Dear Reader

With the principal aim of providing a service to our readers, the strength of The Red Guide has always been our independence, expertise and appreciation.

The independence of The Red Guide is unquestionable:
Firstly, our inspectors visit anonymously and always settle their own bills. Secondly, the Guide retains its impartiality by refusing to include any form of publicity.

The Guide relies on the expertise of our inspectors; dedicated professionals who spend every year travelling inconspicuously around the country seeking out, testing and digesting a wide range of accommodation and cuisine.

And as much as the Guide is written for you, it is also influenced by you. Every year we receive thousands of comments, recommendations and appreciations, all of which contribute to the following year's edition.

These key values mean that every year The Red Guide gives you a reliable, accurate and up-to-date selection to suit every occasion and every pocket.

Look out for us on-line at www.michelin-travel.com.

The Red Guide is influenced by you and is developed for your benefit, which is all the more reason to send us your comments!

Contents

Choosing a hotel or restaurant

This guide offers a selection of hotels and restaurants to help motorists on their travels. In each category establishments are listed in order of preference according to the degree of comfort they offer.

Categories

	XXXXX	*Luxury in the traditional style*
	XXXX	*Top class comfort*
	XXX	*Very comfortable*
	XX	*Comfortable*
	X	*Quite comfortable*
		Traditional pubs serving food
⌂		*Other recommended accommodation (Guesthouses, farmhouses and private homes)*
without rest.		*The hotel has no restaurant*
	with rm	*The restaurant also offers accommodation*

Peaceful atmosphere and setting

Certain establishments are distinguished in the guide by the red symbols shown below.

Your stay in such hotels will be particularly pleasant or restful, owing to the character of the building, its decor, the setting, the welcome and services offered, or simply the peace and quiet to be enjoyed there.

to , ⌂	*Pleasant hotels*
XXXXX to X,	*Pleasant restaurants*
« Park »	*Particularly attractive feature*
	Very quiet or quiet, secluded hotel
	Quiet hotel
≤ sea	*Exceptional view*
≤	*Interesting or extensive view*

The maps located at the beginning of each regional section in the guide indicate places with such peaceful, pleasant hotels and restaurants.

By consulting them before setting out and sending us your comments on your return you can help us with our enquiries.

Hotel facilities

In general the hotels we recommend have full bathroom and toilet facilities in each room. This may not be the case, however, for certain rooms in categories ⌂ and ⌂.

30 rm	*Number of rooms*
	Lift (elevator)
	Air conditioning
TV	*Television in room*
	Establishment either partly or wholly reserved for non-smokers
	Modem point in the bedrooms
	Rooms accessible to disabled people
	Meals served in garden or on terrace
	Outdoor or indoor swimming pool
S	*Exercise room – Sauna*
	Garden
	Park
18	*Hotel tennis court – Golf course and number of holes*
	Landing stage
	Fishing available to hotel guests. A charge may be made
150	*Equipped conference hall: maximum capacity*
	Hotel garage (additional charge in most cases)
P	*Car park for customers only*
	Dogs are excluded from all or part of the hotel
Fax	*Telephone document transmission*
May-October	*Dates when open, as indicated by the hotelier*
season	*Probably open for the season – precise dates not available. Where no date or season is shown, establishments are open all year round.*
LL35 OSB	*Postal code*

Cuisine

Stars

Certain establishments deserve to be brought to your attention for the particularly fine quality of their cooking. ***Michelin stars*** *are awarded for the standard of meals served. For such restaurants we list three culinary specialities typical of their style of cooking to assist you in your choice.*

✿✿✿ **Exceptional cuisine, worth a special journey**

One always eats here extremely well, sometimes superbly. Fine wines, faultless service, elegant surroundings. One will pay accordingly!

✿✿ **Excellent cooking, worth a detour**

Specialities and wines of first class quality. This will be reflected in the price.

✿ **A very good restaurant in its category**

The star indicates a good place to stop on your journey. But beware of comparing the star given to an expensive « de luxe » establishment to that of a simple restaurant where you can appreciate fine cooking at a reasonable price.

The "Bib Gourmand"

Good food at moderate prices

You may also like to know of other restaurants with less elaborate, moderately priced menus that offer good value for money and serve carefully prepared meals.

We bring them to your attention by marking them with the **"Bib Gourmand"** ☺ *and* Meals *in the text of the Guide, e.g.* Meals 19.00/25.00.

Please refer to the map of star-rated restaurants ✿✿✿, ✿✿, ✿ and the **"Bib Gourmand"** ☺, *located at the beginning of each regional section in the guide.*

Prices

Prices quoted are valid for autumn 2000. Changes may arise if goods and service costs are revised.

Hotels and restaurants in bold type have supplied details of all their rates and have assumed responsibility for maintaining them for all travellers in possession of this guide.

In some towns, when commercial or tourist events are taking place, the hotel rates are likely to be considerably higher.

Prices are given in £ sterling, except for the Republic of Ireland where Irish pounds (punt) are quoted. Where no mention **s.**, **t.**, *or* **st.** *is shown, prices may be subject to the addition of service charge, V.A.T., or both (V.A.T. does not apply in the Channel Islands).*

Your recommendation is self-evident if you always walk into a hotel guide in hand.

Meals

Meals 13.00/28.00	**Set meals** *Lowest* 13.00 *and highest* 28.00 prices for set meals – *including cover charge, where applicable*
Meals 19.00/25.00	*See page 5*
s.	*Service only included*
t.	*V.A.T. only included*
st.	*Service and V.A.T. included*
6.00	*Price of 1/2 bottle or carafe of house wine*
Meals a la carte 20.00/35.00	**A la carte meals** *The prices represent the range of charges from a simple to an elaborate 3 course meal and include a cover charge where applicable*

⌂: *Dinner in this category of establishment will generally be offered from a fixed price menu of limited choice, served at a set time to residents only. Lunch is rarely offered. Many will not be licensed to sell alcohol.*

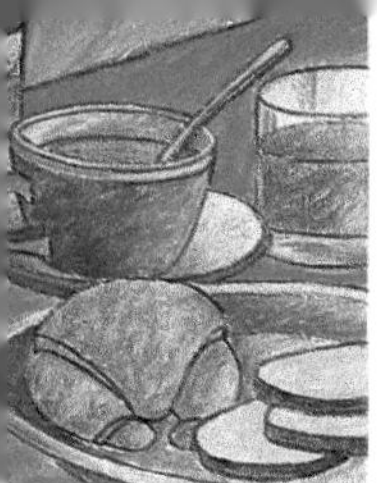

Rooms

rm 50.00/90.00	*Lowest price* 50.00, *per room for a comfortable single and highest price* 90.00 *per room for the best double or twin*
suites	*Check with the hotelier for prices*
rm ☕ 55.00/85.00	*Full cooked breakfast (whether taken or not) is included in the price of the room*
☕ 6.00	*Price of breakfast*

Short breaks (SB)

Many hotels offer a special rate for a stay of two or more nights which comprises dinner, room and breakfast usually for a minimum of two people. Please enquire at hotel for rates.

Alcoholic beverages-conditions of sale

The sale of alcoholic drinks is governed in Great Britain and Ireland by licensing laws which vary greatly from country to country.

Allowing for local variations, restaurants may stay open and serve alcohol with a bona fide meal during the afternoon. Hotel bars and public houses are generally open between 11am and 11pm at the discretion of the licensee. Hotel residents, however, may buy drinks outside the permitted hours at the discretion of the hotelier.

Children under the age of 14 are not allowed in bars.

Deposits

Some hotels will require a deposit, which confirms the commitment of customer and hotelier alike. Make sure the terms of the agreement are clear.

Credit cards

Credits cards accepted by the establishment: MasterCard (Eurocard) – American Express – Diners Club – Visa – Japan Credit Bureau

Towns

✉ *York*	*Postal address*
401 M 27, ⑩	*Michelin map and co-ordinates or fold*
West Country G.	*See the Michelin Green Guide The West Country of England*
pop. 1057	*Population. (Crown copyright 1991. Published by permission of the Controller of Her Majesty's Sationery Office.)*
BX A	*Letters giving the location of a place on the town plan*
18	*Golf course and number of holes (handicap sometimes required, telephone reservation strongly advised)*
✳ ⋖	*Panoramic view, viewpoint*
✈	*Airport*
⛴	*Shipping line*
⛴	*Passenger transport only*
🛈	*Tourist Information Centre*

Standard Time

In winter standard time throughout the British Isles is Greenwich Mean Time (G.M.T.). In summer British clocks are advanced by one hour to give British Summer Time (B.S.T.). The actual dates are announced annually but always occur over weekends in March and October.

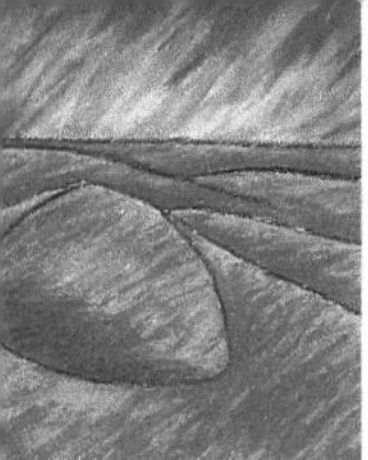

Sights

Star-rating

★★★	*Worth a journey*
★★	*Worth a detour*
★	*Interesting*
AC	*Admission charge*

Location

See	*Sights in town*
Envir.	*On the outskirts*
Exc.	*In the surrounding area*
N, S, E, W	*The sight lies north, south, east or west of the town*
A 22	*Take road A 22, indicated by the same symbol on the Guide map*
2 m.	*Mileage*

Local maps

May we suggest that you consult them

Should you be looking for a hotel or restaurant not too far from Leeds, for example, you can now consult the map along with the town plan.
The local map (opposite) draws your attention to all places around the town or city selected, provided they are mentioned in the Guide.
Places located within a range of 25 km/16 miles are clearly identified by the use of a different coloured background.
The various facilities recommended near the different regional capitals can be located quickly and easily.

Note:

Entries in the Guide provide information on distances to nearby towns.
Whenever a place appears on one of the local maps, the name of the town or city to which it is attached is printed in BLUE.

Example:

ILKLEY is to be found on the local map LEEDS

IKLEY *W. Yorks.* 402 O 22 – pop. 13 530
Myddleton ℘ *(01943) 607277*
Station Rd, LS29 8HA ℘ *(01943) 602319*
London 210 – Bradford 13 – Harrogate 13 – Leeds 16 – Preston 46

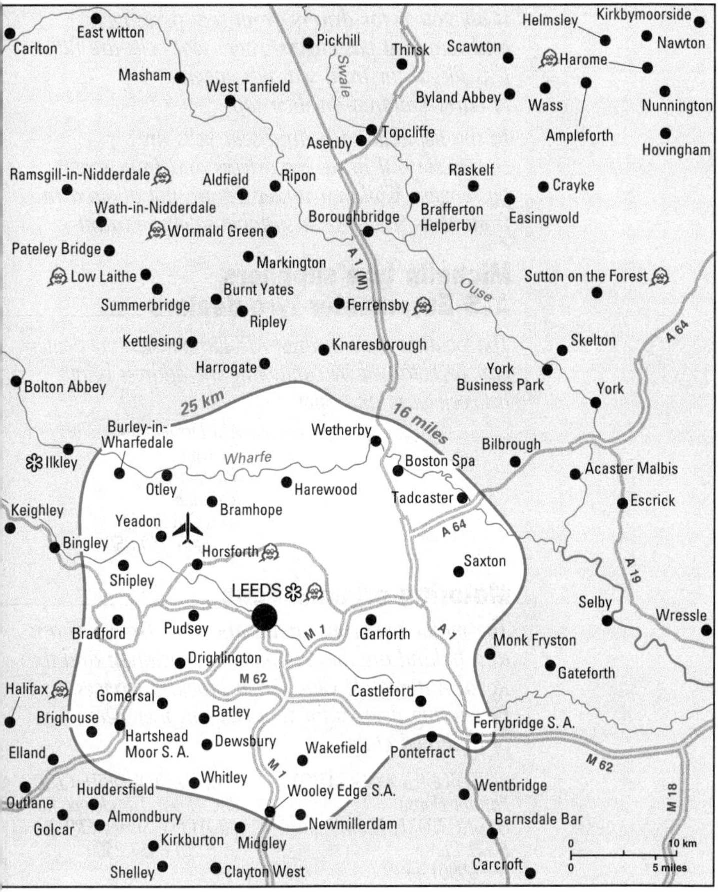

Carlton
East witton
Masham
West Tanfield
Pickhill
Swale
Thirsk
Scawton
Helmsley
Kirkbymoorside
Nawton
Harome
Byland Abbey
Wass
Nunnington
Ampleforth
Hovingham
Topcliffe
Asenby
Ramsgill-in-Nidderdale
Aldfield
Ripon
Raskelf
Crayke
Wath-in-Nidderdale
Boroughbridge
Brafferton Helperby
Easingwold
Wormald Green
Pateley Bridge
Markington
A 1 (M)
Low Laithe
Burnt Yates
Ouse
Sutton on the Forest
Summerbridge
Ferrensby
Ripley
Kettlesing
Knaresborough
Skelton
A 64
Harrogate
York Business Park
Bolton Abbey
York
25 km
16 miles
Burley-in-Wharfedale
Wetherby
Bilbrough
Ilkley
Wharfe
Boston Spa
Acaster Malbis
Otley
Harewood
Keighley
Tadcaster
Escrick
Bramhope
Yeadon
A 64
Bingley
Horsforth
Saxton
A 19
Shipley
LEEDS
Selby
Wressle
Bradford
Pudsey
M 1
Garforth
A 1
Monk Fryston
Drighlington
Gateforth
M 62
Halifax
Gomersal
Castleford
Brighouse
Batley
Ferrybridge S. A.
Hartshead Moor S. A.
Dewsbury
Elland
Wakefield
Pontefract
M 62
M 1
Whitley
Outlane
Huddersfield
Wooley Edge S.A.
Wentbridge
M 18
Almondbury
Golcar
Newmillerdam
Barnsdale Bar
Kirkburton
Midgley
0
10 km
Shelley
Clayton West
Carcroft
0
5 miles

All the local maps are indicated on the thematic map on pages 76 to 85.

Car, tyres

The wearing of seat belts in Great Britain is obligatory for drivers, front seat passengers and rear seat passengers where seat belts are fitted. It is illegal for front seat passengers to carry children on their lap.

In the Republic of Ireland seat belts are compulsory, if fitted, for drivers and front seat passengers. Children under 12 are not allowed in front seats unless in a suitable safety restraint.

Michelin tyre suppliers ATS Euromaster tyre dealers

The location of the nearest ATS Euromaster tyre dealer can be obtained by contacting the address below between 9am and 5pm.

ATS Euromaster
Jill Lane
Sambourne
Redditch
Worcs. B96 6ES
☎ 0800 750 850

Motoring organisations

The major motoring organisations in Great Britain and Ireland are the Automobile Association and the Royal Automobile Club. Each provides services in varying degrees for non-resident members of affiliated clubs.

AUTOMOBILE ASSOCIATION
Fanum House
BASINGSTOKE, Hants
RG21 2EA
☎ (0990) 448866

ROYAL AUTOMOBILE CLUB
RAC House, Lansdowne Rd.
CROYDON, Surrey CR9 2JA
☎ (020) 8917 2500

AUTOMOBILE ASSOCIATION
23 Rock Hill
BLACKROCK
Co-Dublin
☎ (01) 283 3555

ROYAL AUTOMOBILE CLUB
RAC IRELAND
New Mount House
22-24 Lower Mount St.
DUBLIN 2
☎ (01) 676 0113

Town plans

a — *Hotels – Restaurants*

Sights

Place of interest

Interesting place of worship

Roads

M 1 — *Motorway*

4 4 — *Junctions: complete, limited*

Dual carriageway with motorway characteristics

Main traffic artery

A 2 — *Primary route (GB) and National primary route (IRL)*

One-way street – Unsuitable for traffic, street subject to restrictions

Pedestrian street – Tramway

Piccadilly P R — *Shopping street – Car park – Park and Ride*

Gateway – Street passing under arch – Tunnel

15'5 — *Low headroom (16'6" max.) on major through routes*

Station and railway

Funicular – Cable-car

B — *Lever bridge – Car ferry*

Various signs

Tourist Information Centre

Mosque – Synagogue

Communications tower or mast – Ruins

Garden, park, wood – Cemetery

9 — *Stadium – Racecourse – Golf course*

Golf course (with restrictions for visitors) – Skating rink

Outdoor or indoor swimming pool

View – Panorama

Monument – Fountain – Hospital – Covered market

Pleasure boat harbour – Lighthouse

Airport – Underground station – Coach station

Ferry services:

- passengers and cars

Main post office with poste restante, telephone

Public buildings located by letter:

C H J — *County Council Offices – Town Hall – Law Courts*

M T U — *Museum – Theatre – University, College*

POL. — *Police (in large towns police headquarters)*

London

BRENT WEMBLEY — *Borough – Area*

Borough boundary – Area boundary

Ami lecteur

Indépendance, compétence et écoute : depuis toujours Le Guide Rouge a placé ces valeurs au cœur de son service aux lecteurs.

L'indépendance pour Le Guide Rouge, c'est celle de ses inspecteurs qui visitent les hôtels et les restaurants et règlent toutes leurs additions, dans un total anonymat. C'est aussi celle du Guide lui-même qui refuse toute forme de publicité dans ses pages.

La compétence du Guide Rouge passe par celle de ses inspecteurs, professionnels passionnés, qui toute l'année explorent, testent, goûtent, apprécient, comme de simples voyageurs particulièrement attentifs.

À la fois complice et conseiller, Le Guide Rouge est continuellement à votre écoute. Des milliers d'appréciations sur les hôtels et les restaurants sont ainsi reçues chaque année et constituent autant de témoignages précieux qui viendront orienter la prochaine édition.

C'est de cette façon que Le Guide Rouge peut vous proposer une sélection toujours fiable, actualisée et adaptée à tous les budgets. Retrouvez-la aujourd'hui sur le site www.michelin-travel.com.

Le Guide Rouge vit et progresse pour vous et grâce à vous : écrivez-nous !

Sommaire

Le choix d'un hôtel, d'un restaurant

Ce guide vous propose une sélection d'hôtels et restaurants établie à l'usage de l'automobiliste de passage. Les établissements, classés selon leur confort, sont cités par ordre de préférence dans chaque catégorie.

Catégories

	XXXXX	*Grand luxe et tradition*
	XXXX	*Grand confort*
	XXX	*Très confortable*
	XX	*De bon confort*
	X	*Assez confortable*
		Traditionnel "pub" anglais servant des repas
		Autres formes hébergement conseillé (Logis à la ferme, maison d'hôtes et cottages)
without rest.		*L'hôtel n'a pas de restaurant*
	with rm	*Le restaurant possède des chambres*

Agrément et tranquillité

Certains établissements se distinguent dans le guide par les symboles rouges indiqués ci-après.
Le séjour dans ces hôtels se révèle particulièrement agréable ou reposant.

Cela peut tenir d'une part au caractère de l'édifice, au décor original, au site, à l'accueil et aux services qui sont proposés, d'autre part à la tranquillité des lieux.

à	*Hôtels agréables*
XXXXX à X	*Restaurants agréables*
« Park »	*Élément particulièrement agréable*
	Hôtel très tranquille ou isolé et tranquille
	Hôtel tranquille
≤ sea	*Vue exceptionnelle*
≤	*Vue intéressante ou étendue*

Les localités possédant des établissements agréables ou tranquilles sont repérées sur les cartes au début de chacune des régions traitées dans ce guide.

Consultez-les pour la préparation de vos voyages et donnez-nous vos appréciations à votre retour, vous faciliterez ainsi nos enquêtes.

L'intallation

Les chambres des hôtels que nous recommandons possèdent, en général, des installations sanitaires complètes. Il est toutefois possible que dans les catégories 🏠 et ⌂, certaines chambres en soient dépourvues.

30 rm	*Nombre de chambres*
	Ascenseur
	Air conditionné
TV	*Télévision dans la chambre*
	Établissement entièrement ou en partie réservé aux non-fumeurs
	Prise modem dans la chambre
	Chambres accessibles aux handicapés physiques
	Repas servis au jardin ou en terrasse
	Piscine : de plein air ou couverte
S	*Salle de remise en forme – Sauna*
	Jardin de repos
	Parc
18	*Tennis à l'hôtel – Golf et nombre de trous*
	Ponton d'amarrage
	Pêche ouverte aux clients de l'hôtel (éventuellement payant)
150	*Salles de conférences : capacité maximum*
	Garage dans l'hôtel (généralement payant)
P	*Parking réservé à la clientèle*
	Accès interdit aux chiens (dans tout ou partie de l'établissement)
Fax	*Transmission de documents par télécopie*
May-October	*Période d'ouverture, communiquée par l'hôtelier*
season	*Ouverture probable en saison mais dates non précisées. En l'absence de mention, l'établissement est ouvert toute l'année*
LL35 OSB	*Code postal de l'établissement*

La table

Les étoiles

Certains établissements méritent d'être signalés à votre attention pour la qualité de leur cuisine. Nous les distinguons par **les étoiles de bonne table.** *Nous indiquons, pour ces établissements, trois spécialités culinaires qui pourront orienter votre choix.*

✿✿✿ **Une des meilleures tables, vaut le voyage**

On y mange toujours très bien, parfois merveilleusement. Grands vins, service impeccable, cadre élégant... Prix en conséquence.

✿✿ **Table excellente, mérite un détour**

Spécialités et vins de choix...
Attendez-vous à une dépense en rapport.

✿ **Une très bonne table dans sa catégorie**

L'étoile marque une bonne étape sur votre itinéraire.
Mais ne comparez pas l'étoile d'un établissement de luxe à prix élevés avec celle d'une petite maison où, à prix raisonnables, on sert également une cuisine de qualité.

Le "Bib Gourmand"

Repas soignés à prix modérés

Vous souhaitez parfois trouver des tables plus simples, à prix modérés; c'est pourquoi nous avons sélectionné des restaurants proposant, pour un rapport qualité-prix particulièrement favorable, un repas soigné.
Ces restaurants sont signalés par le **"Bib Gourmand"** ☺ *et* **Meals**
Ex **Meals** 19.00/25.00.

Consultez les cartes des étoiles de bonne table ✿✿✿, ✿✿, ✿ et des **"Bib Gourmand"** ☺, *placées au début de chacune des régions traitées dans ce guide.*

Les prix

Les prix que nous indiquons dans ce guide ont été établis en automne 2000. Ils sont susceptibles de modifications, notamment en cas de variations des prix des biens et services.

Dans certaines villes, à l'occasion de manisfestations commerciales ou touristiques, les prix demandés par les hôteliers risquent d'être considérablement majorés. Les prix sont indiqués en livres sterling (1 £ = 100 pence), sauf en République d'Irlande où ils sont donnés en « Punts ». Lorsque les mentions **s.**, **t.**, *ou* **st.** *ne figurent pas, les prix indiqués peuvent être majorés d'un pourcentage pour le service, la T.V.A., ou les deux (la T.V.A. n'est pas appliquée dans les Channel Islands). Les hôtels et restaurants figurent en gros caractères lorsque les hôteliers nous ont donné tous leurs prix et se sont engagés, sous leur propre responsabilité, à les appliquer aux touristes de passage porteurs de notre guide.*

Entrez à l'hôtel le guide à la main, vous montrerez ainsi qu'il vous conduit là en confiance.

Repas

Meals 13.00/28.00	**Repas à prix fixe** *Minimum* 13.00, *maximum* 28.00. *Ces prix s'entendent couvert compris*
Meals 19.00/25.00	*Voir page 19*
s.	*Service compris*
t.	*T.V.A. comprise*
st.	*Service et T.V.A. compris (prix nets)*
6.00	*Prix de la 1/2 bouteille ou carafe de vin ordinaire*
Meals à la carte 20.00/35.00	**Repas à la carte** *Le 1er prix correspond à un repas simple mais soigné, comprenant : petite entrée, plat du jour garni, dessert. Le 2e prix concerne un repas plus complet, comprenant : entrée, plat principal, fromage ou dessert. Ces prix s'entendent couvert compris.*

⌂ : *Dans les établissements de cette catégorie, le dîner est servi à heure fixe exclusivement aux personnes ayant une chambre. Le menu, à prix unique, offre un choix limité de plats. Le déjeuner est rarement proposé. Beaucoup de ces établissements ne sont pas autorisés à vendre des boissons alcoolisées.*

Chambres

rm 50.00/90.00	*Prix minimum 50.00 d'une chambre pour une personne et prix maximum 90.00 de la plus belle chambre occupée par deux personnes*
suites	*Se renseigner auprès de l'hôtelier*
rm ☕ 55.00/85.00	*Le prix du petit déjeuner à l'anglaise est inclus dans le prix de la chambre, même s'il n'est pas consommé*
☕ 6.00	*Prix du petit déjeuner*

Short breaks (SB)

Certains hôtels proposent des conditions avantageuses ou «Short Break» pour un séjour minimum de 2 nuits. Ce forfait, calculé par personne, pour 2 personnes au minimum, comprend la chambre, le dîner et le petit déjeuner. Se renseigner auprès de l'hôtelier.

La vente de boissons alcoolisées

En Grande-Bretagne et en Irlande, la vente de boissons alcoolisées est soumise à des lois pouvant varier d'une région à l'autre.
D'une façon générale, les restaurants peuvent demeurer ouverts l'après-midi et servir des boissons alcoolisées dans la mesure où elles accompagnent un repas suffisamment consistant. Les bars d'hôtel et les pubs sont habituellement ouverts de 11 heures à 23 heures. Néanmoins, l'hôtelier a toujours la possibilité de servir, à sa clientèle, des boissons alcoolisées en dehors des heures légales. Les enfants au-dessous de 14 ans n'ont pas accès aux bars.

Les arrhes

Certains hôteliers demandent le versement d'arrhes. Il s'agit d'un dépôt-garantie qui engage l'hôtelier comme le client. Bien faire préciser les dispositions de cette garantie.

Cartes de crédit

Cartes de crédit acceptées par l'établissement : MasterCard (Eurocard) – American Express – Diners Club – Visa – Japan Credit Bureau

Les villes

✉ *York*	*Bureau de poste desservant la localité*
401 M 27, ⑩	*Numéro des cartes Michelin et carroyage ou numéro du pli*
West Country G.	*Voir le guide vert Michelin The West Country of England*
pop. 1057	*Population*
BX A	*Lettres repérant un emplacement sur le plan*
[golf] 18	*Golf et nombre de trous (Handicap parfois demandé, réservation par téléphone vivement recommandée)*
✻ ⋖	*Panorama, point de vue*
[avion]	*Aéroport*
[bateau]	*Transports maritimes*
[bateau]	*Transports maritimes (pour passagers seulement)*
[i]	*Information touristique*

Heure légale

Les visiteurs devront tenir compte de l'heure officielle.
En Grande-Bretagne : une heure de retard sur l'heure française.

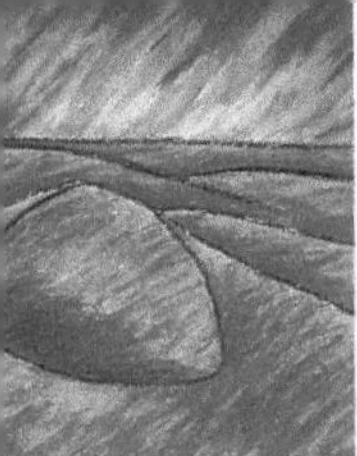

Les curiosités

Intérêt

★★★	*Vaut le voyage*
★★	*Mérite un détour*
★	*Intéressant*
AC	*Entrée payante*

Situation

See	*Dans la ville*
Envir.	*Aux environs de la ville*
Exc.	*Excursions dans la région*
N, S, E, W	*La curiosité est située : au Nord, au Sud, à l'Est, à l'Ouest*
A 22	*On s'y rend par la route A 22, repérée par le même signe sur le plan du Guide*
2 m.	*Distance en miles*

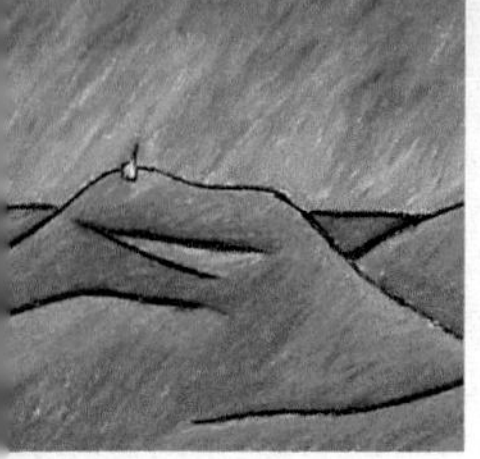

Les cartes de voisinage

Avez-vous pensé à les consulter ?

Vous souhaitez trouver une bonne adresse, par exemple, aux environs de Leeds ? Consultez la carte qui accompagne le plan de la ville.

La « carte de voisinage » (ci-contre) attire votre attention sur toutes les localités citées au Guide autour de la ville choisie, et particulièrement celles situées dans un rayon de 25 km/16 miles (limite de couleur).

Les « cartes de voisinage » vous permettent ainsi le repérage rapide de toutes les ressources proposées par le Guide autour des métropoles régionales.

Nota :

Lorsqu'une localité est présente sur une « carte de voisinage », sa métropole de rattachement est imprimée en BLEU sur la ligne des distances de ville à ville.

Vous trouverez ILKLEY sur la carte de voisinage LEEDS

Example:

IKLEY *W. Yorks.* **402** O 22 – pop. 13 530
Myddleton ✆ (01943) 607277
Station Rd, LS29 8HA ✆ (01943) 602319
London 210 – Bradford 13 – Harrogate 13 – Leeds 16 – Preston 46

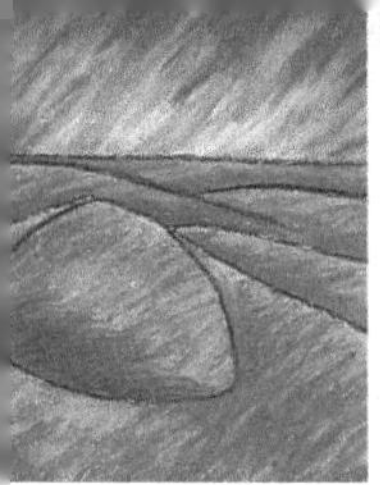

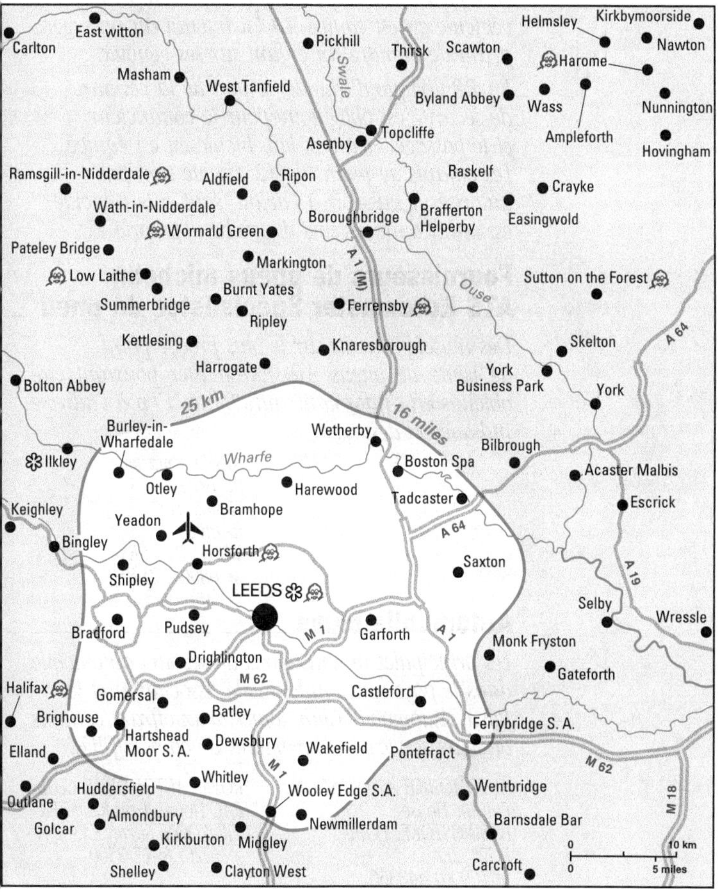

Carlton
East witton
Masham
West Tanfield
Pickhill
Swale
Thirsk
Scawton
Helmsley
Kirkbymoorside
Nawton
Harome
Byland Abbey
Wass
Nunnington
Ampleforth
Hovingham
Asenby
Topcliffe
Ramsgill-in-Nidderdale
Aldfield
Ripon
Raskelf
Crayke
Wath-in-Nidderdale
Boroughbridge
Brafferton Helperby
Easingwold
Wormald Green
Pateley Bridge
Markington
A 1 (M)
Low Laithe
Ouse
Sutton on the Forest
Summerbridge
Burnt Yates
Ferrensby
Ripley
Kettlesing
Knaresborough
Skelton
A 64
Harrogate
York Business Park
Bolton Abbey
York
25 km
16 miles
Burley-in-Wharfedale
Wetherby
Bilbrough
Ilkley
Wharfe
Boston Spa
Acaster Malbis
Otley
Harewood
Tadcaster
Escrick
Keighley
Bramhope
Yeadon
A 64
Bingley
Horsforth
Saxton
A 19
Shipley
LEEDS
Selby
Wressle
Bradford
Pudsey
M 1
Garforth
A 1
Monk Fryston
Drighlington
Gateforth
M 62
Halifax
Gomersal
Castleford
Brighouse
Batley
Ferrybridge S. A.
Hartshead Moor S. A.
Dewsbury
Elland
Wakefield
Pontefract
M 62
M 1
Whitley
Huddersfield
Wooley Edge S.A.
Wentbridge
M 18
Outlane
Almondbury
Newmillerdam
Barnsdale Bar
Golcar
Kirkburton
Midgley
Carcroft
Shelley
Clayton West
0 10 km
0 5 miles

Toutes les « Cartes de voisinage » sont localisées sur la carte thématique pages 76 à 85.

La voiture, les pneus

En Grande-Bretagne, le port de la ceinture de sécurité est obligatoire pour le conducteur et le passager avant ainsi qu'à l'arrière, si le véhicule en est équipé. La loi interdit au passager avant de prendre un enfant sur ses genoux.

En République d'Irlande, le port de la ceinture de sécurité est obligatoire pour le conducteur et le passager avant si le véhicule en est équipé. Les enfants de moins de 12 ans ne sont pas autorisés à s'asseoir à l'avant, sauf si le véhicule est muni d'un système d'attache approprié.

Fournisseurs de pneus michelin ATS Euromaster Spécialistes du pneu

Des renseignements sur le plus proche point de vente de pneus ATS Euromaster pourront être obtenus en s'informant entre 9 h et 17 h à l'adresse indiquée ci-dessous.

ATS Euromaster
Jill Lane
Sambourne
Redditch
Worcs. B96 6ES
✆ 0800 750 850

Automobile clubs

Les principales organisations de secours automobile dans le pays sont l'Automobile Association et le Royal Automobile Club, toutes deux offrant certains de leurs services aux membres de clubs affiliés.

AUTOMOBILE ASSOCIATION
Fanum House
BASINGSTOKE, Hants
RG21 2EA
✆ (0990) 448866

AUTOMOBILE ASSOCIATION
23 Rock Hill
BLACKROCK
Co-Dublin
✆ (01) 283 3555

ROYAL AUTOMOBILE CLUB
RAC House, Lansdowne Rd.
CROYDON, Surrey CR9 2JA
✆ (020) 8917 2500

ROYAL AUTOMOBILE CLUB
RAC IRELAND New Mount House
22-24 Lower Mount St.
DUBLIN 2
✆ (01) 676 0113

Les plans

a ● a *Hôtels – Restaurants*

Curiosités

Bâtiment intéressant

Édifice religieux intéressant

Voirie

M 1 *Autoroute*

4 4 *- échangeurs : complet, partiel*

Route à chaussées séparées de type autoroutier

Grand axe de circulation

A 2 *Itinéraire principal (Primary route : GB)*
(National primary route : IRL)

Sens unique – Rue impraticable, réglementée

Rue piétonne – Tramway

Piccadilly P R *Rue commerçante – Parking – Parking Relais*

Porte – Passage sous voûte – Tunnel

15'6 *Passage bas (inférieur à 16'6") sur les grandes voies de circulation*

Gare et voie ferrée

Funiculaire – Téléphérique, télécabine

Pont mobile – B *Bac pour autos*

Signes divers

Information touristique

Mosquée – Synagogue

Tour ou pylône de télécommunication – Ruines

Jardin, parc, bois – Cimetière

Stade – Hippodrome – Golf – Patinoire

Golf (réservé)

Piscine de plein air, couverte

Vue – Panorama

Monument – Fontaine – Hôpital – Marché couvert

Port de plaisance – Phare

Aéroport – Station de métro – Gare routière

Transport par bateau :
- passagers et voitures

Bureau principal de poste restante, téléphone

Bâtiment public repéré par une lettre :

C H *- Bureau de l'Administration du Comté – Hôtel de ville*

M T U *- Musée – Théâtre – Université, grande école*

POL. J *- Police (commissariat central) – Palais de Justice*

Londres

BRENT WEMBLEY *Nom d'arrondissement (borough) – de quartier (area)*

Limite de « borough » – d'« area »

Amico lettore

Indipendenza, competenza e attenzione : da sempre La Guida Rossa ha collocato questi valori al centro del suo servizio al lettori.

L'indipendenza è, per La Guida Rossa, quella dei suoi ispettori, che visitano gli alberghi e i ristoranti pagando sempre il conto, in totale anonimato. È anche quella di una Guida che all'interno delle sue pagine rifiuta ogni forma di pubblicità.

La competenza per La Guida Rossa passa attraverso quella dei suoi ispettori, professionisti appassionati, che durante l'anno cercano, verificano, assaggiano, valutano, come dei semplici viaggiatori, ma particolarmente attenti.

Ad un tempo complice e consigliere, La Guida Rossa è costantemente attenta ai vostri suggerimenti. Ogni anno infatti riceviamo numerosissime informazioni su alberghi e ristoranti : costituiscono osservazioni preziose, che andranno ad orientare la prossima edizione.

È per questi motivi che La Guida Rossa è in grado di proporvi una selezione sempre affidabile, aggiornata e adatta a tutte le tasche. Oggi la potete trovare anche sul sito www.michelin-travel.com.

La Guida Rossa vive e si evolve per voi e grazie a voi : scriveteci !

Sommario

La scelta di un albergo, di un ristorante

Questa guida propone una selezione di alberghi e ristoranti per orientare la scelta dell'automobilista. Gli esercizi, classificati in base al confort che offrono, vengono citati in ordine di preferenza per ogni categoria.

Categorie

	XXXXX	*Gran lusso e tradizione*
	XXXX	*Gran confort*
	XXX	*Molto confortevole*
	XX	*Di buon confort*
	X	*Abbastanza confortevole*
		Pub tradizionali con cucina
		Altra forme di alloggio consigliate (Pensioni, Fattorie e Case private)
without rest.		*L'albergo non ha ristorante*
	with rm	*Il ristorante dispone di camere*

Amenità e tranquillità

Alcuni esercizi sono evidenziati nella guida dai simboli rossi indicati qui di seguito. Il soggiorno in questi alberghi si rivela particolarmente ameno o riposante.

Ciò può dipendere sia dalle caratteristiche dell'edificio, dalle decorazioni non comuni, dalla sua posizione e dal servizio offerto, sia dalla tranquillità dei luoghi.

a ,	*Alberghi ameni*
XXXXX a X,	*Ristoranti ameni*
« Park »	*Un particolare piacevole*
	Albergo molto tranquillo o isolato e tranquillo
	Albergo tranquillo
sea	*Vista eccezionale*
	Vista interessante o estesa

Le località che possiedono degli esercizi ameni o tranquilli sono riportate sulle carte che precedono ciascuna delle regioni trattate nella guida.

Consultatele per la preparazione dei vostri viaggi e, al ritorno, inviateci i vostri pareri; in tal modo agevolerete le nostre inchieste.

Installazioni

Le camere degli alberghi che raccomandiamo possiedono, generalmente, delle installazioni sanitarie complete. È possibile tuttavia che nelle categorie e alcune camere ne siano sprovviste.

30 rm	*Numero di camere*
	Ascensore
	Aria condizionata
	Televisione in camera
	Esercizio riservato completamente o in parte ai non fumatori
	Presa modem in camera
	Camere di agevole accesso per portatori di handicap
	Pasti serviti in giardino o in terrazza
	Piscina: all'aperto, coperta
	Palestra – Sauna
	Giardino
	Parco
18	*Tennis appatenente all'albergo – Golf e numero di buche*
	Pontile d'ormeggio
	Pesca aperta ai clienti dell'albergo (eventualmente a pagamento)
150	*Sale per conferenze: capienza massima*
	Garage nell'albergo (generalmente a pagamento)
P	*Parcheggio riservato alla clientela*
	Accesso vietato ai cani (in tutto o in parte dell'esercizio
Fax	*Trasmissione telefonica di documenti*
May-October	*Periodo di apertura, comunicato dall'albergatore*
season	*Probabile apertura in stagione, ma periodo non precisato. Gli esercizi senza tali menzioni sono aperti tutto l'anno.*
LL35 OSB	*Codice postale dell'esercizio*

La tavola

Le stelle

*Alcuni esercizi meritano di essere segnalati alla vostra attenzione per la qualità particolare della loro cucina; li abbiamo evidenziati con le «**stelle di ottima tavola**».*
Per ognuno di questi ristoranti indichiamo tre specialità culinarie e alcuni vini locali che potranno aiutarvi nella scelta.

✿✿✿ **Una delle migliori tavole, vale il viaggio**

Vi si mangia sempre molto bene, a volte meravigliosamente. Grandi vini, servizio impeccabile, ambientazione accurata... Prezzi conformi.

✿✿ **Tavola eccellente, merita una deviazione**

Specialità e vini scelti...
Aspettatevi una spesa in proporzione.

✿ **Un'ottima tavola nella sua categoria**

La stella indica una tappa gastronomica sul Vostro itinerario.
Non mettete però a confronto la stella di un esercizio di lusso, dai prezzi elevati, con quella di un piccolo esercizio dove, a prezzi ragionevoli, viene offerta una cucina di qualità.

Il "Bib Gourmand"

Pasti accurati a prezzi contenuti

Per quando desiderate trovare delle tavole più semplici a prezzi contenuti abbiamo selezionato dei ristoranti che, per un rapporto qualità-prezzo particolarmente favorevole, offrono un pasto accurato.
Questi ristoranti sono evidenziali nel testo con il **"Bib Gourmand"** *e* Meals, *evidenziata in rosso, davanti ai prezzi.*
Ex. Meals 19.00/25.00.

Consultate le carte delle stelle ✿✿✿, ✿✿, ✿ e con il **"Bib Gourmand"**, *che precedono ciascuna delle regioni trattate nella guida.*

I prezzi

I prezzi che indichiamo in questa guida sono stati stabiliti nel l'autunno 2000 e potranno pertanto subire delle variazioni in relazione ai cambiamenti dei prezzi di beni e servizi.

Gli alberghi e i ristoranti vengono menzionati in carattere grassetto quando gli albergatori ci hanno comunicato tutti i loro prezzi e si sono impegnati, sotto la propria responsabilità, ad applicarli ai turisti di passaggio, in possesso della nostra guida.

In alcune città, in occasione di manifestazioni turistiche o commerciali, i prezzi richiesti dagli albergatori potrebbero risultare considerevolmente più alti. I prezzi sono indicati in lire sterline (1 £ = 100 pence) ad eccezione per la Repubblica d'Irlanda dove sono indicati in «punts». Quando non figurano le lettere s., t., *o* st. *i prezzi indicati possono essere maggiorati per il servizio o per l'I.V.A. o per entrambi. (L'I.V.A. non viene applicata nelle Channel Islands).*

Entrate nell'albergo o nel ristorante con la guida in mano, dimostrando in tal modo la fiducia in chi vi ha indirizzato.

Pasti

Meals 13.00/28.00 — **Prezzo fisso**

Prezzo minimo 13.00, *e massimo* 28.00. *Questi prezzi comprendono il coperto*

Meals 19.00/25.00 — *Vedere p. 33*

s. — *Servizio compreso*

t. — *I.V.A. compresa*

st. — *Servizio ed I.V.A. compresi (prezzi netti)*

6.00 — *Prezzo della mezza bottiglia o di una caraffa di vino*

Meals a la carte 20.00/35.00 — **Alla carta**

Il 1° prezzo corrisponde ad un pasto semplice comprendente: primo piatto, piatto del giorno con contorno, dessert. Il 2° prezzo corrisponde ad un pasto più completo comprendente: antipasto, piatto principale, formaggio e dessert
Questi prezzi comprendono il coperto

⌂: *Negli alberghi di questa categoria, la cena viene servita, ad un'ora stabilita, esclusivamente a chi vi allogia. Il menu, a prezzo fisso, offre una scelta limitata di piatti. Raramente viene servito anche il pranzo. Molti di questi esercizi non hanno l'autorizzazione a vendere alcolici.*

Camere

rm 50.00/90.00 — *Prezzo minimo* 50.00, *per una camera singola e prezzo massimo* 90.00 *per la camera più bella per due persone*

suites — *Informarsi presso l'albergatore*

rm 55.00/85.00 — *Il prezzo della prima colazione inglese è compreso nel prezzo della camera anche se non viene consumata*

6.00 — *Prezzo della prima colazione*

«Short Breaks» (SB.)

Alcuni alberghi propongono delle condizioni particolarmente vantaggiose o short break per un soggiorno minimo di due notti. Questo prezzo, calcolato per persona e per un minimo di due persone, comprende: camera, cena e prima colazione. Informarsi presso l'albergatore.

La vendita di bevande alcoliche

La vendita di bevande alcoliche in Gran Bretagna è regolata da leggi che variano considerevolmente da regione a regione.

Eccezion fatta per varianti locali, i ristoranti possono rimanere aperti o servire bevande alcoliche con i pasti il pomeriggio. I bar degli hotel e i pub sono generalmente aperti dalle 11 alle 23, a discrezione del gestore. I clienti dell'hotel, comunque, possono acquistare bevande al di fuori delle ore stabilite se il direttore lo permette.

Il bambini al di sotto del 14 anni non possono entrare nei bar.

La caparra

Alcuni albergatori chiedono il versamento di una caparra. Si tratta di un deposito-garanzia che impegna tanto l'albergatore che il cliente. Vi consigliamo di farvi precisare le norme riguardanti la reciproca garanzia di tale caparra.

Carte di credito

Carte di credito accettate dall'esercizio MasterCard (Eurocard) – American Express – Diners Club – Visa – Japan Credit Bureau

Le città

✉ York	Sede dell'ufficio postale
401 M 27, ⑩	Numero della carta Michelin e del riquadro o numero della piega
West Country G.	Vedere la Guida Verde Michelin The West Country of England
pop. 1057	Popolazione
BX A	Lettere indicanti l'ubicazione sulla pianta
18	Golf e numero di buche (handicap generalmente richiesto, prenotazione telefonica vivamente consigliata)
✻ ⋞	Panorama, vista
✈	Aeroporto
⛴	Trasporti marittimi
⛴	Trasporti marittimi (solo passeggeri)
ℹ	Ufficio informazioni turistiche

Ora legale

I visitatori dovranno tenere in considerazione l'ora ufficiale in Gran Bretagna: un'ora di ritardo sull'ora italiana.

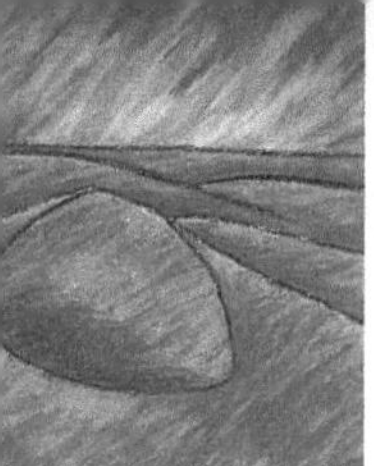

Luoghi d'interesse

Grado di interesse

★★★	*Vale il viaggio*
★★	*Merita una deviazione*
★	*Interessante*
AC	*Entrata a pagamento*

Ubicazione

See	*Nella città*
Envir.	*Nei dintorni della città*
Exc.	*Nella regione*
N, S, E, W	*Il luogo si trova : a Nord, a Sud, a Est a Ovest*
A 22	*Ci si va per la strada A 22 indicata con lo stesso segno sulla pianta*
2 m.	*Distanza in miglia*

Le carte dei dintorni

Sapete come usarle?

Se desiderate, per esempio, trovare un buon indirizzo nei dintorni di Leeds, la « carta dei dintorni » (qui accanto) richiama la vostra attenzione su tutte le località citate nella Guida che si trovino nei dintorni della città prescelta, e in particolare su quelle raggiungibili nel raggio di 25 km/16 miles (limite di colore). Le « carte dei dintorni » coprono l'intero territorio e permettono la localizzazione rapida di tutte le risorse proposte dalla Guida nei dintorni delle metropoli regionali.

Nota:

Quando una località è presente su una « carta dei dintorni », la città a cui ci si riferisce è scritta in BLU nella linea delle distanze da città a città.

Esempio:

Troverete ILKLEY sulla carta dei dintorni di LEEDS

IKLEY *W. Yorks.* 402 O 22 – pop. 13 530
18 *Myddleton* ✆ *(01943) 607277*
Station Rd, LS29 8HA ✆ *(01943) 602319*
London 210 – Bradford 13 – Harrogate 13 – Leeds 16 – Preston 46

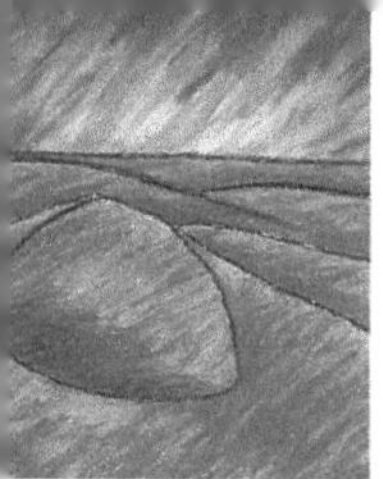

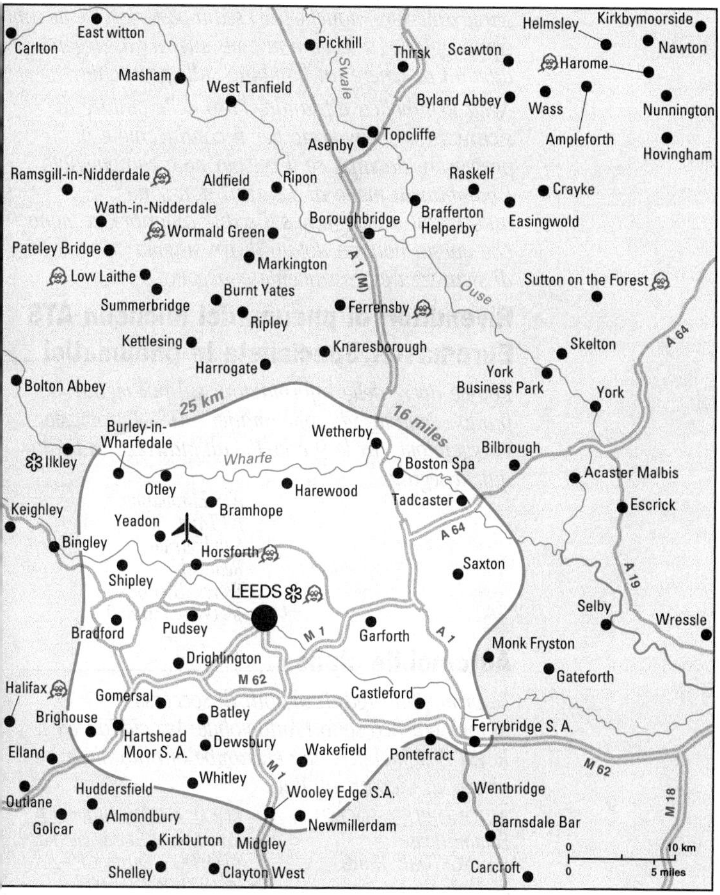

Tutte le «carte dei dintorni» sono localizzate sulla carta tematica e le pagine 76 a 85.

L'automobile, I pneumatici

In Gran Bretagna, l'uso delle cinture di sicurezza è obbligatorio per il conducente ed il passeggero del sedile anteriore, nonchè per i sedili posteriori, se ne sono equipaggiati. La legge non consente al passaggero davanti di tenere un bambino sulle ginocchia.

Nella Repubblica d'Irlanda, l'uso delle cinture di sicurezza è obbligatorio per il conducente e il passeggero davanti, se il veicolo ne è equipaggiato. I bambini di meno di 12 anni non sono autorizzati a viaggiare sul sedile anteriore, a meno che questo non sia dotato di un sistema di sicurezza esprassamente concepito.

Rivenditori di pneumatici Michelin ATS Euromaster Specialista in pneumatici

Potrete avere delle informazioni sul piú vicino punto vendita di pneumatici ATS Euromaster, rivolgendovi, tra le 9 e le 17, all'indirizzo indicato qui di seguito:

ATS Euromaster
Jill Lane
Sambourne
Redditch
Worcs. B96 6ES
✆ 0800 750 850

Automobile clubs

Le principali organizzazioni di soccorso automobilistico sono l'Automobile Association ed il Royal Automobile Club: entrambe offrono alcuni servizi ai membri affiliati.

AUTOMOBILE ASSOCIATION
Fanum House
BASINGSTOKE, Hants
RG21 2EA
✆ (0990) 448866

AUTOMOBILE ASSOCIATION
23 Rock Hill
BLACKROCK
Co-Dublin
✆ (01) 283 3555

ROYAL AUTOMOBILE CLUB
RAC House, Lansdowne Rd.
CROYDON, Surrey CR9 2JA
✆ (020) 8917 2500

ROYAL AUTOMOBILE CLUB
RAC IRELAND
New Mount House
22-24 Lower Mount St.
DUBLIN 2
✆ (01) 676 0113

Le piante

a	*Alberghi – Ristoranti*

Curiosità

Edificio interessante

Costruzione religiosa interessante

Viabilità

M 1	*Autostrada*
4 4	*- svincoli: completo, parziale*
	Strada a carreggiate separate di tipo autostradale
	Asse principale di circolazione
A 2	*Itinerario principale (Primary route : GB) (National Primary Route : IRL)*
	Senso unico – Via impraticable, a circolazione regolamentata
	Via pedonale – Tranvia
Piccadilly P	*Via commerciale – Parcheggio – Parcheggio Ristoro*
	Porta – Sottopassaggio – Galleria
15'5	*Sottopassaggio (altezza inferiore a 16'6") sulle grandi vie di circolazione*
	Stazione e ferrovia
	Funicolare – Funivia, Cabinovia
B	*Ponte mobile – Traghetto per auto*

Simboli vari

	Ufficio informazioni turistiche
	Moschea – Sinagoga
	Torre o pilone per telecomunicazioni – Ruderi
	Giardino, parco, bosco – Cimitero
9	*Stadio – Ippodromo – Golf – Pattinaggio*
	Golf riservato
	Piscina all'aperto, coperta
	Vista – Panorama
	Monumento – Fontana – Ospedale – Mercato coperto
	Porto per imbarcazioni da diporto – Faro
	Aeroporto – Stazione della Metropolitana – Autostazione
	Trasporto con traghetto: - passeggeri ed autovetture
	Ufficio centrale di fermo posta, telefono
	Edificio pubblico indicato con lettera:
C H	*- Sede dell'Amministrazione di Contea – Municipio*
M T U	*- Museo – Teatro – Università, grande scuola*
POL. J	*- Polizia (Questura, nelle grandi città) – Palazzo di Giustizia*

Londra

BRENT WEMBLEY	*Nome del distretto amministrativo (borough) – del quartiere (area)*
	Limite del « borough » – di « area »

Lieber Leser

Unabhängigkeit, Kompetenz und Aufmerksamkeit : dies waren schon immer die Maximen die Der Rote Michelin in den Mittelpunkt seiner Dienstleistung für den Leser gestellt hat.

Die Unabhängigkeit des Roten Michelin ist die seiner Inspektoren. Sie besuchen Hotels und Restaurants und bezahlen alle ihre Rechnungen, und dies unter Wahrung ihrer vollen Anonymität.

Es ist auch die des Führers selbst, der auf seinen Seiten jede Form der Werbung nach wie vor ablehnt.

Kompetent ist Der Rote Michelin durch seine passionierten und fachlich gut ausgebildeten Inspektoren. Das ganze Jahr über sind sie für Sie unterwegs wie ganz normale, nur etwas aufmerksamere Reisende.

Der Rote Michelin ist Ihnen Begleiter und Berater hat immer ein offenes Ohr für Sie. Die sehr zahlreichen Zuschriften, die wir jedes Jahr erhalten, liefern wertvolle Hinweise für die jeweils nächste Ausgabe.

Dadurch ist Der Rote Michelin stets in der Lage eine zuverlässige, aktuelle und für alle Budgets passende Auswahl zu bieten. Besuchen Sie auch unsere Homepage: www.michelin-travel.com.

Der Rote Michelin lebt für Sie und entwickelt sich mit Ihrer Hilfe weiter:

Schreiben Sie uns !

Inhaltsverzeichnis

Wahl eines Hotels, eines Restaurants

Die Auswahl der in diesem Führer aufgeführten Hotels und Restaurants ist für Durchreisende gedacht. In jeder Kategorie drückt die Reihenfolge der Betriebe (sie sind nach ihrem Komfort klassifiziert) eine weitere Rangordnung aus.

Kategorien

		Großer Luxus und Tradition
		Großer Komfort
		Sehr komfortabel
		Mit gutem Komfort
		Mit standard Komfort
		Traditionelle Pubs die Speisen anbieten
		Andere empfohlene Übernachtungsmöglichkeiten (Gästehäuser, Bauernhäuser und Private Übernachtungsmöglichkeiten) und Pensionen
without rest.		*Hotel ohne restaurant*
	with rm	*Restaurant vermietet auch Zimmer*

Annehmlichkeiten

Manche Häuser sind im Führer durch rote Symbole gekennzeichnet (s. unten). Der Aufenthalt in diesen ist wegen der schönen, ruhigen Lage, der nicht alltäglichen Einrichtung und Atmosphäre sowie dem gebotenen Service besonders angenehm und erholsam.

bis ,	*Angenehme Hotels*
bis ,	*Angenehme Restaurants*
« Park »	*Besondere Annehmlichkeit*
	Sehr ruhiges, oder abgelegenes und ruhiges Hotel
	Ruhiges Hotel
sea	*Reizvolle Aussicht*
	Interessante oder weite Sicht

Die den einzelnen Regionen vorangestellten Übersichtskarten, auf denen die Orte mit besonders angenehmen oder ruhigen Häusern eingezeichnet sind, helfen Ihnen bei der Reisevorbereitung. Teilen Sie uns bitte nach der Reise Ihre Erfahrungen und Meinungen mit. Sie helfen uns damit, den Führer weiter zu verbessern.

Einrichtung

Die meisten der empfohlenen Hotels verfügen über Zimmer, die alle oder doch zum größten Teil mit einer Naßzelle ausgestattet sind. In den Häusern der Kategorien und kann diese jedoch in einigen Zimmern fehlen.

30 rm	*Anzahl der Zimmer*
	Fahrstuhl
	Klimaanlage
TV	*Fernsehen im Zimmer*
	Hotel ganz oder teilweise reserviert für Nichtraucher
	Modemanschluß im Zimmer
	Für Körperbehinderte leicht zugängliche Zimmer
	Garten-, Terrassenrestaurant
	Freibad, Hallenbad
	Fitneßraum – Sauna
	Liegewiese, Garten
	Park
18	*Hoteleigener Tennisplatz – Golfplatz und Lochzahl*
	Bootssteg
	Angelmöglichkeit für Hotelgäste, evtl. gegen Gebühr
150	*Konferenzräume: Höchstkapazität*
	Hotelgarage (wird gewöhnlich berechnet)
P	*Parkplatz reserviert für Gäste*
	Hunde sind unerwünscht (im ganzen Haus bzw. in den Zimmern oder im Restaurant)
Fax	*Telefonische Dokumentenübermittlung*
May-October	*Öffnungszeit, vom Hotelier mitgeteilt*
season	*Unbestimmte Öffnungszeit eines Saisonhotels. Die Häuser, für die wir keine Schließungszeiten angeben, sind im allgemeinen ganzjährig geöffnet*
LL35 OSB	*Angabe des Postbezirks (hinter der Hoteladresse)*

Küche

Die Sterne

Einige Häuser verdienen wegen ihrer überdurchschnittlich guten Küche Ihre besondere Beachtung. Auf diese Häuser weisen die Sterne hin.

*Bei den mit «**Stern**» ausgezeichneten Betrieben nennen wir drei kulinarische Spezialitäten, die Sie probieren sollten.*

✿✿✿ **Eine der besten Küchen : eine Reise wert**

Mar ißt hier immer sehr gut, öfters auch hervorragend, edle Weine, tadelloser Service, gepflegte Atmosphäre... entsprechende Preise.

✿✿ **Eine hervorragende Küche : verdient einen Umweg**

Ausgesuchte Menus und Weine... angemessene Preise.

✿ **Eine sehr gute Küche : verdient Ihre besondere Beachtung**

Der Stern bedeutet eine angenehme Unterbrechung Ihrer Reise.

Vergleichen Sie aber bitte nicht den Stern eines sehr teuren Luxusrestaurants mit dem Stern eines kleineren oder mittleren Hauses, wo man Ihnen zu einem annehmbaren Preis eine ebenfalls vorzügliche Mahlzeit reicht.

Der "Bib Gourmand"

Sorgfältig zubereitete, preiswerte Mahlzeiten

Für Sie wird es interessant sein, auch solche Häuser kennenzulernen, die eine sehr gute, Küche zu einem besonders günstigen Preis/Leistungs-Verhältnis bieten.

Im Text sind die betreffenden Restaurants durch rote Angabe **"Bib Gourmand"** *und* Meals *kenntlich gemacht, z.B.* Meals 19.00/25.00.

Preise

Die in diesem Führer genannten Preise wurden uns im Herbst 2000 angegeben. Sie können sich mit den Preisen von Waren und Dienstleistungen ändern.

In einigen Städten werden bei kommerziellen oder touristischen Veranstaltungen von den Hotels beträchtlich erhöhte Preise verlangt.

Die Preise sind in Pfund Sterling angegeben (1£ = 100 pence) mit Ausnahme der Republik Irland wo sie in Punts angegeben sind.

Wenn die Buchstaben s., t., *oder* st. *nicht hinter den angegebenen Preisen aufgeführt sind, können sich diese um den Zuschlag für Bedienung und/oder MWSt erhöhen (keine MWSt auf den Channel Islands).*

Die Namen der Hotels und Restaurants, die ihre Preise genannt haben, sind fett gedruckt. Gleichzeitig haben sich diese Häuser verpflichtet, die von den Hoteliers selbst angegebenen Preise den Benutzern des Michelin-Führers zu berechnen.

Halten Sie beim Betreten des Hotels den Führer in der Hand. Sie zeigen damit, daß Sie aufgrund dieser Empfehlung gekommen sind.

Mahlzeiten

Feste Menupreise

Meals 13.00/28.00	*Mindestpreis* 13.00, *Höchstpreis* 28.00 *für ein angebotenes Menü*
Meals 19.00/25.00	*Siehe Seite 47*
s.	*Bedienung inkl.*
t.	*MWSt inkl.*
st.	*Bedienung und MWSt inkl.*
🍾 6.00	*Preis für 1/2 Flasche oder eine Karaffe Tafelwein*

Mahlzeiten «à la carte»

Meals a la carte 20.00/35.00	*Der erste Preis entspricht einer einfachen aber sorgfältig zubereiteten Mahlzeit, bestehend aus kleiner Vorspeise, Tagesgericht mit Beilage und Nachstisch. Der zweite Preis entspricht einer reichlicheren Mahlzeit mit Vorspeise, Hauptgericht, Käse oder Nachtisch (inkl. Couvert)*

⌂: *In dieser Hotelkategorie wird ein Abendessen normalerweise nur zu bestimmten Zeiten für Hotelgäste angeboten. Es besteht aus einem Menu mit begrenzter Auswahl zu festgesetztem Preis. Mittagessen wird selten angeboten. Viele dieser Hotels sind nicht berechtigt, alkoholische Getränke auszuschenken.*

Zimmer

rm 50.00/90.00 — *Mindestpreis* 50.00, *für ein Einzelzimmer und Höchstpreis* 90.00 *für das schönste Doppelzimmer*

suites — *Preise auf Anfrage*

rm ☕ 55.00/85.00 — *Übernachtung mit englischem Frühstück, selbst wenn dieses nicht eingenommen wird*

☕ 6.00 — *Preis des Frühstücks*

« Short breaks » (SB.)

Einige Hotels bieten Vorzugskonditionen für einen Mindestaufenthalt von zwei Nächten oder mehr (Short Break). Der Preis ist pro Person kalkuliert, bei einer Mindestbeteiligung von zwei Personen und schließt das Zimmer, das Abendessen und das Frühstück ein.

Ausschank alkoholischer Getränke

In Großbritanien und Irland unterliegt der Ausschank alkoholischer Getränke gesetzlichen Bestimmungen die von Land zu Land sehr verschieden sind.

Restaurants können nachmittags geöffnet sein und alkoholische Getränke ausschenken, wenn diese zu einer entsprechenden Mahlzeit genossen werden. Hotelbars und Pubs sind generell von 11 Uhr vormittags bis 23 Uhr abends geöffnet: Hotelgäste können alkoholische Getränke jedoch auch außerhalb der Offnungszeiten serviert werden.

Kindern unter 14 Jahren ist der Aufenthalt in Bars untersagt.

Anzahlung

Einige Hoteliers verlangen eine Anzahlung. Diese ist als Garantie sowohl für den Hotelier als auch für den Gast anzusehen.

Kreditkarten

Vom Haus akzeptierte Kreditkarten: MasterCard (Eurocard) – American Express – Diners Club – Visa – Japan Credit Bureau

Städte

✉ *York*	*Zuständiges Postamt*
401 M 27, ⑩	*Nummer der Michelin-Karte und Koordinaten des Planfeldes oder Faltseite*
West Country G.	*Siehe auch den grünen Michelinführer The West Country of England*
pop. 1057	*Einwohnerzahl*
BX A	*Markierung auf dem Stadtplan*
18	*Öffentlicher Golfplatz und Lochzahl (Handicap manchmal erforderlich, telefonische Reservierung empfehlenswert)*
✳ ⋞	*Rundblick, Aussichtspunkt*
✈	*Flughafen*
⛴	*Autofähre*
⛴	*Personenfähre*
ℹ	*Informationsstelle*

Uhrzeit

In Großbritannien ist eine Zeitverschiebung zu beachten und die Uhr gegenüber der deutschen Zeit um 1 Stunde zurückzustellen.

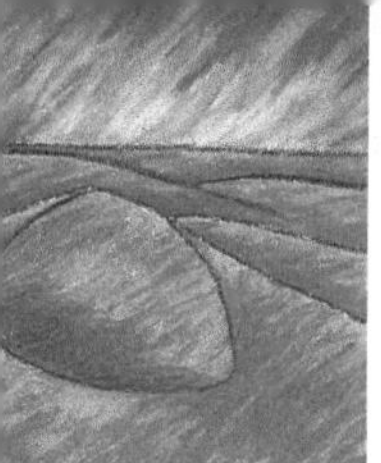

Sehenswürdigkeiten

Bewertung

★★★	*Eine Reise wert*
★★	*Verdient einen Umweg*
★	*Sehenswert*
AC	*Eintritt (gegen Gebühr)*

Lage

See	*In der Stadt*
Envir.	*In der Umgebung der Stadt*
Exc.	*Ausflugsziele*
N, S, E, W	*Im Norden (N), Süden (S), Osten (E), Westen (W) der Stadt*
A 22	*Zu erreichen über die Straße A 22*
2 m.	*Entfernung in Meilen*

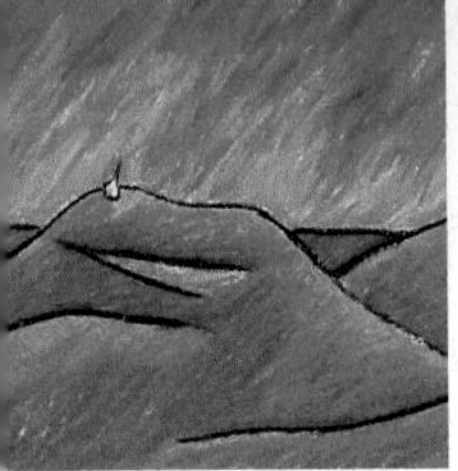

Umgebungskarten

Denken Sie daran sie zu benutzen

Die Umgebungskarte erleichtert Ihnen die Suche nach einem Hotel oder Restaurant in der Nähe einer größeren Stadt.
Wenn Sie zum Beispiel eine gute Adresse in der Nähe von Leeds suchen, gibt Ihnen die Umgebungskarte schnell einen Überblick über alle Orte, die in diesem Führer erwähnt sind.
Innerhalb der in Kontrastfarbe gedruckten Grenze liegen Orte, die im in einer Entfernung von 25 km/16 miles zu erreichen sind.

Anmerkung:

All Orte die auf einer Nachbarschaftskarte verzeichnet sind haben im Ortsblock einen Hinweis. Der entsprechende Ortsname ist in diesem Falle in den Entfernungsangaben in „BLAU" gedruckt.

Beispiel:

Sie finden ILKLEY auf der Umgebungskarte von LEEDS

IKLEY *W. Yorks.* 402 O 22 – pop. 13 530
Myddleton ℘ (01943) 607277
Station Rd, LS29 8HA ℘ (01943) 602319
London 210 – Bradford 13 – Harrogate 13 – Leeds 16 – Preston 46

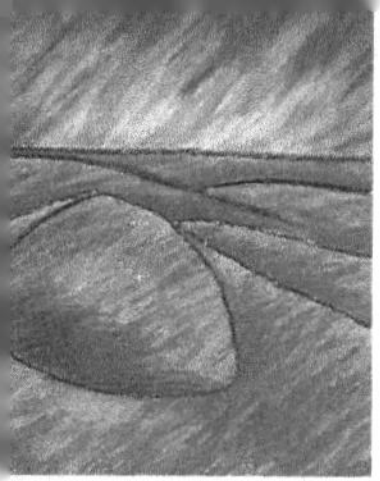

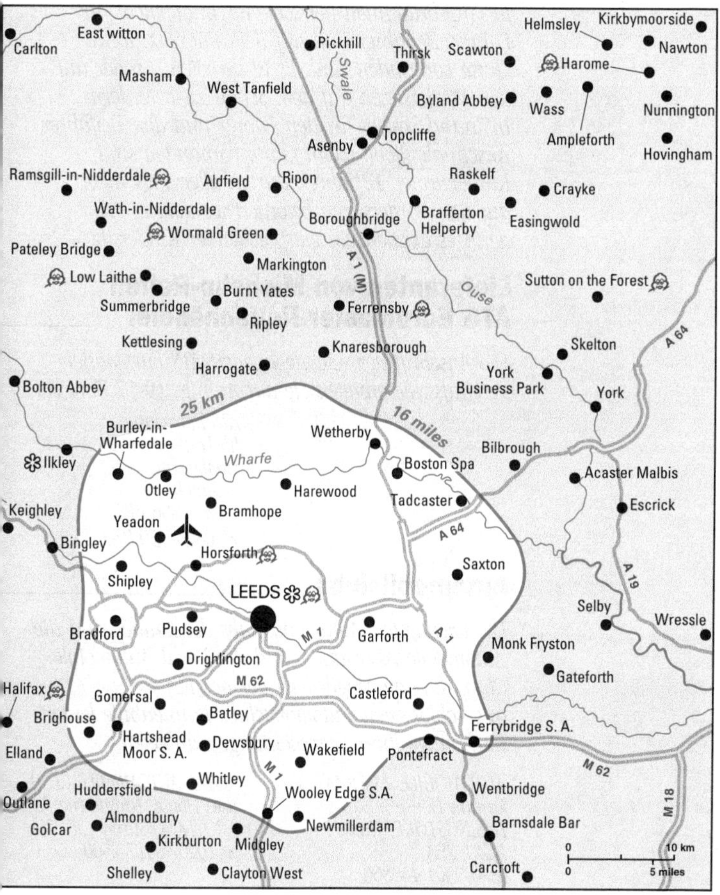

Die Umgebungskarten finden Sie auf der Themenkarte S. 76, S. 85.

Das Auto, die Reifen

In Großbritannien herrscht Anschnallpflicht für Fahrer, Beifahrer und auf dem Rücksitz, wenn Gurte vorhanden sind. Es ist verboten, Kinder auf den Vordersitzen auf dem Schoß zu befördern. In Irland besteht für den Fahrer und den Beifahrer Anschnallpflicht, wenn Gurte vorhanden sind, Kinder unter 12 Jahren dürfen allerdings nicht auf den Vordersitzen befördert werden, es sei denn es existiert ein entsprechender Kindersitz.

Lieferanten von Michelin-Reifen ATS Euromaster Reifenhändler

Die Anschrift der nächstgelegenen ATS Euromaster-Verkaufsstelle erhalten Sie auf Anfrage (9-17 Uhr) bei

ATS Euromaster
Jill Lane
Sambourne
Redditch
Worcs. B96 6ES
✆ 0800 750 850

Automobilclubs

Die wichtigsten Automobilsclubs des Landes sind die Automobile Association und der Royal Automobile Club, die den Mitgliedern der der FIA angeschlossenen Automobilclubs Pannenhilfe leisten und einige ihrer Dienstleistungen anbieten.

AUTOMOBILE ASSOCIATION
Fanum House
BASINGSTOKE, Hants
RG21 2EA
✆ (0990) 448866

ROYAL AUTOMOBILE CLUB
RAC House, Lansdowne Rd.
CROYDON, Surrey CR9 2JA
✆ (020) 8917 2500

AUTOMOBILE ASSOCIATION
23 Rock Hill
BLACKROCK
Co-Dublin
✆ (01) 283 3555

ROYAL AUTOMOBILE CLUB
RAC IRELAND
New Mount House
22-24 Lower Mount St.
DUBLIN 2
✆ (01) 676 0113

Stadtpläne

Hotels – Restaurants

Sehenswürdigkeiten

Sehenswertes Gebäude
Sehenswerter Sakralbau

Straßen

M 1 *Autobahn*
- Anschlußstellen: Autobahneinfahrt und/oder-ausfahrt,
Schnellstraße mit getrennten Fahrbahnen
Hauptverkehrsstraße
A 2 *Fernverkehrsstraße (Primary route : GB)*
(National primary route : IRL)
Einbahnstraße – Gesperrte Straße, mit Verkehrsbeschränkungen
Fußgängerzone – Straßenbahn
Piccadilly *Einkaufsstraße – Parkplatz, Parkhaus*
Tor – Passage – Tunnel – Park-and-Ride-Plätze
15'5 *Unterführung (Höhe angegeben bis 16'6") auf Hauptverkehrsstraßen*
Bahnhof und Bahnlinie
Standseilbahn – Seilschwebebahn
B *Bewegliche Brücke – Autofähre*

Sonstige Zeichen

Informationsstelle
Moschee – Synagoge
Funk-, Fernsehturm – Ruine
Garten, Park, Wäldchen – Friedhof
Stadion – Pferderennbahn – Golfplatz – Eisbahn
Golfplatz (Zutritt bedingt erlaubt)
Freibad – Hallenbad
Aussicht – Rundblick
Denkmal – Brunnen – Krankenhaus – Markthalle
Jachthafen – Leuchtturm
Flughafen – U-Bahnstation – Autobusbahnhof
Schiffsverbindungen: Autofähre
Hauptpostamt (postlagernde Sendungen), Telefon
Öffentliches Gebäude, durch einen Buchstaben gekennzeichnet:
C H J *- Sitz der Grafschaftsverwaltung – Rathaus – Gerichtsgebäude*
M T U *- Museum – Theater – Universität, Hochschule*
POL. *- Polizei (in größeren Städten Polizeipräsidium)*

London

BRENT WEMBLEY *Name des Verwaltungsbezirks (borough) – des Stadtteils (area)*
Grenze des « borough » – des « area »

Beer

Beer is one of the oldest and most popular alcoholic drinks in the world. Traditional draught beer is made by grinding malted barley, heating it with water and adding hops which add the familiar aroma and bitterness.

Beers in Britain can be divided into 2 principal types: Ales and Lagers which differ principally in their respective warm and cool fermentations. In terms of sales the split between the two is approximately equal. Beer can also be divided into keg or cask.

Keg beer – *is filtered, pasteurised and chilled and then packed into pressurised containers from which it gets its name.*

Cask beer – *or 'Real Ale' as it is often referred to, is not filtered, pasteurised or chilled and is served from casks using simple pumps. It is considered by some to be a more characterful, flavoursome and natural beer.*

There are several different beer styles in Britain and Ireland:

Bitter – *whilst it is the most popular traditional beer in England and Wales it is now outsold by lager. Although no precise definition exists it is usually paler and dryer than Mild with a high hop content and slightly bitter taste.*

Mild – *is largely found in Wales, the West Midlands and the North West of England. The name refers to the hop character as it is gentle, sweetish and full flavoured beer. It is generally lower in alcohol and sometimes darker in colour, caused by the addition of caramel or by using dark malt.*

Stout – *the great dry stouts are brewed in Ireland and are instantly recognisable by their black colour and creamy head. They have a pronounced roast flavour with plenty of hop bitterness.*

In Scotland the beers produced are full bodied and malty and are often known simply as Light, Heavy, or Export which refers to the body and strength of the beer.

Although Ireland is most famous for its stouts, it also makes a range of beers which have variously been described as malty, buttery, rounded and fruity with a reddish tinge.

Whisky

The term whisky is derived from th Scottish Gealic uisage beatha *and the Irish Gaelic* uisce beathadh, *both meaning "water of life". When spelt without an e it usually refers to Scotch Whisky which can only be produced in Scotland by the distillation of malted and unmalted barley, maize, rye, and mixtures of two or more of these. Often simply referred to as Scotch it can be divided into 2 basic types: malt whisky and grain whisky.*

Malt whisky – *is made only from malted barley which is traditionally dried over peat fires. The malt is then milled and mixed with hot water before mashing turns the starches into sugars and the resulting liquid, called wort, is filtered out. Yeast is added and fermentation takes place followed by two distilling processes using a pot still. The whisky is matured in oak, ideally sherry casks, for at least three years which affects both its colour and flavour. All malts have a more distinctive smell and intense flavour than grain whiskies and each distillery will produce a completely individual whisky of great complexity. A single malt is the product of an individual distillery. There are approximately 100 malt whisky distilleries in Scotland.*

Grain whisky – *is made from a mixture of any malted or unmalted cereal such as maize or wheat and is distilled in the Coffey, or patent still, by a continuous process. Very little grain whisky is ever drunk unblended.*

Blended whisky – *is a mix of more than one malt whisky or a mix of malt and grain whiskies to produce a soft, smooth and consistent drink. There are over 2,000 such blends which form the vast majority of Scottish whisky production.*

Irish Whiskey – *differs from Scotch whisky both in its spelling and method of production. It is traditionally made from cereals, distilled three times and matured for at least 7 years. The different brands are as individual as straight malt and considered by some to be gentler in character.*

La bière

La bière est l'une des plus anciennes et populaires boissons alcoolisées dans le monde. Pour produire la bière pression traditionnelle, on écrase l'orge maltée que l'on chauffe ensuite avec de l'eau à laquelle on ajoute le houblon. C'est ce qui lui donne son arôme et son goût amer bien connus.
Deux types de bières sont principalement vendues en Grande-Bretagne : les Ales *fermentées à chaud et les* Lagers *fermentées à froid. Elles se divisent en « keg beer » et en « cask beer ».*

Bière en keg : *elle est filtrée, pasteurisée et refroidie, puis versée dans des tonnelets pressurisés appelés kegs.*

Bière en cask *ou « Real Ale » : elle n'est ni filtrée, ni pasteurisée, ni refroidie mais tirée directement du tonneau à l'aide d'une simple pompe. Selon certains, cette bière, de qualité bien distincte, a plus de saveur et est plus naturelle.*

Types de bières vendues au Royaume-Uni et en Irlande :

Bitter – *C'est la bière traditionnelle la plus populaire en Angleterre et au pays de Galles mais ses ventes diminuent au profit des lagers. La Bitter est généralement plus pâle et son goû plus sec que la* Mild. *Son contenu en houblon est élevé et elle a un goût légèrement amer.*

La Mild *se consomme surtout au pays de Galles, dans le Midlands de l'Ouest et dans le Nord-Ouest de l'Angleterre. On l'appelle ainsi en raison de son goût moelleux légèrement douceâtre conféré par le houblon. Cette bière, généralement moins alcoolisée, est plus foncée par le caramel qui lui est ajouté ou par l'utilisation de malt plus brun.*

Stout – *les grandes marques de bières brunes sont brassées en Irlande et sont reconnaissables par leur couleur noire rehaussé de mousse crémeuse. Elles ont un goût prononcé de houblon grillé et une saveur amère.*

Celles produites en Écosse sont maltées; elles ont du corps et se dénomment le plus souvent Light, Heavy ou Export en référence au corps et à leur teneur en alcool.

Whisky

Le mot whisky est un dérivé du gaélique écossais uisage beatha *et du gaélique irlandais* uisce beathadh *signifiant tous deux « eau de vie ». Quand il est écrit sans* e, *il se réfère au whisky écossais qui ne peut être produit qu'en Écosse par la distillation de céréales maltées ou non comme l'orge, le maïs, le seigle ou d'un mélange de deux ou plus de ces céréales. Souvent appelé tout simplement Scotch il se réfère à deux types de whiskies : whisky pur malt ou whisky de grain.*

Le whisky pur malt est fait seulement à partir d'orge maltée qui est traditionnellement séchée au-dessus de feux de tourbe. Le malt est moulu et mélangé avec de l'eau chaude, puis le brassage transforme l'amidon en sucre; le moût est ensuite filtré. On y ajoute de la levure et après la fermentation on fait distiller deux fois dans un alambic. Le whisky est alors vieilli pendant au moins trois ans dans des fûts de chêne, ayant contenu de préférence du sherry, ce qui transforme son goût et sa couleur. Tous les whiskies pur malt ont un arôme particulier et une saveur plus intense que les whiskies de grain et chaque distillerie produit son propre whisky avec des qualités bien distinctes. Il y a environ une centaine de distilleries de whiskies pur malt en Écosse.

Le whisky de grain est fait d'un mélange de céréales, maltées ou non, comme le maïs ou le froment et est distillé dans un alambic de type Coffey suivant un procédé continu. Très peu de whiskies de grain sont consommés à l'état pur. On procède à des mélanges pour la consommation.

Blended whisky est le mélange d'un ou de plusieurs whiskies pur malt et de whiskies de grain afin de produire un alcool léger, moelleux et de qualité. Il existe plus de 2 000 marques de blended whiskies qui forment la majeure partie de la production écossaise.

Le whisky irlandais, différent du whisky écossais par sa fabrication, est traditionnellement produit à partir de céréales; il est ensuite distillé trois fois et vieilli pendant au moins sept ans. Certains le trouvent plus moelleux.

Birra

La birra è una delle bevande alcoliche più antiche e popolari. La tradizionale birra alla spina si ottiene macinando l'orzo, riscaldandolo con l'acqua e aggiungendo il luppolo, che le conferiscono l'aroma e il tipico sapore amaro.

Le birre britanniche si dividono in due tipi principali: Ales e Lagers, *che differiscono essenzialmente per la fermentazione, rispettivamente calda e fredda. In termini di vendita, i due tipi approssimativamente si equivalgono. La birra può anche dividersi in* keg *(lett,* barilotto*), e* cask *(lett* botte*).*

La keg beer *è filtrata, pastorizzata e raffreddata, e poi messa in contenitori pressurizzati, da cui deriva il nome.*

La cask beer, *o* Real Ale, *come viene comunemente indicata, non è filtrata, pastorizzata o raffeddata, ed è servita dalle botti, usando semplici pompe. Alcuni la considerano una birra più ricca di carattere e di gusto e più naturale.*

In Gran Bretagna e Irlanda, le birre si caratterizzano anche in base a « stili » diversi.

Le bitter *costituisce la birra tradizionalmente più popolare in Inghilterra e nel Galles, ma è ora « superata » dalla* lager. *Non esiste definizione specifica per la birra* bitter, *ma si può dire che si tratta in genere di una birra più pallida e secca della* mild, *dall'alto contenuto di luppolo e dal gusto leggermente amaro.*

La mild *è diffusa in Galles, West Midlands e Inghilterra nord-occidentale. Il nome richiama il carattere del luppolo, essendo delicata, dolce e dal gusto pieno. Contiene solitamente una limitata quantità di alcol ed è talvolta scura per l'aggiunta di caramello e per l'impiego di malto scuro.*

La secche stouts *vengono prodotte in Irlanda e sono immediatamente riconoscibili dal colore nero e dalla schiuma cremosa. Hanno una decisa fragranza di tostatura e un gusto amaro di luppolo.*

Whisky

Il termine whisky deriva dal gealico scozzese uisage beatha *e dal gaelico irlandese* uisce beathadh, *che significano « acqua di vita ». Se scritto senza la* e, *indica di solito lo* Scotch Whisky, *che può essere unicamente prodotto in Scozia dalla distillazione di malto e orzo, granturco e segale, e dall'unione di due o più di questi ingredienti. Spesso chiamato semplicemente Scoveri, si divide in due tipi:* malt whisky e grain whisky.

Il malt whisky *viene prodotto unicamente con malto, tradizionalmente seccato su fuochi alimentati con torba. Il malto viene poi macinato e gli viene aggiunta acqua bollente prima che l'impasto muti gli amidi in zuccheri e il liquido che ne deriva, chiamato* wort *(mosto di malto), venga filtrato. Si amalgama poi il lievito e avviene la fermentazione, seguita da due processi di distillazione nell'alambicco. Il whisky è lasciato invecchiare in legno di quercia, idealmente in botti di sherry, per almeno tre anni, perchè acquisti colore e sapore. Ogni tipo di* malt whisky *ha un profumo più distintivo e un gusto più intenso del* grain whisky. *Ogni distilleria produce un whisky dal carattere individuale, che richiede un processo di grande complessità. Un solo* malt whisky *è il prodotto di una specifica distilleria. In Scozia, esistono circa 100 distillerie di* malt whisky.

Il grain whisky *è il risultato della fusione di qualsiasi cereale con o senza malto, come il granturco o il frumento, en viene distillato nel Coffey, o alambicco brevettato, grazie ad un processo continuo. È molto scarsa la quantità di* grain whisky *che si beve puro.*

Il blended whisky *nasce dalla fusione di più di un* malt whisky, *o da quella di* malt e grain whiskies. *Il risultato è una bevanda dal gusto delicato, dolce e pieno. Esistono più di 2000 whisky di questo tipo, che costituiscono la parte più consistente della produzione scozzese.*

Bier

Bier ist eines der ältesten und beliebtesten alkoholischen Getränke der Welt. Das traditionelle Faßbier wird aus gemahlener und gemalzter Gerste hergestellt, die in Wasser erhitzt wird. Durch Beigabe von Hopfen werden das bekannte Aroma und der typische bittere Geschmack erzeugt.

Die Biersorten in Großbritannien unterteilen sich in zwei Hauptgruppen: Ales *und* Lagers, *wobei die Art der Gärung – im einen Fall warm, im anderen kalt – ausschlaggebend für das Endresultat ist. Beide Sorten haben hierzulande einen ungefähr gleichen Marktanteil. Da sich die meisten Brauvorgänge anfangs gleichen, entscheiden erst die Endphasen des Brauens, welche der verschiedenen Biersorten entsteht.*

Darüber hinaus kann das englische Bier auch nach der Art seiner Abfüllung in Keg- *bzw.* Cask-*Bier unterschieden werden:*

Keg beer *wird gefiltert, pasteurisiert, abgekühlt und anschlienßend in luftdichte, unter Druck gesetzte Metallbehälter gefüllt, von denen das Bier auch seinen Namen erhält.*

Cask beer, *gewöhnlich* Real Ale *genannt, wird weder gefiltert, noch pasteurisiert oder gekühlt, sondern mit einfachen (zumeist Hand-) Pumpen vom Faß gezapft.*

Es gibt folgende Biersorten in Großbritannien und Irland:
Bitter ist das meistbekannte traditionelle Bier in England und Wales. Eine genaue Definition, was ein Bitter ausmacht, sucht man vergeblich; es ist gewöhnlich heller und trockener als das Mild, *hat einen hohen Hopfenanteil und einen leicht bitteren Geschmack. In den letzten Jahren hat das – meist importierte oder in Lizenz gebraute –* Lager *ihm jedoch den Rang abgelaufen.*

Mild *ist übergiegend in Wales, in den westlichen Midlands und Nordwestengland zu finden. Der Name bezieht sich auf den Hopfenanteil, der es zu einem milden, etwas süßlichen und vollmundigen Bier macht. Es hat einen geringeren Alkoholgehalt und besitz wegen der Zugabe von Karamel oder dunklem Malz bisweilen eine dunklere Farbe.*

Stouts *von hervorragendem trockenem Geschmack werden in Irland gebraut und sind unmittelbar an ihrer schwarzen Farbe und der cremigen Blume erkennbar. Sie haben einen ausgesprochen starken Geschmack nach bitterem Hopfen.*

In Schottland hergestellte Biere sind alkoholstark und malzig; sie sind oft einfach bekannt als: Light, Heavy oder Export *– Bezeichnungen, die auf Körper und Stärke des Bieres hinweisen.*

Whisky

Die Bezeichnung Whisky entstammt dem Gälischen, wo im Schottischen der Ausdruck uisage beatha, *im Irischen des Ausdruck* uisce beathadh *jeweils « Wasser des Lebens » bedeuten. Wird Whisky ohne ein e am Ende geschrieben, ist* Scotch Whisky *gemeint, der nur in Schottland aus gemalzter und ungemalzter Gerste, Mais, Roggen oder aus Mischungen zweier oder mehrerer dieser Zutaten gebrannt werden darf. Oft auch nur als* Scotch *bezeichnet, kann dieser in zwei Grundarten unterschieden werden:* malt whisky *und* grain whisky.

Malt (Malz) whisky *wird nur aus gemalzter Gerste hergestellt, die traditionell über Torffeuern getrocknet wird. Danach wird das Malz gemahlen und mit heißem Wasser vermischt, wonach in der Maische die Stärke in Zucker umgewandelt wird. Die dadurch entstandene Flüssigkeit,* « wort » *genannt, wird gefiltert und mit Hefe versetzt, was den Gärungsprozess einleitet. Anschließend folgen zwei Destillierungen im herkömmlichen Topf über offenem Feuer. Der Whisky reift danach mindestens drei Jahre lang in Eichenholz, idealerweise in Sherry-Fässern, was sich sowohl auf Farbe wie auf Geschmack des Whiskys auswirkt. Alle* malts *haben einen ausgeprägteren Geruch und intensiveren Geschmack als die* grain-*Whiskies; und jede Destillerie erzeugt einen völlig eigenen Whisky mit individueller Geschmacksnote und großer Komplexität. Ein sogenannter* single malt *enstammt aus einer einzigen Destillerie. Es gibt ungefähr 100 Malt Whisky-Destillerien in Schottland.*

Grain (Korn) whisky *wird aus Mischungen von gemalzten und ungemalzten Getreidesorten, wie Mais oder Weizen, hergestellt und wird in einem kontinuierlichen Prozeß in dem sogenannten « Coffey » destilliert. Nur sehr wenige Kornwhisky-Sorten sind nicht das Ergebnis von* blending, *dem Abstimmen des Geschmacks durch Mischung.*

Blended whisky *wird aus mehr als einer Sorte Malt Whisky oder aus Malt und Grain Whiskies gemischt, um ein weiches, geschamcklich harmonisches Getränk von beständiger Güte zu garantieren. Die über 2000 im Handel zu findenden* blends *stellen den Großteil der schottischen Whiskyerzeugung dar.*

Irish Whiskey *unterscheidet sich vom Scotch Whisky sowohl in der Schreibweise wie auch dem Herstellungsverfahren. Er wird traditionell aus Getreide hergestellt, wird dreifach destilliert und reift mindestens sieben Jahre lang. Die verschiedenen Sorten sind so individuell ausgeprägt wie reine Malt Whiskies und werden oft als weicher und gefälliger empfunden.*

Menu

Starred establishments
Les établissements à étoiles
Gli esercizi con stelle
Die Stern-Restaurants

✿✿✿

England

Bray-on-Thames *Waterside Inn*
London *Gordon Ramsay*

✿✿

England

Bath *Lettonie*
Chagford *Gidleigh Park*
Cheltenham *Le Champignon Sauvage*
London *Capital*
- *Le Gavroche*
- *John Burton-Race*
- *The Square*
- *La Tante Claire*
Oxford *Le Manoir aux Quat' Saisons*
Winteringham *Winteringham Fields*

Scotland

Ullapool *Altnaharrie Inn*

Ireland

Republic of Ireland

Dublin *Patrick Guilbaud*
– *Thornton's*

✿

England

Altrincham *Juniper*
Baslow *Fischer's at Baslow Hall*
Bath *Bath Priory*
- *Moody Goose*
Blackburn *Northcote Manor*
Blakeney *Morston Hall*
Bourton-on-the-Water *Lords of the Manor*
Bray-on-Thames *Fat Duck*
Bristol *Harveys*
Channels Islands
Gorey (Jersey) *Village Bistro*
St Saviour (Jersey) *Longueville Manor*
Chester *Arkle*
Chipping Norton *Chavignol*
Cuckfield *Ockenden Manor*
East Grinstead *Gravetye Manor*
Emsworth *36 on the Quay*
Faversham *Read's*
Folkestone *La Terrasse*
Grantham *Harry's Place*
Grasmere *Michaels Nook Country House*
Great Malvern *Croque-en-Bouche*
Ilkley *Box Tree*
Kenilworth *Simpson's*
King's Lynn *Rococo*
Kington *Stagg Inn*
Leeds *Pool Court at 42*
London *Aubergine*
- *Chapter One*
- *Chez Bruce*
- *City Rhodes*
- *Connaught*
- *L'Escargot*
- *The Halkin*
- *High Holborn*
- *Mirabelle*
- *Monsieur Max*
- *Nobu*
- *The Oak Room Marco Pierre White*
- *1 Lombard Street (Restaurant)*
- *L'Oranger*
- *Orrery*
- *Pétrus*
- *Pied à Terre*

- *Putney Bridge*
- *Rhodes in the Square*
- *Richard Corrigan at Lindsay House*
- *River Café*

Roussillon

Tamarind

- *Zafferano*

Zaika

Longridge *Paul Heathcote's*

Ludlow *Hibiscus*

- *Merchant House*
- *Mr Underhill's at Dinham Weir*

Lyndhurst *Le Poussin at Parkhill*

Newbury *Vineyard*

New Milton *Chewton Glen*

Norwich *Adlard's*

Oakham *Hambleton Hall*

Plymouth *Chez Nous*

Sheffield *Old Vicarage*

Shepton Mallet *Charlton House*

Storrington *Fleur de Sel*

Taplow *Waldo's*

Tavistock *Horn of Plenty*

Ullswater *Sharrow Bay Country House*

Waterhouses *Old Beams*

Wight (Isle of)

Yarmouth *The George*

Winchester *Chesil Rectory*

Windermere *Holbeck Ghyll*

Woodstock *Feathers*

Scotland

Achiltibuie *Summer Isle*

Balloch *Georgian Room*

Castle Douglas *Plumed Horse*

Dalry *Braidwood*

Edinburgh *Martin Wishar*

Fort William *Inverlochy Castle*

Glasgow *One Devonshire Garden*

Port Appin *Aird*

Portpatrick *Knockinaam Lodge*

Wales

Llansanffraid Glan Conwy *Old Rector*

Llyswen *Llangoed Ha*

Ireland

Northern Ireland

Bangor *Shank*

Belfast *Restaurant Michael Dean*

Republic of Ireland

Ahakista *Shir*

Ballyconneely *Erriseask Hous*

Dublin *Peacock Alle*

"Bib Gourmand"

Good food at moderate prices

Repas soignés à prix modérés

Pasti accurati a prezzi contenuti

Sorgfältig zubereitete, preiswerte Mahlzeiten

Meals

England

Aldeburgh *Lighthouse*
Alderley Edge *The Wizard*
Baslow *Café-Max*
Bath *Hole in the Wall*
Birmingham *Gilmore*
- *Metro Bar & Grill*
- *Le Petit Blanc*
Blackpool *September Brasserie*
Brighton and Hove *Black Chapati*
- *Terre à Terre*
Bristol *Markwicks*
Burnham Market *The Restaurant (at Hoste Arms H.)*
Burnsall *Devonshire Fell*
Cambridge *22 Chesterton Road*
Carlisle *Magenta's*
Channel Islands
Green Island (Jersey) *Green Island*
Cheltenham *Le Petit Blanc*
Chipping Campden *Churchill Arms*
Cirencester *Village Pub*
Coln St.Aldwyns *The Courtyard Bar (at New Inn at Coln)*
Devizes *George & Dragon*
Durham *Bistro 21*
Faversham *Dove Inn*
Four Marks *Yew Tree*
Great Missenden *Berts at the Barley Mow*
Halifax *Design House*
Helmsley *The Star Inn*
Horncastle *The Magpies*
Kendal *Punch Bowl Inn*
Keyston *Pheasant*
Knaresborough *The General Tarleton Inn (Bar/Brasserie)*
Ledbury *The Malthouse*
Leeds *Brasserie Forty Four*
- *The Calls Grill*
- *Leodis*
London *L'Accento*
- *L'Anis*
- *Al Duca*
- *Cafe Spice Namaste*
- *Cafe Spice Namaste*
- *Cantina Vinopolis (Brasserie)*
- *I Cardi*
- *Chada Chada*
- *Chapter Two*
- *Il Forno*
- *The Glasshouse*
- *Jak's*
- *Light House*
- *Luca*
- *Malabar*
- *Metrogusto*
- *Passione*
- *The Phoenix*
- *Redmond's*
- *Sabras*
- *Sarkhel's*
- *The Vale*
Long Melford *Scutchers Bistro*
Loughborough *Lang's*
Maldon *Chigborough Lodge*
Nailsworth *Waterman's*
Nayland *White Hart*
Newcastle upon Tyne *Café 21*
- *Café 21*
Nottingham *Hart's*
Old Burghclere *Dew Pond*
Oldham *Brasserie (at White Hart Inn)*
Orford *The Trinity*
Oxford *Le Petit Blanc*

Pateley Bridge	*Dusty Miller*
-	*Yorke Arms*
Preston	*Heathcotes Brasserie*
Reading	*New Inn*
Ripon	*Olives*
Rushlake Green	*Stone House*
St Albans	*Sukiyaki*
Salisbury	*Howard's House*
Sheffield	*Rafters*
-	*Smith's of Sheffield*
Skipton	*Angel Inn (Bar Brasserie)*
Southport	*Warehouse Brasserie*
Sowerby Bridge	*The Millbank*
Standish	*The Mulberry Tree*
Stanton	*Leaping Hare*
Storrington	*Old Forge*
Sunderland	*Brasserie 21*
Sutton on the Forest	*Rose & Crown*
Telford	*Hundred House*
Towcester	*Vine House*
Turville	*Bull & Butcher*
Virginstow	*Percy's*
Wells	*Ritchers*
Windsor	*Al Fassia*
Winkleigh	*Pophams*
Woodbridge	*The Captain's Table*

Scotland

Edinburgh	*Atrium*
-	*Rhodes & Co.*
Glasgow	*No. Sixteen*
Strathyre	*Creagan House*

Wales

Cardiff	*Gilby*
-	*Woods Brasser*
Colwyn Bay	*Café Niçoi*
Knighton	*The Waterdin*
Llandudno	*Nikki Ip*
Llanwrtyd Wells	*Carlton Hou*
Pwllheli	*Plas Bodegro*
Talbot Green	*Brook*

Ireland

Northern Ireland

Belfast	*Alder*
-	*Cayenn*
-	*Deanes Brasser*
Holywood	*Fontan*
Portrush	*Ramo*

Republic of Ireland

Baltimore	*Customs Hou*
Cork	*Jacobs on the Ma*
Dingle	*The Chart Hou*
Dublin	*Blueberry*
-	*Chapter Or*
-	*Ernie*
-	*Jacobs Ladd*
-	*Mermaid Ca*
-	*Morels at Stephen's Ho*
Dungarvan	*The Tanne*
Dun Laoghaire	*Duzy's Ca*
Galway	*Archw*
Kenmare	*An Leath Phing*
-	*The Lime Tr*
Kilbrittain	*Casino Hou*

Particularly pleasant Hotels
Hôtels agréables
Alberghi ameni
Angenehme Hotels

England

London *The Berkeley*
- *Claridge's*
- *Dorchester*
- *Mandarin Oriental Hyde Park*
- *Ritz*
- *Savoy*

New Milton *Chewton Glen*
Taplow *Cliveden*

Ireland *Republic of Ireland*

Straffan *Kildare H. & Country Club*

England

Aylesbury *Hartwell House*
Bath *Lucknam Park*
- *The Royal Crescent*

Ipswich *Hintlesham Hall*
London *Connaught*
Melton Mowbray *Stapleford Park*
Oxford *Le Manoir aux Quat' Saisons*

Scotland

Ballantrae *Glenapp Castle*
Dunkeld *Kinnaird*
Fort William *Inverlochy Castle*
Glasgow *One Devonshire Gardens*

Wales

Llyswen *Llangoed Hall*

Ireland *Republic of Ireland*

Dublin *The Merrion*
Kenmare *Park*
- *Sheen Falls Lodge*

England

Abberley *The Elms*
Amberley *Amberley Castle*
Bath *Bath Priory*
- *Homewood Park*

Bolton Abbey *Devonshire Arms Country House*
Bourton-on-the-Water *Lords of the Manor*
- *Lower Slaughter Manor*

Bristol *Hunstrete House*
Broadway *Buckland Manor*
Castle Combe *Manor House*
Chagford *Gidleigh Park*

Channel Islands

La Pulente (Jersey) *Atlantic*
Rozel Bay (Jersey) *Chateau La Chaire*
St Saviour (Jersey) *Longueville Manor*

East Grinstead *Gravetye Manor*
Evershot *Summer Lodge*
Gillingham *Stock Hill Country House*
Grasmere *Michaels Nook Country House*
Leeds *42 The Calls*
Littlehampton *Bailiffscourt*
London *Blakes*
- *Capital*
- *Charlotte Street*
- *Cliveden Town House*

London	*Covent Garden*
-	*Durley House*
-	*The Goring*
-	*The Halkin*
-	*One Aldwych*
-	*Pelham*
Newbury	*Vineyard*
Oakham	*Hambleton Hall*
Royal Leamington Spa	*Mallory Court*
Sandiway	*Nunsmere Hall*
Scilly *(Isles of)*	
St Martin's	*St Martin's on the Isle*
Tresco	*The Island*
Shepton Mallet	*Charlton House*
Sutton Coldfield	*New Hall*
Taunton	*The Castle*
Tetbury	*The Close*
Ullswater	*Sharrow Bay Country House*
York	*Middlethorpe Hall*

Scotland

Arisaig	*Arisaig Hous*
Dunblane	*Cromlix Hous*
Edinburgh	*The Bonhar*
-	*The Howar*
Eriska *(Isle of)*	*Isle of Erisk*
Inverness	*Culloden Hous*
Newton Stewart	*Kirroughtree Hous*
Port Appin	*Air*

Wales

Llandudno	*Bodysgallen Ha*
Llangammarch Wells	*Lake Countr Hous*

Ireland *Republic of Ireland*

Cashel	*Cashel Hous*
Dublin	*The Clarenc*
Gorey	*Marlfield Hous*
Mallow	*Longueville Hous*
Wicklow	*Tinakilly Hous*

England

Bradford-on-Avon	*Woolley Grange*
Brampton	*Farlam Hall*
Bridgnorth	*The Old Vicarage*
Burrington	*Northcote Manor*
Cheltenham	*On the Park*
Cuckfield	*Ockenden Manor*
Frome	*Babington House*
Hereford	*Castle House*
Horley	*Langshott Manor*
King's Lynn	*Congham Hall*
Lewdown	*Lewtrenchard Manor*
London	*22 Jermyn Street*
Oxford	*Old Parsonage*
Purton	*Pear Tree at Purton*
Rushlake Green	*Stone House*
St Mawes	*Tresanton*
Tetbury	*Calcot Manor*
Ullswater	*Old Church Priory*
Wareham	
Wellington	*Bindon Country House*
Wight *(Isle of)*	
Yarmouth	*The George*
Windermere	*Gilpin Lodge*
-	*Holbeck Ghyll*
Woodstock	*Feathers*

Scotland

Achiltibuie	*Summer Isles*
Arran *(Isle of)*	*Kilmichael Country House*
Gullane	*Greywalls*
Lewis & Harris *(Isle of)*	
Ardvourlie (Harris)	*Ardvourlie Cast*
Portpatrick	*Knockinaam Lodg*
Skye *(Isle of)*	*The House Over-B*
Strontian	*Kilcamb Lodg*
Ullapool	*Altnaharrie In*
Whitebridge	*Knockie Lodg*

Wales

Llandrillo	*Tyddyn Lla Country Hous*
Machynlleth	*Ynyshir Ha*
Swansea	*Fairyh*
Talsarnau	*Maes-y-Neuad*

Ireland *Republic of Ireland*

Arthurstown	*Dunbrody Country Hous*
Ballingarry	*Mustard Seed Echo Lodg*
Cashel	*Zetland Country Hou*
Castlebaldwin	*Cromleach Lodg*
Craughwell	*St Cleran*
Glin	*Glin Cast*
Kanturk	*Assolas Country Hou*
Kinsale	*Perryville House (without res*
Shanagarry	*Ballymaloe Hou*

England

Blakeney *Morston Hall*
Chipping Campden *Malt House*
Cranbrook *Kennel Holt*
Dartmouth *Nonsuch House*
Dulverton *Ashwick House*
Keswick *Swinside Lodge*
Nottingham *Morgans (without rest)*
Porlock *Oaks*
Salisbury *Howard's House*
Staverton *Kingston House*
Swaffham *Strattons*
Teignmouth *Thomas Luny House (without rest)*
Tintagel *Trebrea Lodge*
Wiveliscombe *Langley House*

Scotland

Kelso *Edenwater House*
Kentallen *Ardsheal House*
Lochinver *The Albannach*
Maybole *Ladyburn*
Muir of Ord *Dower House*
Mull *(Isle of)* *Killiechronan House*
Nairn *Boath House*
Perth *Dupplin Castle*
Shetland Islands *Burrastow House*
Tain *Glenmorangie House*

Wales

Betws-y-Coed *Tan-y-Foel Country House*
Llansanffraid Glan Conwy *Old Rectory*

Ireland

Northern Ireland
Holywood *Rayanne House*
Republic of Ireland
Bagenalstown *Kilgraney Country House*
Lahinch *Moy House*
Leenane *Delphi Lodge*
Riverstown *Coopershill*

England

Alnmouth *High Buston Hall*
Askrigg *Helm*
Aylmerton *Felbrigg Lodge*
Bath *Haydon House (without rest)*
Billingshurst *Old Wharf (without rest)*
Blockley *The Old Bakery*
Calne *Chilvester Hill House*
Carlisle *Number Thirty One*
Caxton *Church Farm*
Cockermouth *New House Farm*
- *Winder Hall*
Coniston *Appletree Holme*
Crackington Haven *Manor Farm*
Cranbrook *Old Cloth Hall*
Dover *Old Vicarage (without rest)*
East Hoathly *Old Whyly*
Faversham *Frith Farm House*
Grindon *Porch Farmhouse*
Honiton *Cokesputt House*
Kettlewell *High Fold (without rest)*
Kirkby Malham *Holgate Head*
Lavenham *Lavenham Priory (without rest)*
Lewes *Millers (without rest)*
Lizard *Landewednack House*
Malpas *Tilston Lodge (without rest)*
Marazion *Ednovean Farm (without rest)*
Melksham *Sandridge Park*
North Bovey *The Gate House*
Norton St. Philip *Monmouth Lodge (without rest)*
Petworth *Old Railway Station (without rest)*
Plymouth *The Barn*
Ripley *High Winsley Cottage*
St Blazey *Nanscawen Manor House (without rest)*
Seaford *Old Parsonage (without rest)*
Shrewsbury *Pinewood House (without rest)*

Tavistock *Quither Mill*
- *Tor Cottage (without rest)*
Tetbury *Tavern House (without rest)*
Veryan *Crugsillick Manor*
Wareham *Gold Court House*
Woodstock *Shipton Glebe*

Scotland

Arran *(Isle of)* *Apple Lodge*
Banchory *Old West Manse*
Earlston *Birkhill*
Edinburgh *17 Abercromby Place (without rest)*
- *27 Heriot Row (without rest)*
Fort William *Crolinnhe (without rest)*
- *The Grange (without rest)*
Gairloch *Little Lodge*
Glenborrodale *Feorag House*
Inverness *Millwood House (without rest)*
Islay *(Isle of)* *Kilmeny Country Guest House*
Shetland Islands *Buness Hous*
Skye *(Isle of)* *Kinlochfolla*
Stathpeffer *Craigvar (without res*

Wales

Bala *Fron Feuno Ha*
Dollgellau *Abergwynant Ha*

Ireland

Northern Ireland
Dungannon *Grange Lodg*
Republic of Ireland
Ardee *Red Hous*
Castlelyons *Ballyvolane Hous*
Castlerea *Clonalis Hous*
Cong *Ballywarren Hous*
Inistioge *Berryh*
Kanturk *Glenloha*
Kenmare *Sallyport House (without res*
Kilkenny *Blanchville Hous*

Particularly pleasant Restaurants
Restaurants agréables
Ristoranti ameni
Angenehme Restaurants

XXXXX

England

London *The Restaurant (at Ritz H.)*

XXXX

England

Bray-on-Thames *Waterside Inn (with rm)*
London *Grill Room (at Dorchester H.)*
Taplow *Waldo's*
Winteringham *Winteringham Fields (with rm)*

XXX

England

Baslow *Fischer's at Baslow Hall (with rm)*
Bath *Lettonie (with rm)*
Cambridge *Midsummer House*
Dedham *Le Talbooth*
Emsworth *36 on the Quay*
London *Orrery*
- *Oxo Tower*
- *Le Pont de la Tour*
Moulsford *Beetle & Wedge (with rm)*
Romsey *Old Manor House*
Welwyn Garden City *Auberge du Lac*

Scotland

Peat Inn *The Peat Inn (with rm)*

XX

England

Channel Islands

Gorey (Jersey) *Jersey Pottery (Garden Rest)*
- *Suma's*
St Peter in the Wood (Guernsey) *Café du Moulin*
Eastbourne *Hungry Monk*
Goring *Leatherne Bottel*
Grantham *Harry's Place*
Great Driffield *Rockingham (with rm)*
London *Quaglino's*
Moreton-in-Marsh *Marsh Goose*
Newcastle upon Tyne *Horton Grange (with rm)*
Padstow *The Seafood (with rm)*
Waterhouses *Old Beams (with rm)*

Scotland

Darvel *Scoretulloch House (with rm)*
Kingussie *The Cross (with rm)*

Ireland

Republic of Ireland

Ahakista *Shiro*

Scotland

Skye *(Isle of)*	*Three Chimneys*

Ireland

Republic of Ireland

Kenmare	*The Lime Tre*

England

Aylesbury	*Bottle & Glass*
Bray-on-Thames	*The Fish*
Broadhembury	*Drewe Arms*
Exeter	*Nobody Inn*
Great Yeldham	*White Hart*
Helmsley	*The Star Inn*
Henley-in-Arden	*Crabmill*
Keyston	*Pheasant*
Oundle	*The Falcon In*
Skipton	*Angel Inn (Bar/Brasserie*
Stadhampton	*Crazy Bear (with rm*
Stow-on-the-Wold	*Fox Inn (with rm*
Winchester	*Wykeham Arms (with rm*
Witney	*The Boot In*
Woburn	*The Birc*

Wales

Caersws	*The Talkhouse (with rm*
Conwy	*Groes Inn (with rm*

England

Channel Islands, Isle of Man

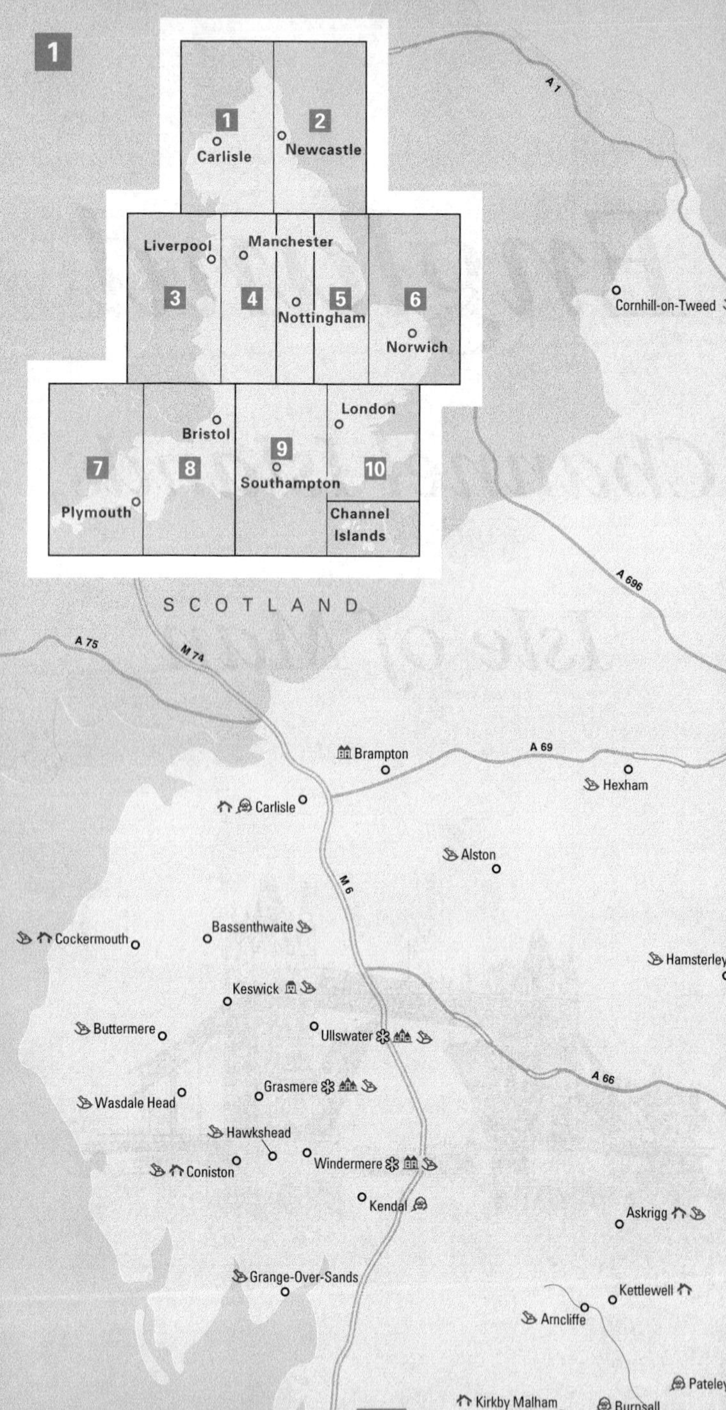
1
1
Carlisle
2
Newcastle
Liverpool
Manchester
3
4
5
6
Nottingham
Norwich
London
Bristol
9
7
8
10
Southampton
Plymouth
Channel
Islands
A 1
Cornhill-on-Tweed
A 696
SCOTLAND
A 75
M 74
Brampton
A 69
Hexham
Carlisle
Alston
M 6
Bassenthwaite
Cockermouth
Hamsterley
Keswick
Buttermere
Ullswater
Grasmere
A 66
Wasdale Head
Hawkshead
Windermere
Coniston
Kendal
Askrigg
Grange-Over-Sands
Kettlewell
Arncliffe
Kirkby Malham
Burnsall

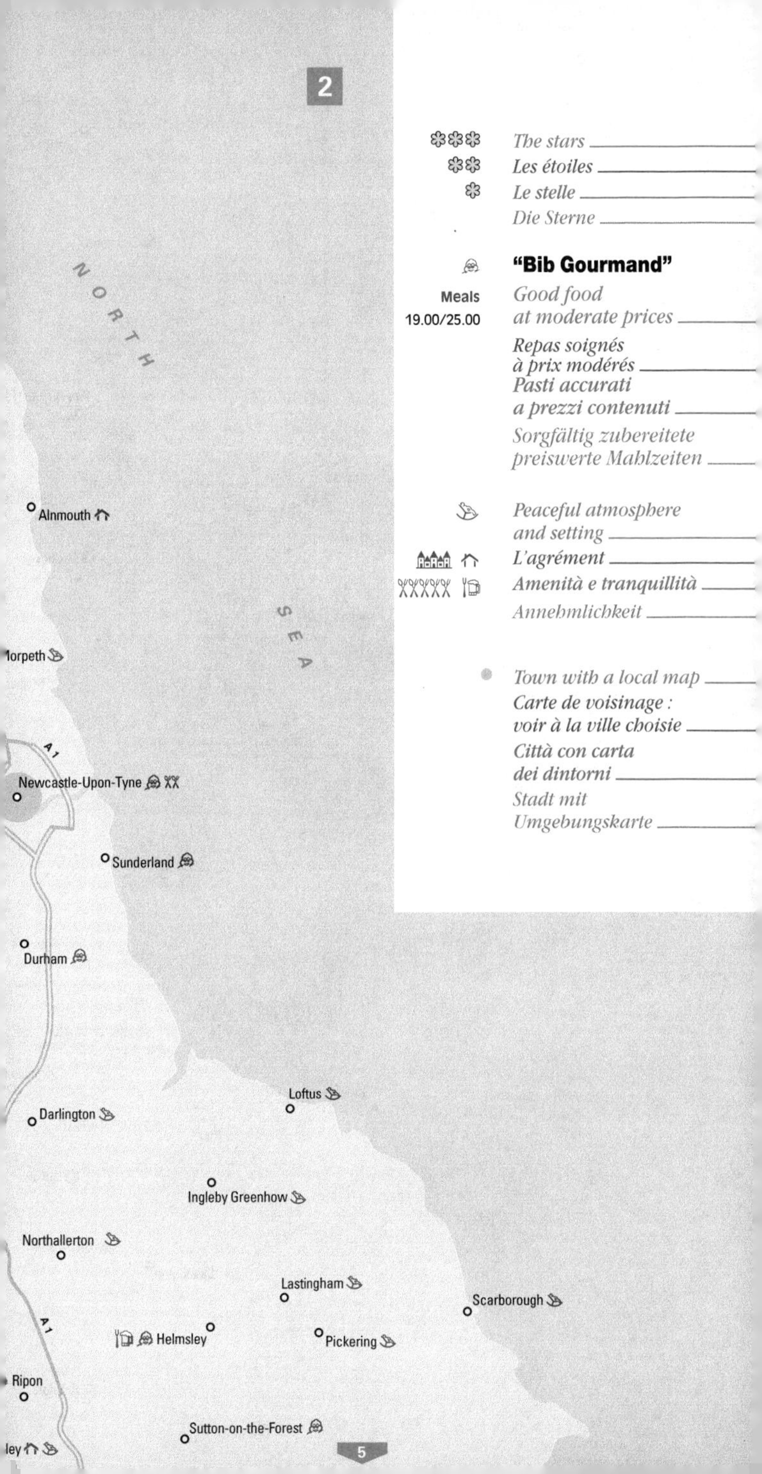

✿✿✿ *The stars*
✿✿ *Les étoiles*
✿ *Le stelle*
Die Sterne

"Bib Gourmand"

Meals 19.00/25.00 — *Good food at moderate prices*
Repas soignés à prix modérés
Pasti accurati a prezzi contenuti
Sorgfältig zubereitete preiswerte Mahlzeiten

Peaceful atmosphere and setting
L'agrément
Amenità e tranquillità
Annehmlichkeit

Town with a local map
Carte de voisinage : voir à la ville choisie
Città con carta dei dintorni
Stadt mit Umgebungskarte

NORTH SEA

Alnmouth
Morpeth
A1
Newcastle-Upon-Tyne XX
Sunderland
Durham
Loftus
Darlington
Ingleby Greenhow
Northallerton
Lastingham
Scarborough
Helmsley
Pickering
A1
Ripon
Sutton-on-the-Forest
ley

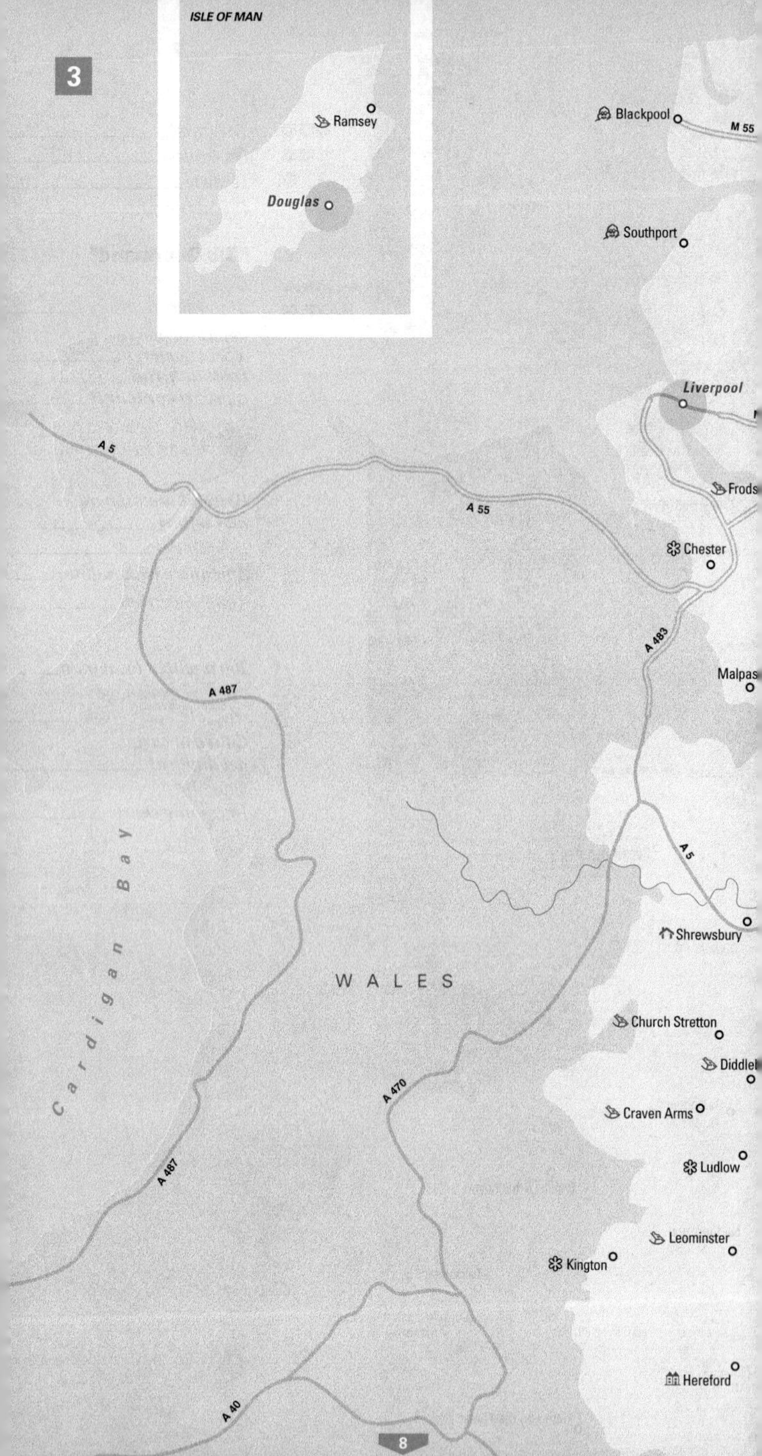

3
ISLE OF MAN
Ramsey
Douglas
Blackpool
M 55
Southport
Liverpool
A 5
A 55
Frods
Chester
A 483
Malpas
A 487
Cardigan Bay
A 5
Shrewsbury
WALES
Church Stretton
Diddle
A 470
Craven Arms
A 487
Ludlow
Leominster
Kington
Hereford
A 40

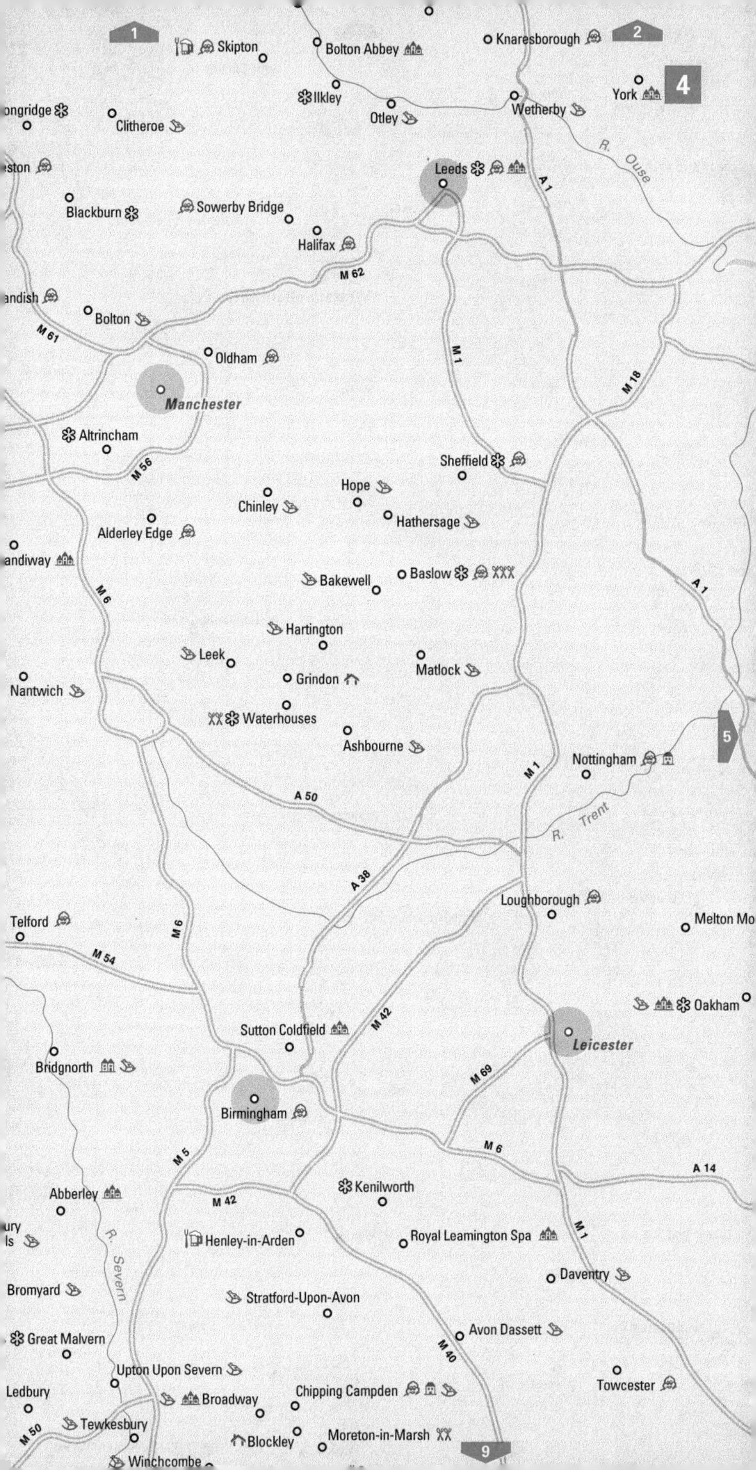

1
2
4
Skipton
Bolton Abbey
Knaresborough
York
Ilkley
Otley
Wetherby
Clitheroe
R. Ouse
Leeds
A 1
Blackburn
Sowerby Bridge
Halifax
M 62
Bolton
M 61
Oldham
Manchester
M 1
M 18
Altrincham
M 56
Sheffield
Hope
Chinley
Hathersage
Alderley Edge
Bakewell
Baslow
M 6
Hartington
Leek
Matlock
Grindon
Nantwich
Waterhouses
Ashbourne
5
Nottingham
A 50
R. Trent
A 38
Loughborough
Telford
Melton Mo
M 54
Oakham
M 42
Sutton Coldfield
Leicester
Bridgnorth
M 69
Birmingham
M 5
A 14
Abberley
Kenilworth
Henley-in-Arden
Royal Leamington Spa
R. Severn
Bromyard
Daventry
Stratford-Upon-Avon
Avon Dassett
Great Malvern
M 40
Upton Upon Severn
Towcester
Ledbury
Broadway
Chipping Campden
Tewkesbury
M 50
Blockley
Moreton-in-Marsh
9
Winchcombe

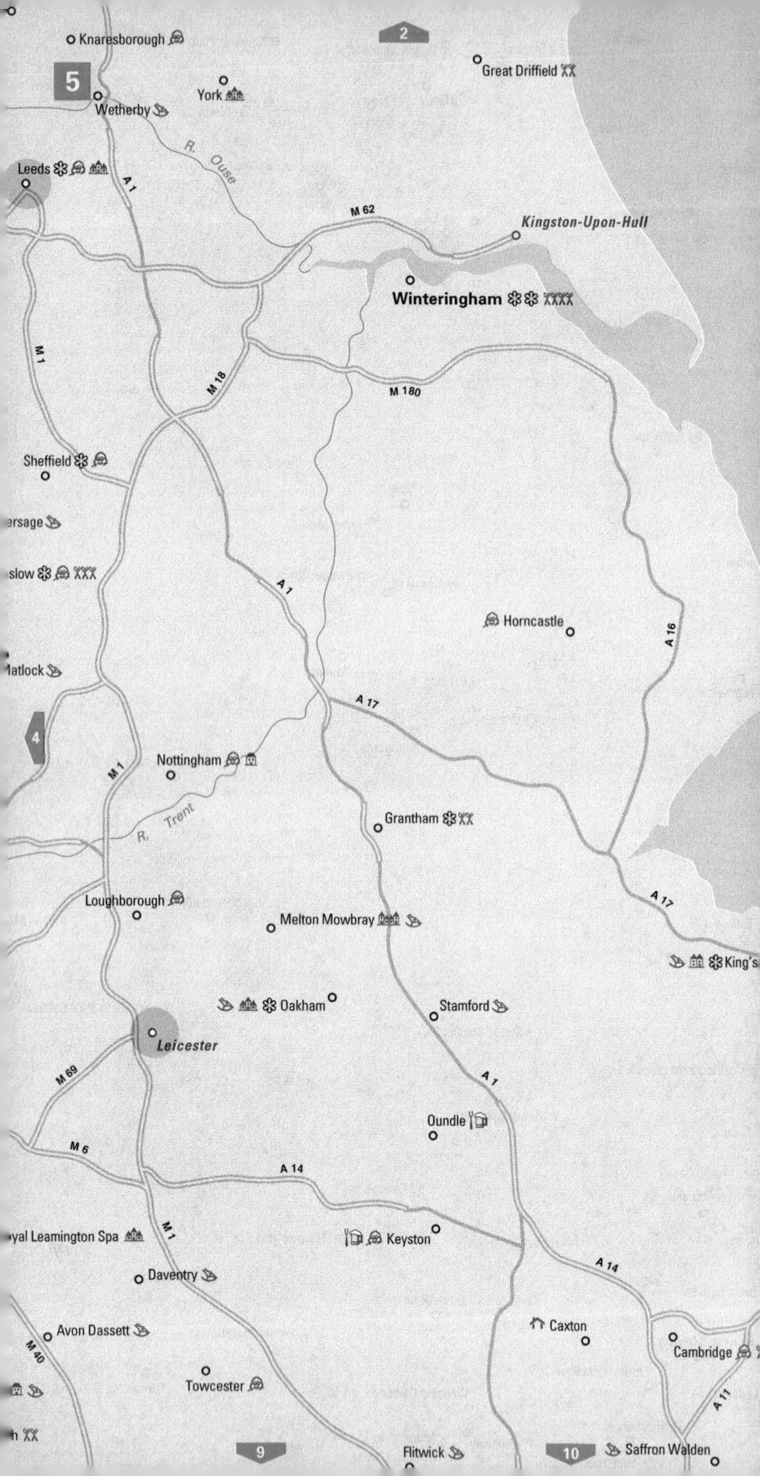
5
2
Knaresborough
York
Great Driffield
Wetherby
R. Ouse
Leeds
A 1
M 62
Kingston-Upon-Hull
Winteringham
M 1
M 18
M 180
Sheffield
ersage
slow
A 1
Horncastle
A 16
Matlock
A 17
4
Nottingham
M 1
R. Trent
Grantham
A 17
Loughborough
Melton Mowbray
King's
Oakham
Stamford
Leicester
M 69
A 1
Oundle
M 6
A 14
M 1
yal Leamington Spa
Keyston
A 14
Daventry
Caxton
Avon Dassett
Cambridge
M 40
Towcester
A 11
9
Flitwick
10
Saffron Walden

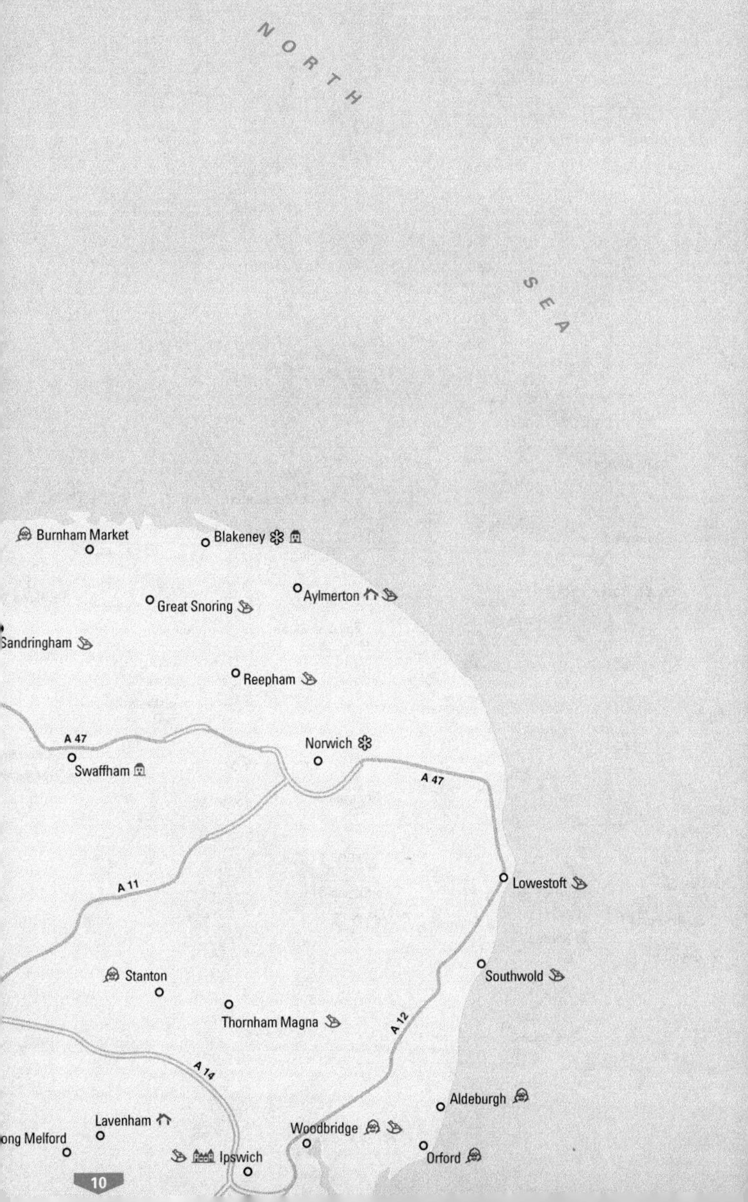

NORTH SEA

Burnham Market
Blakeney
Great Snoring
Aylmerton
Sandringham
Reepham
A 47
Swaffham
Norwich
A 47
A 11
Lowestoft
Stanton
Southwold
Thornham Magna
A 12
A 14
Aldeburgh
Lavenham
Woodbridge
ong Melford
Ipswich
Orford

10

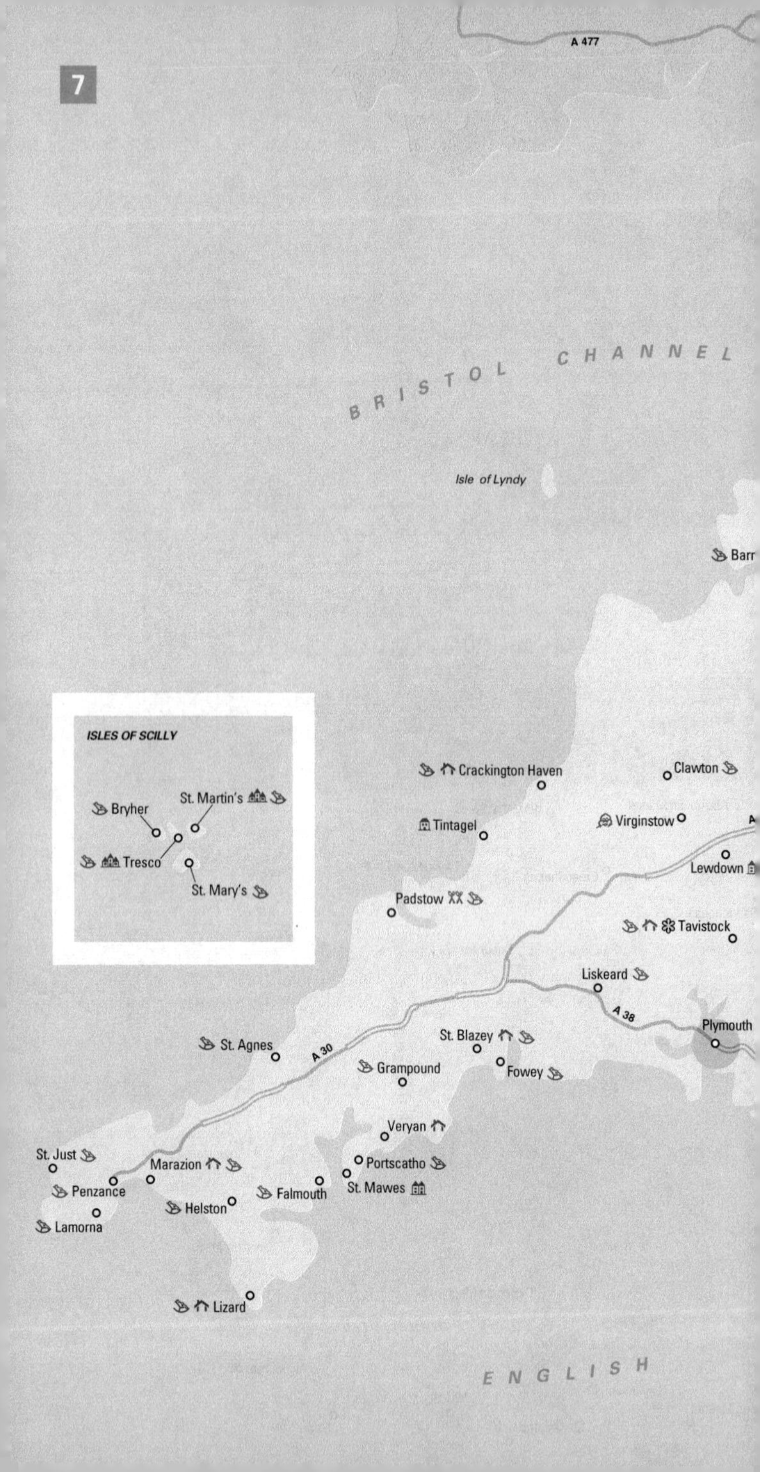

7

A 477

BRISTOL CHANNEL

Isle of Lyndy

Barr

ISLES OF SCILLY

Bryher

St. Martin's

Tresco

St. Mary's

Crackington Haven

Clawton

Tintagel

Virginstow

Lewdown

Padstow

Tavistock

Liskeard

A 38

Plymouth

St. Blazey

St. Agnes

A 30

Grampound

Fowey

Veryan

St. Just

Marazion

Portscatho

Penzance

St. Mawes

Falmouth

Helston

Lamorna

Lizard

ENGLISH

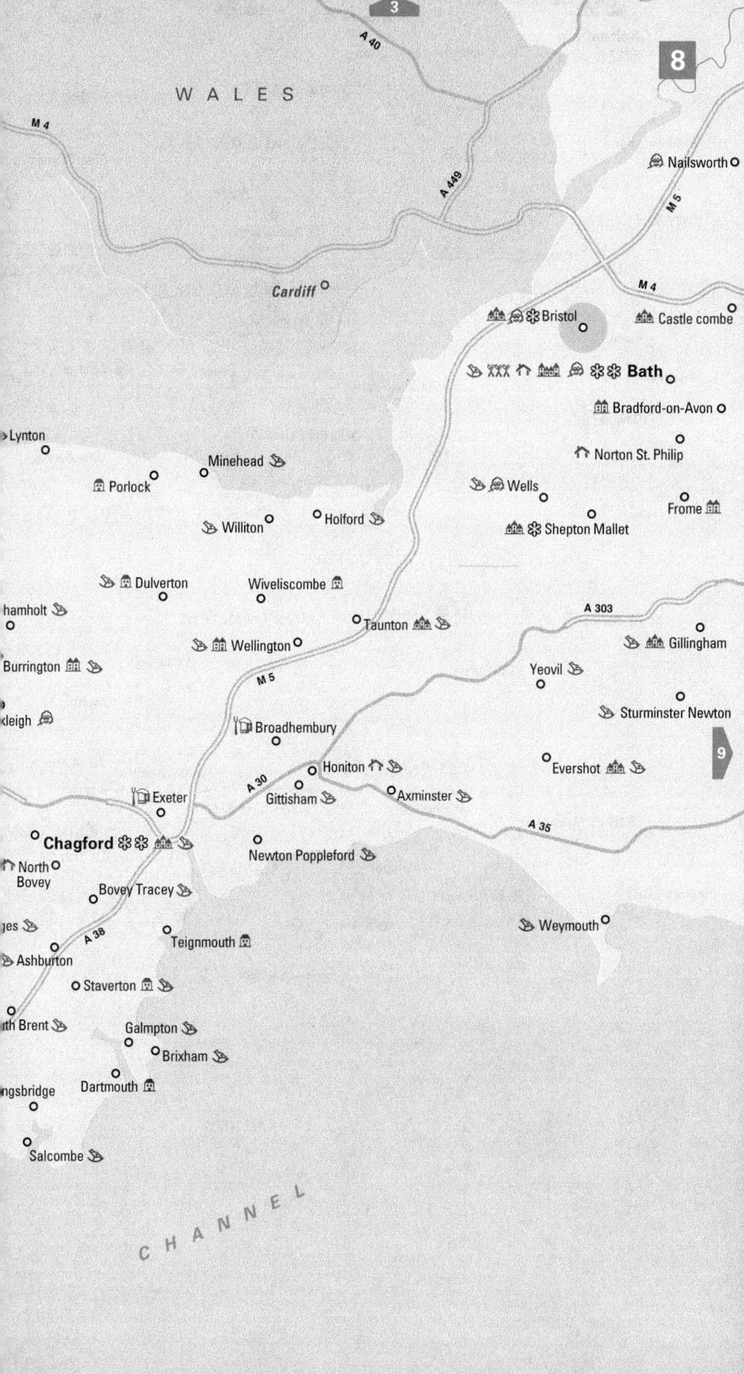
3
8
WALES
M 4
A 40
A 449
Nailsworth
M 5
Cardiff
M 4
Bristol
Castle combe
Bath
Bradford-on-Avon
Lynton
Norton St. Philip
Minehead
Porlock
Wells
Frome
Williton
Holford
Shepton Mallet
Dulverton
Wiveliscombe
hamholt
A 303
Taunton
Gillingham
Wellington
Burrington
Yeovil
M 5
Sturminster Newton
kleigh
Broadhembury
9
Honiton
Evershot
A 30
Exeter
Gittisham
Axminster
A 35
Chagford
Newton Poppleford
North Bovey
Bovey Tracey
ges
Weymouth
A 38
Teignmouth
Ashburton
Staverton
th Brent
Galmpton
Brixham
Dartmouth
ngsbridge
Salcombe
CHANNEL

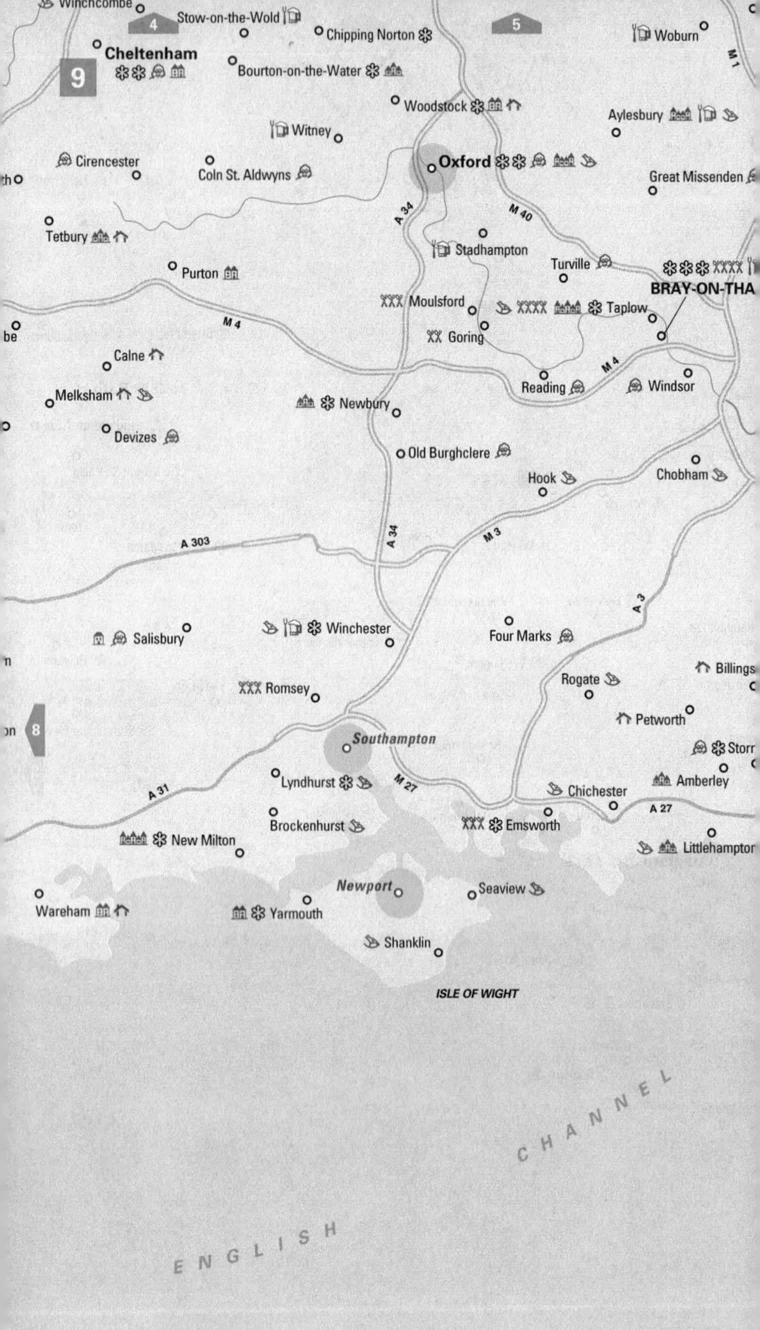

Winchcombe
4
Stow-on-the-Wold
Chipping Norton
5
Woburn
M 1
Cheltenham
9
Bourton-on-the-Water
Woodstock
Aylesbury
Witney
Cirencester
Coln St. Aldwyns
Oxford
Great Missenden
A 34
M 40
Tetbury
Stadhampton
Turville
Purton
BRAY-ON-THA
Moulsford
Taplow
M 4
Goring
Calne
M 4
Reading
Windsor
Melksham
Newbury
Devizes
Old Burghclere
Hook
Chobham
A 303
A 34
M 3
A 3
Salisbury
Winchester
Four Marks
Billings
Rogate
Romsey
Petworth
8
Southampton
Storr
Lyndhurst
M 27
Amberley
A 31
Chichester
A 27
Brockenhurst
Emsworth
New Milton
Littlehampton
Newport
Seaview
Wareham
Yarmouth
Shanklin
ISLE OF WIGHT
ENGLISH CHANNEL

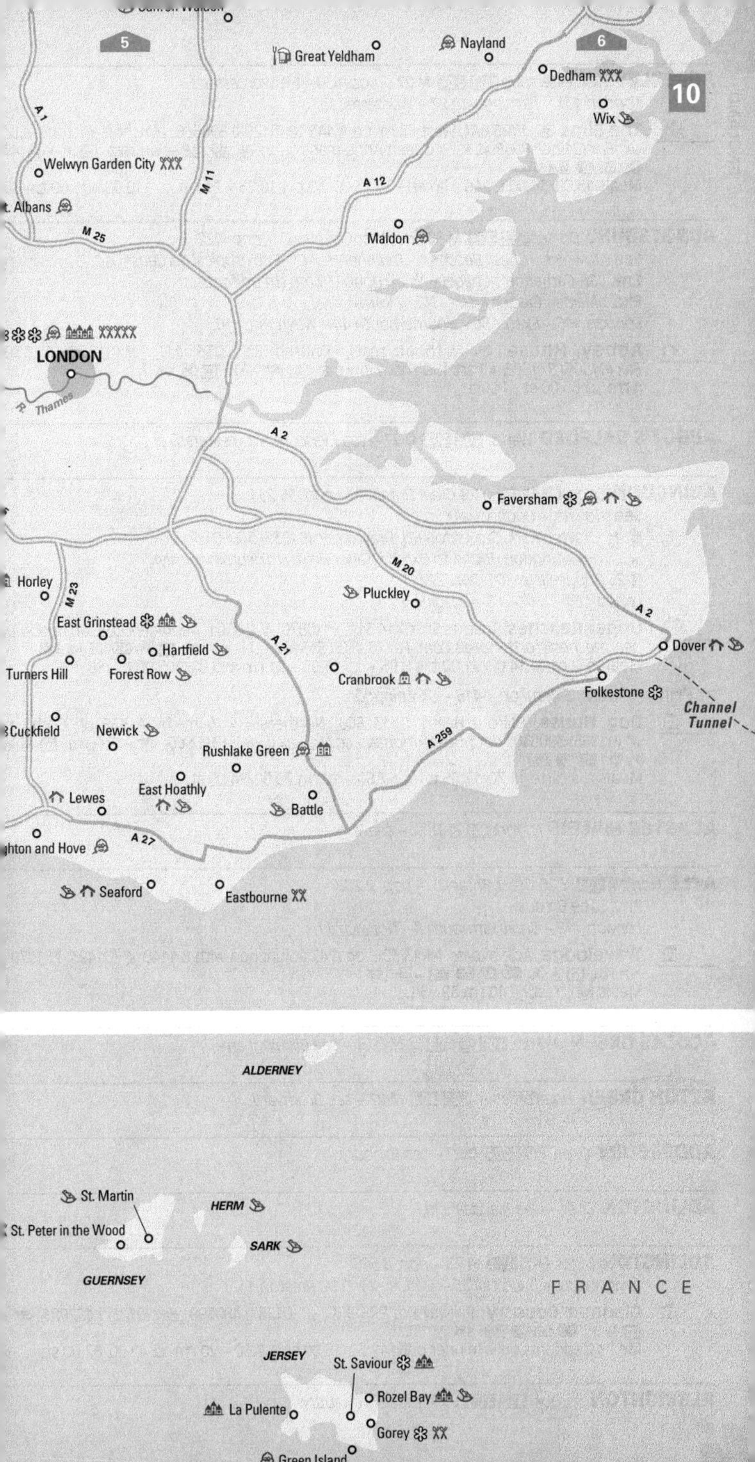

5
6
10
Great Yeldham
Nayland
Dedham
Wix
A 1
Welwyn Garden City
M 11
t. Albans
M 25
A 12
Maldon
LONDON
Thames
A 2
Faversham
M 20
Horley
M 23
East Grinstead
Pluckley
A 2
Hartfield
A 21
Dover
Turners Hill
Forest Row
Cranbrook
Folkestone
Channel Tunnel
Cuckfield
Newick
Rushlake Green
A 259
East Hoathly
Lewes
Battle
hton and Hove
A 27
Seaford
Eastbourne
ALDERNEY
St. Martin
HERM
St. Peter in the Wood
SARK
GUERNSEY
FRANCE
JERSEY
St. Saviour
Rozel Bay
La Pulente
Gorey
Green Island

ABBERLEY *Worcestershire* 403 404 M 27 – *pop. 654* – ✉ *Worcester.*
London 137 – Birmingham 27 – Worcester 13.

The Elms ⑤, WR6 6AT, West : 2 m. on A 443 ✆ (01299) 896666, *elmshotel@ukonline.co.uk, Fax (01299) 896804*, ≤, « Queen Anne mansion », ⊕, ⊕, ⊕ – ⊕ rest, TV P – ⊕ 40. MC AE ⓓ VISA JCB
Meals 15.00/34.00 **t.** and a la carte 35.35/41.40 **t.** ⊕ 10.25 – **21 rm** ⊕ 110.00/175.00 **t.** – SB

ABBOTSBURY *Dorset* 403 404 M 32 *The West Country G.* – *pop. 422.*
See : *Town★★ - Chesil Beach★★ - Swannery★ AC – Sub-Tropical Gardens★ AC.*
Env. : *St. Catherine's Chapel★, ½ m. uphill (30 mn rtn on foot).*
Exc. : *Maiden Castle★★ (≤★) NE : 7½ m.*
London 146 – Exeter 50 – Bournemouth 44 – Weymouth 10.

Abbey House ⑤ without rest., Church St., DT3 4JJ, ✆ (01305) 871330, *Fax (01305) 871088*, « Part 15C abbey infirmary », ⊕ – ⊕ TV P. ⊕
4 rm ⊕ 60.00 **st.**, 1 suite.

ABBOT'S SALFORD *Warks.* 403 404 O 27 – *see Evesham (Worcestershire).*

ABINGDON *Oxon.* 403 404 Q 28 *Great Britain G.* – *pop. 35 234.*
See : *Town★ – County Hall★.*
18, 9 *Drayton Park, Steventon Rd, Drayton ✆ (01235) 550607.*
⊕ *from Abingdon Bridge to Oxford (Salter Bros. Ltd) (summer only).*
ℹ *25 Bridge St. ✆ (01235) 522711.*
London 64 – Oxford 6 – Reading 25.

Upper Reaches, Thames St., OX14 3JA, ✆ (0870) 400 8101, *heritagehotels_abingdon.upper_reaches@forte-hotels.com, Fax (01235) 555182* – ⊕, ⊕ rm, TV P. MC AE ⓓ VISA
Meals a la carte 14.00/31.00 **t.** ⊕ 8.95 – ⊕ 11.95 – **31 rm** 115.00/205.00 **t.** – SB.

at Frilford *West : 3 ¾ m. on A 415* – ✉ *Abingdon.*

Dog House, Frilford Heath, OX13 6QJ, Northeast : 1 ¼ m. by A 338 on Cothill rd ✆ (01865) 390830, *doghouse@morland.co.uk, Fax (01865) 390860*, ⊕ – ⊕ rm, TV ⊕ ⊕ P. MC AE ⓓ VISA
Meals a la carte 11.70/17.45 **t.** – ⊕ 7.50 – **19 rm** 73.00/84.00 **st.**

ACASTER MALBIS *N. Yorks.* 402 Q 22 – *see York.*

ACLE *Norfolk* 404 Y 26 *Great Britain G.* – *pop. 2 208.*
Env. : *The Broads★.*
London 118 – Great Yarmouth 8 – Norwich 11.

Travelodge, Acle bypass, NR13 3BE, on A 47 at junction with B 1140 ✆ (01493) 751970 – ⊕ rm, TV ⊕ P. MC AE ⓓ VISA JCB. ⊕
Meals (grill rest.) – **40 rm** 39.95 **t.**

ACOCKS GREEN *W. Mids* 402 ⑩ 403 ㉒ 404 ⑳ – *see Birmingham.*

ACTON GREEN *Herefordshire* 403 404 M 27 – *see Bromyard.*

ADDERBURY *Oxon.* 403 404 Q 27 – *see Banbury.*

ADLINGTON *Ches.* – *see Macclesfield.*

ADLINGTON *Lancs.* 402 404 M 23 – *pop. 8 556.*
London 217 – Liverpool 35 – Manchester 21 – Preston 16.

Gladmar Country, Railway Rd, PR6 9RG, ✆ (01257) 480398, *Fax (01257) 482681*, ⊕ – TV ⊕ P. MC AE ⓓ VISA. ⊕
Meals (residents only) (dinner only) 12.50/15.00 **st.** ⊕ 7.50 – **20 rm** ⊕ 42.00/62.00 **st.**

ALBRIGHTON *Shrops.* 402 403 L 25 – *see Shrewsbury.*

ALCESTER *Warks.* 403 404 O 27 – *pop. 6 282.*
London 104 – Birmingham 20 – Cheltenham 27 – Stratford-upon-Avon 8.

Kings Court, Kings Coughton, B49 5QQ, North : 1 ½ m. on A 435 ✆ (01789) 763111, *Fax (01789) 400242,* – 130. *closed 24 to 31 December* – **Meals** a la carte 17.20/21.20 **t.** – **42 rm** 57.00/82.00 **t.**

Travelodge, Birmingham Rd, Oversley Hill Roundabout, B49 6AA, South : 1 m. at junction of A 46 with A 435 ✆ (01789) 766987, *Fax (01789) 766987* – rm, rest, .
Meals (grill rest.) – **40 rm** 49.95 **t.**

ALDBOURNE *Wilts.* 403 404 P 29 – *pop. 1 682.*
London 77 – Oxford 36 – Southampton 53 – Swindon 9.

Raffles, 1 The Green, SN8 2BW, ✆ (01672) 540700, *Fax (01672) 540038* – *closed 2 weeks September, 26 to 31 December, Monday, Sunday dinner and lunch Tuesday and Saturday and Bank Holidays* – **Meals** 10.50 **t.** (lunch) and a la carte 15.60/25.35 **t.** 5.50.

ALDBURY *Herts.* 404 S 28 – *pop. 891.*
London 39 – Aylesbury 12 – Luton 20 – Oxford 36.

Valiant Trooper, Trooper Rd, HP23 5RW, ✆ (01442) 851203, – *closed Sunday dinner Monday and Bank Holidays* – **Meals** a la carte 13.50/20.00 **t.**

ALDEBURGH *Suffolk* 404 Y 27 – *pop. 2 654.*
Thorpeness Golf Hotel, Thorpeness ✆ (01728) 452176.
51 High St. ✆ (01728) 453637.
London 97 – Ipswich 24 – Norwich 41.

Wentworth, Wentworth Rd, IP15 5BD, ✆ (01728) 452312, *wentworth_hotel@anglianet.co.uk, Fax (01728) 454343,* ←, – rm, *closed 28 December-5 January* – **Meals** 12.50/15.50 **t.** 7.75 – **37 rm** 66.00/128.00 **t.** – SB.

Lighthouse, 77 High St., IP15 5AU, ✆ (01728) 453377, *Fax (01728) 453377* – *closed 2 weeks January and 1 week October* – **Meals** 15.75 **t.** (dinner) and lunch a la carte 15.75/22.75 **t.** 5.50.

Regatta, 171-173 High St., IP15 5AN, ✆ (01728) 452011, *Fax (01728) 452011* – *closed Monday-Wednesday, November-March* – **Meals** 10.00 **t.** and a la carte.

ALDERLEY EDGE *Ches.* 402 403 404 N 24 – *pop. 5 280.*
Wilmslow, Great Warford, Mobberley ✆ (01565) 872148.
London 187 – Chester 34 – Manchester 14 – Stoke-on-Trent 25.

Alderley Edge, Macclesfield Rd, SK9 7BJ, ✆ (01625) 583033, *sales@alderley_edge_hotel.co.uk, Fax (01625) 586343,* – 120. **Meals** – (see ***The Alderley*** below) – 9.50 – **45 rm** 99.50/175.00 **t.**, 1 suite.

The Alderley (at Alderley Edge H.), Macclesfield Rd, SK9 7BJ, ✆ (01625) 583033, *sales@alderley_edge_hotel.co.uk, Fax (01625) 586343,* – **Meals** 14.50/25.95 **t.** and a la carte 8.50.

The Wizard, Macclesfield Rd, SK10 4UB, Southeast : 1 ¼ m. on B 5087 ✆ (01625) 584000, *Fax (01625) 585105,* – *closed Monday and Sunday dinner* – **Meals** a la carte 19.75/23.00 **t.** 7.95.

Est, Est, Est, 75 London Rd, SK9 7DY, ✆ (01625) 583993, *Fax (01625) 583814,* – *closed 25 December* – **Meals** - Italian - a la carte 11.00/25.60 **t.** 9.95.

ALDERNEY 403 Q 33 and 230 ⑨ – *see Channel Islands.*

ALDERSHOT *Hants.* 404 R 30.

Military Museum, Queens Av. (01252) 320968.
London 45 – Portsmouth 38 – Reading 22 – Winchester 32.

Potters International, 1 Fleet Rd, GU11 2ET, off A 325 (01252) 34400C *Fax (01252) 311611,* – rest, – 350. VISA.
Meals (bar lunch saturday) 14.50/17.50 **st.** and a la carte 5.00 – **95 rm** 115.00 135.00 **st.**, 2 suites.

Travel Inn, Wellington Av., GU11 1SQ, East : on A 323 (01252) 34406 *Fax (01252) 344073* – rm, rest, VISA.
Meals (grill rest.) – **60 rm** 40.95 **t.**

ALDFIELD *N. Yorks. – see Ripon.*

ALDRIDGE *W. Mids.* 402 403 404 O 26 – *pop. 16 862* – *Walsall.*
London 130 – Birmingham 12 – Derby 32 – Leicester 40 – Stoke-on-Trent 38.

Plan : see Birmingham p. 5

Fairlawns, 178 Little Aston Rd, WS9 0NU, East : 1 m. on A 454 (01922) 455122, *welcor e@fairlawns.co.uk, Fax (01922) 743210,* – rest, – 80. VISA. CT
closed 25 and 26 December – **Meals** *(closed Saturday lunch and Bank Holidays)* 14.95 27.50 **st.** 6.50 – **44 rm** 62.50/109.50 **st.**, 6 suites – SB.

ALFRETON *Derbs.* 402 403 404 P 24 – *pop. 22 822.*

Shirland, Lower Delves (01773) 834935 – Ormonde Fields, Nottingham Rd, Codno Ripley (01773) 742987.
London 134 – Derby 13 – Nottingham 19 – Sheffield 27.

Travelodge, Old Swanwick Colliery Rd, DE55 1HJ, South : ¾ m. by A 61 at junction with 38 (01773) 520040, *Fax (01773) 520040* – rm, rest, – 50. VIS JCB.
Meals (grill rest.) – **60 rm** 39.95 **t.**

ALFRISTON *E. Sussex* 404 U 31 – *pop. 1 721* – *Polegate.*
London 66 – Eastbourne 9 – Lewes 10 – Newhaven 8.

Star Inn, High St., BN26 5TA, (01323) 870495, *heritagehotels_alfriston.star_inn@forte hotels.com, Fax (01323) 870922,* « Part 14C coaching inn » – – 30. VISA
Meals (bar lunch Monday to Saturday)/dinner 17.00 **t.** and a la carte 7.75 – 12.00 **37 rm** 100.00/120.00 **t.** – SB.

ALLENDALE *Northd.* 401 402 N 19 – *pop. 2 123* – *Hexham.*

High Studdon, Allenheads Rd (01434) 683926.
London 314 – Carlisle 39 – Newcastle upon Tyne 33.

Thornley House, NE47 9NH, West : ½ m. on Whitfield rd (01434) 683255, *e.finn@uk nline.co.uk,* –
Meals (by arrangement) (communal dining) 11.00 **st.** – **3 rm** 25.00/39.00 **st.**

ALLESLEY *W. Mids.* 403 404 P 26 – *see Coventry.*

ALMONDBURY *W. Yorks.* 402 ⑲ – *see Huddersfield.*

ALNMOUTH *Northd.* 401 402 P 17 *Great Britain G.* – *pop. 586.*

Env. : *Warkworth Castle★ AC, S : 4 m. by B 1338 and A 1068.*
Alnmouth Village, Marine Rd (01665) 830370.
London 314 – Edinburgh 90 – Newcastle upon Tyne 37.

Marine House, 1 Marine Rd, NE66 2RW, (01665) 830349, *tanney@marinehouse.frees rve.co.uk,* – VISA
closed 3-18 January – **Meals** (dinner only) 15.95 **t.** 7.95 – **10 rm** (dinner included 86.00/96.00 **t.** – SB.

High Buston Hall without rest., High Buston, NE66 3QH, Southwest : 2 ¼ m. by B 1338 off A 1068 (01665) 830606, *highbuston@aol.com, Fax (01665) 830707*, ≤, « Georgian house », – P.
closed Christmas – **3 rm** 60.00/75.00.

ALNWICK *Northd.* 401 402 O 17 *Great Britain G. – pop. 7 419.*

See : *Town* ★ – *Castle*★★ *AC.*

Exc. : *Dunstanburgh Castle*★ *AC, NE : 8 m. by B 1340 and Dunstan rd (last 2½ m. on foot).*

18 *Swansfield Park (01665) 602632.*

2 The Shambles (01665) 510665.

London 320 – Edinburgh 86 – Newcastle upon Tyne 34.

White Swan, Bondgate Within, NE66 1TD, (01665) 602109, *Fax (01665) 510400*, « Furnishings from SS Olympic » – P – 150. MC AE VISA
Meals (bar lunch Monday to Saturday)/dinner 21.00/31.00 **t.** 7.25 – **55 rm** 69.00/84.00 **t.** – SB.

Charlton House without rest., 2 Aydon Gdns., South Rd, NE66 2NT, Southeast : ½ m. (01665) 605185, *charltonhouse@talk21.com* – P.
closed Christmas and New Year – **5 rm** 20.00/40.00 **st.**

Bondgate House, 20 Bondgate Without, NE66 1PN, (01665) 602025, *kenforbes@lineone.net, Fax (01665) 602025* – rest, P. MC VISA JCB.
Meals (by arrangement) 13.00 **st.** 3.50 – **8 rm** 25.00/47.00 **st.**

at Newton on the Moor *South : 5½ m. on A 1 – Alnwick.*

Cook and Barker Inn with rm, NE65 9JY, (01665) 575234, *Fax (01665) 575234* – P. MC AE VISA.
closed 26 December – **Meals** 14.00/18.50 **st.** (dinner) and a la carte 13.75/27.75 **st.** 6.00 – **4 rm** 37.50/70.00 **st.** – SB.

ALREWAS *Staffs.* 402 403 404 O 25 – *pop. 4 409 – Burton-upon-Trent.*

London 127 – Birmingham 24 – Derby 32 – Stoke-on-Trent 30.

The Old Boat, Kings Bromley Rd, DE13 7DB, (01283) 791468, *Fax (01283) 791468*, – P. MC VISA
closed 25,26 and 31 December and 1 January – **Meals** 13.55/21.00 **t.**

ALSAGER *Ches.* 402 403 404 N 24 *Great Britain G. – pop. 13 435 – Stoke-on-Trent (Staffs.).*

Env. : *Little Moreton Hall*★★ *AC, NE : 4 m. by A 50 and A 34.*

London 180 – Chester 36 – Liverpool 49 – Manchester 32 – Stoke-on-Trent 11.

Manor House, Audley Rd, ST7 2QQ, Southeast : ¾ m. (01270) 884000, *mhres@compasshotels.co.uk, Fax (01270) 882483*, – rm, P – 200. MC AE VISA.
Meals *(closed Saturday lunch, Sunday dinner and Bank Holidays)* 13.50/21.00 **t.** and a la carte 5.95 – **57 rm** 89.00/109.00 **st.** – SB.

Sappho Cottage, 118 Crewe Rd, ST7 2JA, (01270) 882033, *reception@sappho-cottage.demon.co.uk, Fax (01270) 883556*, – P.
Meals (by arrangement) (communal dining) 15.00 **st.** – **3 rm** 30.00/45.00 **st.**

ALSTON *Cumbria* 401 402 M 19 – *pop. 2 065.*

9 *Alston Moor, The Hermitage (01434) 381675.*

The Railway Station (01434) 381696.

London 309 – Carlisle 28 – Newcastle upon Tyne 45.

Lovelady Shield Country House , Nenthead Rd, CA9 3LF, East : 2 ½ m. on A 689 (01434) 381203, *enquiries@lovelady.co.uk, Fax (01434) 381515*, ≤, – rest, P. MC AE VISA JCB
Meals (bar lunch)/dinner 29.50 **t.** 9.00 – **10 rm** (dinner included) 87.50/175.00 **t.** – SB.

Nent Hall Country House, CA9 3LQ, East : 2 ½ m. on A 689 (01434) 381584, *Fax (01434) 382668*, – P. MC VISA
closed 24-26 December – **Meals** 13.50/26.00 **t.** 5.70 – **17 rm** (dinner included) 42.00/60.00 **st.** – SB.

High Windy Hall , Middleton in Teesdale Rd, CA9 3EZ, Southeast : 4 m. on B 6277 (01434) 381547, *sales@hwh.u_net.com, Fax (01434) 382477*, ≤, – P. MC VISA JCB.
April-November – **Meals** (by arrangement) 23.00 **t.** 6.00 – **5 rm** 40.00/70.00 **t.** – SB.

ALTARNUN *Cornwall* 403 G 32 *The West Country G. – pop. 2 405 – ✉ Launceston.*
See : *Church★.*
Env. : *Bodmin Moor★★, Laneast (St. Sidwell's★), N : 2½ m. by minor roads.*
London 279 – Exeter 56 – Plymouth 34 – Truro 39.

Penhallow Manor Country House, PL15 7SJ, (01566) 86206, *Fax (01566) 86179*, – , TV P. VISA.
closed January-16 February **Meals** (dinner only) 23.00 **t.** 8.50 – **9 rm** 60.00/110.00 **t.** – SB.

ALTON *Hants.* 404 R 30 – *pop. 16 005.*
Old Odiham Rd (01420) 82042.
7 Cross and Pillory Lane (01420) 88448.
London 53 – Reading 24 – Southampton 29 – Winchester 18.

Grange, London Rd, GU34 4EG, Northeast : 1 m. on A 3004 (01420) 86565, *info@altongrange.co.uk, Fax (01420) 541346*, – TV P – 80. AE VISA JCB.
closed 24 December-1 January – ***Truffles :*** **Meals** a la carte 17.85/27.40 **t.** 5.95 – **30 rm** 77.00/105.00 **t.**

ALTON TOWERS *Staffs.* 402 403 404 O 25.
London 158 – Birmingham 48 – Derby 23 – Stafford 24 – Stoke-on-Trent 13.

Alton Towers, ST10 4DB, (0870) 5001100, *info@alton-towers, Fax (01538) 704657*, « Fantasy themed », , , , , – , rest, TV P – 200. AE VISA.
closed 25-30 December – ***Secret Garden :*** **Meals** (light lunch)/dinner a la carte 14.15/20.40 **t.** – 4.95 – **175 rm** 99.00/139.00 **t.**

The Guide is updated annually so renew your Guide every year.

ALTRINCHAM *Gtr. Manchester* 402 403 404 N 23 – *pop. 40 042.*
Altrincham Municipal, Stockport Rd, Timperley (0161) 928 0761 – Dunham Forest Oldfield Lane (0161) 928 2605 – Ringway, Hale Mount, Hale Barns (0161) 904 9609.
20 Stamford New Rd (0161) 912 5931.
London 191 – Chester 30 – Liverpool 30 – Manchester 8.

Cresta Court, Church St., WA14 4DP, on A 56 (0161) 927 7272, *info@cresta-court.co.uk, Fax (0161) 926 9194*, – , rest, TV P – 320. AE VISA
Meals *(closed Monday lunch)* 7.50/12.95 **st.** and dinner a la carte 6.50 – 8.95 – **136 rm** 76.50/86.50 **st.** – SB.

Woodland Park, Wellington Rd, WA15 7RG, off A 560 (0161) 928 8631, *info@woodlandpark.co.uk, Fax (0161) 941 2821* – , rest, TV P – 150. AE VISA JCB.
The Terrace : **Meals** *(closed lunch Saturday, Sunday and Bank Holidays)* 12.95/14.95 **t.** and a la carte 6.50 – **46 rm** 77.50/145.00 **t.** – SB.

Quality H., Langham Rd, WA14 2HT, Southwest : 1 m. (0161) 928 7121, *admin@gb064.u-net.com, Fax (0161) 927 7560*, , , – TV P – 130. AE VISA.
Meals (bar lunch Saturday) 18.50 **t.** (dinner) and a la carte 19.70/31.90 **t.** 6.95 – 9.95 – **89 rm** 85.00/99.00 **t.** – SB.

Premier Lodge, Manchester Rd, WA14 4PH, on A 56 (0870) 7001306, *Fax (0870) 7001307* – , rm, TV P – 40. AE VISA
Meals (grill rest.) a la carte 10.80/19.40 **st.** 3.95 – 6.00 – **46 rm** 46.00 **st.**

Premier Lodge, Manchester Rd, West Timperley, WA14 5NH, North : 2 m. on A 56 (0161) 962 7414, *Fax (0161) 962 3456* – rm, TV P – 50. AE VISA JCB.
Meals (grill rest.) a la carte approx. 10.80/19.40 **st.** 3.95 – 6.00 – **48 rm** 46.00 **st.**

Juniper, 21 The Downs, WA14 2QD, (0161) 929 4008, *Fax (0161) 929 4009* – . AE VISA
closed lunch Monday, Saturday and Bank Holidays and Sunday – **Meals** a la carte 26.00/32.00 **t.** 8.00
Spec. White truffle bouillon with scrambled eggs and lemon toast. Assiette of fishes with Noilly Prat cream sauce. Assiette of strawberries.

Snockers-On-The-Green, 9 Goose Green, WA14 1DW, (0161) 929 8929 – AE VISA JCB
closed Sunday and Bank Holidays – **Meals** 8.00/20.00 **t.** and a la carte 6.00.

at Hale *Southeast : 1 m. on B 5163 – ✉ Altrincham.*

Est, Est, Est, 183 Ashley Rd, WA15 9SD, (0161) 928 1811, *Fax (0161) 928 3468* – . AE VISA
closed 25 and 26 December – **Meals** - Italian - a la carte 9.40/26.60 **st.** 3.45.

t Halebarns *Southeast : 3 m. on A 538 – ✉ Altrincham.*

Swallow Four Seasons, Manchester Airport, Hale Rd, WA15 8XW, ☎ (0161) 904 0301, *sfsh@lineone.net, Fax (0161) 980 1787,* – |♦|, ⇎ rm, ▤ rest, TV ☎ P – 🏫 120. MC AE ① VISA. ✻
The Four Seasons : **Meals** *(closed Saturday lunch)* 20.95 **st.** (dinner) and a la carte 27.20/35.00 **st.** 🍷 7.75 – ☕ 10.50 – **144 rm** 105.00/145.00 **st.**, 3 suites – SB.

ALVECHURCH *Worcs.* 403 404 O 26 – *pop. 5 829.*
London 113 – Birmingham 11 – Bromsgrove 6.

Alcott Farm without rest., Weatheroak, B48 7EH, Northeast : 2 ¾ m. by Radford Rd on Beoley rd (Icknield St.) ☎ (01564) 824051, *Fax (01564) 824051,* 🌳, – ⇎ TV P. ✻
4 rm ☕ 30.00/50.00.

ALVELEY *Shrops. – see Bridgnorth.*

ALWALTON *Cambs.* 402 404 T 26 – *see Peterborough.*

AMBERLEY *W. Sussex* 404 S 31 *Great Britain G. – pop. 525 – ✉ Arundel.*
Env. : *Bignor Roman Villa (mosaics★)* **AC**, *NW : 3½ m. by B 2139 via Bury.*
London 56 – Brighton 24 – Portsmouth 31.

Amberley Castle ♨, BN18 9ND, Southwest : ½ m. on B 2139 ☎ (01798) 831992, *info@amberleycastle.co.uk, Fax (01798) 831998,* « 14C castle, 12C origins », 🌳, – ⇎ TV P – 🏫 40. MC AE ① VISA. ✻
Queen's Room : **Meals** (booking essential) 17.50/35.00 **t.** and a la carte 🍷 12.95 – ☕ 17.00 – **15 rm** 145.00/300.00 **t.**, 5 suites.

AMBLESIDE *Cumbria* 402 L 20 *Great Britain G. – pop. 2 905.*
Env. : *Lake Windermere★★ – Dove Cottage, Grasmere★* **AC AY A** – *Brockhole National Park Centre★* **AC**, *SE : 3 m. by A 591* **AZ**.
Exc. : *Wrynose Pass★★, W : 7½ m. by A 593* **AY** – *Hard Knott Pass★★, W : 10 m. by A 593* **AY**.
ℹ *Central Buildings, Market Cross ☎ (015394) 32582 (closed Sunday and Monday in winter)* **AZ** – *Main Car Park, Waterhead ☎ (015394) 32729 (summer only)* **BY**.
London 278 – Carlisle 47 – Kendal 14.

Plan on next page

Rothay Manor, Rothay Bridge, LA22 0EH, South : ½ m. on A 593 ☎ (015394) 33605, *hotel@rothaymanor.co.uk, Fax (015394) 33607,* ←, 🌳 – ⇎ rest, TV ♿ P. MC AE ① VISA JCB. ✻ — BY r
closed 3 January-9 Febuary – **Meals** (buffet lunch Monday to Saturday)/dinner 28.00 **t.** 🍷 6.50 – **16 rm** ☕ 80.00/140.00 **t.**, 2 suites – SB.

Ambleside Salutation, Lake Rd, LA22 9BX, ☎ (015394) 32244, *enquiries@hotelambleside.uk.com, Fax (015394) 34157* – ⇎ TV P – 🏫 30. MC AE VISA JCB — AZ r
Meals (bar lunch)/dinner 16.50/19.50 **st.** and a la carte 🍷 5.95 – **42 rm** ☕ 52.00/104.00 **st.** – SB.

Borrans Park, Borrans Rd, LA22 0EN, ☎ (015394) 33454, *mail@borranspark.co.uk, Fax (015394) 33003,* ←, 🌳 – ⇎ TV ♿ P. MC VISA JCB. ✻ — BY a
Meals (booking essential to non-residents) (dinner only) 20.00 **st.** 🍷 6.95 – **12 rm** ☕ 60.00/90.00 **st.** – SB.

Elder Grove without rest., Lake Rd, LA22 0DB, ☎ (015394) 32504, *mcdougall-eldergrove@hotmail.com, Fax (015394) 32504* – ⇎ TV P. MC VISA JCB — AZ a
closed 4 days Christmas and 2 weeks in winter – **10 rm** ☕ 30.00/68.00 **t.**

Ambleside Lodge without rest., Rothay Rd, LA22 0EJ, ☎ (015394) 31681, *cherryho@globalnet.co.uk, Fax (015394) 34547,* 🌳 – ⇎ TV P. MC ① VISA JCB. ✻ — AZ x
20 rm ☕ 30.00/95.00 **st.**

Crow How ♨, Rydal Rd, LA22 9PN, Northwest : ½ m. on A 591 ☎ (015394) 32193, *patredman200@netscapeonline.co.uk, Fax (015394) 31770,* ←, 🌳 – ⇎ TV P. MC VISA — BY x
closed January – **Meals** (dinner only) 16.95 **st.** 🍷 6.95 – **9 rm** ☕ 49.00/80.00 **st.** – SB.

Rowanfield Country House ♨, Kirkstone Rd, LA22 9ET, Northeast : ¾ m. ☎ (015394) 33686, *email@rowanfield.com, Fax (015394) 31569,* ← Lake Windermere and Coniston Old Man, 🌳 – ⇎ TV P. MC VISA. ✻ — AZ u
Mid March-November and Christmas and New Year – **Meals** (by arrangement) 23.00 **st.** – **8 rm** ☕ 65.00/80.00 **st.** – SB.

AMBLESIDE
GRASMERE

Borrans Rd .... **BY** 2
Broadgate.................. **BZ** 3
Cheapside .... **AZ** 4
Church St.................. **AZ** 6
Compston St.............. **AZ** 8
Easedale Rd............... **BZ** 10
Kelswick Rd............... **AZ** 12
King St .... **AZ** 13
Lake Rd .... **AZ**
Market Pl.................... **AZ** 1
North Rd .... **AZ** 1
Old Lake Rd .... **AZ** 2
St. Mary's Lane .... **AZ** 2
Smithy Brow................. **AZ** 2
Swan Hill .... **AY** 2

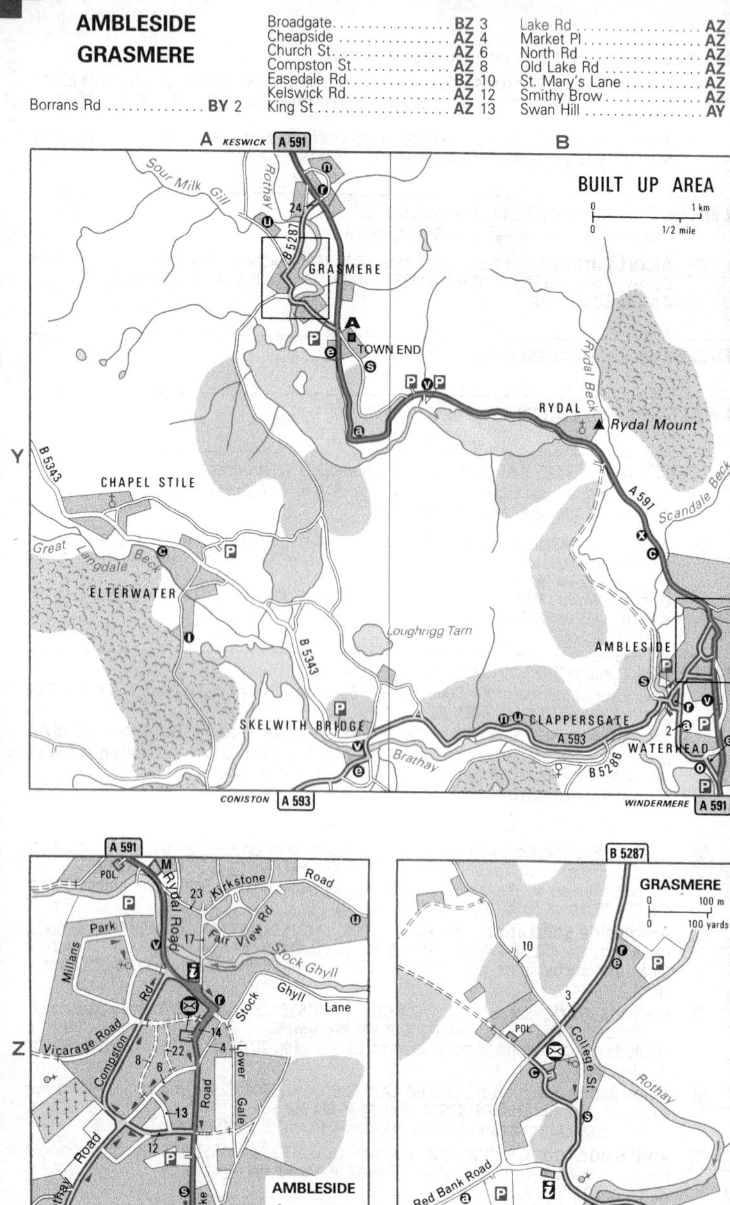

Town plans: *roads most used by traffic and those on which guide listed hotels and restaurants stand are fully drawn; the beginning only of lesser roads is indicated.*

Scandale Brow without rest., Rydal Rd, LA22 9PL, Northwest : ½ m. on A 591 (015394) 34528, *enquiries@scandalebrow.co.uk, Fax (015394) 34528,* – rest. BY c
closed Christmas and restricted opening in winter – **3 rm** 39.00/60.00 **st.**

Laurel Villa without rest., Lake Rd, LA22 0DB, (015394) 33240, *laurelvilla@hotel-ambleside.co.uk, Fax (015394) 33240* – AZ s
8 rm 30.00/60.00 **t.**

Riverside without rest., Under Loughrigg, LA22 9LJ, (015394) 32395, *hotel@riverside-ambleside.co.uk, Fax (015394) 32395,* – BY s
5 rm 32.00/70.00 **s.** – SB.

The Log House, Lake Rd, LA22 0DN, (015394) 31077, *edmondson@kencomp.net* – BY v
Meals 8.50/15.45 **t.** and a la carte 7.50.

Glass House, Rydal Rd, LA22 9AN, (015394) 32137, *theglasshouserestaurant.co.uk, Fax (015394) 31139,* « Converted 15C mill » – AZ v
closed 2 weeks January and 25 December – **Meals** (booking essential) a la carte 18.00/27.00 **t.** 7.50.

Drunken Duck Inn with rm, Barngates, LA22 0NG, Southwest : 3 m. by A 593 and B 5286 on Tarn Hows rd (015394) 36347, *info@drunkenduckinn.co.uk, Fax (015394) 36781,* « Part 16C » – rest, BY v
closed 24 and 25 December – **Meals** a la carte 18.00/25.00 **t.** – **11 rm** 60.00/120.00 **t.**

t Waterhead *South : 1 m. on A 591 – Ambleside.*

Wateredge, Borrans Rd, LA22 0EP, (015394) 32332, *info.m@wateredgehotel.co.uk, Fax (015394) 31878,* « Part 17C fishermen's cottages, lakeside setting », – rest, BY o
closed mid December-mid January – **Meals** (light lunch)/dinner 29.00 **t.** 8.80 – **23 rm** (dinner included) 64.00/156.00 **t.** – SB.

Regent, LA22 0ES, (015394) 32254, *info@regentlakes.co.uk, Fax (015394) 31474* – BY e
Meals (bar lunch)/dinner 17.50/25.00 **t.** and a la carte 7.95 – **30 rm** 65.00/105.00 **t.** – SB.

t Clappersgate *West : 1 m. on A 593 – Ambleside.*

Nanny Brow Country House, LA22 9NF, (015394) 32036, *reservation@nannybrowhotel.demon.co.uk, Fax (015394) 32450,* « Landscaped gardens », – BY u
Meals (dinner only) 22.50/27.50 **t.** and a la carte 8.00 – **15 rm** (dinner included) 65.00/145.00 **t.**, 3 suites – SB.

Grey Friar Lodge, LA22 9NE, (015394) 33158, *greyfriar@veen.freeserve.co.uk, Fax (015394) 33158,* – BY n
closed 14 December-10 February – **Meals** *(closed Sunday)* (residents only) (dinner only) 18.50 **st.** 4.45 – **8 rm** 36.00/85.00 **st.**

t Skelwith Bridge *West : 2½ m. on A 593 – Ambleside.*

Skelwith Bridge, LA22 9NJ, (015394) 32115, *skelwithbr@aol.com, Fax (015394) 34254* – rest, AY v
closed 17-21 December – **Meals** (bar lunch Monday to Saturday)/dinner 19.45 **st.** 8.50 – **29 rm** 48.00/86.00 **st.** – SB.

Greenbank without rest., LA22 9NW, on A 593 (015394) 33236, *greenbank@bigwig.net,* – AY e
mid February-mid November – **3 rm** 34.00/48.00.

t Elterwater *West : 4½ m. by A 593 off B 5343 – Ambleside.*

Langdale H. & Country Club, Great Langdale, LA22 9JD, Northwest : ½ m. on B 5343 (015394) 37302, Reservations (Freephone) 0500 051197, *info@langdale.co.uk, Fax (015394) 37694,* squash – rest, – 100. AY c
Meals a la carte approx. 20.00 **t.** 6.95 – ***Purdeys :*** **Meals** (light lunch)/dinner 16.00/25.00 **t.** and a la carte 8.50 – **65 rm** 130.00/210.00 – SB.

Eltermere Country House, LA22 9HY, (015394) 37207, *colin@hensington.demon.co.uk, Fax (015394) 37540,* – rest, AY i
Meals (dinner only) 19.95 **st.** 5.75 – **19 rm** (dinner included) 59.00/118.00 **st.** – SB.

t Little Langdale *West : 5 m. by A 593 – Langdale.*

Three Shires Inn, LA22 9NZ, (015394) 37215, *enquiry@threeshiresinn.co.uk, Fax (015394) 37127,* – rest, AY z
closed 25 December and restricted opening in January – **Meals** (bar lunch)/dinner 19.95/21.95 **st.** and a la carte 5.10 – **10 rm** 36.00/76.00 **t.** – SB.

AMERSHAM (Old Town) *Bucks.* 404 S 28 – *pop. 21 711.*
Little Chalfont, Lodge Lane ☎ (01494) 764877.
Tesco's Car Park, London Road West ☎ (01494) 729492.
London 29 – Aylesbury 16 – Oxford 33.

Crown, 16 High St., HP7 0DH, ☎ (0870) 4008103, *Fax (01494) 431283,* « Part 16C former coaching inn », – rm, P – 30. MC AE VISA JCB.
Meals 11.00/20.00 **t.** and a la carte 7.00 – 12.50 – **23 rm** 125.00/175.00 **st.** – SB.

King's Arms (Restaurant), High St., HP7 0DJ, ☎ (01494) 726333, *Fax (01494) 43348* « Part 15C inn » – P. MC AE VISA JCB
closed 26 to 31 December, Sunday dinner and Monday – **Meals** 13.50/25.00 **t.** and a la carte 5.10.

Gilbey's, 1 Market Sq., HP7 0DF, ☎ (01494) 727242, *gilbeysamersham@cs.com* *Fax (01494) 531243,* – MC AE VISA
closed 24 to 28 December – **Meals** (booking essential) a la carte 18.45/23.50 **t.** 4.85.

AMESBURY *Wilts.* 403 404 O 30 *The West Country G.* – *pop. 6 333.*
Env. : *Stonehenge*** AC, W : 2 m. by A 303.*
Exc. : *Wilton Village* (Wilton House** AC, Wilton Carpet Factory* AC), SW : 13 m. by 303, B 3083 and A 36.*
Redworth House, Flower Lane ☎ (01980) 622833.
London 87 – Bristol 52 – Taunton 66.

Travelodge, SP4 7AS, North : ¼ m. at junction of A 303 with A 345 ☎ (01980) 62496 *Fax (01980) 624966* – rm, P. MC AE VISA JCB.
Meals (grill rest.) – **48 rm** 49.95 **t.**

Mandalay without rest., 15 Stonehenge Rd, SP4 7BA, ☎ (01980) 62373 *Fax (01980) 626642,* – P. MC AE VISA JCB.
5 rm 32.00/46.00 **st.**

AMPFIELD *Hants.* 403 404 P 30 – *pop. 1 523* – ✉ *Romsey.*
Ampfield (Par Three), Winchester Rd ☎ (01794) 368480.
London 79 – Bournemouth 31 – Salisbury 19 – Southampton 11 – Winchester 7.

Potters Heron, Winchester Rd, SO51 9ZF, on A 3090 ☎ (02380) 26661 *Fax (02380) 251359,* – , rest, P – 150. MC AE VISA
Meals (bar lunch Monday to Saturday)/dinner 17.95 **t.** – 9.75 – **54 rm** 90.00/100.00 **t.** SB.

Keats, Winchester Rd, SO51 9BQ, on A 3090 ☎ (01794) 368252 – P. MC AE VISA JCB.
closed Christmas, Sunday and Monday – **Meals** - Italian - 12.50 **t.** (lunch) and a la carte 18.15/28.45 **t.** 6.00.

AMPLEFORTH *N. Yorks.* 402 Q 21 – ✉ *York.*
London 237 – Leeds 53 – Middlesbrough 29 – York 24.

Shallowdale House , YO62 4DY, West : ½ m. ☎ (01439) 788325, *Fax (01439) 78888* Gilling Gap, – P. MC VISA.
closed Christmas, New Year and restricted opening in winter – **Meals** (by arrangement) 21.00 **st.** 6.00 – **3 rm** 55.00/80.00 **st.** – SB.

AMPNEY CRUCIS *Glos.* 403 404 O 28 – *see Cirencester.*

ANNITSFORD *Northd.* 401 P 18 – *see Newcastle upon Tyne (Tyne and Wear).*

APPLEBY-IN-WESTMORLAND *Cumbria* 402 M 20 – *pop. 2 570 (inc. Bongate).*
Appleby, Brackenber Moor ☎ (017683) 51432.
Moot Hall, Boroughgate ☎ (017683) 51177.
London 285 – Carlisle 33 – Kendal 24 – Middlesbrough 58.

Appleby Manor Country House , Roman Rd, CA16 6JB, East : 1 m. by B 6542 and Station Rd ☎ (017683) 51571, *reception@applebymanor.co.uk, Fax (017683) 52888,* – P – 40. MC AE VISA JCB.
Meals a la carte 16.95/26.35 **st.** 6.25 – **30 rm** 78.00/116.00 **st.** – SB.

Tufton Arms, Market Sq., CA16 6XA, ☎ (017683) 51593, *info@tuftonarmshotel.co.uk* *Fax (017683) 52761,* – P – 100. MC AE VISA JCB
Meals 23.00 **t.** (dinner) and a la carte 12.65/23.00 **t.** 4.75 – **19 rm** 57.00/95.00 **t.** 2 suites – SB.

PPLEDORE *Devon* 403 H 30 *The West Country G. – pop. 2 187.*
See : *Town*★.
London 228 – Barnstaple 12 – Exeter 46 – Plymouth 61 – Taunton 63.

West Farm, Irsha St., EX39 1RY, West : ¼ m. ✆ (01237) 425269, *westfarm@appledore-devon.co.uk*, « 17C house », – rm, TV P.
Meals (by arrangement) (communal dining) 25.00 – **3 rm** 60.00/80.00.

RMSCOTE *Warks..*
London 91 – Birmingham 36 – Oxford 38.

The Fox and Goose Inn with rm, CV37 8DD, ✆ (01608) 682293, *Fax (01608) 682293*, – TV P. MC AE VISA.
closed 1 January and 25-26 December – **Meals** a la carte 15.95/22.50 **t.** 5.00 – **4 rm** 40.00/90.00 **t.**

RNCLIFFE *N. Yorks.* 402 N 21 – *pop. 79* – ✉ *Skipton.*
London 232 – Kendal 41 – Leeds 41 – Preston 50 – York 52.

Amerdale House , BD23 5QE, ✆ (01756) 770250, *Fax (01756) 770250*, ←, – rest, TV P. MC VISA.
mid March-mid November – **Meals** (dinner only) 30.00 6.50 – **11 rm** (dinner included) 79.50/143.00 **st.** – SB.

RUNDEL *W. Sussex* 404 S 31 *Great Britain G. – pop. 3 033.*
See : *Castle*★★ *AC.*
61 High St. ✆ (01903) 882268.
London 58 – Brighton 21 – Southampton 41 – Worthing 9.

Norfolk Arms, 22 High St., BN18 9AD, ✆ (01903) 882101, *nka/forestdale@forestdale.com*, *Fax (01903) 884275* – rest, TV P – 100. MC AE VISA JCB
Meals (bar lunch Monday-Saturday)/dinner 18.00 **t.** 7.45 – **37 rm** 65.00/105.00 **t.** – SB.

Swan, 27-29 High St., BN18 9AG, ✆ (01903) 882314, *info@swan-hotel.co.uk*, *Fax (01903) 883759* – , rest, TV P. MC AE VISA.
Meals 11.95/15.95 **st.** and a la carte 6.50 – **15 rm** 60.00/100.00 **st.** – SB.

Comfort Inn, Crossbush, BN17 7QQ, Southeast : 1 ¼ m. by A 27 on A 284 ✆ (01903) 840840, *admin@gb642.u_net.com*, *Fax (01903) 849849* – , rest, TV P – 30. MC AE VISA JCB
Meals (dinner only) 10.75 **t.** and a la carte – **53 rm** 51.75/69.50 **t.** – SB.

Travel Inn, Crossbush, BN18 9PQ, East : 1 m. on A 27 ✆ (01903) 882655, *Fax (01903) 884381* – , rest, TV P. MC AE VISA.
Meals (grill rest.) – **30 rm** 40.95 **t.**

t Burpham *Northeast : 3 m. by A 27* – ✉ *Arundel.*

Burpham Country , BN18 9RJ, ✆ (01903) 882160, *Fax (01903) 884627*, ←, – TV P. MC AE VISA.
closed 2 weeks February, 1 week September and 25 December – **Meals** *(closed Monday)* (booking essential to non-residents) (dinner only) 19.50/23.50 **t.** 7.50 – **10 rm** 45.00/110.00 **t.** – SB.

George and Dragon, BN18 9RR, ✆ (01903) 883131, *Fax (01903) 883341* – . MC AE VISA
closed 25 December and Sunday dinner – **Meals** (bar lunch Monday to Saturday)/dinner 18.50/24.95 **t.** 6.75.

t Walberton *West : 3 m. by A 27 off B 2132* – ✉ *Arundel.*

Hilton Avisford Park, Yapton Lane, BN18 0LS, on B 2132 ✆ (01243) 551215, *reservations@avisford.stakis.co.uk*, *Fax (01243) 552485*, ←, , , heated, , 18, , , , squash – TV P – 300. MC AE VISA
Meals *(closed Saturday lunch)* (buffet lunch)/dinner 19.75/21.75 **t.** and a la carte – 10.50 – **134 rm** 110.00/140.00 **st.**, 5 suites – SB.

SCOT *Windsor & Maidenhead* 404 R 29 – *pop. 15 761 (inc. Sunningdale).*
18 *Mill Ride, Ascot ✆ (01344) 886777.*
London 36 – Reading 15.

Royal Berkshire , London Rd, Sunninghill, SL5 0PP, East : 2 m. on A 329 ✆ (01344) 623322, *Fax (01344) 627100*, « Queen Anne mansion », , , , , – TV P – 70. MC AE VISA
Meals *(closed Saturday lunch)* (booking essential) 22.50/29.50 **t.** and a la carte 15.00 – 15.50 – **60 rm** 195.00/250.00 **t.**, 3 suites – SB.

Berystede, Bagshot Rd, Sunninghill, SL5 9JH, South : 1 ½ m. on A 330 ☏ (0870) 400 811 heritagehotels-ascot.berystede@forte-hotels.com, Fax (01344) 873061, heated, – rest, – 120.
Meals 16.95/25.00 **t.** and dinner a la carte 9.50 – 12.95 – **89 rm** 175.00 **t.**, 1 suite – S

Ciao Ninety, 6 Hermitage Par., High St., SL5 7TE, ☏ (01344) 622285, Fax (01344) 62228
closed Sunday – **Meals** - Italian - 14.00/18.50 **t.** and a la carte 5.00.

at Sunninghill South : 1½ m. by A 329 on B 3020 – ✉ Ascot.

Highclere, Kings Rd, SL5 9AD, ☏ (01344) 625220, Fax (01344) 872528 – rest,
Meals (lunch booking essential) a la carte 15.30/24.95 **t.** – **11 rm** 80.00/110.00 **t.**

Jade Fountain, 38 High St., SL5 9NE, ☏ (01344) 627070, Fax (01344) 627070 –
closed Christmas – **Meals** - Chinese (Canton, Peking) - 18.00/24.00 **t.** and a la carte 5.00

ASENBY N. Yorks. – see Thirsk.

ASHBOURNE Derbs. 402 403 404 O 24 Great Britain G. – pop. 6 300.
Env. : Dovedale★★ (Ilam Rock★) NW : 6 m. by A 515.
13 Market Pl. ☏ (01335) 343666.
London 146 – Derby 14 – Manchester 48 – Nottingham 33 – Sheffield 44.

Callow Hall , Mappleton Rd, DE6 2AA, West : ¾ m. by Union St. (off Market P ☏ (01335) 300900, Fax (01335) 300512, ←, « Victorian country house », –
closed 25-26 December and 1 Jan – **Meals** – (see ***The Restaurant*** below) – **15 r** 85.00/165.00 **t.**, 1 suite – SB.

Hanover International, Derby Rd, DE6 1XH, Southeast : 1 m. following signs for the 52 (Derby) ☏ (01335) 346666, Fax (01335) 346549, – rm, 200.
Meals (bar lunch)/dinner 19.95 **st.** and a la carte 7.50 – 8.50 – **48 rm** 85.00/105.00 s 2 suites – SB.

Lichfield House without rest., Bridge View, Mayfield, DE6 2HL, Northwest : 1 ¾ m. by 52 (Leek rd) on B 5032 ☏ (01335) 344422, brionybull@ukonline.co.uk, Fax (01335) 34442 –
closed 25 December – **3 rm** 35.00/50.00 **t.**

The Restaurant (at Callow Hall), Mappleton Rd, DE6 2AA, West : ¾ m. by Union St. (c Market Pl.) ☏ (01335) 300900, Fax (01335) 300512 –
closed 25-26 December 1 Jan and Sunday dinner – **Meals** (dinner only and Sunday lunch dinner 20.50/38.00 **t.** 6.00.

ASHBURTON Devon 403 I 32 The West Country G. – pop. 3 660.
Env. : Dartmoor National Park★★.
London 220 – Exeter 20 – Plymouth 25.

Holne Chase , TQ13 7NS, West : 3 m. on Two Bridges rd ☏ (01364) 631471, info@ho e_chase.co.uk, Fax (01364) 631453, ←, –
Meals – (see ***The Restaurant*** below) – **10 rm** 100.00/150.00 **st.**, 7 suites – SB.

Gages Mill, Buckfastleigh Rd, TQ13 7JW, Southwest : 1 m. on Buckfastleigh/Totnes r ☏ (01364) 652391, moore@gagesmill.co.uk, Fax (01364) 652391, – rest,
March-mid November – **Meals** (by arrangement) 13.50 **st.** 5.00 – **8 rm** 29.50/59.00 t

The Restaurant (at Holne Chase H.), TQ13 7NS, West : 3 m. on Two Bridges ☏ (01364) 631471, Fax (01364) 631453, – –
Meals (booking essential) 20.00/32.50 **st.** 10.00.

at Holne West : 4½ m. by Two Bridges rd – ✉ Ashburton.

Wellpritton Farm , TQ13 7RX, Northeast : 1 m. ☏ (01364) 631273, –
Meals (by arrangement) 10.00 – **4 rm** 20.00/40.00 **st.**

ASHBY DE LA ZOUCH *Leics.* 402 403 404 P 25 – *pop. 10 595.*

Willesley Park, Measham Rd (01530) 411532.

North St. (01530) 411767.

London 119 – Birmingham 29 – Leicester 18 – Nottingham 22.

Rajni, 48 Tamworth Rd, LE65 2PR, South : ½ m. on B 5006 (01530) 560349, *Fax (01530) 560347* – P. MC AE VISA
closed 25 December – **Meals** - Indian - (lunch by arrangement)/dinner 7.95/25.00 **t.** and a la carte 7.95.

ASHFORD *Kent* 404 W 30 – *pop. 52 002.*

Channel Tunnel : Eurostar information and reservations (0990) 186186.

18 The Churchyard (01233) 629165.

London 56 – Canterbury 14 – Dover 24 – Hastings 30 – Maidstone 19.

Eastwell Manor, Eastwell Park, Boughton Lees, TN25 4HR, North : 3 m. by A 28 on A 251 (01233) 213000, *eastwell@btinternet.com, Fax (01233) 213017,* « Reconstructed period mansion in formal gardens », heated, – , rest, P – 250. MC AE VISA
Meals 15.00/30.00 **st.** and a la carte 22.50 – ***Pavilion Restaurant :*** **Meals** *(closed Sunday dinner)* a la carte approx. 30.00 **t.** – **20 rm** 150.00/340.00 **t.**, 3 suites – SB.

Ashford International, Simone Weil Av., TN24 8UX, North : 1 ½ m. by A 20 (01233) 219988, *sales@ashfordinthotel.co.uk, Fax (01233) 647743,* – , rm, P – 400. MC AE VISA
Alhambra : **Meals** *(closed Sunday)* 9.95/12.95 **st.** and a la carte 5.95 – ***Mistral Brasserie :*** **Meals** (dinner only) a la carte 12.95/23.40 – 9.95 – **199 rm** 99.00 **st.**, 2 suites – SB.

Posthouse Ashford, Canterbury Rd, TN24 8QQ, North : ¾ m. on A 28 (0870) 400 9001, *Fax (01233) 643176,* – rm, P – 100. MC AE VISA.
Meals 7.50/18.00 **t.** and a la carte – 11.95 – **103 rm** 69.00 **st.** – SB.

Pilgrims Rest, Canterbury Rd, Kennington, TN24 9QR, Northeast : 2 m. on A 28 (01233) 636863, *pilgrimsrest@fullers.co.uk, Fax (01233) 610119,* – rm, rest, P – 70. MC AE VISA
Meals a la carte 11.65/18.45 **st.** – 7.50 – **34 rm** 49.00 **st.** – SB.

Travel Inn, Hall Av., Orbital Park, Sevington, TN24 0GA, Southeast : 3 m. by A 292 off A 2070 (01233) 500755, *Fax (01233) 500712* – , rm, rest, P. MC AE VISA.
Meals (grill rest.) – **60 rm** 40.95 **t.**

at Hothfield *Northwest : 3½ m. by A 20 – Ashford.*

Holiday Inn Garden Court, Maidstone Rd, TN26 1AR, North : 1 m. on A 20 (01233) 713333, *sales@holidayinn-ashford.freeserve.co.uk, Fax (01233) 712082,* – , rm, P – 80. MC AE VISA JCB
Meals *(closed Saturday and Sunday lunch)* 10.00/15.00 **st.** and a la carte – 8.95 – **100 rm** 59.00 **t.** – SB.

Travel Inn, Maidstone Rd, Hothfield Common, TN26 1AP, North : ¾ m. on A 20 (01233) 712571, *Fax (01233) 713945* – rm, P. MC AE VISA.
Meals (grill rest.) – **60 rm** 40.95 **t.**

ASHFORD-IN-THE-WATER *Derbs.* 402 403 404 O 24 – *see Bakewell.*

ASHINGTON *W. Sussex* 404 S 31 – *pop. 2 852* – *Pulborough.*

London 50 – Brighton 20 – Worthing 9.

Mill House, Mill Lane, RH20 3BZ, (01903) 892426, *millinfo@aol.com, Fax (01903) 892855,* – P – 40. MC AE VISA
Meals 22.50 **t.** (dinner) and a la carte 17.95/22.50 **t.** 6.95 – **11 rm** 49.00/89.00 **st.** – SB.

ASHTON-IN-MAKERFIELD *Gtr. Manchester* 402 M 23 – *pop. 28 105* – *Wigan.*

London 199 – Liverpool 19 – Manchester 20.

Premier Lodge, 53 Warrington Rd, WN4 9PJ, South : ½ m. on A 49 (0870) 7001572, *Fax (0870) 7001573* – rm, P. MC AE VISA JCB.
Meals (grill rest.) a la carte 9.80/15.50 **st.** 4.20 – 6.00 – **28 rm** 42.00 **st.**

ASHTON-UNDER-LYNE *Gtr. Manchester* 402 403 404 N 23 – *pop. 43 906.*

32 Market St. ℘ (0161) 343 4343.

London 209 – Leeds 40 – Manchester 7 – Sheffield 34.

York House, York Pl., off Richmond St., OL6 7TT, ℘ (0161) 330 9000, *Fax (0161) 343 161*
– TV P – 40. MC AE VISA JCB
accomodation closed 25 December – **Meals** 10.50/15.00 **st.** and a la carte 5.50 – **34 rm** 52.00/80.00 **st.** – SB.

Woodlands without rest., 33 Shepley Rd, Audenshaw, M34 5DL, Southwest : 2 m. by 635 and A 6017 on B 6169 ℘ (0161) 336 4241 – TV P. MC VISA.
3 rm 45.00/65.00 **s.**

ASKRIGG *N. Yorks.* 402 N 21 – *pop. 1 002* – ✉ *Leyburn.*

London 251 – Kendal 32 – Leeds 70 – York 63.

Helm, Helm, DL8 3JF, West : 1 ½ m., turning right at No Through Rd sign after 1 m ℘ (01969) 650443, *holiday@helmyorkshire.com, Fax (01969) 650443,* ≤ Wensleydale, « Pa 17C stone cottage » – TV P. MC VISA JCB.
Restricted opening in winter – **Meals** (by arrangement) 19.50 **s.** 7.45 – **3 rm** 54.00 78.00 **s.** – SB.

ASPLEY GUISE *Beds.* 404 S 27 – *pop. 2 236.*

Woburn Sands, West Hill ℘ (01908) 582264 – Lyshott Heath, Ampthill ℘ (0152 840252.

London 52 – Bedford 13 – Luton 16 – Northampton 22.

Moore Place, The Square, MK17 8DW, ℘ (01908) 282000, *info@mooreplace.co.u Fax (01908) 281888,* « Georgian mansion », – TV P – 50. MC AE VISA JCB
Meals *(closed lunch Saturday and Bank Holidays)* 16.50/24.95 **t.** and a la carte – **53 rm** 90.00/120.00 **st.**, 1 suite – SB.

Les prix

Pour toutes précisions sur les prix indiqués dans ce guide, reportez-vous aux pages de l'introduction.

ASTON CANTLOW *Warks.* 403 404 O 27 – *pop. 1 843* – ✉ *Solihull.*

London 103 – Birmingham 21 – Stratford-upon-Avon 4 – Warwick 20 – Worcester 24.

The King's Head, Bearley Rd, B95 6HY, ℘ (01789) 488242, *Fax (01789) 488137,* « Part 15C », – P. MC AE VISA
Meals (booking essential) a la carte 18.35/24.15 **t.** 4.95.

ASTON CLINTON *Bucks.* 404 R 28 – *pop. 3 467* – ✉ *Aylesbury.*

London 42 – Aylesbury 4 – Oxford 26.

West Lodge, London Rd, HP22 5HL, ℘ (01296) 630362, *JB@westlodge.co.u Fax (01296) 630151,* – rest, TV P. MC AE VISA JCB.
***Montgolfier* :** **Meals** (residents only) (dinner only) 22.00/30.00 **st.** 11.00 – **7 rm** 50.00 70.00 **st.**

ATHERSTONE *Warks.* 403 404 P 26 – *pop. 10 677.*

London 120 – Birmingham 22 – Coventry 15 – Leicester 30.

Chapel House with rm, Friar's Gate, CV9 1EY, ℘ (01827) 718949, *Fax (01827) 71770* « Part Georgian former dower house », – rest, TV. MC AE VISA JCB.
closed 25 and 26 December and 1 January – **Meals** *(closed Sunday dinner and Bar Holidays)* (lunch by arrangement)/dinner a la carte 18.95/31.20 **t.** 10.00 – **14 rm** 54.00 90.00 **t.** – SB.

AUSTWICK *N. Yorks.* 402 M 21 – *pop. 467* – ✉ *Lancaster (Lancs.).*

London 259 – Kendal 28 – Lancaster 20 – Leeds 46.

Austwick, LA2 8BY, ℘ (015242) 51224, *Fax (015242) 51796,* – TV P – 7
MC VISA.
Meals *(closed Sunday and Monday)* (dinner only) 8.50/25.00 **st.** and a la carte 8.50 – **9 rm** 40.00/110.00 **st.** – SB.

Wood View, The Green, LA2 8BB, ℘ (015242) 51268, – TV P. MC VISA
Meals (by arrangement) 15.00 **st.** 6.50 – **6 rm** 35.00/60.00 – SB.

AVON DASSETT *Warks. – pop. 191 – ✉ Leamington Spa.*
London 82 – Birmingham 37 – Coventry 22 – Oxford 34.

Crandon House without rest., CV47 2AA, Northeast : 1 ¼ m. by Fenny Compton rd on Farnborough rd ☎ (01295) 770652, *crandonhouse@talk21.com, Fax (01925) 770632,* ←, – TV P. MC VISA JCB.
closed 1 week Christmas – **5 rm** 30.00/50.00.

AXBRIDGE *Somerset* 403 L 30 – *pop. 1 773.*
London 142 – Bristol 17 – Taunton 27 – Weston-Super-Mare 11.

The Parsonage without rest., Parsonage Lane, Cheddar Rd, BS26 2DN, East : ¾ m. on A 371 ☎ (01934) 733078, *Fax (01934) 733078,* – TV P.
3 rm 38.00/48.00 **st.**

AXMINSTER *Devon* 403 L 31 *The West Country G. – pop. 3 472.*
Env. : *Lyme Regis★ - The Cobb★, SE : 5½ m. by A 35 and A 3070.*
The Old Courthouse, Church St. ☎ (01297) 34386 (restricted opening in winter).
London 156 – Exeter 27 – Lyme Regis 5.5 – Taunton 22 – Yeovil 24.

Fairwater Head Country House, Hawkchurch, EX13 5TX, Northeast : 5 ¼ m. by B 3261 and A 35 off B 3165 ☎ (01297) 678349, *reception@fairwaterhead.demon.co.uk, Fax (01297) 678459,* ← Axe Vale, , – TV P. MC AE VISA.
restricted opening in winter – **Meals** 12.50/29.50 **t.** 8.25 – **20 rm** 76.00/152.00 **t.** – SB.

at Membury *North : 4½ m. by A 35 and Stockland rd – ✉ Axminster.*

Lea Hill, EX13 7AQ, South : ½ m. ☎ (01404) 881881, *Fax (01404) 881890,* ←, « Part 14C Devon longhouse », – TV P. MC AE VISA
closed January-mid March – **Meals** *(closed Sunday)* (bar lunch)/dinner 24.95/26.00 **t.** 9.00 – **9 rm** (dinner included) 89.00/158.00 **t.**, 2 suites – SB.

Le Guide change, changez de ***guide Michelin*** *tous les ans.*

AYCLIFFE *Darlington – see Darlington.*

AYLESBURY *Bucks.* 404 R 28 *Great Britain G. – pop. 58 058.*
Env. : *Waddesdon Manor★★, NW : 5½ m. by A 41 – Chiltern Hills★.*
Weston Turville, New Rd ☎ (01296) 424084 – Hulcott Lane, Bierton ☎ (01296) 393644.
8 Bourbon St. ☎ (01296) 330559.
London 46 – Birmingham 72 – Northampton 37 – Oxford 22.

Hartwell House, Oxford Rd, HP17 8NL, Southwest : 2 m. on A 418 ☎ (01296) 747444, *info@hartwell_house.com, Fax (01296) 747450,* ←, « Part Jacobean, part Georgian house, former residence of Louis XVIII », , , , , , , – TV P – 80. MC VISA.
Meals 22.00/45.00 **st.** 6.95 – 16.90 – **33 rm** 135.00/215.00 **st.**, 13 suites 305.00/600.00 **st.** – SB.

Posthouse Aylesbury, Aston Clinton Rd, HP22 5AA, Southeast : 2 m. on A 41 ☎ (0870) 400 9002, *Fax (01296) 392 2211,* , , , – rm, TV P – 100. MC AE VISA
Meals *(closed Saturday lunch)* a la carte 19.30/28.00 **t.** 11.45 – 11.95 – **138 rm** 99.00/119.00 **t.**, 2 suites – SB.

Holiday Inn Garden Court, Buckingham Rd, Watermead, HP19 3FY, North : 1 m. on A 413 ☎ (01296) 398839, *aylesbury@holidayinns.co.uk, Fax (01296) 394108,* , – rm, TV P – 30. MC AE VISA JCB.
Meals (residents only) (dinner only) a la carte 16.00/20.00 **st.** – 8.50 – **40 rm** 82.00 **st.**

Bottle & Glass, Gibraltar, HP17 8TY, Southwest : 5 m. on A 418 ☎ (01296) 748488, *junesouthwood@aol.com, Fax (01296) 747673,* « 17C thatched inn » – P. MC AE VISA
closed Sunday dinner – **Meals** - Seafood specialities - a la carte 17.45/38.40 **st.**

AYLMERTON *Norfolk* 404 X 25.
London 139 – Norwich 27.

Felbrigg Lodge, NR11 8RA, Southeast : 1 m. by Metton Rd ☎ (01263) 837588, *info@felbrigglodge.co.uk, Fax (01263) 838012,* , – TV P. MC VISA.
Meals (by arrangement) 26.50 **st.** – **4 rm** 55.00/120.00 **st.** – SB.

AYMESTREY *Herefordshire* 403 L 27 – *pop. 301.*
London 156 – Birmingham 54 – Hereford 17 – Shrewsbury 35 – Worcester 31.

Riverside Inn, HR6 9ST, ✆ (01568) 708440, *Fax (01568) 709058,* « 16C », ⌒, 🌳 – P. MC VISA JCB
Meals 16.95 **t.** (lunch) and a la carte 15.70/24.95 **t.** 🍷 6.95.

BADINGHAM *Suffolk* 404 Y 27 – *see Framlingham.*

BADMINTON *South Gloucestershire* 403 404 N 29 – *pop. 2 167.*
London 114 – Bristol 19 – Gloucester 26 – Swindon 33.

Bodkin House, Petty France, GL9 1AF, Northwest : 3 m. on A 46 ✆ (01454) 238310, *hot@bodkin_house.demon.co.uk, Fax (01454) 238422* – ⅍ rest, TV P. MC AE VISA. ⅍
Meals 16.95/18.95 **st.** and a la carte – **9 rm** ⊆ 52.00/75.00 **st.** – SB.

BAGINTON *Warks.* 403 404 P 26 – *see Coventry.*

BAGSHOT *Surrey* 404 R 29 – *pop. 5 190.*
18 *Windlesham, Grove End* ✆ *(01276) 452220.*
London 37 – Reading 17 – Southampton 49.

Pennyhill Park ⛰, London Rd, GU19 5EU, Southwest : 1 m. on A 30 ✆ (01276) 47177*4*, *pennyhillpark1@msn.com, Fax (01276) 473217,* ≤, « Gardens and parklands », Fš, ⛱ heated, 9, ⌒, ✗ – ⅍ rest, TV ♿ P – 🏛 150. MC AE ⓓ VISA. ⅍
St. James : **Meals** - Italian - 17.50/60.00 and dinner a la carte 🍷 10.00 – (see also ***The Latymer*** below) – ⊆ 15.00 – **113 rm** 155.00/250.00, 10 suites – SB.

Travel Inn, London Rd, GU19 5HR, North : ½ m. on A 30 ✆ (01276) 473196 *Fax (01276) 451357,* 🌳 – ⅍ rm, ▤ rest, TV ♿ P. MC AE ⓓ VISA. ⅍
Meals (grill rest.) – **40 rm** 40.95 **t.**

The Latymer (at Pennyhill Park H.), London Rd, GU19 5EU, Southwest : 1 m. on A 3*0* ✆ (01276) 471774, *pennyhillpark@msn.com, Fax (01276) 473217,* 🌳 – ⅍ ▤ P. MC AE ⓓ VISA
closed Sunday and Monday – **Meals** (booking essential) 19.00/50.00 **st.** and a la cart*e* 🍷 13.00.

BAINBRIDGE *N. Yorks.* 402 N 21 – *pop. 474* – ✉ *Wensleydale.*
London 249 – Kendal 31 – Leeds 68 – York 61.

Rose and Crown, DL8 3EE, ✆ (01969) 650225, *stay@rose-and-crown.freeserve.co.uk Fax (01969) 650735* – TV P. MC VISA
Meals (bar lunch)/dinner 18.00 **t.** and a la carte 🍷 4.00 – **12 rm** ⊆ 32.00/64.00 **st.** – SB.

BAKEWELL *Derbs.* 402 403 404 O 24 *Great Britain G.* – *pop. 3 818.*
Env. : *Chatsworth**** *(Park and Garden**** *) **AC**, NE : 2½ m. by A 619 – Haddon Hall*** ***AC** SE : 2 m. by A 6.*
Old Market Hall, Bridge St. ✆ *(01629) 813227.*
London 160 – Derby 26 – Manchester 37 – Nottingham 33 – Sheffield 17.

Rutland Arms, The Square, DE45 1BT, ✆ (01629) 812812, *rutland@bakewell.demon.co.k, Fax (01629) 812309* – ⅍ TV P – 🏛 100. MC AE ⓓ VISA JCB
Meals (bar lunch)/dinner 19.50/22.00 **st.** 🍷 6.50 – **35 rm** ⊆ 52.00/109.00 **st.** – SB.

at Great Longstone *North : 4 m. by A 619 off B 6001* – ✉ *Bakewell.*

Croft Country House ⛰, DE45 1TF, ✆ (01629) 640278, 🌳 – |⇅|, ⅍ rest, TV P. MC VISA JCB. ⅍
closed 27 December-8 February – **Meals** (dinner only) 26.50 **t.** – **9 rm** ⊆ 50.00/99.00 **t.** SB.

at Ashford-in-the-Water *Northwest : 1¾ m. by A 6 and A 6020* – ✉ *Bakewell.*

Riverside House, Fennel St., DE45 1QF, ✆ (01629) 814275, *riversidehouse@enta.net Fax (01629) 812873,* 🌳 – ⅍ TV P. MC AE ⓓ VISA. ⅍
Meals 23.95/39.95 **t.** 🍷 9.50 – **15 rm** ⊆ 95.00/135.00 **t.** – SB.

BALDERSTONE *Lancs.* – *see Blackburn.*

BALDOCK *Herts.* 404 T 28 – *pop. 9 232.*
London 42 – Bedford 20 – Cambridge 21 – Luton 15.

Travelodge, A 1 Great North Road, Hinxworth (southbound carriageway), SG7 5EX, Northwest : 3 m. by A 507 on A 1 ✆ (01462) 835329, *Fax (01462) 835329* – rm, TV, P. MC AE VISA JCB.
Meals (grill rest.) – **40 rm** 44.95 **t.**

BALLASALLA *Isle of Man* 402 G 21 – *see Man (Isle of).*

BALSALL COMMON *W. Mids. – see Coventry.*

BAMBER BRIDGE *Lancs.* 402 M 22 – *see Preston.*

BAMBURGH *Northd.* 401 402 O 17 *Great Britain G.* – *pop. 582.*
See : *Castle★ AC.*
London 337 – Edinburgh 77 – Newcastle upon Tyne 51.

Lord Crewe Arms, Front St., NE69 7BL, ✆ (01668) 214243, *lca@tinyonline.co.uk, Fax (01668) 214273* – rest, TV P. MC VISA
closed January and February – **Meals** (bar lunch)/dinner a la carte 14.25/17.95 **t.** 7.50 – **12 rm** 60.00/98.00 **t.**

at Waren Mill *West : 2 ¾ m. on B 1342 – Belford.*

Waren House, NE70 7EE, ✆ (01668) 214581, *enquiries@warehousehotel.co.uk, Fax (01668) 214484,* ←, – TV P – 30. MC AE VISA JCB
Meals (dinner only) 22.45 **st.** 8.75 – **8 rm** 85.00/135.00 **st.**, 2 suites – SB.

BAMPTON *Devon* 403 J 31 – *pop. 1 617.*
London 189 – Exeter 18 – Minehead 21 – Taunton 15.

Bark House, Oakfordbridge, EX16 9HZ, West : 3 m. by B 3227 on A 396 ✆ (01398) 351236, – rest, TV P
restricted opening November-March – **Meals** (booking essential) (dinner only) 23.00 **t.** 6.75 – **5 rm** 45.00/85.00 **t.** – SB.

BANBURY *Oxon.* 403 404 P 27 *Great Britain G.* – *pop. 39 906.*
Exc. : *Upton House★ AC, NW : 7 m. by A 422.*
Cherwell Edge, Chacombe ✆ (01295) 711591.
Banbury Museum, 8 Horsefair ✆ (01295) 259855.
London 76 – Birmingham 40 – Coventry 25 – Oxford 23.

Whately Hall, Horsefair, by Banbury Cross, OX16 0AN, ✆ (01295) 263451, *heritagehotels _banbury.whatelyhall@forte-hotels.com, Fax (01295) 271736,* « Part 17C », – rm, TV P – 80. MC AE VISA JCB.
Meals *(closed Saturday lunch)* 7.95/9.95 **t.** (lunch) and a la carte 17.85/27.85 **t.** 5.95 – 10.95 – **66 rm** 100.00 **st.**, 6 suites – SB.

Banbury House, Oxford Rd, OX16 9AH, ✆ (01295) 259361, *banbury@compuserve.com, Fax (01295) 270954* – rm, TV P – 70. MC AE VISA.
closed 24 December-2 January – **Meals** (bar lunch Monday-Saturday)/dinner 19.50 **st.** and a la carte 12.00 – 10.50 – **63 rm** 87.00/140.00 **st.** – SB.

at Adderbury *South : 3 m. on A 4260 – Banbury.*

Red Lion, The Green, OX17 3LU, ✆ (01295) 810269, *Fax (01295) 811906,* « Part 16C inn » – rest, TV P. MC AE VISA JCB
Meals 10.95/15.95 **t.** (dinner) and a la carte 14.00/18.50 **t.** 7.95 – **12 rm** 60.00/95.00 **t.** – SB.

at North Newington *West : 2¼ m. by B 4035 – Banbury.*

La Madonette Country Guest House without rest., OX15 6AA, ✆ (01295) 730212, *lamadonett@aol.com, Fax (01295) 730363,* – TV P. MC VISA JCB.
5 rm 45.00/64.00 **st.**

at Wroxton *Northwest : 3 m. by B 4100 on A 422 – Banbury.*

Wroxton House, Silver St., OX15 6QB, ✆ (01295) 730777, *wroxtonhse@aol.com, Fax (01295) 730800* – TV P – 40. MC AE VISA.
Meals 13.50/26.00 **t.** and a la carte 10.50 – 9.95 – **32 rm** 95.00/105.00 **t.** – SB.

ENGLAND

at Shenington *Northwest : 6 m. by B 4100 off A 422 – ✉ Banbury.*

Sugarswell Farm ⊗, OX15 6HW, Northwest : 2 ¼ m. on Edge Hill rd ☎ (01295) 680512 *Fax (01295) 688149*, ←, 🌳, ⊛ – ⊭ P. ✻
Meals (by arrangement) (communal dining) 22.50 **st.** – **3 rm** ☐ 35.00/70.00 **st.**

BANTHAM *Devon – see Kingsbridge.*

BARFORD *Warks.* 403 404 P 27 – *see Warwick.*

BAR HILL *Cambs.* 404 U 27 – *see Cambridge.*

BARLBOROUGH *Derbs.* 402 403 404 Q 24 – *pop. 1 917.*
London 160 – Derby 45 – Lincoln 37 – Nottingham 30 – Sheffield 12.

Ibis without rest., 3 Tallys End, Chesterfield Rd, S43 4TX, on A 619 ☎ (01246) 813222, Reservations (Freephone) 0800 897121, *Fax (01246) 813444* – |≡| ⊭ TV ☎ ♿ P – 🎤 35. MC AE ⊕ VISA
86 rm 45.00 **st.**

BARNARD CASTLE *Durham* 402 O 20 *Great Britain G. – pop. 6 084.*
See : *Bowes Museum★ AC.*
Exc. : *Raby Castle★ AC, NE : 6½ m. by A 688.*
18 *Harmire Rd ☎ (01833) 638355.*
ℹ *Woodleigh, Flatts Rd ☎ (01833) 690909.*
London 258 – Carlisle 63 – Leeds 68 – Middlesbrough 31 – Newcastle upon Tyne 39.

Jersey Farm ⊗, Darlington Rd, DL12 8TA, East : 1 ½ m. on A 67 ☎ (01833) 638223, *jerseyfarmhotel@enta.net, Fax (01833) 631988*, ⊛ – ⊭ rest, TV P – 🎤 200. MC VISA
Meals 13.90 **t.** and a la carte – **16 rm** ☐ 57.50/69.00 **t.**, 4 suites.

Demesnes Mill ⊗ without rest., DL12 8PE, Southeast : ½ m. by The Bank and Gray Lane through the playing field ☎ (01833) 637929, *millbb@msn.com, Fax (01833) 637974*, ← « Part 15C former cornmill on banks of River Tees », 🌳 – ⊭ TV 🚗. MC VISA JCB
closed January-February – **3 rm** ☐ 40.00/75.00 **st.**

Homelands, 85 Galgate, DL12 8ES, ☎ (01833) 638757, 🌳 – ⊭ rm, TV. ✻
closed 23 December-2 January – **Meals** (by arrangement) 14.95 **st.** 🍷 5.00 – **5 rm** ☐ 26.00/45.00 **s.**

Marwood House, 98 Galgate, DL12 8BJ, ☎ (01833) 637493, *john@kilgarriff.demon.co.uk, Fax (01833) 637493*, ≘s – ⊭ TV. ✻
Meals (by arrangement) 12.00 **st.** – **4 rm** ☐ 21.00/44.00 **st.**

at Romaldkirk *Northwest : 6 m. by A 67 on B 6277 – ✉ Barnard Castle.*

Rose and Crown, DL12 9EB, ☎ (01833) 650213, *hotel@rose-and-crown.co.uk Fax (01833) 650828*, « Part 18C coaching inn » – ⊭ rest, TV P. MC VISA
closed 25 and 26 December – **Meals** *(closed Sunday dinner to non-residents)* (bar lunch Monday to Saturday)/dinner 25.00 **st.** 🍷 7.95 – **10 rm** ☐ 64.00/100.00 **st.**, 2 suites – SB.

BARNARD GATE *Oxon.* 403 404 P 28 – *see Witney.*

BARNEY *Norfolk* 404 W 25 – ✉ *Fakenham.*
London 187 – Cambridge 71 – King's Lynn 21 – Norwich 29.

Old Brick Kilns, Little Barney Lane, NR21 0NL, East : ¾ m. ☎ (01328) 878305, *enquire@old-brick-kilns.co.uk, Fax (01328) 878948*, 🌳 – ⊭ TV ☎ P. MC ⊕ VISA JCB. ✻
Meals (by arrangement) (communal dining) 15.00 **st.** 🍷 3.00 – **3 rm** ☐ 25.00/50.00 **st.** – SB

BARNSDALE BAR *W. Yorks.* 402 404 Q 23 – ✉ *Pontefract.*
London 181 – Leeds 22 – Nottingham 53 – Sheffield 26.

Travelodge, WF8 3JB, on A 1 (southbound carriageway) ☎ (01977) 620711 *Fax (01977) 620711* – ⊭ rm, ▤ rest, TV ♿ P. MC AE ⊕ VISA JCB. ✻
Meals (grill rest.) – **56 rm** 39.95 **t.**

BARNSLEY *Glos.* 403 404 O 28 – *see Cirencester.*

BARNSLEY *S. Yorks.* 402 404 P 23 – *pop. 75 120.*

Wakefield Rd, Staincross ☎ (01226) 382856 – Silkstone, Field Head, Elmhirst Lane ☎ (01226) 790328 – Wombwell Hillies, Wentworth View, Wombwell ☎ (01226) 754433.

Central Library, Shambles St. ☎ (01226) 206757.

London 177 – Leeds 21 – Manchester 36 – Sheffield 15.

Ardsley House H. and Health Club, Doncaster Rd, Ardsley, S71 5EH, East : 2 ¾ m. on A 635 ☎ (01226) 309955, *sales@ardsley-house.co.uk, Fax (01226) 205374,* – rm, rest, – 450.
Meals (bar lunch Saturday and Bank Holidays) 9.95/21.50 **st.** and a la carte – 10.50 – **74 rm** 79.00/94.00 **st.** – SB.

Tankersley Manor, Church Lane, S75 3DQ, South : 6 ¼ m. on A 61 ☎ (01226) 744700, *info@tankersleymanor.co.uk, Fax (01226) 745405,* – – 340.
Meals *(closed Saturday lunch and Sunday dinner)* 17.95/19.95 **st.** (dinner) and a la carte 21.00/32.40 **t.** 7.95 – **69 rm** 77.50/82.50 **st.**

Travel Inn, Maple Rd, Tankersley, S74 3DL, South : 6 ½ m. by A 61 at junction with A 616 ☎ (01226) 350035, *Fax (01226) 741524* – rm, rest,
Meals (grill rest.) – **42 rm** 40.95 **t.**

Travelodge, Doncaster Rd, S70 3PE, East : 2 m. on A 635 ☎ (01226) 298799, *Fax (01226) 298799* – rm,
Meals (grill rest.) – **32 rm** 39.95 **t.**

La guida cambia, cambiate la guida ogni anno.

BARNSTAPLE *Devon* 403 H 30 *The West Country G.* – *pop. 20 740.*

See : *Town★ - Long Bridge★.*

Env. : *Arlington Court★★ (Carriage Collection★)* **AC**, *NE : 6 m. by A 39.*

Chulmleigh, Leigh Rd ☎ (01769) 580519.

36 Boutport St. ☎ (01271) 374037.

London 222 – Exeter 40 – Taunton 51.

Imperial, Taw Vale Par., EX32 8NB, ☎ (01271) 345861, *info@brend-imperial.co.uk, Fax (01271) 324448* – rest, rest, – 60.
Meals 12.50/20.00 **t.** and a la carte – **65 rm** 59.00/118.00 **st.** – SB.

Barnstaple, Braunton Rd, EX31 1LE, West : 1 ½ m. on A 361 ☎ (01271) 376221, *info@barnstaplehotel.co.uk, Fax (01271) 324101,* heated, – rest, – 350.
Meals (bar lunch Monday to Saturday)/dinner 18.50 **t.** and a la carte 5.75 – **60 rm** 59.00/104.00 **st.** – SB.

Lynwood House with rm, Bishops Tawton Rd, EX32 9EF, South : 1 ½ m. by A 361 and Newport rd ☎ (01271) 343695, *info@lynwoodhouse.co.uk, Fax (01271) 379340* – rest,
Meals - Seafood - *(closed Saturday lunch and Sunday)* a la carte 23.00/31.50 **t.** 6.05 – **5 rm** 47.50/67.50 **t.** – SB.

at Bishop's Tawton *South : 2 ¾ m. by A 39 on A 377 – ✉ Barnstaple.*

Downrew House , EX32 0DY, Southeast : 1 ½ m. on Chittlehampton rd ☎ (01271) 342497, *downrew@globalnet.co.uk, Fax (01271) 323947,* heated, – rest, – 40.
Meals (bar lunch Monday-Saturday)/dinner 22.50 **st.** and a la carte 5.50 – **12 rm** 55.00/130.00 **st.** – SB.

Halmpstone Manor , EX32 0EA, Southeast : 3 m. by Chittlehampton rd ☎ (01271) 830321, *Fax (01271) 830826,* – rest,
closed Christmas and New Year – **Meals** (set menu only) (lunch by arrangement)/dinner 25.00/30.00 **st.** 12.30 – **5 rm** 70.00/140.00 **st.**

BARROW-IN-FURNESS *Cumbria* 402 K 21 – *pop. 48 947.*

Rakesmoore Lane, Hawcoat ☎ (01229) 825444 – Furness, Walney Island ☎ (01229) 471232.

Forum 28, Duke St. ☎ (01229) 894784.

London 295 – Kendal 34 – Lancaster 47.

Arlington House, 200-202 Abbey Rd, LA14 5LD, North : 1 m. ☎ (01229) 831976, *Fax (01229) 870990,* heated –
closed 23 December-4 January – **Meals** *(closed Sunday)* (dinner only) a la carte 18.75/25.50 **t.** 6.30 – **8 rm** 65.00/85.00 **t.**

BARTON MILLS *Suffolk.* 404 V 26 – *pop. 832.*

London 72 – Cambridge 21 – Ipswich 37 – Norwich 40.

Travelodge, Fiveways Roundabout, IP28 6AE, on A 11 ✆ (01638) 717675 – rm, TV & P. MC AE D VISA JCB.
Meals (grill rest.) – **32 rm** 49.95 **t.**

BARTON-ON-SEA *Hants.* 403 404 P 31.

London 108 – Bournemouth 11 – Southampton 24 – Winchester 35.

XX **Oysters** with rm, Marine Drive, BH25 7DZ, ✆ (01425) 627777, *Fax (01425) 617714,* Christchurch Bay, Isle of Wight and The Needles, – rest, rest, TV P. MC AE VISA
closed 1-14 January and Monday – **Meals** - Seafood - 14.75/23.50 **t.** – **3 rm** 75.00/110.00 **t.**

BARTON STACEY *Hants.* 403 404 P 30 – *pop. 741.*

London 76 – Andover 10 – Bath 60 – Salisbury 22 – Winchester 8.

Travelodge, SO21 3NP, North : 1 ¼ m. on A 303 (westbound carriageway) ✆ (01264) 720260 – rm, TV & P. MC AE D VISA JCB.
Meals (grill rest.) – **20 rm** 49.95 **t.**

BARTON UNDER NEEDWOOD *Staffs. – see Burton-upon-Trent.*

BARWICK *Somerset* 403 404 M 31 – *see Yeovil.*

BASILDON *Essex* 404 V 29 – *pop. 100 924.*

18 *Clayhill Lane, Sparrow's Hearne ✆ (01268) 533297 –* 9 *Langdon Hills, Lower Dunton Rd, Bulphan ✆ (01268) 548444.*

London 30 – Chelmsford 17 – Southend-on-Sea 13.

Posthouse Basildon, Cranes Farm Rd, SS14 3DG, Northwest : 2 ¼ m. by A 176 off A 1235 ✆ (0870) 400 9003, *Fax (01268) 530119,* – TV & P – 300. MC AE D VISA JCB
Meals 13.50/20.00 **t.** and a la carte 6.95 – 11.95 – **149 rm** 119.00/149.00 **st.** – SB.

Travel Inn, High Rd, Fobbing, SS17 9NR, Southwest : 2 ¼ m. by A 176 at junction with A 13 ✆ (01268) 554500, *Fax (01268) 581752* – rm, TV & P. MC AE D VISA
Meals (grill rest.) – **60 rm** 40.95 **t.**

Travel Inn, Felmores, East Mayne, SS13 1BW, North : 1 ½ m. on A 132 ✆ (01268) 522227, *Fax (01268) 530092* – rm, TV & P. MC AE D VISA.
Meals (grill rest.) – **32 rm** 40.95 **t.**

at Wickford *North : 5 ¼ m. by A 132 – ✉ Basildon.*

Chichester, Old London Rd, Rawreth, SS11 8UE, East : 2 ¾ m. by A 129 ✆ (01268) 560555, *Fax (01268) 560580,* – rest, rest, TV & P – 100. MC AE VISA.
closed 1 week Christmas – **Meals** *(closed Saturday lunch)* 12.50/14.50 **t.** 6.00 – 8.95 – **33 rm** 72.00 **t.**

BASINGSTOKE *Hants.* 403 404 Q 30 – *pop. 77 837.*

18 *Test Valley, Micheldever Rd, Overton ✆ (01256) 771737 –* 18 *Weybrook Park, Rooksdown Lane, Basingstoke ✆ (01256) 320347.*

Willis Museum, Old Town Hall, Market Pl. ✆ (01256) 817618.

London 55 – Reading 17 – Southampton 31 – Winchester 18.

Plan opposite

Audleys Wood , Alton Rd, RG25 2JT, South : 1 ½ m. on A 339 ✆ (01256) 817555, *audleyswood@thistle.co.uk, Fax (01256) 817500,* « Gothic Renaissance mansion », – rm, TV & P – 50. MC VISA Z v
Meals 21.50/29.00 **t.** and a la carte 8.95 – 11.50 – **70 rm** 145.00/155.00 **st.**, 2 suites – SB.

Hilton Basingstoke, Old Common Rd, Black Dam, RG21 3PR, ✆ (01256) 460460, *Fax (01256) 840441,* – rm, rest, TV & P – 150. MC AE D VISA JCB
Meals *(closed Saturday lunch)* (carving rest.) a la carte 18.15/30.85 **st.** – 10.50 – **141 rm** 145.00/170.00 **st.** – SB. Z

Fernbank without rest., 4 Fairfields Rd, RG21 3DR, ✆ (01256) 321191, *hotelfernbank@hemscott.net, Fax (01256) 321191* – TV P. MC AE VISA. Y a
closed 2 weeks Christmas – **16 rm** 62.00/75.00 **st.**

BASINGSTOKE

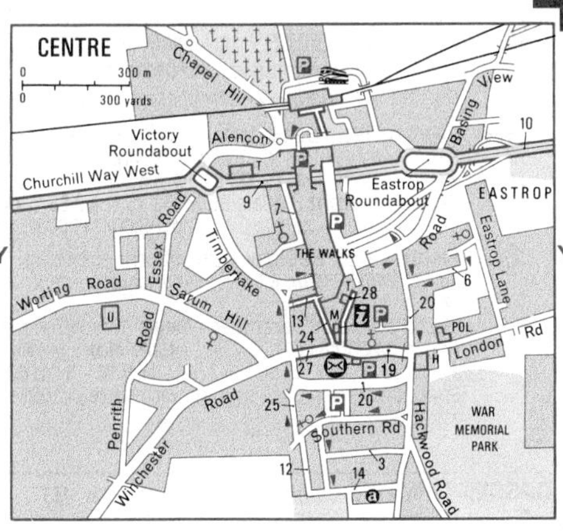

Aldermaston Road . . . . Z 2
Beaconsfield Road . . . . Y 3
Buckland Avenue . . . . Z 5
Chequers Road . . . . Y 6
Church Street . . . . Y 7
Churchill Way . . . . Z 9
Churchill Way East . . . . Z 10
Council Road . . . . Y 12
Cross Street . . . . Y 13
Fairfields Road . . . . Y 14
Houndmills Road . . . . Z 17
London Street . . . . Y 19
New Road . . . . Y 20
Reading Road . . . . Z 22
Southern Ringway . . . . Z 23
Upper Church Street . . . . Y 24
Victoria Street . . . . Y 25
Walks (The) Shopping Centre . Y
Winchester Street . . . . Y 27
Wote Street . . . . Y 28

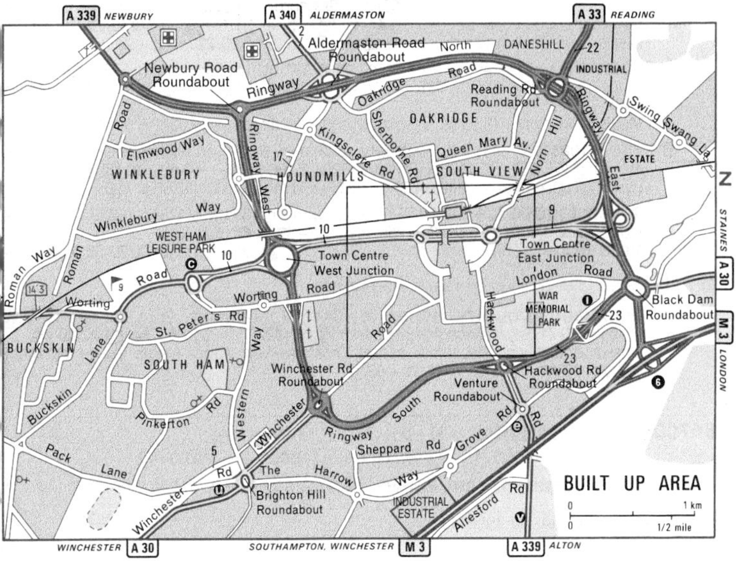

A 339 NEWBURY
A 340 ALDERMASTON
A 33 READING
Aldermaston Road Roundabout
Newbury Road Roundabout
Reading Rd Roundabout
DANESHILL INDUSTRIAL ESTATE
OAKRIDGE
WINKLEBURY
HOUNDMILLS
SOUTH VIEW
WEST HAM LEISURE PARK
Town Centre West Junction
Town Centre East Junction
Black Dam Roundabout
BUCKSKIN
SOUTH HAM
Winchester Rd Roundabout
Venture Roundabout
Hackwood Rd Roundabout
Brighton Hill Roundabout
INDUSTRIAL ESTATE
WAR MEMORIAL PARK
STAINES A 30
M 3 LONDON
BUILT UP AREA
0 1 km
0 1/2 mile
WINCHESTER A 30
SOUTHAMPTON, WINCHESTER M 3
A 339 ALTON

Travel Inn, Worting Rd, RG22 6PG, ✆ (01256) 811477, *Fax (01256) 819329* – rm, TV, P. MC AE VISA. — Z c
Meals (grill rest.) – **71 rm** 40.95 **t.**

Travelodge, Winchester Rd, RG22 5HN, Southwest : 2 ¼ m. by A 30 ✆ (01256) 843566 – rm, TV, P. MC AE VISA JCB. — Z u
Meals (grill rest.) – **32 rm** 59.95 **t.**

at Oakley *West : 4 ¾ m. on B 3400 –* **Z.**

Beach Arms, RG23 7EP, on B 3400 ✆ (01256) 780210, *Fax (01256) 780557,* – TV, P – 30. MC AE VISA JCB.
Meals (grill rest.) a la carte approx. 11.25 **st.** – 6.00 – **32 rm** 64.00 **st.**

Si vous cherchez un hôtel tranquille,
consultez d'abord les cartes de l'introduction
ou repérez dans le texte les établissements indiqués avec le signe ou .

BASLOW *Derbs.* 402 403 404 P 24 *Great Britain G. – pop. 1 184 – ✉ Bakewell.*

See : *Chatsworth★★★ (Park and Garden★★★) AC.*

London 161 – Derby 27 – Manchester 35 – Sheffield 13.

Cavendish, DE45 1SP, on A 619 ☎ (01246) 582311, *info@cavendish-hotel.net Fax (01246) 582312,* ≤ Chatsworth Park, « Collection of paintings and fine art », – rest, TV P – 25. AE VISA.
The Restaurant : Meals 26.75/38.75 **t.** 9.65 – ***Garden Room :*** Meals a la carte 21.00/34.20 **t.** 9.65 – 10.60 – **23 rm** 95.00/145.00 **t.**, 1 suite – SB.

XXX **Fischer's at Baslow Hall** with rm, Calver Rd, DE45 1RR, on A 623 ☎ (01246) 583259, *Fax (01246) 583818,* « Edwardian manor house », – rest, TV P. AE VISA JCB
closed 25 and 26 December – **Meals** *(closed Sunday dinner to non-residents and Saturday lunch)* 24.00/48.00 **t.** 7.50 – ***Café-Max :*** **Meals** *(closed Sunday and Saturday dinner)* a la carte approx. 25.00 **t.** 7.50 – 8.50 – **5 rm** 80.00/140.00 **t.**, 1 suite
Spec. Chargrilled duck sausage with apple jus. Slow braised suckling pig . Fischer's dessert assiette.

BASSENTHWAITE *Cumbria* 401 402 K 19 – *pop. 433.*

London 300 – Carlisle 24 – Keswick 7.

Armathwaite Hall, CA12 4RE, West : 1 ½ m. on B 5291, ✉ Keswick ☎ (017687) 76551, *Fax (017687) 76220,* ≤ Bassenthwaite Lake, « Part 18C mansion in extensive grounds », – TV P – 80. AE VISA.
Meals 16.95/36.95 **t.** and dinner a la carte – **42 rm** 65.00/220.00 **t.** – SB.

Castle Inn, CA12 4RG, West : 1 m. on A 591 at junction with B 5291, ✉ Keswick ☎ (017687) 76401, *Fax (017687) 76604,* – TV P – 120. AE VISA
Meals (dinner only) 18.95 **st.** and a la carte 6.95 – **48 rm** 75.00/115.00 **st.** – SB.

The Pheasant, CA13 9YE, Southwest : 3 ¼ m. by B 5291 on Wythop Mill rd, ✉ Cockermouth ☎ (017687) 76234, *Fax (017687) 76002,* « 16C », – rest, P. VISA JCB.
closed 25 December – **Meals** 14.50/19.95 **t.** – **18 rm** 65.00/150.00 **t.** – SB.

Ravenstone Lodge, CA12 4QG, South : 1 ½ m. on A 591 ☎ (017687) 76629, *ravenstone.lodge@tack21.com, Fax (017687) 76629,* ≤, – TV P. VISA JCB
Meals (residents only) (dinner only) 16.50/20.50 **st.** 5.00 – **10 rm** 30.50/65.00 **st.**

at Ireby *North : 5 m. by A 591 on Ireby rd – ✉ Carlisle.*

Woodlands Country House, CA7 1EX, Northwest : ¼ m. on Mealsgate rd ☎ (016973) 71791, *hj@woodindu-net.com, Fax (016973) 71482,* – TV P. VISA
closed January and December except Christmas-New Year – **Meals** (by arrangement) 17.00 **s.** – **7 rm** 35.00/70.00 **st.** – SB.

BATCOMBE *Somerset* 403 404 M 30 – *pop. 391 – ✉ Shepton Mallet.*

London 130 – Bristol 24 – Bournemouth 50 – Salisbury 40 – Taunton 40.

Three Horseshoes Inn, BA4 6HE, ☎ (01749) 850359, *Fax (01749) 850615,* – P. VISA JCB
Meals a la carte 17.95/23.40 **t.**

BATH *Bath & North East Somerset* 403 404 M 29 *The West Country G. – pop. 85 202.*

See : *City★★★ – Royal Crescent★★★* **AV** *(No 1 Royal Crescent★★* **AC AV A**) – *The Circus★★★* **AV** – *Museum of Costume★★★* **AC AV M7** – *Royal Photographic Society National Centre of Photography★★* **AC BV M8** – *Roman Baths★★* **AC BX D** – *Holburne Museum and Crafts Study Centre★★* **AC Y M5** – *Pump Room★* **BX B** - *Assembly Rooms★* **AV** – *Bath Abbey★* **BX** – *Pulteney Bridge★* **BV** – *Bath Industrial Heritage Centre★* **AC AV M1** – *Lansdown Crescent★★ (Somerset Place★)* **Y** – *Camden Crescent★* **Y** – *Beckford Tower and Museum* **AC** *(prospect★)* **Y M6** – *Museum of East Asian Art★* **AV M9** – *Orange Grove★* **BX.**

Env. : *Claverton (American Museum★★ AC, Claverton Pumping Station★ AC) E : 3 m. by A 36* **Y.**

Exc. : *Corsham Court★★ AC, NE : 8½ m. by A 4 – Dyrham Park★ AC, N : 6½ m. by A 4 and A 46.*

9, 9, 9, *Tracy Park, Bath Rd, Wick ☎ (0117) 937 2251 –* 18 *Lansdown ☎ (01225) 422138 –* 9 *Entry Hill ☎ (01225) 834248.*

Abbey Chambers, Abbey Churchyard ☎ (01225) 477101.

London 119 – Bristol 13 – Southampton 63 – Taunton 49.

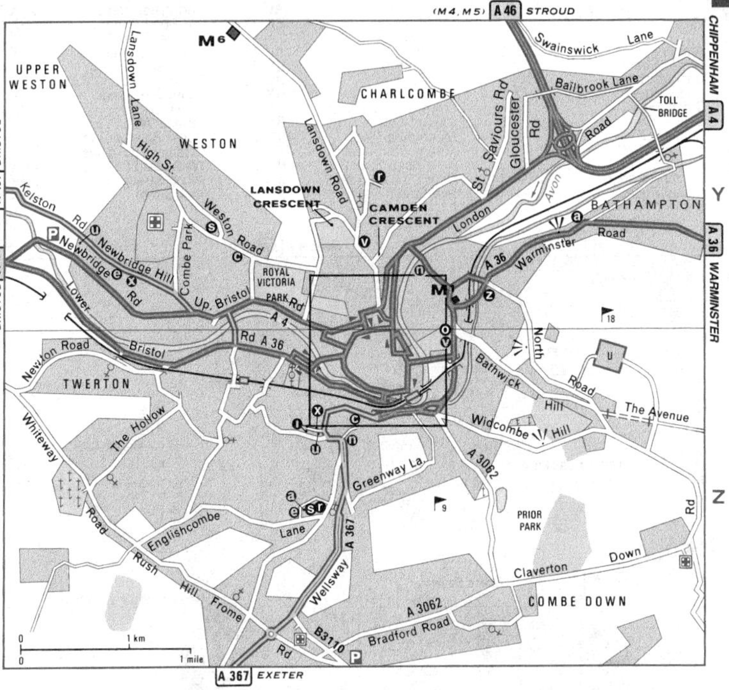

Bath Spa ⑤, Sydney Rd, BA2 6JF, ☎ (0870) 4008222, *fivestar@bathspa.u-net.com, Fax (01225) 444006*, ≤, « Part 19C mansion in landscaped gardens », Ⅎ6, ≘s, ⌂, ✂ – |♦| ⇔ TV ♿ P – 🏛 120. ⓒ AE ⓘ VISA JCB Y Z
Alfresco : **Meals** a la carte 16.50/31.00 **t.** 🍷 7.00 – ***Vellore :*** **Meals** (dinner only and Sunday lunch)/dinner 35.00 **t.** and a la carte 🍷 10.00 – ☕ 14.75 – **98 rm** 140.00/209.00 **t.**, 5 suites – SB.

The Royal Crescent, 16 Royal Cres., BA1 2LS, ☎ (01225) 823333, *reservations@royalcrescent.co.uk, Fax (01225) 447427*, ≤, ≤, « Restored 18C town houses in magnificent Georgian crescent », ≘s, ⌂, ✈ – |♦| ⇔ ▤ TV ☎ 🚗 – 🏛 100. ⓒ AE ⓘ VISA AV a
Pimpernels : **Meals** 22.00 **t.** (lunch) and dinner a la carte 35.00/49.00 **t.** 🍷 12.00 – ☕ 17.50 – **34 rm** 195.00 **t.**, 11 suites 395.00/750.00 **t.** – SB.

Bath Priory, Weston Rd, BA1 2XT, ☎ (01225) 331922, *bathprioryhotel@compuserve.com, Fax (01225) 448276*, ≤, ≤, « Gardens », Ⅎ6, ≘s, ⌂ heated, ⌂ – ⇔ TV ☎ ♿ P. ⓒ AE ⓘ VISA JCB. ✗ Y C
Meals 20.00/45.00 **t.** 🍷 12.00 – **28 rm** ☕ (dinner included) 140.00/310.00 **t.** – SB
Spec. Grilled red mullet with sweet pepper couscous. Best end of lamb with chicken ravioli, red wine sauce. Chocolate marquise with raspberry ripple ice cream.

Homewood Park, BA3 6BB, Southeast : 6½ m. on A 36 ☎ (01225) 723731, *res@homewoodpark.com, Fax (01225) 723820*, ≤, « Part Georgian country house », ⌂ heated, ✈, ♣, ✂ – ⇔ rest, TV P. ⓒ AE ⓘ VISA JCB. ✗
Meals 19.50/46.00 **st.** 🍷 9.00 – **17 rm** ☕ 109.00/210.00 **st.**, 2 suites – SB.

Queensberry, Russel St., BA1 2QF, ☎ (01225) 447928, *queensberry@dial.pipex.com, Fax (01225) 446065*, ✈ – |♦| TV. ⓒ VISA. ✗ AV x
closed 24-28 December – **Meals** – (see ***Olive Tree*** below) – ☕ 9.50 – **29 rm** 90.00/185.00 **t.** – SB.

The Francis on the Square, Queen Sq., BA1 2HH, ☎ (0870) 4008223, *heritagehotels_bath.francis@forte-hotels.com, Fax (01225) 319715* – |♦| ⇔ TV P – 🏛 80. ⓒ AE ⓘ VISA JCB
Meals (bar lunch Monday to Saturday)/dinner 19.95 **t.** and a la carte 🍷 8.00 – ☕ 13.50 – **95 rm** 114.00/184.00 **t.** – SB. AV i

BATH

Ambury . . . . **BX** 2
Argyle Street . . . . **BV** 3
Bennett Street . . . . **AV** 4
Bridge Street . . . . **BVX** 6
Broad Quay . . . . **BX** 7
Chapel Row . . . . **AVX** 9
Charles Street . . . . **AX** 10
Charlotte Street . . . . **AV** 12
Cheap Street . . . . **BX** 13
Churchill Bridge . . . . **BX** 14
Circus Place . . . . **AV** 16
Gay Street . . . . **AV**
Grand Parade . . . . **BX** 17
Great Stanhope Street . . . . **AV** 18
Green Street . . . . **BV** 21
Guinea Lane . . . . **BV** 23
Henry Street . . . . **BX** 24
Lower Borough Walls . . . . **BX** 26
Milsom Street . . . . **BV**
Monmouth Place . . . . **AVX** 28
Monmouth Street . . . . **AX** 30
New Bond Street . . . . **BV** 31
New Orchard Street . . . . . **BX** 32
Nile Street . . . . **AV** 34
Northgate Street . . . . **BVX** 35
Old Bond Street . . . . **BX** 36
Orange Grove . . . . **BX** 38
Pierrepont Street . . . . **BX** 39
Quiet Street . . . . **BV** 41
Russell Street . . . . **AV** 42
Southgate Street . . . . **BX** 43
Stanley Road . . . . **BX** 45
Terrace Walk . . . . **BX** 46
Upper Borough Walls . . . . . **BX** 48
Westgate Buildings . . . . **AX** 49
Westgate Street . . . . **ABX** 50
Wood Street . . . . **AV** 52
York Street . . . . **BX** 53

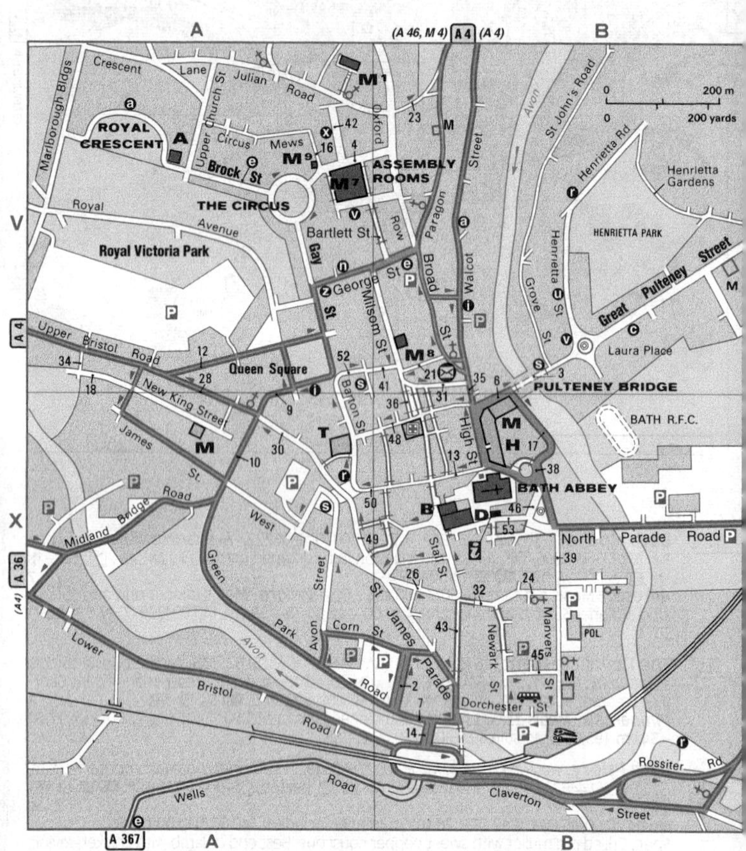

Hilton Bath City, Walcot St., BA1 5BJ, ☎ (01225) 463411, *bathhnhngm@hilton.com, Fax (01225) 464393,* – 240. BV i
Meals a la carte 14.60/32.15 **st.** – 11.00 – **150 rm** 143.00/183.00 **st.**

Hilton Bath Waterside, Rossiter Rd, Widcombe Basin, BA2 4JP, ☎ (01225) 338855, *Fax (01225) 428941* – rm, – 130. BX r
Meals *(closed Saturday lunch)* a la carte 17.40/25.15 **st.** – 13.95 – **113 rm** 106.00/126.00 **t.** – SB.

Lansdown Grove, Lansdown Rd, BA1 5EH, ☎ (01225) 483888, *lansdown@marstonhotels.com, Fax (01225) 483838,* – 80. Y v
Meals (bar lunch Monday to Saturday)/dinner 19.50 **st.** and a la carte 6.75 – 11.00 – **50 rm** 79.00/105.00 **t.** – SB.

Apsley House without rest., 141 Newbridge Hill, BA1 3PT, (01225) 336966, *info@apsley-house.co.uk, Fax (01225) 425462*, – . VISA. Y x
closed 25-26 December – **9 rm** 60.00/115.00 **st.**

The Windsor, 69 Great Pulteney St., BA2 4DL, (01225) 422100, *sales@bathwindsorhotel.com, Fax (01225) 422550* – . VISA JCB. BV c
Meals - Japanese - *(closed Sunday and Monday)* (dinner only) 32.50 **st.** 8.95 – **13 rm** 135.00/240.00 **t.** – SB.

Bath Tasburgh, Warminster Rd, BA2 6SH, East : 1 m. on A 36 (01225) 425096, *reservations@bathtasburgh.co.uk, Fax (01225) 463842*, – . VISA. Y a
Meals (booking essential) (dinner only) 22.50/25.00 **t.** 7.20 – **12 rm** 52.00/98.00 **st.**

County without rest., 18-19 Pulteney Rd, BA2 4EZ, (01225) 425003, *reservations@county-hotel.co.uk, Fax (01225) 466493* – . VISA. Z o
closed 23 December-15 January – **22 rm** 60.00/155.00 **t.**

Villa Magdala without rest., Henrietta Rd, BA2 6LX, (01225) 466329, *office@villamagdala.co.uk, Fax (01225) 483207*, – . VISA JCB. BV r
closed Christmas and New Year – **18 rm** 75.00/130.00 **t.**

The Ayrlington without rest., 24-25 Pulteney Rd, BA2 4EZ, (01225) 425495, *mail@ayrlington.com, Fax (01225) 469029*, – . VISA JCB Z v
12 rm 75.00/100.00 **st.**

Paradise House without rest., 86-88 Holloway, BA2 4PX, (01225) 317723, *info@paradise-house.co.uk, Fax (01225) 482005*, – . VISA. Z c
closed 25-26 December – **11 rm** 65.00/130.00 **st.**

Holly Lodge without rest., 8 Upper Oldfield Park, BA2 3JZ, (01225) 424042, *stay@hollylodge.co.uk, Fax (01225) 481138*, – . VISA JCB. Z x
7 rm 48.00/97.00 **st.**

Bloomfield House without rest., 146 Bloomfield Rd, BA2 2AS, (01225) 420105, *bloomfield_house.co.uk, Fax (01225) 481958*, – . VISA JCB. Z r
closed mid-week January and February – **5 rm** 55.00/95.00 **st.**

Laura Place without rest., 3 Laura Pl., Great Pulteney St., BA2 4BH, (01225) 463815, *Fax (01225) 310222* – . VISA. BV v
closed 22 December-March – **8 rm** 60.00/90.00 **st.**

Dorian House without rest., 1 Upper Oldfield Park, BA2 3JX, (01225) 426336, *dorian.house@which.net, Fax (01225) 444699*, – . VISA JCB. Z u
8 rm 47.00/85.00 **st.**

Leighton House without rest., 139 Wells Rd, BA2 3AL, (01225) 314769, *welcome@leighton-house.co.uk, Fax (01225) 443079*, – . VISA JCB. AX e
8 rm 80.00/95.00 **st.**

Kennard without rest., 11 Henrietta St., BA2 6LL, (01225) 310472, *kennard@dircon.co.uk, Fax (01225) 460054* – . VISA JCB. BV u
closed Christmas and New Year – **13 rm** 48.00/108.00 **st.**

Cheriton House without rest., 9 Upper Oldfield Park, BA2 3JX, (01225) 429862, *cheriton@which.net, Fax (01225) 428403*, – . VISA JCB. Z u
10 rm 42.00/74.00 **st.**

Brompton House without rest., St. John's Rd, Bathwick, BA2 6PT, (01225) 420972, *bromptonhouse@btinternet.com, Fax (01225) 420505*, – . VISA JCB. Y n
closed Christmas and New Year – **17 rm** 48.00/95.00 **t.**

Cranleigh without rest., 159 Newbridge Hill, BA1 3PX, (01225) 310197, *cranleigh@btinternet.com, Fax (01225) 423143*, – . VISA. Y e
closed 24-26 December – **8 rm** 50.00/80.00 **t.**

Travelodge without rest., 1 York Buildings, George St., BA1 2EB, (01225) 448999, *Fax (01225) 442061* – . VISA JCB. BV e
66 rm 49.95 **t.**

Gainsborough without rest., Weston Lane, BA1 4AB, (01225) 311380, *Fax (01225) 447411*, – . VISA. Y s
closed Christmas – **17 rm** 59.00/94.00 **st.**

Harington's, 8-10 Queen St., BA1 1HE, (01225) 461728, *post@haringtonshotel.co.uk, Fax (01225) 444804* – . VISA JCB. AV s
closed Christmas – **Meals** (light lunch only) a la carte approx. 14.25 **t.** 4.20 – **13 rm** 65.00/98.00 **t.**

Haydon House without rest., 9 Bloomfield Park, off Bloomfield Rd, BA2 2BY, (01225) 444919, *stay@haydonhouse.co.uk, Fax (01225) 427351*, – . VISA JCB. Z a
5 rm 50.00/98.00 **st.**

ENGLAND

Meadowland without rest., 36 Bloomfield Park, off Bloomfield Rd, BA2 2BX ℘ (01225) 311079, *meadowland@bath92.freeserve.co.uk, Fax (01225) 311079,* – TV P. MC VISA. Z 6
3 rm 60.00/85.00.

Badminton Villa without rest., 10 Upper Oldfield Park, BA2 3JZ, ℘ (01225) 426347, *bad mintonvilla@cableinet.co.uk, Fax (01225) 420393,* ←, – TV P. MC VISA JCB. Z
closed 23 December-3 January – **4 rm** 48.00/65.00 **st.**

Lavender House, 17 Bloomfield Park, off Bloomfield Rd, BA2 2BY, ℘ (01225) 314500, *la venderhouse@btinternet.com, Fax (01225) 448564,* – TV. MC VISA JCB. Z
closed January – **Meals** (by arrangement) 18.00 – **5 rm** 50.00/80.00.

Brocks without rest., 32 Brock St., BA1 2LN, ℘ (01225) 338374, *marion@brocksguesthou e.co.uk, Fax (01225) 334245* – TV. MC VISA. AV
closed Christmas and New Year – **6 rm** 50.00/75.00 **st.**

Blairgowrie House without rest., 55 Wellsway, BA2 4RT, ℘ (01225) 332266 *Fax (01225) 484535* – TV. Z
3 rm 38.00/58.00 **st.**

Oakleigh without rest., 19 Upper Oldfield Park, BA2 3JX, ℘ (01225) 315698, *oakleigh@wh ch.net, Fax (01225) 448223* – TV P. MC AE VISA. Z
3 rm 50.00/72.00 **st.**

Lettonie (Blunos) with rm, 35 Kelston Rd, BA1 3QH, ℘ (01225) 446676 *Fax (01225) 447541,* ←, – TV P. MC AE VISA. Y
closed 2 weeks Christmas and 2 weeks August – **Meals** *(closed Sunday and Monday)* 25.00-47.50/60.00 **t.** – **4 rm** 95.00/150.00 **t.**
Spec. Tortellini of smoked huss with Sauternes cream sauce. "Châteaubriand" of lamb with mini shepherd's pie. Apple and vanilla savarin with apple sorbet.

Olive Tree (at Queensberry H.), Russel St., BA1 2QF, ℘ (01225) 447928, *queensberry@dia pipex.com, Fax (01225) 446065* – . MC VISA AV
closed 24-28 December and Sunday lunch – **Meals** 13.50/24.00 **t.** and a la carte 11.50.

Moody Goose (Shore), 7A Kingsmead Sq., BA1 2AB, ℘ (01225) 466688 *Fax (01225) 466688* – MC AE VISA AX
closed 2 weeks January, Sunday and Bank Holidays except Good Friday – **Meals** 16.00 23.00 **t.** and dinner a la carte 27.00/32.00 **t.** 12.50
Spec. Parfait of foie gras and guinea fowl with sherry and red wine jelly. Fillet of veal tomato compote and cocotte potatoes. Dark chocolate fondant with white chocolate and tarragon sorbet.

Hole in the Wall, 16 George St., BA1 2EH, ℘ (01225) 425242, *Fax (01225) 425242* – MC AE VISA AV
closed 25, 26 and 31 December and Sunday – **Meals** 9.50/21.50 **t.** and a la carte 20.50 24.50 **t.** 7.00.

Clos du Roy, 1 Seven Dials, Saw Close, BA1 1EN, ℘ (01225) 444450, *Fax (01225) 404044* MC AE VISA JCB AX
Meals 13.95/19.50 **st.** and a la carte 7.75.

Collingbourne Ducis, 12 George St., BA1 2EH, ℘ (01225) 333303, *Fax (01225) 23967* MC AE VISA JCB AV
closed christmas-New Year, 1 week Easter, and dinner Sunday and Monday – **Meals** (light lunch)/dinner a la carte 29.00/42.50 **st.** 12.50.

Rajpoot, Rajpoot House, Argyle St., BA2 4BA, ℘ (01225) 466833, *achowdhury@talk21.co m, Fax (01225) 444527* – . MC AE VISA BV
closed 25 and 26 December – **Meals** - Indian - a la carte 17.75/24.00 **t.**

Sukhothai, 90a Walcot St., BA1 5BG, ℘ (01225) 462463, *Fax (01225) 462463* – . MC VISA JCB BV
closed Sunday and 1 week January – **Meals** - Thai - 6.90/25.00 **t.** and a la carte.

Woods, 9-13 Alfred St., BA1 2QX, ℘ (01225) 314812, *Fax (01225) 443146,* – MC VISA AV
closed 25-26 December and 1 January – **Meals** 8.00/16.50 **t.** and a la carte 5.50.

No. 5 Bistro, 5 Argyle St., BA2 4BA, ℘ (01225) 444499, *charleshome@no-5-bistro.ftbus ess.co.uk, Fax (01225) 318668* – . MC AE VISA JCB BV
closed 1 week Christmas, Monday lunch and Sunday – **Meals** a la carte 19.15/27.00 7.95.

Richmond Arms, 7 Richmond Pl., Lansdown, BA1 5PZ, North : 3/4 m. by Lansdown Rd o Richmond Rd ℘ (01225) 316725, *cunifletch@aol.com,* Y
closed 25 December, 1 January, Sunday dinner and Monday – **Meals** a la carte 9.00/17.50 5.00.

at Colerne *(Wilts.) Northeast : 6 ½ m. by A 4 – Y – , Batheaston rd and Bannerdown Rd – ✉ Chippenham.*

Lucknam Park ⛰, SN14 8AZ, North : ½ m. on Marshfield rd ☎ (01225) 742777, *reservations@lucknampark.co.uk, Fax (01225) 743536,* ←, « Early 18C country house in park », 🏋, ≘s, ☒, 🛋, ✂ – ⇔ rest, TV P – 🏛 25. MC AE ⓓ VISA JCB. ✂
Meals (dinner only and Sunday lunch)/dinner 45.00 **t.** 🍷 16.00 – ☐ 18.00 – **37 rm** 150.00/405.00 **t.**, 4 suites – SB.

at Bathford *East : 3½ m. by A 4 – Y – off A 363 – ✉ Bath.*

The Lodge without rest., Bathford Hill, BA1 7SL, ☎ (01225) 858467, *lodgethe@aol.com, Fax (01225) 858172,* 🏊 heated, 🛋 – TV P. MC VISA
closed Christmas and New Year – **5 rm** ☐ 65.00/95.00 **st.**, 1 suite.

at Monkton Combe *Southeast : 4½ m. by A 36 – Y – ✉ Bath.*

Monkshill ⛰ without rest., Shaft Rd, BA2 7HL, ☎ (01225) 833028, *monks.hill@virgin.net, Fax (01225) 833028,* ← Limpley Stoke Valley, « Antiques », 🛋 – ⇔ TV P. MC VISA JCB
closed 10 days Christmas-New Year – **3 rm** ☐ 65.00/80.00 **st.**

at Limpley Stoke (Lower) *Southeast : 5½ m. by A 36 – Y – off B 3108 – ✉ Bath.*

Cliffe, Cliffe Drive, Crowe Hill, BA3 6HY, ☎ (01225) 723226, *cliffe@bestwestern.co.uk, Fax (01225) 723871,* ←, 🏠, 🏊 heated, 🛋 – ⇔ rest, TV P. MC AE VISA JCB
Meals 12.75/18.75 **st.** (lunch) and a la carte 20.95/28.75 **st.** 🍷 8.25 – **11 rm** ☐ 75.00/125.00 **st.** – SB.

BATHFORD *Bath & North East Somerset* 403 404 M 29 – *see Bath.*

BATLEY *W. Yorks.* 402 O 22 – *pop. 48 030.*
London 205 – Leeds 9 – Manchester 40 – Middlesbrough 76 – Sheffield 31.

Alder House, Towngate Rd, WF17 7HR, Southwest : 1 m. by B 6123 ☎ (01924) 444777, *info@alderhousehotel.co.uk, Fax (01924) 442644,* 🛋 – ⇔ TV P – 🏛 80. MC AE ⓓ VISA JCB. ✂
Meals *(closed Sunday dinner and Monday lunch)* 9.95/19.95 **st.** 🍷 5.95 – **20 rm** ☐ 47.50/72.00 **st.** – SB.

BATTLE *E. Sussex* 404 V 31 *Great Britain G.* – *pop. 5 235.*
See : *Town★ – Abbey and Site of the Battle of Hastings★ AC.*
ℹ *88 High St.* ☎ *(01424) 773721.*
London 55 – Brighton 34 – Folkestone 43 – Maidstone 30.

Netherfield Place ⛰, Netherfield Rd, TN33 9PP, Northwest : 2 m. by A 2100 on Netherfield rd ☎ (01424) 774455, *reservations@netherfieldplace.co.uk, Fax (01424) 774024,* ←, « Georgian style country house, gardens », 🎾, ✂ – TV P – 🏛 50. MC AE ⓓ VISA JCB. ✂
closed 2 weeks Christmas-New Year – **Meals** 17.00/29.00 **t.** and a la carte 🍷 7.50 – **13 rms** ☐ 72.00/170.00 **t.** – SB.

PowderMills ⛰, Powdermill Lane, TN33 0SP, South : 1 ½ m. by A 2100 on Catsfield rd ☎ (01424) 775511, *powdc@aol.com, Fax (01424) 774540,* ←, 🏠, « Part Georgian gunpowdermill, antiques », 🏊, 🎣, 🛋, 🎾 – TV P – 🏛 250. MC AE ⓓ VISA JCB
***Orangery* :** **Meals** *(closed Sunday dinner January-February)* 14.95/19.90 **t.** and a la carte 🍷 8.50 – **35 rm** ☐ 75.00/160.00 **t.** – SB.

Fox Hole Farm ⛰ without rest., Kane Hythe Rd, TN33 9QU, Northwest : 2 ½ m. by A 2100 and A 271 on B 2096 ☎ (01424) 772053, *Fax (01424) 773771,* « 18C woodcutters cottage », 🛋, 🎾 – ⇔ TV P. MC VISA
3 rm ☐ 33.00/54.00 **st.**

Abbey View without rest., Caldbec Hill, TN33 0JS, North : ¼ m. by Mount St. ☎ (01424) 775513, *Fax (01424) 775517,* ←, 🛋 – ⇔ TV P. ✂
3 rm ☐ 35.00/60.00.

BEACONSFIELD *Bucks.* 404 S 29 – *pop. 12 292.*
⛳18 *Beaconsfield Seer Green* ☎ *(01494) 676545.*
London 26 – Aylesbury 19 – Oxford 32.

De Vere Bellhouse, Oxford Rd, HP9 2XE, East : 1 ¾ m. on A 40 ☎ (01753) 887211, *devere.bellhouse@airtime.co.uk, Fax (01753) 888231,* 🏋, ≘s, ☒, 🛋, squash – 🛗 ⇔ TV P – 🏛 450. MC AE ⓓ VISA JCB
***Archways* :** **Meals** *(closed Saturday lunch and Sunday dinner)* a la carte 24.15/31.35 **st.** –
***Brasserie* :** **Meals** a la carte 12.25/24.80 **st.** – **133 rm** ☐ 145.00/165.00 **t.**, 3 suites – SB.

ENGLAND

at Wooburn Common *Southwest : 3½ m. by A 40 – Beaconsfield.*

Chequers Inn, Kiln Lane, HP10 0JQ, Southwest : 1 m. on Bourne End rc (01628) 529575, *info@chequers-inn.com, Fax (01628) 850124*, – – 45 VISA JCB.
Meals 17.95/21.95 and a la carte 8.95 – **17 rm** 92.50/125.00 **t.** – SB.

BEADNELL *Northd.* 401 402 P 17.
London 341 – Edinburgh 81 – Newcastle upon Tyne 47.

Beach Court without rest., Harbour Rd, NE67 5BJ, (01665) 720225, *info@beachcourt com, Fax (01665) 721499*, Beadnell Bay – . VISA JCB.
closed Christmas – – 3.95 – **3 rm** 44.50/79.00 **s.** – SB.

BEAMINSTER *Dorset* 403 L 31 – *pop. 2 769.*
Chedington Court, South Perrott (01935) 891413.
London 154 – Exeter 45 – Taunton 30 – Weymouth 29.

Bridge House, 3 Prout Bridge, DT8 3AY, (01308) 862200, *enquiries@bridge-house.cc uk, Fax (01308) 863700*, – . VISA
Meals 14.00/28.25 **t.** and lunch a la carte 6.00 – **14 rm** 51.50/128.00 **t.** – SB.

BEARSTED *Kent* 404 V 30 – *see Maidstone.*

BEAULIEU *Hants.* 403 404 P 31 *Great Britain G.* – *pop. 726* – *Brockenhurst.*
See : *Town★★ - National Motor Museum★★ AC.*
Env. : *Buckler's Hard★ (Maritime Museum★ AC) SE : 2 m.*
London 102 – Bournemouth 24 – Southampton 13 – Winchester 23.

Montagu Arms, Palace Lane, SO42 7ZL, (01590) 612324, *enquires@montagu_arms.c .uk, Fax (01590) 612188*, « Part 18C inn, gardens » – – 40. VISA.
Restaurant : **Meals** 12.50/29.95 **t.** and dinner a la carte 6.00 – ***Monty's Brasserie*** **Meals** 12.50/29.95 **t.** and dinner a la carte 6.00 – **22 rm** 78.00/125.00 **t.**, 2 suites – SB

at Bucklers Hard *South : 2½ m. – Brockenhurst.*

Master Builder's House, SO42 7XB, (01590) 616253, *res@themasterbuilders.cc uk, Fax (01590) 616297*, , , « Located in 18C maritime village », – rm, 40. VISA JCB.
Riverview : **Meals** 19.95/29.50 **t.** and a la carte 9.00 – ***Yachtsman Gallery*** : **Meal** a la carte 16.50/21.70 **t.** – **24 rm** 115.00/155.00 **t.**, 1 suite – SB.

BECKINGTON *Somerset* 403 404 N 30 – *pop. 903* – *Bath (Bath & North East Somerset).*
London 110 – Bristol 27 – Southampton 54 – Swindon 37.

Travelodge, BA3 6SF, on A 36 (01373) 830251, *Fax (01373) 830251* – rm, VISA JCB.
Meals (grill rest.) – **40 rm** 59.95 **t.**

BEDFORD *Beds.* 404 S 27 – *pop. 73 917.*
Bedfordshire, Bromham Rd, Biddenham (01234) 261669 **Y** – *Mowsbury, Kimboltc Rd (01234) 216374.*
10 St. Paul's Sq. (01234) 215226.
London 59 – Cambridge 31 – Colchester 70 – Leicester 51 – Lincoln 95 – Luton 20 – Oxfo 52 – Southend-on-Sea 85.

Plan opposite

Barns, Cardington Rd, MK44 3SA, East : 2 m. on A 603 (01234) 27004 *Fax (01234) 273102*, – – 120. VISA **Y**
Meals - Seafood - *(closed Saturday lunch)* a la carte 18.65/24.95 **t.** 7.00 – 10.50 – **48 r** 95.00/155.00 **t.** – SB.

Bedford Swan, The Embankment, MK40 1RW, (01234) 346565, *sales@patenhotels. .uk, Fax (01234) 212009*, – , rm, rest, – 250. VISA **X**
Meals 10.95/16.50 **st.** and a la carte 8.00 – 8.95 – **109 rm** 76.00/84.50 **st.**, 1 suite – S

Travel Inn, Priory Country Park, Barkers Lane, MK41 9DJ, (01234) 35288 *Fax (01234) 325697* – rm, . VISA. **Y**
Meals (grill rest.) – **32 rm** 40.95 **t.**

BEDFORD

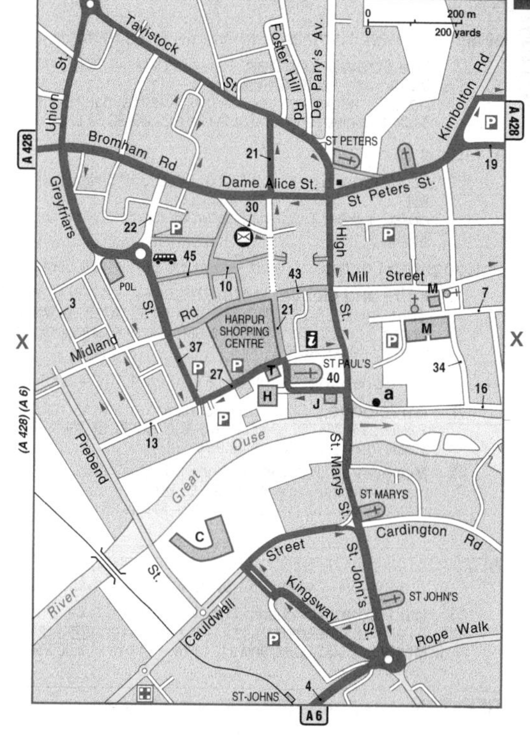

A 6 KETTERING
B 660
A 428
PETERBOROUGH CAMBRIDGE
12
31
BEDFORD PARK
Kimbolton Rd
PUTNOE
Polhill
36
9
24
GOLDINGTON
Goldington Rd
18
42
Av.
U
A 421
Bromham Rd
Goldington
Duse
Lane
Great
7
MIDLAND
6
33
RUSSEL PARK
Barkers
New Cut
QUEEN'S PARK
18
P
R
s
PRIORY COUNTRY PARK
28
River
39
A 603
Cardington
Rd
Kempston Rd
London
n
Y
26
Bedford Rd
Rd
JUBILEE PARK
15
Rd
Sprind Rd
Ampthill
Elstow
Rd
Bedford Rd
Mile Rd
Harrowden
r
25
CARDINGTON
Elstow Rd
46
The Highway
SHORTSTOWN
ELSTOW
0 1 km
0 1/2 mile
A 421
B 530
A 6 LUTON
A 600 HICHTIN

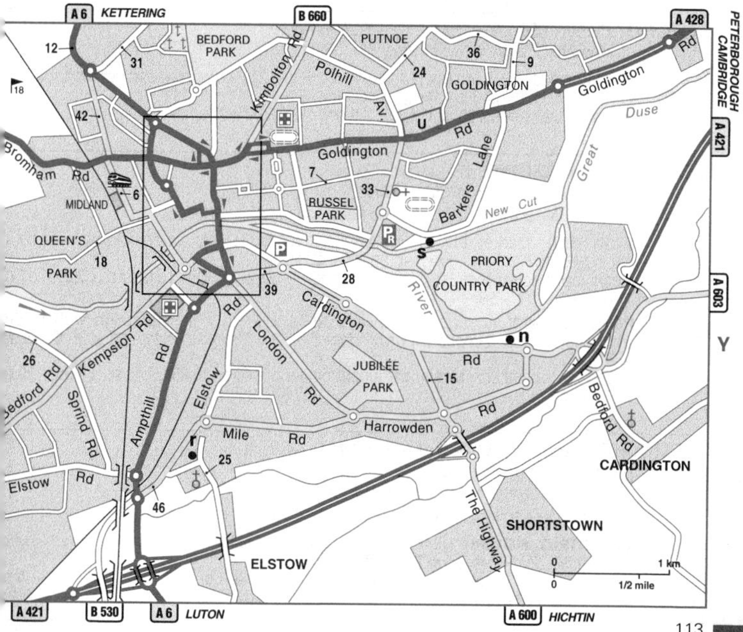

ENGLAND

at Milton Ernest *Northwest : 5 m. on A 6 – Y – ✉ Bedford.*

XX **The Strawberry Tree,** Radwell Rd, MK44 1RY, ✆ (01234) 823633, « 18C thatched cottage », – P. MC VISA JCB
closed 2 weeks January, Monday, Tuesday, Saturday lunch and Sunday dinner – **Meals** 34.00 **t.** (dinner) and lunch a la carte 29.00/32.50 **t.** 9.00.

at Elstow *South : 2 m. by A 6 off A 5134 – ✉ Bedford.*

XX **St. Helena,** High St., MK42 9XP, ✆ (01234) 344848, « Part 16C house », – P. MC AE VISA Y
closed 1 week Christmas, Saturday lunch, Sunday and Monday – **Meals** 18.50/30.00 t 9.50.

at Houghton Conquest *South : 6½ m. by A 6 – Y – ✉ Bedford.*

XX **Knife and Cleaver** with rm, The Grove, MK45 3LA, ✆ (01234) 740387, *cleaver@callnetu.com, Fax (01234) 740900,* – TV P. MC AE VISA JCB.
closed 27 to 30 December – **Meals** *(closed Sunday dinner)* 11.95/20.00 **t.** and a la carte – **9 rm** 49.00/74.00 **t.**

at Marston Moretaine *Southwest : 6¼ m. by A 6 – Y – off A 421 – ✉ Bedford.*

Travelodge, Beancroft Rd junction, MK43 0PZ, on A 421 ✆ (01234) 766755 *Fax (01234) 766755* – rm, TV P. MC AE VISA JCB.
Meals (grill rest.) – **32 rm** 49.95 **t.**

XX **Moreteyne Manor,** Woburn Rd, MK43 0NG, ✆ (01234) 767003, « 16C moated manor house », – P. MC AE VISA
closed Sunday dinner and Monday – **Meals** 16.95/28.50 **t.** 5.50.

BEESTON *Ches.* 402 403 404 L 24 – *pop. 196* – ✉ *Tarporley.*
London 186 – Chester 15 – Liverpool 30 – Shrewsbury 32.

Wild Boar, Whitchurch Rd, CW6 9NW, on A 49 ✆ (01829) 260309, *Fax (01829) 26108*, « Part 17C timbered house » – rm, rest, TV P – 100. MC AE VISA
Meals 21.95/35.00 **st.** and a la carte – **37 rm** 75.00/90.00 **t.**

BEESTON *Notts.* 402 403 404 Q 25 – *see Nottingham.*

BEETHAM *Cumbria* 402 L 21 – *pop. 1 692* – ✉ *Milnthorpe.*
London 270 – Carlisle 64 – Lancaster 12 – Leeds 72.

The Wheatsheaf with rm, LA7 7AL, ✆ (015395) 62123, *munrowheatsheaf@compuserv.com, Fax (015395) 64840* – TV P. MC VISA JCB
Meals a la carte 14.95/25.40 **t.** 7.50 – **5 rm** 55.00/70.00 **t.** – SB.

BELFORD *Northd.* 401 402 O 17 – *pop. 1 177.*
Belford, South Rd ✆ (01668) 213433.
London 335 – Edinburgh 71 – Newcastle upon Tyne 49.

Blue Bell, Market Pl., NE70 7NE, ✆ (01668) 213543, *bluebel@globalnet.co.u Fax (01668) 213787,* – rest, TV P. MC AE VISA
Meals (bar lunch Monday to Saturday)/dinner 23.00/25.00 **t.** and a la carte 7.25 – **17 rm** 46.00/96.00 **t.** – SB.

Purdy Lodge, Adderstone Services, NE70 7JU, on A 1 at junction with B 134 ✆ (01668) 213000, *reception@purdylodge.co.uk, Fax (01668) 213111* – TV P. MC AE VISA JCB
closed 25 December – **Meals** (bar lunch)/dinner a la carte 10.85/23.45 **st.** 4.95 – **20 rm** 39.95 **st.** – SB.

BELLINGHAM *Northd.* 401 402 N 18 – *pop. 1 164* – ✉ *Hexham.*
Boggle Hole ✆ (01434) 220530.
Fountain Cottage, Main St. ✆ (01434) 220616.
London 315 – Carlisle 48 – Newcastle upon Tyne 33.

Westfield House, NE48 2DP, ✆ (01434) 220340, *westfield.house@virgin.ne Fax (01434) 220694,* – TV P. MC VISA.
April-October – **Meals** (by arrangement) (communal dining) 15.50 **s.** 5.50 – **4 rm** 28.00/56.00 **st.** – SB.

BELPER *Derbs.* 402 403 404 P 24 – *pop. 18 213.*

London 141 – Derby 8 – Manchester 55 – Nottingham 17.

Makeney Hall Country House ⑤, Makeney, Milford, DE56 0RS, South : 2 m. by A 6 on Makeney rd ✆ (01332) 842999, *Fax (01332) 842777*, – |♦|, ⇔ rm, TV P – 150. MC AE ① VISA JCB
Meals *(closed Saturday lunch)* 9.95/19.50 **st.** and a la carte 8.00 – 9.75 – **45 rm** 85.00/150.00 **st.** – SB.

The Green Room, 61 King St., DE56 1QA, ✆ (01773) 828800, *greenroombelper@aol.com, Fax (01773) 828184* – MC AE VISA JCB
closed Sunday dinner, Monday and Tuesday – **Meals** 15.00 **t.** (lunch) and a la carte 20.40/27.45 **t.** 11.00.

at Shottle *Northwest : 4 m. by A 517 – ✉ Belper.*

Dannah Farm ⑤, Bowmans Lane, DE56 2DR, North : ¼ m. by Alport rd ✆ (01773) 550273, *reservations@dannah.demon.co.uk, Fax (01773) 550590*, « Working farm », – ⇔ TV P. MC VISA JCB.
closed Christmas – **Meals** (by arrangement) 17.95 **st.** 8.65 – **8 rm** 49.50/110.00 **st.**, 2 suites.

BEPTON *W. Sussex – see Midhurst.*

BERKELEY *Glos.* 403 404 M 28 *Great Britain G. – pop. 1 550.*

See : *Berkeley Castle★★ AC.*

Exc. : *Wildfowl and Wetlands Trust, Slimbridge★ AC, NE : 6½ m. by B 4066 and A 38.*

London 129 – Bristol 20 – Cardiff 50 – Gloucester 18.

Prince of Wales, Berkeley Rd, GL13 9HD, Northeast : 2 ½ m. by B 4066 on A 38 ✆ (01453) 810474, *Fax (01453) 511370*, – ⇔ rm, TV P – 200. MC AE ① VISA
Meals - Italian - (bar lunch)/dinner a la carte 15.40/22.65 **st.** – 6.00 – **43 rm** 55.00/65.00 **st.** – SB.

The Old School House, Canonbury St., GL13 9BG, ✆ (01453) 811711, *oldschoolhouse@btinternet.com, Fax (01453) 511761* – ⇔ rest, TV P. MC AE ① VISA.
Meals (booking essential to non-residents) (dinner only) a la carte 20.00/23.75 **t.** 7.95 – **8 rm** 55.00/75.00 **st.**

BERKSWELL *W. Mids.* 403 404 P 26 – *see Coventry.*

BERWICK-UPON-TWEED *Northd.* 401 402 O 16 *Great Britain and Scotland G. – pop. 13 544.*

See : *Town★ - Walls★.*

Env. : *Foulden★, NW : 5 m. – Paxton House (Chippendale furniture★) AC, W : 5 m. by A 6105, A 1 and B 6461.*

Exc. : *St. Abb's Head★★ (≤★), NW : 12 m. by A 1, A 1107 and B 6438 – SW : Tweed Valley★★ – Eyemouth Museum★ AC, N : 7½ m. by A 1 and A 1107 – Holy Island★ (Priory ruins★ AC, Lindisfarne Castle★ AC), SE : 9 m. by A 1167 and A 1 – Manderston★ (stables★), W : 13 m. by A 6105 – Ladykirk (Kirk o'Steil★), SW : 8½ m. by A 698 and B 6470.*

18 *Goswick ✆ (01289) 387256* – 18 *Magdalene Fields ✆ (01289) 306384.*

106 Marygate ✆ (01289) 330733.

London 349 – Edinburgh 57 – Newcastle upon Tyne 63.

Marshall Meadows Country House ⑤, TD15 1UT, North : 2 ¾ m. by A 1 ✆ (01289) 331133, *stay@marshallmeadows.co.uk, Fax (01289) 331438*, – ⇔ rest, TV P – 180. MC VISA JCB
Meals 7.90/25.00 **t.** 5.90 – **18 rm** 70.00/100.00 **t.**, 1 suite – SB.

High Letham Farmhouse ⑤, TD15 1UX, West : 2 ¼ m. by A 6105 and A 1 on Low Cocklaw rd ✆ (01289) 306585, *Fax (01289) 304194*, ≤, – ⇔ TV P. MC VISA.
closed Christmas – **Meals** (by arrangement) (communal dining) 20.00 **t.** 4.20 – **3 rm** 42.00/64.00 **s.** – SB.

BEVERLEY *East Riding* 402 S 22 *Great Britain G. – pop. 23 632 – ✉ Kingston-upon-Hull.*

See : *Town★ - Minster★★ – St. Mary's Church★.*

18 *The Westwood ✆ (01482) 867190.*

34 Butcher Row ✆ (01482) 867430.

London 188 – Kingston-upon-Hull 8 – Leeds 52 – York 29.

Tickton Grange, Tickton, HU17 9SH, Northeast : 3 ¾ m. on A 1035 ✆ (01964) 543666, *maggy@tickton-grange.demon.co.uk, Fax (01964) 542556*, – TV P – 200. MC AE VISA.
closed 25 and 26 December **Meals** – (see ***Squires Dining Room*** below) – 8.50 – **17 rm** 65.00/75.00 **st.** – SB.

Squires Dining Room (at Tickton Grange), Tickton, HU17 9SH, Northeast : 3 ¾ m. on A 1035 ✆ (01964) 543666, *Fax (01964) 542556* – P. MC AE VISA
Meals 22.50/25.00 **t.** (dinner) and a la carte 8.95.

at Walkington *Southwest : 3½ m. by A 164 on B 1230 – ✉ Beverley.*

Manor House with rm, Northlands, Newbald Rd, HU17 8RT, Northeast : 1 m. by Northgate on Beverley rd ✆ (01482) 881645, *derek@the-manorhouse.co.uk Fax (01482) 866501*, « Late 19C house, conservatory », – TV P. MC VISA JCB
closed 25-26 December, 1 January and Bank Holiday Mondays – **Meals** *(closed Sunday)* (dinner only) 18.50 **t.** and a la carte 8.50 – 10.50 – **7 rm** 70.00/80.00 **t.** – SB.

BEWDLEY *Worcs.* 402 403 404 N 26 – *see Kidderminster.*

BEXHILL *E. Sussex* 404 V 31 – *pop. 38 905.*
Cooden Beach ✆ (01424) 842040 – Highwoods, Ellerslie Lane ✆ (01424) 212625.
51 Marina ✆ (01424) 732208.
London 66 – Brighton 32 – Folkestone 42.

Leet Lychgates, 5a Church St., Old Town, TN40 2HE, ✆ (01424) 212193, *leet@tesco.net Fax (01424) 212193* – . MC VISA
closed Sunday and Monday – **Meals** (booking essential) (dinner only) 16.95.

Don't confuse:

Comfort of hotels : ... ,
Comfort of restaurants : XXXXX ..... X,
Quality of the cuisine : ✿✿✿, ✿✿, ✿, Meals

BIBURY *Glos.* 403 404 O 28 *Great Britain G.* – *pop. 570* – ✉ *Cirencester.*
See : *Village*★.
London 86 – Gloucester 26 – Oxford 30.

Swan, GL7 5NW, ✆ (01285) 740695, *swanhotl@swanhotel-cotswolds.co.uk Fax (01285) 740473*, « Attractively furnished inn with gardens and trout stream », – TV – 50. MC AE VISA JCB.
Signet Room : **Meals** (dinner only and Sunday lunch)/dinner 35.00 **st.** 8.95 – ***Jankowski's Brasserie :*** **Meals** a la carte 14.20/16.90 **st.** 8.75 – **18 rm** 99.00/260.00 **st.** – SB.

Cotteswold House without rest., Arlington, GL7 5ND, on B 4425 ✆ (01285) 740609, *cotteswold.house@btclick.com, Fax (01285) 740609* – TV P. VISA.
3 rm 35.00/48.00.

BICKLEIGH *Devon* 403 J 31 *The West Country G.* – *pop. 3 595* – ✉ *Tiverton.*
See : *Village*★★ - *Devonshire's Centre, Bickleigh Mill*★★ *AC* – *Bickleigh Castle*★ *AC.*
Env. : *Knightshayes Court*★ *AC, N : 4 m. by A 396.*
Exc. : *Uffculme (Coldharbour Mill*★★ *AC) NE : 7½ m.*
Post Hill, Tiverton ✆ (01884) 252114.
London 195 – Exeter 9 – Taunton 31.

Fisherman's Cot, EX16 8RW, on A 396 ✆ (01884) 855237, *Fax (01884) 855241*, « Riverside setting », – rm, TV P – 30. MC AE VISA
Meals (carving lunch)/dinner a la carte 12.15/20.95 **t.** – **21 rm** 54.00/69.00 **t.**

Bickleigh Cottage, Bickleigh Bridge, EX16 8RJ, on A 396 ✆ (01884) 855230, « Part 17 thatched cottage, riverside setting », – rest, P. MC VISA.
April-October – **Meals** (residents only) (dinner only) 12.50 – **9 rm** 30.00/50.00 **t.**

BICKLEY MOSS *Ches.* 402 404 L 24 – ✉ *Malpas.*
London 180 – Birmingham 63 – Chester 16 – Shrewsbury 27 – Stoke-on-Trent 25.

Cholmondeley Arms with rm, Cholmondeley, SY14 8BT, North : 1 ½ m. on A 4 ✆ (01829) 720300, *cholmondeleyarms@cwcom.net, Fax (01829) 720123*, « Converte schoolhouse », – TV P. MC VISA
Meals a la carte 13.00/20.45 **t.** – **6 rm** 45.00/60.00 **t.** – SB.

BIDDENDEN *Kent* 404 V 30 *Great Britain G. – pop. 2 205 – ✉ Ashford.*
Env. : *Sissinghurst Castle Garden★ AC, W : 3 m. by A 262.*
Chart Hills, Weeks Lane ☎ (01580) 292222.
London 50 – Folkestone 28 – Hastings 25 – Maidstone 14.

West House, 28 High St., TN27 8AH, ☎ (01580) 291341, *westhouse.restaurant@virginet.co.uk, Fax (01580) 291341,* « Part 16C former weavers cottage » – P. MC AE VISA JCB
closed 2 weeks June, 2 weeks January, 25-26 December, 1 January and Sunday-Tuesday – **Meals** (booking essential) (dinner only) 27.50 **t.** 7.00.

BIDEFORD *Devon* 403 H 30 *The West Country G. – pop. 13 066.*
See : *Bridge★★ – Burton Art Gallery★ AC.*
Env. : *Appledore★, N : 2 m.*
Exc. : *Clovelly★★, W : 11 m. by A 39 and B 3237 – Lundy Island★★, NW : by ferry – Rosemoor★ – Great Torrington (Dartington Crystal★ AC) SE : 7½ m. by A 386.*
Royal North Devon, Golf Links Rd, Westward Ho ☎ (01237) 473824 – Torrington, Weare Trees ☎ (01805) 622229.
to Lundy Island (Lundy Co. Ltd) (1 h 45 mn).
Victoria Park, The Quay ☎ (01237) 477676.
London 231 – Exeter 43 – Plymouth 58 – Taunton 60.

Yeoldon House, Durrant Lane, EX39 2RL, North : 1 ½ m. by B 3235 off A 386 ☎ (01237) 474400, *yeoldonhouse@aol.com, Fax (01237) 476618,* ←, – rest, TV P. MC AE VISA
Meals *(closed Sunday)* (dinner only) 19.50 **st.** and a la carte 8.00 – **10 rm** 55.00/95.00 **st.**

at Instow *North : 3 m. by A 386 on B 3233 – ✉ Bideford.*

Commodore, Marine Par., EX39 4JN, ☎ (01271) 860347, *admin@the-commodore.freeserve.co.uk, Fax (01271) 861233,* ← Taw and Torridge estuaries, – rest, TV P – 250. MC AE VISA.
Meals (dinner only and Sunday lunch)/dinner a la carte 19.00/40.50 **t.** 4.50 – **20 rm** (dinner included) 62.50/140.00 **t.** – SB.

at Eastleigh *Northeast : 2½ m. by A 386 (via Old Barnstaple Rd) – ✉ Bideford.*

The Pines at Eastleigh, Old Barnstaple Rd, EX39 4PA, ☎ (01271) 860561, *barry@thepineateastleigh.co.uk, Fax (01271) 861248,* ←, – TV P. MC VISA
restricted opening in winter – **Meals** (by arrangement) 15.00 **st.** 4.00 – **6 rm** 39.00/78.00 **st.**

BIGBURY-ON-SEA *Devon* 403 I 33 *– pop. 600 – ✉ Kingsbridge.*
London 196 – Exeter 42 – Plymouth 23.

Henley, Folly Hill, TQ7 4AR, ☎ (01548) 810240, *Fax (01548) 810020,* ← Bigbury Bay and Bolt Tail, – TV P. MC AE VISA
February-19 December – **Meals** (residents only) (dinner only) 18.50 **t.** 7.00 – **6 rm** 50.00/80.00 **t.** – SB.

BIGGLESWADE *Beds.* 404 T 27 *– pop. 12 350.*
John O'Gaunt, Sutton Park, Sandy ☎ (01767) 260360.
London 44 – Bedford 11 – Cambridge 23 – Peterborough 37.

Stratton House, London Rd, SG18 8ED, ☎ (01767) 312442, *reception@strattonhouse.demon.co.uk, Fax (01767) 600416* – , rest, TV P – 40. MC AE VISA
Meals (bar lunch)/dinner 12.00/20.00 **st.** and a la carte 5.00 – **31 rm** 58.00/100.00 **st.** – SB.

BILBROUGH *N. Yorks.* 402 Q 22 *– see York.*

BILLESLEY *Warks. – see Stratford-upon-Avon.*

Remember the speed limits that apply in the United Kingdom, unless otherwise signposted.
- 60 mph on single carriageway roads
- 70 mph on dual carriageway roads and motorways

BILLINGSHURST *W. Sussex* 404 S 30 – *pop. 4 980.*
London 44 – Brighton 24 – Guildford 25 – Portsmouth 40.

Travelodge, Five Oaks, Staines St., RH14 9AE, North : 1 m. on A 29 ☎ (01403) 782711, *Fax (01403) 782711* – rm, rest, TV, P. MC AE VISA JCB.
Meals (grill rest.) – **26 rm** 49.95 **t.**

Old Wharf without rest., Wharf Farm, Newbridge, RH14 0JG, West : 1 ¾ m. on A 272 ☎ (01403) 784096, *david.mitchell@farming.co.uk, Fax (01403) 784096,* ≤, « Restored canalside warehouse », – TV P. MC AE VISA.
closed 2 weeks Christmas and New Year – **3 rm** 45.00/90.00 **st.**

Badgers Bistro, 87 High St., RH14 9QX, ☎ (01403) 783547, *nigel@jolliffe48.freeserve.co.uk, Fax (01403) 783547* – P. MC AE VISA
closed 1 week in spring, 2 weeks in autumn, Sunday dinner and Monday – **Meals** - French - a la carte 20.00/25.00 **t.** 7.95.

BILSBORROW *Lancs. – see Garstang.*

BINFIELD HEATH *Oxon. – see Henley-on-Thames.*

BINGHAM *Notts.* 402 404 R 25 – *pop. 7 057.*
London 125 – Lincoln 28 – Nottingham 11 – Sheffield 35.

Yeung Sing, Market St., NG13 8AB, ☎ (01949) 831831, *Fax (01949) 838833* – TV P. MC AE VISA JCB.
closed 25 and 26 December – **Meals** – (see below) – **15 rm** 43.00/75.00 **t.** – SB.

Yeung Sing (at Yeung Sing H.), Market St., NG13 8AB, ☎ (01949) 831222 *Fax (01949) 838833* – P. MC AE VISA JCB
closed 25 and 26 December – **Meals** - Chinese (Canton) - 11.00/18.00 **t.** and a la carte 7.50.

Les prix — Pour toutes précisions sur les prix indiqués dans ce guide, reportez-vous aux pages de l'introduction.

BINGLEY *W. Yorks.* 402 O 22 – *pop. 19 585* – ✉ *Bradford.*
St. Ives Est. ☎ (01274) 562436.
London 204 – Bradford 6 – Skipton 13.

Five Rise Locks, Beck Lane, BD16 4DD, via Park Rd ☎ (01274) 565296, *info@five-rise-locks.co.uk, Fax (01274) 568828,* – TV P. MC VISA JCB
Oxley's Bistro : **Meals** (lunch by arrangement) a la carte 11.00/21.00 **t.** 4.50 – **9 rm** 50.00/60.00 **st.** – SB.

Travel Inn, Bradford Rd, Sandbeds, BD20 5NH, Northwest : 1 ½ m. by A 650 ☎ (01274) 566662, *Fax (01274) 566114* – rm, rest, TV P. MC AE VISA.
Meals (grill rest.) – **40 rm** 40.95 **t.**

BINHAM *Norfolk* 404 W 25 – *pop. 281* – ✉ *Fakenham.*
London 123 – Cambridge 75 – King's Lynn 31 – Norwich 29.

Field House, Walsingham Rd, NR21 0BU, Southwest : 1 ½ m. on Walsingham rd ☎ (01328) 830639, « Georgian farmhouse », – TV P.
closed November-mid February – **Meals** (by arrangement) 19.00 **s.** – **3 rm** 41.00/66.00 **s.**

BINLEY *W. Mids. – see Coventry.*

BINTON *Warks. – see Stratford-upon-Avon.*

BIRCHINGTON *Kent* 404 X 29 – *pop. 9 859.*
London 71 – Dover 20 – Maidstone 40 – Margate 5.

Crown Inn (Cherry Brandy House), Ramsgate Rd, Sarre, CT7 0LF, Southwest : 4 m on A 28 ☎ (01843) 847808, *crown@shepherd_neame.co.uk, Fax (01843) 847914,* – TV P. MC AE VISA
Meals a la carte 13.40/23.95 **t.** 6.40 – **12 rm** 43.50/75.00 **t.** – SB.

ENGLAND

BIRCH SERVICE AREA *Gtr. Manchester* 402 ㉒ 403 ③ 404 ⑩ – ✉ *Heywood (Lancs.).*

(westbound) junctions 18/19, M 62 ℘ (0161) 643 0988.

Travelodge, OL10 2HQ, on M 62 between junctions 18 and 19 ℘ (0161) 655 3403, *Fax (0161) 655 3358* – TV & P. MC AE VISA JCB.
Meals (grill rest.) – **55 rm** 39.95 **t.**

Travelodge without rest., OL10 2HQ, M 62 (westbound) between junctions 18 and 19 ℘ (0161) 643 9419 – TV & P. MC AE VISA JCB.
35 rm 39.95 **t.**

BIRKENHEAD *Mersey.* 402 403 K 23 – *pop. 93 087.*

18 Arrowe Park, Woodchurch ℘ (0151) 677 1527 – 18 Prenton, Golf Links Rd, Prenton ℘ (0151) 608 1461.
Mersey Tunnels (toll).
to Liverpool and Wallasey (Mersey Ferries) frequent services daily.
Woodside Ferry Booking Hall ℘ (0151) 647 6780.
London 222 – Liverpool 2.

Plan : see Liverpool p. 3

Bowler Hat, 2 Talbot Rd, Prenton, CH43 2HH, ℘ (0151) 652 4931, *Fax (0151) 653 8127,* – TV P – 200. MC AE VISA.
Blades : **Meals** *(closed Saturday lunch)* a la carte 14.00/25.00 **t.** – **32 rm** 75.00/95.00 **t.**

BIRMINGHAM

W. Mids. 403 404 O 26 *Great Britain G. – pop. 965 928.*

London 122 – Bristol 91 – Liverpool 103 – Manchester 86 – Nottingham 50.

TOURIST INFORMATION

Convention & Visitor Bureau, 2 City Arcade ℘ (0121) 643 2514, Fax (0121) 616 1038
Convention & Visitor Bureau, National Exhibition Centre ℘ (0121) 780 4321
Birmingham Airport, Information Desk ℘ (0121) 767 7145.
Visitor Information Centre, 130 Colmore Row ℘ (0121) 693 6300.

PRACTICAL INFORMATION

18 *Edgbaston, Church Road ℘ (0121) 454 1736,* **FX**.
18 *Hilltop, Park Lane, Handsworth ℘ (0121) 554 4463,* **CU**.
18 *Hatchford Brook, Coventry Road, Sheldon ℘ (0121) 743 9821.*
18 *Brandhall, Heron Road, Oldbury, Warley ℘ (0121) 552 7475,* **BU**.
9 *Harborne Church Farm, Vicarage Road, Harborne ℘ (0121) 427 1204,* **EX**.
Birmingham International Airport : ℘ (0121) 767 5511, E : 6½ m. by A 45 **DU**.

SIGHTS

See : *City★ – Museum and Art Gallery★★* **JZ M2** – *Barber Institute of Fine Arts★★ (at Birmingham University)* **EX** – *Cathedral of St. Philip (stained glass portrayals★)* **KYZ**.

Env. : *Aston Hall★★* **FV M.**

Exc. : *Black Country Museum★, Dudley, NW : 10 m. by A 456 and A 4123* **AU**. – *Bournville★, SW : 4 m. on A 38 and A 441.*

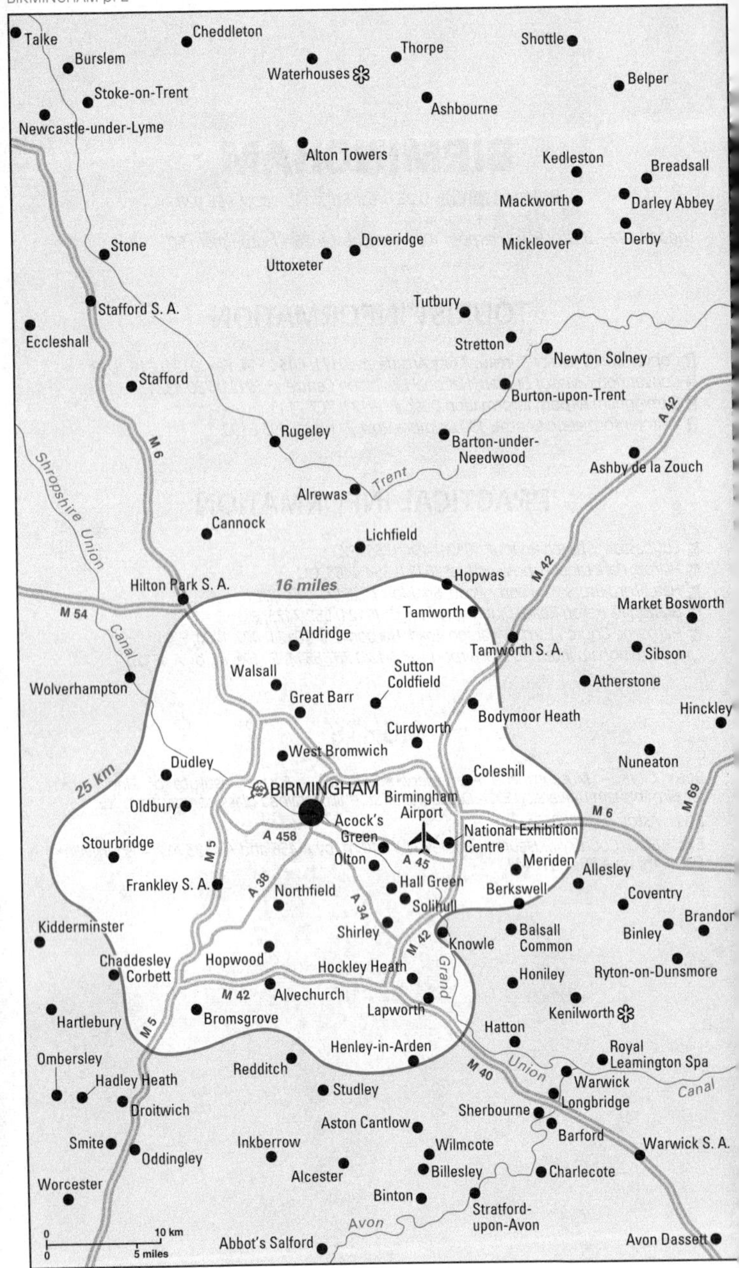

The Guide is updated annually so renew your Guide every year.

STREET INDEX TO BIRMINGHAM TOWN PLANS

«**Short Breaks**» (SB)

De nombreux hôtels proposent des conditions avantageuses pour un séjour de deux nuits comprenant la chambre, le dîner et le petit déjeuner.

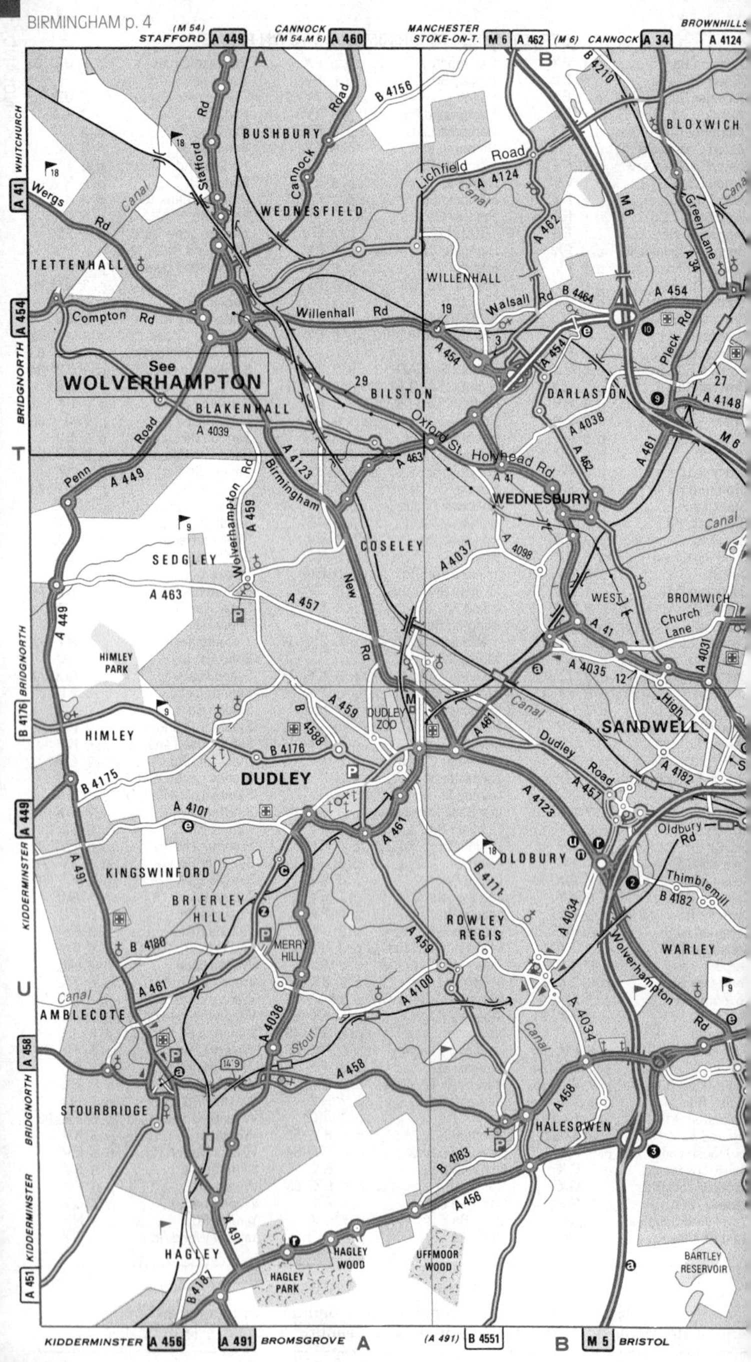
(M 54) STAFFORD A 449
CANNOCK (M 54. M 6) A 460
MANCHESTER STOKE-ON-T. M 6 A 462 (M 6) CANNOCK A 34
BROWNHILLS A 4124
WHITCHURCH A 41
BRIDGNORTH A 454
BRIDGNORTH B 4176
KIDDERMINSTER A 449
BRIDGNORTH A 458
KIDDERMINSTER A 451
KIDDERMINSTER A 456
A 491 BROMSGROVE
(A 491) B 4551
M 5 BRISTOL
BUSHBURY
WEDNESFIELD
TETTENHALL
See WOLVERHAMPTON
BLAKENHALL
BILSTON
WILLENHALL
BLOXWICH
DARLASTON
WEDNESBURY
COSELEY
SEDGLEY
HIMLEY PARK
HIMLEY
DUDLEY
DUDLEY ZOO
WEST BROMWICH
SANDWELL
KINGSWINFORD
BRIERLEY HILL
MERRY HILL
OLDBURY
ROWLEY REGIS
WARLEY
AMBLECOTE
STOURBRIDGE
HALESOWEN
HAGLEY
HAGLEY WOOD
HAGLEY PARK
UFFMOOR WOOD
BARTLEY RESERVOIR

BIRMINGHAM AND WOLVERHAMPTON
ENLARGED AREA

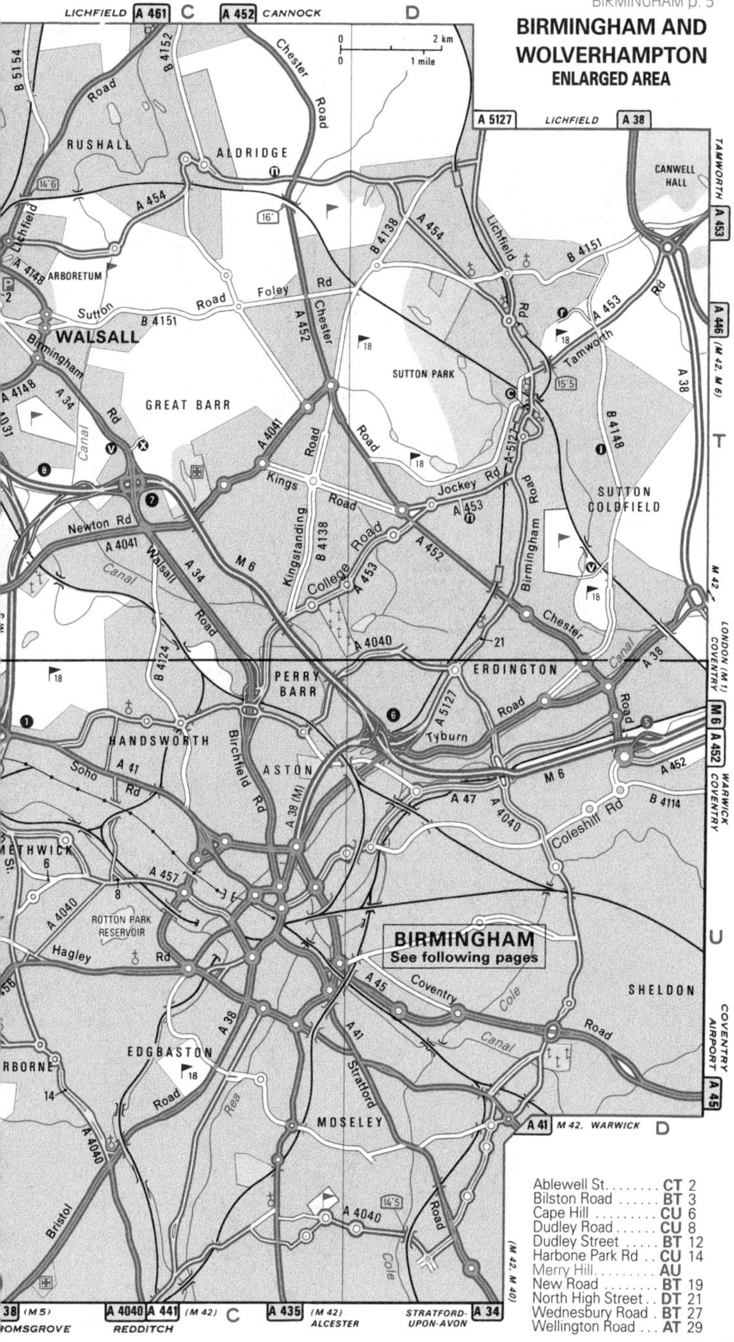

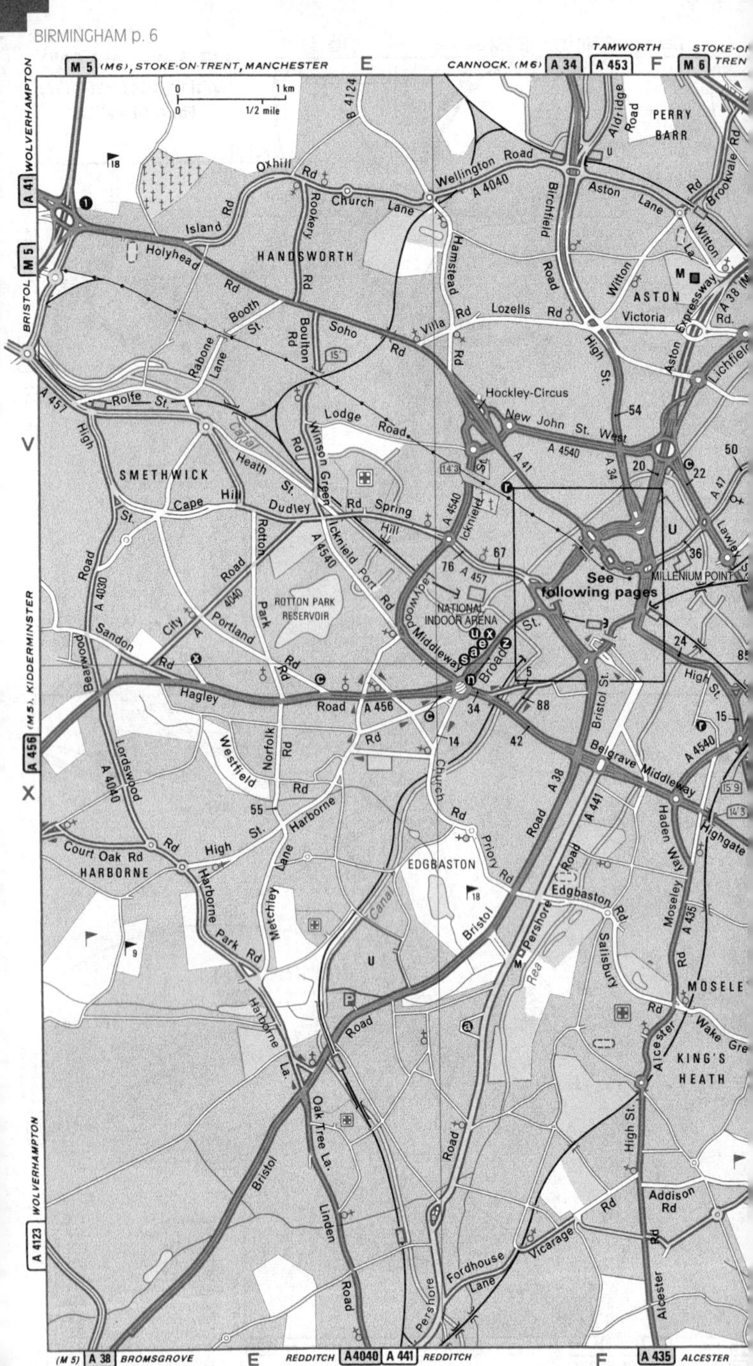
M 5 (M6), STOKE-ON-TRENT, MANCHESTER
E
CANNOCK (M6) A 34
TAMWORTH A 453
F
STOKE-ON-TRENT M 6
WOLVERHAMPTON A 41
BRISTOL M 5
KIDDERMINSTER (M5) A 456
WOLVERHAMPTON A 4123
V
X
HANDSWORTH
PERRY BARR
ASTON
SMETHWICK
ROTTON PARK RESERVOIR
NATIONAL INDOOR ARENA
MILLENIUM POINT
See following pages
EDGBASTON
HARBORNE
MOSELEY
KING'S HEATH
Hockley-Circus
New John St. West
Wellington Road
Aston Lane
Lozells Rd
Holyhead Rd
Soho Rd
Dudley Rd
Hagley Road
Belgrave Middleway
Bristol Road
Pershore Road
Alcester Rd
(M 5) A 38 BROMSGROVE
REDDITCH A 4040 A 441 REDDITCH
A 435 ALCESTER

BUILT UP AREA

Street	Grid	No.
Bath Row	FX	5
Bordesley Middleway	FX	10
Calthorpe Rd	FX	14
Camp Hill	FX	15
Darmouth Middleway	FV	22
Digbeth	FV	24
Dudley Park Rd	GX	25
High St.	GV	31
Islington Row Middleway	FX	34
Jennen's Rd	FV	36
Lee Bank Middleway	FX	42
Nechell's Parkway	FV	50
New Town Row	FV	54
Nursery Rd	EX	55
Saltley Rd	GV	66
Sand Pits Parade	FV	67
Solihull Lane	GX	74
Summer Hill Rd	FV	76
Watery Lane	FV	85
Westley Rd	GX	87
Wheeley's Lane	FX	88

For Street Index see Birmingham p. 3

CENTRE

Albert St. . . . . **KZ** 2
Bull Ring Centre . . . . **KZ**
Bull St. . . . . **KY** 13
Corporation St. . . . . **KYZ**
Dale End. . . . . **KZ** 21
Hall St. . . . . **JY** 29
Holloway Circus. . . . . **JZ** 32
James Watt Queensway. . . **KY** 35
Jennen's Rd . . . . **KY** 36
Lancaster Circus. . . . . **KY** 39
Lancaster St. . . . . **KY** 41
Masshouse Circus . . . . **KY** 43
Moor St. Queensway. . . . . . **KZ** 46
Navigation St.. . . . . **JZ** 49
New St. . . . . **JKZ**
Newton St. . . . . **KY** 53
Paradise Circus . . . . **JZ** 56
Paradise Forum
Shopping Centre . . . . **JZ**
Priory Queensway . . . . **KY** 5
St Chads Circus . . . . **JKY** 6
St Chads Ringway . . . . **KY** 6
St Martin's Circus. . . . . **KZ** 6
Shadwell St. . . . . **KY** 7
Smallbrook
Queensway . . . . **KZ** 7
Snow Hill Queensway . . . . . **KY** 7
Summer Row . . . . **JY** 7
Temple Row . . . . **KZ** 8
Waterloo St. . . . . **JZ** 8

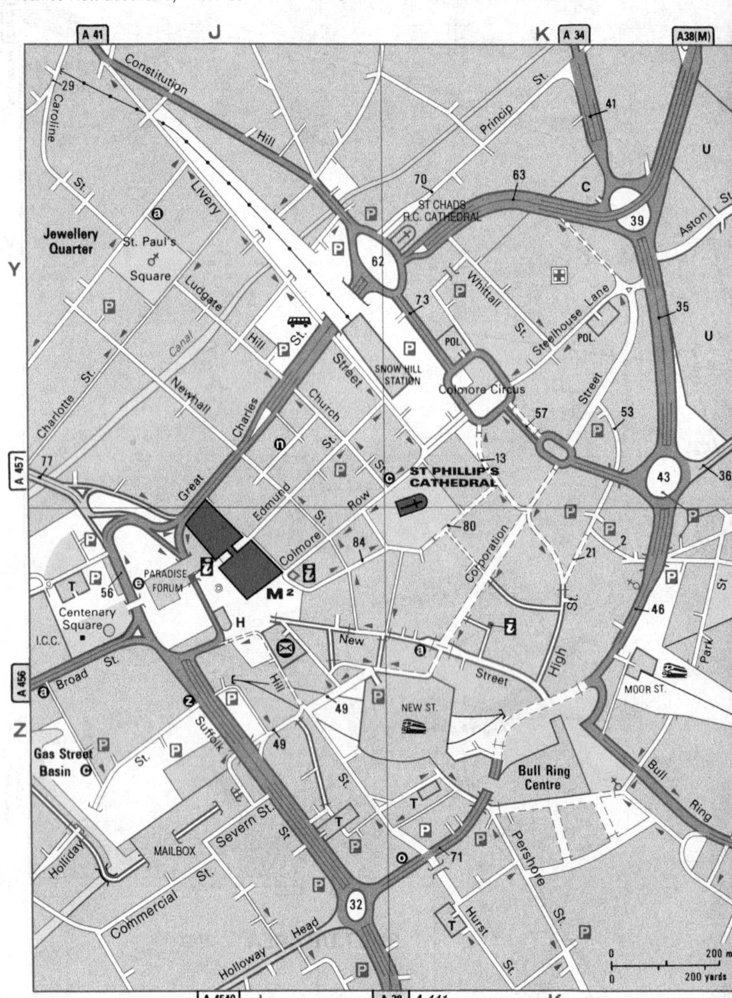

«Short Breaks»

Many hotels now offer a special rate for a stay of 2 nights which includes dinner, bed and breakfast.

Town plans : Birmingham pp. 3-8

Hyatt Regency, 2 Bridge St., B1 2JZ, (0121) 643 1234, *hrbirm@hrb.co.uk, Fax (0121) 616 2323*, <, – , rm, – 250. VISA JCB. JZ a
closed 7 to 11 October – **Meals** – (see ***Number 282*** below) – 12.75 – **315 rm** 125.00/160.00 **st.**, 4 suites.

Birmingham Marriott, 12 Hagley Rd, B16 8SJ, (0121) 452 1144, *Fax (0121) 456 3442*, – , rm, – 25. VISA. FX c
Langtrys : **Meals** a la carte 21.00/39.00 **t.** 7.00 – (see also ***Sir Edward Elgar's*** below) – 12.50 – **94 rm** 120.00/140.00 **st.**, 4 suites – SB.

Crowne Plaza Birmingham, Central Sq., B1 1HH, (0121) 631 2000, *Fax (0121) 643 9018*, – , rm, – 150. VISA JCB.
closed Christmas – **Meals** *(closed Saturday lunch)* (carving rest.) 15.00/19.50 **st.** and a la carte 6.95 – 13.95 – **281 rm** 139.00/149.00 **st.**, 3 suites – SB. JZ z

The Burlington, Burlington Arcade, 126 New St., B2 4JQ, (0121) 643 9191, *mail@burlingtonhotel.com, Fax (0121) 643 5075*, – , rm, rest, – 400. VISA KZ a
closed 24-30 December – ***Berlioz :*** **Meals** 18.00/22.00 **t.** and a la carte 10.50 – 13.50 – **107 rm** 147.00/171.00 **st.**, 5 suites.

Copthorne, Paradise Circus, B3 3HJ, (0121) 200 2727, *sales.birmingham@mill-cop.com, Fax (0121) 200 1197*, – , rm, rest, – 180. VISA. JZ e
Goldsmiths : **Meals** (dinner only) 26.95 **st.** 12.25 – ***Goldies :*** **Meals** 18.95 **st.** and a la carte 8.00 – 12.95 – **209 rm** 140.00/160.00 **st.**, 3 suites – SB.

Jonathan's, 16-24 Wolverhampton Rd, Oldbury, B68 0LH, West : 4 m. by A 456 (0121) 429 3757, *sales@jonathans.co.uk, Fax (0121) 434 3107*, « Authentic Victorian furnishings and memorabilia » – , rest, – 100. VISA JCB. BU e
Victorian Restaurant : **Meals** - English - *(closed Saturday lunch and Sunday dinner)* (booking essential) 15.90 **t.** and a la carte 12.00 – ***Secret Garden :*** **Meals** 9.50 **t.** and a la carte 13.35/21.30 **t.** 12.00 – **46 rm** 88.00/170.00 **t.**, 2 suites – SB.

Birmingham Grand Moat House, Colmore Row, B3 2DA, (0121) 607 9988, *revbgd@queensmoat.co.uk, Fax (0121) 233 1465* – , rm, rest, – 500. VISA JKY c
Hugo's : **Meals** a la carte 16.40/21.40 **st.** – 11.45 – **170 rm** 120.00/165.00 **st.**, 3 suites – SB.

Posthouse Birmingham City, Smallbrook, Queensway, B5 4EW, (0870) 400 9008, *Fax (0121) 631 2528*, , squash – , rm, – 630. VISA JCB
Meals *(closed Saturday lunch and Bank Holidays)* (carving rest.) 12.95/17.25 **t.** 6.95 – 11.95 – **251 rm** 89.00 **st.** – SB. KZ o

Novotel, 70 Broad St., B1 2HT, (0121) 643 2000, *hlo77@accor-hotels.com, Fax (0121) 643 9796*, – , rm, rest, – 300. VISA JCB FV e
Meals 10.00/18.00 **st.** and a la carte 7.50 – 10.25 – **148 rm** 95.00/120.00 **st.** – SB.

Chamberlain Tower, Broad St., B1 2HQ, (0121) 626 0626, *info@chamberlain.co.uk, Fax (0121) 626 0627* – , rest, – 400. VISA. FV z
Meals (carving rest.) 10.00 **st.** – **445 rm** 55.00 **st.**

Chamberlain Park, Alcester St., B12 0PJ, (0121) 627 0627, *info@chamberlain.co.uk, Fax (0121) 627 0628* – , rest, – 400. VISA. FX r
Meals (carving rest.) 10.00 **st.** 3.75 – **250 rm** 35.00/45.00 **t.**

Asquith House, 19 Portland Rd, off Hagley Rd, Edgbaston, B16 9HN, (0121) 454 5282, *Fax (0121) 456 4668*, « Victorian house », – . VISA. EX c
closed 25-26 December and 1 January – **Meals** (by arrangement Saturday and Sunday) 16.95/27.95 **t.** and a la carte 4.95 – **10 rm** 60.00/83.00 **t.**

Westbourne Lodge, 27-29 Fountain Rd, Edgbaston, B17 8NJ, (0121) 429 1003, *info@westbournelodge.co.uk, Fax (0121) 429 7436*, , – rm, . VISA EV x
closed Christmas – **Meals** *(closed Saturday and Sunday)* (booking essential to non-residents) 14.95 **st.** 5.00 – **22 rm** 52.00/72.00 **st.** – SB.

Copperfield House, 60 Upland Rd, Selly Park, B29 7JS, (0121) 472 8344, *info@copperfieldhousehotel.fsnet.co.uk, Fax (0121) 415 5655*, – rest, . VISA.
Meals *(closed Saturday and Sunday)* (dinner only) a la carte 15.50/22.50 **st.** 6.00 – **17 rm** 60.00/80.00 **t.** – SB. FX a

Premier Lodge, 80 Broad St., BI5 1LY, (0870) 7001316, *Fax (0870) 7001317* – , rm, rest, . VISA. FVX s
closed 25-26 December – **Meals** (grill rest.) a la carte 10.95/19.05 **t.** – 6.00 – **60 rm** 46.00 **t.**

Travel Inn, Richard St., Waterlinks, B7 4AA, (0121) 333 6484, *Fax (0121) 333 6490* – , rm, rest, . VISA. FV c
Meals (grill rest.) (dinner only) – **60 rm** 40.95 **t.**

ENGLAND

Travelodge, 1741 Coventry Rd, Yardley, B26 1DS, Southeast : 5 m. by A 41 on A 4 (0121) 764 5882, *Fax (0121) 764 5882* – rm, . HX
Meals (grill rest.) – **40 rm** 49.95 **t.**

Travelodge, 230 Broad St., B15 1AY, (0121) 644 5266, *Fax (0121) 644 5251* – . FV
Meals (grill rest.) – **136 rm** 49.95 **t.**

Travel Inn, 20-22 Bridge St., B1 2JH, (0121) 633 4820, *Fax (0121) 633 4779* – , rm – 40. . JZ
Meals (grill rest.) – **53 rm** 40.95 **t.**

Ibis, 1 Bordesley Park Rd, B10 0PD, (0121) 506 2600, *h2178@accor-hotels.com*, *Fax (0121) 506 2610* – . GX
Meals (dinner only) a la carte approx. 15.70 **st.** – **87 rm** 42.00 **st.**

Sir Edward Elgar's (at Birmingham Marriott H.), 12 Hagley Rd, B16 8S (0121) 452 1144, *Fax (0121) 456 3442* – . FX
closed Saturday lunch – **Meals** 21.00/36.00 **t.** and a la carte 7.50.

Number 282 (at Hyatt Regency H.), 2 Bridge St., B1 2JZ, (0121) 643 123 *Fax (0121) 616 2323* – . JZ
closed Sunday dinner, Monday lunch and Bank Holidays – **Meals** 16.50/19.95 **s** and a la carte 12.95.

Bank, 4 Brindleyplace, B1 2JB, (0121) 633 4466, *Fax (0121) 633 4465*, – . FV
closed Christmas, New Year and Sunday dinner – **Meals** a la carte 20.50/29.95 **t.** 7.45.

Gilmore, 27 Warstone Lane, Hockley, B18 6JQ, (0121) 233 3655, *Fax (01543) 41551* « Former rolling mill » – FV
closed 1 week Easter, 2 weeks August, 24 December-mid January, Sunday, Monday, Tuesd after Bank Holidays and Saturday lunch – **Meals** 14.00/23.00 **t.** 7.50.

Metro Bar and Grill, 73 Cornwall St., B3 2DF, (0121) 200 1911, *Fax (0121) 200 1611* . JY
closed 24-31 December, Saturday lunch, Sunday and Bank Holidays – **Meals** (bookir essential) a la carte 20.20/27.15 **t.** 4.95.

Henry's, 27 St. Paul's Sq., B3 1RB, (0121) 200 1136, *Fax (0121) 200 1190* – . JY
closed 25-26 December and Bank Holiday Monday – **Meals** - Chinese (Canton) - 16.5 30.00 **t.** and a la carte.

Leftbank, 79 Broad St., B15 1AH, (0121) 643 4464, *Fax (0121) 643 5793* – FV
closed 1 week Christmas, Saturday lunch, Sunday and Bank Holidays – **Meals** a la car 18.85/29.50 **t.**

Le Petit Blanc, Nine Brindleyplace, B1 2HS, (0121) 633 7333, *petitblanc.birmingham virginnet.co.uk, Fax (0121) 633 7444* – . FV
Meals 12.50/15.00 **t.** (lunch) and a la carte 18.45/25.90 **t.**

at Hall Green *Southeast : 5 3/4 m. by A 41 on A 34* – *Birmingham.*

Mizan, 1347 Stratford Rd, B28 9HW, (0121) 777 3185 – . GX
Meals - Indian - (dinner only and Thursday lunch)/dinner a la carte 8.05/13.05 **t.**

at Birmingham Airport *Southeast : 9 m. by A 45* – **DU** – *Birmingham.*

Posthouse Birmingham Airport, Coventry Rd, B26 3QW, on A (0870) 400 9007, *Fax (0121) 782 2476* – – 130.
Meals 15.00 **st.** a la carte 8.45 – **141 rm** 109.00/129.00 **st.** – SB.

Novotel, Passenger Terminal, B26 3QL, (0121) 782 7000, *Fax (0121) 782 0445* – rm, – 35. .
Meals *(closed lunch Saturday and Sunday)* 12.50/19.50 **st.** and a la carte – **195 r** 112.00/121.00 **st.**

at National Exhibition Centre *Southeast : 9 1/2 m. on A 45* – **DU** – *Birmingham.*

Hilton Birmingham Metropole, Bickenhill, B40 1PP, (0121) 780 42 *Fax (0121) 780 3923*, , , – , rm, – 2000.
closed 25 December – **Meals** (carving rest.) 18.00/28.50 **t.** – ***Primavera :*** **Meals** - Italia (dinner only) 31.95 **t.** and a la carte – 13.50 – **779 rm** 245.00/300.00 **st.**, 15 suites – SB

Express by Holiday Inn without rest., Bickenhill, Parkway, B40 1 (0121) 782 3222, *sales.nec@ingram.hotel.co.uk, Fax (0121) 780 4224* – , rm, – 100.
179 rm 79.95.

at Acocks Green *Southwest : 5 m. by A 41 – ✉ Birmingham.*

Westley, Westley Rd, B27 7UJ, ☎ (0121) 706 4312, *reservations@westley_hotel.co.uk, Fax (0121) 706 2824* – TV P – 200. MO AE ① VISA. ✻ GX c
closed 25 December – **Meals** (bar lunch Monday to Saturday)/dinner 13.95/18.95 **t.** and a la carte 6.20 – 8.50 – **35 rm** 75.00/83.00 **t.**, 1 suite.

at Northfield *Southwest : 6 m. by A 38* – **CU** – *✉ Birmingham.*

Norwood, 87-89 Bunbury Rd, B31 2ET, via Church Rd ☎ (0121) 411 2202, *Fax (0121) 411 2202,* – TV P. MO AE ① VISA JCB. ✻
closed Christmas and New Year – **Meals** (bar lunch)/dinner 18.50 **st.** – **18 rm** 62.50/85.00 **st.** – SB.

at Oldbury *West : 7 ¾ m. by A 456 on A 4123 – ✉ Birmingham.*

Express by Holiday Inn without rest., Birchley Park, B69 2BD, ☎ (0121) 511 0000, *Fax (0121) 511 0051* – |‡|, ⇔ rm, ▤ rest, TV ☎ & P – 30. MO AE ① VISA JCB BU r
109 rm 58.50 **st.**

Travel Inn, Wolverhampton Rd, B69 2BH, on A 4123 ☎ (0121) 552 3031, *Fax (0121) 552 1012* – ⇔ rm, ▤ rest, TV & P. MO AE ① VISA. ✻ BU u
Meals (grill rest.) – **40 rm** 40.95 **t.**

Travelodge, Wolverhampton Rd, B69 2BH, on A 4123 ☎ (0121) 552 2967 – ⇔ rm, TV & P. MO AE ① VISA JCB. ✻ BU n
Meals (grill rest.) – **33 rm** 39.95 **t.**

at Great Barr *Northwest : 6 m. on A 34 – ✉ Birmingham.*

Posthouse Birmingham, Chapel Lane, B43 7BG, ☎ (0870) 400 9009, *Fax (0121) 357 7503,* Lδ, ≘s, ▧ – ⇔ rm, TV P – 120. MO AE ① VISA CT x
Meals a la carte 15.85/32.85 **t.** 6.45 – 11.95 – **192 rm** 79.00 **t.** – SB.

Express by Holiday Inn without rest., Birmingham Rd, B43 7AG, ☎ (0121) 358 4044, *Fax (0121) 358 4644* – ⇔ rm, TV ☎ & P. MO AE ① VISA. ✻ CT v
32 rm 49.95 **t.**

at West Bromwich *Northwest : 6 m. on A 41 – ✉ Birmingham.*

Moat House Birmingham, Birmingham Rd, B70 6RS, ☎ (0121) 609 9988, *revbwb@queensmoat.co.uk, Fax (0121) 525 7403,* Lδ, ≘s, ▧ – |‡|, ⇔ rm, ▤ rest, TV P – 180. MO AE ① VISA BU c
Meals a la carte 14.65/26.85 **st.** 6.50 – 11.50 – **168 rm** 109.00/125.00 **st.** – SB.

BIRMINGHAM AIRPORT *W. Mids.* 403 404 O 26 – *see Birmingham.*

BISHOP'S HULL *Somerset – see Taunton.*

BISHOP'S STORTFORD *Herts.* 404 U 28 – *pop. 28 403.*

Stansted Airport : ☎ (0870) 0000303, NE : 3½ m.

The Old Monastery, Windhill ☎ (01279) 655831.

London 34 – Cambridge 27 – Chelmsford 19 – Colchester 33.

The Cottage ⑤ without rest., 71 Birchanger Lane, CM23 5QA, Northeast : 2 ¼ m. by B 1383 on Birchanger rd ☎ (01279) 812349, *Fax (01279) 815045,* « Part 17C and 18C cottages », – ⇔ TV P. MO VISA JCB. ✻
closed Easter and Christmas-New Year – **15 rm** 40.00/65.00 **t.**

The Lemon Tree, 14-16 Water Lane, CM23 2LB, ☎ (01279) 757788, *Fax (01279) 757766* – MO VISA JCB
closed Sunday dinner, Monday, Christmas and first week January – **Meals** 10.00/20.00 **t.** and a la carte 6.75.

at Hatfield Heath *(Essex) Southeast : 6 m. on A 1060 – ✉ Bishop's Stortford.*

Down Hall Country House ⑤, CM22 7AS, South : 1 ½ m. by Matching Lane ☎ (01279) 731441, *reservations@downhall.co.uk, Fax (01279) 730416,* ≤, « 19C Italianate mansion », Lδ, ≘s, ▧, , , ✂ – |‡|, ⇔ rest, ▤ rest, TV P – 250. MO AE ① VISA
Ibbetsons : **Meals** (carving lunch) 18.50/29.50 **st.** 8.50 – ***Downham :*** **Meals** *(closed Monday and Sunday dinner)* a la carte 39.00/56.50 **st.** 8.50 – 15.95 – **99 rm** 120.00/195.00 **t.** – SB.

BISHOP'S TAWTON *Devon* 403 H 30 – *see Barnstaple.*

BLABY *Leics.* 402 403 404 Q 26 – *see Leicester.*

BLACKBURN *Blackburn* 402 M 22 – *pop. 105 994.*

Pleasington ☎ *(01254) 202177* – *Wilpshire, 72 Whalley Rd* ☎ *(01254) 248260* – *Grea Harwood, Harwood Bar* ☎ *(01254) 884391.*

King George's Hall, Northgate ☎ *(01254) 53277.*

London 228 – Leeds 47 – Liverpool 39 – Manchester 24 – Preston 11.

at Langho *North : 4½ m. on A 666 –* ✉ *Whalley.*

Mytton Fold H. and Golf Club, Whalley Rd, BB6 8AB, Northeast : 1 m. by A 666 c Whalley rd ☎ (01254) 240662, *mytton_fold.hotel@virgin.net, Fax (01254) 248119,* rest, 250. VISA. Meals (bar lunch Monday to Saturday)/dinner 13.25/22.20 **t.** 6.50 – **28 rm** 52.0 80.00 **t.** – SB.

Petre Lodge, Northcote Rd, BB6 8BG, Northeast : ½ m. ☎ (01254) 245506, *aslambert@ bdial.co.uk, Fax (01254) 245506* – VISA. *closed Christmas* – **Meals** (residents only) (dinner only Monday-Thursday) a la carte 9.9 15.00 **st.** – **9 rm** 45.00/55.00 **st.**

Northcote Manor (Haworth) with rm, Northcote Rd, BB6 8BE, North : ½ m. on A 59 junction with A 666 ☎ (01254) 240555, *admin@northcotemanor.com, Fax (01254) 24656* – rest, VISA. **Meals** *(closed 25 December, 1 January and Saturday lunch)* 16.00/25.00 **t.** and a la car 30.15/47.50 **t.** 16.50 – **14 rm** 90.00/110.00 **t.** – SB
Spec. Black pudding and trout, mustard and watercress sauce. Terrine of foie gras wi sultana brioche. Brown shrimp soup with garlic croutons.

at Clayton-le-Dale *North : 4¾ m. by A 666 on B 6245 –* ✉ *Blackburn.*

Shajan, Longsight Rd, BB1 9EX, Southwest : ½ m. on A 59 ☎ (01254) 813234 – VISA
Meals - Indian - (buffet lunch Sunday) a la carte 13.25/22.90 **t.** 4.95.

at Mellor *Northwest : 4 m. by A 677 –* ✉ *Blackburn.*

Millstone, Church Lane, BB2 7JR, ☎ (01254) 813333, *millstone@shireinns.co.u Fax (01254) 812628* – – 25. VISA
Millers : **Meals** a la carte 24.00/39.00 **st.** – **23 rm** 88.00/108.00 **st.**, 1 suite – SB.

at Balderstone *Northwest : 6½ m. by A 677 off A 59 –* ✉ *Blackburn.*

Premier Lodge, Myerscough Rd, BB2 7LE, on A 59 ☎ (0870) 700133 *Fax (0870) 7001331* – rm, rest, VISA JCB.
Meals (grill rest.) (in bar) a la carte 8.00/15.00 **st.** – 6.00 – **20 rm** 46.00 **st.**

BLACKPOOL *Blackpool* 402 K 22 *Great Britain G.* – *pop. 146 262.*

See : *Tower* AC AY A.*

Blackpool Park, North Park Dr., ☎ *(01253) 397910* **BY** – *Poulton-le-Fylde, Myrtle Far Breck Rd* ☎ *(01253) 892444.*

Blackpool Airport : ☎ *(01253) 343434, S : 3 m. by A 584.*

1 Clifton St. ☎ *(01253) 478222 – Pleasure Beach, Unit 25, Ocean Boulevard, Sou Promenade* ☎ *(01253) 403223.*

London 246 – Leeds 88 – Liverpool 56 – Manchester 51 – Middlesbrough 123.

Plan opposite

Imperial, North Promenade, FY1 2HB, ☎ (01253) 623971, *imperialblackpool@paramou -hotels.co.uk, Fax (01253) 751784,* – rm, – 400. **AY**
closed 4-11 October – ***Palm Court :*** **Meals** 6.50/19.50 **st.** and dinner a la carte 8.15 **171 rm** 99.00/190.00 **st.**, 10 suites – SB.

Hilton Blackpool, North Promenade, FY1 2JQ, ☎ (01253) 623434, *Fax (01253) 2943* – rm, rest, – 900. VISA **AY**
The Promenade : **Meals** (carving rest.) (bar lunch)/dinner 17.50 **st.** and a la carte 7.0 9.50 – **268 rm** 160.00/180.00 **st.**, 6 suites – SB.

De Vere, East Park Drive, FY3 8LL, ☎ (01253) 838866, *michelle.kelso@devere.hotel.co Fax (01253) 798800,* squash – rest, – 500. VISA. **BZ**
Park Brasserie : **Meals** 19.95/25.00 **st.** (dinner) and a la carte 13.50/25.00 **st.** 7.95 **162 rm** 135.00/145.00, 2 suites – SB.

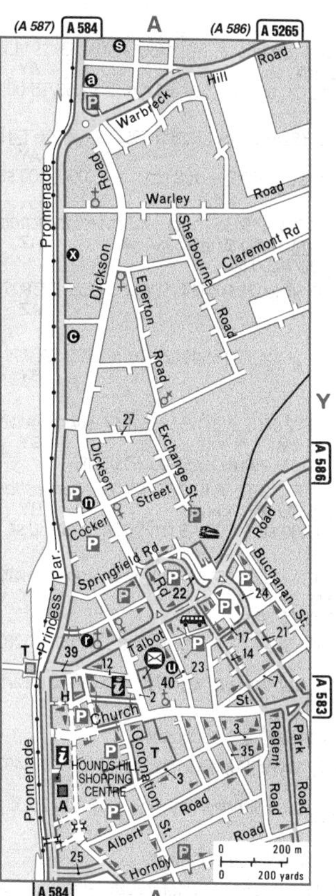
(A 587)
A 584
A
(A 586)
A 5265
Promenade
Warbreck
Hill
Road
Dickson
Road
Warley
Road
Sherbourne
Claremont Rd
Egerton
Road
Exchange St.
Dickson
Street
Cocker
Springfield Rd
Princess Par.
Talbot
Buchanan
St.
Church
St.
Regent
Road
Park
Road
Coronation
St.
Albert
Road
Hornby
Road
HOUNDS HILL SHOPPING CENTRE
Y
A 586
A 583
A 584
0 200 m
0 200 yards

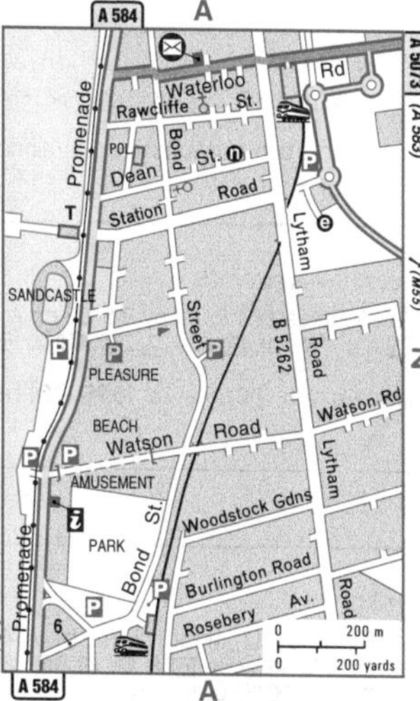
A 584
A
A 5073
(A 583)
Waterloo
Rd
Rawcliffe
St.
Bond
St.
Dean
Road
Station
Road
Lytham
Road
Promenade
SANDCASTLE
Street
B 5262
PLEASURE
BEACH
AMUSEMENT
PARK
Watson
Road
Watson Rd
Woodstock Gdns
Bond
St.
Burlington Road
Rosebery
Av.
(M 55)
Z
A 584
0 200 m
0 200 yards

BLACKPOOL

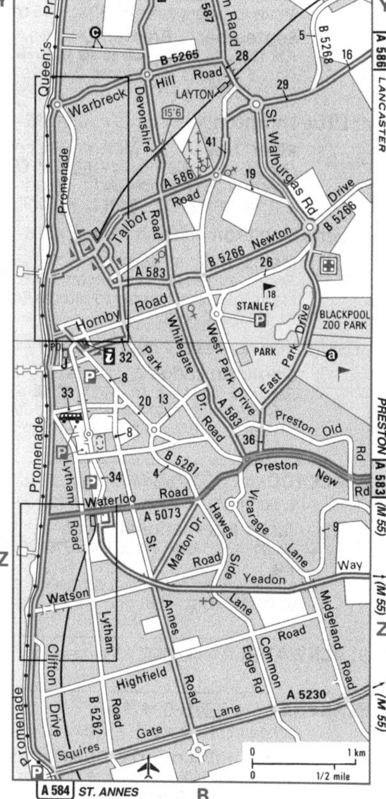
B
FLEETWOOD
A 587
Queen's
Promenade
A 584
Fleetwood Rd
Road
A 587
Red Bank Rd
Devonshire
B 5124
Bispham
Road
A 587
B 5265
Hill
Road
LAYTON
Warbreck
Devonshire
St. Walburgas Rd
B 5268
A 586
LANCASTER
A 586
Road
Talbot
Road
B 5266 Newton
Drive
B 5266
A 583
Hornby
Road
Park
Whitegate
West Park Drive
Dr. Road
A 583
STANLEY
PARK
East Park Drive
BLACKPOOL ZOO PARK
Preston Old
Rd
PRESTON
A 583
Preston New
Rd
(M 55)
B 5261
Road
Waterloo
A 5073
St.
Marton Dr.
Road
Hawes Side
Lane
Vicarage
Lane
Yeadon
Way
(M 55)
Promenade
Lytham
Road
Watson
Lytham
Annes
Road
Common
Edge Rd
Road
Midgeland
Road
Clifton
Drive
B 5262
Road
Highfield
A 5230
Lane
Gate
Squires
Promenade
A 584
ST. ANNES
Y
Z
0 1 km
0 1/2 mile

ENGLAND

Libertys on the Square, Cocker Sq., North Promenade, FY1 1RX, (01253) 291155 *Fax (01253) 752271*, <, – TV P. MC AE VISA. AY r
Meals (dinner only and Sunday lunch)/dinner 8.95/20.00 **t.** 4.50 – **64 rm** 39.50/73.00 t – SB.

Savoy, Queens Promenade, FY2 9SJ, (01253) 352561, *Fax (01253) 595549* – TV P – 300. MC AE VISA. AY a
Meals (bar lunch)/dinner a la carte 15.20/25.20 **st.** 7.95 – **128 rm** 45.00/90.00 **st.** 3 suites.

Old Coach House, 50 Dean St., FY4 1BP, (01253) 349195, *blackpool@theoldcoachhouse.freeserve.co.uk, Fax (01253) 344330*, – TV P. MC AE VISA JCB. AZ r
Meals (dinner only) 10.00/22.45 **t.** – **7 rm** 40.00/70.00 **st.**

Travel Inn, Yeadon Way, South Shore, FY1 6BF, (01253) 341415, *Fax (01253) 343805* – rm, rest, TV P – 40. MC AE VISA. AZ
Meals (grill rest.) – **40 rm** 40.95 **t.**

Travel Inn, Devonshire Rd, Bispham, FY2 0AR, (01253) 354942, *Fax (01253) 590498* – rm, rest, TV P – 40. MC AE VISA BY
Meals (grill rest.) – **39 rm** 40.95 **t.**

Sunray, 42 Knowle Av., off Queens Promenade, FY2 9TQ, (01253) 351937, *sunray@cwcom.net, Fax (01253) 593307* – rest, TV P. MC AE VISA BY
March-November – **Meals** (by arrangement) 13.00 **st.** – **9 rm** 30.00/60.00 **st.**

Burlees, 40 Knowle Av., off Queen's Promenade, FY2 9TQ, (01253) 354535, *burleeshotel@btinternet.com, Fax (01253) 354535* – TV P. MC VISA JCB. BY
February-November – **Meals** (by arrangement) 12.00 **st.** 4.00 – **9 rm** 24.00/52.00 **st.** – SB.

Grosvenor View, 7-9 King Edward Av., FY2 9TD, (01253) 352851, *grosvenor-view@yahoo.co.uk, Fax (01253) 352109* – P. MC AE VISA. AY
Meals (by arrangement) 7.50 **st.** – **16 rm** 19.00/50.00 **st.**

September Brasserie, 15-17 Queen St., FY1 1PU, (01253) 623282 *Fax (01253) 299455* – MC AE VISA JCB AY
closed 2 weeks in summer, 2 weeks in winter, Sunday and Monday – **Meals** a la carte 17.00/23.00 **t.** 7.00.

at Little Thornton *Northeast : 5 m. by A 586 –* **BY** *– off A 588 – Blackpool.*

River House with rm, Skippool Creek, Wyre Rd, FY5 5LF, (01253) 883497 *Fax (01253) 892083*, <, – TV P. MC VISA
closed 25-26 December and 1 January – **Meals** *(closed Sunday)* (booking essential) 25.00 t and a la carte 7.50 – **4 rm** 70.00/90.00 **t.** – SB.

at Little Singleton *Northeast : 6 m. by A 586 –* **BY** *– on A 585 – Blackpool.*

Mains Hall, 86 Mains Lane, FY6 7LE, (01253) 885130, *enquiries@mainshall.co.uk Fax (01253) 894132*, – rm, TV P. MC AE VISA JCB
Meals (bar lunch Monday to Saturday)/dinner 16.00/25.00 **st.** and a la carte 6.00 – **12 rm** 45.00/120.00 **st.** – SB.

at Singleton *Northeast : 7 m. by A 586 –* **BY** *– on B 5260 – Blackpool.*

Singleton Lodge, Lodge Lane, FY6 8LT, North : ¼ m. on B 5260 (01253) 883854 *Fax (01253) 894432*, – TV P. MC AE VISA
closed Bank Holidays – **Meals** *(closed Sunday dinner)* (dinner only and Sunday lunch)/dinner a la carte 15.00/21.50 **t.** 5.20 – **12 rm** 55.00/80.00 **t.** – SB.

BLACKROD *Lancs.* 402 404 M 23 – *pop. 5 681.*

London 220 – Burnley 25 – Liverpool 31 – Manchester 16 – Preston 18.

Jarvis International, Manchester Rd, BL6 5RU, Southeast : 1 ½ m. by B 5408 on A (01942) 814598, *Fax (01942) 816026*, – rm, TV P – 250. MC AE VISA
Meals *(closed Saturday lunch)* 10.95/17.50 **st.** and a la carte 6.85 – 10.95 – **91 rm** 92.00/102.00 **st.** – SB.

BLACKWATER *Cornwall* 403 E 33 – *see Truro.*

BLAKENEY *Glos.* 403 404 M 28.

London 134 – Bristol 31 – Gloucester 16 – Newport 31.

Viney Hill Country Guesthouse, Viney Hill, GL15 4LT, West : ¾ m. by A 4 (01594) 516000, *info@vineyhill.co.uk, Fax (01594) 516018*, – TV P. MC AE VISA.
Meals (by arrangement) 17.00/20.00 **st.** 5.00 – **6 rm** 35.00/56.00 **st.** – SB.

BLAKENEY *Norfolk* 404 X 25 – *pop. 1 628* – ✉ *Holt.*
London 127 – King's Lynn 37 – Norwich 28.

Blakeney, The Quay, NR25 7NE, ☎ (01263) 740797, *reception@blakeney.hotel.co.uk, Fax (01263) 740795,* ≤, – rest, TV P – 200. MC AE VISA
Meals (light lunch Monday-Saturday)/dinner 19.00 **t.** and a la carte 4.90 – **59 rm** (dinner included) 68.00/200.00 **t.** – SB.

White Horse with rm, 4 High St., NR25 7AL, ☎ (01263) 740574, *Fax (01263) 741303* – TV P. MC AE VISA.
closed 2 weeks January – **Meals** (bar lunch and Sunday and Monday dinner) a la carte 17.40/24.85 **t.** 6.50 – **10 rm** 40.00/90.00 **t.**

at Cley next the Sea *East : 1½ m. on A 149* – ✉ *Holt.*

Cley Mill, NR25 7RP, ☎ (01263) 740209, *Fax (01263) 740209,* ≤, « 18C redbrick windmill on saltmarshes », – P. MC VISA
Meals (by arrangement) (communal dining) 17.50 **st.** – **7 rm** 60.00/100.00 **st.**

at Morston *West : 1½ m. on A 149* – ✉ *Holt.*

Morston Hall (Blackiston), The Street, NR25 7AA, ☎ (01263) 741041, *reception@morstonhall.com, Fax (01263) 740419,* – rest, TV P. MC AE
closed 1-26 January and 25-26 December – **Meals** (booking essential) (set menu only) (dinner only and Sunday lunch)/dinner 34.00 **t.** – **6 rm** (dinner included) 130.00/220.00 **t.** – SB
Spec. Cheddar soufflé with galette of roasted tomatoes. Roast loin of veal with roasted salsify and truffle jus. Crème brûlée with apricot sorbet.

BLANCHLAND *Northd.* 401 402 N 19 – *pop. 135* – ✉ *Consett (Durham).*
London 298 – Carlisle 47 – Newcastle upon Tyne 24.

Lord Crewe Arms, DH8 9SP, ☎ (01434) 675251, *lord@crewearms.freeserve.co.uk, Fax (01434) 675337,* « Part 13C abbey », – TV. MC AE VISA
Meals (bar lunch Monday to Saturday)/dinner 28.00 **st.** 7.00 – **19 rm** 80.00/110.00 **st.** – SB.

BLANDFORD FORUM *Dorset* 403 404 N 31 *The West Country G.* – *pop. 8 880.*
See : *Town*★.
Env. : *Kingston Lacy*★★ *AC, SE : 5½ m. by B 3082 – Royal Signals Museum*★, *NE : 2 m. by B 3082.*
Exc. : *Milton Abbas*★, *SW : 8 m. by A 354 – Sturminster Newton*★, *NW : 8 m. by A 357.*
18 *Ashley Wood, Wimbourne Rd* ☎ *(01258) 452253.*
Marsh & Ham Car Park, West St. ☎ *(01258) 454770.*
London 124 – Bournemouth 17 – Dorchester 17 – Salisbury 24.

Crown, West St., DT11 7AJ, ☎ (01258) 456626, *Fax (01258) 451084,* – TV P – 200. MC AE VISA
closed Christmas – **Meals** *(closed Saturday lunch)* 8.95/14.95 **t.** and a la carte 5.95 – **32 rm** 70.00/92.00 **t.** – SB.

at Chettle *Northeast : 7¼ m. by A 354* – ✉ *Blandford Forum.*

Castleman with rm, DT11 8DB, ☎ (01258) 830096, *chettle@globalnet.co.uk, Fax (01258) 830051,* ≤, « Part 16C dower house with Victorian additions », – rest, TV P. MC VISA.
closed February and 25-26 December – **Meals** (dinner only and Sunday lunch)/dinner a la carte 15.50/22.00 **t.** 4.50 – **8 rm** 40.00/75.00 **t.**

BLAWITH *Cumbria* 402 K 21 – *see Coniston.*

BLEDINGTON *Glos.* 403 404 P 28 – *see Stow-on-the-Wold.*

BLOCKLEY *Glos.* 403 404 O 27 – *pop. 1 668* – ✉ *Moreton-in-Marsh.*
London 91 – Oxford 34 – Birmingham 39.

The Old Bakery, High St., GL56 9EU, ☎ (01386) 700408, *Fax (01386) 700408,* ≤, « Converted Victorian cottage », – TV P. MC AE VISA JCB.
closed 2 weeks June, December and January – **Meals** (by arrangement) 6.50 – **3 rm** (dinner included) 80.00/160.00 **st.** – SB.

BLUBBERHOUSES *N. Yorks.* 402 O 22.
London 246 – Harrogate 17 – Leeds 21.

The Stone House Inn, Thruscross, HG3 4AH, North : 2 m. on Greenhow R… ℘ (01943) 880325, *Fax (01943) 880325* – ⇔ P. MC VISA JCB
closed 25 December and Monday except Bank Holidays – **Meals** a la carte 18.85/24.85 t
🍷 5.95.

BLUNSDON *Wilts.* 403 404 O 29 – *see Swindon.*

BLYTH *Notts.* 402 403 404 Q 23 – *pop. 1 867* – ✉ *Worksop.*
London 166 – Doncaster 13 – Lincoln 30 – Nottingham 32 – Sheffield 20.

Charnwood, Sheffield Rd, S81 8HF, West : ¾ m. on A 634 ℘ (01909) 591610, *info@char… woodhotel.com, Fax (01909) 591429,* ⇔, – ⇔ rest, TV P – 120. MC AE VISA JCB
Meals 12.75/18.95 **t.** and a la carte 🍷 6.50 – **33 rm** ☐ 65.00/90.00 **t.**

Travelodge without rest., Hilltop roundabout, S81 8HG, North : ¾ m. by B 6045 a… junction of A 1 (M) with A 614 ℘ (01909) 591841, *Fax (01909) 591831* – ⇔ TV ♿ P. MC A… VISA JCB.
39 rm 39.95 **t.**

BODENHAM *Herefordshire* 403 404 L 27.
London 140 – Birmingham 55 – Hereford 10 – Shrewsbury 48 – Worcester 25.

England's Gate Inn, HR1 3HU, North : ¾ m. ℘ (01568) 797286, *englandsgate@hotma… com,* – P. MC VISA
Meals a la carte 11.30/19.45 **t.**

BODMIN *Cornwall* 403 F 32 *The West Country G.* – *pop. 12 553.*
See : *St. Petroc Church★.*
Env. : *Bodmin Moor★★ – Lanhydrock★★, S : 3 m. by B 3269 – Blisland★ (Church★), N : 5½ m. by A 30 and minor roads – Pencarrow★, NW : 4 m. by A 389 and minor roads Cardinham (Church★), NE : 4 m. by A 30 and minor rd – St. Mabyn (Church★), N : 5½ m. b… A 389, B 3266 and minor rd.*
Exc. : *St. Tudy★, N : 7 m. by A 389, B 3266 and minor rd.*
ℹ *Shire House, Mount Folly Sq.* ℘ *(01208) 76616.*
London 270 – Newquay 18 – Plymouth 32 – Truro 23.

Mount Pleasant Farmhouse, Mount, PL30 4EX, East : 7 ¼ m. by A 30 o… Warleggan rd ℘ (01208) 821342, *colettecapper@hotmail.com,* ≤, heated, – ⇔ P… MC VISA JCB.
restricted opening October-April – **Meals** (by arrangement) 13.00 **s.** – **7 rm** ☐ 32.00… 60.00 **s.**

Bokiddick Farm without rest., Lanivet, PL30 5HP, South : 6 m. by A 30 followin… signs for Lanhydrock and Bokiddick ℘ (01208) 831481, *Fax (01208) 831481,* « Workin… farm », , – ⇔ TV P.
closed Christmas and New Year – **3 rm** ☐ 30.00/46.00.

BODYMOOR HEATH *Staffs.* 402 403 404 O 26 – *see Tamworth.*

BOGNOR REGIS *W. Sussex* 404 R 31 – *pop. 19 836.*
ℹ *Belmont St.* ℘ *(01243) 823140.*
London 65 – Brighton 29 – Portsmouth 24 – Southampton 36.

Premier Lodge, Shripney Rd, PO22 9PA, North : 3 m. on A 29 ℘ (01243) 82232… *Fax (01243) 841430* – ⇔ rm, TV P – 80. MC AE VISA JCB.
Meals 10.95 **st.** and a la carte 🍷 7.95 – ☐ 5.95 – **24 rm** 42.00 **t.**

Inglenook, 255 Pagham Rd, Nyetimber, PO21 3QB, West : 2 ½ m. by B 2166 followin… signs for Pagham ℘ (01243) 262495, *inglenook@btinternet.com, Fax (01243) 2626…* « Part 16C », – ⇔ TV P – 100. MC AE VISA
Meals 11.50/16.95 **t.** and a la carte 🍷 5.00 – **18 rm** ☐ 50.00/90.00 **t.** – SB.

BOLDON *Tyne and Wear* 401 402 O 19 – *see Sunderland.*

BOLLINGTON *Ches.* 402 403 404 N 24 – *see Macclesfield.*

BOLTON Gtr. Manchester 402 404 M 23 – pop. 139 020.

Regent Park, Links Rd, Chorley New Rd ☎ (01204) 844170 – Lostock Park ☎ (01204) 843278 – Boston Old Links, Chorley Old Rd, Montserrat ☎ (01204) 840050.

Town Hall, Victoria Sq. ☎ (01204) 334400.

London 214 – Burnley 19 – Liverpool 32 – Manchester 11 – Preston 23.

Bolton Moat House, 1 Higher Bridge St., BL1 2EW, ☎ (01204) 879988, *cbbol@queensmoat.co.uk, Fax (01204) 380777,* « Cloisters restaurant in 19C church », rm, rest, – 340. MC AE VISA.
Meals *(closed Saturday lunch)* a la carte 13.50/24.50 **st.** – 10.50 – **130 rm** 99.00/115.00 – SB.

New Pack Horse, Nelson Sq., Bradshawgate, BL1 1DP, ☎ (01204) 527261, *info@packhorse.macdonald-hotels.co.uk, Fax (01204) 364352* – rm, – 250. MC AE VISA.
Meals *(closed Sunday)* a la carte 15.45/24.25 **st.** 7.00 – **74 rm** 60.00/80.00 **st.**

at Egerton North : 3½ m. on A 666 – Bolton.

Egerton House, Blackburn Rd, BL7 9PL, ☎ (01204) 307171, *info@egerton.macdonald-hotels.co.uk, Fax (01204) 593030,* – – 150. MC AE VISA JCB
Meals *(closed Saturday lunch)* a la carte 20.00/27.00 **st.** 8.00 – **32 rm** 75.00/110.00 **st.** – SB.

at Bromley Cross North : 3¼ m. by A 676 on B 6472 – Bolton.

Last Drop Village, Hospital Rd, BL7 9PZ, Northwest : 1 m. by B 6472 on Hospital Rd ☎ (01204) 591131, *info@lastdrop-macdonald-hotels.co.uk, Fax (01204) 304122,* « Village created from restored farm buildings », squash – rm, – 700. MC AE VISA.
Meals *(closed Saturday lunch)* a la carte 19.85/33.85 **t.** 9.95 – **125 rm** 75.00/175.00 **t.**, 3 suites – SB.

Quarlton Manor Farm, Plantation Rd, Edgworth, BL7 0DD, Northeast : 4 ¾ m. by B 6472 and B 6391 following signs for Edgeworth and Blackburn ☎ (01204) 852277, *Fax (01204) 852286,* « Part 17C farmhouse », – MC VISA
Meals 26.50 **t.** and a la carte 5.50 – **4 rm** 44.00/88.00 **t.**, 1 suite – SB.

Les prix — Pour toutes précisions sur les prix indiqués dans ce guide, reportez-vous aux pages de l'introduction.

BOLTON ABBEY N. Yorks. 402 O 22 *Great Britain G.* – pop. 117 – Skipton.

See : *Bolton Priory* AC.*

London 216 – Harrogate 18 – Leeds 23 – Skipton 6.

The Devonshire Arms Country House, BD23 6AJ, ☎ (01756) 710441, *sales@thedevonshirearms.co.uk, Fax (01756) 710564,* « Part 17C restored coaching inn, collection of fine art and antiques », – – 90. MC AE VISA
The Burlington :* Meals** (dinner only and Sunday lunch) 42.00 **st.** – (see also ***Devonshire Brasserie and Bar below) – **38 rm** 120.00/205.00 **st.**, 3 suites – SB.

Devonshire Brasserie and Bar (at The Devonshire Arms Country House), BD23 6AJ, ☎ (01756) 710710, *Fax (01756) 710564,* « Contemporary decor » – MC AE VISA
Meals (booking essential) a la carte 18.50/22.00 **st.**

BOREHAMWOOD Herts. 404 T 29 – pop. 29 837.

London 10 – Luton 20.

Plan : see Greater London (North West) p. 9

Elstree Moat House, Barnet bypass, WD6 5PU, at junction of A 5135 with A 1 ☎ (020) 8214 9988, *cbels@queensmoat.co.uk, Fax (020) 8207 3194,* – rm, rest, – 400. MC AE VISA JCB.
CT s
Meals *(closed Saturday lunch)* 14.50/19.50 **t.** and a la carte 7.50 – 11.50 – **131 rm** 145.00/195.00 **t.** – SB.

BOROUGHBRIDGE N. Yorks. 402 P 21 – pop. 1 903.

Fishergate ☎ (01423) 323373 (summer only).

London 215 – Leeds 19 – Middlesbrough 36 – York 16.

Rose Manor, Horsefair, YO51 9LL, ☎ (01423) 322245, *rosemanorhotel@ukf.net, Fax (01423) 324920,* – rm, – 250. MC AE VISA.
closed 25 and 26 December – **Meals** 18.00 **st.** (dinner) and a la carte 18.15/23.85 **st.** 5.95 – **19 rm** 79.50/116.00 **st.**, 1 suite – SB.

ENGLAND

Crown, Horsefair, YO51 9LB, ✆ (01423) 322328, *sales@crownboroughbridge.co.uk Fax (01423) 324512,* ⬚, ⬚, ⬚ – ⬚, ⬚ rm, ⬚ ⬚ – ⬚ 180. ⬚ ⬚ ⬚ VISA
Meals (bar lunch Monday to Saturday)/dinner 19.95 and a la carte – **37 rm** ⬚ 65.00/95.00 **t.** – SB.

thediningroom, 20 St. James's Sq., YO51 9AR, ✆ (01423) 326426, *lee@thediningroomreeserve.co.uk* – ⬚ rest. ⬚ VISA
closed 25-26 December, 1-24 January and Sunday dinner-Tuesday – (dinner only and Sunday lunch)/dinner a la carte 18.50/24.50 **t.** ⬚ 8.50.

at Brafferton Helperby *Northeast : 5 m. by B 6265 and Easingwold rd on Helperby rd* – ⬚ *York*

Laurel Manor Farm ⬚ without rest., YO61 2NZ, by Hall Lane ✆ (01423) 360436, *laurelmf@aol.com, Fax (01423) 360437,* « 18C farmhouse », ⬚, ⬚, ⬚, ⬚ – ⬚ ⬚
3 rm ⬚ 30.00/55.00 **t.**

BORROWDALE *Cumbria* 402 K 20 – *see Keswick.*

BOSCASTLE *Cornwall* 403 F 31 *The West Country G.*

See : *Village*★.
Env. : *Church*★ – *Old Post Office*★.
London 260 – Bude 14 – Exeter 59 – Plymouth 43.

Bottreaux House, PL35 0BG, South : ¾ m. by B 3263 on B 3266 ✆ (01840) 250231, *botreauxhotel@dircon.co.uk, Fax (01840) 250170* – ⬚ ⬚ ⬚. ⬚ ⬚ VISA JCB
Meals *(closed Sunday)* (dinner only) a la carte approx. 16.00 **t.** ⬚ 4.40 – **7 rm** ⬚ 30.00/60.00 **t.**

Trerosewill Farm ⬚ without rest., Paradise, PL35 0DL, South : 1 m. off B 3266 ✆ (01840) 250545, *nicholls@trerosewill.telme.com, Fax (01840) 250545,* ⬚, « Working farm », ⬚, ⬚ – ⬚ ⬚ ⬚. ⬚ VISA JCB. ⬚
closed Christmas and New Year – **6 rm** ⬚ 30.00/59.00.

Le Grand Londres *(GREATER LONDON) est composé de la City et de 32 arrondissements administratifs (Borough) eux-mêmes divisés en quartiers ou en villages ayant conservé leur caractère propre (Area).*

BOSHAM *W. Sussex* 404 R 31 – *see Chichester.*

BOSTON *Lincs.* 402 404 T 25 *Great Britain G.* – *pop. 34 606.*

See : *St. Botolph's Church*★.
Exc. : *Tattershal Castle*★, *NW : 15 m. by A 1121, B 1192 and A 153 – Battle of Britain Memorial Flight, RAF Coningsby*★, *NW : 14 m. on A 1121, B 1192 and A 153.*
⬚ *Cowbridge, Horncastle Rd* ✆ *(01205) 362306.*
⬚ *Market Pl.* ✆ *(01205) 356656.*
London 122 – Lincoln 35 – Nottingham 55.

Comfort Inn, Donnington Rd, Bicker Bar Roundabout, PE20 3AN, Southwest : 8 m. at junction of A 17 with A 52 ✆ (01205) 820118, *admin@gb607.u_net.com Fax (01205) 820228* – ⬚ rm, ⬚ rest, ⬚ ⬚ ⬚ – ⬚ 70. ⬚ ⬚ ⬚ VISA
Meals (bar lunch)/dinner 10.75/12.75 **st.** and a la carte ⬚ 5.95 – ⬚ 7.75 – **54 rm** 45.00 **st.** – SB.

BOSTON SPA *W. Yorks.* 402 P 22 – *pop. 4 135.*

London 127 – Harrogate 12 – Leeds 12 – York 16.

Four Gables ⬚ without rest., Oaks Lane, LS23 6DS, West : ¼ m. by A 659 ✆ (01937) 849031, *info@four.gables.co.uk, Fax (01937) 849031,* ⬚ – ⬚ ⬚ ⬚. ⬚
3 rm ⬚ 32.00/60.00 **st.**

Harts, 182 High St., LS23 6BT, ✆ (01937) 849555, *Fax (01937) 541036* – ⬚ ⬚. ⬚ ⬚ VISA
closed Monday and Sunday dinner – **Meals** 15.95 **st.** (dinner) and a la carte 19.90/26.75 **st.**

Spice Box, 152 High St., LS23 6BW, ✆ (01937) 842558, *Fax (01937) 849955* – ⬚. ⬚ VISA
closed 26 December-3 January, Sunday dinner and Monday lunch – **Meals** (dinner booking essential) 14.95 **t.** and a la carte ⬚ 5.95.

OTLEY *Hants.* 403 404 Q 31 – *pop.* 2 297 – ✉ *Southampton.*

Botley Park H. Golf & C.C., Winchester Rd, Boorley Green ☎ (01489) 780888 ext : 451.
London 83 – Portsmouth 17 – Southampton 6 – Winchester 11.

Botley Park H. Golf & Country Club, Winchester Rd, Boorley Green, SO32 2UA, Northwest : 1 ½ m. on B 3354 ☎ (01489) 780888, *Fax (01489) 789242*, squash – rest, – 250.
Meals *(closed Saturday lunch)* (dancing Saturday evening) 15.00/26.50 **t.** and dinner a la carte 7.25 – 10.50 – **100 rm** 93.00/188.50 **t.** – SB.

OUGHTON *Kent – see Faversham.*

OURNE *Lincs.* 402 404 S 25 – *pop.* 8 777.

London 101 – Leicester 42 – Lincoln 35 – Nottingham 42.

t Toft *Southwest : 3 m. by A 151 on A 6121 – ✉ Bourne.*

Toft House, Main Rd, Toft, PE10 0JT, ☎ (01778) 590614, *Fax (01778) 590264*, – – 70.
Meals *(closed Sunday dinner)* 15.95 **st.** 4.50 – **22 rm** 43.00/65.00 **st.** – SB.

t Grimsthorpe *West : 4 m. on A 151 – ✉ Bourne.*

Black Horse Inn with rm, PE10 0LY, ☎ (01778) 591247, *dine@blackhorseinn.co.uk, Fax (01778) 591373*, – rest,
Meals *(closed Sunday dinner)* a la carte 14.20/22.05 **t.** 6.95 – **5 rm** 55.00/69.00 **t.**, 1 suite.

OURNEMOUTH *Bournemouth* 403 404 O 31 *The West Country G.* – *pop.* 155 488.

See : *Compton Acres★★ (English Garden ≤★★★) AC* **AX** – *Russell-Cotes Art Gallery and Museum★★ AC* **DZ** - *Shelley Rooms AC* **EX**.

Env. : *Poole★, W : 4 m. by A 338 – Brownsea Island★ (Baden-Powell Stone ≤★★) AC, by boat from Sandbanks* **BX** *or Poole Quay – Christchurch★ (priory★) E : 4½ m. on A 35.*

Exc. : *Corfe Castle★, SW : 18 m. by A 35 and A 351 – Lulworth Cove★ (Blue Pool★) W : 8 m. of Corfe Castle by B 3070 – Swanage★, E : 5 m. of Corfe Castle by A 351.*

Queens Park, Queens Park West Dr. ☎ (01202) 396198, **DV** – *Bournmouth and Meyrick Park, Central Dr. ☎ (01202) 290307,* **CY**.

Bournemouth (Hurn) Airport : ☎ (01202) 364000, N : 5 m. by Hurn - **DV**.

Westover Rd ☎ (0906) 8020234.

London 114 – Bristol 76 – Southampton 34.

Plans on following pages

Swallow Highcliff (becoming a Marriott spring 2001), St. Michael's Rd, West Cliff, BH2 5DU, ☎ (01202) 557702, *bournemouth@swallow.hotel.co.uk, Fax (01202) 292734*, ≤, heated, – rm, – 450. CZ z
Meals 9.75/24.00 **st.** and a la carte 7.75 – **154 rm** 85.00/175.00 **st.**, 3 suites – SB.

Royal Bath, Bath Rd, BH1 2EW, ☎ (01202) 555555, *devere.royalbath@airtime.co.uk, Fax (01202) 554158*, ≤, – – 400.
Meals (dinner only) a la carte 26.50/37.50 **st.** – (see also ***Oscars*** below) – **133 rm** 135.00/230.00 **st.**, 7 suites – SB. DZ a

Carlton, East Overcliff, BH1 3DN, ☎ (01202) 552011, *carlton@menzieshotels.co.uk, Fax (01202) 299573*, ≤, heated, – rest, – 160. EZ a
Meals 13.25/32.50 **st.** and a la carte 7.50 – **68 rm** 110.00/190.00 **st.**, 5 suites – SB.

Norfolk Royale, Richmond Hill, BH2 6EN, ☎ (01202) 551521, *norfolkroyal@englishrosehotels.co.uk, Fax (01202) 299729*, – rest, – 90. CY u
The Orangery : **Meals** 12.50/22.50 **t.** and a la carte 11.55 – **90 rm** 105.00/175.00 **st.**, 5 suites – SB.

Hilton Bournemouth, Westover Rd, BH1 2BZ, ☎ (01202) 557681, *reservations@bournemouth.stakis.co.uk, Fax (01202) 554918*, ≤, – rm, – 300. DZ n
Meals *(closed Saturday lunch)* 10.50/21.00 **st.** and dinner a la carte – 9.50 – **114 rm** 120.00/170.00 **st.**, 6 suites – SB.

Chine, Boscombe Spa Rd, BH5 1AX, ☎ (01202) 396234, *reservations@chinehotel.co.uk, Fax (01202) 391737*, ≤, heated, – rm, – 120. DX e
Meals 14.50/18.50 **st.** and a la carte – **92 rm** (dinner included) 95.00/190.00 **st.** – SB.

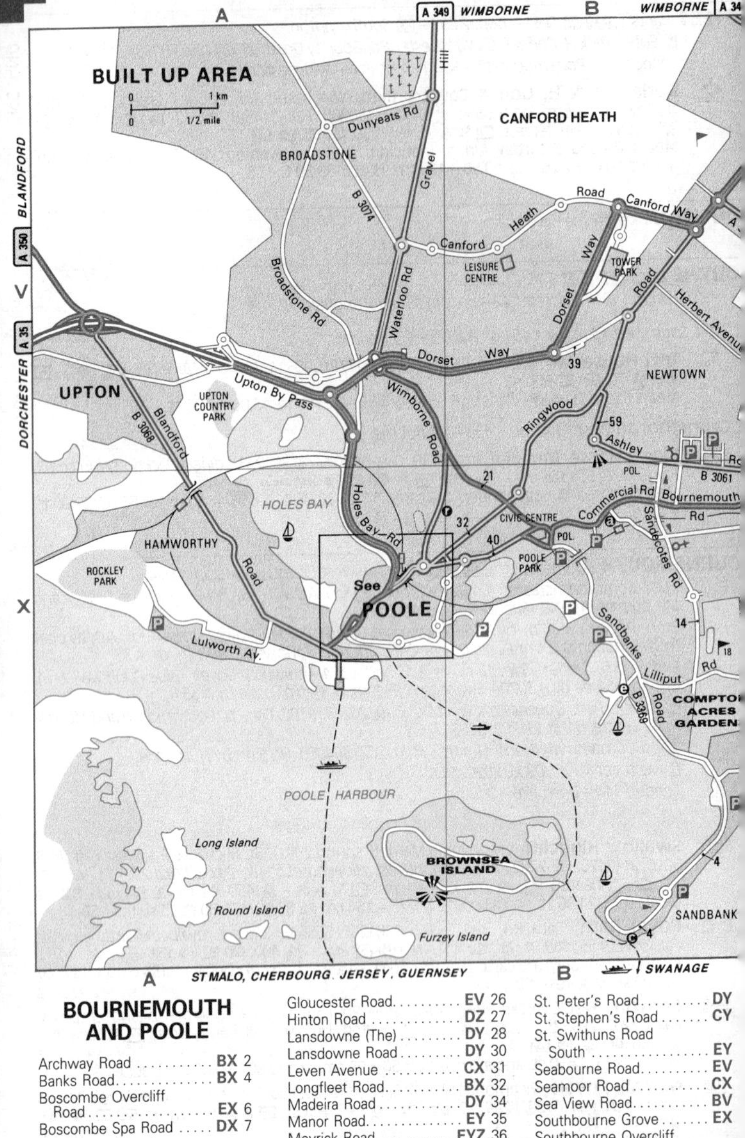

BOURNEMOUTH AND POOLE

Archway Road .... **BX** 2
Banks Road.............. **BX** 4
Boscombe Overcliff Road .... **EX** 6
Boscombe Spa Road ..... **DX** 7
Branksome Wood Road .... **CY** 9
Chessel Avenue .... **EX** 10
Clarendon Road .... **CX** 12
Commercial Road .... **CY** 13
Compton Avenue.......... **BX** 14
Cranleigh Road........... **EV** 16
Durley Road.............. **CZ** 17
Ensbury Park Road ...... **CV** 19
Exeter Road .... **CDZ** 20
Fernside Road.......... **ABX** 21
Fir Vale Road............ **DY** 23
Gervis Place .... **DY** 24
Gloucester Road.......... **EV** 26
Hinton Road .... **DZ** 27
Lansdowne (The)......... **DY** 28
Lansdowne Road.......... **DY** 30
Leven Avenue .... **CX** 31
Longfleet Road........... **BX** 32
Madeira Road............. **DY** 34
Manor Road.............. **EY** 35
Meyrick Road........... **EYZ** 36
Old Christchurch Road .... **DY**
Old Wareham Road....... **BV** 39
Parkstone Road .... **BX** 40
Pinecliff Road............ **CX** 42
Post Office Road .... **CY** 43
Priory Road .... **CZ** 45
Queen's Road .... **CX** 46
Richmond Hill............ **CY** 47
Richmond Park Road ..... **DV** 48
Russell Cotes Road....... **DZ** 49
St. Michael's Road........ **CZ** 51
St. Paul's Road........... **EY** 52
St. Peter's Road.......... **DY**
St. Stephen's Road .... **CY**
St. Swithuns Road South .... **EY**
Seabourne Road.......... **EV**
Seamoor Road .... **CX**
Sea View Road........... **BV**
Southbourne Grove .... **EX**
Southbourne Overcliff Drive.................. **EX**
Sovereign Shopping Centre **EX**
Square (The) .... **CY**
Suffolk Road .... **CY**
Surrey Road .... **CX**
Triangle (The) .... **CY**
Upper Hinton Road .... **DZ**
Wessex Way .... **CX**
West Cliff Promenade .... **CZ**
Western Road .... **CX**
Westover Road............ **DZ**

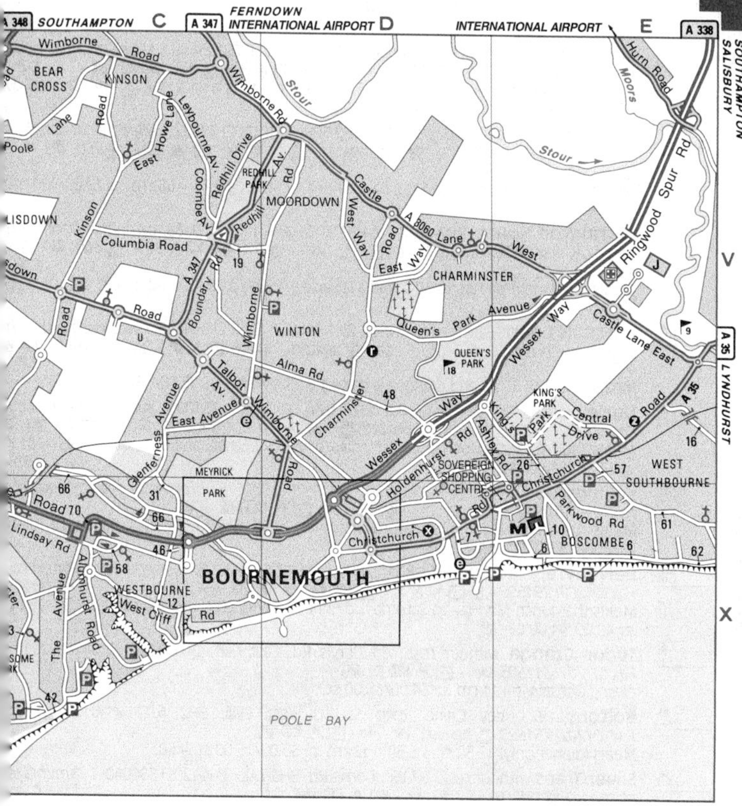

A 348 SOUTHAMPTON C A 347 FERNDOWN INTERNATIONAL AIRPORT D INTERNATIONAL AIRPORT E A 338

SOUTHAMPTON SALISBURY

Wimborne Road
BEAR CROSS
KINSON
Poole Lane
Road
East Howe Lane
Leybourne Av.
Coombe Av.
Redhill Drive
Wimborne Rd
Stour
Moors
Hurn Road
Stour
Ringwood Spur Rd
REDHILL PARK
Redhill Av.
Rd
MOORDOWN
Castle
West Way
Road
A 3060 Lane
West
LISDOWN
Kinson
Columbia Road
A 347
Boundary Rd
19
East Way
CHARMINSTER
Ringwood
V
Road
Road
U
Wimborne
WINTON
Queen's Park Avenue
Wessex Way
Castle Lane East
9
A 35
LYNDHURST
Talbot Av.
Alma Rd
Charminster
QUEEN'S PARK
18
48
KING'S PARK
Central Drive
King's Park
Road
A 35
16
East Avenue
Glenferness Avenue
Wimborne Road
Wessex
Holdenhurst Rd
Ashley Rd
MEYRICK PARK
26
Christchurch
57
WEST SOUTHBOURNE
66
31
SOVEREIGN SHOPPING CENTRE
Parkwood Rd
Road 70
66
Lindsay Rd
46
Christchurch
7
Rd
10
BOSCOMBE 6
61
62
Alumhurst Road
58
6
The Avenue
BOURNEMOUTH
WESTBOURNE
West Cliff
12
Rd
X
42
POOLE BAY

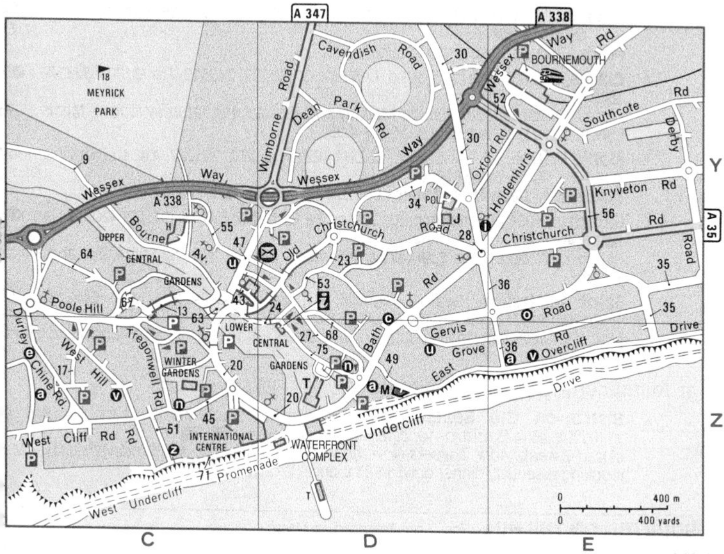

A 347
A 338
Cavendish Road
30
Wessex Way Rd
BOURNEMOUTH
18
MEYRICK PARK
Wimborne Road
Dean Park Rd
52
Southcote Rd
Derby
30
Oxford Rd
Holdenhurst
Way
9
Wessex
Way
Wessex
Y
A 338
34 POL
Knyveton Rd
Christchurch
Road
56
Rd
A 35
Bourne Av.
55
47
UPPER CENTRAL GARDENS
Old
Christchurch
28
Christchurch
Road
64
23
35
53
Rd
36
Poole Hill
67
13
43
24
Road
35
63
LOWER CENTRAL GARDENS
27
68
Bath
Gervis
Drive
Durley Chine Rd.
West Hill
Tregonwell Rd
WINTER GARDENS
20
75
GARDENS
49
Grove
36
Overcliff
Rd
East
17
Drive
Z
20
45
51
West Cliff Rd
Rd
INTERNATIONAL CENTRE
Undercliff
WATERFRONT COMPLEX
71
Promenade
West Undercliff
0 400 m
0 400 yards
C D E

ENGLAND

Miramar, 19 Grove Rd, East Overcliff, BH1 3AL, (01202) 556581, *sales@miramar-bourr mouth.com, Fax (01202) 291242,* – 150. VISA DZ
Meals *(closed Saturday lunch)* 10.00/25.00 **t.** and dinner a la carte 7.75 – **44 rm** 65.0(140.00 **t.** – SB.

Connaught, West Hill Rd, West Cliff, BH2 5PH, (01202) 298020, *sale@theconnaught.c uk, Fax (01202) 298028,* heated, – 250. CZ
VISA
Meals (bar lunch Monday to Saturday)/dinner 19.50 **st.** 4.75 – **55 rm** 70.00/120.00 1 suite – SB.

Carrington House, Knyveton Rd, BH1 3QQ, (01202) 369988, *carrington@zoffanyh els.co.uk, Fax (01202) 292221,* – 300. DX
VISA
Meals (bar lunch)/dinner 16.50 **t.** and a la carte 5.95 – 9.75 – **145 rm** 85.00/105.00 **t.** SB.

East Cliff Court, East Overcliff Drive, BH1 3AN, (01202) 554545, *eastcliff@menzies-h els.co.uk, Fax (01202) 557456,* heated – 100. EZ
JCB
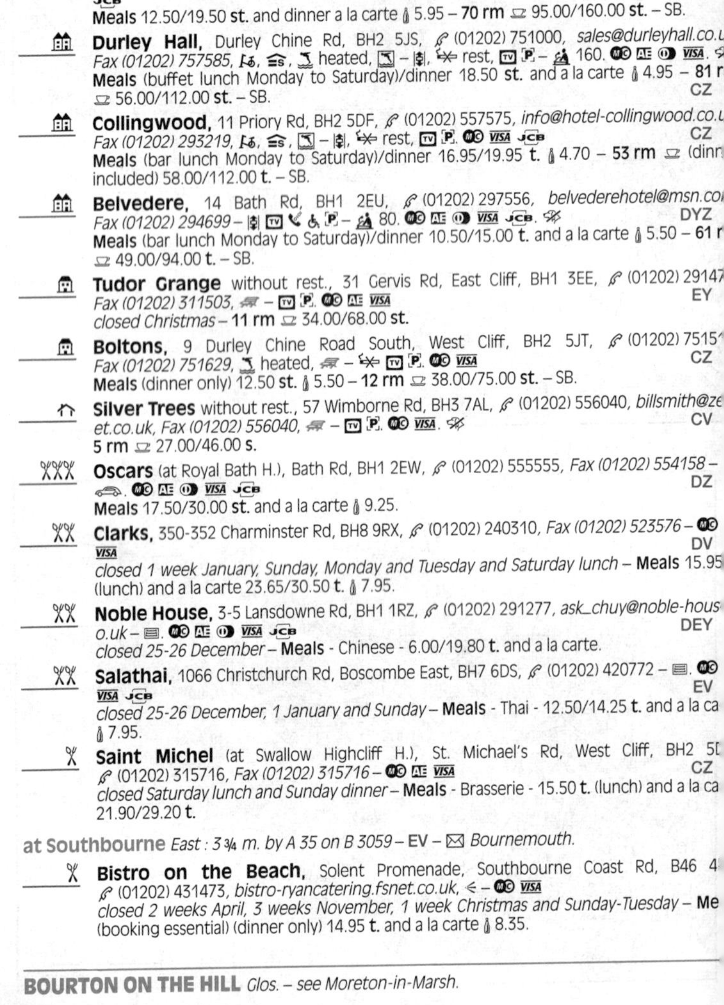
Meals 12.50/19.50 **st.** and dinner a la carte 5.95 – **70 rm** 95.00/160.00 **st.** – SB.

Durley Hall, Durley Chine Rd, BH2 5JS, (01202) 751000, *sales@durleyhall.co.u Fax (01202) 757585,* heated, – rest, – 160. VISA. CZ
Meals (buffet lunch Monday to Saturday)/dinner 18.50 **st.** and a la carte 4.95 – **81 r** 56.00/112.00 **st.** – SB.

Collingwood, 11 Priory Rd, BH2 5DF, (01202) 557575, *info@hotel-collingwood.co.u Fax (01202) 293219,* – rest, VISA JCB CZ
Meals (bar lunch Monday to Saturday)/dinner 16.95/19.95 **t.** 4.70 – **53 rm** (dinn included) 58.00/112.00 **t.** – SB.

Belvedere, 14 Bath Rd, BH1 2EU, (01202) 297556, *belvederehotel@msn.co Fax (01202) 294699* – 80. VISA JCB. DYZ
Meals (bar lunch Monday to Saturday)/dinner 10.50/15.00 **t.** and a la carte 5.50 – **61 r** 49.00/94.00 **t.** – SB.

Tudor Grange without rest., 31 Gervis Rd, East Cliff, BH1 3EE, (01202) 29147 *Fax (01202) 311503,* – VISA EY
closed Christmas – **11 rm** 34.00/68.00 **st.**

Boltons, 9 Durley Chine Road South, West Cliff, BH2 5JT, (01202) 7515 *Fax (01202) 751629,* heated, – VISA CZ
Meals (dinner only) 12.50 **st.** 5.50 – **12 rm** 38.00/75.00 **st.** – SB.

Silver Trees without rest., 57 Wimborne Rd, BH3 7AL, (01202) 556040, *billsmith@ze et.co.uk, Fax (01202) 556040,* – VISA. CV
5 rm 27.00/46.00 **s.**

Oscars (at Royal Bath H.), Bath Rd, BH1 2EW, (01202) 555555, *Fax (01202) 554158* – VISA JCB DZ
Meals 17.50/30.00 **st.** and a la carte 9.25.

Clarks, 350-352 Charminster Rd, BH8 9RX, (01202) 240310, *Fax (01202) 523576* – DV
VISA
closed 1 week January, Sunday, Monday and Tuesday and Saturday lunch – **Meals** 15.95 (lunch) and a la carte 23.65/30.50 **t.** 7.95.

Noble House, 3-5 Lansdowne Rd, BH1 1RZ, (01202) 291277, *ask_chuy@noble-hous o.uk* – VISA JCB DEY
closed 25-26 December – **Meals** - Chinese - 6.00/19.80 **t.** and a la carte.

Salathai, 1066 Christchurch Rd, Boscombe East, BH7 6DS, (01202) 420772 – EV
VISA JCB
closed 25-26 December, 1 January and Sunday – **Meals** - Thai - 12.50/14.25 **t.** and a la ca 7.95.

Saint Michel (at Swallow Highcliff H.), St. Michael's Rd, West Cliff, BH2 5I (01202) 315716, *Fax (01202) 315716* – VISA CZ
closed Saturday lunch and Sunday dinner – **Meals** - Brasserie - 15.50 **t.** (lunch) and a la ca 21.90/29.20 **t.**

at Southbourne *East : 3 ¾ m. by A 35 on B 3059* – **EV** – *Bournemouth.*

Bistro on the Beach, Solent Promenade, Southbourne Coast Rd, B46 4 (01202) 431473, *bistro-ryancatering.fsnet.co.uk,* – VISA
closed 2 weeks April, 3 weeks November, 1 week Christmas and Sunday-Tuesday – **Me** (booking essential) (dinner only) 14.95 **t.** and a la carte 8.35.

BOURTON ON THE HILL *Glos.* – *see Moreton-in-Marsh.*

OURTON-ON-THE-WATER *Glos.* 403 404 O 28 *Great Britain G. – pop. 2 239.*

See : *Town★.*

Env. : *Northleach (Church of SS. Peter and Paul★, Wool Merchants' Brasses★), SW : 5 m. by A 429.*

London 91 – Birmingham 47 – Gloucester 24 – Oxford 36.

Dial House, The Chestnuts, High St., GL54 2AN, ✆ (01451) 822244, *info@dialhousehotel.com, Fax (01451) 810126,* – TV P. MC AE VISA.
Meals a la carte 20.50/25.95 **t.** 7.50 – **14 rm** 52.00/129.00 **t.** – SB.

Coombe House without rest., Rissington Rd, GL54 2DT, ✆ (01451) 821966, *stephie.etherington@virgin.net, Fax (01451) 810477,* – TV P. MC VISA.
March-November – **6 rm** 50.00/60.00 **s.**

Lansdowne Villa, Lansdowne, GL54 2AR, ✆ (01451) 820673, *Fax (01451) 822099* – TV P. MC VISA JCB.
closed 2 weeks Christmas – **Meals** (by arrangement) 13.95 **st.** – **12 rm** 32.00/55.00 **t.** – SB.

Broadlands without rest., Clapton Row, GL54 2DN, ✆ (01451) 822002, *Fax (01451) 821776* – TV P. MC VISA JCB.
closed 24-26 December and 2 weeks January – **11 rm** 38.00/58.00 **st.**

The Lawns without rest., Station Rd, GL54 2ER, ✆ (01451) 821195, *Fax (01451) 821195* – TV P.
closed 24 December-5 January – **5 rm** 45.00/65.00 **s.**

: Great Rissington *Southeast : 3¼ m. – ✉ Cheltenham.*

Lamb Inn, GL54 2LP, ✆ (01451) 820388, *Fax (01451) 820724,* « Part 17C Cotswold stone inn », – P. MC AE VISA
Meals a la carte 11.80/25.00 **t.** 4.40 – **14 rm** 55.00/80.00 **t.**

: Lower Slaughter *Northwest : 1¾ m. by A 429 – ✉ Cheltenham.*

Lower Slaughter Manor, GL54 2HP, ✆ (01451) 820456, *lowsmanor@aol.com, Fax (01451) 822150,* ←, « 17C manor house, gardens », – rest, TV P – 25. MC AE VISA.
Meals 12.95/42.00 **t.** 22.00 – **13 rm** 200.00/375.00 **t.**, 3 suites – SB.

Washbourne Court, GL54 2HS, ✆ (01451) 822143, *washbourne@classic.msn.com, Fax (01451) 821045,* « Part 17C house », – rest, TV P – 25. MC AE VISA JCB.
Meals 16.00/21.00 **t.** (lunch) and dinner a la carte approx. 40.00 **t.** 13.75 – **19 rm** 130.00/270.00 **t.**, 9 suites – SB.

: Upper Slaughter *Northwest : 2¾ m. by A 429 – ✉ Cheltenham.*

Lords of the Manor, GL54 2JD, ✆ (01451) 820243, *lordsofthemanor@btinternet.com, Fax (01451) 820696,* ←, « Part 17C manor house », – rest, TV P – 30. MC AE VISA JCB.
Meals 17.95/21.95 **t.** (lunch) and a la carte 35.00/47.00 **t.** – **26 rm** 99.00/299.00 **st.**, 1 suite – SB
Spec. Wild salmon with spiced lentils and foie gras. Fillet of beef with foie gras and truffle ravioli. Peach and Champagne soufflé with basil ice cream.

OVEY TRACEY *Devon* 403 I 32 *The West Country G. – pop. 3 492 – ✉ Newton Abbot.*

See : *St. Peter, St. Paul and St. Thomas of Canterbury Church★.*

Env. : *Dartmoor National Park★★.*

18 *Newton Abbot ✆ (01626) 52460.*

London 214 – Exeter 14 – Plymouth 32.

Edgemoor, Haytor Rd, TQ13 9LE, West : 1 m. on B 3387 ✆ (01626) 832466, *edgemoor@btinternet.com, Fax (01626) 834760,* – rest, TV P – 50. MC AE VISA JCB
closed New Year **Meals** (booking essential) 16.95/27.45 **t.** 5.75 – **16 rm** 58.50/100.00 **t.** – SB.

Coombe Cross, Coombe Lane, TQ13 9EY, East : ½ m. on B 3344 ✆ (01626) 832476, *Fax (01626) 835298,* ←, – rest, TV P. MC AE VISA.
closed mid November-27 December – **Meals** (dinner only) 15.00/22.95 **t.** 7.00 – **24 rm** 60.00/100.00 **st.** – SB.

Front House Lodge, East St., TQ13 9EL, ✆ (01626) 832202, *fronthouselodge@yahoo.co.uk, Fax (01626) 832202,* – TV P. MC VISA.
restricted opening in winter – **Meals** (by arrangement) 20.00 **st.** – **6 rm** 30.00/50.00 **t.**

ENGLAND

at Haytor *West : 2½ m. on B 3387 – ✉ Bovey Tracey.*

Bel Alp House ⟟, TQ13 9XX, on B 3387 ☎ (01364) 661217, *Fax (01364) 661292,* countryside, ⟟ – ⟟ rest, ⟟ ⟟ ⟟. ⟟ ⟟ ⟟ VISA JCB. ⟟
restricted opening in winter and closed 22 December-6 January – **Meals** (booking essent to non-residents) (light lunch)/dinner 22.50 **st.** 🍷 8.00 – **6 rm** ⟟ 60.00/150.00 **st.**

at Haytor Vale *West : 3½ m. by B 3387 – ✉ Newton Abbot.*

Rock Inn, TQ13 9XP, ☎ (01364) 661305, *rockinn@eclipse.co.uk, Fax (01364) 66124* « 18C », ⟟ – ⟟ ⟟ ⟟ ⟟. ⟟ ⟟ ⟟ VISA
Meals a la carte 18.20/25.85 **t.** 🍷 8.95 – **9 rm** ⟟ 60.50/95.00 **t.** – SB.

BOVINGDON *Herts.* 404 S 28 – *pop. 4 491.*
London 35 – Aylesbury 29 – Maidenhead 21 – Oxford 31.

Bobsleigh Inn, Hempstead Rd, HP3 0DS, on B 4505 ☎ (01442) 833276, *info@bobsleig macdonald.hotels.co.uk, Fax (01442) 832471,* ⟟, ⟟, ⟟ – ⟟ ⟟ ⟟ – ⟟ 60. ⟟ ⟟ ⟟ V JCB
Meals 15.95/37.50 **t.** and a la carte 🍷 7.95 – **47 rm** ⟟ 67.00/140.00 **t.** – SB.

BOW BRIDGE *Devon – see Totnes.*

Le Guide change, changez de ***guide Michelin*** *tous les ans.*

BOWBURN *Durham* 401 402 P 19 – *pop. 3 296.*
London 265 – Durham 3 – Middlesbrough 20.

Travel Inn without rest., Tursdale Rd, DH6 5NP, at junction 61 of A 1(☎ (0191) 377 3666, *Fax (0191) 377 1448* – ⟟ ⟟ ⟟ ⟟. ⟟ ⟟ ⟟ VISA. ⟟
closed Christmas and New Year – **40 rm** 40.95 **t.**

BOWNESS-ON-WINDERMERE *Cumbria* 402 L20 – *see Windermere.*

BRACKNELL *Bracknell Forest* 404 R 29 – *pop. 60 895.*
⛳ Downshire, Easthampstead Park, Wokingham ☎ (01344) 302030.
ℹ The Look Out, Nine Mile Ride ☎ (01344) 354409.
London 35 – Reading 11.

Coppid Beech, John Nike Way, RG12 8TF, Northwest : 3 m. by A 329 on B 34 ☎ (01344) 303333, *sales@coppid-beech-hotel.co.uk, Fax (01344) 301200,* ⟟, ⟟, ⟟ – ⟟ rm, ⟟ rest, ⟟ ⟟ ⟟ ⟟ – ⟟ 350. ⟟ ⟟ ⟟ VISA. ⟟
Rowans : **Meals** 23.95 **t.** and a la carte 🍷 6.50 – **195 rm** ⟟ 155.00/175.00 **st.**, 10 suite SB.

Hilton Bracknell, Bagshot Rd, RG12 0QJ, South : 2 m. on A 322 ☎ (01344) 4248 *Fax (01344) 487454,* ⟟, ⟟, ⟟ – ⟟ ⟟ ⟟ ⟟ ⟟ ⟟ – ⟟ 260. ⟟ ⟟ ⟟ VISA
Meals *(closed Saturday lunch)* 14.95/25.00 **t.** and dinner a la carte – ⟟ 12.50 – **215** 185.00/235.00 **st.** – SB.

Travelodge without rest., London Rd, Binfield, RG4 2AA, Northwest : 3 ½ m. by A 329 B 3408 ☎ (01344) 485940, *Fax (01344) 485940* – ⟟ ⟟ ⟟ ⟟. ⟟ ⟟ ⟟ VISA JCB. ⟟
35 rm 59.95 **t.**

Travel Inn, Arlington Sq., Wokingham Rd, RG42 1NA, West : ½ m. on A 329 at "3. roundabout ☎ (01344) 319520, *Fax (01344) 319526* – ⟟ rm, ⟟ rest, ⟟ ⟟ ⟟. ⟟ ⟟ VISA
Meals (grill rest.) – **60 rm** 40.95 **t.**

BRADFORD *W. Yorks.* 402 O 22 *Great Britain G.* – *pop. 289 376.*
See : *City★ – National Museum of Photography, Film and Television★.*
⛳ West Bowling, Newall Hall, Rooley Lane ☎ (01274) 724449 **BY** – *⛳ Woodhall H Woodhall Rd, Calverley, Pudsey ☎ (0113) 256 4771, – ⛳ Bradford Moor, Scarr Hill, Poll Lane ☎ (01274) 771716* **BX** – *⛳ East Brierley, South View Rd ☎ (01274) 681023* **BX** – *Queensbury, Brighouse Rd, Queensbury ☎ (01274) 882155* **AY**.
✈ Leeds and Bradford Airport : ☎ (0113) 250 9696, NE : 6 m. by A 658 **BX**.
ℹ Central Library, Prince's Way ☎ (01274) 753678.
London 212 – Leeds 9 – Manchester 39 – Middlesbrough 75 – Sheffield 45.

Plan of Enlarged Area : see Leeds

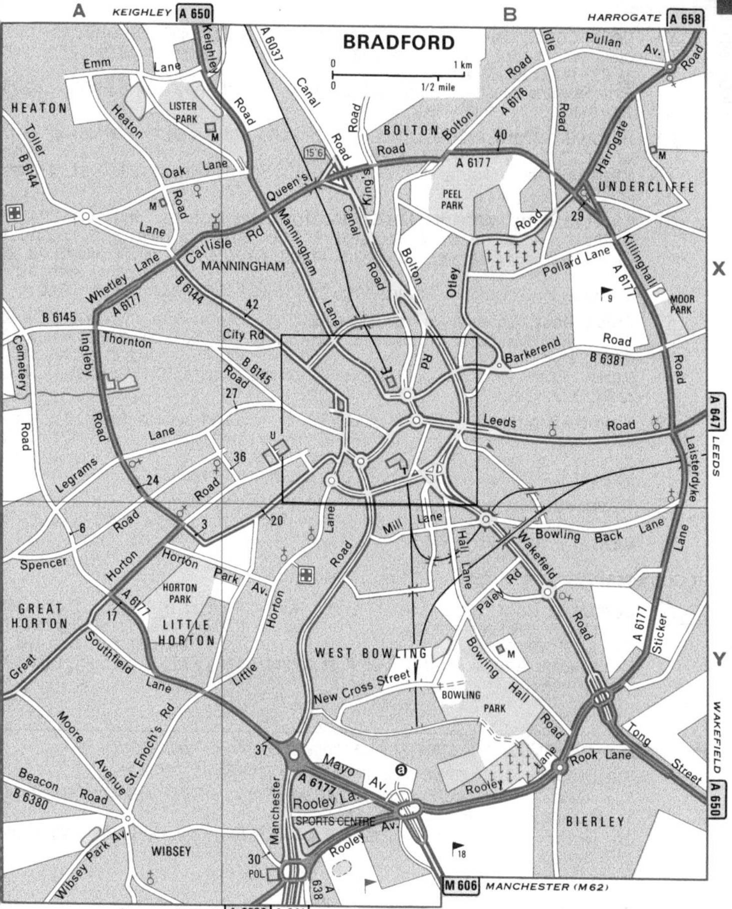

BRADFORD

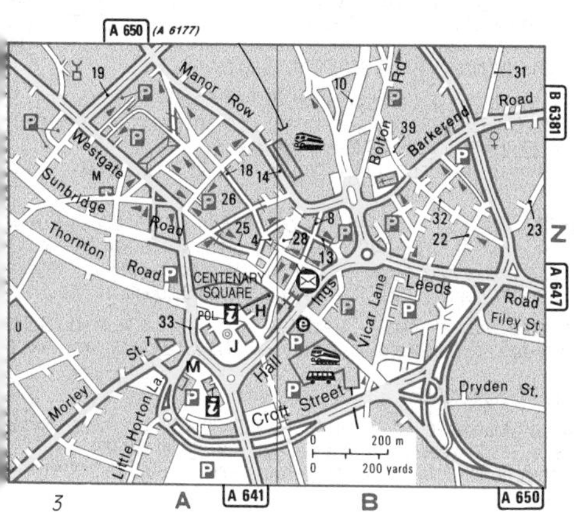

Street	Grid	No.
All Saints Road	AY	3
Bank Street	AZ	4
Beckside Road	AY	6
Broadway	BZ	8
Canal Road	BZ	10
Charles Street	BZ	13
Cheapside	BZ	14
Cross Lane	AY	17
Darley Street	AZ	18
Drewton Road	AZ	19
Easby Road	BY	20
East Parade	BZ	22
Harris Street	BZ	23
Horton Grange Road	AX	24
Ivegate	AZ	25
Kirkgate Centre	AZ	26
Listerhills Road	BX	27
Market Street	BZ	28
Northcote Road	BX	29
Odsal Road	BY	30
Otley Road	BZ	31
Peckover Street	BZ	32
Prince's Way	AZ	33
Shearbridge Road	BX	36
Smiddles Lane	BY	37
Stott Hill	BZ	39
Valley View Grove	BX	40
White Abbey Road	BX	42

ENGLAND

Cedar Court, Mayo Av., off Rooley Lane, BD5 8HZ, ☎ (01274) 406606, *sales@cedarcourt-otel-bradford.co.uk, Fax (01274) 406600,* – rm, rest, – 800. VISA JCB BY
Four Seasons : **Meals** (bar lunch Saturday) 10.95/19.50 **st.** and a la carte 8.95 – 9.75 – **130 rm** 99.00 **st.**, 1 suite – SB.

Hilton Bradford, Hall Ings, BD1 5SH, ☎ (01274) 734734, *Fax (01274) 306146* – rm, rest, – 700. VISA BZ
Meals (grill rest.) a la carte 11.95/24.95 **st.** – 12.50 – **116 rm** 89.00/95.00 **st.**, 4 suites – SB.

Courtyard by Marriott Leeds/Bradford, The Pastures, Tong Lane, BD4 0RP, Southeast : 4 ¾ m. by A 650 and B 6135 on Tong Lane ☎ (0113) 2854646, *Fax (0113) 2853661,* – rm, rest, – 250. VISA on Leeds town plan BU
Meals (bar lunch Saturday) a la carte 18.00/25.00 **t.** – 10.00 – **53 rm** 85.00/100.00 **st.**

Guide Post, Common Rd, Low Moor, BD12 0ST, South : 3 m. by A 641 off A 638 ☎ (01274) 607866, *bookings@guidepost.net, Fax (01274) 671085* – rm, – 100. VISA on Leeds town plan AU
Meals *(closed Sunday dinner)* 9.95 **t.** (lunch) and a la carte 20.15/23.85 **st.** – **43 rm** 62.50/92.50 **st.** – SB.

Novotel Bradford, Euroway Trading Estate, Merrydale Rd, BD4 6SA, South : 3 ½ m. by A 641 and A 6117 off M 606 ☎ (01274) 683683, *hosio@accorhotels.com, Fax (01274) 651342,* heated – rm, – 300. VISA on Leeds town plan AU
Meals 10.50/15.80 **st.** and a la carte 5.00 – 8.95 – **127 rm** 57.50 **st.**

Travel Inn, Whitehall Rd, Cleckheaton, BD19 6HG, South : 5 ½ m. by A 650, A 6177, M 606 off A 58 ☎ (01274) 862828, *Fax (01274) 852973* – rm, rest, VISA. on Leeds town plan BU
Meals (grill rest.) – **40 rm** 40.95 **t.**

at Gomersal *Southeast : 7 m. by A 650 on A 651 – ✉ Bradford.*

Gomersal Park, Moor Lane, BD19 4LJ, Northeast : 1 ½ m. by A 651 off A 65 ☎ (01274) 869386, *gomersal@bestwestern.co.uk, Fax (01274) 861042,* – – 200. VISA on Leeds town plan BU
Meals *(closed Saturday lunch)* 8.95/23.95 **st.** and a la carte 6.95 – 9.25 – **52 rm** 83.00/94.00 **st.** – SB.

BRADFORD-ON-AVON *Wilts.* 403 404 N 29 *The West Country G. – pop. 8 815.*

See : *Town★★ - Saxon Church of St. Lawrence★★ - Tithe Barn★ – Bridge★.*

Env. : *Great Chalfield Manor★ (All Saints★)* **AC**, *NE : 3 m. by B 3109 – Westwood Manor★* **AC**, *S : 1 ½ m. by B 3109 – Top Rank Tory (★).*

Exc. : *Bath★★★, NW : 7 ½ m. by A 363 and A 4 – Corsham Court★★* **AC**, *NE : 6 ½ m. by B 3109 and A 4.*

34 Silver St. ☎ (01225) 865797.

London 118 – Bristol 24 – Salisbury 35 – Swindon 33.

Woolley Grange, Woolley Green, BA15 1TX, Northeast : ¾ m. by B 3107 on Woolley St ☎ (01225) 864705, *info@woolleygrange.com, Fax (01225) 864059,* , « 17C manor house, special facilities for young children », heated, – rest, – 40. VISA
Meals 20.00/34.50 **st.** 7.00 – **20 rm** 90.00/200.00 **st.**, 3 suites – SB.

Widbrook Grange, Trowbridge Rd, Widbrook, BA15 1UH, Southeast : 1 m. on A 363 ☎ (01225) 864750, *Fax (01225) 862890,* « Georgian farmhouse and converted outbuildings », – – 25. VISA JCB.
Meals *(closed Friday to Sunday)* (residents only) (dinner only) 25.50 **t.** 8.50 – **21 rm** 49.00/120.00 **t.**

Bradford Old Windmill, 4 Masons Lane, BA15 1QN, on A 363 ☎ (01225) 866842, *oldwindmill@netscapeonline.co.uk, Fax (01225) 866648,* – VISA.
closed January, February and weekends only November and December – **Meals** - Vegetarian - (by arrangement) (communal dining) 19.00 **s.** – **2 rm** 69.00/99.00 **s.**, 1 suite.

The Beeches Farmhouse without rest., Holt Rd, BA15 1TS, East : 1 ¼ m. on B 3107 ☎ (01225) 863475, *beeches-farmhouse@netgates.co.uk, Fax (01225) 863475,* – VISA JCB
closed Christmas – **3 rm** 40.00/60.00 **s.**

Priory Steps, Newtown, off Market St., BA15 1NQ, ☎ (01225) 862230, *priorysteps@clara.co.uk, Fax (01225) 866248,* , « 17C weavers cottages », – VISA.
Meals (by arrangement) (communal dining) 21.00 **st.** 6.00 – **5 rm** 60.00/80.00 **st.**

Midway Cottage without rest., Farleigh Wick, BA15 2PU, Northwest : 2 3/4 m. on A 363 ☎ (01225) 863932, *Fax (01225) 866836*, – TV P
3 rm 30.00/45.00.

Georgian Lodge with rm, 25 Bridge St., BA15 1BY, ☎ (01225) 862268, *georgianlodge.hotel@btinternet.com, Fax (01225) 862218* – rest, TV. MC AE D VISA.
closed 1 week January – **Meals** *(closed Monday lunch)* a la carte 20.00/26.50 **st.** 12.00 – **10 rm** 30.00/88.00 **st.**

t Winsley *West : 2½ m. by A 363 off B 3108 – ✉ Bradford-on-Avon.*

Burghope Manor without rest., BA15 2LA, ☎ (01225) 723557, *burghope.manor@virgin.net, Fax (01225) 723113,* « 13C manor house », – TV P. MC AE VISA JCB.
closed Christmas and New Year – **5 rm** 80.00/95.00.

t Monkton Farleigh *Northwest : 4 m. by A 363 – ✉ Bradford-on-Avon.*

Fern Cottage without rest., BA15 2QJ, ☎ (01225) 859412, *ferncottage@tinyworld.co.uk, Fax (01225) 859018,* « Part 17C », – TV P.
3 rm 40.00/60.00 **t.**

RADWELL *Derbs.* 402 403 404 O 24 – *pop. 1 728* – ✉ *Sheffield.*
London 181 – Derby 51 – Manchester 32 – Sheffield 16 – Stoke-on-Trent 41.

StoneyRidge without rest., Granby Rd, S33 9HU, West : 3/4 m. via Town Lane ☎ (01433) 620538, *toneyridge@aol.com, Fax (01433) 623154*, ≤, , – TV P. MC AE D VISA JCB
4 rm 31.00/56.00.

RAFFERTON HELPERBY *N. Yorks.* 402 P 21 – *see Boroughbridge.*

RAINTREE *Essex* 404 V 28 – *pop. 33 229.*
18 *Kings Lane, Stisted* ☎ *(01376) 346079* – 9 *Towerlands, Panfield Rd* ☎ *(01376) 326802.*
Town Hall Centre, Market Pl. ☎ *(01376) 550066.*
London 45 – Cambridge 38 – Chelmsford 12 – Colchester 15.

White Hart, Bocking End, CM7 9AB, ☎ (01376) 321401, *geaves@cix.co.uk, Fax (01376) 552628,* – rm, TV P – 30. MC AE VISA.
Meals (grill rest.) a la carte 15.75/22.55 **st.** – **31 rm** 60.00/70.00 **st.** – SB.

Express by Holiday Inn without rest., Galley's corner, Cressing Rd, CM7 8DJ, Southeast : 2 1/4 m. on B 1018 ☎ (01376) 551141, *Fax (01376) 551142* – rm, rest, TV P – 25. MC AE D VISA JCB.
– **47 rm** 49.95 **t.**

Travel Inn, Galley's Corner, CM7 8GG, Southeast : 2 m. by B 1018 on A 120 ☎ (01376) 340914, *Fax (01376) 370437* – rm, rest, TV P. MC AE D VISA
Meals (grill rest.) – **40 rm** 40.95 **t.**

RAMHALL *Gtr. Manchester* 402 403 404 N 23 – *pop. 39 730 (inc. Hazel Grove)* – ✉ *Stockport.*
London 190 – Chesterfield 35 – Manchester 11.

County H. Bramhall, Bramhall Lane South, SK7 2EB, on A 5102 ☎ (0161) 455 9988, *Fax (0161) 440 8071* – TV P – 200. MC AE D VISA
Meals 10.00/20.00 **t.** and a la carte 9.95 – 9.95 – **65 rm** 85.00/110.00 **st.** – SB.

RAMHOPE *W. Yorks.* 402 P 22 – *see Leeds.*

RAMPTON *Cambs.* 402 404 T 27 – *pop. 4 673.*
London 72 – Bedford 22 – Cambridge 18 – Northampton 36.

Travel Inn, Brampton Hut, Great North Rd, PE18 8NQ, Northwest : 2 m. by B 1514 at junction of A 1 and A 14 ☎ (01480) 810800, *Fax (01480) 811298* – , rm, rest, TV P – 45. MC AE D VISA.
Meals (grill rest.) – **60 rm** 40.95 **t.**

RAMPTON *Cumbria* 401 402 L 19 *Great Britain G.* – *pop. 3 957.*
Env. : *Hadrian's Wall*★★, *NW : by A 6077.*
18 *Talkin Tarn* ☎ *(016977) 2255* – 18 *Brampton Park, Huntingdon* ☎ *(01480) 434700.*
Moot Hall, Market Sq. ☎ *(016977) 3433.*
London 317 – Carlisle 9 – Newcastle upon Tyne 49.

Farlam Hall, CA8 2NG, Southeast : 2 ¾ m. on A 689 ✆ (016977) 46234, *farlamhall@o l.pipex.com, Fax (016977) 46683*, ≤, « Victorian country house, ornamental gardens » – TV P. MC VISA
closed 25 to 30 December – **Meals** (booking essential to non-residents) (dinner onl 31.00 **t.** 6.75 – **12 rm** (dinner included) 120.00/250.00 **t.** – SB.

Kirby Moor Country House, Longtown Rd, CA8 2AB, North : ½ m. on A 607 ✆ (016977) 3893, *info@kirbymoor-hotel.com, Fax (016977) 41847*, ≤, – rest, TV MC VISA
Meals a la carte approx. 10.15/18.65 **st.** – **6 rm** 42.00/64.00 **st.** – SB.

at Kirkcambeck *North : 7 ¾ m. by A 6071 and Walton rd – Brampton.*

Cracrop Farm without rest., CA8 2BW, West : 1 m. by B 6318 on Stapleton r ✆ (016977) 48245, *Fax (016977) 48333*, ≤, « Working farm », – TV P. VISA.
4 rm 25.00/50.00 **st.**

BRANCASTER STAITHE *Norfolk* 404 V 25.
London 131 – Cambridge 74 – Norwich 39.

The White Horse with rm, Main Rd, PE31 8BW, ✆ (01485) 210262, *whitehorse.branca er@virgin.net, Fax (01485) 210262*, ≤, – TV P. MC AE VISA
closed 25 December – **Meals** a la carte 15.00/24.00 **t.** 5.95 – **8 rm** 64.00/98.00 **t.** – SB

Wenn Sie ein ruhiges Hotel suchen,
benutzen Sie zuerst die Karte in der Einleitung
oder wählen Sie im Text ein Hotel mit dem Zeichen oder .

BRANDESBURTON *East Riding* 402 T 22 – *pop. 1 835 – Great Driffield.*
London 197 – Kingston-upon-Hull 16 – York 37.

Burton Lodge, YO25 8RU, Southwest : ½ m. on Leven rd ✆ (01964) 542847, *burton@lo ge5755.freeserve.co.uk, Fax (01964) 544771*, 18, – rest, TV P. MC AE VISA JCB
closed 25-26 December – **Meals** (residents only) (dinner only) 14.00 **t.** 5.50 – **9 r** 36.00/52.00 **st.** – SB.

BRANDON *Warks.* 403 404 P 26 – *see Coventry (W. Mids.).*

BRANDS HATCH *Kent* 404 (44) – *Dartford.*
9 *Corinthian, Gay Dawn Farm, Fawkham, Dartford ✆ (01474) 707559.*
London 22 – Maidstone 18.

Thistle Brands Hatch, DA3 8PE, on A 20 ✆ (01474) 854900, *brands.hatch@thistle.co.u , Fax (01474) 853220*, – rm, rest, TV P – 270. MC AE VISA JCB.
Genevieves :* Meals** *(closed Saturday lunch and Sunday dinner)* 23.50/34.00 **st.** – ***Buga
***Bistro :* Meals** *(closed Sunday lunch)* a la carte approx. 15.00 **t.** 6.25 – 11.50 – **121 r** 121.00/161.00 **st.**

at Fawkham Green *East : 1½ m. by A 20 – Ash Green.*

Brands Hatch Place, DA3 8NQ, ✆ (01474) 872239, *Fax (01474) 879652*, , squash – TV P – 120. MC AE VISA.
Meals *(closed Saturday lunch)* 16.00/22.95 **st.** – **41 rm** 77.00/130.00 **st.** – SB.

BRANSCOMBE *Devon* 403 K 31 *The West Country G. – pop. 501 – Seaton.*
See : *Village★.*
Env. : *Seaton (≤★★), NW : 3 m – Colyton★.*
London 167 – Exeter 20 – Lyme Regis 11.

Masons Arms, EX12 3DJ, ✆ (01297) 680300, *Fax (01297) 680500*, « 14C inn » rest, TV P – 100. MC VISA.
Meals (dinner only) 22.00 **t.** 8.00 – **22 rm** 64.00/120.00 **t.** – SB.

BRANSTON *Lincs.* 402 404 S 24 – *see Lincoln.*

BRAYE *Alderney (Channel Islands)* 403 Q 33 and 230 (9) – *see Channel Islands.*

BRAY-ON-THAMES *Windsor & Maidenhead* 404 R 29 – *pop. 8 121* – ✉ *Maidenhead.*
London 34 – Reading 13.

Plan : see Maidenhead

Monkey Island, SL6 2EE, Southeast : ¾ m. by Upper Bray Rd and Old Mill Lane ☎ (01628) 623400, *monkeyisland@btconnect.com, Fax (01628) 784732,* ≤, « Island on River Thames », – 150. **Meals** a la carte 30.25/44.25 **t.** 9.75 – **25 rm** 160.00/195.00 **t.**, 1 suite – SB.

Chauntry House, 1 High St., SL6 2AB, ☎ (01628) 673991, *res@chauntryhouse.com, Fax (01628) 773089,* – rest, – 30. X a
closed Christmas and New Year – **Meals** 22.00/35.00 **t.** and a la carte 11.00 – **15 rm** 110.00/150.00 **t.**

Waterside Inn (Roux) with rm, Ferry Rd, SL6 2AT, ☎ (01628) 620691, *waterinn@aol.com, Fax (01628) 784710,* « ≤ Thames-side setting » –
closed 26 December-1 February and 16-19 April – **Meals** - French - *(closed Tuesday except dinner June-August and Monday)* 32.00-48.50/72.50 **t.** and a la carte 62.00/95.50 **t.** 16.00 – **8 rm** 150.00/175.00 **st.**, 1 suite X s
Spec. Tronçonnettes de homard poêlées minute au Porto blanc. Filets de lapereau grillés aux marrons glacés. Soufflé chaud aux framboises.

Fat Duck (Blumenthal), High St., SL6 2AQ, ☎ (01628) 580333, *Fax (01628) 776188,* – X e
closed 2 weeks December, Sunday dinner and Monday – **Meals** 24.50 **t.** (lunch) and a la carte 41.45/55.75 **t.** 9.50
Spec. Crab feuillantine with foie gras, marinated salmon and oyster vinaigrette. Veal sweetbread roast in salt crust with cockles and asparagus. Bavarois of butternut squash, goat's cheese ice cream.

The Fish, Old Mill Lane, SL6 2BG, ☎ (01628) 781111, *jeanatfish@demon.co.uk, Fax (01628) 623571,* – X r
closed 24-28 December, Sunday dinner and Monday – **Meals** - Seafood - a la carte 21.00/35.00 **t.** 6.50.

BREADSALL *Derby* – *see Derby.*

BREDE *E. Sussex* 404 V 31 – *pop. 1 764.*
London 62 – Brighton 43 – Canterbury 41 – Hastings 7 – Maidstone 25.

Arndale Cottage without rest., Northiam Rd, Broad Oak, TN31 6EP, North : 1 ½ m. on A 28 ☎ (01424) 882813, *Fax (01424) 882813,* –
closed 22 December-2 January – **3 rm** 30.00/48.00 **s.**

BRENTWOOD *Essex* 404 V 29 – *pop. 49 463.*
Bentley G. & C.C., Ongar Rd ☎ (01277) 373179 – 18, 9 Warley Park, Magpie Lane, Little Warley ☎ (01277) 224891.
Pepperell House, 44 High St. ☎ (01277) 200300.
London 22 – Chelmsford 11 – Southend-on-Sea 21.

Marygreen Manor, London Rd, CM14 4NR, Southwest : 1 ¼ m. on A 1023 ☎ (01277) 225252, *info@marygreenmanor.co.uk, Fax (01277) 262809,* – – 50.
Meals 17.50/26.00 **t.** and a la carte 10.00 – 11.00 – **42 rm** 115.50/134.00 **st.**, 1 suite.

Posthouse Brentwood, Brook St., CM14 5NF, Southwest : 1 ½ m. on A 1023 ☎ (0870) 4009012, *Fax (01277) 264264,* – rm, rest, – 100.
Meals a la carte 21.00/26.50 **t.** 12.95 – 11.95 – **145 rm** 119.00/169.00 **st.** – SB.

BRIDGNORTH *Shrops.* 402 403 404 M 26 *Great Britain G.* – *pop. 11 229.*
Exc. : *Ironbridge Gorge Museum★★ AC (The Iron Bridge★★ - Coalport China Museum★★ - Blists Hill Open Air Museum★★ - Museum of the River and Visitor Centre★) NW : 8 m. by B 4373.*
Stanley Lane ☎ (01746) 763315.
The Library, Listley St. ☎ (01746) 763257.
London 146 – Birmingham 26 – Shrewsbury 20 – Worcester 29.

at Worfield *Northeast : 4 m. by A 454* – ✉ *Bridgnorth.*

The Old Vicarage , WV15 5JZ, ☎ (01746) 716497, *admin@the_old_vicarage.demon.co.uk, Fax (01746) 716552,* « Edwardian parsonage », –
Meals (booking essential) (lunch by arrangement Monday to Saturday)/dinner 22.50/36.50 **st.** 10.00 – **13 rm** 80.00/175.00 **st.**, 1 suite – SB.

ENGLAND

at Alveley *Southeast : 7 m. by A 442 – ✉ Bridgnorth.*

Mill, Birdsgreen, WV15 6HL, Northeast : ¾ m. ☎ (01746) 780437, *Fax (01746) 780850*, lift, ⇆ rest, TV P – 200. MC AE D VISA.
Meals 12.50/25.00 **t.** and a la carte 7.50 – ☐ 12.50 – **21 rm** 68.00/110.00 **t.** – SB.

BRIDGWATER *Somerset* 403 L 30 *The West Country G. – pop. 34 610.*

See : *Town★ – Castle Street★ – St. Mary's★ – Admiral Blake Museum★ AC.*

Env. : *Westonzoyland (St. Mary's Church★★) SE : 4 m. by A 372 – North Petherton (Churc Tower★★) S : 3½ m. by A 38.*

Exc. : *Stogursey Priory Church★★, NW : 14 m. by A 39.*

18 Enmore Park, Enmore ☎ (01278) 671244.

50 High St. ☎ (01278) 453489 (restricted opening in winter).

London 160 – Bristol 39 – Taunton 11.

Walnut Tree, North Petherton, TA6 6QA, South : 3 m. on A 38 ☎ (01278) 662255, *reserv tions@walnut-tree-hotel.co.uk, Fax (01278) 663946*, ← – ⇆ rm, ▤ rest, TV P – 120. MC AE D VISA JCB.
closed 25-26 December – ***Duke's :*** **Meals** a la carte 14.65/20.75 **t.** – ***Duke's Bistro :*** **Meal** (bookings not accepted) a la carte 14.65/20.95 **t.** – ☐ 8.00 – **31 rm** 59.00/74.00 **t.**, 1 suite.

at Woolavington *Northeast : 5 m. by A 39 on B 3141 – ✉ Bridgwater.*

Chestnut House, Hectors Stone, Lower Road, TA7 8EQ, ☎ (01278) 683658, *jon@chestn thouse.freeserve.co.uk, Fax (01278) 684333*, « Part 16C farmhouse », – ⇆ rest, TV P MC VISA
Meals a la carte 18.00/23.50 **t.** 5.00 – **6 rm** ☐ 45.00/80.00 **t.** – SB.

at Cannington *Northwest : 3½ m. by A 39 – ✉ Bridgwater.*

Blackmore Farm without rest., TA5 2NE, Southwest : 1 ½ m. by A 39 on Bradley Gree rd ☎ (01278) 653442, *dyerfarm@aol.com, Fax (01278) 653427*, « Part 14C manor house working farm », – ⇆ TV ♿ P. MC VISA.
3 rm ☐ 35.00/60.00 **s.**, 1 suite.

BRIDLINGTON *East Riding* 402 T 21 *Great Britain G. – pop. 31 334.*

Env. : *Flamborough Head★, NE : 5 ½ m. by B 1255 and B 1259 – Burton Agnes Hall★ AC SW : 6 m. by A 166.*

18 Belvedere Rd ☎ (01262) 672092 – 18 Flamborough Head, Lighthouse Rd, Flamboroug ☎ (01262) 850333.

25 Prince St. ☎ (01262) 673474.

London 236 – Kingston-upon-Hull 29 – York 41.

Expanse, North Marine Drive, YO15 2LS, ☎ (01262) 675347, *expanse@brid.demon.u Fax (01262) 604928*, ← – lift TV P – 200. MC AE VISA JCB.
Meals 9.00/17.00 **st.** and dinner a la carte 4.50 – **48 rm** ☐ 34.00/84.00 **st.** – SB.

BRIDPORT *Dorset* 403 L 31 *The West Country G. – pop. 7 278.*

Env. : *Parnham House★★ AC, N : 6 m. by A 3066 – Mapperton Gardens★, N : 4 m. by A 306 and minor rd.*

Exc. : *Lyme Regis★ – The Cobb★, W : 11 m. by A 35 and A 3052.*

18 Bridport and West Dorset, East Cliff, West Bay ☎ (01308) 422597.

32 South St. ☎ (01308) 424901.

London 150 – Exeter 38 – Taunton 33 – Weymouth 19.

Roundham House, Roundham Gdns, West Bay Rd, DT6 4BD, South : 1 m. by B 315 ☎ (01308) 422753, *cyprencom@compuserve.com, Fax (01308) 421500*, ←, – ⇆ TV P MC VISA JCB
April-1 January – **Meals** (dinner only) 17.95 **t.** 5.95 – **8 rm** ☐ 40.00/80.00 **st.**

Britmead House, West Bay Rd, DT6 4EG, South : 1 m. on B 3157 ☎ (01308) 422941, *br mead@talk21.com, Fax (01308) 422516*, – ⇆ TV P. MC VISA JCB.
restricted opening in winter – **Meals** 16.00 **t.** 4.50 – **7 rm** ☐ 39.00/62.00 **t.**

Riverside, West Bay, DT6 4EZ, South : 1 ¾ m. by B 3157 ☎ (01308) 422011, ←, – MC VISA JCB
mid February-November – **Meals** - Seafood - *(closed Sunday dinner and Monday excep Bank Holidays)* (booking essential) (restricted dinner March-April and October-Novembe a la carte 20.00/30.00 **t.** 6.00.

at Shipton Gorge *Southeast : 3 m. by A 35 – ✉ Bridport.*

Innsacre Farmhouse, Shipton Lane, DT6 4LJ, North : 1 m. ☎ (01308) 456137, *Fax (01308) 456137*, « 17C », – TV P. MC VISA JCB
closed 23 December-2 January and last week October – **Meals** (by arrangement) 16.50 **t.** 8.00 – **4 rm** 45.00/75.00 **t.**

BRIGHOUSE *W. Yorks.* 402 O 22 – *pop. 32 198.*

Crow Nest Park, Coach Rd, Hove Edge ☎ (01484) 401121.
London 213 – Bradford 12 – Burnley 28 – Manchester 35 – Sheffield 39.

Posthouse Leeds Brighouse, Clifton Village, HD6 4HW, Southeast : 1 m. on A 644 ☎ (0870) 400 9013, *GM1736@forte-hotels.com, Fax (01484) 400068*, – rm, TV P – 200. MC AE VISA
Meals 10.95/17.95 **t.** and a la carte 5.95 – 10.95 – **92 rm** 89.00/109.00 **st.**, 2 suites – SB.

Brook's, 6 Bradford Rd, HD6 1RW, ☎ (01484) 715284, *brooks@legend.co.uk*, *Fax (01484) 712641* – . MC VISA
closed 2 weeks January, 1 week August and Sunday – **Meals** (dinner only and lunch in December)/dinner 23.50 **t.** 7.50.

BRIGHTON AND HOVE *Brighton and Hove* 404 T 31 *Great Britain G. – pop. 192 453.*

See : *Town*★★ - *Royal Pavilion*★★★ **AC CZ** – *Seafront*★★ – *The Lanes*★ **BCZ** – *St. Bartholomew's*★ **AC CX B** – *Art Gallery and Museum (20C decorative arts*★*)* **CY M.**

Env. : *Devil's Dyke (*★*) NW : 5 m. by Dyke Rd (B 2121)* **BY.**

East Brighton, Roedean Rd ☎ (01273) 604838 **CV** – *The Dyke, Devil's Dyke, Dyke Rd ☎ (01273) 857296,* **BV** – *Hollingbury Park, Ditchling Rd ☎ (01273) 552010,* **CV** – *Waterhall, Waterhall Rd ☎ (01273) 508658,* **AV.**

Shoreham Airport : ☎ (01273) 296900, W : 8 m. by A 27 **AV.**

10 Bartholomew Sq. ☎ (0906) 711 2255.

London 53 – Portsmouth 48 – Southampton 61.

Plans on following pages

Grand, Kings Rd, BN1 2FW, ☎ (01273) 224300, *reservations@grandbrighton.co.uk*, *Fax (01273) 224321*, – TV – 800. MC AE VISA **BZ v**
Meals 19.50/30.00 **t.** and a la carte – **195 rm** 155.00/220.00 **t.**, 5 suites – SB.

Thistle Brighton, Kings Rd, BN1 2GS, ☎ (01273) 206700, *brighton@thistle.co.uk*, *Fax (01273) 820692*, – TV – 300. MC AE VISA JCB
Promenade : Meals 14.75/18.50 **st.** and a la carte – 12.00 – **204 rm** 191.00 **st.**, 4 suites – SB. **CZ n**

Hilton Brighton Metropole, Kings Rd, BN1 2FU, ☎ (01273) 775432, *Fax (01273) 207764*, – rm, rest, TV – 1500. MC AE VISA.
Meals *(closed Saturday lunch)* 19.50/29.95 **st.** and a la carte – 12.95 – **323 rm** 177.50/212.00 **st.**, 10 suites – SB. **BZ s**

Hilton Brighton West Pier, Kings Rd, BN1 2JF, ☎ (01273) 329744, *Fax (01273) 775877*, – , rest, TV – 450. MC AE VISA. **BZ c**
Meals *(closed Saturday lunch)* (carving rest.) 14.95/17.95 **st.** – 13.95 – **129 rm** 180.00 **st.**, 2 suites – SB.

Belgrave, 64 Kings Rd, BN1 1NA, ☎ (01273) 323221, *Fax (01273) 312485*, – , rm, rest, TV – 70. MC AE VISA. **BZ x**
Meals 13.00/15.00 **t.** 7.50 – **59 rm** 105.00/140.00 **t.**, 2 suites.

Jarvis Preston Park, 216 Preston Rd, BN1 6UU, North : 1 ½ m. on A 23 ☎ (01273) 507853, *Fax (01273) 540039*, – rest, TV P – 60. MC AE VISA.
Meals (bar lunch Monday to Saturday)/dinner 16.00 **t.** and a la carte – 9.95 – **33 rm** 79.00/105.00 st. – SB. **BV a**

Topps without rest., 17 Regency Sq., BN1 2FG, ☎ (01273) 729334, *Fax (01273) 203679* – TV. MC AE VISA JCB. **BZ a**
15 rm 49.00/129.00 **st.**

Adelaide without rest., 51 Regency Sq., BN1 2FF, ☎ (01273) 205286, *adelaide@pavilion.co.uk, Fax (01273) 220904* – TV. MC AE VISA. **BZ z**
closed Christmas **12 rm** 43.00/88.00 **st.**

Premier Lodge, 144 North St., BN1 1DN, ☎ (01273) 746833, *Fax (01273) 323878* – , rest, TV – 80. MC AE VISA **CZ a**
Meals (dinner only) a la carte 15.00/19.50 **t.** – 6.00 – **160 rm** 46.000.

Travelodge without rest., 165-167 Preston Rd, BN1 6AU, ☎ (01273) 550245, *Fax (01273) 554917* – TV P. MC AE VISA JCB. **BV z**
94 rm 49.95 **t.**

BRIGHTON AND HOVE

Street	Grid	No.
Adelaide Crescent	AY	2
Brunswick Place	AY	3
Brunswick Square	AYZ	4
Carlton Terrace	AV	5
Chatham Place	BX	6
Churchill Square Shopping Centre	BYZ	
Denmark Road	BY	7
East Street	CZ	8
Eastern Road	CV	9
George Street	AV	10
Gladstone Terrace	CX	12
Gloucester Place	CY	13
Gloucester Road	CY	14
Goldsmid Road	BX	15
Grand Junction Road	CZ	16
Hollingbury Park Av	BV	17
Hollingdean Road	CV	18
Hove Street	AV	19
London Road	CX	
Market Place	CX	20
Marlborough Place	CY	21
Montpelier Place	BY	22
North Street	CZ	
Old Steine	CZ	23
Pavillon Parade	CZ	26
Richmond Place	CY	27
Richmond Terrace	CX	28
St. George's Place	CY	30
St. Peter's Place	CX	31
Terminus Road	BCX	32
Upper Lewes Road	CX	33
Warren Road	CV	37
Waterloo Place	CX	39
Wellington Road	AV	40
Western Road	ABY	
York Place	CY	42

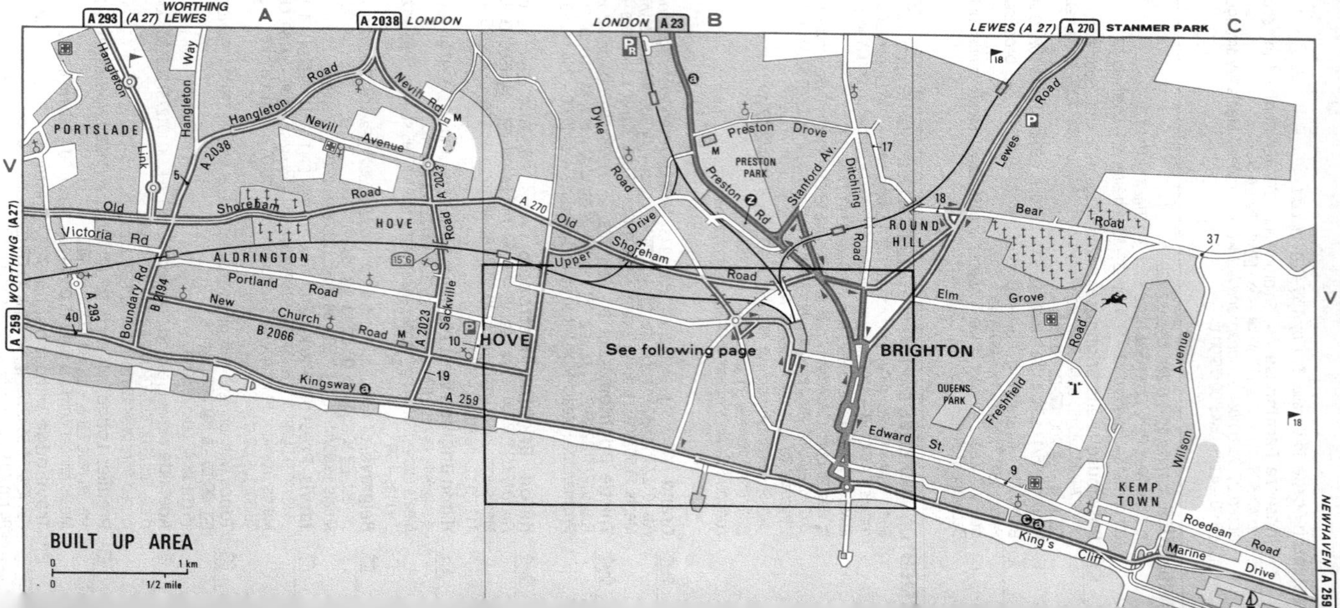

A 293 (A 27) WORTHING LEWES — A — A 2038 LONDON — LONDON A 23 — B — LEWES (A 27) A 270 STANMER PARK — C

WORTHING (A27) A 259 — NEWHAVEN A 259

PORTSLADE — HOVE — ALDRINGTON — BRIGHTON — ROUND HILL — PRESTON PARK — QUEENS PARK — KEMP TOWN

See following page

BUILT UP AREA

0 — 1 km
0 — 1/2 mile

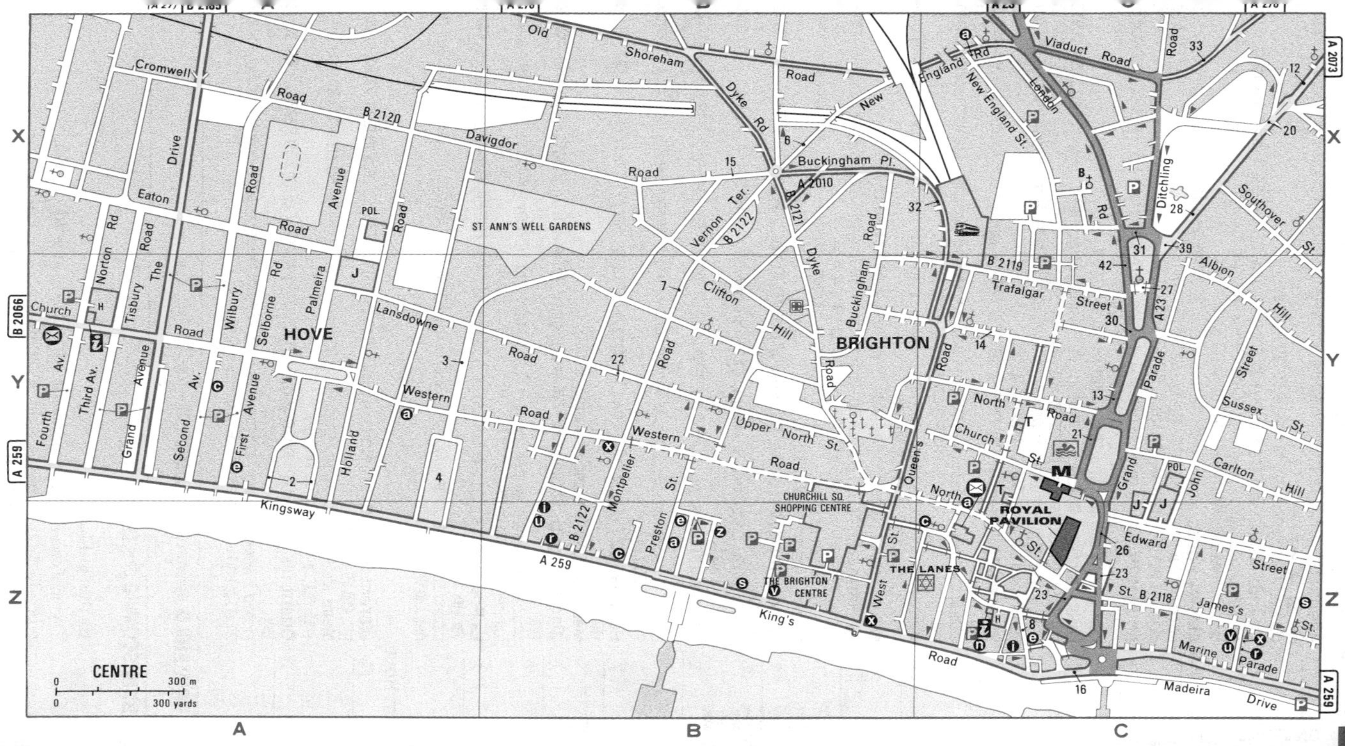

HOVE
BRIGHTON
ROYAL PAVILION
THE LANES
ST. ANN'S WELL GARDENS
CHURCHILL SQ. SHOPPING CENTRE
THE BRIGHTON CENTRE
CENTRE
0 300 m
0 300 yards
Kingsway
King's Road
Madeira Drive
Marine Parade
Western Road
Church Road
Dyke Road
Queen's Road
North Road
Church St.
North St.
Grand Parade
Old Shoreham Road
Cromwell Road
Davigdor Road
Lansdowne Road
Clifton Hill
Upper North St.
Montpelier Road
Preston St.
West St.
Holland Road
Palmeira Avenue
Selborne Rd
Wilbury Road
The Drive
Eaton Road
Tisbury Road
Norton Rd
Fourth Av.
Third Av.
Grand Avenue
Second Av.
First Avenue
Buckingham Pl.
Buckingham Road
Vernon Ter.
New England Rd
New England St.
London Rd
Viaduct Road
Ditchling Road
Southover St.
Albion Hill
Trafalgar Street
Sussex Street
Carlton Hill
John St.
Edward Street
St. James's St.
A 259
A 2073
A 23
B 2066
B 2120
B 2119
B 2118
B 2122
A 2010
B 2121
A
B
C
X
Y
Z

ENGLAND

Allendale without rest., 3 New Steine, BN2 1PB, ☎ (01273) 675436, *Fax (01273) 602603* – TV. MC JCB. ⛔ CZ
closed Christmas Meals – **13 rm** ▭ 35.00/90.00 **st.**

Arlanda without rest., 20 New Steine, BN2 1PD, ☎ (01273) 699300, *arlanda@brighton.co.uk, Fax (01273) 600930* – TV. MC AE VISA JCB. ⛔ CZ
closed 2 weeks Christmas – – **14 rm** ▭ 40.00/80.00 **st.**

Ainsley House without rest., 28 New Steine, BN2 1PD, ☎ (01273) 605310, *ahhotel@fastnet.co.uk, Fax (01273) 688604* – TV. MC AE VISA JCB. ⛔ CZ
closed 1 week Christmas – **11 rm** ▭ 30.00/78.00 **t.**

Amblecliff without rest., 35 Upper Rock Gdns., BN2 1QF, ☎ (01273) 681161, *amblecliff.brighton@virgin.net, Fax (01273) 676945* – TV. MC AE VISA. ⛔ CZ
closed Christmas and New Year – **8 rm** ▭ 50.00/80.00 **t.**

One Paston Place, 1 Paston Pl., Kemp Town, BN2 1HA, ☎ (01273) 606933, *Fax (01273) 675686* – ▤. MC AE VISA JCB CV
closed first 2 weeks January, first 2 weeks August, Sunday and Monday – **Meals** 21.00 **t.** (lunch) and a la carte 35.50/43.00 **st.** 🌢 7.00.

Whytes, 33 Western St., BN1 2PG, ☎ (01273) 776618, *janthony@lineone.net* – . MC AE VISA JCB BZ
closed 2 weeks late February, 25 December, Sunday and Monday – **Meals** (booking essential) (dinner only) 24.00 **t.** and a la carte 🌢 7.50.

Victor's, 11 Little East St., BN1 1HT, ☎ (01273) 774545, *rosario@victors.co.uk, Fax (01273) 325529* – MC AE VISA CZ
Meals - French - (booking essential) 19.95/30.00 **t.** and a la carte 🌢 9.95.

La Marinade, 77 St. Georges Rd, Kemp Town, BN2 1EF, ☎ (01273) 600992, *violavincent@yahoo.co.uk, Fax (01273) 600992* – ▤. MC AE VISA JCB CV
closed 1 week in spring, 1 week in summer, Monday, Tuesday lunch and Sunday dinner – **Meals** - French - 13.00/23.00 **t.** 🌢 8.00.

Terre à Terre, 71 East St., BN1 1HQ, ☎ (01273) 729051, *Fax (01273) 327561* – ▤. MC AE VISA CZ
closed 24-26 December, 1 January and Monday lunch – **Meals** - Vegetarian - a la carte 11.50/21.40 **t.**

The Gingerman, 21A Norfolk Sq., BN1 2PD, ☎ (01273) 326688, *Fax (01273) 326688* – MC AE VISA BZ
closed 2 weeks summer, 2 weeks winter, Sunday and Monday – **Meals** (booking essential) 9.95/21.50 **t.** 🌢 6.70.

Havana, 32 Duke St., BN1 1AG, ☎ (01273) 773388, *Fax (01273) 748923* – MC AE VISA CZ
Meals 19.95/29.95 **t.** and a la carte 🌢 10.95.

Black Chapati, 12 Circus Par., off New England Rd, BN1 4GW, ☎ (01273) 699011 – MC AE VISA CX
closed 2 weeks December, 2 weeks July, Sunday and Monday – **Meals** - Asian specialities - (dinner only) a la carte 19.75/25.70 **t.**

La Fourchette, 101 Western Rd, BN1 2AA, ☎ (01273) 722556, *Fax (01273) 722556.* MC AE VISA BY
closed Sunday, Monday lunch and 26 December – **Meals** - French - 10.00/20.00 **t.** and dinner a la carte 🌢 12.00.

at Hove.

Claremont House, Second Av., BN3 2LL, ☎ (01273) 735161, *Fax (01273) 735161*, TV. MC AE VISA AY
Meals *(closed Sunday and Monday)* (bar lunch)/dinner 10.50/16.50 **st.** and a la carte 🌢 3.2 – **12 rm** ▭ 45.00/88.00 **st.** – SB.

Quentin's, 42 Western Rd, BN3 1JD, ☎ (01273) 822734, *Fax (01273) 822734* – MC AE VISA AZ
closed 2 weeks August, Christmas-New Year, Saturday lunch, Sunday and Monday – **Meals** 21.00 **t.** and lunch a la carte 🌢 5.00.

BRIMFIELD *Herefordshire* 403 404 L 27 – *see Ludlow.*

BRIMSCOMBE *Glos.* 403 404 N 28 – *see Stroud.*

In this guide

a symbol or a character, printed in red or black, in **bold** or light type, does not have the same meaning.
Pay particular attention to the explanatory pages.

BRISTOL

Bristol 403 404 M 29 *The West Country G. – pop. 407 992.*

London 121 – Birmingham 91.

TOURIST INFORMATION

St. Nicholas Church, St. Nicholas St. ☎ (0117) 926 0767.

PRACTICAL INFORMATION

Mangotsfield, Carsons Rd ☎ (0117) 956 5501, **BV**.
Beggar Bush Lane, Failand, Clifton ☎ (01275) 393117, **AX**.
Knowle, Fairway, West Town Lane, Brislington ☎ (0117) 977 6341, **BX**.
Long Ashton, Clarken Coombe ☎ (01275) 392229, **AX**.
Stockwood Vale, Stockwood Lane, Keynsham ☎ (0117) 986 6505, **BX**.
Severn Bridge (toll).
Bristol Airport : ☎ (01275) 474444, SW : 7 m. by A 38 **AX**.

SIGHTS

See : *City★★ – St. Mary Redcliffe★★* **DZ** – *Brandon Hill★★* **AX** – *Georgian House★★* **AX K** – *Harbourside Industrial Museum★★* **CZ M3** – *SS Great Britain★★ AC* **AX S2** – *The Old City★* **CYZ** : *Theatre Royal★★* **CZ T** – *Merchant Seamen's Almshouses★* **CZ Q** – *St. Stephen's City★* **CY S1** – *St. John the Baptist★* **CY** – *College Green★* **CYZ** *(Bristol Cathedral★, Lord Mayor's Chapel★) – The Exploratory Hands-on Science Centre★* **DZ** – *City Museum and Art Gallery★* **AX M1**.

Env. : *Clifton★★* **AX** *(Suspension Bridge★★ (toll), R.C. Cathedral of St. Peter and St. Paul★★* **F1**, *Bristol Zoological Gardens★★ AC, Village★) – Blaise Hamlet★★ – Blaise Castle House Museum★, NW : 5 m. by A 4018 and B 4057* **AV**.

Exc. : *Bath★★★, SE : 13 m. by A 4* **BX** – *Chew Magna★ (Stanton Drew Stone Circles★ AC) S : 8 m. by A 37 –* **BX** *– and B 3130 – Clevedon★ (Clevedon Court★ AC, ≤★) W : 11½ m. by A 370, B 3128 –* **AX** *– and B 3130.*

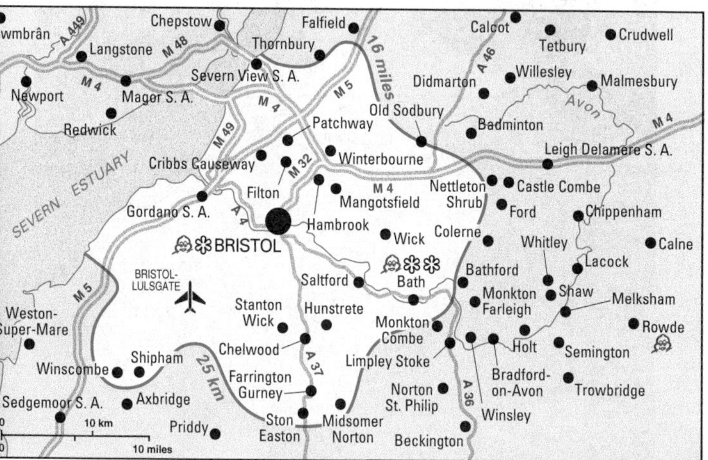

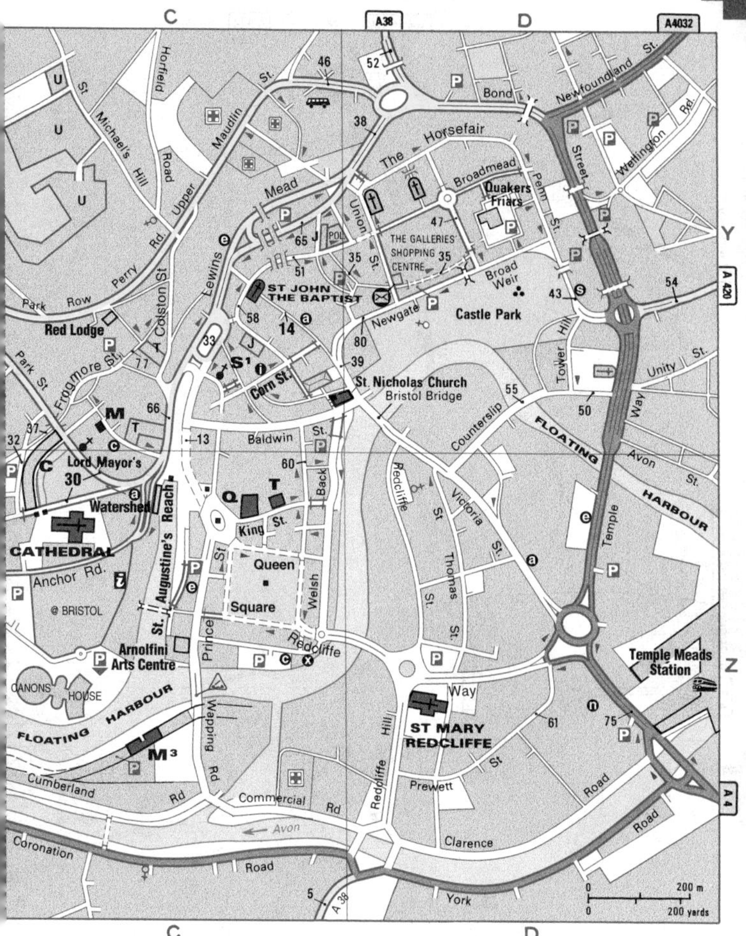

STREET INDEX TO BRISTOL TOWN PLANS

ir Balloon Road . . . . **BX** 3
shton Avenue . . . . **AX** 4
edminster Parade . . . . **CZ** 5
lack Boy Hill . . . . **AX** 8
road Quay . . . . **CYZ** 13
road Street . . . . **CY** 14
roadmead . . . . **DY**
runel Way . . . . **AX** 16
anford Road . . . . **AV** 17
assel Road . . . . **BV** 18
heltenham Road . . . . **AX** 20
hurch School Road . . . . . . **BX** 21
larence Road . . . . **BX** 22
liff House Road . . . . **AX** 24
lifton Down Road . . . . **AX** 25
lifton Hill . . . . **AX** 26
lifton Park . . . . **AX** 28
louds Hill Road . . . . **BX** 29
ollege Green . . . . **CZ** 30
ollege Street . . . . **CYZ** 32

Colston Avenue . . . . **CY** 33
Eastgate Shopping Centre . **BX**
Fairfax Street . . . . **CDY** 35
Frog Lane . . . . **CY** 37
Galleries' (The)
Shopping Centre . . . . **DY**
Haymarket . . . . **DY** 38
High Street . . . . **CDY** 39
Horse Fair (The) . . . . **DY**
Lawrence Hill . . . . **BX** 41
Lodge Hill . . . . **BX** 42
Lower Castle St. . . . . **DY** 43
Malago Road . . . . **AX** 44
Marlborough St. . . . . **CDY** 46
Merchant Street . . . . **DY** 47
Nags Head Hill . . . . **BX** 49
Narrow Plain . . . . **DY** 50
Nelson Street . . . . **CY** 51
North Street . . . . **DY** 52
Old Market St. . . . . **DY** 54

Park Street . . . . **CY**
Passage Street . . . . **DY** 55
Pembroke Road . . . . **AX** 56
Philip Street . . . . **AX** 57
Quay Street . . . . **CY** 58
Queen Charlotte St. . . . . . . **CZ** 60
Redcliffe Mead Lane . . . . . **DZ** 61
Regent Street . . . . **AX** 62
Royal York Crescent . . . . . **AX** 63
Rupert Street . . . . **CY** 65
St. Augustine's Parade . . . . **CY** 66
Sheene Road . . . . **AX** 67
Sion Hill . . . . **AX** 70
Stokes Croft . . . . **AX** 72
Summerhill Road . . . . **BX** 73
Temple Gate . . . . **DZ** 75
Thicket Road . . . . **BV** 76
Trenchard Street . . . . **CY** 77
Victoria Street . . . . **BV** 79
Wine Street . . . . **DY** 80

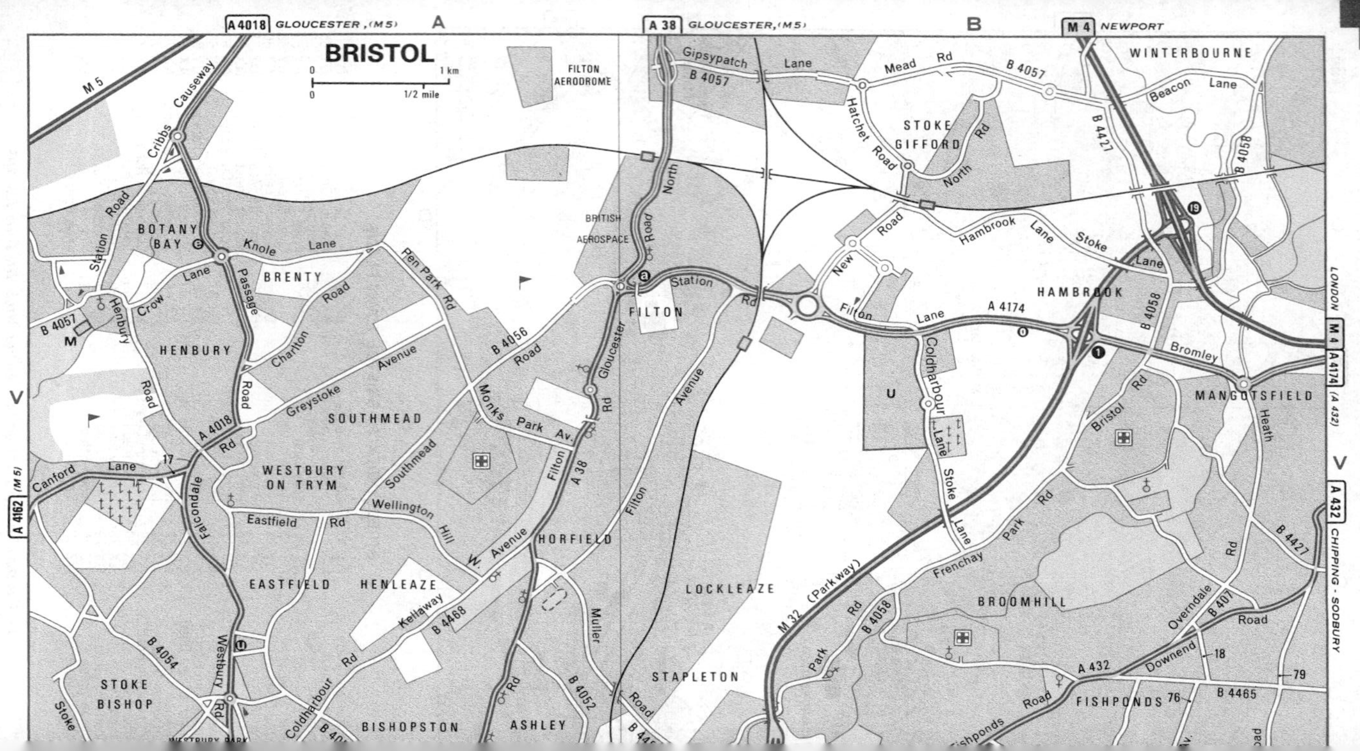
BRISTOL
0 1 km
0 1/2 mile
A 4018 GLOUCESTER ,(M5)
A
A 38 GLOUCESTER,(M5)
B
M 4 NEWPORT
LONDON M 4 A 4174 (A 432)
A 432 CHIPPING - SODBURY
A 4162 (M 5)
M 5
Cribbs Causeway
FILTON AERODROME
BRITISH AEROSPACE
Gipsypatch Lane
B 4057
Mead Rd
WINTERBOURNE
Beacon Lane
B 4427
B 4058
STOKE GIFFORD
Hatchet Road
North Rd
Station Road
BOTANY BAY
Knole Lane
BRENTY
Passage Road
Crow Lane
Henbury
HENBURY
B 4057
M
Charlton Road
Pen Park Rd
B 4056 Road
North Road
Station Rd
FILTON
New Road
Hambrook Lane
Stoke Lane
HAMBROOK
A 4174
Filton Lane
Coldharbour Lane
Stoke Lane
U
B 4058
Bromley
MANGOTSFIELD
Heath Rd
Bristol Rd
Greystoke Avenue
SOUTHMEAD
Gloucester Rd
Avenue
A 4018 Rd
Monks Park Av.
Filton A 38
WESTBURY ON TRYM
Southmead
Canford Lane
17
Falcondale Rd
Wellington Hill
Eastfield Rd
W. Avenue
HORFIELD
Filton Avenue
M 32 (Parkway)
Frenchay Park Rd
B 4427
EASTFIELD
HENLEAZE
Kellaway
B 4468
Muller
LOCKLEAZE
BROOMHILL
Overndale Rd
B 407 Road
B 4054
Westbury Rd
Coldharbour Rd
STOKE BISHOP
Stoke
BISHOPSTON
ASHLEY
B 4052
Rd
STAPLETON
Road
Park Rd
B 4058
A 432
Downend
18
79
FISHPONDS
76
B 4465
Fishponds Road

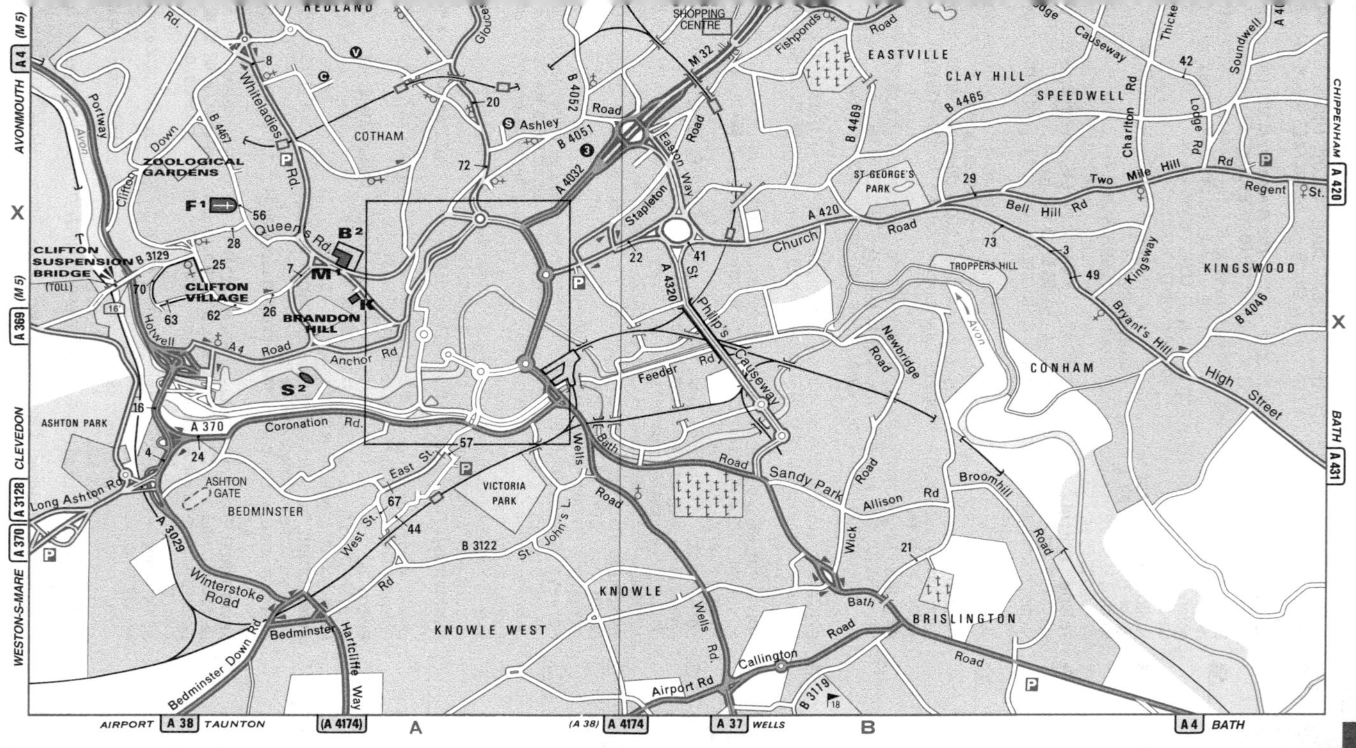

CHIPPENHAM A 420
BATH A 431
A 4 BATH
A 37 WELLS
(A 38) A 4174
(A 4174)
AIRPORT A 38 TAUNTON
AVONMOUTH A 4 (M 5)
A 369 (M 5)
CLEVEDON A 3128
WESTON-S-MARE A 370
A
B
REDLAND
COTHAM
SHOPPING CENTRE
EASTVILLE
CLAY HILL
SPEEDWELL
KINGSWOOD
CONHAM
ST. GEORGE'S PARK
TROPPERS HILL
BRISLINGTON
KNOWLE
KNOWLE WEST
BEDMINSTER
ASHTON GATE
ASHTON PARK
VICTORIA PARK
ZOOLOGICAL GARDENS
CLIFTON VILLAGE
CLIFTON SUSPENSION BRIDGE (TOLL)
BRANDON HILL
Portway
Avon
Clifton Down Rd.
B 4467
Whiteladies Rd.
Queen's Rd.
B 3129
Hotwell Road
A 4
Anchor Rd
Coronation Rd.
A 370
Long Ashton Rd
A 3029
Winterstoke Road
Bedminster Down Rd
Bedminster
Hartcliffe Way
West St.
East St.
B 3122
St. John's L.
Wells Road
Wells Rd.
Bath Road
Airport Rd
Callington Road
B 3119
Sandy Park Road
Wick Road
Allison Rd
Broomhill Road
Newbridge Road
Feeder Rd
Philip's Causeway
A 4320
St
Stapleton Road
Easton Way
A 4032
B 4051
B 4052
Ashley
Gloucester
M 32
Fishponds Road
B 4469
B 4465
Causeway
Charlton Rd
Lodge Rd
Soundwell
A 420
Church Road
Bell Hill Rd
Two Mile Hill Rd
Regent St.
Kingsway
Bryant's Hill
B 4046
High Street

Bristol Marriott City Centre, 2 Lower Castle St., Old Market, BS1 3AD (0117) 929 4281, *Fax (0117) 922 5838,* – rm, – 600 VISA JCB. DY
Le Chateau : Meals (dinner only) 25.00 **st.** 7.75 – ***The Brasserie :*** Meals (dinner only) 15.95 **st.** and a la carte 7.75 – 12.50 – **281 rm** 106.00 **st.**, 8 suites – SB.

Hotel du Vin, The Sugar House, Narrow Lewins Mead, BS1 2NU, (0117) 925 5577, *admin@bristol.hotelduvin.co.uk, Fax (0117) 925 1199,* « Converted 18C sugar refinery, contemporary wine themed interior » – – 85. VISA JCB. CY
Meals – (see ***Bistro*** below) – 11.50 – **40 rm** 99.00/125.00 **t.**

Holiday Inn Bristol, Victoria St., BS1 6HY, (0117) 976 9988, *Fax (0117) 925 5040,* rm, rest, – 180. VISA. DZ
Meals 17.95/19.95 **st.** (dinner) and a la carte 17.05/29.85 **st.** 6.95 – 11.50 – **128 rm** 127.00/210.00 **st.** – SB.

Thistle Bristol, Broad St., BS1 2EL, (0117) 929 1645, *bristol@thistle.co.uk, Fax (0117) 922 7619* – rm, – 550. VISA JCB CY
Meals *(closed Saturday lunch)* 21.50 **st.** and a la carte 6.10 – 11.00 – **178 rm** 128.00/141.00 **st.**, 4 suites – SB.

Jurys Bristol, Prince St., BS1 4QF, (0117) 923 0333, *bristol-hotel@jurysdoyle.com, Fax (0117) 923 0300,* – rm, rest, – 300. VISA. CZ
Unicorn : **Meals** (dinner only) 17.95 **st.** and a la carte 8.00 – ***Quayside :*** **Meals** (carving lunch Sunday) 15.95 **st.** (dinner) and a la carte approx. 16.00 **st.** – 9.00 – **186 rm** 125.00/145.00 **st.**, 1 suite.

City Inn, Temple Way, BS1 6BF, (0117) 925 1001, *bristolreservations@cityinn.com, Fax (0117) 907 4116,* – rm, – 50. VISA DY
closed 25-26 December – ***City Café :*** **Meals** (bar lunch Saturday and Sunday) 13.00/30.00 **st.** – 8.50 – **167 rm** 57.50 **st.**

Express by Holiday Inn without rest., Templegate, BS1 6PL, (01179) 304800, *bristol@premierhotels.co.uk, Fax (01179) 304900* – – 30. VISA JCB
94 rm 59.50 **st.** DZ

Travel Inn, Hengrove Leisure Park, Hengrove Way, BS14 0HR, South : 4 m. by A 37 off A 4174 (01275) 834340, *Fax (01275) 834721* – rm, rest, VISA.
Meals (grill rest.) – **40 rm** 40.95 **t.**

Courtlands, 1 Redland Court Rd, Redland, BS6 7EE, (0117) 942 4432, *Fax (0117) 923 2432,* – rest, VISA AX
*closed 23 December-3 January***Meals** *(closed Friday, Saturday and Sunday)* (dinner only) (residents only) a la carte 10.45/16.45 **st.** 5.25 – **25 rm** 52.00/62.00 **st.**

Westbury Park without rest., 37 Westbury Rd, BS9 3AU, (0117) 962 0465, *Fax (0117) 962 8607* – . VISA. AV
closed Christmas-New Year – **8 rm** 38.00/56.00 **t.**

Harveys, 12 Denmark St., BS1 5DQ, (0117) 927 5034, *danielgalmiche@adswnet.com, Fax (0117) 927 5003,* « Medieval cellars and wine museum » – . VISA CY
closed first 2 weeks August, 25-26 December, 1 week February, Sunday, Saturday lunch and Bank Holidays – **Meals** 22.00-24.50/39.00-53.00 **st.** 12.00
Spec. Grilled scallops with potato, truffle and mixed salad. Roast farm pigeon with sauté potatoes, sherry vinegar jus. Warm bitter chocolate tart with citrus fruits.

Markwicks, 43 Corn St., BS1 1HT, (0117) 926 2658, *Fax (0117) 926 2658* – VISA JCB CY
closed 2 weeks August, 1 week Easter, 1 week Christmas, Sunday, Saturday lunch and Bank Holidays – **Meals** 17.50/25.00 **t.** and a la carte 26.00/31.00 **t.**

Bistro (at Hotel du Vin), The Sugar House, Narrow Lewins Mead, BS1 2NU (0117) 925 5577, *Fax (0117) 925 1199* – VISA JCB CY
Meals (booking essential) a la carte approx 25.50 **t.** 9.50.

Riverstation, The Grove, Harbourside, BS1 4RB, (0117) 914 4434, *Fax (0117) 934 9990,* « Harbourside setting » – VISA CZ
closed Christmas and New Year – **Meals** (booking essential) 14.25 **t.** (lunch) and a la carte 21.50/30.50 **t.** 7.95.

Severnshed, The Grove, Harbourside, BS1 4RB, (0117) 925 1212, *info@severnshed.co.uk, Fax (0117) 925 1214,* « Converted boat shed, harbourside setting » – VISA
closed Christmas-New Year – **Meals** - Organic Middle Eastern - (live music Tuesday evening) a la carte 13.95/22.50 **t.** 6.95. CV

Bell's Diner, 1 York Rd, Montpelier, BS6 5QB, (0117) 924 0357, *Fax (0117) 924 4280* . VISA JCB AX
closed Christmas, Saturday lunch, Monday lunch, Sunday dinner and Bank Holidays – **Meals** a la carte 17.00/26.50 **t.** 8.00.

Red Snapper, 1 Chandos Rd, Redland, BS6 6PG, (0117) 973 7999, *redsnapper@cix.co.uk* – VISA AX
closed10 days Christmas, Sunday dinner and Monday lunch – **Meals** 14.00/20.00 (lunch) and dinner a la carte 19.50/25.00 **t.**

at Filton *North : 4½ m. on A 38 – ✉ Bristol.*

Premier Lodge, Shield Retail Park, Gloucester Road North, BS12 7AA, on A 4174 (eastbound carriageway) ✆ (0117) 979 1011, *Fax (0870) 700 1337* – ⇔ rm, ▤ rest, TV ✆ ♿ P. MC AE ⓓ VISA. ✂ BV a
Meals (grill rest.) a la carte 8.75/23.05 **t.** – ☕ 6.00 – **61 rm** 49.50 **t.**

at Patchway *(South Gloucestershire) North : 6½ m. on A 38 –* **BV** *– ✉ Bristol.*

Aztec, Aztec West Business Park, BS12 4TS, North : 1 m. by A 38 ✆ (01454) 201090, *aztec@shireinns.co.uk, Fax (01454) 201593,* ⛲, Fs, ⛽, ▣, 🛏, squash – ⬍ ⇔, ▤ rm, TV ✆ ♿ P – 🏃 200. MC AE ⓓ VISA
Meals a la carte 26.00/38.00 **st.** – **125 rm** ☕ 149.00/169.00 **st.**, 3 suites – SB.

Hilton Bristol, Ashridge Rd, BS32 4JF, North : 1 m. by A 38 ✆ (01454) 201144, *res.manager@bristol.stakis.co.uk, Fax (01454) 612022,* Fs, ⛽, ▣ – ⇔, ▤ rest, TV ✆ ♿ P – 🏃 200. MC AE ⓓ VISA. ✂
Meals *(closed lunch Saturday and Bank Holidays)* (carving rest.) 12.95/17.95 **t.** and dinner a la carte – ☕ 9.95 – **142 rm** 155.00/180.00 **st.** – SB.

at Cribbs Causeway *North : 6¾ m. on A 4018 – ✉ Bristol.*

Travelodge without rest., BS10 7TL, on A 4018 (northbound carriageway) ¼ m. before junction 17 of M 4 ✆ (0117) 501530, *Fax (0117) 501530* – ⇔ TV ♿ P. MC AE ⓓ VISA JCB. ✂ AV e
56 rm 49.95 **t.**

at Hambrook *(South Gloucestershire) Northeast : 5½ m. by M 32 on A 4174 – ✉ Bristol.*

Posthouse Bristol, Filton Rd, BS16 1QX, ✆ (0870) 400 9014, *Fax (0117) 956 9735,* Fs, ⛽, ▣, ♣ – ⬍, ⇔ rm, ▤ rest, TV P – 🏃 250. MC AE ⓓ VISA BV o
Meals *(closed Saturday lunch)* a la carte 27.85/30.85 **t.** 🍷 8.45 – ☕ 11.95 – **194 rm** 99.00/139.00 **t.**, 4 suites – SB.

at Mangotsfield *Northeast : 5¾ m. by M 32 on A 4174 –* **BV** *– ✉ Bristol.*

Travel Inn, 200-202 Westerleigh Rd, Emersons Green, BS16 7AN, East : ¾ m. off A 4174 ✆ (0117) 956 4755, *Fax (0117) 956 4644* – ⇔ rm, TV ♿ P. MC AE ⓓ VISA
Meals (grill rest.) – **40 rm** 40.95 **t.**

at Winterbourne *(South Gloucestershire) Northeast : 7½ m. by M 32 and A 4174 on B 4058 –* **BV** *– ✉ Bristol.*

Grange H. & Country Club, Northwoods, BS36 1RP, Northwest : 2 m. by B 4057 on B 4427 (Rudgeway rd) ✆ (01454) 777333, *Fax (01454) 777447,* ⛽, ▣, ♣ – ⇔ TV P – 🏃 150. MC AE ⓓ VISA
Meals *(closed Saturday lunch)* a la carte 19.00/26.25 **st.** 🍷 7.60 – ☕ 10.95 – **68 rm** 119.00/129.00 – SB.

at Wick *East : 7½ m. on A 420 – ✉ Bristol.*

Tracy Park Golf & Country Club ⛰, Bath Rd, BS30 5RN, Southeast : 1 m. on Lansdown rd ✆ (0117) 937 2251, *hotel@tracypark.com, Fax (0117) 937 4288,* « Part Georgian manor house », ⛳18, ♣, squash – ⇔ TV P – 🏃 120. MC VISA. ✂
Cavaliers Kitchen : **Meals** (dinner only) 17.95/26.45 **t.** and a la carte 🍷 7.00 – **18 rm** ☕ 35.00/75.00 **st.**

at Saltford *(Bath & North East Somerset) Southeast : 7½ m. on A 4 –* **BX** *– ✉ Bristol.*

Brunel's Tunnel House, High St., BS31 3BQ, off Beech Rd ✆ (01225) 873873, *info@brunelstunnelhouse.com, Fax (01225) 874875,* 🛏 – ⇔ TV P. MC AE VISA JCB. ✂
closed Christmas and New Year – **Meals** *(closed Friday to Sunday)* (by arrangement) (residents only) (dinner only) 17.00 **st.** 🍷 4.50 – **8 rm** ☕ 55.00/65.00 **st.**

at Chelwood *(Bath & North East Somerset) Southeast : 8½ m. by A 37 –* **BX** *– on A 368 – ✉ Bristol.*

Chelwood House, BS39 4NH, Southwest : ¾ m. on A 37 ✆ (01761) 490730, *chelwoodhouse.com, Fax (01761) 490072,* ⩽, 🛏 – ⇔ rest, TV P. MC AE VISA. ✂
Meals *(closed Sunday)* (dinner only) a la carte 21.50/31.00 **t.** 🍷 6.00 – **12 rm** ☕ 60.00/110.00 **t.**

at Hunstrete *(Bath & North East Somerset) Southeast : 10 m. by A 4 and A 37 –* **BX** *– off A 368 – ✉ Bristol.*

Hunstrete House ⛰, BS39 4NS, ✆ (01761) 490490, *reservations@hunstretehouse.co.uk, Fax (01761) 490732,* ⩽, ⛲, « Late 17C country house, gardens and deer park », ⛱ heated, 🎾 – ⇔ rest, TV P – 🏃 40. MC AE ⓓ VISA JCB. ✂
closed 3-11 January – **Meals** 15.95/19.95 **t.** (lunch) and a la carte 42.50/49.50 **t.** 🍷 9.75 – **21 rm** ☕ 125.00/195.00 **t.**, 1 suite – SB.

ENGLAND

at Stanton Wick *Bath & North East Somerset South : 9 m. by A 37 and A 368 on Stanton Wick rd – ✉ Bristol.*

Carpenters Arms, BS39 4BX, ✆ (01761) 490202, *carpenters@dial.pipex.com* *Fax (01761) 490763* – TV P. MC AE ① VISA
closed 25-26 December and 1 January **Meals** a la carte 17.20/24.40 **t.** 6.25 – **12 rm** 59.50/79.50 **t.** – SB.

BRITWELL SALOME *Oxon. – pop. 187.*

London 75 – Oxford 21 – Reading 19.

The Goose, OX9 5LG, ✆ (01491) 612304, *Fax (01491) 614822,* – P. MC VISA
closed Monday and Sunday dinner – **Meals** 10.00/30.00 **t.** and lunch a la carte 6.95.

BRIXHAM *Devon 403 J 32 The West Country G. – pop. 15 865.*

Env. : *Berry Head★ (≤★★★) NE : 1½ m.*

The Old Market House, The Quay ✆ (01803) 852861.

London 230 – Exeter 30 – Plymouth 32 – Torquay 8.

Berry Head ⛰, Berry Head Rd, TQ5 9AJ, ✆ (01803) 853225, *berryhd@aol.com* *Fax (01803) 882084,* ≤ Torbay, – rest, TV P – 300. MC AE VISA
Meals 12.00/20.00 **st.** and a la carte – **32 rm** 48.00/116.00 – SB.

Quayside, 41 King St., TQ5 9TJ, ✆ (01803) 855751, *quayside.hotel@virgin.net* *Fax (01803) 882733,* ≤ – rest, TV P. MC AE ① VISA JCB
Meals (bar lunch)/dinner 18.00 **st.** and a la carte 5.50 – **30 rm** 50.00/80.00 **st.** – SB.

BROAD CAMPDEN *Glos. –* *see Chipping Campden.*

BROADHEMBURY *Devon 403 K 31 – pop. 617 – ✉ Honiton.*

London 191 – Exeter 17 – Honiton 5 – Taunton 23.

Drewe Arms, EX14 3NF, ✆ (01404) 841267, *drewe.arms@btinternet.com* *Fax (01404) 841765,* « Part 13C thatched inn », – P. MC VISA
closed Sunday dinner – **Meals** - Seafood - 24.00 **t.** and a la carte 26.00/42.50 **t.** 9.50.

BROADWAY *Worcs. 403 404 O 27 Great Britain G. – pop. 2 328.*

See : *Town★.*

Env. : *Country Park (Broadway Tower ✻★★), SE : 2 m. by A 44 – Snowshill Manor★ (Terrace Garden★) AC, S : 2½ m.*

1 Cotswold Court ✆ (01386) 852937.

London 93 – Birmingham 36 – Cheltenham 15 – Worcester 22.

The Lygon Arms, High St., WR12 7DU, ✆ (01386) 852255, *info@the_lygon_arms.co.uk* *Fax (01386) 858611,* « Part 16C inn », – rest, TV P – 80 MC AE ① VISA JCB
The Restaurant : **Meals** 22.00/45.00 **t.** and a la carte 10.50 – (see also ***Oliver's*** below) – 9.20 – **61 rm** 110.00/250.00, 4 suites – SB.

The Broadway, The Green, WR12 7AA, ✆ (01386) 852401, *bookings@cotswold-inns-hotels.co.uk, Fax (01386) 853879,* « Part 15C », – TV P. MC AE VISA.
Meals 10.95/19.95 **st.** – **20 rm** 68.50/110.00 **t.** – SB.

Collin House ⛰, Collin Lane, WR12 7PB, Northwest : 1 ¼ m. by B 4632 at junction with A 44. ✆ (01386) 858354, *collin.house@virgin.net, Fax (01386) 858697,* « 17C », – rest TV P. MC AE VISA.
closed 24 to 28 December – **Meals** *(closed Sunday and Monday)* a la carte approx. 14.45 **t.** 8.85 – **6 rm** 69.00/120.00 **t.**

Barn House without rest., 152 High St., WR12 7AJ, ✆ (01386) 858633 *Fax (01386) 858633,* « 17C », – TV P
3 rm 35.00/75.00 **st.**, 1 suite.

Windrush House, Station Rd, WR12 7DE, ✆ (01386) 853577, *richard@broadway-windrush.co.uk,* – TV P
Meals 10.00/15.00 **s. 5 rm** 35.00/55.00 **s.**

Whiteacres without rest., Station Rd, WR12 7DE, ✆ (01386) 852320, *whiteacres@btinternet.com* – TV P.
closed 24-26 December – **5 rm** 40.00/54.00 **st.**

The Olive Branch without rest., 78 High St., WR12 7AJ, (01386) 853440, *broadway@theolive-branch.co.uk, Fax (01386) 859070* – VISA JCB – **8 rm** 35.00/65.00 **t.** – SB.

Oliver's, High St., WR12 7DU, (01386) 854418, *info@the-lygon-arms.co.uk, Fax (01386) 858611,* « 16C » – AE VISA JCB
Meals a la carte 17.40/23.85 **t.**

at Willersey Hill *(Glos.) East : 2 m. by A 44 – Broadway.*

Dormy House, WR12 7LF, (01386) 852711, *reservations@dormyhouse.co.uk, Fax (01386) 858636,* – rest, – 180. AE VISA JCB
closed 24 to 26 December – ***Tapestries :*** **Meals** *(closed Saturday lunch)* a la carte 31.35/39.90 **t.** 9.65 – ***Barn Owl :*** **Meals** a la carte 15.75/22.20 **t.** 9.65 – **45 rm** 75.00/150.00 **t.**, 3 suites – SB.

at Buckland *(Glos.) Southwest : 2 ¼ m. by B 4632 – Broadway.*

Buckland Manor, WR12 7LY, (01386) 852626, *buckland-manor-uk@msn.com, Fax (01386) 853557,* « Part 13C manor house in extensive gardens », heated, – rest, AE VISA.
Meals (booking essential to non-residents) 28.50 **t.** (lunch) and a la carte 40.75/52.00 **t.** 9.80 – **13 rm** 195.00/345.00 **t.** – SB.

at Wormington *(Glos.) Southwest : 4 ¼ m. by B 4632 on Wormington rd – Broadway.*

Leasow House without rest., Laverton Meadow, WR12 7NA, East : 1 ¼ m. (01386) 584526, *leasow@clara.net, Fax (01386) 584596,* – AE VISA
7 rm 43.00/65.00 **st.**

The Guide is updated annually so renew your Guide every year.

BROCKDISH *Norfolk* 404 X 26 – *see Diss.*

BROCKENHURST *Hants.* 403 404 P 31 *Great Britain G. – pop. 3 048.*
Env. : *New Forest★★ (Rhinefield Ornamental Drive★★, Bolderwood Ornamental Drive★★).*
Brockenhurst Manor, Sway Rd (01590) 623332.
London 99 – Bournemouth 17 – Southampton 14 – Winchester 27.

Rhinefield House, Rhinefield Rd, SO42 7QB, Northwest : 3 m. (01590) 622922, *Fax (01590) 622800,* « Victorian country mansion, formal gardens », heated, – – 120. AE VISA.
Armada : **Meals** 16.95/25.50 **st.** and dinner a la carte 9.50 – **34 rm** 90.00/125.00 **st.** – SB.

New Park Manor, Lyndhurst Rd, SO42 7QH, North : 1 ½ m. on A 337 (01590) 623467, *enquiries@newparkmanorhotel.co.uk, Fax (01590) 622268,* heated, – – 150. AE VISA
Stag : **Meals** 14.00/27.00 **t.** and dinner a la carte 14.80 – **24 rm** 80.00/160.00 **t.**

Careys Manor, Lyndhurst Rd, SO42 7RH, on A 337 (01590) 623551, *careysmanorhotel@btinternet.com, Fax (01590) 622799,* – – 100. AE VISA
Meals 13.95/24.95 **t.** and a la carte 7.95 – ***Blaireau's*** *((01590) 623032)* **: Meals** - French - 7.95/11.95 **t.** and a la carte 6.95 – **78 rm** 79.00/129.00 **st.**, 1 suite – SB.

Whitley Ridge, Beaulieu Rd, SO42 7QL, East : 1 m. on B 3055 (01590) 622354, *whitleyridge@brockenhurst.co.uk, Fax (01590) 622856,* « Part Georgian », – rest, AE VISA
Meals (bar lunch Monday to Saturday)/dinner 23.50/25.00 **st.** and a la carte 8.00 – **14 rm** 70.00/126.00 – SB.

Cloud, Meerut Rd, SO42 7TD, (01590) 622165, *enquiries@cloudhotel.co.uk, Fax (01590) 622818,* – rest, VISA
closed 27 December-19 January – **Meals** 7.95/25.00 **t.** – **18 rm** 75.00/150.00 **t.** – SB.

Cottage without rest., Sway Rd, SO42 7SH, (01590) 622296, *100604.22@compuserve.com, Fax (01590) 623014,* – VISA
March-November – **7 rm** 60.00/90.00 **t.**

Simply Poussin, The Courtyard, rear of 49-51 Brookley Rd, SO42 7RB, (01590) 623063, *sales@simplypoussin.co.uk, Fax (01590) 623144* – AE VISA.
closed 2 weeks January, Sunday and Monday – **Meals** (booking essential) 10.50/25.00 **t.** 12.50.

Thatched Cottage with rm, 16 Brookley Rd, SO42 7RR, (01590) 623090, *sales@thatchedcottage.co.uk, Fax (01590) 623479,* « 17C farmhouse » – rest, AE VISA JCB
closed 1 January-12 February – **Meals** *(closed Sunday dinner and Monday)* (booking essential) (light lunch)/dinner 15.00/36.00 **t.** 9.00 – **5 rm** 70.00/170.00 **st.** – SB.

at Sway *Southwest : 3 m. by B 3055 – ✉ Lymington.*

String of Horses Country House, Mead End Road, SO41 6EH, ✆ (01590) 682631 *relax@stringofhorses.co.uk, Fax (01590) 682911*, heated, – rest, TV P. MC AE VISA JCB.
Meals *(closed Sunday dinner)* (dinner only and Sunday lunch) 14.50/23.00 and a la carte 9.50 – **8 rm** 70.00/118.00 **st.** – SB.

Nurse's Cottage, Station Rd, SO41 6BA, ✆ (01590) 683402, *nurses.cottage@lineone.ne, Fax (01590) 683402*, – TV P. MC AE VISA JCB
closed 2 weeks March, 3 weeks November – **Meals** (dinner only and Sunday lunch)/dinne 19.75 **t.** 8.15 – **3 rm** 55.00/95.00 **t.** – SB.

BROMBOROUGH *Mersey.* 402 403 L 24 – *pop. 14 518* – ✉ *Wirral.*
Raby Hall Rd ✆ (0151) 334 2155.
London 210 – Chester 14 – Liverpool 6 – Manchester 46.

The Village H. & Leisure Club, Pool Lane, CH62 4UE, on A 41 ✆ (0151) 643 1616 *Fax (0151) 643 1420*, squash – rest, TV P – 150. MC AE VISA
Meals 12.95 **t.** and a la carte – **93 rm** 89.00/99.00 **t.**

Travel Inn, High St., L62 7HZ, ✆ (0151) 334 2917, *Fax (0151) 334 0443* – rm, TV P – 80. MC AE VISA.
Meals (grill rest.) – **32 rm** 40.95 **t.**

Jährlich eine neue Ausgabe
Aktuellste Informationen, jährlich für Sie!

BROME *Suffolk* 404 X 26 – *see Diss (Norfolk).*

BROMFIELD *Shrops.* 403 L 26 – *see Ludlow.*

BROMLEY CROSS *Gtr. Manchester* 402 404 M 23 – *see Bolton.*

BROMSGROVE *Worcs.* 403 404 N 26 – *pop. 26 366.*
Bromsgrove Museum, 26 Birmingham Rd ✆ (01527) 831809.
London 117 – Birmingham 14 – Bristol 71 – Worcester 13.

Hilton Bromsgrove, Birmingham Rd, B61 0JB, North : 2 ½ m. on A 38 ✆ (0121) 447 7888, *Fax (0121) 447 7273*, – rm, rest, TV P – 250. MC AE VISA
Meals *(closed Saturday lunch)* (carving lunch) 13.50/17.00 **st.** and a la carte – 9.50 – **146 rm** 150.00/170.00 **st.**, 2 suites – SB.

Hanover International, 85 Kidderminster Rd, B61 9AB, West : 1 m. on A 448 ✆ (01527) 576600, *Fax (01527) 878981*, – rest, TV P – 200. MC AE VISA.
Meals (closed Saturday lunch) a la carte 15.40/21.70 **st.** 8.25 – 9.75 – **113 rm** 115.00/130.00 **st.**, 1 suite – SB.

Grafton Manor, Grafton Lane, B61 7HA, Southwest : 1 ¾ m. by Worcester Rd ✆ (01527) 579007, *steven@grafton.u-net.com, Fax (01527) 575221*, « 16C and 18C manor », – rest, TV P. MC AE VISA.
Meals (lunch by arrangement) 18.50/29.50 **st.** 10.40 – **7 rm** 85.00/125.00 **st.**, 2 suites – SB.

Bromsgrove Country, 249 Worcester Rd, Stoke Heath, B61 7JA, Southwest : 2 m ✆ (01527) 835522, *Fax (01527) 871257*, – TV P. MC VISA.
closed 1 week August and 2 weeks Christmas – **Meals** (residents only) (dinner only a la carte approx. 12.00 **st.** 6.00 – 6.00 – **7 rm** 49.00/55.00 **st.**

BROMYARD *Herefordshire* 403 404 M 27 – *pop. 3 117.*
T.I.C. & Heritage Centre, 1 Rowberry St. ✆ (01684) 482038.
London 138 – Hereford 15 – Leominster 13 – Worcester 14.

Granary, Church House Farm, Collington, HR7 4NA, North : 4 ¼ m. by B 4214, Edvin Loach rd and Ripplewood rd ✆ (01885) 410345, *Fax (01885) 410555*, « Working farm », – TV P.
closed 2 weeks November – **Meals** (by arrangement) 17.00 **t.** – **5 rm** 22.50/44.00 **t.**

at Acton Green *Southeast : 4 ¾ m. by A 44 on B 4220 – ✉ Bromyard.*

Hidelow House, Acton Beauchamp, WR6 5AH, South : ¼ m. ☎ (01886) 884547, *mg@hidelow.co.uk, Fax (01886) 884060*, – TV P.
closed 25-26 December – **Meals** (by arrangement) (communal dining) 14.50 **st.** – **3 rm** 30.50/61.00 **st**

BROOK *Hants.* 403 404 P 31 – *✉ Lyndhurst.*
London 92 – Bournemouth 24 – Southampton 14.

Bell Inn, SO43 7HE, ☎ (023) 8081 2214, *bell@bramshaw.co.uk, Fax (023) 8081 3958*, 18 – TV P – 40. MC AE VISA.
Meals (bar lunch Monday to Saturday)/dinner 20.00/26.50 **t.** 8.50 – **26 rm** 57.00/85.00 **t.** – SB.

BROOKMANS PARK *Herts.* 404 T 28 – *pop. 3 315.*
London 21 – Luton 21.

Villa Rosa, 3 Great North Rd, AL9 6LB, Southeast : 1 ¾ m. on A 1000 ☎ (01707) 651444, *Fax (01707) 654970* – P. MC AE VISA JCB
closed 3 weeks August, 25 December, Saturday lunch, Sunday and Bank Holidays – **Meals** - Italian - a la carte 16.00/28.80 **t.** 5.00.

BROUGHTON *Lancs.* 402 L 22 – *see Preston.*

BROXTED *Essex* 404 U 28 – *see Stansted Airport.*

BROXTON *Ches.* 402 403 L 24 – *pop. 417.*
London 197 – Birmingham 68 – Chester 12 – Manchester 44 – Stoke-on-Trent 29.

Carden Park, CH3 9DQ, West : 1 ½ m. on A 534 ☎ (01829) 731000, *sales@cardenpark.co.uk, Fax (01829) 731032*, 18 – rest, TV P – 400. MC AE VISA.
***Garden Restaurant* : Meals** (dinner only and Sunday lunch) 25.00 **t.** and a la carte 9.50 – ***Brasserie Renard* : Meals** a la carte 17.65/26.40 **t.** 9.50 – 10.95 – **179 rm** 110.00/125.00 **st.**, 13 suites – SB.

Broxton Hall Country House, Whitchurch Rd, CH3 9JS, on A 41 at junction with A 534 ☎ (01829) 782321, *reservation@broxtonhall.co.uk, Fax (01829) 782330*, « Part 17C timbered house, antiques », – TV P. MC AE VISA JCB
closed 25-26 December and 1 January – **Meals** 18.00/26.50 **t.** (dinner) and lunch a la carte 13.00/25.00 **t.** 6.25 – **10 rm** 65.00/130.00 **t.**

BRUTON *Somerset* 403 404 M 30 *The West Country G.* – *pop. 2 111.*
Exc. : *Stourhead★★★ AC, W : 8 m. by B 3081.*
London 118 – Bristol 27 – Bournemouth 44 – Salisbury 35 – Taunton 36.

Truffles, 95 High St., BA10 0AR, ☎ (01749) 812255, *trufflesbruton@tinyworld.co.uk, Fax (01749) 812255* – MC VISA
closed 2 weeks February, 1 week October, Sunday dinner and Monday – **Meals** (dinner only and Sunday lunch)/dinner 23.95 **st.** 6.50.

BRYHER *Cornwall* 403 ㉚ – *see Scilly (Isles of).*

BUCKDEN *Cambs.* 404 T 27 – *pop. 2 534* – *✉ Huntingdon.*
London 65 – Bedford 15 – Cambridge 20 – Northampton 31.

George, High St., PE18 9XA, ☎ (01480) 810307, *Fax (01480) 811274* – rest, TV P. MC AE VISA.
Meals a la carte 14.10/18.65 **t.** – **16 rm** 42.00 **st.** – SB.

BUCKINGHAM *Bucks.* 403 404 Q27 *Great Britain G.* – *pop. 10 168.*
Env. : *Stowe Gardens★★, NW : 3 m. by minor rd.*
Exc. : *Claydon House★ AC, S : 8 m. by A 413.*
18 *Silverstone, Silverstone Rd, Stowe ☎ (01280) 850005* – 18 *Tingewick Rd ☎ (01280) 813282.*
London 64 – Birmingham 61 – Northampton 20 – Oxford 25.

Villiers, 3 Castle St., MK18 1BS, ✆ (01280) 822444, *villiers-hotels@demon.co.uk* *Fax (01280) 822113* – |≡| TV P – 200. MC AE ① VISA. ✂
Meals – (see ***Henry's*** below) – **34 rm** ⊐ 105.00/120.00 **st.**, 4 suites – SB.

Buckingham Four Pillars, Buckingham Ring Rd, MK18 1RY, South : 1 ¼ m. by Bridge St. on A 421 ✆ (01280) 822622, *enquiries@four-pillars.co.uk, Fax (01280) 823074,* – rest, TV P – 160. MC AE ① VISA
Meals (dancing Saturday evening) (carving lunch Sunday) 7.95/18.95 **st.** and dinner a la carte 5.25 – ⊐ 8.75 – **70 rm** 85.00/95.00 **st.** – SB.

Henry's (at Villiers H.), 3 Castle St., MK18 1BS, ✆ (01280) 822444, *Fax (01280) 822113* – P. MC AE ① VISA
closed Sunday dinner – **Meals** (dinner only and Sunday lunch)/dinner 26.50 **st** and a la carte 10.00.

BUCKLAND *Glos.* 403 404 O 27 – *see Broadway (Worcestershire).*

BUCKLAND *Oxon.* 403 404 P 28 – ✉ *Faringdon.*
London 78 – Oxford 16 – Swindon 15.

Lamb Inn with rm, Lamb Lane, SN7 8QN, ✆ (01367) 870484, *Fax (01367) 870675,* – rest, TV P. MC AE VISA JCB. ✂
closed 25 and 26 December – **Meals** a la carte 12.45/34.50 **t.** – **4 rm** ⊐ 39.00/58.00 **t.**

BUCKLERS HARD *Hants.* 403 404 P 31 – *see Beaulieu.*

BUDE *Cornwall* 403 G 31 *The West Country G.* – *pop. 3 681.*
See : *The Breakwater★★ – Compass Point (≤★).*
Env. : *Poughill★ (church★★), N : 2½ m. – E : Tamar River★★ – Kilkhampton (Church★), NE : 5½ m. by A 39 – Stratton (Church★), E : 1½ m. – Launcells (Church★), E : 3 m. by A 3072 – Marhamchurch (St. Morwenne's Church★), SE : 2½ m. by A 39 – Poundstock★ (≤★★, church★, guildhouse★), S : 4½ m. by A 39.*
Exc. : *Morwenstow (cliffs★★, church★), N : 8½ m. by A 39 and minor roads – Jacobstow (Church★), S : 7 m. by A 39.*
Burn View ✆ (01288) 352006.
Bude Visitor Centre, The Crescent ✆ (01288) 354240.
London 252 – Exeter 51 – Plymouth 50 – Truro 53.

Falcon, Breakwater Rd, EX23 8SD, ✆ (01288) 352005, *reception@falconhotel.com* *Fax (01288) 356359,* ≤, – rest, TV P – 60. MC AE ① VISA
closed 25 December – **Meals** (bar lunch Monday to Saturday)/dinner 17.50/20.00 **st** and a la carte – **26 rm** ⊐ 40.00/84.00 **st.** – SB.

Hartland, Hartland Terr., EX23 8JY, ✆ (01288) 355661, *hartlandhotel@aol.com* *Fax (01288) 355664,* ≤, heated – |≡|, rm, TV P
March-November – **Meals** (bar lunch)/dinner 20.00/22.00 **t.** 5.50 – **28 rm** ⊐ 50.00/84.00 **t.**

Cliff, Crooklets Beach, EX23 8NG, ✆ (01288) 353110, *Fax (01288) 353110,* – rest, TV P. MC VISA JCB
March-October – **Meals** (bar lunch)/dinner 12.50 **st.** 3.80 – **15 rm** ⊐ (dinner included) 40.20/93.00 **st.**

Camelot, DownsView, EX23 8RE, ✆ (01288) 352361, *stay@camelot-hotel.co.uk* *Fax (01288) 355470* – TV P. MC AE VISA JCB. ✂
closed Christmas-New Year – **Meals** (dinner only) 17.50 **t.** 5.25 – **24 rm** ⊐ 34.00/68.00 **t.** – SB.

Bude Haven, Flexbury Av., EX23 8NS, ✆ (01288) 352305, *Fax (01258) 352305* – TV P. MC VISA. ✂
closed 2 weeks January – **Meals** (bar lunch)/dinner a la carte 12.75/21.65 **t.** 3.50 – **11 rm** ⊐ 27.50/70.00 **t.** – SB.

BUDLEIGH SALTERTON *Devon* 403 K 32 *The West Country G. – pop. 3 759.*

Env. : *East Budleigh (Church★), N : 2½ m. by A 376 – Bicton★ (Gardens★)* **AC**, *N : 3 m. by A 376.*

18 *East Devon, North View Rd ☎ (01395) 442018.*

Fore St. ☎ (01395) 445275.

London 182 – Exeter 16 – Plymouth 55.

Long Range, 5 Vales Rd, EX9 6HS, by Raleigh Rd ☎ (01395) 443321, *long.range@eclipse.co.uk, Fax (01395) 445220,* – TV P. MC VISA.
Meals 17.50 **t.** 6.80 – **7 rm** 30.00/65.00 **t.**

BUDOCK WATER *Cornwall – see Falmouth.*

BUNBURY *Ches.* 402 403 404 M 24 – *see Tarporley.*

BURFORD *Oxon.* 403 404 P 28 – *pop. 1 171.*

18 *☎ (01993) 822583.*

The Brewery, Sheep St. ☎ (01993) 823558.

London 76 – Birmingham 55 – Gloucester 32 – Oxford 20.

Bay Tree, 12-14 Sheep St., OX18 4LW, ☎ (01993) 822791, *bookings@cotswold-inns-hotels.co.uk, Fax (01993) 823008,* « 16C house, antique furnishings », – rest, TV P – 30. MC AE VISA.
Meals *(closed Saturday lunch)* 15.95/25.95 **st.** and dinner a la carte – **19 rm** 90.00/165.00 **t.**, 2 suites – SB.

Lamb Inn, Sheep St., OX18 4LR, ☎ (01993) 823155, *Fax (01993) 822228,* « Part 14C, antique furnishings », – rest, TV. MC VISA JCB
closed 25 and 26 December – **Meals** (bar lunch Monday to Saturday)/dinner 25.00/27.00 **t.** 6.50 – **15 rm** 70.00/120.00 **t.** – SB.

Burford House without rest., 99 High St., OX18 4QA, ☎ (01993) 823151, *Fax (01993) 823240,* « Part 17C », – TV. MC AE VISA.
closed 2 weeks February – **7 rm** 75.00/120.00 **t.**

Golden Pheasant, 91 High St., OX18 4QA, ☎ (01993) 823223, *Fax (01993) 822621* – rest, TV P. MC AE VISA.
Meals (bar lunch Monday to Saturday)/dinner a la carte 14.40/26.50 **t.** 9.00 – **12 rm** 70.00/85.00 **t.** – SB.

Inn For All Seasons, The Barringtons, OX18 4TN, West : 3 ¼ m. on A 40 ☎ (01451) 844324, *Fax (01451) 844375,* – TV P – 35. MC AE VISA
Meals a la carte 13.95/26.95 **st.** 7.50 – **10 rm** 52.50/115.00 **st.** – SB.

Travelodge, Bury Barn, OX7 5TB, on A 40 (Burford roundabout) ☎ (01993) 822699 – rm, TV P. MC AE VISA JCB.
Meals (grill rest.) – **40 rm** 49.95 **t.**

BURGH-LE-MARSH *Lincs.* 402 404 U24 – *pop. 2 718.*

London 110 – Boston 29 – Great Grimsby 38 – Lincoln 40.

Windmill, 46 High St., PE24 5JT, ☎ (01754) 810281, *Fax (01754) 811011* – P. MC AE VISA
closed Sunday dinner, and Monday – **Meals** (dinner only and Sunday lunch)/dinner a la carte 17.50/20.95 **st.** 7.00.

BURLEY *Hants.* 403 404 O 31 *Great Britain G. – pop. 1 438 – ✉ Ringwood.*

Env. : *New Forest★★ (Rhinefield Ornamental Drive★★, Bolderwood Ornamental Drive★★).*

London 102 – Bournemouth 17 – Southampton 17 – Winchester 30.

The Burley Inn, The Cross, BH24 4AB, ☎ (01425) 403448, *Fax (01425) 402058* – TV P. MC VISA
closed 25 December – **Meals** a la carte 13.50/24.50 **t.** 5.00 – **9 rm** 45.00/75.00 **t.**

BURLEY IN WHARFEDALE *W. Yorks.* 402 O 22 – *pop. 5 528.*

London 218 – Bradford 14 – Harrogate 15 – Leeds 14 – Preston 52.

David Woolley's, 78 Main St., LS29 7BT, ☎ (01943) 864602, *david@davidwoolleysrestaurant.co.uk* – P. MC VISA
closed 25 December, 1 January, Sunday and Bank Holidays – **Meals** (dinner only) 12.50/16.00 **t.** and a la carte 5.00.

BURNHAM *Bucks.* 404 S 29 – *pop. 11 169.*
London 33 – Oxford 37 – Reading 17.

County H. Burnham Beeches, Grove Rd, SL1 8DP, Northwest : 1 m. by Britwell Rd *(01628) 429955, Fax (01628) 603994*, – rm, – 180. *VISA*.
closed 27-30 December – ***Grays :*** **Meals** *(closed Saturday lunch)* 19.50/25.00 **t.** and a la carte 9.50 – 12.50 – **80 rm** 120.00/160.00 **t.**, 2 suites – SB.

BURNHAM MARKET *Norfolk* 404 W 25 *Great Britain G. – pop. 898.*
Env. : *Holkham Hall★★ AC, E : 3 m. by B 1155.*
18 Lambourne, Dropmore Rd (01628) 666755.
London 128 – Cambridge 71 – Norwich 36.

Hoste Arms, The Green, PE31 8HD, (01328) 738777, *thehostearms@compuserve.com* *Fax (01328) 730103*, « 17C inn », – *VISA*
Meals – (see ***The Restaurant*** below) – **28 rm** 64.00/86.00 **t.** – SB.

Railway Inn, Creake Rd, PE31 8EN, (01328) 730505, *thehostearms@compuserve.com* *Fax (01328) 730103* – *VISA*
Meals – (see ***The Restaurant*** below) – **6 rm** 38.00/48.00 **t.** – SB.

The Restaurant (at Hoste Arms H.), The Green, PE31 8HD, (01328) 738777 *Fax (01328) 730103*, – *VISA*
Meals (booking essential) a la carte 14.55/27.80 **t.** 7.25.

When visiting the West Country,
*use the **Michelin Green Guide*** **"The West Country of England".**
- *Detailed descriptions of places of interest*
- *Touring programmes by county*
- *Maps and street plans*
- *The history of the region*
- *Photographs and drawings of monuments, beauty spots, houses...*

BURNHAM-ON-CROUCH *Essex* 404 W 29 – *pop. 7 067.*
Burnham-on-Crouch, Ferry Rd, Creeksea (01621) 782282.
London 52 – Chelmsford 19 – Colchester 32 – Southend-on-Sea 25.

Contented Sole, 80 High St., CM0 8AA, (01621) 782139 – *VISA*
closed Christmas-New Year, last 2 weeks July, Sunday dinner and Monday – **Meals** (dinner only and Sunday lunch)/dinner 15.95 **t.** and a la carte 6.50.

BURNLEY *Lancs.* 402 N 22 – *pop. 74 661.*
18, 9 Towneley, Towneley Park, Todmorden Rd (01282) 451636 – 18 Glen View (01282) 421045.
Burnley Mechanics, Manchester Rd (01282) 455485.
London 236 – Bradford 32 – Leeds 37 – Liverpool 55 – Manchester 25 – Middlesbrough 10. – Preston 22 – Sheffield 68.

Oaks, Colne Rd, Reedley, BB10 2LF, Northeast : 2 ½ m. on A 56 (01282) 414141, *oaks@hireinns.co.uk, Fax (01282) 433401*, – rm, – 120. *VISA*
Quills : **Meals** (dinner only) a la carte 24.00/32.00 **st.** – ***Archives Brasserie :*** **Meals** (lunch only) a la carte 6.00 **st.** – **51 rm** 96.00/116.00 **st.** – SB.

Rosehill House, Rosehill Av., Manchester Rd, BB11 2PW, South : 1 ¼ m. by A 56 (01282) 453931, *rosehillhousehotel@fsmail.net, Fax (01282) 455628*, – rest, *VISA* JCB
closed 1 January – **Meals** a la carte 17.00/23.00 **t.** 6.95 – **23 rm** 40.00/75.00 **t.**, 2 suites

The Alexander, 2 Tarleton Av., off Todmorden Rd, BB11 3ET, Southeast : ¾ m. on A 67 (01282) 422684, *phleisure@aol.com, Fax (01282) 424094*, – *VISA*.
Meals 7.95/13.95 **st.** and a la carte – **16 rm** 42.00/53.00 **st.** – SB.

Travel Inn, Queen Victoria, Queen Victoria Rd, BB10 3EF, Northeast : ¾ m. on A 611 (01282) 450250, *Fax (01282) 452811* – rm, rest, – 40. *VISA*.
Meals (grill rest.) – **40 rm** 40.95 **t.**

Travelodge, Cavalry Barracks, Barracks Rd, BB11 4AS, West : ½ m. at junction of A 67 with A 679 (01282) 416039, *Fax (01282) 416039* – rm, *VISA* JCB.
Meals (grill rest.) – **32 rm** 39.95 **t.**

BURNSALL *N. Yorks.* 402 O 21 – *pop. 108* – ✉ *Skipton.*

London 223 – Bradford 26 – Leeds 29.

Red Lion, BD23 6BU, ☎ (01756) 720204, *redlion@daelnet.co.uk, Fax (01756) 720292,* ≤, « Part 16C inn », – ⇔ TV P. MC AE ① VISA JCB. ✂
Meals – (see ***The Restaurant*** below) – **11 rm** ☐ (dinner included) 75.00/150.00 **st.** – SB.

Devonshire Fell with rm, BD23 6BT, ☎ (01756) 729000, *sales@thedevonshirearms.co.uk, Fax (01756) 729009,* ≤, – ⇔ TV ☎ P – 🏛 50. MC AE ① VISA
Meals a la carte 18.50/22.00 **st.** – **10 rm** ☐ 70.00/120.00 **st.**, 2 suites – SB.

The Restaurant (at Red Lion H.), BD23 6BU, ☎ (01756) 720204, *Fax (01756) 720292,* « Part 16C inn » – ⇔ P. MC AE ① VISA JCB
Meals (bar lunch Monday to Saturday)/dinner 25.95 **t.** 6.95.

BURNT YATES *N. Yorks.* – *see Ripley.*

BURPHAM *W. Sussex* 404 S 30 – *see Arundel.*

BURRINGTON *Devon* 403 I 31 – *pop. 533.*

London 260 – Barnstaple 14 – Exeter 28 – Taunton 50.

Northcote Manor ⛰, EX37 9LZ, Northwest : 2 m. on A 377 ☎ (01769) 560501, *rest@northcotemanor.co.uk, Fax (01769) 560770,* ≤, « 17C manor house », , , – ⇔ rest, TV P. MC AE ① VISA
Meals (booking essential) (dinner only) 32.00/35.00 **t.** – **10 rm** ☐ (dinner included) 138.75/200.00 **t.**, 1 suite – SB.

BURSLEM *Stoke-on-Trent* 402 403 404 N 24 – *see Stoke-on-Trent.*

BURSTALL *Suffolk* – *see Ipswich.*

BURTON-IN-KENDAL SERVICE AREA *Cumbria* 402 L 21 – ✉ *Carnforth.*

Travelodge without rest., LA6 1JF, on M 6 northbound carriageway between junctions 35 and 36 ☎ (01524) 784012, *Fax (01524) 784014* – ⇔ TV ♿ P. MC AE ① VISA JCB. ✂
47 rm 49.95 **t.**

BURTON-ON-THE-WOLDS *Leics.* 402 403 404 Q 25 – *see Loughborough.*

BURTON-UPON-TRENT *Staffs.* 402 403 404 O 25 – *pop. 60 525.*

18 Branston G. & C.C., Burton Rd ☎ (01283) 512211 – 18 Craythorne, Craythorne Rd, Stretton ☎ (01283) 564329.

183 High St. ☎ (01283) 516609.

London 128 – Birmingham 29 – Leicester 27 – Nottingham 27 – Stafford 27.

Stanhope Arms, Ashby Road East, DE15 0PU, Southeast : 2 ½ m. on A 511 ☎ (01283) 217954, *info@stanhopearmshotel.com, Fax (01283) 226199,* – ▤ rest, TV P – 🏛 150. MC VISA. ✂
Meals (grill rest.) a la carte 10.00/22.00 **st.** – ☐ 5.95 – **24 rm** 47.50 **st.**

Express by Holiday Inn without rest., 2nd Av., Centrum 100, DE14 2WF, Southwest : 2 m. by A 5121 ☎ (01283) 504300, *Fax (01283) 504301* – |♦| ⇔ TV ☎ ♿ P – 🏛 60. MC AE ① VISA JCB
82 rm 57.50 **st.**

Travelodge, DE13 8EH, Southwest : 4 ¾ m. by A 5121 on A 38 (southbound carriageway) ☎ (01283) 716784, *Fax (01283) 716784* – ⇔ rm, TV ♿ P. MC AE ① VISA JCB. ✂
Meals (grill rest.) – **40 rm** 39.95 **t.**

Travelodge, DE13 8EG, Southwest : 5 ¼ m. by A 5121 on A 38 (northbound carriageway) ☎ (01283) 716343, *Fax (01283) 716343* – ⇔ rm, TV ♿ P. MC AE ① VISA JCB. ✂
Meals (grill rest.) – **20 rm** 39.95 **t.**

at Stretton *North : 3½ m. by A 50 off A 5121* – ✉ *Burton-upon-Trent.*

Dovecliff Hall ⛰ with rm, Dovecliff Rd, DE13 0DJ, Northeast : 1 m. ☎ (01283) 531818, *Fax (01283) 516546,* ≤, « Restored Georgian house, gardens », , – ⇔ TV P. MC AE VISA JCB. ✂
closed 28 May-1 June – **Meals** *(closed Monday and Saturday lunch and Sunday dinner)* 15.50/24.50 **t.** and a la carte 9.50 – **7 rm** ☐ 65.00/130.00 **t.** – SB.

ENGLAND

at Newton Solney *Northeast : 3 m. by A 50 on B 5008 – ✉ Burton-upon-Trent.*

Jarvis Newton Park, Newton Rd, DE15 0SS, ☎ (01283) 703568, *Fax (01283) 703214,* – ⇅ ⇔ TV P – 100. MC AE ① VISA.
Meals (bar lunch Monday to Saturday)/dinner 18.50 **st.** and a la carte 11.00 – ☐ 8.95 – **50 rm** 105.00/165.00 **st.** – SB.

at Barton-under-Needwood *Southwest : 6 m. by A 5121 on B 5016 – ✉ Burton-upon-Trent.*

Fairfield without rest., 55 Main St., DE13 8AB, ☎ (01283) 716396, *bookings@fairfield.f25 com, Fax (01283) 716396* – ⇔ TV P. MC VISA.
closed 25 and 26 December – – **3 rm** ☐ 35.00/45.00 **st.**

BURTONWOOD SERVICE AREA *Ches.* 402 M23 – ✉ *Warrington.*
Liverpool 16.

Days Inn, WA5 3AX, M 62 (westbound carriageway) ☎ (01925) 710376, Reservations (Freephone) 0800 0280400, *Fax (01925) 710378* – ⇔ rm, TV & P. MC AE ① VISA
Meals (grill rest.) a la carte 8.65/13.90 **t.** – ☐ 7.45 – **40 rm** 39.95/44.00 **t.**

BURY *Gtr. Manchester* 402 N 23 403 ③ 404 N 23 – *pop. 62 633.*
Greenmount ☎ (01204) 883712.
The Mets Art Centre, Market St. ☎ (0161) 253 5111.
London 211 – Leeds 45 – Liverpool 35 – Manchester 9.

Bolholt Country Park, Walshaw Rd, BL8 1PU, Northeast : ¾ m. by B 621 ☎ (0161) 762 4000, *enquiries@bolholt.co.uk, Fax (0161) 762 4100,* – ⇔ rm, TV P – 300. MC AE ① VISA
Meals 15.00/35.00 **st.** and dinner a la carte 8.90 – **66 rm.** ☐ 64.00/89.00 **st.**

Est, Est, Est, 703 Manchester Rd, BL9 9SS, South : 2 m. on A 56 ☎ (0161) 766 4869 *Fax (0161) 796 5338* – P. MC AE ① VISA JCB
closed 25-26 December, 1 January and Saturday lunch – **Meals** - Italian - a la carte 13.10/19.85 **t.** 6.85.

at Walmersley *North : 1 ¾ m. on A 56 – ✉ Bury.*

Red Hall, Manchester Rd, BL9 5NA, North : 1 ¼ m. on A 56 ☎ (01706) 822476 *Fax (01706) 828086* – ⇔ TV P – 40. MC AE ① VISA.
closed Christmas and New Year – **Meals** *(closed lunch Monday and Saturday)* 11.25/14.20 **t** (dinner) and a la carte 12.20/20.45 **t.** 5.80 – **20 rm** ☐ 53.00/66.00 **st.**

BURY ST. EDMUNDS *Suffolk* 404 W 27 *Great Britain G.* – *pop. 31 237.*
See : *Town★ – Abbey and Cathedral★.*
Env. : *Ickworth House★ AC, SW : 3 m. by A 143.*
18 Suffolk G. & C.C., St. John's Hill Plantation, The Street, Fornham All Saints ☎ (01284) 706777.
6 Angel Hill ☎ (01284) 764667.
London 79 – Cambridge 27 – Ipswich 26 – Norwich 41.

Angel, 3 Angel Hill, IP33 1LT, ☎ (01284) 714000, *sales@theangel.co.uk, Fax (01284) 71400* – ⇔ rm, TV P – 140. MC AE ① VISA JCB
Abbeygate : **Meals** 15.00/35.00 **t.** – ***The Vaults :*** **Meals** 13.00/19.00 **t.** 7.15 – ☐ 11.95 – **42 rm** 68.00/98.00 **t.**, 1 suite – SB.

Priory, Tollgate, IP32 6EH, North : 1 ¾ m. on A 1101 ☎ (01284) 766181, *reservations@prioryhotel.co.uk, Fax (01284) 767604,* – ⇔ TV P – 60. MC AE ① VISA JCB
Meals *(closed Saturday lunch)* 15.50/23.25 **st.** and a la carte 8.95 – **39 rm** ☐ 75.00/113.00 **st.** – SB.

Butterfly, Symonds Rd, IP32 7BW, Southeast : 1 ½ m. by A 1302 and A 134 at junction with A 14 ☎ (01284) 760884, *burybutterfly@lineone.net, Fax (01284) 755476* – ⇔ rm, TV & P – 60. MC AE ① VISA JCB
Meals 15.00 **st.** and a la carte 7.50 – ☐ 7.50 – **65 rm** 67.50 **st.** – SB.

Ounce House without rest., Northgate St., IP33 1HP, ☎ (01284) 761779, *pott@globalnet.co.uk, Fax (01284) 768315,* – ⇔ TV P. MC AE ① VISA.
3 rm ☐ 65.00/95.00 **st.**

The Abbey without rest., 35 Southgate St., IP33 2AZ, ☎ (01284) 762020, *reservations@theabbeyhotel.demon.co.uk, Fax (01284) 724770* – ⇔ TV P. MC AE ① VISA.
10 rm ☐ 55.00/75.00 **t.**, 2 suites.

Maison Bleue, 30-31 Churchgate St., IP33 1RG, ☎ (01284) 760623, *Fax (01284) 761611* – ⇔. MC AE VISA JCB
closed3 weeks January and Sunday – **Meals** - Seafood - 14.95/18.95 **t.** and a la carte 7.20

at Ixworth *Northeast : 7 m. by A 143 – ✉ Bury St. Edmunds.*

XX **Theobalds,** 68 High St., IP31 2HJ, ☏ (01359) 231707, *Fax (01359) 231707*, « Part 17C cottage » – MC VISA
closed 2 weeks August, Saturday lunch, Sunday dinner and Monday – **Meals** a la carte 26.95/32.65 **t.**

at Rougham Green *Southeast : 4 m. by A 1302 and A 134 off A 14 – ✉ Bury St. Edmunds.*

Ravenwood Hall, IP30 9JA, ☏ (01359) 270345, *enquiries.ravenwoodhall.co.uk, Fax (01359) 270788*, heated, – TV P – 150. MC AE VISA
Meals 19.95/28.95 **t.** and a la carte 9.00 – **14 rm** 69.00/125.00 **t.** – SB.

at Horringer *Southwest : 3 m. on A 143 – ✉ Bury St. Edmunds.*

Beehive, IP29 5SN, ☏ (01284) 735260, *Fax (01284) 830321*, – P. MC VISA
closed 25 and 26 December and Sunday dinner – **Meals** a la carte 15.45/20.65 **t.** 6.00.

BUSHEY *Herts.* 404 S 29.

Bushey Hall, Bushey Hall Dr. ☏ *(01923) 222253*, **BT** – *Bushey G. & C.C., High St.* ☏ *(020) 8950 2283*, **BT**.

London 18 – Luton 21 – Watford 3.

Plan : see Greater London (North-West) p. 8

XX **st James,** 30 High St., WD2 3DN, ☏ (020) 8950 2480, *Fax (020) 8950 4107* – . MC AE VISA
closed Sunday and Bank Holidays – **Meals** 12.95/17.95 **t.** and a la carte 7.50.

BT c

BUTTERMERE *Cumbria* 402 K 20 – *pop. 139* – ✉ *Cockermouth.*

London 306 – Carlisle 35 – Kendal 43.

Bridge, CA13 9UZ, ☏ (017687) 70252, *enquiries@bridge-hotel.com, Fax (017687) 70215*, – P. MC VISA
Meals (booking essential) (bar lunch)/dinner 21.00 **t.** 8.50 – **21 rm** (dinner included) 60.00/136.00 **t.** – SB.

Wood House , CA13 9XA, Northwest : ½ m. on B 5289 ☏ (017687) 70208, Crummock Water and Melbreak, « Lakeside setting », – P.
mid February-mid November – **Meals** (by arrangement) (communal dining) 14.00/23.95 **st.** 3.90 – **3 rm** 43.00/70.00 **st.**

BUXTON *Derbs.* 402 403 404 O24 – *pop. 19 854.*

Buxton and High Peak, Townend ☏ *(01298) 23453.*

The Crescent ☏ *(01298) 25106.*

London 172 – Derby 38 – Manchester 25 – Stoke-on-Trent 24.

Lee Wood, The Park, SK17 6TQ, on A 5004 ☏ (01298) 23002, *leewoodhotel@btinternet.com, Fax (01298) 23228*, – , rm, TV P – 100. MC AE VISA.
Meals 14.00/23.95 **st.** and a la carte 6.50 11.00 – **40 rm** 60.00/95.00 **st.** – SB.

Coningsby without rest., 6 Macclesfield Rd, SK17 9AH, ☏ (01298) 26735, *coningsby@btinternet.com, Fax (01298) 26735*, – TV P. MC VISA.
March-October – **3 rm** 75.00 **s.**

BYFORD *Herefordshire* 403 L 27 – *see Hereford.*

BYLAND ABBEY *N. Yorks.* 402 Q 21 – *see Helmsley.*

CADNAM *Hants.* 403 404 P 31 – *pop. 1 866.*

London 91 – Salisbury 16 – Southampton 8 – Winchester 19.

Walnut Cottage without rest., Old Romsey Rd, SO40 2NP, off A 3090 ☏ (023) 8081 2275, *Fax (023) 8081 2275*, – TV P.
closed 24 to 27 December – **3 rm** 30.00/46.00.

CAISTOR ST. EDMUND *Norfolk* 404 X 26 – *see Norwich.*

CALCOT *Glos. – see Tetbury.*

CALLINGTON *Cornwall* 403 H 32.
London 237 – Exeter 53 – Plymouth 15 – Truro 46.

The Thyme and Plaice, 3 Church St., PL17 7RE, (01579) 384933, *dine@thymeandplace.com, Fax (01579) 384933* – . VISA JCB
closed 3 weeks January – **Meals** (booking essential) (Sunday to Wednesday by arrangement) (dinner only) (set menu only) 19.95 **t.** 4.50.

CALNE *Wilts.* 403 404 O 29 *The West Country G.* – *pop. 11 516.*
Env. : *Bowood House★ AC, (Library ←★) SW : 2 m. by A 4 – Avebury★★ (The Stones★, Church★) E : 6 m. by A 4.*
London 91 – Bristol 33 – Swindon 17.

Chilvester Hill House, SN11 0LP, West : ¾ m. by A 4 on Bremhill rd (01249) 813981 *Fax (01249) 814217,* – rest, TV P. AE VISA.
Meals (by arrangement) (communal dining) 18.00/25.00 **st.** 5.50 – **3 rm** 50.00/85.00 **st.**

CAMBERLEY *Surrey* 404 R 29 – *pop. 46 120 (inc. Frimley).*
18 *Camberley Heath, Golf Dr. (01276) 23258.*
London 40 – Reading 13 – Southampton 48.

Frimley Hall, Lime Av. via Conifer Drive, GU15 2BG, East : ¾ m. off Portsmouth Rd (A 325) (0870) 400 8224, *heritagehotels-camberley.frimley-hall@forte-hotels.com Fax (01276) 691253,* – TV P – 60. AE VISA
Meals 11.00/21.50 **t.** and (dinner) a la carte 7.50 – 13.95 – **86 rm** 170.00 **st.** – SB.

Travel Inn, 221 Yorktown Rd, GU47 0RT, West : 2 m. by A 30 and A 321 on A 3095 (01276) 878181, *Fax (01276) 890648* – rm, rest, TV P. AE VISA.
Meals (grill rest.) – **40 rm** 40.95 **t.**

CAMBORNE *Cornwall* 403 E 33 *The West Country G.* – *pop. 35 915 (inc. Redruth).*
Env. : *Carn Brea (←★★), NE : 3 m. by A 3047 and minor rd.*
London 299 – Falmouth 14 – Penzance 16 – Truro 14.

Tyack's, 27 Commercial St., TR14 8LD, (01209) 612424, *Fax (01209) 612435* – TV P AE VISA.
Meals 14.95 **t.** and a la carte 4.50 – **13 rm** 45.00/60.00 **st.**, 2 suites – SB.

CAMBRIDGE *Cambs.* 404 U 27 *Great Britain G.* – *pop. 95 682.*
See : *Town★★★ – St. John's College★★★* **AC Y** – *King's College★★ (King's College Chapel★★★)* **Z** *The Backs★★* **YZ** – *Fitzwilliam Museum★★* **Z M1** – *Trinity College★★* **Y** – *Clare College★* **Z B** – *Kettle's Yard★* **Y M2** – *Queen's College★* **AC Z.**
Exc. : *Audley End★★, S : 13 m. on Trumpington Rd, A 1309, A 1301 and B 1383 – Imperial War Museum★, Duxford, S : 9 m. on M 11.*
18 *Cambridgeshire Moat House Hotel, Bar Hill (01954) 780555* **X.**
Cambridge Airport : (01223) 373737, E : 2 m. on A 1303 **X.**
Wheeler St. (01223) 322640.
London 55 – Coventry 88 – Kingston-upon-Hull 137 – Ipswich 54 – Leicester 74 – Norwich 61 – Nottingham 88 – Oxford 100.

Plan opposite

Cambridge Garden House Moat House, Granta Pl., off Mill Lane, CB2 1RT (01223) 259988, *gmcgh@queensmoat.co.uk, Fax (01223) 316605,* ←, , , , – , rest, TV P – 250. AE VISA. Z r
Meals 21.95 **st.** (lunch) and a la carte approx. 21.40/32.15 **st.** 7.25 – 13.50 – **117 rm** 154.00/269.00 **st.** – SB.

Crowne Plaza, Downing St., CB2 3DT, (01223) 464466, *sales@cpcam.demon.co.uk Fax (01223) 464440* – , rm, TV P – 250. AE VISA JCB. Z a
Meals (bar lunch)/dinner a la carte 18.00/30.00 **st.** – 12.95 – **194 rm** 169.00 **st.**, 2 suites – SB.

University Arms, Regent St., CB2 1AD, (01223) 351241, *dug.sales@devere-hotels.com, Fax (01223) 315256* – TV P – 300. AE VISA. Z e
Meals *(closed Saturday lunch)* a la carte 23.00/30.00 **st.** – 11.95 – **114 rm** 115.00/165.00 **st.**, 1 suite – SB.

Gonville, Gonville Pl., CB1 1LY, (01223) 366611, *info@gonville.hotel.co.uk Fax (01223) 315470* – , rest, rest, TV P – 200. AE VISA. Z
Meals (bar lunch)/dinner 18.50 **st.** and a la carte 5.95 – 9.50 – **64 rm** 95.00/120.00 **st.** – SB.

CAMBRIDGE

ridge Street	Y 2	Northampton St.	Y 22
orn Exchange St.	Z 6	Parker Street	Z 23
owning Street	Z 7	Peas Hill	Z 25
ree School Lane	Z 12	Pembroke Street	Z 26
rafton Centre	Y	Petty Cury	Z 27
obson Street	Y 14	Rose Crescent	Y 28
ing's Parade	Z 15	St. Andrew's St.	Z 30
ion Yard Centre	Z	St. John's Street	Y 31
adingley Rd	X, Y 16	Short Street	Y 32
agdalene St.	Y 17	Sidney Street	Y 34
arket Hill	Z 18	Trinity Street	Y 36
arket Street	Y 19	Trumpington Road	Z 37
ilton Road	Y 20	Wheeler Street	Z 39
ewmarket Road	Y 21		

COLLEGES

HRIST'S	Y A	NEW HALL	X D
HURCHILL	X B	NEWNHAM	X E
LARE	Z B	PEMBROKE	Z N
LARE HALL	X N	PETERHOUSE	Z O
ORPUS CHRISTI	Z G	QUEENS'	Z
ARWIN	Z D	ROBINSON COLLEGE	X K
OWNING	Z E	ST CATHARINE'S	Z R
MMANUEL	Z F	ST EDMUNDS HOUSE	Y U
TZWILLIAM	X G	ST JOHN'S	Y
ONVILLE AND CAIUS	Y G	SELWYN	X F
UGUES HALL	Z K	SIDNEY SUSSEX	Y P
ESUS	Y K	TRINITY	Y
ING'S	Z	TRINITY HALL	Y V
UCY CAVENDISH	Y O	WOLFSON	X U
AGDALENE	Y N		

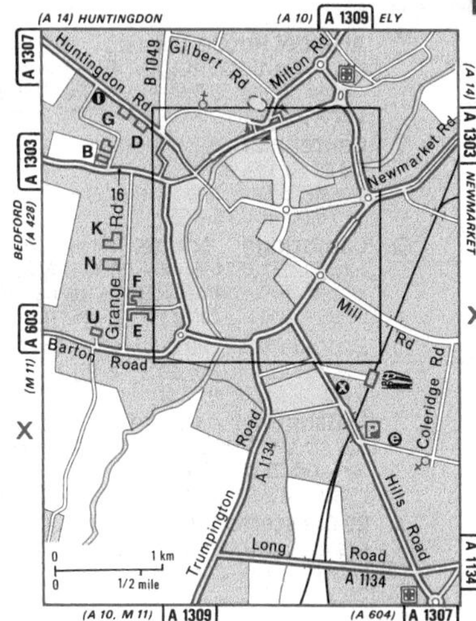

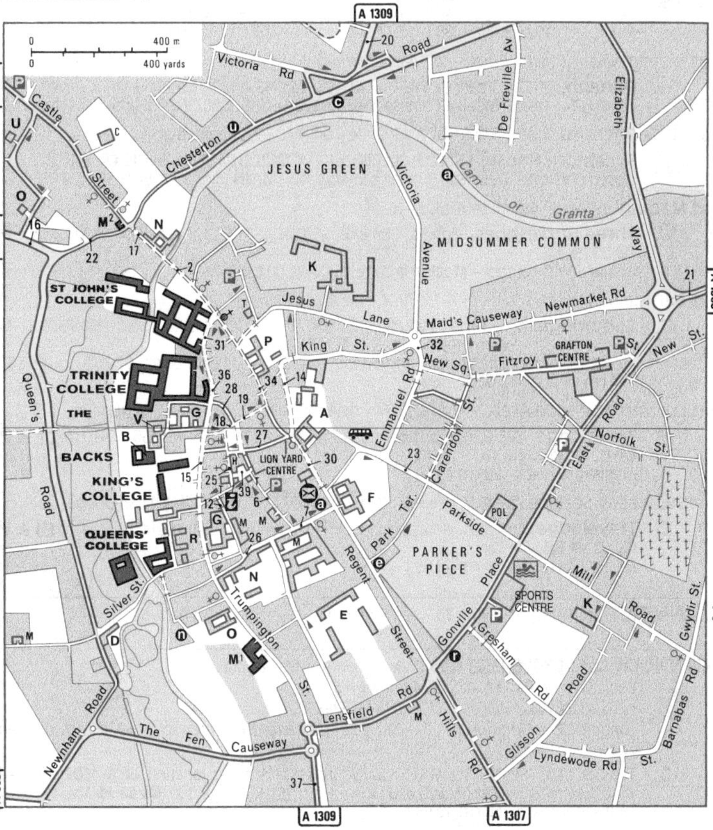

Arundel House, Chesterton Rd, CB4 3AN, ✆ (01223) 367701, *info@arundelhousehotels.co.uk, Fax (01223) 367721,* – , rest, – 40. VISA. Y
closed 25 and 26 December – ***Restaurant :*** **Meals** 16.75 **t.** and a la carte 5.25 – ***Conservatory :*** **Meals** a la carte 11.45/16.15 **t.** 5.25 – 4.95 – **105 rm** 55.00/99.00 **t.** – SB.

Centennial, 63-71 Hills Rd, CB2 1PG, ✆ (01223) 314652, *Fax (01223) 315443* – VISA. X
closed 25 December-1 January – **Meals** (dinner only) 13.50 **t.** and a la carte 5.00 – **39 rm** 70.00/95.00 **t.** – SB.

Cambridge Lodge, 139 Huntingdon Rd, CB3 0DQ, ✆ (01223) 352833, *Fax (01223) 355166,* – – 25. VISA. X
closed 25 December – **Meals** (dinner only and lunch Saturday and Sunday)/dinner 14.95/20.95 **t.** and a la carte 6.00 – **15 rm** 64.00/97.50 **t.**

Brooklands without rest., 95 Cherry Hinton Rd, CB1 4BS, ✆ (01223) 242035, *Fax (01223) 242035,* – . VISA JCB. X
5 rm 30.00/50.00 **st.**

XXX **Midsummer House,** Midsummer Common, CB4 1HA, ✆ (01223) 369299, *Fax (01223) 302672,* « Attractively situated beside River Cam, on Midsummer Common » – VISA JCB Y
closed 14-29 August, Christmas and New Year – **Meals** 18.50/39.50 **t.** 7.95.

XX **22 Chesterton Road,** 22 Chesterton Rd, CB4 3AX, ✆ (01223) 351880, *davidcarter@restaurant22.co.uk, Fax (01223) 323814* – . VISA JCB Y
closed 1 week Christmas, Sunday and Monday – **Meals** (booking essential) (dinner only) 23.50 **t.** 7.95.

at Impington *North : 2 m. on B 1049 at junction with A 14* – **X** – ✉ *Cambridge.*

Posthouse Cambridge, Lakeview, Bridge Rd, CB4 9PH, ✆ (0870) 400 9015, *Fax (01223) 233426,* , , , – rm, – 70. VISA
Meals a la carte 19.85/28.85 **t.** 8.50 – 11.95 – **165 rm** 99.00 **st.** – SB.

at Histon *North : 3 m. on B 1049* – **X** – ✉ *Cambridge.*

XX **Phoenix,** 20 The Green, CB4 4JA, ✆ (01223) 233766 – . VISA
closed Christmas – **Meals** - Chinese (Peking, Szechuan) - 6.50/26.00 **t.** and a la carte.

at Little Shelford *South : 5½ m. by A 1309* – **X** – *off A 10* – ✉ *Cambridge.*

XX **Sycamore House,** 1 Church St., CB2 5HG, ✆ (01223) 843396 – . VISA
closed Christmas-New Year, Sunday and Monday – **Meals** (dinner only) 23.50 **t** 9.00.

at Madingley *West : 4½ m. by A 1303* – **X.**

XX **Three Horseshoes,** High St., CB3 8AB, ✆ (01954) 210221, *Fax (01954) 212043,* – VISA
closed Sunday dinner – **Meals** a la carte 16.00/21.00 **t.** 5.00.

at Bar Hill *Northwest : 5½ m. by A 1307* – **X** – *off A 14.*

Cambridgeshire Moat House, CB3 8EU, ✆ (01954) 249988, *Fax (01954) 780010,* , , , – rm, – 200. VISA
Meals *(closed lunch Saturday and Sunday)* a la carte 22.00/34.00 **st.** 6.25 – 13.50 – **134 rm** 115.00/130.00 **st.** – SB.

at Lolworth Service Area *Northwest : 6 m. by A 1307* – **X** – *on A 14* – ✉ *Cambridge.*

Travelodge, CB3 8DR, (northbound carriageway) ✆ (01954) 781335 – rm, VISA JCB.
Meals (grill rest.) – **20 rm** 49.95 **t.**

at Swavesey Service Area *Northwest : 8 m. by A 1307* – **X** – *on A 14* – ✉ *Cambridge.*

Travelodge, CB4 5QA, (southbound carriageway) ✆ (01954) 789113 – rm, VISA JCB.
Meals (grill rest.) – **36 rm** 49.95 **t.**

CANNINGTON *Somerset* 403 K 30 – *see Bridgwater.*

CANNOCK *Staffs.* 402 403 404 N 25 *Great Britain G.* – *pop. 60 106.*

Exc. : *Weston Park★★ AC, W : 11 m. by A 5.*

Cannock Park, Stafford Rd ✆ *(01543) 578850.*

London 135 – Birmingham 20 – Derby 36 – Leicester 51 – Shrewsbury 32 – Stoke-on-Trent 28.

Travel Inn, Watling St., WS11 1SJ, Southwest : 1 m. at junction of A 4601 with A 5 ✆ (01543) 572721, *Fax (01543) 466130* – rm, – 100. VISA.
Meals (grill rest.) – **60 rm** 40.95 **t.**

CANTERBURY *Kent* 404 X 30 *Great Britain G. – pop. 36 464.*

See : *City*★★★ - *Cathedral*★★★ **Y** - *St. Augustine's Abbey*★★ *AC* **YZ K** – *King's School*★ **Y B** – *Mercery Lane*★ **Y 12** - *Christ Church Gate*★ **Y A** – *Weavers*★ **Y D** – *Hospital of St. Thomas the Martyr, Eastbridge*★ **Y E** – *Poor Priests Hospital*★ *AC* **Y M1** – *St. Martin's Church*★ **Y N** – *West Gate*★ *AC* **Y R.**

34 St. Margaret's St. ☎ (01227) 766567.

London 59 – Brighton 76 – Dover 15 – Maidstone 28 – Margate 17.

CANTERBURY

Beercart Lane	**YZ** 2
Borough (The)	**Y** 4
Burgate	**Y**
Butchery Lane	**Y** 5
Guildhall Street	**Y** 6
High Street	**Y** 8
Lower Bridge Street	**Z** 9
Lower Chantry Lane	**Z** 10
Mercery Lane	**Y** 12
Palace Street	**Y**
Rhodaus Town	**Z** 13
Rosemary Lane	**Z** 14
St. George's Place	**Z** 16
St. George's Street	**Z** 17
St. Margaret's Street	**YZ** 18
St. Mary's Street	**Z** 19
St. Radigund's Street	**Y** 21
St. Peter's Street	**Y** 20
Upper Bridge Street	**Z** 23
Watling Street	**Z** 25

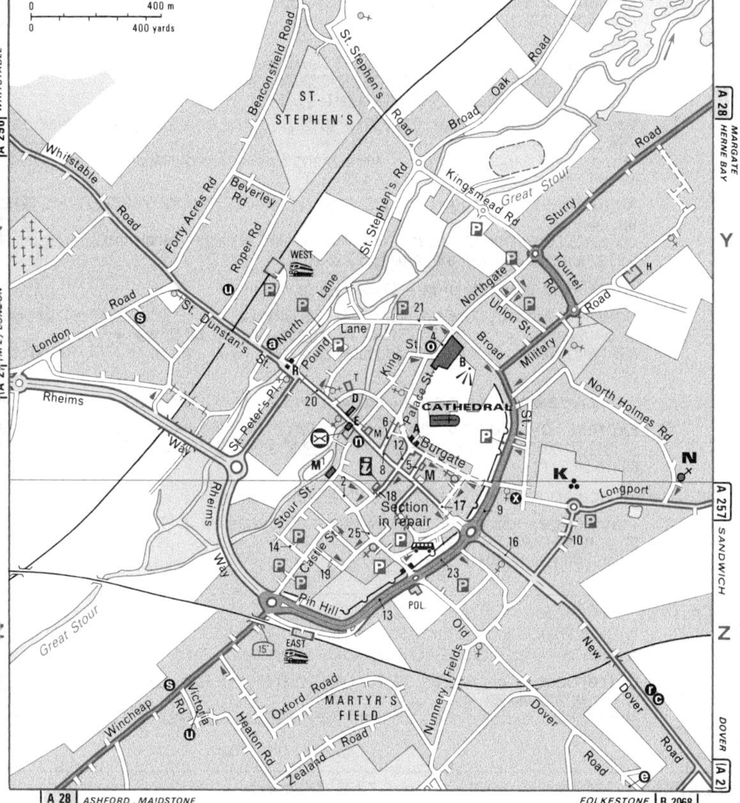

County, High St., CT1 2RX, ☎ (01227) 766266, *info@county.macdonald-hotels.co.uk, Fax (01227) 451512* – rm, P – 140. VISA JCB. **Y n**
Sullys : **Meals** 17.00/24.00 **st.** and a la carte – 10.50 – **72 rm** 79.00/82.00 **st.**, 1 suite – SB.

Falstaff, 8-10 St. Dunstan's St., CT2 8AF, ☎ (01227) 462138, *Fax (01227) 463525,* « Part 15C coaching inn » – P. VISA **Y a**
Othello's : **Meals** 14.95/16.95 **t.** and a la carte 7.25 – 9.50 – **47 rm** 91.00/100.00 **t.** – SB.

ENGLAND

Thanington without rest., 140 Wincheap, CT1 3RY, ✆ (01227) 453227, *thanington@lined ne.net, Fax (01227) 453225*, ⊠, – ⇆ TV P. MC AE VISA JCB Z
closed 24-26 December – **15 rm** 55.00/89.00 **st.**

Ebury, 65-67 New Dover Rd, CT1 3DX, ✆ (01227) 768433, *info@ebury-hotel.co.uk Fax (01227) 459187*, – rest, TV P. MC AE VISA JCB. Z
closed 23 December-14 January – **Meals** *(closed Sunday)* (dinner only) a la carte 18.70/22.40 **st.** 5.90 – **15 rm** 50.00/79.00 **st.** – SB.

Magnolia House, 36 St. Dunstan's Terr., CT2 8AX, ✆ (01227) 765121, *magnolia_house_canterbury@yahoo.com, Fax (01227) 765121*, – TV P. MC AE VISA. Y
Meals (by arrangement in winter) 18.00/22.00 **st.** – **7 rm** 45.00/110.00 **st.**

Clare Ellen without rest., 9 Victoria Rd, CT1 3SG, ✆ (01227) 760205, *loraine.williams@clare-ellenguesthouse.co.uk, Fax (01227) 784482*, – TV P. MC VISA JCB. Z
6 rm 26.00/52.00 **st.**

Zan Stel Lodge without rest., 140 Old Dover Rd, CT1 3NX, ✆ (01227) 453654, – TV P. Z
4 rm 30.00/52.00.

Alexandra House without rest., 1 Roper Rd, CT2 7EH, ✆ (01227) 767011 *Fax (01227) 786617*, – TV P. Y
7 rm 28.00/52.00.

La Bonne Cuisine (at Canterbury H.), 71 New Dover Rd, CT1 3DZ, ✆ (01227) 450551, *canterbury.hotel@btinternet.com, Fax (01227) 780145* – P. MC AE VISA Z
Meals - French - 16.95/19.00 **t.** and a la carte 6.90.

Tuo e Mio, 16 The Borough, CT1 2DR, ✆ (01227) 761471, *james@greggio.freeserve.co.uk* – MC AE VISA JCB Y
closed 2 weeks August, Christmas, Monday and Tuesday lunch – **Meals** - Italian - 12.50 **t.** (lunch) and a la carte 16.50/24.50 **t.** 4.25.

Augustine's, 1-2 Longport, CT1 1PE, ✆ (01227) 453063, *Fax (01227) 453063* – . MC AE VISA JCB Z
closed 25 December-12 January, Sunday dinner and Monday – **Meals** (booking essential) 8.95 **t.** (lunch) and dinner a la carte 15.50/26.00 **t.**

at Chartham Hatch *West : 3¼ m. by A 28 – Z – ✉ Canterbury.*

Howfield Manor, Howfield Lane, CT4 7HQ, Southeast : 1 m. ✆ (01227) 738294, *@howfield.invictanet.co.uk, Fax (01227) 731535*, – TV P – 100. MC AE VISA JCB.
Old Well : **Meals** 14.95/18.95 **st.** and dinner a la carte 5.50 – **15 rm** 75.00/105.00 **st.** – SB.

at Upper Harbledown Service Area *West : 4 m. on A 2 – Y – ✉ Canterbury.*

Express by Holiday Inn without rest., CT2 9HX, (eastbound carriageway) ✆ (01227) 865000, *Fax (01227) 865100* – TV P – 35. MC AE VISA.
89 rm 54.50 **st.**

at Gate Service Area *West : 4½ m. on A 2 – Y – ✉ Faversham.*

Travelodge, Dunkirk, ME13 9LN, (westbound carriageway) ✆ (01227) 752781 – rm, TV P. MC AE VISA JCB.
Meals (grill rest.) – **40 rm** 39.95 **t.**

CANVEY ISLAND *Essex* 404 V 29 – *pop. 36 859.*

Castle Point, Waterside Farm, Somnes Av. ✆ (01268) 510830.
London 35 – Chelmsford 19 – Maidstone 44 – Southend-on-Sea 13.

Oysterfleet, Knightswick Rd, SS8 7UX, ✆ (01268) 510111, *Fax (01268) 511420*, – TV P – 200. MC VISA.
Meals *closed Sunday dinner* (grill rest.) 9.85/16.35 **st.** and a la carte – 4.50 – **40 rm** 39.50 **st.**

CAPEL ST. MARY *Suffolk* 404 X 27 – *pop. 3 176 – ✉ Ipswich.*

London 78 – Cambridge 52 – Colchester 18 – Ipswich 3.

Travelodge, Bentley Services, IP9 2JP, West : ½ m. on A 12 ✆ (01473) 312157 *Fax (01473) 312157* – rm, TV P. MC AE VISA JCB.
Meals (grill rest.) – **32 rm** 39.95 **t.**

CARBIS BAY *Cornwall* 403 D 33 – *see St. Ives.*

CARCROFT *S. Yorks.* 402 403 404 Q 23 – *see Doncaster.*

CARLISLE *Cumbria* 401 402 L 19 *Great Britain G. – pop. 72 439.*

See : *Town★ - Cathedral★ (Painted Ceiling★)* **AY E** – *Tithe Barn★* **BY A**.

Env. : *Hadrian's Wall★★, N : by A 7* **AY**.

18 *Aglionby ℘ (01228) 513029* **BY** – 18 *Stony Holme, St. Aidan's Rd ℘ (01228) 625511* **BY** – 9 *Dalston Hall, Dalston ℘ (01228) 710165,* **AZ**.

Carlisle Airport ℘ (01228) 573641, NW : 5½ m. by A 7 – **BY** – *and B 6264* – **Terminal** : *Bus Station, Lowther St.*

Green Market ℘ (01228) 625600.

London 317 – Blackpool 95 – Edinburgh 101 – Glasgow 100 – Leeds 124 – Liverpool 127 – Manchester 122 – Newcastle upon Tyne 59.

CARLISLE

- nnetwell Street .... **AY** 2
- otchergate.............. **BZ**
- ridge Street............. **AY** 3
- runswick Street .... **BZ** 4
- astle Street............. **BY** 5
- ecil Street .... **BZ** 6
- Charlotte Street .... **AZ** 7
- Chiswick Street .... **BY** 8
- Church Street .... **AY** 10
- Eden Bridge .... **BY** 12
- English Street............ **BY** 13
- Lonsdale Street .... **BY** 14
- Lowther Street........... **BY** 15
- Port Road................ **AY** 16
- St. Marys Gate........... **BY** 17
- Scotch Street .... **BY** 19
- Spencer Street........... **BY** 20
- Tait Street .... **BZ** 21
- The Lanes Shopping Centre .... **BY**
- Victoria Viaduct .... **ABZ** 24
- West Tower Street .... **BY** 26
- West Walls............. **ABY** 27
- Wigton Road............. **AZ** 29

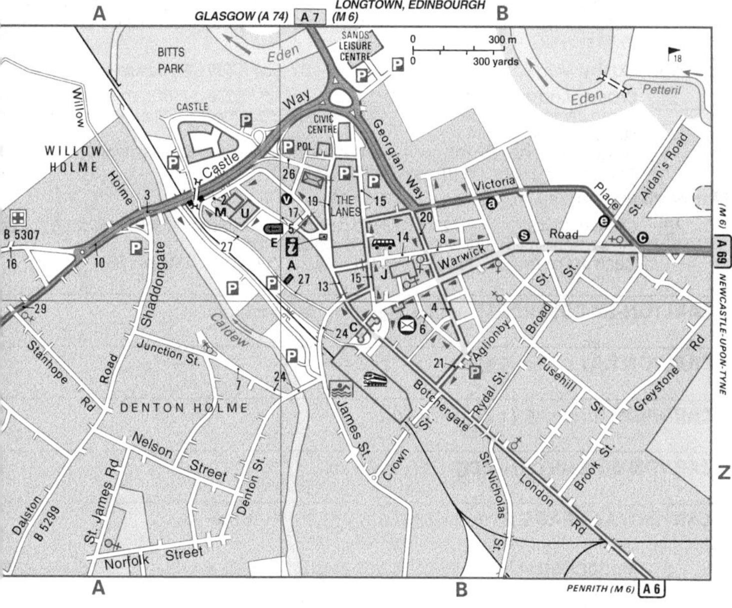

Cumbria Park, 32 Scotland Rd, CA3 9DG, North : 1 m. on A 7 ℘ (01228) 522887, *enquiries@cumbriaparkhotel.co.uk, Fax (01228) 514796* – |♦|, ⇄ TV P – 120. MO AE ① VISA JCB.
closed 25 and 26 December – **Meals** (bar lunch Sunday) 12.50/15.95 **t.** and a la carte 6.25 – **47 rm** 74.00/120.00 **t.**

Premier Lodge, Kingstown Rd, CA3 0AT, North : 1 ¾ m. on A 7 ℘ (0870) 7001348, *Fax (0870) 7001349* – ⇄ TV & P. MO AE ① VISA.
Meals (grillrest.) – **49 rm** 46.00 **t.**

Travel Inn, Warwick Rd, CA1 2WF, East : 1 ½ m. on A 69 ℘ (01228) 545290, *Fax (01228) 545354* – |♦|, ⇄ rm, TV & P. MO AE ① VISA.
Meals (grill rest.) – **44 rm** 40.95 **t.**

Travelodge, Todhills, CA6 4HA, Northwest : 3 m. by A 7 on A 74 (southbound) ℘ (0870) 9056343 – ⇄ rm, TV & P. MO AE ① VISA JCB.
Meals (grill rest.) – **40 rm** 49.95 **t.**

ENGLAND

Number Thirty One, 31 Howard Pl., CA1 1HR, ☎ (01228) 597080, *bestpep@aol.com*, *Fax (01228) 597080*, « Victorian town house » – ⇔ TV. MC AE VISA. ✻ BY
March-October – **Meals** (by arrangement) 25.00 **s.** – **3 rm** 55.00/90.00 **s.**

Fern Lee, 9 St. Aidan's Rd, CA1 1LT, ☎ (01228) 511930, *Fax (01228) 511930* – ⇔ TV P. ✻ BY
Meals (by arrangement) 12.00 **st.** – **8 rm** 30.00/50.00 **st.** – SB.

Courtfield House without rest., 169 Warwick Rd, CA1 1LP, ☎ (01228) 522767 – TV. ✻ BY
closed 25 December – **5 rm** 25.00/40.00 **st.**

Langleigh House without rest., 6 Howard Pl., CA1 1HR, ☎ (01228) 530440, *Fax (01228) 530440* – ⇔ TV P. ✻ BY
closed Christmas **4 rm** 25.00/40.00 **s.**

Magenta's, 18 Fisher St., CA3 8RH, ☎ (01228) 546363, *Fax (01228) 546363* – ⇔. MC VISA JCB BY
closed 1-26 January, Sunday and Bank Holiday Monday – **Meals** (dinner only) 18.00 **t.** and a la carte 18.95/24.40 **t.** 9.35.

No. 10, 10 Eden Mount, Stanwix, CA3 9LY, North : ¾ m. on A 7. ☎ (01228) 524183 – MC AE VISA
closed February, 1 week late October, Sunday and Monday – **Meals** (booking essential) (dinner only) a la carte 16.85/22.75 **t.** 6.00.

at Kingstown *North : 3 m. by A 7* – **BY** – ✉ *Carlisle.*

Posthouse Carlisle, Park House Rd, CA3 0HR, at junction 44 of M 6 ☎ (0870) 400 9018, *Fax (01228) 543178*, Fő, ≘s, ▣ – ⇔ rm, ≡ rest, TV & P – 🔺 120. MC AE ⓓ VISA JCB
Meals *(closed Saturday lunch)* 15.00 **t.** and a la carte 6.95 – 11.95 – **127 rm** 69.00/89.00 **st.** – SB.

at High Crosby *Northeast : 5 m. by A 7 and B 6264* – **BY** – *off A 689* – ✉ *Carlisle.*

Crosby Lodge Country House ⛰, CA6 4QZ, ☎ (01228) 573618, *crosbylodge@crosby-eden.demon.co.uk*, *Fax (01228) 573428*, ←, « 18C country mansion », 🌳 – ⇔ rest, TV P. MC AE VISA JCB. ✻
closed Christmas-mid January – **Meals** (Sunday dinner booking essential) 16.50/30.00 **t.** and a la carte 8.40 – **11 rm** 82.00/140.00 **t.** – SB.

at Wetheral *East : 6¼ m. by A 69* – **BZ** – ✉ *Carlisle.*

Crown, CA4 8ES, ☎ (01228) 561888, *crown@shireinns.co.uk*, *Fax (01228) 561637*, Fő, ≘s, ▣, 🌳, squash – ⇔ TV ☏ & P – 🔺 175. MC AE ⓓ VISA
Meals a la carte 26.00/36.00 **st.** – **49 rm** 102.00/122.00 **st.**, 2 suites – SB.

CARLTON-IN-COVERDALE *N. Yorks.* 402 O 21 – *see Middleham.*

CARLYON BAY *Cornwall* 403 F 33 – *see St. Austell.*

CARNFORTH *Lancs.* 402 L 21 – *see Lancaster.*

CARNON DOWNS *Cornwall* 403 E 33 – *see Truro.*

CARTERWAY HEADS *Northd.* 401 402 O 19 – ✉ *Shotley Bridge.*
London 272 – *Carlisle 59* – *Newcastle upon Tyne 21.*

Manor House Inn, DH8 9LX, on A 68 ☎ (01207) 255268, *Fax (01207) 255268* – ⇔ P. MC AE VISA
closed dinner 25 December **Meals** a la carte 15.45/23.40 **t.** 7.00.

CARTMEL *Cumbria* 402 L 21 – *see Grange-over-Sands.*

CARTMELL FELL *Cumbria* 402 L 21 – *see Newby Bridge.*

CASTERTON *Cumbria* 402 M 21 – *see Kirkby Lonsdale.*

CASTLE ASHBY *Northants.* 404 R 27 – *pop. 138* – ✉ *Northampton.*
London 76 – *Bedford 15* – *Northampton 11.*

The Falcon ⛰, NN7 1LF, ☎ (01604) 696200, *falcon@castleashby.co.uk*, *Fax (01604) 696673*, 🍽, « Part 16C inn », 🌳 – TV & P. MC AE VISA
Meals 23.95 **t.** (dinner) and a la carte 27.50/35.45 **t.** 10.95 – **16 rm** 79.50/95.50 **t.** – SB.

CASTLE CARY *Somerset* 403 404 M 30 – *pop. 2 904.*

London 125 – Bristol 28 – Taunton 31 – Yeovil 13.

Bond's with rm, Ansford Hill, Ansford, BA7 7JL, North : ¾ m. by Ansford Rd on A 371 ℘ (01963) 350464, *Fax (01963) 350464*, – TV P. MC VISA JCB. *closed 1 week Christmas, Monday, Sunday dinner and Tuesday lunch* – **Meals** (light lunch)/ dinner a la carte 13.40/22.40 **st.** 6.00 – **7 rm** 56.00/68.00 **t.**

ENGLAND

CASTLE COMBE *Wilts.* 403 404 N 29 *The West Country G. – pop. 347 –* ✉ *Chippenham.*

See : *Village*★★.

London 110 – Bristol 23 – Chippenham 6.

Manor House, SN14 7HR, ℘ (01249) 782206, *enquiries@manor_house.co.uk, Fax (01249) 782159*, « Part 14C manor house in park », heated, 18, – rest, TV P – 50. MC AE VISA. **Meals** 16.95/45.00 **t.** 12.50 – 15.00 – **43 rm** 145.00/350.00 **t.**, 2 suites – SB.

Castle Inn, SN14 7HN, ℘ (01249) 783030, *res@castleinn.co.uk, Fax (01249) 782315*, « Part 12C » – rest, TV. MC AE VISA JCB. **Meals** a la carte 21.60/24.05 **t.** – **11 rm** 67.50/105.00 **t.** – SB.

at Ford *South : 1 ¾ m. on A 420 –* ✉ *Chippenham.*

White Hart Inn, SN14 8RP, ℘ (01249) 782213, *Fax (01249) 783075* – TV P. MC AE VISA **Meals** 15.75 **t.** (lunch) and a la carte 15.95/23.25 **t.** 10.50 – **11 rm** 69.00/84.00 **st.**

at Nettleton Shrub *West : 2 m. by B 4039 on Nettleton rd (Fosse Way) –* ✉ *Chippenham.*

Fosse Farmhouse, SN14 7NJ, ℘ (01249) 782286, *caroncooper@compuserve.com, Fax (01249) 783066*, – rest, TV P. MC AE VISA JCB. **Meals** (by arrangement) 25.00 **st.** 6.50 – **6 rm** 65.00/125.00 **st.**

CASTLE DONINGTON *Leics.* 402 403 404 P 25 – *pop. 6 007 –* ✉ *Derby.*

East Midlands Airport : ℘ (01332) 852852, S : by B 6540 and A 453.

London 123 – Birmingham 38 – Leicester 23 – Nottingham 13.

Priest House on the River, Kings Mills, DE74 2RR, West : 1 ¾ m. by Park Lane ℘ (01332) 810649, *priesthouse@arcadianhotels.co.uk, Fax (01332) 811141*, ←, « Riverside setting », – rest, TV P – 130. MC AE VISA **Meals** 13.50/24.50 **st.** and dinner a la carte 8.00 – – **43 rm** 80.00/100.00 **st.**, 2 suites – SB.

Donington Manor, High St., DE74 2PP, ℘ (01332) 810253, *engrist@dmhgrist.demon.co.uk, Fax (01332) 850330*, – TV P – 80. MC AE VISA. *closed 27 to 30 December* – **Meals** 8.50/14.00 **st.** and a la carte 5.50 – **28 rm** 66.00/ 92.00 **st.**, 2 suites.

CASTLEFORD *W. Yorks.* 402 P/Q 22.

London 197 – Leeds 11 – Manchester 53 – Nottingham 70 – Sheffield 37 – YOrk 29.

Premier Lodge, Commerce Park, Pioneer Way, WF10 5TG, Southwest : 2 m. by A 655 ℘ (01977) 665400, *Fax (01977) 667240* – |‡|, rest, TV P. MC AE VISA. **Meals** (grill rest.) (dinner only) a la carte 8.85/18.40 **st.** – 6.00 – **62 rm** 46.00 **st.**

CASTLETON *Derbs.* 402 403 404 O 23 *Great Britain G. – pop. 689 –* ✉ *Sheffield (S. Yorks.).*

Env. : *Blue John Caverns*★ *AC, W : 1 m.*

London 181 – Derby 49 – Manchester 30 – Sheffield 16 – Stoke-on-Trent 39.

Ye Olde Nags Head, Cross St., S33 8WH, ℘ (01433) 620248, *Fax (01433) 621604* – rest, TV P. MC AE VISA JCB **Meals** *closed Sunday dinner and Monday* 11.95/24.95 **t.** – **8 rm** (dinner included) 49.50/164.00 **t.** – SB.

CASTLETOWN *Isle of Man* 402 G 21 – *see Man (Isle of).*

CASTOR *Peterborough* 404 S 26 – *see Peterborough.*

CATEL *Guernsey (Channel Islands)* 403 P 33 and 230 ⑨ – *see Channel Islands.*

CAUNTON *Notts.* 402 404 R 24 – *see Newark-on-Trent.*

CAWSTON *Norfolk* 404 X 25 *Great Britain G. – pop. 2 265 –* ✉ *Norwich.*

Env. : *Blicking Hall*★★ *AC, NE : 5 m. by B 1145 and B 1354.*

London 122 – Cromer 15 – King's Lynn 42 – Norwich 13.

The Walnuts without rest., 8-12 New St., NR10 4AL, ✆ (01603) 871357 *Fax (01603) 871357,* heated, – *P.* *closed 25 and 26 December* – **3 rm** 36.00/50.00.

CAXTON *Cambs.*

London 67 – Bedford 18 – Cambridge 12 – Huntingdon 7.

Church Farm, Gransden Rd, CB3 8PL, ✆ (01954) 719543, *churchfarm@aol.com, Fax (01954) 718999,* « Part 17C farmhouse », – P. VISA.
Meals (communal dining) 21.50 5.75 – **4 rm** 42.50/80.00 – SB.

CHADDESLEY CORBETT *Worcs.* 403 404 N 26 – *see Kidderminster.*

CHAGFORD *Devon* 403 I 31 *The West Country G. – pop. 1 417.*

Env. : *Dartmoor National Park*★★.

London 218 – Exeter 17 – Plymouth 27.

Gidleigh Park, TQ13 8HH, Northwest : 2 m. by Gidleigh Rd ✆ (01647) 432367, *gidleighpark@gidleigh.co.uk, Fax (01647) 432574,* ≤ Teign Valley, woodland and Meldon Hill, « Timbered country house, water garden », – rest, P. VISA
Meals (booking essential) 33.00/65.00-70.00 **st.** 12.50 – **12 rm** (dinner included) 260.00/475.00 **st.**, 3 suites
Spec. Ravioli of langoustine with courgette tagliatelle. Local beef fillet with shallots and red wine sauce. Millefeuille of chocolate and banana parfait, lime sorbet.

Glendarah House without rest., Lower St., TQ13 8BZ, ✆ (01647) 433270, *enquiries@glendarah-house.co.uk, Fax (01647) 433483,* ≤, – P. VISA JCB.
closed Christmas-New Year – **7 rm** 30.00/60.00 **s.**

22 Mill Street with rm, 22 Mill St., TQ13 8AW, ✆ (01647) 432244, *Fax (01647) 433101* – rest, VISA
closed 2 weeks January, 10 days May and 25-26 December – **Meals** *(closed Sunday and lunch Monday and Tuesday)* 16.95/31.00 **st.** 8.75 – **2 rm** 35.00/45.00 **st.**

at Sandypark *Northeast : 2¼ m. on A 382 –* ✉ *Chagford.*

Mill End, TQ13 8JN, on A 382 ✆ (01647) 432282, *Fax (01647) 433106,* « Country house with water mill », – rest, P. VISA JCB
– **Meals** (light lunch)/dinner 27.50 **t.** 9.00 – **17 rm** 47.00/110.00 **t.** – SB.

CHALGROVE *Oxon.* 403 404 Q 29 – *pop. 2 832.*

London 57 – Aylesbury 12 – Oxford 17 – Reading 32.

Red Lion Inn, 115 High St., OX44 7SS, ✆ (01865) 890625, *Fax (01865) 890795,* – VISA JCB
closed 25 December and Sunday dinner – **Meals** a la carte 9.80/16.45 **t.** 5.00.

CHANNEL ISLANDS 403 OPQ 33 and 230 ⑨ ⑩ ⑪ *The West Country G. – pop. 145 920.*

ALDERNEY

403 Q 33 and 230 ⑨ *The West Country G. – pop. 2 297.*

See : *Braye Bay★ – Mannez Garenne (≤★ from Quesnard Lighthouse) – Telegraph Bay★ Vallee des Trois Vaux★ – Clonque Bay★.*

✈ ☎ (01481) 822886 - Booking Office : Aurigny Air Services ☎ (01481) 822888.

ℹ States Office, Queen Elizabeth II St. ☎ (01481) 822994/822811.

Braye.

✗ **First and Last,** GY9 3TH, ☎ (01481) 823162, ≤ harbour – MC AE ⓓ VISA
May-October – **Meals** *(closed Sunday and Monday)* (dinner only) a la carte 16.75/26.0 ⅰ 4.00.

St. Anne.

Belle Vue, The Butes, GY9 3UN, ☎ (01481) 822844, *bellevue@alderney.ne Fax (01481) 823601* – ⇔ rest, TV. MC VISA JCB. ✽
closed Christmas and New Year – **Meals** a la carte 11.70/24.75 ⅰ 6.25 – **17 rm** ☐ 46.0 92.00 – SB.

Chez Nous without rest., Les Venelles, GY9 3TW, ☎ (01481) 823633, *Fax (01481) 823732* ⇔ TV
April-October – **3 rm** 33.00/56.00 **s.**

Bonjour, 16 High St., GY9 3UG, ☎ (01481) 822152 – ⇔ rm, TV. ✽
Meals (by arrangement) 12.00 **s.** – **3 rm** ☐ 25.00/50.00 **s.** – SB.

GUERNSEY

403 OP 33 and 230 ⑨ ⑩ *The West Country G. – pop. 58 867.*

See : *Island★ – Pezeries Point★★ – Icart Point★★ – Côbo Bay★★ – St. Martin's Point★★ – Apolline's Chapel★ – Vale Castle★ – Fort Doyle★ – La Gran'mere du Chimquiere★ – Rc quaine Bay★ – Jerbourg Point★.*

✈ Service Air ☎ (01481) 237682, Aurigny Air ☎ (01481) 37426.

⛴ from St. Peter Port to France (St. Malo) and Jersey (St. Helier) (Emeraude Lines) – frc St. Peter Port to Jersey (St. Helier) and Weymouth (Condor Ferries Ltd).

⛴ – from St. Peter Port to France (St. Malo) and Jersey (St. Helier) (Condor Ferries Ltd weekly – from St. Peter Port to France (Dielette) (Emeraude Lines) (summer only) (1 h mn) – from St. Peter Port to Herm (Herm Seaway) (25 mn) – from St. Peter Port to Sark (Is of Sark Shipping Co. Ltd) (45 mn) – from St. Peter Port to Jersey (St. Helier) (Emeraude Lin (50 mn) – from St. Peter Port to Jersey (St. Helier) (Condor Ferries Ltd) daily except Sund

ℹ P.O. Box 23, North Esplanade ☎ (01481) 2723552 – The Airport, La Villiaze, For ☎ (01481) 237267.

Catel/Castel.

Hougue du Pommier ♨, Hougue du Pommier Rd, GY5 7FQ, ☎ (01481) 256531, *hc @houguedupommier.guernsey.net, Fax (01481) 256260,* ⛱, ≘s, ⛵ heated – ⇔ TV MC AE ⓓ VISA
Meals (dinner only) 16.50 and a la carte ⅰ 6.80 – **43 rm** ☐ 48.00/96.00 – SB.

Cobo Bay, Cobo Coast Rd, GY5 7HB, ☎ (01481) 257102, *Fax (01481) 254542,* ≤, ≘s – ▤ rest, TV P. MC VISA. ✽
closed January-21 February – **Meals** (dinner only and Sunday lunch) 18.50 **st.** and a la ca ⅰ 5.00 – **36 rm** ☐ 44.00/108.00 **st.** – SB.

Fermain Bay – ✉ *St. Peter Port.*

La Favorita ♨, Fermain Lane, GY4 6SD, ☎ (01481) 235666, *info@favorita.co Fax (01481) 235413,* ≤, ⛱, ≘s, ⛵, ⛱ – |‡| ⇔ TV P. MC AE ⓓ VISA. ✽
closed January, February and Christmas – **Meals** (bar lunch)/dinner 14.95 **s.** and a la ca ⅰ 6.00 – **37 rm** ☐ 53.00/98.50 **s.** – SB.

Forest – *pop. 1 386.*

Tudor Lodge Deer Farm without rest., Forest Rd, GY8 0AG, (01481) 237849, *Fax (01481) 235662*, – TV P.
April-September – **5 rm** 35.00/60.00.

Mon Plaisir without rest., Route de Farras, GY8 0DY, (01481) 264498, *monplaisir@guernsey.net, Fax (01481) 263493*, – TV P. MC VISA.
closed Christmas and New Year – **5 rm** 31.00/52.00 **s.**

Maison Bel Air without rest., Le Chene, GY8 0AL, (01481) 238503, *Fax (01481) 239403*, – TV P.
6 rm 30.00/50.00.

Kings Mills.

Fleur du Jardin with rm, GY5 7JT, (01481) 257996, *info@fleurdujardin.guernsey.net, Fax (01481) 256834*, heated, – TV P. MC AE VISA JCB.
Meals (lunch in bar)/dinner 14.95/22.95 and a la carte 3.90 – **17 rm** 66.00/120.00 **s.**

Pembroke Bay – Vale.
St. Peter Port 5.

Pembroke Bay, GY3 5BY, (01481) 247573, *info@pembroke.guernseyci.com, Fax (01481) 248838*, heated, – rm, TV P. MC VISA
Easter-September – **Meals** *(closed Monday dinner)* (lunch residents only)/dinner 13.50 **s.** and a la carte 5.50 – **12 rm** 60.00/98.00 **s.**

St. Martin – *pop. 6 082.*
St. Peter Port 2.

Jerbourg, Jerbourg Point, GY4 6BJ, (01481) 238826, *hjerb8765@aol.com, Fax (01481) 238238*, sea and neighbouring Channel Islands, – , rest, TV P. MC VISA.
Meals 17.00 (dinner) and a la carte 10.25/27.50 4.50 – **32 rm** 55.00/135.00 – SB.

Idlerocks, Jerbourg Point, GY4 6BJ, (01481) 237711, *info@idlerocks.com, Fax (01481) 235592*, sea and neighbouring Channel Islands, heated, – TV P. MC AE VISA.
Meals (bar lunch Monday to Saturday)/dinner 14.50 and a la carte 8.50 – **28 rm** 43.00/86.00 – SB.

Bon Port, Moulin Huet Bay, GY4 6EW, (01481) 239249, *mail@bonport.com, Fax (01481) 239596*, Moulin Huet Bay and Jerbourg Point, – rest, TV P. MC AE VISA.
Meals 18.50 (dinner) and a la carte 12.50/25.00 5.50 – **17 rm** 61.85/150.00 – SB.

Green Acres, Les Hubits, GY4 6LS, (01481) 235711, *greenacres@guernsey.net, Fax (01481) 235978*, heated, – rest, rest, TV P – 40. MC AE VISA.
2 April-22 October – **Meals** (bar lunch)/dinner 14.50 and a la carte 4.80 – **47 rm** 55.00/90.00.

Saints Bay, Icart, GY4 6JG, (01481) 238888, *saintsbayhotel.fsnet.co.uk, Fax (01481) 235558*, heated, – rm, TV P. MC AE VISA.
Meals (bar lunch)/dinner 16.00/18.50 and a la carte 4.70 – **36 rm** 41.00/101.00.

La Barbarie, Saints Bay, GY4 6ES, (01481) 235217, *barbarie@guernsey.net, Fax (01481) 235208*, heated, – TV P. MC VISA.
Meals (bar lunch Monday to Saturday)/dinner 12.40/22.15 and a la carte 6.00 – **22 rm** 53.50/83.00, 1 suite – SB.

Bella Luce, La Fosse, Moulin Huet, GY4 6EB, (01481) 238764, *info@bellalucehotel.guernsey.net, Fax (01481) 239561*, heated, – rest, TV P. MC AE VISA
Meals (bar lunch Monday to Saturday)/dinner 14.00 and a la carte 3.75 – **31 rm** 53.50/103.00 – SB.

La Michele, Les Hubits, GY4 6NB, (01481) 238065, *lamichelehotel@ukgateway.net, Fax (01481) 2339492*, heated, – rest, TV P. MC AE VISA.
11 April-October – **Meals** (residents only) (dinner only) 4.50 – **16 rm** (dinner included) 32.00/86.00 – SB.

The Auberge, Jerbourg Rd, GY4 6BH, (01481) 238485, *dixneuf@itl.net, Fax (01481) 710936*, Sea and neighbouring Channel Islands, – P. MC AE VISA JCB
closed Sunday dinner in winter – **Meals** a la carte 16.70/22.90.

St. Peter in the Wood – *pop. 2 242* – ✉ *St. Peters.*

XX **Café du Moulin,** Rue de Quanteraine, GY7 9DP, ☎ (01481) 265944, *vincentfam@guerns y.net, Fax (01481) 267343,* 🏠, « Converted granary », 🚗 – MC VISA
closed 2 weeks February, 2 weeks November, Monday and Tuesday lunch – **Meals** 14.5(
24.00 **s.** and a la carte 19.50/28.50 **s.** 🍷 8.00.

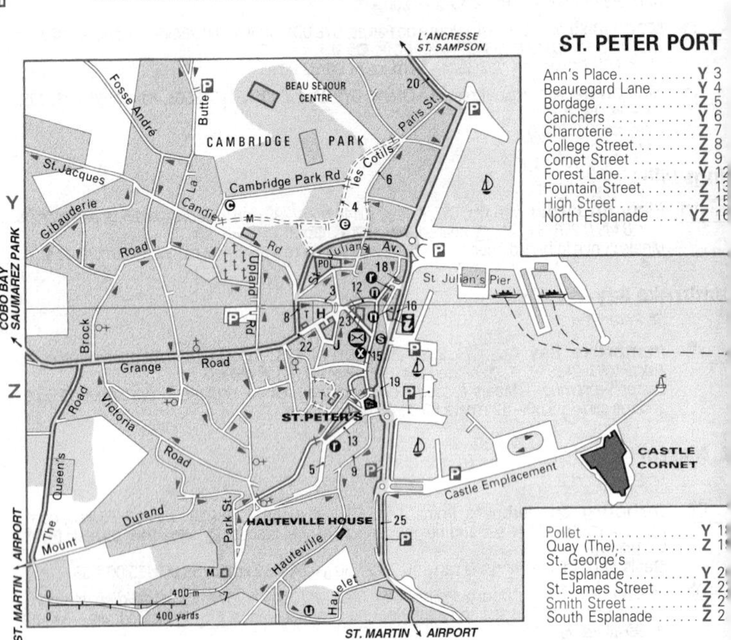

St. Peter Port *The West Country G.* – *pop. 16 648.*

See : *Town*★★ – *St. Peter's Church*★ **Z** – *Hauteville House*★ **AC Z** – *Castle Cornet*★ (≤★) A
Z.

Env. : *Saumarez Park*★ *(Guernsey Folk Museum*★*), W : 2 m. by road to Catel* **Z** – *Lit Chapel*★, *SW : 2¼ m. by Mount Durand road* **Z**.

⛳18 *Rohais, St. Pierre Park* ☎ *(01481) 727039,* **Z**.

St. Pierre Park, Rohais, GY1 1FD, West : 1½ m. by Grange Rd ☎ (01481) 728282, *enqu es@stpierrepark.co.uk, Fax (01481) 712041,* ≤, ⛹, ≘s, 🏊, ⛳9, 🚗, 🎾, ✂ – 🛗, ▤ rest, 📺 – 🏃 200. MC AE ⓞ VISA. ✂
Café Renoir **:** **Meals** a la carte approx. 14.50 **s.** 🍷 7.00 – (see also ***Victor Hugo*** below)
132 rm ☕ 130.00/170.00 **s.** – SB.

Duke of Richmond, Cambridge Park, GY1 1UY, ☎ (01481) 726221, *duke@guernsey.n Fax (01481) 728945,* ≤, 🏊 heated – 🛗, ✂ rm, 📺 – 🏃 100. MC AE ⓞ VISA **Y**
Meals 9.00/16.00 **s.** and a la carte 🍷 6.50 – **71 rm** ☕ 70.00/120.00 **s.**, 1 suite – SB.

Les Rocquettes, Les Gravees, GY1 1RN, West : ¾ m. by Grange Rd ☎ (01481) 722146, *r quettes@sarniahotels.com, Fax (01481) 7214543,* ⛹, ≘s, 🏊, 🚗 – 🛗 ✂ 📺 P. MC AE
VISA. ✂
Meals (bar lunch Monday to Saturday)/dinner 10.00/18.50 and a la carte 🍷 4.50 – **51**
☕ 60.00/110.00.

De Havelet, Havelet, GY1 1BA, ☎ (01481) 722199, *havelet@sarniahotels.co Fax (01481) 714057,* ≘s, 🏊, 🚗 – 📺 P. MC AE ⓞ VISA. ✂ **Z**
Wellington Boot **:** **Meals** (dinner only and Sunday lunch)/dinner 15.00/16.00 and a la ca
– ***Havelet Grill*** **:** **Meals** *(closed Sunday lunch and Monday dinner)* 15.00/16.00 and a la ca
🍷 6.00 – **34 rm** ☕ 60.00/120.00.

Moore's Central, Le Pollet, GY1 1WH, ☎ (01481) 724452, *moores@sarniahotels.co Fax (01481) 714037,* ⛹, ≘s – 🛗 📺. MC AE ⓞ VISA. ✂ **Y**
Conservatory **:** **Meals** 9.00/16.00 and a la carte 🍷 4.70 – ***Library*** **:** **Meals** (carving re a la carte 9.00/15.00 🍷 4.70 – **49 rm** ☕ 52.00/166.00 – SB.

ENGLAND

La Frégate, Les Cotils, GY1 1UT, (01481) 724624, *lafregate@guernsey.net*, *Fax (01481) 720443*, town and harbour, – rest. Y e
The Restaurant : **Meals** 14.95/20.00 and a la carte – **13 rm** 63.00/105.00.

Victor Hugo (at St. Pierre Park H.), Rohais, GY1 1FD, West : 1 ½ m. by Grange Rd (01481) 728282, *Fax (01481) 712041* – VISA
closed Saturday lunch, Sunday dinner and Bank Holidays – **Meals** - Seafood - 25.00/31.95 **s.** and a la carte 10.50.

Le Nautique, Quay Steps, GY1 2LE, (01481) 721714, *Fax (01481) 721786*, – VISA Z s
closed Saturday lunch and Sunday – **Meals** - Seafood specialities - a la carte 17.00/28.50 6.00.

Merchant House, 38 High St., GY1 2JU, (01481) 728019, *dgmann@cinergy.co.uk*, *Fax (01481) 725875* – . VISA Z x
closed 25-26 December and Sunday – **Meals** 10.00/12.95 and a la carte.

The Absolute End, Longstore, GY1 2BG, North : ¾ m. by St. George's Esplanade (01481) 723822, *Fax (01481) 729129* – VISA JCB
closed January and Sunday – **Meals** - Seafood - 11.90 (lunch) and a la carte 16.70/27.70 5.50.

Frogs, 6 Tower Hill, GY1 1DF, (01481) 710088, *frenchrestaurant@gtonline.net*, *Fax (01481) 710878*, – . VISA Z r
closed 25-26 December and 1 January, Saturday lunch and Sunday – **Meals** - French - 8.45/10.45 **s.** (lunch) and a la carte 18.80/26.45 **s.**

Sawatdi, North Plantation, GY1 2LH, (01481) 2725805, *kalam@gitonline.net*, *Fax (01481) 2716455* – . VISA JCB Z n
closed 25-26 December and Sunday lunch – **Meals** - Thai - 8.95/25.95 and a la carte 6.50.

Christies (Restaurant), Le Pollet, GY1 1WQ, (01481) 726624, *Fax (01481) 729138*, – . VISA Y r
Meals a la carte 18.90/27.50 5.95.

St. Saviour – *pop. 2 419.*

St. Peter Port 4.

L'Atlantique, Perelle Bay, GY7 9NA, (01481) 264056, *enquiries@perellebay.com*, *Fax (01481) 263800*, , heated, – . VISA.
March-December – **Meals** (bar lunch Monday to Saturday)/dinner 18.50 and a la carte 4.50 – (see also ***L'Atlantique*** below) – **23 rm** 47.00/94.00 – SB.

Les Piques Country H., Rue des Piques, GY7 9FW, (01481) 264515, *Fax (01481) 265857*, « Part 15C farmhouse », , , , – . VISA.
restricted opening in winter – **Meals** *(closed Monday lunch)* 8.95/15.95 (dinner) and a la carte 4.50 – **17 rm** 70.00/120.00, 3 suites.

L'Atlantique (at L'Atlantique H.), Perelle Bay, GY7 9NA, (01481) 264056, *Fax (01481) 263800*, – . VISA
March-December – **Meals** (dinner only and Sunday lunch)/dinner 17.50 and a la carte 4.50.

Auberge du Val, Sous L'Eglise, GY7 9FX, (01481) 263862, *aubduval@guernsey.net*, *Fax (01481) 264835*, , « Converted 19C farmhouse, herb garden », – . VISA JCB.
closed 25-26 December – **Meals** *(closed Sunday dinner and Monday except lunch Bank Holidays)* (booking essential) a la carte approx. 20.40 – **8 rm** 30.00/60.00.

Vale.

Bordeaux, Bordeaux Bay, GY3 5LX, (01481) 247461, *Fax (01481) 243669*, –
early April-October – **Meals** (by arrangement) 10.00 **s.** – **8 rm** 37.00/54.00 **s.**

Vazon Bay – *Catel.*

La Grande Mare, Vazon Coast Rd, GY5 7LL, (01481) 256576, *Fax (01481) 256532*, , , , heated, , , , – – 30. VISA.
Meals 10.50/17.95 and a la carte 6.45 – **11 rm** 69.00/138.00, **13 suites** 104.00 – SB.

HERM

403 P 33 and 230 ⑩ *The West Country G. – pop. 97.*

See : *Le Grand Monceau★.*

to Guernsey (St. Peter Port) (Herm Seaway) (20 mn).

White House, GY1 3HR, (01481) 722159, *hotel@herm-island.cor* *Fax (01481) 710066*, « Private island setting ≤ Belle Greve Bay and Guernsey », heate , , – rest. MC AE VISA.
7 April-7 October – ***Conservatory*** **: Meals** (booking essential) 12.95/18.80 6.70 – ***Sh*** ***Inn*** **: Meals** *closed dinner Sunday and Monday* (bar lunch)/dinner 15.00 6.75 – **39 rm** (dinner included) 70.00/166.00 – SB.

JERSEY

403 OP 33 and 230 ⑪ *The West Country G. – pop. 85 150.*

See : *Island★★ – Jersey Zoo★★ AC – Jersey Museum★ – Eric Young Orchid Foundation★* *St. Catherine's Bay★ (≤★★) – Grosnez Point★ – Devil's Hole★ – St. Matthews Churc* *Millbrook (glasswork★) – La Hougue Bie★ (Neolithic tomb★ AC) – Waterworks Valley* *Hamptonne Country Life Museum★ – St. Catherine's Bay★ (≤★★) – Noirmont Point★.*

States of Jersey Airport : (01534) 490999.

from St. Helier to France (St. Malo) and Guernsey (St. Peter Port) (Emeraude Lines, from St. Helier to France (Granville) (Emeraude Lines) (summer only) (1 h) – from St. Helier France (Dielette) (Emeraude Lines) (summer only) (1 h 10 mn) – from St. Helier to Fran (Carteret) (Emeraude Lines) (summer only) (55 mn) – from St. Helier to Sark (Emerau Lines) (50 mn) – from St. Helier to Guernsey (St. Peter Port) and Weymouth (Condor Ferr Ltd).

from St. Helier to France (Granville and St. Malo) (Emeraude Lines and Condor Ferr Ltd) (summer only) – from St. Helier to France (St. Malo) (Condor Ferries Ltd) 3 weekly from Gorey to France (Carteret) (Emeraude Lines) (summer only) (30-40 mn) – from Helier to Guernsey (St. Peter Port) (Condor Ferries Ltd) (50 mn) – from St. Helier to Guerns (St. Peter Port) (Condor Ferries Ltd) daily except Sunday.

Liberation Square, St. Helier (01534) 500777.

Corbiere – ✉ *St. Brelade.*

St. Helier 8.

XXX **Sea Crest** with rm, Petit Port, JE3 8HH, (01534) 746353, *seacrest@super.net.* *Fax (01534) 747316*, ≤, , , – rest, TV P. MC AE VISA.
closed 15 February-15 March – **Meals** (*closed Sunday dinner October-March and Mond* 14.75/19.50 and a la carte 7.50 – **7 rm** 85.00/130.00.

Gorey *The West Country G.* – ✉ *St. Martin.*

See : *Mont Orgueil Castle★ (≤★★) AC.*

St. Helier 4.

Old Court House, Gorey Village, JE3 9FS, (01534) 854444, *ochhotel@itl.n* *Fax (01534) 853587*, , heated, – TV P. MC AE VISA JCB.
mid April-mid October – **Meals** (bar lunch)/dinner 16.50 **s.** and a la carte 4.50 – **58 rm** (dinner included) 58.50/134.00 **s.**

Moorings, Gorey Pier, JE3 6EW, (01534) 853633, *casino@itl.net, Fax (01534) 85761* rest, TV. MC AE VISA.
Meals 14.25/30.00 **s.** and a la carte 8.50 – **15 rm** 49.00/98.00 – SB.

XX **Jersey Pottery (Garden Restaurant)**, Gorey Village, JE3 9EP, (01534) 851119, *pot@itl.net, Fax (01534) 856403*, , « Working pottery », – P. MC AE VISA JCB
closed 23 December-26 January and Monday – **Meals** - Seafood - (lunch only) a la ca 21.25/32.25 **s.** 6.00.

XX **Suma's**, Gorey Hill, JE3 6ET, (01534) 853291, *Fax (01534) 851913*, ≤, – . MC AE VISA
closed 23 December-18 January and Sunday dinner – **Meals** (booking essential) 14.5C (lunch) and a la carte 19.50/33.20 **s.**

X **Village Bistro**, Gorey Village, JE3 9EP, (01534) 853429, *Fax (01534) 853429*, – AE VISA JCB
closed 3 weeks January-February, Tuesday lunch and Monday except Bank Holidays – **Me** 13.50 (lunch) and a la carte 25.15/28.35 4.95
Spec. Lobster risotto with sea bass. Scallop and King prawn ravioli, mussel and mushroo cream. Assiette of seafood.

Green Island.

X **Green Island**, St. Clement, JE2 6LS, (01534) 857787, *amw@psilink.co.* *Fax (01534) 619309*, , « Beachside setting » – MC VISA JCB
closed 2 weeks February-March, 3 weeks November, 1 week Christmas, Monday a Sunday dinner – **Meals** - Seafood specialities - (booking essential) a la carte 18.95/24 4.75.

rève De Lecq – ✉ *St. Ouen.*

Des Pierres, JE3 2DT, on B 65 ☏ (01534) 481858, *despierres@localdial.com, Fax (01534) 485273* – TV P. MC AE Ⓓ VISA.
Meals (residents only) (dinner only) 9.85 **s.** – **16 rm** (dinner included) 37.00/74.00.

rouville – *pop. 4 658.*

Lavender Villa, Rue a Don, JE3 9DX, on A 3 ☏ (01534) 854937, *Fax (01534) 856147*, – rest, TV P. MC VISA.
mid March-October – **Meals** (residents only) (dinner only) 10.00 4.50 – **21 rm** (dinner included) 37.00/74.00.

a Haule – ✉ *St. Brelade.*

La Place, Route du Coin, JE3 8BT, by B 25 on B 43 ☏ (01534) 744261, *hotlaplace@aol.com, Fax (01534) 745164*, heated, – rest TV P – 100. MC AE Ⓓ VISA.
Knights: **Meals** (dinner only and Sunday lunch September to May)/dinner 26.00 **s.** and a la carte 8.00 – **42 rm** 108.00/156.00 **s.** – SB.

La Haule Manor, St. Aubin's Bay, JE3 8BS, ☏ (01534) 741426, *Fax (01534) 745501*, ← St. Aubin's Fort and Bay, – rest, TV P. MC VISA JCB.
April-October – **Meals** 14.50/18.95 6.80 – **14 rm** 87.45/113.00.

Au Caprice, Route de la Haule, JE3 8BA, on A 1 ☏ (01534) 722083, *aucaprice@cinergy.co.uk, Fax (01534) 280058* – TV. MC VISA.
April-October – **Meals** (by arrangement) 7.00 **s.** 3.00 – **12 rm** 22.00/56.00.

a Pulente – ✉ *St. Brelade.*

18 *Les Mielles G. & C.C., St. Ouens Bay ☏ (01534) 482787.*
St. Helier 7.

Atlantic, Le Mont de la Pulente, JE3 8HE, on B 35 ☏ (01534) 744101, *info@theatlantichotel.com, Fax (01534) 744102*, ←, heated, – TV P – 60. MC AE Ⓓ VISA.
closed January and February – **Meals** 16.50/25.00 **s.** and dinner a la carte 27.25/40.50 **s.** 10.00 – **49 rm** 155.00/255.00 **s.**, 1 suite – SB.

a Rocque.

St. Helier 8.

Borsalino Rocque, JE3 9FF, ☏ (01534) 852111, *Fax (01534) 856404*, – P. MC AE VISA
closed 25-26 December and Tuesday – **Meals** - Seafood - 7.25/22.50 and a la carte 6.40.

ozel Bay – ✉ *St. Martin.*

St. Helier 6.

Chateau La Chaire, Rozel Valley, JE3 6AJ, ☏ (01534) 863354, *res@chateau-la-chaire.co.uk, Fax (01534) 865137*, « Victorian country house », – rest, TV P. MC AE Ⓓ VISA JCB.
Meals 27.50 6.50 – **13 rm** 105.00/180.00 **s.**, 1 suite – SB.

Beau Couperon, JE3 6AN, ☏ (01534) 865522, *southern@itl.net, Fax (01534) 865332*, ←, heated – rest, TV P. MC AE VISA.
April-December – **Meals** 17.50 (dinner) and a la carte 12.50/25.50 5.00 – **33 rm** 72.30/96.40 – SB.

Frere de Mer, Le Mont de Rozel, JE3 6AN, East : ½ m. on B 38 ☏ (01534) 861000, *Fax (01534) 864007*, ← Sea and French coastline, – P. MC AE VISA
closed Monday – **Meals** - Seafood specialities - 8.95/12.95 (lunch) and a la carte 18.45/33.00 5.00.

. Aubin – ✉ *St. Brelade.*

St. Helier 4.

La Tour, High St., JE3 8BZ, ☏ (01534) 743770, *Fax (01534) 747143*, ← St. Aubin's Fort and Bay, – TV P. MC Ⓓ VISA.
closed 2 January-16 March – ***Rooks:*** **Meals** (light lunch)/dinner 12.50 **s.** and a la carte 4.50 – **24 rm** 44.50/111.00 **s.**, 1 suite.

Somerville, Mont du Boulevard, JE3 8AD, South : ¾ m. via harbour ☏ (01534) 741226, *somerville@dolanhotels.com, Fax (01534) 746621*, ← St. Aubin's Bay, heated, – TV P. MC VISA.
closed January – **Meals** (live music and dancing Saturday) (bar lunch Monday to Saturday)/dinner 15.00/24.00 6.50 – **59 rm** 48.00/96.00.

ENGLAND

Mont de La Roque, Mont de La Roque, JE3 8BQ, (01534) 742942, *mdlrq@supernet k, Fax (01534) 747841,* ≤ St. Aubin's Fort and Bay, – rest, TV P. MC AE VISA.
23 January-October – ***Le Mirage :*** **Meals** (dinner only and Sunday lunch)/dinner a la car 18.75/28.15 4.95 – **31 rm** 60.00/150.00, 2 suites.

Panorama without rest., La Rue du Crocquet, JE3 8BZ, (01534) 74242 *Fax (01534) 745940,* ≤ St. Aubin's Fort and Bay, – TV. MC AE VISA.
mid March-early November – **15 rm** 46.00/92.00.

St. Magloire, High St., JE3 8BZ, (01534) 741302, *Fax (01534) 744148* – rest, TV. VISA.
March-October – **Meals** (residents only) (dinner only) 7.50 **s.** 2.75 – **12 rm** 31.0 52.00 **s.**

Sabots d'or, High St., JE3 8BZ, (01534) 43732, *Fax (01534) 490142* – rest, TV. AE VISA
Meals (by arrangement) 7.00 **s.** 3.50 – **12 rm** 25.00/54.00 **s.**

Porthole Cottage without rest., La Route au Moestre (Market Hill), JE3 8A (01534) 745007, *portcott@itt.net, Fax (01534) 490336,* ≤, – TV P. MC AE VISA JCB.
10 March-28 October – **11 rm** 30.00/60.00 **s.**

Old Court House Inn with rm, St. Aubin's Harbour, JE3 8AB, (01534) 7464 *Fax (01534) 745103,* ≤, – TV. MC AE VISA.
Meals *(closed 25 December)* 12.00/18.00 and a la carte 4.95 – **8 rm** 50.00/100.0 1 suite – SB.

St. Brelade's Bay *The West Country G. – pop. 9 560 –* St. Brelade.

See : *Fishermen's Chapel (frescoes★).*
St. Helier 6.

L'Horizon, JE3 8EF, (01534) 743101, *Fax (01534) 746269,* ≤ St. Brelade's Bay, – TV P – 150. MC AE VISA.
Crystal Room : **Meals** (dinner only and Sunday lunch)/dinner 26.00 **s.** and a la carte 8. – (see also ***The Grill*** below) – **104 rm** 140.00/240.00 **s.**, 3 suites – SB.

St. Brelade's Bay, Rue de la Baie, JE3 8EF, (01534) 746141, *Fax (01534) 747278,* ≤ Brelade's Bay, « Gardens », heated, – TV P. MC AE VISA.
27 April-7 October – **Meals** 18.00/30.00 and a la carte 8.00 – **80 rm** 101.00/244.00 1 suite.

Golden Sands, La Route de la Baie, JE3 8EF, (01534) 741241, *goldensands@dolanho s.com, Fax (01534) 499366,* ≤ – rest, TV. MC VISA.
April-October – **Meals** (bar lunch)/dinner 12.50/20.00 **s.** 6.75 – **62 rm** 54.00/124.00

Chateau Valeuse, Rue de la Valeuse, JE3 8EE, (01534) 746281, *chatval@itl.n Fax (01534) 747110,* heated, – rest, TV P. MC VISA JCB.
6 April-23 October – **Meals** *(closed Sunday dinner)* 11.00/18.00 and dinner a la carte 6 – **34 rm** 51.00/122.00 – SB.

XXX **The Grill** (at L'Horizon H.), JE3 8EF, (01534) 490082, *Fax (01534) 746269* – P. MC VISA
closed lunch Sunday and Monday – **Meals** 18.00 **s.** (lunch) and a la carte 26.00/37.0 8.00.

St. Helier *The West Country G. – pop. 27 523.*

See : *Jersey Museum★ AC Z – Elizabeth Castle (≤★) AC Z – Fort Regent (≤★ AC) Z.*
Env. : *St. Peter's Valley - German Underground Hospital★ AC, NW : 4 m. by A 1, A 11 Peter's Valley rd and C 112.*

Plan opposite

De Vere Grand, Esplanade, JE4 8WD, (01534) 722301, *grand.jersey@devere-hotels m, Fax (01534) 737815,* ≤, – rest, TV – 180. MC AE Y
Meals (bar lunch)/dinner 21.00 7.50 – (see also ***Victoria's*** below) – **109 rm** 130. 190.00 **s.**, 5 suites – SB.

Hotel de France, St. Saviours Rd, JE1 7XP, (01534) 614000, *enggen@defrance.co. Fax (01534) 614299,* heated, squash – TV P – 1000. MC AE Y
closed 21-28 December – **Meals** (dinner only) a la carte 23.90/29.75 **s.** 8.25 – **312** 99.00/295.00 **s.**, 8 suites.

Pomme d'Or, Liberation Sq., JE1 3UF, (01534) 880110, *pomme@seymour-hotels- ey.com, Fax (01534) 737781* – rm, rest, TV – 180. MC AE VISA Z
Harbour Room : **Meals** (carving rest.) 13.50/17.50 **s.** and a la carte 5.25 – (see also ***Petite Pomme*** below) – **139 rm** 80.00/130.00 **s.**, 2 suites.

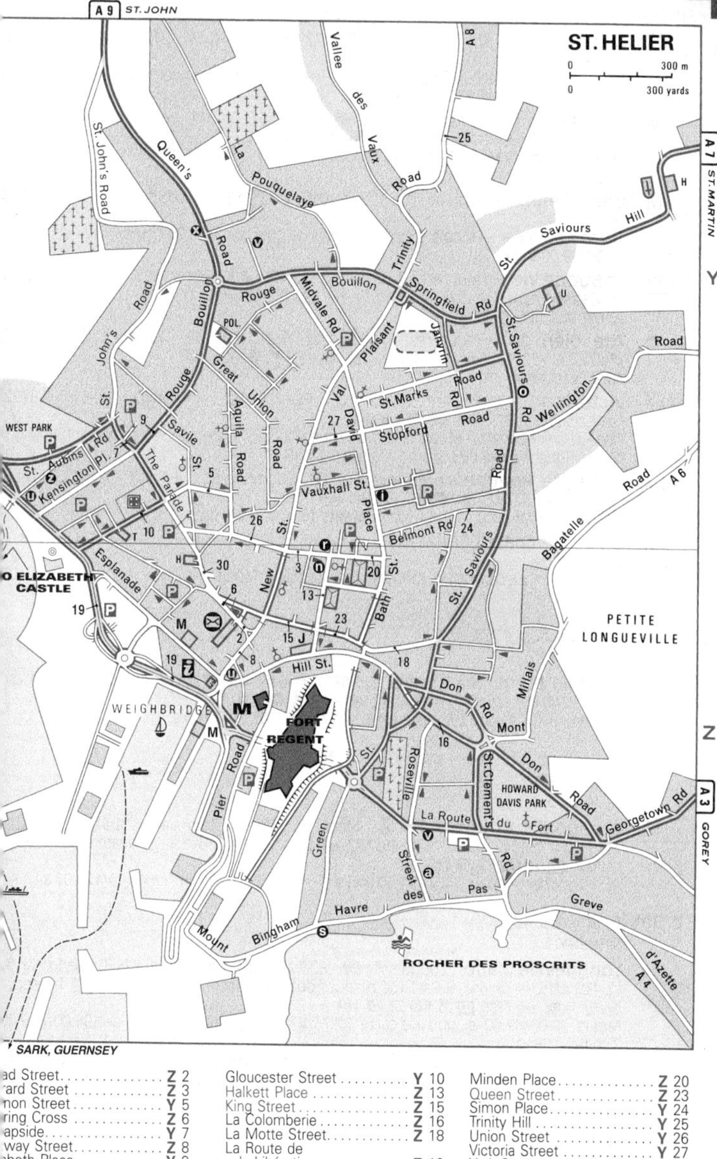

ad Street . . . . Z 2
ard Street . . . . Z 3
non Street . . . . Y 5
ring Cross . . . . Z 6
apside . . . . Y 7
way Street . . . . Z 8
abeth Place . . . . Y 9

Gloucester Street . . . . Y 10
Halkett Place . . . . Z 13
King Street . . . . Z 15
La Colomberie . . . . Z 16
La Motte Street . . . . Z 18
La Route de
la Libération . . . . Z 19

Minden Place . . . . Z 20
Queen Street . . . . Z 23
Simon Place . . . . Y 24
Trinity Hill . . . . Y 25
Union Street . . . . Y 26
Victoria Street . . . . Y 27
York Street . . . . Z 30

[hotel symbol] **Royal,** David Pl., JE2 4TD, ✆ (01534) 726521, *royalhot@itl.net, Fax (01534) 724035* – [lift] [TV] – [conference] 400. [MC] [AE] [D] [VISA] Y i
Meals *(bar lunch Monday-Saturday)/dinner* 15.50 **s.** and a la carte – **81 rm** [room] 59.50/89.50 **s.** – SB.

[hotel symbol] **De la Plage,** Havre des Pas, JE4 9NJ, ✆ (01534) 723474, *enquiries@delaplagehotel.com, Fax (01534) 768642,* ≤, [gym] – [lift] [TV] [P]. [MC] [AE] [D] [VISA] [JCB]. [no dogs] Z s
9 April-18 October – **Meals** (bar lunch)/dinner 16.50 **s.** [wine] 5.50 – **78 rm** [room] 45.00/118.00 **s.**

Queens, Queens Rd, JE2 3GR, ☎ (01534) 722239, *Fax (01534) 721930* – |‡|, ⊁ rest, TV MO ⓓ VISA JCB. ✠ Y
closed 21 December-7 January – **Meals** (residents only) (dinner only) a la carte 12.95 ⅟ 4.00 – **37 rm** ☐ 50.00/130.00 **s.** – SB.

Laurels, La route du Fort, JE2 4PA, ☎ (01534) 736444, *reservations@seabird.co. Fax (01534) 759904* – ⊁ rest, TV P. MO AE ⓓ VISA Z
March-October – **Meals** (residents only) (dinner only) 12.00 ⅟ 5.00 – **37 rm** ☐ 55.00/100. – SB.

Brookfield, 24 Raleigh Av., JE2 3ZG, ☎ (01534) 723168, *Fax (01534) 721543* – TV. MO V ✠ Y
March-November – **Meals** (residents only) (dinner only) – **20 rm** ☐ (dinner include 21.00/69.00 **s.**

La Bonne Vie without rest., Roseville St., JE2 4PL, ☎ (01534) 735955, *labonnevieguest use@yahoo.com, Fax (01534) 733357* – ⊁ TV. MO VISA JCB. ✠ Z
10 rm ☐ 28.00/56.00 **s.**

The Glen without rest., Vallee des Vaux, JE2 3GB, North : 1 ¼ m. by A ☎ (01534) 732062, *Fax (01534) 880738,* – TV P. MO VISA. ✠
April-October – **7 rm** ☐ 30.00/62.00 **s.**

Victoria's (at De Vere Grand H.), Peirson Rd, JE4 8WD, ☎ (01534) 8722 *Fax (01534) 737815* – ▤. MO AE ⓓ VISA Y
closed Bank Holidays – **Meals** (live music and dancing Friday and Saturday) (dinner only a Sunday lunch)/dinner 23.50 and a la carte ⅟ 7.50.

La Petite Pomme (at Pomme d'Or H.), Liberation Sq., JE1 3UF, ☎ (01534) 7666 *Fax (01534) 737781* – ▤. MO AE ⓓ VISA JCB Z
closed Saturday lunch and Sunday – **Meals** 18.00 and a la carte ⅟ 4.50.

La Capannina, 65-67 Halkett Pl., JE2 4WG, ☎ (01534) 734602, *Fax (01534) 877628* – MO AE ⓓ VISA Z
closed 25-26 December, 1 January and Sunday – **Meals** - Italian - a la carte 14.60/30 ⅟ 6.50.

St. Lawrence – *pop. 4 773.*

St. Helier 3.

Elmdale Farm, Ville Emphrie, JE3 1EF, ☎ (01534) 734779, *elmdalefarm@psilink.co. Fax (01534) 601115,* , heated, – TV P. MO VISA. ✠
Meals 8.95/14.95 and a la carte ⅟ 4.60 – **19 rm** ☐ 39.50/79.00 **s.**

St. Peter *The West Country C.* – *pop. 4 228.*

See : *Living Legend*★.
St. Helier 5.

Greenhill's Country H., Mont de l'Ecole, Coin Varin, JE3 7EL, on C ☎ (01534) 481042, *Fax (01534) 485322,* « Part 17C farmhouse », heated, – ⊁ r ▤ rest, TV P. MO AE ⓓ VISA. ✠
April-October – **Meals** 14.50/21.50 and a la carte ⅟ 5.50 – **24 rm** ☐ 48.00/128.00 **s.**, 1 su

St. Saviour – *pop. 12 680.*

St. Helier 1.

Longueville Manor, Longueville Rd, JE2 7WF, on A 3 ☎ (01534) 725501, *longman@ et, Fax (01534) 731613,* « Part 13C manor house with Jacobean panelling », heated, – |‡|, ⊁ rest, TV P. MO AE ⓓ VISA
Meals 20.00/42.00 **s.** and a la carte 22.75/47.00 **s.** ⅟ 9.00 – **28 rm** ☐ 195.00/300.0 2 suites – SB
Spec. Suprême of cod, salad of baby vegetables. Suprême of sea bass, baked auberg terrine, sauce vierge. Roast rump and loin of lamb with potato gratin and ratatouille.

Champ Colin without rest., Rue du Champ Colin, Hougue, JE2 7 ☎ (01534) 851877, *Fax (01534) 854902,* « Part 19C farmhouse, antiques », – ⊁ TV MO AE VISA JCB. ✠
3 rm ☐ 35.00/50.00.

Trinity – *pop. 2 639.*

The Highfield Country H., Route d'Ebenezer, JE3 5DT, Northwest : ½ m. on ☎ (01534) 862194, *highfield@localdial.com, Fax (01534) 865342,* , , , – ⊁ rest, TV P. MO AE VISA JCB. ✠
April-28 October – **Meals** (dinner only) 14.00 **s.** and a la carte – **28 rm** ☐ 52.50/125 10 suites.

The Guide is updated annually so renew your Guide every year.

ENGLAND

SARK

403 P 33 and 230 ⑩ *The West Country G. – pop. 550.*

See : *Island*★★ – *La Coupée*★★★ – *Port du Moulin*★★ – *Creux Harbour*★ – *La Seigneurie*★ *AC* – *Pilcher Monument*★ – *Hog's Back*★.

to Jersey (St. Helier) (Emeraude Lines) (50 mn).

to France (St. Malo) via Jersey (St. Helier) (Condor Ferries Ltd) 3 weekly – to Guernsey (St. Peter Port) (Isle of Sark Shipping Co. Ltd) (summer only) (45 mn).

Harbour Hill ☎ (01481) 832345 (restricted opening in winter).

Dixcart, GY9 0SD, ☎ (01481) 832015, *Fax (01481) 832164*, « Part 16C farmhouse », – rest, TV. MC AE D VISA JCB
Meals (bar meals in winter) 16.00 (dinner) and a la carte 15.00/25.75 4.75 – **15 rm** 50.00/100.00.

Aval du Creux, Harbour Hill, GY9 0SB, ☎ (01481) 832036, *avalducreux@freeuk.com, Fax (01481) 832368*, heated, – rest, TV. MC AE VISA JCB
May-October – **Meals** 17.95 and a la carte 3.50 – 4.95 – **20 rm** 57.55/96.50 **s.**

Stocks Island, GY9 0SD, ☎ (01481) 832001, *stocks@sark.net, Fax (01481) 832130*, heated, – rest. MC AE D VISA JCB
April-October – **Meals** (bar lunch)/dinner 18.00/25.00 **s.** and a la carte 6.00 – **21 rm** (dinner included) 50.00/140.00 **s.** – SB.

Petit Champ, GY9 0SF, ☎ (01481) 832046, *hpc@island_of_sark.co.uk, Fax (01481) 832469*, ≤ coast, Herm, Jetou and Guernsey, heated, – rest. MC AE D VISA.
12 April-28 September – **Meals** 18.25 **s.** (dinner) and a la carte 11.35/21.80 **s.** 5.75 – **16 rm** (dinner included) 57.00/110.00.

La Sablonnerie with rm, Little Sark, GY9 0SD, ☎ (01481) 832061, *Fax (01481) 832408*, « Part 16C farmhouse », – MC AE VISA.
Easter-mid October – **Meals** 23.80/25.80 and a la carte 5.50 – **22 rm** (dinner included) 59.50/149.00, 1 suite.

Founiais, Harbour Hill, GY9 0SB, ☎ (01481) 832626, *founais@gtonline, Fax (01481) 832642*, – MC VISA
April-September – **Meals** - Seafood specialities - *(closed Sunday)* and a la carte 15.35/21.85 3.95.

HANNEL TUNNEL *Kent* 404 X 30 – *see Folkestone.*

HAPELTOWN *N. Yorks.* 402 403 404 P 23 – *see Sheffield.*

HARD *Somerset* 403 L 31 – *pop. 10 770.*

The Guildhall, Fore St. ☎ (01460) 67463.

London 157 – Exeter 32 – Lyme Regis 12 – Taunton 18 – Yeovil 17.

Lordleaze, Henderson Drive, TA20 2HW, Southeast : 1 ½ m. by A 358 off Forton rd ☎ (01460) 61066, *Fax (01460) 66468* – TV P – 120. MC AE VISA
Meals a la carte 13.75/21.70 **t.** 4.25 – **16 rm** 55.00/75.00 **t.** – SB.

HARINGWORTH *Glos. – see Chipping Campden.*

HARLBURY *Oxon.* 403 404 P 28 – *pop. 2 694.*

London 72 – Birmingham 50 – Oxford 15.

Bull Inn with rm, Sheep St., OX7 3RR, ☎ (01608) 810689, « Part 17C inn » – TV P. MC VISA.
closed 25 and 31 December, 1 January and Monday – **Meals** *(closed Sunday dinner)* a la carte 14.85/29.40 **t.** 5.95 – **3 rm** 50.00/60.00 **t.**

HARLECOTE *Warks.* 403 404 P 27 – *see Stratford-upon-Avon.*

HARLESTOWN *Cornwall* 403 F 32 – *see St. Austell.*

HARLTON *W. Sussex* 404 R 31 – *see Chichester.*

CHARLWOOD *Surrey* 404 T 30 – *pop. 1 969* – ✉ *Horley.*
London 30 – Brighton 29 – Royal Tunbridge Wells 28.

Stanhill Court ⛰, Stan Hill, RH6 0EP, Northwest : 1 m. by Norwood Hill R ✆ (01293) 862166, *enquiries@stanhillcourthotel.co.uk, Fax (01293) 862773,* ←, « 19C Scottish baronial style interior », ⛳, 🌳, 🎾 – ⛔ rest, TV P – 🎤 180. MC AE Ⓓ VISA JCB. ⛔
Meals *(closed Saturday lunch)* 12.95/29.50 **t.** and a la carte – **14 rm** ☕ 120.00/175.00 **t.** SB.

CHARMOUTH *Dorset* 403 L 31 – *pop. 1 497* – ✉ *Bridport.*
London 157 – Dorchester 22 – Exeter 31 – Taunton 27.

Thatch Lodge, The Street, DT6 6PQ, ✆ (01297) 560407, *thatchlodgehotel@cs.com, Fax (01297) 560407,* « Part 14C thatched cottage », 🌳 – ⛔ TV P. MC VISA JCB. ⛔
mid March-late December – **Meals** *(closed Sunday and Monday)* (by arrangement) (dinner only) 27.50 **t.** 🍷 6.50 – **6 rm** ☕ 76.00/120.00 **t.** – SB.

White House, 2 Hillside, The Street, DT6 6PJ, ✆ (01297) 560411, *white-house@lineonet, Fax (01297) 560702* – ⛔ TV P. MC AE VISA JCB. ⛔
mid February-mid November – **Meals** (dinner only) 19.50 **t.** 🍷 9.00 – **10 rm** ☕ (dinner included) 68.00/116.00 **st.** – SB.

CHARTHAM HATCH *Kent* 404 X 30 – *see Canterbury.*

There is no paid advertising in this Guide.

CHATTERIS *Cambs.* 402 404 U 26 – *pop. 7 261.*
London 85 – Cambridge 26 – Norwich 71.

Cross Keys, 12-16 Market Hill, PE16 6BA, ✆ (01354) 693036, *Fax (01354) 694454,* « P... 17C inn » – ⛔ rm, TV. MC VISA JCB. ⛔
Meals (bar meals Sunday dinner) a la carte 17.75/22.75 **st.** 🍷 4.50 – **12 rm** ☕ 35.0... 68.00 **st.** – SB.

CHEADLE *Ches.* 402 403 N 23.
London 200 – Manchester 7 – Stoke-on-Trent 33.

Village H. & Leisure Club, Cheadle Rd, SK8 1HW, South : ¾ m. by A 51... ✆ (0161) 428 0404, *Fax (0161) 428 1191,* 🏋, ♨, 🏊, squash – 🛗 ⛔, ▤ rest, TV ✆ ♿ ... 🎤 200. MC AE Ⓓ VISA JCB
Meals (grill rest.) 14.95 **st.** and a la carte – **78 rm** ☕ 89.00/119.00 **st.**

Travel Inn, Royal Crescent, Cheadle Royal Retail Park, SK8 3FE, Southwest : 2 m. by A 5... off A 34 ✆ (0161) 491 5884, *Fax (0161) 491 5886* – 🛗, ⛔ rm, ▤ rest, TV ♿ P. MC AE VISA. ⛔
Meals (grill rest.) – **40 rm** 40.95 **t.**

CHEDDLETON *Staffs.* 402 403 404 N 24 – *pop. 3 534* – ✉ *Leek.*
London 125 – Birmingham 48 – Derby 33 – Manchester 42 – Stoke-on-Trent 11.

Choir Cottage without rest., Ostlers Lane, via Hollow Lane (opposite Red Lion on A 52... ST13 7HS, ✆ (01538) 360561, *elaine.sutcliffe@rc24.net* – ⛔ TV P. ⛔
closed 25 December – **3 rm** ☕ 35.00/60.00 **st.**

CHEDWORTH *Glos.* 403 404 O 28.
London 93 – Oxford 36 – Birmingham 59 – Gloucester 14 – Swindon 25.

Hare and Hounds, Foss Cross, GL54 4NN, Southeast : 2 m. by Fossebridge rd on A 4... ✆ (01285) 720288, 🌳 – P. MC VISA
closed 25 December – **Meals** (bookings not accepted) a la carte 13.00/24.45 **t.**

CHELMSFORD *Essex* 404 V 28 – *pop. 97 451.*
ℹ *County Hall, Market Rd* ✆ *(01245) 283400.*
London 33 – Cambridge 46 – Ipswich 40 – Southend-on-Sea 19.

Travel Inn, Chelmsford Service Area, Colchester Rd, Springfield, CM2 5PY, Northeast junction of A 12 with A 138 and A 130 ✆ (01245) 464008, *Fax (01245) 464010* – 🛗, ⛔ TV ♿ P – 🎤 35. MC AE Ⓓ VISA. ⛔
Meals (grill rest.) – **61 rm** 40.95 **t.**

t Great Baddow *Southeast : 3 m. by A 414 – ✉ Chelmsford.*

Pontlands Park , West Hanningfield Rd, CM2 8HR, ☎ (01245) 476444, *sales@pontlandsparkhotel.co.uk, Fax (01245) 478393,* ←, , heated, , – TV P – 40. MC AE VISA.
closed 24 to 31 December – ***The Conservatory :*** Meals *(closed Monday and Saturday lunch and Sunday dinner to non-residents)* (dancing Friday evening) 16.00/18.50 **t.** and dinner a la carte 8.75 – 10.00 – **16 rm** 90.00/140.00 **t.**, 1 suite – SB.

: Margaretting *Southwest : 3½ m. by A 1016 – ✉ Chelmsford.*

Ivy Hill, Writtle Rd, CM4 0EH, West : ½ m. by Wantz Rd ☎ (01277) 353040, *sales@ivyhillhotel.co.uk, Fax (01277) 355038,* heated, , – TV P – 80. MC AE VISA.
Meals *(closed Saturday lunch)* 22.95 **t.** and a la carte 7.95 – 9.50 – **33 rm** 90.00/160.00 **t.**

HELTENHAM *Glos.* 403 404 N 28 *Great Britain G. – pop. 91 301.*

See : *Town★ – Pittville Pump Room★* **AC A A.**

Exc. : *Sudeley Castle★ (Paintings★)* **AC**, *NE : 7 m. by B 4632* **A.**

18 *Cleeve Hill ☎ (01242) 672025* **A** – 18 *Cotswold Hills, Ullenwood ☎ (01242) 515317* **A.**

77 Promenade ☎ (01242) 522878.

London 99 – Birmingham 48 – Bristol 40 – Gloucester 9 – Oxford 43.

Plan on next page

Queen's, Promenade, GL50 1NN, ☎ (0870) 4008107, *gm1050@forte_hotels.com, Fax (01242) 224145,* – TV P – 80. MC AE VISA B n
Napier : Meals 21.95 **t.** (dinner) and a la carte 15.00/26.00 **t.** 6.00 – 12.25 – **79 rm** 110.00/175.00 **st.** – SB.

Thistle Cheltenham, Gloucester Rd, GL51 0TS, West : 2 m. on A 40 ☎ (01242) 232691, *cheltenham@thistle.co.uk, Fax (01242) 221846,* , , , , – , rm, rest, TV P – 220. MC AE VISA JCB
Burford Room : Meals *(closed Saturday lunch)* 18.50/23.00 **st.** (dinner) and a la carte 22.00/37.00 **st.** 8.00 – 11.75 – **118 rm** 118.00 **st.**, 4 suites – SB.

Cheltenham Park, Cirencester Rd, Charlton Kings, GL53 8EA, ☎ (01242) 222021, *cheltenhampark@paramount.hotels.co.uk, Fax (01242) 226935,* , , , – , rest, TV P – 350. MC AE VISA A e
Meals 11.95/21.50 **st.** 8.95 – **143 rm** 99.00/128.00 **st.**, 1 suite – SB.

On the Park, 38 Evesham Rd, GL52 2AH, ☎ (01242) 518898, *stay@hotelonthepark.co.uk, Fax (01242) 511526,* « Regency town house », – TV . MC AE VISA. C r
Meals – (see ***Bacchanalian*** below) – 8.50 – **12 rm** 80.50/159.50 **t.** – SB.

Kandinsky, Bayshill Rd, GL50 3AS, ☎ (01242) 527788, *reservations@hotelkandinsky.com, Fax (01242) 226412,* « Contemporary interior » – , rest, TV P. MC AE VISA JCB
Café Paradiso : Meals 12.00/15.00 **st.** (lunch) and a la carte 13.50/26.50 **st.** 8.00 – 10.50 – **46 rm** 65.00/90.00 **st.**, 2 suites. B x

Prestbury House, The Burgage, GL52 3DN, Northeast : 1 ½ m. by Prestbury Rd (B 4632) off Tatchley Lane ☎ (01242) 529533, *Fax (01242) 227076,* – TV P – 60. MC AE VISA. A r
Meals 14.00 **st.** and a la carte 3.50 – **16 rm** 66.00/80.00 – SB.

Charlton Kings, London Rd, Charlton Kings, GL52 6UU, ☎ (01242) 231061, *Fax (01242) 241900,* – TV P. MC AE VISA JCB A c
Meals (dinner only and Sunday lunch)/dinner 18.75 **t.** 5.80 – **13 rm** 61.00/105.00 **t.** – SB.

Lypiatt House without rest., Lypiatt Rd, GL50 2QW, ☎ (01242) 224994, *lypiatthouse@gofornet.co.uk, Fax (01242) 224996* – TV P. MC AE VISA B c
10 rm 55.00/85.00 **st.**

Acanthus Court without rest., 59 Leckhampton Rd, GL53 0BS, ☎ (01242) 576083, *res@acanthus.co.uk, Fax (01242) 224579* – TV P. MC AE VISA JCB. A e
closed 21 December-15 January – **5 rm** 69.00/79.00 **t.**

Wyastone, Parabola Rd, GL50 3BG, ☎ (01242) 245549, *reservations@wyastonehotel.co.uk, Fax (01242) 522659* – TV P. MC VISA. B i
closed Christmas-New Year – **Meals** (residents only) (dinner only) a la carte approx. 18.00 5.50 – **13 rm** 53.00/79.00 **st.**

Milton House without rest., 12 Royal Par., Bayshill Rd, GL50 3AY, ☎ (01242) 582601, *info@miltonhousehotel.co.uk, Fax (01242) 222326* – TV P. MC AE VISA. B e
closed 28 December-3 January – **8 rm** 45.00/80.00 **st.**

Beaumont House, Shurdington Rd, GL53 0JE, ☎ (01242) 245986, *rocking.horse@virgin.net, Fax (01242) 520044,* – rest, TV P. MC AE VISA JCB. A u
Meals (residents only) (dinner only) 16.50 **st.** – **16 rm** 42.00/68.00 **st.** – SB.

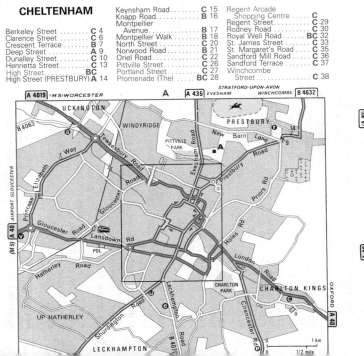

CHELTENHAM

Street	Grid	No.
Berkeley Street	C	4
Clarence Street	C	6
Crescent Terrace	B	7
Deep Street	A	9
Dunalley Street	C	10
Henrietta Street	C	13
High Street	BC	
High Street (PRESTBURY)	A	14
Keynsham Road	C	15
Knapp Road	B	16
Montpellier Avenue	B	17
Montpellier Walk	B	18
North Street	C	20
Norwood Road	B	21
Oriel Road	C	22
Pittville Street	C	26
Portland Street	C	27
Promenade (The)	BC	28
Regent Arcade Shopping Centre	C	29
Regent Street	C	30
Rodney Road	C	30
Royal Well Road	BC	32
St. James Street	C	33
St. Margaret's Road	C	35
Sandford Mill Road	C	36
Sandford Terrace	C	37
Winchcombe Street	C	38

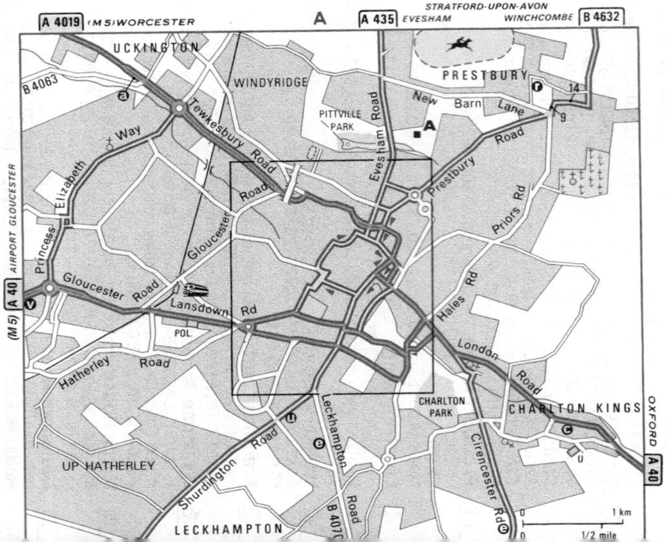

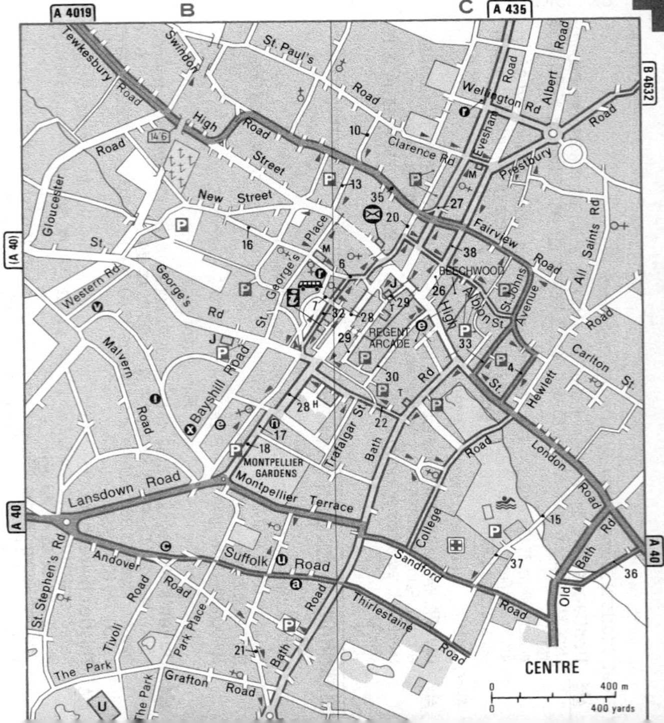

CENTRE

Stretton Lodge, Western Rd, GL50 3RN, ☎ (01242) 570771, *info@strettonlodge.demon.co.uk, Fax (01242) 528724,* – rm, TV, P. MC AE VISA JCB B v
Meals (residents only) (lunch by arrangement)/dinner a la carte 19.65/26.20 **st.** 6.95 – **8 rm** 50.00/90.00 **st.** – SB.

Travel Inn, Tewkesbury Rd, Uckington, GL51 9SL, Northwest : 1 ¾ m. on A 4019 at junction with B 4634 ☎ (01242) 233847, *Fax (01242) 244887* – rm, TV, P. MC AE VISA. A a
Meals (grill rest.) – **40 rm** 40.95 **t.**

Travel Inn, 374 Gloucester Rd, GL51 7AY, ☎ (01242) 260103, *Fax (01242) 260042* – rm, TV, P. MC AE VISA. A v
Meals (grill rest.) – **42 rm** 40.95 **t.**

Le Champignon Sauvage (Everitt-Matthias), 24-26 Suffolk Rd, GL50 2AQ, ☎ (01242) 573449, *Fax (01242) 254365* – MC AE VISA JCB B a
closed 3 weeks June, 10 days Christmas-New Year, 2 days after Easter, Sunday and Monday – **Meals** 19.50/39.50 **t.** 5.95
Spec. Roasted foie gras with walnuts and quince, Banyuls sauce. Fillet of pork, chou farci and black pudding. Feuillantine of mango, Thai spiced cream and red wine syrup.

Bacchanalian (at On the Park H.), 38 Evesham Rd, GL52 2AH, ☎ (01242) 227713 – rest. MC AE VISA C r
Meals (booking essential) 15.95/23.50 **t.** and dinner a la carte 8.00.

Mayflower, 32-34 Clarence St., GL50 3NX, ☎ (01242) 522426, *Fax (01242) 251667* – . MC AE VISA JCB B r
closed 24 to 26 December and Sunday lunch – **Meals** - Chinese - 6.95/32.50 **t.** and a la carte 6.95.

Le Petit Blanc, Promenade, GL50 1NN, ☎ (01242) 266800, *Fax (01242) 266801* – . MC AE B n
closed 25 December – **Meals** - Brasserie - 15.00 **st.** (lunch) and a la carte 17.25/26.25 **st.**

The Daffodil, 18-20 Suffolk Par., GL50 2AE, ☎ (01242) 700055, *daffodilrest@c5.com, Fax (01242) 700088,* « Converted cinema » – . MC AE VISA JCB B u
closed 25-26 December and Sunday – **Meals** a la carte 18.95/26.75 **st.** 5.00.

Vanilla, 9-10 Cambray Pl., GL50 1JS, ☎ (01242) 228228, *Fax (01242) 228228* – MC AE VISA JCB C e
closed 25-26 December 1 January, Monday and Sunday dinner – **Meals** 7.45/11.95 **t.** (lunch) and a la carte 16.95/24.00 **t.** 8.00.

Woolstone *North : 6 ¼ m. by A 435* – **A** – ✉ *Cheltenham.*

Old Rectory without rest., GL52 4RG, ☎ (01242) 673766, *fesey@aol.com, Fax (01242) 677011,* ≤, – TV P. MC VISA.
closed Christmas and New Year **3 rm** 40.00/75.00 **t.**

Cleeve Hill *Northeast : 4 m. on B 4632* – **A** – ✉ *Cheltenham.*

Cleeve Hill without rest., GL52 3PR, ☎ (01242) 672052, *gbtoncleevehill@aol.com, Fax (01242) 679969,* ≤, – TV P. MC VISA.
10 rm 60.00/95.00 **t.**

Shurdington *Southwest : 3 ¾ m. on A 46* – **A** – ✉ *Cheltenham.*

The Greenway , GL51 5UG, ☎ (01242) 862352, *greenway@btinternet.com, Fax (01242) 862780,* ≤, « Part 16C Cotswold country house, gardens », – TV P – 30. MC AE VISA.
Meals 14.00/35.00 **t.** 10.00 – **19 rm** 99.00/229.00 **t.** – SB.

Cheltenham and Gloucester Moat House, Shurdington Rd, GL3 4PB, Southwest : 1 ¼ m. on A 46 ☎ (01452) 519988, *cbcgl@queensmoat.co.uk, Fax (01452) 519977,* , , , – , rm, rest, TV & P – 340. MC AE VISA JCB
Meals *(closed Saturday lunch)* (carving lunch Sunday) 15.50/19.50 **st.** and a la carte 6.50 – 11.50 – **94 rm** 120.00/155.00 **st.**, 2 suites – SB.

Staverton *West : 4 ¼ m. by A 40* – **A** – ✉ *Cheltenham.*

White House, Gloucester Rd, GL51 0ST, on B 4063 ☎ (01452) 713226, *Fax (01452) 857590* – rm, TV P – 200. MC AE VISA JCB
Meals *(closed Saturday lunch)* 9.50/35.00 **st.** and dinner a la carte 6.75 – **49 rm** 80.00/115.00 **t.** – SB.

ELWOOD *Bath & North East Somerset* – *see Bristol.*

es prix — Pour toutes précisions sur les prix indiqués dans ce guide, reportez-vous aux pages de l'introduction.

CHENIES *Bucks.* 404 S 28 – *pop. 258* – ✉ *Rickmansworth (Herts.).*
London 30 – Aylesbury 18 – Watford 7.

Bedford Arms, WD3 6EQ, ✆ (01923) 283301, *info@bedfordarms-hotel-chenies.co*
Fax (01923) 284825, , – rm, TV P. MC AE VISA JCB.
Meals *(closed Sunday dinner)* (bar lunch Saturday) 23.00 **t.** and a la carte 7.25 – 13.5
10 rm 155.00 **st.** – SB.

CHERWELL VALLEY SERVICE AREA *Oxon.* 403 404 Q 28 – ✉ *Bicester.*
Motorway Service Area, junction 10 M 40, Northampton Rd, Bicester ✆ *(01869) 34588*

Travelodge, Northampton Rd, Ardley, OX6 9RD, M 40, junction 10 ✆ (01869) 3460
Fax (01869) 345030 – rm, TV P. MC AE VISA JCB.
Meals (grill rest.) – **98 rms** 59.95 **t.**

CHESHUNT *Herts.* 404 T 28 – *pop. 51 998* – ✉ *Broxbourne.*
Cheshunt, Park Lane ✆ *(01992) 29777.*
London 22 – Cambridge 40 – Ipswich 70 – Luton 34 – Southend-on-Sea 39.

Cheshunt Marriott, Halfhide Lane, Turnford, EN10 6NG, Northwest : 1 ¼ m. off B
✆ (01992) 451245, *Fax (01992) 440120,* , , – TV P – 120. MC
VISA.
Meals (bar lunch Monday to Saturday)/dinner a la carte 17.75/27.50 **t.** 7.95 – 10.5
131 rm 119.00 **t.**, 12 suites – SB.

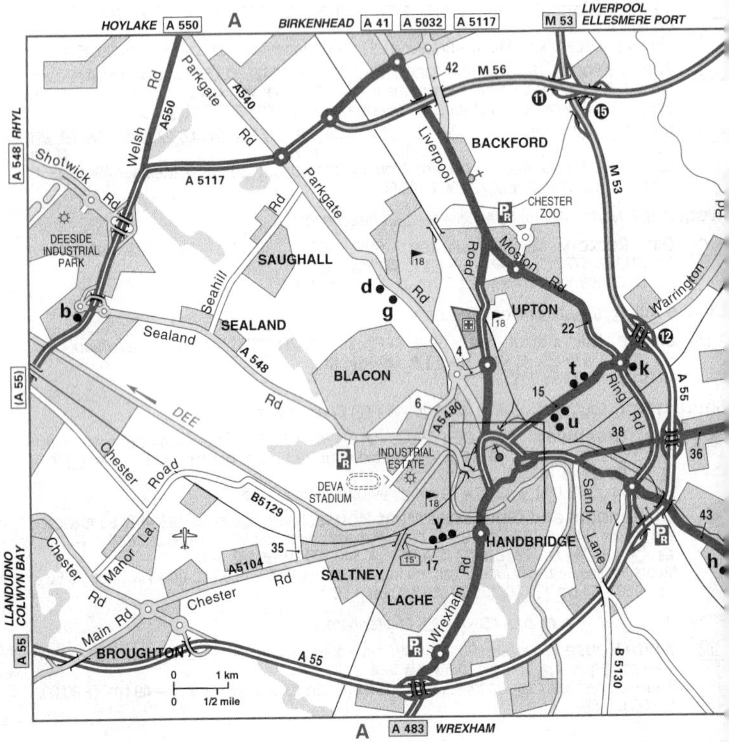

CHESTER BUILT UP AREA

Caldy Valley Road . . . . **A** 4
Countess Way . . . . **A** 5
Deva Link. . . . . **A** 6
Hoole Road . . . . **A** 15
Hough Green . . . . **A** 17
Long Lane . . . . **A** 22
Saltney Ferry Road . . . . **A** 35
Tarvin Road . . . . **A**
Vicar's Cross Road . . . . **A**
Whitby Lane . . . . **A**
Whitchurch Road . . . . **A**

ENGLAND

HESTER *Ches.* 402 403 L 24 *Great Britain G. – pop. 80 110.*

See : *City*★★ - *The Rows*★★ **B** – *Cathedral*★ **B** – *City Walls*★ **B**.

Env. : *Chester Zoo*★ **AC**, *N : 3 m. by A 5116.*

18 *Upton-by-Chester, Upton Lane* ☎ *(01244) 381183* **A** – 18 *Curzon Park* ☎ *(01244) 675130* **A**.

ℹ *Town Hall, Northgate St.* ☎ *(01244) 402111 – Chester Visitor and Craft Centre, Vicars Lane* ☎ *(01244) 402111.*

London 207 – Birkenhead 7 – Birmingham 91 – Liverpool 21 – Manchester 40 – Preston 52 – Sheffield 76 – Stoke-on-Trent 38.

CHESTER

ughton . . . . **B** 2
dge Street . . . . **B** 3
tgate Street . . . . **B** 7
dsham Street . . . . **B** 9
Grosvenor Park Road . . . . . . **B** 10
Grosvenor Street . . . . **B** 12
Handbridge . . . . **B** 13
Little St. John Street . . . . . **B** 19
Liverpool Road . . . . **B** 21
Lower Bridge Street . . . . **B** 23
Nicholas Street . . . . **B** 25
Northgate Street . . . . **B** 26
Parkgate Road . . . . **B** 28
Pepper Street . . . . **B** 30
St. John Street . . . . **B** 32
St. Martins Way . . . . **B** 33
Vicar's Lane . . . . **B** 40
Watergate Street . . . . **B**

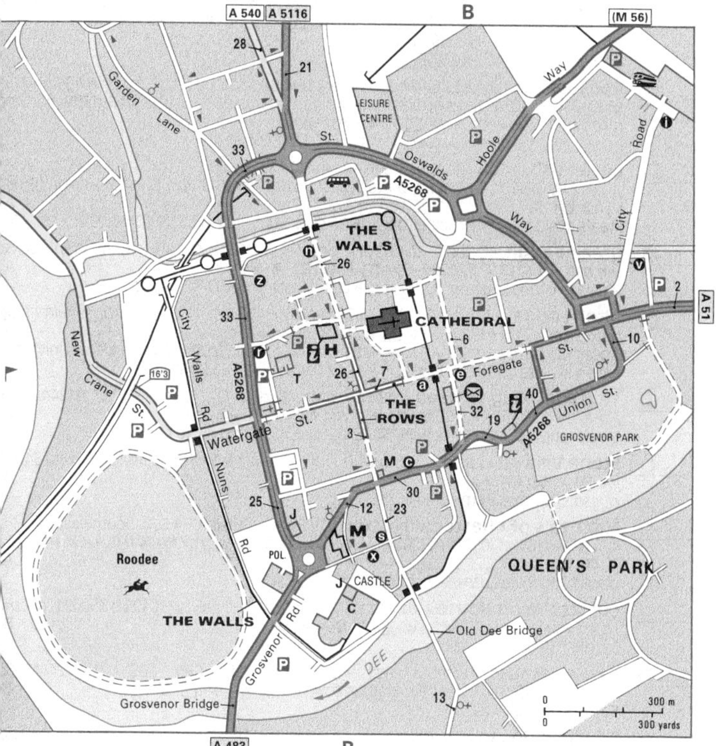

Chester Grosvenor, Eastgate, CH1 1LT, ☎ (01244) 324024, *chesgrov@chestergrosvenor.co.uk, Fax (01244) 313246,* – – 250. *closed 25 and 26 December* – **Meals** – (see ***Arkle*** and ***La Brasserie*** below) – 14.50 – **84 rm** 135.00/235.00, 1 suite. B a

Crabwall Manor, Parkgate Rd, Mollington, CH1 6NE, Northwest : 2 ¼ m. on A 540 ☎ (01244) 851666, *sales@crabwall.com, Fax (01244) 851400,* « Part 16C manor », – rest, – 100. A d
Meals – (see ***the Restaurant*** below) – **42 rm** 125.00/150.00 **st.**, 6 suites.

ENGLAND

Moat House Chester, Trinity St., CH1 2BD, ✆ (01244) 899988, *rvch9@queensmoat.co k*, *Fax (01244) 316118*, – rm, rest, – 600. VISA JCB B
Meals 10.00/17.00 **st.** and a la carte 7.25 – 11.50 – **158 rm** 125.00/200.00 **st.**, 2 suites – SB.

Mollington Banastre, Parkgate Rd, Mollington, CH1 6NN, Northwest : 2 ¼ m. on A 5 ✆ (01244) 851471, *Fax (01244) 851165*, squash – , rest, 250. VISA JCB A
Meals *(closed Sunday lunch)* 23.00 **st.** and a la carte 7.50 – **63 rm** 78.00/100.00 **st.** – SB

Hoole Hall, Warrington Rd, Hoole, CH2 3PD, Northeast : 2 m. on A 56 ✆ (01244) 4088 *Fax (01244) 320251*, – – 150. VISA. A
The Atrium : **Meals** *(closed Saturday lunch)* (buffet lunch Monday to Friday)/dinn a la carte 13.95/22.40 **st.** 6.95 – 11.75 – **97 rm** 80.00/95.00 **st.** – SB.

The Queen, City Rd, CH1 3AH, ✆ (01244) 350100, *reservations.queens@principalhote. o.uk*, *Fax (01244) 318483*, – – 220. VISA JCB B
The Garden : **Meals** 12.50/30.00 **st.** and a la carte 6.95 – **127 rm** 109.00/145.00 1 suite – SB.

Blossoms, St. John St., CH1 1HL, ✆ (01244) 323186, *heritagehotels-chester.blossoms@ rte_hotels.com*, *Fax (01244) 346433* – – 100. VISA JCB B
Brookes : **Meals** 7.95/13.95 **t.** (lunch) and a la carte 15.70/22.15 **t.** 7.50 – 9.95 – **63** 85.00/105.00 **st.**, 1 suite – SB.

Redland without rest., 64 Hough Green, CH4 8JY, Southwest : 1 m. by A 483 on A 5 ✆ (01244) 671024, *teresawhite@redlandhotelfsnet.co.uk.*, *Fax (01244) 681309*, « Victor mansion house », – . VISA. A
closed 20 December-1 January **12 rm** 45.00/75.00 **st.**

Cavendish, 42-44 Hough Green, CH4 8JQ, Southwest : 1 m. by A 483 on A 5 ✆ (01244) 675100, *cavendish@hotel_chester.com*, *Fax (01244) 678844* – rest, . VISA. A
Meals (residents only) (dinner only) 18.95 **st.** 5.00 – **19 rm** 45.00/60.00 **t.** – SB.

Green Bough, 60 Hoole Rd, CH2 3NL, on A 56 ✆ (01244) 326241, *greenboughhotel@c om.net*, *Fax (01244) 326265* – . VISA. A
Meals (bar lunch)/dinner 17.50 **st.** 8.00 – **18 rm** 59.50/125.00 **st.** – SB.

Alton Lodge, 78 Hoole Rd, CH2 3NT, on A 56 ✆ (01244) 310213, *enquiries@altonlodg o.uk*, *Fax (01244) 319206* – . VISA JCB. A
closed Christmas and New Year – **Meals** *(closed Friday to Sunday)* (residents only) (din only) a la carte 10.70/19.95 **st.** 5.50 – **17 rm** 45.00/65.00 **st.** – SB.

Ye Olde King's Head, 48-50 Lower Bridge St., CH1 1RS, ✆ (01244) 3248 *Fax (01244) 315693*, « 16C inn » – . VISA JCB. B
Meals (grill rest.) a la carte 9.45/14.35 **t.** – 6.45 – **8 rm** 45.50 **t.**

Stone Villa without rest., 3 Stone Pl., CH2 3NR, off A 56 (Hoole Rd) ✆ (01244) 34501 . VISA JCB. A
closed Christmas **9 rm** 35.00/56.00 **st.**

Mitchell's of Chester without rest., 28 Hough Green, CH4 8JQ, Southwest : 1 m. b 483 on A 5104 ✆ (01244) 679004, *mitoches@dialstart.net*, *Fax (01244) 659567*, – . VISA. A
closed 22-28 December – **7 rm** 32.00/54.00 **st.**

Chester Town House without rest., 23 King St., CH1 2AH, ✆ (01244) 350021, *dbcth l.com*, *Fax (01244) 350021* – . VISA. B
5 rm 35.00/50.00 **st.**

Castle House without rest., 23 Castle St., CH1 2DS, ✆ (01244) 3503 *Fax (01244) 350354*, « Part Elizabethan town house » – . VISA B
5 rm 24.00/48.00.

Edwards House without rest., 61-63 Hoole Rd, CH2 3NJ, on A 56 ✆ (01244) 318055, *anerob@supernet.com*, *Fax (01244) 310948* – . VISA. A
10 rm 25.00/54.00 **st.**

Arkle (at Chester Grosvenor H.), Eastgate, CH1 1LT, ✆ (01244) 324024, *Fax (01244) 313* – . VISA JCB B
closed 19-28 August, 25 December-23 January except 31 December, Sunday and Mond.
Meals 25.00/45.00-48.00 **t.** 11.75
Spec. Veal sweetbread with pasta and asparagus. Bresse pigeon with truffle bouillon foie gras. Steamed turbot with langoustine sabayon.

The Restaurant (at Crabwall Manor H.), Parkgate Rd, Mollington, CH1 6NE, Northwes ¼ m. on A 540 ✆ (01244) 851666, *Fax (01244) 851400*, – . VISA JCB A
– **Meals** a la carte 36.00/48.50 **t.**

XX **La Brasserie** (at Chester Grosvenor H.), Eastgate, CH1 1LT, (01244) 324024, *Fax (01244) 313246* – ▤ P. MC AE O VISA JCB B a
closed 25 and 26 December – **Meals** a la carte 21.75/38.25 **t.** 8.75.

X **Est, Est, Est,** Newgate House, Newgate St., CH1 1DE, (01244) 400507, *Fax (01244) 400507* – ▤. MC AE O VISA B c
closed 25 and 26 December – **Meals** - Italian - a la carte 12.20/26.55 **t.** 6.85.

X **Blue Bell,** 65 Northgate St., CH1 2HQ, (01244) 317758, *Fax (01244) 317759*, « Converted 15C inn » – ⇜. MC VISA JCB B n
closed 25-26 December and 1 January **Meals** 18.50/29.95 **t.** (dinner) and a la carte 13.90/ 30.00 **t.** 7.25.

Old Harkers Arms, 1 Russell St., CH3 5AL, (01244) 344525, *Fax (01244) 344812* – MC AE VISA. ✻ A v
closed dinner 25 December-1 January and Friday dinner – **Meals** a la carte 9.85/19.15 4.40.

Rowton *Southeast : 3 m. by A 41* – ✉ *Chester.*

Rowton Hall, Whitchurch Rd, CH3 6AD, (01244) 335262, *rowtonhall@rowtenhall.co.uk*, *Fax (01244) 335464*, Fб, ≘s, ▣, ⛱, ✂ – TV ♿ P – 🏠 200. MC AE O VISA. ✻ A h
Meals 14.50/22.50 **t.** and a la carte 8.95 – **38 rm** ▭ 85.00/200.00 **t.** – SB.

Two Mills *Northwest : 5 ¾ m. on A 540* – **A** – *at junction with A 550* – ✉ *Ledsham.*

Premier Lodge, Parkgate Rd, CH66 9PD, (0870) 7001580, *Fax (0870) 7001581* – |‡| ⇜ TV ☏ ♿ P. MC AE O VISA. ✻
Meals (grill rest.) – **31 rm** 42.00 **t.**

Puddington *Northwest : 6 m. by A 540* – **A** – ✉ *South Wirral.*

Craxton Wood, Parkgate Rd, CH66 9PB, on A 540 (0151) 347 4000, *info@craxton.macdonald-hotels.co.uk*, *Fax (0151) 347 4040*, ⩽, Fб, ≘s, ▣, ⛱, ⚲ – |‡| ⇜, ▤ rest, TV ☏ ♿ P – 🏠 400. MC AE O VISA JCB. ✻
Meals (bar lunch Saturday) 16.95/25.00 **t.** and a la carte 8.50 – **71 rm** ▭ 85.00/105.00 **st.**, 1 suite – SB.

Le Grand Londres (GREATER LONDON) est composé de la City et de 32 arrondissements administratifs (Borough) eux-mêmes divisés en quartiers ou en villages ayant conservé leur caractère propre (Area).

[CH]ESTERFIELD *Derbs.* 402 403 404 P 24 *Great Britain G.* – *pop. 71 945.*

Env. : *Bolsover Castle* AC, E : 5 m. by A 632.*

18, 9 Chesterfield Municipal, Murray House, Crow Lane (01246) 273887 – 18 Grassmoor, North Wingfield Rd (01246) 856044.

Peacock Information Centre, Low Pavement (01246) 345777.

London 152 – Derby 24 – Nottingham 25 – Sheffield 12.

Ibis (without rest.), Lordsmill St, S41 7RW, at junction of A 619 and A 632 (01246) 221333, Reservations (Freephone) 0800 897121, *Fax (01246) 221444* – |‡| ⇜, ▤ rest, TV ☏ ♿ P – 🏠 40. MC AE O VISA
86 rm 49.50 **st.**

Travelodge, Brimington Road North, Wittington Moor, S41 9BE, North : 2 m. on A 61 (01246) 455411, *Fax (01246) 455411* – ⇜ rm, ▤ rest, TV ♿ P. MC AE O VISA JCB. ✻
Meals (grill rest.) – **20 rm** 49.95 **t.**

[CH]ESTER-LE-STREET *Durham* 401 402 P 19 – *pop. 35 123.*

18 Lumley Park (0191) 388 3218 – 18 Roseberry Grange, Grange Villa (0191) 370 0670.

London 275 – Durham 7 – Newcastle upon Tyne 8.

Lumley Castle, DH3 4NX, East : 1 m. on B 1284 (0191) 389 1111, *Fax (0191) 389 1881*, « 14C », ⛱ – ⇜ rest, TV P – 🏠 150. MC AE O VISA JCB. ✻
closed 25-26 December and 1 January – **Meals** *(closed Saturday lunch)* 15.50/26.50 **st.** and a la carte 7.00 – ▭ 12.50 – **58 rm** 95.00/185.00, 1 suite – SB.

[CH]ESTER SERVICE AREA *Ches.* – ✉ *Chester.*

Travel Inn without rest., Elton, CH2 4QZ, at M 56 junction 14 (01928) 728500, *Fax (01928) 728511* – ⇜ TV ♿ P – 🏠 25. MC AE O VISA. ✻
40 rm 40.95 **t.**

ENGLAND

CHESTERTON *Oxon.* 404 Q 28 – *pop. 806* – ✉ *Bicester.*

18 *Bicester* ✆ *(01869) 241204.*

London 69 – Birmingham 65 – Northampton 36 – Oxford 15.

Bignell Park, OX6 8UE, on A 4095 ✆ (01869) 241444, *Fax (01869) 241444*, – TV P 25. MC AE D VISA. ✻
Meals *(closed Sunday lunch)* 15.00/20.00 **st.** (lunch) and dinner a la carte 23.00/36.00 6.95 – **23 rm** ☕ 65.00/135.00 **st.**

CHETTLE *Dorset* – *see Blandford Forum.*

CHICHESTER *W. Sussex* 404 R 31 *Great Britain G.* – *pop. 26 572.*

See : *City★ – Cathedral★* **BZ A** – *St. Mary's Hospital★* **BY D** – *Pallant House★ AC* **BZ M.**

Env. : *Fishbourne Roman Palace (mosaics★) AC* **AZ R.**

Exc. : *Weald and Downland Open Air Museum★ AC, N : 6 m. by A 286* **AY.**

18 *Goodwood, Kennel Hill* ✆ *(01243) 785012,* **AY** – 18, 18, 9 *Chichester Golf Centre, Hunst Village* ✆ *(01243) 533833,* **AZ.**

ℹ *29a South St.* ✆ *(01243) 775888.*

London 69 – Brighton 31 – Portsmouth 18 – Southampton 30.

CHICHESTER

Street	Grid	No.
Birdham Road	AZ	2
Bognor Road	AZ	3
Cathedral Way	AZ	4
Chapel Street	BY	6
Chichester Arundel Road	AY	7
East Pallant	BZ	9
East Street	BZ	

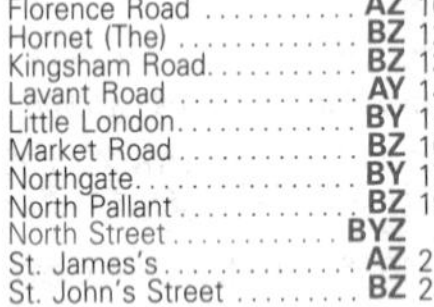

Street	Grid	No.
Florence Road	AZ	10
Hornet (The)	BZ	12
Kingsham Road	BZ	13
Lavant Road	AY	14
Little London	BY	15
Market Road	BZ	16
Northgate	BY	17
North Pallant	BZ	19
North Street	BYZ	
St. James's	AZ	21
St. John's Street	BZ	23

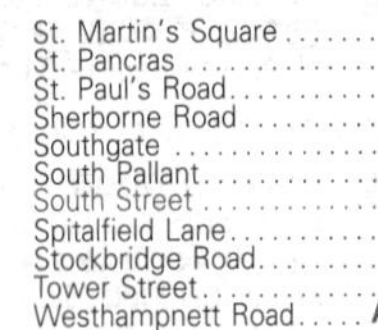

Street	Grid
St. Martin's Square	BY
St. Pancras	BY
St. Paul's Road	BY
Sherborne Road	AZ
Southgate	BZ
South Pallant	BZ
South Street	BZ
Spitalfield Lane	BY
Stockbridge Road	AZ
Tower Street	BY
Westhampnett Road	AYZ

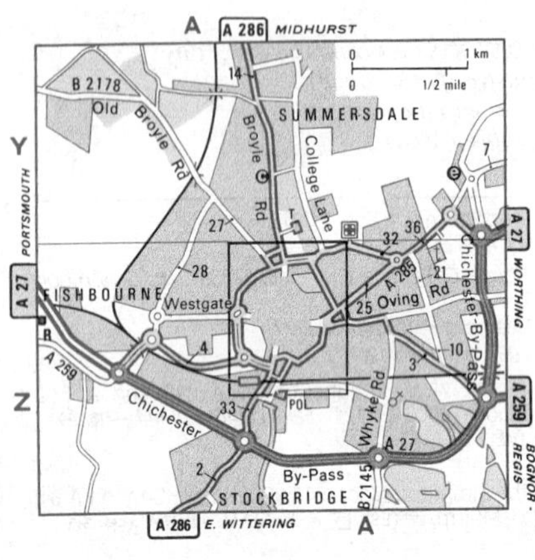

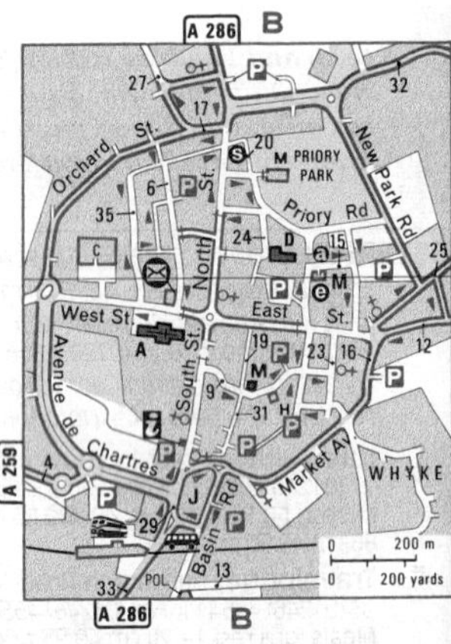

Jarvis Chichester, Westhampnett, PO19 4UL, ✆ (01243) 786351, *Fax (01243) 7823* ... **AY**
S, – ✻, rest, TV & P – 300. MC AE D VISA JCB
Meals (bar lunch Monday to Saturday)/dinner 15.95 **t.** and a la carte 7.50 – **76**
☕ 94.00/129.00 **t.**, 1 suite – SB.

The Ship, North St., PO19 1NH, ✆ (01243) 778000, *bookings@shiphotel.co* ... **BY**
Fax (01243) 788000 – ✻ rest, TV P – 70. MC AE D VISA JCB
Meals 16.95/19.95 **st.** and a la carte 5.40 – **36 rm** ☕ 75.00/114.00 **st.** – SB.

Suffolk House, 3 East Row, PO19 1PD, ✆ (01243) 778899, *reservations@suffolkhsho demon.co.uk, Fax (01243) 787282*, – ✻ rest, TV. MC AE D VISA JCB. ✻ **BY**
Meals *(closed Sunday dinner)* (dinner only and Sunday lunch)/dinner 16.50 **t.** 5.75 – **11**
☕ 59.00/125.00 **st.** – SB.

Crouchers Bottom, Birdham Rd, Apuldram, PO20 7EH, Southwest : 2 ½ m. on A
✆ (01243) 784995, *Fax (01243) 539797*, – ✻ TV & P. MC AE VISA
Meals (dinner only) a la carte 18.85/28.15 **t.** 8.65 – **16 rm** ☕ 52.00/105.00 **t.** – SB.

XX **Comme ça,** 67 Broyle Rd, PO19 4BD, on A 286 ✆ (01243) 788724, *comme.ca@btinternet.com, Fax (01243) 530052,* , – P. MO AE VISA AY c
closed Monday and Sunday dinner – **Meals** - French - 17.95 **t.** (lunch) and a la carte 19.45/24.55 **t.** 7.65.

Charlton *North : 6¼ m. by A 286* – **AY** – ✉ *Chichester.*

Woodstock House, PO18 0HU, ✆ (01243) 811666, *Fax (01243) 811666,* – TV P. MO AE VISA.
closed 24-26 December – **Meals** *(closed Sunday and Monday)* (dinner only) 19.95 **t.** 7.00 – **11 rm** 55.00/120.00 **t.** – SB.

Chilgrove *North : 6½ m. by A 286* – **AY** – *on B 2141* – ✉ *Chichester.*

Forge, PO18 9HX, ✆ (01243) 535333, *reservations@forgehotel.com, Fax (01243) 535363,* « Converted 17C forge », – rm, TV P. MO AE VISA JCB.
closed last week October – **Meals** (by arrangement) (communal dining) 25.00 **st.** – **5 rm** 45.00/110.00 **st.** – SB.

Halnaker *Northeast : 3¼ m. on A 285* – **BY** – ✉ *Chichester.*

The Old Store without rest., Stane St., PO18 0QL, on A 285 ✆ (01243) 531977, *alandavis@theoldstore.fsnet.co.uk, Fax (01243) 531977,* – TV P. MO VISA.
7 rm 28.00/55.00 **st.**

Goodwood *Northeast : 3½ m. by A 27* – **AY** – *on East Dean Rd* – ✉ *Chichester.*

Marriott Goodwood Park H. & Country Club, PO18 0QB, ✆ (01243) 775537, *Fax (01243) 520120,* , , , 18, , , – TV P – 150. MO AE VISA.
Meals 20.00/27.50 **st.** and dinner a la carte 7.45 – **93 rm** 85.00/145.00 **st.**, 1 suite – SB.

Bosham *West : 4 m. by A 259* – **AZ** – ✉ *Chichester.*

Millstream, Bosham Lane, PO18 8HL, ✆ (01243) 573234, *info@millstream-hotel.co.uk, Fax (01243) 573459,* – , rest, TV P. MO AE VISA
Meals 14.95/21.95 **s.** 6.50 – **35 rm** 75.00/115.00 **t.** – SB.

Hatpins without rest., Bosham Lane, PO18 8HG, ✆ (01243) 572644, *mary@hatpins.co.uk, Fax (01243) 572644,* , – TV P.
5 rm 39.50/80.00.

Chidham *West : 6 m. by A 259* – **AZ** – ✉ *Chichester.*

Old Rectory without rest., Cot Lane, PO18 8TA, ✆ (01243) 572088, *peter.blencowe@lineone.net, Fax (01243) 572088,* , – TV P
restricted opening in winter **4 rm** 24.00/56.00 **st.**

Funtington *Northwest : 4¾ m. by B 2178 on B 2146* – **AY** – ✉ *Chichester.*

XX **Hallidays,** Watery Lane, PO18 9LF, ✆ (01243) 575331, « Part 13C thatched cottages » – P. MO VISA
closed 2 weeks March, 1 week September, Monday, Saturday lunch and Sunday dinner – **Meals** 11.00/13.00 **t.** (lunch) and a la carte 20.75/27.00 **t.** 8.00.

IDHAM *W. Sussex* – *see Chichester.*

IEVELEY SERVICE AREA *Newbury* 403 404 Q29 – ✉ *Thatcham.*

Travelodge, Oxford Rd, Hermitage, RG18 9XX, at junction 13 of M 4 ✆ (01635) 248024, *Fax (01635) 247886* – rm, TV P. MO AE VISA JCB.
Meals (grill rest.) – **64 rm** 59.95 **t.**

ILDER THORNTON *Ches.* – ✉ *Wirral.*
London 200 – *Birkenhead 7* – *Chester 12* – *Liverpool 10.*

Travel Inn, New Chester Rd, L66 1QW, on A 41 ✆ (0151) 339 8101, *Fax (0151) 347 1401* – rm, TV P. MO AE VISA.
Meals (grill rest.) – **31 rm** 40.95 **t.**

ILGROVE *W. Sussex* 404 R 31 – *see Chichester.*

ILLATON *Devon* 403 H 32 – *see Tavistock.*

CHILLINGTON *Devon* 403 I 33 – *see Kingsbridge.*

CHINLEY *Derbs.* 402 403 404 O 23 – ✉ *Stockport (Ches.).*
London 187 – *Manchester* 24 – *Sheffield* 25.

Ashen Clough ⛰, High Peak, SK23 6AH, North : 1 m. by Maynestone R
✆ (01663) 750311, ≤, 🌳, 🏇 – ⇔ 🅿. ✗
Meals (by arrangement) (communal dining) 22.00 🍷 5.00 – **3 rm** ☐ 47.00/74.00.

CHINNOR *Oxon.* 404 R 28 *The West Country G. – pop. 5 599.*
Exc. : *Ridgeway Path*★★.
London 45 – Oxford 19.

Cross Lanes Cottage without rest., West Lane, Bledlow, HP27 9PF, Northeast : 1 ½
on B 4009 ✆ (01844) 345339, *Fax (01844) 274165,* « Part 16C », 🌳 – ⇔ 📺 🅿. ✗
3 rm ☐ 45.00/55.00 **st.**

at Sprig's Alley *Southeast : 2½ m. by Bledlow Ridge rd* – ✉ *Chinnor.*

Sir Charles Napier Inn, OX9 4BX, ✆ (01494) 483011, *Fax (01494) 485311,* 🍽, 🌳 –
MC AE ① VISA
closed 25-26 December, Monday and Sunday dinner – **Meals** a la carte 25.00/31.00 **t.**

Wenn Sie ein ruhiges Hotel suchen,
benutzen Sie zuerst die Karte in der Einleitung
oder wählen Sie im Text ein Hotel mit dem Zeichen ⛰ *oder* ⛰.

CHIPPENHAM *Wilts.* 403 404 N 29 *The West Country G. – pop. 26 376.*
See : *Yelde Hall*★.
Env. : *Corsham Court*★★ *AC, SW : 4 m. by A 4 – Sheldon Manor*★ *AC, W : 1½ m. by A 42*
Biddestone★, *W : 3½ m. – Bowood House*★ *AC (Library* ≤★*) SE : 5 m. by A 4 and A 342.*
Exc. : *Castle Combe*★★, *NW : 6 m. by A 420 and B 4039.*
⛳9 *Monkton Park (Par Three)* ✆ *(01249) 653928.*
ℹ *The Citadel, Bath Rd* ✆ *(01249) 706333.*
London 106 – Bristol 27 – Southampton 64 – Swindon 21.

Crown Inn, Giddea Hall, Yatton Keynell, SN14 7ER, Northwest : 4 ½ m. on A 4
✆ (01249) 782229, *Fax (01249) 782337* – 📺 🅿. MC AE VISA. ✗
Meals a la carte 11.40/23.85 **t.** – **8 rm** ☐ 55.00/65.00 **t.**

at Stanton Saint Quintin *North : 5 m. by A 429* – ✉ *Chippenham.*

Stanton Manor ⛰, SN14 6DQ, ✆ (01666) 837552, *reception@stantonmanor.co.*
Fax (01666) 837022, 🍽, 🌳, 🏇 – ⇔ 📺 📞 🅿 – 🎪 40. MC AE VISA JCB. ✗
Meals a la carte 13.85/19.85 **st.** 🍷 6.95 – **14 rm** ☐ 65.00/125.00 **st.** – SB.

CHIPPERFIELD *Herts.* 404 ㊷ *– pop. 1 680 –* ✉ *Kings Langley.*
London 27 – Hemel Hempstead 5 – Watford 6.

Two Brewers Inn, The Common, WD4 9BS, ✆ (01923) 265266, *Fax (01923) 26188*
⇔ rm, 📺 🅿 – 🎪 25. MC AE VISA. ✗
Meals a la carte 13.95/23.15 **t.** – ☐ 6.95 – **20 rm** 89.50 **st.**

CHIPPING *Lancs.* 402 M 22 *– pop. 1 392 –* ✉ *Preston.*
London 233 – Lancaster 30 – Leeds 54 – Manchester 40 – Preston 12.

Gibbon Bridge ⛰, PR3 2TQ, East : 1 m. on Clitheroe rd ✆ (01995) 61456, *reception@*
bon-bridge.co.uk, Fax (01995) 61277, ≤, 🏋, ♨, 🌳, 🏇, 🎾 – 🛗 📺 ♿ 🅿 – 🎪 120. MC AE
VISA
Meals 13.00/23.50 **t.** and dinner a la carte 🍷 7.25 – **12 rm** ☐ 70.00/100.00 **t.**, **18 sui**
☐ 120.00/225.00 **t.** – SB.

IPPING CAMPDEN *Glos.* 403 404 O 27 *Great Britain G. – pop. 1 741.*
See : *Town*★.
Env. : *Hidcote Manor Garden*★★ AC, *NE : 2½ m.*
Unit 2, Rosary Cottage, High St. (01386) 841206.
London 93 – Cheltenham 21 – Oxford 37 – Stratford-upon-Avon 12.

Cotswold House, The Square, GL55 6AN, (01386) 840330, *reception@cotswoldhouse.com, Fax (01386) 840310,* « Attractively converted Regency town house », – rest, – 30.
Garden Room : **Meals** (dinner only and Sunday lunch)/dinner 35.00 **st.** 7.50 – ***Hicks' Brasserie :*** **Meals** a la carte approx. 22.00 **st.** 6.00 – **15 rm** 90.00/180.00 **st.** – SB.

Seymour House, High St., GL55 6AH, (01386) 840429, *enquiry@seymourhousehotel.com, Fax (01386) 840369,* « Part 17C mature grapevine in restaurant », – rest, – 65.
Meals 9.75/32.00 **t.** and a la carte 7.00 – **11 rm** 72.50/120.00 **st.**, 4 suites – SB.

Noel Arms, High St., GL55 6AT, (01386) 840317, *bookings@cotswold-inns-hotels.co.uk, Fax (01386) 841136,* « Part 14C » – rest, – 40.
Meals (bar lunch Monday to Saturday)/dinner a la carte 18.95/27.85 **st.** 5.60 – **26 rm** 75.00/110.00 **t.** – SB.

Eight Bells Inn with rm, Church St., GL55 6JG, (01386) 840371, *Fax (01386) 841669,* « 14C inn » – .
closed Sunday dinner – **Meals** a la carte 15.20/24.25 **st.** – **5 rm** 35.00/60.00 **st.**

Mickleton *North : 3¼ m. by B 4035 and B 4081 on B 4632 – Chipping Campden.*

Three Ways House, GL55 6SB, (01386) 438429, *threeways@puddingclub.com, Fax (01386) 438118,* – rest, – 80.
Meals (bar lunch Monday to Saturday)/dinner 23.50 **t.** and a la carte 7.50 – **41 rm** 75.00/98.00 **st.** – SB.

Charingworth *East : 3 m. by B 4035 – Chipping Campden.*

Charingworth Manor , GL55 6NS, on B 4035 (01386) 593555, *charingworthmanor@englishrosehotels.co.uk, Fax (01386) 593353,* , « Part early 14C manor house with Jacobean additions », , , , , – rest, – 30.
Meals 12.95/39.95 **t.** 13.00 – **26 rm** 115.00/300.00 **t.** – SB.

Paxford *Southeast : 3 m. by B 4035 – Chipping Campden.*

Churchill Arms with rm, GL55 6XH, (01386) 594000, *the-churchill-arms@hotmail.co.uk, Fax (01386) 594005,* – .
Meals (bookings not accepted) a la carte 19.00/23.50 **t.** 8.75 – **4 rm** 40.00/60.00 **t.**

Broad Campden *South : 1¼ m. by B 4081 – Chipping Campden.*

Malt House , GL55 6UU, (01386) 840295, *nick@the-malt-house.freeserve.co.uk, Fax (01386) 841334,* « 17C », – .
closed 24 to 26 December – **Meals** *(closed Tuesday and Wednesday)* (booking essential to non-residents) (dinner only) 27.50/29.50 **t.** 14.00 – **7 rm** 89.50/108.50 **st.**, 1 suite.

Marnic House without rest., GL55 6UR, (01386) 841473, *marnic@zoom.co.uk, Fax (01386) 840441,* – .
closed 20 December-20 January – **3 rm** 45.00/50.00.

IPPING NORTON *Oxon.* 403 404 P28 *Great Britain G. – pop. 5 386.*
Env. : *Chastleton House*★★, *NW : 4 m. by A 44.*
Lyneham (01993) 831841 – Southcombe (01608) 642383.
London 77 – Birmingham 44 – Gloucester 36 – Oxford 21.

Chavignol, 7 Horsefair, OX7 5AL, (01608) 644490, *chavignol@virginbiz.com, Fax (01608) 644490* – .
closed 3 weeks January, Sunday and Monday – **Meals** (booking essential) 26.00 **t.** (lunch) and a la carte 36.50/41.00 **t.** 7.00
Spec. Assiette of shellfish. Braised pig cheek on parsley mash with truffle sauce. Apple and frangipane tart, caramel sauce.

ISELDON *Wilts.* 403 404 O 29 – *see Swindon.*

In this guide

a symbol or a character, printed in red or **black**, in **bold** or light type, does not have the same meaning.
Pay particular attention to the explanatory pages.

CHITTLEHAMHOLT *Devon* 403 I 31 – *pop. 194* – ✉ *Umberleigh.*
London 216 – Barnstaple 14 – Exeter 28 – Taunton 45.

Highbullen ⛝, EX37 9HD, ☎ (01769) 540561, *highbullen@sosi.net, Fax (01769) 5404*, ≤, ⛝, ⛝ heated, ⛝, 18, ⛝, ⛝, ⛝, ⛝indoor/outdoor, squash – ⛝ rest, TV P – ⛝ MC VISA. ⛝
Meals (lunch by arrangement)/dinner 22.00 **st.** 8.00 – ⛝ 3.50 – **40 rm** (dinner includ 75.00/195.00 **st.** – SB.

CHOBHAM *Surrey* 404 S 29 – *pop. 3 411* – ✉ *Woking.*
London 35 – Reading 21 – Southampton 53.

Knaphill Manor ⛝ without rest., Carthouse Lane, GU21 4XT, Southwest : 1 m. by Cas Grove Rd and Guildford Rd ☎ (01276) 857962, *Fax (01276) 855503*, ≤, ⛝ – TV P. MC ⛝
closed Easter and Christmas-New Year – **3 rm** ⛝ 50.00/75.00.

Quails, 1 Bagshot Rd, GU24 8BP, ☎ (01276) 858491, *Fax (01276) 858491* – ⛝. MC AE VISA
closed 25 December-1 January, Saturday lunch, Sunday and Monday – **Meals** 15.95 (lunch) and a la carte 26.00/30.65 **t.** 5.95.

CHOLLERFORD *Northd.* 401 402 N 18 *Great Britain G.* – ✉ *Hexham.*
Env. : *Hadrian's Wall*★★ – *Chesters*★ *(Bath House*★*)* **AC**, *W : ½ m. by B 6318.*
London 303 – Carlisle 36 – Newcastle upon Tyne 21.

George, NE46 4EW, ☎ (01434) 681611, *Fax (01434) 681727*, ≤, « Riverside gardens », ⛝, ⛝, ⛝ – ⛝ TV ⛝ P – ⛝ 65. MC AE ⛝ VISA
Meals 9.00/40.00 **st.** and a la carte 8.00 – **47 rm** ⛝ 80.00/120.00 **st.** – SB.

CHORLEY *Lancs.* 402 404 M 23 – *pop. 33 536.*
18 *Duxbury Park, Duxbury Hall Rd* ☎ *(01257) 265380* – 18 *Shaw Hill Hotel G. & C.C., Pres Rd, Whittle-le-Woods* ☎ *(01257) 269221.*
London 222 – Blackpool 30 – Liverpool 33 – Manchester 26.

Premier Lodge, Moss Lane, Whittle-le-Woods, PR6 8AD, Northeast : 1 m. by A 6 an 674 on B 6229 ☎ (0870) 7001354, *Fax (01257) 232 912* – ⛝, ⛝ rm, TV ⛝ ⛝ P. MC AE ⛝
Meals a la carte 11.50/22.50 **st.** – ⛝ 6.00 – **82 rm** 42.00 **st.**

Premier Lodge, Bolton Rd, PR7 4AB, South : 1 m. on A 6 ☎ (0870) 70013 *Fax (0870) 7001353* – ⛝ TV ⛝ ⛝ P. MC AE ⛝ VISA. ⛝
Meals (grill rest.) a la carte 8.95/16.35 **t.** 7.25 – ⛝ 6.00 – **29 rm** 42.00 **t.** – SB.

at Whittle-le-Woods *North : 2 m. on A 6* – ✉ *Chorley.*

Shaw Hill H. Golf & Country Club, Preston Rd, PR6 7PP, ☎ (01257) 269221, *info@sh hill.co.uk, Fax (01257) 261223*, ⛝, ⛝, ⛝, 18 – TV P – ⛝ 200. MC AE VISA. ⛝
Vardon : **Meals** (bar lunch Saturday) 13.95/15.00 **t.** 9.75 – **30 rm** ⛝ 73.00/120.00 **t.** –

Parkville Country House, 174 Preston Rd, PR6 7HE, ☎ (01257) 2618 *Fax (01257) 273171*, ⛝ – TV P. MC AE ⛝ VISA JCB. ⛝
Meals *(closedSunday)* (dinner only) 12.95 **t.** and a la carte 8.95 – **8 rm** ⛝ 70.00/80.00 s

CHORLTON CUM HARDY *Gtr. Manchester* 402 403 404 N 23 – *see Manchester.*

CHRISTCHURCH *Dorset* 403 404 O 31 *The West Country G.* – *pop. 36 379.*
See : *Town*★ – *Priory*★.
Env. : *Hengistbury Head*★ *(≤★★) SW : 4½ m. by A 35 and B 3059.*
18 *Highcliffe Castle, 107 Lymington Rd, Highcliffe-on-Sea* ☎ *(01425) 272953* – 9 *Barrack Iford* ☎ *(01202) 473817.*
23 High St. ☎ *(01202) 471780.*
London 111 – Bournemouth 6 – Salisbury 26 – Southampton 24 – Winchester 39.

Travel Inn, Barrack Rd, BH23 2BN, West : ¾ m. on A 35 ☎ (01202) 485215 – ⛝, ⛝ rm, ⛝ P. MC AE ⛝ VISA. ⛝
Meals (grill rest.) – **40 rm** 40.95 **t.**

Travel Inn, Somerford Rd, BH23 3QG, East : 2 m. on B 3059 ☎ (01202) 4853 *Fax (01202) 474939* – ⛝ rm, TV ⛝ P. MC AE ⛝ VISA. ⛝
Meals (grill rest.) – **70 rm** 40.95 **t.**

Splinters, 12 Church St., BH23 1BW, ☎ (01202) 483454, *eating@splinters.uk.c Fax (01202) 480180* – MC AE ⛝ VISA
closed 26 December, Sunday and Monday – **Meals** a la carte 27.00/32.00 **t.**

Mudeford *Southeast : 2 m. – ✉ Christchurch.*

Avonmouth, 95 Mudeford, BH23 3NT, ✆ (0870) 400 8120, *heritagehotels_mudeford_christchurch.avonmouth@forte-hotels.com, Fax (01202) 479004,* ←, heated, – TV P – 60. MC AE VISA JCB
Meals (bar lunch Monday to Saturday)/dinner 10.95/23.95 **t.** and a la carte 7.95 – 13.95 – **40 rm** 85.00/130.00 **t.** – SB.

Waterford Lodge, 87 Bure Lane, Friars Cliff, BH23 4DN, ✆ (01425) 272948, *waterford@bestwestern.co.uk, Fax (01425) 279130,* – rest, TV P – 80. MC AE VISA.
Meals 14.50/25.50 **t.** 8.50 – 10.50 – **18 rm** 82.00/95.00 **t.** – SB.

HURCHILL *Oxon.* 403 404 P 28 – *pop. 502 – ✉ Chipping Norton.*
London 79 – Birmingham 46 – Cheltenham 29 – Oxford 23 – Swindon 31.

The Forge without rest., OX7 6NJ, ✆ (01608) 658173, *jon.price1@virgin.net, Fax (01608) 659262* – TV P. MC VISA.
6 rm 40.00/60.00 **t.**

HURCH STRETTON *Shrops.* 402 403 L 26 *Great Britain G. – pop. 3 435.*
Env. : *Wenlock Edge★, E : by B 4371.*
18 *Trevor Hill ✆ (01694) 722281.*
London 166 – Birmingham 46 – Hereford 39 – Shrewsbury 14.

Mynd House, Ludlow Rd, Little Stretton, SY6 6RB, Southwest : 1 ¼ m. on B 4370 ✆ (01694) 722212, *info@myndhouse.co.uk, Fax (01694) 724180,* – TV P. MC AE VISA.
Meals (booking essential) (dinner only and Sunday lunch) 17.50/22.50 **st.** 7.00 – **5 rm** 45.00/120.00 **st.**, 2 suites – SB.

Jinlye without rest., Castle Hill, All Stretton, SY6 6JP, North : 2 ¼ m. by B 4370 turning left beside telephone box in All Stretton ✆ (01694) 723243, *info@jinlye.co.uk, Fax (01694) 723243,* ←, « 16C », , – TV P. MC VISA.
8 rm 50.00/70.00 **t.** – SB.

The Studio, 59 High St., SY6 6BY, ✆ (01694) 722672, *Fax (01694) 722672,* – . MC VISA
closed 25-26 December, Sunday and Monday – **Meals** 11.50 **t.** (lunch) and a la carte 15.15/21.40 **t.** 7.50.

RENCESTER *Glos.* 403 404 O 28 *Great Britain G. – pop. 15 221.*
See : *Town★ – Church of St. John the Baptist★ – Corinium Museum★ (Mosaic pavements★) AC.*
Env. : *Fairford : Church of St. Mary★ (stained glass windows★★) E : 7 m. by A 417.*
18 *Cheltenham Rd, Bagendon ✆ (01285) 653939.*
Corn Hall, Market Pl. ✆ (01285) 654180.
London 97 – Bristol 37 – Gloucester 19 – Oxford 37.

Wimborne House without rest., 91 Victoria Rd, GL7 1ES, ✆ (01285) 643653, *Fax (01285) 653890,* – TV P.
closed 24 December-1 January – **6 rm** 35.00/45.00.

The Ivy House without rest., 2 Victoria Rd, GL7 1EN, ✆ (01285) 656626, *ivyhousebed@ukonline.co.uk* – TV P.
4 rm 38.00/45.00 **t.**

Harry Hare's, 3 Gosditch St., GL7 2AG, ✆ (01285) 652375, *Fax (01285) 641691,* , – MC AE VISA
Meals a la carte 16.40/25.85 **t.**

Barnsley *Northeast : 4 m. by A 429 on B 4425 – ✉ Cirencester.*

Village Pub with rm, GL7 5EF, ✆ (01285) 740421, *reservations@thevillagepub.co.uk, Fax (01285) 740142* – TV P. MC VISA.
closed 25 December – **Meals** a la carte 14.95/26.95 **t.** – **6 rm** 55.00/70.00 **st.**

Ampney Crucis *East : 2 ¾ m. by A 417 – ✉ Cirencester.*

Crown of Crucis, GL7 5RS, on A 417 ✆ (01285) 851806, *Fax (01285) 851735,* – rm, TV P – 100. MC AE VISA
closed 25 December – **Meals** (bar lunch)/dinner a la carte 14.80/18.60 **t.** 4.80 – **25 rm** 60.00/86.00 **t.** – SB.

ENGLAND

at Ewen *Southwest : 3 1/4 m. by A 429 – ✉ Cirencester.*

Wild Duck Inn with rm, Drake's Island, GL7 6BY, ☎ (01285) 770310, *wduckinn@aol.co…*
Fax (01285) 770924, « Part 17C former farm buildings », – TV P. MC AE VISA
Meals a la carte 12.85/25.90 **t.** – 6.95 – **11 rm** 55.00/75.00 **t.**

at Kemble *Southwest : 4 m. on A 429 – ✉ Cirencester.*

Smerrill Barns without rest., GL7 6BW, North : 1 1/4 m. on A 429 ☎ (01285) 770907, *gs…her@hotmail.com, Fax (01285) 770706*, « Converted 18C barn » – TV P. MC VISA JCB
closed 23 December-3 January **7 rm** 45.00/55.00.

at Stratton *Northwest : 1 1/4 m. on A 417 – ✉ Cirencester.*

Stratton House, Gloucester Rd, GL7 2LE, ☎ (01285) 651761, *Fax (01285) 640024*,
TV P – 150. MC AE D VISA
Meals (bar lunch Monday to Saturday)/dinner 18.75/25.75 **t.** and a la carte – **41**…
85.00/125.00 **t.** – SB.

CLACKET LANE SERVICE AREA *Surrey* 404 U 30 – ✉ *Westerham.*
M 25 Motorway Services, junctions 5-6, Westerham ☎ (01959) 565063.

Travel Inn Metro without rest., TN16 2ER, M 25 between junctions 5 and 6 (westbou… carriageway) ☎ (01959) 565577, *Fax (01959) 561311* – TV P. MC AE D VISA.
closed Christmas and New Year – **58 rm** 46.95 **t.**

CLACTON-ON-SEA *Essex* 404 X 28 – *pop. 45 065.*
West Rd ☎ (01255) 424331.
23 Pier Av. ☎ (01255) 423400.
London 76 – Chelmsford 37 – Colchester 14 – Ipswich 28.

Chudleigh, 13 Agate Rd, Marine Parade West, CO15 1RA, ☎ (01255) 4254…
Fax (01255) 470280 – TV P. MC AE D VISA JCB
Meals *(closed Friday to Sunday October-March)* (dinner only) 12.50/15.00 **t.** 5.00 – **10 r…**
37.00/54.00 **t.**

CLANFIELD *Oxon.* 403 404 P 28 – *pop. 1 709 (inc. Shilton).*
London 75 – Oxford 24 – Swindon 16.

Plough at Clanfield, Bourton Rd, OX18 2RB, on A 4095 ☎ (01367) 8102…
Fax (01367) 810596, « Elizabethan manor house », – TV P. MC AE D VISA JCB.
closed 25 December-4 January – **Meals** *(closed to non-residents Sunday dinner and Mo…day)* 32.50 **t.** (dinner) and a la carte 20.10/29.75 **t.** 9.25 – **6 rm** 75.00/110.00 **t.** – SB.

CLAPPERSGATE *Cumbria – see Ambleside.*

CLARE *Suffolk* 404 V 27 – *pop. 1 976 – ✉ Sudbury.*
London 67 – Cambridge 27 – Colchester 24 – Ipswich 32 – Bury St.Edmunds 16.

Ship Stores, 22 Callis St., CO10 8PX, ☎ (01787) 277834 – rm, TV. MC VISA JCB.
Meals (by arrangement) 8.50 **st.** – **5 rm** 41.00/46.00 **s.** – SB.

CLAVERING *Essex* 404 U 28 – *pop. 1 663 – ✉ Saffron Walden.*
London 44 – Cambridge 25 – Colchester 44 – Luton 29.

Cricketers with rm, CB11 4QT, ☎ (01799) 550442, *cricketers@lineone.n…*
Fax (01799) 550882, – TV P. MC AE VISA.
closed 25 and 26 December – **Meals** (lunch in bar)/dinner a la carte 14.00/23.00 **st.** 7.6…
6 rm 65.00/90.00 **st.**

CLAWTON *Devon* 403 H 31 *The West Country G.* – *pop. 292* – ✉ *Holsworthy.*
Env. : *W : Tamar River*★★.
London 240 – Exeter 39 – Plymouth 36.

Court Barn Country House, EX22 6PS, West : 1/2 m. ☎ (01409) 2712…
Fax (01409) 271309, – TV P. MC AE D VISA JCB.
Meals (booking essential) 13.95/21.00 **st.** and a la carte 7.50 – **8 rm** 38.00/80.00 **st…**
SB.

CLAYDON *Suffolk* 404 X 27 – *see Ipswich.*

AYGATE *Surrey* 404 ㊷ – *see Esher.*

AYTON-LE-DALE *Lancs. – see Blackburn.*

AYTON-LE-MOORS *Lancs.* 402 M 22 – *pop. 6 961* – ✉ *Accrington.*
London 232 – Blackburn 3.5 – Lancaster 37 – Leeds 44 – Preston 14.

Dunkenhalgh, Blackburn Rd, BB5 5JP, Southwest : 1 ½ m. on A 678 ☎ (01254) 398021, *dunkenhalgh@macdonald-hotels.co.uk, Fax (01254) 872230,* – P – 400. MC AE VISA.
***Cameo :* Meals** *(closed Saturday lunch)* 14.95/35.00 **t.** 9.00 – **120 rm** 75.00/95.00 **t.**, 1 suite – SB.

Sparth House, Whalley Rd, BB5 5RP, ☎ (01254) 872263, *Fax (01254) 872263,* – rest, TV P – 100. MC AE VISA.
Meals 11.95 **st.** (lunch) and a la carte 13.65/23.65 **st.** – **16 rm** 63.50/120.00 **st.** – SB.

AYTON-LE-WOODS *Lancs.* 402 M 24 – *pop. 14 173* – ✉ *Chorley.*
London 220 – Liverpool 34 – Manchester 26 – Preston 5.5.

The Pines, 570 Preston Rd, PR6 7ED, on A 6 at junction with B 5256 ☎ (01772) 338551, *info@thepineshotel.fsbusiness.co.uk, Fax (01772) 629002,* – rm, TV P – 200. MC AE VISA JCB.
closed 26 December – **Meals** 10.00 **t.** (lunch) and a la carte 15.50/27.00 **t.** – **34 rm** 70.00/110.00 **t.**, 2 suites.

Travelodge, Preston Rd, PR6 7JB, on A 6 ☎ (01772) 311963 – rm, TV P. MC AE VISA JCB.
Meals (grill rest.) – **40 rm** 39.95 **t.**

AYTON WEST *W. Yorks.* 402 404 P 23 – *pop. 7 988 (inc. Skelmanthorpe)* – ✉ *Huddersfield.*
London 190 – Leeds 19 – Manchester 35 – Sheffield 24.

Bagden Hall, Wakefield Rd, Scissett, HD8 9LE, Southwest : 1 m. on A 636 ☎ (01484) 865330, *info@bagdenhall.demon.co.uk, Fax (01484) 861001,* 9, – rest, TV P – 70. MC AE VISA.
Meals 10.75/17.95 **st.** and dinner a la carte 4.95 – **17 rm** 60.00/100.00 **st.**

EARWELL *Glos. – see Coleford.*

EATOR MOOR *Cumbria* 402 J 20 – *pop. 6 410.*
London 317 – Carlisle 31 – Keswick 25 – Whitehaven 7.

Ennerdale Country House, Cleator, CA23 3DT, South : 1 ½ m. by B 5295 on A 5086 ☎ (01946) 813907, *ennerdale@bestwestern.co.uk, Fax (01946) 815260,* – TV P – 35. MC AE VISA JCB
Meals 9.95/44.50 **st.** and a la carte 6.95 – **28 rm** 109.00/149.00 **st.**, 2 suites – SB.

EETHORPES *N.E. Lincs.* 402 404 U 23 – *pop. 32 719.*
Humberside Airport : ☎ (01652) 688456, W : 16 m. by A 46 and A 18 Y.
42-43 Alexandra Rd ☎ (01472) 323111.
London 171 – Boston 49 – Lincoln 38 – Sheffield 77.

Kingsway, Kingsway, DN35 0AE, ☎ (01472) 601122, *Fax (01472) 601381,* – TV P. MC AE VISA.
closed 25 and 26 December – **Meals** 14.75/18.95 **t.** and a la carte 5.90 – **50 rm** 68.00/90.00 **t.** – SB.

EEVE HILL *Glos.* 403 404 N 28 – *see Cheltenham.*

EY NEXT THE SEA *Norfolk* 404 X 25 – *see Blakeney.*

IFFORD'S MESNE *Glos. – see Newent.*

IMPING *W. Sussex* 404 S 31 – *see Littlehampton.*

CLITHEROE *Lancs.* 402 M 22 – *pop. 13 548.*

Whalley Rd ☎ (01200) 422618.

12-14 Market Pl. ☎ (01200) 425566.

London 64 – Blackpool 35 – Manchester 31.

Brooklyn, 32 Pimlico Rd, BB7 2AH, ☎ (01200) 428268 – rm, TV. MC VISA JCB.
closed 24-26 December – **Meals** (by arrangement) 10.00 **s.** – **4 rm** 27.50/43.00 **s.**

Auctioneer, New Market St., BB7 2JW, ☎ (01200) 427153, *Fax (01200) 444518* – MC VISA
closed Monday, Sunday dinner and lunch Tuesday and Wednesday – **Meals** 11.95/19.75 and a la carte 6.50.

at Waddington *North : 1 3/4 m. on B 6478 – ✉ Clitheroe.*

Peter Barn without rest., Rabbit Lane, via Cross Lane, BB7 3JH, Northwest : 1 1/2 m. B 6478 ☎ (01200) 428585, – P.
closed Christmas and New Year – **3 rm** 27.00/50.00.

CLOVELLY *Devon* 403 G 31 *The West Country G.* – *pop. 439* – ✉ *Bideford.*

See : *Village★★.*

Env. : *SW : Tamar River★★.*

Exc. : *Hartland : Hartland Church★ – Hartland Quay★ (viewpoint★★) – Hartland Point ≤★★ W : 6 1/2 m. by B 3237 and B 3248 – Morwenstow (Church★, cliffs★★), SW : 11 1/2 m. by A 3*

to Lundy Island (Lundy Co. Ltd) (summer only) (1 h).

London 241 – Barnstaple 18 – Exeter 52 – Penzance 92.

Red Lion , The Quay, EX39 5TF, ☎ (01237) 431237, *redlion@clovelly.demon.co.*
Fax (01237) 431044, ≤ – rest, TV P. MC AE VISA.
Meals (bar lunch)/dinner 25.00 **st.** 7.00 – **11 rm** (dinner included) 85.75/141.50 **st.** SB.

New Inn, High St., EX39 5TQ, ☎ (01237) 431303, *newinn@clovelly.demon.co.*
Fax (01237) 431636, « 17C » – rest, TV. MC AE VISA.
Meals (bar lunch)/dinner 20.00 **t.** 7.00 – **8 rm** 41.00/82.00 **t.** – SB.

Les prix — Pour toutes précisions sur les prix indiqués dans ce guide, reportez-vous aux pages de l'introduction.

COATHAM MUNDEVILLE *Durham* 402 P 20 – *see Darlington.*

COBHAM *Surrey* 404 S 30 – *pop. 15 254 (inc. Oxshott).*

London 24 – Guildford 10.

Plan : see Greater London (South-West) p. 12

Hilton Cobham, Seven Hills Road South, KT11 1EW, West : 1 1/2 m. by A 2
☎ (01932) 864471, *Fax (01932) 868017,* – rm, TV P – 3
MC AE VISA
Meals (bar lunch Saturday) (dancing Saturday evening) a la carte 13.75/30.95 **st.** – 13
– **152 rm** 179.00/199.00 **st.**, 3 suites – SB.

Premier Lodge, Portsmouth Rd, Fairmile, KT11 1BW, Northeast : 1 m. on A
☎ (01932) 868141, *Fax (01932) 866478,* – rm, TV P. MC AE VISA.
Meals (grill rest.) a la carte approx. 18.00 **t.** – 6.00 – **48 rm** 49.50. AZ

at Stoke D'Abernon *Southeast : 1 1/2 m. on A 245 – ✉ Cobham.*

Woodlands Park, Woodlands Lane, KT11 3QB, on A 245 ☎ (01372) 843933, *info@woodlandspark.co.uk, Fax (01372) 842704,* – rm, TV P – 280. MC AE VISA.
Oak Room* :** **Meals** (dinner only and Sunday lunch) 29.50/37.50 **t.** – ***Quotes Brasserie **Meals** a la carte 16.15/24.80 **t.** – 12.50 – **59 rm** 130.00/190.00 **t.** – SB.

COCKERMOUTH *Cumbria* 401 402 J 20 – *pop. 7 702.*

Embleton ☎ (017687) 76223.

Town Hall, Market St. ☎ (01900) 822634.

London 306 – Carlisle 25 – Keswick 13.

Trout, Crown St., CA13 0EJ, ☎ (01900) 823591, *enquiries@trouthotel.co*
Fax (01900) 827514, – TV P – 50. MC AE VISA
Meals 10.95/22.45 **t.** and a la carte – **29 rm** 59.95/130.00 **t.** – SB.

Lorton *Southeast : 4 ¼ m. by B 5292 – ✉ Cockermouth.*

Winder Hall Country House ⑤, CA13 9UP, on B 5289 ℘ (01900) 85107, *stay@winderhall.co.uk, Fax (01900) 85107,* ≤, « Part 17C manor house », – ⇔ TV P. MO VISA JCB. ⌘
Meals 20.00 ♁ 9.00 – **6 rm** ☐ (dinner included) 55.00 **st.** – SB.

New House Farm, CA13 9UU, South : 1 ¼ m. on B 5289 ℘ (01900) 85404, *hazel@newhouse-farm.co.uk, Fax (01900) 85404,* ≤, « Part 17C and 19C farmhouse », – ⇔ P
Meals 22.00 **st.** ♁ 7.50 – **5 rm** ☐ 50.00/84.00 **st.** – SB.

OGGESHALL *Essex* 404 W 28 – *pop. 3 927 – ✉ Colchester.*
London 49 – Braintree 6 – Chelmsford 16 – Colchester 9.

White Hart, Market End, CO6 1NH, ℘ (01376) 561654, *wharthotel@ndirect.co.uk, Fax (01376) 561789,* « Part 15C guildhall », – TV P. MO AE VISA JCB. ⌘
Meals - Italian - (in bar Sunday dinner) 15.00 **t.** and a la carte ♁ 6.50 – **18 rm** ☐ 61.50/97.00 **t.** – SB.

Baumann's Brasserie, 4-6 Stoneham St., CO6 1TT, ℘ (01376) 561453, *food@baumanns.fsbusiness.co.uk, Fax (01376) 563762* – MO AE VISA JCB
closed first 2 weeks January, Monday, Saturday lunch and Sunday dinner – **Meals** 12.50/15.50 **t.** and a la carte ♁ 9.50.

Don't confuse:

Comfort of hotels : ... ,
Comfort of restaurants : XXXXX ..... X,
Quality of the cuisine : ✿✿✿, ✿✿, ✿, **Meals**

OLCHESTER *Essex* 404 W 28 *Great Britain G.* – *pop. 96 063.*
See : *Castle and Museum★ AC* **BZ.**
Birch Grove, Layer Rd ℘ (01206) 734276.
Visitor Information Centre, 1 Queen St. ℘ (01206) 282920.
London 52 – Cambridge 48 – Ipswich 18 – Luton 76 – Southend-on-Sea 41.

Plans on following pages

George, 116 High St., CO1 1TD, ℘ (01206) 578494, *Fax (01206) 761732,* « 15C former coaching inn » – ⇔ rm, ▤ rest, TV P – 70. MO AE VISA JCB. ⌘ BZ b
Meals *(closed dinner 25 and 26 December)* 11.55 **t.** (lunch) and a la carte 12.85/20.20 **t.** ♁ 6.25 – ☐ 8.75 – **48 rm** 74.50/104.50 **t.** – SB.

Rose and Crown, East St., Eastgates, CO1 2TZ, ℘ (01206) 866677, *info@rose-and-crown.com, Fax (01206) 866616,* « Part 15C inn » – ⇔ rm, TV ♿ P – 100. MO AE ① VISA JCB. ⌘ CZ d
closed 27 to 30 December – **Meals** (in bar Sunday dinner) 9.95/24.95 **st.** and a la carte ♁ 9.00 – ☐ 8.95 – **29 rm** 74.00/99.00 **st.** – SB.

Butterfly, Old Ipswich Rd, CO7 7QY, Northeast : 4 ¼ m. by A 1232 at junction of A 12 with A 120 (via sliproad to A 120) ℘ (01206) 230900, *cobutterfly@lineone.net, Fax (01206) 231095* – ⇔ rm, TV ♿ P – 80. MO AE ① VISA JCB
Meals 15.00/17.50 **t.** (dinner) and a la carte ♁ 7.50 – ☐ 8.50 – **50 rm** 67.50 **t.** – SB.

Travel Inn, Severalls Business Park, Ipswich Rd, CO4 4NP, North : 2 ¾ m. on A 1232 ℘ (01206) 855001, *Fax (01206) 211388* – ⇔ rm, ▤ rest, TV ♿ P. MO AE ① VISA
Meals (grill rest.) – **40 rm** 40.95 **t.**

Warehouse Brasserie, 12a Chapel St. North, CO2 7AT, ℘ (01206) 765656, *Fax (01206) 542969* – ▤. MO VISA BZ e
closed 20 August-4 September, 23 December-9 January, Sunday and Monday – **Meals** 10.95/14.95 **t.** and a la carte.

Eight Ash Green *West : 4 m. by A 1124* – **AZ** – *✉ Colchester.*

Posthouse Colchester, Abbotts Lane, CO6 3QL, at junction of A 1124 with A 12 ℘ (0870) 400 9020, *gm1064@forte-hotel.com, Fax (01206) 766577,* Lδ, ≘s, – ⇔ rm, ▤ rest, TV ♿ P – 150. MO AE ① VISA
Meals 15.00 **t.** and a la carte ♁ 7.50 – ☐ 11.95 – **110 rm** 69.00 **st.** – SB.

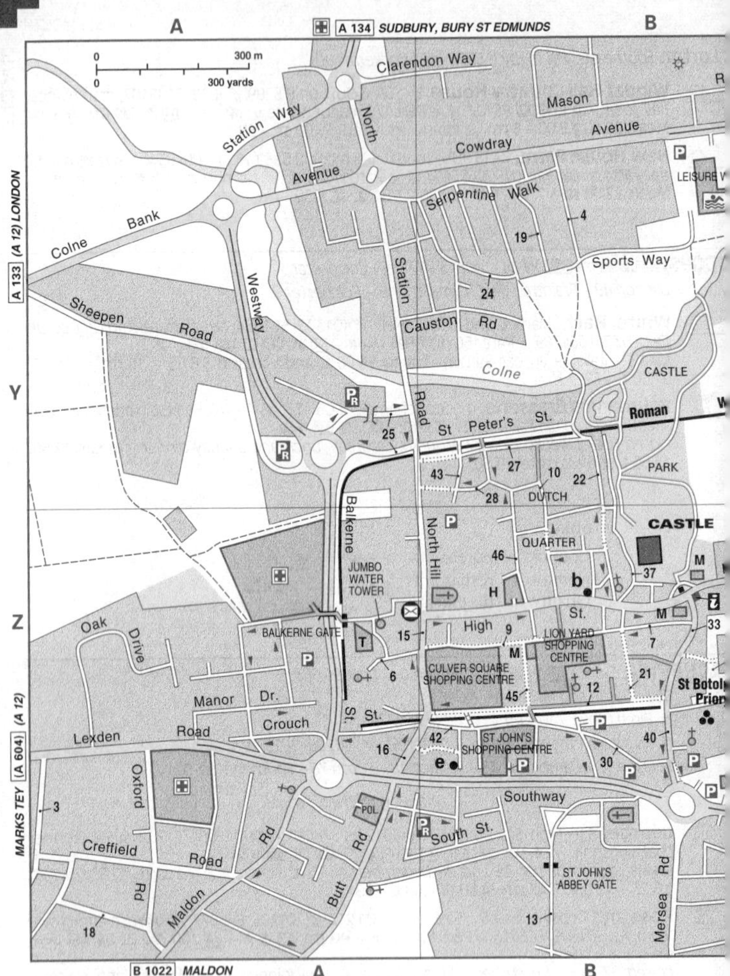

at Marks Tey *West : 5 m. by A 12 at junction with A 120* – **AZ** – ✉ *Colchester.*

Marks Tey, London Rd, CO6 1DU, on B 1408 ☎ (01206) 210001, *sales@patenhotels.co* *Fax (01206) 212167*, – rm, rest, – 200.
Meals 10.95/16.50 **st.** and a la carte 8.00 – 8.95 – **109 rm** 72.00/79.50 **st.**, 1 suite –

LES GUIDES VERTS MICHELIN

Paysages, monuments
Routes touristiques
Géographie
Histoire, Art
Itinéraires de visite
Plans de villes et de monuments

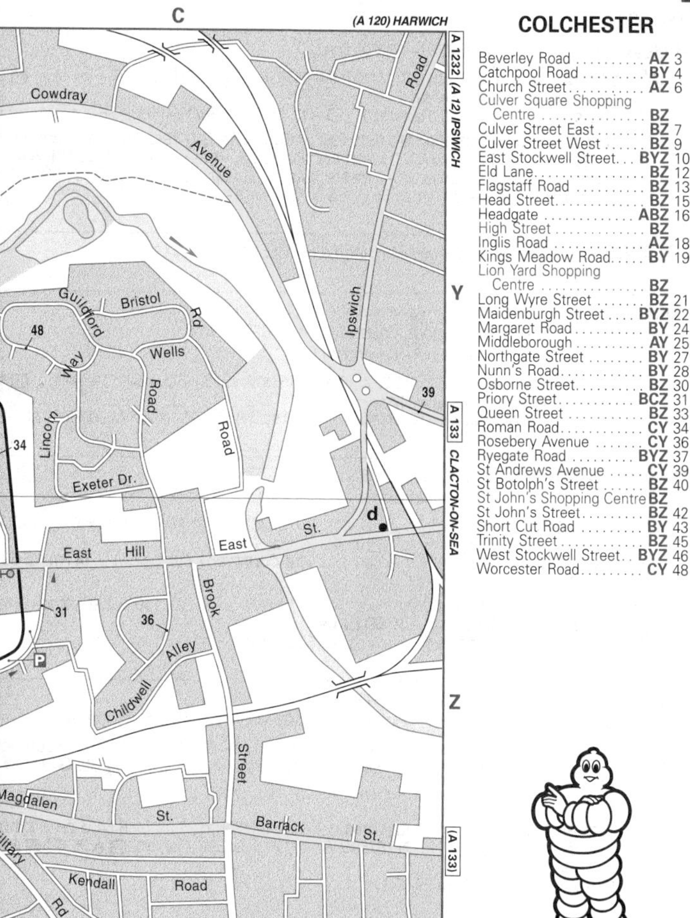

COLCHESTER

Beverley Road . . . . **AZ** 3
Catchpool Road . . . . **BY** 4
Church Street. . . . . **AZ** 6
Culver Square Shopping
Centre . . . . **BZ**
Culver Street East . . . . **BZ** 7
Culver Street West . . . . . . **BZ** 9
East Stockwell Street. . . **BYZ** 10
Eld Lane. . . . . **BZ** 12
Flagstaff Road . . . . **BZ** 13
Head Street. . . . . **BZ** 15
Headgate . . . . **ABZ** 16
High Street . . . . **BZ**
Inglis Road . . . . **AZ** 18
Kings Meadow Road. . . . . **BY** 19
Lion Yard Shopping
Centre . . . . **BZ**
Long Wyre Street . . . . **BZ** 21
Maidenburgh Street . . . . **BYZ** 22
Margaret Road . . . . **BY** 24
Middleborough . . . . **AY** 25
Northgate Street . . . . **BY** 27
Nunn's Road. . . . . **BY** 28
Osborne Street. . . . . **BZ** 30
Priory Street. . . . . **BCZ** 31
Queen Street . . . . **BZ** 33
Roman Road. . . . . **CY** 34
Rosebery Avenue . . . . **CY** 36
Ryegate Road . . . . **BYZ** 37
St Andrews Avenue . . . . . **CY** 39
St Botolph's Street . . . . . . **BZ** 40
St John's Shopping Centre **BZ**
St John's Street. . . . . **BZ** 42
Short Cut Road . . . . **BY** 43
Trinity Street . . . . **BZ** 45
West Stockwell Street. . **BYZ** 46
Worcester Road. . . . . **CY** 48

LEFORD *Devon* 403 I 31 – ✉ *Crediton.*
London 214 – Barnstaple 29 – Exeter 14 – Plymouth 43 – Taunton 42.

New Inn with rm, EX17 5BZ, ✆ (01363) 84242, *new-inn@eurobell.co.uk, Fax (01363) 85044,* , « Part 13C thatched inn » – rm, TV P. MC AE VISA JCB. *closed 25 and 26 December* – **Meals** a la carte 18.45/22.90 **t.** 6.50 – **6 rm** 50.00/75.00 **t.**

LEFORD *Glos.* 403 404 M 28 *Great Britain G. – pop. 9 567.*
Env. : *W : Wye Valley*★.
Forest of Dean, Lords Hills ✆ (01594) 832583 – Forest Hills, Mile End Rd ✆ (01594) 810620.
High St. ✆ (01594) 812388.
London 143 – Bristol 28 – Gloucester 19 – Newport 29.

Speech House, Forest of Dean, GL16 7EL, Northeast : 3 m. by B 4028 on B 4226 ✆ (01594) 822607, *Fax (01594) 823658,* – TV P – 60. MC AE VISA
Meals (bar lunch)/dinner a la carte 18.15/24.45 **t.** 7.50 – **30 rm** 49.75/101.50 **t.**, 1 suite – SB.

at Clearwell *South : 2 m. by B 4228 – ✉ Coleford.*

Wyndham Arms, GL16 8JT, ✆ (01594) 833666, *Fax (01594) 836450* – ⇆ rest, TV P – 55. MC AE O VISA JCB. ✻
Meals 13.75/21.25 **t.** and a la carte 5.85 – **18 rm** ☐ 52.50/100.00 **t.** – SB.

Tudor Farmhouse, High St., GL16 8JS, ✆ (01594) 833046, *reservations@tudorfarmhu_net.com, Fax (01594) 837093,* « Part 13C and 16C », – ⇆ TV P. MC AE VISA JCB
closed 23 to 30 December – **Meals** *(closed Sunday)* (dinner only) 21.50/27.00 and a la carte 7.50 – **20 rm** ☐ 55.00/85.00 **t.**, 1 suite – SB.

COLERNE *Wilts.* 403 404 M 29 – *see Bath (Bath & North East Somerset).*

COLESHILL *Warks.* 403 404 O 26 – *pop. 6 324* – ✉ *Birmingham (W. Mids.).*
Atherstone, The Outwoods, Coleshill Rd ✆ (01827) 713110.
London 113 – Birmingham 8 – Coventry 11.

Coleshill, 152 High St., B46 3BG, ✆ (01675) 465527, *Fax (01675) 464013* – ⇆ rm, TV – 150. MC AE O VISA JCB. ✻
***Gregorys Bistro :* Meals** a la carte 12.00/14.00 **st.** 8.95 – **23 rm** ☐ 75.00/85.00 **st.** – S

COLN ST. ALDWYNS *Glos.* 403 404 O 28 – *pop. 260* – ✉ *Cirencester.*
London 101 – Bristol 53 – Gloucester 20 – Swindon 15.

New Inn at Coln, GL7 5AN, ✆ (01285) 750651, *stay@new_inn.co.uk, Fax (01285) 7506* « 16C coaching inn » – ⇆ rest, TV P. MC AE VISA. ✻
Meals 22.50/26.50 **t.** 10.00 – (see also ***The Courtyard Bar*** below) – **14 rm** ☐ 68. 115.00 **t.** – SB.

The Courtyard Bar (at New Inn at Coln), GL7 5AN, ✆ (01285) 750651, *stay@new_inn.uk, Fax (01285) 750657,* – P. MC AE VISA
Meals (bookings not accepted) a la carte 16.75/24.75 **t.** 10.00.

COLSTERWORTH *Lincs.* 402 404 S 25 – *pop. 1 452.*
London 105 – Grantham 8 – Leicester 29 – Nottingham 32 – Peterborough 14.

Travelodge without rest., Granada Service Area, NG33 5JR, at A 151/A 1 (southbou carriageway) ✆ (01476) 861077, *Fax (01476) 861078* – ⇆ TV ♿ P – 30. MC AE O JCB. ✻
36 rm 39.95 **t.**

Travelodge, New Fox, South Witham, NG33 5LN, South : 3 m. by B 6403 on A 1 (nor bound carriageway) ✆ (01572) 767586, *Fax (01572) 767586* – ⇆ rm, TV ♿ P. MC AE O JCB. ✻
Meals (grill rest.) – **32 rm** 29.95 **t.**

COLSTON BASSETT *Notts.* 402 404 R 25 – *pop. 239* – ✉ *Nottingham.*
London 129 – Lincoln 40 – Nottingham 15 – Sheffield 51.

Martins Arms, School Lane, NG12 3FD, ✆ (01949) 81361, *Fax (01949) 81309,* , – MC VISA. ✻
closed 25 December and Sunday dinner – **Meals** a la carte 22.85/32.40 **t.** 10.25.

COLTISHALL *Norfolk* 404 Y 25 *Great Britain G.* – *pop. 1 992* – ✉ *Norwich.*
Env. : *The Broads*★.
London 133 – Norwich 8.

Norfolk Mead , NR12 7DN, ✆ (01603) 737531, *norfolkmead@aol.com. Fax (01603) 737521,* heated, , – ⇆ TV P. MC AE O VISA JCB
Meals 8.50/10.50 **t.** (lunch) and dinner a la carte 24.00/31.50 **t.** 8.50 – **9 rm** ☐ 65 120.00 **t.** – SB.

Kings Head with rm, Wroxham Rd, NR12 7EA, ✆ (01603) 737426, *Fax (01603) 7365* TV P. MC VISA. ✻
Meals *(closed Sunday dinner January-March)* a la carte 15.85/23.20 **t.** 6.50 – 4 ☐ 25.00/60.00 **t.**

COLWALL *Herefordshire* – *see Great Malvern.*

OLYFORD Devon 403 K 31 *Great Britain G.* – ✉ *Colyton.*

Env. : *Colyton★ (Church★), N : 1 m. on B 3161 – Axmouth (≤★), S : 1 m. by A 3052 and B 3172.*

London 168 – Exeter 21 – Taunton 30 – Torquay 46 – Yeovil 32.

Swallows Eaves, EX24 6QJ, ☎ (01297) 553184, *Fax (01297) 553574,* – TV P. MC VISA JCB.
Meals (dinner only) 22.50 **st.** 7.40 – **8 rm** 44.00/88.00 **st.** – SB.

ENGLAND

OMPTON ABBAS *Dorset – see Shaftesbury.*

ONGLETON *Ches.* 402 403 404 N 24 *Great Britain G.* – *pop. 24 897.*

Env. : *Little Moreton Hall★★ AC, SW : 3 m. by A 34.*

Biddulph Rd ☎ (01260) 273540.

Town Hall, High St. ☎ (01260) 271095.

London 183 – Liverpool 50 – Manchester 25 – Sheffield 46 – Stoke-on-Trent 13.

Sandhole Farm without rest., Hulme Walfield, CW12 2JH, North : 2 ¼ m. on A 34 ☎ (01260) 224419, *veronica@sandholefarm.co.uk, Fax (01260) 224766,* – TV P. MC AE VISA.
17 rm 40.00/50.00 **t.**

ONISTON *Cumbria* 402 K 20 *Great Britain G.* – *pop. 1 304.*

Env. : *Coniston Water★ – Brantwood★ AC, SE : 2 m. on east side of Coniston Water.*

Exc. : *Hard Knott Pass★★, Wrynose Pass★★, NW : 10 m. by A 593 and minor road.*

Ruskin Av. ☎ (015394) 41533.

London 285 – Carlisle 55 – Kendal 22 – Lancaster 42.

Coniston Lodge, Station Rd, LA21 8HH, ☎ (015394) 41201, *robinson@conistonlodge.freeserve.co.uk, Fax (015394) 41201* – TV P. MC AE VISA.
closed January – **Meals** *(closed Sunday and Monday)* (dinner only) 20.50 **t.** 7.75 – **6 rm** 47.50/81.00 **t.**

Water Yeat *South : 6½ m. by A 593 on A 5084* – ✉ *Ulverston.*

Water Yeat, LA12 8DJ, ☎ (01229) 885306, *Fax (01229) 885306,* ≤, « Part 17C », – P.
mid February-November and New Year – **Meals** (by arrangement) 20.00 **st.** 5.00 – **5 rm** 40.00/64.00 **st.**

Blawith *South : 7¼ m. by A 593 on A 5084* – ✉ *Ulverston.*

Appletree Holme, LA12 8EL, West : 1 m. taking unmarked road opposite church and then right hand fork after ¼ m. ☎ (01229) 885618, ≤, – TV P. MC VISA.
Meals 25.00 **st.** – **4 rm** (dinner included) 78.50/145.00 **st.** – SB.

Torver *Southwest : 2¼ m. on A 593* – ✉ *Coniston.*

Wheelgate Country House without rest., Little Arrow, LA21 8AU, Northeast : ¾ m. on A 593 ☎ (015394) 41418, *wheelgate@conistoncottages.co.uk, Fax (015394) 41114,* « Part 17C farmhouse », – TV P. MC VISA JCB.
March-November – **5 rm** 28.00/56.00.

Old Rectory, LA21 8AX, Northeast : ¼ m. by A 593 ☎ (015394) 41353, *enquire@theoldrectoryhotel.com, Fax (015394) 41156,* ≤, – TV P. MC VISA
Meals (residents only) (dinner only) 6.50 – **8 rm** (dinner included) 60.00/104.00 **st.** – SB.

Arrowfield Country without rest., Little Arrow, LA21 8AU, Northeast : ¾ m. on A 593 ☎ (015394) 41741, ≤, – TV P.
March-November – **5 rm** 24.00/48.00 **st.**

NISTON COLD *N. Yorks. – see Skipton.*

NSTABLE BURTON *N. Yorks.* 402 O 21 – *see Leyburn.*

Groß-London *(GREATER LONDON) besteht aus der City und 32 Verwaltungsbezirken (Borough). Diese sind wiederum in kleinere Bezirke (Area) unterteilt, deren Mittelpunkt ehemalige Dörfer oder Stadtviertel sind, die oft ihren eigenen Charakter bewahrt haben.*

CONSTANTINE *Cornwall* 403 E 33 – ✉ *Falmouth.*

Env. : *Mawgan-in-Meneage (Church★), S : 3 m. by minor roads.*
London 303 – Falmouth 15 – Penzance 25 – Truro 24.

Trengilly Wartha Inn with rm, Nancenoy, TR11 5RP, South : 1 ½ m. by Fore St. Port Navas rd ✆ (01326) 340332, *trengilly@compuserve.com, Fax (01326) 340332,* – TV P. MC AE O VISA JCB
Meals (bar lunch)/dinner 27.00 **t.** 6.00 – **8 rm** 46.00/86.00 **t.** – SB.

CONSTANTINE BAY *Cornwall* 403 E 32 – *see Padstow.*

COOKHAM *Windsor & Maidenhead* 404 R 29 *Great Britain G.* – *pop. 6 096* – ✉ *Maidenhead.*

See : *Stanley Spencer Gallery★ AC.*
to Marlow, Maidenhead and Windsor (Salter Bros. Ltd) (summer only).
London 32 – High Wycombe 7 – Reading 16.

Alfonso's, 19 Station Hill Par., SL6 9BR, ✆ (01628) 525775, *Fax (01628) 525775* – MC AE VISA
closed 2 weeks August, 1 week Christmas, Saturday lunch, Sunday and Bank Holiday.
Meals 18.50/23.00 **t.** and a la carte 8.00.

Bel and the Dragon, High St., SL6 9SQ, ✆ (01628) 521263, *cookham@belandthedrag.co.uk, Fax (01628) 851008,* – MC AE VISA
Meals a la carte 20.40/32.40 **t.**

COPTHORNE *W. Sussex* 404 T 30 – *see Crawley.*

CORBIERE *Jersey (Channel Islands)* 403 P 33 and 230 ⑩ ⑪ – *see Channel Islands.*

CORBRIDGE *Northd.* 401 402 N 19 *Great Britain G.* – *pop. 2 719.*

Env. : *Hadrian's Wall★★, N : 3 m. by A 68 – Corstopitum★ AC, NW : ½ m.*
Hill St. ✆ (01434) 632815 (Easter-October).
London 300 – Hexham 3 – Newcastle upon Tyne 18.

Angel Inn, Main St., NE45 5LA, ✆ (01434) 632119, *Fax (01434) 632119,* « 18C form posting inn » – rest, TV P. MC AE O VISA.
Meals 16.95 **t.** (dinner) and a la carte 12.45/15.95 **t.** 5.45 – **5 rm** 49.50/74.00 **t.**

Riverside without rest., Main St., NE45 5LE, ✆ (01434) 632942, *riverside@ukonline.co. Fax (01434) 633883* – TV P. MC AE VISA JCB
closed 2 weeks November and Christmas-New Year – **10 rm** 30.00/59.00 **st.**

Lion of Corbridge, Bridge End, NE45 5AX, ✆ (01434) 632504, *Fax (01434) 63257* rest, TV P. MC AE O VISA JCB.
closed Christmas and New Year – **Meals** (bar lunch Monday to Saturday and dinner Sun and Monday) a la carte 13.45/19.40 **t.** 4.95 – **14 rm** 48.00/74.00 **t.**

The Courtyard without rest., Mount Pleasant, Sandhoe, NE46 4LX, Northwest : 2 m. by A 68 on Stagshaw rd ✆ (01434) 606850, *Fax (01434) 607962,* ←, – TV P.
restricted opening in winter – **3 rm** 55.00/80.00 **s.**

Ramblers Country House, Farnley, NE45 5RN, South : 1 m. on Riding Mill ✆ (01434) 632424, *Fax (01434) 633656* – P. MC AE O VISA JCB
closed Sunday dinner and Monday – **Meals** (dinner only and Sunday lunch)/dinner 19.9 and a la carte 4.95.

Valley, The Old Station House, Station Rd, NE45 5AY, South : ½ m. by Riding Mill ✆ (01434) 633434, *Fax (01434) 633923* – MC AE O VISA
closed 25 December and Sunday – **Meals** - Indian - (dinner only) a la carte 11.95/19.85 s

CORBY *Northants.* 404 R 26 *Great Britain G.* – *pop. 49 053.*

Env. : *Boughton House★★ AC, S : 5½ m. by A 6116 and A 43.*
Priors Hall, Stamford Rd, Weldon ✆ (01536) 260756.
George St. ✆ (01536) 407507.
London 100 – Leicester 26 – Northampton 22 – Peterborough 24.

Hilton Corby, Geddington Rd, NN18 8ET, East : 2 ½ m. on A 6116 at junction with A ✆ (01536) 401020, *reservations_corby@hilton.com, Fax (01536) 400767,* – TV P – 200. MC AE O VISA JCB.
Seasons : **Meals** *(closed Saturday lunch and Sunday dinner)* (live music and dancing Saturday evening) 18.50/20.00 **t.** – ***Millers :*** **Meals** a la carte 11.40/21.65 **t.** – 10.95 – **103** 110.00/125.00 **st.**, 2 suites – SB.

)RFE CASTLE *Dorset* 403 404 N 32 *The West Country G.* – *pop. 1 335* – ✉ *Wareham.*

See : *Castle★ (≤★★) AC.*

London 129 – Bournemouth 18 – Weymouth 23.

Mortons House, 45 East St., BH20 5EE, ☎ (01929) 480988, *stay@mortonshouse.co.uk, Fax (01929) 480820,* ≤, « Part Elizabethan manor », – rest, TV P. MC AE ⓓ VISA
Meals 16.00/24.00 **t.** and a la carte 6.50 – **16 rm** 90.00/106.00 **t.**, 1 suite – SB.

)RNHILL-ON-TWEED *Northd.* 401 402 N 17 *Scotland G.* – *pop. 317.*

Env. : *Ladykirk (Kirk o'Steil★), NE : 6 m. by A 698 and B 6470.*

London 345 – Edinburgh 49 – Newcastle upon Tyne 59.

Tillmouth Park ⛷, TD12 4UU, Northeast : 2 ½ m. on A 698 ☎ (01890) 882255, *el@tillmouthpark.f9.co.uk, Fax (01890) 882540,* ≤, « 19C country house », , , – TV P. MC AE ⓓ VISA
Meals (bar lunch Monday to Saturday)/dinner 26.00/30.00 **t.** 8.00 – **14 rm** 90.00/170.00 **t.** – SB.

Coach House, Crookham, TD12 4TD, East : 4 m. on A 697 ☎ (01890) 820293, *thecoachhouse@englandmail.com, Fax (01890) 820284,* – rest, TV ♿ P. MC VISA
Easter-October – **Meals** (dinner only) 17.50 **t.** 4.50 – **9 rm** 25.00/78.00 **t.**

)RSCOMBE *Dorset* 403 L 31 – ✉ *Dorchester.*

London 153 – Exeter 47 – Taunton 30 – Weymouth 24.

Fox Inn with rm, DT2 0NS, Northeast : ¾ m. on Halstock rd ☎ (01935) 891330, *dine@fox-inn.co.uk, Fax (01935) 891330,* « Thatched inn » – rm, TV P. MC AE VISA.
closed 25 December – **Meals** a la carte 15.95/23.95 **t.** 8.50 – **3 rm** 55.00/85.00 **t.**

)RSE LAWN *Worcs.* – *see Tewkesbury (Glos.).*

)SGROVE *Northants.* 404 R 27 – *see Stony Stratford.*

)SHAM *Portsmouth* 403 404 Q 31 – *see Portsmouth and Southsea.*

)VENEY *Cambs.* – *see Ely.*

)VENTRY *W. Mids.* 403 404 P 26 *Great Britain G.* – *pop. 299 316.*

See : *City★ - Cathedral★★★* **AC AV** – *Old Cathedral★* **AV A** – *Museum of British Road Transport★* **AC AV M1.**

18 Windmill Village, Birmingham Rd, Allesley ☎ (024) 7640 4041 – 9 Sphinx, Sphinx Drive ☎ (024) 7645 1361.

Bayley Lane ☎ (024) 7622 7264.

London 100 – Birmingham 18 – Bristol 96 – Nottingham 52.

Plans on following pages

Hilton Coventry, Paradise Way, The Triangle, Walsgrave, CV2 2ST, Northeast : 4 m. by A 4600 ☎ (024) 7660 3000, *ctthnhngm@hilton.com, Fax (024) 7660 3011,* , , – , rm, , TV ♿ P – 600. MC AE ⓓ VISA BX c
closed Christmas and New Year – **Meals** (bar lunch Saturday) 13.95/20.95 **st.** and a la carte – 11.50 – **169 rm** 165.00 **st.**, 3 suites – SB.

Posthouse Coventry, Hinckley Rd, Walsgrave, CV2 2HP, Northeast : 3 ½ m. on A 4600 ☎ (0870) 400 9021, *Fax (024) 7662 1736,* , – rm, rest, TV P – 300. MC AE ⓓ VISA BX r
Meals *(closed Saturday lunch)* (grill rest.) 15.00 **t.** (dinner) and a la carte 17.45/25.15 **t.** 6.95 – 11.95 – **160 rm** 89.00 **t.** – SB.

Village H. and Leisure Club, Dolomite Av., Coventry Business Park, CV4 9GZ, West : 2 m. by B 4101 ☎ (024) 7671 9000, *village.coventry@village-hotels.com, Fax (024) 7671 9100,* , , , squash – , rest, TV ♿ P – 250. MC AE ⓓ VISA. AY z
Meals (grill rest.) 10.95/12.95 **st.** and a la carte – **98 rm** 82.00/95.00 **st.**

Brooklands Grange, Holyhead Rd, CV5 8HX, Northwest : 2 ½ m. on A 4114 ☎ (024) 7660 1601, *enquiries@brooklands_grange.co.uk, Fax (024) 7660 1277,* – rest, TV P. MC AE ⓓ VISA. AY e
closed 26 December – **Meals** *(closed Saturday lunch and Bank Holiday lunch)* 18.50 **st.** and a la carte 8.50 – **31 rm** 90.00/125.00 **st.** – SB.

COVENTRY

Street	Grid	No.
Bayley Lane	AV	3
Bishop Street	AV	5
Broadgate	AV	6
Burges	AV	7
Corporation Street	AV	
Earl Street	AV	10
Fairfax Street	AV	12
Far Gosford Street	AV	13
Gosford Street	AV	15
Greyfriars Lane	AV	16
Hales Street	AV	17
Hearsall Lane	AY	21
High Street	AV	22
Ironmonger Road	AV	23
Jordan Well	AV	26
Leicester Row	AV	29
Light Lane	AV	30
Little Park Street	AV	31
Precincts Shopping	AV	
Primrose Hill Street	AV	34
Queen Victoria Road	AV	35
St. Johns (Ringway)	AV	38
St. Nicholas (Ringway)	AV	39
Swanswell (Ringway)	AV	40
Trinity Street	AV	41
Upper Well Street	AV	43
Vecqueray Street	AV	45
Victoria Street	AV	46
Warwick Road	AV	49
White Street	AV	51
Windsor Street	AV	52
White Friars (Ringway)	AV	54

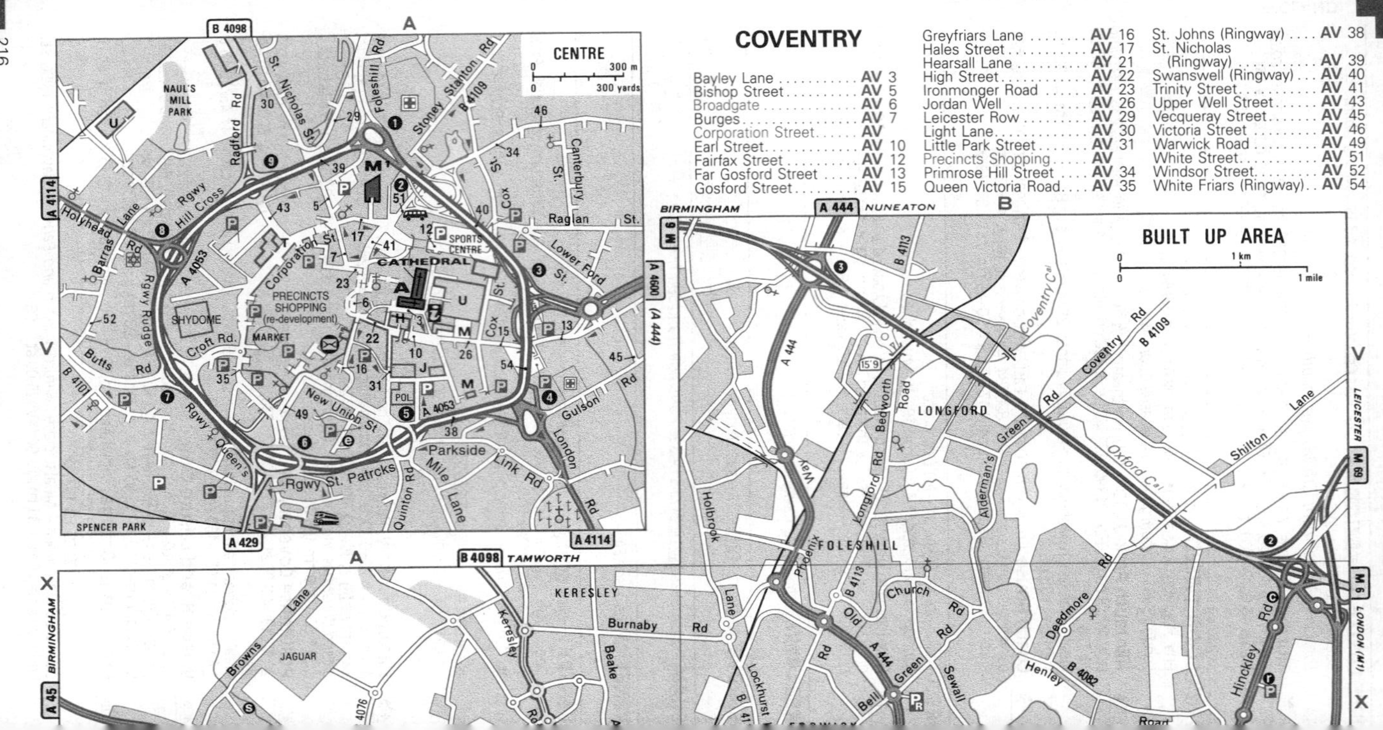

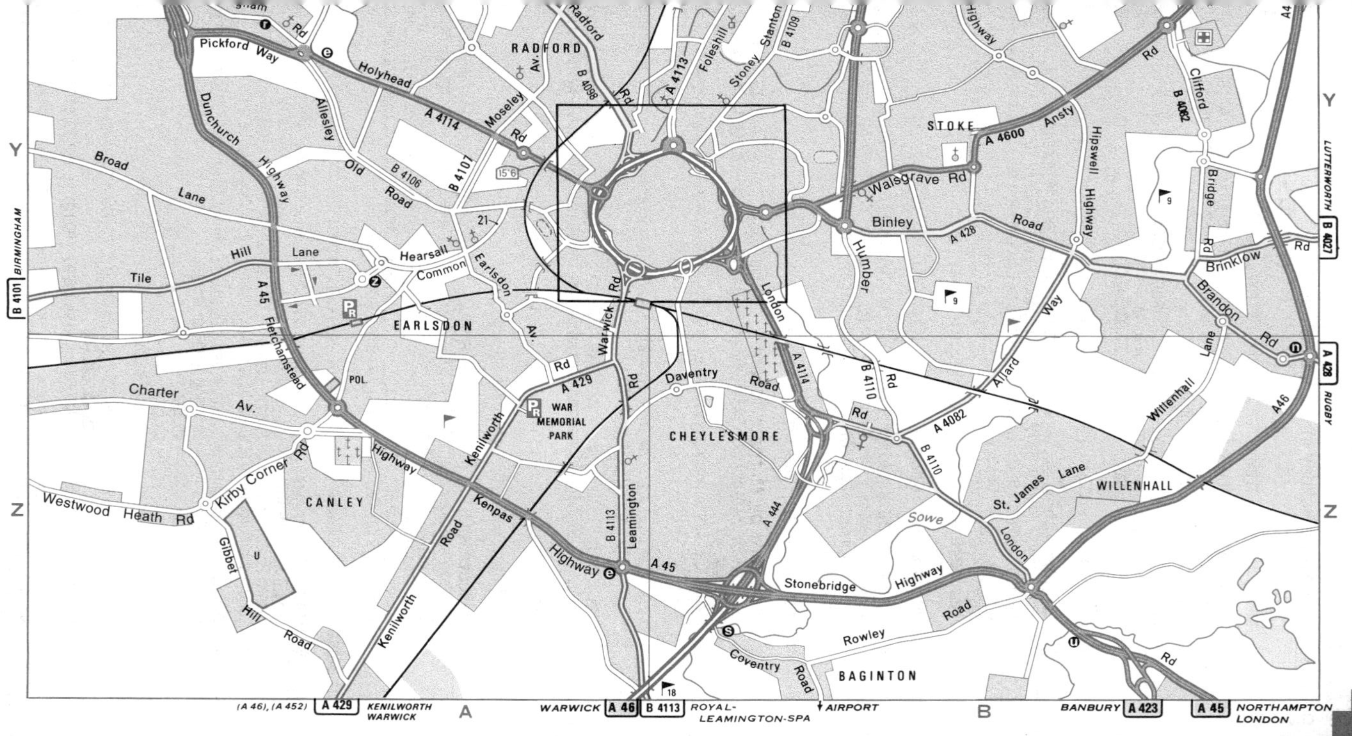

LUTTERWORTH
B 4027
A 428
RUGBY
B 4101
BIRMINGHAM
(A 46), (A 452)
A 429
KENILWORTH
WARWICK
A
WARWICK
A 46
B 4113
ROYAL-
LEAMINGTON-SPA
AIRPORT
B
BANBURY
A 423
A 45
NORTHAMPTON
LONDON
Y
Z
Pickford Way
Holyhead
A 4114
Moseley
Rd
RADFORD
Av.
Radford
B 4098
Rd
A 4113
Foleshill
Stoney Stanton
B 4109
Highway
Rd
Clifford
B 4082
STOKE
A 4600
Ansty
Hipswell
Highway
Bridge
Rd
Brinklow
Rd
Dunchurch
Highway
Allesley
Old
Road
B 4106
B 4107
Broad
Lane
Walsgrave Rd
Binley
A 428
Road
Humber
Brandon
Rd
Hearsall
Common
Earlsdon
Hill
Lane
Tile
A 45
Fletchamstead
EARLSDON
Av.
Warwick
Rd
London
Way
Lane
Rd
A 429
Rd
Daventry
Road
A 4114
B 4110
Rd
Allard
Willenhall
A46
Charter
Av.
POL.
WAR
MEMORIAL
PARK
CHEYLESMORE
Rd
A 4082
B 4110
Kenilworth
Highway
Kirby Corner
Rd
CANLEY
St. James
Lane
WILLENHALL
Westwood Heath Rd
Kenpas
Road
B 4113
Leamington
A 444
Sowe
London
Gibbet
Hill
Road
Highway
A 45
Stonebridge
Highway
Road
Kenilworth
Rowley
Coventry
Road
BAGINTON
Rd

ENGLAND

Express by Holiday Inn, Kenpas Highway, CV3 6PB, at junction of A 45 with B 41 ☎ (024) 7641 7555, *Fax (024) 7641 3388* – rm, rest, TV, P – 30. MC AE VISA JCB. AZ
Meals (grill rest.) a la carte 12.50/17.00 **t.** – **37 rm** 49.95 **t.**

Travel Inn, Rugby Rd, Binley Woods, CV3 2TA, at junction of A 46 with A 4 ☎ (024) 7663 6585, *Fax (024) 7643 1178* – rm, rest, TV, P. MC AE VISA. BZ
Meals (grill rest.) – **73 rm** 40.95 **t.**

Crest without rest., 39 Friars Rd, CV1 2LJ, ☎ (024) 7622 7822, *alanharve@aol.cc Fax (024) 7622 7244* – TV. MC VISA JCB. AV
closed 25 and 26 December – **4 rm** 27.00/54.00.

at Binley *East : 3½ m. on A 428* – **BY** – ✉ *Coventry.*

Coombe Abbey, Brinklow Rd, CV3 2AB, East : 2 m. following signs for Coom Abbey Country Park (B 4027) ☎ (024) 7645 0450, *Fax (024) 7663 5101*, ≤, « Former Cist cian abbey of 12C origins with formal gardens by Capability Brown », – rm, P – 120. MC AE VISA.
closed 24-27 December – **Meals** (bar lunch Monday to Saturday)/dinner 26.50 and a la carte – 12.00 – **82 rm** 135.00/365.00 **st.**, 1 suite – SB.

at Brandon *(Warks.) East : 6 m. on A 428* – **BZ** – ✉ *Coventry.*

Brandon Hall, Main St., CV8 3FW, ☎ (0870) 400 8105, *brandonhall@forte-hotels.co , Fax (024) 7654 4909*, squash – TV P – 100. MC AE VISA JCB
Meals (bar lunch Saturday) 12.50/26.00 **t.** and dinner a la carte 8.50 – 12.50 – **60** 125.00 **t.** – SB.

at Ryton on Dunsmore *Southeast : 4 ¾ m. by A 45* – ✉ *Coventry.*

Courtyard by Marriott Coventry, London Rd, CV8 3DY, on A 45 (northbou carriageway) ☎ (024) 7630 1585, *Fax (024) 7630 1610* – , rest, TV P – 250. AE VISA. BZ
Meals (bar lunch Saturday) a la carte 17.00/21.00 **st.** 8.00 – 10.00 – **47 rm** 75.(85.00 **st.**, 2 suites.

at Baginton *(Warks.) South : 3 m. by A 4114 and A 444 off A 45 (off westbound carriageway a Howes Lane turning)* – ✉ *Coventry.*

Old Mill, Mill Hill, CV8 3AH, ☎ (024) 7630 2241, *oldmill.bag@btclick.cc Fax (024) 7630 7070*, « Converted corn mill » – rm, rest, TV P – 25. MC AE VISA. BZ
Meals (grill rest.) a la carte 11.70/24.10 **t.** – 6.95 – **28 rm** 85.00 **t.**

at Berkswell *West : 6½ m. by B 4101* – **AY** – ✉ *Coventry.*

Nailcote Hall, Nailcote Lane, CV7 7DE, South : 1 ½ m. on B 4101 ☎ (024) 7646 6174, *i @nailcotehall.co.uk, Fax (024) 7647 0720*, « Part 17C timbered house », TV P – 100. MC AE VISA JCB.
Oak Room : **Meals** *(closed Saturday lunch, Sunday and dinner Bank Holiday Monc* (booking essential) 21.50/29.50 **t.** 10.50 – ***Rick's :*** **Meals** (booking essential) a la ca 17.95/40.45 **t.** 10.50 – **38 rm** 145.00/275.00 **t.** – SB.

at Balsall Common *West : 6 ¾ m. by B 4101* – **AY** – ✉ *Coventry.*

Haigs, 273 Kenilworth Rd, CV7 7EL, on A 452 ☎ (01676) 533004, *Fax (01676) 535132*, TV P. MC AE VISA.
closed 26 December-5 January – ***Poppy's :*** **Meals** *(closed Sunday dinner)* (dinner only a Sunday lunch)/dinner 18.50/33.00 **t.** and a la carte 5.25 – **23 rm** 66.00/89.50 **st.**

Travel Inn, Kenilworth Rd, CV7 7EX, Northwest : ½ m. on A 452 ☎ (01676) 5331 *Fax (01676) 535929* – rm, TV P. MC AE VISA
Meals (grill rest.) – **42 rm** 40.95 **t.**

at Allesley *Northwest : 3 m. on A 4114* – ✉ *Coventry.*

Allesley, Birmingham Rd, CV5 9GP, ☎ (024) 7640 3272, *Fax (024) 7640 5190* – , re rest, TV P – 450. MC AE VISA JCB AY
Meals *(closed Saturday lunch)* 17.50/21.00 **st.** 6.95 – **90 rm** 102.00/130.00 **st.** – SB.

Brookfields without rest., 134 Butt Lane, CV5 9FE, ☎ (024) 7640 48 *Fax (024) 7640 2022*, – P. AX
closed New Year – **4 rm** 30.00/50.00.

Meriden *Northwest : 6 m. by A 45 on B 4104* – **AX** – ✉ *Coventry.*

Marriott Forest of Arden H. & Country Club, Maxstoke Lane, CV7 7HR, Northwest : 2 ¾ m. on Maxstoke rd ✆ (01676) 522335, *Fax (01676) 523711,* – ⇆, ▤ rest, TV ✆ ♿ P – 360. MC AE ◑ VISA JCB. ✗
The Broadwater : **Meals** *(closed Saturday lunch)* 12.95/16.50 **st.** (lunch) and dinner a la carte 23.70/35.50 **st.** 7.45 – ***The Long Weekend :*** **Meals** a la carte 14.95/21.35 **t.** 7.45 – ☕ 12.95 – **214 rm** 129.00/179.00 **st.** – SB.

The Manor, Main Rd, CV7 7NH, ✆ (01676) 522735, *Fax (01676) 522186,* – ⇆, ▤ rest, TV ✆ ♿ P – 275. MC AE ◑ VISA
restricted opening 24 December-2 January – **Meals** *(closed Saturday lunch)* 19.95/21.95 **st.** and a la carte 8.00 – **110 rm** ☕ 120.00/130.00 **st.**, 2 suites – SB.

VERACK *Cornwall* 403 E 33.
London 300 – Penzance 25 – Truro 27.

Bay, TR12 6TF, ✆ (01326) 280464, *enquiries@thebayhotel.co.uk, Fax (01326) 280464,* ≤, – ⇆ rest, TV P. MC VISA
7 March-3 November and 2 weeks Christmas – **Meals** (bar lunch)/dinner 18.50/27.50 **t.** 5.25 – **14 rm** ☕ (dinner included) 48.50/120.00 **t.**

WAN BRIDGE *Cumbria* 402 M 21 – *see Kirkby Lonsdale.*

WLEY *Oxon. – see Oxford.*

ACKINGTON HAVEN *Cornwall* 403 G 31 *The West Country G.* – ✉ *Bude.*
Env. : *Poundstock★ (≤★★, church★, guildhouse★), NE : 5 ½ m. by A 39 – Jacobstow (Church★), E : 3½ m.*
London 262 – Bude 11 – Plymouth 44 – Truro 42.

Manor Farm ⛰, EX23 0JW, Southeast : 1 ¼ m. by Boscastle rd taking left turn onto Church Park Rd after 1.1 m. then taking first right onto unmarked lane ✆ (01840) 230304, ≤, « Part 11C manor », – ⇆ P. ✗
closed 25 December – **Meals** (by arrangement) (communal dining) 18.00 **s.** – **4 rm** ☕ 35.00/70.00 **s.** – SB.

Trevigue ⛰, EX23 0LQ, Southeast : 1 ¼ m. on High Cliff rd ✆ (01840) 230418, *Fax (01840) 230418,* « 16C farmhouse, working farm » – ⇆ P. MC VISA. ✗
closed 25 December – **Meals** (by arrangement) (communal dining) 18.00 – **3 rm** ☕ 36.00/60.00 – SB.

ANBROOK *Kent* 404 V 30 *Great Britain G.* – *pop. 3 522.*
Env. : *Sissinghurst Castle★ AC, NE : 2½ m. by A 229 and A 262.*
ℹ *Vestry Hall, Stone St. ✆ (01580) 712538 (summer only).*
London 53 – Hastings 19 – Maidstone 15.

Kennel Holt ⛰, Goudhurst Rd, TN17 2PT, Northwest : 2 ¼ m. by A 229 on A 262 ✆ (01580) 712032, *hotel@kennelholt.demon.co.uk, Fax (01580) 715495,* « Elizabethan manor house with Edwardian additions, gardens » – ⇆ rest, TV P. MC VISA JCB. ✗
closed 2 weeks February – **Meals** *(closed Sunday dinner to non-residents and Monday)* (dinner only) 27.50/32.50 **t.** 7.50 – **10 rm** ☕ 90.00/175.00 **st.**

Old Cloth Hall ⛰, TN17 3NR, East : 1 m. by Tenterden Rd ✆ (01580) 712220, *Fax (01580) 712220,* ≤, « Tudor manor house, gardens », – ⇆ rm, TV P. ✗
closed Christmas – **Meals** (by arrangement) (communal dining) 22.00 – **3 rm** ☕ 50.00/105.00.

Soho South, 23 Stone St., TN17 3HF, ✆ (01580) 714666, *Fax (01580) 715653* – MC VISA
closed 1 week in spring, 1 week in autumn, 25-26 December, 1 January and Sunday-Tuesday – **Meals** a la carte 12.75/28.25 **t.** 9.20.

Sissinghurst *Northeast : 1 ¾ m. by B 2189 on A 262* – ✉ *Cranbrook.*

Rankins, The Street, TN17 2JH, on A 262 ✆ (01580) 713964 – MC VISA
restricted opening in winter, closed Monday, Tuesday and Bank Holidays – **Meals** (dinner only and Sunday lunch)/dinner 25.00/28.00 **t.** 4.75.

ANTOCK *Cornwall* 403 E 32 – *see Newquay.*

CRAVEN ARMS *Shrops.* 402 403 L 26 *Great Britain G. – pop. 1 892.*

Env. : *Wenlock Edge★, NE : by B 4368.*

London 170 – Birmingham 47 – Hereford 32 – Shrewsbury 21.

Old Rectory ⑤, Hopesay, SY7 8HD, West : 4 m. by B 4368 ✆ (01588) 6602
Fax (01588) 660502, ⩽, « Part 17C », ⚘ – ⇔ TV P. ✱
closed Christmas – **Meals** (by arrangement) (communal dining) 22.50 ⚱ 8.00 – 3
⊡ 75.00.

CRAWLEY *W. Sussex* 404 T 30 – *pop. 88 203.*

18, 18 Cottesmore, Buchan Hill, Pease Pottage ✆ (01293) 528256 – 18, 9 Tilgate Fore Titmus Dr., Tilgate ✆ (01293) 530103 – 9 Gatwick Manor, London Rd, Lowfield Heath (01293) 538587 – 9 Pease Pottage, Horsham Rd ✆ (01293) 521706.

London 33 – Brighton 21 – Lewes 23 – Royal Tunbridge Wells 23.

Plan of enlarged Area : see Gatwick

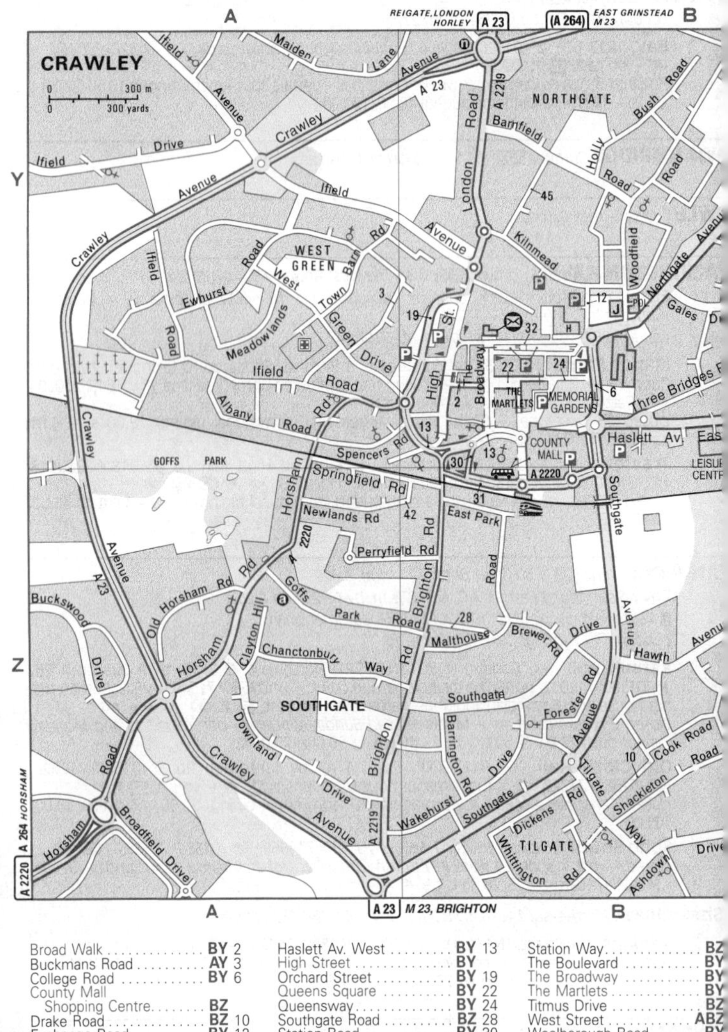

Broad Walk .... **BY** 2	Haslett Av. West .... **BY** 13	Station Way.............. **BZ**
Buckmans Road .... **AY** 3	High Street .... **BY**	The Boulevard .... **BY**
College Road .... **BY** 6	Orchard Street .... **BY** 19	The Broadway .... **BY**
County Mall Shopping Centre.......... **BZ**	Queens Square .... **BY** 22	The Martlets .... **BY**
Drake Road .... **BZ** 10	Queensway .... **BY** 24	Titmus Drive .... **BZ**
Exchange Road .... **BY** 12	Southgate Road .... **BZ** 28	West Street .... **ABZ**
	Station Road .... **BY** 30	Woolborough Road .... **BY**

Holiday Inn London Gatwick, Langley Drive, Tushmore Roundabout, RH11 7SX, ℘ (01293) 529991, *Fax (01293) 510653*, – rm, – 275. BY n
Colonnade : Meals *(closed Sunday dinner)* (dinner only and Sunday lunch)/dinner 21.50 **t.** and a la carte – ***La Brasserie :*** Meals a la carte 15.00/21.50 **t.** – 12.50 – **219 rm** 140.00 **st.**, 2 suites.

Premier Lodge, Goffs Park Rd, Southgate, RH11 8AX, ℘ (01293) 535447, *Fax (01293) 542050*, – , rest, – 150.
Meals (grill rest.) 5.95/10.95 **st.** and a la carte – 6.00 – **57 rm** 49.50 **st.** – SB. AZ a

Express by Holiday Inn (without rest.), The Squareabout, Haslett Avenue East, RH10 1UA, ℘ (01293) 525523, *Fax (01293) 525529* – , rm, – 35. Z a
74 rm 52.50 **t.**

Copthorne *Northeast : 4½ m. on A 264* – **BY**.

Copthorne London Gatwick, Copthorne Way, RH10 3PG, ℘ (01342) 348800, *coplgw@mill-cop.com, Fax (01342) 348833*, , squash – rm, rest, – 100.
Lion D'Or : Meals *(closed Saturday lunch and Sunday)* 23.95 **t.** (dinner) and a la carte 24.25/38.00 **t.** 10.50 – ***Brasserie :*** Meals (carving lunch) 15.50/18.50 **t.** and a la carte 8.50 – 13.50 – **227 rm** 134.00/144.00 **t.**

Copthorne Effingham Park, West Park Rd, RH10 3EU, on B 2028 ℘ (01342) 714994, *events.effingham@mill-cop.com, Fax (01342) 716039*, – , rest, – 600.
Meals (bar lunch)/dinner a la carte 17.20/31.50 **t.** 6.75 – 13.50 – **119 rm** 134.00/144.00 **t.**, 3 suites.

Three Bridges *East : 1 m. on Haslett Avenue East* – **BY** – ✉ *Crawley.*

Jarvis International Gatwick, Tinsley Lane South, RH10 2XH, North : ½ m. by Hazelwick Av. ℘ (01293) 561186, *Fax (01293) 561169*, – – 210.
on Gatwick town plan Y n
Meals *(closed 25 December and lunch Saturday, Sunday and 1 January)* (bar lunch)/dinner a la carte 21.00/27.00 **t.** 8.60 – 10.95 – **151 rm** 115.00/135.00 **t.** – SB.

RAYKE *N. Yorks. – see Easingwold.*

RESSAGE *Shrops.* 402 403 404 M 26 – *pop. 810* – ✉ *Shrewsbury.*
London 163 – Birmingham 46 – Chester 48 – Manchester 73 – Shrewsbury 6 – Stoke-on-Trent 34.

Cholmondeley Riverside Inn with rm, SY5 6AF, Northwest : 1 ½ m. on A 458 ℘ (01952) 510900, *Fax (01952) 510980*, ≤, « Riverside setting », –
Meals *(closed 25 December)* a la carte 14.55/22.70 **t.** 5.95 – **7 rm** 50.00/90.00 **t.** – SB.

REWE *Ches.* 402 403 404 M 24 – *pop. 63 351.*
Queen's Park, Queen's Park Dr. ℘ (01270) 666724 – Fields Rd, Haslington ℘ (01270) 584227.
London 174 – Chester 24 – Liverpool 49 – Manchester 36 – Stoke-on-Trent 15.

Travel Inn, Coppenhall Lane, Woolstanwood, CW2 8SD, West : 2 m. on A 532 at junction with A 530 ℘ (01270) 251126, *Fax (01270) 256316* –
Meals (grill rest.) – **41 rm** 40.95 **t.**

Travelodge, Alsager Rd, Barthomley, CW2 5PT, Southeast : 5 ½ m. by A 5020 on A 500 at junction with M 6 ℘ (01270) 883157, *Fax (01270) 883157* – rm,
Meals (grill rest.) – **42 rm** 49.95 **t.**

RIBBS CAUSEWAY *Bristol – see Bristol.*

RICK *Northants.* 403 404 Q 26 – *see Rugby.*

---

e confondez pas :

Confort des hôtels : ... ,
Confort des restaurants : ..... ,
Qualité de la table : , , , Meals

CRICKET MALHERBIE *Somerset* 403 L 31 – *see Ilminster.*

CRICKLADE *Wilts.* 403 404 O 29 – *pop. 3 808.*

Cricklade Hotel, Common Hill (01793) 750751.
London 90 – Bristol 45 – Gloucester 27 – Oxford 34 – Swindon 6.

Cricklade H. & Country Club, Common Hill, SN6 6HA, Southwest : 1 m. on B 40 (01793) 750751, *Fax (01793) 751767,* – 120. AE VISA.
Meals 16.50/24.00 **st.** 9.50 – **46 rm** 90.00/130.00 **s.** – SB.

CROCKERTON *Wilts. – see Warminster.*

CROFT-ON-TEES *Durham* 402 P 20 – *see Darlington.*

CROMER *Norfolk* 404 X 25 – *pop. 7 267.*

Royal Cromer, Overstrand Rd (01263) 512884.
Prince of Wales Rd (01263) 512497.
London 132 – Norwich 23.

Morden House, 20 Cliff Av., NR27 0AN, (01263) 513396, *rosemary@broadland.co*
closed Christmas-New Year – **Meals** 14.00 – **6 rm** 26.00/42.00 – SB.

at Overstrand *Southeast : 2½ m. by B 1159 – Cromer.*

Sea Marge, High St., NR27 0AB, (01263) 579579, *seamarge.hotel@virgin.n*
Fax (01263) 579524, VISA JCB
Meals (bar lunch Monday to Saturday)/dinner a la carte 15.00/24.95 **st.** – **18 rm** 60.0 80.00 **st.** – SB.

at Northrepps *Southeast : 3 m. by A 149 and Northrepps rd – Cromer.*

Shrublands Farm, NR27 0AA, (01263) 579297, *youngman@farming.co.*
Fax (01263) 579297, « Working farm »,
closed 24-26 December – **Meals** (by arrangement) (winter only) (communal dining) 15.00 – **3 rm** 27.00/48.00.

CRONDALL *Hants.* 404 R 30 – *pop. 6 113.*

London 56 – Reading 21 – Winchester 30.

The Chesa, Bowling Alley, GU10 5RJ, North : 1 m. (01252) 850328, *chesa@totalise.co k, Fax (01252) 850328* – AE VISA
closed 3 weeks August, 3 weeks January and Sunday-Tuesday – **Meals** (booking essent (dinner only) a la carte approx. 33.50 7.00.

CRONTON *Mersey.* 402 403 404 L 23 – *see Widnes.*

CROOK *Durham* 401 402 O 19 – *pop. 8 246 – Bishop Auckland.*

Low Job's Hill (01388) 762429.
London 261 – Carlisle 65 – Middlesbrough 34 – Newcastle upon Tyne 27.

Duke of York Inn, Fir Tree, DL15 8DG, Southwest : 3 ½ m. by A 689 off A (01388) 762848 – VISA.
Meals a la carte 15.70/26.65 **t.** 5.75 – **5 rm** 52.00/69.00 **t.** – SB.

Greenhead Country House without rest., Fir Tree, DL15 8BL, Southwest : 3 ½ m. b 689 off A 68 (01388) 763143, *Fax (01388) 763143,* AE VISA.
7 rm 42.00/55.00 **s.**

CROPTON *N. Yorks.* 402 R 21 – *see Pickering.*

CROSBY *Mersey.* 402 403 K 23 – *see Liverpool.*

CROSS HOUSES *Shrops.* 402 403 L 25 – *see Shrewsbury.*

CROSTHWAITE *Cumbria* 402 L 21 – *see Kendal.*

ROWTHORNE *Bracknell Forest* 404 R 29 – *pop. 21 500.*

London 42 – Reading 15.

Waterloo, Duke's Ride, RG45 6DW, on B 3348 ℘ (01344) 777711, *Fax (01344) 778913,* – rm, rest, TV P – 60. MC AE VISA JCB
closed 26 December-3 January – **Meals** *(closed Sunday dinner)* (bar lunch)/dinner a la carte 16.85/21.85 **t.** – 9.50 – **58 rm** 115.00/139.00 **st.** – SB.

Beijing, 103 Old Wokingham Rd, RG45 6LH, Northeast : ¾ m. by A 3095 ℘ (01344) 778802 – P. MC AE VISA JCB
closed 25-26 December, 1 January and Sunday lunch – **Meals** - Chinese - 13.50/25.00 **t.** and a la carte 4.25.

ROYDE *Devon* 403 H 30 – ✉ *Braunton.*

London 232 – Barnstaple 10 – Exeter 50 – Taunton 61.

Croyde Bay House, Moor Lane, Croyde Bay, EX33 1PA, Northwest : 1 m. by Baggy Point rd ℘ (01271) 890270, ≤ Croyde Bay, – rest, TV P. MC AE VISA JCB
March-mid November – **7 rm** (dinner included) 60.00/120.00 **t.**

Kittiwell House, St. Mary's Rd, EX33 1PG, ℘ (01271) 890247, *kittiwell@aol.com, Fax (01271) 890469,* « 16C thatched Devon longhouse » – rm, TV P. MC VISA
closed 4-29 January – **Meals** (dinner only) 21.50 **t.** and a la carte 7.50 – **12 rm** 44.00/74.00 **t.** – SB.

Whiteleaf, Hobbs Hill, EX33 1PN, ℘ (01271) 890266, – TV P. MC AE VISA JCB
Meals (by arrangement) 17.50 **t.** 7.35 – **4 rm** 38.00/60.00 **t.** – SB.

Le Grand Londres (GREATER LONDON) est composé de la City et de 32 arrondissements administratifs (Borough) eux-mêmes divisés en quartiers ou en villages ayant conservé leur caractère propre (Area).

RUDWELL *Wilts.* 403 404 N 29 – *see Malmesbury.*

UCKFIELD *W. Sussex* 404 T 30 – *pop. 2 879.*

London 40 – Brighton 15.

Ockenden Manor, Ockenden Lane, RH17 5LD, ℘ (01444) 416111, *ockenden@hshotels.co.uk, Fax (01444) 415549,* « Part 16C manor house », – rest, TV P – 50. MC AE VISA.
Meals 18.50/31.00-42.00 **t.** 15.50 – **20 rm** 105.00/240.00 **t.**, 2 suites – SB
Spec. Ballottine of salmon with grain mustard and dill vinaigrette. Roasted cod fillet with haricot beans, chicory and truffles. Tulip of fresh fruits with vanilla ice cream.

JLLOMPTON *Devon* 403 J 31 *The West Country G.* – *pop. 5 676.*

See : *Town★ – St. Andrew's Church★.*
Env. : *Uffculme (Coldharbour Mill★★ AC) NE : 5½ m. by B 3181 and B 3391.*
Exc. : *Killerton★★, SW : 6½ m. by B 3181 and B 3185.*
Padbrook Park ℘ (01884) 38286.
London 197 – Exeter 15 – Taunton 29.

Manor, 2-4 Fore St., EX15 1JL, ℘ (01884) 32281, *Fax (01884) 38344* – TV P. MC VISA
Meals (bar lunch)/dinner a la carte 9.50/15.00 **t.** 4.50 – **10 rm** 46.50/59.50 **t.**

JRDWORTH *W. Mids.* 402 ⑩ 403 ㉛ 404 ⑳ – *see Sutton Coldfield.*

ALTON *N. Yorks.* 402 O 20 – *see Richmond.*

ALTON-IN-FURNESS *Cumbria* 402 K 21 – *pop. 7 550.*

The Dunnerholme, Duddon Rd, Askham-in-Furness ℘ (01229) 462675.
London 283 – Barrow-in-Furness 3.5 – Kendal 30 – Lancaster 41.

Clarence House Country, Skelgate, LA15 8BQ, Northwest : ½ m. on Askam rd ℘ (01229) 462508, *vba1761186@aol.com, Fax (01229) 467177,* – TV P. MC AE VISA JCB
closed 25 and 26 December – **Meals** a la carte 20.95/30.00 **t.** 6.25 – **17 rm** 68.00/85.00 **t.** – SB.

DARESBURY *Warrington* 402 403 404 M 23 – *pop. 1 579* – ✉ *Warrington.*
London 197 – Chester 16 – Liverpool 23 – Manchester 25.

Daresbury Park, Chester Rd, WA4 4BB, on A 56 ☎ (01925) 267331, *daresburyparksales@devere-hotels.com, Fax (01925) 601496,* ⛶, ⛶, ⛶, squash – ⛶, ⛶ rm, ⛶ rest, ⛶ ⛶ – ⛶ 500. ⛶ ⛶ ⛶ *VISA* JCB
The Terrace : **Meals** (carving rest.) a la carte 14.75/20.70 **st.** 4.60 – ***The Looking Glass :*** **Meals** *(closed Saturday lunch)* a la carte 14.75/20.70 **st.** 4.60 – ⛶ 9.95 – **181 rm** 130.00/195.00 **st.** – SB.

DARGATE *Kent – see Faversham.*

DARLEY ABBEY *Derbs.* 402 403 404 P 25 – *see Derby.*

Wenn Sie ein ruhiges Hotel suchen,
benutzen Sie zuerst die Karte in der Einleitung
oder wählen Sie im Text ein Hotel mit dem Zeichen ⛶ oder ⛶.

DARLINGTON *Darlington* 402 P 20 – *pop. 86 767.*
Blackwell Grange, Briar Close ☎ (01325) 464464 – Stressholme, Snipe Lane ☎ (01325) 461002.
Teesside Airport : ☎ (01325) 332811, E : 6 m. by A 67.
13 Horsemarket ☎ (01325) 388666.
London 251 – Leeds 61 – Middlesbrough 14 – Newcastle upon Tyne 35.

New Grange, Southend Av., DL3 7HZ, Northwest : ¾ m. by A 167 on B 62.. ☎ (01325) 365859, *Fax (01325) 487111* – ⛶ ⛶ ⛶ – ⛶ 100. ⛶ ⛶ *VISA*. ⛶
Meals (dinner only and Sunday lunch)/dinner a la carte 13.00/22.15 **st.** – ⛶ 6.00 – **24 r..** 60.00/72.00 **st.**

Balmoral without rest., 63 Woodland Rd, DL3 7BQ, ☎ (01325) 4619.. *Fax (01325) 461908* – ⛶ ⛶. ⛶
closed Christmas – **9 rm** ⛶ 22.00/45.00.

at Coatham Mundeville *North : 4 m. on A 167* – ✉ *Darlington.*

Hall Garth Golf & Country Club, DL1 3LU, East : ¼ m. on Brafferton ☎ (01325) 300400, *Fax (01325) 310083,* ⛶, ⛶, ⛶, ⛶, ⛶ – ⛶ ⛶ ⛶ ⛶ – ⛶ 250. ⛶ ⛶ *VISA*
Hugo's : **Meals** (bar lunch Monday to Saturday)/dinner 19.95/22.95 **st.** and a la carte 7.. – ⛶ 10.50 – **38 rm** 104.00/150.00 **st.**, 3 suites – SB.

at Aycliffe *North : 5½ m. on A 167* – ✉ *Darlington.*

The County, 13 The Green, DL5 6LX, ☎ (01325) 312273, *Fax (01325)308780* – ⛶ ⛶. ⛶ ⛶ *VISA*
closed Sunday dinner – **Meals** (booking essential) a la carte 14.00/35.00 **t.**

at Croft-on-Tees *South : 3½ m. on A 167* – ✉ *Darlington.*

Clow Beck House ⛶, Monk End Farm, DL2 2SW, West : ½ m. by South Para.. ☎ (01325) 721075, *amjuser@clowbeckhouse.co.uk, Fax (01325) 720419,* ⛶, « Worki.. farm », ⛶, ⛶, ⛶ – ⛶ ⛶ ⛶. ⛶ ⛶ *VISA*. ⛶
closed Christmas and New Year – **Meals** (residents only) (dinner only) a la carte 16.0.. 23.50 **st.** 6.00 – **13 rm** ⛶ 47.00/75.00 **st.**

at Headlam *Northwest : 6 m. by A 67* – ✉ *Gainford.*

Headlam Hall ⛶, DL2 3HA, ☎ (01325) 730238, *admin@headlamhall.co.u.. Fax (01325) 730790,* ⛶, « Part Jacobean and part Georgian manor house, gardens », ⛶, ⛶, ⛶, ⛶, ⛶ – ⛶ ⛶ ⛶ ⛶ – ⛶ 150. ⛶ ⛶ ⛶ *VISA* JCB
closed 25 and 26 December – **Meals** a la carte 21.25/27.00 **st.** 4.50 – **34 rm** ⛶ 74.0.. 89.00 **st.**, 2 suites – SB.

at Heighington *Northwest : 6 m. by A 68 off A 6072* – ✉ *Darlington.*

Eldon House without rest., East Green, DL5 6PP, ☎ (01325) 312270, *kbartram@btinternet.com, Fax (01325) 315580,* « Part 17C », ⛶, ⛶ – ⛶
3 rm ⛶ 30.00/50.00 **s.**

at Redworth *Northwest : 7 m. by A 68 on A 6072 – ✉ Bishop Auckland.*

Redworth Hall H. & Country Club, DL5 6NL, on A 6072 ✆ (01388) 772442, *redworth @paramount-hotels.co.uk, Fax (01388) 775112,* « Part 18C and 19C manor house of Elizabethan origins », – rm, rest, – 300. VISA.
Conservatory : **Meals** 14.50/19.95 **t.** and a la carte 8.95 – (see also ***The Blue Room*** below) – **96 rm** 105.00/135.00 **t.**, 4 suites – SB.

The Blue Room (at Redworth Hall H. & Country Club), DL5 6NL, on A 6072 ✆ (01388) 772442, *Fax (01388) 775112,* « Part 18C and 19C manor house of Elizabethan origins », – . VISA
closed Sunday – **Meals** (dinner only) 37.50 **t.** 8.95.

DARTFORD *Kent* 404 U 29 – *pop. 59 411.*
Dartford Tunnel and Bridge (toll).
London 20 – Hastings 51 – Maidstone 22.

Hilton Dartford Bridge, Masthead Close, Crossways Business Park, DA2 6QF, Northeast : 2 ½ m. by A 226, Cotton Lane and Crossways Boulevard ✆ (01322) 284444, *Fax (01322) 288225,* – rm, – 240. VISA.
Meals *(closed lunch Saturday and Bank Holidays)* 16.95/29.00 **st.** and a la carte 7.50 – 11.95 – **171 rm** 134.00/144.00 **st.**, 4 suites – SB.

Express by Holiday Inn without rest., University Way, DA1 5PA, Northeast : 3 m. by A 226 and Cotton Lane on A 206 (westbound carriageway) ✆ (01322) 290333, *dartford@premierhotels.co.uk, Fax (01322) 290444* – – 35. VISA.
126 rm 62.50 **st.**

Les prix — Pour toutes précisions sur les prix indiqués dans ce guide, reportez-vous aux pages de l'introduction.

DARTMOUTH *Devon* 403 J 32 *The West Country G.* – *pop. 5 676.*
See : *Town★★ (<★) – Old Town - Butterwalk★ - Dartmouth Castle (<★★★) AC.*
Exc. : *Start Point (<★) S : 13 m. (including 1 m. on foot).*
The Engine House, Mayor's Av. ✆ *(01803) 834224.*
London 236 – Exeter 36 – Plymouth 35.

Royal Castle, 11 The Quay, TQ6 9PS, ✆ (01803) 833033, *enquiry@royalcastle.co.uk, Fax (01803) 835445,* < – rest, VISA
Meals 7.50/9.95 **st.** and a la carte 6.95 – **25 rm** 68.95/140.00 **st.** – SB.

Dart Marina, Sandquay, TQ6 9PH, ✆ (01803) 832580, *heritagehotels-dartmouth.dart_marina@forte-hotels.com, Fax (01803) 835040,* < Dart Marina – , rest, VISA.
Meals (bar lunch Monday to Saturday)/dinner a la carte 12.85/30.40 **t.** 5.95 – 12.00 – **50 rm** 80.00/135.00 **t.**

Ford House, 44 Victoria Rd, TQ6 9DX, ✆ (01803) 834047, *richard@ford-house-freeserve.co.uk, Fax (01803) 834047,* – VISA
April-October – **Meals** (residents only) (communal dining) (dinner only) (unlicensed) 32.00 **st.** – **3 rm** 55.00/75.00 **st.** – SB.

The Gunfield, Castle Rd, TQ6 0JN, ✆ (01803) 834571, *enquiry@gunfield.co.uk, Fax (01803) 834772,* < Dart Estuary and Kingswear, – VISA
closed January and 25 December – **Meals** *(closed Sunday dinner)* (lunch by arrangement except summer and weekends)/dinner a la carte 18.65/21.15 **t.** – **10 rm** 120.00 **t.**

Boringdon House without rest., 1 Church Rd, TQ6 9HQ, ✆ (01803) 832235, « Georgian house », –
3 rm 39.00/55.00 **st.**

Wadstray House without rest., Blackawton, TQ9 7DE, West : 4 ½ m. on A 3122 ✆ (01803) 712539, *Fax (01803) 712539,* –
closed 25 and 26 December – **3 rm** 45.00/60.00 **st.**

Hedley House without rest., Newcomen Rd, TQ6 9BN, ✆ (01803) 832885, *hedleyhouse @yahoo.com,* < Dart Estuary and Kingswear – .
3 rm 40.00/65.00 **s.**

Woodside Cottage without rest., Blackawton, TQ9 7BL, West : 5 ½ m. by A 3122 on Blackawton rd ✆ (01803) 712375, *bandb@woodside-cottage.demon.co.uk, Fax (01803) 712605,* <, –
March-October – **3 rm** 30.00/50.00.

ENGLAND

XX **The Carved Angel,** 2 South Embankment, TQ6 9BH, ✆ (01803) 832465, *enquiries@th arvedangel.com, Fax (01803) 835141,* ≤ Dart Estuary – ⅔. MC VISA
closed first 2 weeks January, 25-26 December, Monday lunch and Sunday dinner – **Mea** 29.50/39.50 **st.** 11.00.

XX **Hooked,** 5 Higher St., TQ6 9RB, ✆ (01803) 832022, *Fax (01803) 832022.* MC VISA JCB
closed last week December-first week February, Sunday and Monday lunch – **Meals** Seafood - 29.50 **t.** (dinner) and lunch a la carte 14.85/29.50 **t.** 7.00.

at Kingswear *East : via lower ferry taking first right onto Church Hill before Steam Packet Inn* ✉ *Dartmouth.*

Nonsuch House, Church Hill, TQ6 0BX, ✆ (01803) 752829, *enquiries@nonsuch-house. .uk, Fax (01803) 752357,* ≤ Dartmouth Castle and Warfleet, – TV. MC VISA JCB.
Meals *(closed Wednesday in summer and Sunday in winter)* (residents only) (dinner on (set menu only) (unlicensed) 19.50/24.00 – **5 rm** 52.50/75.00.

at Stoke Fleming *Southwest : 3 m. on A 379* – ✉ *Dartmouth.*

Stoke Lodge, Cinders Lane, TQ6 0RA, ✆ (01803) 770523, *mail@stokelodge.co.u Fax (01803) 770851,* ≤, heated, – rest, TV P. MC AE VISA
Meals 11.95/17.50 **t.** and a la carte 6.25 – **24 rm** 53.00/86.00 **t.** – SB.

DARWEN *Blackburn* 402 404 **M 22.**

Winterhill ✆ (01254) 701287.

London 222 – Manchester 24 – Blackburn 5 – Blackpool 34 – Leeds 59 – Liverpool 43.

Astley Bank, Bolton Rd, BB3 2QB, South : ¾ m. on A 666 ✆ (01254) 777700, *sales@astl bank.co.uk, Fax (01254) 777707,* – TV P – 70. MC AE VISA JCB.
Meals 14.50/23.00 and a la carte 5.50 – **37 rm** 78.00/118.00 **t.** – SB.

DAVENTRY *Northants.* 404 **Q 27** – *pop. 18 099.*

Norton Rd ✆ (01327) 702829 – , Hellidon Lakes Hotel & C.C., Hellidon ✆ (0132 62550 – Staverton Park, Staverton ✆ (01327) 302000.

Moot Hall, Market Sq. ✆ (01327) 300277.

London 79 – Coventry 23 – Northampton 13 – Oxford 46.

Fawsley Hall , Fawsley, NN11 3BA, South : 6 ½ m. by A 45 off A 3 ✆ (01327) 892000, *fawsley@compuserve.com, Fax (01327) 892001,* ≤, « Tudor man house with Georgian and Victorian additions », – TV P – 100. MC AE VISA
Meals 14.95/29.90 **t.** and a la carte 10.50 – **28 rm** 135.00/225.00 **st.**, 2 suites – SB.

Hanover International, Sedgemoor Way, off Ashby Rd, NN11 5SG, North : 2 m. o 361 ✆ (01327) 307000, *Fax (01327) 706313,* – rest, TV P – 6 MC AE VISA JCB
– **Meals** *(closed lunch Saturday, July and August)* (bar lunch)/dinner 18.95 **st.** and a la ca 9.95 – 10.50 – **136 rm** 110.00 **st.**, 2 suites – SB.

at Flore *East : 6 m. on A 45* – ✉ *Northampton.*

Courtyard by Marriott Daventry, High St., NN7 4LP, East : ½ m. on A ✆ (01327) 349022, *Fax (01327) 349017,* – rm, rest, TV P – 80. MC AE JCB.
Meals *(closed Saturday lunch)* a la carte 17.00/21.00 **st.** 8.00 – 10.00 – **53 rm** 75.00

at Staverton *Southwest : 2 ¾ m. by A 45 off A 425* – ✉ *Daventry.*

Colledges House, Oakham Lane, NN11 6JQ, off Glebe Lane ✆ (01327) 7027 *Fax (01327) 300851,* « Part 17C », – rm, TV P. MC VISA
closed Christmas and New Year – **Meals** (by arrangement) (communal dining) 24.50 – **4** 46.00/72.00.

at Everdon *Southeast : 7 m. by A 45, A 361 and B 4037 on Everdon rd* – ✉ *Daventry.*

Threeways House without rest., NN11 6BL, ✆ (01327) 361631, *elizabethbarwoo hotmail.com, Fax (01327) 361359,* – TV P.
closed 2 weeks Christmas and New Year **4 rm** 30.00/50.00 **st.**

Remember the speed limits that apply in the United Kingdom, unless otherwise signposted.

- 60 mph on single carriageway roads
- 70 mph on dual carriageway roads and motorways

AWLISH *Devon* 403 J 32 – *pop. 9 648.*

Warren ℘ (01626) 862255.

The Lawn ℘ (01626) 863589.

London 215 – Exeter 13 – Plymouth 40 – Torquay 11.

Langstone Cliff, Dawlish Warren, EX7 0NA, North : 2 m. by A 379 ℘ (01626) 868000, *reception@langstone-hotel.co.uk, Fax (01626) 868006,* heated, , , , – , rest, – 400. VISA
Meals (lunch by arrangement Monday to Saturday) 12.00/18.50 **st.** 4.70 – **68 rm** 55.00/94.00 – SB.

EAL *Kent* 404 Y 30 – *pop. 28 504.*

Walmer & Kingsdown, The Leas, Kingsdown ℘ (01304) 373256.

Town Hall, High St. ℘ (01304) 369576.

London 78 – Canterbury 19 – Dover 8.5 – Margate 16.

Royal, Beach St., CT14 6JD, ℘ (01304) 375555, *royalhotel@theroyalhotel.com, Fax (01304) 372270,* , – rm, . VISA .
The Boathouse Brasserie : **Meals** *(closed Monday lunch and Sunday dinner)* 15.50 **t.** (lunch) and a la carte 16.30/28.40 **st.** – **22 rm** 45.00/130.00 **st.** – SB.

Dunkerley's, 19 Beach St., CT14 7AH, ℘ (01304) 375016, *dunkerleysofdeal@btinternet.com, Fax (01304) 380187,* – rest, rest, . VISA JCB.
Meals – (see ***Restaurant*** below) – **16 rm** 55.00/120.00 **t.** – SB.

Sutherland House, 186 London Rd, CT14 9PT, ℘ (01304) 362853, *Fax (01304) 381146,* – rm, . VISA JCB.
Meals (by arrangement) 21.00 **st.** 5.00 – **5 rm** 45.00/57.00 **st.** – SB.

Restaurant (at Dunkerley's H.), 19 Beach St., CT14 7AH, ℘ (01304) 375016, *Fax (01304) 380187* – . VISA JCB
Meals (bar meals Monday) 10.50 **t.** (lunch) and a la carte 20.15/32.85 **t.** 6.95.

EDDINGTON *Oxon.* 403 404 Q 28 – *pop. 2 319.*

London 72 – Birmingham 46 – Coventry 33 – Oxford 18.

Holcombe, High St., OX15 0SL, ℘ (01869) 338274, *reception@holcombehotel.freeserve.co.uk, Fax (01869) 337167,* – . VISA JCB.
closed 25-30 December – **Meals** 14.50/35.00 **t.** and a la carte 7.50 – **17 rm** 69.00/115.00 **t.** – SB.

Deddington Arms, Horsefair, OX15 0SH, ℘ (01869) 338364, *deddarms@aol.com, Fax (01869) 337010* – – 30. VISA
Meals a la carte 17.00/25.00 **t.** 7.00 – **27 rm** 69.00/110.00 **t.** – SB.

Dexter's, Market Pl., OX15 0SA, ℘ (01869) 338813, *dexteruk@globalnet.co.uk, Fax (01869) 338813* – VISA JCB
closed 27 August-8 September, Sunday and Monday – **Meals** 19.50 **t.** and a la carte 21.00/33.50 **t.** 10.00.

EDHAM *Essex* 404 W 28 *Great Britain G.* – *pop. 1 847* – ✉ *Colchester.*

Env. : *Stour Valley★ – Flatford Mill★, E : 6 m. by B 1029, A 12 and B 1070.*

London 63 – Chelmsford 30 – Colchester 8 – Ipswich 12.

Maison Talbooth , Stratford Rd, CO7 6HN, West : ½ m. ℘ (01206) 322367, *mtreception@talbooth.co.uk, Fax (01206) 322752,* , – . VISA .
Meals – (see ***Le Talbooth*** below) – 7.50 – **9 rm** 120.00/195.00 **t.**, 1 suite – SB.

Le Talbooth, Gun Hill, CO7 6HP, West : 1 m. ℘ (01206) 323150, *ltreception@talbooth.co.uk, Fax (01206) 322309,* , « Part Tudor house in attractive riverside setting », – . VISA
closed Sunday dinner – **Meals** 17.00/27.00 **t.** and a la carte 29.40/41.85 **t.** 8.95.

Fountain House & Dedham Hall with rm, Brook St., CO7 6AD, ℘ (01206) 323027, *jimsarton@dedhamhall.demon.co.uk, Fax (01206) 323293,* – rest, . VISA .
closed 25-26 December – **Meals** *(closed Sunday and Monday)* (dinner only) 21.50 **t.** 8.00 – **6 rm** 50.00/75.00 **t.** – SB.

ENMEAD *Hants.* 403 Q 31 – *pop. 5 626.*

London 70 – Portsmouth 11 – Southampton 27.

Barnard's, Hambledon Rd, PO7 6NU, ℘ (023) 9225 7788, *Fax (023) 9225 7788,* – . VISA JCB
closed 25-26 December, Saturday lunch, Sunday and Monday – **Meals** a la carte 19.50/27.00 **t.** 6.25.

DENTON *Gtr. Manchester* 402 404 N 23 – *pop. 37 785.*

Denton, Manchester Rd ☎ *(0161) 336 3218.*

London 196 – Chesterfield 41 – Manchester 6.

Old Rectory, Meadow Lane, Haughton Green, M34 1GD, South : 2 m. by A 6017, Tw Trees Lane and Haughton Green Rd ☎ (0161) 336 7516, *reservations@oldrectoryhotel.m chester.co.uk, Fax (0161) 320 3212,* – , rest, – 100.
Meals *(closed Saturday lunch)* 8.95/25.00 **t.** and a la carte 8.50 – **36 rm** 69.00/90.00 – SB.

Travel Inn, Manchester Rd, M34 3SH, West : 1 m. by A 57 at junction of M 60 and M ☎ (0161) 320 1116, *Fax (0161) 320 1098* – rm, rest, .
Meals (grill rest.) – **40 rm** 40.95 **t.**

DERBY *Derby* 402 403 404 P 25 *Great Britain G.* – *pop. 223 836.*

See : *City★ – Museum and Art Gallery★ (Collection of Derby Porcelain★)* **YZ M1** – *Ro Crown Derby Museum★ AC* **Z M2.**

Env. : *Kedleston Hall★★ AC, NW : 4½ m. by Kedleston Rd* **X**.

Wilmore Rd, Sinfin ☎ (01332) 766323 – Mickleover, Uttoxeter Rd ☎ (01332) 51333 Kedleston Park, Kedlston, Quardon ☎ (01332) 840035 – , Breadsall Priory Hotel C C.C., Moor Rd, Morley ☎ (01332) 832235 – Allestree Park, Allestree Hall, Allestr ☎ (01332) 550616.

East Midlands Airport, Castle Donington : ☎ (01332) 852852, SE : 12 m. by A 6 **X**.

Assembly Rooms, Market Pl. ☎ (01332) 255802.

London 132 – Birmingham 40 – Coventry 49 – Leicester 29 – Manchester 62 – Nottingha 16 – Sheffield 47 – Stoke-on-Trent 35.

Plan opposite

Midland, Midland Rd, DE1 2SQ, ☎ (01332) 345894, *sales@midland-derby.co. Fax (01332) 293522,* – , rm, – 150. Z
Meals *(closed Saturday lunch)* 14.50/30.00 **st.** 10.00 – 11.00 – **99 rm** 80.00/104.50 1 suite – SB.

La Gondola, 220 Osmaston Rd, DE23 8JX, ☎ (01332) 332895, *lagondola@rapidial.co. Fax (01332) 384512* – – 70. X
Meals - Italian - *(closed Sunday dinner to non-residents)* (dancing Saturday) 6.90/14.50 and a la carte 7.00 – **20 rm** 53.00/58.00 **t.**, 1 suite.

Premier Lodge, Foresters Leisure Park, Osmaston Park Rd, DE23 8A ☎ (01332) 270027, *Fax (01332) 270528* – rm, – 40. X
Meals (grill rest.) 10.95 **st.** (dinner) and a la carte 11.35/18.45 **st.** – 6.00 – **26 rm** 46.00

Express by Holiday Inn without rest., Roundhouse Rd, Pride Park, DE24 8I ☎ (01332) 388000, *Fax (01332) 388038* – – 30.
103 rm 51.00 **st.** X

European Inn without rest., Midland Rd, DE1 2SL, ☎ (01332) 292000, *admin@euro_de y.co.uk, Fax (01332) 293940* – – 120. Z
6.75 – **86 rm** 48.50 **t.**

Travel Inn, Wyvern Business Park, DE21 6BF, ☎ (01332) 667826, *Fax (01332) 667827* – rm, rest, . X
Meals (grill rest.) (dinner only) – **82 rm** 40.95 **t.**

Travel Inn, Manor Park Way, Uttoxeter New Rd, DE22 3NA, ☎ (01332) 2030 *Fax (01332) 207506* – rm, rest, . X
Meals (grill rest.) – **43 rm** 40.95 **t.**

at Darley Abbey *North : 2½ m. off A 6* – **X** – ✉ *Derby.*

Darleys, Darley Abbey Mill, DE22 1DZ, ☎ (01332) 364987, *davidpinchbeck@darleys.cc Fax (01332) 364987,* « Converted cotton mill in attractive riverside setting » – .
closed Sunday dinner and Bank Holidays – **Meals** 12.50/22.00 **t.** and a la carte.

at Breadsall *Northeast : 4 m. by A 52 off A 61* – **X** – ✉ *Derby.*

Marriott Breadsall Priory H. & Country Club, Moor Rd, Morley, DE7 6 Northeast : 1 ¼ m. by Rectory Lane ☎ (01332) 832235, *Fax (01332) 833509,* ≤, , , , , – , rest, – 120.
Priory : **Meals** 12.50/23.00 **t.** and dinner a la carte 10.95 – ***Long Weekend :*** **Me** a la carte 19.20/25.25 **t.** 10.95 – 11.95 – **107 rm** 130.00 **st.**, 5 suites – SB.

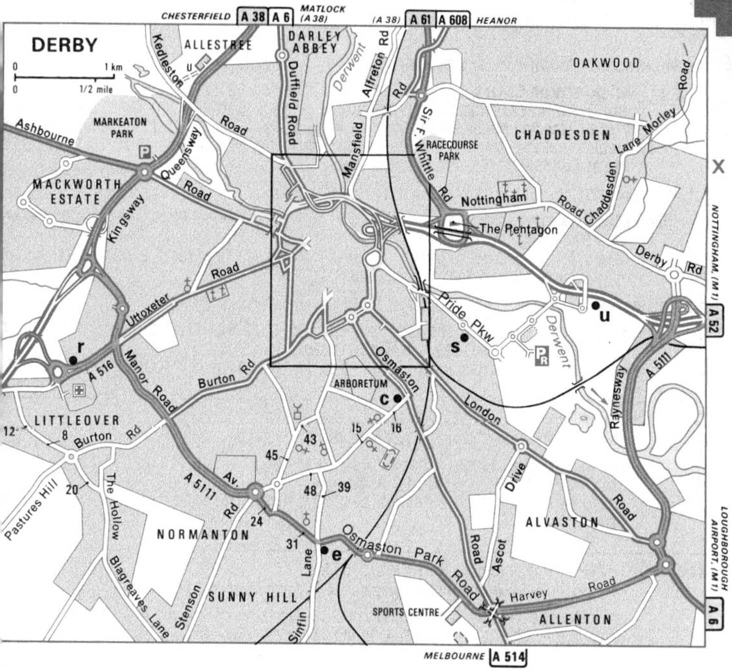

CHESTERFIELD A 38 A 6 MATLOCK (A 38) (A 38) A 61 A 608 HEANOR

DERBY

0 1 km
0 1/2 mile

ALLESTREE
DARLEY ABBEY
OAKWOOD
Kedleston Road
Duffield Road
Derwent
Alfreton Rd
Mansfield
Sir F. Whittle Rd
RACECOURSE PARK
CHADDESDEN
Morley Road
Lane Chaddesden
Ashbourne Road
MARKEATON PARK
Queensway
MACKWORTH ESTATE
Kingsway
Nottingham Road
The Pentagon
Derby Rd
X
NOTTINGHAM, (M 1)
A 52
Uttoxeter Road
Pride Pkw
Derwent
Raynesway
A 5111
r
s
u
A 516
Manor Road
Burton Rd
ARBORETUM
Osmaston Road
London Road
c
LITTLEOVER
12
8
Burton Rd
15
16
43
45
48
39
20
Pastures Hill
The Hollow
A 5111 Av. Rd
24
NORMANTON
Drive
ALVASTON
Road
31
e
Osmaston Park Road
Lane
Ascot
Road
LOUGHBOROUGH AIRPORT, (M 1)
Blagreaves Lane
Stenson
SUNNY HILL
Sinfin
SPORTS CENTRE
Harvey Road
ALLENTON
A 6
MELBOURNE A 514

ert Street . . . . Z 2
bington Lane . . . . Z 3
d Lane . . . . Y 4
dshaw Way . . . . Z 5
thedral Road. . . . . Y 7
ain Lane . . . . X 8
arnwood Street . . . . . . Z 9
rden Avenue . . . . X 12
rn Market . . . . Z 13
rporation Street . . . . YZ 14
ry House Road . . . . . . X 15
uglas Street . . . . X 16
ffield Road . . . . Y 17
gle Shopping
Centre . . . . Z
st Street . . . . Z 18
Street . . . . Y 19
sway . . . . X 20
Gate . . . . Y 22
y Street . . . . Y 23
nilworth
venue. . . . . X 24
g Street . . . . Y 25
ersage St. . . . . Z 26
rket Place . . . . YZ 27
dland Road . . . . Z 28
rledge . . . . Z 29
unt Street . . . . Z 30
wdigate Street . . . . . . X 31
rmanton Road . . . . Z 33
een Street . . . . Y 34
Mary's Gate . . . . Y 36
Peter's Street . . . . Z 37
Thomas Road. . . . . X 39
heveral Street. . . . . . . Z 40
fford Street . . . . Z 42
nhope Street. . . . . X 43
per Dale Road. . . . . . . X 45
toria Street. . . . . Z 46
lbrook Road. . . . . X 48
rdwick. . . . . Z 50

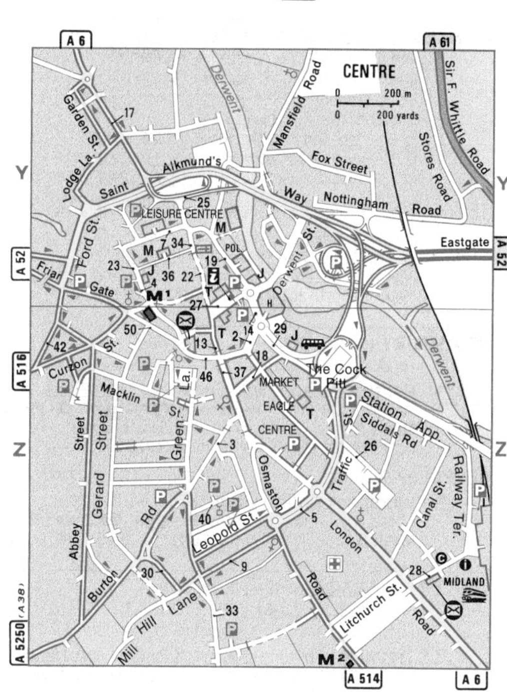

ENGLAND

at Mickleover *Southwest : 3 m. by A 38 and A 516 – X – ✉ Derby.*

Mickleover Court, Etwall Rd, DE3 5XX, ☎ (01332) 521234, *info@menzies-hotels.co.u* *Fax (01332) 521238,* – rm, – 200.
The Brasserie : **Meals** 14.50 **t.** (lunch) and a la carte 17.85/24.15 **t.** – ***Stelline Trattori*** **Meals** - Italian - *(closed Sunday-Tuesday)* (dinner only) a la carte 13.20/26.40 **t.** 6.50 **91 rm** 135.00/175.00 **st.**, 8 suites – SB.

at Mackworth *Northwest : 2 ¾ m. by A 52 – X – ✉ Derby.*

Mackworth, Ashbourne Rd, DE22 4LY, on A 52 ☎ (01332) 824324, *Fax (01332) 8246* – – 160.
closed 24-26 December and 1 January – **Meals** (carving rest.) 6.25/13.50 **t.** and di ner a la carte 5.50 – **14 rm** 49.00/80.00 **t.**

at Kedleston *Northwest : 4 m. by Kedleston Rd – X – ✉ Derby.*

Kedleston Country House, Kedleston Rd, DE22 5JD, East : 2 m. ☎ (01332) 5592 *Fax (01332) 558822,* ← – .
Meals *(closed Sunday dinner)* 6.95/18.95 **st.** 6.25 – **14 rm** 48.00/65.00 **st.**

DERSINGHAM *Norfolk* 402 404 V 25 – *pop. 3 961.*
London 112 – King's Lynn 10 – Norwich 48.

Dersingham Hall, Chapel Rd, PE31 6PJ, on B 1440 ☎ (01485) 54351 *Fax (01485) 543433* – rest, .
closed 1 week Christmas – **Meals** 4.50/12.50 **t.** (lunch) and a la carte 13.90/20.90 **t.** 4.95 **4 rm** 40.00/55.00 **t.**

DESBOROUGH *Northants.* 404 R 26 – *pop. 7 351.*
London 83 – Birmingham 52 – Leicester 20 – Northampton 20.

Travelodge, Harborough Rd, NN14 2UG, North : 1 ½ m. on A 6 ☎ (01536) 7620 *Fax (01536) 762034* – rm, .
Meals (grill rest.) – **32 rm** 39.95 **t.**

DEVIZES *Wilts.* 403 404 O 29 *The West Country G. – pop. 13 205.*
See : *St. John's Church★★ – Market Place★ – Devizes Museum★ AC.*
Env. : *Potterne (Porch House★★) S : 2½ m. by A 360 – E : Vale of Pewsey★.*
Exc. : *Stonehenge★★★ AC, SE : 16 m. by A 360 and A 344 – Avebury★★ (The Stones Church★) NE : 7 m. by A 361.*
Erlestoke Sands, Erlestoke ☎ (01380) 831069.
Cromwell House, Market Sq. ☎ (01380) 729408.
London 98 – Bristol 38 – Salisbury 25 – Swindon 19.

at Rowde *Northwest : 2 m. by A 361 on A 342 – ✉ Devizes.*

George & Dragon, High St., SN10 2PN, on A 342 ☎ (01380) 723053, *gd-rowde@lineon et, Fax (01380) 724738,* – .
closed 25 December, 1 January, Sunday and Monday – **Meals** (booking essential) 10.0 12.50 **t.** (lunch) and a la carte 19.00/30.00 **t.** 9.25.

DEWSBURY *W. Yorks.* 402 P 22 – *pop. 50 168.*
London 205 – Leeds 9 – Manchester 40 – Middlesbrough 76 – Sheffield 31.

Heath Cottage, Wakefield Rd, WF12 8ET, East : ¾ m. on A 638 ☎ (01924) 4653 *Fax (01924) 459405* – , rest, – 70. .
Meals *(closed Sunday dinner and Bank Holidays to non-residents)* 10.50/13.95 **t.** and d ner a la carte 6.00 – **29 rm** 52.00/70.00 **t.** – SB.

at Whitley *Southwest : 4 m. by B 6409 and B 6117 on Whitley rd – ✉ Dewsbury.*

Woolpack Country Inn, Whitley Rd, WF12 0LZ, ☎ (01924) 499999, *enquiries@wool khotel.co.uk, Fax (01924) 495289* – .
Meals 8.25 **st.** (lunch) and a la carte 15.25/25.70 **st.** 5.25 – **14 rm** 44.50/60.00 **st.**

DIDCOT *Oxon.* 403 404 Q 29 – *✉ Abingdon.*
Car park, Station Rd ☎ (01235) 813243.
London 58 – Oxford 15 – Reading 20 – Swindon 31.

Travel Inn, Milton Heights, Milton, OX14 4DP, Northwest : 3 ¼ m. by B 4493 on A 4 ☎ (01235) 835168, *Fax (01235) 835187* – rm, rest, .
Meals (grill rest.) – **60 rm** 40.95 **t.**

IDDLEBURY *Shrops.* 402 403 L 26 *Great Britain G. – pop. 911 – ✉ Craven Arms.*
Env. : *NW : Wenlock Edge*★.
London 169 – Birmingham 46.

Delbury Hall ⛰, SY7 9DH, entrance on B 4368 beside lodge, opposite 40 mph sign ☎ (01584) 841267, *wrigley@delbury.com, Fax (01584) 841441*, ←, « Georgian mansion », ... – ✈ TV P. MC VISA JCB.
closed Christmas – **Meals** (booking essential) (residents only) (communal dining) (dinner only) 30.00 **st.** 8.00 – **4 rm** 55.00/110.00 **st.**

IDMARTON *Glos.* 403 404 N 29 – *pop. 429 – ✉ Tetbury.*
London 120 – Bristol 20 – Gloucester 27 – Swindon 33.

Old Rectory without rest., GL9 1DS, on A 433 ☎ (01454) 238233, *Fax (01454) 238909*, – TV P.
closed Christmas and New Year – **3 rm** 30.00/48.00.

Kings Arms with rm, GL9 1DT, on A 433 ☎ (01454) 238245, *kingsarm@kingsarm.freeserve.co.uk, Fax (01454) 238249*, – rm, TV P – 25. MC VISA.
closed 25 December – **Meals** (bar dinner Sunday) a la carte 18.45/29.15 **t.** – **4 rm** 45.00/70.00 **t.**

IDSBURY *Gtr. Manchester* 402 403 404 N 23 – *see Manchester.*

Prices — For notes on the prices quoted in this Guide, see the introduction.

ISLEY *Ches.* 402 403 404 N 23 – *pop. 3 743 – ✉ Stockport.*
London 187 – Chesterfield 35 – Manchester 12.

Hilton Moorside ⛰, Mudhurst Lane, Higher Disley, SK12 2AP, Southeast : 2 m. by Buxton Old Rd ☎ (01663) 764151, *general.manager@moorside.stakis.co.uk, Fax (01663) 762794*, ←, ..., squash – |$|, rm, TV P – 300. MC AE VISA.
Meals (bar lunch Saturday) 11.50/19.95 **t.** and dinner a la carte – 10.95 – **94 rm** 79.00/170.00 **t.** – SB.

SS *Norfolk* 404 X 26 – *pop. 6 538.*
Meres Mouth, Mere St. ☎ (01379) 650523.
London 98 – Ipswich 25 – Norwich 21 – Thetford 17.

Weavers, Market Hill, IP22 4JZ, ☎ (01379) 642411, « Part 15C weaver's cottage » – MC AE VISA JCB
closed 2 weeks Christmas, Sunday and lunch Saturday and Monday – **Meals** 8.75/14.95 **t.** and Saturday dinner a la carte 18.85/23.15 **t.** 9.75.

Brockdish *East : 7 m. by A 1066, A 140 and A 143 – ✉ Diss.*

Grove Thorpe ⛰, Grove Rd, IP21 4JE, North : ¾ m. ☎ (01379) 668305, *Fax (01379) 668305*, « 17C bailiffs house », – P.
closed 25 December – **Meals** (by arrangement) (communal dining) 17.00 **s.** – **3 rm** 40.00/64.00 **s.** – SB.

Brome *(Suffolk) Southeast : 2 ¾ m. by A 1066 on B 1077 – ✉ Eye.*

Cornwallis Arms ⛰, IP23 8AJ, ☎ (01379) 870326, *info@thecornwallis.com, Fax (01379) 870051*, « Part 16C dower house, topiary gardens », – TV P – 30. MC VISA
Meals 23.00 **t.** 8.95 – **16 rm** 72.50/90.00 **t.** – SB.

Wingfield *Southeast : 7 m. by A 1066, A 140 and B 1118.*

De La Pole Arms, Church Rd, IP21 5RA, ☎ (01379) 384545, *Fax (01379) 384377*, « Part 17C inn » – P. MC VISA
Meals a la carte 15.45/25.20 **t.** 7.95.

Fersfield *Northwest : 7 m. by A 1066 – ✉ Diss.*

Strenneth ⛰ without rest., Airfield Rd, IP22 2BP, ☎ (01379) 688182, *ken@strenneth.co.uk, Fax (01379) 688260*, « Part 17C farmhouse », – TV P. MC VISA JCB
7 rm 28.00/50.00.

ODDISCOMBSLEIGH *Devon* 403 J 31 – *see Exeter.*

DONCASTER *S. Yorks.* 402 403 404 Q 23 – *pop. 71 595.*

Doncaster Town Moor, Bawtry Rd, Belle Vue ℘ (01302) 533778, **B** – *Crookhill Pa Conisborough ℘ (01709) 862979 – Wheatley, Amthorpe Rd ℘ (01302) 831665,* **B** – *Owston Park, Owston Hall, Owston ℘ (01302) 330821.*

Central Library, Waterdale ℘ (01302) 734309.

London 173 – Kingston-upon-Hull 46 – Leeds 30 – Nottingham 46 – Sheffield 19.

DONCASTER

Arksey Lane . . . . **A** 7
Bentley Road . . . . **A** 10
Church Lane . . . . **B** 15
Cusworth Lane . . . . **A** 19
Doncaster Road . . . . **B** 22
Goodison Boulevard . . . . **B** 26
Great North Road . . . . **A** 28
Green Lane . . . . **A** 32
High Road . . . . **A** 34
Jossey Lane . . . . **A** 38
Sandford Road . . . . **A** 49
Sandringham Road . . . . **B** 52
Springwell Lane . . . . **A**
Sprotbrough Road . . . . **A**
Station Road . . . . **A**
Stoops Lane . . . . **B**
Tickhill Road . . . . **A**
Warmsworth Road . . . . **A**
Wentworth Road . . . . **B**

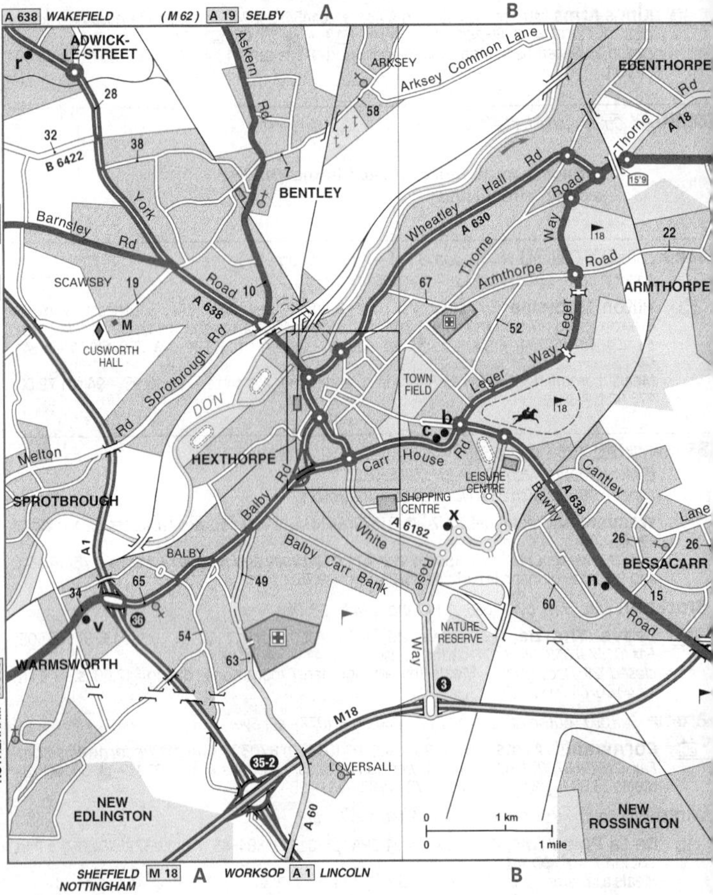

Doncaster Moat House, Warmsworth, DN4 9UX, Southwest : 2 ¾ m. on A 6
℘ (01302) 799988, *cbdan@queensmoat.co.uk, Fax (01302) 310197,* – rest, – 400. AE VISA **A**
Meals (bar lunch Monday to Saturday)/dinner 15.95 **st.** and a la carte 7.95 – 11.5
98 rm 99.00/125.00 **st.**, 2 suites – SB.

DONCASTER

bion Place . . . . C 3
oley Road . . . . C 5
alby Road . . . . C 8
'oxholme Lane C
arr House Road C
nequer Avenue . . . . C 12
nequer Road C
nrist Church Road C
nurch Way C
eveland Street C
olonnades Shopping
Centre C
unningham Road . . . . . . C 17
ast Laith Gate . . . . C 24
enchgate Schopping
Centre C
'ey Friars Road C
all Gate C
gh Street . . . . C 36
ghfield Road C
ilton Walk . . . . C 40
ether hall Road . . . . C 43
orth Bridge Road . . . . . . C 44
ueen's Road . . . . C 46
Jame's Bridge . . . . C 48
Jame's Street C
ver Street C
outh Parade C
orne Road C
afford Way C
aterdale C
aterdale Shopping
Centre C
hite Rose Way . . . . C 70
ood Street C

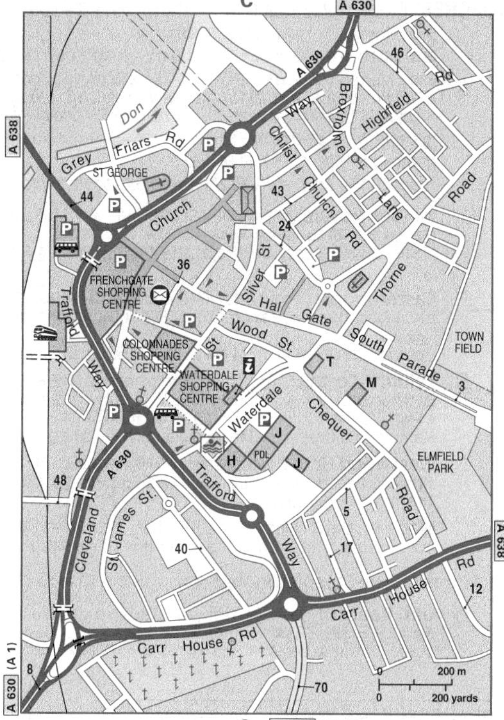

Mount Pleasant, Great North Rd, DN11 0HP, Southeast : 6 m. on A 638 ✆ (01302) 868219, *mountpleasant@fax.co.uk, Fax (01302) 865130,* – TV P – 100. MC AE VISA JCB.
closed 25 December – **Meals** 12.00/20.00 **t.** (lunch) and dinner a la carte 17.70/25.50 **t.** 7.00 – **38 rm** 59.00/99.00 **t.**, 2 suites – SB.

Grand St. Leger, Racecourse Roundabout, Bennetthorpe, DN2 6AX, Southeast : 1 ½ m. on A 638 ✆ (01302) 364111, *grandstleger.hotel@virgin.net, Fax (01302) 329865* – TV P – 80. MC AE VISA JCB. B b
Meals 9.95/14.95 **t.** (lunch) and a la carte 17.90/29.00 **t.** 5.00 – **20 rm** 75.00/125.00 **t.** – SB.

Punch's Toby, Bawtry Rd, Bessacarr, DN4 7BS, Southeast : 3 m. on A 638 ✆ (01302) 370037, *Fax (01302) 379021* – TV P – 40. MC VISA. B n
Meals (carving rest.) a la carte 9.90/15.90 **st.** – **25 rm** 44.95 **st.** – SB.

Travel Inn, South Entry Drive, White Rose Way, DN4 5JH, South : 1 ½ m. by A 6182 ✆ (01302) 361134, *Fax (01302) 364811* – rm, rest, TV P. MC AE VISA B x
Meals (grill rest.) – **42 rm** 40.95 **t.**

Hamilton's with rm, Carr House Rd, DN4 5HP, Southeast : 2 m. on A 638 ✆ (01302) 760770, *ham760770@freeserve, Fax (01302) 768101,* « Victorian town house » – TV P – 30. MC AE VISA JCB. B c
Meals *(closed Sunday dinner and Monday except Bank Holidays)* 10.95/25.95 **s.** and dinner a la carte 9.95 – **4 rm** 70.00/90.00 **st.** – SB.

Aagrah, Great North Rd, Woodlands, DN6 7RA, Northwest : 4 m. on A 638 ✆ (01302) 728888 – P. MC AE VISA JCB A r
closed 25 December – **Meals** - Indian (Kashmiri) - (booking essential) (dinner only) a la carte 8.65/13.15 **t.**

Carcroft *Northwest : 6½ m. by A 638 on A 1* – **A** – ✉ *Doncaster.*

Travelodge, Great North Rd, DN6 8LR, (northbound carriageway) ✆ (01302) 330841, *Fax (01302) 330841* – rm, rest, TV P. MC AE VISA JCB.
Meals (grill rest.) – **40 rm** 39.95 **t.**

DORCHESTER *Dorset* 403 404 M 31 *The West Country G. – pop. 15 037.*

See : *Town★ - Dorset County Museum★ AC.*

Env. : *Maiden Castle★★ (≤★) SW : 2½ m. – Puddletown Church★, NE : 5½ m. by A 35.*

Exc. : *Moreton Church★★, E : 7½ m. – Bere Regis★ (St. John the Baptist Church★ - Roof★ NE : 11 m. by A 35 – Athelhampton House★ AC, NE : 6½ m. by A 35 - Cerne Abbas★, N : m. by A 352 – Milton Abbas★, NE : 12 m. on A 354 and by-road.*

18 Came Down ☎ (01305) 812531.

Antelope Walk ☎ (01305) 267992.

London 135 – Bournemouth 27 – Exeter 53 – Southampton 53.

Wessex Royale, 32 High West St., DT1 1UP, ☎ (01305) 262660, *Fax (01305) 251941* – TV – 80. MC AE VISA JCB
Meals *(closed Sunday lunch)* a la carte 14.40/21.20 **st.** 4.95 – **25 rm** 49.00/69.00 **st.** SB.

Casterbridge without rest., 49 High East St., DT1 1HU, ☎ (01305) 264043, *reception@casterbridgehotel.co.uk, Fax (01305) 260884,* « Georgian town house » – TV. MC AE VISA JCB.
closed 25-26 December – **14 rm** 45.00/85.00 **t.**

Yalbury Cottage, Lower Bockhampton, DT2 8PZ, East : 2 ¼ m. by B 3150 and Bockhampton rd ☎ (01305) 262382, *yalbury.cottage@virgin.net, Fax (01305) 26641* « Part 17C cottage », – TV P. MC VISA JCB.
February-28 December – **Meals** (dinner only) 26.00 **t.** 6.50 – **8 rm** 53.00/82.00 **st.** – S

Westwood House without rest., 29 High West St., DT1 1UP, ☎ (01305) 268018, *reservations@westwoodhouse.co.uk, Fax (01305) 250282* – TV. MC AE VISA JCB
7 rm 49.00/69.00 **t.**

Mock Turtle, 34 High West St., DT1 1UP, ☎ (01305) 264011 – MC AE VISA
closed Sunday and lunch Saturday and Monday – **Meals** a la carte 14.75/22.50 **t.** 6.75.

at Winterbourne Steepleton *West : 4 ¾ m. by B 3150 and A 35 on B 3159 – ✉ Dorchester.*

Old Rectory without rest., DT2 9LG, ☎ (01305) 889468, *trees@eurobell.co.uk Fax (01305) 889737,* – TV P.
closed Christmas and New Year – **4 rm** 45.00/100.00 **st.**

DORCHESTER *Oxon.* 403 404 Q 29 *Great Britain G. – pop. 2 256.*

See : *Town★.*

Exc. : *Ridgeway Path★★.*

London 51 – Abingdon 6 – Oxford 8 – Reading 17.

George, 25 High St., OX10 7HH, ☎ (01865) 340404, *Fax (01865) 341620,* « Part 14C coaching inn », – TV P – 40. MC AE VISA
Meals (bar lunch Monday-Friday)/dinner a la carte 20.00/24.00 **t.** 6.00 – 3.50 – **18 rm** 65.00/85.00 **t.** – SB.

White Hart, 26 High St., OX10 7HN, ☎ (01865) 340074, *Fax (01865) 341082,* « 17C coaching inn » – TV P – 40. MC AE VISA
Meals a la carte 15.75/26.20 **st.** 6.50 – **15 rm** 65.00/85.00 **st.**, 4 suites – SB.

DORKING *Surrey* 404 T 30 – *pop. 15 658.*

18 Betchworth Park, Reigate Rd ☎ (01306) 882052.

London 26 – Brighton 39 – Guildford 12 – Worthing 33.

Burford Bridge, Box Hill, RH5 6BX, North : 1 ½ m. on A 24 ☎ (0870) 400 8283, *gb1071@forte-hotels.com, Fax (01306) 880386,* heated, – TV P – 300. MC AE VISA
Meals 15.00/30.00 **t.** and a la carte 6.00 – 13.50 – **57 rm** 165.00 **t.** – SB.

White Horse, High St., RH4 1BE, ☎ (0870) 4008282, *heritagehotels-dorking.white-horse@forte-hotels.com, Fax (01306) 887241* – TV P – 50. MC AE VISA JCB
Meals 8.00/19.75 **t.** and a la carte 8.50 – 12.50 – **69 rm** 150.00/170.00 **t.** – SB.

Travelodge, Reigate Rd, RH4 1QB, East : ½ m. on A 25 ☎ (01306) 74036 *Fax (01306) 740361* – , rest, TV P. MC AE VISA JCB.
Meals (grill rest.) – **54 rm** 59.95 **t.**

Prices — For notes on the prices quoted in this Guide, see the introduction.

ORRINGTON *Shrops.* 402 403 L 26 – *see Shrewsbury.*

DOUGLAS *Isle of Man* 402 G 21 – *see Man (Isle of).*

DOVER *Kent* 404 Y 30 *Great Britain G.* – *pop. 34 179.*

See : *Castle*★★ *AC* Y.

to France (Calais) (P & O Stena Line) frequent services daily (1 h 15 mn) – to France (Calais) (SeaFrance S.A.) frequent services daily (1 h 30 mn) – to France (Calais) (Hoverspeed Ltd) frequent services daily (35 mn) – to Belgium (Ostend) (Hoverspeed Ltd) 5 daily (2 h).

Townwall St. ℘ *(01304) 205108.*

London 76 – Brighton 84.

DOVER

ench Street . . . . Y 3
ggin Street . . . . Y 4
annon Street . . . . Y 5
astle Street . . . . Y 6
harlton Green . . . . Y 7
rabble Hill . . . . Z 9
aton Road . . . . Z 10
igh Street . . . . Y
ng Street . . . . Y 13
adywell, Park Street . . . . Y 15
ondon Road . . . . Y 17
encester Road . . . . Y
iory Road . . . . Y 18
iory Street . . . . Y 19
ueen St. . . . . Y 20
andwich Road . . . . Z 21
wer Street . . . . Z 24
orthington Street . . . . Y 25

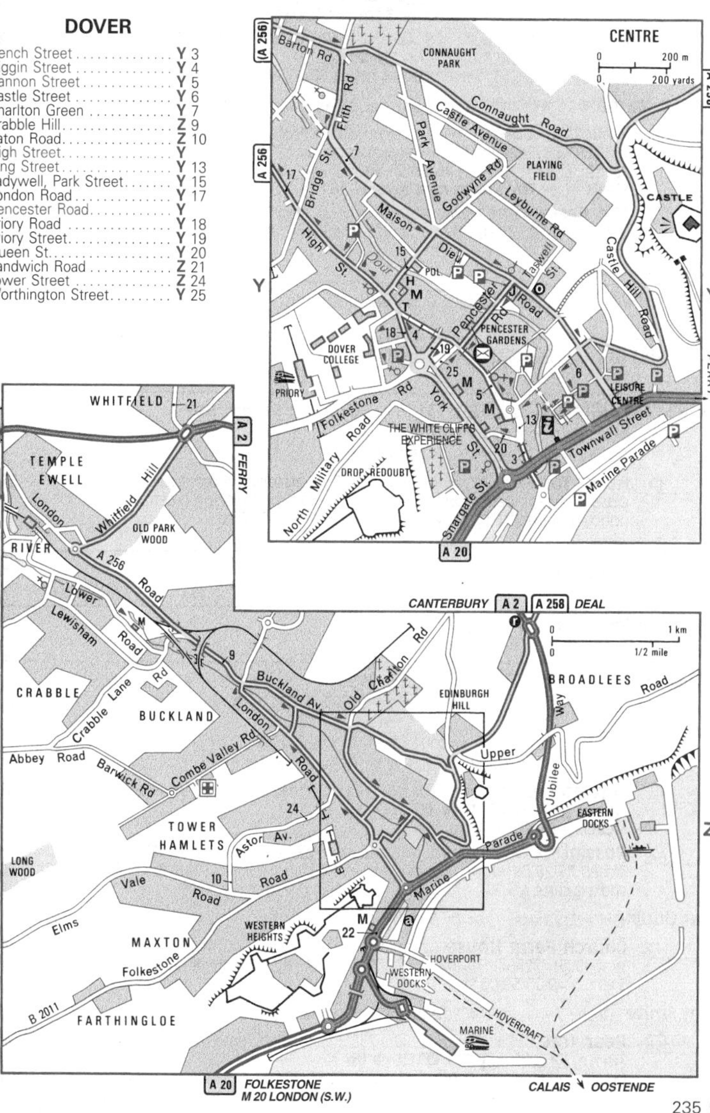

ENGLAND

Churchill, Dover Waterfront, CT17 9BP, ℘ (01304) 203633, *enquiries@churchill-hotel.c m, Fax (01304) 216320,* ≤, ₣₺, ≘ – |‡| ⇹ TV P – 🎓 120. MO AE ⓘ VISA. ✂ Z
Meals 14.50/18.95 **t.** 7.50 – 9.00 – **66 rm** 59.00/79.00 **st.**

Travel Inn, Jubilee Way, Guston Wood, CT15 5FD, Northeast : 2 m. by A 258 at junctic with A 2 ℘ (01304) 204660, *Fax (01304) 215273* – ⇹ rm, TV ♿ P. MO AE ⓘ VISA. ✂ Z
Meals (grill rest.) – **40 rm** 40.95 **t.**

Travel Inn, Folkestone Rd, CT15 7AB, Southwest : 2 ½ m. on B 2011 ℘ (01304) 21333 *Fax (01304) 214504* – ⇹ rm, TV ♿ P. MO AE ⓘ VISA. ✂
Meals (grill rest.) – **62 rm** 40.95 **t.**

Old Vicarage without rest., Chilverton Elms, Hougham, CT15 7AS, West : 2 ¾ m. 2011 and Elms Vale Rd on West Hougham rd ℘ (01304) 210668, *vicarage@csi.cor Fax (01304) 225118,* ≤, – TV P. MO VISA. ✂
closed 23 December-2 January – **3 rm** 80.00 **st.**

East Lee without rest., 108 Maison Dieu Rd, CT16 1RT, ℘ (01304) 210176, *eastlee@eclip. .co.uk, Fax (01304) 206705* – ⇹ TV. MO VISA. ✂ Y
closed 25, 26 and 31 December – **4 rm** 50.00.

at St. Margaret's at Cliffe *Northeast : 4 m. by A 258* – Z – ✉ *Dover.*

Wallett's Court, West Cliffe, CT15 6EW, Northwest : ¾ m. on Dover ℘ (01304) 852424, *wc@wallettscourt.com, Fax (01304) 853430,* « Part 17C manor house ₣₺, ≘, ⊠, , ✂ – TV P. MO AE ⓘ VISA JCB. ✂
Meals – (see ***The Restaurant*** below) – **16 rm** 70.00/150.00 **t.** – SB.

The Restaurant (at Wallett's Court H.), West Cliffe, CT15 6EW, Northwest : ¾ m. c Dover rd ℘ (01304) 852424, *Fax (01304) 853430,* – ⇹ P. MO AE ⓘ VISA JCB
Meals 17.50/40.00 **t.** 7.50.

DOVERIDGE *Derbs.* 402 403 404 O 25 – *see Uttoxeter.*

DOWNTON *Wilts.* 403 404 O 31 – *see Salisbury.*

DREWSTEIGNTON *Devon* 403 I 31 *The West Country G. – pop. 668.*

Env. : *Dartmoor National Park★★.*

London 216 – Exeter 15 – Plymouth 32.

Hunts Tor, EX6 6QW, ℘ (01647) 281228, *huntstorhotel@netscapeonline.co.uk* – ⇹ TV
closed 2 weeks December – **Meals** (set menu only) (booking essential-minimum 24 hou notice required) 20.00 **st.** 7.25 – **3 rm** 45.00/75.00 **st.**

DRIFT *Cornwall – see Penzance.*

DRIGHLINGTON *W. Yorks.* 402 P 22 – *see Leeds.*

DROITWICH *Worcs.* 403 404 N 27 – *pop. 20 966.*

18 Ombersley, Bishopswood Rd ℘ (01905) 620747 – 18 Droitwich G & C.C., Ford Lane (01905) 770129.

St. Richard's House, Victoria Sq. ℘ (01905) 774312.

London 129 – Birmingham 20 – Bristol 66 – Worcester 6.

Travelodge, Rashwood Hill, WR9 8DA, Northeast : 1 ½ m. on A 38 ℘ (01527) 861545 ⇹ rm, TV ♿ P. MO AE ⓘ VISA JCB. ✂
Meals (grill rest.) – **32 rm** 49.95 **t.**

Rossini's, 6 Worcester Rd, WR9 8AB, ℘ (01905) 794799 – ≣ P. MO AE VISA JCB
closed 25-26 December, Sunday dinner and Bank Holidays – **Meals** - Italian - 12.90/22.50 and a la carte 5.90.

at Oddingley *Southeast : 3 m. by B 4090.*

Church Farm House (without rest.), WR9 7NE, Southeast : ¼ m. on Netherwood ℘ (01905) 772387, *Fax (01905) 772387,* , , ✂ – ⇹ TV P. ✂
3 rm 40.00/59.00 **st.**

at Smite *South : 3 ¾ m. by B 4090 and A 38 off A 4538* – ✉ *Worcester.*

Pear Tree, WR3 8SY, ℘ (01905) 756565, *thepeartreeuk@aol.com, Fax (01905) 75677* ⇹ rm, TV ♿ P – 🎓 300. MO AE ⓘ VISA. ✂
Meals (carving lunch Sunday) a la carte 14.85/25.20 **t.** – **21 rm** 75.00/95.00 **t.**, 3 suites

t Hadley Heath *Southwest : 4 m. by Ombersley Way, A 4133 and Ladywood rd – ✉ Droitwich.*

Hadley Bowling Green Inn, WR9 0AR, ☎ (01905) 620294, *hbinn@backissues.freeserve.co.uk, Fax (01905) 620771* – TV ☎ P. MO AE ⓓ VISA. ✂
Meals *(closed Sunday dinner)* a la carte 14.90/25.30 **t.** – **14 rm** ☕ 58.00/69.00 **st.** – SB.

Old Farmhouse without rest., WR9 0AR, ☎ (01905) 620837, *judylambe@ombersley.demon.co.uk, Fax (01905) 621722*, ⛺, ✂ – ⊁ TV P
closed 25 December – **5 rm** ☕ 30.00/55.00 **s.**

RONFIELD *Derbs.* 402 403 404 P 24 – *pop. 22 985* – ✉ *Sheffield (S. Yorks.).*
London 158 – Derby 30 – Nottingham 31 – Sheffield 6.

Manor House with rm, 10-15 High St., Old Dronfield, S18 1PY, ☎ (01246) 413971, *sales@barrelsandbottles, Fax (01246) 412104* – ⊁ TV ☎ P. MO AE VISA JCB
closed 25-26 December – **Meals** (lunch by arrangement)/dinner 21.95 **st.** and a la carte 8.50 – **8 rm** ☕ 59.50/79.50 **st.**, 2 suites – SB.

UDLEY *W. Mids.* 402 403 404 N 26 *Great Britain G.* – *pop. 304 615.*
See : *Black Country Museum*★.
🅸 *39 Churchill Centre ☎ (01384) 812830.*
London 132 – Birmingham 10 – Wolverhampton 6.

Plan : see Birmingham p. 4

Copthorne Merry Hill, The Waterfront, Level St., Brierley Hill, DY5 1UR, Southwest : 2 ¼ m. by A 461 ☎ (01384) 482882, *Fax (01384) 482773*, Fₛ, ≘s, 🏊 – |$|, ⊁ rm, ▤ rest, TV ☎ ♿ P – 🔺 570. MO AE ⓓ VISA. ✂ AU z
Meals 12.95/16.00 **st.** and a la carte – ☕ 12.95 – **129 rm** 135.00/145.00 **st.**, 9 suites – SB.

Ward Arms, Birmingham Rd, DY1 4RN, Northeast : ¾ m. on A 461 ☎ (01384) 458070, *113566,1360@compuserve.com, Fax (01384) 457502* – ⊁ rm, TV ♿ P – 🔺 150. MO AE ⓓ VISA JCB BT a
Meals *(closed lunch Saturday and Bank Holiday Mondays)* (carving rest.) 9.95/15.00 **st.** 7.50 – ☕ 9.50 – **72 rm** 80.00 **st.** – SB.

Travel Inn, Dudley Rd, Kingswinford, DY6 8WT, West : 3 m. on A 4101 ☎ (01384) 291290, *Fax (01384) 277593* – |$|, ⊁ rm, ▤ rest, TV ♿ P – 🔺 35. MO AE ⓓ VISA. ✂ AU e
Meals (grill rest.) – **43 rm** 40.95 **t.**

Travelodge without rest., Dudley Rd, Brierley Hill, DY5 1LQ, Southwest : 2 m. on A 461 ☎ (01384) 481579 – ⊁ TV ♿ P. MO AE ⓓ VISA JCB. ✂ AU c
32 rm 39.95 **t.**

ULVERTON *Somerset* 403 J 30 *The West Country G.* – *pop. 1 870 (inc. Brushford).*
See : *Village*★.
Env. : *Exmoor National Park*★★ – *Tarr Steps*★★, *NW : 6 m. by B 3223.*
London 198 – Barnstaple 27 – Exeter 26 – Minehead 18 – Taunton 27.

Ashwick House 🐦, TA22 9QD, Northwest : 4 ¼ m. by B 3223 turning left after second cattle grid ☎ (01398) 323868, *ashwickhouse@talk21.com, Fax (01398) 323868*, ≤, ⛲, « Edwardian country house in extensive gardens » – ⊁ rest, TV P. ✂
Meals (booking essential to non-residents) (set menu only) (light lunch Monday to Saturday residents only)/dinner 19.75 **t.** 6.75 – **6 rm** ☕ (dinner included) 79.00/150.00 **t.** – SB.

Highercombe, TA22 9PT, Northwest : 2 ½ m. on B 3223 ☎ (01398) 323451, *Fax (01398) 323451*, « Georgian house of 14C origin », ⛺ – ⊁ rm, TV P. MO AE ⓓ VISA
Meals (by arrangement) (communal dining) 17.50 **st.** – **2 rm** ☕ 45.00/90.00 **s.**, 1 suite.

UNSLEY *N. Yorks.* – *see Whitby.*

UNSTABLE *Beds.* 404 S 28 – *pop. 49 666.*
⛳18 *Tilsworth, Dunstable Rd ☎ (01525) 210721.*
🅸 *The Library, Vernon Pl. ☎ (01582) 471012.*
London 40 – Bedford 24 – Luton 4.5 – Northampton 35.

Hanover International, Church St., LU5 4RT, ☎ (01582) 662201, *Fax (01582) 696422* – |$|, ⊁ rm, ▤ rest, TV P – 🔺 40. MO AE ⓓ VISA
Meals (bar lunch Saturday) a la carte 20.40/30.40 **st.** 8.50 – ☕ 9.95 – **68 rm** 109.00/130.00 – SB.

Highwayman, London Rd, LU6 3DX, Southeast : 1 m. on A 5 ✆ (01582) 60112[illegible] *Fax (01582) 603812* – TV ♿ P – 🏛 50. MC AE VISA
Meals (bar lunch Monday to Saturday)/dinner 13.00 **t.** and a la carte – **53 rm** ☕ 55.0[illegible] 85.00 **t.** – SB.

Travel Inn, 350 Luton Rd, LU5 4LL, Northeast : 1 ¾ m. on A 505 ✆ (01582) 60993[illegible] *Fax (01582) 664114* – rm, rest, TV ♿ P. MC AE D VISA
Meals (grill rest.) – **42 rm** 40.95 **t.**

Travel Inn, Watling St., Kensworth, LU6 3QP, Southeast : 2 ½ m. on A 5 ✆ (01582) 84050[illegible] *Fax (01582) 842811* – rm, TV ♿ P. MC AE D VISA.
Meals (grill rest.) – **40 rm** 40.95 **t.**

at Hockliffe *Northwest : 3 ¼ m. on A 5 – ✉ Dunstable.*

Travelodge, LU7 9LZ, Southeast : ¾ m. on A 5 ✆ (01525) 211177, *Fax (01525) 211177* rm, TV ♿ P. MC AE D VISA JCB.
Meals (grill rest.) – **28 rm** 49.95 **t.**

DUNSTER *Somerset* 403 **J 30** *The West Country G. – pop. 848 – ✉ Minehead.*

See : *Town★★ – Castle★★* **AC** *(Upper rooms ≤★) – Dunster Water Mill★* **AC** *– St. George[illegible] Church★ – Dovecote★.*

Env. : *Exmoor National Park★★ (Dunkery Beacon★★★ (≤★★★), Watersmeet★, Valley of th[illegible] Rocks★, Vantage Point★) – Cleeve Abbey★★* **AC**, *SE : 5 m. by A 39 – Timberscomb[illegible] (Church★) SW : 3 ½ m. by A 396.*

London 184 – Bristol 61 – Exeter 40 – Taunton 22.

Luttrell Arms, 36 High St., TA24 6SG, ✆ (01643) 821555, *heritagehotels-dunster.luttrell rms@forte-hotels.com, Fax (01643) 821567,* « Part 15C inn », – TV . MC AE [illegible] VISA JCB
Meals 10.00/25.00 **t.** and a la carte 12.50 – ☕ 12.50 – **27 rm** 110.00 **t.** – SB.

The Guide is updated annually so renew your Guide every year.

DURHAM *Durham* 401 402 **P 19** *Great Britain G. – pop. 36 937.*

See : *City★★★ - Cathedral★★★ (Nave★★★, Chapel of the Nine Altars★★★, Sanctuary Knoc[illegible] er★)* **B** *– Oriental Museum★★* **AC** *(at Durham University by A 167)* **B** *– City and Riversic[illegible] (Prebends' Bridge ≤★★★* **A** *, Framwellgate Bridge ≤★★* **B***) – Monastic Buildings (Cathedr[illegible] Treasury★, Central Tower≤★)* **B** *– Castle★ (Norman chapel★)* **AC B.**

Exc. : *Hartlepool Historic Quay★, SE : 14 m. by A 181, A 19 and A 179.*

18 *Mount Oswald, South Rd ✆ (0191) 386 7527.*

Market Pl. ✆ (0191) 384 3720.

London 267 – Leeds 77 – Middlesbrough 23 – Sunderland 12.

Plan opposite

Ramside Hall, Carrville, DH1 1TD, Northeast : 3 m. on A 690 ✆ (0191) 386 528[illegible] *Fax (0191) 386 0399,* 18, 9, – , rm, TV ♿ P – 🏛 400. MC AE D VISA
Meals 15.00/26.00 **st.** and a la carte – **78 rm** ☕ 102.00/122.00 **st.**, 2 suites – SB.

Royal County (becoming a Marriott spring 2001), Old Elvet, DH1 3JN, ✆ (0191) 386 682[illegible] *info@swallowhotels.com, Fax (0191) 386 0704,* , , – , rm, TV ♿ P 🏛 120. MC AE D VISA **B**
County : **Meals** 16.50/25.50 **st.** and a la carte 7.75 – ***Bowes :*** **Meals** a la carte 13.6[illegible] 24.85 **st.** 7.75 – **147 rm** ☕ 110.00/170.00 **st.**, 4 suites – SB.

Swallow Three Tuns, New Elvet, DH1 3AQ, ✆ (0191) 386 4326, *three.tuns@swallow-h[illegible] tels.co.uk, Fax (0191) 386 1406* – rm, TV P – 🏛 350. MC AE D VISA JCB **B**
Meals (bar lunch Monday to Saturday)/dinner a la carte 22.50/28.50 **st.** 6.50 – **49 r[illegible]** ☕ 105.00/140.00 **st.**, 1 suite – SB.

Bracken, Shincliffe, DH1 2PD, Southeast : 2 m. on A 177 ✆ (0191) 386 296[illegible] *Fax (0191) 384 5423,* – TV ♿ P. MC VISA.
Meals *(closed Sunday lunch)* 12.50/25.00 **st.** and dinner a la carte 6.50 – **12 rm** ☕ 50.0[illegible] 95.00 **st.**

Travel Inn, Arnison Retail Centre, DH1 5GB, North : 3 m. by A 167 ✆ (0191) 383 914[illegible] *Fax (0191) 383 9107* – rm, rest, TV ♿ P. MC AE D VISA
Meals (grill rest.) – **40 rm** 40.95 **t.**

Bistro 21, Aykley Heads House, Aykley Heads, DH1 5TS, Northwest : 1 ½ m. by A 691 and 6532 ✆ (0191) 384 4354, *Fax (0191) 384 1149,* , « Part 17C Mediterranean villa » – [illegible] MC AE D VISA
closed Easter, 25 and 26 December, 1 January, Sunday and Bank Holidays – **Meals** 14.50 (lunch) and a la carte 16.50/26.50 **t.** 8.30.

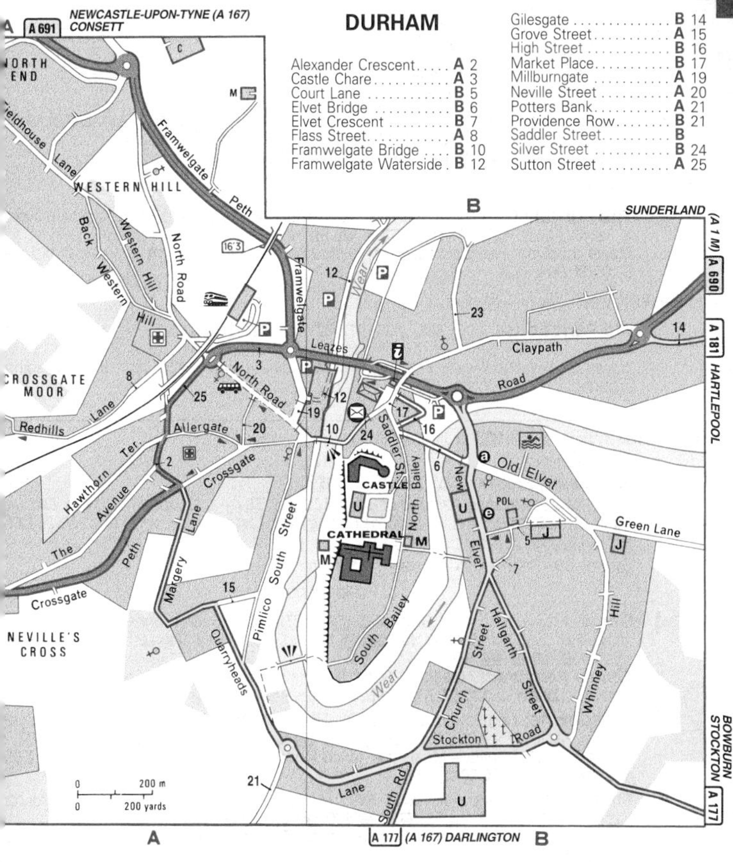

DUXFORD Cambs. 404 U 27 – *pop. 1 848* – ✉ *Cambridge.*

London 50 – Cambridge 11 – Colchester 45 – Peterborough 45.

Duxford Lodge, Ickleton Rd, CB2 4RU, ☎ (01223) 836444, *duxford@btclick.com, Fax (01223) 832271,* ⊼ – TV P – 🏃 30. MC AE D VISA. ✂
closed 26-30 December – ***Le Paradis :*** **Meals** *(closed Saturday lunch)* 14.00/22.50 **t.** and a la carte 5.00 – **15 rm** ☐ 78.00/110.00 **t.**

EAGLESCLIFFE *Stockton-on-Tees* 402 P 20 – *see Stockton-on-Tees.*

EARL'S COLNE *Essex* 404 W 28 – *pop. 3 420* – ✉ *Colchester.*

London 55 – Cambridge 33 – Chelmsford 22 – Colchester 10.

Elm House, 14 Upper Holt St., CO6 2PG, on A 1124 ☎ (01787) 222197, ⊼ – ⇆ rm,
closed Easter and Christmas – **Meals** (by arrangement) (communal dining) 18.00 **s.** – **4 rm** ☐ 25.00/50.00 – SB.

EASINGTON *Bucks..*

London 54 – Aylesbury 13 – Oxford 18.

Mole & Chicken, The Terrace, HP18 9EY, ☎ (01844) 208387, *Fax (01844) 208250,* « Characterful inn » – P. MC AE VISA. ✂
closed 25 December – **Meals** (booking essential) a la carte 19.00/25.00 **t.**

EASINGWOLD *N. Yorks.* 402 Q 21 – *pop. 2 816* – ✉ *York.*

Stillington Rd ✆ *(01347) 821486.*

Chapel Lane ✆ *(01347) 821530 (summer only).*

London 217 – Middlesbrough 37 – York 14.

Old Vicarage without rest., Market Pl., YO61 3AL, ✆ (01347) 821015, *kirman@oldvic-easingwold.freeserve.co.uk, Fax (01347) 823465,* – TV P. MC VISA.
closed December and January – **4 rm** 40.00/65.00.

at Crayke *East : 2 m. on Helmsley Rd* – ✉ *York.*

The Durham Ox with rm, Westway, YO61 4TE, ✆ (01347) 821506, *@the-durham-ox.co k, Fax (01347) 823326* – rest, TV P. MC VISA.
Meals (booking essential) a la carte 16.85/29.85 **t.** 10.00 – **6 rm** (dinner include 50.00/90.00 **t.** – SB.

at Raskelf *West : 2 ¾ m.* – ✉ *York.*

Old Farmhouse, YO61 3LF, ✆ (01347) 821971, *Fax (01347) 822392* – TV P. MC VI
closed 22 December-early February – **Meals** (dinner only) 19.50 **st.** – **9 rm** (dinn included) 32.50/96.00 **st.** – SB.

EASTBOURNE *E. Sussex* 404 U 31 *Great Britain G.* – *pop. 94 793.*

See : *Seafront*★.

Env. : *Beachy Head*★★★, *SW : 3 m. by B 2103* **Z**.

Royal Eastbourne, Paradise Dr. ✆ *(01323) 729738* **Z** – *Eastbourne Downs, East De Rd* ✆ *(01323) 720827* – *Eastbourne Golfing Park, Lottbridge Drove* ✆ *(01323) 520400.*

Cornfield Rd ✆ *(01323) 411400.*

London 68 – Brighton 25 – Dover 61 – Maidstone 49.

Plan opposite

Grand, King Edward's Par., BN21 4EQ, ✆ (01323) 412345, *reservations@grandeastbourr co.uk, Fax (01323) 412233,* ←, heated, – rest, rest, TV P 300. MC AE VISA JCB — Z
***Garden Restaurant* : Meals** 15.50/32.00 **st.** and a la carte 9.50 – (see also **Mirabe** below) – **128 rm** 120.00/200.00 **st.**, 24 suites – SB.

Lansdowne, King Edward's Par., BN21 4EE, ✆ (01323) 725174, *the.lansdowne@btinte et.com, Fax (01323) 739721,* ← – rest, TV – 120. MC AE VISA JCB — Z
closed 1 to 18 January – **Meals** (bar lunch Monday to Saturday)/dinner 17.95 **t.** 6.95 **115 rm** 59.00/106.00 **st.** – SB.

Chatsworth, Grand Par., BN21 3YR, ✆ (01323) 411016, *stay@chatsworth-hotel.co Fax (01323) 643270,* ← – TV – 100. MC AE VISA — X
Meals (bar lunch Monday to Saturday)/dinner 17.50 **st.** 5.25 – **46 rm** 56.00/86.00 **s** 1 suite – SB.

Cherry Tree, 15 Silverdale Rd, BN20 7AJ, ✆ (01323) 722406, *anncherrytree@aol.co Fax (01323) 648838* – TV. MC AE VISA JCB. — Z
Meals (by arrangement) 12.50 **st.** 4.95 – **10 rm** 30.00/66.00 **st.** – SB.

Brayscroft, 13 South Cliff Av., BN20 7AH, ✆ (01323) 647005, *braycroft@hotmail.co Fax (01323) 720705* – TV. MC VISA JCB — Z
Meals (by arrangement) 12.00 **st.** – **5 rm** 29.00/58.00 **st.** – SB.

Southcroft, 15 South Cliff Av., BN20 7AH, ✆ (01323) 729071, *southcroft@eastbourne3 reeserve.co.uk* – TV. — Z
Meals (by arrangement) 12.00 **st.** 3.50 – **6 rm** 28.00/56.00 **st.** – SB.

Mirabelle (at Grand H.), King Edward's Par., BN21 4EQ, ✆ (01323) 435066, *reservations randeastbourne.co.uk, Fax (01323) 412233* – P. MC AE VISA JCB — Z
closed 2 weeks January, 2 weeks September, dinner 25 December,26 December, Sund and Monday – **Meals** (booking essential) 19.00/32.00 **st.** and dinner a la carte.

at Jevington *Northwest : 6 m. by A 259* – **Z** – *on Jevington Rd* – ✉ *Polegate.*

Hungry Monk, The Street, BN26 5QF, ✆ (01323) 482178, *Fax (01323) 483989,* « Pa Elizabethan cottages », – P. MC AE VISA
closed 24-26 and 31 December, 1 January and Bank Holiday Monday – **Meals** (bookir essential) (dinner only and Sunday lunch)/dinner 26.50 **t** 11.00.

at Wilmington *Northwest : 6½ m. by A 22 on A 27* – **Y** – ✉ *Eastbourne.*

Crossways with rm, Lewes Rd, BN26 5SG, ✆ (01323) 482455, *crossways@fastnet.co.u Fax (01323) 487811,* – rest, TV P. MC AE VISA JCB.
closed 24 December-24 January – **Meals** *(closed Sunday and Monday)* (dinner only) 28.95 6.95 – **7 rm** 50.00/80.00 **st.** – SB.

EASTBOURNE

ndale Centre V
shford Road . . . . V 2
edfordwell Road. . . . . V 3
hurch Street . . . . Z 4
ornfield Road . . . . V 5
evonshire Place . . . . X 6
ldredge Road. . . . . V 7
ove Road V
ailsham Road . . . . Y 8
gh Street. . . . . Z 9
ewes Road . . . . Y 13
smore Road . . . . V 14
orth Street . . . . V 15
olegate By-Pass . . . . Y 18
. Anthony's
Avenue . . . . Y 21

Seaside Rd. V
South Street. V
Station Road. . . . . Y 24
Susan's Road. . . . . V 25

Terminus Road V
The Goffs. . . . . Z 26
Trinity Trees. . . . . V 27
Upperton Road. . . . . V, Z 28

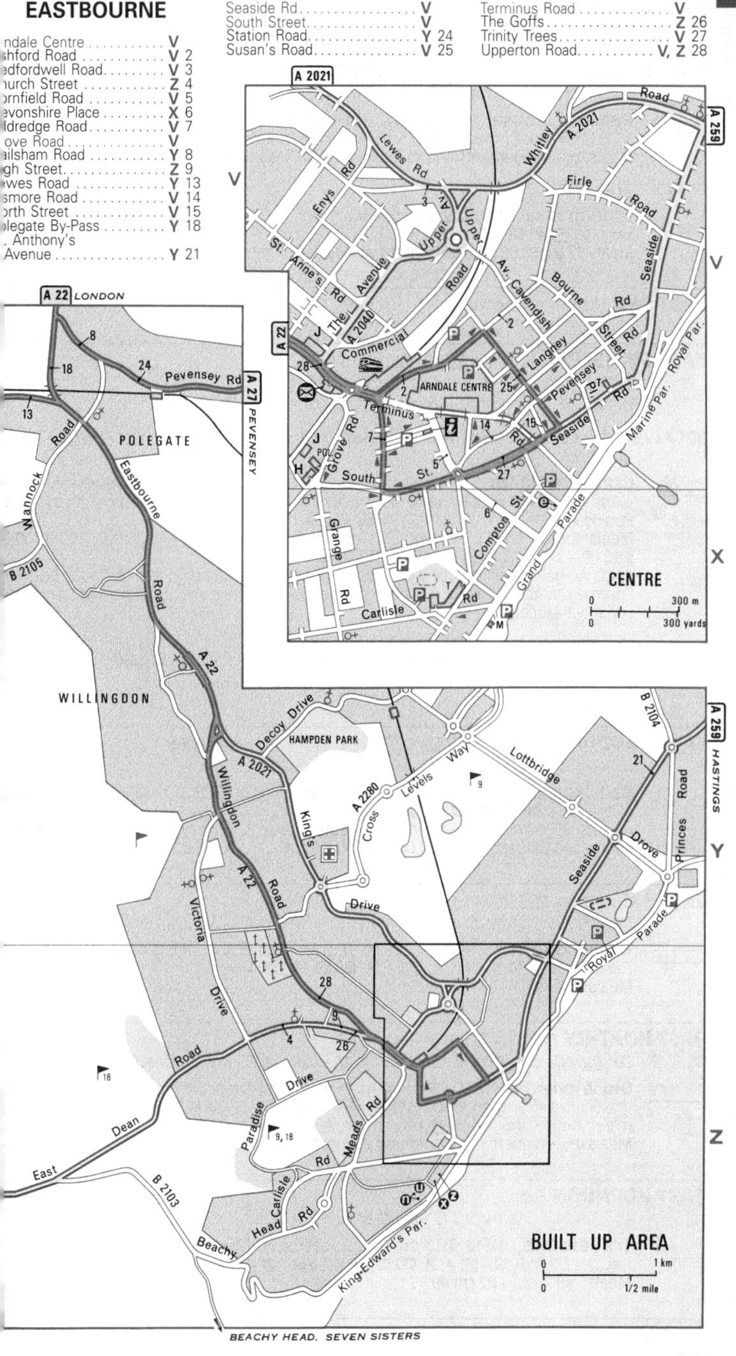

EAST CHILTINGTON *E. Sussex – see Lewes.*

EAST DEREHAM *Norfolk* 404 W 25 – *pop. 12 974.*
London 109 – Cambridge 57 – King's Lynn 27 – Norwich 16.

Peacock House, Peacock Lane, Old Beetley, NR20 4DG, North : 3 ½ m. on B 11… *(01362) 860371, peackh@aol.co,* « Part 17C farmhouse », – [P]
Meals (by arrangement) (communal dining) 14.50 **s.** – **3 rm** 25.00/45.00 **s.**

at Wendling *West : 5½ m. by A 47.*

Greenbanks Country H., Swaffham Rd, NR19 2AR, (01362) 687742, rest, [TV] [P]. MC VISA
Meals 12.50/30.00 **st.** 6.50 – **8 rm** 48.00/76.00 **st.**

EAST END *Hants. – see Lymington.*

EAST GRINSTEAD *W. Sussex* 404 T 30 – *pop. 24 383.*
18 *Copthorne, Borers Arm Rd (01342) 712508.*
London 48 – Brighton 30 – Eastbourne 32 – Lewes 21 – Maidstone 37.

at Gravetye *Southwest : 4½ m. by B 2110 taking second turn left towards West Hoathly – Ea… Grinstead.*

Gravetye Manor, Vowels Lane, RH19 4LJ, (01342) 810567, *gravetye@relaischat…ux.fr, Fax (01342) 810080,* « 16C manor house with gardens and grounds by Willia… Robinson », – rest, [TV] [P]. MC VISA.
Meals *(closed to non-residents 25 December)* (booking essential) 26.00/37.00-52.00 … 10.00 – 16.00 – **18 rm** 145.00/310.00 **st.**
Spec. Medallions of lobster with essence of tomato and basil. Fillet of Angus beef wi… Fourme d'Ambert, celeriac purée, red wine sauce. Roast turbot with scallops, ginger a… coriander sauce.

Les prix	Pour toutes précisions sur les prix indiqués dans ce guide, reportez-vous aux pages de l'introduction.

EAST HADDON *Northants.* 403 404 Q 27 – *pop. 607 – Northampton.*
London 78 – Birmingham 47 – Leicester 32 – Northampton 6.

Red Lion with rm, High St., NN6 8BU, (01604) 770223, *Fax (01604) 770767,* « Pa… 17C », – [TV] [P]. MC AE VISA JCB.
closed 25 and 26 December – **Meals** *(closed Sunday dinner)* 15.00/21.00 (lunch) and a la carte 17.00/28.00 **t.** 7.00 – **5 rm** 60.00/75.00 **t.**

EASTHAM *Mersey.* 402 403 L 24 – *pop. 15 011 – Wirral.*
London 209 – Birmingham 45 – Chester 13 – Liverpool 8 – Manchester 45.

Travelodge, New Chester Rd, L62 9AQ, at junction of A 41 with M 53 (0151) 327 248… *Fax (0151) 327 2489* – rm, [TV] [P]. MC AE VISA JCB.
Meals (grill rest.) – **31 rm** 39.95 **t.**

EAST HOATHLY *E. Sussex* 404 U 31 – *pop. 1 206.*
London 60 – Brighton 16 – Eastbourne 13 – Hastings 25 – Maidstone 32.

Old Whyly, BN8 6EL, West : ½ m., turning right after post box on right, taking cent… gravel drive after approx. 400 metres (01825) 840216, *Fax (01825) 840738,* « Georgi… manor house, antiques », heated, – rm, [P].
Meals (by arrangement) (communal dining) 22.00 **s.** – **3 rm** 67.50/90.00 **s.**

EAST HORNDON *Essex.*
London 21 – Chelmsford 13 – Southend-on-Sea 17.

Travelodge, CM13 3LL, on A 127 (eastbound carriageway) (01277) 8108… *Fax (01277) 810819* – [TV] [P]. MC AE VISA JCB.
Meals (grill rest.) – **22 rm** 49.95 **t.**

EASTLEIGH *Devon* 403 H 30 – *see Bideford.*

ASTLEIGH *Hants.* 403 P 31 – *pop. 49 934.*

Fleming Park, Magpie Lane (023) 8061 2797.

Southampton (Eastleigh) Airport : (023) 8062 0021.

The Point, Leigh Rd (023) 8064 1261.

London 74 – Winchester 8 – Southampton 4.

Posthouse Eastleigh, Leigh Rd, SO50 9PG, West : 1/4 m. on A 335 (0870) 4009075, *Fax (023) 8064 3945,* – rm, rest, – 200. MC AE VISA JCB
Meals (bar lunch Saturday) a la carte 15.65/24.85 **t.** – 11.95 – **117 rm** 94.00/114.00 **t.** – SB.

Travel Inn, Leigh Rd, SO50 9YX, West : 1/2 m. on A 335 (023) 8065 0541, *Fax (023) 8065 0531* – rm, MC AE VISA
Meals (grill rest.) – **60 rm** 40.95 **t.**

Travelodge, Twyford Rd, SO50 4LF, North : 1 m. on A 335 (023) 8061 6813 – rm, MC AE VISA JCB.
Meals (grill rest.) – **32 rm** 49.95 **t.**

ASTLING *Kent* 404 W 30 – *see Faversham.*

AST MIDLANDS AIRPORT *Leics.* 402 403 404 P/Q 25 – *Derby.*

London 125 – Nottingham 15 – Derby 13 – Birmingham 40 – Leicester 24.

Hilton East Midlands Airport, Derby Rd, Lockington, DE74 2YW, Northeast : 2 3/4 m. by A 453 on A 50 at junction 24 of M 1 (01509) 674000, *Fax (01509) 672412,* – rm, – 300. MC AE VISA
Meals *(closed Saturday lunch)* (carving lunch) 15.95/21.95 **st.** and dinner a la carte – 11.95 – **150 rm** 135.00/155.00 **st.**, 2 suites.

Thistle East Midlands Airport, DE74 2SH, (01332) 850700, *east.midlandsairport@thistle.co.uk, Fax (01332) 850823,* – – 250. MC AE VISA.
Meals (bar lunch Saturday) 19.95 **st.** and a la carte – 10.75 – **164 rm** 147.00 **st.** – SB.

Travelodge, Donington Park, DE74 2TN, East : 1/2 m. by A 453 at junction with A 42 and 23a of M 1 (01509) 670900, *Fax (01509) 686316* – rm, rest, MC AE VISA JCB
Meals (grill rest.) – **80 rm** 49.95 **t.**

ASTON *Somerset – see Wells.*

AST TYTHERLEY *Hants. – see Romsey.*

AST WITTERING *W. Sussex* 404 R 31 – *pop. 4 630 – Chichester.*

London 74 – Brighton 37 – Portsmouth 25.

Clifford's Cottage, Bracklesham Lane, Bracklesham Bay, PO20 8JA, East : 1 m. by B 2179 on B 2198 (01243) 670250 – MC AE VISA
closed first week February, 2 weeks November, Monday, Tuesday and Sunday dinner – **Meals** (dinner only and Sunday lunch)/dinner 19.50 **st.** and a la carte 4.75.

AST WITTON *N. Yorks.* 402 O 21 – *pop. 153 – Leyburn.*

London 238 – Leeds 45 – Middlesbrough 30 – York 39.

Blue Lion with rm, DL8 4SN, (01969) 624273, *Fax (01969) 624189,* « Part 18C former coaching inn », – MC VISA
The Restaurant : **Meals** (dinner only and Sunday lunch)/dinner a la carte 19.15/30.85 **st.** 6.95 – (see also ***The Bar*** below) – **12 rm** 60.00/95.00 **st.**

The Bar (at Blue Lion), DL8 4SN, (01969) 624273, *Fax (10969) 624189,* « Part 18C former coaching inn », – MC VISA
Meals (booking essential) a la carte 13.95/29.65 **st.** 6.95.

BCHESTER *Durham* 401 402 O 19 – *Consett.*

Consett and District, Elmfield Rd, Consett (01207) 502186.

London 275 – Carlisle 64 – Newcastle upon Tyne 16.

Raven Country, Broomhill, DH8 6RY, Southeast : 3/4 m. on B 6309 (01207) 562562, *enquiries@ravenhotel.co.uk, Fax (01207) 560262,* – – 120. MC AE VISA.
Meals a la carte 13.00/23.00 **st.** 4.95 – **29 rm** 55.00/69.00 **st.** – SB.

ECCLES *Gtr. Manchester* 402 403 404 M 23 – *see Manchester.*

ECCLESHALL *Staffs.* 403 404 N 25 – *pop. 5 892.*
London 154 – Birmingham 37 – Stoke-on-Trent 13.

Julians, 21 High St., ST21 6BW, ☎ (01785) 851200, *Fax (01785) 859097* – . MC AE VISA
Meals (light lunch)/dinner a la carte 17.15/31.85 **st.** 7.50.

EDENBRIDGE *Kent* 404 U 30 *Great Britain G. – pop. 7 196.*
Env. : *Hever Castle★ AC, E : 2½ m. – Chartwell★ AC, N : 3 m. by B 2026.*
18, 18, 9 *Edenbridge G & C.C., Crouch House Rd ☎ (01732) 867381.*
London 35 – Brighton 36 – Maidstone 29.

Honours Mill, 87 High St., TN8 5AU, ☎ (01732) 866757, , « Renovated 18C mill » – MC VISA
closed 2 weeks Christmas, Monday, Sunday dinner and Saturday lunch – **Meals** 12.50/32.75 **t.** 9.95.

Haxted Mill, Haxted Rd, TN8 6PU, West : 2 ¼ m. on Haxted Rd ☎ (01732) 862914, *david@haxtedmill.co.uk, Fax (01732) 865705*, , « Converted 17C stables, riverside setting », – P. MC VISA
closed 22 December-5 January, Monday, Tuesday, Sunday dinner and Saturday lunch October-May – **Meals** 17.00 **t.** (lunch) and a la carte 23.90/35.90 **t.** 12.15.

at Four Elms *Northeast : 2½ m. on B 2027 – ✉ Edenbridge.*

Oak House Barn without rest., Mapleton Rd, TN8 6PL, Northwest : 1 m. off B 2027 ☎ (01732) 700725, « Converted part 16C barn », – TV P.
closed December – **3 rm** 40.00/60.00 **t.**

EGERTON *Gtr. Manchester* 402 ㉑ 403 ② 404 ⑨ – *see Bolton.*

EGGESFORD *Devon* 403 I 31.
London 215 – Barnstaple 18 – Exeter 22 – Taunton 48.

Eggesford Country H., EX18 7JZ, ☎ (01769) 580345, *relax@eggesfordhotel.co.uk, Fax (01769) 580262*, , , – rm, TV P – 80. MC VISA
closed 2 weeks January – **Meals** a la carte 12.05/19.20 **t.** – **15 rm** 36.00/80.00 **t.**

EGHAM *Surrey* 404 S 29 – *pop. 23 816.*
London 29 – Reading 21.

Runnymede, Windsor Rd, TW20 0AG, on A 308 ☎ (01784) 436171, *info@runnymedehotel.com, Fax (01784) 436340*, « Riverside setting », , , , , – , rm, P – 350. MC AE VISA JCB.
Meals – (see ***Left Bank*** below) – 13.95 – **177 rm** 152.00/215.00 **st.**, 3 suites – SB.

Great Fosters, Stroude Rd, TW20 9UR, South : 1 ¼ m. by B 388 ☎ (01784) 433822, *greatfosters@compuserve.com, Fax (01784) 472455*, « Elizabethan mansion, gardens », heated, , – rest, TV P – 100. MC AE VISA.
Meals *(closed Saturday lunch)* 16.95/32.50 **st.** and a la carte 6.75 – 12.75 – **39 rm** 95.00/295.00 **st.**, 3 suites.

Left Bank (at Runnymede H.), Windsor Rd, TW20 0AG, on A 308 ☎ (01784) 43740 « Riverside setting », – P. MC AE VISA JCB
closed Saturday lunch and Sunday dinner – **Meals** 18.95 **t.** (lunch) and dinner a la carte 24.10/29.25 **t.** 9.50.

EIGHT ASH GREEN *Essex* 404 W 28 – *see Colchester.*

ELLAND *W. Yorks.* 402 O 22 – *pop. 10 931 – ✉ Halifax.*
9 *Hammerstones Leach Lane, Hullen Edge ☎ (01422) 372505.*
London 204 – Bradford 12 – Burnley 29 – Leeds 17 – Manchester 30.

La Cachette, 7-10 Town Hall Buildings, HX5 0EU, ☎ (01422) 378833, *Fax (01422) 377899* . MC AE VISA
closed 26-27 December, Sunday and Bank Holiday lunch – **Meals** 11.95 **st.** (dinner) and a la carte 15.00/22.00 **st.** 4.95.

LLESMERE PORT *Mersey.* 402 403 L 24 – *pop. 64 504.*
London 211 – Birkenhead 9 – Chester 9 – Liverpool 12 – Manchester 44.

Holiday Inn Ellesmere Port Chester, Centre Island, Waterways, Lower Mersey St., CH65 2AL, Northeast : 1 ½ m. by A 5032 (M 53 junction 9) ☎ (0151) 356 8111, *Fax (0151) 356 8444,* « Marina setting overlooking Boat Museum », rm, rest, 120.
Waterways : **Meals** *(closed Sunday lunch)* 10.50 **t.** (lunch) and a la carte 19.20/26.20 **t.** 6.95 – 9.50 – **83 rm** 100.00/110.00 **t.**

LMDON *Essex* 404 U 27 – *see Saffron Walden.*

LSING *Norfolk* 404 X 25 – *pop. 261* – ✉ *East Dereham.*
London 118 – Cambridge 66 – King's Lynn 33 – Norwich 15.

Bartles Lodge without rest., Church St., NR20 3EA, ☎ (01362) 637177,
7 rm 35.00/46.00 **st.**

LSLACK *N. Yorks.* 402 N 22 – *see Skipton.*

LSTED *W. Sussex* 404 R 31 – *see Midhurst.*

LSTED MARSH *W. Sussex* 404 R 31 – *see Midhurst.*

LSTOW *Beds.* 404 S 27 – *see Bedford.*

LSTREE *Herts.* 404 T 29 – *pop. 2 196.*
Watling St. ☎ *(020) 8953 6115.*
London 10 – Luton 22.

Plan : see Greater London (North West) pp. 8 and 9

Edgwarebury, Barnet Lane, WD6 3RE, ☎ (020) 8953 8227, *edgwarebury@corushotels.com, Fax (020) 8207 3668,* 80. CT e
Meals – (see ***The Cavendish*** below) – 11.75 – **47 rm** 115.00/195.00 **st.** – SB.

The Cavendish (at Edgwarebury H.), Barnet Lane, WD6 3RE, ☎ (020) 8953 8227, *Fax (020) 8207 3668,* CT e
closed Saturday lunch – **Meals** (booking essential) a la carte 22.00/38.95 **t.** 6.50.

LTERWATER *Cumbria* – *see Ambleside.*

LY *Cambs.* 404 U 26 *Great Britain G.* – *pop. 10 329.*
See : *Cathedral★★ AC.*
Exc. : *Wicken Fen★, SE : 9 m. by A 10 and A 1123.*
107 Cambridge Rd ☎ *(01353) 662751.*
Oliver Cromwells House, 29 St. Mary's St. ☎ *(01353) 662062.*
London 74 – Cambridge 16 – Norwich 60.

Lamb, 2 Lynn Rd, CB7 4EJ, ☎ (01353) 663574, *Fax (01353) 662023* – rest, 30.
Meals 11.50/16.95 **t.** and a la carte – **32 rm** 67.00/90.00 **t.** – SB.

Travelodge, Witchford Rd, CB6 3NN, West : 1 m. on A 10/A 142 roundabout, Ely bypass ☎ (01353) 668499 – rm,
Meals (grill rest.) – **39 rm** 49.95 **t.**

t Littleport *North : 5 ¾ m. on A 10* – ✉ *Ely.*

Fen House, 2 Lynn Rd, CB6 1QG, ☎ (01353) 860645 –
closed 1 week Christmas and Sunday to Tuesday – **Meals** (booking essential) (dinner only) 28.75 **t.** 6.25.

t Coveney *Northwest : 4 m. by West Fen rd* – ✉ *Ely.*

Hill House Farm without rest., 9 Main St., CB6 2DJ, ☎ (01353) 778369,
closed 25 and 26 December – **3 rm** 50.00.

ENGLAND

at Sutton Gault *West : 8 m. by A 142 off B 1381 – ✉ Ely.*

Anchor Inn with rm, CB6 2BD, ✆ (01353) 778537, *anchor@sutton-gault.freeserve.co.u*
Fax (01353) 776180, « Part 17C inn » – ⅍ TV P. MC AE VISA. ⅍
closed 25-26 December – **Meals** a la carte 19.40/25.95 **t.** 6.95 – **1 rm** 51.00/95.00
1 suite.

EMSWORTH *Hants.* 404 R 31 – *pop. 18 310 (inc. Southbourne).*
London 75 – Brighton 37 – Portsmouth 10.

Brookfield, 93-95 Havant Rd, PO10 7LF, East : 1 m. on A 259 ✆ (01243) 37336
Fax (01243) 376342, – rm, rest, TV P – 50. MC AE VISA JCB.
closed 1 week Christmas – ***Hermitage :*** **Meals** 12.95/24.95 **t.** 6.95 – **40 rm** 70.0
150.00 **t.** – SB.

Travelodge, PO10 7RB, Northeast : 1 ½ m. on A 27 (eastbound carriagewa
✆ (01243) 370877 – rm, TV P. MC AE VISA JCB.
Meals (grill rest.) – **36 rm** 39.95 **t.**

36 on the Quay (Farthing), 47 South St., The Quay, PO10 7EG, ✆ (01243) 37559
Fax (01243) 375593, ← – . MC AE VISA JCB
closed 2 weeks January, 1 week October, Sunday, lunch Saturday and Monday and Bar
Holidays – **Meals** (booking essential) 16.95/19.95 **t.** (lunch) and a la carte 34.50/42.50
7.50
Spec. Fillets of red mullet with langoustine and pesto. Seared scallops with chicken ar
duck liver sausage, creamed garlic potato. "36's lemon dessert".

Spencers, 36 North St., PO10 7DG, ✆ (01243) 372744, *Fax (01243) 372744* – . MC AE
VISA
closed 24-26 December, Sunday and Monday – **Meals** (dinner only) a la carte 15.05/23.75
7.00.

Fat Olives, 30 South St., PO10 7EH, ✆ (01243) 377914, *fatolives@lemjm.fsnet.co.uk,*
– . MC VISA
closed 2 weeks Christmas and New Year, Sunday and Monday – **Meals** 14.50
(lunch) and a la carte 17.45/25.40 **t.** 9.00.

ENSTONE *Oxon.* 403 404 P 28 – *pop. 1 523* – ✉ *Chipping Norton.*
London 73 – Birmingham 48 – Gloucester 32 – Oxford 18.

Swan Lodge without rest., OX7 4NE, on A 44 ✆ (01608) 678736, *Fax (01608) 677963,*
– TV P.
3 rm 40.00/50.00 **st.**

EPSOM *Surrey* 404 ㉚ – *pop. 64 405 (inc. Ewell).*
Longdown Lane South, Epsom Downs ✆ (01372) 721666 – Horton Park C.C., Hook
✆ (020) 8393 8400.
London 17 – Guildford 16.

Chalk Lane, Chalk Lane, KT18 7BB, Southwest : ½ m. by A 24 and Woodcote R
✆ (01372) 721179, *chalklane@compuserve.com, Fax (01372) 727878* – TV P – 15
MC AE VISA.
Meals *(closed Saturday lunch and Sunday dinner)* 10.00/23.50 **t.** and a la carte 8.00
26 rm 80.00/155.00 **t.** – SB.

Travel Inn Metro, 2-4 St. Margarets Drive, KT18 7LB, Southwest : ½ m. on A 2
✆ (01372) 739786, *Fax (01372) 739761* – rm, rest, TV P – 40. MC AE VISA
Meals (grill rest.) – **40 rm** 46.95 **t.**

Le Raj, 211 Fir Tree Rd, Epsom Downs, KT19 3LB, Southeast : 2 ¼ m. by B 289 and B 284 c
B 291 ✆ (01737) 371371, *booking@leraj.com, Fax (01737) 211903* – . MC AE VISA
closed 25 and 26 December – **Meals** - Indian - 20.00/40.00 **t.** and a la carte.

ERPINGHAM *Norfolk* 404 X 25 – *pop. 1 871.*
London 123 – Cromer 8 – King's Lynn 46 – Norwich 16.

The Ark with rm, The Street, NR11 7QB, ✆ (01263) 761535, – TV P.
closed 2 weeks October and 25-28 December – **Meals** *(closed Sunday dinner and Monda*
(dinner only and Sunday lunch)/dinner 28.00 **t.** 7.00 – **3 rm** (dinner included) 72.5
135.00 **t.**

Saracen's Head with rm, Wolterton, NR11 7LX, West : 1 ½ m. ✆ (01263) 76890
Fax (01263) 768993, – rm, P. MC AE VISA JCB.
closed 25 December – **Meals** a la carte 15.95/20.20 **t.** 5.00 – **4 rm** 45.00/65.00 **t.** – SE

SCRICK *N. Yorks.* 402 Q 22 – *see York.*

SHER *Surrey* 404 S 29 – *pop. 46 599 (inc. Molesey).*

Thames Ditton & Esher, Portsmouth Rd (020) 8398 1551 **BZ** – *Moore Place, Portsmouth Rd (01372) 463533* **BZ** – *Sandown Park, More Lane (01372) 461234* **BZ**.

London 20 – Portsmouth 58.

Plan : see Greater London (South-West) p. 12

Good Earth, 14-18 High St., KT10 9RT, (01372) 462489, *Fax (01372) 460668* – . MC AE VISA BZ e
closed 23-30 December – **Meals** - Chinese - 12.00/28.50 **t.** and a la carte 7.50.

Claygate *Southeast : 1 m. by A 244 – Esher.*

Le Petit Pierrot, 4 The Parade, KT10 0NU, (01372) 465105, *Fax (01372) 467642* – MC AE VISA BZ r
closed 2 weeks September, 1 week Christmas, Saturday lunch, Sunday and Bank Holidays – **Meals** - French - 14.75/24.50 **t.** 6.15.

SHOTT *Northd. – see Morpeth.*

VERDON *Northants. – see Daventry.*

Si vous cherchez un hôtel tranquille,
consultez d'abord les cartes de l'introduction
ou repérez dans le texte les établissements indiqués avec le signe ou .

VERSHOT *Dorset* 403 404 M 31 – *pop. 225* – *Dorchester.*

London 149 – Bournemouth 39 – Dorchester 12 – Salisbury 53 – Taunton 30 – Yeovil 10.

Summer Lodge , Summer Lane, DT2 0JR, (01935) 83424, *reception@summerlodgehotel.com, Fax (01935) 83005,* , « Part Georgian dower house », heated, , – rest, MC AE VISA
Meals 15.75 **st.** (lunch) and a la carte 30.00/42.00 **st.** 7.00 – 15.00 – **18 rm** 125.00/285.00 **st.** – SB.

VESHAM *Worcs.* 403 404 O 27 – *pop. 17 823.*

The Almonry, Abbey Gate (01386) 446944.

London 99 – Birmingham 30 – Cheltenham 16 – Coventry 32.

Wood Norton Hall, WR11 4YB, Northwest : 2 ¼ m. on A 4538 (01386) 420007, *woodnortonhall@bbc.co.uk, Fax (01386) 420190,* « Victorian country house », , , , , squash – – 70. MC AE VISA.
closed 24 December-3 January – ***Duc's :*** **Meals** *(closed Saturday lunch)* (booking essential) 19.50/38.50 **t.** 7.25 – **44 rm** 115.00/155.00 **t.**, 1 suite – SB.

Evesham, Coopers Lane, WR11 6DA, off Waterside (01386) 765566, Reservations (Freephone) 0800 716969, *reception@eveshamhotel.com, Fax (01386) 765443,* , – MC AE VISA
closed 25 and 26 December – **Meals** a la carte 18.00/29.50 **st.** 5.50 – **40 rm** 65.00/117.00 **st.** – SB.

Waterside, 56-59 Waterside, WR11 6JZ, (01386) 442420, *Fax (01386) 446272,* , – MC AE VISA JCB
closed 20 December-4 January – **Meals** (grill rest.) a la carte 9.30/16.60 **t.** – **15 rm** 63.80/82.50 **t.** – SB.

Riverside, The Parks, Offenham Rd, WR11 5JP, Northeast : 2 m. by Waterside and B 4035 off B 4510 (01386) 446200, *riversidehotel@theparksoffenham.freeserve.co.uk, Fax (01386) 40021,* , , – , rest, MC VISA JCB.
closed Sunday, Monday and 25 December – **Meals** 17.95/28.95 **st.** and lunch a la carte 7.95 – **7 rm** 60.00/90.00 **st.** – SB.

Harvington *Northeast : 4½ m. by A 4184 and B 4088 off Bidford rd – Evesham.*

Mill at Harvington , Anchor Lane, WR11 5NR, Southeast : 1 ½ m. (01386) 870688, *Fax (01386) 870688,* , « 18C mill with riverside garden », heated, , – rest, MC AE VISA JCB.
closed 1 week Christmas – **Meals** 13.95/24.00 **t.** and a la carte 5.75 – **21 rm** 63.00/121.00 **t.** – SB.

at Abbot's Salford *(Warks.) Northeast : 5 m. by A 4184 and B 4088 on Bidford rd –* ✉ *Evesham.*

Salford Hall, WR11 5UT, ✆ (01386) 871300, *reception@salfordhall.co.u* *Fax (01386) 871301,* « Tudor mansion with early 17C extension and gatehouse », – rest, TV P – 50. MC AE ① VISA JCB. *closed 24-30 December* – ***Stanford Room :*** **Meals** *(closed Saturday lunch)* 15.95/35.00 8.65 – **33 rm** 85.00/150.00 **t.** – SB.

EWELL *Surrey* 404 T 29 – *pop. 4 862.*
London 13 – Crawley 26 – Guildford 22.

Plan : see Greater London (South-West) p. 13

Premier Lodge, 272 Kingston Rd, KT19 0SH, ✆ (020) 8393 2666, *Fax (020) 8394 178C* rm, TV P. MC AE ① VISA. CZ
Meals (grill rest.) 11.75 **t.** and a la carte – 6.00 – **29 rm** 46.00 **t.**

EWEN *Glos.* 403 404 O 28 – *see Cirencester.*

EXETER *Devon* 403 J 31 *The West Country G. – pop. 94 717.*
See : *City★★ - Cathedral★★* **Z** – *Royal Albert Memorial Museum★* **Y**.
Exc. : *Killerton★★* ***AC****, NE : 7 m. by B 3181* **V** – *Ottery St. Mary★ (St. Mary's★) E : 12 m. by 3183 –* **Y** – *A 30 and B 3174 – Crediton (Holy Cross Church★), NW : 9 m. by A 377.*
Downes Crediton, Hookway ✆ (01363) 773991.
Exeter Airport : ✆ (01392) 367433, E : 5 m. by A 30 **V** – **Terminal :** *St. David's a Central Stations.*
Civic Centre, Paris St. ✆ (01392) 265700.
London 201 – Bournemouth 83 – Bristol 83 – Plymouth 46 – Southampton 110.

EXETER
BUILT UP AREA

Blackboy Road . . . . V 8
Buddle Lane . . . . X 9
Butts Road. . . . . X 12
East Wonford Hill. . . . . X 17
Heavitree Road . . . . VX 20
Hill Lane . . . . V 21
Marsh Barton Road . . . . X 25
Mount Pleasant Road . . . . . . V 29
North Street
HEAVITREE . . . . X 32
Old Tiverton Road. . . . . V 35
Polsloe Road . . . . V 39
Prince Charles Road. . . . . . . V 41
Prince of Wales Road . . . . . V 42
St. Andrew's Road. V
Summer Lane V
Sweetbriar Lane VX
Trusham Road. X
Union Road V
Whipton Lane X
Wonford Road. X
Wonford Street. X
Woodwater Lane X

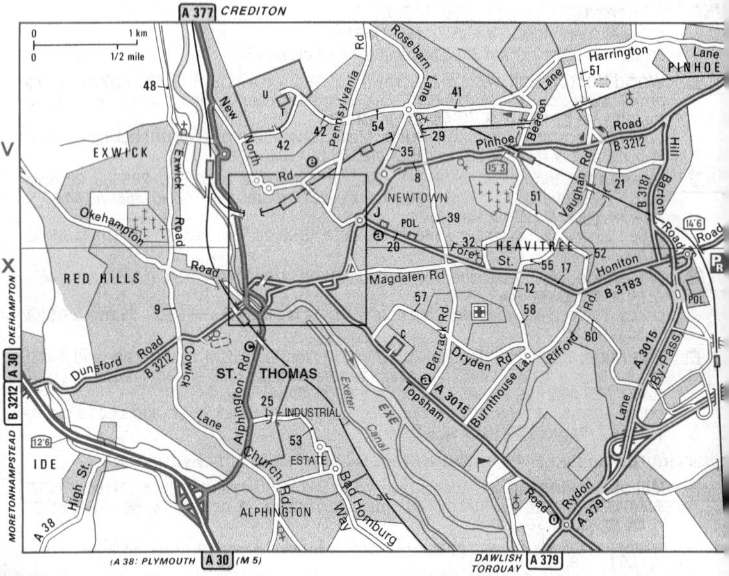

A 377 CREDITON
EXWICK
RED HILLS
ST. THOMAS
NEWTOWN
HEAVITREE
PINHOE
IDE
ALPHINGTON
INDUSTRIAL ESTATE
MORETONHAMPSTEAD B 3212 A 30 OKEHAMPTON
(A 38: PLYMOUTH A 30 (M 5)
DAWLISH TORQUAY A 379

EXETER
CENTRE

›hington Rd . . . . Z 2
›rnfield Rd . . . . Z 3
›dford St. . . . . Y 4
›stle St. . . . . Y 13
›thedral Close Walk . . . . . YZ 14
Cowick St. . . . . Z 15
Edmund St. . . . . Z 18
Fore St. . . . . Z
Guildhall Shopping Centre . . . Y
Harlequins Shopping Centre . Y
High St. . . . . Y
King St. . . . . Z 22
Mary Arches St. . . . . Z 26
Mint (The) . . . . Z 28
New Bridge St. . . . . Z 31
Palace Gate . . . . Z 36
Paul St. . . . . Y 37
Preston St. . . . . Z 40
Princesshay . . . . Y 44
Quay Hill . . . . Z 45
Queen's Terrace . . . . Y 46
St. Martin's Lane . . . . Y 49
Stepcote Hill. . . . . Z 50

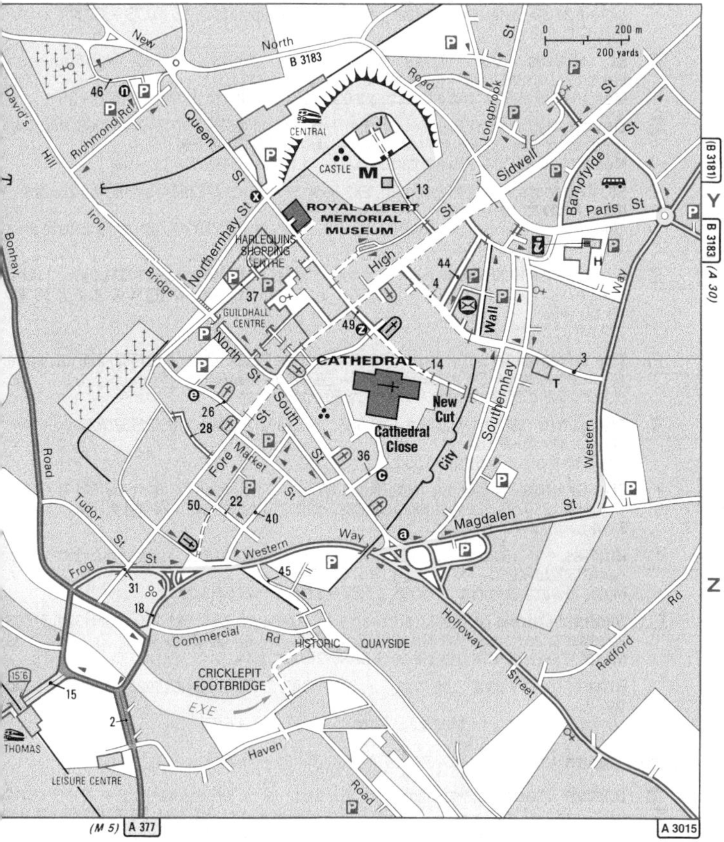

Southgate, Southernhay East, EX1 1QF, ☎ (01392) 412812, *GB1083@forte_hotels.com, Fax (01392) 413549*, – rm, TV, P – 150. MC AE VISA JCB Z a
Meals *(closed Saturday lunch)* 22.00 **t.** (dinner) and a la carte 20.90/32.70 **t.** 9.00 – 12.95 – **109 rm** 110.00, 1 suite – SB.

Thistle Exeter, Queen St., EX4 3SP, ☎ (01392) 254982, *Fax (01392) 420928* – rm, rest, TV P – 300. MC AE VISA. Y x
Meals (bar lunch)/dinner 14.00/20.00 **st.** and a la carte 6.95 – 9.95 – **88 rm** 103.00/125.00 **st.**, 2 suites – SB.

Royal Clarence, Cathedral Yard, EX1 1HD, ☎ (01392) 319955, *Fax (01392) 439423* – TV – 120. MC AE VISA. Y z
St. Martin's Cafe Bar : **Meals** a la carte 12.50/22.40 **t.** 12.25 – (see also ***Michael Caines*** below) – 9.50 – **56 rm** 99.00/135.00 **st.**, 1 suite – SB.

Buckerell Lodge, Topsham Rd, EX2 4SQ, ☎ (01392) 221111, *Fax (01392) 491111*, – rm, TV P – 50. MC AE VISA X a
Meals 19.95 **t.** (dinner) and a la carte 19.95/25.00 **t.** 9.95 – 9.95 – **53 rm** 80.00/110.00 **t.** – SB.

The Queens Court, Bystock Terr., EX4 4HY, ☎ (01392) 272709, *sales@queenscourt-ho .co.uk, Fax (01392) 491390,* – ▮ ⇔ TV P – 🎤 50. MC AE ◑ VISA Y
closed 25 December-1 January – a la carte 5.95 ***Olive Tree :*** **Meals** - Mediterranean *(closed lunch Saturday and Sunday)* 9.95/15.95 **t.** – ☕ 5.00 – **18 rm** 59.00/69.00 **t.**

Gipsy Hill ⛇, Gipsy Hill Lane, via Pinn Lane, EX1 3RN, East : 2 m. by Honiton Rd (A 30) Gipsy Hill rd ☎ (01392) 465252, *gipsyhill@bestwestern.co.uk, Fax (01392) 464302,* ⇔ TV P – 🎤 120. MC AE ◑ VISA
closed 24-30 December – **Meals** 10.00/20.00 **t.** and a la carte 6.75 – **37 rm** ☕ 80.0 110.00 **t.** – SB.

St. Olaves, Mary Arches St., EX4 3AZ, ☎ (01392) 217736, *info@olaves.co. Fax (01392) 413054,* – TV P. MC AE ◑ VISA Z
Meals 12.50/15.50 **t.** and a la carte 6.00 – ☕ 6.00 – **15 rm** 85.00/120.00 **t.** – SB.

Devon, Matford, EX2 8XU, South : 3 m. by A 377 on A 379 ☎ (01392) 259268, *info@dev hotel.co.uk, Fax (01392) 413142* – TV P – 🎤 160. MC AE ◑ VISA
Meals 11.75/15.00 **t.** and a la carte 5.50 – **41 rm** ☕ 65.00/75.00 **t.** – SB.

St. Andrews, 28 Alphington Rd, EX2 8HN, ☎ (01392) 276784, *Fax (01392) 250249* – TV ♿ P. MC AE ◑ VISA. ✻ X
closed 24 December-first week January – **Meals** (bar lunch)/dinner a la carte appro 14.65 **t.** 6.95 – **17 rm** ☕ 45.00/65.00 **t.**

Express by Holiday Inn without rest., Exeter Business Park, EX1 3PE, East : 2 ¾ m. Honiton Rd (A 30) ☎ (01392) 261000, *Fax (01392) 261061* – ▮ ⇔ TV ☎ ♿ P – 🎤 30. MC ◑ VISA JCB
122 rm 52.50 **st.**

The Edwardian without rest., 30-32 Heavitree Rd, EX1 2LQ, ☎ (01392) 276102, *edwar x@globalnet.co.uk, Fax (01392) 253393* – TV. MC AE VISA JCB V
closed 25 and 26 December – **12 rm** ☕ 36.00/56.00 **st.**

Travel Inn, 398 Topsham Rd, EX2 6HE, ☎ (01392) 875441, *Fax (01392) 876174* – ⇔ r TV ♿ P. MC AE ◑ VISA. ✻ X
Meals (grill rest.) – **45 rm** 40.95 **t.**

The Grange ⛇ without rest., Stoke Hill, EX4 7JH, North : 1 ¾ m. by Old Tiverton R ☎ (01392) 259723, *dudleythegrange@aol.com,* heated, – ⇔ TV P. ✻
3 rm ☕ 25.00/42.00 **st.**

Raffles, 11 Blackall Rd, EX4 4HD, ☎ (01392) 270200, *raffleshtl@btinternet.co Fax (01392) 270200* – ⇔ rest, TV. MC AE VISA V
Meals (by arrangement) 17.00 **st.** 3.50 – **6 rm** ☕ 34.00/48.00 **st.**

Michael Caines (at The Royal Clarence H.), Cathedral Yard, EX1 1HD, ☎ (01392) 31003 *ables@michaelcaines.com, Fax (01392) 310032* – ⇔ ▤. MC AE ◑ VISA Y
Meals 17.00 **t.** (lunch) and a la carte 22.80/28.00 **t.** 11.95.

Brazz, 10-12 Palace Gate, EX1 1JA, ☎ (01392) 252525, *Fax (01392) 253045* – ▤. MC VISA Z
closed 25 December – **Meals** a la carte 15.85/32.85 **t.** 6.75.

at Stoke Canon *North : 5 m. by A 377 off A 396* – V – ✉ *Exeter.*

Barton Cross ⛇, Huxham, EX5 4EJ, East : ½ m. on Huxham rd ☎ (01392) 8412 *Fax (01392) 841942,* « Part 17C thatched cottages », – ⇔ rest, TV P. MC AE VISA JCB
Meals (dinner only) 20.50/25.00 **t.** 6.00 – **8 rm** ☕ 65.50/90.00 **t.** – SB.

at Whimple *Northeast : 9 m. by A 30* – V – ✉ *Exeter.*

Woodhayes ⛇, EX5 2TD, ☎ (01404) 822237, *info@woodhayes-hotel.co. Fax (01404) 822337,* « Georgian country house », – ⇔ TV P. MC AE ◑ VISA. ✻
Meals (booking essential) (dinner only) (set menu only) 30.00 **t.** 8.50 – **6 rm** ☕ 65.0 90.00 **t.**

at Kennford *South : 5 m. on A 30 off A 38* – X – ✉ *Exeter.*

Fairwinds, EX6 7UD, ☎ (01392) 832911, *Fax (01392) 832911* – ⇔ TV P. MC VISA. ✻
closed mid November-December – **Meals** (residents only) (dinner only) a la carte 12.9 14.85 4.50 – **6 rm** ☕ 37.00/50.00 – SB.

at Doddiscombsleigh *Southwest : 10 m. by B 3212 off B 3193* – X – ✉ *Exeter.*

Nobody Inn, EX6 7PS, ☎ (01647) 252394, *inn.nobody@virgin.net, Fax (01647) 252978,* « Part 16C », – P. MC AE VISA
closed 25-26 December – **Meals** a la carte 12.40/19.50 **t.** 3.50.

XETER SERVICE AREA *Devon* 403 J 31 – ✉ *Exeter.*

Travelodge, Moor Lane, Sandygate, EX2 4AR, M 5 junction 30 ℘ (01392) 74044, *Fax (01392) 410406* – ⇔ rm, TV & P – 70. MO AE ① VISA JCB. ⚘
Meals (grill rest.) – **76 rm** 59.95 **t.**

XFORD *Somerset* 403 J 30 *The West Country G.*
See : *Church★.*
Env. : *Exmoor National Park★★.*
London 193 – Exeter 41 – Minehead 14 – Taunton 33.

Crown, TA24 7PP, ℘ (01643) 831554, *bradleyhotelsexmoor@easynet.co.uk, Fax (01643) 831665,* « Attractively furnished country inn, water garden », – TV P. MO AE VISA
Meals (in bar) a la carte 14.00/21.25 **t.** 6.00 – (see also ***The Restaurant*** below) – **17 rm** 47.50/116.00 **t.** – SB.

The Restaurant (at Crown H.), TA24 7PP, ℘ (01643) 831554, *Fax (01643) 831665* – P. MO AE VISA
Meals (dinner only and Sunday lunch)/dinner 25.00 **t.** 6.50.

XMOUTH *Devon* 403 J 32 *The West Country G.* *pop. 30 386.*
Env. : *A la Ronde★ AC, N : 2 m. by B 3180.*
Alexandra Terr. ℘ (01395) 222299.
London 210 – Exeter 11.

Barn ⚘, Foxholes Hill, EX8 2DF, East : 1 m. via Esplanade and Queens Drive ℘ (01395) 224411, *Fax (01395) 225445,* ≤, heated, – ⇔ TV P – 50. MO AE ① VISA. ⚘
closed 24 December-2 January – **Meals** (dinner only and Sunday lunch)/dinner 15.00 **st.** 5.50 – **11 rm** 34.00/68.00 **st.**

Lympstone *North : 3 m. by A 376 – ✉ Exmouth.*

River House with rm, The Strand, EX8 5EY, ℘ (01395) 265147, *theriverhouse@talk21.com,* ≤ Exe Estuary – ⇔ rest, TV. MO AE VISA. ⚘
closed 26-28 December, 1-2 January and Bank Holiday Monday – **Meals** *(closed Sunday and Monday to non-residents)* 15.00/37.00 **t.** and lunch a la carte 7.50 – 7.00 – **3 rm** 62.00/108.00 **t.** – SB.

YE *Cambs.* 402 404 T 26 – *see Peterborough.*

YNSHAM *Oxon.* 403 404 P 28 – *pop. 4 764.*
London 65 – Gloucester 40 – Oxford 8.

Off the Square, 4 Lombard St., OX8 1HT, ℘ (01865) 881888, *christiano.butler@virgin.net, Fax (01865) 883537* – ⇔ P. AE ① VISA
closed first week September, first 2 weeks January, Sunday dinner and Monday – **Meals** 19.50/31.00 **t.** 12.00.

ADMOOR *N. Yorks.* – *see Kirkbymoorside.*

AKENHAM *Norfolk* 404 W 25 – *pop. 6 471.*
Fakenham, The Racecourse ℘ (01328) 862867.
Red Lion House, Market Pl. ℘ (01328) 851981.
London 111 – Cambridge 64 – Norwich 27.

Sculthorpe Mill ⚘, Lynn Rd, Sculthorpe, NR21 9QG, West : 2 ½ m. by A 148 ℘ (01328) 856161, *Fax (01328) 856651,* ≤, « Converted late 18C watermill », – ⇔ TV P. MO AE VISA
Meals (bar lunch)/dinner 15.00 **t.** and a la carte – **6 rm** 50.00/60.00 **t.** – SB.

ALFIELD *South Gloucestershire* 403 404 M 29.
London 132 – Bristol 16 – Gloucester 22.

Gables, Bristol Rd, GL12 8DL, North : ½ m. on A 38 ℘ (01454) 260502, *Fax (01454) 261821,* – ⇔ rest, TV & P – 150. MO AE ① VISA. ⚘
Meals (bar lunch)/dinner 16.50 **t.** and a la carte 5.25 – 7.25 – **32 rm** 71.50/85.00 **st.**

FALMOUTH

Street	Grid	No.
Arwenack Street	B	2
Avenue Road	B	3
Beacon Road	A	4
Belmont Road	A	7
Berkeley Vale	A	8
Boscawen Road	A	9
Budock Terrace	A	13
Church Street	B	
Conway Road	A	14
De Pass Road	B	15
Emslie Road	B	18
Fenwick Road	A	19
Glasney Road	A	20
Grovehill Crescent	B	23
Gyllyngvase Hill	B	24
Gyllyngvase Road	B	25
High Street	A	
Kimberley Place	A	28
Langton Road	A	29
Madeira Walk	A	30
Market Street	A	33
Marlborough Crescent	A	34
Park Terrace	A	35
Pendennis Road	B	38
Swanpool Road	A	39
Symons Hill	A	40
Tredova Crescent	A	43
Trescobeas Road	A	44
Wellington Terrace	A	45
Windsor Terrace	A	48
Wodehouse Terrace	A	49

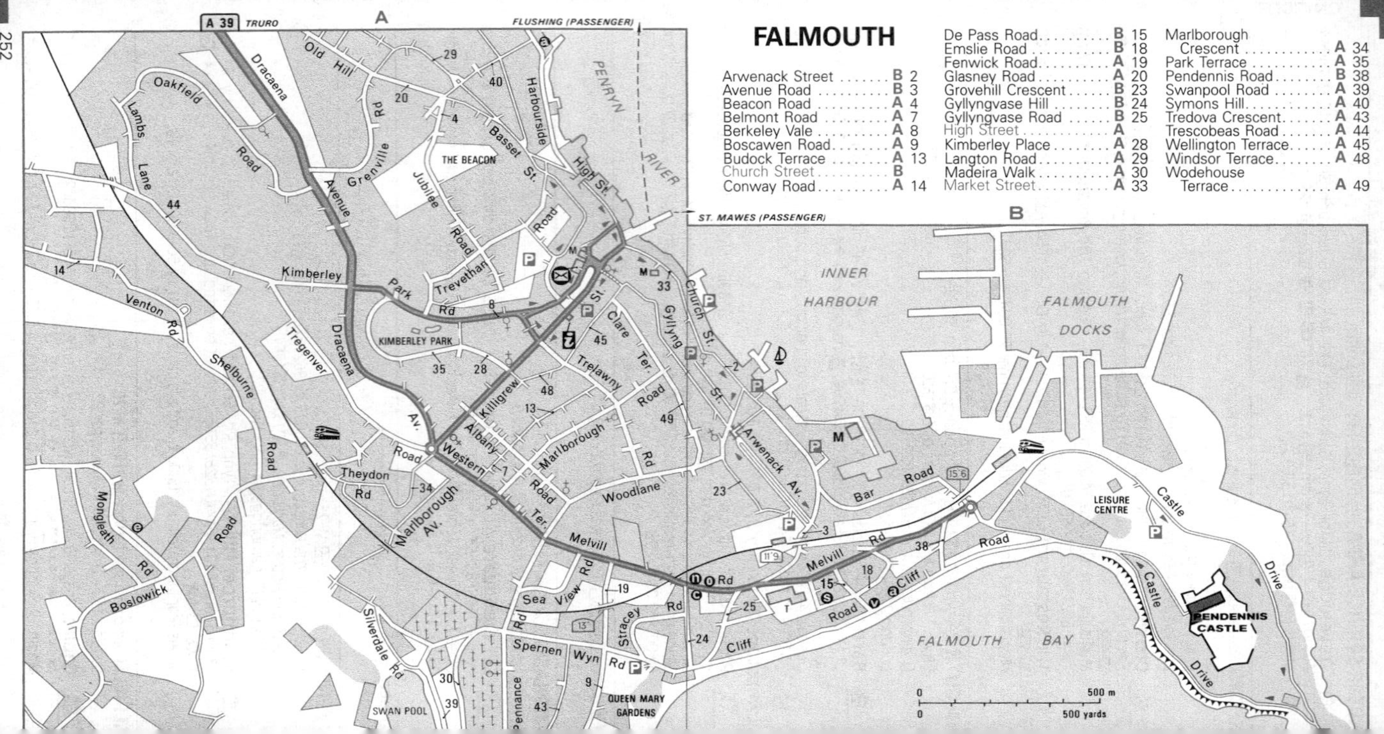

FALMOUTH Cornwall 403 E 33 *The West Country G.* – pop. 19 217.

See : *Town*★ – *Pendennis Castle*★ (≤★★) **AC** B.

Env. : *Glendurgan Garden*★★ **AC** – *Trebah Garden*★, SW : 4 ½ m. by Swanpool Rd A – *Mawnan Parish Church*★ (≤★★) S : 4 m. by Swanpool Rd A – *Cruise along Helford River*★.

Exc. : *Trelissick*★★ (≤★★) NW : 13 m. by A 39 and B 3289 A – *Carn Brea* (≤★★) NW : 10 m. by A 393 A – *Gweek (Setting*★, *Seal Sanctuary*★) SW : 8 m. by A 39 and Treverva rd – *Wendron (Poldark Mine*★) **AC**, SW : 12½ m. by A 39 – A – and A 394.

18 Swanpool Rd ℘ (01326) 311262 A – 9 Budock Vean Hotel, Mawnan Smith ℘ (01326) 250892.

28 Killigrew St. ℘ (01326) 312300.

London 308 – Penzance 26 – Plymouth 65 – Truro 11.

Plan opposite

Royal Duchy, Cliff Rd, TR11 4NX, ℘ (01326) 313042, *info@royalduchy.co.uk, Fax (01326) 319420*, ≤, – MO AE VISA. B a
Meals 9.95/22.00 **t.** and a la carte 5.50 – **42 rm** 70.00/192.00 **t.**, 1 suite – SB.

Greenbank, Harbourside, TR11 2SR, ℘ (01326) 312440, *thegreenbankhotel@btinternet.com, Fax (01326) 211362*, ≤ harbour – – 160. MO AE VISA A a
***Conservatory :* Meals** a la carte 15.75/20.00 **t.** 9.75 – **60 rm** 72.00/145.00 **t.**, 1 suite.

Penmere Manor, Mongleath Rd, TR11 4PN, ℘ (01326) 211411, *reservations@penmere.co.uk, Fax (01326) 317588*, heated, – – 60. MO AE VISA
closed 24 to 27 December – ***Bolitho's :* Meals** (bar lunch)/dinner 19.00/22.00 **t.** 6.50 – **37 rm** 60.50/119.00 **t.** – SB. A e

Carthion, Cliff Rd, TR11 4AP, ℘ (01326) 313669, *info@carthion.f9.co.uk, Fax (01326) 212828*, ≤, – MO AE VISA. B v
closed 22 December-31 January – **Meals** (bar lunch Monday to Saturday)/dinner 8.00/14.00 **t.** and a la carte 5.25 – **18 rm** 51.00/88.00 **t.** – SB.

Prospect House without rest., 1 Church Rd, Penryn, TR10 8DA, Northwest : 2 m. by A 39 on B 3292 ℘ (01326) 373198, *bbudd@freeuk.com, Fax (01326) 373198*, – MO VISA
3 rm 30.00/55.00.

Rosemullion without rest., Gyllyngvase Hill, TR11 4DF, ℘ (01326) 314690, *gail@rosemullionhotel.demon.co.uk, Fax (01326) 210098* – . B c
closed Christmas – **13 rm** 25.00/50.00 **t.**

Melvill House, 52 Melvill Rd, TR11 4DQ, ℘ (01326) 316645, *crawfords@crawfords.eurobell.co.uk, Fax (01326) 211608* – MO VISA. B o
Meals (by arrangement) 9.50 **s.** 3.50 – **7 rm** 25.00/49.00.

Dolvean without rest., 50 Melvill Rd, TR11 4DQ, ℘ (01326) 313658, *reservations@dolvean.freeserve.co.uk, Fax (01326) 313995* – MO AE VISA JCB. B n
closed Christmas – **12 rm** 30.00/60.00 **st.**

Chelsea House, 2 Emslie Rd, TR11 4BG, ℘ (01326) 212230, *info@chelseahousehotel.com, Fax (01326) 212230*, ≤, – MO VISA. B s
closed December – **Meals** (by arrangement) 9.95 **st.** 4.25 – **7 rm** 24.00/48.00 **s.** – SB.

at Mylor Bridge *North : 4½ m. by A 39 and B 3292 on Mylor rd – A – ✉ Falmouth.*

Pandora Inn, Restronguet Creek, TR11 5ST, Northeast : 1 m. by Passage Hill off Restronguet Hill ℘ (01326) 372678, *Fax (01326) 372678*, ≤, « Thatched inn of 13C origins » – MO VISA
Meals (bar lunch)/dinner a la carte 16.80/24.30 **t.**

at Mawnan Smith *Southwest : 5 m. by Trescobeas Rd – A – ✉ Falmouth.*

Meudon, TR11 5HT, East : ½ m. by Carwinion Rd ℘ (01326) 250541, *info@meudon.co.uk, Fax (01326) 250543*, « Landscaped sub-tropical gardens », – MO AE VISA
closed 2 January-13 February – **Meals** 12.50/25.00 **st.** and a la carte 7.00 – **27 rm** (dinner included) 95.00/190.00 **t.**, 2 suites – SB.

Trelawne, Maenporth, TR11 5HS, East : ¾ m. by Carwinion Rd ℘ (01326) 250226, *Fax (01326) 250909*, ≤, – MO AE VISA
closed 19 December-12 February – ***The Hutches :* Meals** (bar lunch)/dinner 19.50/24.50 **t.** 5.90 – **14 rm** (dinner included) 48.00/96.00 **t.** – SB.

at Budock Water *West : 2¼ m. by Trescobeas Rd – A – ✉ Falmouth.*

Crill Manor, TR11 5BL, South : ¾ m. ℘ (01326) 211880, *Fax (01326) 211229*, – MO AE VISA JCB
Meals (dinner only and Sunday lunch)/dinner 19.50 **st.** 5.95 – **14 rm** 43.00/86.00 **st.** – SB.

FAREHAM *Hants.* 403 404 Q 31 *Great Britain G. – pop. 54 866 (inc. Portchester).*
Env. : *Portchester castle★ AC, SE : 2½ m. by A 27.*
Westbury Manor, West St. (01329) 221342.
London 77 – Portsmouth 9 – Southampton 13 – Winchester 19.

Solent, Rookery Av., Whiteley, PO15 7AJ, Northwest : 5 m. by A 27 (01489) 880000, *so nt@shireinns.co.uk, Fax (01489) 880007,* , , , , , , squash – , rm, – 250. AE VISA
Meals a la carte 26.00/36.00 **st.** – **117 rm** 122.00/142.00 **st.** – SB.

Posthouse Fareham, Cartwright Drive, Titchfield, PO15 5RJ, West : 2 ¾ m. on A 2 (0870) 400 9028, *Fax (01329) 844666,* , , – rm, – 140. AE VISA JCB.
Meals 15.00 **t.** (dinner) and a la carte 14.15/27.35 **t.** 6.95 – 11.95 – **125 rm** 99.00 **t.** SB.

Red Lion, East St., PO16 0BP, (01329) 822640, *Fax (01329) 823579,* – – 80. AE VISA.
Meals (bar lunch Monday to Saturday)/dinner a la carte 10.70/17.45 **t.** – **42 rm** 62.50 75.00 **t.**

Lysses House, 51 High St., PO16 7BQ, (01329) 822622, *lysses@lysses.co.u Fax (01329) 822762,* – , rest, – 100. AE VISA.
closed Christmas – ***The Richmond :*** **Meals** *(closed Saturday lunch, Sunday and Bar Holidays)* 13.95/19.50 **st.** and a la carte 6.70 – **21 rm** 65.00/80.00 **st.**

Avenue House without rest., 22 The Avenue, PO14 1NS, West : ½ m. on A 2 (01329) 232175, *Fax (01329) 232196,* – . AE VISA.
closed Christmas and New Year – **19 rm** 49.50/75.00 **t.**

Travel Inn, Southampton Rd, Park Gate, SO3 6AF, West : 4 m. by A 27 (01489) 57985 *Fax (01489) 577238* – rm, . AE VISA.
Meals (grill rest.) – **40 rm** 40.95 **t.**

Springfield without rest., 67 The Avenue, PO14 1PE, West : 1 m. on A 2 (01329) 828325, – . VISA.
closed 2 weeks Christmas – **6 rm** 45.00/52.00 **st.**

FARINGDON *Oxon.* 403 404 P 29.
7A Market Pl. (01367) 242191.
London 81 – Oxford 19 – Newbury 29 – Swindon 12.

The Trout at Tadpole Bridge, Buckland Marsh, SN7 8RF, Northeast : 4 ½ m. by A 4 off A 420 on Bampton rd (01367) 870382, *hammick@troutinn.freeserve.co.u Fax (01367) 870515,* – . AE VISA
closed 25 December-1 January and Sunday dinner – **Meals** a la carte 15.90/24.85 **t.** 4.50

FARNBOROUGH *Hants.* 404 R 30 – *pop. 52 535.*
Southwood, Ively Rd (01252) 548700.
London 41 – Reading 17 – Southampton 44 – Winchester 33.

Posthouse Farnborough, Lynchford Rd, GU14 6AZ, South : 1 ½ m. on A 3 (0870) 400 9029, *Fax (01252) 377210,* , , – rm, rest, – 11 AE VISA
Meals *(closed Saturday lunch)* 15.00 **st.** (lunch) and a la carte 16.85/19.15 **st.** 7.50 – 11.95 – **143 rm** 129.00 **st.** – SB.

Falcon, 68 Farnborough Rd, GU14 6TH, South : ¾ m. on A 325 (01252) 545378, *falcor meridianleisure.com, Fax (01252) 522539* – . AE VISA.
Meals *(closed lunch Saturday and Sunday)* 14.50/19.50 **st.** and a la carte 7.00 – **30 r** 82.50/95.50 **st.**

Travel Inn, Ively Rd, Southwood, GU14 0JP, Southwest : 2 m. by A 325 on A 3 (01252) 546654, *Fax (01252) 546427* – rm, . AE VISA JCB.
Meals (grill rest.) – **40 rm** 40.95 **t.**

Wings Cottage, 32 Alexandra Rd, GU14 6DA, South : 1 ¼ m. by A 325 off Boundary (01252) 544141, *Fax (01252) 519071* – . AE VISA JCB
Meals - Chinese - 20.00/25.00 **st.** and a la carte 4.50.

FARNHAM *Surrey* 404 R 30 – *pop. 36 178.*

Farnham Park (Par Three) *(01252) 715216.*

Locality Office, South St. *(01252) 715109.*

London 45 – Reading 22 – Southampton 39 – Winchester 28.

Bush, The Borough, GU9 7NN, (0870) 4008225, *heritagehotels-farnham.bush@forte-hotels.com, Fax (01252) 733530,* – – 60. VISA JCB
Thackeray's : **Meals** a la carte 15.15/29.35 **t.** 6.50 – 12.50 – **83 rm** 145.00/189.75 – SB.

Bishop's Table, 27 West St., GU9 7DR, (01252) 710222, *welcome@bishopstable.com, Fax (01252) 733494,* – rest, . VISA.
closed 25 December-4 January – **Meals** *(closed lunch Saturday and Bank Holidays)* 22.50/28.50 **t.** and a la carte 9.00 – **17 rm** 95.00/115.00 **t.** – SB.

FARRINGTON GURNEY *Bath & North East Somerset* 403 404 M 30 *The West Country G.* – *pop. 780* – Bristol.

Env. : *Downside Abbey★ (Abbey Church★) SE : 5 m. by A 37 and B 3139.*

Exc. : *Wells★★ - Cathedral★★★, Vicars' Close★, Bishop's Palace★ AC (≤★★) SW : 8 m. by A 39 – Chew Magna★ (Stanton Drew Stone Circles★ AC) NW : 9½ m. by A 37 and B 3130.*

London 132 – Bath 13 – Bristol 12 – Wells 8.

Country Ways, Marsh Lane, BS39 6TT, off A 362 (01761) 452449, *janet.richards@ukonline.co.uk, Fax (01761) 452706,* – rest, . VISA.
closed 1 week Christmas – **Meals** *(closed Sunday)* (dinner only) a la carte 19.70/26.50 **t.** 9.00 – **6 rm** 65.00/100.00 **st.**

FAR SAWREY *Cumbria* 402 L 20 – *see Hawkshead.*

FAVERSHAM *Kent* 404 W 30 – *pop. 17 070.*

Fleur de Lis Heritage Centre, 13 Preston St. *(01795) 534542.*

London 52 – Dover 26 – Maidstone 21 – Margate 25.

Preston Lea without rest., Canterbury Rd, ME13 8XA, East : 1 m. on A 2 (01795) 535266, *preston.lea@which.net, Fax (01795) 533388,* « Late 19C neo-Gothic house », – . VISA JCB.
3 rm 35.00/52.00 **st.**

Albion Tavern, Front Brents, Faversham Creek, ME13 7DH, (01795) 591411, *patrickcoevoet@freeuk.com,* – . VISA
*closed Sunday dinner***Meals** (booking essential) a la carte 17.95/26.15 **t.** 6.95.

at Dargate *East : 6 m. by A 2 off A 299 – Faversham.*

Dove Inn, Plum Pudding Lane, ME13 9HB, (01227) 751360, *Fax (01227) 751360,* – . VISA JCB
closed Monday and dinner Sunday and Tuesday – **Meals** a la carte 18.00/25.00 **st.**

at Boughton *Southeast : 3 m. by A 2 – Faversham.*

The Garden, 167-169 The Street, ME13 9BH, (01227) 751411, *garden-hotel@lineone.net, Fax (01227) 751801,* – rest, . VISA JCB
Meals 14.50/19.95 **t.** and a la carte 6.50 – **10 rm** 50.00/70.00 **t.** – SB.

at Painter's Forstal *Southwest : 2¼ m. by A 2 and Brogdale Rd – Faversham.*

XXX **Read's** (Pitchford), ME13 0EE, (01795) 535344, *Fax (01795) 591200,* , – . VISA JCB
closed Sunday and Monday – **Meals** 18.50/24.00-38.00 **t.** 8.00
Spec. Selection of Whitstable smoked haddock dishes. Roast loin of lamb with wild mushroom crust, pea purée, rosemary jus. Harlequin soufflé, chocolate and vanilla ice cream.

at Eastling *Southwest : 5 m. by A 2 – Faversham.*

Frith Farm House , Otterden, ME13 0DD, Southwest : 2 m. by Otterden rd on Newnham rd (01795) 890701, *markham@frith.force9.co.uk, Fax (01795) 890009,* – . VISA.
Meals (by arrangement) (communal dining) 22.00 – **3 rm** 38.00/64.00.

FAWKHAM GREEN *Kent* 404 (44) – *see Brands Hatch.*

FEERING *Essex* 404 W 28.
London 56 – Braintree 10 – Chelmsford 23 – Colchester 14.

Travelodge, London Rd, CO5 9EL, on A 12 (northbound carriageway) (01376) 57284[8] *Fax (01376) 572848* – rm, TV, P. MC AE VISA JCB.
Meals (grill rest.) – **39 rm** 39.95 **t.**

FELIXSTOWE *Suffolk* 404 Y 28 – *pop. 28 606.*
18, 9 *Felixstowe Ferry, Ferry Rd (01394) 283060.*
Leisure Centre, Undercliff Road West (01394) 276770.
London 84 – Ipswich 11.

Orwell, Hamilton Rd, IP11 7DX, (01394) 285511, *Fax (01394) 670687*, – res TV P – 250. MC AE VISA.
Meals 14.00/16.50 **st.** and a la carte 6.95 – 9.25 – **57 rm** 62.50/75.00 **st.**, 1 suite – SB.

FELTON *Herefordshire* 403 404 M 27 – *pop. 93.*
London 130 – Birmingham 54 – Hereford 14 – Shrewsbury 50 – Worcester 27.

Felton House without rest., HR1 3PH, (01432) 820366, *bandb@ereal.ne* *Fax (01432) 820366*, – P
closed Christmas – **4 rm** 23.00/46.00 **s.**

FERMAIN BAY *Guernsey (Channel Islands)* 403 P 33 and 230 ⑩ – *see Channel Islands.*

FERNDOWN *Dorset* 403 404 O 31 – *pop. 25 177.*
18 *Ferndown Forest, Forest Links Rd (01202) 876096.*
London 108 – Bournemouth 6 – Dorchester 27 – Salisbury 23.

The Dormy, New Rd, BH22 8ES, on A 347 (01202) 872121, *devere.dormy@airtime.co k, Fax (01202) 895388*, 18, squash – TV P – 250. MC VISA
Hennessys :* Meals** *(closed Saturday lunch, Sunday and Monday)* (dancing Saturday eve ning) 22.50/30.00 **st.** (dinner) and a la carte 18.40/33.50 **st.** – ***Garden :* Meals** *(closed Sa urday lunch)* (carvery) 8.00/25.00 **st.** – ***Pavilion Brasserie : Meals *closed 25 Decemb* a la carte 15.40/19.95 **st.** – **109 rm** 110.00/145.00 **st.**, 5 suites – SB.

Travel Inn, Ringwood Rd, Tricketts Cross, BH22 9BB, Northeast : 1 m. on A 34 (01202) 874210, *Fax (01202) 897794* – rm, TV P. MC AE VISA.
Meals (grill rest.) – **32 rm** 40.95 **t.**

FERNHURST *W. Sussex* 404 R 30.
London 50 – Southampton 46 – Brighton 40.

King's Arms, Midhurst Rd, GU27 3HA, South : 1 m. on A 286 (01428) 652005, – MC VISA
closed first 2 weeks January and Sunday dinner – **Meals** a la carte 19.00/22.25 **t.**

FERRENSBY *N. Yorks.* – *see Knaresborough.*

FERRYBRIDGE SERVICE AREA *W. Yorks.* 402 Q 22 – Leeds.
London 178 – Leeds 14 – Doncaster 14 – Rotherham 28 – York 28.

Travelodge, WF11 0AF, at junction 33 of M 62 with A 1 (01977) 6727[6] *Fax (01977) 622509* – TV P. MC AE VISA JCB.
Meals (grill rest.) – **36 rm** 49.95 **t.**

FERSFIELD *Norfolk* – *see Diss.*

FILEY *N. Yorks.* 402 T 21 – *pop. 6 619.*
London 238 – Kingston-upon-Hull 42 – Leeds 68 – Middlesbrough 58.

White Lodge, The Crescent, YO14 9JX, (01723) 514771, *white.lodge@lineone.n* *Fax (01723) 516590*, – TV P. MC VISA
Meals (bar lunch Monday to Saturday)/dinner 14.50 **t.** and a la carte 4.95 – **20 r** 47.00/94.00 **t.** – SB.

Downcliffe House, The Beach, YO14 9LA, (01723) 513310, *paulmanners@btintern com, Fax (01723) 513773*, – rest, TV P. MC VISA.
closed January – **Meals** a la carte 13.70/19.75 **t.** 5.25 – **11 rm** (dinner included) 51.0 102.00 **t.** – SB.

ILTON *Bristol* 403 404 M 29 – *see Bristol.*

INDON *W. Sussex* 404 S 31 – *pop. 1 776* – ✉ *Worthing.*
London 49 – Brighton 13 – Southampton 50 – Worthing 4.

Findon Manor, High St., BN14 0TA, off A 24 ☎ (01903) 872733, *findon@dircon.co.uk, Fax (01903) 877473,* « Part 16C stone and flint house », – rest, TV P – 40. MC AE VISA.
Meals 18.95/24.00 **t.** 6.95 – **11 rm** 53.00/110.00 **t.** – SB.

INEDON *Northants.* 404 S 26 – *see Wellingborough.*

LAMSTEAD *Herts.* 404 S 28 – *pop. 1 399* – ✉ *St. Albans.*
London 32 – Luton 5.

Hertfordshire Moat House, London Rd, AL3 8HH, on A 5 ☎ (01582) 449988, *Fax (01582) 449041,* – rest, TV P – 180. MC AE VISA JCB.
– **Meals** 22.00/35.00 **st.** – 11.50 – **140 rm** 104.00/138.00 **st.** – SB.

LEET *Hants.* 404 R 30 – *pop. 30 391.*
North Hants, Minley Rd ☎ (01252) 616443.
The Harlington Centre, 236 Fleet Rd ☎ (01252) 811151.
London 40 – Basingstoke 11 – Reading 17.

Lismoyne, Church Rd, GU13 8NA, ☎ (01252) 628555, *Fax (01252) 811761,* – rest, rest, TV P – 100. MC AE VISA.
Meals *(closed Sunday dinner)* 10.00/18.50 **st.** and dinner a la carte 5.50 – **44 rm** 85.00/110.00 **st.**

LEET SERVICE AREA *Hants.* 404 R 30 – ✉ *Basingstoke.*

Days Inn (without rest.), Hartley Witney, RG27 8BN, M 3 between junctions 4a and 5 (southbound carriageway) ☎ (01252) 815587, Reservations (Freephone) 0800 0280400, *Fax (01252) 815587* – TV P. MC AE VISA JCB
7.45 – **58 rm** 55.00/60.00 **t.**

LEETWOOD *Lancs.* 402 K 22 – *pop. 27 227.*
Fleetwood, Golf House, Princes Way ☎ (01253) 873114.
to Northern Ireland (Larne) (P & O Irish Sea) daily (8 h).
Old Ferry Office, The Esplanade ☎ (01253) 773953.
London 245 – Blackpool 10 – Lancaster 28 – Manchester 53.

North Euston, The Esplanade, FY7 6BN, ☎ (01253) 876525, *admin@northeustonhotel.co.uk, Fax (01253) 777842,* – TV P – 150. MC AE VISA.
Meals *(closed Saturday lunch)* 7.25/19.25 **t.** and a la carte 7.50 – **53 rm** 56.00/104.00 **t.** – SB.

LETCHING *E. Sussex* 404 U 30/31 – *pop. 1 722.*
London 45 – Brighton 20 – Eastbourne 24 – Maidstone 20.

The Griffin Inn with rm, TN22 3SS, ☎ (01825) 722890, *Fax (01825) 722810,* « 16C coaching inn », – rm, TV P. MC AE VISA.
closed 25 December – **Meals** (meals in bar Sunday dinner in winter) a la carte 17.50/22.95 **t.** 10.50 – **8 rm** 60.00/95.00 **st.**

LITWICK *Beds.* 404 S 27 – *pop. 11 063.*
London 45 – Bedford 13 – Luton 12 – Northampton 28.

Flitwick Manor, Church Rd, MK45 1AE, off Dunstable Rd ☎ (01525) 712242, *flitwick@menzies-hotels.co.uk, Fax (01525) 718753,* « 18C manor house », – TV P. MC AE VISA JCB
Meals 19.50/35.50 **t.** and dinner a la carte 9.00 – 14.00 – **17 rm** 120.00/195.00 **t.** – SB.

This Guide is not a comprehensive list of all hotels and restaurants, nor even of all good hotels and restaurants in Great Britain and Ireland.

Since our aim is to be of service to all motorists, we must show establishments in all categories and so we have made a selection of some in each.

FLORE *Northants.* 403 404 *Q 27 – see Daventry.*

FOLKESTONE *Kent* 404 *X 30 Great Britain G. – pop. 45 587.*

See : *The Leas★ (≤★) Z.*

Channel Tunnel : Eurotunnel information and reservations ☎ (0990) 353535.

to France (Boulogne) (Hoverspeed Ltd) 4 daily (55 mn).

Harbour St. ☎ (01303) 258594.

London 76 – Brighton 76 – Dover 8 – Maidstone 33.

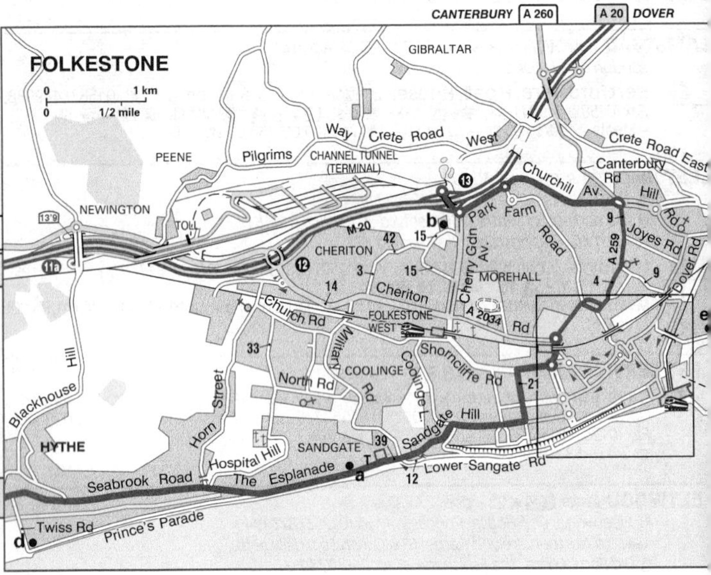

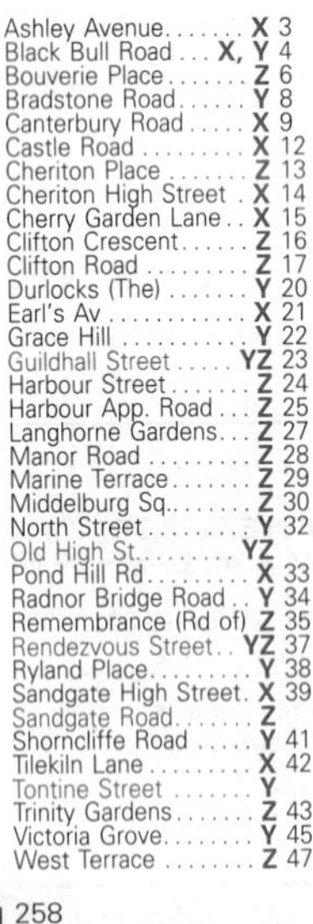

Ashley Avenue .... X 3
Black Bull Road ... X, Y 4
Bouverie Place .... Z 6
Bradstone Road ...... Y 8
Canterbury Road ..... X 9
Castle Road .... X 12
Cheriton Place .... Z 13
Cheriton High Street . X 14
Cherry Garden Lane .. X 15
Clifton Crescent ...... Z 16
Clifton Road .... Z 17
Durlocks (The) .... Y 20
Earl's Av .... X 21
Grace Hill .... Y 22
Guildhall Street ..... YZ 23
Harbour Street .... Z 24
Harbour App. Road ... Z 25
Langhorne Gardens ... Z 27
Manor Road .... Z 28
Marine Terrace .... Z 29
Middelburg Sq. .... Z 30
North Street .... Y 32
Old High St. .... YZ
Pond Hill Rd. .... X 33
Radnor Bridge Road .. Y 34
Remembrance (Rd of) Z 35
Rendezvous Street .. YZ 37
Ryland Place .... Y 38
Sandgate High Street. X 39
Sandgate Road .... Z
Shorncliffe Road ..... Y 41
Tilekiln Lane .... X 42
Tontine Street .... Y
Trinity Gardens ...... Z 43
Victoria Grove .... Y 45
West Terrace .... Z 47

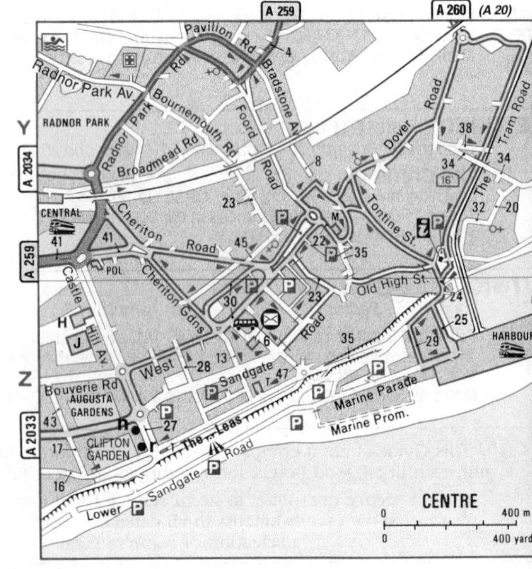

Clifton, The Leas, CT20 2EB, ✆ (01303) 851231, *reservations@thecliftonhotel.com, Fax (01303) 223949,* ← – |♦| TV – 80. MC AE ⓓ VISA Z r
Meals 10.50/19.00 **t.** and a la carte 4.75 – 8.50 – **80 rm** 52.00/85.00 **t.** – SB.

Travel Inn, Cherry Garden Lane, CT19 4AP, Northwest : 1 ¼ m. by A 259 at junction 13 of M 20 ✆ (01303) 273620, *Fax (01303) 273641* – rm, TV P. MC AE ⓓ VISA. X b
Meals (grill rest.) – **40 rm** 40.95 **t.**

Harbourside without rest., 13-14 Wear Bay Rd, CT19 6AT, ✆ (01303) 256528, *r.pye@lineone.net, Fax (01303) 241299,* ←, – TV. MC AE ⓓ VISA. X e
7 rm 50.00/90.00 **s.**

La Tavernetta, Leaside Court, Clifton Gdns., CT20 2ED, ✆ (01303) 254955, *Fax (01303) 244732* – MC AE VISA JCB Z n
closed Sunday and Bank Holidays – **Meals** - Italian - 9.50 **t.** (lunch) and a la carte 15.70/21.40 **t.** 5.90.

at Sandgate *West : 1 ¾ m. on A 259 – ✉ Folkestone.*

Sandgate, The Esplanade, CT20 3DY, West : ½ m. ✆ (01303) 220444, *Fax (01303) 220496,* ← – |♦| TV. MC AE ⓓ VISA. X a
closed 4 weeks January and first week October – **Meals** – (see ***La Terrasse*** below) – **14 rm** 45.00/76.00 **t.**

La Terrasse (Gicqueau) (at Sandgate H.), The Esplanade, CT20 3DY, West : ½ m. ✆ (01303) 220444, *Fax (01303) 220496,* ← – . MC AE ⓓ VISA X a
closed 4 weeks January, first week October, Monday, Sunday dinner and Tuesday lunch – **Meals** - French - (booking essential) 22.50/31.00 **t.** and a la carte 38.00/43.00 **t.** 8.50
Spec. Pan-fried scallops, potato purée with black truffles. Fillets of sea bass, black truffle coulis and chicory. Valhrona chocolate dessert with almond cream and coffee ice cream.

ONTWELL *W. Sussex* 404 S 31 – ✉ *Arundel.*

Little Chef Complex ✆ (01243) 543269.
London 60 – Chichester 6 – Worthing 15.

Travelodge, BN18 0SB, at A 27/A 29 roundabout ✆ (01243) 543973, *Fax (01243) 543973* – rm, TV P. MC AE ⓓ VISA JCB.
Meals (grill rest.) – **62 rm** 49.95 **t.**

ORD *Wilts. – see Castle Combe.*

ORDINGBRIDGE *Hants.* 403 404 O 31 – *pop. 4 301.*

Town Hall, 63 High St. ✆ (01425) 654560 (summer only).
London 101 – Bournemouth 17 – Salisbury 11 – Winchester 30.

Three Lions with rm, Stuckton Rd, Stuckton, SP6 2HF, Southeast : 1 m. by B 3078 ✆ (01425) 652489, *the3lions@btinternet.com, Fax (01425) 656144,* – rm, TV P. MC VISA.
closed last 2 weeks January and first week February – **Meals** *(closed Sunday dinner and Monday)* a la carte 25.25/29.25 **t.** 9.50 – 5.75 – **3 rm** 75.00/85.00 **st.** – SB.

OREST *Guernsey (Channel Islands)* 403 P 33 and 230 ⑨ ⑩ – *see Channel Islands.*

OREST ROW *E. Sussex* 404 U 30 – *pop. 3 508.*

18, 18 *Royal Ashdown Forest, Chapel Lane, Forest Row ✆ (01342) 822018.*
London 35 – Brighton 26 – Eastbourne 30 – Maidstone 32.

Wych Cross *South : 2½ m. on A 22 – ✉ Forest Row.*

Ashdown Park , RH18 5JR, East : ¾ m. on Hartfield rd ✆ (01342) 824988, *reservation s@ashdownpark.com, Fax (01342) 826206,* ←, « Part 19C manor house in extensive gardens », , , , 18, , – rest, TV P – 150. MC AE ⓓ VISA.
Anderida : **Meals** 23.00/35.00 **st.** and a la carte – **102 rm** 120.00/200.00 **st.**, 5 suites – SB.

ORMBY *Mersey.* 402 K 23 – ✉ *Southport.*

London 213 – Liverpool 14 – Manchester 46 – Preston 27.

Est, Est, Est, 29 Three Tuns Lane, L37 4FB, ✆ (01704) 833775, *Fax (01704) 879168,* – . MC AE ⓓ VISA
Meals - Italian - 10.00 **t.** and a la carte 6.85.

FOULSHAM *Norfolk* 404 X 25 – *pop. 1 379* – ✉ *East Dereham.*
London 121 – Cambridge 69 – King's Lynn 31 – Norwich 18.

XX **The Gamp,** Claypit Lane, NR20 5RW, ☎ (01362) 684114, – P. MC VISA
closed 26 December-12 January, Monday, Sunday dinner and Tuesday lunch – **Meals** 11.95 (lunch) and a la carte 16.55/24.55 **t.** 5.95.

FOUR ELMS *Kent* 404 U 30 – *see Edenbridge.*

FOUR MARKS *Hants.* 403 404 Q 30 – *pop. 3 843 (inc. Medstead)* – ✉ *Alton.*
London 58 – Guildford 24 – Reading 29 – Southampton 24.

Travelodge, 156 Winchester Rd, GU34 5HZ, on A 31 ☎ (01420) 562659 – TV P. MC VISA JCB.
Meals (grill rest.) – **31 rm** 39.95 **t.**

at Lower Wield *Northwest : 4 m. taking Wield rd through Medstead* – ✉ *Four Marks.*

Yew Tree, SO24 9RX, ☎ (01256) 389224, *Fax (01256) 389224*, , – P. MC VISA
Meals 16.95/19.95 **t.** (lunch) and a la carte 18.95/24.50 **t.**

FOWEY *Cornwall* 403 G 32 *The West Country G.* – *pop. 2 123.*
See : *Town*★★.
Env. : *Gribbin Head*★★ (<★★) *6 m. rtn on foot* – *Bodinnick* (<★★) - *Lanteglos Church*★, *E m. by ferry* – *Polruan* (<★★) *SE : 6 m. by ferry* – *Polkerris*★, *W : 2 m. by A 3082.*
4 Custom House Hill ☎ *(01726) 833616.*
London 277 – Newquay 24 – Plymouth 34 – Truro 22.

Fowey Hall , Hanson Drive, PL23 1ET, West : ½ m. off A 3082 ☎ (01726) 8338
Fax (01726) 834100, <, « Part Victorian country house, special facilities for children heated, – rest, TV P – 40. MC AE VISA
Meals (light lunch Monday to Saturday)/dinner 32.50 **t.** 9.50 – **17 rm** 170.00 **t.**, 8 sui – SB.

Marina, 17 The Esplanade, PL23 1HY, ☎ (01726) 833315, *marina.hotel@dial.pipex.co*
Fax (01726) 832779, < Fowey river and harbour, – rest, TV. MC AE VISA
Meals (bar lunch)/dinner 22.00/25.00 **t.** and a la carte 7.45 – **13 rm** 76.00/130.00 **t** SB.

Carnethic House , Lambs Barn, PL23 1HQ, Northwest : ¾ m. on A 30 ☎ (01726) 833336, *carnethic@btinternet.com*, *Fax (01726) 833296*, heated, , rest, TV P. MC AE VISA.
closed December and January – **Meals** (bar lunch)/dinner 16.00 **st.** 5.00 – **8 rm** 40.(75.00 **st.** – SB.

XX **Food for Thought,** The Quay, PL23 1AT, ☎ (01726) 832221, *Fax (01726) 832077*, « converted coastguard's cottage on quayside » – MC VISA
closed Christmas, January, February and Sunday – **Meals** (dinner only) 19.95 **t.** and a la ca 5.95.

at Golant *North : 3 m. by B 3269* – ✉ *Fowey.*

Cormorant , PL23 1LL, ☎ (01726) 833426, *Fax (01726) 833426*, < River Fowey, , – rest, TV P. MC VISA.
Meals (light lunch)/dinner 21.00 **st.** 6.50 – **11 rm** 60.50/96.00 **st.** – SB.

FOWNHOPE *Herefordshire* 403 404 M 27 – *pop. 900* – ✉ *Hereford.*
London 132 – Cardiff 46 – Hereford 6 – Gloucester 27.

Green Man Inn, HR1 4PE, ☎ (01432) 860243, *Fax (01432) 860207*, , , , , rest, TV P. MC AE VISA
Meals (bar lunch Monday-Saturday)/dinner a la carte 15.80/21.05 **t.** 5.85 – **20** 38.75/64.00 **t.** – SB.

FRADDON *Cornwall* 403 F 32 – ✉ *St. Columbus Major.*
London 264 – Exeter 77 – Penzance 35 – Newquay 7 – Plymouth 44 – Truro 12.

Travel Inn, Penhale, TR9 6NA, on A 30 (eastbound carriageway) ☎ (01726) 861
Fax (01726) 861336 – rm, rest, TV P. MC AE VISA.
Meals (grill rest.) – **40 rm** 40.95 **t.**

Le Guide change, changez de **guide Michelin** *tous les ans.*

RAMLINGHAM *Suffolk* 404 Y 27 – *pop. 2 697* – ✉ *Woodbridge.*
London 92 – Ipswich 19 – Norwich 42.

Crown, Market Hill, IP13 9AN, ☎ (01728) 723521, *Fax (01728) 724274,* « 16C inn » – TV P. MC AE VISA JCB
Meals (bar lunch Monday to Saturday)/dinner 8.95/16.95 **t.** and a la carte – **12 rm** 55.00/95.00 **t.** – SB.

Badingham *Northeast : 3 ¼ m. by B 1120 on A 1120* – ✉ *Woodbridge.*

Colston Hall without rest., IP13 8LB, East : ¾ m. by A 1120 on Bruisyard rd ☎ (01728) 638375, *Fax (01728) 638084,* « Working farm », – P.
6 rm 35.00/55.00 **st.**

RAMPTON ON SEVERN *Glos.* 403 404 M 28 – *pop. 1 383.*
London 115 – Bristol 30 – Cardiff 56 – Gloucester 14.

Restaurant on the Green, The Green, GL2 7DY, ☎ (01452) 740077 – MC
closed 25 December, Sunday and Monday – **Meals** (booking essential) (lunch by arrangement)/dinner 23.95.

RANKLEY SERVICE AREA *W. Mids.* 403 404 ⑲ – ✉ *Birmingham.*

Plan : see Birmingham p. 4

Travelodge, B32 4AR, M 5 between junctions 3 and 4 ☎ (0121) 550 3131, *Fax (0121) 501 2880* – TV P. MC AE VISA JCB. BU a
Meals (grill rest.) – **62 rm** 49.95 **t.**

RANT *E. Sussex* 404 U 30 – *see Royal Tunbridge Wells.*

RESHWATER BAY *I.O.W.* 403 404 P 31 – *see Wight (Isle of).*

RILFORD *Oxon.* 403 404 P 28-29 – *see Abingdon.*

RIMLEY *Surrey* 404 R 30 – *pop. 5 661* – ✉ *Camberley.*
London 39 – Reading 17 – Southampton 47.

Toby Carvery and Lodge, 114 Portsmouth Rd, GU15 1HS, Northeast : 1 m. on A 325 ☎ (01276) 691939, Reservations (01738) 444123, *Fax (01276) 605902,* – TV P – 30. MC AE VISA.
Meals (carving rest.) 6.45 **t.** (lunch) and a la carte 10.35/12.00 **t.** 7.25 – **43 rm** 79.95 **t.**

ODSHAM *Ches.* 402 403 404 L 24 – *pop. 8 903* – ✉ *Warrington.*
Frodsham, Simons Lane ☎ (01928) 732159.
London 203 – Chester 11 – Liverpool 21 – Manchester 29 – Stoke-on-Trent 42.

Old Hall, Main St., WA6 7AB, ☎ (01928) 732052, *Fax (01928) 739046,* – rm, TV P – 30. MC AE VISA
Meals 11.95/21.50 **t.** and a la carte 6.50 – **24 rm** 64.50/79.50 **st.**, 1 suite.

Heathercliffe Country House, Manley Rd, WA6 6HB, South : 1 ½ m. by B 5152 ☎ (01928) 733722, *manager@heathercliffe.freeserve.co.uk, Fax (01928) 735667,* – TV P. MC AE VISA JCB
closed 27-28 December and 1 January – **Meals** *(closed Sunday dinner)* 17.50/19.50 **t.** and dinner a la carte 6.50 – **9 rm** 67.50/95.00 **st.** – SB.

OME *Somerset* 403 404 M/N 30.
London 118 – Bristol 24 – Southampton 52 – Swindon 44.

Babington House, Babington, BA11 3RW, Northwest : 6 ½ m. by A 362 on Vobster rd ☎ (01373) 812266, *babhouse@babingtonhouse.co.uk, Fax (01373) 812112,* « Georgian manor house, contemporary interior and informal atmosphere », heated, – TV P – 45. MC AE VISA
Meals a la carte 21.00/32.00 **t.** 6.50 – 10.50 – **27 rm** 150.00/300.00 **t.** – SB.

NTINGTON *W. Sussex* 404 R 31 – *see Chichester.*

GALMPTON *Devon* 403 J 32 – ✉ *Brixham.*
London 229 – Plymouth 32 – Torquay 6.

Maypool Park 🙛, Maypool, TQ5 0ET, Southwest : 1 m. by Greenway R
☎ (01803) 842442, peacock@maypoolpark.co.uk, Fax (01803) 845782, ≤, – ⇋ TV
MC AE VISA. ⧄
Meals (lunch by arrangement in summer) (dinner only and Sunday lunch)/dinner 19.50 s
ⅆ 5.75 – **10 rm** ⊏ 48.00/80.00 **st.** – SB.

GARFORTH *W. Yorks.* 402 P 22 – *see Leeds.*

GARSTANG *Lancs.* 402 L 22 – *pop. 5 697.*
Discovery Centre, Council Offices, High St. ☎ (01995) 602125.
London 233 – Blackpool 13 – Manchester 41.

Garstang Country H. and Golf Club, Bowgreave, PR3 1YE, South : 1 ¼ m. on B 64
☎ (01995) 600100, reception@garstanghotelandgolf.co.uk, Fax (01995) 600950, 18 – |‡|
TV P – 200. MC AE ⓓ VISA. ⧄
Meals 10.95/12.95 **st.** and a la carte ⅆ 4.95 – **32 rm** ⊏ 60.00/80.00 **st.** – SB.

Crofters, Cabus, PR3 1PH, West : ¾ m. on A 6 *☎ (01995) 604128, Fax (01995) 60164*
⇋ rest, TV P – 200. MC AE ⓓ VISA JCB
Meals (dancing Saturday evening) (bar lunch Monday to Saturday)/dinner a la carte 13.8
20.15 **st.** ⅆ 5.50 – ⊏ 6.00 – **19 rm** 40.00/67.00 **st.**

Pickering Park, Garstang Rd, Catterall, PR3 0HD, South : 1 ½ m. on B 64
☎ (01995) 600999, hotel@pickeringpark.demon.co.uk, Fax (01995) 602100, – ⇋ re
TV P – 60. MC AE ⓓ VISA JCB. ⧄
Meals a la carte 17.40/27.95 **t.** – **16 rm** ⊏ 60.00/80.00 **t.** – SB.

at Bilsborrow *South : 3 ¾ m. by B 6430 on A 6 –* ✉ *Preston.*

Guy's Thatched Hamlet, Canalside, St. Michaels Rd, PR3 0RS, off A
☎ (01995) 640010, guyshamlet@aol.com, Fax (01995) 640141 – TV P. MC AE VISA JCB
closed 25 December – **Meals** a la carte 11.50/24.80 **st.** ⅆ 4.50 – ⊏ 5.50 – **53 rm** 42.
56.00 **st.** – SB.

Olde Duncombe House without rest., Garstang Rd, PR3 0RE, ☎ (01995) 6403
Fax (01995) 640336 – TV P. MC AE VISA
9 rm ⊏ 35.00/45.00 **st.**

GATEFORTH *N. Yorks. – pop. 176.*
London 203 – Leeds 22 – Manchester 70 – York 16.

XXX **Restaurant Martel** 🙛, Gateforth Hall, YO8 9LJ, West : ½ m. *☎ (01757) 228225, ma*
@uk.packardbell.org, Fax (01757) 228189, « Early 19C former hunting lodge », – P.
VISA
closed 25 December-4 January, Saturday lunch, Sunday dinner and Monday – **Meals** 14.
17.00 **t.** (lunch) and a la carte 28.50/36.00 **t.** ⅆ 7.00.

GATE SERVICE AREA *Kent* 404 X 30 – *see Canterbury.*

GATESHEAD *Tyne and Wear* 401 402 P 19 *Great Britain G. – pop. 83 159.*
EXC. : *Beamish : North of England Open Air Museum★★ AC, SW : 6 m. by A 692 and A 6*
BX.
18 *Ravensworth, Moss Heaps, Wrekenton ☎ (0191) 487 6014* – 18 *Heworth, Gingling C*
☎ (0191) 469 9832 BX.
Tyne Tunnel (toll).
Central Library, Prince Consort Rd ☎ (0191) 477 3478 BX – *Metrocentre, Portcullis, 7*
Arcade ☎ (0191) 460 6345 AX.
London 282 – Durham 16 – Middlesbrough 38 – Newcastle upon Tyne 1 – Sunderland 1

Plan : see Newcastle upon Tyne

Newcastle Marriott, Cameron Park, Metro Centre, NE11 9XF, West : 5 m. off
☎ (0191) 493 2233, reservation@newcastlemarriott.co.uk, Fax (0191) 493 2030, Fö, ≘s
– |‡|, ⇋ rm, ▤ TV ☏ ♿ P – 450. MC AE ⓓ VISA JCB. ⧄ AX
Meals (bar lunch)/dinner a la carte 19.45/27.40 **st.** – ⊏ 9.95 – **148 rm** 97.00/105.00 **st.**

Gibside Arms, Front St., Whickham, NE16 4JG, ✆ (0191) 488 9292, *reception@gibside_hotel.co.uk, Fax (0191) 488 8000* – ▤ rest, TV ♿ – 120. MO AE ⓓ VISA AX s
Meals (bar lunch Monday to Saturday)/dinner 15.95/19.95 **st.** and a la carte 6.50 – 8.95 – **45 rm** 57.50/69.00 **st.** – SB.

Travel Inn, Derwenthaugh Rd, NE16 3BL, ✆ (0191) 414 6308, *Fax (0191) 414 5032* – , rest, TV ♿ P. MO AE ⓓ VISA AX c
Meals (grill rest.) – **40 rm** 40.95 **t.**

at Low Fell *South : 2 m. by A 167* – **BX** – ✉ *Gateshead.*

Eslington Villa, 8 Station Rd, NE9 6DR, West : ½ m. by Belle Vue Bank, turning left at T junction ✆ (0191) 487 6017, *Fax (0191) 420 0667,* – rest, TV P. MO AE ⓓ VISA.
closed 25 December and 1 January – **Meals** *(closed Saturday lunch and Sunday dinner)* 11.50/16.95 **t.** (lunch) and a la carte 19.50/25.50 **t.** 6.50 – **18 rm** 59.50/69.50 **st.**

GATWICK AIRPORT *W. Sussex* 404 T 30 – ✉ *Crawley.*

Gatwick Airport : ✆ (01293) 535353.
London 29 – Brighton 28.

Plan on next page

Hilton London Gatwick Airport, South Terminal, RH6 0LL, ✆ (01293) 518080, *gathitwsal@hilton.com, Fax (01293) 528980,* , , – , rm, TV ♿ P – 500. MO AE ⓓ VISA. Y u
Meals a la carte 24.50/42.50 **t.** 8.00 – 14.95 – **565 rm** 180.00 **t.**

Le Meridien London Gatwick, Gatwick Airport (North Terminal), RH6 0PH, ✆ (0870) 400 8494, *meridienbuscent@hotmail.com, Fax (01293) 567739,* , , – , rm, TV ♿ P – 300. MO AE ⓓ VISA JCB. Y e
Gatwick Oriental : **Meals** - Asian - 17.00/27.00 **t.** and a la carte 8.00 – ***Brasserie :*** **Meals** *(closed lunch Saturday and Sunday)* (buffet lunch) 16.50/19.95 **t.** and dinner a la carte 9.25 – 13.95 – **489 rm** 200.00 **st.**, 6 suites – SB.

Renaissance London Gatwick, Povey Cross Rd, RH6 0BE, ✆ (01293) 820169, *alex.holmes@renaissancehotels.com, Fax (01293) 820259,* , , , squash – , rm, TV ♿ P – 180. MO AE ⓓ VISA. Y a
Meals *(closed Sunday lunch)* 16.95/19.95 **st.** and dinner a la carte – 11.50 – **253 rm** 110.00 **st.**, 2 suites.

Posthouse Gatwick, Povey Cross Rd, RH6 0BA, ✆ (0870) 400 9030, *gm1090@forte-hotels.com, Fax (01293) 771054* – , rm, rest, TV P – 300. MO AE ⓓ VISA. Y c
Meals *(closed Saturday lunch)* 13.95 **t.** (lunch) and a la carte 17.35/27.35 **t.** 6.95 – 11.95 – **210 rm** 109.00 **st.** – SB.

Gatwick Moat House, Longbridge Roundabout, Povey Cross Rd, RH6 0AB, ✆ (01293) 899988, *cegat@queensmoat.co.uk, Fax (01293) 785991,* – rm, TV ♿ P – 150. MO AE ⓓ VISA JCB Y n
Meals (bar lunch)/dinner a la carte 14.65/26.85 **st.** 5.95 – 10.50 – **124 rm** 115.00/130.00 **st.** – SB.

Travel Inn Metro, Longbridge Way, Gatwick Airport (North Terminal), RH6 0NX, ✆ (01293) 568158, *Fax (01293) 568278* – , rm, rest, TV ♿ P. MO AE ⓓ VISA. Y s
Meals (grill rest.) (dinner only) – **219 rm** 46.95 **t.**

Premier Lodge, London Rd, Lowfield Heath, RH10 2ST, ✆ (0870) 7001388, *Fax (0870) 7001389,* « Part 15C manor house », – , rm, TV ♿ P – 220. MO AE ⓓ VISA. Y x
Meals a la carte 11.00/22.00 **t.** – 6.00 – **100 rm** 46.00 **t.**

Travelodge, Church Rd, Lowfield Heath, RH11 0PQ, ✆ (01293) 533441, *Fax (01293) 535369* – , rm, rest, TV ♿ P – 40. MO AE ⓓ VISA JCB. Y r
Meals (grill rest.) – **186 rm** 49.95 **t.**

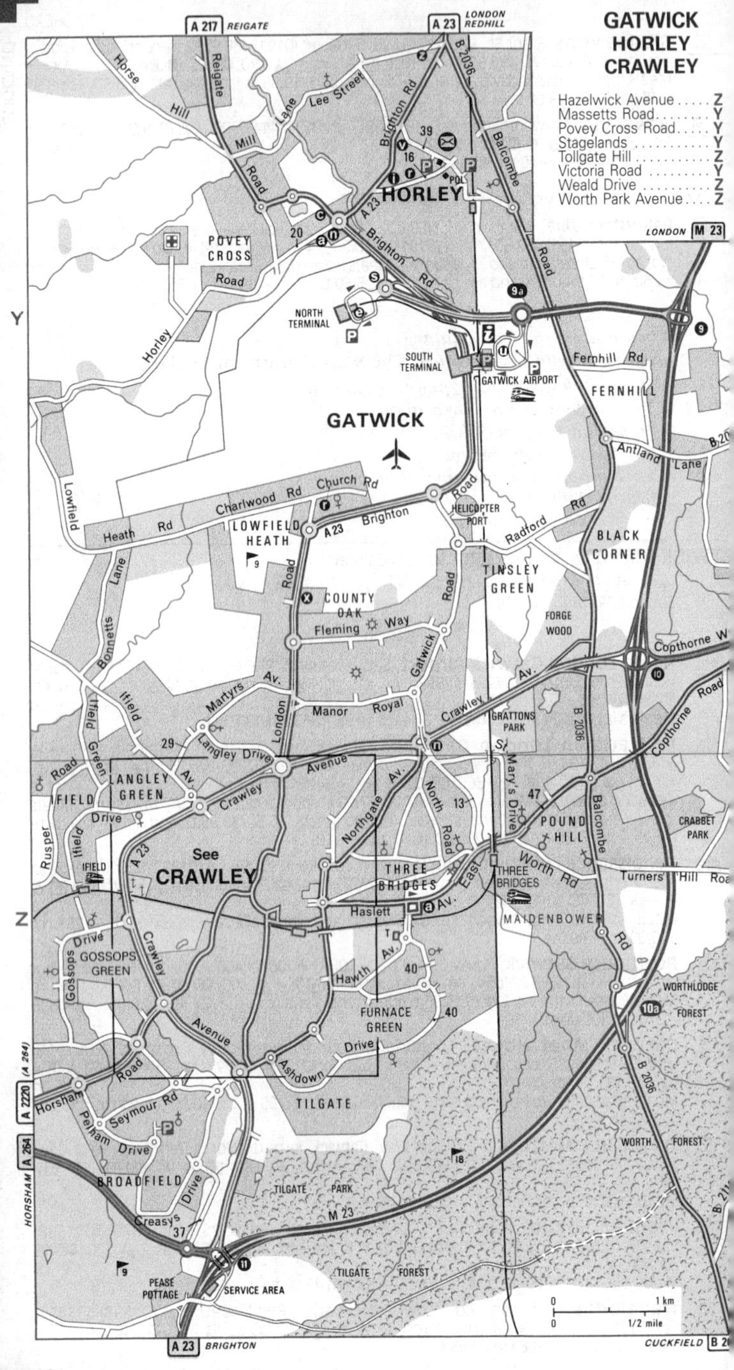
GATWICK
HORLEY
CRAWLEY
Hazelwick Avenue ..... Z
Massetts Road .... Y
Povey Cross Road ..... Y
Stagelands .... Y
Tollgate Hill .... Z
Victoria Road .... Y
Weald Drive .... Z
Worth Park Avenue .... Z
A 217 REIGATE
A 23 LONDON REDHILL
LONDON M 23
HORLEY
POVEY CROSS
NORTH TERMINAL
SOUTH TERMINAL
GATWICK AIRPORT
GATWICK
FERNHILL
LOWFIELD HEATH
HELICOPTER PORT
BLACK CORNER
TINSLEY GREEN
COUNTY OAK
FORGE WOOD
GRATTONS PARK
LANGLEY GREEN
IFIELD
See CRAWLEY
THREE BRIDGES
POUND HILL
CRABBET PARK
MAIDENBOWER
GOSSOPS GREEN
FURNACE GREEN
WORTHLODGE FOREST
TILGATE
BROADFIELD
TILGATE PARK
WORTH FOREST
TILGATE FOREST
PEASE POTTAGE
SERVICE AREA
A 23 BRIGHTON
CUCKFIELD B 2036
HORSHAM A 264
A 2220 (A 264)
Y
Z

AYTON *Mersey.* 402 ㉜ 403 ⑫ – *see Heswall.*

ERRARDS CROSS *Bucks.* 404 S 29 – *pop. 19 523 (inc. Chalfont St. Peter).*
London 22 – Aylesbury 22 – Oxford 36.

Bull, Oxford Rd, SL9 7PA, on A 40 ☎ (01753) 885995, *bull@sarova.co.uk, Fax (01753) 885504,* – 200. VISA.
Meals *(closed lunch Saturday and Bank Holidays)* 19.95/23.50 **st.** – 10.75 – **107 rm** 160.00/230.00 **st.**, 2 suites – SB.

ILLAN *Cornwall* 403 E 33 – ✉ *Helston.*
London 301 – Falmouth 23 – Penzance 25 – Truro 26.

Tregildry , TR12 6HG, ☎ (01326) 231378, *trgildry@globalnet.co.uk, Fax (01326) 231561,* VISA
March-October – ***Herra :*** **Meals** (dinner only) 24.00 **t.** 8.25 – **10 rm** (dinner included) 75.00/160.00 **t.** – SB.

ILLINGHAM *Dorset* 403 404 N 30 *The West Country G.* – *pop. 6 404.*
Exc. : *Stourhead*** AC, N : 9 m. by B 3092, B 3095 and B 3092.*
London 116 – Bournemouth 34 – Bristol 46 – Southampton 52.

Stock Hill Country House , Stock Hill, SP8 5NR, West : 1 ½ m. on B 3081 ☎ (01747) 823626, *reception@stockhill.net, Fax (01747) 825628,* « Victorian country house, antiques and gardens », – rest, VISA.
Meals *(closed lunch Saturday and Monday)* (booking essential) 22.00/35.00 **t.** 12.45 – **8 rm** (dinner included) 125.00/300.00 **t.** – SB.

Les prix

Pour toutes précisions sur les prix indiqués dans ce guide, reportez-vous aux pages de l'introduction.

SLINGHAM *Suffolk* 404 X 27 – *pop. 822* – ✉ *Eye.*
London 93 – Cambridge 45 – Ipswich 20 – Norwich 30.

Old Guildhall, Mill St., IP23 8JT, ☎ (01379) 783361, « 15C former guildhall », –
closed January – **Meals** (by arrangement) 14.00 **s.** 3.50 – **4 rm** 39.00/58.00 **st.** – SB.

TTISHAM *Devon* 403 K 31 – *pop. 602* – ✉ *Honiton.*
London 168 – Exeter 18 – Southampton 95 – Taunton 21.

Combe House , EX14 3AD, ☎ (01404) 540400, *stay@thishotel.com, Fax (01404) 46004,* « Elizabethan mansion », – 60. VISA
Meals (booking essential to non-residents) 14.00/28.50 **t.** 9.50 – **14 rm** 75.00/120.00 **t.**, 1 suite – SB.

EWSTONE *Herefordshire* – *see Ross-on-Wye.*

OSSOP *Derbs.* 402 403 404 O 23 – *pop. 30 771 (inc. Hollingworth).*
9 *Sheffield Rd ☎ (01457) 865247.*
The Gatehouse, Victoria St. ☎ (01457) 855920.
London 194 – Manchester 18 – Sheffield 25.

The Wind in the Willows , Hurst Rd, Derbyshire Level, SK13 7PT, East : 1 m. by A 57 ☎ (01457) 868001, *info@windinthewillows.co.uk, Fax (01457) 853354,* – rest, VISA.
Meals (residents only) (dinner only) 24.00 **st.** 10.00 – **12 rm** 74.00/119.00 **st.**

OUCESTER *Glos.* 403 404 N 28 *Great Britain G.* – *pop. 114 003.*
See : *City* - Cathedral** Y – The Docks* Y – Bishop Hooper's Lodging* AC* Y **M.**
18, 9 *Gloucester Hotel, Matson Lane ☎ (01452) 525653.*
28 Southgate St. ☎ (01452) 421188.
London 106 – Birmingham 52 – Bristol 38 – Cardiff 66 – Coventry 57 – Northampton 83 – Oxford 48 – Southampton 98 – Swansea 92 – Swindon 35.

GLOUCESTER

Street	Grid	No.
Barnwood By-Pass	Z	3
Black Dog Way	Y	5
Commercial Road	Y	6
Cotteswold Road	Z	8
Derby Road	Z	9
Eastgate Shopping Centre	Y	
Eastgate Street	Y	10
Great Western Road	Y	12
Heathville Road	Y	13
King Edward's Avenue	Z	14
Lower Westgate Street	Y	15
Northgate Street	Y	16
Parkend Road	Z	17
Parliament Street	Y	18
Pitt Street	Y	19
Quay Street	Y	20
Royal Oak Road	Y	21
St. Aldate Street	Y	22
St. Johns Lane	Y	23
Southern Avenue	Z	24
Southgate Street	Y	
Spa Road	Y	26
Stroud Road	Z	28
Tredworth Road	Z	30
Worcester Street	Y	31

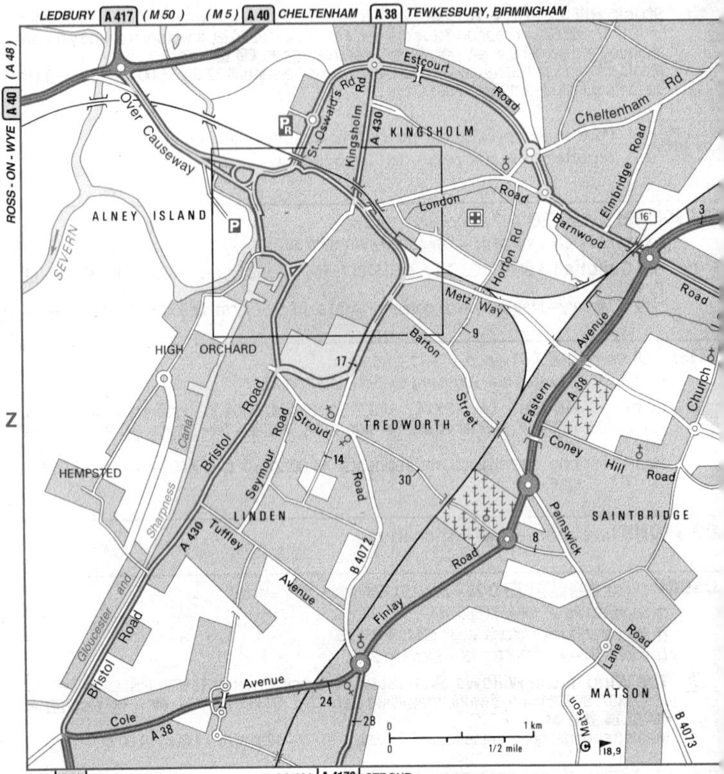

Y

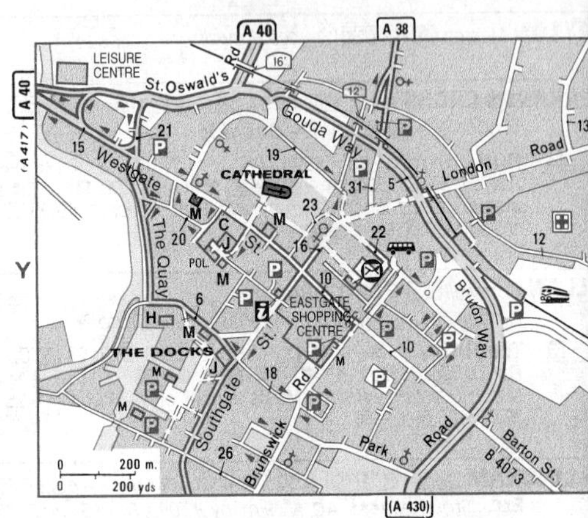

LEDBURY A 417 (M 50) (M 5) A 40 CHELTENHAM A 38 TEWKESBURY, BIRMINGHAM

ROSS-ON-WYE A 40 (A 48)

Z

ALNEY ISLAND
KINGSHOLM
HIGH ORCHARD
TREDWORTH
HEMPSTED
LINDEN
SAINTBRIDGE
MATSON

Over Causeway
Estcourt Road
Cheltenham Rd
Elmbridge Road
London Road
Barnwood Road
Horton Rd
Metz Way
Barton Street
Eastern Avenue
Coney Hill Road
Church
Bristol Road
Stroud Road
Seymour Road
Tuffley Avenue
Painswick Road
Finlay Road
Cole Avenue
Gloucester and Sharpness Canal
Lane Road
B 4072
B 4073
A 430
A 38
SEVERN

1 km
1/2 mile

A 38 (M 5), BRISTOL (A 46) A 4173 STROUD

Benutzen Sie auf Ihren Reisen in Europa
die **Michelin-Länderkarten** 1 : 1 000 000.

Jarvis Gloucester H. & Country Club, Robinswood Hill, GL4 6EA, Southeast : 3 m. by B 4073 (01452) 525653, *Fax (01452) 307212*, squash – 180. VISA JCB. Z c
closed 25-26 December **Meals** (closed Saturday lunch) 12.80/17.50 **st.** – 8.95 – **102 rm** 99.00/135.00 **st.**, 5 suites – SB.

Premier Lodge, Tewkesbury Rd, Twigworth, GL2 9PG, Northeast : 2 ½ m. on A 38 (01452) 730266, *Fax (01452) 730099* – rm, – 40. VISA.
Meals (grill rest.) a la carte 10.15/16.35 **t.** – 6.00 – **52 rm** 42.00 **t.**

Express by Holiday Inn without rest., Waterwells Business Park, Nr. Quedgeley, GL2 4SA, Southwest : 3 m. on A 38 (01452) 726400, *Fax (01452) 722922* – – 35. VISA JCB.
106 rm 56.00 **t.**

Travel Inn, Tewkesbury Rd, Longford, GL2 9BE, North : 1 ¼ m. on A 38 (01452) 523519, *Fax (01452) 300924* – rm, – 40. VISA.
Meals (grill rest.) – **60 rm** 40.95 **t.**

Upton St. Leonards *Southeast : 3½ m. by B 4073 – Z – Gloucester.*

Hatton Court, Upton Hill, GL4 8DE, South : ¾ m. on B 4073 (01452) 617412, *res@hatton_court.co.uk, Fax (01452) 612945*, heated, – rest, rest, – 60. VISA JCB.
Carringtons : **Meals** 14.95/25.00 **t.** and a la carte 6.00 – **45 rm** 89.00/99.00 **t.** – SB.

Jarvis Bowden Hall, Bondend Lane, GL4 8ED, East : 1 m. by Bondend rd (01452) 614121, *Fax (01452) 611885*, – – 85. VISA.
Meals (dinner only and Sunday lunch) (carving lunch Sunday)/dinner a la carte 17.75/24.25 **t.** 7.60 – 9.95 – **72 rm** 104/00/124.00 **t.** – SB.

Bullens Manor Farm without rest., High St., GL4 8DL, Southeast : ½ m. (01452) 616463, « Working farm », –.
closed Christmas and New Year – **3 rm** 22.00/40.00.

Witcombe *Southeast : 7 m. by A 40 and A 417 – Z – off A 46 – Gloucester.*

Travel Inn, GL3 4SS, (01452) 862521, *Fax (01452) 864926* – rm, VISA.
Meals (grill rest.) – **39 rm** 40.95 **t.**

ATHLAND *N. Yorks.* 402 R 20 – *pop. 444* – *Whitby.*
London 248 – Middlesbrough 36 – York 38.

Mallyan Spout, The Common, YO22 5AN, (01947) 896486, *mallyan@ukgateway.net, Fax (01947) 896327*, – VISA
closed one week Christmas – **Meals** (bar lunch Monday to Saturday)/dinner 21.50 **t.** and a la carte 5.50 – **26 rm** 55.00/130.00 **t.** – SB.

Heatherdene, The Old Vicarage, The Common, YO22 5AN, (01947) 896334, *info@heatherdenehotel.co.uk*, – rest, VISA.
restricted opening in winter – **Meals** (by arrangement) 15.00 7.00 **6 rm** 40.00/70.00.

DALMING *Surrey* 404 S 30 – *pop. 20 630.*
West Surrey, Enton Green (01483) 421275 – Shillinglee Park, Chiddingfold (01428) 653237.
London 39 – Guildford 5 – Southampton 48.

Bel and the Dragon, Bridge St., GU7 3DU, (01483) 527333, *Fax (01483) 427833*, « Converted church » – VISA JCB
Meals a la carte 20.40/32.40 **t.**

DSTONE *Surrey* 404 T 30 – *pop. 2 399.*
London 22 – Brighton 36 – Maidstone 28.

Tutu L'Auberge, Tilburstow Hill, South Godstone, RH9 8JY, South : 2 ¼ m. (01342) 892318, *hr36@dial.pipex.com, Fax (01342) 893435*, – – 100. VISA JCB
closed 26 to 30 December, Sunday dinner and Monday – **Meals** - French - 16.90/18.50 **st.** and a la carte 6.50.

LANT *Cornwall* 403 G 32 – *see Fowey.*

LCAR *W. Yorks.* – *see Huddersfield.*

GOMERSAL *W. Yorks.* 402 O 22 – *see Bradford.*

GOODWOOD *W. Sussex* 404 R 31 – *see Chichester.*

GOOSNARGH *Lancs.* 402 L 22 – *pop. 1 087* – ✉ *Preston.*
London 238 – Blackpool 18 – Preston 6.

XX **Solo,** Goosnargh Lane, PR3 2BN, ✆ (01772) 865206, *Fax (01772) 865206* – ⊁ P. MC AE JCB
closed 26 December and Monday **Meals** (dinner only and Sunday lunch)/dinner 23.90 and a la carte 8.90.

Ye Horns Inn with rm, Horns Lane, PR3 2FJ, Northeast : 2 ½ m. by B 52 ✆ (01772) 865230, *enquiries@yehornsinn.co.uk, Fax (01772) 864299,* « Part 18C », – P. MC AE VISA JCB.
Meals *(closed Monday lunch)* 12.50/17.50 **t.** and a la carte 6.00 – **6 rm** 49.00/75.00 SB.

GORDANO SERVICE AREA *North Somerset* – ✉ *Bristol.*
Severn Bridge (toll).

Days Inn without rest., BS20 9XG, M 5 junction 19 ✆ 460275) 373709, Reservations (Fr phone) 0800 0280400, *Fax (01275) 374104* – ⊁ rm, TV ✆ ♿ P. MC AE VISA JCB
7.45 **60 rm** 49.00 **t.**

GOREY *Jersey (Channel Islands)* 403 P 33 and 230 ⑪ – *see Channel Islands.*

GORING *Oxon.* 403 404 Q 29 *The West Country G.* – *pop. 4 193 (inc. Streatley).*
Exc. : *Ridgeway Path*★★.
London 56 – Oxford 16 – Reading 12.

XX **Leatherne Bottel,** RG8 0HS, North : 1 ½ m. by B 4009 ✆ (01491) 872667, *leatherneb el@aol.com, Fax (01491) 875308,* ≤, « Thames-side setting » – P. MC AE VISA
closed 25 December and Sunday dinner – **Meals** (booking essential) a la carte 30. 40.00 **st.**

at South Stoke *North : 2 m. by B 4009* – ✉ *Goring.*

Perch and Pike, RG8 0JS, ✆ (01491) 872415, *Fax (01491) 875852,* « Part 17C inn ⊁ P. MC VISA
closed dinner Sunday and Monday – **Meals** (booking essential) a la carte 16.00/23.00.

GORLESTON-ON-SEA *Norfolk* 404 Z 26 – *see Great Yarmouth.*

GOSFORTH *Cumbria* 402 J 20 – *pop. 1 568* – ✉ *Seascale.*
London 317 – Kendal 55 – Workington 21.

Westlakes, Gosforth Rd, CA20 1HP, Southwest : ¼ m. on B 5344 ✆ (019467) 25221, *w akeshotel@compuserve.com, Fax (019467) 25099,* – ⊁ rest, TV ✆ P. MC AE VISA
closed 24 December-7 January **Meals** *(closed lunch Saturday and Sunday)* a la carte 14. 25.95 **st.** 4.50 – **9 rm** 50.50/67.50 **st.**

GOSFORTH *Tyne and Wear* 401 402 P 18 – *see Newcastle upon Tyne.*

GOUDHURST *Kent* 404 V 30 – *pop. 2 498.*
London 50 – Hastings 25 – Maidstone 17.

West Winchet without rest., Winchet Hill, TN17 1JX, North : 2 ½ m. on B 2 ✆ (01580) 212024, *annieparker@jpaltd.co.uk, Fax (01580) 212250,* – ⊁ TV P
closed 24 December-3 January – **3 rm** 35.00/50.00 **s.**

GRAMPOUND *Cornwall* 403 F 33 *The West Country G.* – ✉ *Truro.*
Env. : *Trewithen*★★★ *AC, W : 2 m. by A 390 – Probus*★ *(tower*★, *Country Demonstra Garden*★ *AC) W : 2½ m. by A 390.*
London 287 – Newquay 16 – Plymouth 44 – Truro 8.

Creed House without rest., Creed, TR2 4SL, South : 1 m. by Creed rd turning left just past the church ☎ (01872) 530372, ←, « Georgian rectory, gardens » – P
closed Christmas and New Year – **4 rm** 40.00/70.00 **st.**

Eastern Promise, 1 Moor View, TR2 4RT, ☎ (01726) 883033 – P. MC AE VISA JCB
closed Wednesday – **Meals** - Chinese - (booking essential) (dinner only) 20.00 **st.** and a la carte 4.90.

GRANGE-IN-BORROWDALE *Cumbria* 402 K 20 – *see Keswick.*

GRANGE-OVER-SANDS *Cumbria* 402 L 21 *Great Britain G. – pop. 4 473.*

Env. : *Cartmel Priory*, NW : 3 m.*

Meathop Rd ☎ (015395) 33180 – Grange Fell, Fell Rd ☎ (015395) 32536.

Victoria Hall, Main St. ☎ (015395) 34026 (restricted opening in winter).

London 268 – Kendal 13 – Lancaster 24.

Netherwood, Lindale Rd, LA11 6ET, ☎ (015395) 32552, *blawith@aol.com, Fax (015395) 34121,* ← Morecambe Bay, « Victorian country house, gardens », – , rest, TV P – 150. MC VISA
Meals 9.00/24.00 **t.** 4.95 – **28 rm** 55.00/130.00 **t.** – SB.

Graythwaite Manor, Fernhill Rd, LA11 7JE, ☎ (015395) 32001, *sales@graythwaitemanor.co.uk, Fax (015395) 35549,* ←, « Extensive flowered gardens », – rest, TV P. MC AE VISA JCB.
closed 8-27 January – **Meals** 12.00/25.00 **t.** and a la carte 4.50 – **21 rm** 65.00/99.00 **t.** – SB.

Mount Eden, Eden Mount, LA11 6BZ, ☎ (015395) 34794, – TV P.
March-October – **Meals** (by arrangement) 12.50 – **3 rm** 25.00/50.00.

Lindale *Northeast : 2 m. on B 5277 – Grange-over-Sands.*

Greenacres, LA11 6LP, ☎ (015395) 34578, *Fax (015395) 34578* – TV P. MC VISA JCB.
closed Christmas and New Year – **Meals** (by arrangement) 13.00 **st.** – **5 rm** 28.00/56.00 **st.**

Witherslack *Northeast : 5 m. by B 5277 off A 590.*

Old Vicarage, Church Rd, LA11 6RS, Northwest : ¾ m. ☎ (015395) 52381, *hotel@oldvicarage.com, Fax (015395) 52373,* « Part Georgian country house », – rest, TV P. MC AE VISA JCB
Meals (dinner only and Sunday lunch)/dinner a la carte 21.00/27.00 **t.** 7.50 – **14 rm** 65.00/150.00 **t.** – SB.

Cartmel *Northwest : 3 m.*

Aynsome Manor, LA11 6HH, North : ¾ m. by Cartmel Priory rd on Wood Broughton rd ☎ (015395) 36653, *info@aynsomemanorhotel.co.uk, Fax (015395) 36016,* – rest, TV P. MC AE VISA JCB
closed January – **Meals** *(closed Sunday dinner to non-residents)* (dinner only and Sunday lunch)/dinner 17.00/21.00 **t.** 7.75 – **12 rm** (dinner included) 70.00/120.00 – SB.

Uplands, Haggs Lane, LA11 6HD, East : 1 m. ☎ (015395) 36248, *uplands@kencomp.net, Fax (015395) 36848,* ←, – rest, TV P. MC AE VISA
closed January and February – **Meals** *(closed Monday and lunch Tuesday and Wednesday)* (booking essential) 15.50/29.00 **t.** 7.50 – **5 rm** (dinner included) 86.00/154.00 **t.** – SB.

GRANTHAM *Lincs.* 402 404 S 25 *Great Britain G. – pop. 33 243.*

See : *St. Wulfram's Church*.*

Env. : *Belton House* AC, N : 2½ m. by A 607.*

Exc. : *Belvoir Castle** AC, W : 6 m. by A 607.*

9, 9, 9 Belton Park, Belton Lane, Londonthorpe Rd ☎ (01476) 567399 – 18, 18, 9 Belton Woods Hotel ☎ (01476) 593200.

The Guildhall Centre, St. Peter's Hill ☎ (01476) 406166.

London 113 – Leicester 31 – Lincoln 29 – Nottingham 24.

Belton Woods, Belton, NG32 2LN, North : 2 m. on A 607 ☎ (01476) 593200, *devere.belton@airtime.co.uk, Fax (01476) 574547,* , , , , 18, 9, , , , squash – TV P – 245. MC AE VISA JCB
Manor : **Meals** (dinner only) 29.50 **t.** and a la carte 9.50 – ***Plus Fours :*** **Meals** 16.00/21.50 **t.** 11.50 – 11.50 – **132 rm** 125.00/170.00 **t.**, 4 suites – SB.

Swallow (becoming a Courtyard by Marriott spring 2001), Swingbridge Rd, NG31 7 South : 1 ¼ m. at junction of A 607 with A 1 southbound sliproad ✆ (01476) 593000, *info wallowhotels.com, Fax (01476) 592592*, – rm, rest, – 2 MC AE VISA
Tapestry : Meals a la carte 16.00/27.50 **st.** – **90 rm** 90.00/110.00 **st.** – SB.

Angel and Royal, High St., NG31 6PN, ✆ (01476) 565816, *Fax (01476) 567149*, « P 13C » – – 30. MC AE VISA JCB.
Meals (bar lunch Monday to Saturday)/dinner 11.95/14.95 **st.** and a la carte 5.95 – **28** 50.00/80.00 **st.** – SB.

at Great Gonerby *Northwest : 2 m. on B 1174 – ✉ Grantham.*

Harry's Place (Hallam), 17 High St., NG31 8JS, ✆ (01476) 561780 – MC VISA
closed 25 and 26 December, Sunday, Monday and Bank Holidays – **Meals** (booking essent a la carte 39.50/50.00 **t.** 10.00
Spec. Terrine of chicken with leeks, coriander and balsamic dressing. Seared scallops w sauce of their coral, prawns, white wine and basil. Roast partridge with bacon and Jeru lem artichoke.

at Grantham Service Area *Northwest : 3 m on B 1174 at junction with A 1 – ✉ Grantham.*

Travelodge, NG32 2AB, ✆ (01476) 577500, *Fax (01476) 577500* – rm, MC VISA JCB.
Meals (grill rest.) – **40 rm** 39.95 **t.**

GRASMERE *Cumbria* 402 K 20 *Great Britain G.* – ✉ *Ambleside.*
See : *Dove Cottage*★ *AC* AY A.
Env. : *Lake Windermere*★★, *SE : by A 591* **AZ**.
Redbank Rd ✆ (015394) 35245 (summer only) **BZ**.
London 282 – Carlisle 43 – Kendal 18.

Plans : see Ambleside

Michaels Nook, LA22 9RP, Northeast : ½ m. off A 591, turning by Swan ✆ (015394) 35496, *m-nook@wordsworth-grasmere.co.uk, Fax (015394) 35645*, mo tains and countryside, « Victorian country house extensively furnished with antiqu landscaped gardens », – rest, MC AE VISA. AY
Meals (booking essential) 25.00/58.00 **t.** 8.75 – **12 rm** (dinner included) 148. 275.00 **st.**, 2 suites – SB
Spec. Assiette of Périgord duckling and foie gras. Pavé of sea bass with artichokes, Hermitage. Bramley apple mousse, vanilla foam.

Wordsworth, Stock Lane, LA22 9SW, ✆ (015394) 35592, *enquiry@wordsworth_grasi e.co.uk, Fax (015394) 35765*, – rest, rest, – 130. MC VISA. BZ
Prelude : Meals 19.50/30.00 and a la carte 10.50 – **35 rm** (dinner included) 120. 230.00 **t.**, 2 suites – SB.

Gold Rill, Red Bank Rd, LA22 9PU, ✆ (015394) 35486, *enquiries@gold-rill.c Fax (015394) 35486*, – rest, rest, MC VISA JCB. BZ
closed 1 week December and two weeks January – **Meals** (bar lunch)/dinner 20.00 and a la carte 6.25 – **24 rm** (dinner included) 66.00/132.00 **st.**, 1 suite – SB.

Swan, LA22 9RF, on A 591 ✆ (015394) 35551, *heritagehotels-grasmere.swan@forte_h s.com, Fax (015394) 35741*, – MC AE VISA JCB AY
Meals 13.95/24.00 **t.** 8.75 – **38 rm** (dinner included) 69.00/138.00 **st.** – SB.

Red Lion, Red Lion Sq., LA22 9SS, ✆ (015394) 35456, *enquiries@hotelgrasmere.uk.c Fax (015394) 35579*, – rest, – 60. MC AE VISA JCB. BZ
Meals (bar lunch)/dinner 19.50 **st.** and a la carte 5.95 – **46 rm** 55.50/111.00 **st.**, 1 s – SB.

Thistle Grasmere, Keswick Rd, LA22 9PR, on A 591 ✆ (015394) 35666, *grasmere@th .co.uk, Fax (015394) 35565*, « Lakeside setting », – – 100. MC AE VISA JCB AY
Meals (bar lunch)/dinner a la carte 15.00/20.00 **st.** 8.95 – 9.00 – **70 rm** 97. 117.00 **st.** – SB.

White Moss House, Rydal Water, LA22 9SE, South : 1 ½ m. on A 591 ✆ (015394) 35 *dixon@whitemoss.demon.co.uk, Fax (015394) 35516*, – rest, MC AE BY
March-November – **Meals** *(closed Sunday)* (booking essential) (dinner only) 29.00 **t.** 7. **7 rm** (dinner included) 89.00/180.00 **st.**, 1 suite – SB.

Bridge House, Stock Lane, LA22 9SN, ✆ (015394) 35425, *enquiries@bridgehousegra re.co.uk, Fax (015394) 35523*, – MC VISA JCB. BZ
closed 15-24 December – **Meals** (dinner only) 16.00 **st.** and a la carte 9.95 – **18 rm** (dinner included) 55.00/100.00 **st.** – SB.

Oak Bank, Broadgate, LA22 9TA, (015394) 35217, *grasmereoakbank@btinternet.com, Fax (015394) 35685,* – rest, TV P. MC VISA JCB BZ e
closed 25 December and 3 January-10 February – **Meals** (bar lunch)/dinner 19.50 **t.** 6.50 – **15 rm** (dinner included) 45.00/130.00 **t.** – SB.

Grasmere, Broadgate, LA22 9TA, (015394) 35277, *enquiries@grasmerehotel.co.uk, Fax (015394) 35277,* – TV P. MC AE VISA JCB BZ r
closed January – **Meals** (dinner only) 15.00/18.50 **st.** 6.00 – **12 rm** (dinner included) 50.00/124.00 **st.** – SB.

Lancrigg Vegetarian Country House, Easedale Rd, LA22 9QN, West : ½ m. on Easedale Rd (015394) 35317, *info@lancrigg.co.uk, Fax (015394) 35058,* Easedale Valley, – rest, TV P. MC AE VISA AY u
Meals (lunch by arrangement)/dinner 25.00 **t.** 9.95 – **13 rm** (dinner included) 70.00/198.00 **t.** – SB.

Woodland Crag without rest., How Head Lane, LA22 9SG, Southeast : ¾ m. by B 5287 (015394) 35351, – TV P. AY s
closed 25 December – **5 rm** 29.00/60.00 **st.**

Banerigg without rest., Lake Rd, LA22 9PW, South : ¾ m. on A 591 (015394) 35204, – P. AY a
6 rm 26.00/55.00 **s.**

RASSENDALE *Mersey.* 402 403 L 23 – *see Liverpool.*

RASSINGTON *N. Yorks.* 402 O 21 – *pop. 1 102* – *Skipton.*
National Park Centre, Colvend, Hebden Rd (01756) 752774.
London 240 – Bradford 30 – Burnley 28 – Leeds 37.

Ashfield House, Summers Fold, BD23 5AE, (01756) 752584, *keilin@talk21.com, Fax (01756) 752584,* « Part 17C », – TV P. MC VISA.
closed 25-26 December, January and restricted opening in February and March – **Meals** (by arrangement) 17.00 **st.** 4.50 – **7 rm** 44.00/68.00 **st.** – SB.

Grassington Lodge without rest., 8 Wood Lane, BD23 5LU, (01756) 752518, *grassington.lodge@totalise.co.uk, Fax (01756) 752518* – TV P.
closed 2 weeks November and 1 week Christmas – **7 rm** 40.00/65.00 **s.**

RAVESEND *Kent* 404 V 29 – *pop. 51 435.*
to Tilbury (White Horse Fast Ferries) frequent services daily (approx. 8 mn).
Town Centre, 18a St. George's Sq. (01474) 337600.
London 25 – Dover 54 – Maidstone 16 – Margate 53.

Manor, Hever Court Rd, Singlewell, DA12 5UQ, Southeast : 2 ½ m. by A 227 off A 2 (eastbound carriageway) (01474) 353100, *manorhotel@clara.net, Fax (01474) 354978,* – , rest, TV P – 200. MC AE VISA.
Meals *(closed Saturday and Sunday)* (bar lunch)/dinner 18.95 **st.** and a la carte 6.00 – **52 rm** 80.00/90.00 **st.**

Overcliffe, 15-16 Overcliffe, DA11 0EF, on A 226 (Dartford rd) (01474) 322131, *Fax (01474) 536737,* – TV P. MC AE VISA
Meals (dinner only) a la carte 18.50/22.50 **t.** 5.00 – **29 rm** 75.00/90.00 **st.**

Travel Inn, Wrotham Rd, DA11 7LF, South : 1 m. on A 227 (01474) 533556, *Fax (01474) 323776* – rm, TV P. MC AE VISA JCB
Meals (grill rest.) – **36 rm** 40.95 **t.**

AVETYE *W. Sussex* – *see East Grinstead.*

AZELEY GREEN *Wokingham* – *see Reading.*

EASBY *Mersey.* 402 (32) 403 (12) – *pop. 56 077 (inc. Moreton)* – *Wirral.*
London 220 – Liverpool 9.

Premier Lodge, Greasby Rd, CH49 2PP, on B 5139 (0870) 7001582, *Fax (0870) 7001583* – rm, TV P. MC AE VISA.
Meals (grill rest.) 10.95 **t.** and a la carte – 6.00 – **30 rm** 42.00 **st.**

EAT BADDOW *Essex* 404 V 28 – *see Chelmsford.*

EAT BARR *W. Mids.* 403 404 O 26 – *see Birmingham.*

GREAT BROUGHTON *N. Yorks.* 402 Q 20 – *pop. 937 (inc. Little Broughton)* – ✉ *Middlesbroug*
London 241 – Leeds 61 – Middlesbrough 10 – York 54.

Wainstones, 31 High St., TS9 7EW, ☎ (01642) 712268, *wstones@netcomuk.co.*
Fax (01642) 711560 – TV P – 120. MC AE VISA JCB.
Meals a la carte 18.45/23.50 **t.** – **24 rm** 62.50/78.95 **t.** – SB.

GREAT DUNMOW *Essex* 404 V 28 – *pop. 4 907.*
London 42 – Cambridge 27 – Chelmsford 13 – Colchester 24.

Saracen's Head, High St., CM6 1AG, ☎ (01371) 873901, *Fax (01371) 875743* – TV
60. MC AE VISA JCB
Meals (bar lunch)/dinner 10.95/12.95 **st.** 6.95 – 9.75 – **24 rm** 75.00/105.00 **st.** – SB.

The Starr with rm, Market Pl., CM6 1AX, ☎ (01371) 874321, *terry@starrdunmow.demo*
o.uk, Fax (01371) 876337 – TV P – 35. MC AE VISA JCB
closed 1 week Christmas – **Meals** *(closed Sunday dinner)* 20.00/35.00 **t.** 6.00 – 8
67.00/124.00 **t.**

GREAT GONERBY *Lincs.* 402 404 S 25 – *see Grantham.*

GREAT GRIMSBY *N.E. Lincs.* 402 404 T 23.
London 173 – Boston 51 – Kingston-upon-Hull 33 – Lincoln 37 – Sheffield 73.

Travel Inn, Europa Park, off Gilbey Rd, DN31 2UT, ☎ (01472) 242630, *Fax (01472) 250*
– rm, rest, TV P. MC AE VISA.
Meals (grill rest.) – **40 rm** 40.95 **t.**

GREAT LONGSTONE *Derbs.* 402 403 404 O 24 – *see Bakewell.*

GREAT MALVERN *Worcs.* 403 404 N 27 – *pop. 31 537.*
21 Church St. ☎ *(01684) 892289* **B**.
London 127 – Birmingham 34 – Cardiff 66 – Gloucester 24.
Plan opposite

Red Gate without rest., 32 Avenue Rd, WR14 3BJ, ☎ (01684) 565013, *red_gate@lineon*
et, Fax (01684) 565013, – TV P. MC VISA JCB. **B**
closed Christmas and New Year – **6 rm** 30.00/57.00.

Pembridge, 114 Graham Rd, WR14 2HX, ☎ (01684) 574813, *pembridgehotel@aol.co*
Fax (01684) 566885, – TV P. MC AE VISA. **B**
closed 22 December-10 January – **Meals** *(closed Sunday)* 15.00/17.50 **t.** 6.95 – 8
48.00/68.00 **t.** – SB.

Cowleigh Park Farm without rest., Cowleigh Rd, WR13 5HJ, Northwest : 1 ½ m. b
4232 on B 4219 ☎ (01684) 566750, *cowleighparkfarm@talk21.com, Fax (01684) 566*
« Part 17C farmhouse », – TV P **A**
closed Christmas and New Year – **3 rm** 48.00/54.00 **st.**

at Welland *Southeast : 4½ m. by A 449 on A 4104* – **A** – ✉ *Great Malvern.*

Holdfast Cottage, Marlbank Rd, WR13 6NA, West : ¾ m. on A 4
☎ (01684) 310288, *Fax (01684) 311117,* « 17C country cottage », – TV P.
VISA **A**
closed Christmas – **Meals** (booking essential) (dinner only) 24.00 **st.** 6.25 – **8 rm** 50.
90.00 **st.** – SB.

at Malvern Wells *South : 2 m. on A 449* – ✉ *Malvern.*

Cottage in the Wood, Holywell Rd, WR14 4LG, ☎ (01684) 575859, *proprietor@co*
geinthewood.co.uk, Fax (01684) 560662, ≤ Severn and Evesham Vales, – r
rest, TV P. MC AE VISA JCB. **A**
Meals 13.95 **st.** (lunch) and dinner a la carte 28.15/30.45 **st.** 7.50 – **20 rm** 75.
145.00 **st.** – SB.

Croque-en-Bouche (Marion Jones), 221 Wells Rd, WR14 4HF, ☎ (01684) 565612, *m*
croque-en-bouche.co.uk, Fax (0870) 7066232 – . MC VISA **A**
closed 1 week May, 1 week September, Christmas-New Year and Sunday to Wednesd
Meals (booking essential) (dinner only) 26.50/33.50 **st.** 7.50
Spec. Crab and lobster croustade with bouillabaisse sauce. Japanese style selections. Sa
and herbs from the garden.

Planters, 191-193 Wells Rd, WR14 4HE, ☎ (01684) 575065 – MC VISA **A**
closed 25 December, Tuesday in winter, Sunday and Monday – **Meals** - South East Asi
(booking essential) (dinner only) 28.50 **t.** and a la carte 8.00.

Town plans
roads most used
by traffic and those
on which guide listed
hotels and restaurants
stand are fully drawn;
the beginning only
of lesser roads
is indicated.

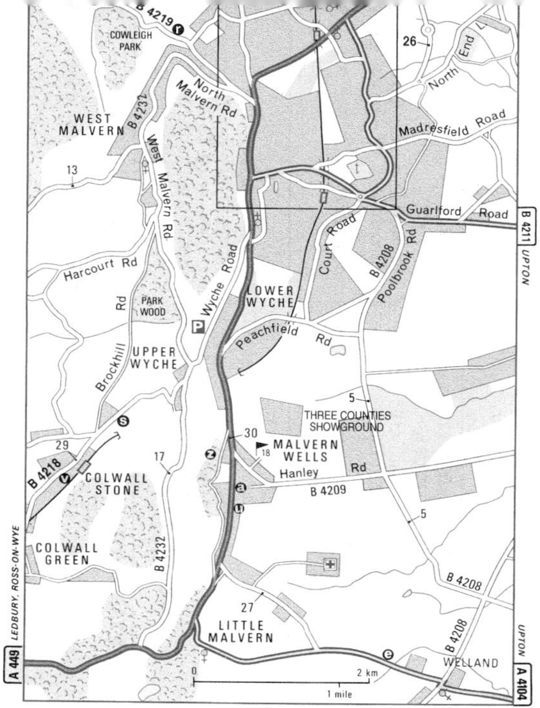

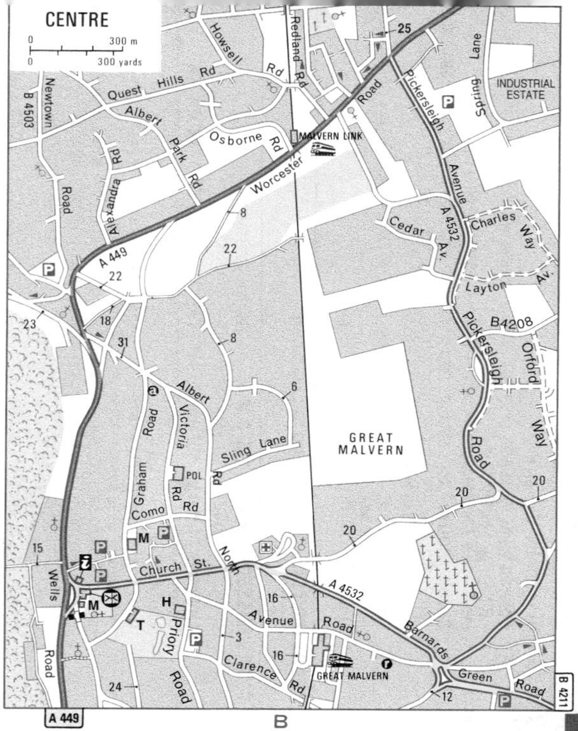

CENTRE

A

B

ENGLAND

at Colwall *Southwest : 3 m. on B 4218 – ✉ Great Malvern.*

Colwall Park, WR13 6QG, ✆ (01684) 540000, *hotel@colwall.com, Fax (01684) 540847,* – TV P – 120. MC AE VISA A
Meals – (see ***The Restaurant*** below) – **20 rm** 65.00/120.00, 2 suites – SB.

Brook House without rest., Walwyn Rd, WR13 6QX, ✆ (01684) 5406(
Fax (01684) 540604, « Jacobean manor house, gardens » – TV P. A
closed 1 week Christmas – **3 rm** 39.50/59.00.

The Restaurant (at Colwall Park H.), WR13 6QG, ✆ (01684) 540000, *Fax (01684) 54084*
rest. MC AE VISA A
Meals 13.95/22.95 **t.** and dinner a la carte 6.25.

GREAT MILTON *Oxon.* 403 404 Q 28 – *see Oxford.*

GREAT MISSENDEN *Bucks.* 404 R 28 – *pop. 7 980 (inc. Prestwood).*
London 34 – Aylesbury 10 – Maidenhead 19 – Oxford 35.

La Petite Auberge, 107 High St., HP16 0BB, ✆ (01494) 865370 – MC VISA JCB
closed 2 weeks Easter, 2 weeks Christmas and Sunday – **Meals** - French - (dinner or
a la carte 24.20/29.60 **t.** 8.30.

Berts at The Barley Mow, Chesham Rd, HP16 0QT, East : 1 m. on B 4
✆ (01494) 865625, *Fax (01494) 866406,* – P. MC AE VISA
closed Sunday, Monday, Saturday lunch and Bank Holidays – **Meals** - Mediterranea
(booking essential) 15.00 **t.** (lunch) and dinner a la carte 17.10/26.30 **t.**

40° (at Cross Keys), 40 High St., H16 0AU, ✆ (01494) 864544, *Fax (01494) 791065* –
MC AE VISA JCB
closed 24 December-4 January, Sunday dinner and Monday – **Meals** a la carte 20.4
28.45 **t.** 6.75.

GREAT RISSINGTON *Glos. – see Bourton-on-the-Water.*

GREAT SNORING *Norfolk* 404 W 25 – *pop. 191 – ✉ Fakenham.*
London 115 – Cambridge 68 – Norwich 28.

Old Rectory , Barsham Rd, NR21 0HP, ✆ (01328) 820597, *greatsnoring.oldrectory*
ompuserve.com, Fax (01328) 820048, « Part 15C manor house », – rest, TV P.
AE VISA JCB,
closed 24 to 27 December – **Meals** (booking essential) (dinner only) 25.00/27.00 **t.** 5.9
6 rm 78.00/101.00 **t.** – SB.

GREAT TEW *Oxon.* 403 404 P 28 – *pop. 145.*
London 75 – Birmingham 50 – Gloucester 42 – Oxford 21.

Falkland Arms with rm, OX7 4DB, ✆ (01608) 683653, *sjcourage@btconnect.cc*
Fax (01608) 683656, « 17C inn in picturesque village », – TV. MC AE VISA JCB.
Meals *(closed Sunday dinner)* (dinner booking essential) a la carte 13.70/19.00 **t.** – 6
40.00/85.00 **t.**

GREAT YARMOUTH *Norfolk* 404 Z 26 *Great Britain G. – pop. 56 190.*
Env. : *The Broads★.*
Gorleston, Warren Rd ✆ (01493) 661911 – Beach House, Caister-on-Sea ✆ (014
728699.
Marine Par. ✆ (01493) 842195.
London 126 – Cambridge 81 – Ipswich 53 – Norwich 20.

Elizabeth, Marine Par., NR30 3AG, ✆ (01493) 855551, *Fax (01493) 853338* – TV
150. MC AE VISA JCB.
Meals 9.95/19.95 **t.** and a la carte 6.95 – **47 rm** 55.00/95.00 **st.**, 3 suites – SB.

Imperial, North Drive, NR30 1EQ, ✆ (01493) 851113, *imperial@scs_datacom.co*
Fax (01493) 852229 – , rm, rest, TV P – 140. MC AE VISA
Rambouillet : **Meals** *(closed lunch Saturday and Bank Holidays)* 12.50/20.50
and a la carte 6.55 – **39 rm** 68.00/84.00 **st.** – SB.

Star, Hall Quay, NR30 1HG, ✆ (01493) 842294, *star.hotel@rjt.co.uk, Fax (01493) 33021*
, rm, rest, TV P – 70. MC AE VISA
Terrace : **Meals** (bar lunch Monday to Saturday)/dinner 16.95/22.95 **t.** and a la carte 9
– **40 rm** 66.00/94.00 **t.** – SB.

Gorleston-on-Sea *South : 3 m. on A 12 – ✉ Great Yarmouth.*

Cliff, Cliff Hill, NR31 6DH, ☎ (01493) 662179, *cliffhotel@aol.com, Fax (01493) 653617,* – rest, TV P – 170. MC AE ① VISA.
Meals 16.50 **t.** and a la carte 9.50 – **38 rm** 69.00/97.00 **st.**, 1 suite – SB.

GREAT YELDHAM *Essex* 404 V 27 – *pop. 1 513 – ✉ Colchester.*
London 58 – Cambridge 29 – Chelmsford 24 – Colchester 21 – Ipswich 37.

White Hart, Poole St., CO9 4HJ, ☎ (01787) 237250, *Fax (01787) 238044,* , « 16C inn », – P. MC AE ① VISA
Meals a la carte 10.40/28.20 **t.** 9.00.

GREEN ISLAND *Jersey (Channel Islands) – see Channel Islands.*

GRENOSIDE *S. Yorks.* 402 403 404 P 23 – *see Sheffield.*

GRETA BRIDGE *Durham* 402 O 20.
London 253 – Carlisle 63 – Leeds 63 – Middlesbrough 32.

Morritt Arms, DL12 9SE, ☎ (01833) 627232, *relax@themorritt.co.uk, Fax (01833) 627392,* « 17C former coaching inn », , – TV P – 200. MC AE ① VISA
Copperfield : **Meals** 12.95/18.95 **t.** and a la carte 4.40 – ***Pallatts :*** **Meals** a la carte 11.15/19.45 **t.** 4.40 – **23 rm** 59.50/99.50 **st.** – SB.

In this guide

a symbol or a character, printed in **red** or **black**, in **bold** or light type, does not have the same meaning.
Pay particular attention to the explanatory pages.

GREVE DE LECQ *Jersey (Channel Islands)* 403 P 33 and 230 ⑪ – *see Channel Islands.*

GRIMSBY *N.E Lincs.* 402 404 T 23 – *see Great Grimsby.*

GRIMSTHORPE *Lincs.* 402 404 S 25 – *see Bourne.*

GRIMSTON *Norfolk* 404 V 25 – *see King's Lynn.*

GRINDLEFORD *Derbs.* 402 403 404 P 24 – ✉ *Sheffield (S. Yorks.).*
London 165 – Derby 31 – Manchester 34 – Sheffield 10.

Maynard Arms, Main Rd, S32 2HE, on B 6521 ☎ (01433) 630321, *Fax (01433) 630445,* ≤, – rest, TV P – 130. MC AE VISA JCB
Meals *(closed Saturday lunch)* 17.50/21.50 **t.** 7.35 – **8 rm** 69.00/99.00 **t.**, 2 suites – SB.

GRINDON *Staffs.* 403 404 O 24 – *pop. 242 – ✉ Leek.*
London 118 – Birmingham 70 – Derby 26 – Manchester 42 – Stoke-on-Trent 20.

Porch Farmhouse , ST13 7TP, ☎ (01538) 304545, *porchfarmhouse@msn.com, Fax (01538) 304545,* « Part 17C », – TV P. MC VISA.
closed Christmas and New Year – **Meals** (by arrangement) (communal dining) 17.50 **s.** – **3 rm** 37.50/55.00 **s.** – SB.

GRIZEDALE *Cumbria* 402 K 20 – *see Hawkshead.*

GROUVILLE *Jersey (Channel Islands)* 403 P 33 and 230 ⑪ – *see Channel Islands.*

GUERNSEY 403 OP 33 and 230 ⑨ ⑩ – *see Channel Islands.*

GUILDFORD *Surrey* 404 S 30 – *pop. 65 998.*
14 Tunsgate ✆ *(01483) 444333* Y.
London 33 – Brighton 43 – Reading 27 – Southampton 49.

GUILDFORD

Bedford Road	Y	2
Bridge Street	Y	3
Castle Street	Y	5
Chertsey Street	Y	6
Commercial Road	Y	8
Eastgate Gardens	Y	9
Friary Bridge	Y	12
Friary Centre	Y	
High Street	Y	
Ladymead	Z	13
Leapale Lane	Y	15
Leapale Road	Y	16
Leas Road	Y	17
Market Street	Y	18
Mary Road	Y	19
Midleton Road	Z	20
Millbrook	Y	21
New Inn Lane	Z	22
North Street	Y	
One Tree Hill Road	Z	24
Onslow Street	Y	25
Park Street	Y	27
Quarry Street	Y	28
Stoughton Road	Z	30
Trood's Lane	Z	31
Tunsgate Shopping Centre	Y	
Tungsgate	Y	33
Warwick's Bench	Y	34
Woodbridge Road	Z	37

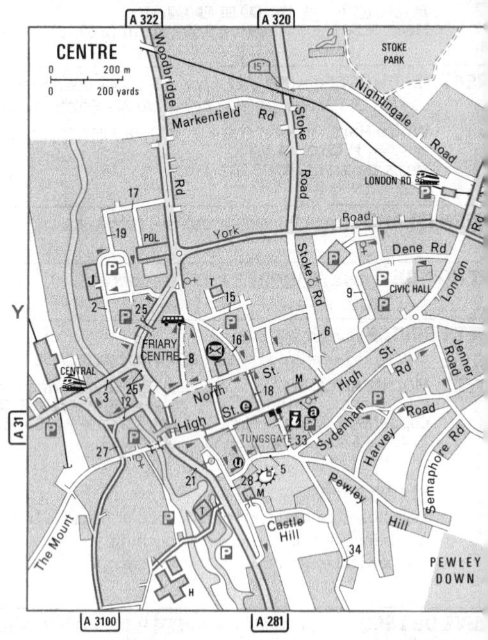

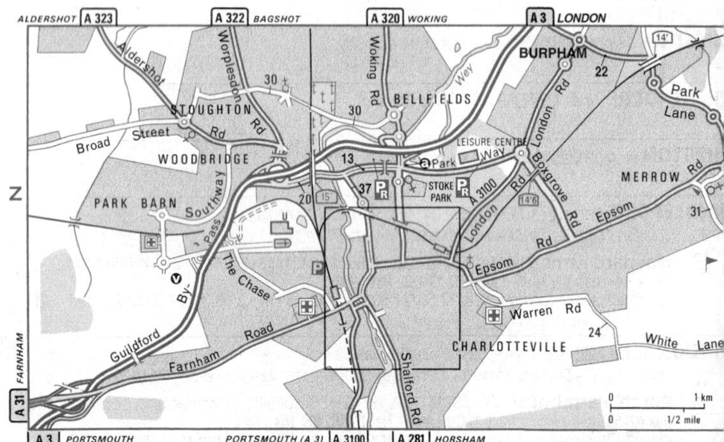

Angel Posting House and Livery, High St., GU1 3DP, ✆ (01483) 564555, *angelh@hotmail.com, Fax (01483) 533770,* « 16C coaching inn with 13C vaulted cellar restaurar – |‡|, ⇆ rest, ▤ rest, TV ♿ – 🏛 70. MC AE O VISA Y
No. 1 Angel Gate : Meals 14.50/24.50 **t.** and dinner a la carte 🍷 10.50 – ☕ 12.50 – **14** 135.00/180.00 **t.**, 7 suites – SB.

Posthouse Guildford, Egerton Rd, GU2 5XZ, ✆ (0870) 400 9036, *Fax (01483) 3029* Z
Meals *(closed lunch Saturday)* a la carte 22.85/28.15 **st.** 🍷 6.95 – ☕ 11.95 – **162** 129.00 **st.**, 4 suites – SB.

Travel Inn, Parkway, GU1 1UP, North : 1 ½ m. by A 320 on A 25 ☎ (01483) 304932, *Fax (01483) 304935* – |‡|, ⇔ rm, ▤ rest, TV ♿ P – 🏛 45. MO AE ⓓ VISA. ⚹ Z a
Meals (grill rest.) – **87 rm** 40.95 **t.**

Café de Paris, 35 Castle St., GU1 3UQ, ☎ (01483) 534896, *tniel.cafedeparis@aol.com, Fax (01483) 224340* – MO AE VISA Y u
closed last week July, first week August, Sunday and Bank Holidays – **Meals** - French - 14.95 **t.** and a la carte 🍾 6.20.

The Gate, No. 3 Milkhouse Gate, GU1 3EZ, ☎ (01483) 576300, *keithrussell@thegaterestaurant.co.uk* – ⇔. MO AE VISA Y a
closed Sunday – **Meals** 13.50 **t.** (lunch) and a la carte 23.95/30.85 **t.** 🍾 7.00.

Shere *East : 6 ¾ m. by A 246 off A 25* – **Z** – ✉ *Guildford.*

Kinghams, Gomshall Lane, GU5 9HE, ☎ (01483) 202168, *Fax (01483) 202168*, « 17C cottage » – P. MO AE ⓓ VISA JCB
closed 25 December-6 January, Sunday dinner and Monday – **Meals** (booking essential) 13.95/15.95 **t.** and a la carte 🍾 5.00.

JITING POWER *Glos.* 403 404 O 28 – ✉ *Cheltenham.*
London 95 – Birmingham 47 – Gloucester 30 – Oxford 39.

Guiting Guest House, Post Office Lane, GL54 5TZ, ☎ (01451) 850470, *guiting.guest_house@virgin.net, Fax (01451) 850034*, « 16C farmhouse » – ⇔ TV. MO VISA JCB
closed 2 weeks January and 2 weeks February – **Meals** (by arrangement) 20.00 **st.** – **5 rm** ☕ 38.00/60.00 **st.**

Le Grand Londres (GREATER LONDON) est composé de la City et de 32 arrondissements administratifs (Borough) eux-mêmes divisés en quartiers ou en villages ayant conservé leur caractère propre (Area).

JLWORTHY CROSS *Devon* 403 H 32 – *see Tavistock.*

JNTHORPE *Notts.* 402 403 404 R 25 – *pop. 646.*
London 132 – Lincoln 32 – Nottingham 12 – Sheffield 40.

Unicorn, Gunthorpe Bridge, NG14 7FB, Southeast : 1 ½ m. by A 6097 and Gunthorpe (riverside) rd ☎ (0115) 966 3612, *Fax (0115) 966 4801*, ≤, 🐟 – ⚓, ▤ rest, TV P. MO AE VISA. ⚹
Meals (grill rest.) (bar lunch Monday to Saturday)/dinner a la carte 11.15/22.00 **t.** – **15 rm** ☕ 49.50/59.50 **t.**

JNWALLOE *Cornwall* 403 E 33 – *see Helston.*

ACKNESS *N. Yorks.* 402 S 21 – *see Scarborough.*

ADDENHAM *Bucks.* 404 R 28 – *pop. 4 906.*
London 54 – Aylesbury 8 – Oxford 21.

Green Dragon, Churchway, HP17 8AA, ☎ (01844) 291403, *the.greendragon@virgin.net, Fax (01844) 299532*, 🌳 – P. MO AE VISA
closed Sunday dinner – **Meals** (booking essential) 14.95/16.95 **st.** (dinner) and a la carte 18.00/22.00 **st.** 🍾 9.00.

ADLEIGH *Suffolk* 404 W 27 – *pop. 6 595.*
🅱 *Hadleigh Library, 29 High St.* ☎ *(01473) 823778.*
London 72 – Cambridge 49 – Colchester 17 – Ipswich 10.

Edge Hall, 2 High St., IP7 5AP, ☎ (01473) 822458, *Fax (01473) 827751*, 🌳 – ⇔ TV P
Meals (by arrangement) 22.00 **st.** 🍾 4.50 – **9 rm** ☕ 37.50/80.00 **st.** – SB.

ADLEY HEATH *Worcs.* – *see Droitwich.*

AILEY *Oxon.* 403 404 P 28 – *see Witney.*

HAILSHAM *E. Sussex* 404 U 31 – *pop. 18 426.*

Wellshurst G. & C.C., North St., Hellingly ☎ (01435) 813636.
London 57 – Brighton 23 – Eastbourne 7 – Hastings 20.

Boship Farm, Lower Dicker, BN27 4AT, Northwest : 3 m. by A 295 on A ☎ (01323) 844826, *boship.farm@forestdale.com, Fax (01323) 843945,* heated, – rm, – 120.
Meals (bar lunch Monday to Saturday)/dinner 22.00 **t.** and a la carte 5.85 – **45 r** 60.00/85.00 **t.**, 2 suites – SB.

Travelodge, Boship Roundabout, Lower Dicker, BN27 4DT, Northwest : 3 m. by A 295 a A 22 on A 267 ☎ (01323) 844556, *Fax (01323) 844556* – rm, rest,
Meals (grill rest.) – **58 rm** 49.95 **t.**

at Magham Down *Northeast : 2 m. by A 295 on A 271 – ✉ Hailsham.*

Olde Forge, BN27 1PN, ☎ (01323) 842893, *theoldforgehotelandrestaurant@tesco.n Fax (01323) 842893* –
Meals (dinner only) 23.50 **t.** – **7 rm** 44.00/58.00 **st.**

HALE *Gtr. Manchester* 402 403 404 M 23 – *see Altrincham.*

HALEBARNS *Gtr. Manchester* 402 ㉝ 403 ③ 404 ⑨ – *see Altrincham.*

HALFWAY BRIDGE *W. Sussex* 404 R 31 – *see Petworth.*

HALIFAX *W. Yorks.* 402 O 22 – *pop. 91 069.*

Halifax Bradley Hall, Holywell Green ☎ (01422) 374108 – Halifax West End, Paddc Lane, Highroad Well ☎ (01422) 353608, Union Lane, Ogden ☎ (01422) 244171 – Ryburn, Norland, Sowerby Bridge ☎ (01422) 831355 – Lightcliffe, Knowle Top Rd (01422) 202459.
Piece Hall ☎ (01422) 368725.
London 205 – Bradford 8 – Burnley 21 – Leeds 15 – Manchester 28.

Holdsworth House, Holmfield, HX2 9TG, North : 3 m. by A 629 and Shay La ☎ (01422) 240024, *info@holdsworthhouse.co.uk, Fax (01422) 245174,* « Part 17C mar house », – – 150.
closed 26 to 30 December – **Meals** *(closed lunch Saturday and Sunday)* 13.00/24.50 **t.** 7. – 8.25 – **36 rm** 85.00/124.00 **t.**, 4 suites – SB.

Imperial Crown, 42-46 Horton St., HX1 1QE, ☎ (01422) 342342, *Fax (01422) 34986* rm, – 150.
Meals (bar lunch Monday to Saturday)/dinner 17.50 **st.** and a la carte 7.25 – 9.7 **39 rm** 89.00/99.00 **st.**, 2 suites – SB.

Design House (Restaurant), Dean Clough (Gate 5), HX3 5AX, ☎ (01422) 383242, *en ries@designhouserestaurant.co.uk, Fax (01422) 322732* –
closed 25 December, 1 January, Sunday and Saturday lunch – **Meals** a la carte 21.90/27.8 10.80.

HALLAND *E. Sussex* 404 U 31 – – ✉ *Lewes.*

London 59 – Brighton 17 – Eastbourne 15 – Maidstone 35.

Shortgate Manor Farm without rest., BN8 6PJ, Southwest : 1 m. on B 2 ☎ (01825) 840320, *ewalt@shortgate.co.uk, Fax (01825) 840320,* –
3 rm 35.00/60.00.

HALL GREEN *W. Mids.* 402 403 404 O 26 – *see Birmingham.*

HALNAKER *W. Sussex – see Chichester.*

HALTWHISTLE *Northd.* 401 402 M 19 *Great Britain G.* – *pop. 3 773.*

Env. : *Hadrian's Wall★★, N : 4½ m. by A 6079 – Housesteads★★* **AC**, *NE : 6 m. by B 631 Roman Army Museum★* **AC**, *NW : 5 m. by A 69 and B 6318 – Vindolanda (Museum★) NE : 5 m. by A 69 – Steel Rig (<★) NE : 5½ m. by B 6318.*
Wallend Farm, Greenhead ☎ (01697) 747367.
Railway Station, Station Rd ☎ (01434) 322002.
London 335 – Carlisle 22 – Newcastle upon Tyne 37.

Centre of Britain, Main St., NE49 0BZ, ☎ (01434) 322422, *enquiries@centre-of-britain.org.uk, Fax (01434) 322655* – TV P. MC AE D VISA
Meals 9.45/15.50 **t.** and a la carte 4.55 – **9 rm** 55.00/80.00 **t.** – SB.

Ashcroft without rest., Lantys Lonnen, NE49 0DA, ☎ (01434) 320213, *Fax (01434) 320213,* « Gardens » – TV P. MC VISA.
7 rm 26.00/55.00 **st.**

AMBLETON *Rutland – see Oakham.*

AMBROOK *South Gloucestershire* 403 404 M 29 – *see Bristol.*

AMSTEAD MARSHALL *Newbury* 403 404 P29 – *see Newbury.*

AMSTERLEY *Durham* 401 402 O 19 – *pop. 397* – ✉ *Bishop Auckland.*
London 260 – Carlisle 75 – Middlesbrough 30 – Newcastle upon Tyne 22.

Grove House, Hamsterley Forest, DL13 3NL, West : 3 ¾ m. via Bedburn on Hamsterley Forest Toll rd ☎ (01388) 488203, *x047@dial.pipex.com, Fax (01388) 488174,* – P.
closed 15 December-15 January – **Meals** (by arrangement) 19.50 **st.** – **3 rm** 26.50/57.00.

ANDFORTH *Ches.* 402 403 404 N 23 – *see Wilmslow.*

ANWOOD *Shrops.* 402 403 L 25 – *see Shrewsbury.*

AREWOOD *W. Yorks.* 402 P 22 – *pop. 3 222* – ✉ *Leeds.*
London 214 – Harrogate 9 – Leeds 10 – York 20.

Harewood Arms, Harrogate Rd, LS17 9LH, on A 61 ☎ (0113) 288 6566, *Fax (0113) 288 6064,* – rest, TV P. MC AE D VISA
Meals (bar lunch Monday to Saturday)/dinner 17.50/21.50 **t.** and a la carte 4.10 – **24 rm** 55.00/70.00 **st.** – SB.

ARLOW *Essex* 404 U 28 – *pop. 74 629.*
18 *Nazeing, Middle St.* ☎ *(01992) 893798.*
London 22 – Cambridge 37 – Ipswich 60.

Swallow Churchgate Manor, Churchgate St., Old Harlow, CM17 0JT, East : 3 ¼ m. by A 414 and B 183 ☎ (01279) 420246, *info@swallowhotels.com, Fax (01279) 437720,* – TV P – 170. MC AE D VISA
Meals (bar lunch Saturday) 21.00/23.00 **t.** (dinner) and a la carte 22.80/28.70 **t.** 6.50 – **82 rm** 102.00/135.00 **t.**, 3 suites – SB.

Harlow Moat House, Southern Way, CM18 7BA, Southeast : 2 ¼ m. by A 1025 on A 414 ☎ (01279) 829988, *revhar@queensmoat.co.uk, Fax (01279) 635094,* – , rest, TV P – 200. MC AE D VISA
Meals (carving rest.) (bar lunch Saturday) 17.95 **st** (dinner) and a la carte 18.50/22.50 **st.** 6.95 – 11.50 – **119 rm** 115.00/135.00 **st.** – SB.

Green Man, Mulberry Green, Old Harlow, CM17 0ET, East : 2 ¼ m. by A 414 and B 183 ☎ (01279) 442521, *Fax (01279) 626113* – rm, TV P – 60. MC AE D VISA
Meals (bar lunch Saturday) a la carte 15.85/28.15 **t.** 5.95 – 9.75 – **55 rm** 95.00/99.00 **st.** – SB.

Travel Inn, Cambridge Rd, Old Harlow, CM20 2EP, Northeast : 3 ¼ m. by A 414 on A 1184 ☎ (01279) 442545, *Fax (01279) 452169* – rm, TV P. MC AE D VISA.
Meals (grill rest.) – **38 rm** 40.95 **t.**

ARNHAM *Wilts.* 403 404 O 30 – *see Salisbury.*

AROME *N. Yorks. – see Helmsley.*

ARPENDEN *Herts.* 404 S 28 – *pop. 28 097.*
18 *Harpenden Common, East Commmon* ☎ *(01582) 712856* – 18 *Hammonds End,* ☎ *(01582) 712580.*
London 32 – Luton 6.

Hanover International, 1 Luton Rd, AL5 2PX, ✆ (01582) 760271, *david.hunter9@vir .net, Fax (01582) 460819,* – |‡|, ⋟ rm, ▤ rest, TV ✆ ♿ P – 150. AE VISA JC *closed 25 December-2 January* – **Meals** (bar meals Saturday lunch, Sunday dinner and Ba Holidays) a la carte 16.25/24.45 **t.** – ☕ 8.95 – **58 rm** 105.00/140.00, 2 suites – SB.

Chef Peking, 5-6 Church Green, AL5 2TP, ✆ (01582) 769358, *Fax (01582) 462094* – ▤. AE VISA
Meals - Chinese (Peking, Szechuan) - 15.00/24.00 **st.** and a la carte 🍷 4.00.

HARROGATE *N. Yorks.* 402 P 22 *Great Britain G.* – *pop. 66 178.*

See : *Town*★.

Exc. : *Fountains Abbey*★★★ *AC :- Studley Royal*★★ *AC (≤★ from Anne Boleyn's Sea Fountains Hall (Façade*★*), N : 13 m. by A 61 and B 6265* **AY** – *Harewood House*★★ *(Gallery*★*) AC, S : 7½ m. by A 61* **BZ**.

Forest Lane Head ✆ (01423) 863158 – Follifoot Rd, Pannal ✆ (01423) 871641 – Oakdale ✆ (01423) 567162 – Crimple Valley, Hookstone Wood Rd ✆ (01423) 883485.

Royal Baths Assembly Rooms, Crescent Rd ✆ (01423) 537300.

London 211 – Bradford 18 – Leeds 15 – Newcastle upon Tyne 76 – York 22.

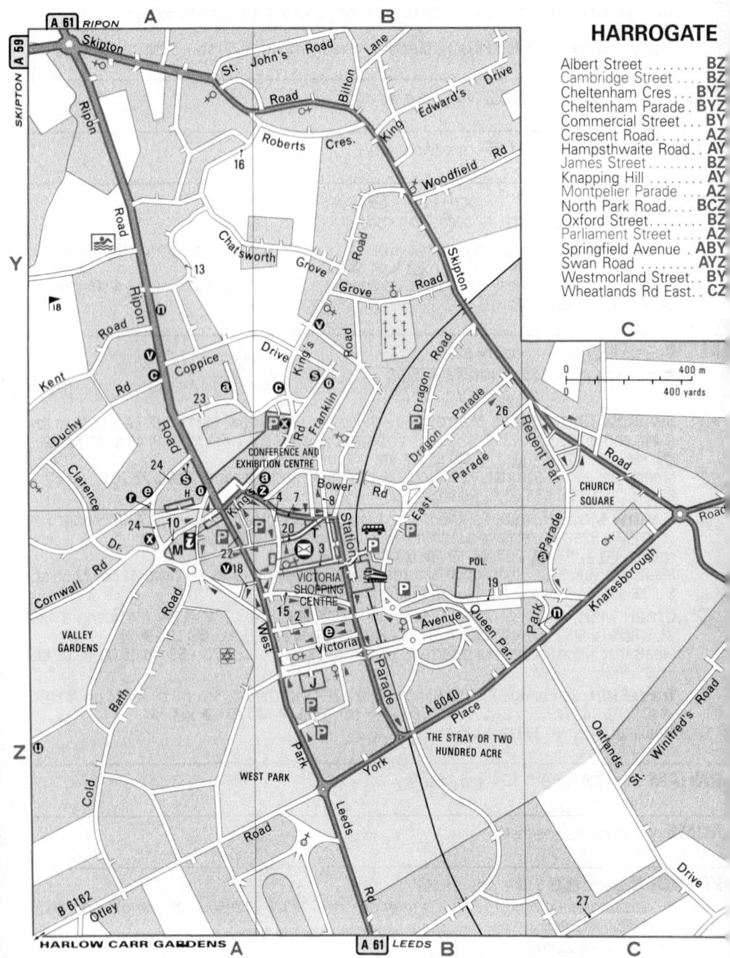

Rudding Park, Rudding Park, Follifoot, HG3 1JH, Southeast : 3 ¾ m. by A 661 ✆ (01423) 871350, *sales@rudding-park.co.uk, Fax (01423) 872286,* 18, – rm, rest, P – 300. AE VISA.
The Clocktower : **Meals** 12.50/24.90 **t.** and dinner a la carte 7.50 – **48 rm** 110.00/140.00 **st.**, 2 suites – SB.

Cedar Court, Queen Building, Park Par., HG1 5AH, ✆ (01423) 858585, *sales@cedarcourt.karoo.co.uk, Fax (01423) 504950,* – rm, rest, P – 325. AE VISA CZ n
Queens : **Meals** *(closed Saturday lunch)* 12.50/18.50 **t.** 7.95 – 11.95 – **100 rm** 100.00/160.00 **st.** – SB.

Harrogate Moat House, Kings Rd, HG1 1XX, ✆ (01423) 849988, *cbhgt@queensmoat.co.uk, Fax (01423) 524435,* – rm, rest, P – 400. AE VISA JCB BY x
Abbey : **Meals** (carving rest.) (dinner only) 16.95/19.95 **st.** 6.50 – ***Boulevard :*** **Meals** (dinner only) a la carte 16.50/22.50 **st.** 6.50 – 11.50 – **205 rm** 115.00/130.00 **st.**, 9 suites – SB.

St. George Swallow, 1 Ripon Rd, HG1 2SY, ✆ (01423) 561431, *info@swallowhotels.com, Fax (01423) 530037,* P – 120. AE VISA AY o
Meals (bar lunch)/dinner 18.50 **st.** and a la carte 6.25 – **89 rm** 95.00/120.00 **st.**, 1 suite.

Old Swan, Swan Rd, HG1 2SR, ✆ (01423) 500055, *info@oldswan.macdonald-hotels.co.uk, Fax (01423) 501154,* P – 400. AE VISA JCB. AY e
Wedgewood Room : **Meals** (dinner only and Sunday lunch)/dinner 19.95/23.95 **st.** 8.50 – ***Library :*** **Meals** *(closed Sunday)* (dinner only) a la carte 23.25/29.50 **st.** 8.50 – **127 rm** 105.00/130.00 **st.**, 9 suites – SB.

The Balmoral, Franklin Mount, HG1 5EJ, ✆ (01423) 508208, *info@balmoralhotel.co.uk, Fax (01423) 530652,* « Antique furnishings », – P. AE VISA BY v
closed Christmas and New Year – **Meals** – (see ***Villu Toots*** below) – 8.50 – **16 rm** 84.00/114.00 **st.**, 4 suites – SB.

Grants, Swan Rd, HG1 2SS, ✆ (01423) 560666, *enquiries@grantshotel-harrowgate.com, Fax (01423) 502550* – rest, rest, P – 70. AE VISA JCB. AY s
Chimney Pots Bistro : **Meals** a la carte 17.40/25.40 **t.** 5.95 – **41 rm** 99.00/155.00 **t.**, 1 suite – SB.

White House, 10 Park Par., HG1 5AH, ✆ (01423) 501388, *info@whitehouse-hotel.demon.co.uk, Fax (01423) 527973,* « Victorian house, antique furnishings », – . AE VISA. CZ a
Meals (booking essential) (lunch by arrangement)/dinner a la carte 24.50/28.25 **t.** 7.50 – **9 rm** 75.00/135.00 **t.**, 1 suite – SB.

Studley, 28 Swan Rd, HG1 2SE, ✆ (01423) 560425, *studley@hotels.activebooking.com, Fax (01423) 530967* – P. AE VISA AZ x
Le Breton : **Meals** 7.95/17.95 **t.** and dinner a la carte 6.00 – **34 rm** 68.00/100.00 **t.**, 2 suites – SB.

Quality Kimberley without rest., 11-19 Kings Rd, HG1 5JY, ✆ (01423) 505613, *info@kimberley.scotnet.co.uk, Fax (01423) 530276* – P – 40. AE VISA. BY c
closed 22 December-3 January – – 8.50 – **48 rm** 69.50/89.50 **t.**

Ruskin, 1 Swan Rd, HG1 2SS, ✆ (01423) 502045, *ruskin.hotel@virgin.net, Fax (01423) 506131,* – P. AE VISA JCB AY s
Meals (residents only) (dinner only) 22.50 **st.** 6.75 – **7 rm** 75.00/125.00 **st.** – SB.

Britannia Lodge without rest., 16 Swan Rd, HG1 2SA, ✆ (01423) 508482, *britlodge3@aol.com, Fax (01423) 526840,* – P. AE VISA. AYZ r
12 rm 45.00/75.00 **st.**

Alexa House, 26 Ripon Rd, HG1 2JJ, ✆ (01423) 501988, *alexahouse@msn.com, Fax (01423) 504086* – P. AE VISA. AY n
Meals (by arrangement) (dinner only) 14.50 **st.** 4.50 – **13 rm** 50.00/75.00 **st.** – SB.

The Delaine without rest., 17 Ripon Rd, HG1 2JL, ✆ (01423) 567974, *Fax (01423) 561723,* – P. VISA JCB AY c
10 rm 45.00/62.00 **st.**

Alexandra Court without rest., 8 Alexandra Rd, HG1 5JS, ✆ (01423) 502764, *Fax (01423) 523151* – P. AE VISA BY o
12 rm 38.00/65.00 **t.**

Acacia Lodge without rest., 21 Ripon Rd, HG1 2JL, ✆ (01423) 560752, *Fax (01423) 503725* – P. AY v
7 rm 58.00/78.00 **st.**

Brookfield House without rest., 5 Alexandra Rd, HG1 5JS, ✆ (01423) 506646, *brookfieldhouse@hotmail.com, Fax (01423) 566470* – P. AE VISA BY s
closed Christmas and New Year – **8 rm** 30.00/55.00 **st.**

Ashwood House without rest., 7 Spring Grove, HG1 2HS, ✆ (01423) 560081, *ashwoo ouse@aol.com, Fax (01423) 527928* – ✻ 📺 P. ✻ AY
closed 24 December-2 January – **9 rm** ☕ 37.00/58.00 **t.**

Knox Mill House ✻ without rest., Knox Mill Lane, HG3 2AE, North : 1 ½ m. by A ✆ (01423) 560650, *Fax (01423) 560650,* ← – ✻ P. ✻
closed Christmas and New Year – **3 rm** ☕ 35.00/45.00 **s.**

Garden House (without rest.), 14 Harlow Moor Drive, HG2 0JX, ✆ (01423) 503059, *gar nhouse@hotels.harrogate.com, Fax (01423) 503059* – 📺. MC AE ① VISA. ✻ AZ
7 rm ☕ 26.00/52.00 **st.**

Villu Toots (at The Balmoral H.), Franklin Mount, HG1 5EJ, ✆ (01423) 705805, *info@bal ralhotel.co.uk, Fax (01423) 530652* – ▤ P. MC AE VISA BY
closed Christmas, New Year and Saturday lunch – **Meals** 13.50/20.00 **t.** and a la carte 🍷 5.

Olivers 24, 24 Kings Rd, HG1 5JW, ✆ (01423) 568600, *Fax (01423) 531838* – MC AE JCB BY
closed 25-26 December, 1 January, Sunday and Monday – **Meals** (dinner only) 10.50/13.9 and a la carte 🍷 8.95.

Courtyard, 1 Montpellier Mews, HG1 2TQ, ✆ (01423) 530708, *Fax (01423) 530708,* ✻ ✻. MC VISA JCB AZ
closed 25-26 December, Sunday and Bank Holidays – **Meals** a la carte 17.15/24.85 **t.** 🍷 6.9

Sasso, 8-10 Princes Sq., HG1 1LX, ✆ (01423) 508838, *Fax (01423) 508838* – MC VISA
closed 25 December-3 January, Sunday and Monday lunch – **Meals** - Italian - a la ca 16.85/21.70 **t.** 🍷 7.35. BZ

Est, Est, Est, 16 Cheltenham Cres., HD1 1DL, ✆ (01423) 566453, *Fax (01423) 521737* – MC AE ① VISA BY
closed 25 and 26 December – **Meals** - Italian - a la carte 13.45/21.10 **t.**

at Kettlesing *West : 6½ m. by A 59* – **AY** – ✉ *Harrogate.*

Knabbs Ash without rest., Skipton Rd, HG3 2LT, South : 2 m. on A 59 ✆ (01423) 77104 *olin+sheila@knabbsash.freeserve.co.uk, Fax (01423) 771515,* ←, ✻, ✻ – ✻ 📺 P. ✻
closed 25-26 December – **3 rm** ☕ 35.00/50.00.

HARTFIELD *E. Sussex* 404 U 30 – *pop. 2 026.*

London 47 – Brighton 28 – Maidstone 25.

Bolebroke Mill ✻ without rest., Edenbridge Rd, TN7 4JP, North : 1 ¼ m. by B 2 turning right onto unmarked rd ✆ (01892) 770425, *etb@bolebrokemill.demon.co. Fax (01892) 770425,* « Part early 17C cornmill, original features », ✻ – ✻ 📺 P. MC AE VISA JCB. ✻
closed mid December-mid February – **5 rm** ☕ 59.00/78.00.

HARTFORD *Ches.* 402 403 404 M 24 – *pop. 4 605.*

London 188 – Chester 15 – Liverpool 31 – Manchester 25.

Hartford Hall, 81 School Lane, CW8 1PW, ✆ (01606) 75711, *Fax (01606) 782285,* ✻ ✻ rm, 📺 P – ✻ 35. MC AE ① VISA. ✻
Meals 6.00/11.00 **t.** (lunch) and a la carte 16.50/24.40 **t.** 🍷 4.50 – ☕ 6.95 – **19 rm** 55. 70.00 **t.**, 1 suite.

HARTINGTON *Derbs.* 402 403 404 O 24 – *pop. 1 604 (inc. Dovedale)* – ✉ *Buxton.*

London 168 – Derby 36 – Manchester 40 – Sheffield 34 – Stoke-on-Trent 22.

Biggin Hall ✻, Biggin, SK17 0DH, Southeast : 2 m. by B 5054 ✆ (01298) 84451, *biggi l@compuserve.com, Fax (01298) 84681,* ←, « Part 17C », ✻ – ✻ 📺 P. MC AE VISA. ✻
Meals (booking essential to non-residents) (dinner only) 14.50 **st.** 🍷 5.50 – ☕ 3.50 – **19** 55.00/90.00 – SB.

This Guide is not a comprehensive list of all hotels and restaurants, nor even of all good hotels and restaurants in Great Britain and Ireland.

Since our aim is to be of service to all motorists, we must show establishments in all categories and so we have made a selection of some in each.

ARTLEBURY *Worcs.* 403 N 26 – *pop. 2 253.*
London 135 – Birmingham 20 – Worcester 11.

Travelodge, Crossway Green, DY13 9SH, South : 2 ½ m. by B 4193 on A 449 (southbound carriageway) ✆ (01299) 250553, *Fax (01299) 251774* – rm, TV P. MC AE VISA JCB.
Meals (grill rest.) – **32 rm** 49.95 **t.**

ARTLEPOOL *Hartlepool* 402 Q 19 – *pop. 87 310.*
18, 18 Seaton Carew, Tees Rd ✆ (01429) 266249 – 18 Castle Eden & Peterlee ✆ (01429) 836220 – 18 Hart Warren ✆ (01429) 274398.
Teesside Airport : ✆ (01325) 332811, SW : 20 m. by A 689, A 1027, A 135 and A 67.
Hartlepool Art Gallery, Church Sq. ✆ (01429) 869706.
London 263 – Durham 19 – Middlesbrough 9 – Sunderland 21.

Grand, Swainson St., TS24 8AA, ✆ (01429) 266345, *Fax (01429) 265217* – TV P – 200. MC AE VISA.
Meals *(closed Sunday dinner)* (bar lunch)/dinner a la carte 10.40/25.35 **t.** 5.50 – **46 rm** 54.50/100.00 **t.**

Travel Inn, Old West Quay, Hartlepool Marina, TS24 0XZ, ✆ (01429) 890115, *Fax (01429) 868674,* – rm, rest, TV P. MC AE VISA.
Meals (grill rest.) – **40 rm** 40.95 **t.**

Seaton Carew *Southeast : 2 m. on A 178.*

Staincliffe, The Cliff, TS25 1AB, ✆ (01429) 264301, *Fax (01429) 421366,* – rm, TV P – 200. MC AE VISA JCB.
Meals a la carte 10.00/14.00 **st.** 5.00 – **20 rm** 48.00/100.00 **t.** – SB.

Krimo's, Nephine House, The Marina, TS24 0YB, ✆ (01429) 266120, *krimos@krimos.co.uk* – MC VISA JCB
closed 25-26 December, 1 January, Sunday and Monday – **Meals** 8.95/12.00 **st.** (lunch) and a la carte 17.85/24.40 **st.** 4.50.

Great Britain and Ireland is now covered by an Atlas at a scale of 1 inch to 4.75 miles.

Three easy to use versions: Paperback, Spiralbound and Hardback.

ARTSHEAD MOOR SERVICE AREA *W. Yorks.* 402 O 22 – ✉ *Brighouse.*
London 213 – Bradford 8 – Burnley 31 – Manchester 35 – Sheffield 39.

Days Inn without rest., Clifton, HD6 4JX, M 62 between junctions 25 and 26 (eastbound carriageway) ✆ (01274) 851706, Reservations (Freephone) 0800 0280400, *Fax (01274) 855169* – TV P. MC AE VISA JCB
7.45 **38 rm** 45.00 **t.**

ARVINGTON *Worcs.* 403 404 O27 – *see Evesham.*

ARWELL *Oxon.* 403 404 Q 29 – *pop. 2 236.*
London 64 – Oxford 16 – Reading 18 – Swindon 22.

Kingswell, Reading Rd, OX11 0LZ, South : ¾ m. on A 417 ✆ (01235) 833043, *kingswell@breathemail.net, Fax (01235) 833193* – TV P – 30. MC AE VISA JCB.
closed 26 December-3 January – **Meals** 15.75/19.75 **t.** and a la carte – **19 rm** 90.00/110.00 **t.** – SB.

ARWICH and DOVERCOURT *Essex* 404 X 28 – *pop. 18 436 (Harwich).*
9 Station Rd, Parkeston ✆ (01255) 503616.
to Germany (Hamburg) (DFDS Seaways A/S) daily (19 h 30 mn) – to Denmark (Esbjerg) (DFDS Seaways A/S) 1-3 daily (21 h) – to The Netherlands (Hook of Holland) (Stena Line) 2 daily (3 h 30 mn).
Iconfield Park, Parkeston ✆ (01255) 506139.
London 78 – Chelmsford 41 – Colchester 20 – Ipswich 23.

Pier at Harwich, The Quay, CO12 3HH, ✆ (01255) 241212, *info@thepieratharwich.co.uk, Fax (01255) 551922,* – TV P. MC AE VISA.
Harbourside : **Meals** - Seafood - 17.50/19.50 **t.** and a la carte 6.95 – 5.50 – **14 rm** 62.50/150.00 **st.** – SB.

HASLEMERE *Surrey* 404 R 30 – *pop. 12 218.*

London 47 – Brighton 46 – Southampton 44.

Lythe Hill, Petworth Rd, GU27 3BQ, East : 1 ½ m. on B 2131 ☎ (01428) 651251, *lythe@lythehill.co.uk, Fax (01428) 644131*, ≤, – rest, TV ♿ P – 100. MC AE D JCB
Meals *(closed Saturday and Sunday)* 19.50/22.50 and a la carte 8.50 – ***Auberge de France :*** **Meals** - French - (dinner only and Sunday lunch)/dinner a la carte 32.50/39.75 8.50 – 12.00 – **28 rm** 98.00/120.00 **st.**, 12 suites – SB.

Georgian House, High St., GU27 2JY, ☎ (01428) 656644, *mail@georgianhousehotel.co..., Fax (01428) 645600*, – TV P – 120. MC AE D VISA.
Meals a la carte 14.50/22.05 **st.** 5.00 – 8.50 – **24 rm** 70.00 **st.**

HASLINGDEN *Lancs.* 402 N 22.

London 228 – Blackpool 40 – Burnley 9 – Leeds 39 – Manchester 28 – Liverpool 52.

Sykeside Country House, Rawtenstall Road End, BB4 6QE, South : 1 m. by A 680 on A 681 ☎ (01706) 831163, *Fax (01706) 830090*, – TV ♿ P. MC AE D VISA JCB.
Meals *(closed Monday lunch and Sunday dinner)* 11.95/12.95 **t.** (lunch) and dinner a la carte 20.40/25.40 **t.** 8.95 – **10 rm** 62.00/80.00 **t.** – SB.

When visiting Great Britain,
use the Michelin Green Guide **"Great Britain".**
- *Detailed descriptions of places of interest*
- *Touring programmes*
- *Maps and street plans*
- *The history of the country*
- *Photographs and drawings of monuments, beauty spots, houses...*

HASTINGS and ST. LEONARDS *E. Sussex* 404 V 31 – *pop. 81 139 (Hastings).*

18 *Beauport Park, Battle Rd, St. Leonards-on-Sea ☎ (01424) 852977.*

Town Hall, Queen's Sq., Priory Meadow ☎ (01424) 781111 – Old Town Hall ☎ (01424) 781111 (summer only).

London 65 – Brighton 37 – Folkestone 37 – Maidstone 34.

Plan opposite

Beauport Park , Battle Rd, TN38 8EA, Northwest : 3 ½ m. at junction of A 2100 with B 2159 ☎ (01424) 851222, *reservations@beauportprkhotel.demon.co.uk, Fax (01424) 852465*, ≤, « Formal garden », heated, 18, – , rest, TV – 60. MC AE D VISA JCB
Meals 16.00/24.00 **st.** and a la carte – ***Brasserie :*** **Meals** a la carte approx. 22.90 **st.** – 26 rm 90.00/115.00 **st.**

Cinque Ports, Summerfields, Bohemia Rd, TN34 1ET, ☎ (01424) 439222, *enquiries@cinqueports.co.uk, Fax (01424) 437277* – TV P – 200. MC AE D VISA JCB. AZ
Meals (bar lunch Monday to Saturday) (carving lunch Sunday)/dinner 13.95/20.00 and a la carte 7.95 – **40 rm** 65.00/85.00 **st.** – SB.

Tower House, 26-28 Tower Road West, TN38 0RG, ☎ (01424) 427217, *towerhot@dialex.com, Fax (01424) 427217*, – TV. MC AE D VISA. AY
Meals (residents only) (dinner only) 16.50/18.50 **st.** 4.00 – **10 rm** 39.50/65.00 **st.** –

Travel Inn, 1 John Macadam Way, TN37 7DB, ☎ (01424) 754070, *Fax (01424) 753139* – rm, TV ♿ P. MC AE D VISA. AY
Meals (grill rest.) – **44 rm** 40.95 **t.**

Parkside House without rest., 59 Lower Park Rd, TN34 2LD, ☎ (01424) 433096, *Fax (01424) 421431*, – TV. MC VISA. BY
5 rm 30.00/56.00 **s.**

Lionsdown House without rest., 116 High St., Old Town, TN34 3ET, ☎ (01424) 420802, *haronlionsdown@aol.com, Fax (01424) 420802*, « Medieval Wealden hall house with Georgian facade » – TV. MC AE VISA JCB. BY
closed 25 and 26 December **3 rm** 30.00/46.00 **st.**

Röser's, 64 Eversfield Pl., TN37 6DB, ☎ (01424) 712218, *gerald@rosers.co.uk, Fax (01424) 712218* – MC AE D VISA BZ
closed last 2 weeks June, first 2 weeks January, 25 and 26 December, Saturday lunch, Sunday and Monday – **Meals** 20.95/23.95 **st.** and a la carte 7.50.

HASTINGS AND ST. LEONARDS

pert Road . . . . BZ 3
urne (The) . . . . BY 4
mbridge Gardens . . . . BZ 5
stle Street . . . . BZ 7
stle Hill Road . . . . BZ 8
rnwallis Gardens . . . . BZ 9
rnwallis Terrace . . . . BZ 10
nmark Place . . . . BZ 13
Dorset Place . . . . BZ 15
Gensing Road . . . . AZ 16
George Street . . . . BY 18
Grosvenor Crescent . . . . AY 19
Harold Place . . . . BZ 20
Havelock Road . . . . BZ 21
King's Road . . . . AZ 22
London Road . . . . AZ
Marine Court . . . . AZ 23
Middle Street . . . . BZ 24
Norman Road . . . . AZ
Priory Meadow Shopping Centre . . . . BZ
Queen's Road . . . . BZ
Robertson Street . . . . BZ 27
Rock-a-Nore Road . . . . BY 30
St. Helen's Park Road . . . . . BY 31
Sedlescombe Road South . AY 32
Silchester Road . . . . AZ 33
Warrior Square . . . . AZ 34
Wellington Place . . . . BZ 35
Wellington Square . . . . BZ 36
White Rock Road . . . . BZ 38

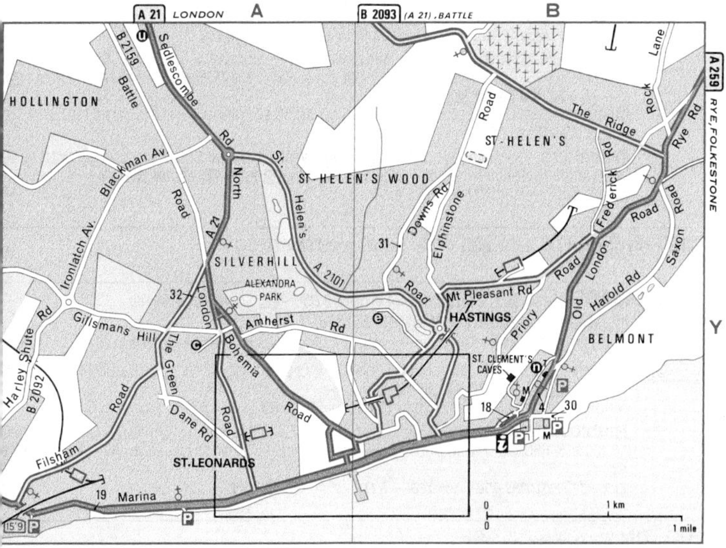

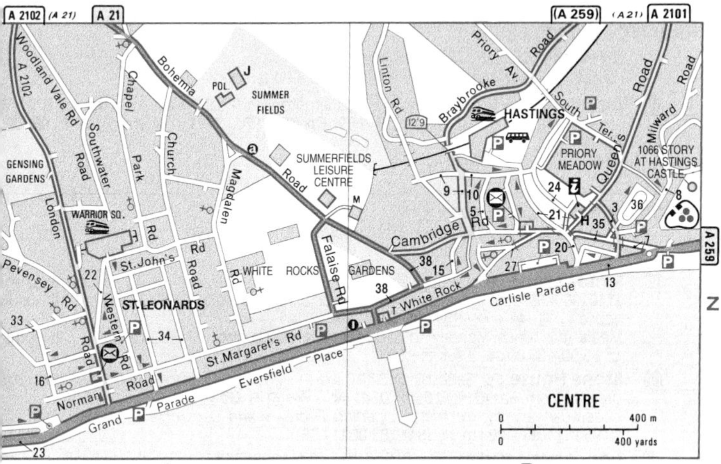

Dieser Führer ist kein vollständiges Hotel- und Restaurantverzeichnis.
Um den Ansprüchen aller Touristen gerecht zu werden,
haben wir uns auf eine Auswahl in jeder Kategorie beschränkt.

HATCH BEAUCHAMP *Somerset* 403 K 30 – *see Taunton.*

HATFIELD *Herts.* 404 T 28 *Great Britain G. – pop. 31 104.*
See : *Hatfield House★★ AC.*
Hatfield London C.C., Bedwell Park, Essendon (01707) 642624.
London 27 – Bedford 38 – Cambridge 39.

Jarvis International Hatfield, 301 St. Albans Rd West, AL10 9RH, West : 1 m. by 6426 on A 1057 at junction with A 1001 (01707) 265411, *Fax (01707) 264019,* – rm, TV, P – 150. MC AE VISA
Meals 8.00/25.00 **st.** and a la carte 6.95 – 9.95 – **128 rm** 105.00/125.00 **st.** – SB.

Quality Hatfield, Roehyde Way, AL10 9AF, South : 2 m. by B 6426 on A 10 (01707) 275701, *admin@gbo59.u-net.com, Fax (01707) 266033* – rm, rest, TV P – 120. MC AE VISA
Meals (residents only Saturday lunch) 15.00/17.50 **st.** (dinner) and a la carte 11.05/19.35 – 9.75 – **76 rm** 95.00/115.00 – SB.

Travel Inn, Comet Way, AL10 0DA, Northwest : 1 m. by B 197 at junction with A 10 (01707) 268990, *Fax (01707) 268293* – rm, TV P. MC AE VISA.
Meals (grill rest.) – **40 rm** 40.95 **t.**

HATFIELD HEATH *Essex* 404 U 28 – *see Bishop's Stortford (Herts.).*

HATHERSAGE *Derbs.* 402 403 404 P 24 – *pop. 2 858 – Sheffield (S. Yorks.).*
Sickleholme, Bamford (01433) 651306.
London 177 – Derby 39 – Manchester 34 – Sheffield 11 – Stoke-on-Trent 44.

George, S32 1BB, (01433) 650436, *info@george_hotel.net, Fax (01433) 65009* rest, TV P – 70. MC AE VISA
Meals a la carte 16.50/27.50 **t.** – **19 rm** 59.50/89.50 **t.** – SB.

Highlow Hall without rest., Hope Valley, S32 1AX, South : 2 m. by B 6001 on Abney (01433) 650393, *Fax (01433) 659505,* « Part 16C manor house », – P. MC
closed Christmas and New Year – **3 rm** 40.00/60.00 **st.**

HATTON *Warks. – see Warwick.*

HAVANT *Hants.* 404 R 31.
1 Park Rd South (023) 9248 0024.
London 75 – Southampton 24 – Brighton 39 – Portsmouth 12.

Travel Inn, 65 Bedhampton Hill, Bedhampton, PO9 3JN, West : 1 ½ m. by B 2177 junction with A 3 (M) (023) 9247 2619, *Fax (023) 9245 3471* – rm, TV P. MC AE VISA.
Meals (grill rest.) – **36 rm** 40.95 **t.**

HAWES *N. Yorks.* 402 N 21 – *pop. 1 117.*
Dales Countryside Museum, Station Yard (01969) 667450.
London 253 – Kendal 27 – Leeds 72 – York 65.

Simonstone Hall, Simonstone, DL8 3LY, North : 1 ½ m. on Muker (01969) 667255, *simonstone@demon.co.uk, Fax (01969) 667741,* « Part 18C cour house », – TV P. MC AE VISA
Meals (bar lunch Monday to Saturday)/dinner a la carte 17.40/25.90 **st.** 7.95 – **18** 55.00/180.00 **st.**, 2 suites – SB.

Stone House, Sedbusk, DL8 3PT, North : 1 m. by Muker rd (01969) 667571, *dal otel@aol.com, Fax (01969) 667720,* – TV P. MC VISA
closed January and restricted opening February and December – **Meals** (dinner o 18.95 **t.** 5.95 – **22 rm** 38.00/89.00 **t.** – SB.

Cockett's, Market Pl., DL8 3RD, (01969) 667312, *cocketts@callnetuk.cc Fax (01969) 667162,* – TV. MC VISA JCB.
Meals *(closed lunch Monday, Tuesday, Friday and Saturday)* 8.00/16.00 **t.** (c ner) and a la carte 10.20/17.70 **t.** 6.25 – **8 rm** 25.00/59.00 **t.** – SB.

Herriot's, Main St., DL8 3QW, (01969) 667536, *herriotshotel@aol.cc Fax (01969) 667810* – TV. MC VISA JCB
weekends only mid November-March and closed January – **Meals** (dinner only) a la ca 14.50/20.75 **st.** 5.80 – **7 rm** 35.00/55.00 **st.** – SB.

Rookhurst Georgian Country House, Gayle, DL8 3RT, South : ½ m. by Gayle rd (01969) 667454, *rookhurst@lineone.net, Fax (01969) 667128*, – TV P. MC VISA.
closed Christmas – **Meals** (booking essential) (residents only) (dinner only) 18.00 **st.** 6.00 – **5 rm** (dinner included) 75.00/130.00 **st.** – SB.

Brandymires, DL8 3PR, North : ¼ m. on Muker rd (01969) 667482 – P
mid February-October – **Meals** (by arrangement) 13.50 **st.** – **4 rm** 27.00/40.00 **st.**

HAWKHURST *Kent* 404 V 30 – *pop. 4 217.*
London 55 – Folkestone 37 – Hastings 18 – Maidstone 18.

The Wren's Nest without rest., Hastings Rd, TN18 4RT, South : 1 ½ m. by A 229 on B 2244 (01580) 754919, *Fax (01580) 754919*, – TV P.
closed January-mid February and Christmas – **3 rm** 40.00/55.00 **st.**

HAWKSHEAD *Cumbria* 402 L 20 *Great Britain G.* – *pop. 570* – ✉ *Ambleside.*
See : *Village*★.
Env. : *Lake Windermere*★★ – *Coniston Water*★ *(Brantwood*★*, on east side), SW : by B 5285.*
Main Car Park (015394) 36525 (summer only).
London 283 – Carlisle 52 – Kendal 19.

Highfield House Country H., Hawkshead Hill, LA22 0PN, West : ¾ m. on B 5285 (Coniston rd) (015394) 36344, *highfield.hawkshead@btinternet.com, Fax (015394) 36793*, ← Kirkstone Pass and Fells, – rest, TV P. MC VISA JCB
closed 24 to 26 December and 3 to 31 January – **Meals** (bar lunch)/dinner 18.00/20.00 **st.** 8.00 – **11 rm** (dinner included) 64.00/135.00 **st.** – SB.

Rough Close Country House, LA22 0QF, South : 1 ½ m. on Newby Bridge rd (015394) 36370, *Fax (015394) 36002*, – TV P. MC VISA.
April-October and restricted opening in March and November – **Meals** (booking essential) (residents only) (dinner only) 12.00 **t.** 5.50 – **5 rm** (dinner included) 55.00/90.00 **t.**

Ivy House, Main St., LA22 0NS, (015394) 36204, *ivyhousehotel@btinternet.com*, – rest, TV P. MC VISA JCB
March-October – **Meals** (by arrangement) 13.00 **st.** 4.00 – **11 rm** (dinner included) 37.50/91.00 **t.** – SB.

Bracken Fell without rest., Barngates Rd, Outgate, LA22 0NH, North : 1 ¼ m. by B 5286 on Barngates rd (015394) 36289, *hart.brackenfell@virgin.net, Fax (015394) 36413*, – TV P.
6 rm 49.00 **st.**

Near Sawrey *Southeast : 2 m. on B 5285* – ✉ *Ambleside.*

Sawrey House Country H., LA22 0LF, (015394) 36387, *enquiries@sawrey-house.com, Fax (015394) 36010*, ← Esthwaite Water and Grizedale Forest, – TV P. MC VISA
closed January and restricted opening in winter – **Meals** (booking essential) (dinner only) 30.00 **st.** 10.00 – **11 rm** (dinner included) 65.00/150.00 **st.** – SB.

Ees Wyke Country House, LA22 0JZ, (015394) 36393, *Fax (015394) 36393*, ← Esthwaite Water and Grizedale Forest, – rest, TV P. AE
closed January and February – **Meals** (booking essential) (dinner only) 24.00 **t.** 6.50 – **8 rm** (dinner included) 60.00/120.00 **t.**

Far Sawrey *Southeast : 2½ m. on B 5285* – ✉ *Ambleside.*

West Vale, LA22 0LQ, (015394) 42817, *Fax (015394) 88214*, ← – P. MC VISA JCB.
March-October – **Meals** (by arrangement) 13.00 **st.** 5.20 – **6 rm** 29.00/52.00 **st.** – SB.

Grizedale *Southwest : 2 ¾ m.* – ✉ *Ambleside.*

Grizedale Lodge without rest., LA22 0QL, (015394) 36532, *enquiries@grizedale-lodge.com, Fax (015394) 36572*, ← – TV P. MC AE VISA JCB
February-November – **9 rm** 37.50/80.00 **t.**

HAWNBY *N. Yorks.* 402 Q 21 – ✉ *Helmsley.*
London 245 – Newcastle upon Tyne 69 – Middlesbrough 27 – York 30.

Hawnby, YO62 5QS, (01439) 798202, *info@hawnbyhotel.co.uk, Fax (01439) 798344*, ←, – rm, TV P. MC VISA JCB.
Meals a la carte 10.70/18.00 **t.** – **6 rm** 45.00/60.00 **t.** – SB.

Laskill *Northeast : 1½ m. by B 1257* – ✉ *Hawnby.*

Laskill Farm, Easterside, YO62 5BN, (01439) 798268, *Fax (01439) 798498*, « Working farm », – TV P. MC VISA
Meals (by arrangement) (communal dining) 13.50 **st.** 6.00 – **6 rm** 30.00/60.00 **st.**

HAWORTH *W. Yorks.* 402 O 22 *Great Britain G. – pop. 4 956 – ✉ Keighley.*
See : Town★.
2-4 West Lane ✆ (01535) 642329.
London 213 – Burnley 22 – Leeds 22 – Manchester 34.

Ashmount without rest, Mytholmes Lane, BD22 8EZ, ✆ (01535) 645726, *ashmounthaw th@aol.com, Fax (01535) 645726,* ≤, « Victorian country house », – TV P. MC VISA
closed 3 days at Christmas – **6 rm** 25.00/39.00 **s.**

Weaver's with rm, 15 West Lane, BD22 8DU, ✆ (01535) 643822, *colinjane@aol.co Fax (01535) 644832,* « Former weavers cottages » – rest, TV. MC AE VISA JCB.
closed last week June and 1 week Christmas – **Meals** *(closed Sunday and Monday)* (dinr only) 13.50 **t.** and a la carte 5.50 – **3 rm** 50.00/75.00 **t.** – SB.

HAYDOCK *Mersey.* 402 403 404 M 23 – *pop. 16 705 – ✉ St. Helens.*
London 198 – Liverpool 19 – Manchester 18.

Thistle Haydock, Penny Lane, WA11 9SG, Northeast : ½ m. on A 599 ✆ (01942) 2720 *haydock@thistle.co.uk, Fax (01942) 711092,* – rm, rest, TV P 300. MC AE VISA JCB
The Restaurant : **Meals** *(closed lunch Saturday and Bank Holidays)* 14.95/19.50 **t.** and d ner a la carte 8.00 – 11.50 – **134 rm** 116.00/136.00 **st.**, 4 suites – SB.

Posthouse Haydock, Lodge Lane, Newton-le-Willows, WA12 0JG, Northeast : 1 m. o 49 ✆ (0870) 400 9039, *gmmail1117@forte-hotels.com, Fax (01942) 718419,* – rm, rest, TV P – 180. MC AE VISA JCB
Meals *(closed Saturday lunch)* 6.95/15.95 **t.** and a la carte 6.95 – 11.95 – **138** 79.00/139.00 **st.** – SB.

Travelodge, Piele Rd, WA11 9TL, on A 580 ✆ (01942) 272055, *Fax (01942) 27206* rm, TV P. MC AE VISA JCB.
Meals (grill rest.) – **62 rm** 39.95 **t.**

HAYLE *Cornwall* 403 D 33.
London 288 – Penzance 9 – Truro 20.

Travel Inn, Loggans Moor, Carwin Rise, TR27 4PN, North : 1 m. by B 3301 off A ✆ (01736) 755025, *Fax (01736) 757029* – rm, rest, TV P. MC AE VISA.
Meals (grill rest.) – **40 rm** 40.95 **t.**

HAYLING ISLAND *Hants.* 404 R 31 – *pop. 14 054.*
Links Lane ✆ (023) 9246 3712.
Beachlands, Seafront ✆ (023) 9246 7111 (summer only).
London 77 – Brighton 45 – Southampton 28.

Cockle Warren Cottage without rest., 36 Seafront, PO11 9HL, ✆ (023) 9246 49 *Fax (023) 9246 4838,* heated, – TV P. MC VISA JCB
– **5 rm** 35.00/80.00 **t.**

HAYTOR *Devon – see Bovey Tracey.*

HAYTOR VALE *Devon – see Bovey Tracey.*

HAYWARDS HEATH *W. Sussex* 404 T 31 – *pop. 28 923.*
Paxhill Park, East Mascalls Lane, Lindfield ✆ (01444) 484467.
London 41 – Brighton 16.

Birch, Lewes Rd, RH17 7SF, East : ¾ m. on A 272 ✆ (01444) 451565, *info@birch-hotel.c k, Fax (01444) 440109* – rest, TV P – 60. MC AE VISA.
closed 25-30 December – **Meals** *(closed Saturday lunch, Sunday dinner)* 10.95/17.50 6.95 – **51 rm** 80.00/100.00 **st.** – SB.

Jeremy's at Borde Hill, Borde Hill Gdns., RH16 1XP, North : 1 ¾ m. by B 2028 Balcombe Rd ✆ (01444) 441102, *jeremys.bordehill@btinternet.com., Fax (01494) 443* , « Converted 19C stables ≤ Victorian walled garden » – P. MC AE VISA
closed Sunday dinner and Monday – **Meals** 19.50 **t** and a la carte 8.75.

Dining Room 2, 65 The Broadway, RH16 3AS, ✆ (01444) 417755, *Fax (01444) 4177* MC AE VISA
closed 25 December to 4 January, 1 week Easter, first 2 weeks August, Sunday, Satu lunch and Bank Holidays – **Meals** 13.50/18.95 **t.** and a la carte 9.50.

ADLAM *Durham* 402 O 20 – *see Darlington.*

ATHROW AIRPORT *Middx.* 404 S 29 – *see Hillingdon (Greater London).*

BDEN BRIDGE *W. Yorks.* 402 N 22 – *pop. 3 681* – ✉ *Halifax.*

Great Mount, Wadsworth ℘ (01422) 842896.

1 Bridge Gate ℘ (01422) 843831.

London 223 – Burnley 13 – Leeds 24 – Manchester 25.

Carlton, Albert St., HX7 8ES, ℘ (01422) 844400, *ctonhotel@aol.com, Fax (01422) 843117* – rest, – 150. VISA JCB
Meals 8.95/17.95 **st.** and dinner a la carte 6.95 – **16 rm** 56.00/75.00 **st.**

The White Lion, Bridge Gate, HX7 8EX, ℘ (01422) 842197, *Fax (01422) 846619,* « Part 17C inn » – rm, VISA JCB.
closed 25 December – **Meals** (in bar Sunday to Thursday) a la carte 8.70/20.15 **st.** 5.75 – **10 rm** 35.00/55.00 **st.**

Redacre Mill, Mytholmroyd, HX7 5DQ, Southeast : 1 ½ m. by A646 off Westfield Terr. ℘ (01422) 881569, *peters@redacremill.freeserve.co.uk, Fax (01422) 885563,* « Converted canalside warehouse », – VISA.
Meals (by arrangement) (communal dining) 20.00 **st.** 4.75 – **5 rm** 39.00/59.00 **st.** – SB.

IGHINGTON *Durham* 402 P20 – *see Darlington.*

LMSLEY *N. Yorks.* 402 Q 21 *Great Britain G.* – *pop. 1 833.*

Env. : *Rievaulx Abbey★★ AC, NW : 2½ m. by B 1257.*

Ampleforth College, Court Cottage, Cawton, York ℘ (01653) 628555.

Town Hall, Market Pl. ℘ (01439) 770173.

London 239 – Middlesbrough 28 – York 24.

The Black Swan, Market Pl., YO62 5BJ, ℘ (01439) 770466, *heritagehotels-helmsley.blackswan@forte-hotels.com, Fax (01439) 770174,* « Part 16C inn », – VISA
***The Rutland Room* : Meals** 15.00/26.00 **t.** and dinner a la carte 7.50 – 12.00 – **45 rm** 120.00/160.00 **st.** – SB.

Carlton Lodge, Bondgate, YO62 5EY, ℘ (01439) 770557, *carlton.lodge@dial.pipex.com, Fax (01439) 770623,* – rest, – 130. VISA
***The Stirrings* : Meals** *(closed Sunday)* (dinner only) a la carte 12.65/23.70 **t.** 6.00 – **11 rm** 39.50/75.00 **st.** – SB.

The Feathers, Market Pl., YO62 5BH, ℘ (01439) 770275, *Fax (01439) 771101,* – rest, VISA JCB.
Meals (carving lunch Sunday) (bar lunch Monday to Saturday) 5.00 **st.** and a la carte – **14 rm** 45.00/60.00 **st.** – SB.

Lemm's with rm, 19 Bridge St., YO62 5BG, ℘ (01439) 771555, *cuisine_eclairee@compuserve.com, Fax (01439) 771515* – . VISA JCB
closed Monday and Tuesday except August – **Meals** - Bistro - a la carte 19.00/23.45 **st.** – **3 rm** 21.50/50.00 **st.** – SB.

Nawton *East : 3¼ m. on A 170* – ✉ *York.*

Plumpton Court, High St., YO62 7TT, ℘ (01439) 771223, *plumptoncourt@ukgateway.net, Fax (01439) 771223,* – .
Meals (by arrangement) 14.00 **st.** – **7 rm** 35.00/50.00 **st.**

Harome *Southeast : 2¾ m. by A 170* – ✉ *York.*

The Pheasant, YO62 5JG, ℘ (01439) 771241, *Fax (01439) 771744,* , – rest, VISA JCB.
March-November – **Meals** (bar lunch)/dinner 19.50/22.50 **t.** 6.50 – **10 rm** (dinner included) 68.50/150.00 **t.**, 2 suites – SB.

The Star Inn, YO62 5JE, ℘ (01439) 770397, *Fax (01439) 771833,* , « Part 14C thatched inn », – VISA
closed 1 week November, 3 weeks January, 25 December, Monday, Sunday dinner and Bank Holidays – **Meals** (booking essential) a la carte 20.85/26.95 **t.** 9.50.

Nunnington *Southeast : 6¼ m. by A 170 off B 1257* – ✉ *Helmsley.*

Ryedale Country Lodge with rm, YO62 5XB, West : 1 m. ℘ (01439) 748246, *Fax (01439) 748346,* « Converted railway station », , – VISA
closed Monday and Tuesday to non-residents – **Meals** a la carte 16.00/22.00 **st.** – **7 rm** 45.00/75.00 **st.** – SB.

ENGLAND

at Wass *Southwest : 6 m. by A 170 – ✉ Helmsley.*

Wombwell Arms, YO61 4BE, ☎ (01347) 868280 – ⇔ P. MC VISA
closed 2 weeks January, Sunday dinner and Monday – **Meals** a la carte 13.45/17.00 **t.** 7.

at Byland Abbey *Southwest : 6½ m. by A 170 – ✉ Helmsley.*

Abbey Inn with rm, YO61 4BD, ☎ (01347) 868204, *Fax (01347) 868678,* ←, ⛱, ⇔ rest, TV P. MC VISA
Meals *(closed Sunday dinner and Monday lunch)* a la carte 14.75/25.00 **t.** 6.50 – 3 ☐ 70.00/110.00 **t.** – SB.

at Scawton *West : 4½ m. by B 1257 – ✉ Helmsley.*

The Hare Inn, YO7 2HG, ☎ (01845) 597289, *Fax (01845) 597289,* « Part 17C » – P. MC JCB
closed first week February, 25 December and Monday lunch – **Meals** a la carte 16. 20.95 **t.** 6.75.

HELSTON *Cornwall* 403 E 33 *The West Country G. – pop. 8 505.*
See : *The Flora Day Furry Dance★★.*
Env. : *Lizard Peninsula★ – Gunwalloe Fishing Cove★, S : 4 m. by A 3083 and minor r Culdrose (Flambards Village Theme Park★), SE : 1 m. – Wendron (Poldark Mine★), NE : m. by B 3297 – Gweek (Seal Sanctuary★ – setting★), E : 4 m. by A 394 and minor rd.*
London 306 – Falmouth 13 – Penzance 14 – Truro 17.

Nansloe Manor ⚲, Meneage Rd, TR13 0SB, ☎ (01326) 574691, *info@nansloe-mano .uk, Fax (01326) 564680,* ⇔ – ⇔ rest, TV P. MC VISA JCB. ⚔
Meals (bar lunch Monday to Saturday)/dinner 23.50/25.00 **t.** 10.00 – **7 rm** ☐ 59. 140.00 **t.**

at Gunwalloe *South : 5 m. by A 394 off A 3083 – ✉ Helston.*

The Halzephron Inn ⚲ with rm, TR12 7QB, ☎ (01326) 240406, *Fax (01326) 241442* ⛱ – ⇔ rest, TV P. MC AE VISA. ⚔
closed 25 December – **Meals** a la carte 15.10/24.00 **t.** 5.50 – **2 rm** ☐ 38.00/68.00 **t.**

HEMEL HEMPSTEAD *Herts.* 404 S 28 – *pop. 79 235.*
Little Hay Golf Complex, Box Lane, Bovingdon ☎ (01442) 833798 – Boxmoor, 18 Lane ☎ (01442) 242434.
Dacorum Information Centre ☎ (01442) 234222.
London 30 – Aylesbury 16 – Luton 10 – Northampton 46.

Posthouse Hemel Hempstead, Breakspear Way, HP2 4UA, East : 2 ½ m. on A ☎ (0870) 400 9041, *Fax (01442) 211812,* Lo, ≘s, ⊠ – |‡|, ⇔ rm, TV & P. – 60. MC AE VISA JCB
Meals *(closed Saturday lunch)* a la carte approx. 20.00 **t.** – ☐ 11.95 – **145 rm** 139. 179.00 **st.** – SB.

Watermill, London Rd, Bourne End, HP1 2RJ, West : 2 ¼ m. on A 4251 ☎ (01442) 349 *watermill@sarova.co.uk, Fax (01442) 866130,* ⛱ – ⇔ TV & P. – 100. MC AE ⊕ VISA ⚔
Meals (bar lunch)/dinner 19.95 **st.** 5.95 – ☐ 9.95 – **75 rm** 99.00/114.00 **st.** – SB.

Boxmoor Lodge, London Rd, HP1 2RA, West : 1 m. on A 4251 ☎ (01442) 230 *Fax (01442) 252230,* ⇔ – ⇔ rest, TV & P. – 25. MC AE ⊕ VISA JCB. ⚔
closed 25 December-4 January – **Meals** *(closed Sunday and lunch Saturday and Mon* a la carte 20.50/29.00 **t.** 6.00 – **25 rm** ☐ 80.00/110.00 **t.** – SB.

Travel Inn, Stoney Lane, Bourne End, HP1 2SB, West : 3 ½ m. by A 4251 off A ☎ (01442) 879149, *Fax (01442) 879147* – |‡|, ⇔ rm, TV & P. – 35. MC AE ⊕ VISA. ⚔
Meals (grill rest.) – **60 rm** 40.95 **t.**

Travelodge without rest., Wolsey House, Wolsey Rd, HP2 5SF, ☎ (01442) 244 *Fax (01442) 266887* – ⇔ rm, TV & P. MC AE ⊕ VISA JCB. ⚔
53 rm 59.95 **t.**

HENFIELD *W. Sussex* 404 T 31 – *pop. 4 111.*
London 47 – Brighton 10 – Worthing 11.

Tottington Manor, Edburton, BN5 9LJ, Southeast : 3 ½ m. by A 2037 on Fulkin ☎ (01903) 815757, *tottingtonmanor@compuserve.com, Fax (01903) 879331,* ←, ⛱, ⇔ rest, TV P. MC AE ⊕ VISA JCB. ⚔
closed 1-15 January – **Meals** *(closed Saturday lunch and Sunday dinner)* 28.00/32.5 (dinner) and a la carte 23.00/31.25 **t.** 7.50 – **6 rm** ☐ 55.00/80.00 **t.**

Wineham *Northeast : 3½ m. by A 281, B 2116 and Wineham Lane – ✉ Henfield.*

Frylands without rest., BN5 9BP, West : ¼ m. taking left turn at telephone box ✆ (01403) 710214, *fowler@pavilion.co.uk, Fax (01403) 711449,* ←, « Part Elizabethan farmhouse », heated, ..., ... – ... TV P. ...
closed 20 December-2 January – **3 rm** ▭ 25.00/45.00 **s.**

ENLADE *Somerset – see Taunton.*

ENLEY-IN-ARDEN *Warks.* 403 404 O 27 – *pop. 2 803.*
London 104 – Birmingham 15 – Stratford-upon-Avon 8 – Warwick 8.5.

Ardencote Manor H. & Country Club ..., Lye Green Rd, Claverdon, CV35 8LS, East : 3 ¾ m. by A 4189 on Shrewley rd ✆ (01926) 843111, *hotel@ardencote.com, Fax (01926) 842646,* ..., ..., ..., 9, ..., ..., ..., ..., squash – ... rest, TV P – 180. MO AE ① VISA. ...
***Oak Room :* Meals** (booking essential) (dinner only and Sunday lunch)/dinner 14.25/ 24.95 **st.** 6.50 – **75 rm** ▭ 95.00/160.00 **st.** – SB.

Jago, 64 High St., B95 5BX, ✆ (01564) 795255, *Fax (01564) 795255* – MO AE VISA
closed 25 December-1 January, Monday, Saturday lunch and Sunday dinner – **Meals** a la carte 14.65/28.20 **st.** 8.50.

Crabmill, Preston Bagot, Claverdon, B95 5DR, East : 1 m. on A 4189 ✆ (01926) 843342, *Fax (01926) 843989,* ... – P. MO AE VISA
closed Sunday dinner – **Meals** (booking essential) a la carte 17.75/28.60 **t.** 9.95.

ENLEY-ON-THAMES *Oxon.* 404 R 29 – *pop. 10 558.*
18 Huntercombe, Nuffield ✆ (01491) 641207.
to Reading (Salter Bros. Ltd) (summer only) – to Marlow (Salter Bros. Ltd) (summer only).
Town Hall, Market Pl. ✆ (01491) 578034.
London 40 – Oxford 23 – Reading 9.

Red Lion, RG9 2AR, ✆ (01491) 572161, *reservations@redlionhenley.co.uk, Fax (01491) 410039* – TV P – 30. MO AE VISA. ...
Meals 16.00/19.00 **t.** and a la carte 7.00 – ▭ 12.50 – **26 rm** 99.00/135.00 **st.**

The Rise without rest., Rotherfield Rd, RG9 1NR, ✆ (01491) 579360, *Fax (01491) 578691,* ... – ... TV P
3 rm ▭ 45.00/55.00 **s.**

Lenwade without rest., 3 Western Rd, RG9 1JL, ✆ (01491) 573468, *lenwadeuk@compuserve.com, Fax (01491) 573468,* ... – ... TV P. ...
3 rm ▭ 40.00/60.00 **st.**

Villa Marina, 18 Thameside, RG9 1BH, ✆ (01491) 575262, *Fax (01491) 411394* – ... MO AE ① VISA
Meals - Italian - 12.00 **t.** (lunch) and a la carte 18.00/31.00 **t.**

Stonor *North : 4 m. by A 4130 on B 480 – ✉ Henley-on-Thames.*

Stonor Arms, RG9 6HE, ✆ (01491) 638866, *stonorarms.hotel@virgin.net, Fax (01491) 638863,* ..., ... – ... rest, TV P. MO AE VISA
Meals 15.25/25.00 **t.** and a la carte 10.75 – **10 rm** ▭ 99.00/155.00 **t.** – SB.

Binfield Heath *Southwest : 4 m. by A 4155 – ✉ Henley-on-Thames.*

Holmwood ... without rest., Shiplake Row, RG9 4DP, ✆ (0118) 947 8747, *Fax (0118) 947 8637,* « Part Georgian country house », ..., ..., ... – TV P. MO VISA. ...
5 rm ▭ 40.00/60.00 **st.**

REFORD *Herefordshire* 403 L 27 *Great Britain G. – pop. 54 326.*
See : *City★ - Cathedral★★ (Mappa Mundi★)* **A A** – *Old House★* **A B.**
Exc. : *Kilpeck (Church of SS. Mary and David★★) SW : 8 m. by A 465* **B.**
18 Raven's Causeway, Wormsley ✆ (01432) 830219 – 18 Belmont Lodge, Belmont ✆ (01432) 352666 – 18 Burghill Valley, Tillington Rd, Burghill ✆ (01432) 760456 – 9 Hereford Municipal, Holmer Rd ✆ (01432) 344376 **B.**
1 King St. ✆ (01432) 268430.
London 133 – Birmingham 51 – Cardiff 56.

Plan on next page

HEREFORD

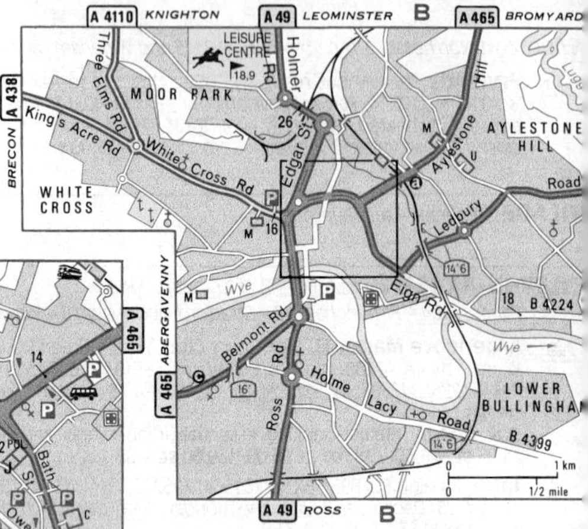

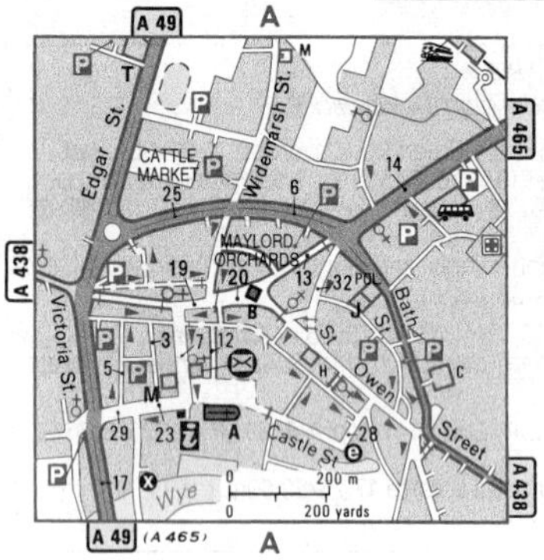

Castle House, Castle St., HR1 2NW, (01432) 356321, *info@castlehse.co* *Fax (01432) 365909*, « Contemporary interior », – rest, A
Meals 18.95/29.95 **st.** 9.50 – 19.00 – **15 rm** 90.00/210.00 **st.** – SB.

Three Counties, Belmont Rd, HR2 7BP, Southwest : 1 ½ m. on A 465 (01432) 2999 *Fax (01432) 275114* – rm, – 350. B
Meals (bar lunch)/dinner 17.50 **st.** – **60 rm** 59.50/78.50 **st.** – SB.

Aylestone Court, Aylestone Hill, HR1 1HS, (01432) 341891, *ayleshotel@aol.co* *Fax (01432) 267691*, – rest, – 40. B
Meals (dinner only) 24.95 **t.** and a la carte – **9 rm** 65.00/100.00 **t.**

Travel Inn, Holmer Rd, Holmer, HR4 9RS, North : 1 ¾ m. on A 49 (01432) 2748 *Fax (01432) 343003* – rm,
Meals (grill rest.) – **42 rm** 40.95 **t.**

Grafton Villa Farm without rest., Grafton, HR2 8ED, South : 2 ¼ m. on A (01432) 268689, *Fax (01432) 268689*, « Working farm », –
closed 23-26 December – **3 rm** 30.00/45.00 **st.**

La Rive, Left Bank Village, Bridge St., HR4 9DG, (01432) 349008, *Fax (01432) 349(* « River-side setting » – A
closed Saturday lunch and Sunday dinner – **Meals** 12.95/42.95 **t.** 7.25.

Floodgates Brasserie, Left Bank Village, Bridge St., HR4 9DG, (01432) 349008, *inf eftbank.co.uk, Fax (01432) 349012*, « River-side setting » – A
Meals a la carte 16.15/24.70 **t.** 5.45.

at Marden *North : 5 ¾ m. by A 49* – **B** – *Hereford.*

The Vauld Farm, HR1 3HA, Northeast : 1 ½ m. by Litmarsh rd (01568) 797(« 16C timbered farmhouse », – rest,
Meals (by arrangement) (communal dining) 20.00 – **3 rm** 30.00/60.00, 1 suite.

at Madley *West : 6 m. by A 465 on B 4352* – **B** – *Hereford.*

Comet Inn, HR2 9NJ, (01981) 250600, *Fax (01981) 250643* –
Meals a la carte 13.95/18.70 **t.** 5.65.

at Ruckhall *West : 5 m. by A 49 off A 465* – **B** – *Eaton Bishop.*

Ancient Camp Inn with rm, HR2 9QX, (01981) 250449, *campinn@btinternet.c* *Fax (01981) 251581*, River Wye and countryside, –
closed first 2 weeks January – **Meals** *(closed Sunday dinner and Monday except E Holidays)* (booking essential) a la carte 17.85/28.15 **t.** 5.50 – **4 rm** 45.00/70.00 **t.**, 1 te – SB.

: **Byford** *West : 7½ m. by A 438 – B – ✉ Hereford.*

Old Rectory, HR4 7LD, ☎ (01981) 590218, *jo@cm-ltd.com, Fax (01981) 590499,* – TV P.
March-November – **Meals** (by arrangement) 15.00 **s.** – **3 rm** 35.00/46.00.

ERM 403 P 33 and 230 ⑩ – *see Channel Islands.*

ERMITAGE *Dorset – see Sherborne.*

ERSTMONCEUX *E. Sussex* 404 U 31 – *pop. 3 898.*
London 63 – Eastbourne 12 – Hastings 14 – Lewes 16.

Sundial, Gardner St., BN27 4LA, ☎ (01323) 832217, *Fax (01323) 832909,* « Converted 16C cottage », – P. MC AE VISA JCB
closed 7-31 August, Christmas-20 January, Sunday dinner and Monday – **Meals** - French - 15.50/27.50 **t.** and a la carte 7.50.

Wartling *Southeast : 3 ¾ m. by A 271 and Wartling rd – ✉ Herstmonceux.*

Wartling Place without rest., BN27 1RY, ☎ (01323) 832590, *accom@wartlingplace.prestel.co.uk, Fax (01323) 831558,* « Part Georgian », – TV P. MC AE VISA JCB.
3 rm 55.00/85.00.

ERTINGFORDBURY *Herts.* 404 T 28 – *pop. 633 – ✉ Hertford.*
London 26 – Luton 18.

White Horse, Hertingfordbury Rd, SG14 2LB, ☎ (0870) 400 8114, *white_horse@forte-hotels.com, Fax (01992) 550809,* – TV P – 50. MC AE VISA
Meals *(closed Saturday lunch)* 10.95 **t.** (lunch) and dinner a la carte 15.25/25.95 **t.** 7.75 – 11.45 – **42 rm** 100.00/110.00 **t.** – SB.

ESWALL *Mersey.* 402 403 K 24 – *pop. 16 569.*
London 212 – Birkenhead 12 – Chester 14 – Liverpool 11.

Est, Est, Est, 146-148 Telegraph Rd, L60 0AH, ☎ (0151) 342 9550, *Fax (0151) 349 9905* – MC AE VISA
Meals - Italian - a la carte 10.85/23.65 **t.** 6.85.

Gayton *Southeast : ½ m. on A 540 – ✉ Heswall.*

Travel Inn, Chester Rd, L60 3FD, ☎ (0151) 342 1982, *Fax (0151) 342 8983* – rm, TV & P. MC AE VISA.
Meals (grill rest.) – **37 rm** 40.95 **t.**

ETHERSETT *Norfolk* 404 X 26 – *see Norwich.*

ETTON *N. Yorks.* 402 N 21 – *see Skipton.*

EVERSHAM *Cumbria* 402 L 21 – *pop. 639 – ✉ Milnthorpe.*
London 270 – Kendal 7 – Lancaster 18 – Leeds 72.

Blue Bell, Princes Way, LA7 7EE, on A 6 ☎ (015395) 62018, *stay@bluebellhotel.co.uk, Fax (015395) 62455,* – rest, TV P – 80. MC AE VISA
Meals a la carte 12.85/21.85 **t.** 6.95 – **21 rm** 52.50/66.00 **t.** – SB.

EXHAM *Northd.* 401 402 N 19 *Great Britain G.* – *pop. 11 008.*
See : *Abbey★ (Saxon Crypt★★, Leschman chantry★).*
Env. : *Hadrian's Wall★★, N : 4½ m. by A 6079.*
Exc. : *Housesteads★★, NW : 12½ m. by A 6079 and B 6318.*
18 *Spital Park ☎ (01434) 602057* – 18 *Slaley Hall G. & C.C., Slaley ☎ (01434) 673350* – 9 *Tynedale, Tyne Green ☎ (01434) 608154.*
Hallgate ☎ (01434) 605225.
London 304 – Carlisle 37 – Newcastle upon Tyne 21.

Beaumont, Beaumont St., NE46 3LT, ☎ (01434) 602331, *beaumont.hotel@btinternet.com, Fax (01434) 606184* – TV – 80. MC AE VISA JCB.
Meals 6.50/16.75 **t.** and dinner a la carte 9.50 – 6.50 – **25 rm** 65.00/85.00 **t.** – SB.

East Peterel Field Farm, NE46 2JT, South : 2 m. by B 6306 off Whiteley Chapel ☎ (01434) 607209, *ben@petfield.demon.uk, Fax (01434) 601753*, ≤, – 🅿
Meals (by arrangement) (communal dining) 25.00 **st.** – **4 rm** 40.00/65.00 **st.**

West Close House without rest., Hextol Terr., NE46 2AD, by Allendale ☎ (01434) 603307, – 🅿.
closed Christmas and New Year – **4 rm** 21.00/52.00.

Dene House without rest., Juniper, NE46 1SJ, South : 3 ¾ m. by B 306 following signs Dye House ☎ (01434) 673413, *margaret@dene-house-freeserve.co.uk, Fax (01434) 6734* – 🅿
closed 25 and 26 December – **3 rm** 25.00/50.00.

at Slaley *Southeast : 5½ m. by B 6306 – ✉ Hexham.*

Slaley Hall, NE47 0BY, Southeast : 2 ¼ m. ☎ (01434) 673350, *slaley@deverehotels.m, Fax (01434) 673962*, ≤, – 🅿 – 400. AE VISA JCB.
Meals (bar lunch Monday to Saturday)/dinner 23.50 **st.** and a la carte – **129 rm** 130.(175.00 **st.**, 10 suites – SB.

HEYTESBURY *Wilts.* 403 404 N 30 – *see Warminster.*

HICKSTEAD *W. Sussex.*
London 40 – Brighton 8.

Travelodge, Jobs Lane, RH17 5NX, off A 23 ☎ (01444) 881377, *Fax (01444) 88137* rm, rest, 🅿. AE VISA JCB.
Meals (grill rest.) – **55 rm** 49.95 **t.**

*Keine Aufnahme in den **Michelin-Führer** durch*
- falsche Information oder
- Bezahlung!

HIGHCLIFFE *Dorset* 403 404 O 31.
London 112 – Bournemouth 10 – Salisbury 21 – Southampton 26 – Winchester 37.

Lord Bute, Lymington Rd, BH23 4JS, ☎ (01425) 278884, *mail@lordbute.co. Fax (01425) 279258* – rest, 🅿 – 30. AE VISA
Meals *(closed Sunday dinner and Monday)* 13.95/24.95 **t.** and a la carte 6.25 – 7.0
10 rm 65.00/95.00 **t.** – SB.

HIGH CROSBY *Cumbria* 401 402 L 19 – *see Carlisle.*

HIGH WYCOMBE *Bucks.* 404 R 29 *Great Britain G.* – *pop. 71 718.*
Env. : *Chiltern Hills*★.
Hazlemere G & C.C., Penn Rd, Hazlemere ☎ (01494) 714722 – , Wycombe Heigl Rayners Av., Loudwater ☎ (01494) 816686.
Paul's Row ☎ (01494) 421892.
London 34 – Aylesbury 17 – Oxford 26 – Reading 18.

Posthouse High Wycombe, Handycross, HP11 1TL, Southwest : 1 ½ m. by A 404 junction 4 of M 40 ☎ (0870) 400 9042, *Fax (01494) 439071* – rm, rest, 200. AE VISA
Meals a la carte 18.95/32.80 **st.** – 11.95 – **109 rm** 129.00 **st.** – SB.

Alexandra, Queen Alexandra Rd, HP11 2JX, ☎ (01494) 463494, *alexandra.hotel@btint et.com, Fax (01494) 463560* – rm, 🅿. AE VISA.
Meals *(closed Friday to Sunday)* (dinner only) a la carte 15.20/25.00 **st.** – 8.90 – **28** 79.00 **st.**

Travel Inn, London Rd, HP10 9YL, Southeast : 3 m. on A 40 ☎ (01494) 5370 *Fax (01494) 446855* – rm, 🅿. AE VISA.
Meals (grill rest.) – **59 rm** 40.95 **t.**

HILTON PARK SERVICE AREA *W. Mids.* – ✉ *Wolverhampton.*

Travelodge, WV11 2AT, M 6 between junctions 10A and 11 (southbound carriagew ☎ (01922) 701997, *Fax (01922) 701967* – 🅿. AE VISA JCB.
Meals (grill rest.) – **64 rm** 49.95 **t.**

INCKLEY *Leics.* 402 403 404 P 26 – *pop. 40 608.*
Hinckley Library, Lancaster Rd (01455) 635106.
London 103 – Birmingham 31 – Coventry 12 – Leicester 14.

Sketchley Grange, Sketchley Lane, LE10 3HU, South : 1 ½ m. by B 4109 (Rugby Rd) (01455) 251133, *sketchleygrange@btinternet.com, Fax (01455) 631384,* , , , – , rest, – 280. VISA
The Willow : **Meals** 14.50/21.95 **st.** and a la carte 6.00 – ***The Terrace :*** **Meals** a la carte 15.35/19.85 **st.** 5.50 – 10.95 – **54 rm** 99.00 **st.**, 1 suite – SB.

NDON *Wilts.* 403 404 N 30 – *pop. 493* – *Salisbury.*
London 107 – Exeter 71 – Salisbury 21 – Taunton 47.

Grosvenor Arms with rm, SP3 6DJ, (01747) 820696, *Fax (01747) 820869,* – . AE VISA JCB
Meals a la carte 18.15/35.75 **t.** 9.50 – **7 rm** 55.00/95.00 **t.**

NTLESHAM *Suffolk* 404 X 27 – *see Ipswich.*

STON *Cambs.* 404 U 27 – *see Cambridge.*

TCHIN *Herts.* 404 T 28 – *pop. 32 221.*
London 40 – Bedford 14 – Cambridge 26 – Luton 9.

Thistle Stevenage, Blakemore End Rd, Little Wymondley, SG4 7JJ, Southeast : 2 ½ m. by A 602 (01438) 355821, *stevenage@thistle.co.uk, Fax (01438) 742114,* heated, – rm, – 200. AE VISA
Meals 12.95/21.95 **st.** and dinner a la carte 6.00 – 10.75 – **80 rm** 116.00/130.00 **st.**, 2 suites.

Redcoats Farmhouse with rm, Redcoats Green, Little Wymondley, SG4 7JR, Southeast : 3 m. by A 602 (01438) 729500, *sales@redcoats.co.uk, Fax (01438) 723322,* « Part 15C », – rm, . AE VISA
closed 1 week after Christmas and Bank Holiday Monday – **Meals** *(closed Sunday dinner)* 14.00/17.00 **t.** (lunch) and a la carte 28.50/36.00 **t.** 6.00 – **12 rm** 80.00/110.00 **t.** – SB.

OCKLEY HEATH *W. Mids.* 403 404 O 26 – *pop. 14 538* – *Solihull.*
London 117 – Birmingham 11 – Coventry 17.

Nuthurst Grange Country House, Nuthurst Grange Lane, B94 5NL, South : ¾ m. by A 3400 (01564) 783972, *info@nuthurstgrange.co.uk, Fax (01564) 783919,* – – 80. AE VISA.
closed 25-26 December – **Meals** – (see ***The Restaurant*** below) – **15 rm** 135.00/185.00 **t.** – SB.

Travel Inn, Stratford Rd, B94 6NX, on A 3400 (01564) 782144, *Fax (01564) 783197* – rm, – 35. AE VISA.
Meals (grill rest.) – **40 rm** 40.95 **t.**

The Restaurant (at Nuthurst Grange Country House), Nuthurst Grange Lane, B94 5NL, South : ¾ m. by A 3400 (01564) 783972, *Fax (01564) 783919,* – . AE VISA
closed 25-26 December and Saturday lunch – **Meals** 29.50/45.00 **t.** (dinner) and lunch a la carte 20.50/27.50 **t.** 9.50.

Lapworth *Southeast : 2 m. on B 4439* – *Warwick.*

The Boot, Old Warwick Rd, B94 6JU, on B 4439 (01564) 782464, *Fax (01564) 784989,* , – . AE VISA JCB
closed 25 December – **Meals** (booking essential) a la carte 16.15/22.45 **t.** 10.25.

OCKLIFFE *Beds.* 404 S 28 – *see Dunstable.*

OLBROOK *Suffolk* 404 X 28 – *see Ipswich.*

Bitte beachten Sie die Geschwindigkeitsbeschränkungen in Großbritannien
- 60 mph (= 96 km/h) außerhalb geschlossener Ortschaften
- 70 mph (= 112 km/h) auf Straßen mit getrennten Fahrbahnen und Autobahnen.

HOLFORD *Somerset* 403 K 30 *Great Britain G. – pop. 307 – ✉ Bridgwater.*
Env. : *Stogursey Priory Church★★, W : 4½ m.*
London 171 – Bristol 48 – Minehead 15 – Taunton 22.

Combe House ⛰, TA5 1RZ, Southwest : 1 m., turning off A 39 at Elf petrol stati
✆ (01278) 741382, *enquiries@combehouse.co.uk, Fax (01278) 741322,* ⛰, 🎾 – ⇔ re
📺 🅿. MC AE VISA JCB
closed 4 January-mid February – **Meals** (bar lunch)/dinner 19.75 **st.** 5.60 – **15**
☕ 38.00/87.00 **st.**, 1 suite – SB.

HOLMES CHAPEL *Ches.* 402 403 404 M 24 – *pop. 5 465.*
London 181 – Chester 25 – Liverpool 41 – Manchester 24 – Stoke-on-Trent 20.

Old Vicarage, Knutsford Rd, Cranage, CW4 8EF, Northwest : ½ m. on A
✆ (01477) 532041, *oldvichotel@aol.com, Fax (01477) 535728* – ⇔ rest, 📺 ✆ ♿ 🅿 – 🎪
MC AE ⓓ VISA. ✗
Church's Brasserie : **Meals** 15.50/16.75 **st.** and a la carte – **29 rm** ☕ 70.50/82.50 **st.** –

Holly Lodge, 70 London Rd, CW4 7AS, on A 50 ✆ (01477) 537033, *sales@hollylodgeho*
co.uk, Fax (01477) 535823 – ⇔ 📺 ♿ 🅿 – 🎪 120. MC AE ⓓ VISA
Meals (bar lunch Monday to Saturday)/dinner 15.50 **st.** and a la carte – **42 rm** ☕ 75.
125.00 **st.** – SB.

Cottage Rest. and Lodge, London Rd, Allostock, WA16 9LU, North : 3 m. on A
✆ (01565) 722470, *Fax (01565) 722749* – ⇔ rm, 📺 🅿 – 🎪 60. MC AE ⓓ
Meals *(closed Saturday lunch and Sunday dinner)* a la carte 11.95/19.00 **t.** 5.60 – **12**
☕ 65.00/80.00 **t.** – SB.

Les prix — Pour toutes précisions sur les prix indiqués dans ce guide, reportez-vous aux pages de l'introduction.

HOLNE *Devon* 403 I 32 – *see Ashburton.*

HOLT *Norfolk* 404 X 25 – *pop. 2 972.*
London 124 – King's Lynn 34 – Norwich 22.

Yetman's, 37 Norwich Rd, NR25 6SA, ✆ (01263) 713320 – ⇔. MC AE VISA
closed 3 weeks October-November, 25, 26 and 31 December and Sunday-Tuesday – **Me**
(dinner only and Sunday lunch)/dinner 28.25 **t.**.

HOLT *Wilts.* 403 404 N 29 – *see Trowbridge.*

HOLYWELL *Cambs.* 404 T 27 – *see St. Ives.*

HONILEY *Warks.* – *see Warwick*

HONITON *Devon* 403 K 31 *The West Country G. – pop. 9 008.*
See : *All Hallows Museum★ AC.*
Env. : *Ottery St. Mary★ (St. Mary's★) SW : 5 m. by A 30 and B 3177.*
Exc. : *Faraway Countryside Park (<★) AC, SE : 6½ m. by A 375 and B 3174.*
ℹ *Lace Walk Car Park ✆ (01404) 43716.*
London 186 – Exeter 17 – Southampton 93 – Taunton 18.

Deer Park ⛰, Buckerell Village, Weston, EX14 0PG, West : 2 ½ m. by A
✆ (01404) 41266, *Fax (01404) 46598,* <, ≘, 🏊 heated, 🎣, ⛰, 🌳, 🎾, squash – 📺
🎪 70. MC AE ⓓ VISA. ✗
Meals 15.00/25.00 **st.** and a la carte 8.00 – **22 rm** ☕ 50.00/140.00 **st.** – SB.

at Yarcombe *Northeast : 8 m. on A 30 – ✉ Honiton.*

Belfry Country H., EX14 9BD, on A 30 ✆ (01404) 861234, *Fax (01404) 861579,* < –
📺 🅿. MC AE VISA
Meals (dinner only) 22.00 **st.** 6.50 – **6 rm** ☕ 45.00/80.00 – SB.

at Wilmington *East : 3 m. on A 35 – ✉ Honiton.*

Home Farm, EX14 9JR, on A 35 ✆ (01404) 831278, *Fax (01404) 831411,* « Part
thatched farmhouse », ⛰ – ⇔ 📺 🅿. MC VISA
Meals 16.50/25.00 **t.** and a la carte 5.50 – **13 rm** ☕ 37.50/80.00 **st.** – SB.

Payhembury *Northwest : 7 m. by A 373 – ✉ Honiton.*

Colestocks Country House, EX14 0JR, South : 1 m. on Colestocks rd ✆ (01404) 850633, *Fax (01404) 850633,* « Part 16C thatched house », – TV P. MC VISA.
April-October – **Meals** (dinner only) (residents only) 16.00/18.50 and a la carte 4.00 – **8 rm** 29.50/55.00 **st.**

Cokesputt House, EX14 3HD, West : ¼ m. on Tale rd ✆ (01404) 841289, « Part 17C and 18C, gardens » – P. MC AE VISA.
closed January – **Meals** (booking essential) (communal dining) 21.00 – **3 rm** 33.00/66.00 **s.** – SB.

OO GREEN *Ches. – see Knutsford.*

OOK *Hants.* 404 R 30 – *pop. 6 471* – *✉ Basingstoke.*
London 47 – Reading 13 – Southampton 35.

Hanover International H. & Club Basingstoke, Scures Hill, Nately Scures, RG27 9JS, West : 1 m. on A 30 ✆ (01256) 764161, *Fax (01256) 768341,* , , , – , rm, rest, TV P – 200. MC AE VISA JCB.
Meals *(closed Saturday lunch, Sunday dinner and Bank Holidays)* a la carte 24.30/35.25 **st.** 10.25 – 11.25 – **100 rm** 125.00/195.00 **st.**

Hook House, London Rd, RG27 9EQ, East : ½ m. on A 30 ✆ (01256) 762630, *Fax (01256) 760232,* « Part Georgian house », – TV P. MC AE VISA JCB.
closed 25-26 December – **Meals** *(closed Sunday)* (residents only) (dinner only) a la carte 16.95/21.85 **st.** 6.00 – **17 rm** 60.00/90.00 **st.**

Rotherwick *North : 2 m. by A 30 and B 3349 on Rotherwick rd – ✉ Basingstoke.*

Tylney Hall, RG27 9AZ, South : 1 ½ m. by Newnham rd on Ridge Lane ✆ (01256) 764881, *sales@tylneyhall.com, Fax (01256) 768141,* « 19C mansion in extensive gardens by Gertrude Jekyll », , , heated, , , – rm, TV P – 120. MC AE VISA JCB.
Meals 23.00/35.00 **st.** and a la carte 9.00 – **101 rm** 120.00/330.00 **st.**, 9 suites – SB.

OOK *Wilts. – see Swindon.*

OPE *Derbs.* 402 403 404 O 23 – *✉ Sheffield.*
London 180 – Derby 50 – Manchester 31 – Sheffield 15 – Stoke-on-Trent 40.

Underleigh House without rest., Hope Valley, S33 6RF, North : 1 m. by Edale rd ✆ (01433) 621372, *underleigh.house@btinternet.com, Fax (01433) 621324,* , – TV P. MC VISA.
closed 2 weeks Christmas and New Year – **5 rm** 46.00/80.00 **st.**, 1 suite.

OPE COVE *Devon* 403 I 33 – *see Salcombe.*

OPTON WAFERS *Shrops.* 403 404 M 26 – *pop. 609* – *✉ Kidderminster.*
London 150 – Birmingham 32 – Shrewsbury 38.

The Crown Inn with rm, DY14 0NB, on A 4117 ✆ (01299) 270372, *desk@crownathopton.co.uk, Fax (01299) 271127,* – rm, TV P. MC AE VISA JCB.
closed 25 December and 4-5 January – **Meals** *(closed Sunday dinner and Monday lunch)* 19.95/27.50 **t.** (dinner) and lunch a la carte 16.50/25.90 **t.** 6.95 – **7 rm** 47.00/78.00 **t.** – SB.

OPWAS *Staffs.* 402 ⑩ 403 ㉒ 404 ⑩ – *see Tamworth.*

OPWOOD *W. Mids.* 402 ⑨ 403 ㉒ 404 ⑳ – *✉ Birmingham.*
London 131 – Birmingham 8.

Westmead, Redditch Rd, B48 7AL, on A 441 ✆ (0121) 445 1202, *reservations@corushotels.com, Fax (0121) 445 6163* – , rest, TV P – 250. MC AE VISA.
closed 25-26 December and 1 January – **Meals** 16.95 and a la carte – 10.50 – **56 rm** 95.00/130.00 **st.**, 2 suites – SB.

HORLEY *Surrey* 404 T 30 – *pop. 19 267.*
London 27 – Brighton 26 – Royal Tunbridge Wells 22.

Plan : see Gatwick

Langshott Manor, Langshott, RH6 9LN, North : by A 23 turning right at Thistle Gatw H. onto Ladbroke Rd ☎ (01293) 786680, *admin@langshottmanor.com, Fax (01293) 7839* , « Part Elizabethan manor house, gardens » – ⇔ TV P. MO AE ① VISA
Meals (booking essential) 25.00/37.50 **st.** and dinner a la carte 32.50/49.50 **st.** 8.00
14 rm ⊇ 145.00/225.00 **st.**, 1 suite – SB.

Thistle Gatwick, Brighton Rd, RH6 8PH, on A 23 ☎ (01293) 786992, *gatwick@thistle.uk, Fax (01293) 820625,* – ⇔, ▤ rest, TV P – 60. MO AE ① VISA. Y
Meals (bar lunch Saturday) 15.00/20.00 **t.** 6.50 – ⊇ 10.75 – **78 rm** 127.00/162.00 **st.** –

Lawn without rest., 30 Massetts Rd, RH6 7DE, ☎ (01293) 775751, *info@lawnguesthouse.co.uk, Fax (01293) 821803,* – ⇔ TV P. MO AE VISA JCB Y
12 rm ⊇ 45.00/50.00 **t.**

The Turret without rest., 48 Massetts Rd, RH6 7DS, ☎ (01293) 782490, *theturret@tesco.net, Fax (01293) 431492* – ⇔ TV P. MO VISA. Y
10 rm ⊇ 38.00/50.00 **st.**

Rosemead without rest., 19 Church Rd, RH6 7EY, ☎ (01293) 784965, *rosemead@globalnet.co.uk, Fax (01293) 430547* – ⇔ TV P. MO AE VISA JCB. Y
6 rm ⊇ 38.00/50.00 **st.**

HORNCASTLE *Lincs.* 402 404 T 24 – *pop. 4 994.*
Trinity Centre, 52 East St. ☎ (01507) 526636 (summer only).
London 140 – Boston 19 – Great Grimsby 31 – Lincoln 21.

Admiral Rodney, North St., LN9 5DX, ☎ (01507) 523131, *admiralrodney@bestwestern.co.uk, Fax (01507) 523104* – |‡|, ⇔ rm, TV P – 140. MO AE ① VISA JCB.
Meals (carving lunch)/dinner 12.95 **t.** and a la carte 5.25 – **31 rm** ⊇ 49.00/76.00 **t.** – SB

The Magpies, 71-75 East St., LN9 6AA, ☎ (01507) 527004, *magpies@fsbdial.co. Fax (01507) 524064* – ⇔. MO VISA
closed 3 weeks August, Monday, Tuesday, Sunday dinner and restricted opening January-February – **Meals** (dinner only and Sunday lunch)/dinner 20.00/25.00 **t.** 6.00.

HORNDON-ON-THE-HILL *Essex* 404 V 29.
London 25 – Chelmsford 22 – Maidstone 34 – Southend-on-Sea 16.

Bell Inn with rm, High Rd, SS17 8LD, ☎ (01375) 642463, *bell-inn@fdn.co. Fax (01375) 361611,* « 16C coaching inn » – ⇔ rm, TV P. MO AE VISA JCB.
Meals *(closed 25-26 December and Bank Holiday Mondays)* 17.95 **t.** (lunch) and a la carte 17.10/25.95 **t.** 6.95 – ⊇ 8.00 – **4 rm** 40.00/85.00 **st.**

HORNS CROSS *Devon* 403 H 31 *The West Country G.* – ✉ *Bideford.*
Exc. : *Clovelly★★, NW : 7 m. by A 39 and B 3237.*
London 237 – Barnstaple 15 – Exeter 48.

Lower Waytown without rest., EX39 5DN, Northeast : 1 ¼ m. on A ☎ (01237) 451787, *Fax (01237) 451787,* « Part 17C thatched cottage », – ⇔ TV P.
closed Christmas-New Year – **3 rm** ⊇ 41.00/59.00 **st.**

HORRINGER *Suffolk* 404 W 27 – *see Bury St. Edmunds.*

HORSFORTH *W. Yorks.* 402 P 22 – *see Leeds.*

HORSHAM *W. Sussex* 404 T 30 – *pop. 42 552.*
18, 18 *Fullers, Hammerpond Rd, Mannings Heath ☎ (01403) 210228.*
9 Causeway ☎ (01403) 211661.
London 39 – Brighton 23 – Guildford 20 – Lewes 25 – Worthing 20.

South Lodge , Brighton Rd, Lower Beeding, RH13 6PS, Southeast : 5 m. on A ☎ (01403) 891711, *enquiries@southlodgehotel.co.uk, Fax (01403) 891766,* ≤, « Victorian mansion, gardens », , 18, , , – ⇔ rest, TV P – 80. MO AE ① VISA JCB.
Meals 18.50/50.50 **t.** and dinner a la carte 15.00 – ⊇ 12.95 – **37 rm** 150.00/350.00 4 suites – SB.

Cisswood House, Sandygate Lane, Lower Beeding, RH13 6NF, Southeast : 3 ¾ m. on A 281 ✆ (01403) 891216, *cisswood@pageant.co.uk, Fax (01403) 891621,* – rest, P – 150. VISA.
Meals *(closed Saturday lunch)* 15.00/30.00 **t.** and dinner a la carte 7.50 – **32 rm** 82.50/99.00 **t.**, 2 suites – SB.

Travel Inn, The Station, 57 North St., RH12 1RB, ✆ (01403) 250141, *Fax (01403) 270797* – rm, rest, P. VISA.
Meals (grill rest.) – **40 rm** 40.95 **t.**

Southwater *South : 3 m. by B 2237 – ✉ Horsham.*

Cole's, Worthing Rd, RH13 7BS, ✆ (01403) 730456, *colesrestaurant@dial.pipex.com, Fax (01403) 738299* – P. VISA JCB
closed 2 weeks in summer, 1 week in winter, Saturday lunch, Sunday dinner and Monday – **Meals** 12.95/15.00 **t.** (lunch) and a la carte 21.95/30.85 **t.** 6.50.

Slinfold *West : 4 m. by A 281 off A 264 – ✉ Horsham.*

Random Hall, Stane St., RH13 7QX, West : ½ m. on A 29 ✆ (01403) 790558, *Fax (01403) 791046,* « Part 16C farmhouse » – rest, P. VISA.
closed 27 December-10 January – **Meals** 11.50/22.50 **st.** – **15 rm** 80.00/90.00 **st.** – SB.

...RTON *Northants.* 404 R 27 – *pop. 574 – ✉ Northampton.*

London 66 – Bedford 18 – Northampton 6.

French Partridge, Newport Pagnell Rd, NN7 2AP, ✆ (01604) 870033, *french@partridge.com, Fax (01604) 870032* – P
closed 2 weeks Easter, 3 weeks July and August, 2 weeks Christmas, Sunday and Monday – **Meals** (booking essential) (dinner only) 30.00 **st.** 9.00.

...RTON-CUM-STUDLEY *Oxon.* 403 404 Q 28 – *pop. 453 – ✉ Oxford.*

London 57 – Aylesbury 23 – Oxford 7.

Studley Priory , OX33 1AZ, ✆ (01865) 351203, *res@studley-priory.co.uk, Fax (01865) 351613,* ←, « Elizabethan manor house in park », 18, , – P – 50. VISA JCB.
Meals 15.00/27.50 **t.** and a la carte – 8.50 – **17 rm** 105.00/140.00 **t.**, 1 suite – SB.

...RWICH *Lancs.* 402 404 M 23 – ✉ *Bolton.*

London 217 – Liverpool 35 – Manchester 21 – Preston 16.

Express by Holiday Inn without rest., 3 Arena Approach, BL6 6LB, Southeast : 2 ½ m. by A 673 on A 6027 ✆ (01204) 469111, *Fax (01204) 469222* – P – 30. VISA JCB.
74 rm 49.95 **st.**

...THFIELD *Kent* 404 W 30 – *see Ashford.*

...UGHTON CONQUEST *Beds.* 404 S 27 – *see Bedford.*

...VE *Brighton and Hove* 404 T 31 – *see Brighton and Hove.*

...VINGHAM *N. Yorks.* 402 R 21 – *pop. 322 – ✉ York.*

London 235 – Middlesbrough 36 – York 25.

Worsley Arms, YO62 4LA, ✆ (01653) 628234, *worsleyarms@aol.com, Fax (01653) 628130,* « Part 19C coaching inn », – P – 25. VISA JCB
***Wyvern :* Meals** (dinner only and Sunday lunch)/dinner 25.00/30.00 **t.** and a la carte 7.00 – ***Cricketer's Bistro :* Meals** a la carte 16.50/21.50 **t.** 7.00 – **19 rm** 60.00/90.00 **t.** – SB.

...DDERSFIELD *W. Yorks.* 402 404 O 23 – *pop. 143 726.*

18, 9 Bradley Park, Bradley Rd ✆ (01484) 223772 – 18 Woodsome Hall, Fenay Bridge ✆ (01484) 602971 – 18 Outlane, Slack Lane ✆ (01422) 374762 A – *18 Meltham, Thick Hollins Hall ✆ (01484) 850227 – 18 Fixby Hall, Lightridge Rd ✆ (01484) 420110* B – *18 Crosland Heath, Felks Stile Rd ✆ (01484) 653216* A.

3 Albion St. ✆ (01484) 223200.

London 191 – Bradford 11 – Leeds 15 – Manchester 25 – Sheffield 26.

HUDDERSFIELD

Acre Street .... **AB** 3
Armitage Road .... **B** 4
Ashes Lane .... **B** 6
Balmoral Avenue........... **B** 7
Bolstermoor Road .... **A** 12
Brighouse Road .... **AB** 15
Butternab Road............ **B** 16
Church Lane .... **B** 19
Clough Road .... **A** 24
Crosland Factory Lane...... **A** 27
Dog Kennel Bank .... **B** 28
East Street............... **A** 31
Edgerton Road .... **B** 33
Fartown Green Road .... **B** 36
Gillroyd Lane .... **A** 40
Glead Road .... **A** 42

Gleholt Road .... **B** 43
Grimescar Road .... **B** 46
Haeton Road .... **B** 48
Halifax Old Road.......... **B** 49
Halifax Road.............. **B** 51
Helme Lane................ **A** 54
Hey Lane .... **B** 55
Huddersfield Road .... **B** 58
Kaye Lane .... **B** 61
King's Mill In .... **B** 64
Knowl Road .... **A** 66
Leymoor Road.............. **A** 72
Lindley Moor .... **A** 73
Lockwood Road .... **B** 75
Lockwood Scar .... **B** 76
Longwood Gate .... **A** 78
Manchester Road .... **B** 84
New Mill Road .... **B** 97
Norttgate .... **B** 106

Pack Road .... **B** 1
Pike Low Road............. **A** 1
Quarmby Road .... **A** 1
Reinwood Road .... **A** 1
Rochdale Road .... **A** 1
St. John's Road .... **B** 1
St. Thomas Road .... **B** 1
Scar Lane................. **A** 1
Scotgate Road............. **B** 1
Slades Lane............... **A** 1
Station Road .... **A** 1
Swallow Lane .... **A** 1
Udget Street .... **A** 1
Vicarage Road............. **A** 1
Waingate .... **B** 1
Walpde Road............... **B** 1
West Bourne Road.......... **B** 1
Whitehead Lane .... **B** 1
Woodhead Road............. **B** 1

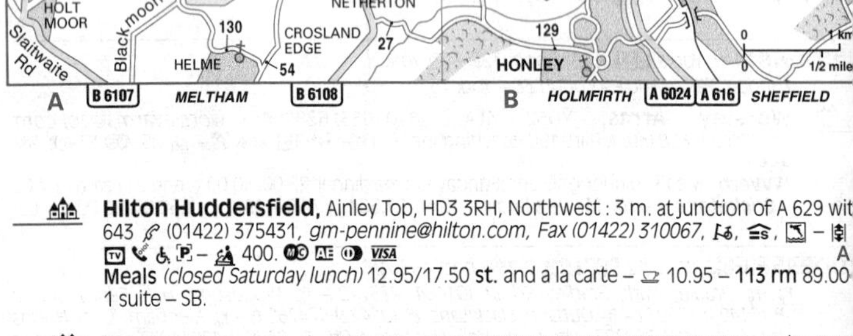

Hilton Huddersfield, Ainley Top, HD3 3RH, Northwest : 3 m. at junction of A 629 wit 643 ☎ (01422) 375431, *gm-pennine@hilton.com, Fax (01422) 310067,* – 400. *VISA* A
Meals *(closed Saturday lunch)* 12.95/17.50 **st.** and a la carte – 10.95 – **113 rm** 89.00 1 suite – SB.

George, St. George's Sq., HD1 1JA, ☎ (01484) 515444, *Fax (01484) 435056* – – 200. *VISA* JCB C
Meals (bar lunch Saturday) 9.95/28.80 **st.** and a la carte 5.95 – 10.00 – **59 rm** 85. 105.00 **st.**, 1 suite – SB.

HUDDERSFIELD

pel Hill . . . . C 18
emont Street . . . . C 21
william Street . . . . C 37
woors Street. . . . . C 39
at Northerh Street . . . . . C 45
erial Arcade. . . . . C 60
Street. . . . . C 63
ver Fitzwilliam Street . . . C 79
nchester Road. . . . . C 84
ket Place . . . . C 85
ket Street . . . . C 87
rton Street . . . . C 91
v North Road . . . . C 100
thumberland Street . . . C 105
cote Bank . . . . C 108
tland Street . . . . C 112
een Street . . . . C 115
een Street South . . . . . C 117
way Street. . . . . C 120
Peter's Street . . . . C 125
ng Street. . . . . C 133
ngwood Avenue . . . . . C 136
ity Street . . . . C 141
n Street . . . . C 145
oria Lane . . . . C 148
efield Road . . . . C 151
er Street . . . . C 156

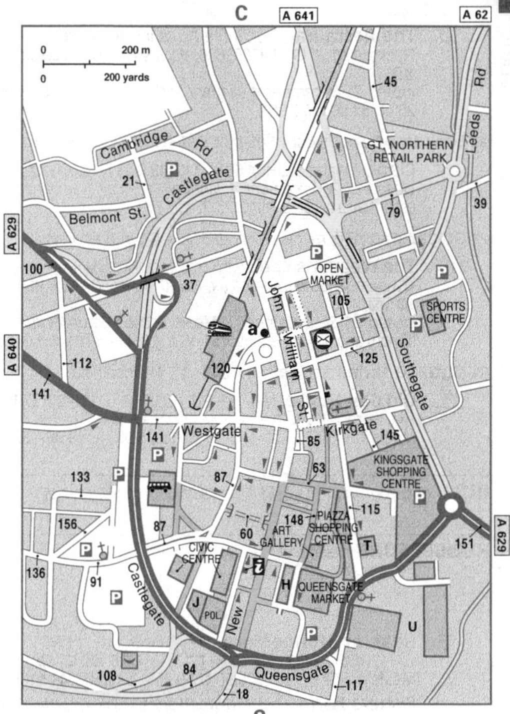

eat Britain and
land is now covered
an Atlas at a scale
1 inch to 4.75 miles.

ree easy
use versions:
perback, Spiralbound
d Hardback.

Briar Court, Halifax Rd, Birchencliffe, HD3 3NT, Northwest : 2 m. on A 629 ℘ (01484) 519902, *briarcourthotel@btconnect.com, Fax (01484) 431812* – rm, TV, P – 150. MC AE VISA JCB. A n
closed Christmas and Bank Holidays – **Meals** *(closed Saturday lunch)* a la carte 13.00/26.00 **t.** – ***Da Sandro :*** **Meals** - Italian - *(closed Saturday lunch)* a la carte 13.00/26.00 **st.** 6.00 – **47 rm** 65.00/75.00 **st.**, 1 suite.

The Lodge, 48 Birkby Lodge Rd, Birkby, HD2 2BG, North : 1 ½ m. by A 629 and Blacker Rd ℘ (01484) 431001, *Fax (01484) 421590,* – TV P – 30. MC AE VISA. B f
closed 26 December and Bank Holiday Monday – **Meals** *(closed Saturday lunch)* (residents only Sunday dinner) 14.95/26.00 **t.** 6.50 – **12 rm** 60.00/80.00 **st.**

Premier Lodge, New Hey Rd, Fixby, HD2 2EA, Northwest : 3 ½ m. by A 629 off A 643 (Brighouse rd) ℘ (0870) 7001408, *Fax (0870) 7001409* – TV P. MC AE VISA.
Meals (carving rest.) 11.75 **st.** – 6.00 – **40 rm** 42.00 **st.** A a

Almondbury *Southeast : 1 ¾ m. by A 629 on Almondbury rd* – **B** – ✉ *Huddersfield.*

Thorpe Grange Manor, Thorpe Lane, HD5 8TA, ℘ (01484) 425115, *admin@thorpegrangemanor.com, Fax (01484) 425115,* – P. MC VISA JCB
closed 30 June-15 August, 1-8 January, Saturday lunch, Sunday dinner and Monday – **Meals** 14.95 **st.** and a la carte 7.95.

Kirkburton *Southeast : 5 m. by A 629 on B 6116* – **B** – ✉ *Huddersfield.*

Hanover International, Penistone Rd, HD8 0PE, on A 629 ℘ (01484) 607788, *Fax (01484) 607961* – TV P – 150. MC AE VISA
closed 26-30 December – ***Brasserie 209 :*** **Meals** (dinner only) 16.95 **st.** and a la carte 6.80 – 8.50 – **47 rm** 69.00/79.00 **st.** – SB.

Shelley *Southeast : 6 ¼ m. by A 629 on B 6116* – **B** – ✉ *Huddersfield.*

Three Acres Inn, Roydhouse, HD8 8LR, Northeast : 1 ½ m. on Flockton rd ℘ (01484) 602606, *3acres@globalnet.co.uk, Fax (01484) 608411* – TV P. MC AE VISA.
closed 25 December and 1 January – **Meals** – (see ***The Restaurant*** below) – **20 rm** 55.00/75.00 **t.**

ENGLAND

XX **The Restaurant** (at Three Acres Inn H.), Roydhouse, HD8 8LR, Northeast : 1 ½ m. Flockton rd ✆ (01484) 602606, *3acres@globalnet.co.uk, Fax (01484) 608411* – ▤ P. MC VISA
closed 25 December, 1 January and Saturday lunch – **Meals** 16.95 **t.** (lunch) and a la ca 20.40/37.90 **t.** 6.95.

at Lockwood *Southwest : 1 m. by A 616 – B – ✉ Huddersfield.*

X **Ciao!,** 2 Water St., HD4 6EJ, ✆ (01484) 534444, *Fax (01484) 536655* – ▤ P. MC AE VISA
closed 25-26 December, 1 January, Saturday lunch and Sunday – **Meals** - Italian - (book essential) a la carte 14.40/23.95 **t.**

at Golcar *West : 3½ m. by A 62 on B 6111 – ✉ Huddersfield.*

XXX **The Weaver's Shed** with rm, Knowl Rd, via Scar Lane, HD7 4AN, ✆ (01484) 654284, *@weaversshed.demon.co.uk, Fax (01484) 650980,* « Part 18C woollen mill » – TV P. MC VISA
A
closed 25-26 December – **Meals** *(closed Saturday lunch, Sunday and Monday)* 13.9 (lunch) and a la carte 21.95/31.15 **t.** 8.95 – **5 rm** 50.00/65.00 **t.** – SB.

at Outlane *Northwest : 4 m. on A 640 – ✉ Huddersfield.*

Old Golf House, New Hey Rd, HD3 3YP, ✆ (01422) 379311, *Fax (01422) 372694,* ▤ rest, TV P – 100. MC AE VISA
A
Meals 10.00/17.95 **st.** and a la carte 6.95 – 9.95 – **52 rm** 89.00/109.00 **st.** – SB.

HULL *Kingston-upon-Hull* 402 S 22 – *see Kingston-upon-Hull.*

HUNGERFORD *Newbury* 403 404 P 29 *The West Country G. – pop. 5 046.*

Exc. : *Savernake Forest★★ (Grand Avenue★★★), W : 7 m. by A 4 – Crofton Beam Engine SW : 8 m. by A 338 and minor roads.*

London 74 – Bristol 57 – Oxford 28 – Reading 26 – Southampton 46.

Bear at Hungerford, 17 Charnham St., RG17 0EL, on A 4 ✆ (01488) 6825 *Fax (01488) 684357,* – TV P – 75. MC AE VISA
Meals a la carte 16.50/28.50 **t.** 9.95 – 9.50 – **41 rm** 86.00/125.00 **st.** – SB.

Fishers Farm, Shefford Woodlands, RG17 7AB, Northeast : 4 m. by A 4 and A 338 o 4000 ✆ (01488) 648466, *mail@fishersfarm.co.uk, Fax (01488) 648706,* « Working farm – P.
Meals (by arrangement) (communal dining) 20.00 **st.** – **3 rm** 35.00/56.00 **st.**

Marshgate Cottage without rest., Marsh Lane, RG17 0QX, West : ¾ m. by Church ✆ (01488) 682307, *reservations@marshgate.co.uk, Fax (01488) 685475,* – TV P. VISA
closed 25 and 26 December – **10 rm** 36.50/55.00 **st.**

at Little Bedwyn *Southwest : 3 m. by A 4 – ✉ Hungerford.*

XX **The Harrow Inn,** SN8 3JP, ✆ (01672) 870871, *dining@harrowinn.co Fax (01672) 870871,* – . MC AE VISA
closed 3 weeks August, 1 week December, 2 weeks January, Sunday dinner and Monda **Meals** a la carte 25.50/30.00 **t.** 10.00.

HUNSTANTON *Norfolk* 402 404 V 25 – *pop. 4 634.*

18 *Golf Course Rd ✆ (01485) 532811.*

Town Hall, The Green ✆ (01485) 532610.

London 120 – Cambridge 60 – Norwich 45.

Le Strange Arms, Golf Course Rd, Old Hunstanton, PE36 6JJ, North : 1 m. by A ✆ (01485) 534411, *lestrangearms@netmatters.co.uk, Fax (01485) 534724,* – r TV P – 150. MC AE VISA JCB
Meals (bar lunch Monday to Saturday)/dinner 18.00/25.00 **t.** and a la carte 6.50 – **33** 57.50/103.00 **t.**, 3 suites – SB.

Oriel Lodge without rest., 24 Homefields Rd, PE36 5HJ, ✆ (01485) 532368, *info@orie ge.co.uk, Fax (01485) 532388,* – TV P.
5 rm 35.00/58.00.

Claremont without rest., 35 Greevegate, PE36 6AF, ✆ (01485) 533171 – TV
7 rm 23.00/48.00 **t.**

HUNSTRETE *Bath & North East Somerset* 403 404 M 29 – *see Bristol.*

NTINGDON *Cambs.* 404 T 26 – *pop. 15 575* – 9 *Hemingford Abbots, New Farm Lodge, Cambridge Rd* ℘ *(01480) 495000.*
The Library, Princes St. ℘ *(01480) 388588.*
London 69 – Bedford 21 – Cambridge 16.

Huntingdon Marriott, Kingfisher Way, Hinchingbrooke Business Park, PE18 8FL, West : 1 ½ m. by A 141 at junction with A 14 ℘ (01480) 446000, *huntingdon@marriotthotels.co.uk, Fax (01480) 451111,* – – 260. MO AE VISA
Meals 12.50/21.50 **st.** and a la carte 7.95 – **146 rm** 95.00 **st.**, 4 suites – SB.

Old Bridge, 1 High St., PE18 6TQ, ℘ (01480) 424300, *oldbridge@huntsbridge.co.uk, Fax (01480) 411017,* – , rm, – 50. MO AE VISA
Meals a la carte 21.00/30.00 **st.** 6.00 – **24 rm** 79.50/125.00 **st.**

Travelodge, PE18 9JF, Southeast : 5 ½ m. on A 14 (eastbound carriageway) ℘ (01954) 230919, *Fax (01954) 230919* – rm, rest, . MO AE VISA JCB.
Meals (grill rest.) – **40 rm** 49.95 **t.**

NTON *Kent* – *pop. 603* – ✉ *Maidstone.*
London 37 – Canterbury 28 – Folkestone 34 – Hastings 35 – Maidstone 5.

The Woolhouse without rest., Grove Lane, ME15 0SE, ℘ (01622) 820778, *Fax (01622) 820645,* « Converted 17C barn », , –
closed Christmas and New Year – **4 rm** 25.00/50.00.

When looking for a quiet hotel use the maps found in the introduction or look for establishments with the sign or .

RLEY-ON-THAMES *Windsor & Maidenhead* 404 R 29 – *pop. 1 712* – ✉ *Maidenhead.*
London 38 – Oxford 26 – Reading 12.

Ye Olde Bell, High St., SL6 5LX, ℘ (01628) 825881, *Fax (01628) 825871,* « Part 12C inn », – rm, – 130. MO AE VISA
Meals 17.95/26.95 **st.** and a la carte 9.50 – 10.95 – **45 rm** 135.00/170.00 **st.**, 1 suite – SB.

RST *Berks.* 403 404 Q 29 – *see Reading.*

RSTBOURNE TARRANT *Hants.* 403 404 P 30 – *pop. 700* – ✉ *Andover.*
London 77 – Bristol 77 – Oxford 38 – Southampton 33.

Esseborne Manor , SP11 0ER, Northeast : 1 ½ m. on A 343 ℘ (01264) 736444, *esseborne-manor@compuserve.com, Fax (01264) 736725,* , – – 40. MO AE VISA
Meals 15.00/20.00 **st.** (lunch) and dinner a la carte 23.00/31.00 **st.** 8.00 – **15 rm** 100.00/135.00 **st.** – SB.

RST GREEN *Lancs.* 402 M 22 – ✉ *Clitheroe.*
London 236 – Blackburn 12 – Burnley 13 – Preston 12.

Shireburn Arms, Whalley Rd, BB7 9QJ, on B 6243 ℘ (01254) 826518, *sales@shireburn-hotel.co.uk, Fax (01254) 826208,* – . MO AE VISA JCB
Meals 7.95/13.95 **t.** and a la carte 6.50 – **18 rm** 45.00/65.00 **t.** – SB.

TTON-LE-HOLE *N. Yorks.* 402 R 21 – *pop. 162.*
London 244 – Scarborough 27 – York 33.

Hammer and Hand, YO62 6UA, ℘ (01751) 417300, *info@hammerandhandhouse.com, Fax (01751) 417711,* « 18C former beer house », – . MO VISA
closed 10-21 February, Christmas and New Year – **Meals** (by arrangement) 15.00 **st.** 4.00 – **3 rm** 35.00/50.00 **st.**

Quaker Cottage, YO62 6UA, ℘ (01751) 417300, *info@hammerandhandhouse.com, Fax (01751) 417711,* « 17C Yorkshire longhouse », – . MO VISA
closed 10-21 February, Christmas and New Year – **Meals** (by arrangement) 15.00 4.00 – **4 rm** 27.00/50.00 **st.**

YTON *Mersey.* 402 403 L 23 – *see Liverpool.*

HYDE *Gtr. Manchester* 402 403 404 N 23 – *pop. 30 666.*
London 202 – Manchester 10.

Village Leisure, Captain Clarke Rd, Dukinfield, SK14 4QG, Northwest : 1 ¼ m. by A 6
(0161) 368 1456, *gary.lewis@village-hotels.com, Fax (0161) 367 8343,* squa
– 150.
Meals (grill rest.) a la carte 10.00/22.85 **t.** – **89 rm** 75.00/87.00 **t.** – SB.

Premier Lodge, Stockport Rd, SK14 3AU, East : 2 m. by A 57 (0870) 70014
Fax (0870) 7001479 – rm,
Meals (grill rest.) a la carte 9.90/16.15 **t.** – 6.00 – **83 rm** 42.00 **t.**

HYTHE *Kent* 404 X 30 – *pop. 14 569.*
Sene Valley, Sene, Folkestone (01303) 268513.
En Route Travel, Red Lion Sq. (01303) 267799.
London 68 – Folkestone 6 – Hastings 33 – Maidstone 31.

Plan : see Folkestone

Hythe Imperial, Prince's Par., CT21 6AE, (01303) 267441, *hytheimperial@marston*
els.com, Fax (01303) 264610, squash –
250.
Meals *(closed Saturday lunch)* 19.50/27.00 **st.** and dinner a la carte 8.50 – ***The Terra***
Meals (light lunch)/dinner a la carte 15.00/25.00 **st.** – 11.00 – **97 rm** 87.00/120.00
3 suites – SB.

Stade Court, West Par., CT21 6DT, (01303) 268263, *stadecourt@marstonhotels.co.*
Fax (01303) 261803, – rest, – 35.
Meals (bar lunch Monday to Saturday)/dinner 22.00 **t.** and a la carte 6.75 – 10.0
42 rm 69.00/89.00 **t.** – SB.

Jährlich eine neue Ausgabe
Aktuellste Informationen, jährlich für Sie!

IFFLEY *Oxon – see Oxford.*

ILCHESTER *Somerset* 403 L 30 – *pop. 1 733.*
London 138 – Bridgwater 21 – Exeter 48 – Taunton 24 – Yeovil 5.

Ilchester Arms, The Square, BA22 8LN, (01935) 840220, *Fax (01935) 841353,* –
Meals (bar lunch)/dinner 14.95/19.95 **t.** and a la carte – **8 rm** 65.00/95.00 **st.** – SB.

ILKLEY *W. Yorks.* 402 O 22 – *pop. 13 530.*
Myddleton (01943) 607277.
Station Rd (01943) 436200.
London 210 – Bradford 13 – Harrogate 17 – Leeds 16 – Preston 46.

Rombalds, 11 West View, Wells Rd, LS29 9JG, (01943) 603201, *reception@rombalds*
mon.co.uk, Fax (01943) 816586, « Georgian town house » – – 70.
Meals a la carte 13.20/23.50 **st.** 6.75 – **11 rm** 69.50/104.00 **st.**, 4 suites – SB.

The Crescent, Brook St., LS29 8DG, (01943) 600012, *creshot@dialstart.r*
Fax (01943) 601513 – rm, – 100.
Meals (bar lunch and Sunday dinner)/dinner 9.95/12.95 **t.** and a la carte – **20 rm** 57.
75.00 **t.**

Cow and Calf, Hangingstone Rd, LS29 8BT, Southeast : 1 ¼ m. by Cowpasture
(01943) 607335, *Fax (01943) 604712,* – rm, – 25.
Meals (in bar) a la carte 10.50/16.95 **st.** – **16 rm** 45.00/55.00 **st.**

The Grove without rest., 66 The Grove, LS29 9PA, (01943) 600298, *info@grovehote*
g, Fax (0870) 706 5587 –
– **6 rm** 45.00/64.00 **st.**

Box Tree, 37 Church St., LS29 9DR, on A 65 (01943) 608484, *info@theboxtree.co.*
Fax (01943) 607186, « 18C stone farmhouse, collection of paintings and objets d'art
closed last 2 weeks January, 26 to 30 December, Monday and Sunday dinner – **Me**
a la carte 22.50/35.00 **st.** 6.50
Spec. Bavarois of artichoke and crab with tomato coulis. Suprême of guinea fowl w
herbs and asparagus. Dark chocolate 'hat', passion fruit coulis.

LOGAN *Cornwall* 403 E 33 *The West Country G. – pop. 13 095 –* ✉ *Redruth.*
Env. : *Portreath*★, *NW : 2 m. by B 3300 – Hell's Mouth*★, *SW : 5 m. by B 3301.*
London 305 – Falmouth 14 – Penzance 17 – Truro 11.

Aviary Court, Mary's Well, TR16 4QZ, Northwest : ¾ m. by Alexandra Rd ☎ (01209) 842256, *aviarycourt@connexions.co.uk, Fax (01209) 843744,* – rest, TV P. MC VISA.
Meals *(closed Sunday dinner to non-residents)* (dinner only and Sunday lunch)/dinner a la carte 16.75/21.20 **t.** 5.00 – **6 rm** 42.50/62.50.

MINSTER *Somerset* 403 L 31 *The West Country G. – pop. 4 162.*
See : *Town*★ – *Minster*★★.
Env. : *Barrington Court Gardens*★ *AC, NE : 3½ m. by B 3168 – Chard (Museum*★*), S : 6 m. by B 3168 and A 358.*
London 145 – Taunton 12 – Yeovil 17.

Travelodge, Southfield Roundabout, Horton Cross, TA19 9PT, Northwest : 1 ½ m. at junction of A 303 with A 358 ☎ (01460) 53748 – rm, TV P. MC AE VISA JCB.
Meals (grill rest.) – **32 rm** 39.95 **t.**

Cricket Malherbie *South : 2½ m. by Chard rd –* ✉ *Ilminster.*

Old Rectory, TA19 0PW, ☎ (01460) 54364, *theoldrectory@malherbie.freeserve.co.uk, Fax (01460) 57374,* – TV P. MC VISA JCB.
closed 25 and 26 December – **Meals** (by arrangement) (communal dining) 17.50 **st.** 6.00 – **4 rm** 48.00/80.00 **st.** – SB.

Groß-London (GREATER LONDON) besteht aus der City und 32 Verwaltungsbezirken (Borough). Diese sind wiederum in kleinere Bezirke (Area) unterteilt, deren Mittelpunkt ehemalige Dörfer oder Stadtviertel sind, die oft ihren eigenen Charakter bewahrt haben.

IPINGTON *Cambs. – see Cambridge.*

IGLEBY GREENHOW *N. Yorks.* 402 Q 20 – *pop. 391.*
London 262 – Darlington 28 – Leeds 62 – Middlesbrough 12 – Scarborough 50 – York 49.

Manor House Farm, TS9 6RB, South : 1 m. via lane to manor, next to church ☎ (01642) 722384, *mbloom@globalnet.co.uk,* «, « Working farm », – P. MC VISA JCB.
closed 1 week Christmas – **Meals** 17.50 **st.** 5.50 – **3 rm** (dinner included) 47.50/95.00 **st.** – SB.

IGLETON *N. Yorks.* 402 M 21 – *pop. 1 979 –* ✉ *Carnforth (Lancs.).*
The Community Centre car park ☎ (015242) 41049 (summer only).
London 266 – Kendal 21 – Lancaster 18 – Leeds 53.

Pines Country House, Kendal Rd, LA6 3HN, Northwest : ¼ m. on A 65 ☎ (015242) 41252, *pineshotel@aol.com, Fax (015242) 41252,* – TV P. MC VISA
March-November – **Meals** (booking essential) (residents only) (dinner only) 14.00 **st.** – **7 rm** 34.00/56.00 – SB.

Ferncliffe House (without rest.), 55 Main St., LA6 3HJ, ☎ (015242) 42405, *ferncliffe@hotmail.com* – TV P. MC VISA.
closed 25-26 December – **5 rm** 29.00/46.00 **t.**

Riverside Lodge without rest., 24 Main St., LA6 3HJ, ☎ (015242) 41359, *andrew@foleya.fsnet.co.uk,* «, , – TV P. MC VISA
8 rm 30.00/46.00 **st.**

IKBERROW *Worcs.* 403 404 O 27 – ✉ *Worcester.*
London 116 – Birmingham 21 – Cheltenham 25 – Stratford-upon-Avon 12.

The Old Windmill, Withybed Lane, off Stonepit Lane, WR7 4JL, ☎ (01386) 792801, *sheila@theoldwindmill.co.uk, Fax (01386) 792801,* «, – TV P. MC VISA JCB.
Meals (by arrangement) (communal dining) 21.00 **s.** – **3 rm** 60.00/90.00 **s.**

ISTOW *Devon* 403 H 30 – *see Bideford.*

IPSWICH *Suffolk* 404 X 27 *Great Britain G. – pop. 130 157.*

See : *Christchurch Mansion (collection of paintings★)* X B.

Rushmere, Rushmere Heath ☎ (01473) 727109 – Purdis Heath, Bucklesham ☎ (01473) 727474 – Fynn Valley, Witnesham ☎ (01473) 785267.

St. Stephens Church, St. Stephens Lane ☎ (01473) 258070.

London 76 – Norwich 43.

Plan opposite

Swallow Belstead Brook, Belstead Rd, IP2 9HB, Southwest : 2 ½ ☎ (01473) 684241, *info@swallowhotels.com, Fax (01473) 681249,* – 200. VISA. Z
Meals *(closed Saturday lunch)* 14.50/40.00 **st.** and a la carte 7.00 – **86 rm** 99.(108.75 **st.**, 2 suites – SB.

Posthouse Ipswich, London Rd, IP2 0UA, Southwest : 2 ¼ m. by A 1214 on A 10 ☎ (0870) 400 9045, *Fax (01473) 680412,* – rm, – 100. VISA Z
Meals *(closed Saturday lunch)* 15.00/45.00 **t.** and a la carte 7.95 – 11.95 – **110 r** 69.00 **st.** – SB.

Courtyard by Marriott Ipswich, The Havens, Ransomes Europark, IP3 9SJ, Sou east : 3 ½ m. by A 1156 and Nacton Rd at junction with A 14 ☎ (01473) 2722 *Fax (01473) 272484,* – rm, rest, – 180. VISA.
Meals a la carte 14.15/22.20 **st.** 7.45 – 10.00 – **60 rm** 72.00 **st.** – SB.

Marlborough, Henley Rd, IP1 3SP, ☎ (01473) 257677, *reception@themarlborough.co. Fax (01473) 226927,* – rest, – 50. VISA Y
Meals *(closed Saturday lunch)* 16.00/23.95 **st.** and a la carte 10.95 – 10.65 – **21** 69.00/89.00 **st.**, 1 suite – SB.

Novotel, Greyfriars Rd, IP1 1UP, ☎ (01473) 232400, *Fax (01473) 232414* – rm, – 180. VISA JCB X
Meals 15.00 **st.** and a la carte – 10.00 – **100 rm** 76.00 **st.** – SB.

Highview House without rest., 56 Belstead Rd, IP2 8BE, ☎ (01473) 6016 *Fax (01473) 688659,* – VISA JCB Z
closed 2 weeks Christmas-New Year – **9 rm** 45.00/58.00 **t.**

Travel Inn, Bourne Hill, Wherstead, IP2 8ND, South : 1 ¾ m. by A 137 (Wherstead ☎ (01473) 692372, *Fax (01473) 692283* – rm, VISA
Meals (grill rest.) – **40 rm** 40.95 **t.**

Mortimer's, Wherry Quay, IP4 1AS, ☎ (01473) 230225, *Fax (01473) 761611* – VISA JCB X
closed 24 December-5 January, Saturday lunch, Sunday and Bank Holidays – **Meals** Seafood - a la carte 15.15/27.50 **t.** 5.30.

at Claydon *Northwest : 4½ m. by A 1156 off A 14* – Y – ✉ *Ipswich.*

Claydon Country House, 16-18 Ipswich Rd, IP6 0AR, ☎ (01473) 830382, *kayshotel@ .com, Fax (01473) 832476,* – VISA.
Meals *(closed Sunday dinner)* 15.40 **st.** and a la carte – **14 rm** 64.00/74.00 **st.** – SB.

Travel Inn, Mockbeggars Hall Farm, Paper Mill Lane, IP6 0AP, Southwest : ½ m. off A roundabout ☎ (01473) 833125, *Fax (01473) 833127* – rm, VISA
Meals (grill rest.) (dinner only) – **59 rm** 40.95 **t.**

at Woolverstone *South : 5½ m. by A 137* – Z – *off B 1456* – ✉ *Ipswich.*

Woolverstone House, Mannings Lane, IP9 1AN, ☎ (01473) 780940, *cooks@ente ise.net, Fax (01473) 780959,* « Lutyens house, Gertrude Jekyll gardens », –
closed 21 December-6 January – **Meals** (by arrangement) (communal dining) 17.50/27.5 – **3 rm** 60.00/90.00 **s.**

at Holbrook *South : 5 ¾ m. by A 137* – Z – *and B 1456 on B 1080* – ✉ *Ipswich.*

Highfield without rest., Harkstead Rd, IP9 2RA, East : ½ m. by Fishponds La ☎ (01473) 328250, *Fax (01473) 328250,* –
closed mid December-mid January – **3 rm** 30.00/46.00 **st.**

at Burstall *West : 4½ m. by A 1214 off A 1071* – Y – ✉ *Ipswich.*

Mulberry Hall, IP8 3DP, ☎ (01473) 652348, *mulberryhall@hotmail.co Fax (01473) 652110,* « 16C farmhouse », –
closed Christmas-New Year – **Meals** (by arrangement) 17.00 **st.** – **3 rm** 20.00/40.00 **st**

IPSWICH

yle Street .... X 2
:k Hamlet .... Z 3
:field Drive .... Z 5
nd Street .... X 6
dgwater Road .... Z 7
termarket Centre.... X 9
r Street .... X 10
evallier Street........ Y 13
llege Street .... X 15
n Hill.......... X 16
gs Head Street ...... X 18
nbrook Road.......... Z 19
con Street .... X 21
e Hamlet .... Z 22
nciscan Way .... X 24
rs Street .... X 25
y Friars Road .... X 26
ve Lane.......... YZ 28
dford Road ...... X, Y 30
yds Avenue .... X 31
wer Orwell Street...... X 32
thgate Street .... X 33
well Place.......... X 34
een Street .... X 37
Helen's Street ... X, Y 39
Margarets Street.... X 40
Nicholas Street ..... X 41
Peter's Street....... X 42
thouse Street .... X 43
ent Street .... X 46
ern Street X
ver Ramparts
Centre .... X 47
per Orwell Street .... X 49
terworks Street ..... X 51
stgate Street.......... X 52
mouth Road......... Y 54

Europe

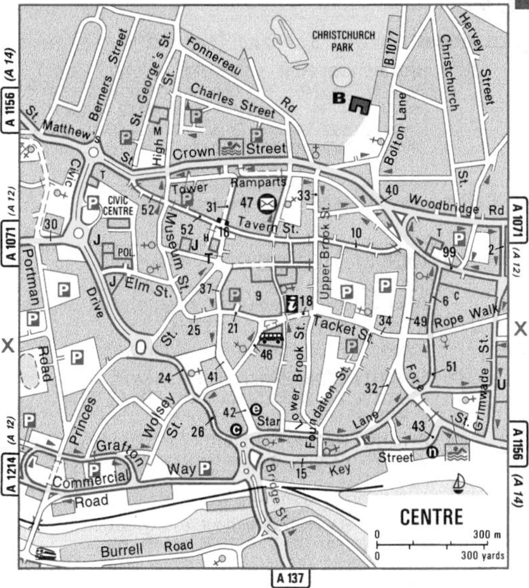

If the name of the hotel
is not in bold type,
on arrival ask the hotelier his prices.

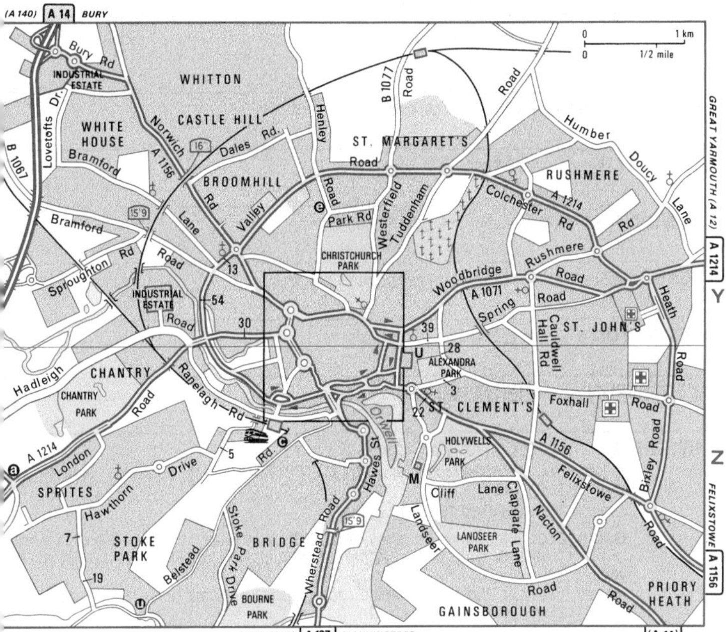

at Hintlesham *West : 5 m. by A 1214 on A 1071 – Y – ✉ Ipswich.*

Hintlesham Hall ⛯, IP8 3NS, ✆ (01473) 652334, *reservations@hintlesham-hall.co. Fax (01473) 652463,* ≤, « Georgian country house of 16C origins », ⛯, ⛯, ⛯ heated, ⛯, ⛯, ⛯ – ⛯ rest, TV P – ⛯ 80. MC AE ⛯ VISA
Meals *(closed Saturday lunch)* 21.00/27.00 **st.** and a la carte 32.95/41.95 **st.** – ⛯ 8.05
29 rm 94.00/230.00 **st.**, 4 suites – SB.

IREBY *Cumbria* 401 402 K 19 – *see Bassenthwaite.*

IRONBRIDGE *Wrekin* 403 404 M 26 *Great Britain G. – pop. 2 184.*

See : *Ironbridge Gorge Museum*★★ **AC** *(The Iron Bridge*★★, *Coalport China Museum*★ *Blists Hill Open Air Museum*★★, *Museum of the River and visitors centre*★ *).*

ℹ *The Wharfage* ✆ *(01952) 432166.*

London 135 – Birmingham 36 – Shrewsbury 18.

Severn Lodge ⛯ without rest., New Rd, TF8 7AS, ✆ (01952) 432148, *enquiries@seve odge.com, Fax (01952) 432062,* ⛯ – ⛯ TV P. ⛯
3 rm ⛯ 45.00/59.00.

Bridge House without rest., Buildwas, TF8 7BN, West : 2 m. on B 43 ✆ (01952) 432105, *janethedges@talk21.com, Fax (01952) 432105,* « 17C cottage », ⛯ TV P. ⛯
closed Christmas and New Year – **4 rm** ⛯ 45.00/60.00.

The Library House without rest., 11 Severn Bank, TF8 7AN, ✆ (01952) 432299, *libhou @enta.net, Fax (01952) 433967,* ⛯ – ⛯ TV
closed January and 25-26 December – **4 rm** ⛯ 45.00/55.00 **st.**

da Vinci's, 26 High St., TF8 7AD, ✆ (01952) 432250, *nlord43303@aol.co Fax (01952) 433039* – ⛯ MC VISA
closed 25 December-23 January, 1 week in summer and 1 week in autumn – **Meals** - Italia (booking essential) (dinner only Tuesday-Saturday and Sunday lunch) a la carte 15.9 23.45 **t.**

ISLE OF MAN 402 FG 21 – *see Man (Isle of).*

IVY HATCH *Kent – see Sevenoaks.*

IXWORTH *Suffolk* 404 W 27 – *see Bury St. Edmunds.*

JERSEY 403 OP 33 and 230 ⑩ ⑪ – *see Channel Islands.*

JEVINGTON *E. Sussex* 404 U 31 – *see Eastbourne.*

KEDLESTON *Derbs.* 402 403 404 P 25 – *see Derby.*

KEIGHLEY *W. Yorks.* 402 O 22 – *pop. 49 567.*

⛳18 *Branshaw, Branshaw Moor, Oakworth* ✆ *(01535) 643235* – ⛳18 *Riddlesden, Howden Rou* ✆ *(01535) 602148.*

London 200 – Bradford 10 – Burnley 20.

Dalesgate, 406 Skipton Rd, Utley, BD20 6HP, Northwest : 1 ¼ m. on B 6265 (Utley ✆ (01535) 664930, *stephen.e.atha@btinternet.com, Fax (01535) 611253* – TV P. MC AE VISA
closed 1 week at Christmas – **Meals** *(closed Sunday)* (dinner only) 12.95 **t.** and a la ca ⛯ 5.75 – **20 rm** ⛯ 45.00/65.00 **t.** – SB.

KELLING *Norfolk* 404 X 25 – *pop. 161 – ✉ Holt.*

London 125 – King's Lynn 39 – Norwich 30.

The Pheasant, Coast Rd, NR25 7EG, on A 149 ✆ (01263) 588382, *enquiries@pheasan telnorfolk.co.uk, Fax (01263) 588101,* ⛯ – ⛯ TV ♿ P. MC VISA
Meals (bar lunch)/dinner 17.95 **st.** ⛯ 4.75 – **30 rm** ⛯ 38.00/76.00 **st.** – SB.

ELSALE *Suffolk* 404 Y 27 – *pop. 1 309* – ✉ *Saxmundham.*
London 103 – Cambridge 68 – Ipswich 23 – Norwich 37.

Mile Hill Barn, North Green, IP17 2RG, North : 1 ½ m. on (main) A 12 ✆ (01728) 668519, *richard@milehillbarn.freeserve.co.uk,* « Converted barn », – TV P. Meals (by arrangement) 16.00 **s.** – **3 rm** 50.00/65.00 **s.** – SB.

Hedgehogs, IP17 2RF, North : 1 m. on (main) A 12 ✆ (01728) 604444, *Fax (01728) 604499,* « 16C house » – P. MO AE VISA
closed 1 week spring, one week October, Sunday dinner and Monday – **Meals** 7.95/10.50 **t.** and a la carte 7.75.

EMBLE *Glos.* 403 404 N 28 – *see Cirencester.*

EMERTON *Glos.* – *see Tewkesbury.*

ENDAL *Cumbria* 402 L 21 *Great Britain G.* – *pop. 25 461.*
Env. : *Levens Hall and Garden★ AC, S : 4½ m. by A 591, A 590 and A 6.*
Exc. : *Lake Windermere★★, NW : 8 m. by A 5284 and A 591.*
The Heights ✆ (01539) 723499.
Town Hall, Highgate ✆ (01539) 725758.
London 270 – Bradford 64 – Burnley 63 – Carlisle 49 – Lancaster 22 – Leeds 72 – Middlesbrough 77 – Newcastle upon Tyne 104 – Preston 44 – Sunderland 88.

Stonecross Manor, Milnthorpe Rd, LA9 5HP, South : 1 ½ m. on A 6 ✆ (01539) 733559, *info@stonecrossmanor.co.uk, Fax (01539) 736386,* – rest, TV P – 180. MO AE VISA JCB.
Meals a la carte 17.00/24.00 **t.** 8.00 – **30 rm** 63.50/119.00 **t.** – SB.

Lane Head House, Helsington, LA9 5RJ, South : 2 m. off A 6 ✆ (01539) 731283, *Fax (01539) 721023,* – TV P. MO AE VISA JCB.
Meals (dinner only) (residents only) a la carte 12.00/23.50 **t.** 5.00 – **6 rm** 45.00/85.00 **t.**

Burrow Hall without rest., Plantation Bridge, LA8 9JR, Northwest : 3 ¼ m. by A 5284 on A 591 ✆ (01539) 821711, – TV P. MO AE VISA JCB.
closed December and January – **4 rm** 35.00/50.00 **s.**

The Moon, 129 Highgate, LA9 4EN, ✆ (01539) 729254, *moon@129highgate.freeserve.co.uk, Fax (01539) 729254* – . MO VISA JCB
closed 25 December, 1 January, Monday dinner, Tuesday, Thursday and Saturday lunch – **Meals** (light lunch)/dinner a la carte 16.45/23.25 **t.**

Selside *North : 6 m. on A 6* – ✉ *Kendal.*

Low Jock Scar, LA8 9LE, off A 6 ✆ (01539) 823259, *philip@low-jock-scar.freeserve.co.uk, Fax (01539) 823259,* – P. MO VISA
mid March-October – **Meals** (by arrangement) 17.00 **st.** 4.50 – **5 rm** 33.50/58.00 **st.**

Crosthwaite *West : 5 ¼ m. by All Hallows Lane* – ✉ *Kendal.*

Crosthwaite House, LA8 8BP, ✆ (015395) 68264, *crosthwaite.house@kencomp.net, Fax (015395) 68264,* – rest, TV. AE
March-mid November – **Meals** (by arrangement) 15.00 **st.** 4.50 – **6 rm** 25.00/50.00 **st.** – SB.

Punch Bowl Inn with rm, LA8 8HR, ✆ (015395) 68237, *enquiries@punchbowl.fsnet.co.uk, Fax (015395) 68875,* , « Part 17C inn » – TV P. MO VISA.
closed 2 weeks November and 25 December – **Meals** *(closed Sunday dinner and Monday October-March)* (booking essential) a la carte 17.20/23.15 **st.** 7.00 – **3 rm** 37.50/55.00 **st.** – SB.

ENILWORTH *Warks.* 403 404 P 26 *Great Britain G.* – *pop. 21 623.*
See : *Castle★ AC.*
The Library, 11 Smalley Pl. ✆ (01926) 852595.
London 102 – Birmingham 19 – Coventry 5 – Warwick 5.

Chesford Grange, Chesford Bridge, CV8 2LD, Southeast : 1 ¾ m. on A 452 ✆ (01926) 859331, *samantha.brown@principlehotels.co.uk, Fax (01926) 859075,* , – TV P – 860. MO AE VISA.
Meals 13.95/18.50 **st.** and a la carte – **154 rm** 120.00/140.00 **st.** – SB.

Victoria Lodge without rest., 180 Warwick Rd, CV8 1HU, ✆ (01926) 512020, *info@victorialodgehotel.co.uk, Fax (01926) 858703,* – TV P. MO AE VISA JCB.
closed 21 December-1 January – **9 rm** 40.00/59.00 **st.**

ENGLAND

Castle Laurels without rest., 22 Castle Rd, CV8 1NG, North : ½ m. on Stonebridge
☎ (01926) 856179, *moore22@aol.com, Fax (01926) 854954* – TV P. MO VISA.
closed 4 days Christmas – **11 rm** 37.00/65.00 **st.**

Simpson's (Antona), 101-103 Warwick Rd, CV8 1HL, ☎ (01926) 8645
Fax (01926) 864510 – P. MO AE VISA JCB
closed last 2 weeks August, Saturday lunch, Sunday and Bank Holidays – **Meals** 15.0
29.95 **t.** and a la carte 20.00/29.95 **t.** 7.50
Spec. Roast sea bass, caramelised endive, with citrus vinaigrette. Assiette of pork, rö
potatoes and dried apricot. Turrón parfait with raspberries.

Bosquet, 97a Warwick Rd, CV8 1HP, ☎ (01926) 852463 – MO AE VISA JCB
closed 3 weeks August, 10 days Christmas – **Meals** - French - (lunch by arrangeme
25.00 **t.** (lunch) and a la carte 28.00/31.50 **t.** 6.50.

KENNFORD *Devon* 403 J 32 – *see Exeter.*

KERNE BRIDGE *Herefordshire* 403 404 M 28 – *see Ross-on-Wye.*

KESWICK *Cumbria* 402 K 20 *Great Britain G. – pop. 4 836.*

Env. : *Derwentwater★* X – *Thirlmere (Castlerigg Stone Circle★), E : 1½ m.* X **A.**
18 *Threlkeld Hall* ☎ *(017687) 79010.*
Moot Hall, Market Sq. ☎ *(017687) 72645 – at Seatoller, Seatoller Barn, Borrowd*
☎ *(017687) 77294 (summer only).*
London 294 – Carlisle 31 – Kendal 30.

Plan opposite

Underscar Manor , Applethwaite, CA12 4PH, North : 1 ¾ m. by A 591 on Unders
rd ☎ (017687) 75000, *Fax (017687) 74904,* ← Derwent Water and Fells, « Victorian Italian
country house », – TV P. MO AE VISA.
Meals – (see ***The Restaurant*** below) – **11 rm** (dinner included) 110.00/250.00 **t.**

Lyzzick Hall , Underskiddaw, CA12 4PY, Northwest : 2 ½ m. on A 5
☎ (017687) 72277, *lyzzickhall@netscapeonline.co.uk, Fax (017687) 72278,* ←,
rest, TV P – 25. MO VISA JCB.
closed mid January-mid February and 24 to 26 December – **Meals** 21.00/24.00 **t.** (d
ner) and a la carte 12.10/28.95 **t.** 4.70 – **29 rm** 44.00/92.00 **t.**

Dale Head Hall Lakeside , Thirlmere, CA12 4TN, Southeast : 5 ¾ m. on A 5
☎ (017687) 72478, *stay@dale-head-hall.co.uk, Fax (017687) 71070,* ← Lake Thirlmere, «
keside setting », – rest, P. MO AE VISA JCB.
closed January – **Meals** (dinner only) 30.00 **st.** 8.75 – **14 rm** (dinner included) 97.5
145.00 **st.** – SB.

Applethwaite Country House , Applethwaite, CA12 4PL, Northwest : 1 ¾ m. b
591 on Underscar rd ☎ (017687) 72413, *ryan@applethwaite.freeserve.co.*
Fax (017687) 75706, ←, – TV P. MO VISA.
March-mid November – **Meals** (dinner only) 17.50 **t.** 5.50 – **12 rm** 37.00/75.00 **st.** –

Lairbeck , Vicarage Hill, CA12 5QB, ☎ (017687) 73373, *reservations@lairbeckhotel-*
wick.co.uk, Fax (017687) 73144, – TV P. MO VISA JCB. X
March-November and Christmas – **Meals** (dinner only) 16.00 **t.** 6.45 – **14 rm** 38.0
76.00 **t.** – SB.

Brackenrigg Country House, Thirlmere, CA12 4TF, Southeast : 3 m. on A 5
☎ (017687) 72258, *Fax (017687) 72258,* – rest, TV P.
Easter-October – **Meals** (by arrangement) 16.00 **s.** – **6 rm** 36.00/52.00 – SB.

Abacourt House without rest., 26 Stanger St., CA12 5JU, ☎ (017687) 72967, *abacour*
aol.com – TV P. Z
5 rm 44.00.

Greystones without rest., Ambleside Rd, CA12 4DP, ☎ (017687) 73108, *greystones@k*
akes.freeserve.co.uk – TV P. MO VISA. Z
8 rm 25.00/52.00.

Craglands, Penrith Rd, CA12 4LJ, ☎ (017687) 74406, *keswick@craglands.freeserve.co.*
– TV P. X
Meals (by arrangement) 13.00 **st.** – **5 rm** 35.00/50.00 **st.**

Acorn House without rest., Ambleside Rd, CA12 4DL, ☎ (017687) 72553, *acornhouse.*
mon.co.uk, Fax (017687) 75332 – TV P. MO VISA. Z
mid February-mid November – **10 rm** 32.50/60.00 **st.**

Claremont House without rest., Chestnut Hill, CA12 4LT, ☎ (017687) 720
Fax (017687) 72089, ←, – TV P. X
April-October – **4 rm** 35.00/50.00 **st.**

KESWICK

*orth is at the top
all town plans.*

*s plans de villes
nt disposés
Nord en haut.*

A 66 WORKINGTON COCKERMOUTH
A 591 CARLISLE
PENRITH, M 6
By-Pass
Greta
PORTINSCALE
Derwent
B 5292
BRAITHWAITE
Brockle Beck
GREAT WOOD
Borrowdale Road
A 591 WINDERMERE
STAIR
DERWENTWATER
Newlands Beck
BRANDELHOW PARK
HOGS EARTH
Watendlath Beck
BORROWDALE
DERWENT FELLS
GRANGE
ROSTHWAITE B 5289 BUTTERMERE

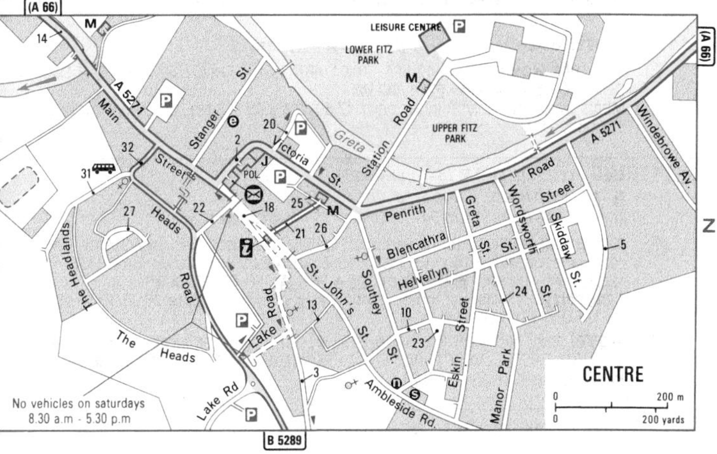

XXX **The Restaurant** (at Underscar Manor H.), Applethwaite, CA12 4PH, North : 1 ¾ m. by A 591 on Underscar rd ✆ (017687) 75000, *Fax (017687) 74904*, < Derwent Water and Fells, « Victorian Italianate country house », – **P**. MC AE VISA
Meals 28.00/30.00 **t.** and a la carte 8.00.

Threlkeld *East : 4 m. by A 66* – X – ✉ *Keswick.*

Scales Farm without rest., CA12 4SY, Northeast : 1 ½ m. off A 66 ✆ (017687) 79660, *scales@scalesfarm.com, Fax (017687) 79660*, « Part 17C », – TV **P**. MC VISA
closed 25-26 December – **6 rm** 31.00/56.00.

ENGLAND

Horse and Farrier Inn, CA12 4SQ, (017687) 79688, *Fax (017687) 79824,* « Part 1 coaching inn » – P. VISA
closed 25 December – **Meals** a la carte 15.25/25.65 **t.** – **9 rm** 30.50/61.00 **t.**

at Borrowdale *South : on B 5289 – Keswick.*

Hilton Keswick Lodore, CA12 5UX, (017687) 77285, *Fax (017687) 77343,* heated, squash – rest, P – 120. VISA
Meals (bar lunch Monday to Saturday)/dinner 17.95 **st.** and a la carte 8.00 – – **70** 79.00/158.00 **st.**, 1 suite – SB. Y

Greenbank Country House, CA12 5UY, (017687) 77215, *Fax (017687) 77215,* – P. VISA. Y
closed 1 week Christmas and 2 weeks January – – **10 rm** (dinner included) 42.0 96.00 **st.**

at Grange-in-Borrowdale *South : 4¾ m. by B 5289 – Keswick.*

Borrowdale Gates Country House, CA12 5UQ, (017687) 77204, *hotel@borrowdale-gates.com, Fax (017687) 77254,* Borrowdale Valley, – rest, P. Y
*closed January***Meals** 29.75/31.00 **t.** (dinner) and a la carte 16.75/39.50 **t.** 8.00 – **29 rm** (dinner included) 91.00/172.00 **t.** – SB.

at Rosthwaite *South : 6 m. on B 5289 – Y – Keswick.*

Hazel Bank, CA12 5XB, (017687) 77248, *enquiries@hazelbankhotel.demon.co.uk Fax (017687) 77373,* – P. VISA JCB.
Meals (dinner only) 17.95 **t.** 6.50 – **8 rm** (dinner included) 59.50/119.00 **t.**, 1 suite.

at Portinscale *West : 1½ m. by A 66 – Keswick.*

Swinside Lodge, Newlands, CA12 5UE, South : 1 ½ m. on Grange (017687) 72948, *info@swinsidelodge-hotel.co.uk, Fax (017687) 72948,* Catbells a Causey Pike, – P. VISA. X
Meals (set menu only) (booking essential) (dinner only) 25.00 **st.** 4.50 – **7 rm** (dinr included) 70.00/172.00 **st.** – SB.

Derwent Cottage, CA12 5RF, (017687) 74838, – P. VISA X
March-October – **Meals** (by arrangement) 14.50 **st.** 7.20 – **6 rm** 47.00/79.00 **st.** – SB

at Thornthwaite *Northwest : 3½ m. by A 66 – X – Keswick.*

Thwaite Howe, CA12 5SA, (017687) 78281, *Fax (017687) 78529,* Skiddaw a Derwent Valley, – P. VISA
Meals (residents only) (dinner only) 17.50 **t.** 6.95 – **8 rm** (dinner included) 72.0 104.00 **t.** – SB.

KETTERING *Northants.* 404 R 26 – *pop. 47 186.*
The Coach House, Sheep St. (01536) 410266.
London 88 – Birmingham 54 – Leicester 16 – Northampton 24.

Kettering Park, Kettering Parkway, NN15 6XT, South : 2 ¼ m. by A 509 (Wellingborou rd) at junction with A 14 (01536) 416666, *kpark@shireinns.co.uk, Fax (01536) 416171,* squash – rm, P – 250. VISA
***Langberrys* :** **Meals** (bar lunch Saturday and Sunday) a la carte 26.00/38.00 **st.** – **127 r** 125.00/145.00 **st.** – SB.

Travel Inn, Rothwell Rd, NN16 8XF, West : 1 ¼ m. at junction of A 14 with A (01536) 310082, *Fax (01536) 310104* – rm, rest, P. VISA.
Meals (grill rest.) – **39 rm** 40.95 **t.**

KETTLESING *N. Yorks.* 402 P 21 – *see Harrogate.*

KETTLEWELL *N. Yorks.* 402 N 21 – *pop. 297 (inc. Starbotton)* – *Skipton.*
London 237 – Bradford 33 – Leeds 40.

Langcliffe Country House, BD23 5RJ, by Church rd on 'Access only' (01756) 760243, – P. VISA.
closed 24-26 December – **Meals** (booking essential to non-residents) (dinner only) 18.00 5.50 – **6 rm** (dinner included) 70.00/100.00 **st.** – SB.

High Fold without rest., BD23 5RJ, By church rd on "Access only" (01756) 760390, *deborah@highfold.fsnet.co.uk, Fax (01756) 760390,* « Convert barn », – P
closed Christmas – **3 rm** 37.00/60.00 **st.**

EYSTON Cambs. 404 S 26 – pop. 257 (inc. Bythorn) – ✉ Huntingdon.

London 75 – Cambridge 29 – Northampton 24.

Pheasant, Village Loop Rd, PE18 0RE, ℘ (01832) 710241, *Fax (01832) 710340*, « Characterful thatched inn » – ⇔ P. MC AE ⓓ VISA JCB
closed dinner 25-26 December and 1 January – **Meals** a la carte 18.85/28.20 **st.** 7.95.

IBWORTH BEAUCHAMP Leics. – pop. 3 550 – ✉ Leicester.

London 85 – Birmingham 49 – Leicester 16 – Northampton 17.

Firenze, 9 Station St., LE8 0LN, ℘ (0116) 279 6260, *Fax (0116) 279 3646* – MC VISA
closed Saturday lunch, Sunday, Monday, 1 week Easter, 1 week Christmas and2 weeks August – **Meals** - Italian - a la carte 12.50/27.00 **st.** 7.20.

IDDERMINSTER Worcestershire 403 404 N 26 – pop. 54 644.

Severn Valley Railway Station, Comberton Hill ℘ (01562) 829400 (summer only).

London 139 – Birmingham 17 – Shrewsbury 34 – Worcester 15.

Stone Manor, Stone, DY10 4PJ, Southeast : 2 ½ m. on A 448 ℘ (01562) 777555, *enquiries@stonemanorhotel.co.uk, Fax (01562) 777834*, ⇔ TV P – 150. MC AE ⓓ VISA.
Fields : **Meals** 14.95/19.50 **t.** and a la carte 6.70 – 8.25 – **56 rm** 75.00/135.00 **t.**, 1 suite – SB.

at Chaddesley Corbett Southeast : 4½ m. by A 448 – ✉ Kidderminster.

Brockencote Hall, DY10 4PY, on A 448 ℘ (01562) 777876, *info@brockencotehall.com, Fax (01562) 777872*, « Part 19C mansion in park », – ⇔ rest, TV P – 25. MC AE ⓓ VISA.
Meals – (see ***The Restaurant*** below) – **17 rm** 110.00/170.00 **st.** – SB.

The Restaurant (at Brockencote Hall), DY10 4PY, on A 448 ℘ (01562) 777876, *Fax (01562) 777872* – ⇔. MC AE ⓓ VISA
closed Saturday lunch – **Meals** - French a la carte 24.30/44.50 **st.** 8.00.

at Bewdley Northeast : 1 m. by A 190 – ✉ Kidderminster.

Jarvis Heath H. & Country Club, Habberley Rd, DY12 1LJ, Northeast : 1 m. by A 190 ℘ (01299) 406400, *Fax (01299) 400921*, – ⇔ TV P – 650. MC AE ⓓ VISA
Meals (bar lunch)/dinner 15.95/18.95 **t.** 7.95 – 9.95 – **44 rm** 92.00/104.00 **t.** – SB.

IDMORE END Oxon. – see Reading.

ILLINGTON LAKE SERVICE AREA Cumbria 402 M 21 – ✉ Kendal.

Killington Lake Services, RoadChef Service Area, M 6 south, near Kendal ℘ (015396) 20138.

Travel Inn without rest., LA8 0NW, M 6 between junctions 36 and 37 (southbound carriageway) ℘ (01539) 621666, *Fax (01539) 621660* – ⇔ TV P. MC AE ⓓ VISA.
closed Christmas and New Year – **40 rm** 40.95 **t.**

IMBOLTON Herefordshire 403 L 27 – see Leominster.

INGHAM Oxon. 403 404 P 28 – pop. 1 434.

London 81 – Gloucester 32 – Oxford 25.

Mill House, OX7 6UH, ℘ (01608) 658188, *stay@millhousehotel.co.uk, Fax (01608) 658492*, – ⇔ rest, TV P – 70. MC AE ⓓ VISA JCB
Meals 13.95/22.75 **st.** (dinner) and a la carte 8.25 – **23 rm** (dinner included) 87.75/155.50 **st.** – SB.

Die im **Michelin-Führer**

verwendeten Zeichen und Symbole haben
- **fett** oder dünn gedruckt, rot oder **schwarz** -
jeweils eine andere Bedeutung.
Lesen Sie daher die Erklärungen aufmerksam durch.

KINGSBRIDGE *Devon* 403 I 33 *The West Country G. – pop. 5 258.*

See : *Town★ – Boat Trip to Salcombe★★ AC.*

Exc. : *Prawle Point (≤★★★) SE : 10 m. around coast by A 379.*

Thurlestone ℘ (01548) 560405.

The Quay ℘ (01548) 853195.

London 236 – Exeter 36 – Plymouth 24 – Torquay 21.

Buckland-Tout-Saints , Goveton, TQ7 2DS, Northeast : 2 ½ m. by A 38 ℘ (01548) 853055, *buckland@tout-saints.co.uk, Fax (01548) 856261,* ≤, « Queen Anne mansion », – rest, 100. VISA
closed 15 January-7 February – **Meals** 13.00/25.00 **t.** 10.50 – **8 rm** 75.00/170.00 2 suites – SB.

at Chillington *East : 5 m. on A 379 – ✉ Kingsbridge.*

White House, TQ7 2JX, ℘ (01548) 580580, *tinwhitehse@cs.com, Fax (01548) 581124,* – . VISA.
closed January – **Meals** (bar lunch Monday-Saturday)/dinner 18.95 **t.** 6.95 – **7 r** 60.00/112.00 **t.**

at Thurlestone *West : 4 m. by A 381 – ✉ Kingsbridge.*

Thurlestone , TQ7 3NN, ℘ (01548) 560382, *enquires@thurlestone.co.u Fax (01548) 561069,* ≤, , , , heated, , , , , squash – , rest, res – 100. VISA JCB
closed 3-11 January – ***Margaret Amelia :*** **Meals** (lunch by arrangement)/dinner 28.00 7.50 – ***Terrace :*** **Meals** (lunch only except Sunday) a la carte 14.00/29.50 **t.** 7.50 – **63 r** (dinner included) 109.00/274.00 **st.**, 4 suites – SB.

at Bantham *West : 5 m. by A 379 – ✉ Kingsbridge.*

Sloop Inn with rm, TQ7 3AJ, ℘ (01548) 560489, *Fax (01548) 561940* –
Meals a la carte 11.40/16.50 **t.** – **5 rm** 66.00 **t.**

KING'S CLIFFE *Northants.* 404 S 26 – ✉ *Peterborough.*

London 93 – Leicester 21 – Northampton 19 – Peterborough 7.

King's Cliffe House, 31 West St., PE8 6XB, ℘ (01780) 470172, *kchr@onetel.net.ukfree rve.co.uk, Fax (01780) 470172,* –
closed 2 weeks spring, 2 weeks autumn, 25 and 26 December, 1 January, Sunday to Tuesd and Bank Holidays – **Meals** (booking essential) (dinner only) a la carte 17.95/26.95 **st.** 5.2

KINGSKERSWELL *Devon* 403 J 32 – *pop. 3 672* – ✉ *Torquay.*

London 219 – Exeter 21 – Plymouth 33 – Torquay 4.

Pitt House, 2 Church End Rd, TQ12 5DS, ℘ (01803) 873374, « 15C thatched dow house », – . VISA
closed 2 weeks January, 1 week May, 1 week August, 1 week October – **Meals** (dinner on 25.00 **t.** 8.50.

KINGS LANGLEY *Herts.* 404 S 28 – *pop. 8 144.*

London 26 – Luton 14.

Premier Lodge, Hempstead Rd, WD4 8BR, ℘ (0870) 7001568, *Fax (0870) 7001569* rm, . VISA.
Meals (grill rest.) a la carte 9.65/16.35 **st.** – 6.00 – **60 rm** 42.00 **st.**

KING'S LYNN *Norfolk* 402 404 V 25 *Great Britain G. – pop. 41 281.*

Exc. : *Houghton Hall★★ AC, NE : 14½ m. by A 148 – Four Fenland Churches★ (Terringt St. Clement, Walpole St. Peter, West Walton, Walsoken) SW : by A 47.*

Eagles, School Rd, Tilney All Saints ℘ (01553) 827147.

The Custom House, Purfleet Quay ℘ (01553) 763044.

London 103 – Cambridge 45 – Leicester 75 – Norwich 44.

Knights Hill, Knights Hill Village, South Wootton, PE30 3HQ, Northeast : 4 ½ m. on A 1 at junction with A 149 ℘ (01553) 675566, *reception@knightshill.co.uk, Fax (01553) 6755* , , , , – – 300. VISA.
Garden : **Meals** (dinner only and Sunday lunch)/dinner 18.95 **t.** and a la carte – ***Farme Arms :*** **Meals** (carving lunch) a la carte 11.95/21.25 – 8.25 – **61 rm** 95.00/105.00 **t.** – S

Butterfly, Beveridge Way, PE30 4NB, Southeast : 2 ¼ m. by Hardwick Rd at junction o 10 with A 47 ℘ (01553) 771707, *kingsbutterfly@lineone.net, Fax (01553) 768027* – r – 40. VISA JCB
Meals 15.00/17.00 **t.** and a la carte – 8.50 – **50 rm** 67.50 **t.** – SB.

Travel Inn, Freebridge Farm, Clenchwarten Rd, PE34 3LJ, Southwest : 3 1/4 m. by Hardwick Rd at junction of A 47 with A 17 (01485) 772221, *Fax (01485) 775827* – rm, rest, TV P. MC AE VISA.
Meals (grill rest.) – **40 rm** 40.95 **t.**

Old Rectory without rest., 33 Goodwins Rd, PE30 5QX, (01553) 768544, « Restored Georgian style Victorian residence », – TV P
4 rm 32.00/42.00.

Fairlight Lodge without rest., 79 Goodwins Rd, PE30 5PE, (01553) 762234, *penny.rowe@lineone.net, Fax (01553) 770280,* – TV P
closed 23 to 27 December – **7 rm** 25.00/40.00.

Rococo (Anderson), 11 Saturday Market Pl., Old Town, PE30 5DQ, (01553) 771483, *rococorest@aol.com, Fax (01553) 771483* – MC AE VISA JCB
closed 24-30 December, Monday lunch and Sunday – **Meals** (booking essential) 17.95/29.50 **t.** 6.00
Spec. Sautéed local wild mushrooms with poached duck egg and toasted brioche. Steamed fillet of turbot with fondant potato and shrimp sauce. Hazelnut mousse with basket of raspberries.

Grimston *East : 6 1/4 m. by A 148 – King's Lynn.*

Congham Hall, Lynn Rd, PE32 1AH, (01485) 600250, *reception@conghamhallhotel.demon.co.uk, Fax (01485) 601191,* « Part Georgian manor house, herb garden », heated, – TV P – 30. MC AE VISA JCB.
Orangery : **Meals** 11.50/34.00 **st.** 10.00 – **12 rm** 85.00/175.00 **st.**, 2 suites – SB.

INGS MILLS *Guernsey (Channel Islands) – see Channel Islands.*

INGSTON BAGPUIZE *Oxon.* 403 404 P 28 – *see Oxford.*

INGSTON-UPON-HULL *Kingston-upon-Hull* 402 S 22 *Great Britain G. – pop. 310 636.*

Exc. : *Burton Constable* AC, NE : 9 m. by A 165 and B 1238* **Z**.

18 *Springhead Park, Willerby Rd (01482) 656309 –* 18 *Sutton Park, Salthouse Rd (01482) 374242.*

Humber Bridge (toll).

Humberside Airport : (01652) 688456, S : 19 m. by A 63 – **Terminal** : *Coach Service.*

to The Netherlands (Rotterdam) (P & O North Sea Ferries) daily (12 h 30 mn) – to Belgium (Zeebrugge) (P & O North Sea Ferries) daily (12 h 45 mn).

1 Paragon St. (01482) 223559 – King George Dock, Hedon Rd (01482) 702118.

London 183 – Leeds 61 – Nottingham 94 – Sheffield 68.

Plan on next page

Posthouse Hull Marina, The Marina, Castle St., HU1 2BX, (0870) 400 9043, *Fax (01482) 213299,* – rm, rest, TV P – 120. MC AE VISA JCB
Y n
Meals *(closed Saturday lunch)* 19.95 **t.** (dinner) and a la carte 19.95/24.95 **t.** – 11.95 – **99 rm** 119.00/145.00 **t.** – SB.

Travel Inn, Kingswood Park, Ennerdale Link Rd, HU7 4HS, North : 5 m. by A 1079 on A 1033 (01482) 820225, *Fax (01482) 820300* – rm, rest, TV P. MC AE VISA
Meals (grill rest.) – **42 rm** 40.95 **t.**

Travel Inn, Ferriby Rd, Hessle, HU13 0JA, West : 7 m. by A 63 off A 164 (01482) 645285, *Fax (01482) 645299* – rm, rest, TV P. MC AE VISA.
Meals (grill rest.) – **40 rm** 40.95 **t.**

Willerby *West : 5 m. by A 1079, Spring Bank –* **Z** *– and Willerby Rd – Kingston-upon-Hull.*

Willerby Manor, Well Lane, HU10 6ER, (01482) 652616, *info@willerbymanor.co.uk, Fax (01482) 653901,* – rm, TV P – 500. MC AE VISA.
closed 25 December – ***Lafite :*** **Meals** (dinner only and Sunday lunch)/dinner 12.50/17.50 **t.** and a la carte 6.15 – ***Everglades :*** **Meals** a la carte 9.95/14.40 **t.** – 9.50 – **51 rm** 74.50/90.00 **st.**

Little Weighton *Northwest : 9 m. by A 1079 –* **Z** *– and B 1233 via Skidby Village – Cottingham.*

Rowley Manor, HU20 3XR, Southwest : 1/2 m. by Rowley Rd (01482) 848248, *info@rowleymanor.com, Fax (01482) 849900,* « Georgian manor house », – TV P – 100. MC AE VISA
Meals 22.50 **t.** 6.65 – **16 rm** 70.00/90.00 **t.** – SB.

KINGSTON-UPON-HULL

Street	Grid	No.
Bond Street	X	3
Carr Lane	Y	
Commercial Road	Y	8
County Road North	Z	9
Dock Office Row	X	10
Dock Street	X	12
Fairfax Avenue	Z	13
Ferensway	XY	14
George Street	X	
Grimston Street	X	15
Humber Dock Street	Y	16
Jameson Street	Y	17
Jarratt Street	X	18
King Edward Street	Y	19
Lowgate	Y	23
Market Place	Y	24
Maybury Road	Z	25
Paragon Street	Y	29
Prince's Avenue	Z	31
Prince's Dock Street	Y	32
Princes Quay Shopping Centre	Y	
Prospect Shopping Centre	X	
Prospect Street	X	
Queen's Road	Z	33
Queen Street	Y	35
Queen's Dock Avenue	X	36
Reform Street	X	37
Sculcoates Bridge	X	42
Southcoates Avenue	Z	43
Southcoates Lane	Z	44
Waterhouse Lane	Y	47
Whitefriargate	Y	49
Wilberforce Drive	X	50
Worship Street	X	52

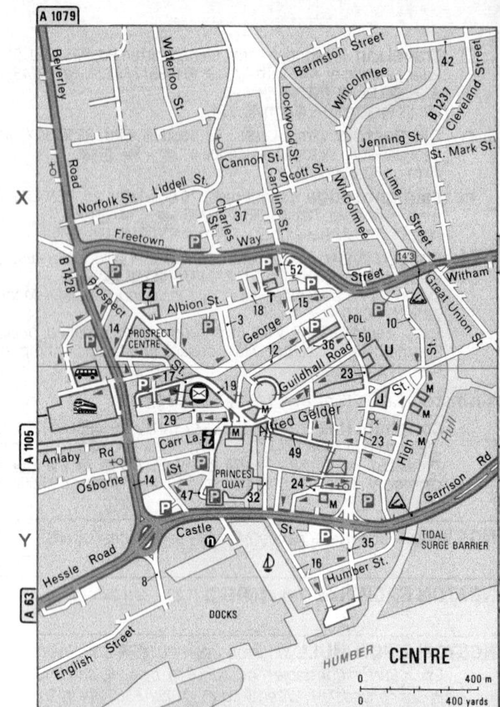

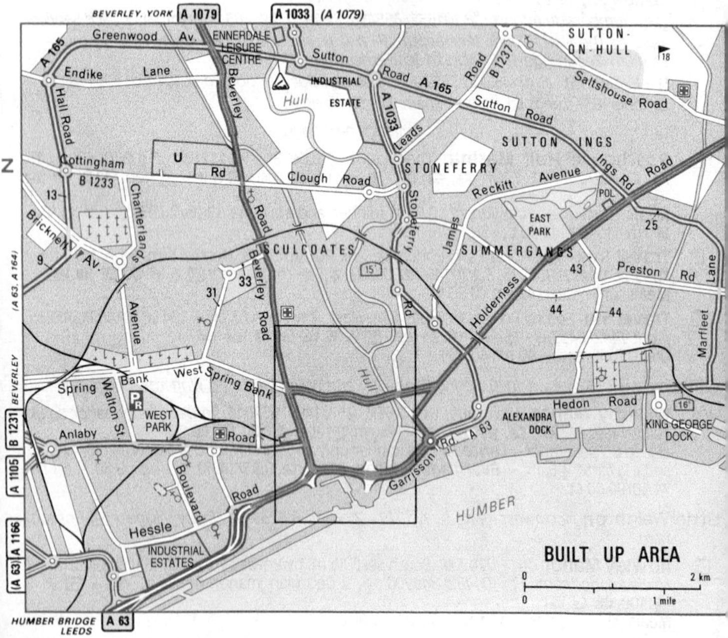

BEVERLEY, YORK A 1079 A 1033 (A 1079)

Greenwood Av.
ENNERDALE LEISURE CENTRE
A 165
Endike Lane
Hall Road
Sutton Road A 165
INDUSTRIAL ESTATE
Hull
A 1033
Leads Road
B 1237
SUTTON-ON-HULL
Saltshouse Road
Sutton Road
SUTTON INGS
Ings Rd
Road
Z
Cottingham Rd
B 1233
Clough Road
STONEFERRY
Reckitt Avenue
Stoneferry Rd
EAST PARK
Chanterlands Avenue
Bricknell Av.
SCULCOATES
Beverley Road
James
SUMMERGANGS
Preston Rd
Lane
Holderness
Marfleet
(A 63, A 164) BEVERLEY
B 1231
A 1105
A 1166
(A 63)
Spring Bank
West Spring Bank
Walton St.
WEST PARK
Anlaby Road
Boulevard
Hessle Road
INDUSTRIAL ESTATES
Hedon Road
ALEXANDRA DOCK
KING GEORGE DOCK
Garrisson Rd. A 63
HUMBER

BUILT UP AREA

0 2 km
0 1 mile

HUMBER BRIDGE LEEDS A 63

NGSTOWN *Cumbria – see Carlisle.*

NGSWEAR *Devon* 403 *J 32 – see Dartmouth.*

NGTON *Herefordshire* 403 *K 27 – pop. 2 197.*

London 152 – Birmingham 61 – Hereford 19 – Shrewsbury 54.

Penrhos Court, HR5 3LH, East : 1 ½ m. on A 44 ☎ (01544) 230720, *Fax (01544) 230754,* « Part 15C and 16C house with medieval cruck hall », – 25. – **Meals** - Organic produce - (booking essential) (dinner only) 31.50/35.00 **t.** and a la carte 6.00 – **15 rm** 65.00/110.00 **t.** – SB.

Titley *Northeast : 3½ m. on B 4355 – ✉ Kington.*

Stagg Inn (Reynolds) with rm, HR5 3RL, ☎ (01544) 230221, *stagginn@titley.kc3ltd.co.uk, Fax (01544) 231390* – *closed 2 weeks November and Monday except Bank Holidays* – **Meals** (booking essential) a la carte 14.30/20.90 **st.** 6.20 – **2 rm** 30.00/50.00 **st.**

Spec. Asparagus and herb risotto. Stuffed tenderloin of local pork with aubergine sauce. Passion fruit jelly with vanilla ice cream.

RKBURTON *W. Yorks.* 402 404 *O 23 – see Huddersfield.*

RKBY LONSDALE *Cumbria* 402 *M 21 – pop. 2 076 – ✉ Carnforth (Lancs.).*

[18] Scaleber Lane, Barbon ☎ (015242) 76365 – [9] Casterton, Sedbergh Rd ☎ (015242) 71592.

24 Main St. ☎ (015242) 71437 (restricted opening in winter).

London 259 – Carlisle 62 – Kendal 13 – Lancaster 17 – Leeds 58.

Whoop Hall Inn, Burrow with Burrow, LA6 2HP, Southeast : 1 m. on A 65 ☎ (015242) 71284, *whoophall@cerbernet.co.uk, Fax (015242) 72154,* – rm, – 140.

Meals 7.50/11.00 **t.** 5.50 – **22 rm** 50.00/70.00 **t.** – SB.

Snooty Fox Tavern with rm, 33 Main St., LA6 2AH, ☎ (015242) 71308, *kim@snootyfox84.freeserve.co.uk, Fax (015242) 72642,* « Jacobean inn » – rm,

Meals a la carte 14.95/25.20 **st.** – **9 rm** 40.00/60.00 **st.**

Casterton *Northeast : 1¼ m. by A 65 on A 683 – ✉ Carnforth.*

Pheasant Inn with rm, LA6 2RX, ☎ (015242) 71230, *pheasant.casterton@eggconnect.net, Fax (015242) 71230,* – rest,

Meals a la carte 12.95/23.75 **t.** – **11 rm** 40.00/72.00 **t.**

Cowan Bridge *(Lancs.) Southeast : 2 m. on A 65 – ✉ Carnforth (Lancs.).*

Hipping Hall, LA6 2JJ, Southeast : ½ m. on A 65 ☎ (015242) 71187, *hippinghal@aol.com, Fax (015242) 72452,* « 15C former hamlet », – *closed Christmas and January* – **Meals** (residents only) (communal dining) (dinner only) a la carte 18.00/24.15 **t.** – **4 rm** 74.00/92.00 **st.**, 2 suites.

RKBY MALHAM *N. Yorks.* 402 *N 21 – pop. 70 – ✉ Skipton.*

London 235 – Bradford 25 – Burnley 30 – Carlisle 97 – Harrogate 25 – York 47.

Holgate Head, BD23 4BJ, ☎ (01729) 830376, *holgate@nildram.co.uk, Fax (01729) 830576,* « Part 17C », – *mid March-mid October* – **Meals** (communal dining) 22.00 **st.** – **3 rm** 52.50/75.00 **st.**

RKBYMOORSIDE *N. Yorks.* 402 *R 21 – pop. 2 650.*

[18] Manor Vale ☎ (01751) 431525.

London 244 – Scarborough 26 – York 33.

George and Dragon, 17 Market Pl., YO62 6AA, ☎ (01751) 433334, *Fax (01751) 432933,* « Part 17C coaching inn », – rest,

Meals (bar lunch Monday to Saturday)/dinner a la carte 16.35/20.40 **t.** 7.90 – **18 rm** 49.00/90.00 **t.** – SB.

Fadmoor *Northwest : 2¼ m. – ✉ Kirbymoorside.*

The Plough Inn, YO62 7HY, ☎ (01751) 431515, – *closed 25-26 December, 1 January, Sunday dinner and Monday* – **Meals** (booking essential) a la carte 14.25/25.00 **t.**

RKCAMBECK *Cumbria* 401 402 *L 18 – see Brampton.*

KIRKHAM *Lancs.* 402 L 22 – *pop. 9 038* – ✉ *Preston.*
London 240 – Blackpool 9 – Preston 7.

Premier Lodge, Fleetwood Rd, PR4 3HE, Northwest : 2 m. by B 5192 on A 585 (M junction 3) ☎ (0870) 7001510, *Fax (0870) 7001511* – ⇔ rm, TV, P. MC AE VISA JC
Meals (grill rest.) a la carte 10.85/15.35 **t.** – ☕ 6.00 – **28 rm** 42.00 **t.**

Cromwellian, 16 Poulton St., PR4 2AB, ☎ (01772) 685680, *Fax (01772) 685680* – MC VISA JCB
closed 2 weeks summer, 1 week spring, 25 December, 1 January, Sunday and Monday
Meals (dinner only) 19.50/26.50 **t.** 5.50.

at Wrea Green *Southwest : 3 m. on B 5259* – ✉ *Kirkham.*

The Villa, Moss Side Lane, PR4 2PE, Southwest : ½ m. on B 5259 ☎ (01772) 68434 *Fax (01772) 687647* – |♦|, ⇔ rm, ≡ rm, TV, P. MC AE VISA JCB.
Meals 6.95/9.00 **t.** (lunch) and a la carte 13.00/21.00 **t.** 6.00 – **25 rm** ☕ 65.00/80.00 **t.** SB.

KIRKWHELPINGTON *Northd.* 401 402 N/O 18 *Great Britain G.* – *pop. 353* – ✉ *Morpeth.*
Env. : *Wallington House★ AC, E : 3½ m. by A 696 and B 6342.*
London 305 – Carlisle 46 – Newcastle upon Tyne 20.

Shieldhall , Wallington, NE61 4AQ, Southeast : 2 ½ m. by A 696 on B 63 ☎ (01830) 540387, *Fax (01830) 540387,* – ⇔ TV P. MC VISA.
February-October – **Meals** (by arrangement) (communal dining) 17.00 6.00 – **4 r** ☕ 35.00/60.00.

KNARESBOROUGH *N. Yorks.* 402 P 21 – *pop. 13 380.*
18 Boroughbridge Rd ☎ (01423) 863219.
9 Castle Courtyard, Market Pl. ☎ (01423) 866886 (summer only).
London 217 – Bradford 21 – Harrogate 3 – Leeds 18 – York 18.

Dower House, Bond End, HG5 9AL, ☎ (01423) 863302, *enquiries@bwdowerhouse.co.u* *Fax (01423) 867665,* – ⇔ TV P – 65. MC AE VISA.
Meals (bar lunch Monday to Saturday)/dinner **st.** a la carte 14.45/24.00 **t.** 7.95 – **30 r** ☕ 60.00/100.00 **t.**, 1 suite – SB.

at Ferrensby *Northeast : 3 m. on A 6055.*

The General Tarleton Inn with rm, Boroughbridge Rd, HG5 0QB, ☎ (01423) 340284, *i@generaltarleton.co.uk, Fax (01423) 340288* – ⇔ TV P – 40. MC AE VISA
closed 25 December – ***The Dining Room :*** **Meals** *(closed Sunday dinner)* (dinner only a Sunday lunch)/dinner 25.00 **t.** 10.00 – (see also below) – **14 rm** ☕ (dinner include 99.95/134.90 **t.** – SB.

The General Tarleton Inn, Boroughbridge Rd, HG5 0QB, ☎ (01423) 340284, *gti@generaltarleton.co.uk, Fax (01423) 340288,* « Characterful 18C inn » – P. MC AE VISA
closed 25 December – ***Bar/Brasserie :*** **Meals** (bookings not accepted) a la carte 19.4 24.35 **t.** 10.00.

KNIGHTWICK *Worcs.* 403 404 M 27 – *pop. 87* – ✉ *Worcester.*
London 132 – Hereford 20 – Leominster 18 – Worcester 8.

Talbot with rm, WR6 5PH, on B 4197 ☎ (01886) 821235, *Fax (01886) 821060,* – P. MC AE VISA.
closed 25 December – **Meals** 14.95/19.95 **t.** and a la carte – **10 rm** ☕ 37.00/67.50 **t.** – SB

KNOWLE *W. Mids.* 403 404 O 26 – *pop. 17 588* – ✉ *Solihull.*
London 108 – Birmingham 9 – Coventry 10 – Warwick 11.

Greswolde Arms, 1657 High St., B93 0LL, ☎ (01564) 772711, *Fax (01564) 770354* ⇔ rm, TV P – 150. MC AE VISA.
Meals 13.95 **st.** and a la carte – **36 rm** ☕ 75.00/95.00 **st.**

KNOWL HILL *Windsor & Maidenhead* 404 R 29 – ✉ *Twyford.*
9, Hennerton, Crazies Hill Rd, Wargrave ☎ (0118) 940 1000.
London 38 – Maidenhead 5 – Reading 8.

Bird in Hand, Bath Rd, RG10 9UP, ☎ (01628) 826622, *Fax (01628) 826748,* – TV P. MC AE VISA
accommodation closed 1 week Christmas – **Meals** a la carte 16.15/26.90 **st.** – **15 r** ☕ 100.00/110.00 **st.** – SB.

NUTSFORD *Ches.* 402 403 404 M 24 – *pop. 13 352.*
Council Offices, Toft Rd (01565) 632611.
London 187 – Chester 25 – Liverpool 33 – Manchester 18 – Stoke-on-Trent 30.

Cottons, Manchester Rd, WA16 0SU, Northwest : 1 1/2 m. on A 50 (01565) 650333, *cottons@shireinns.co.uk, Fax (01565) 755351,* , squash – 200.
AE VISA
Magnolia : **Meals** *(closed lunch Saturday and Sunday)* 12.00/24.00 **t.** and a la carte 8.95 – **90 rm** 120.00/150.00 **st.**, 9 suites – SB.

Royal George, King St., WA16 6EE, (01565) 634151, *Fax (01565) 634955* – rm, – 120. AE VISA.
Meals 9.95/12.50 **t.** and a la carte – 6.95 – **31 rm** 60.00 **t.**

Longview, 55 Manchester Rd, WA16 0LX, (01565) 632119, *enquiries@longviewhotel.com, Fax (01565) 652402* – rest, AE VISA
closed 24 December-6 January – **Meals** *(closed Sunday and Bank Holidays)* (bar lunch)/dinner a la carte 14.25/24.70 **t.** 5.00 – **23 rm** 65.00/110.00 **t.**

Travelodge, Chester Rd, Tabley, WA16 0PP, Northwest : 2 3/4 m. by A 5033 on A 556 (01565) 652187, *Fax (01565) 652187* – rm, AE VISA JCB.
Meals (grill rest.) – **32 rm** 49.95 **t.**

Belle Epoque Brasserie with rm, 60 King St., WA16 6DT, (01565) 633060, *Fax (01565) 634150,* « Art Nouveau », – – 60. AE VISA.
closed 25 December and Bank Holidays – **Meals** *(closed Saturday lunch and Sunday)* a la carte 18.50/26.50 **st.** – 5.00 – **6 rm** 50.00/60.00 **st.**

Est, Est, Est, 81 King St., WA16 6DX, (01565) 755487, *Fax (01565) 633186* – . AE VISA
closed 25 and 26 December – **Meals** - Italian - and a la carte 10.85/23.65 **t.** 6.85.

at Mobberley *Northeast : 2 1/2 m. by A 537 on B 5085 – Knutsford.*

Hinton, Town Lane, WA16 7HH, on B 5085 (01565) 873484, *Fax (01565) 873484,* – AE VISA.
Meals (by arrangement) 14.50 **t.** – **6 rm** 44.00/58.00 **t.**

Laburnum Cottage, Knutsford Rd, WA16 7PU, West : 3/4 m. on B 5085 (01565) 872464, *Fax (01565) 872464,* – .
Meals 15.00 **st.** – **5 rm** 42.00/55.00 **st.**

at Hoo Green *Northwest : 3 1/2 m. on A 50 – Knutsford.*

Mere Court, Warrington Rd, WA16 0RW, Northwest : 1 m. on A 50 (01565) 831000, *sales@merecourt.co.uk, Fax (01565) 831001,* « Edwardian manor house », – – 30. AE VISA.
Meals 13.95/19.95 **t.** a la carte 8.50 – **34 rm** 115.00/160.00 **t.** – SB.

Premier Lodge, Warrington Rd, WA16 0PZ, (0870) 7001482, *Fax (0870) 7001483* – rm, AE VISA.
Meals (grill rest.) a la carte 9.85/15.35 **t.** – 6.00 – **28 rm** 46.00 **st.**

LACOCK *Wilts.* 403 404 N 29 *The West Country G.* – *pop. 1 068* – *Chippenham.*
See : *Village★★ - Lacock Abbey★ AC – High St.★, St. Cyriac★, Fox Talbot Museum of Photography★ AC.*
London 109 – Bath 16 – Bristol 30 – Chippenham 3.

Sign of the Angel, 6 Church St., SN15 2LB, (01249) 730230, *angel@lacock.co.uk, Fax (01249) 730527,* « Part 14C and 15C former wool merchant's house in National Trust village », – AE VISA JCB
closed 1 week Christmas – **Meals** - English - *(closed Monday lunch except Bank Holidays)* a la carte 20.40/29.70 **t.** 6.00 – **10 rm** 71.50/120.00 **t.** – SB.

LADOCK *Cornwall* 403 F 33.
London 268 – Exeter 84 – Penzance 37 – Newquay 12 – Plymouth 51 – Truro 13.

Bissick Old Mill, TR2 4PG, (01726) 882557, *Fax (01726) 884057* – VISA JCB.
Meals (by arrangement) 17.50 **st.** 5.50 – **5 rm** 39.95/69.00 **st.** – SB.

LAMORNA *Cornwall* 403 D 33.
London 303 – Falmouth 30 – Penzance 5 – Plymouth 83 – Truro 32.

The Lamorna Cove , TR19 6XH, (01736) 731411, *reception@lamornacovehotel.co.uk, Fax (01736) 732316,* , heated, – AE VISA.
closed January-Easter – **Meals** 15.00/23.00 **t.** and a la carte – **11 rm** 55.00/110.00 **t.**, 1 suite.

ENGLAND

LANCASTER *Lancs.* 402 L 21 *Great Britain G. – pop. 44 497.*

See : *Castle★ AC.*

Ashton Hall, Ashton-with-Stodday ☎ (01524) 752090 – Lansil, Caton Rd ☎ (0152 39269.

29 Castle Hill ☎ (01524) 32878.

London 252 – Blackpool 26 – Bradford 62 – Burnley 44 – Leeds 71 – Middlesbrough 97 Preston 26.

Lancaster House, Green Lane, Ellel, LA1 4GJ, South : 3 ¼ m. by A 6 ☎ (01524) 844822, *nchouse@elh.co.uk, Fax (01524) 844766,* – rest, – 12 MC AE VISA JCB

The Gressingham : **Meals** 20.95 **t.** and a la carte 8.95 – 9.95 – **80 rm** 99.00 **st.** – SB.

Posthouse Lancaster, Waterside Park, Caton Rd, LA1 3RA, Northeast : 1 ½ m. on A 6 at junction 34 of M 6 ☎ (0870) 4009047, *Fax (01524) 841265,* – – 120. MC AE VISA.

Meals 15.00 **t.** and a la carte 8.95 – 11.95 – **157 rm** 69.00 **st.** – SB.

Edenbreck House without rest., Sunnyside Lane, off Ashfield Av., LA1 5ED, Westbourne Rd, near the station ☎ (01524) 32464, – .

closed 25 December – **3 rm** 30.00/55.00.

at Carnforth *North : 6 ¼ m. on A 6.*

New Capernwray Farm , Capernwray, LA6 1AD, Northeast : 3 m. by B 62 ☎ (01524) 734284, *newcapfarm@aol.com, Fax (01524) 734284,* « 17C former farr house », – . MC VISA JCB

March-October – **Meals** (by arrangement) (communal dining) 24.50 **s.** – **3 rm** 44.0 76.00 **s.**

LANCASTER SERVICE AREA *Lancs.* 402 L 22 – ✉ *Forton.*

(M 6) Service Area, White Carr Lane, Bay Horse ☎ (01524) 792181.

Travelodge, LA2 9DU, on M 6 between junctions 32 and 33 ☎ (01524) 79222 *Fax (01524) 791703* – . MC AE VISA JCB.

Meals (grill rest.) – **53 rm** 49.95 **t.**

LANCING *W. Sussex* 404 S 31 – *pop. 29 575 (inc. Sompting).*

London 59 – Brighton 4 – Southampton 53.

Sussex Pad, Old Shoreham Rd, BN15 0RH, East : 1 m. off A 27 ☎ (01273) 45464 *Fax (01273) 453010,* – rest, . MC AE VISA

Meals 21.00 **t.** and a la carte 7.90 – **20 rm** 60.00/80.00 **t.**

LANGHO *Lancs.* 402 M 22 – *see Blackburn.*

LANGTON GREEN *Kent – see Royal Tunbridge Wells.*

LAPWORTH *Warks. – see Hockley Heath.*

LARKFIELD *Kent* 404 V 30 – *see Maidstone.*

LASKILL *N. Yorks. – see Helmsley.*

LASTINGHAM *N. Yorks.* 402 R 21 – *pop. 87* – ✉ *York.*

London 244 – Scarborough 26 – York 32.

Lastingham Grange , YO62 6TH, ☎ (01751) 417345, *reservations@lastinghamgra e.com, Fax (01751) 417358,* « Part 17C farmhouse, gardens », – rest,

closed December-February – **Meals** (light lunch Monday to Saturday)/dinner 31.75 **t.** 4. – **12 rm** 89.00/165.00 **t.** – SB.

LAUNCESTON *Cornwall* 403 G 32.

Trethorne, Kennards House ☎ (01566) 86324.

London 228 – Bude 23 – Exeter 47 – Plymouth 27.

Springer Spaniel, Treburley, PL15 9NS, South : 4 ½ m. on A 388 ☎ (01579) 37042 *Fax (01579) 370113* – . MC VISA JCB

Meals a la carte 11.95/23.50 **t.** 4.25.

AVENHAM *Suffolk* 404 W 27 *Great Britain G.* – *pop. 1 231* – ✉ *Sudbury.*

See : *Town*★★ – *Church of St. Peter and St. Paul*★.

Lady St. ✆ *(01787) 248207.*

London 66 – Cambridge 39 – Colchester 22 – Ipswich 19.

Swan, High St., CO10 9QA, ✆ (0870) 4008116, *heritagehotels_lavenham.swan@forte_hotels.com, Fax (01787) 248286,* « Part 14C timbered inn », – TV P – 45. MC AE VISA JCB
Meals 15.95/26.95 **t.** 7.95 – 14.95 – **44 rm** 100.00/165.00 **st.**, 2 suites – SB.

Angel, Market Pl., CO10 9QZ, ✆ (01787) 247388, *angellav@aol.com, Fax (01787) 248344,* « 15C inn », – TV P. MC AE VISA.
closed 25 and 26 December – **Meals** a la carte 12.00/18.00 **t.** 3.95 – **8 rm** 45.00/70.00 **t.** – SB.

Lavenham Priory without rest., Water St., CO10 9RW, ✆ (01787) 247404, *mail@lavenhampriory.co.uk, Fax (01787) 248472,* « Part 13C timbered former priory », – TV P. MC VISA JCB.
closed Christmas-New Year – **5 rm** 59.00/98.00 **st.**

Great House with rm, Market Pl., CO10 9QZ, ✆ (01787) 247431, *greathouse@clara.co.uk, Fax (01787) 248007,* , « Part 14C timbered house » – TV. MC AE VISA JCB
closed 3 weeks January – **Meals** - French - *(closed Sunday dinner and Monday to non-residents)* 15.95/21.95 **t.** and a la carte 8.50 – **3 rm** 65.00/99.00 **t.**, 2 suites 99.00/120.00 **t.** – SB.

EA *Lancs.* – *see Preston.*

EAMINGTON SPA *Warks.* 403 404 P 27 – *see Royal Leamington Spa.*

EDBURY *Herefordshire* 403 404 M 27 – *pop. 6 216.*

3 The Homend ✆ *(01531) 636147.*

London 119 – Hereford 14 – Newport 46 – Worcester 16.

The Feathers, High St., HR8 1DS, ✆ (01531) 635266, *Fax (01531) 638955,* « Timbered 16C inn », – TV P – 120. MC AE VISA
Quills : **Meals** a la carte 15.00/25.00 **t.** 10.00 – ***Fuggles :*** **Meals** a la carte 17.00/26.00 **t.** 12.00 – **19 rm** 75.00/140.00 **t.** – SB.

The Barn House without rest., New St., HR8 2DX, ✆ (01531) 632825, « Part 17C », – TV P – 60. MC VISA.
closed 25 and 26 December – **3 rm** 48.00/58.00.

The Malthouse, Church Lane, HR8 1DT, ✆ (01531) 634443, *jtlipton@themalthouse.fsnet.co.uk, Fax (01531) 634443,* – . MC VISA JCB
closed 2 weeks in spring, 24 December-2 January, Sunday and Monday – **Meals** (booking essential) (dinner only and Saturday lunch)/dinner a la carte 16.25/25.00 **t.** 8.95.

LEEDS

W. Yorks. 402 P 22 *Great Britain G.* – *pop. 424 194.*

London 204 – Liverpool 75 – Manchester 43 – Newcastle upon Tyne 95 – Nottingham 74.

TOURIST INFORMATION

The Arcade, City Station ☎ *(0113) 242 5242.*

PRACTICAL INFORMATION

18, 18 *Temple Newsam, Temple Newsam Rd, Halton* ☎ *(0113) 264 5624,* **CT**.
18 *Gotts Park, Armley Ridge Rd, Armley* ☎ *(0113) 234 2019,* **BT**.
18 *Middleton Park, Ring Rd, Beeston Park, Middleton* ☎ *(0113) 270 9506,* **CU**.
18, 9 *Moor Allerton, Coal Rd, Wike* ☎ *(0113) 266 1154.*
18 *Howley Hall, Scotchman Lane, Morley* ☎ *(01924) 472432.*
9 *Roundhay, Park Lane* ☎ *(0113) 266 2695* **CT**.
Leeds – Bradford Airport : ☎ *(0113) 250 9696, NW : 8 m. by A 65 and A 658* **BT**.

SIGHTS

See : *City★ - Royal Armouries Museum★★★ – City Art Gallery★ AC* **GY M**.

Env. : *Kirkstall Abbey★ AC, NW : 3 m. by A 65* **GY** *– Temple Newsam★ (decorative arts★) AC, E : 5 m. by A 64 and A 63* **CU D**.

Exc. : *Harewood House★★ (The Gallery★) AC, N : 8 m. by A 61* **CT** *– Nostell Priory★, SE : 18 m. by A 61 and A 638 – Yorkshire Sculpture Park★, S : 20 m. by M 1 to junction 38 and 1 m. north off A 637 – Brodsworth Hall★, SE : 25 m. by M 1 to junction 40, A 638 and minor rd (right) in Upton.*

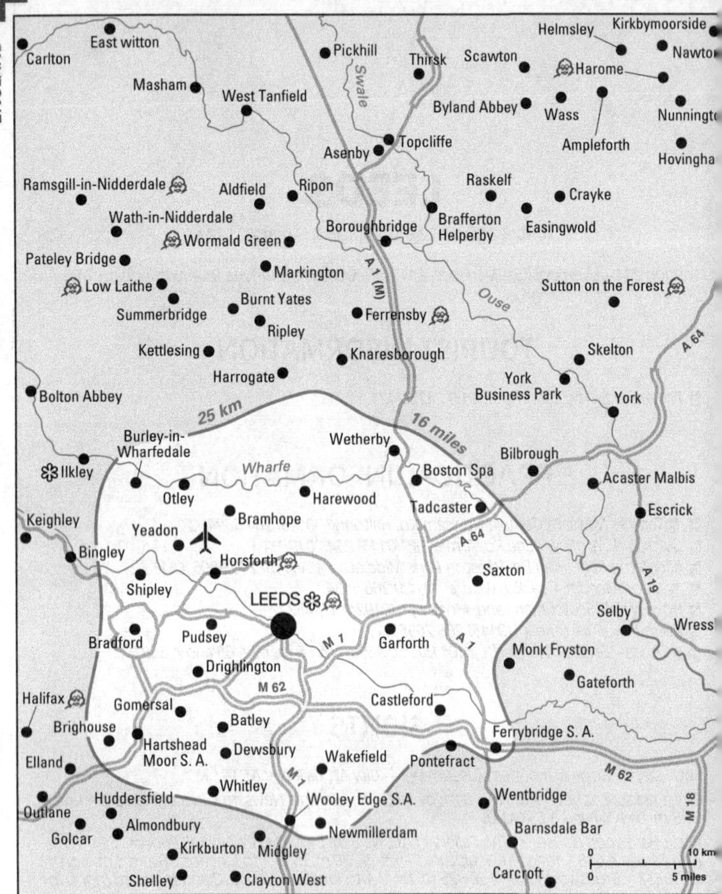

Oulton Hall, Rothwell Lane, Oulton, LS26 8HN, Southeast : 5 ½ m. by A 61 and A 639 on 654 ☎ (0113) 282 1000, *oulton.hall@devere-hotels.com, Fax (0113) 282 8066,* ←, « Part Victorian mansion », Ⓛ, ≘s, ⊠, 18, 9, – |‡|, ⇔, ▤ rest, TV & P – 🔬 330. MC AE VISA CU

Bronte : Meals *(closed Saturday lunch)* 15.00 **st.** (lunch) and a la carte 22.00/39.00 ⅉ 7.50 – ***Blayd's :*** **Meals** a la carte 22.00/39.00 **st.** ⅉ 7.50 – **150 rm** ⊒ 140.00/160.00 s 2 suites – SB.

Leeds Marriott, 4 Trevelyan Sq., Boar Lane, LS1 6ET, ☎ (0113) 236 63 *Fax (0113) 236 6367,* Ⓛ, ≘s, ⊠ – |‡|, ⇔ rm, ▤ TV & – 🔬 280. MC AE ⓓ VISA GZ

John T's : **Meals** a la carte 15.50/33.00 **st.** ⅉ 7.75 – ⊒ 12.50 – **243 rm** 117.00 **st.**, 1 suite SB.

Leeds Crowne Plaza, Wellington St., LS1 4DL, ☎ (0113) 244 2200, *Fax (0113) 244 04* Ⓛ, ≘s, ⊠ – |‡|, ⇔ rm, ▤ TV & P – 🔬 200. MC AE ⓓ VISA. ✻ FZ

Meals *(closed Saturday lunch)* 14.00/20.00 **t.** and a la carte – ⊒ 12.95 – **130 rm** 140.00 5 suites – SB.

42 The Calls, 42 The Calls, LS2 7EW, ☎ (0113) 244 0099, *hotel@42thecalls.co. Fax (0113) 234 4100,* ←, « Converted riverside grain mill » – |‡| TV & – 🔬 85. MC ⓓ VISA GZ

closed Christmas – **Meals** – (see ***Pool Court at 42*** below) – (see also ***Brasserie Forty Fo*** below) – ⊒ 11.50 – **38 rm** 98.00/150.00 **t.**, 3 suites.

Le Meridien Queen's, City Sq., LS1 1PL, (0113) 243 1323, *Fax (0113) 242 5154* – rm, – 600. VISA. GZ u
No. 1 City Square: **Meals** 7.95 **st.** lunch and a la carte 16.65/22.45 **st.** 8.50 – 11.75 – **194 rm** 115.00/135.00 **st.**, 5 suites – SB.

Village H. and Leisure Club, 186 Otley Rd, Headingley, LS16 5PR, Northwest : 3 ½ m. on A 660 (0113) 278 1000, *village.l@cybase.co.uk, Fax (0113) 278 1111,* squash – rest, – 220. VISA. BT s
Meals (grill rest.) 9.95/12.95 **st.** and a la carte 3.90 – **94 rm** 88.00 **t.**

Weetwood Hall, Otley Rd, LS16 5PS, Northwest : 4 m. on A 660 (0113) 230 6000, *sales @weetwood.co.uk, Fax (0113) 230 6095,* – – 150. VISA JCB BT c
Meals (bar lunch Saturday) 12.95/17.50 **t.** and dinner a la carte – 9.75 – **108 rm** 89.00/ 160.00 **t.** – SB.

Hilton Leeds City, Neville St., LS1 4BX, (0113) 244 2000, *leehnhngm@hilton.com, Fax (0113) 243 3577,* – rm, rm, – 400. VISA. GZ r
Meals *(closed lunch Saturday and Sunday)* (bar lunch)/dinner 17.95 **st.** and a la carte – 13.95 – **186 rm** 145.00 **st.**, 20 suites.

Malmaison, Sovereign Quay, LS1 1DQ, (0113) 398 1000, *leeds@malmaison.com, Fax (0113) 398 1002,* « Riverside setting, contemporary interior », – rm, – 40. VISA. GZ n
Meals 15.00/25.00 **st.** and a la carte – 10.75 – **99 rm** 89.00/120.00 **st.**, 1 suite.

Haley's, Shire Oak Rd, Headingley, LS6 2DE, Northwest : 2 m. by A 660 (0113) 278 4446, *info@haleys.co.uk, Fax (0113) 275 3342* – – 25. VISA JCB. DV s
closed 26 to 30 December – **Meals** *(closed Sunday dinner to non-residents)* (dinner only and Sunday lunch)/dinner 24.95 **st.** and a la carte 6.75 – **29 rm** 95.00/230.00 **st.** – SB.

Metropole, King St., LS1 2HQ, (0113) 245 0841, *Fax (0113) 242 5156* – – 250. VISA JCB FZ e
Meals 17.95 **t.** (dinner) and a la carte 14.00/28.00 **st.** 6.00 – 11.95 – **117 rm** 102.00/ 135.00 **st.**, 1 suite – SB.

Merrion, Merrion Centre, 17 Wade Lane, LS2 8NH, (0113) 243 9191, *info@merrion-hotel-leeds.com, Fax (0113) 242 3527* – rm, – 80. VISA JCB.
Meals 17.50 **t.** and a la carte 5.45 – 11.75 – **109 rm** 99.00/130.00 **st.** GY e

Golden Lion, 2 Lower Briggate, LS1 4AE, (0113) 243 6454, *info@goldenlion-hotel-leeds.com, Fax (0113) 242 9327* – rm, – 120. VISA JCB. GZ v
Meals (bar lunch)/dinner a la carte 14.75/20.15 **t.** 5.95 – **115 rm** 99.00/145.00 **st.** – SB.

Premier Lodge, City West One Office Park, Gelderd Rd, LS12 6SN, Southwest : 3 ½ m. by A 62 (0870) 7001414, *Fax (0870) 7001415* – rest, VISA JCB
Meals (grill rest.) (dinner only) a la carte 13.00/18.90 **st.** 4.00 – 6.00 – **126 rm** 46.00 **st.** CU n

Travel Inn Metro, Citygate, Wellington St., LS3 1LH, (0113) 242 8104, *Fax (0113) 242 8105* – rm, rest, VISA. FZ v
Meals (grill rest.) – **140 rm** 46.95 **t.**

Express by Holiday Inn without rest., Cavendish St. (off Kirkstall Rd), LS3 1LY, (0113) 242 6200, *leeds@premierhotels.co.uk, Fax (0113) 242 6300* – – 40. VISA JCB FY e
112 rm 55.00 **st.**

Express by Holiday Inn, Aberford Rd, Oulton, LS26 8EJ, Southeast : 5 ½ m. by A 61 on A 639 (0113) 282 6201, *Fax (0113) 288 7210* – rm, – 40. VISA JCB. CU e
Meals (carving rest.) a la carte 8.00/13.00 **t.** – **77 rm** 49.95 **t.**

Travelodge without rest., Blayds Court, Swinegate, LS1 4AG, (0113) 244 5793, *Fax (0113) 246 0076* – VISA JCB. GZ v
100 rm 49.95 **t.**

Pinewood, 78 Potternewton Lane, LS7 3LW, (0113) 262 2561, *Fax (0113) 262 2561,* – rest, VISA. DV a
closed Christmas-New Year – **Meals** (by arrangement) 11.95 **t.** – **10 rm** 37.00/47.00 **t.**

XXX **gueller,** 3 York Pl., LS1 2DR, (0113) 245 9922, *dine@guellers.com, Fax (0113) 245 9965* – VISA FZ e
closed 25 December-4 January, Sunday and Monday – **Meals** 18.00 **t.** (lunch) and a la carte 28.50/47.50 **t.** 13.00.

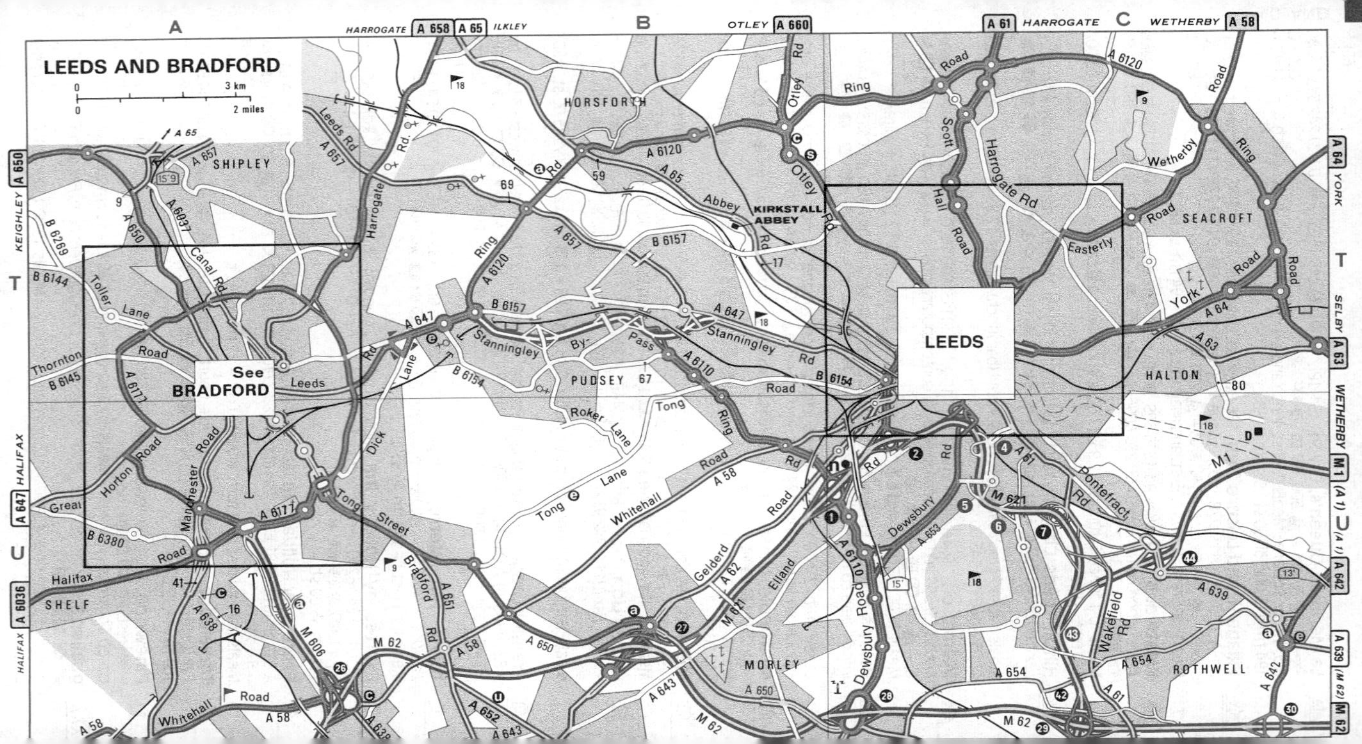
LEEDS AND BRADFORD
0 3 km
0 2 miles
LEEDS
See BRADFORD
SHIPLEY
HORSFORTH
KIRKSTALL ABBEY
PUDSEY
SEACROFT
HALTON
MORLEY
ROTHWELL
SHELF
HARROGATE A 658 A 65 ILKLEY
OTLEY A 660
A 61 HARROGATE
WETHERBY A 58
A 64 YORK
SELBY A 63
WETHERBY M 1 (A 1)
A 642
A 639 (M 62) M 62
KEIGHLEY A 650
HALIFAX A 647
HALIFAX A 6036

LEEDS

Bradford Road . . . . . . **AT** 9
Cambridge Road . . . **DV** 14
Cleckheaton Road . . . . **AU** 16
Commercial Road . . **BT** 17
Domestic Street . . . . **DX** 23
East Park Parade . . . **EX** 28
Gelderd Road . . . . . . **DX** 32
Harrogate Road . . . . **DV** 40
Huddersfield Road . . . . **AU** 41
Hyde Park Road . . . **AV** 43
Ivy Street . . . . **EX** 45
Lupton Avenue . . . . . **EX** 51
New Road Side . . . . . **BT** 59
Oakwood Lane . . . . . **EV** 63
Pudsey Road . . . . **BT** 67
Rodley Lane . . . . **BV** 69
Roseville Road . . . . **EVX** 70
Shaw Lane . . . . **DV** 74
South Accommodation Road . . . . **EX** 77
Stainbeck Road . . . . **DV** 79
Templenewsam Road **CT** 80

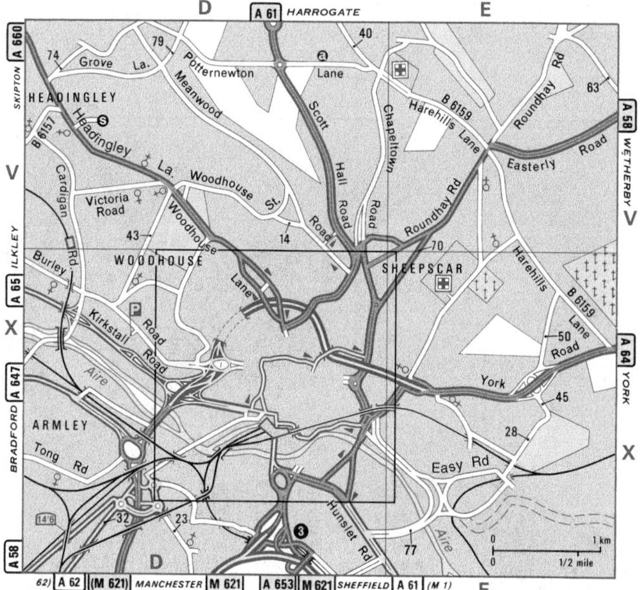

XXX **Pool Court at 42** (at 42 The Calls H.), 44 The Calls, LS2 7EW, ☎ (0113) 244 4242, *pc42@btinternet.com, Fax (0113) 234 3332,* ☂, « Riverside setting » – ⇌ ▤. MC AE (D) VISA GZ z
closed Saturday lunch, Sunday and Bank Holidays – **Meals** 19.00/37.50 **t.** 🍷 8.65
Spec. Basil scented jelly with lobster and crab. Squab pigeon and girolles with truffled consommé. Savarin of strawberries and rhubarb.

XX **Rascasse,** Canal Wharf, Water Lane, LS11 5BB, ☎ (0113) 244 6611, *Fax (0113) 244 0736,* <, « Converted grain warehouse, canalside setting » – ▤. MC AE (D) VISA FZ c
closed Christmas and New Year, Sunday, Saturday lunch and Bank Holiday Mondays – **Meals** 18.00 **t.** (lunch) and a la carte 22.00/37.00 **t.** 🍷 7.00.

XX **Teatro,** The Quays, Concordia St., LS1 4BJ, ☎ (0113) 243 6699, *Fax (0113) 243 2244,* ☂ – ▤. MC AE (D) VISA JCB GZ e
closed 24-30 December – **Meals** 12.50/15.00 **t.** (lunch) and dinner a la carte 22.40/30.95 **t.** 🍷 15.00.

XX **Leodis,** Victoria Mill, Sovereign St., LS1 4BJ, ☎ (0113) 242 1010, *Fax (0113) 243 0432,* ☂, « Converted riverside warehouse » – MC AE (D) VISA GZ b
closed 31 December, Sunday, Saturday lunch and Bank Holidays – **Meals** 14.95 **t.** (lunch) and a la carte 15.75/24.75 **t.** 🍷 6.85.

XX **Brasserie Forty Four** (at 42 The Calls H.), 44 The Calls, LS2 7EW, ☎ (0113) 234 3232, *Fax (0113) 234 3332,* « Riverside setting » – ▤. MC AE (D) VISA GZ z
closed 3 days Christmas, Sunday, Saturday lunch and Bank Holidays – **Meals** 12.95 **t.** (lunch) and a la carte 20.50/25.80 **t.** 🍷 7.95.

XX **Fourth Floor** (at Harvey Nichols), 107-111 Briggate, LS1 6AZ, ☎ (0113) 204 8000, *Fax (0113) 204 8080,* ☂ – ▤. MC AE (D) VISA JCB GZ s
closed 25-26 December, 1 January, and dinner Sunday-Wednesday – **Meals** (lunch bookings not accepted) 13.00/16.00 **t.** (lunch) and a la carte 26.00/31.00 **t.** 🍷 8.00.

XX **Maxi's,** 6 Bingley St., LS3 1LX, off Kirkstall Rd ☎ (0113) 244 0552, *info@maxi-s.co.uk, Fax (0113) 234 3902,* « Pagoda, ornate decor » – ▤ P. MC AE (D) VISA DX a
closed 25 and 26 December – **Meals** - Chinese (Canton, Peking) - 17.50/24.00 **t.** and a la carte.

LEEDS

Aire Street . . . . FZ 2
Albion Street. . . . . GZ 3
Bond Street . . . . GZ 8
Bridge Street . . . . GY 10
Briggate . . . . GZ
City Square . . . . GZ 15
Commercial Street . . . . GZ 18
Cookridge Street . . . . GY 19
County Arcade . . . . GZ 20
Cross Stamford St. . . . . GY 21
Crown Point Road . . . . GZ 22
Duncan Street . . . . GZ 25
East Parade . . . . FGZ 27
Eastgate. . . . . GZ 31
Hanover Way. . . . . FY 38
Headrow (The) . . . . GY
Headrow Centre . . . . GZ 39
Infirmary Street . . . . GZ 44
King Street. . . . . FZ 46
Kirkgate . . . . GZ 48
Lands Lane . . . . GZ 49
Leeds Shopping Plaza. . . . . GZ 50
Marsh Lane. . . . . GZ 52
Meadow Lane . . . . GZ 53
Merrion Centre . . . . GY
Merrion Street . . . . GY 54
Merrion Way. . . . . GY 55
Millennium Square . . . . GY 56
New Briggate . . . . GY 57
New York Road . . . . GY
Park Lane. . . . . FY
Queen Street. . . . . FZ
St. John's Centre . . . . GY
St. Paul's Street . . . . FZ
St. Peter's Street. . . . . GZ
Sheepscar St. South. . . . . . GY
Skinner Lane . . . . GY
South Parade . . . . FGZ
Trinity St. Shopping Centre . . . . GZ
Victoria Road. . . . . GZ
Wade Lane . . . . GY
Wellington Road . . . . FZ
West Street. . . . . FZ
Westgate . . . . FZ

Shears Yard, The Calls, LS2 7EY, ☎ (0113) 244 4144, *shears@ukweb.cc* *Fax (0113) 244 8102* – ▤. MO AE VISA GZ
closed 25 December-1 January, Sunday and Bank Holiday Mondays – **Meals** 12.95/20.95 and a la carte 7.95.

The Calls Grill, Calls Landing, 38 The Calls, LS2 7EW, ☎ (0113) 245 38 *Fax (0113) 243 9035*, « Converted riverside warehouse » – ▤. MO AE ① VISA GZ
closed 24 December-4 January, Monday and Sunday lunch – **Meals** 14.50 **t.** (c ner) and a la carte 11.25/27.45 **t.**

at Garforth *East : 7 m. by A 63 – CT – ✉ Leeds.*

Aagrah, Aberford Rd, LS25 1BA, on A 642 (Garforth rd) ☎ (0113) 287 6606 – ▤ P. MO VISA JCB
closed 25 December – **Meals** - Indian (Kashmiri) - (booking essential) (dinner only) a la ca 8.65/13.15 **t.**

Drighlington *Southwest : 6 m. by A 62 and A 650 on B 6135 – ✉ Leeds.*

Travel Inn, The Old Brickworks, Wakefield Rd, BD11 1EA, ✆ (0113) 287 9132, *Fax (0113) 287 9115,* – rm, rest, TV, P. MC AE VISA. BU a
Meals (grill rest.) – **42 rm** 40.95 **t.**

Pudsey *West : 5 ¾ m. by A 647 – ✉ Leeds.*

Aagrah, 483 Bradford Rd, LS28 8ED, on A 647 ✆ (01274) 668818, *Fax (01274) 669803* – P. MC AE VISA JCB BT e
closed 25 December – **Meals** - Indian (Kashmiri) - (booking essential) (dinner only) a la carte 8.65/13.15 **t.**

Horsforth *Northwest : 5 m. by A 65 off A 6120 – ✉ Leeds.*

Paris, Calverley Bridge, Calverley Lane, Rodley, LS13 1NP, Southwest : 1 m. by A 6120 ✆ (0113) 258 1885, *Fax (0113) 239 0651* – P. MC AE VISA BT a
closed Saturday lunch – **Meals** 13.95/14.95 **t.** and a la carte 14.40/26.35 **t.** 6.50.

Bramhope *Northwest : 8 m. on A 660* – **BT** – *✉ Leeds.*

Posthouse Leeds/Bradford, Leeds Rd, LS16 9JJ, ✆ (0870) 400 9049, *Fax (0113) 284 3451,* – TV P – 160. MC AE VISA
Meals 15.00 **t.** and a la carte 6.95 – 11.95 – **130 rm** 89.00 **st.**, 1 suite – SB.

The Cottages without rest., Moor Rd, LS16 9HH, South : ¼ m. on Cookridge rd ✆ (0113) 284 2754, *Fax (0113) 203 7496,* – TV P.
closed Christmas and New Year – **5 rm** 35.00/48.00.

Yeadon *Northwest : 8 m. by A 65 on A 658* – **BT** – *✉ Leeds.*

Travel Inn, Victoria Av., LS19 7AW, on A 658 ✆ (0113) 250 4284, *Fax (0113) 250 5838* – rm, rest, TV, P. MC AE VISA.
Meals (grill rest.) – **40 rm** 40.95 **t.**

EK *Staffs.* 402 403 404 N 24 – *pop. 18 167.*

Westwood, Newcastle Rd, Wallbridge ✆ (01538) 398385.

1 Market Pl. ✆ (01538) 483741.

London 122 – Derby 30 – Manchester 39 – Stoke-on-Trent 12.

Country Cottage, Back Lane Farm, Winkhill, ST13 7XZ, Southeast : 5 ½ m. by A 523 (turning left opposite Little Chef) ✆ (01538) 308273, *mjb6435@netscapeonline.co.uk, Fax (01538) 308098,* – TV P.
Meals 13.50 **st.** – **4 rm** 22.50/43.00 **st.**

EMING BAR *N. Yorks.* 402 P 21 – *pop. 1 824 – ✉ Northallerton.*

The Yorkshire Maid, Motel Leeming, A1 North ✆ (01677) 424262.

London 235 – Leeds 44 – Middlesbrough 30 – Newcastle upon Tyne 52 – York 37.

Little Holtby, DL7 9LH, Northwest : 2 m. on A 1 (northbound carriageway) ✆ (01609) 748762, *littleholtby@yahoo.co.uk, Fax (01609) 748822,* – TV P.
Meals (by arrangement) (communal dining) 12.50 **s.** – **3 rm** 30.00/50.00 **s.** – SB.

ICESTER *Leicester* 402 403 404 Q 26 *Great Britain G.* – *pop. 318 518.*

See : *Guildhall*★ **BY B** – *Museum and Art Gallery*★ **CY M2** – *St. Mary de Castro Church*★ **BY A.**

Leicestershire, Evington Lane ✆ (0116) 273 8825 **AY** – *Western Park, Scudamore Rd ✆ (0116) 287 6158* – *Humberstone Heights, Gipsy Lane ✆ (0116) 299 5570* **AX** – *Oadby, Leicester Road Racecourse ✆ (0116) 270 0215* **AY** – *Lutterworth Rd, Blaby ✆ (0116) 278 4804.*

East Midlands Airport, Castle Donington : ✆ (01332) 852852 NW : 22 m. by A 50 – **AX** – *and M1.*

7-9 Every St., Town Hall Sq. ✆ (0116) 299 8888.

London 107 – Birmingham 43 – Coventry 24 – Nottingham 26.

Plans on following pages

Hilton Leicester, Junction 21 Approach, Braunstone, LE3 2WQ, Southwest : 3 ½ m. by A 5460 at junction with A 563 ✆ (0116) 263 0066, *reservations@leicester.stakis.co.uk, Fax (0116) 263 0627,* – rest, TV P – 200. MC AE VISA
Meals *(closed lunch Saturday and Bank Holidays)* a la carte 17.70/27.25 **st.** – 11.50 – **177 rm** 155.00 **st.**, 2 suites – SB. AY e

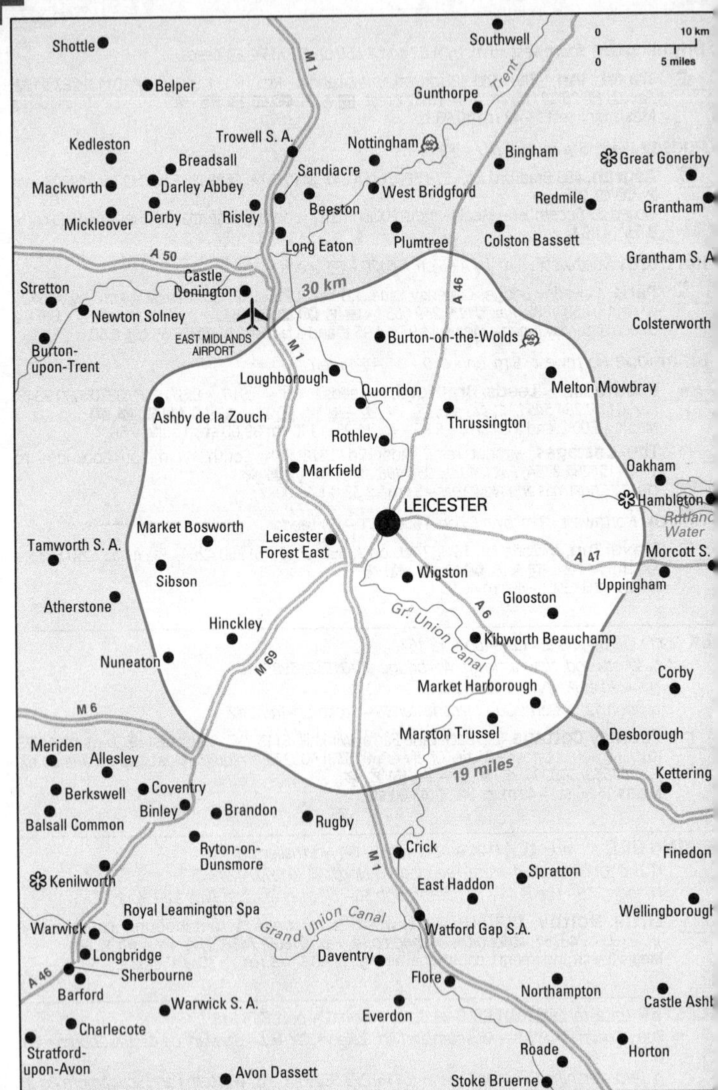

Grand, 73 Granby St., LE1 6ES, (0116) 255 5599, *Fax (0116) 254 4736* – rm, – 500. AE VISA CY
Meals (bar lunch Monday to Saturday)/dinner 16.95 **st.** and a la carte – – **91 rm** 99 114.00 **st.**, 1 suite – SB.

Holiday Inn Leicester, 129 St. Nicholas Circle, LE1 5LX, (0116) 253 1161, *holidayin icester@virgin.net, Fax (0116) 251 3169,* – rm, – 250 AE VISA JCB. BY
Meals 12.95/18.95 **st.** and a la carte 7.50 – 10.95
187 rm 130.00/140.00 **st.**, 1 suite.

LEICESTER
BUILT UP AREA

quith Way . . . . AY 2
lgrave Road . . . . AX 4
aunstone Avenue . . . . AY 10
aunstone Lane East . . . . . AY 13
aunstone Way . . . . AY 14
Checketts Road . . . . AX 17
Fosse Road North . . . . AX 21
Fullhurst Avenue . . . . AY 23
Glenfrith Way . . . . AX 24
Henley Road . . . . AX 29
Humberstone Road . . . . AX 34
King Richards Road . . . . AY 37
Knighton Road . . . . AY 38
Loughborough Road . . . . . . AX 40
Marfitt Street . . . . AX 41
Middleton Street . . . . AY 44
Raw Dykes Road . . . . AY 62
Stoughton Road . . . . AY 66
Upperton Road . . . . AY 68
Walnut Street . . . . AY 69
Wigston Lane . . . . AY 75
Woodville Road . . . . AY 76
Wyngate Drive . . . . AY 78

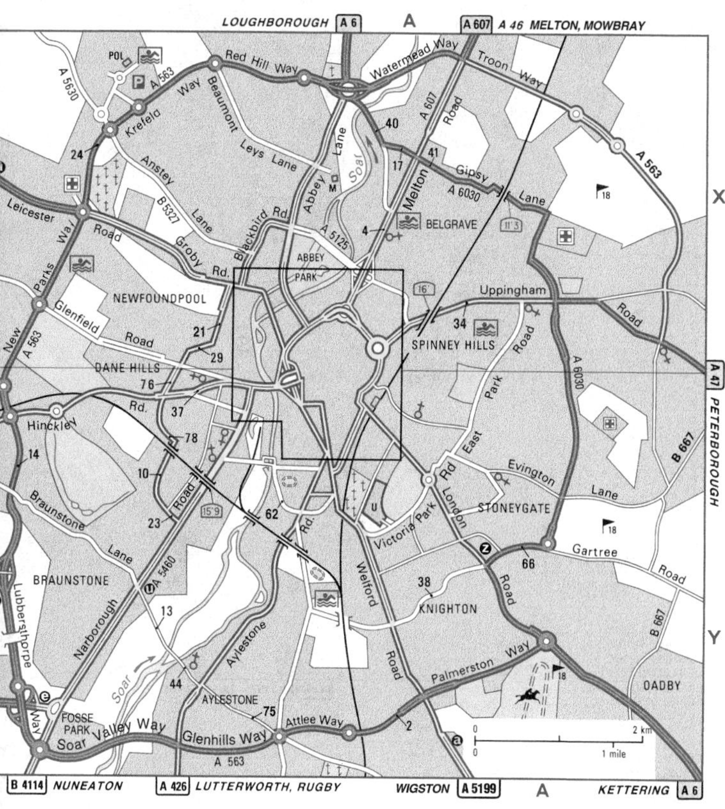

Posthouse Leicester, Braunstone Lane East, LE3 2FW, Southwest : 2 m. on A 5460 (0870) 400 9051, *gm1124@forte-hotels.com, Fax (0116) 282 3623* – rest, – 80. VISA JCB AY u
Meals (bar lunch Saturday) 15.00/25.00 **t.** and a la carte 7.95 – 11.95 – **172 rm** 69.00/89.00 **t.** – SB.

Belmont House, De Montfort St., LE1 7GR, (0116) 254 4773, *Fax (0116) 247 0804* – rm, – 100. VISA JCB. CY c
closed 25 December-3 January – ***Cherry's* : Meals** *(closed Saturday lunch and Sunday dinner)* a la carte 14.50/24.70 **t.** 8.00 – 8.50 – **78 rm** 89.00/107.00 **st.** – SB.

The Regency, 360 London Rd, LE2 2PL, Southeast : 2 m. on A 6 (0116) 270 9634, *Fax (0116) 270 1375* – rest, VISA. AY z
closed 26 December – **Meals** *(closed Saturday lunch)* 12.95 **t.** (dinner) and a la carte 12.50/21.95 **t.** 4.95 – **32 rm** 46.00/67.00 **t.**

Premier Lodge, Glen Rise, Oadby, LE2 4RG, Southeast : 5 ¾ m. on A 6 (0870) 7001418, *Fax (0870) 7001419* – rm, VISA.
Meals (grill rest.) a la carte 9.30/15.45 **st.** – 6.00 – **30 rm** 46.00 **st.**

Premier Lodge, Leicester Rd, Glenfield, LE3 8HB, Northwest : 3 ½ m. on A 50 (0870) 7001416, *Fax (0870) 7001417,* – rm, VISA. AX a
Meals (grill rest.) a la carte 8.95/16.35 **st.** – 6.00 – **43 rm** 46.00 **st.**

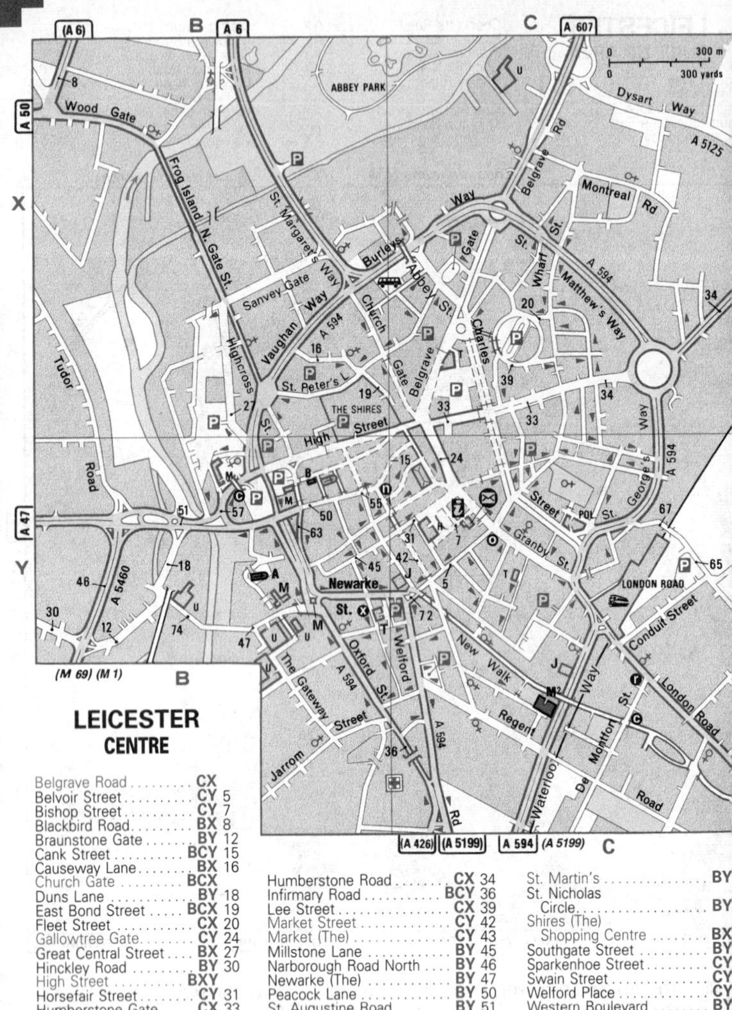

LEICESTER
CENTRE

Travel Inn, Meridian Business Park, Meridian Way, Braunstone, LE3 2LW, Southwest : m. by A 47 off A 563 ☎ (0116) 289 0945, *Fax (0116) 282 7486*, – rm, rest, – **Meals** (grill rest.) – **51 rm** 40.95 **t.** AY

Watsons, 5-9 Upper Brown St., LE1 5TE, ☎ (0116) 222 7770, *Fax (0116) 222 7771*, « C verted Victorian cotton mill » – BY
closed 10 days Christmas-New Year, Sunday and Bank Holidays – **Meals** 11.50 (lunch) and a la carte 20.00/25.50 9.00.

The Tiffin, 1 De Montfort St., LE1 7GE, ☎ (0116) 247 0420, *thetiffin@btclick.c* *Fax (0116) 255 3737* – . CY
closed 24 to 26 December, 1 January, Saturday lunch and Sunday – **Meals** - India (booking essential) 15.00/18.00 **t.** and a la carte 5.95.

The Case, 4-6 Hotel St., St. Martin's, LE1 5AW, ☎ (0116) 251 7675, *Fax (0116) 251 76* BY
closed 24 to 28 and 31 December, 1-2 January, Sunday and Bank Holidays – **Meals** 16.7 and a la carte 13.10/24.10 **t.** 3.95.

Rothley *North : 5 m. by A 6* – **AX** – *on B 5328* – ✉ *Leicester.*

Limes, 35 Mountsorrel Lane, LE7 7PS, ☎ (0116) 230 2531 – rest, TV P. MC AE VISA JCB.
closed 23 December-4 January – **Meals** (residents only) (dinner only) a la carte 11.50/18.40 **st.** – **11 rm** 42.50/55.00 **st.**

Wigston *Southeast : 3 ¼ m. on A 50* – ✉ *Leicester.*

Leicester Stage H., 299 Leicester Rd, LE18 1JW, ☎ (0116) 288 6161, *sales@stagehotel.co.uk, Fax (0116) 281 1874,* – rm, rest, TV P – 500. MC AE VISA.
Meals 16.95 **st.** (dinner) and a la carte 19.00/27.50 **st.** – **75 rm** 85.00/110.00 **st.** – SB.
AY a

Blaby *South : 4 ¼ m. on A 426* – **AY** – ✉ *Leicester.*

Time Out, Enderby Rd, LE8 4GD, ☎ (01162) 787898, *reservations@corushotels.com, Fax (01162) 781974,* – rm, rest, TV P – 70. MC AE VISA JCB
Meals *(closed Saturday lunch)* 11.95/18.95 **st.** and a la carte 8.50 – 10.95 – **48 rm** 90.00/120.00 **st.** – SB.

Leicester Forest East *West : 3 m. on A 47* – **AY** – ✉ *Leicester.*

Red Cow, Hinckley Rd, LE3 3PG, ☎ (0116) 238 7878, *alanjudd@msn.com, Fax (0116) 238 6539* – rm, TV P. MC AE VISA.
Meals (grill rest.) a la carte 11.50/18.00 **t.** 3.00 – 5.00 – **31 rm** 39.75 **st.**

Travel Inn, Hinckley Rd, LE3 3GD, ☎ (0116) 239 4677, *Fax (0116) 239 3429* – , rest, TV P. MC AE VISA.
Meals (grill rest.) – **40 rm** 40.95 **t.**

ICESTER FOREST EAST *Leics.* 402 403 404 Q 26 – *see Leicester.*

IGH *Dorset* 403 404 M 31 – *see Sherborne.*

IGH DELAMERE SERVICE AREA *Wilts.* 403 404 N 29 – ✉ *Chippenham.*

Travelodge, SN14 6LB, M 4 between junctions 18 and 17 (eastbound carriageway) ☎ (01666) 837691, *Fax (01666) 837112* – rm, TV P. MC AE VISA JCB.
Meals (grill rest.) – **70 rm** 59.95 **t.**

INTWARDINE *Shrops.* 403 L 26 – ✉ *Craven Arms.*
London 156 – Birmingham 55 – Hereford 24 – Worcester 40.

Upper Buckton Farm , Buckton, SY7 0JU, West : 2 m. by A 4113 and Buckton rd ☎ (01547) 540634, *Fax (01547) 540634,* ≤, « Working farm », – P.
Meals (by arrangement) 18.00 **s.** – **3 rm** 40.00/60.00.

NHAM *Kent* 404 W 30 – *pop. 2 167* – ✉ *Maidstone.*
London 45 – Folkestone 28 – Maidstone 9.

Chilston Park, Sandway, ME17 2BE, South : 1 ¾ m. off Broughton Malherbe rd ☎ (01622) 859803, *Fax (01622) 858588,* ≤, « Part 17C mansion, antiques », – , rest, TV P – 110. MC AE VISA
Meals *(closed Saturday lunch)* 19.50/32.00 **st.** and dinner a la carte 7.00 – **49 rm** 90.00/120.00 **st.**, 4 suites – SB.

Lime Tree, 8-10 The Limes, The Square, ME17 2PQ, ☎ (01622) 859509, *Fax (01622) 850096* – MC AE VISA JCB
Meals 18.95/27.50 **t.** and a la carte 9.50.

When travelling for business or pleasure
in **England, Wales, Scotland** *and* **Ireland***:*

- use the series of five maps (nos 401, 402, 403, 404 and 923) at a scale of 1:400 000
- they are the perfect complement to this Guide

LEOMINSTER *Herefordshire* 403 L 27 *Great Britain G. – pop. 9 543.*

Env. : *Berrington Hall★ AC, N : 3 m. by A 49.*

Ford Bridge ℘ (01568) 612863.

1 Corn Sq. ℘ (01568) 616460.

London 141 – Birmingham 47 – Hereford 13 – Worcester 26.

at Kimbolton *Northeast : 3 m. by A 49 on A 4112.*

Lower Bache House, HR6 0ER, East : 1 ¾ m. by A 4112 ℘ (01568) 750304, « 1 farmhouse », – rest, P. Meals (by arrangement) 18.50 **st.** 4.40 – **4 rm** 34.50/59.00 **st.** – SB.

at Leysters *Northeast : 5 m. by A 49 on A 4112 – ✉ Leominster.*

The Hills Farm, HR6 0HP, ℘ (01568) 750205, *conolly@bigwig.n* *Fax (01568) 750306*, ≤, « Working farm », – P. VISA JCB *closed November to February and 2 weeks June* – **Meals** (by arrangement) 18.00 **s.** – **5** 38.00/60.00 **s.**

LEWDOWN *Devon* 403 H 32 *The West Country G.*

Env. : *Lydford★★, E : 4 m.*

Exc. : *Launceston★ - Castle★ (≤★) St. Mary Magdalene★, W : 8 m. by A 30 and A 388.*

London 238 – Exeter 37 – Plymouth 29.

Lewtrenchard Manor, EX20 4PN, South : ¾ m. by Lewtrenchard ℘ (01566) 783256, *setj@lewtrenchard.co.uk, Fax (01566) 783332*, « 17C manor house a gardens », – rest, P – 50. AE VISA. **Meals** (booking essential to non-residents) 32.00 **t.** 7.00 – **9 rm** 85.00/170.00 **t.**

LEWES *E. Sussex* 404 U 31 *Great Britain G. – pop. 15 376.*

See : *Town★ (High Street★, Keere Street★) – Castle (≤★) AC.*

Exc. : *Sheffield Park Garden★ AC, N : 9½ m. by A 275.*

Chapel Hill ℘ (01273) 473245.

187 High St. ℘ (01273) 483448.

London 53 – Brighton 8 – Hastings 29 – Maidstone 43.

Shelleys, High St., BN7 1XS, ℘ (01273) 472361, *info@shelleys-hotel-lewes.cc* *Fax (01273) 483152*, « Part Georgian former inn, antiques », – P – 50. AE VISA JCB. **Meals** a la carte 19.50/28.50 **t.** 6.75 – 13.50 – **18 rm** 130.00/180.00 **st.**, 1 suite – SB.

Millers without rest., 134 High St., BN7 1XS, ℘ (01273) 475631, *millers134@aol.cc* *Fax (01273) 486226*, – . *closed 4 and 5 November and 21 December-6 January* – **3 rm** 51.00/57.00 **s.**

at East Chiltington *Northwest : 5½ m. by A 275 and B 2116 off Novington Lane – ✉ Lewes.*

Jolly Sportsman, Chapel Lane, BN7 3BA, ℘ (01273) 890400, *jollysportsman@minstra .uk, Fax (01273) 890400*, – P. VISA *closed Christmas, Sunday dinner and Monday* – **Meals** 14.75/19.85 **t.** (lunch) and a la ca 18.65/23.25 **t.** 5.00.

LEYBURN *N. Yorks.* 402 O 21 – *pop. 2 074.*

4 Central Chambers, Market Pl. ℘ (01969) 623069.

London 251 – Darlington 25 – Kendal 43 – Leeds 53 – York 49.

Greenhills without rest., 5 Middleham Rd, DL8 5EY, ℘ (01969) 623859, *val.pringle@fr et.co.uk* – P *closed Christmas and New Year* – **3 rm** 25.00/45.00.

Sandpiper Inn, Market Pl., DL8 5AT, ℘ (01969) 622206, *hsandpiper.99@aol.c* *Fax (01969) 625367*, « Part 16C », – P. VISA *closed Monday except Bank Holidays* – **Meals** (restricted lunch) a la carte 15.15/22.50 8.00.

at Constable Burton *East : 3½ m. on A 684 – ✉ Leyburn.*

Park Gate House, Constable Burton, DL8 5RG, East : 3 ½ m. on A 684 ℘ (01677) 450 *Fax (01677) 450466*, – P. **Meals** (by arrangement) 12.50 **s.** 4.75 – **4 rm** 40.00/65.00 **s.** – SB.

Wyvill Arms with rm, DL8 5LH, ℘ (01677) 450581 – P. AE VISA. **Meals** - Steak specialities - a la carte 13.85/16.55 **t.** – **3 rm** 28.00/56.00 **t.** – SB.

EYLAND *Lancs.* 402 L 22 – *pop. 3 729.*

London 224 – Blackburn 12 – Lancaster 30 – Leeds 68 – Liverpool 34 – Preston 7.

Jarvis Leyland, Leyland Way, PR5 2JX, East : ¾ m. on B 5256 ✆ (01772) 422922, *Fax (01772) 622282,* – rest, TV P – 230. MC AE VISA. Meals (bar lunch Saturday and Sunday) 13.95 **st.** and dinner a la carte 8.60 – 10.50 – **93 rm** 75.00/88.00 **st.**

EYSTERS *Herefordshire* 403 404 M 27 – *see Leominster.*

CHFIELD *Staffs.* 402 403 404 O 25 *Great Britain G.* – *pop. 28 666.*

See : *City★* - *Cathedral★★ AC.*

18, 9 *Seedy Mill, Elmhurst ✆ (01543) 417333.*

Donegal House, Bore St. ✆ (01543) 308209.

London 128 – Birmingham 16 – Derby 23 – Stoke-on-Trent 30.

Little Barrow, Beacon St., WS13 7AR, ✆ (01543) 414500, *hinecjp@netscape.online.co.uk , Fax (01543) 415734* – TV P – 80. MC AE VISA JCB. *closed 24-26 December* – **Meals** 10.00/16.50 **t.** and a la carte 4.90 – **24 rm** 65.00/80.00 **st.** – SB.

Chandlers Grande Brasserie, Corn Exchange, Conduit St., WS13 6JU, ✆ (01543) 416688, *Fax (01543) 417887* – MC AE VISA *closed 1-8 January and Bank Holiday Mondays* – **Meals** 10.00/12.95 **t.** and a la carte.

Olive Tree, 34 Tamworth St., WS13 6JJ, ✆ (01543) 263363 – MC AE VISA *closed 25 December, 1 January and Sunday* – **Meals** 7.95 **st.** (lunch) and a la carte 13.15/25.70 **st.**

Thrales, 40-44 Tamworth St., WS13 6JJ, (corner of Backcester Lane) ✆ (01543) 255091, *Fax (01543) 415352* – AE VISA *closed Sunday dinner and Bank Holiday Mondays* – **Meals** 9.50/12.50 **t.** and a la carte 9.95.

Les prix — Pour toutes précisions sur les prix indiqués dans ce guide, reportez-vous aux pages de l'introduction.

CKFOLD *W. Sussex* – *see Petworth.*

FTON *Devon* 403 H 32 *The West Country G.* – *pop. 964.*

Env. : *Launceston★ – Castle★ (≤★) St. Mary Magdalene★, W : 4½ m. by A 30 and A 388.*

London 238 – Bude 24 – Exeter 37 – Launceston 4 – Plymouth 26.

Arundell Arms, Fore St., PL16 0AA, ✆ (01566) 784666, *arundellarms@btinternet.com, Fax (01566) 784494,* – rest, TV P – 100. MC AE VISA *closed 3 days Christmas* – **Meals** – (see ***The Restaurant*** below) – **28 rm** 78.00/117.00 **st.** – SB.

Thatched Cottage, Sprytown, PL16 0AY, East : 1 ¼ m. by old A 30 ✆ (01566) 784224, *victoria@thatchedcott.u_net.com, Fax (01566) 784334,* – rest, TV P. MC AE VISA JCB **Meals** 12.95 **t.** (lunch) and a la carte 20.00/23.95 **t.** – **5 rm** 45.00/120.00 **t.** – SB.

The Restaurant (at Arundell Arms H.), Fore St., PL16 0AA, ✆ (01566) 784666, *arundellarms@btinternet.com, Fax (01566) 784494* – . MC AE VISA **Meals** 21.50/37.50 **t.** 7.50.

MPLEY STOKE (LOWER) *Bath & North East Somerset* 403 404 N 29 – *see Bath.*

NCOLN *Lincs.* 402 404 S 24 *Great Britain G.* – *pop. 80 281.*

See : *City★★ – Cathedral and Precincts★★★ AC* Y – *High Bridge★★* Z 9 – *Usher Gallery★ AC* YZ **M1** – *Jew's House★* Y – *Castle★ AC* Y.

Env. : *Doddington Hall★ AC, W : 6 m. by B 1003* – Z – *and B 1190.*

Exc. : *Gainsborough Old Hall★ AC, NW : 19 m. by A 57* – Z – *and A 156.*

18 *Carholme, Carholme Rd ✆ (01522) 523725.*

Humberside Airport : ✆ (01652) 688456, N : 32 m. by A 15 – Y – *M 180 and A 18.*

9 Castle Sq. ✆ (01522) 873700.

London 140 – Bradford 81 – Cambridge 94 – Kingston-upon-Hull 44 – Leeds 73 – Leicester 53 – Norwich 104 – Nottingham 38 – Sheffield 48 – York 82.

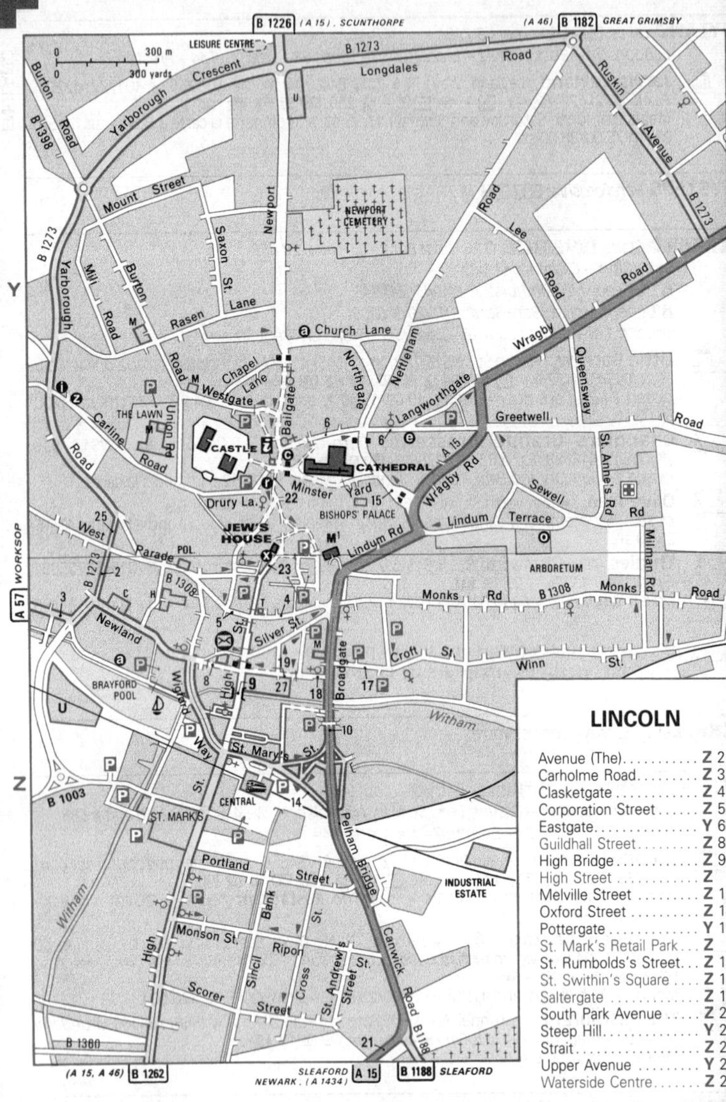

White Hart, Bailgate, LN1 3AR, ☎ (01522) 526222, *heritagehotels-lincoln.thewhitehar ortehotels.com, Fax (01522) 531798,* « Antique furniture » – |‡|, ⇹ TV – 🚗 – 🏛 70. MC Y
Ⓓ VISA JCB
Orangery Bistro : **Meals** a la carte 17.95/22.00 **t.** – ☕ 10.95 – **39 rm** 115.00 **st.**, 9 suit
SB.

Courtyard by Marriott, Brayford Wharf North, LN1 1YW, ☎ (01522) 544 *Fax (01522) 560805,* Fō – |‡|, ⇹ rm, ▤ TV ☎ ♿ P – 🏛 30. MC AE Ⓓ VISA JCB. ⛔ Z
Meals a la carte 15.45/21.95 **st.** 🍷 7.45 – ☕ 10.00 – **95 rm** 76.00 **st.** – SB.

Bentley, Newark Rd, South Hykeham, LN6 9NH, Southwest : 5 ¾ m. by A 15 on B 143 junction with A 46 ☎ (01522) 878000, *info@thebentleyhotel.uk.com, Fax (01522) 878*
Fō, ≘s, 🏊 – |‡| ⇹, ▤ rest, TV ☎ ♿ P – 🏛 325. MC AE Ⓓ VISA. ⛔
Meals (carvery lunch)/dinner 16.25/28.00 **st.** and a la carte 🍷 4.95 – **53 rm** ☕ 65
85.00 **st.**

Hillcrest, 15 Lindum Terr., LN2 5RT, ☎ (01522) 510182, *jennifer@hillcresthotel.freeserve.co.uk, Fax (01522) 510182,* ≤, – TV P. MC AE VISA JCB Y o
closed 23 December-5 January – **Meals** *(closed Sunday)* (bar lunch)/dinner 16.00 **t.** and a la carte – **15 rm** 52.00/89.00 **t.** – SB.

D'Isney Place without rest., Eastgate, LN2 4AA, ☎ (01522) 538881, *info@disney-place.freeserve.co.uk, Fax (01522) 511321,* – TV. MC AE VISA JCB Y e
17 rm 51.50/123.00 **t.**

Pride of Lincoln, off Whisby Rd, LN6 3QZ, Southwest : 6 m. by A 15, A 1434, B 1190 on A 46 ☎ (01522) 686878, *Fax (01522) 500664,* – |, rm, TV & P – 200. MC AE VISA.
Meals (grill rest.) a la carte 14.00/18.00 **t.** – 4.95 – **20 rm** 39.95 **t.**

Ibis without rest., off Whisby Rd, LN6 3QZ, Southwest : 6 m. by A 15, A 1434 and B 1190 on A 46 ☎ (01522) 698333, *Fax (01522) 698444* – | TV & P – 25. MC AE VISA
86 rm 45.00 **st.**

Damons Motel, 997 Doddington Rd, LN6 3SE, Southwest : 4 ¼ m. by A 15 and A 1434 on B 1190 at junction with A 46 ☎ (01522) 887733, *Fax (01522) 887734,* – rm, TV & P. MC AE VISA.
Meals (grill rest.) (booking essential) a la carte approx. 19.00 **t.** 5.40 – 5.00 – **47 rm** 40.50/42.50 **t.**

Travel Inn, Lincoln Rd, Canwick Hill, LN4 2RF, Southeast : 1 ¾ m. by B 1188 on B 1131 ☎ (01522) 525216, *Fax (01522) 542521,* – rm, TV & P. MC AE VISA.
Meals (grill rest.) – **40 rm** 40.95 **t.**

Travelodge, Thorpe on the Hill, LN6 9AJ, Southwest : 6 m. by A 15 and A 1434 at junction with A 46 ☎ (01522) 697213, *Fax (01522) 697213* – rm, TV & P. MC AE VISA.
Meals (grill rest.) – **32 rm** 39.95 **t.**

Minster Lodge without rest., 3 Church Lane, LN2 1QJ, ☎ (01522) 513220, *minsterlodge@cs.com, Fax (01522) 513220* – TV P. MC AE VISA. Y a
6 rm 60.00/90.00 **st.**

Carline without rest., 1-3 Carline Rd, LN1 1HL, ☎ (01522) 530422, *Fax (01522) 530422* – TV P. Y i
closed Christmas and New Year – **9 rm** 35.00/44.00 **t.**

Tennyson without rest., 7 South Park Av., LN5 8EN, South : 1 ¼ m. on A 15 ☎ (01522) 521624, *tennyson.hotel@virgin.net, Fax (01522) 521624* – TV P. MC VISA.
closed 24-28 December – **8 rm** 29.00/42.00 **t.**

Abbottsford House without rest., 5 Yarborough Terr., LN1 1HN, ☎ (01522) 826696, *Fax (01522) 826696* – TV P. Y z
restricted opening in winter – **3 rm** 30.00/45.00.

Jew's House, Jew's House, 15 The Strait, LN2 1JD, ☎ (01522) 524851, *Fax (01522) 520084,* « 12C town house » – . MC AE VISA YZ x
closed 25, 26 and 31 December, 1 January, Sunday and Monday – **Meals** 10.00/29.50 **t.** and a la carte 6.00.

Wig and Mitre, first floor, 30 Steep Hill, LN2 1TL, ☎ (01522) 523705, *Fax (01522) 532402,* « Part 14C » – MC AE VISA JCB Y r
Meals a la carte 17.25/25.70 **st.** 8.65.

Washingborough *East : 3 m. by B 1188 – Z – on B 1190 – ✉ Lincoln.*

Washingborough Hall , Church Hill, LN4 1BE, ☎ (01522) 790340, *washingborough.hall@btinternet.com, Fax (01522) 792936,* heated, – TV P – 40. MC AE VISA
Meals (carving lunch Monday to Friday)/dinner 22.50/30.00 **t.** and a la carte 6.00 – **12 rm** 67.50/99.50 **t.** – SB.

Branston *Southeast : 3 m. on B 1188 – Z – ✉ Lincoln.*

Moor Lodge, Sleaford Rd, LN4 1HU, ☎ (01522) 791366, *moorlodge@bestwestern.co.uk, Fax (01522) 794389* – TV P – 150. MC AE VISA
Meals a la carte 14.90/18.95 **t.** 6.50 – **23 rm** 48.00/60.00 **t.** – SB.

IDALE *Cumbria* 402 L 21 – *see Grange-over-Sands.*

LIPHOOK *Hants.* 404 R 30.
London 51 – Brighton 48 – Guildford 16 – Portsmouth 30 – Southampton 41 – Winchest 30.

Travelodge, GU30 7TT, Southwest : 2 m. by B 2131 on A 3 (northbound carriagewa ☎ (01428) 727619, *Fax (01428) 727619* – rm, rest, TV P. VISA JCB.
Meals (grill rest.) – **40 rm** 39.95 **t.**

LISKEARD *Cornwall* 403 G 32 *The West Country G. – pop. 7 044.*
See : *Church*★.
Exc. : *Lanhydrock*★★, *W : 11½ m. by A 38 and A 390 – NW : Bodmin Moor*★★ *- St. Endelli Church*★★ *- Altarnun Church*★ *- St. Breward Church*★ *- Blisland*★ *(church*★*) - Camelford*★ *Cardinham Church*★ *- Michaelstow Church*★ *- St. Kew*★ *(church*★*) - St. Mabyn Church*★ *– Neot*★ *(Parish Church*★★*) - St. Sidwell's, Laneast*★ *- St. Teath Church*★ *- St. Tudy*★ *Launceston*★ *– Castle*★ *(≤*★*) St. Mary Magdalene*★, *NE : 19 m. by A 390 and A 388.*
London 261 – Exeter 59 – Plymouth 19 – Truro 37.

The Well House, St. Keyne, PL14 4RN, South : 3 ½ m. by B 3254 on St. Keyne Well ☎ (01579) 342001, *enquiries@wellhouse.co.uk, Fax (01579) 343891*, ≤, « Victorian coun house », heated, – TV P. VISA JCB
Meals (booking essential to non-residents) 28.50 **t.** 5.00 – **9 rm** 70.00/160.00 **t.**

Old Rectory, Duloe Rd, St. Keyne, PL14 4RL, South : 3 ¼ m. on B 32 ☎ (01579) 342617, *savillelyons@freenet.co.uk, Fax (01579) 342293*, – TV P. V
closed Christmas and New Year – **Meals** *(closed Sunday)* (booking essential) (dinner or 25.00 **st.** 4.80 – **6 rm** 75.00/130.00 **st.** – SB.

Pencubitt Country House, Station Rd, PL14 4EB, South : ½ m. by B 3254 Lamellion rd ☎ (01579) 342694, *claire@penc.co.uk, Fax (01579) 342694*, – rest, P. VISA
Meals (booking essential) (dinner only) 20.00 **st.** 7.00 – **5 rm** 39.00/76.00 **st.** – SB.

LITTLE BEDWYN *Newbury* 403 404 P 29 – *see Hungerford.*

LITTLEBURY GREEN *Essex* 404 O 27 – *see Saffron Walden.*

LITTLEHAMPTON *W. Sussex* 404 S 31 – *pop. 50 408.*
London 64 – Brighton 18 – Portsmouth 31.

Bailiffscourt, Climping St., Climping, BN17 5RW, West : 2 ¾ m. by A 2 ☎ (01903) 723511, *bailiffscourt@h.s.hotels.co.uk, Fax (01903) 723107*, « Reconstru ed "medieval" house », heated, – rest, TV P – 35. VISA JC
Meals 18.50/35.00 **st.** 11.00 – **31 rm** 145.00/270.00 **st.** – SB.

Travelodge, Worthing Rd, Rustington, BN17 6JN, East : 1 ¼ m. on B 2 ☎ (01903) 733150, *Fax (01903) 733150* – rm, TV P. VISA JCB.
Meals (grill rest.) – **36 rm** 39.95 **t.**

Amberley Court without rest., Crookthorn Lane, Climping, BN17 5SN, West : 1 ¾ m B 2187 off A 259 ☎ (01903) 725131, *Fax (01903) 734555*, – TV P.
closed 16 December-6 January – **3 rm** 27.00/58.00.

LITTLE LANGDALE *Cumbria* 402 K 20 – *see Ambleside.*

LITTLE LANGFORD *Wilts. – see Salisbury.*

LITTLE PETHERICK *Cornwall* 403 F 32 – *see Padstow.*

LITTLEPORT *Cambs.* 404 U 26 – *see Ely.*

LITTLE SHELFORD *Cambs.* 404 U 27 – *see Cambridge.*

LITTLE SINGLETON *Lancs. – see Blackpool.*

TTLE SUTTON *Ches.* 402 ㉜ 403 ⑫ – ✉ *South Wirral.*
London 208 – Chester 12 – Liverpool 11 – Manchester 48.

Quality H. Chester, Berwick Rd, L66 4PS, on A 550 ℘ (0151) 339 5121, *admin@gb066.u-net.com, Fax (0151) 339 3214,* , – , rest, – 200. VISA. **Meals** (dinner only) a la carte 19.00/25.45 **st.** 6.95 – 9.95 – **53 rm** 76.00/102.00 **st.** – SB.

TTLE THORNTON *Lancs.* 402 L 22 – *see Blackpool.*

TTLE WALSINGHAM *Norfolk* 404 W 25 – ✉ *Walsingham.*
London 117 – Cambridge 67 – Cromer 21 – Norwich 32.

Old Bakehouse with rm, 33-35 High St., NR22 6BZ, ℘ (01328) 820454, *chris@pandley.freeserve.co.uk, Fax (01328) 820454* – . VISA JCB.
closed 2 weeks February, 1 week October and 25-26 December – **Meals** (Sunday to Wednesday set menu only, residents only) (dinner only) 13.75 and a la carte 21.35/25.35 7.70 – **3 rm** 27.50/45.00.

TTLE WEIGHTON *East Riding* 402 S 22 – *see Kingston-upon-Hull.*

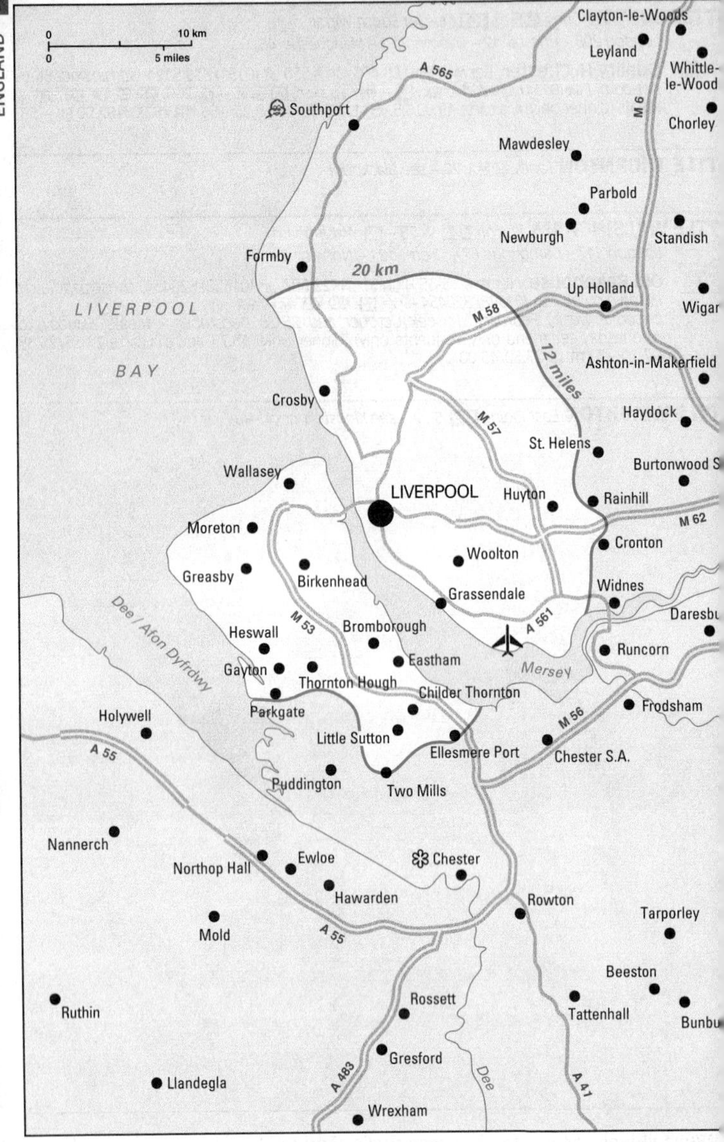

Particularly pleasant hotels and restaurants are shown in the Guide by a **red symbol**.

Please send us the names of anywhere you have enjoyed your stay.

Your **Michelin Guide** will be even better.

ENGLAND

VERPOOL *Mersey.* 402 403 L 23 *Great Britain G. – pop. 481 786.*

See : *City★ – Walker Art Gallery★★* **DY M3** – *Liverpool Cathedral★★ (Lady Chapel★)* **EZ** – *Metropolitan Cathedral of Christ the King★★* **EY** – *Albert Dock★* **CZ** *(Merseyside Maritime Museum★* **AC M2** - *Tate Liverpool★).*

Exc. : *Speke Hall★* **AC**, *SE : 8 m. by A 561* **BX**.

18, 9 Allerton Municipal, Allerton Rd (0151) 428 1046 – 18 Liverpool Municipal, Ingoe Lane, Kirkby (0151) 546 5435, **BV** – *9 Bowring, Bowring Park, Roby Rd (0151) 489 1901.*

Mersey Tunnels (toll) **AX**.

Liverpool Airport : (0151) 288 4000, SE : 6 m. by A 561 **BX** – **Terminal** : *Pier Head.*

to Isle of Man (Douglas) (Isle of Man Steam Packet Co. Ltd) (2 h 30 mn/4 h) – to Northern Ireland (Belfast) (Norse Irish Ferries Ltd) 1-2 daily (8 h 30 mn) – to Dublin (Merchant Ferries Ltd) 2 daily (approx. 7 h 45 mn) – to Dublin (P & O Irish Sea) daily (8 h) – to Dublin (Sea Containers Ferries Scotland Ltd) daily (3 h 45 mn).

to Birkenhead and Wallasey (Mersey Ferries) frequent services daily.

Merseyside Welcome Centre, Queens Sq., Roe St. (0151) 709 3631 – Atlantic Pavilion, Albert Dock (0151) 708 8854.

London 219 – Birmingham 103 – Leeds 75 – Manchester 35.

Town plans : Liverpool pp. 2-5

Liverpool Marriott, One Queen Sq., L1 1RH, (0151) 476 8000, *Fax (0151) 474 5000,* – 250. MO AE VISA DY e
Meals *(closed lunch Saturday and Bank Holidays)* 23.00 **st.** (dinner) and a la carte 23.00/28.50 **st.** 7.00 – **143 rm** 109.00/119.00 **st.**, 3 suites.

Crowne Plaza Liverpool, St. Nicholas Pl., Princes Dock, Pier Head, L3 1QN, (0151) 243 8000, *sales@crowneplaza-liverpool.co.uk, Fax (0151) 243 8111,* – rm, – 700. MO AE VISA. CY a
closed 24-26 December – **Meals** *(closed lunch Saturday, Sundayand Bank Holidays)* 12.95/15.95 **st.** and a la carte 6.95 – 12.95 – **155 rm** 125.00 **st.**, 4 suites – SB.

Liverpool Moat House, Paradise St., L1 8GT, (0151) 471 9988, *gmliv@queensmoathouse.co.uk, Fax (0151) 709 2706,* – rm, – 500. MO AE VISA
Meals (buffet lunch)/dinner a la carte 20.95/27.00 **t.** 6.25 – 11.50 – **259 rm** 115.00/135.00 **st.**, 4 suites – SB. DZ n

Thistle Liverpool, 30 Chapel St., L3 9RE, (0151) 227 4444, *liverpool@thistle.co.uk, Fax (0151) 236 3973,* – rm, – 100. MO AE VISA. CY r
Meals *(closed lunch Saturday and Sunday)* 17.00/21.00 **st.** (dinner) and a la carte 18.40/28.95 **st.** 7.50 – 10.25 – **223 rm** 124.00/134.00 **st.**, 3 suites – SB.

Devonshire House, 293-297 Edge Lane, L7 9LD, East : 2 ¼ m. on A 5047 (0151) 264 6600, *Fax (0151) 263 2109,* – – 300. MO AE VISA.
Meals a la carte 6.00/18.00 **st.** 7.00 – **54 rm** 75.00/95.00 **st.** – SB. BX a

Express by Holiday Inn without rest., Britannia Pavilion, Albert Dock, L3 4AD, (0151) 709 1133, *liverpool@premierhotels.co.uk, Fax (0151) 709 1194,* – – 35. MO AE VISA JCB CZ r
117 rm 69.50 **t.**

Premier Lodge, Dunningsbridge Rd, L30 6YN, North : 6 ¾ m. by A 59 on A 5036 (0870) 7001428, *enquiries@parkhotelliverpool.co.uk, Fax (0151) 525 2481* – rm, – 500. MO AE VISA.
Meals (grill rest.) 8.95 **st.** (dinner) and a la carte 9.50/20.50 **st.** – 6.00 – **62 rm** 42.00 **st.** – SB.

Premier Lodge, 45 Victoria St., L1 6JB, (0151) 236 1366, *Fax (0151) 227 1541* – rm, MO AE VISA. DY z
closed 24-26 December and 1-2 January – **Meals** (grill rest.) a la carte 11.00/20.65 **t.** – 6.00 – **39 rm** 46.00 **t.**

Travel Inn, Northern Perimeter Rd, L30 7PT, North : 6 m. by A 59 on A 5036 (0151) 531 1497, *Fax (0151) 520 1842* – rm, rest, MO AE VISA.
Meals (grill rest.) – **43 rm** 40.95 **t.**

Travel Inn, Queens Dr., West Derby, L13 0DL, East : 4 m. on A 5058 (Ringroad) (0151) 228 4724, *Fax (0151) 220 7610* – rm, rest, MO AE VISA.
Meals (grill rest.) – **40 rm** 40.95 **t.** BV a

Ziba, 15-19 Berry St., L1 9DF, (0151) 708 8870, *Fax (0151) 707 9926* – MO AE VISA
closed 25-26 December, 1 January, Sunday dinner and Bank Holidays – **Meals** 10.50/13.50 **t.** and a la carte **t.** EZ s

60 Hope Street, 60 Hope St., L1 9BZ, (0151) 707 6060, *info@60hopestreet.com, Fax (0151) 707 6016* – MO VISA EZ x
closed25-26 December, Saturday lunch, Sunday dinner and Monday – **Meals** 10.95/13.95 **t.** (lunch) and a la carte 22.40/30.95 **t.** 13.50.

(M 57) A 580 MANCHESTER,(M 57, M 6)

A 565 CROSBY A (A 59, M 57, M 58) A 5036 PRESTON PRESTON A 59 (M 57, M 58) B

DUBLIN BELFAST DUBLIN ISLE OF MAN

LIVERPOOL
BUILT UP AREA

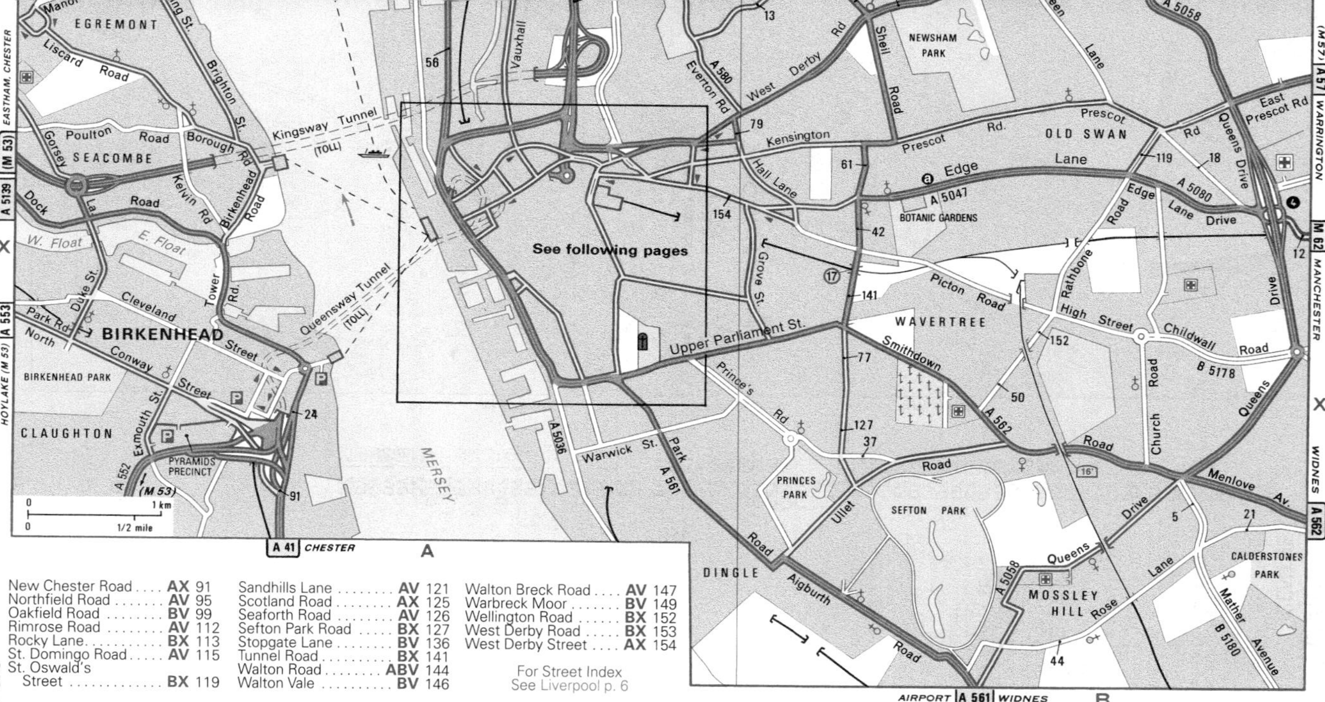

For Street Index
See Liverpool p. 6

LIVERPOOL

CENTRE

Street	Grid	No.
Argyle St.	DZ	6
Blackburne Pl.	EZ	11
Bold St.	DZ	
Brunswick Rd.	EY	19
Canada Boulevard	CYZ	22
Canning Pl.	CZ	23
Church St.	DY	
Churchill Way	DY	25
Clarence St.	EYZ	26
College Lane	DZ	28
Commutation Row	DY	30
Cook St.	CY	32
Crosshall St.	DY	36
Daulby St.	EY	40
Erskine St.	EY	45
Fontenoy St.	DY	48
Forrest St.	DZ	49
George's Dock Gate	CY	51
Grafton St.	DZ	53
Great Charlotte St.	DY	54
Great Howard St.	CY	56
Hatton Garden	DY	57
Haymarket	DY	58
Hood St.	DY	62
Houghton St.	DY	65
Huskisson St.	EZ	66
James St.	CY	68
King Edward St.	CY	69
Knight St.	EZ	72
Leece St.	EZ	73
Lime St.	DY	
Liver St.	CZ	76
London Rd.	DEY	
Lord St.	CDY	
Mansfield St.	DEY	80
Mathew St.	CDY	81
Moss St.	EY	86
Mount St.	EZ	88
Myrtle St.	EZ	89
Newington	DZ	92
New Quay	CY	93
North John St.	CY	96
Norton St.	EY	97
Parker St.	DY	103
Prescot St.	EY	105
Prince's Rd	EZ	107
Ranelagh St.	DY	108
Renshaw St.	DEZ	
Richmond St.	DY	109
Roe St.	DY	114
St. James Pl.	EZ	117
St. Johns Centre	DY	
St. John's Lane	DY	118
School Lane	DYZ	122
Scotland Pl.	DY	123
Sefton St.	DZ	129
Seymour St.	EY	130
Skelhorne St.	DY	133
Stanley St.	CDY	135
Suffolk St.	DZ	137
Tarleton St.	DY	139
Victoria St.	DY	143
Water St.	CY	150
William Brown St.	DY	156
York St.	DZ	157

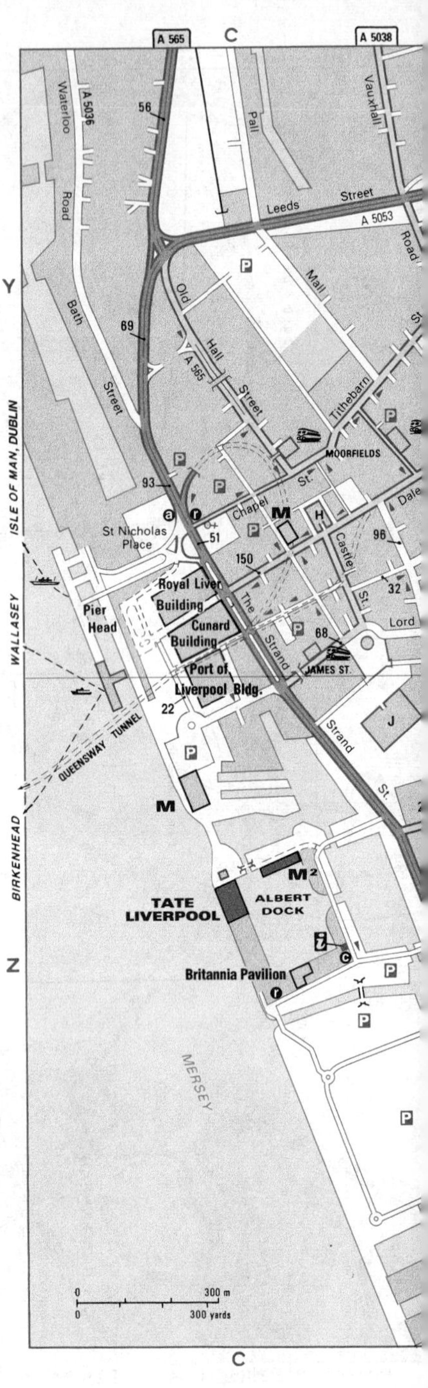

GREEN TOURIST GUIDES

Picturesque scenery, buildings
Attractive routes
Touring programmes
Plans of towns and buildings.

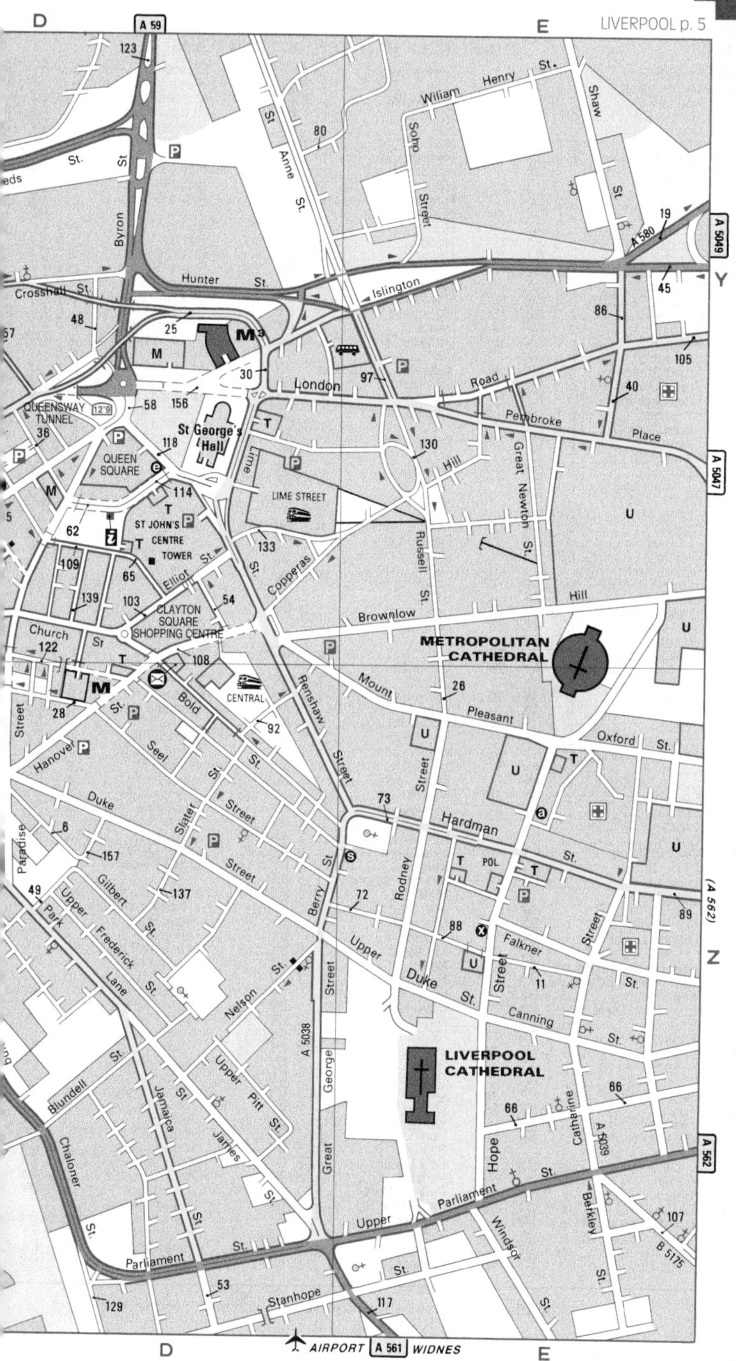

METROPOLITAN CATHEDRAL
LIVERPOOL CATHEDRAL
St George's Hall
QUEEN SQUARE
ST JOHN'S CENTRE TOWER
CLAYTON SQUARE SHOPPING CENTRE
LIME STREET
CENTRAL
QUEENSWAY TUNNEL
AIRPORT A 561 WIDNES

ENGLAND

STREET INDEX TO LIVERPOOL TOWN PLANS

Street	Page	Grid	No.
Aigburth Rd.	p. 3	BX	
Aintree Lane	p. 2	BV	2
Aintree Rd.	p. 2	AV	3
Allerton Rd	p. 3	BX	5
Argyle St.	p. 5	DZ	6
Bailey Drive	p. 2	AV	7
Balliol Rd	p. 2	AV	
Bath St.	p. 4	CY	
Belmont Rd.	p. 3	BX	8
Berkley St.	p. 5	EZ	
Berry St.	p. 5	DZ	
Birkenhead Rd	p. 3	AX	
Blackburne Pl.	p. 5	EZ	11
Blundell St.	p. 5	DZ	
Bold St.	p. 5	DZ	
Borough Rd.	p. 3	AX	
Bowring Park Rd	p. 3	BX	12
Breck Rd	p. 3	ABX	13
Brewster St.	p. 2	AV	14
Bridge Rd	p. 2	AV	16
Brighton St.	p. 3	AX	
Broad Green Rd	p. 3	BX	18
Brownlow Hill	p. 5	DEY	
Brunswick Rd.	p. 5	EY	19
Byron St.	p. 5	DY	
Calderstones Rd	p. 3	BX	21
Canning Pl.	p. 4	CZ	23
Canning St.	p. 5	EZ	
Castle St.	p. 4	CY	
Catharine St.	p. 5	EZ	
Chaloner St.	p. 5	DZ	
Chapel St.	p. 4	CY	
Chester St.	p. 3	AX	24
Childwall Rd	p. 3	BX	
Church Rd	p. 3	BX	
Church Rd LITHERLAND	p. 2	AV	
Church St.	p. 5	DY	
Churchill Way	p. 5	DY	25
Clarence St.	p. 5	EYZ	26
Cleveland St.	p. 3	AX	
College Lane	p. 5	DZ	28
Commercial Rd	p. 2	AV	29
Commutation Row	p. 5	DY	30
Conway St.	p. 3	AX	
Cook St.	p. 4	CY	32
Copperas Hill	p. 5	DE	
Copple House La.	p. 2	BV	33
County Rd	p. 2	AV	34
Crosby Rd South	p. 2	AV	
Crosshall St.	p. 5	DY	36
Croxteth Rd	p. 3	BX	37
Croxteth Hall Lane	p. 2	BV	39
Dale St.	p. 4	CDY	
Daulby St.	p. 5	EY	40
Derby Rd	p. 2	AV	
Duke St.	p. 5	DZ	
Duke St. BIRKENHEAD	p. 3	AX	
Durning Rd	p. 3	BX	42
Dwerry House Lane	p. 2	BV	43
East Lancashire Rd	p. 2	BV	
East Prescot Rd	p. 3	BX	
Edge Lane	p. 3	BX	
Edge Lane Drive	p. 3	BX	
Elliot St.	p. 5	DY	
Elmswood Rd.	p. 3	BX	44
Erskine St.	p. 5	EY	45
Everton Rd.	p. 3	AX	
Exmouth St.	p. 3	AX	
Fontenoy St.	p. 5	DY	48
Forrest St.	p. 5	DZ	49
Freeman St.	p. 3	AX	
Gainsborough Rd	p. 3	BX	50
George's Dock Lane	p. 4	CY	51
Gilbert St.	p. 5	DZ	
Gorsey Lane	p. 3	AX	
Grafton St.	p. 5	DZ	53
Great Charlotte St.	p. 5	DY	54
Great Crosshall St.	p. 5	DY	
Great George St.	p. 5	DY	
Great Howard St.	p. 4	CY	56
Great Newton St.	p. 5	EY	
Green Lane	p. 3	BX	
Grove St.	p. 3	BX	
Hall Lane	p. 3	BX	
Hannover St.	p. 5	DZ	
Hardman St.	p. 5	EZ	
Hatton Garden	p. 5	DY	57
Haymarket	p. 5	DY	58
Hawthorne Rd	p. 2	AV	
High St.	p. 3	BX	
Holt Rd.	p. 3	BX	61
Hood St.	p. 5	DY	62
Hope St.	p. 5	EZ	
Hornby Rd	p. 2	AV	64
Houghton St.	p. 5	DY	65
Hunter St.	p. 5	DY	
Huskisson St.	p. 5	EZ	66
Islington	p. 5	EY	
Jamaica St.	p. 5	DZ	
James St.	p. 4	CY	68
Kelvin Rd	p. 3	AX	
Kensington	p. 3	BX	
King St.	p. 3	AX	
King Edward St.	p. 4	CY	69
Kirkdale Rd	p. 2	AV	71
Knight St.	p. 5	EZ	72
Knowsley Rd.	p. 2	AV	
Leece St.	p. 5	EZ	73
Leeds St.	p. 4	CY	
Lime St.	p. 5	DY	
Linacre Rd	p. 2	AV	74
Linacre Lane	p. 2	AV	
Liscard Rd	p. 3	AX	
Liver St.	p. 5	CZ	76
Lodge Lane	p. 3	BX	77
London Rd.	p. 5	DEY	
Long Lane	p. 2	BV	
Longmoor Lane	p. 2	BV	
Lord St.	p. 4	CDY	
Lower House Lane	p. 2	BV	
Lower Lane	p. 2	BV	
Low Hill	p. 3	ABX	79
Manor Rd.	p. 2	AX	
Mansfield St.	p. 5	DEY	80
Marsh Lane	p. 2	AV	
Mather Av.	p. 3	BX	
Mathew St.	p. 4	CDY	81
Melrose Rd	p. 2	AV	82
Menlove Av.	p. 3	BV	
Merton Rd.	p. 2	AV	
Mill Bank	p. 2	BV	84
Moss Lane	p. 2	AV	85
Moss St.	p. 5	EY	86
Mount Pleasant	p. 5	EZ	
Mount St.	p. 5	EZ	88
Muirhead Av.	p. 2	BV	
Muirhead Av. East	p. 2	BV	
Myrtle St.	p. 5	EZ	89
Nelson St.	p. 5	DZ	
Netherton Way	p. 2	AV	
New Chester Rd.	p. 3	AX	91
Newington	p. 5	DZ	92
New Quay	p. 4	CY	93
Northfield Rd.	p. 2	AV	95
North John St.	p. 4	CY	96
Norton St.	p. 5	EY	97
Oakfield Rd	p. 2	BV	99
Old Hall St.	p. 4	CY	
Oxford St.	p. 5	EZ	
Pall Mall	p. 4	CY	
Paradise St.	p. 5	DZ	
Parker St.	p. 5	DY	103
Park Lane	p. 5	DZ	
Park Rd	p. 3	AX	
Park Rd North	p. 3	AX	
Parliament St.	p. 5	DZ	
Pembroke Pl.	p. 5	EY	
Picton Rd	p. 3	BX	
Poulton Rd.	p. 3	AX	
Prescot Rd.	p. 3	BX	
Prescot St.	p. 5	EY	1
Prince's Rd	p. 5	EZ	1
Queens Drive	p. 3	BX	
Queensway	p. 3	AX	
Ranelagh St.	p. 5	DY	1
Rathbone Rd	p. 3	BX	
Renshaw St.	p. 5	DEZ	
Rice Lane	p. 2	AV	
Richmond St.	p. 5	DY	1
Rimrose Rd	p. 2	AV	1
Rocky Lane	p. 3	BX	1
Rodney St.	p. 5	EZ	
Roe St.	p. 5	DY	1
Rose Lane	p. 3	BX	
Russel St.	p. 5	EY	
St. Anne St.	p. 5	DY	
St. Domingo Rd	p. 2	AV	1
St. James Pl.	p. 5	EZ	1
St. James St.	p. 5	DZ	
St. John's Lane	p. 5	DY	1
St. Johns Centre	p. 5	DY	
St. Nicholas Pl.	p. 4	CY	
St. Oswald's St.	p. 3	BX	1
Sandhills Lane	p. 2	AV	1
School Lane	p. 5	DYZ	1
Scotland Pl.	p. 5	DY	1
Scotland Rd.	p. 3	AX	1
Seaforth Rd	p. 2	AV	1
Seel St.	p. 5	DZ	
Sefton Park Rd	p. 3	BX	1
Sefton St.	p. 3	DZ	1
Seymour St.	p. 5	EY	1
Shaw St.	p. 5	EY	
Sheil Rd	p. 3	BX	
Skelhorne St.	p. 5	EY	1
Slater St.	p. 5	DZ	
Smithdown Rd	p. 3	BX	
Soho St.	p. 5	EY	
South John St.	p. 4	CYZ	
Southport Rd.	p. 2	AV	
Stanhope St.	p. 5	DZ	
Stanley Rd.	p. 2	AV	
Stanley St.	p. 4	CDY	1
Stonebridge Lane	p. 2	BV	
Stopgate Lane	p. 2	BV	
Strand St.	p. 4	CZ	
Strand (The)	p. 4	CY	
Suffolk St.	p. 5	DZ	
Tarleton St.	p. 5	DY	
Tithebarn St.	p. 4	CY	
Townsend Av.	p. 2	BV	
Townsend Lane	p. 2	BV	
Tunnel Rd	p. 3	BX	
Ullet Rd	p. 3	BX	
Upper Duke St.	p. 5	EZ	
Upper Frederick St.	p. 5	DZ	
Upper Parliament St.	p. 5	EZ	
Upper Pitt	p. 5	DZ	
Utting Av.	p. 2	AV	
Utting Av. East	p. 2	BV	
Vauxhall Rd	p. 4	CY	
Victoria St.	p. 5	DY	
Walton Lane	p. 2	AV	
Walton Rd	p. 2	ABV	
Walton Vale	p. 2	BV	
Walton Breck Rd	p. 2	AV	
Walton Hall Av.	p. 2	BV	
Wapping	p. 4	CDZ	
Warbreck Moor	p. 2	BV	
Warwick	p. 3	AX	
Water St.	p. 4	CY	
Waterloo Rd	p. 4	CY	
Wellington Rd	p. 3	BX	
West Derby Rd	p. 3	BX	
West Derby St.	p. 3	AX	
Whitechapel	p. 5	DY	
William Brown St.	p. 5	DY	
William Henry St.	p. 5	EY	
Windsor St.	p. 5	EZ	
York St.	p. 5	DZ	

The names of main shopping streets are indicated in red at the beginning of the list of streets.

ENGLAND

XX **Becher's Brook,** 29a Hope St., L1 9BQ, ℘ (0151) 707 0005, *Fax (0151) 708 7011* – ⇆. MO AE ① VISA EZ a
closed 25 and 31 December, Sunday, Saturday lunch and Bank Holidays – **Meals** 13.50 **t.** (lunch) and a la carte 24.50/39.20 **t.** ▮ 5.00.

X **Mister M's,** 6 Atlantic Pavilion, Albert Dock, L3 4AA, ℘ (0151) 707 2202, *mikemcdonald@misterms.freeserve.co.uk, Fax (0151) 708 8769,* – MO AE ① VISA JCB CZ c
closed 25 December and first 2 weeks January – **Meals** - Seafood - 14.95 **t.** and a la carte 14.95/30.45 **t.**

at Crosby *North : 5½ m. on A 565* – **AV.**

Blundellsands, Blundellsands Road West, L23 6TN, West : 1 ¼ m. via College Rd, Mersey Rd and Agnes Rd ℘ (0151) 924 6515, *info@blundellsands-hotel.co.uk, Fax (0151) 931 5364* – |♦|, ⇆ rm, TV P – 🔺 250. MO AE VISA. ✂
Meals (bar meals Saturday lunch, Sunday dinner and Bank Holidays) 12.50/15.50 **t.** and a la carte ▮ 6.00 – ▭ – **30 rm** 50.00/85.00 **st.**

at Huyton *East : 8¼ m. by A 5047 and A 5080* – **BX** – *on B 5199* – ✉ *Liverpool.*

Village H. and Leisure Club, Fallows Way, L35 1RZ, Southeast : 3 ¼ m. by A 5080 off Windy Arbor Rd ℘ (0151) 449 2341, *village.wh@cybase.co.uk, Fax (0151) 449 3832,* Ⅰ₆, ≘s, ▣, squash – |♦|, ⇆ rm, TV ♿ P – 🔺 250. MO AE ① VISA. ✂
Meals *(closed Sunday dinner)* 10.95/18.50 **t.** and a la carte ▮ 6.80 – **62 rm** ▭ 86.00/145.00 **t.**

Premier Lodge, Roby Rd, L36 4HD, Southwest : 1 m. on A 5080 ℘ (0870) 7001426, *Fax (0870) 7001427,* – ⇆ rm, ▤ rest, TV ☏ ♿ P – 🔺 35. MO AE ① VISA. ✂
Meals (grill rest.) a la carte 8.85/22.65 **t.** – ▭ 6.00 – **53 rm** 46.00 **t.**

Travel Inn, Wilson Rd, Tarbock, L36 6AD, Southeast : 2 ¼ m. on A 5080 ℘ (0151) 480 9614, *Fax (0151) 480 9361* – ⇆ rm, ▤ rest, TV ♿ P. MO AE ① VISA. ✂
Meals (grill rest.) – **40 rm** 40.95 **t.**

at Grassendale *Southeast : 4½ m. on A 561* – **BX** – ✉ *Liverpool.*

XX **Gulshan,** 544-548 Aigburth Rd, L19 3QG, on A 561 ℘ (0151) 427 2273, *Fax (0151) 427 2111* – ▤. MO AE ① VISA
Meals - Indian - (dinner only) a la carte approx. 14.85 **t.**

at Woolton *Southeast : 6 m. by A 562* – **BX** –, *A 5058 and Woolton Rd* – ✉ *Liverpool.*

Woolton Redbourne, Acrefield Rd, L25 5JN, ℘ (0151) 421 1500, *wooltonredbourne@cwcom.net, Fax (0151) 421 1501,* « Victorian house, antiques », – ⇆ rest, TV P. MO AE ① VISA JCB
Meals (residents only) (dinner only) 22.95 **t.** ▮ 8.50 – **20 rm** ▭ 63.00/92.00 **t.**, 1 suite.

LIZARD *Cornwall* 403 E 34 *The West Country G.*

Env. : *Lizard Peninsula★ - Mullion Cove★★ (Church★) - Kynance Cove★★ - Cadgwith★ - Coverack★ – Cury★ (Church★) - Gunwalloe Fishing Cove★ - St. Keverne (Church★) - Landewednack★ (Church★) – Mawgan-in-Meneage (Church★) - Ruan Minor (Church★) - St. Anthony-in-Meneage★.*

London 326 – Penzance 24 – Truro 29.

Housel Bay ⛰, Housel Bay, TR12 7PG, ℘ (01326) 290417, *hotel@houselbay.com, Fax (01326) 290359,* ⋞ Housel Cove, – |♦|, ⇆ rest, TV P. MO AE VISA. ✂
Meals (bar lunch Monday to Saturday)/dinner 15.50/19.50 **t.** ▮ 7.00 – **21 rm** ▭ 29.50/107.00 **t.** – SB.

Landewednack House ⛰, Church Cove, TR12 7PQ, East : 1 m. by A 3083 ℘ (01326) 290909, *landewednack.house@virgin.net, Fax (01326) 290192,* « Part 17C, antique furnished, former rectory overlooking Church Cove », heated, – ⇆ TV P. MO VISA. ✂
closed 24-26 December – **Meals** (by arrangement) (communal dining) 26.00 **st.** ▮ 8.95 – **3 rm** ▭ 49.00/92.00.

South Parc without rest., Lighthouse Rd, TR12 7NL, ℘ (01326) 290441, *timperleyroy@hotmail.com, Fax (01326) 290441,* ⋞, – ⇆ TV P. ✂
closed Christmas and New Year – **3 rm** ▭ 28.00/48.00 **st.**

Tregullas House ⛰ without rest., Housel Bay, TR12 7PF, ℘ (01326) 290351, *judy.hendy@tinyworld.co.uk,* ⋞, – P
closed 1 week Christmas – **3 rm** ▭ 30.00/44.00.

Si vous cherchez un hôtel tranquille, consultez d'abord les cartes de l'introduction ou repérez dans le texte les établissements indiqués avec le signe ⛰ ou ⛰.

LOCKINGTON *East Riding* 402 S 22.
London 211 – Kingston-upon-Hull 16 – Leeds 64 – York 38.

XX **Rockingham** with rm, 52 Front St., YO25 9SH, South : 9 ¾ m. by A 1
☎ (01430) 810607, *Fax (01430) 810734* – rm, TV P. VISA
Meals *(closed Sunday, Monday and Bank HOlidays)* (dinner only) 28.95 **t.** 7.50 – **3 r**
85.00/110.00 **t.**

LOCKWOOD *W. Yorks.* – *see Huddersfield.*

LOFTUS *Redcar & Cleveland* 402 R 20 – *pop. 5 931* – ✉ *Saltburn-by-the-Sea.*
London 264 – Leeds 73 – Middlesbrough 17 – Scarborough 36.

Grinkle Park , Easington, TS13 4UB, Southeast : 3 ½ m. by A 174 on Grinkle
☎ (01287) 640515, *grinkle.parkhotel@bass.com, Fax (01287) 641278*, ←, , , – TV
AE VISA.
Meals 12.00/23.00 **t.** and dinner a la carte 5.75 – **20 rm** 81.50/107.00 **t.** – SB.

LOLWORTH SERVICE AREA *Cambs.* – *see Cambridge.*

LONDON

404 folds ㊷ to ㊹ – *London G.* – *pop. 6 679 699*

SIGHTS

HISTORIC BUILDINGS AND MONUMENTS

Palace of Westminster★★★ : House of Lords★★, Westminster Hall★★ (hammerbeam roof★★★), Robing Room★, Central Lobby★, House of Commons★, Big Ben★, Victoria Tower★ p. 30 LY – *Tower of London★★★ (Crown Jewels★★★, White Tower or Keep★★★, St. John's Chapel★★, Beauchamp Tower★ Tower Hill Pageant★) p. 31* PVX.

Banqueting House★★ p. 30 LX – *Buckingham Palace★★ (Changing of the Guard★★, Royal Mews★★) p. 36* BVX – *Kensington Palace★★ p. 28* FX – *Lincoln's Inn★★ p. 37* EV – *London Bridge★ p. 31* PVX – *Royal Hospital Chelsea★★ p. 35* FU – *St. James's Palace★★ p. 33* EP – *Somerset House★★ p. 37* EXY – *South Bank Arts Centre★★ (Royal Festival Hall★, National Theatre★, County Hall★) p. 30* MX – *The Temple★★ (Middle Temple Hall★) p. 26* MV – *Tower Bridge★★ p. 31* PX.

Albert Memorial★ p. 34 CQ – *Apsley House★ p. 32* BP – *Burlington House★ p. 33* EM – *Charterhouse★ p. 27* NOU – *George Inn★, Southwark p. 31* PX – *Gray's Inn★ p. 26* MU – *Guildhall★ (Lord Mayor's Show★★) p. 27* OU – *International Shakespeare Globe Centre★ p. 31* OX **T** – *Dr Johnson's House★ p. 27* NUV **A** – *Lancaster House★ p. 33* EP – *Leighton House★ p. 28* EY – *Linley Sambourne House★ p. 28* EY – *Lloyds Building★★ p. 27* PV – *Mansion House★ (plate and insignia★★) p. 27* PV **P** – *The Monument★ (✻★) p. 27* PV **G** – *Old Admiralty★ p. 30* KLX – *Royal Albert Hall★ p. 34* CQ – *Royal Exchange★ p. 27* PV **V** – *Royal Opera Arcade★ (New Zealand House) p. 33* FGN – *Royal Opera House★ (Covent Garden) p. 37* DX – *Spencer House★★ p. 33* DP – *Staple Inn★ p. 26* MU **Y** – *Theatre Royal★ (Haymarket) p. 33* GM – *Westminster Bridge★ p. 30* LY.

CHURCHES

The City Churches

St. Paul's Cathedral★★★ (Dome ⋞★★★) p. 27 NOV.

St. Bartholomew the Great★★ (choir★) p. 27 OU **K** – *St. Dunstan-in-the-East★★ p. 27* PV **F** – *St. Mary-at-Hill★★ (woodwork★★, plan★) p. 27* PV **B** – *Temple Church★★ p. 26* MV.

All Hallows-by-the-Tower (font cover★★ brasses★) p. 27 PV **Y** – *Christ Church★ p. 25* OU **E** – *St. Andrew Undershaft (monuments★) p. 27* PV **A** – *St. Bride★ (steeple★★) p. 27* NV **Y** – *St. Clement Eastcheap (panelled interior★★) p. 27* PV **E** – *St. Edmund the King and Martyr (tower and spire★) p. 27* PV **D** – *St-Giles Cripplegate★ p. 27* OU **N** – *St. Helen Bishopsgate★ (monuments★★) p. 27* PUV **R** – *St. James Garlickhythe (tower and spire★, sword rests★) p. 27* OV **R** – *St. Magnus the Martyr (tower★, sword rest★) p. 27* PV **K** – *St. Margaret Lothbury★ (tower and spire★, woodwork★, screen★, font★) p. 27* PU **S** – *St. Margaret Pattens (spire★, woodwork★) p. 27* PV **N** – *St. Martin-within-Ludgate (tower and spire★, door cases★) p. 27* NOV **B** – *St. Mary Abchurch★ (reredos★★, tower and spire★, dome★) p. 27* PV **X** – *St. Mary-le-Bow (tower and steeple★★) p. 27* OV **G** – *St. Michael Paternoster Royal (tower and spire★) p. 27* OV **D** – *St. Nicholas Cole Abbey (tower and spire★) p. 27* OV **F** – *St. Olave★ p. 27* PV **S** – *St. Peter upon Cornhill (screen★) p. 27* PV **L** – *St. Stephen Walbrook★ (tower and steeple★, dome★), p. 27* PV **Z** – *St. Vedast (tower and spire★, ceiling★), p. 27* OU **E**.

Other Churches

Westminster Abbey★★★ (Henry VII Chapel★★★, Chapel of Edward the Confessor★★, Chapter House★★, Poets' Corner★) p. 30 LY.

Southwark Cathedral★★ p. 31 PX.

Queen's Chapel★ p. 33 EP – *St. Clement Danes★ p. 37* EX – *St. James's★ p. 33* EM – *St. Margaret's★ p. 30* LY **A** – *St. Martin-in-the-Fields★ p. 37* DY – *St. Paul's★ (Covent Garden) p. 37* DX – *Westminster Roman Catholic Cathedral★ p. 30* KY **B**.

PARKS

Regent's Park★★★ p. 25 HI *(terraces★★), Zoo★★.*

Hyde Park – Kensington Gardens★★ (Orangery★) pp. 28 and 29 – St. James's Park★★ p. 30 KXY.

STREETS AND SQUARES

The City★★★ p. 27 NV.

Bedford Square★★ p. 26 KLU – *Belgrave Square★★* p. 36 AVX – *Burlington Arcade★★* p. 33 DM – *Covent Garden★★ (The Piazza★★)* p. 37 DX – *The Mall★★* p. 33 FP – *Piccadilly★* p. 33 EM – *The Thames★★* pp. 29-31 – *Trafalgar Square★★* p. 37 DY – *Whitehall★★ (Horse Guards★)* p. 30 LX.

Barbican★ p. 27 OU – *Bond Street★* pp. 32-33 CK-DM – *Canonbury Square★* p. 27 NS – *Carlton House Terrace★* p. 33 GN – *Cheyne Walk★* p. 29 GHZ – *Fitzroy Square★* p. 26 KU – *Jermyn Street★* p. 33 EN – Leicester Square★ p. 33 GM – *Merrick Square★* p. 31 OY – *Montpelier Square★* p. 35 EQ – *Neal's Yard★* p. 37 DV – *Piccadilly Arcade★* p. 33 DEN – *Portman Square★* p. 32 AJ – *Queen Anne's Gate★* p. 30 KY – Regent Street★ p. 33 EM – *Piccadilly Circus★* p. 33 FM – *St. James's Square★* p. 33 FN – *St. James's Street★* p. 33 EN – *Shepherd Market★* p. 32 CN – *Soho★* p. 33 – *Trinity Church Square★* p. 31 OY – *Victoria Embankment gardens★* p. 37 DEXY – *Waterloo Place★* p. 33 FN

MUSEUMS

British Museum★★★ p. 26 LU – *National Gallery★★★* p. 33 GM – *Science Museum★★★* p. 34 CR – *Tate Britain★★★* p. 30 LZ – *Victoria and Albert Museum★★★* p. 35 DR – *Wallace Collection★★★* p. 32 AH.

Courtauld Institute Galleries★★ (Somerset House) p. 37 EXY – *Gilbert Collection★★ (Somerset House)* p. 37 EX Y – *Museum of London★★* p. 27 OU **M** – *National Portrait Gallery★★* p. 33 GM – *Natural History Museum★★* p. 34 CS – *Sir John Soane's Museum★★* p. 26 MU **M** – *Tate Modern★★* p. 31 OX **M**.

Clock Museum★ (Guildhall) p. 26 OU – *Imperial War Museum★* p. 31 NY – *London Transport Museum★* p. 37 DX – *Madame Tussaud's★* p. 25 IU **M** – *Museum of Mankind★* p. 33 DM – *National Army Museum★* p. 35 FU – *Percival David Foundation of Chinese Art★* p. 26 KLT **M** – *Planetarium★* p. 25 IU **M** – *Wellington Museum★ (Apsley House)* p. 32 BP.

OUTER LONDON

Blackheath p. 15 HX *terraces and houses★*, *Eltham Palace★* **A**
Brentford p. 12 BX *Syon Park★★*, *gardens★*
Bromley p. 14 GY *The Crystal Palace Park★*
Chiswick p. 13 CV *Chiswick Mall★★*, *Chiswick House★* **D**, *Hogarth's House★* **E**
Dulwich p. 14 *Picture Gallery★* FX **X**
Greenwich pp. 14 and 15 : *Cutty Sark★★* GV **F**, *Footway Tunnel(⩽ ★★)* – *Fan Museum★* p. 10 GV **A**, – *National Maritime Museum★★ (Queen's House★★)* GV **M**, *Royal Naval College★★ (Painted Hall★, the Chapel★)* GV **G**, *The Park and Old Royal Observatory★ (Meridian Building : collection★★)* HV **K**, *Ranger's House★* GX **N**
Hampstead *Kenwood House★★ (Adam Library★★, paintings★★)* p. 9 EU **P**, *Fenton House★★*, p. 24 ES
Hampton Court p. 12 BY *(The Palace★★★, gardens★★★, Fountain Court★, The Great Vine★)*
Kew p. 13 CX *Royal Botanic Gardens★★★ : Palm House★★, Temperate House★, Kew Palace or Dutch House★★, Orangery★, Pagoda★, Japanese Gateway★*
Hendon★ p. 9, *Royal Air Force Museum★★* CT **M**
Hounslow p. 12 BV *Osterley Park★★*
Lewisham p. 14 GX *Horniman Museum★* **M**
Richmond pp. 12 and 13 : *Richmond Park★★, ✻★★★* CX, *Richmond Hill✻★★* CX, *Richmond Bridge★★* BX **R**, *Richmond Green★★* BX **S** *(Maids of Honour Row★★, Trumpeter's House★)*, *Asgill House★* BX **B**, *Ham House★★* BX **V**
Shoreditch p. 10 FU *Geffrye Museum★* **M**
Tower Hamlets p. 10 GV *Canary Wharf★★* B, *Isle of Dogs★ St. Katharine Dock★* **Y**
Twickenham p. 12 BX *Marble Hill House★* **Z**, *Strawberry Hill★* **A** .

PRACTICAL INFORMATION

Britain Visitor Centre, 1 Regent St, W1

Airports

Heathrow ☎ 08700 000123 p. 12 **AX** - *Terminal: Airbus (A1) from Victoria, Airbus (A2) from Paddington - Underground (Piccadilly line) frequent service daily.*
Gatwick ☎ (01293) 535353 p. 13: *by A23* **EZ** *and M23* - Terminal: *Coach service from Victoria Coach Station (Flightline 777, hourly service) - Railink (Gatwick Express) from Victoria (24 h service).*
London City Airport ☎ (020) 7646 0000 p. 11 **HV**
Stansted, at Bishop's Stortford ☎ 08700 000303, NE: 34m p. 11 *by M11* **JT** *and A120.*

British Airways, Victoria Air Terminal: 115 Buckingham Palace Rd, SW1 ☎ (020) 7707 4750 p. 36 **BX**

Banks

Open, generally 9.30 am to 4.30 pm weekdays (except public holidays). Most have cash dispensers. You need ID (passport) for cashing cheques. Banks levy smaller commissions than hotels.
Many 'Bureaux de Change' around Piccadilly open 7 days.

Medical Emergencies

To contact a doctor for first aid, emergency medical advice and chemists night service: (020) 8900 1000.
Accident & Emergency: dial 999 for Ambulance, Police or Fire Services.

Post Offices

Open Monday to Friday 9 am to 5.30 pm. Late collections made from Leicester Square.

Shopping

Most stores are found in Oxford Street (Selfridges, M & S), Regent Street (Hamleys, Libertys) and Knightsbridge (Harrods, Harvey Nichols). Open usually Monday to Saturday *9 am to 6 pm. Some open later (8 pm) once a week; Knightsbridge* Wednesday, *Oxford Street and Regent Street* Thursday. *Other areas worth visiting include Jermyn Street and Savile Row (mens outfitters), Bond Street (jewellers and haute couture).*

Theatres

The "West End" has many major theatre performances and can generally be found around Shaftesbury Avenue. Most daily newspapers give details of performances. A half-price ticket booth is located in Leicester Square and is open Monday-Saturday 1 - 6.30 pm, Sunday and matinée days 12 noon - 6.30 pm. Restrictions apply.

Tipping

When a service charge is included in a bill it is not necessary to tip extra. If service is not included a discretionary 10% is normal.

Travel

As driving in London is difficult, it is advisable to take the Underground, a bus or taxi. Taxis can be hailed when the amber light is illuminated.

Localities outside the Greater London limits are listed alphabetically throughout the guide.

Les localités situées en dehors des limites de Greater London se trouvent à leur place alphabetique dans le guide.

Alle Städte und Gemeinden außerhalb von Greater London sind in alphabetischer Reihenfolge aufgelistet.

Le località situate al di fuori dei confini della Greater London sono ordinate alfabeticamente all'interno della Guida.

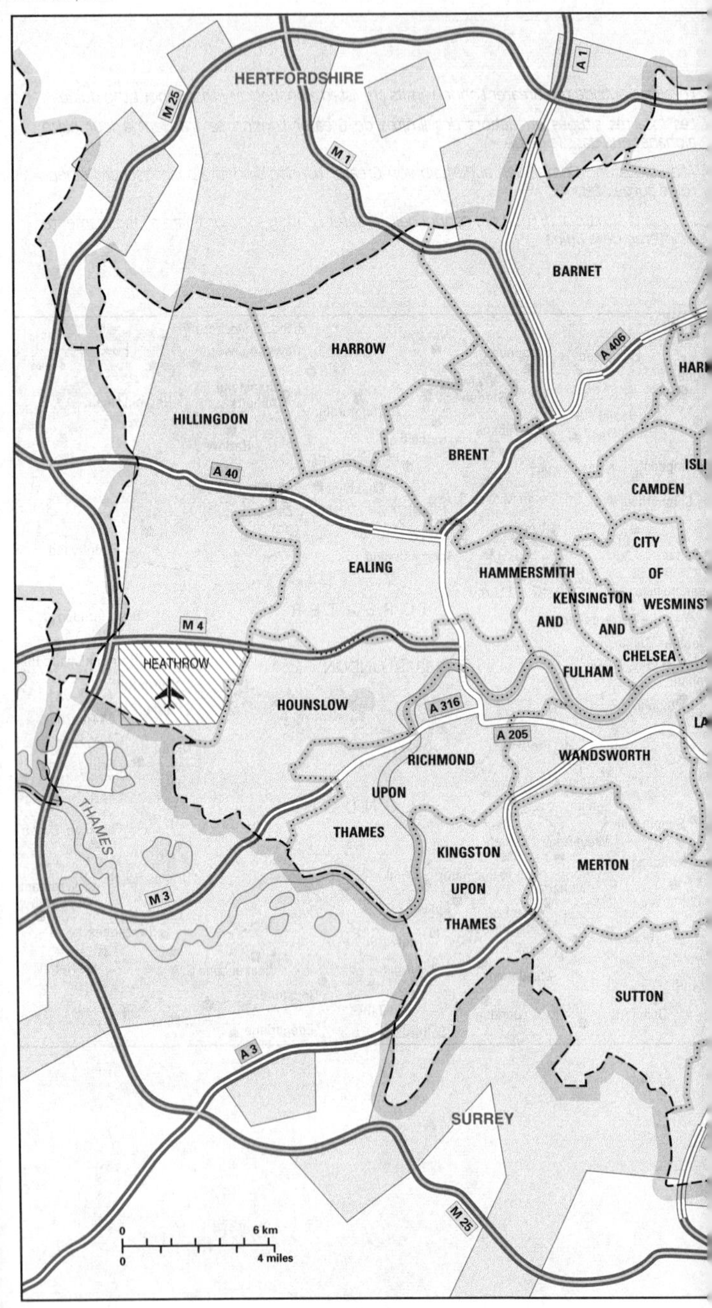
HERTFORDSHIRE
M 25
M 1
A 1
BARNET
HARROW
A 406
HILLINGDON
BRENT
A 40
CAMDEN
CITY
OF
WESMINST
EALING
HAMMERSMITH
AND
FULHAM
KENSINGTON
AND
CHELSEA
M 4
HEATHROW
HOUNSLOW
A 316
A 205
WANDSWORTH
RICHMOND
UPON
THAMES
THAMES
KINGSTON
UPON
THAMES
MERTON
M 3
SUTTON
A 3
SURREY
M 25
0
6 km
0
4 miles

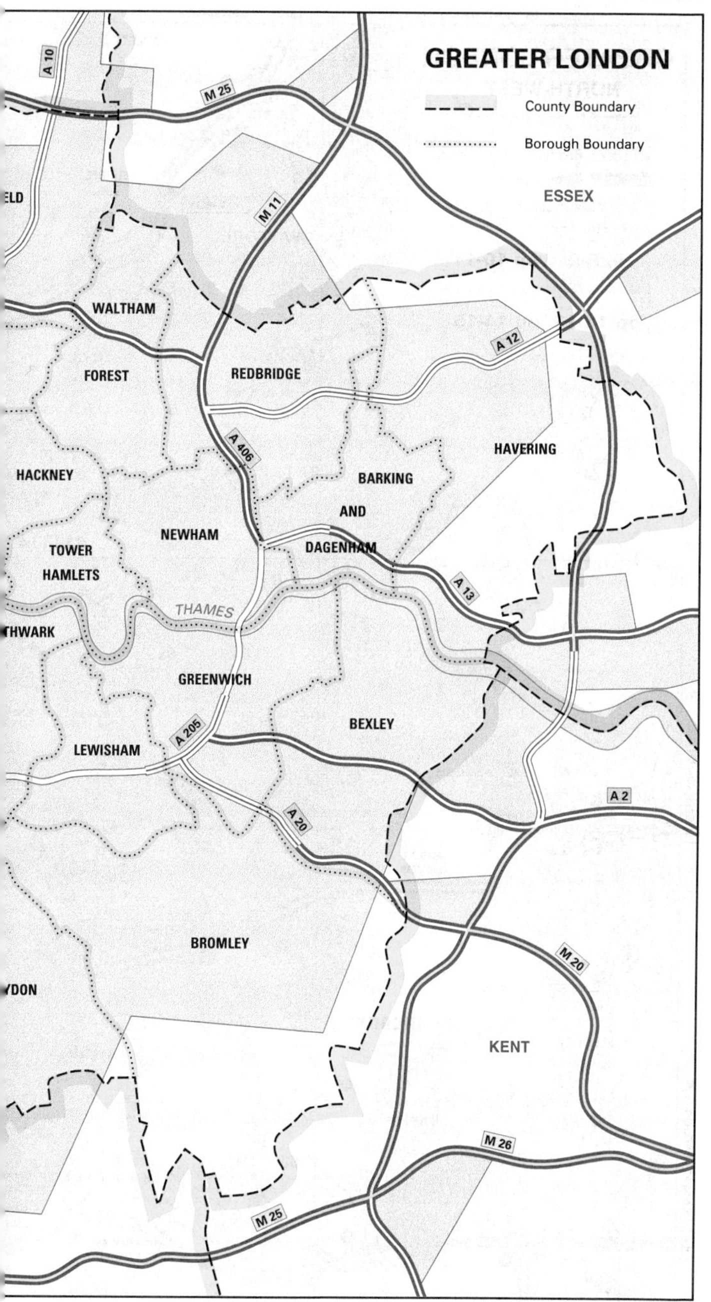
GREATER LONDON
County Boundary
Borough Boundary
ESSEX
A 10
M 25
M 11
ELD
WALTHAM
FOREST
REDBRIDGE
A 12
HAVERING
A 406
HACKNEY
BARKING
AND
DAGENHAM
NEWHAM
TOWER
HAMLETS
A 13
THAMES
THWARK
GREENWICH
BEXLEY
LEWISHAM
A 205
A 2
A 20
BROMLEY
M 20
YDON
KENT
M 26
M 25

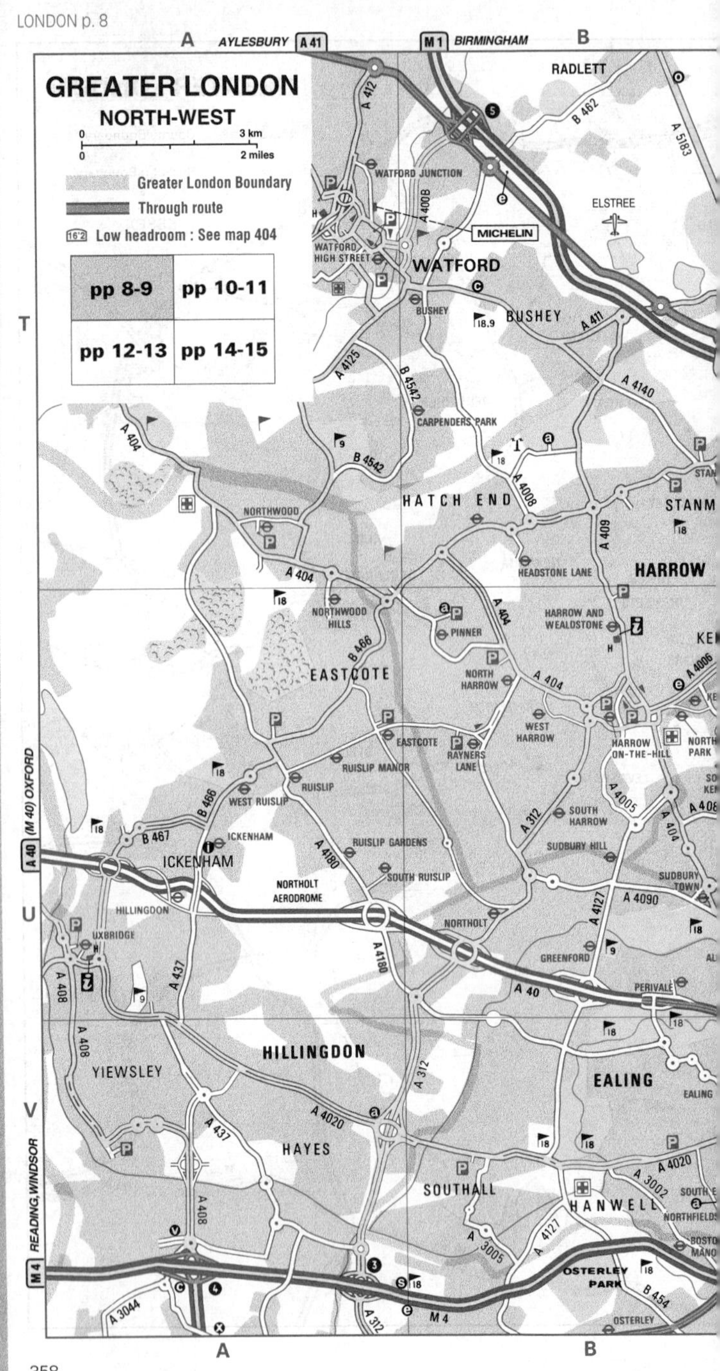

A
AYLESBURY A 41
M 1 BIRMINGHAM
B
GREATER LONDON
NORTH-WEST
0 3 km
0 2 miles
Greater London Boundary
Through route
16'2 Low headroom : See map 404
pp 8-9
pp 10-11
pp 12-13
pp 14-15
RADLETT
B 462
A 5183
A 412
WATFORD JUNCTION
A 4008
ELSTREE
MICHELIN
WATFORD HIGH STREET
WATFORD
BUSHEY
BUSHEY
A 411
A 4125
B 4542
A 4140
CARPENDERS PARK
A 404
B 4542
A 4008
HATCH END
STANM
NORTHWOOD
A 409
HEADSTONE LANE
HARROW
A 404
NORTHWOOD HILLS
PINNER
HARROW AND WEALDSTONE
B 466
EASTCOTE
NORTH HARROW
A 404
A 4006
EASTCOTE
RAYNERS LANE
WEST HARROW
HARROW ON-THE-HILL
NORTH PARK
RUISLIP MANOR
WEST RUISLIP
RUISLIP
A 4005
B 466
A 312
SOUTH HARROW
B 467
ICKENHAM
A 4180
RUISLIP GARDENS
SUDBURY HILL
A 40 (M 40) OXFORD
ICKENHAM
NORTHOLT AERODROME
SOUTH RUISLIP
SUDBURY TOWN
A 4090
A 4127
HILLINGDON
NORTHOLT
UXBRIDGE
GREENFORD
A 4180
A 408
A 437
A 40
PERIVALE
A 408
HILLINGDON
YIEWSLEY
A 312
EALING
EALING
A 4020
A 437
HAYES
A 4020
A 3002
SOUTHALL
HANWELL
NORTHFIELDS
A 408
M 4 READING, WINDSOR
A 3005
A 4127
OSTERLEY PARK
B 454
A 3044
A 312
M 4
OSTERLEY
A
B
T
U
V

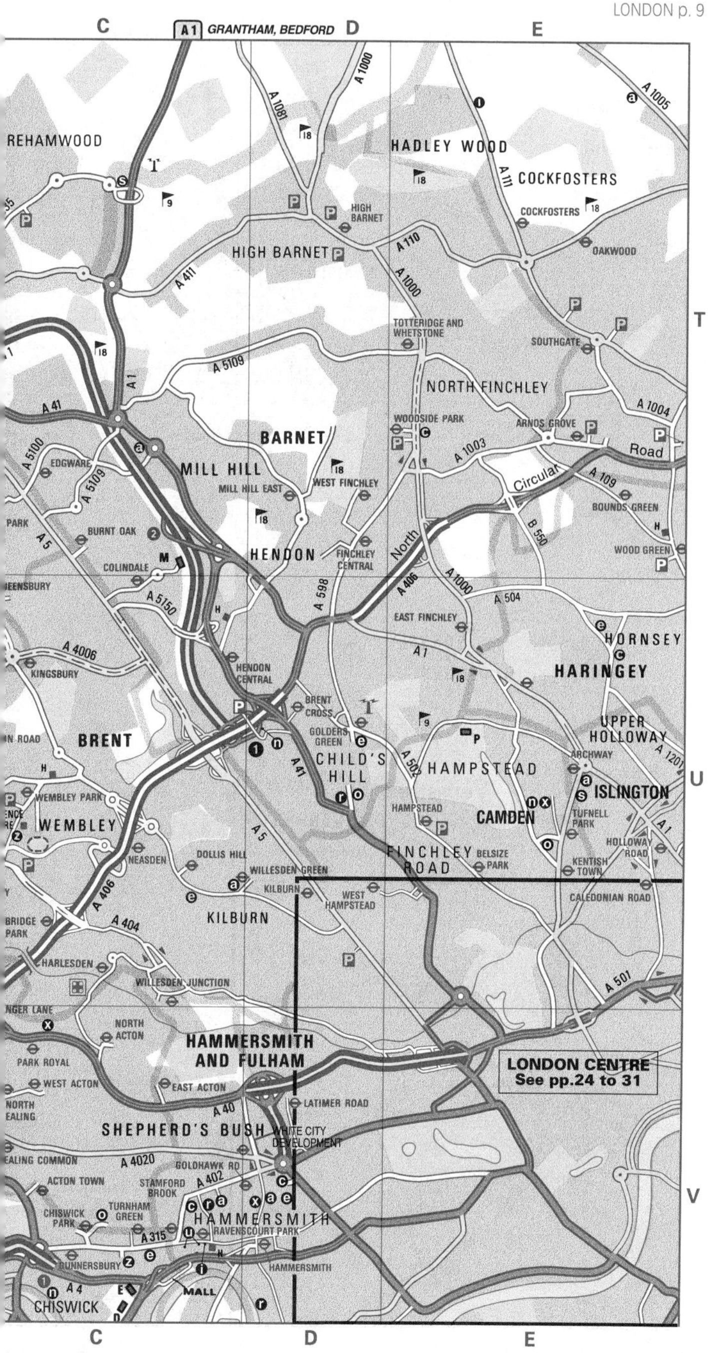

C
D
E
A1 GRANTHAM, BEDFORD
A 1000
A 1081
A 1005
REHAMWOOD
HADLEY WOOD
COCKFOSTERS
A 111
HIGH BARNET
COCKFOSTERS
OAKWOOD
A 110
A 411
A 1000
TOTTERIDGE AND WHETSTONE
SOUTHGATE
T
A 5109
NORTH FINCHLEY
A 1004
A 41
A1
WOODSIDE PARK
ARNOS GROVE
BARNET
A 1003
Road
A 5100
EDGWARE
MILL HILL
MILL HILL EAST
WEST FINCHLEY
Circular
A 109
A 5109
BOUNDS GREEN
PARK
B 550
A 5
BURNT OAK
HENDON
FINCHLEY CENTRAL
North
WOOD GREEN
COLINDALE
A 406
A 1000
A 5150
A 598
A 504
A 4006
EAST FINCHLEY
HORNSEY
KINGSBURY
HENDON CENTRAL
A1
HARINGEY
BRENT CROSS
GOLDERS GREEN
UPPER HOLLOWAY
BRENT
CHILD'S HILL
A 41
A 502
HAMPSTEAD
ARCHWAY
A 1201
ISLINGTON
U
WEMBLEY PARK
WEMBLEY
HAMPSTEAD
CAMDEN
TUFNELL PARK
A1
NEASDEN
DOLLIS HILL
A5
FINCHLEY ROAD
BELSIZE PARK
HOLLOWAY ROAD
WILLESDEN GREEN
KENTISH TOWN
A 406
KILBURN
WEST HAMPSTEAD
CALEDONIAN ROAD
KILBURN
A 404
HARLESDEN
WILLESDEN JUNCTION
A 501
NORTH ACTON
HAMMERSMITH AND FULHAM
LONDON CENTRE
See pp.24 to 31
PARK ROYAL
WEST ACTON
EAST ACTON
A 40
LATIMER ROAD
NORTH EALING
SHEPHERD'S BUSH
WHITE CITY DEVELOPMENT
EALING COMMON
A 4020
GOLDHAWK RD
ACTON TOWN
STAMFORD BROOK
A 402
V
TURNHAM GREEN
CHISWICK PARK
HAMMERSMITH
A 315
RAVENSCOURT PARK
GUNNERSBURY
HAMMERSMITH
A 4
MALL
CHISWICK
C
D
E

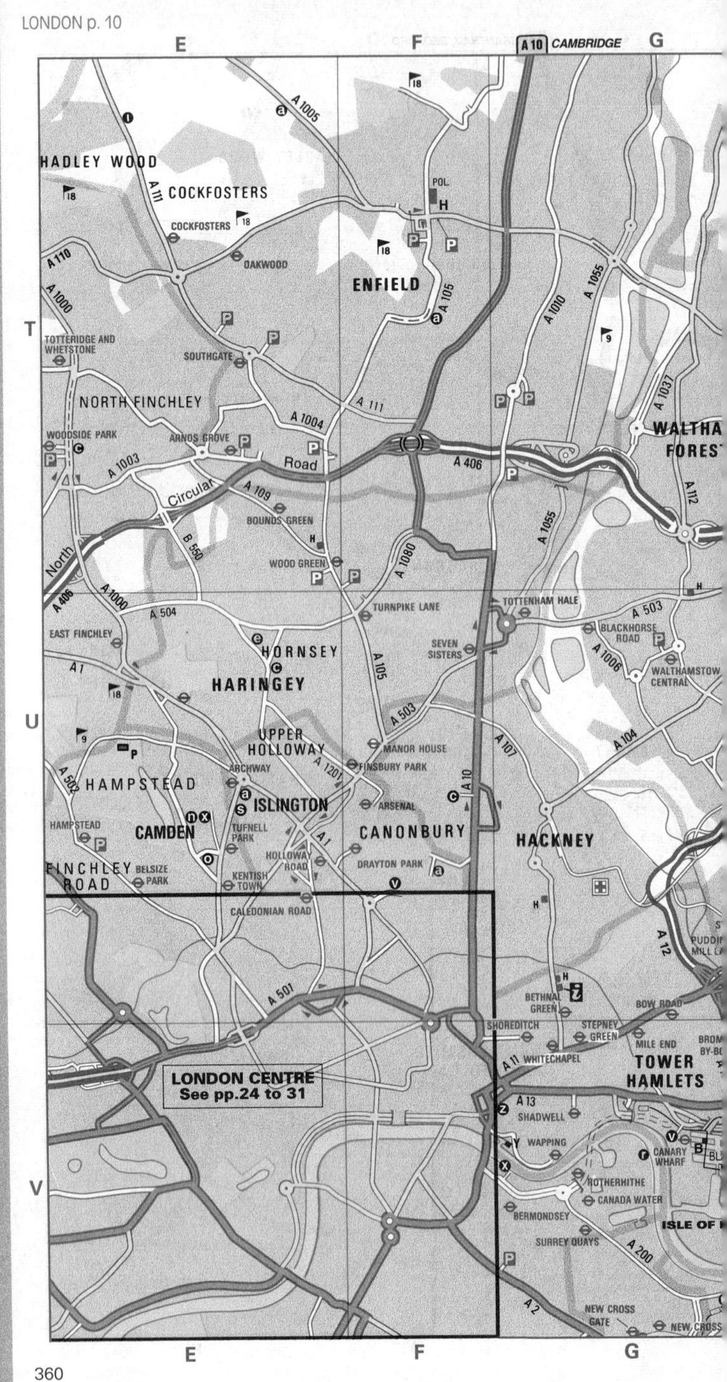
E
F
G
A 10 CAMBRIDGE
HADLEY WOOD
COCKFOSTERS
ENFIELD
TOTTERIDGE AND WHETSTONE
SOUTHGATE
OAKWOOD
NORTH FINCHLEY
WOODSIDE PARK
ARNOS GROVE
BOUNDS GREEN
WOOD GREEN
North Circular Road
TURNPIKE LANE
TOTTENHAM HALE
BLACKHORSE ROAD
WALTHAMSTOW CENTRAL
SEVEN SISTERS
EAST FINCHLEY
HORNSEY
HARINGEY
UPPER HOLLOWAY
MANOR HOUSE
FINSBURY PARK
ARCHWAY
HAMPSTEAD
ISLINGTON
ARSENAL
CAMDEN
TUFNELL PARK
CANONBURY
HACKNEY
HOLLOWAY ROAD
DRAYTON PARK
FINCHLEY ROAD
BELSIZE PARK
KENTISH TOWN
CALEDONIAN ROAD
BETHNAL GREEN
BOW ROAD
SHOREDITCH
STEPNEY GREEN
MILE END
WHITECHAPEL
TOWER HAMLETS
LONDON CENTRE
See pp.24 to 31
SHADWELL
WAPPING
CANARY WHARF
ROTHERHITHE
CANADA WATER
BERMONDSEY
SURREY QUAYS
NEW CROSS GATE
T
U
V

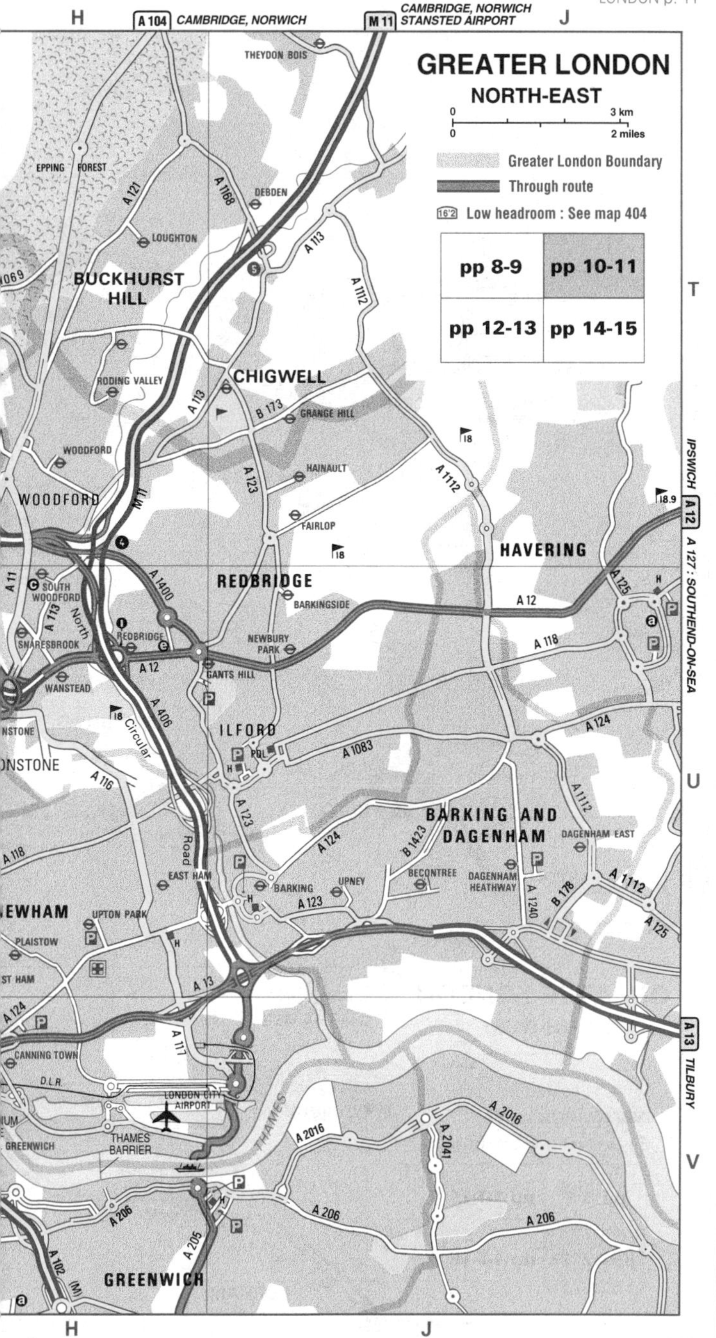
H
A 104 CAMBRIDGE, NORWICH
M 11 CAMBRIDGE, NORWICH STANSTED AIRPORT
J
GREATER LONDON
NORTH-EAST
0 3 km
0 2 miles
Greater London Boundary
Through route
16'2 Low headroom : See map 404
pp 8-9
pp 10-11
pp 12-13
pp 14-15
T
U
V
IPSWICH A 12
A 127 : SOUTHEND-ON-SEA
A 13 TILBURY
THEYDON BOIS
EPPING FOREST
DEBDEN
LOUGHTON
BUCKHURST HILL
RODING VALLEY
CHIGWELL
GRANGE HILL
WOODFORD
HAINAULT
FAIRLOP
HAVERING
REDBRIDGE
SOUTH WOODFORD
BARKINGSIDE
SNARESBROOK
NEWBURY PARK
GANTS HILL
WANSTEAD
North Circular Road
ILFORD
BARKING AND DAGENHAM
DAGENHAM EAST
BECONTREE
DAGENHAM HEATHWAY
EAST HAM
BARKING
UPNEY
NEWHAM
UPTON PARK
PLAISTOW
CANNING TOWN
D.L.R.
LONDON CITY AIRPORT
THAMES BARRIER
GREENWICH
THAMES
GREENWICH
A 121
A 1168
A 113
A 1112
B 173
A 123
M 11
A 1400
A 12
A 118
A 125
A 406
A 116
A 1083
A 124
B 1423
A 1240
B 178
A 13
A 117
A 2016
A 2041
A 206
A 205
A 102 (M)
A 11
H
J

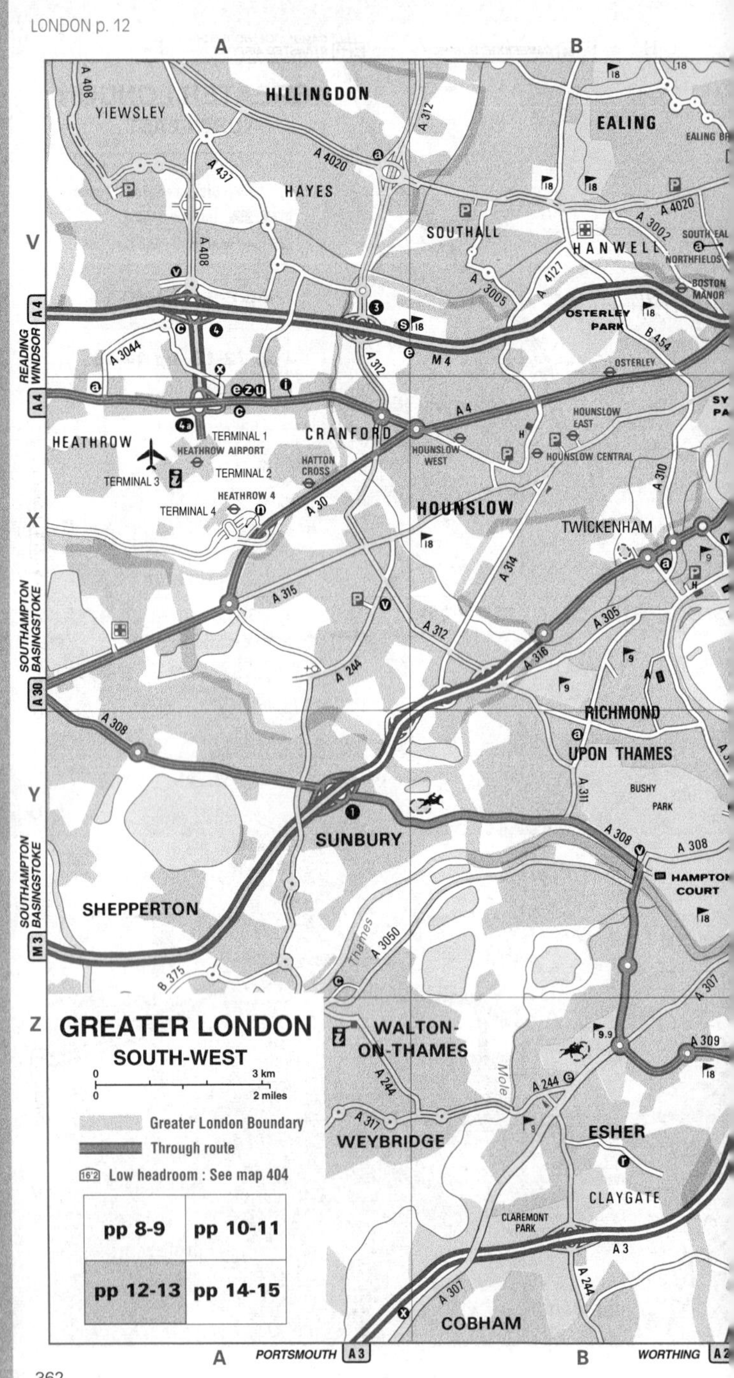

GREATER LONDON
SOUTH-WEST
0 3 km
0 2 miles
Greater London Boundary
Through route
Low headroom : See map 404
pp 8-9
pp 10-11
pp 12-13
pp 14-15
HILLINGDON
YIEWSLEY
HAYES
SOUTHALL
EALING
HANWELL
OSTERLEY PARK
HEATHROW
HEATHROW AIRPORT
TERMINAL 1
TERMINAL 2
TERMINAL 3
TERMINAL 4
HEATHROW 4
HATTON CROSS
CRANFORD
HOUNSLOW WEST
HOUNSLOW EAST
HOUNSLOW CENTRAL
HOUNSLOW
TWICKENHAM
RICHMOND UPON THAMES
BUSHY PARK
HAMPTON COURT
SUNBURY
SHEPPERTON
WALTON-ON-THAMES
WEYBRIDGE
ESHER
CLAYGATE
CLAREMONT PARK
COBHAM
NORTHFIELDS
BOSTON MANOR
OSTERLEY
Thames
Mole
READING WINDSOR
SOUTHAMPTON BASINGSTOKE
PORTSMOUTH
WORTHING

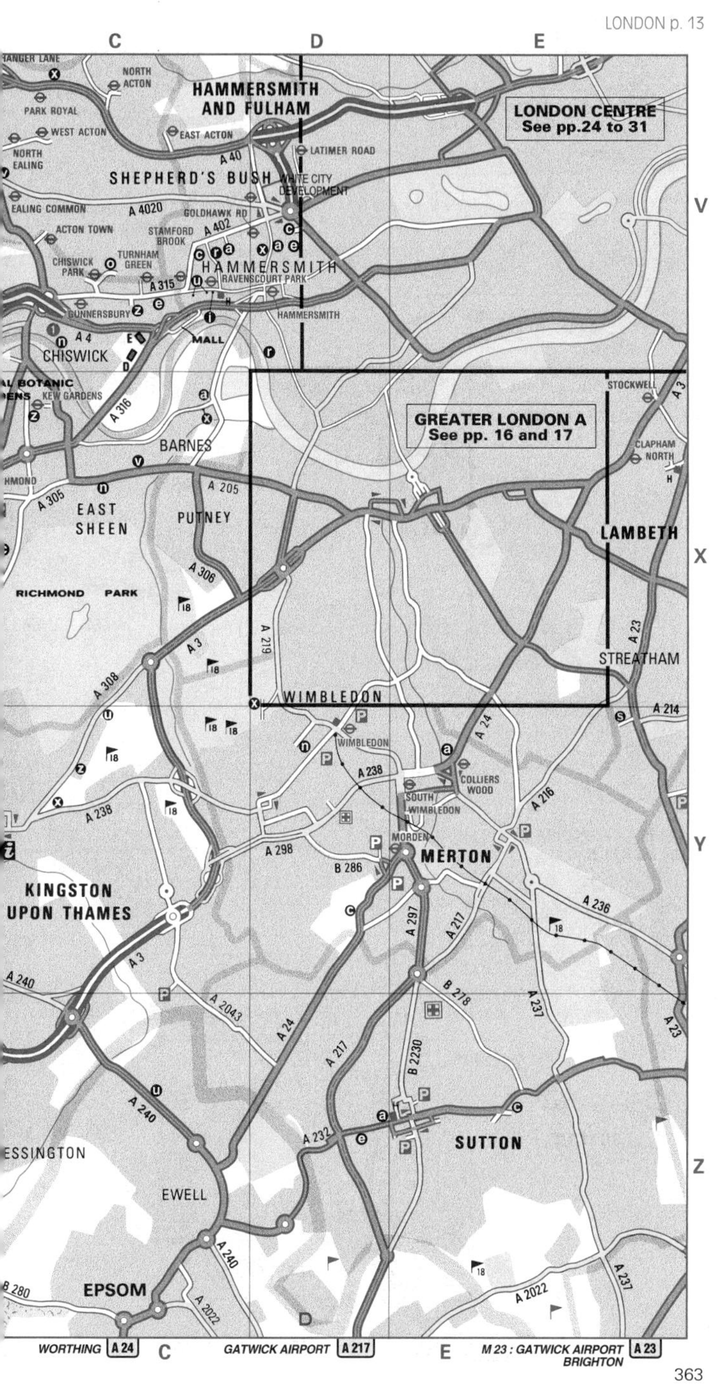
C
D
E
HAMMERSMITH AND FULHAM
LONDON CENTRE
See pp.24 to 31
NORTH ACTON
PARK ROYAL
WEST ACTON
EAST ACTON
LATIMER ROAD
NORTH EALING
SHEPHERD'S BUSH
WHITE CITY DEVELOPMENT
EALING COMMON
A 4020
GOLDHAWK RD
ACTON TOWN
STAMFORD BROOK
A 402
TURNHAM GREEN
CHISWICK PARK
HAMMERSMITH
RAVENSCOURT PARK
A 315
GUNNERSBURY
HAMMERSMITH
A 4
MALL
CHISWICK
KEW GARDENS
STOCKWELL
A 3
GREATER LONDON A
See pp. 16 and 17
A 316
BARNES
CLAPHAM NORTH
A 205
A 305
EAST SHEEN
PUTNEY
LAMBETH
A 306
RICHMOND PARK
A 219
A 23
A 3
STREATHAM
A 308
WIMBLEDON
A 214
A 24
WIMBLEDON
COLLIERS WOOD
A 238
SOUTH WIMBLEDON
A 216
A 238
MORDEN
A 298
MERTON
B 286
KINGSTON UPON THAMES
A 236
A 297
A 217
A 3
A 240
A 2043
B 278
A 237
A 23
A 24
A 217
B 2230
A 240
SUTTON
A 232
ESSINGTON
EWELL
A 240
A 237
EPSOM
B 280
A 2022
A 2022
V
X
Y
Z
WORTHING A 24
C
GATWICK AIRPORT A 217
E
M 23 : GATWICK AIRPORT A 23
BRIGHTON

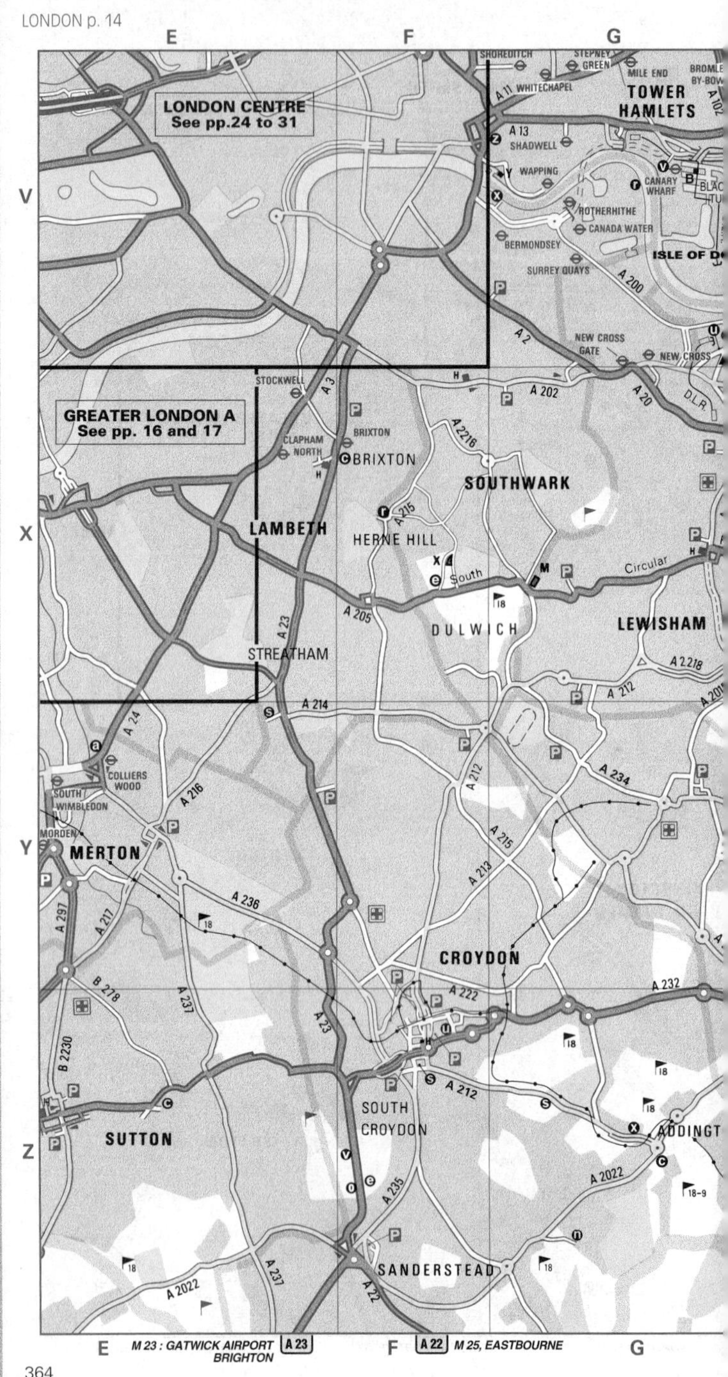
E
F
G
V
X
Y
Z
LONDON CENTRE
See pp.24 to 31
GREATER LONDON A
See pp. 16 and 17
SHOREDITCH
STEPNEY GREEN
MILE END
BROMLEY-BY-BOW
WHITECHAPEL
TOWER HAMLETS
SHADWELL
WAPPING
CANARY WHARF
ROTHERHITHE
CANADA WATER
BERMONDSEY
SURREY QUAYS
ISLE OF D
NEW CROSS GATE
NEW CROSS
D.L.R.
STOCKWELL
CLAPHAM NORTH
BRIXTON
SOUTHWARK
LAMBETH
HERNE HILL
South Circular
DULWICH
LEWISHAM
STREATHAM
COLLIERS WOOD
SOUTH WIMBLEDON
MORDEN
MERTON
CROYDON
SUTTON
SOUTH CROYDON
ADDINGT
SANDERSTEAD
A 11
A 13
A 200
A 2
A 202
A 20
A 3
A 2216
A 215
A 205
A 23
A 214
A 2218
A 212
A 24
A 216
A 234
A 213
A 236
A 297
A 217
B 278
A 237
A 222
A 232
B 2230
A 2022
A 235
A 22
M 23 : GATWICK AIRPORT BRIGHTON
M 25, EASTBOURNE

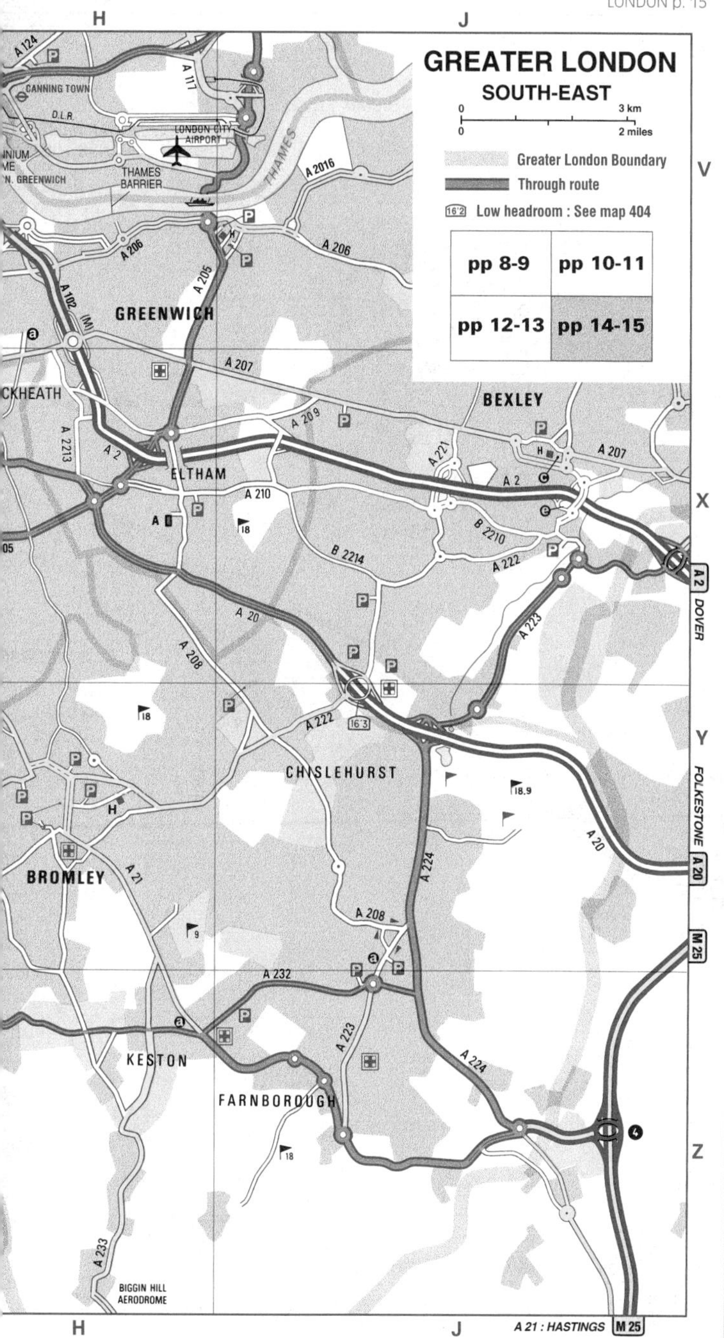
GREATER LONDON
SOUTH-EAST
0 3 km
0 2 miles
Greater London Boundary
Through route
16'2 Low headroom : See map 404
pp 8-9
pp 10-11
pp 12-13
pp 14-15
H
J
V
X
Y
Z
CANNING TOWN
D.L.R.
LONDON CITY AIRPORT
THAMES BARRIER
THAMES
N. GREENWICH
GREENWICH
CKHEATH
ELTHAM
BEXLEY
CHISLEHURST
BROMLEY
KESTON
FARNBOROUGH
BIGGIN HILL AERODROME
A 124
A 117
A 2016
A 206
A 205
A 102 (M)
A 207
A 209
A 2213
A 2
A 210
A 221
B 2210
B 2214
A 222
A 20
A 208
A 223
A 224
A 21
A 232
A 233
M 25
A 2 DOVER
FOLKESTONE A 20
A 21 : HASTINGS M 25

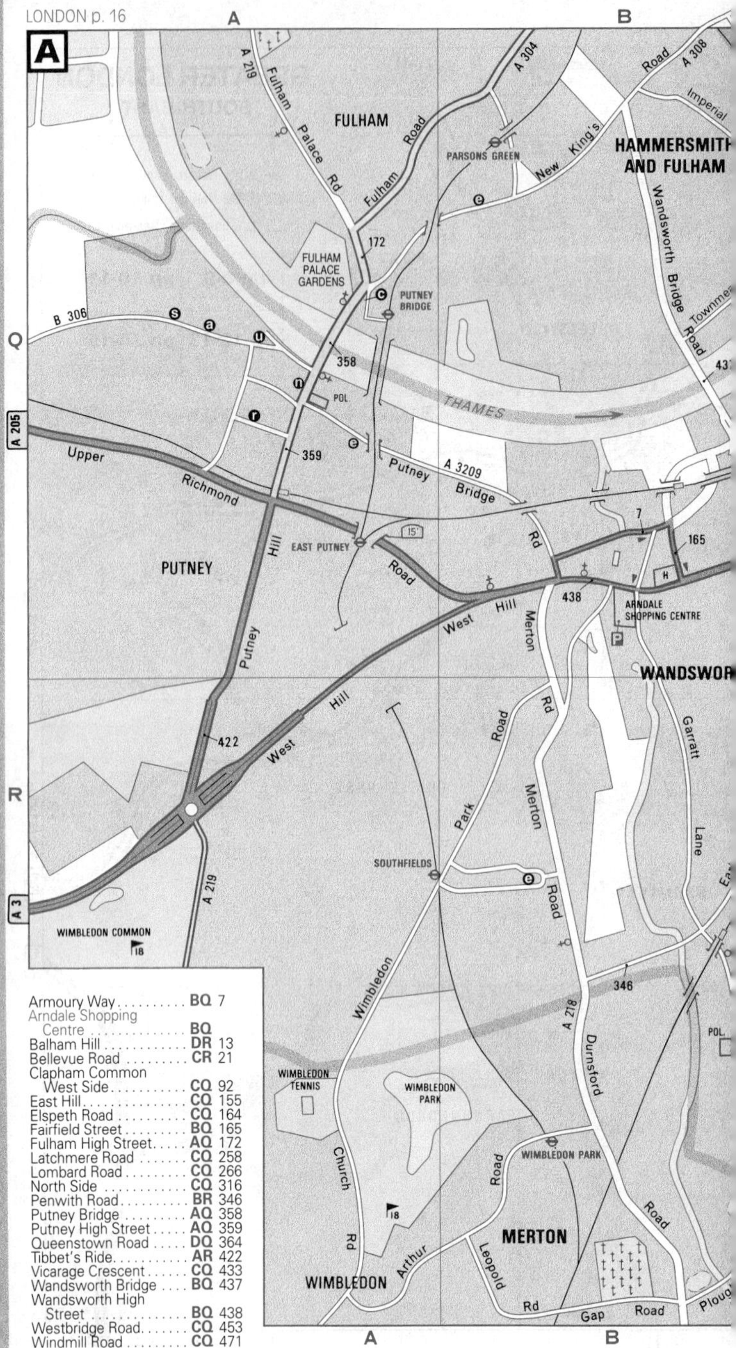

Armoury Way .... BQ 7
Arndale Shopping Centre .... BQ
Balham Hill .... DR 13
Bellevue Road .... CR 21
Clapham Common West Side .... CQ 92
East Hill .... CQ 155
Elspeth Road .... CQ 164
Fairfield Street .... BQ 165
Fulham High Street...... AQ 172
Latchmere Road .... CQ 258
Lombard Road .... CQ 266
North Side .... CQ 316
Penwith Road .... BR 346
Putney Bridge .... AQ 358
Putney High Street ...... AQ 359
Queenstown Road ...... DQ 364
Tibbet's Ride............ AR 422
Vicarage Crescent .... CQ 433
Wandsworth Bridge ..... BQ 437
Wandsworth High Street .... BQ 438
Westbridge Road .... CQ 453
Windmill Road .... CQ 471

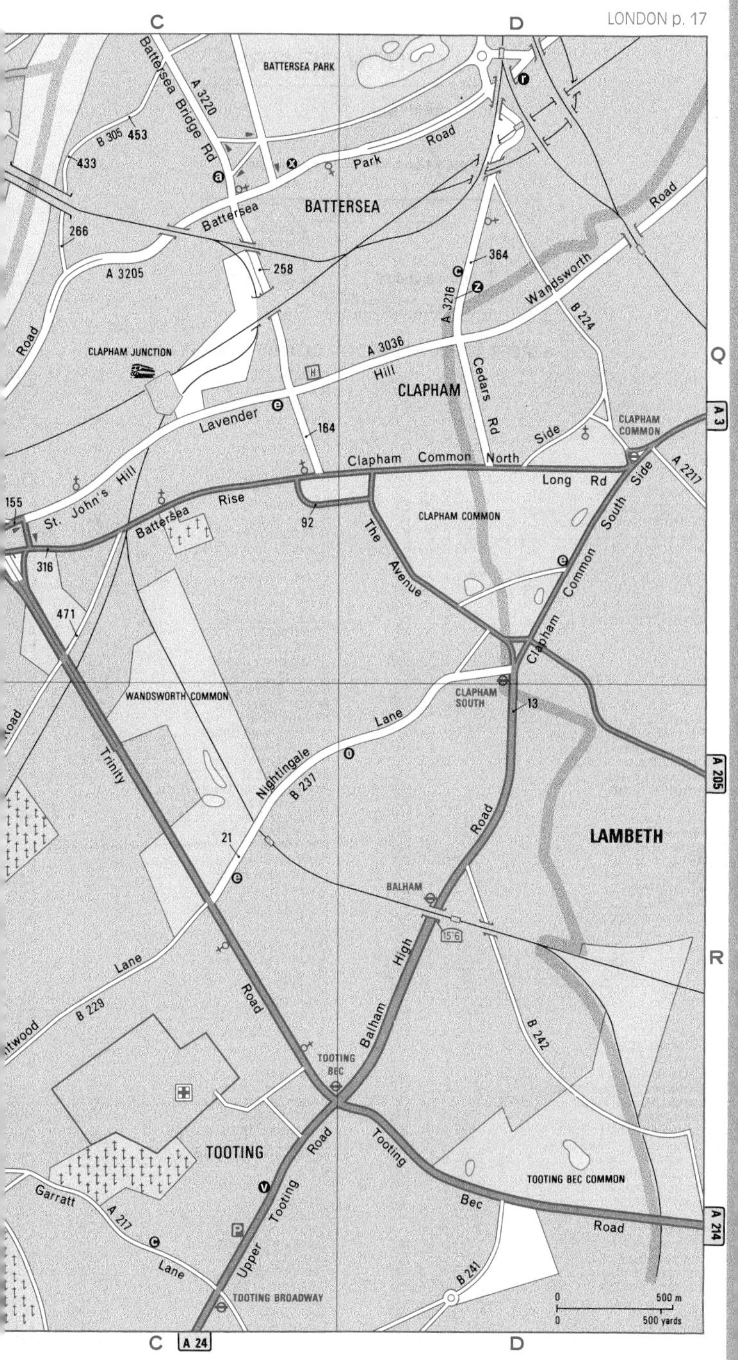

C
D
BATTERSEA PARK
Battersea Bridge Rd
A 3220
B 305
453
433
Park
Road
BATTERSEA
Battersea
266
258
A 3205
364
A 3216
Wandsworth
Road
B 224
Road
CLAPHAM JUNCTION
A 3036
Hill
CLAPHAM
Cedars
Rd
Q
A 3
Lavender
164
Side
CLAPHAM COMMON
Clapham
Common
North
Long
Rd
A 2217
155
St. John's Hill
Battersea
Rise
92
The
Avenue
CLAPHAM COMMON
South
Side
316
471
Clapham
Common
WANDSWORTH COMMON
CLAPHAM SOUTH
13
Lane
Nightingale
B 237
Trinity
A 205
Road
LAMBETH
21
BALHAM
Lane
R
B 229
Road
High
B 242
Balham
TOOTING BEC
TOOTING
Road
Tooting
Garratt
A 217
Lane
Upper
Tooting
Bec
TOOTING BEC COMMON
Road
A 214
B 241
TOOTING BROADWAY
0
500 m
0
500 yards
C
A 24
D

LONDON CENTRE

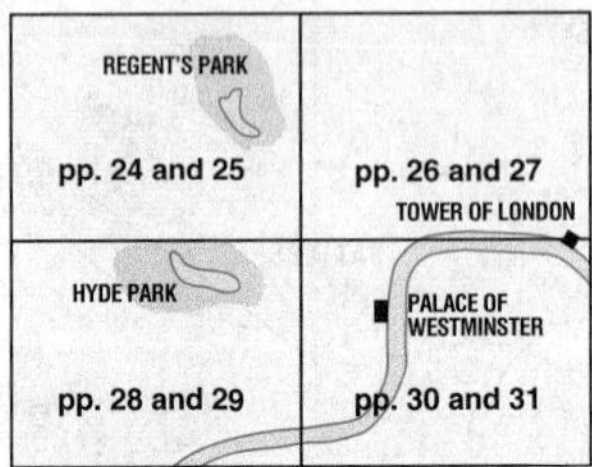

STREET INDEX TO LONDON CENTRE TOWN PLANS

Street	District	Page	Grid	No.
Elystan Street	SW3	p. 35	**DT**	
Endell Street	WC2	p. 37	**DV**	
England's Lane	NW3	p. 25	**HS**	
Englefield Road	N1	p. 27	**PS**	
Ennismore Gardens	SW7	p. 35	**DQ**	
Essex Road	N1	p. 27	**OS**	
Essex Street	WC2	p. 37	**EX**	
Estcourt Road	SW6	p. 28	**EZ**	
Eton Avenue	NW3	p. 25	**GS**	
Euston Road	NW1	p. 26	**LT**	
Evelyn Gardens	SW7	p. 34	**CU**	
Eversholt Street	NW1	p. 26	**KT**	
Exeter Street	WC2	p. 37	**DX**	
Exhibition Road	SW7	p. 34	**CQ**	
Fairfax Road	NW6	p. 24	**FS**	
Fairhazel Gardens	NW6	p. 24	**FS**	
Falmouth Road	SE1	p. 31	**OY**	
Farm Street MAYFAIR	W1	p. 32	**BM**	
Fann Street	W1	p. 27	**OU**	166
Farringdon Road	EC1	p. 27	**NU**	
Farringdon Street	EC4	p. 27	**NU**	168
Fenchurch Street	EC3	p. 27	**PV**	
Fentiman Road	SW8	p. 30	**LZ**	
Fernhead Road	W9	p. 24	**ET**	
Fetter Lane	EC4	p. 27	**NU**	169
Fifth Avenue	W10	p. 24	**ET**	
Filmer Road	SW6	p. 28	**EZ**	
Finborough Road	SW10	p. 34	**AU**	
Finchley Road	NW8, NW3 NW2, NW11	p. 25	**GS**	
Fitzalan Street	SE11	p. 30	**MZ**	
Fitzjohn's Avenue	NW3	p. 25	**GS**	
Fitzroy Square	W1	p. 26	**KU**	
Fleet Road	NW3	p. 24	**ES**	
Fleet Street	EC4	p. 26	**MV**	
Flint Street	SE17	p. 31	**PZ**	
Flood Street	SW3	p. 35	**EU**	
Floral Street	WC2	p. 37	**DX**	
Foulis Terrace	SW7	p. 34	**CT**	170
Foxley Road	SW9	p. 31	**NZ**	
Frampton Street	NW8	p. 25	**GT**	
Francis Street	SW1	p. 36	**CY**	
Franklin's Row	SW3	p. 35	**FU**	
Frith Street	W1	p. 33	**FK**	
Frognal	NW3	p. 24	**ES**	
Frognal Rise	NW3	p. 24	**ES**	171
Fulham Road	SW3, SW10, SW6	p. 28	**EZ**	
Garden Row	SE1	p. 31	**NY**	173
Garrick Street	WC2	p. 37	**DX**	
Garway Road	W2	p. 36	**BZ**	
Gayton Road	NW3	p. 24	**ES**	
George Street	W1	p. 32	**AJ**	
Gerrard Street	W1	p. 33	**GL**	174
Gilbert Street	W1	p. 32	**BL**	175
Gillingham Street	SW1	p. 36	**BY**	
Gilston Road	SW10	p. 34	**BU**	
Giltspur Street	EC1	p. 27	**OU**	178
Glasshouse Street	W1	p. 33	**EM**	179
Glendower Place	SW7	p. 34	**CS**	180
Gliddon Road	W14	p. 28	**EZ**	182
Gloucester Avenue	NW1	p. 25	**IS**	
Gloucester Place	W1, NW1	p. 25	**HU**	
Gloucester Road	SW7	p. 34	**BR**	
Gloucester Square	W2	p. 37	**EZ**	
Gloucester Street	SW1	p. 31	**JZ**	
Gloucester Terrace	W2	p. 36	**CZ**	
Golborne Road	W10	p. 24	**EU**	
Golden Square	W1	p. 33	**EL**	
Goodge Street	W1	p. 26	**KU**	184
Goswell Road	EC1	p. 27	**OT**	
Gower Street	WC1	p. 26	**KU**	
Gracechurch Street	EC3	p. 27	**PV**	187
Grafton Street	W1	p. 33	**DM**	
Grange Road	SE1	p. 31	**PY**	
Granville Place	W1	p. 32	**AK**	188
Gray's Inn Road	WC1	p. 26	**LT**	
Gt. Castle Street	W1	p. 33	**DJ**	189
Gt. Cumberland Place	W1	p. 37	**EZ**	191
Gt. Dover Street	SE1	p. 31	**PY**	
Gt. Eastern Street	EC2	p. 27	**PT**	192
Gt. George Street	SW1	p. 30	**LY**	193
Gt. Marlborough Street	W1	p. 33	**EK**	
Gt. Peter Street	SW1	p. 30	**LY**	
Gt. Queen Street	WC2	p. 37	**DV**	
Gt. Russell Street	WC1	p. 26	**LU**	
Gt. Smith Street	SW1	p. 30	**LY**	196
Gt. Suffolk Street	SE1	p. 31	**OX**	
Gt. Tower Street	EC3	p. 27	**PV**	197
Gt. Western Road	W9, W11	p. 24	**EU**	
Gt. Windmill Street	W1	p. 33	**FM**	
Greek Street	W1	p. 33	**GK**	198
Greencroft Gardens	NW6	p. 24	**FS**	

Street	District	Page	Grid	No.
Green Street	W1	p. 32	**AL**	
Grenville Place	SW7	p. 34	**BS**	
Gresham Street	EC2	p. 27	**OU**	
Greville Place	NW6	p. 24	**FS**	
Greycoat Place	SW1	p. 30	**KY**	2
Greyhound Road	W6, W14	p. 28	**EZ**	
Grosvenor Crescent	SW1	p. 36	**AV**	
Grosvenor Gardens	SW1	p. 36	**BX**	
Grosvenor Place	SW1	p. 36	**AV**	
Grosvenor Road	SW1	p. 30	**JZ**	
Grosvenor Square	W1	p. 32	**BL**	
Grosvenor Street	W1	p. 32	**BL**	
Grove End Road	NW8	p. 25	**GT**	
Guildhouse Street	SW1	p. 36	**BY**	2
Guilford Street	WC1	p. 26	**LU**	
Gunter Grove	SW10	p. 28	**FZ**	2
Gunterstone Road	W14	p. 28	**EZ**	2
Hackney Road	E2	p. 27	**PT**	
Half Moon Street	W1	p. 32	**CN**	
Halford Road	SW6	p. 28	**EZ**	
Halkin Street	SW1	p. 36	**AV**	
Halliford Street	N1	p. 27	**OS**	
Hall Road	NW8	p. 24	**FT**	
Hamilton Place	W1	p. 32	**BP**	2
Hamilton Terrace	NW8	p. 24	**FT**	
Hammersmith Road	W14, W6	p. 28	**EZ**	2
Hampstead Grove	NW3	p. 24	**ES**	2
Hampstead High Street	NW3	p. 24	**ES**	2
Hampstead Road	NW1	p. 26	**KT**	
Hanover Square	W1	p. 32	**CK**	2
Hanover Street	W1	p. 33	**DK**	
Hans Crescent	SW1	p. 35	**ER**	
Hans Place	SW1	p. 35	**ER**	
Hans Road	SW3	p. 35	**ER**	
Harcourt Terrace	SW10	p. 34	**AU**	
Harley Street WESTMINSTER	W1	p. 32	**CH**	
Harleyford Road	SE11	p. 30	**LZ**	
Harleyford Street	SE11	p. 30	**MZ**	2
Harper Road	SE1	p. 31	**OY**	
Harriet Street	SW1	p. 35	**FQ**	2
Harrington Gardens	SW7	p. 34	**BT**	
Harrington Road	SW7	p. 34	**CS**	2
Harrow Road	W2, W9 W10, NW10	p. 24	**FU**	
Harwood Road	SW6	p. 28	**FZ**	
Hasker Street	SW3	p. 35	**ES**	
Haverstock Hill	NW3	p. 25	**HS**	
Haymarket	SW1	p. 33	**FM**	
Hay Galleria Shopping Centre	SE1	p. 31	**PX**	
Hay's Mews	W1	p. 32	**BN**	
Heath Street	NW3	p. 24	**ES**	
Hemingford Road	N1	p. 26	**MS**	
Henrietta Place	W1	p. 32	**BJ**	
Henrietta Street	WC2	p. 37	**DX**	2
Herbrand Street	WC1	p. 26	**LT**	2
Hercules Road	SE1	p. 30	**MY**	2
Hereford Road	W2	p. 36	**AZ**	
Hertford Street	W1	p. 32	**BP**	2
Heygate Street	SE17	p. 31	**OZ**	
High Holborn	WC1	p. 26	**LU**	
Hill Street	W1	p. 32	**BN**	
Hobart Place	SW1	p. 36	**AX**	
Holbein Place	SW1	p. 35	**FT**	
Holbein Mews	SW1	p. 35	**FT**	2
Holborn	EC1	p. 26	**MU**	
Holborn Viaduct	EC1	p. 27	**NU**	
Holland Park	W11	p. 28	**EX**	
Holland Park Avenue	W11	p. 28	**EX**	
Holland Park Gardens	W11	p. 28	**EX**	2
Holland Road	W14	p. 28	**EY**	
Holland Street	W8	p. 28	**EY**	
Holland Walk	W8	p. 28	**EY**	2
Holland Villas Road	W14	p. 28	**EY**	
Holles Street	W1	p. 32	**CJ**	
Hollybush Hill	E11	p. 24	**ES**	2
Hollywood Road	SW10	p. 34	**BU**	
Horseferry Road	SW1	p. 30	**KY**	
Horseguards Avenue	SW1	p. 30	**LX**	2
Hornton Street	W8	p. 28	**FY**	2
Houndsditch	EC3	p. 27	**PU**	
Howick Place	SW1	p. 36	**CX**	
Howland Street	W1	p. 26	**KU**	2
Hoxton Street	N1	p. 27	**PT**	
Hudson's Place	SW1	p. 36	**BY**	
Hugh Street	SW1	p. 36	**BY**	
Hunter Street	WC1	p. 26	**LT**	2
Hyde Park Gardens	W2	p. 37	**DZ**	
Hyde Park Square	W2	p. 37	**EZ**	2
Hyde Park Street	W2	p. 37	**EZ**	
Hyde Road	N1	p. 27	**PS**	2
Ifield Road	SW10	p. 34	**AU**	
Imperial Road	SW6	p. 16	**BQ**	
Inverness Terrace	W2	p. 36	**BZ**	

worth Place NW6 p. 35 DT
ames Street W1 p. 32 BJ
ames Street SOHO WC2 p. 33 EL
ermyn Street SW1 p. 31 EN
ohn Adam Street WC2 p. 37 DY
ohn Islip Street SW1 p. 30 LZ
ohn Ruskin Street SE5 p. 31 OZ
ubilee Place SW3 p. 35 ET
udd Street WC1 p. 26 LT
eat's Grove NW3 p. 24 ES 236
emble Street WC2 p. 37 EV
endal Street W2 p. 37 EZ
ennington Lane SE11 p. 30 MZ
ennington Oval SE11 p. 30 MZ
ennington Park Road SE11 p. 31 NZ
ennington Road SE1, SE11 p. 30 MZ
ensal Road W10 p. 24 ET
ensington Church Street W8 p. 36 AZ 238
ensington Court W8 p. 34 AQ 241
ensington Court Place W8 p. 34 AR 242
ensington Gardens Square W2 p. 36 BZ 243
ensington Gore SW7 p. 34 CQ
ensington High Street W8, W14 p. 26 EY
ensington Palace Gardens W8 p. 28 FX
ensington Park Road W11 p. 24 EV
ensington Place W8 p. 36 AZ
ensington Road W8, SW7 p. 34 BQ
ensington Square W8 p. 34 AQ
entish Town Road NW1, NW5 p. 26 JS
enway Road SW5 p. 28 FZ 245
lburn Lane W10, W9 p. 24 ET
lburn Park Road NW6 p. 24 ET
nightsbridge SW1, SW7 p. 33 EQ
ng's Road SW3, SW10, SW6 p. 33 DU
ng Edward Street EC1 p. 27 OU 247
ngly Street W1 p. 33 DK
ng's Cross Road WC1 p. 26 LT
ngsland Road E2, E8 p. 27 PT
ng Street ST. JAMES'S SW1 p. 33 EN
ng Street STRAND WC2 p. 37 DX
ngsway WC2 p. 37 EV
ng William Street EC4 p. 27 PV 250
aresborough Place SW5 p. 34 AS
dbroke Grove W10, W11 p. 24 EU
mbeth Bridge SW1, SE1 p. 30 LY
mbeth Palace Road SE1 p. 30 MY
mbeth Road SE1 p. 30 MY
mbeth Walk SE11 p. 30 MZ
ncaster Gate W2 p. 36 CDZ 256
ncaster Grove NW3, p. 25 GS
ncaster Place SW19 p. 37 EX
ncaster Terrace W2 p. 37 DZ 257
nsdowne Walk W11 p. 28 EX
uderdale Road W9 p. 24 FT
unceston Place W8 p. 34 BR 259
wn Road NW3 p. 24 ES
adenhall Street EC3 p. 27 PV 260
es Place W1 p. 32 AL
icester Square WC2 p. 33 GM 261
inster Gardens W2 p. 36 CZ
inster Square W2 p. 36 AZ
inster Terrace W2 p. 36 CZ
nnox Gardens NW10 p. 35 ES
nnox Gardens Mews SW3 p. 35 ES 263
ver Street EC1 p. 27 OT
xham Gardens W8 p. 34 AS
xington Street W1 p. 33 EL
lie Road SW6 p. 28 EZ
ncoln's Inn Fields WC2 p. 37 EV
sle Street WC2 p. 33 GL
sson Grove NW1, NW8 p. 25 GT
ttle Boltons (The) SW10 p. 34 BU
ttle Britain EC1 p. 27 OU 264
verpool Road N1, N7 p. 26 MS
verpool Street EC2 p. 27 PU
oyd Baker Street WC1 p. 26 MT 265
mbard Street EC3 p. 27 PV 268
ndon Bridge SE1, EC4 p. 31 PX
ndon Road SE1 p. 31 NY
ndon Street W2 p. 37 DZ
ndon Wall EC2 p. 27 OU
ng Acre WC2 p. 37 DX
ng Lane CITY EC1 p. 27 OU 270
ng Lane SOUTHWARK SE1 p. 31 PY
thbury EC2 p. 27 PU 273
ts Road SW10 p. 28 FZ
udoun Road NW8 p. 24 FS
wer Belgrave Street SW1 p. 36 AX
wer Grosvenor Place SW1 p. 36 BX 274
wer Marsh SE1 p. 30 MY 277
wer Sloane Street SW1 p. 35 FT
wer Terrace NW3 p. 24 ES
wer Thames Street EC3 p. 27 PV 278

Lowndes Square SW1 p. 35 FQ
Lowndes Street SW1 p. 35 FR
Luke Street EC2 p. 27 PT
Lupus Street SW1 p. 30 JZ
Lyall Street SW1 p. 35 FR
Lyndhurst Road NW3 p. 24 ES
Macklin Street WC2 p. 37 DV
Maddox Street W1 p. 33 DK
Maida Avenue W2 p. 24 FU
Maida Vale W9 p. 24 FT
Maiden Lane WC2 p. 37 DY
Mall (The) SW1 p. 33 FP
Malvern Road NW6 p. 24 ET
Manchester Square W1 p. 32 AJ 281
Manchester Street W1 p. 32 AH
Manor Place SE17 p. 31 OZ
Manresa Road SW3 p. 35 DU
Mansell Street E1 p. 27 PV 282
Marble Arch W1 p. 37 EZ
Margaret Street W1 p. 33 DJ
Market Place W1 p. 33 DJ 286
Market Road N7 p. 26 LS
Markham Street SW3 p. 35 ET
Marlborough Place NW8 p. 24 FT
Marloes Road W8 p. 28 FY
Marshall Street W1 p. 33 EK
Marsham Street SW1 p. 30 LY
Marylebone High Street W1 p. 25 IU
Marylebone Lane W1 p. 32 BJ 287
Marylebone Road NW1 p. 25 HU
Melbury Road W14 p. 28 EY
Merrick Square SE1 p. 31 OY
Merton Rise NW3 p. 25 HS
Middlesex Street E1 p. 25 PU
Midland Road NW1 p. 26 LT
Miles Street SW8 p. 30 LZ 290
Millbank SW1 p. 30 LY
Millenium Bridge EC4, SE1 p. 31 OV 291
Milner Street SW3 p. 35 ES
Minories EC3 p. 27 PV
Monmouth Street WC2 p. 37 DX
Montague St. EC1 p. 27 OU 292
Montagu Square W1 p. 32 AH
Montpelier Square SW7 p. 35 EQ
Montpelier Street SW7 p. 35 ER
Montpelier Walk SW7 p. 35 DR
Moore Street SW3 p. 35 ES
Moorgate EC2 p. 27 PU
Moreland Street EC1 p. 27 OT 293
Mortimer Street W1 p. 26 KU
Moscow Road W2 p. 36 BZ
Mossop Street SW3 p. 35 ES
Mount Row W1 p. 32 BM
Mount Street W1 p. 32 BM
Munster Road SW6 p. 28 EZ
Musard Road W6 p. 28 EZ
Museum Street WC1 p. 37 DV 294
Myddelton Street EC1 p. 27 NT 296
Nassington Road NW3 p. 24 ES 297
Neal Street WC2 p. 37 DV
Neate Street SE5 p. 31 PZ
Netherhall Gardens NW3 p. 24 ES
Nevern Place SW5 p. 28 EZ 298
Nevern Square SW5 p. 28 EZ 299
Neville Terrace SW7 p. 34 CT 300
New Bond Street W1 p. 30 CK
New Bridge Street EC4 p. 27 NV 301
Newburn Street SE11 p. 30 MZ
New Cavendish Street W1 p. 32 BH
New Change EC4 p. 27 OV 304
New Church Road SE5 p. 31 PZ
Newcomen Street SE1 p. 31 PX
New End Square NW3 p. 24 ES 305
Newgate Street EC1 p. 27 OU
Newington Butts SE1, SE11 p. 31 OZ 306
Newington Causeway SE1 p. 31 OY 307
New Kent Road SE1 p. 31 OY
Newman Street W1 p. 26 KU
New North Road N1 p. 27 OS
New Oxford Street WC1 p. 37 DV 308
New Row WC2 p. 37 DX
New Square WC2 p. 37 EV
Newton Road W2 p. 36 BZ
Newton Street WC2 p. 37 DV 309
Nine Elms Lane SW8 p. 30 KZ
Noel Street W1 p. 33 EJ
Norfolk Crescent W2 p. 37 EZ 310
Norfolk Square W2 p. 37 DZ 313
North Audley Street W1 p. 32 AK 314
North Carriage Drive W2 p. 37 EZ
North End Road W14, SW6 p. 28 EZ
North Row W1 p. 32 AL
Northumberland Avenue WC2 p. 30 LX 317

Street	District	Page	Grid	No.
Notting Hill Gate	W11	p. 36	**AZ**	
Nutley Terrace	NW3	p. 24	**ES**	
Nuttall Street	N1	p. 27	**PS**	
Oakley Street	SW3	p. 35	**DU**	
Offord Road	N1	p. 26	**MS**	
Old Bailey	EC4	p. 27	**NV**	318
Old Bond Street	W1	p. 31	**DM**	
Old Broad Street	EC2	p. 27	**PU**	319
Old Brompton Road	SW7, SW5	p. 34	**BT**	
Old Burlington Street	W1	p. 33	**DM**	322
Old Church Street	SW3	p. 34	**CU**	
Old Compton Street	W1	p. 33	**GK**	323
Old Kent Road	SE1, SE15	p. 31	**PZ**	
Old Marylebone Road	NW1	p. 25	**HU**	324
Old Park Lane	W1	p. 32	**BP**	
Old Street	EC1	p. 27	**OT**	
Olympia Way	W14	p. 28	**EY**	326
Onslow Gardens	SW7	p. 34	**CT**	
Onslow Square	SW7	p. 34	**CT**	
Orange Street	WC2	p. 33	**GM**	
Orchard Street	W1	p. 32	**AK**	
Ordnance Hill	NW8	p. 25	**GS**	
Orme Court	W2	p. 36	**BZ**	328
Ormonde Gate	SW3	p. 35	**FU**	329
Ornan Road	NW3	p. 24	**ES**	331
Ossulton Street	NW1	p. 26	**LT**	
Outer Circle	NW1	p. 25	**HT**	
Oxford Circus	W1	p. 33	**DJ**	
Oxford Square	W2	p. 37	**EZ**	332
Oxford Street	W1	p. 30	**BK**	
Paddington Street	W1	p. 25	**IU**	333
Page Street	SW1	p. 30	**LZ**	
Page's Walk	SE1	p. 31	**PY**	
Palace Court	W2	p. 36	**BZ**	
Palace Gardens Terrace	W8	p. 36	**AZ**	335
Palace Gate	W8	p. 34	**BQ**	
Palace Street	SW1	p. 36	**BX**	
Pall Mall	SW1	p. 33	**FN**	
Palmer Street	SW1	p. 36	**CV**	
Pancras Road	NW1	p. 26	**KS**	
Panton Street	SW1	p. 33	**FM**	336
Parade (The)	SW11	p. 29	**HZ**	
Park Crescent	W1	p. 25	**IU**	337
Parker Street	WC2	p. 37	**DV**	
Parkgate Road	SW11	p. 29	**HZ**	
Park Lane	W1	p. 32	**AM**	
Park Road	NW1, NW8	p. 25	**HT**	
Park Street	W1	p. 32	**AL**	
Park Village East	NW1	p. 25	**JS**	
Park Walk	SW10	p. 34	**CU**	
Parkway	NW1	p. 25	**JS**	
Parliament Hill	NW3	p. 24	**ES**	
Parliament Street	SW1	p. 30	**LY**	340
Parry Street	SW8	p. 30	**LZ**	341
Paul Street	EC2	p. 27	**PT**	
Pelham Street	SW7	p. 35	**DS**	
Pembridge Gardens	W2	p. 36	**AZ**	
Pembridge Road	W11	p. 36	**AZ**	
Pembridge Square	W2	p. 36	**AZ**	
Pembridge Villas	W11	p. 36	**AZ**	
Pembrocke Gardens	W8	p. 28	**EY**	342
Pembrocke Road	W8	p. 28	**EZ**	
Penn Street	N1	p. 27	**PS**	343
Penton Place	WC1	p. 31	**OS**	
Penton Rise	WC1	p. 26	**MT**	344
Penton Street	N1	p. 26	**MT**	345
Pentonville Road	N1	p. 26	**LT**	
Penywern Road	SW5	p. 28	**FZ**	347
Percival Street	EC1	p. 27	**NT**	
Petty France	SW1	p. 36	**CV**	
Philbeach Gardens	SW5	p. 28	**EZ**	348
Piccadilly	W1	p. 31	**EM**	
Piccadilly Circus	W1	p. 33	**FM**	
Pilgrimage Street	SE1	p. 31	**PY**	349
Pimlico Road	SW1	p. 29	**IZ**	
Pitfield Street	N1	p. 27	**PT**	
Poland Street	W1	p. 33	**EJ**	
Pond Street	NW3	p. 24	**ES**	
Pont Street	SW1	p. 35	**ER**	
Poole Street	N1	p. 27	**PS**	350
Porchester Gardens	W2	p. 36	**BZ**	
Porchester Road	W2	p. 24	**FU**	351
Porchester Terrace	W2	p. 36	**CZ**	
Portland Place	W1	p. 25	**JU**	
Portland Street	SE17	p. 31	**PZ**	
Portman Square	W1	p. 32	**AJ**	
Portobello Road	W11, W10	p. 22	**EV**	
Potman Street	W1	p. 32	**AK**	
Portugal Street	WC2	p. 37	**EV**	
Poultry	EC2	p. 27	**OV**	352
Praed Street	W2	p. 25	**GV**	
Pratt Street	NW1	p. 26	**KS**	
Primrose Hill Road	NW3	p. 25	**HS**	

Street	District	Page	Grid	No.
Prince Albert Road	NW1, NW8	p. 25	**HS**	
Prince Consort Road	SW7	p. 34	**CR**	
Prince's Gardens	SW7	p. 34	**CR**	35
Prince's Street	W1	p. 33	**DK**	
Princes Street	EC2	p. 27	**PV**	35
Queen Anne's Gate	SW1	p. 30	**KY**	
Queen Anne Street	W1	p. 32	**BH**	
Queensberry Place	SW7	p. 34	**CS**	36
Queensborough Terrace	W2	p. 36	**CZ**	
Queen's Circus	SW8	p. 29	**IZ**	36
Queen's Gardens	W2	p. 36	**CZ**	36
Queen's Gate	SW7	p. 34	**BQ**	
Queen's Gate Gardens	SW7	p. 34	**BR**	
Queen's Gate Place	SW7	p. 34	**BR**	36
Queen's Gate Terrace	SW7	p. 34	**BR**	
Queen's Grove	NW8	p. 25	**GS**	
Queen Street	EC4	p. 27	**OV**	36
Queen's Walk	SW1	p. 33	**DN**	
Queensway	W2	p. 36	**BZ**	
Queen Victoria Street	EC4	p. 27	**OV**	
Radnor Place	W2	p. 37	**DZ**	
Radnor Walk	SW3	p. 35	**EU**	
Randolph Avenue	W9	p. 24	**FT**	
Randoplh Street	NW1	p. 26	**KS**	36
Rawlings Street	SW3	p. 35	**ES**	
Redcliffe Gardens	SW10	p. 34	**AU**	
Redcliffe Square	SW10	p. 34	**AU**	
Redesdale Street	SW3	p. 35	**EU**	36
Red Lion Street	WC1	p. 26	**MU**	
Reeves Mews	W1	p. 32	**AM**	
Regent Street	W1	p. 31	**EM**	
Regency Street	SW1	p. 30	**KZ**	
Regent's Park Road	NW1	p. 25	**HS**	
Richmond Avenue	N1	p. 26	**MS**	
Robert Street	NW1	p. 26	**JT**	
Rochester Row	SW1	p. 36	**CY**	
Rodney Road	N1	p. 31	**OZ**	
Roland Gardens	SW7	p. 34	**BT**	
Roman Way	N7	p. 26	**MS**	
Romilly Street	W1	p. 33	**GL**	3
Rosebery Avenue	EC1	p. 26	**MT**	
Rosslyn Hill	NW3	p. 24	**ES**	
Rossmore Road	NW1	p. 25	**HT**	3
Royal College Street	NW1	p. 26	**KS**	
Royal Crescent	W11	p. 28	**EX**	3
Royal Hospital Road	SW3	p. 35	**FU**	
Rupert Street	W1	p. 33	**FL**	
Russell Square	WC1	p. 26	**LU**	
Russell Street	WC2	p. 37	**DX**	
Rutland Gate	SW7	p. 35	**DQ**	
Rylston Road	SW6	p. 28	**EZ**	
Sackville Street	W1	p. 33	**EM**	
St. Albans Grove	W8	p. 32	**AR**	
St. Andrews Street	EC4	p. 27	**NU**	3
St. Bride Street	EC4	p. 27	**NV**	3
St. George's Drive	SW1	p. 30	**KZ**	
St. George's Road	SE1	p. 31	**NY**	
St. George's Square	SW1	p. 30	**KZ**	
St. George Street	W1	p. 33	**DL**	
St. Giles Circus	W1, WC1, WC2	p. 33	**GJ**	
St. Giles High Street	WC2	p. 37	**DV**	3
St. James's Place	SW1	p. 33	**EN**	
St. James's Square	SW1	p. 33	**FN**	
St. James's Street	SW1	p. 33	**EN**	
St. James Street	E17	p. 37	**DX**	
St. John Street	EC1	p. 27	**NT**	
St. John's Wood High Street	NW8	p. 25	**GT**	3
St. John's Wood Park	NW8	p. 25	**GS**	3
St. John's Wood Road	NW8	p. 25	**GT**	
St. Leonard's Terrace	SW3	p. 35	**FU**	
St. Martin's Lane	WC2	p. 37	**DY**	
St. Martin's-le-Grand	EC1	p. 27	**OU**	3
St. Pancras Way	NW1	p. 26	**KS**	
St. Paul's Road	N1	p. 27	**OS**	
St. Petersburgh Place	W2	p. 36	**BZ**	
St. Peter's Street	N1	p. 27	**OS**	
St. Thomas Street	SE1	p. 31	**PX**	
Sardinia Street	WC2	p. 37	**EV**	3
Savile Row	W1	p. 33	**DM**	
Savoy Place	WC2	p. 37	**DY**	
Savoy Street	WC2	p. 37	**EX**	
Scarsdale Villas	W8	p. 28	**EY**	
Seagrave Road	SW6	p. 28	**EZ**	
Serle Street	WC2	p. 37	**EV**	
Serpentine Road	W2	p. 32	**AP**	
Seymour Street	W1, W2	p. 32	**AK**	
Shaftesbury Avenue	W1, WC2	p. 33	**FL**	
Sheffield Terrace	W8	p. 28	**EX**	
Shelton Street	WC2	p. 37	**DX**	
Shepherdess Walk	N1	p. 27	**OT**	
Shepherd Market	W1	p. 32	**CN**	
Shepherd Street	W1	p. 32	**BP**	
Shirland Road	W9	p. 24	**ET**	

ɔreditch High Street ... E1 p. 27 **PT** 384
ɔrts Gardens ... WC2 p. 37 **DV**
mouth Street ... WC1 p. 26 **LT** 385
clair Road ... W14 p. 28 **EY**
ane Avenue ... SW3 p. 35 **ET**
ane Square ... SW1 p. 35 **FT**
ane Street ... SW1 p. 33 **FR**
ith Street ... SW3 p. 35 **EU**
ows Fields ... SE1 p. 31 **PX** 386
no Square ... W1 p. 33 **FJ**
ithampton Row ... WC1 p. 26 **LU** 387
ithampton Street ... WC2 p. 37 **DX** 388
ith Audley Street ... W1 p. 32 **BM**
ith Eaton Place ... SW1 p. 36 **AY** 389
ith End Road ... NW3 p. 24 **ES**
ith Hill ... NW3 p. 24 **ES** 390
ith Lambeth Road ... SW8 p. 30 **LZ**
ith Molton Street ... W1 p. 32 **BK**
ith Parade ... SW3 p. 34 **CU**
ith Place ... EC2 p. 27 **PU** 391
ith Street ... W1 p. 32 **BN**
ith Terrace ... SW7 p. 35 **DS**
ithwark Bridge ... SE1, EC4 p. 31 **OV** 395
ithwark Bridge Road ... SE1 p. 31 **OY**
ithwark Street ... SE1 p. 31 **OX**
ithwick Street ... W2 p. 37 **EZ**
a road ... SE16 p. 31 **PY**
encer Street ... EC1 p. 27 **NT** 398
tal Square ... E1 p. 27 **PU** 399
ing Street ... W2 p. 37 **DZ**
mford Street ... SE1 p. 30 **MX**
nhope Gardens ... SW7 p. 34 **BS**
nhope Place ... W2 p. 37 **EZ** 400
nhope Terrace ... W2 p. 37 **DZ**
r Road ... W14 p. 28 **EZ**
reys Gate ... SW1 p. 30 **LY** 402
and ... WC2 p. 37 **DY**
atton Street ... W1 p. 33 **DN**
nner Place ... SW7 p. 34 **CT**
nner Street ... SE1 p. 31 **OX**
Street ... EC2 p. 27 **PU**
rey Street ... WC2 p. 37 **EX**
sex Gardens ... W2 p. 37 **DZ**
sex Place ... W2 p. 37 **DZ**
sex Square ... W2 p. 37 **DZ** 404
herland Avenue ... W9 p. 24 **FU**
herland Street ... SW1 p. 29 **JZ**
inton Street ... WC1 p. 26 **LT**
Iney Place ... SW7 p. 35 **DT** 405
Iney Street ... SW3 p. 35 **DT**
nons Street ... SW3 p. 35 **FT** 407
ard Street ... SE1 p. 31 **OY** 408
nbrook Street ... SW1 p. 30 **KZ**
arth Road ... W14, W6 p. 28 **EZ**
stock Place ... WC1 p. 26 **LT**
stock Square ... WC1 p. 26 **LT** 409
stock Street ... WC2 p. 37 **DX**
worth Square ... SW3 p. 35 **EU**
nple Place ... WC2 p. 37 **EX**
npleton Place ... SW5 p. 28 **EZ** 410
minus Place ... SW1 p. 36 **BX** 412
yer Street ... W1 p. 32 **BJ** 413
obald's Road ... WC1 p. 26 **LU**
leby Road ... SW1 p. 36 **CX** 416
rnhill Road ... N1 p. 26 **MS**
eadneedle Street ... EC2 p. 27 **PV** 417
ogmorton Street ... EC2 p. 27 **PU** 418
rloe Place ... SW7 p. 34 **CS** 420
rloe Square ... SW7 p. 35 **DS**
rlow Street ... SE17 p. 31 **PZ**
ey Street ... W1 p. 32 **BN** 421
Street ... SW3 p. 35 **EU**
ley Street ... SE1 p. 31 **BX**
hill Street ... SW1 p. 30 **KY**
enham Court Road ... W1 p. 26 **KU**
ver Bridge ... E1 p. 31 **PX**
ver Bridge Road ... SE1 p. 31 **PY**
ver Hill ... EC3 p. 27 **PV** 425
algar Avenue ... SE15 p. 31 **PZ**
algar Square ... WC2, SW1 p. 37 **DY**
bovir Road ... SW5 p. 28 **FZ** 426
gunter Road ... SW10 p. 34 **BU**
vor Place ... SW7 p. 35 **EQ**
vor Square ... SW7 p. 35 **ER**
ity Church Square ... SE1 p. 31 **OY**
ity Street ... SE1 p. 31 **OY**
's Street ... SE11 p. 30 **MZ**
on Street ... SE1 p. 31 **NX**
er Belgrave Street ... SW1 p. 36 **AX**
er Berkeley Street ... W1 p. 37 **EZ**
er Brook Street ... W1 p. 32 **AM**
er Grosvenor Street ... W1 p. 32 **AM**
er Ground ... SE1 p. 31 **NX** 428

Upper St. Martin's Lane ... WC2 p. 37 **DX** 430
Upper Street ... N1 p. 27 **NS**
Upper Thames Street ... EC4 p. 27 **OV** 431
Upper Woburn Place ... WC1 p. 26 **LT** 432
Vale (The) ... SW3 p. 34 **CU**
Vanston Place ... SW6 p. 28 **EZ**
Vassal Road ... SW9 p. 31 **NZ**
Vauxhall Bridge ... SW1, SE1 p. 30 **LZ**
Vauxhall Bridge Road ... SW1 p. 36 **BY**
Vauxhall Street ... SE11 p. 30 **MZ**
Vauxhall Walk ... SE11 p. 30 **LZ**
Vere Street ... W1 p. 32 **BJ**
Victoria Embankment ... SW1
WC2, EC4 p. 37 **DY**
Victoria Grove ... W8 p. 34 **BR**
Victoria Road
KENSINGTON ... W8 p. 34 **BQ**
Victoria Street ... SW1 p. 36 **BX**
Vigo Street ... W1 p. 33 **EM**
Villiers Street ... WC2 p. 37 **DY**
Vincent Square ... SW1 p. 30 **KZ**
Vincent Street ... SW1 p. 30 **LZ** 436
Virginia Road ... E2 p. 27 **PT**
Walterton Road ... W9 p. 24 **ET**
Walton Street ... SW3 p. 35 **ES**
Walworth Road ... SE17 p. 31 **OZ**
Wandsworth Road ... SW8 p. 30 **LZ**
Wardour Street ... W1 p. 33 **FJ**
Warrington Crescent ... W9 p. 24 **FT**
Warwick Avenue ... W2, W9 p. 24 **FU** 441
Warwick Road ... SW5, W14 p. 28 **EZ**
Warwick Street ... W1 p. 33 **EM** 444
Warwick Way ... SW1 p. 29 **JZ**
Waterloo Bridge ... WC2, SE1 p. 37 **EY**
Waterloo Place ... SW1 p. 33 **FN**
Waterloo Road ... SE1 p. 31 **NY**
Waverton Street ... W1 p. 32 **BN**
Webber Street ... SE1 p. 31 **NY**
Weighhouse Street ... W1 p. 32 **BK**
Welbeck Street ... W1 p. 32 **BH**
Wellington Road ... NW8 p. 25 **GT**
Wellington Street ... WC2 p. 37 **DX**
Wells Street ... W1 p. 33 **EJ**
Wells Way ... SE5 p. 31 **PZ**
Well Walk ... NW3 p. 24 **ES**
Westbourne Crescent ... W2 p. 37 **DZ** 448
Westbourne Grove ... W2, W11 p. 36 **AZ**
Westbourne Park Road ... W2, W11 p. 24 **EU**
Westbourne Park Villas ... W2 p. 24 **FU** 449
Westbourne Street ... W2 p. 37 **DZ** 450
Westbourne Terrace ... W2 p. 37 **DZ**
Westbourne Road ... N7 p. 26 **MS**
Westbourne Terrace
Road ... W2 p. 24 **FU** 452
West Cromwell Road ... SW5, W14 p. 28 **EZ**
West Halkin Street ... SW1 p. 35 **FR**
Westminster Bridge ... SW1, SE1 p. 30 **LY**
Westminster Bridge Road ... SE1 p. 30 **MY**
Weston Street ... SE1 p. 31 **PY**
West Smithfield ... EC1 p. 27 **NU** 454
Westway ... N18 p. 24 **EU**
Wetherby Gardens ... SW5 p. 34 **BT**
Wharfdale Road ... N1 p. 26 **LS** 455
Wharf Road ... N1 p. 27 **OT**
Whiston Road ... E2 p. 27 **PS**
Whitcomb Street ... WC2 p. 33 **GM**
Whitechapel High Street ... E1 p. 27 **PU** 456
Whitecross Street ... EC1, EC2 p. 27 **OT**
Whitehall ... SW1 p. 30 **LX**
Whitehall Court ... SW1 p. 30 **LX** 460
Whitehall Place ... SW1 p. 30 **LX** 462
Whitehead's Grove ... SW3 p. 35 **ET** 463
Whitmore Road ... N1 p. 27 **PS** 464
Wigmore Street ... W1 p. 32 **BJ**
Wild Street ... WC2 p. 37 **DV**
William IV Street ... WC2 p. 37 **DY** 467
William Street ... SW1 p. 35 **FQ** 468
Willoughby Road ... NW3 p. 24 **ES** 470
Willow Road ... NW3 p. 24 **ES**
Willow Walk ... SE1 p. 31 **PY**
Wilson Street ... EC2 p. 27 **PU**
Wilton Place ... SW1 p. 35 **FQ**
Wilton Road ... SW1 p. 36 **BY**
Wilton Street ... SW1 p. 36 **AX**
Wimpole Street ... W1 p. 32 **BH**
Woburn Place ... WC1 p. 26 **LT**
Woods Mews ... W1 p. 32 **AL**
Wormwood Street ... EC2 p. 27 **PU** 472
Worship Street ... EC2 p. 27 **PU**
Wyndham Road ... SE5 p. 31 **OZ**
York Road ... SE1 p. 31 **MY**
York Way ... N1, N7 p. 26 **LS**
Young Street ... W8 p. 34 **AQ**

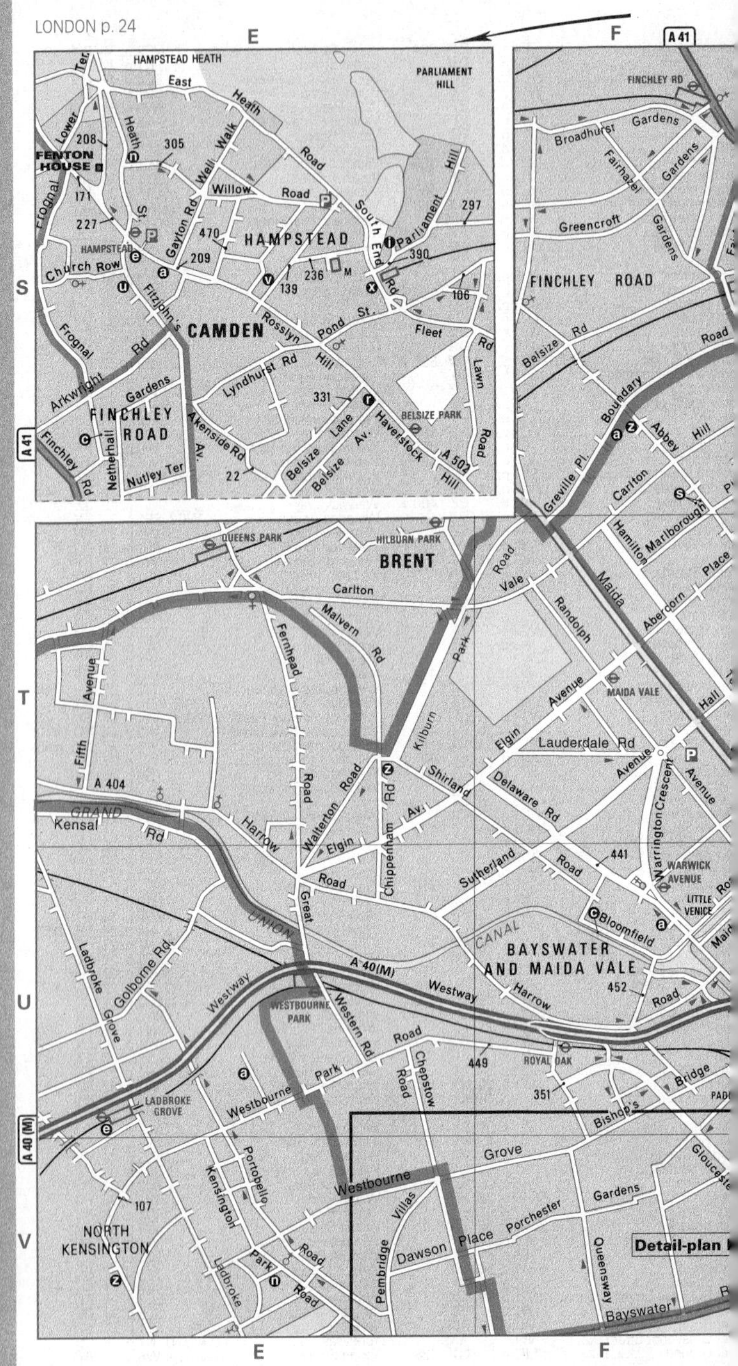
E
F
A 41
HAMPSTEAD HEATH
PARLIAMENT HILL
East Heath Road
Lower Ter.
Heath St.
Well Walk
Willow Road
South End Rd
Parliament Hill
FENTON HOUSE
Frognal
Gayton Rd
HAMPSTEAD
CAMDEN
Church Row
Fitzjohn's Av.
Rosslyn Hill
Pond St.
Fleet Rd
Lawn Road
Lyndhurst Rd
Arkwright Rd
Frognal
Gardens
FINCHLEY ROAD
Netherhall Gardens
Nutley Ter
Finchley Rd
Akenside Rd
Belsize Lane
Belsize Av.
Haverstock Hill
A 502
BELSIZE PARK
FINCHLEY RD
Broadhurst Gardens
Fairhazel Gardens
Greencroft Gardens
Belsize Rd
Boundary Road
Abbey Hill
Greville Pl.
Carlton
Hamilton
Marlborough Place
QUEENS PARK
KILBURN PARK
BRENT
Carlton Vale
Malvern Rd
Fernhead Road
Kilburn Park Road
Randolph
Maida Vale
Abercorn
Hall
MAIDA VALE
Fifth Avenue
Elgin Avenue
Lauderdale Rd
Warrington Crescent
Avenue
Shirland Rd
Delaware Rd
Walterton Road
Chippenham Rd
A 404
GRAND UNION CANAL
Kensal Rd
Harrow Road
Elgin Av.
Sutherland Avenue
WARWICK AVENUE
LITTLE VENICE
Bloomfield
Great Western Rd
BAYSWATER AND MAIDA VALE
A 40(M)
Westway
Ladbroke Grove
Golborne Rd.
Harrow Road
WESTBOURNE PARK
Westbourne Park Road
Chepstow Road
ROYAL OAK
Bishop's Bridge
LADBROKE GROVE
A 40 (M)
Portobello Road
Kensington Park Road
Westbourne Grove
Gloucester
Pembridge Villas
Dawson Place
Porchester Gardens
Queensway
Bayswater
NORTH KENSINGTON
Ladbroke
Detail-plan
S
T
U
V
208
305
171
227
470
209
139
236
M
390
297
106
331
22
441
452
449
351
107

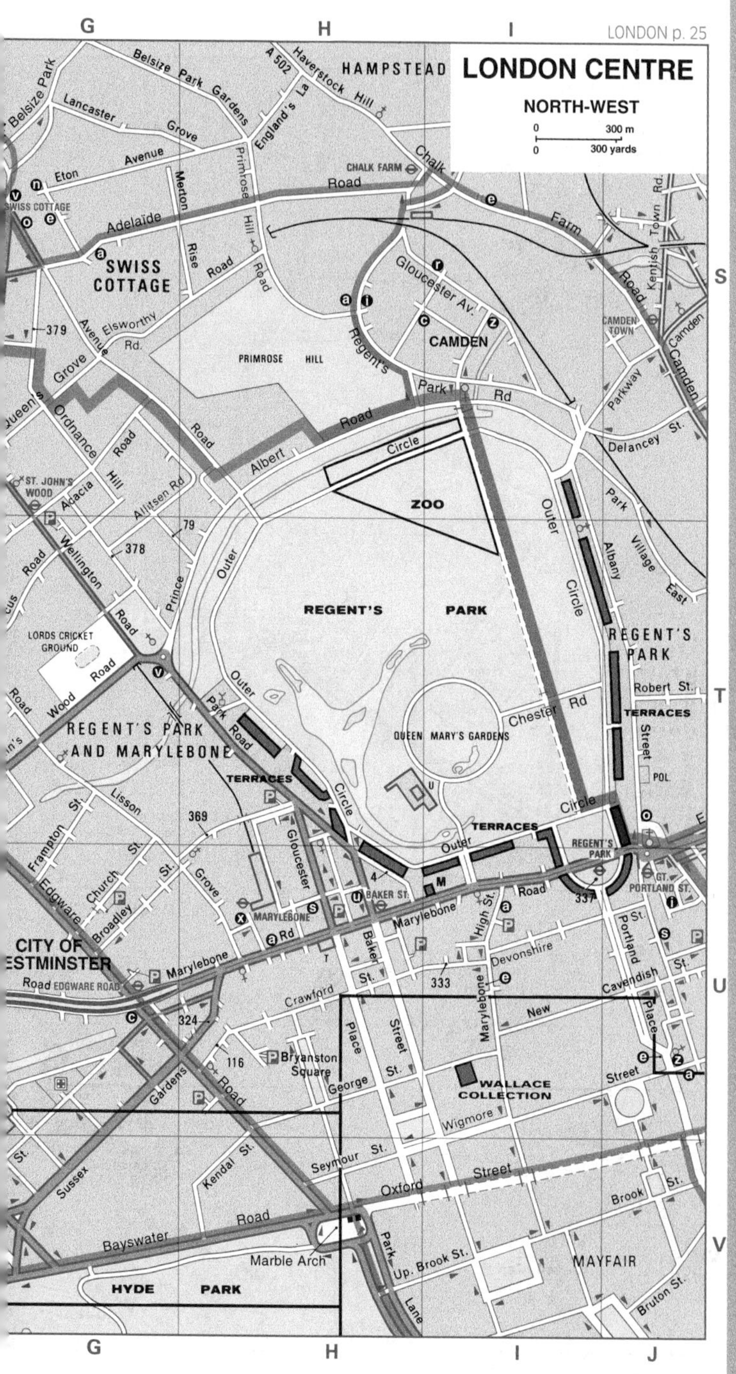
LONDON CENTRE
NORTH-WEST
0 300 m
0 300 yards
HAMPSTEAD
SWISS COTTAGE
CAMDEN
PRIMROSE HILL
ZOO
REGENT'S PARK
QUEEN MARY'S GARDENS
LORDS CRICKET GROUND
REGENT'S PARK AND MARYLEBONE
TERRACES
CITY OF WESTMINSTER
WALLACE COLLECTION
MAYFAIR
HYDE PARK
Marble Arch
Oxford Street
Baker St.
Marylebone Road
Bayswater Road
Edgware Road
Park Lane

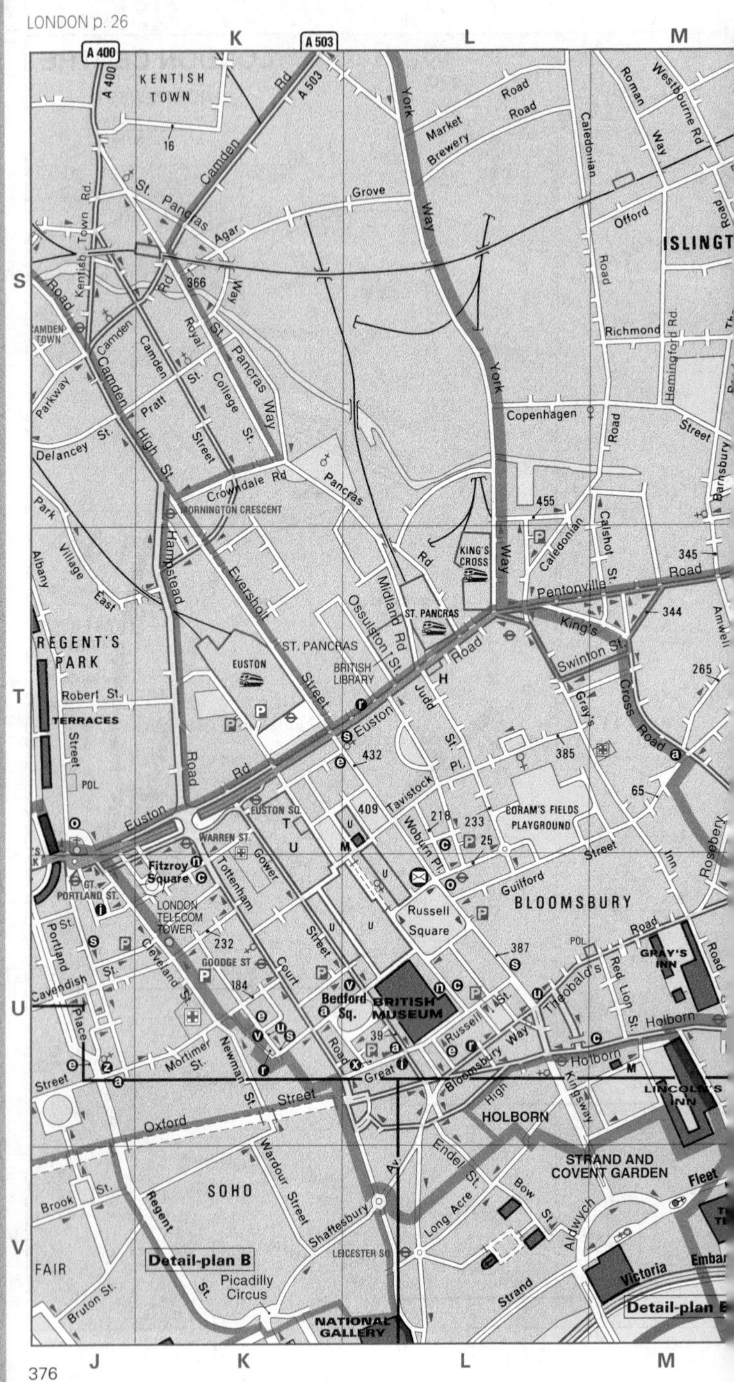
K
L
M
A 400
A 503
KENTISH TOWN
Camden Rd
York Way
Market Road
Brewery Road
Caledonian Road
Roman Way
Westbourne Rd
St. Pancras Way
Agar Grove
Offord Road
ISLINGT
Kentish Town Rd.
Royal College St.
Camden Rd
Camden St.
Camden High St.
Parkway
Pratt St.
Delancey St.
Richmond
Hemingford Rd.
Copenhagen Street
Barnsbury
Crowndale Rd
Pancras Rd
MORNINGTON CRESCENT
Park Village East
Albany Street
Hampstead Road
Eversholt Street
Midland Rd
Ossulston St.
KING'S CROSS
ST. PANCRAS
Calshot St.
Caledonian
Pentonville Road
King's Cross Road
Swinton St.
Amwell
REGENT'S PARK
EUSTON
BRITISH LIBRARY
Euston Road
Judd St.
Gray's Inn Road
Robert St.
TERRACES
POL.
Euston Rd
EUSTON SQ.
Tavistock Pl.
Woburn Pl.
CORAM'S FIELDS PLAYGROUND
WARREN ST.
Fitzroy Square
Gower Street
Tottenham Court Rd
GT. PORTLAND ST.
LONDON TELECOM TOWER
Guilford Street
BLOOMSBURY
Russell Square
Rosebery
Portland Pl.
Cleveland St.
GOODGE ST
Cavendish Place
Bedford Sq.
BRITISH MUSEUM
Theobald's Road
Red Lion St.
GRAY'S INN
Holborn
Mortimer St.
Newman St.
Bedford Road
Russell St.
Bloomsbury Way
Great Russell St.
Kingsway
LINCOLN'S INN
Oxford Street
HOLBORN
High Holborn
Endell St.
STRAND AND COVENT GARDEN
Fleet
Brook St.
SOHO
Wardour Street
Regent St.
Shaftesbury Av.
Long Acre
Bow St.
Aldwych
LEICESTER SQ.
FAIR
Bruton St.
Detail-plan B
Picadilly Circus
NATIONAL GALLERY
Strand
Victoria Embankment
S
T
U
V
J
16
366
455
345
344
265
385
65
432
409
218
233
25
232
184
387
39

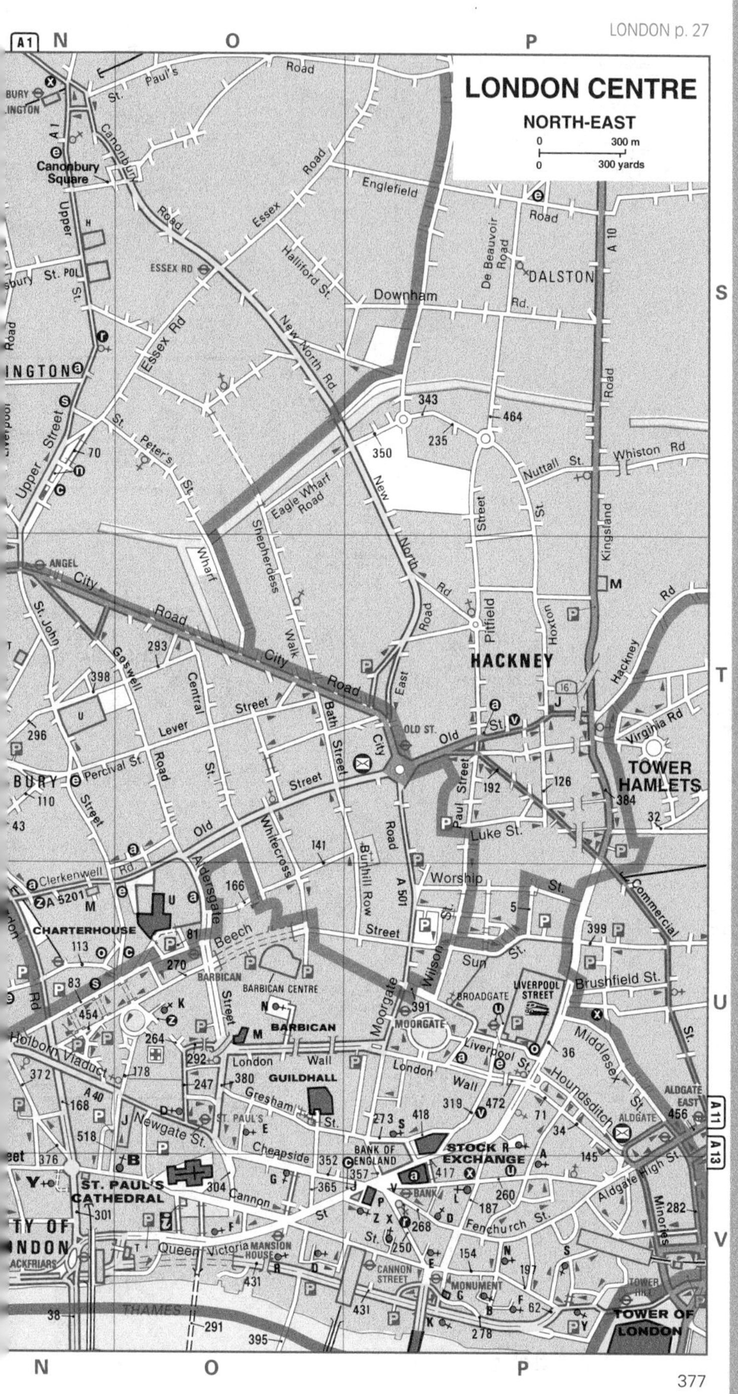
LONDON CENTRE
NORTH-EAST
0 300 m
0 300 yards
Canonbury Square
ESSEX RD
DALSTON
HACKNEY
TOWER HAMLETS
ANGEL
CHARTERHOUSE
BARBICAN
BARBICAN CENTRE
GUILDHALL
MOORGATE
LIVERPOOL STREET
BROADGATE
BANK OF ENGLAND
STOCK EXCHANGE
BANK
ST. PAUL'S CATHEDRAL
MANSION HOUSE
CANNON STREET
MONUMENT
ALDGATE
ALDGATE EAST
TOWER HILL
TOWER OF LONDON
THAMES
CITY OF LONDON
BLACKFRIARS
City Road
Old Street
New North Rd.
Kingsland Road
Upper Street
Essex Rd
Goswell Road
London Wall
Cheapside
Cannon St
Fenchurch St.
Houndsditch
Commercial
Whitecross
Moorgate
Bishopsgate
Aldersgate Street
Holborn Viaduct
Newgate St.
Queen Victoria
Aldgate High St.
Minories

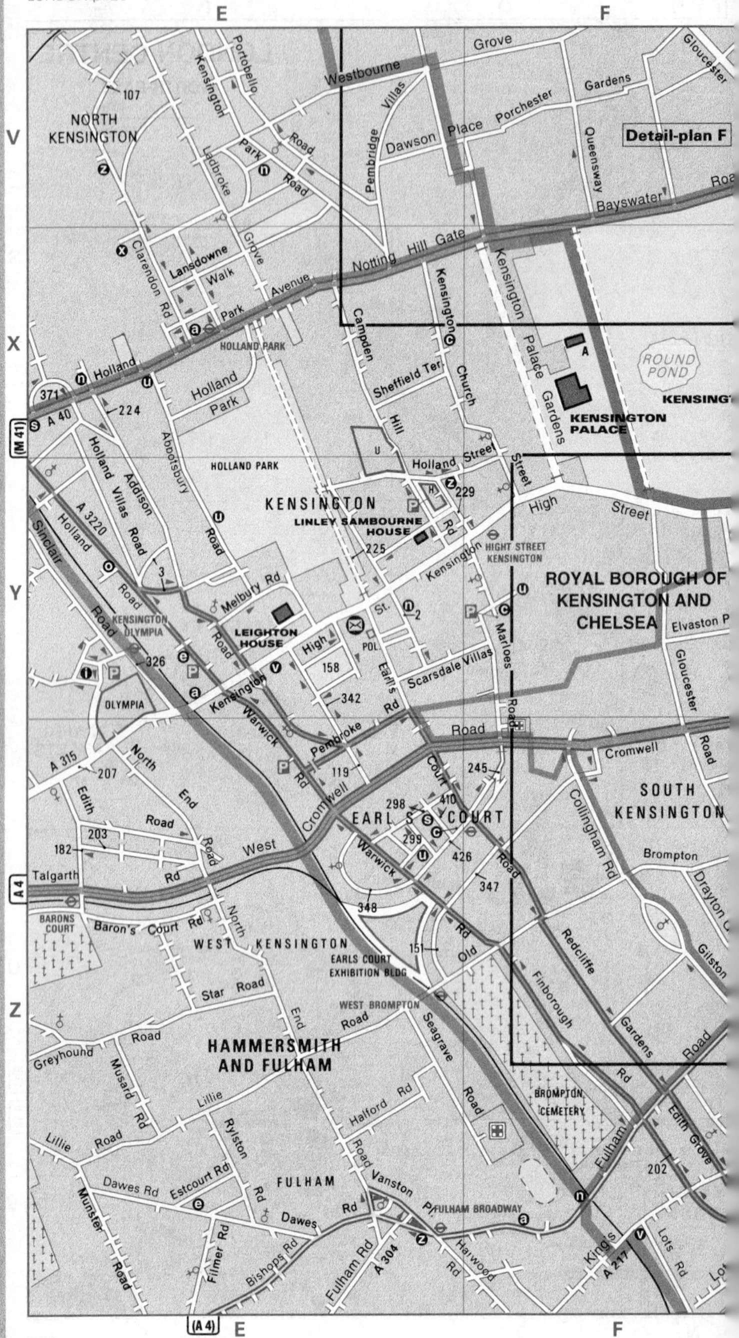

E F

V X Y Z

Detail-plan F

NORTH KENSINGTON

Westbourne Grove
Gloucester
Gardens
Porchester
Queensway
Bayswater Road
Portobello
Kensington Park Road
Ladbroke Grove
Pembridge Villas
Dawson Place
Notting Hill Gate
Lansdowne Walk
Clarendon Rd
Holland Park Avenue
HOLLAND PARK
Holland Park
Campden Hill
Kensington Church Street
Kensington Palace Gardens
Sheffield Ter.
ROUND POND
KENSINGTON PALACE
KENSINGTON
Holland Street
Holland
A 40
M 41
Holland Villas Road
Addison Road
Abbotsbury Road
HOLLAND PARK
KENSINGTON
LINLEY SAMBOURNE HOUSE
Kensington High Street
HIGH STREET KENSINGTON
ROYAL BOROUGH OF KENSINGTON AND CHELSEA
Elvaston Pl
Gloucester Road
Sinclair Road
Holland Road
A 3220
Melbury Rd
KENSINGTON OLYMPIA
LEIGHTON HOUSE
POL.
Earls Court Rd
Scarsdale Villas
Marloes Road
OLYMPIA
Warwick Road
Pembroke Road
Cromwell Road
SOUTH KENSINGTON
A 315
North End Road
Edith Road
EARL'S COURT
Collingham Rd
Brompton
Drayton Gardens
West Cromwell Rd
Talgarth Rd
A 4
BARONS COURT
Baron's Court Rd
WEST KENSINGTON
EARLS COURT EXHIBITION BLDG
Old Brompton Road
Redcliffe Gardens
Gilston
Star Road
WEST BROMPTON
Finborough Road
Greyhound Road
HAMMERSMITH AND FULHAM
Musard Rd
Seagrave Road
Lillie Road
Halford Rd
Rylston Rd
BROMPTON CEMETERY
Fulham Road
Edith Grove
Dawes Rd
Estcourt Rd
FULHAM
Vanston Pl.
FULHAM BROADWAY
Munster Road
Filmer Rd
Bishops Rd
Fulham Rd
A 304
Harwood Rd
King's Road
A 217
Lots Rd

107 371 224 3 229 225 2 326 158 342 207 119 245 298 410 203 182 299 426 347 348 151 202

(A 4) E F

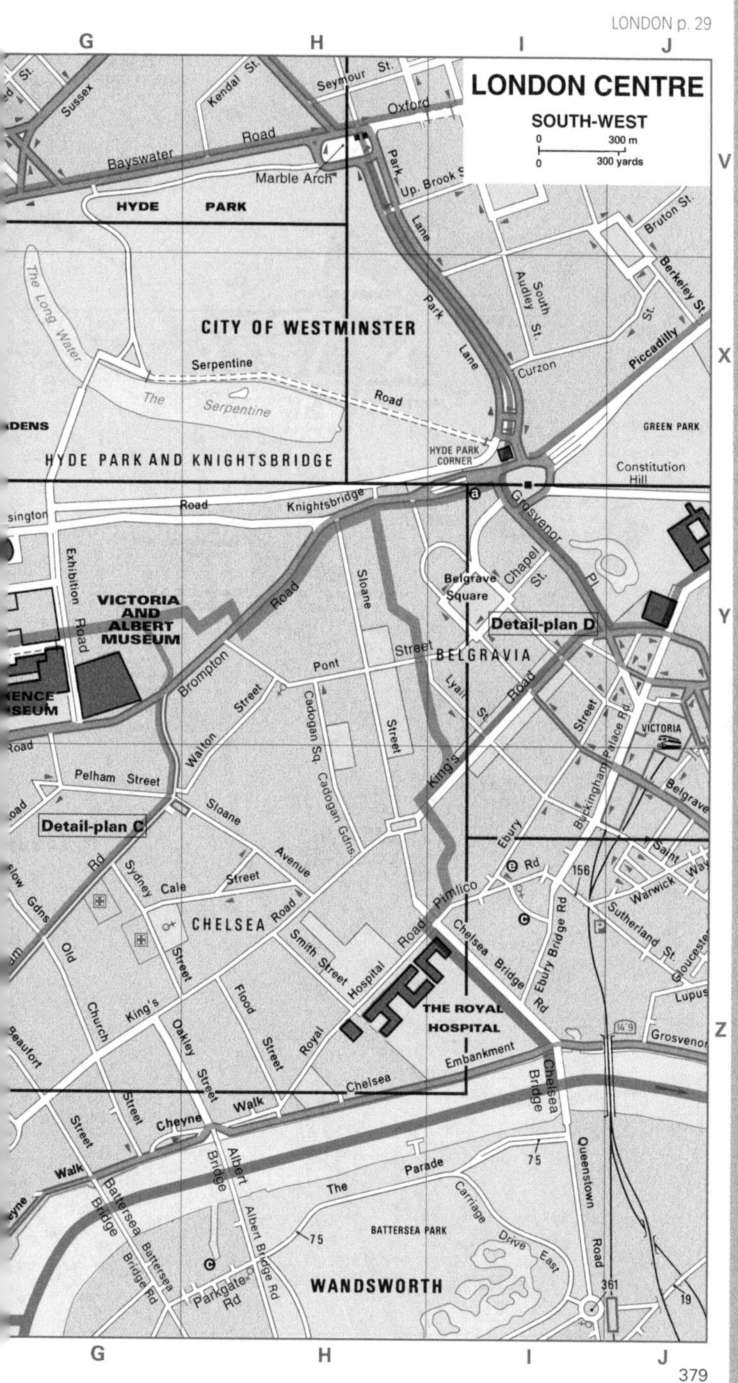
LONDON CENTRE
SOUTH-WEST
0 300 m
0 300 yards
G
H
I
J
V
X
Y
Z
HYDE PARK
CITY OF WESTMINSTER
HYDE PARK AND KNIGHTSBRIDGE
Bayswater Road
Marble Arch
Oxford
Park Lane
Up. Brook St.
South Audley St.
Curzon
Piccadilly
Berkeley St.
Bruton St.
GREEN PARK
HYDE PARK CORNER
Constitution Hill
Serpentine Road
The Serpentine
The Long Water
Knightsbridge
Grosvenor Pl.
Belgrave Square
Chapel St.
Detail-plan D
BELGRAVIA
VICTORIA AND ALBERT MUSEUM
Exhibition Road
Brompton Road
Sloane Street
Pont Street
Lyall St.
King's Road
Walton Street
Cadogan Sq.
Cadogan Gdns.
Pelham Street
Sloane Avenue
Detail-plan C
Sydney Street
Cale Street
CHELSEA
Smith Street
Royal Hospital Road
THE ROYAL HOSPITAL
Pimlico Road
Chelsea Bridge Rd
Ebury Bridge Rd
Ebury Rd
Buckingham Palace Rd.
VICTORIA
Belgrave
Warwick Way
Sutherland St.
Gloucester
Lupus
Grosvenor
Old Church Street
Flood Street
Oakley Street
Beaufort Street
Chelsea Embankment
Cheyne Walk
Albert Bridge
Battersea Bridge
Chelsea Bridge
Queenstown Road
The Parade
Carriage Drive East
BATTERSEA PARK
WANDSWORTH
Albert Bridge Rd
Battersea Bridge Rd
Parkgate Rd
156
75
361
19

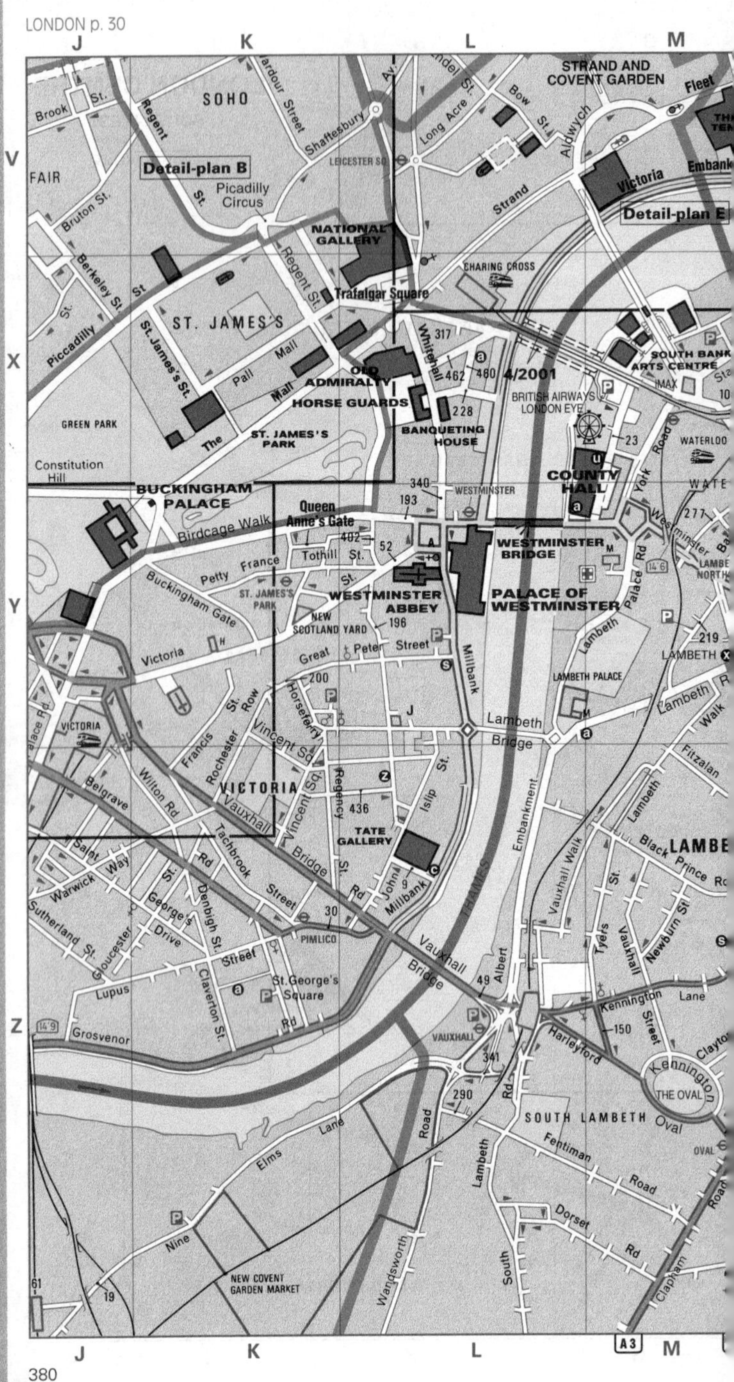
J
K
L
M
V
X
Y
Z
SOHO
STRAND AND
COVENT GARDEN
Fleet
Brook
St.
Regent
Wardour Street
Shaftesbury
Av.
Long Acre
Bow
St.
Aldwych
LEICESTER SQ.
Detail-plan B
FAIR
Picadilly
Circus
St.
Bruton St.
NATIONAL
GALLERY
Strand
Victoria
Embank
Detail-plan E
Berkeley St.
Regent St.
Trafalgar Square
CHARING CROSS
Piccadilly
St. James's St.
ST. JAMES'S
Pall
Mall
OLD
ADMIRALTY
Whitehall
317
462
480
4/2001
SOUTH BANK
ARTS CENTRE
IMAX
BRITISH AIRWAYS
LONDON EYE
HORSE GUARDS
228
GREEN PARK
The
Mall
ST. JAMES'S
PARK
BANQUETING
HOUSE
23
COUNTY
HALL
WATERLOO
York
Road
Constitution
Hill
BUCKINGHAM
PALACE
340
WESTMINSTER
193
Queen
Anne's Gate
Birdcage Walk
402
52
Tothill
St.
WESTMINSTER
BRIDGE
277
Westminster
Petty
France
Buckingham Gate
ST. JAMES'S
PARK
WESTMINSTER
ABBEY
PALACE OF
WESTMINSTER
Palace
Rd
LAMBETH NORTH
NEW
SCOTLAND YARD
196
Lambeth
219
LAMBETH
Victoria
Great
Peter
Street
Millbank
LAMBETH PALACE
200
Horseferry
Rochester
Row
St.
Francis
Lambeth
Bridge
Lambeth
Walk
Vincent Sq.
Regency
St.
Islip
Fitzalan
VICTORIA
Palace Rd
Wilton Rd
Belgrave
VICTORIA
Vauxhall
436
TATE
GALLERY
Embankment
Lambeth
Black Prince
Rd
LAMBE
Saint
Way
Warwick
Tachbrook
Street
Bridge
Rd
John
Millbank
THAMES
Vauxhall Walk
Tyers
St.
Vauxhall
Newburn St
Sutherland St.
Gloucester
George's
Drive
Denbigh St.
30
PIMLICO
Vauxhall
Bridge
Street
Albert
Claverton St.
St.George's
Square
Lupus
49
Kennington
Lane
Rd
150
14'9
Grosvenor
VAUXHALL
341
Harleyford
Kennington
THE OVAL
Clayton
290
SOUTH LAMBETH
Oval
Road
Rd
Lane
Elms
Lambeth
Fentiman
Road
OVAL
Dorset
Rd
Road
Nine
NEW COVENT
GARDEN MARKET
Wandsworth
South
Clapham
61
19
A3

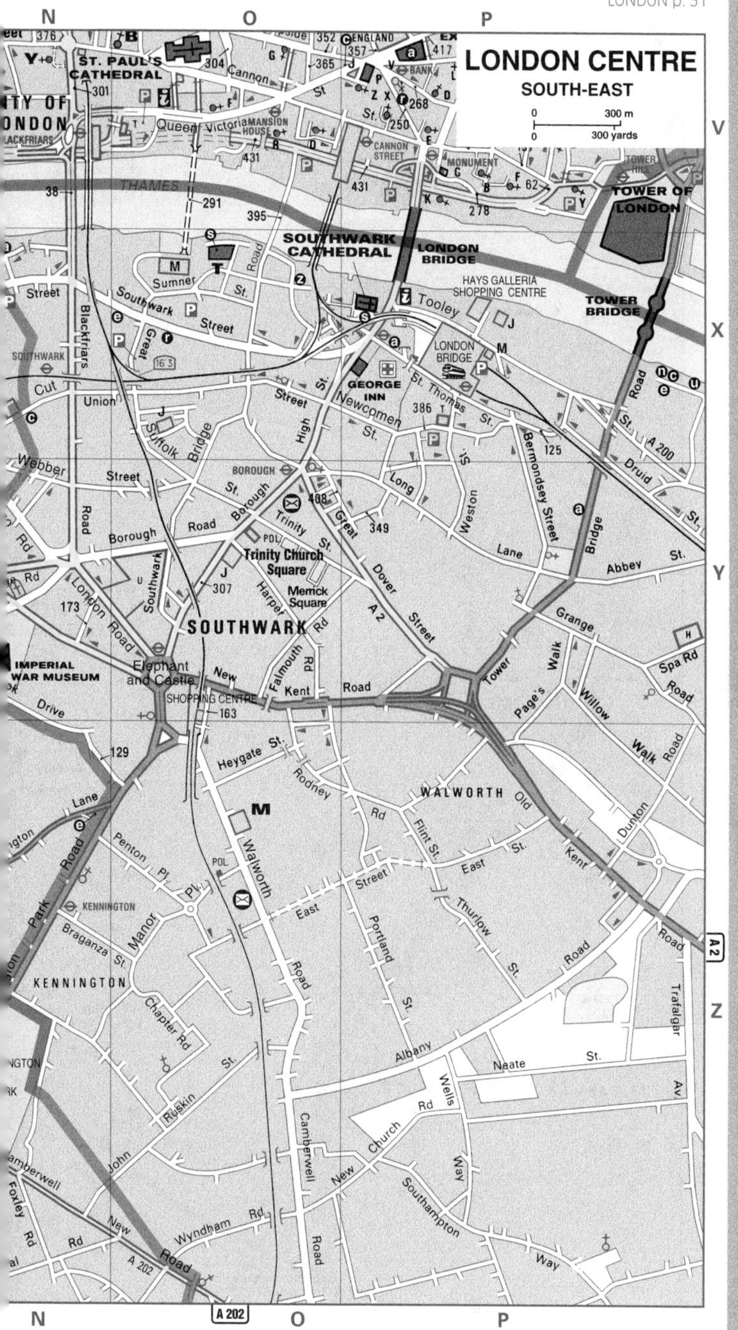
LONDON CENTRE
SOUTH-EAST
0 300 m
0 300 yards
ST. PAUL'S CATHEDRAL
SOUTHWARK CATHEDRAL
LONDON BRIDGE
TOWER OF LONDON
TOWER BRIDGE
HAYS GALLERIA SHOPPING CENTRE
GEORGE INN
Trinity Church Square
Merrick Square
SOUTHWARK
IMPERIAL WAR MUSEUM
Elephant and Castle
SHOPPING CENTRE
WALWORTH
KENNINGTON
THAMES
CANNON STREET
MONUMENT
MANSION HOUSE
BANK
BOROUGH
KENNINGTON
Cannon St
Queen Victoria
Southwark Street
Sumner St.
Great
Blackfriars Road
Union Street
Cut
Webber Street
Suffolk
Borough Road
Borough High St.
Trinity St.
Great Dover Street
A 2
Long Lane
Weston St.
Bermondsey Street
Tower Bridge Road
A 200
Druid St.
Abbey St.
Grange
Spa Rd
Page's Walk
Willow Walk
Tooley St.
St. Thomas St.
Newcomen St.
London Road
Harper Rd
Falmouth Rd
New Kent Road
Heygate St.
Rodney Rd
Flint St.
East St.
Thurlow St.
Portland St.
Walworth Road
Old Kent Road
Dunton Road
Trafalgar Av
Albany Road
Neate St.
Wells Way
Church Rd
New Church
Camberwell Road
Southampton Way
Wyndham Rd
John Ruskin St.
Chapter Rd
Manor Pl.
Penton Pl.
Braganza St.
Kennington Park Road
Kennington Lane
Camberwell New Road
Foxley Rd
A 202
A 2
POL.
N
O
P
V
X
Y
Z

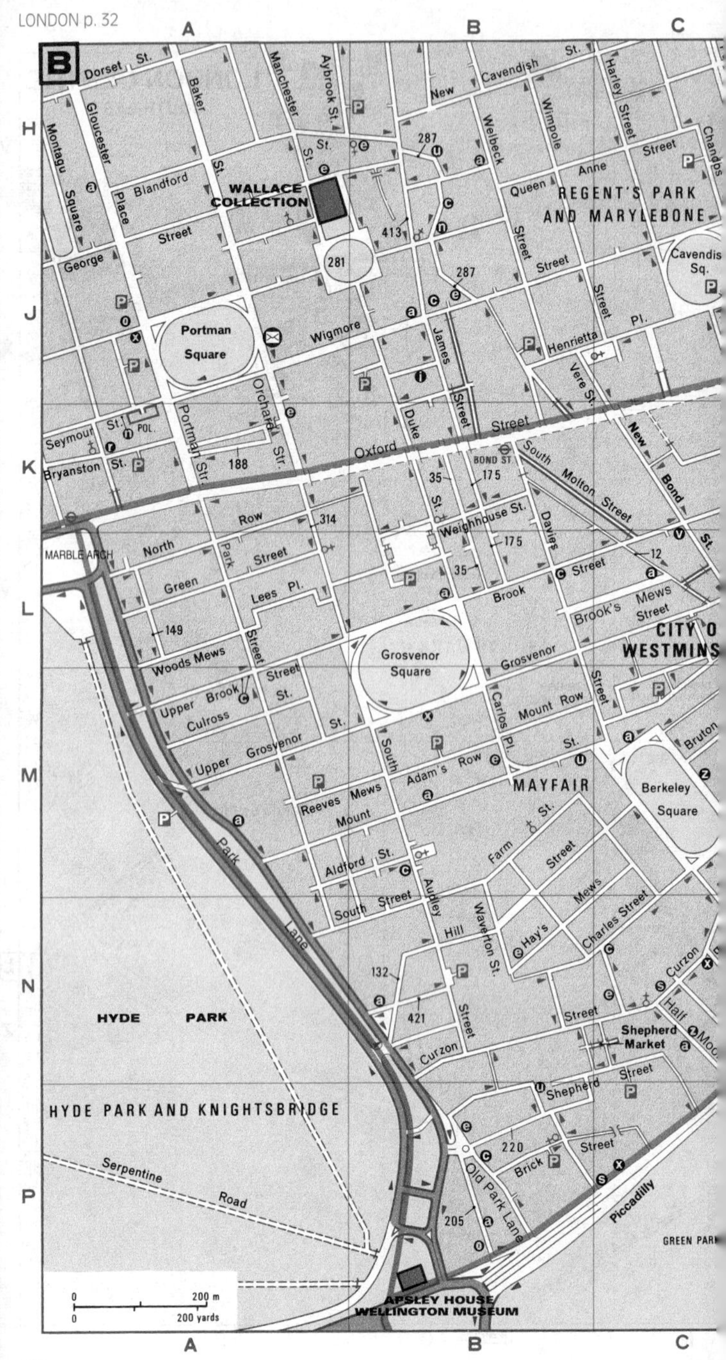
B
A
B
C
H
J
K
L
M
N
P
WALLACE COLLECTION
REGENT'S PARK AND MARYLEBONE
Portman Square
Cavendish Sq.
MARBLE ARCH
Grosvenor Square
CITY OF WESTMINSTER
MAYFAIR
Berkeley Square
HYDE PARK
HYDE PARK AND KNIGHTSBRIDGE
Shepherd Market
GREEN PARK
APSLEY HOUSE WELLINGTON MUSEUM
Dorset St.
Baker St.
Manchester St.
Aybrook St.
New Cavendish St.
Harley Street
Welbeck Street
Wimpole Street
Montagu Square
Gloucester Place
Blandford Street
Queen Anne Street
George Street
Wigmore Street
James Street
Duke St.
Henrietta Pl.
Vere St.
Orchard Str.
Portman Str.
Seymour St.
Bryanston St.
Oxford Street
BOND ST.
South Molton Street
New Bond St.
North Row
Park Street
Green St.
Weighhouse St.
Davies Street
Brook Street
Brook's Mews
Lees Pl.
Woods Mews
Upper Brook Street
Culross St.
Upper Grosvenor St.
Grosvenor Street
Carlos Pl.
Mount Row
Bruton
South Audley Street
Adam's Row
Reeves Mews
Mount St.
Farm Street
Aldford St.
South Street
Hill St.
Waverton St.
Hay's Mews
Charles Street
Curzon Street
Half Moon
Park Lane
Shepherd Street
Brick Street
Old Park Lane
Piccadilly
Serpentine Road
287
413
281
188
175
35
314
12
149
132
421
220
205
0 200 m
0 200 yards

lington Street . . . . **DN** 6	Dunraven Street . . . . **AL** 149	Manchester Square . . . . . . **AJ** 281
very Row . . . . **CL** 12	Gerrard Street . . . . **GL** 174	Market Place . . . . **DJ** 286
ateman Street . . . . **FK** 18	Gilbert Street . . . . **BL** 175	Marylebone Lane . . . . **BJ** 287
erwick Street . . . . **FK** 26	Glasshouse Street . . . . **EM** 179	North Audley Street . . . . . . **AK** 314
nney Street . . . . **BL** 35	Granville Place . . . . **AK** 188	Old Burlington Street . . . . **DM** 322
arlton Gardens . . . . **FP** 74	Great Castle Street . . . . . . **DJ** 189	Old Compton Street . . . . . **GK** 323
eanery Street . . . . **BN** 132	Greek Street . . . . **GK** 198	Panton Street . . . . **FM** 336
enman Street . . . . **FM** 133	Hamilton Place . . . . **BP** 205	Romilly Street . . . . **GL** 368
enmark Street . . . . **GJ** 134	Hanover Square . . . . **CK** 210	Thayer Street . . . . **BJ** 413
uke of York Street . . . . . . **EN** 143	Hertford Street . . . . **BP** 220	Tilney Street . . . . **BN** 421
uke Street ST. JAMES . . **EN** 146	Leicester Square . . . . **GM** 261	Warwick Street . . . . **EM** 444

Oxford Street is closed to private traffic, Mondays to Saturdays : from 7 am to 9 pm between Portman Street and St. Giles Circus

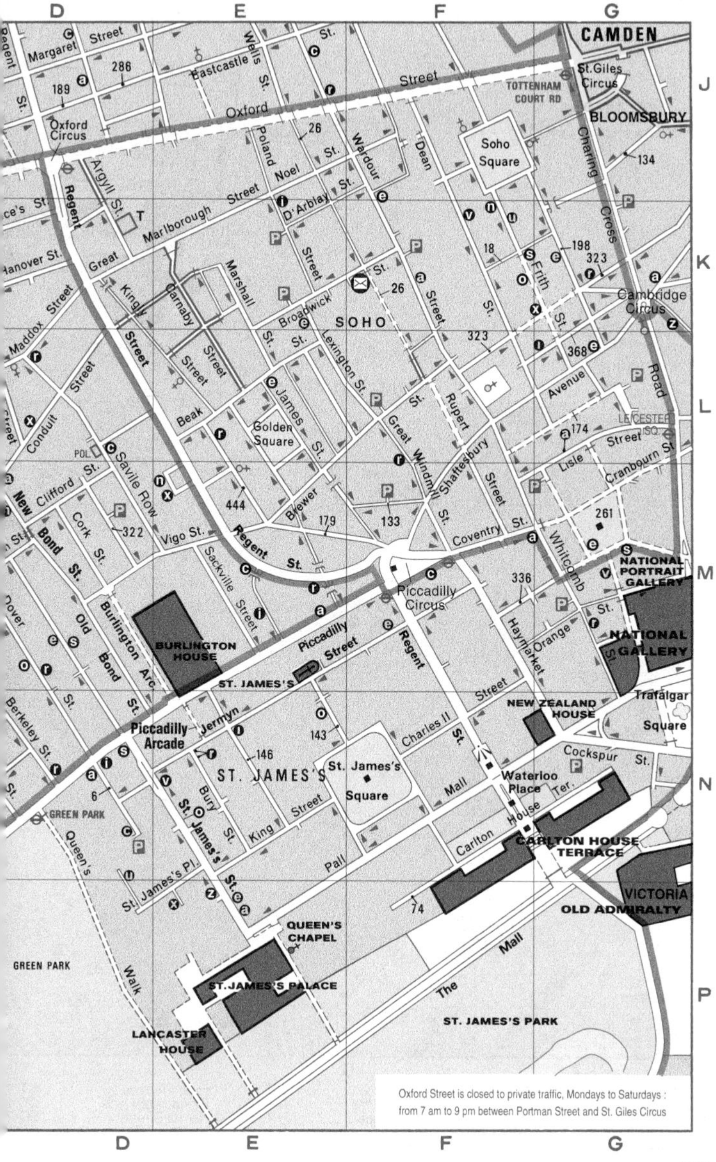

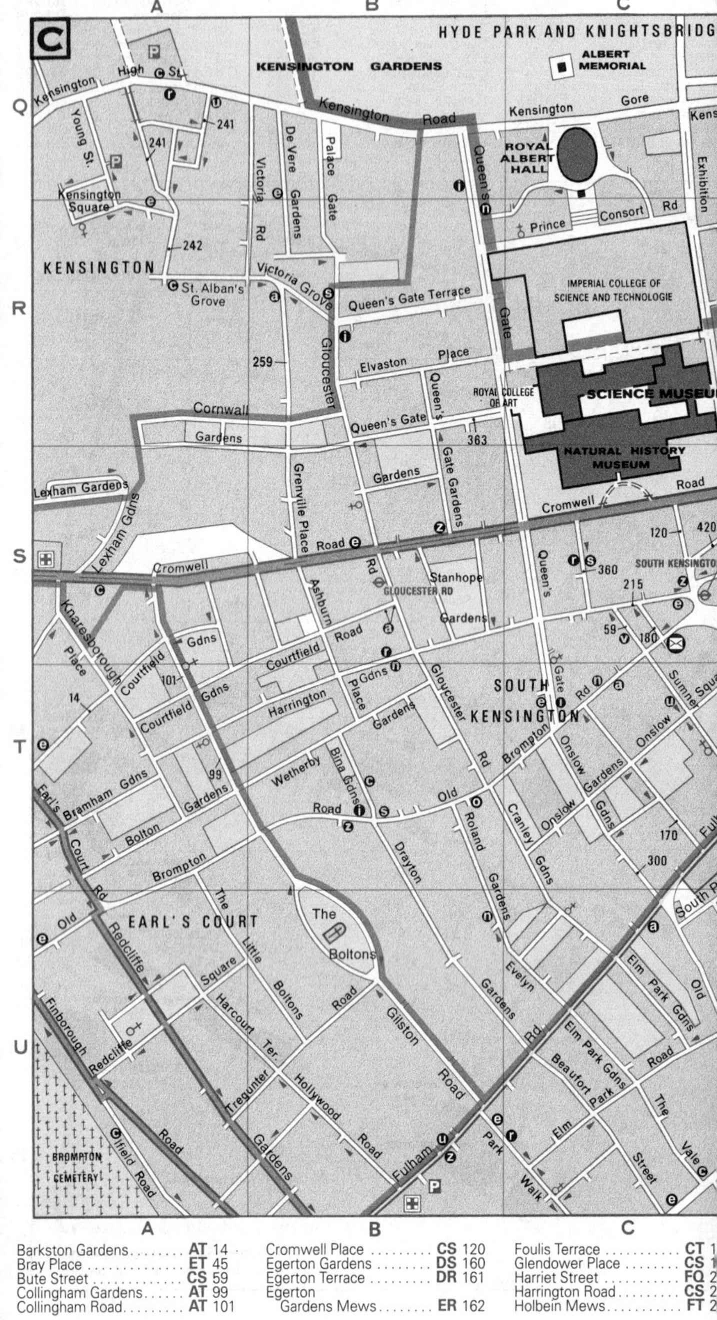
A
B
C
C
HYDE PARK AND KNIGHTSBRIDG
KENSINGTON GARDENS
ALBERT MEMORIAL
Kensington High St.
Kensington Road
Kensington Gore
ROYAL ALBERT HALL
Q
Young St.
241
Kensington Square
Victoria Rd
De Vere Gardens
Palace Gate
Queen's Gate
Exhibition
Prince Consort Rd
242
KENSINGTON
St. Alban's Grove
Victoria Grove
Queen's Gate Terrace
IMPERIAL COLLEGE OF SCIENCE AND TECHNOLOGIE
R
259
Gloucester
Elvaston Place
ROYAL COLLEGE OF ART
SCIENCE MUSEUM
Cornwall Gardens
Queen's Gate
Gardens
363
NATURAL HISTORY MUSEUM
Lexham Gardens
Grenville Place
Gate Gardens
Cromwell Road
Lexham Gdns
120
420
S
Cromwell
Road
Rd
Stanhope
GLOUCESTER RD
Gardens
Queen's
360
SOUTH KENSINGTON
215
Knaresborough Place
Ashburn
Gdns
Courtfield Road
59
180
Courtfield Gdns
101
Gdns
Gloucester
SOUTH KENSINGTON
Gate
Rd
Sumner
14
Courtfield Gardens
Harrington Gardens
Place
Brompton
Rd
Onslow
T
Earl's
Bramham Gdns
99
Gardens
Wetherby
Bina Gdns
Old
Road
Onslow Gardens
Onslow Gdns
Cranley Gdns
Bolton
Court
Brompton
Drayton
Roland Gardens
170
300
Rd
Old
EARL'S COURT
The Little Boltons
The Boltons
South P
Redcliffe
Square
Harcourt Ter.
Bolton Road
Gilston
Evelyn Gardens
Elm Park Gdns
Old
Finborough
Redcliffe
U
Tregunter
Hollywood
Road
Elm Park Gdns
Beaufort
Park
Road
The
BROMPTON CEMETERY
Road
Ifield Road
Gardens
Road
Fulham
Park Walk
Elm
Street
Vale
A
B
C

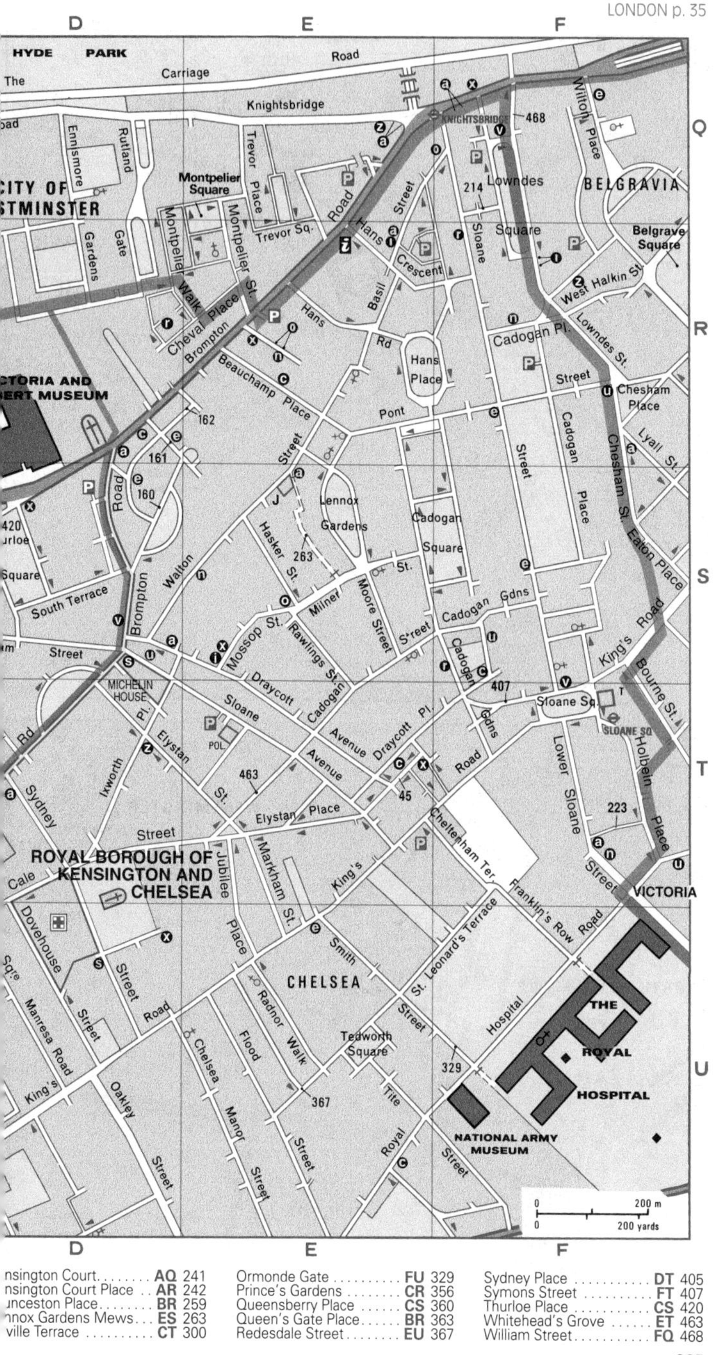

D
E
F
Q
R
S
T
U
HYDE PARK
The Carriage Road
Knightsbridge
KNIGHTSBRIDGE
468
Ennismore Gardens
Rutland Gate
Montpelier Square
Trevor Place
Trevor Sq.
Montpelier Walk
Montpelier St.
CITY OF
STMINSTER
Cheval Place
Brompton Road
Hans Road
Hans Crescent
Basil Street
Hans Rd
Hans Place
Sloane Street
Lowndes Square
214
BELGRAVIA
Wilton Place
Belgrave Square
West Halkin St.
Cadogan Pl.
Lowndes St.
Chesham Place
Lyall St.
Chesham St.
Eaton Place
Beauchamp Place
Pont Street
CTORIA AND
ERT MUSEUM
162
161
160
Walton Street
Lennox Gardens
Cadogan Square
Cadogan Place
Hasker St.
263
Milner St.
Moore Street
Mossop St.
Rawlings St.
Cadogan Street
Cadogan Gdns
Cadogan Gdns
South Terrace
Brompton Road
Street
MICHELIN HOUSE
Draycott Avenue
Sloane Avenue
Draycott Pl.
Cadogan Gdns
407
Sloane Sq.
SLOANE SQ.
King's Road
Bourne St.
Holbein Place
Lower Sloane Street
223
VICTORIA
Elystan Pl.
Elystan St.
463
Elystan Place
45
Road
Ixworth Pl.
POL.
Sydney Street
Cheltenham Ter.
Franklin's Row
ROYAL BOROUGH OF
KENSINGTON AND
CHELSEA
Cale Street
Jubilee Place
Markham St.
King's Road
St. Leonard's Terrace
Smith Street
Dovehouse Street
Manresa Road
Sq.re
CHELSEA
Radnor Walk
Flood Street
Chelsea Manor Street
Tedworth Square
Tite Street
Hospital Road
329
367
King's Road
Oakley Street
Royal Hospital Road
Street
THE ROYAL HOSPITAL
NATIONAL ARMY MUSEUM
0 200 m
0 200 yards

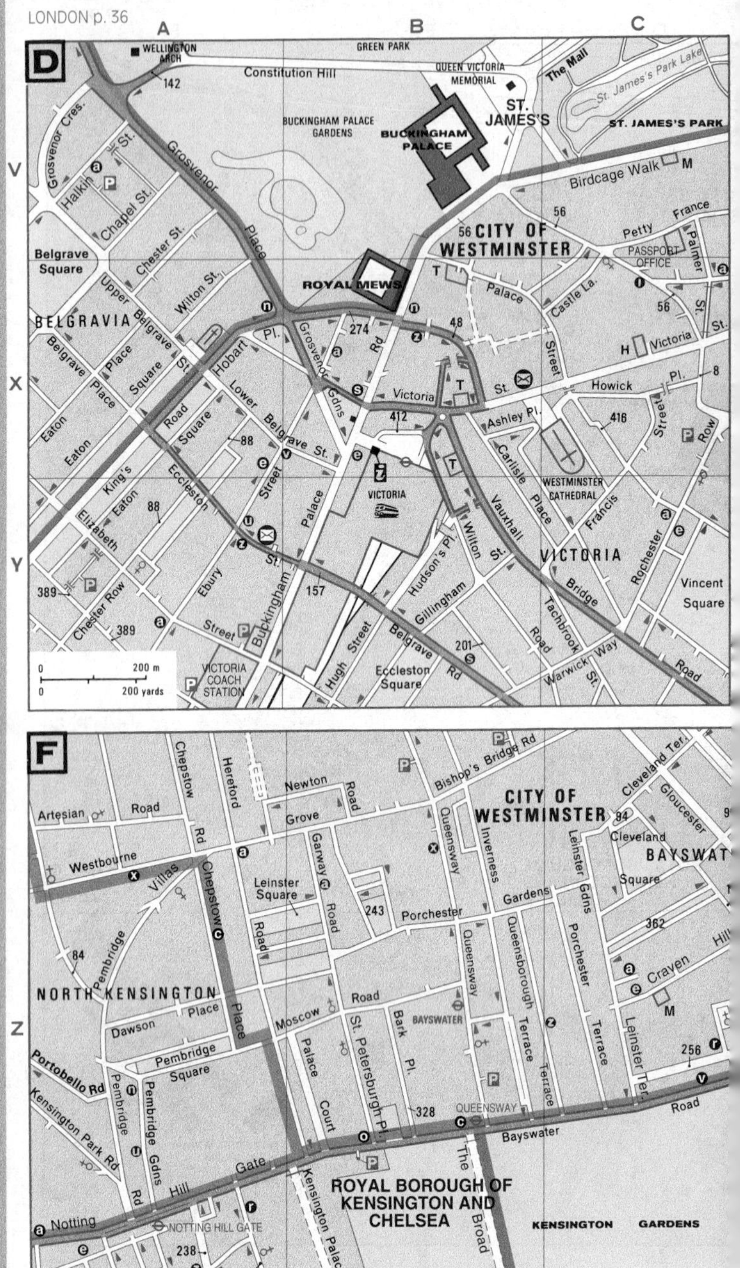
D
WELLINGTON ARCH
GREEN PARK
Constitution Hill
QUEEN VICTORIA MEMORIAL
The Mall
St. James's Park Lake
ST. JAMES'S
ST. JAMES'S PARK
BUCKINGHAM PALACE GARDENS
BUCKINGHAM PALACE
Grosvenor Place
Birdcage Walk
CITY OF WESTMINSTER
Petty France
PASSPORT OFFICE
Belgrave Square
ROYAL MEWS
BELGRAVIA
Victoria St.
WESTMINSTER CATHEDRAL
VICTORIA
Vincent Square
VICTORIA COACH STATION
Eccleston Square
Vauxhall Bridge Road
F
CITY OF WESTMINSTER
BAYSWAT
NORTH KENSINGTON
BAYSWATER
QUEENSWAY
Bayswater Road
Notting Hill Gate
NOTTING HILL GATE
ROYAL BOROUGH OF KENSINGTON AND CHELSEA
KENSINGTON GARDENS
The Broad Walk
Kensington Palace Gardens
KENSINGTON
0 200 m
0 200 yards

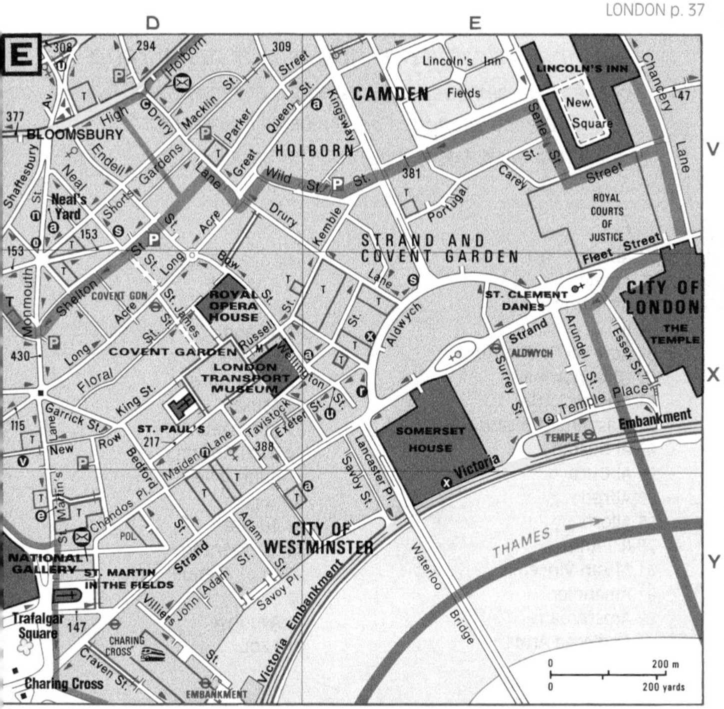

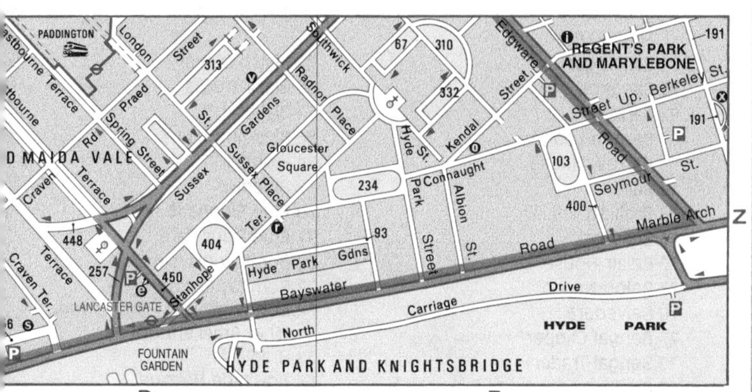
PADDINGTON
London
Street
Praed
Spring Street
Southwick
Radnor
Place
Gardens
Gloucester
Square
Sussex Place
Sussex
MAIDA VALE
Terrace
Craven
Craven Ter.
Terrace
Hyde St.
Kendal
Connaught
Park
Street
Albion
St.
Edgware
Street
Road
REGENT'S PARK
AND MARYLEBONE
Up. Berkeley St.
Street
Seymour
St.
Marble Arch
Road
Hyde Park Gdns
Bayswater
Stanhope
Ter.
LANCASTER GATE
FOUNTAIN
GARDEN
Carriage
Drive
North
HYDE PARK
HYDE PARK AND KNIGHTSBRIDGE

Alphabetical list of hotels and restaurants

Liste alphabétique des hôtels et restaurants

Elenco alfabetico degli alberghi e ristoranti

Alphabetisches Hotel- und Restaurantverzeichnis

C

D

E

F

G

H

I

J

K

L

M

S

T

U - V - W

X - Y - Z

Starred establishments in London

Les établissements à étoiles de Londres
Gli esercizi con stelle a Londra
Die Stern-Restaurants in London

✿✿✿

67	*Chelsea*	XXXX	Gordon Ramsay

✿✿

66	*Chelsea*	🏨	Capital
87	*Regent's Park & Marylebone*	XXXXX	John Burton-Race
84	*Mayfair*	XXXX	Le Gavroche
82	*Belgravia*	XXXX	La Tante Clair
84	*Mayfair*	XXX	The Square

✿

83	*Mayfair*	🏨	Connaught
81	*Belgravia*	🏨	The Halkin
84	*Mayfair*	XXXXX	The Oak Room Marco Pierre White
67	*Chelsea*	XXX	Aubergine
53	*Farnborough*	XXX	Chapter One
57	*City of London*	XXX	City Rhodes
90	*Soho*	XXX	L'Escargot
54	*Bloomsbury*	XXX	High Holborn
84	*Mayfair*	XXX	Mirabelle
57	*City of London*	XXX	1 Lombard Street (Restaurant)
89	*St James's*	XXX	L'Oranger
88	*Regent's Park & Marylebone*	XXX	Orrery
89	*St James's*	XXX	Pétrus
79	*Putney*	XXX	Putney Bridg
93	*Victoria*	XXX	Rhodes in th Square
76	*Hampton Hill*	XX	Monsieur Ma
85	*Mayfair*	XX	Nobu
54	*Bloomsbury*	XX	Pied à Terre
90	*Soho*	XX	Richard Corrigan at Lindsay Hous
61	*Hammersmith*	XX	River Café
93	*Victoria*	XX	Roussillon
85	*Mayfair*	XX	Tamarind
82	*Belgravia*	XX	Zafferano
67	*Chelsea*	XX	Zaika
79	*Wandsworth*	X	Chez Bruce

Good food at moderate prices

Repas soignés à prix modérés

Pasti accurati a prezzi contenuti

Sorgfältig zubereitete, preiswerte Mahlzeiten

 **"Bib Gourmand"**

Kensington	XX	L'Anis
Battersea	XX	Cafe Spice Namaste
Whitechapel	XX	Cafe Spice Namaste
Greenwich	XX	Chapter Two
Kew	XX	The Glasshouse
Chelsea	XX	Jak's
East Sheen	XX	Redmond's
Bayswater & Maida Vale	X	L'Accento
St. James's	X	Al Duca
Southwark	X	Cantina Vinopolis (Brasserie)

Page	Area		Restaurant
68	*Chelsea*	X	(I) Cardi
89	*Regent's Park and Marylebone*	X	Chada Chada
91	*Soho*	X	Il Forno
75	*Wimbledon*	X	Light House
73	*Surbiton*	X	Luca
71	*Kensington*	X	Malabar
79	*Battersea*	X	Metrogusto
55	*Bloomsbury*	X	Passione
79	*Putney*	X	The Phoenix
53	*Brent*	X	Sabras
79	*Southfields*	X	Sarkhels
81	*Bayswater & Maida Vale*	X	The Vale

Particularly pleasant hotels and restaurants

Hôtels et restaurants agréables

Alberghi e ristoranti ameni

Angenehme Hotels und Restaurants

81 *Belgravia* The Berkeley
82 *Mayfair* Claridge's
82 *Mayfair* Dorchester
82 *Hyde Park & Knightsbridge* Mandarin Orient Hyde Park
89 *St James's* Ritz
Savoy
91 *Strand & Covent Garden*

80 *Mayfair* Connaught

71 *South Kensington* Blakes
66 *Chelsea* Capital
87 *Regent's Park & Marylebone* Charlotte Street
66 *Chelsea* Cliveden Town House
54 *Bloomsbury* Covent Garden
66 *Chelsea* Durley House
93 *Victoria* The Goring
81 *Belgravia* The Halkin
92 *Strand & Covent Garden* One Aldwych
71 *South Kensington* Pelham

89 *St. James's* 22 Jermyn Street

89 *St. James's* The Restaurant (at Ritz H.)

84 *Mayfair* Grill Room

88 *Regent's Park & Marylebone* Orrery
77 *Southwark* Oxo Tower
76 *Bermondsey* Le Pont de la Tou

90 *St. James's* Quaglino's

Restaurants classified according to type

Restaurants classés suivant leur genre

Ristoranti classificati secondo il loro genere

Restaurants nach Art und Einrichtung geordnet

hinese

Page	Area	Class	Restaurant
	Mayfair	XXXX	The Oriental
	St James's	XXX	Orient
	Richmond	XX	Four Regions
	Mill Hill	XX	Good Earth
	Chelsea	XX	Good Earth
	South Woodford	XX	Ho-Ho
	City of London	XX	Imperial City
	Mayfair	XX	Kai
	Victoria	XX	Ken Lo's Memories of China
61	*Fulham*	XX	Mao Tai
59	*Ealing*	XX	Maxim
70	*Kensington*	XX	Memories of China
82	*Hyde Park & Knightsbridge*	XX	Mr Chow
81	*Bayswater & Maida Vale*	XX	Poons
53	*Orpington*	XX	Xian
55	*Hampstead*	XX	ZeNW3
90	*St James's*	X	China House
91	*Soho*	X	Fung Shing
59	*Croydon*	X	Tai Tung

anish

Area	Class	Restaurant
South Kensington	XX	Lundum's

astern Mediterranean

Area	Class	Restaurant
Regent's Park & Marylebone	XX	Levant

nglish

Page	Area	Class	Restaurant
	Mayfair	XXXX	Grill Room
	Victoria	XXX	Shepherd's
92	*Strand & Covent Garden*	XX	Rules

lipino

Area	Class	Restaurant
Bloomsbury	X	Josephine's

rench

Page	Area	Class	Restaurant
	Regent's Park & Marylebone	XXXXX	✿✿ John Burton-Race
	Mayfair	XXXX	✿✿ (Le) Gavroche
	Belgravia	XXXX	✿✿ (La) Tante Claire
	North Kensington	XXX	Chez Moi
	Strand & Covent Garden	XX	(The) Admiralty
	Bayswater and Maida Vale	XX	Amandier
	Crouch End	XX	(Les) Associés
68	*Chelsea*	XX	Brasserie St. Quentin
58	*City of London*	XX	Club Gascon
68	*Chelsea*	XX	(Le) Colombier
70	*Kensington*	XX	(L') Escargot Doré
73	*Kingston*	XX	Gravier's
55	*Bloomsbury*	XX	Mon Plaisir
67	*Chelsea*	XX	Poissonnerie de l'Avenue
82	*Belgravia*	XX	Vong (French Thai)
88	*Regent's Park & Marylebone*	X	(L') Aventure

81 *Bayswater and Maida Vale*	X	Bistro Daniel
74 *Kennington*	X	Lobster Pot
64 *Archway*	X	Paris-London Café
94 *Victoria*	X	(La) Poule au P
60 *Dalston*	X	Soulard

Greek

60 *Hackney*	X	Real Greek

Indian & Pakistani

77 *Bermondsey*	XXX	Bengal Clipper
72 *South Kensington*	XXX	Bombay Brasserie
67 *Chelsea*	XXX	Chutney Mary (Anglo-Indian)
93 *Victoria*	XXX	Quilon
78 *Spitalfields*	XX	Bengal Trader
73 *South Kensington*	XX	Café Lazeez
78 *Battersea*	XX	☺ Cafe Spice Namaste
78 *Whitechapel*	XX	☺ Cafe Spice Namaste
85 *Mayfair*	XX	Chor Bizarre
73 *South Kensington*	XX	Khan's of Kensington
55 *Bloomsbury*	XX	Malabar Junction
73 *South Kensington*	XX	Memories of India
58 *Croydon*	XX	Planet Spice
88 *Regent's Park & Marylebone*	XX	(La) Porte des Indes
61 *Hammersmith*	XX	Rafique
88 *Regent's Park & Marylebone*	XX	Rasa Samudra
58 *City of London*	XX	Shimla Pinks
85 *Mayfair*	XX	✿ Tamarind
74 *Herne Hill*	XX	3 Monkeys
68 *Chelsea*	XX	Vama
85 *Mayfair*	XX	Yatra
67 *Chelsea*	XX	✿ Zaika
80 *Wandsworth*	X	Bombay Bicyc Club
64 *Finsbury*	X	Café Lazeez Ci
79 *Tooting*	X	Kastoori (Vegetarian)
71 *Kensington*	X	☺ Malabar
53 *Willesden Green*	X	☺ Sabras (Vegetarian)
79 *Southfields*	X	☺ Sarkhels
91 *Soho*	X	Soho Spice
73 *South Kensington*	X	Star of India
86 *Mayfair*	X	Veeraswamy

Italian

81 *Belgravia*	🏨	✿ (The) Halkin
67 *Chelsea*	XXX	Floriana
93 *Victoria*	XXX	(L') Incontro
82 *Hyde Park & Knightsbridge*	XXX	Isola
93 *Victoria*	XXX	Santini
85 *Mayfair*	XXX	Sartoria
67 *Chelsea*	XXX	Toto's
85 *Mayfair*	XX	Alloro
81 *Bayswater & Maida Vale*	XX	Al San Vincenzo
70 *Kensington*	XX	(The) Ark
88 *Regent's Park & Marylebone*	XX	Bertorelli's
88 *Regent's Park & Marylebone*	XX	Caldesi
68 *Chelsea*	XX	Caraffini
94 *Victoria*	XX	(Il) Convivio
68 *Chelsea*	XX	Daphne's
54 *Bloomsbury*	XX	Neal Street
71 *North Kensington*	XX	Orsino
59 *Ealing*	XX	Riso
61 *Hammersmith*	XX	✿ River Café
88 *Regent's Park & Marylebone*	XX	Rosmarino
86 *Mayfair*	XX	Teca
77 *Bermondsey*	XX	Tentazioni
78 *Carshalton*	XX	(La) Veranda
52 *Barnet*	XX	(The) Villa
82 *Belgravia*	XX	✿ Zafferano
81 *Bayswater & Maida Vale*	X	☺ (L') Accent
90 *St. James's*	X	☺ Al Duca
81 *Bayswater & Maida Vale*	X	Assaggi

Camden	X	Black Truffle
Bermondsey	X	Cantina Del Ponte
Chelsea	X	(I) Cardi
Kensington	X	Cibo
Putney	X	Del Buongustaio
Putney	X	Enoteca Turi
Crouch End	X	Florians
Soho	X	(Il) Forno
Chiswick	X	Grano
Bayswater & Maida Vale	X	Green Olive

88	*Regent's Park & Marylebone*	X	Ibla
59	*Croydon*	X	Mario
79	*Wandsworth*	X	Metrogusto
94	*Victoria*	X	Olivo
55	*Bloomsbury*	X	Passione
88	*Regent's Park & Marylebone*	X	Purple Sage
75	*Barnes*	X	Riva
63	*Ickenham*	X	Roberto's
91	*Soho*	X	Vasco and Piero's Pavillion

panese

St. James's	XXX	Suntory
City of London	XXX	Tatsuso
Regent's Park & Marylebone	XX	Asuka
Hampstead	XX	Benihana
Chelsea	XX	Benihana

90	*St James's*	XX	Matsuri
85	*Mayfair*	XX	✿ Nobu
86	*Mayfair*	XX	Shogun
55	*Camden*	X	Abeno
68	*Chelsea*	X	i'tsu
53	*Brent*	X	Sushi-Say

orean

Islington	X	Bu-San

banese

Belgravia	XX	Al Bustan
Belgravia	XX	Noura Brasserie

70	*Kensington*	XX	Phoenicia

oroccan

South Kensington	XX	Pasha

86	*Mayfair*	X	Momo

orth African

Hammersmith & Fulham	X	Azou

olish

Kensington	X	Wódka

ubs

Chelsea	Admiral Codrington
Hammersmith	Anglesea Arms
Chelsea	Builders Arms
Camden	Bull & Last
Islington	Centuria
Chelsea	Chelsea Ram
Bayswater & Maida Vale	(The) Chepstow
Putney	Coat and Badge
Islington	(The) Crown
Battersea	Duke of Cambridge
Camden	(The) Engineer
Shepherds Bush	Havelock Tavern

56	*Camden*	(The) Lansdowne
55	*Camden*	Lord Palmerston
56	*Hampstead*	(The) Magdala
65	*Finsbury*	(The) Peasant
56	*Primrose Hill*	(The) Queens
61	*Hamersmith & Fulham*	(The) Salisbury Tavern
64	*Archway*	St John's
89	*Regents Park & Marylebone*	(The) Salt House
69	*Chelsea*	Swag and Tails
61	*Hammersmith*	Thatched House
56	*Kentish Town*	(The) Vine

ssian

Mayfair	XXX	Firebird

Seafood

	Area		Restaurant
67	*Chelsea*	XXX	One-O-One
85	*Mayfair*	XXX	Scotts
85	*Mayfair*	XX	Bentley's
73	*Kingston*	XX	Gravier's (French)
81	*Bayswater & Maida Vale*	XX	Jason's
92	*Strand & Covent Garden*	XX	J. Sheekey
67	*Chelsea*	XX	Poissonnerie de l'Avenue (French)
88	*Regent's Park and Marylebone*	XX	Rasa Samudra (Indian)
73	*South Kensington*	XX	(The) Restaurant a One Ninety
68	*Chelsea*	X	Bibendum Oyster Bar
73	*South Kensington*	X	Catch
78	*Southwark*	X	Fish!
78	*Tower Hamlets*	X	Fish !
80	*Wandsworth*	X	Fish!
74	*Kennington*	X	Lobster Pot (French)
77	*Bayswater & Maida Vale*	X	Livebait
81	*Southwark*	X	Livebait
92	*Strand & Covent Garden*	X	Livebait

South African

	Area		Restaurant
65	*Chiswick*	X	Springbok Café

South East Asian

	Area		Restaurant
85	*Mayfair*	XX	Cassia Oriental
58	*City of London*	XX	Pacific Orient

Spanish

	Area		Restaurant
69	*Clerkenwell*	XX	Gaudi
73	*South Kensington*	XX	Cambio De Tercio

Swedish

	Area		Restaurant
64	*Canonbury*	X	Anna's Place

Thai

	Area		Restaurant
60	*Fulham*	XX	Blue Elephant
79	*Battersea*	XX	Chada
81	*Bayswater & Maida Vale*	XX	Nipa
58	*City of London*	XX	Sri Siam City
82	*Belgravia*	XX	Vong (French Thai)
73	*Kingston*	X	Ayudhya
73	*South Kensington*	X	Bangkok
89	*Regent's Park & Marylebone*	X	Chada Chada
79	*Tooting*	X	Oh Boy
81	*Soho*	X	Sri Siam

Turkish

	Area		Restaurant
88	*Regent's Park & Marylebone*	XX	Ozer

Vegetarian

	Area		Restaurant
88	*Regent's Park & Marylebone*	XX	Rasa Samudra (Indian)
79	*Tooting*	XX	Kastoori (India
53	*Willesden Green*	X	Sabras (Indian

Vietnamese

	Area		Restaurant
91	*Soho*	X	Saigon

Boroughs and areas

Greater London *is divided, for administrative purposes, into 32 boroughs plus the City : th sub-divide naturally into minor areas, usually grouped around former villages or quarters, wh often maintain a distinctive character.*

BARNET.

Brent Cross – ✉ *NW2.*

Holiday Inn Brent Cross, Tilling Rd, NW2 1LP, ✆ (020) 8201 8686, *joanna.fielding@ shotels.com, Fax (020) 8455 4660* – |♦|, ⇔ rm, ▤ TV ✆ ♿ P – 🚣 50. MC AE ① VISA J
p. 9 **DU**
Meals (bar lunch)/dinner 15.00 **st.** and a la carte – ☕ 11.95 – **153 rm** 145.00 **st.**

Child's Hill – ✉ *NW2.*

Quincy's, 675 Finchley Rd, NW2 2JP, ✆ (020) 7794 8499, *aaronanita@quincys.freeser o.uk, Fax (020) 7431 4501* – ▤. MC VISA JCB p. 9 **DU**
closed 1 week in spring, 2 weeks August, 25 December, 1 January and Sunday – **Me** (booking essential) (dinner only) 25.00 **t.** 🍷 7.50.

Laurent, 428 Finchley Rd, NW2 2HY, ✆ (020) 7794 3603 – MC AE VISA p. 9 **DU**
closed August, 25 December and 1 January – **Meals** - Couscous - a la carte approx. 14.7

Golders Green – ✉ *NW11.*

The Villa, 38 North End Rd, NW11 7PT, ✆ (020) 8458 6344, *Fax (020) 8458 6344* – ▤. AE ① VISA p. 9 **DU**
closed 25 December, 1 January and Monday – **Meals** - Italian - 14.50/18.0 (lunch) and a la carte 22.20/26.40 **t.** 🍷 6.00.

Mill Hill – ✉ *NW7.*

18 100 Barnet Way, Mill Hill ✆ (020) 8959 2282 **CT.**

Good Earth, 143 The Broadway, NW7 4RN, ✆ (020) 8959 7011, *Fax (020) 8959 1464* – MC AE VISA JCB p. 9 **CT**
closed 23-30 December – **Meals** - Chinese - a la carte 21.80/29.80 **st.**

BEXLEY.

Bexley – ✉ *Kent.*

Posthouse Bexley, Black Prince Interchange, Southwold Rd, DA5 1ND, on ✆ (0870) 400 9006, *Fax (01322) 526113* – |♦|, ⇔ rm, TV ♿ P – 🚣 70. MC AE ① VISA
Meals (closed Saturday lunch) a la carte 17.35/28.60 **t.** 🍷 6.95 – ☕ 11.95 – **105 rm** 89.0 – SB. p. 15 **JX**

Bexleyheath – ✉ *Kent.*

Bexleyheath Marriott, 1 Broadway, DA6 7JZ, ✆ (020) 8298 1000, *bexleyheath@sw w-hotels.co.uk, Fax (020) 8298 1234,* Ls, ▣ – |♦|, ⇔ rm, ▤ TV ♿ P – 🚣 250. MC AE VISA p. 15 **JX**
La Galleria : **Meals** 20.00 **st.** (lunch) and a la carte 27.00/47.00 **st.** 🍷 9.00 – ***Copper :*** **M** (carving rest.) 20.00 **st.** (dinner) and a la carte 25.50/36.00 **st.** 🍷 9.00 – **138 rm** ☕ 105.0 – SB.

BRENT.

Kingsbury – ✉ *NW9.*

Kingsland without rest., Kingsbury Circle, NW9 9RR, ✆ (020) 8206 0 *Fax (020) 8206 0555* – |♦| ⇔ TV ✆ ♿ P. MC ① VISA p. 9 **CU**
28 rm 50.00/65.00 **st.**

embley – Middx.

Wembley Plaza, Empire Way, HA9 8DS, (020) 8902 8839, *Fax (020) 8900 2201*, rest, – 300. VISA JCB p. 9 CU z
Celebrities : Meals *(closed Saturday lunch)* (carving rest.) 15.95/29.75 **t.** and a la carte 8.00 – ***Terracotta :*** Meals *(closed Saturday lunch)* a la carte approx. 26.50 **t.** 8.00 – 12.00 – **306 rm** 150.00/250.00 **st.** – SB.

illesden Green – Middx.

Sabras, 263 High Rd, NW10 2RX, (020) 8459 0340, *Fax (020) 8459 0340* – VISA JCB p. 9 CU e
closed Monday – **Meals** - Indian Vegetarian - (dinner only) a la carte 15.95/22.95 **t.**

Sushi-Say, 33B Walm Lane, NW2 5SH, (020) 8459 2971, *Fax (020) 8459 2971.* VISA JCB p. 9 CU a
closed 25-26 December, 1 January, Easter, 1 week August and Monday – **Meals** - Japanese - (dinner only and lunch Saturday and Sunday)/dinner 17.70/27.90 **t.** and a la carte 9.00.

OMLEY.

18, 9 *Cray Valley, Sandy Lane, St. Paul's Cray, Orpington (01689) 837909* **JY.**

omley – Kent.

9 *Magpie Hall Lane (020) 8462 7014* **HY.**

Bromley Court, Bromley Hill, BR1 4JD, (020) 8464 5011, *bromleyhotel@btinternet.com, Fax (020) 8460 0899*, – rm, rest, – 150. VISA. p. 15 HY z
Meals *(closed Saturday lunch)* 13.90/15.50 **st.** and dinner a la carte 6.50 – **113 rm** 98.00/107.00 **st.**, 2 suites.

rnborough – Kent.

Chapter One, Farnborough Common, Locksbottom, BR6 8NF, (01689) 854848, *pennyatch1@aol.com, Fax (01689) 858439* – . VISA JCB p. 15 HZ a
closed 1-3 January – **Meals** 19.50/23.95 **t.** 8.50
Spec. Sweet pea soup with pea ravioli. Duck leg confit with foie gras sausage and cep ragoût. Chocolate fondant with bitter chocolate sorbet.

pington – Kent.

18 *High Elms, High Elms Rd, Downe, Orpington (01689) 858175.*

Xian, 324 High St., BR6 0NG, (01689) 871881 – . VISA JCB p. 15 JY a
Meals - Chinese (Peking, Szechuan) - 8.50/22.00 **t.** and a la carte.

MDEN.

oomsbury – NW1/W1/WC1.

Holiday Inn Kings Cross, 1 Kings Cross Rd, WC1X 9HX, (020) 7833 3900, *sales@holidayinnlondon.demon.co.uk, Fax (020) 7917 6163*, – rm, – 220. VISA. p. 26 MT a
Simply Spice : Meals - Indian - *(closed Saturday lunch)* a la carte 10.00/23.00 **st.** – ***Carriages :*** Meals a la carte 10.00/25.00 **st.** – 12.50 – **403 rm** 190.00 **st.**, 2 suites.

Russell, Russell Sq., WC1B 5BE, (020) 7837 6470, *reservations.russell@principalhotels.co.uk, Fax (020) 7278 2124* – rm, rest, – 400. VISA.
Fitzroy Doll's : Meals 16.95/26.95 **t.** and a la carte – ***Virginia Woolf's :*** Meals a la carte approx. 16.00 **t.** 6.50 – 14.95 – **349 rm** 178.00/198.00 **t.**, 2 suites – SB. p. 26 LU o

Marlborough, 9-14 Bloomsbury St., WC1B 3QD, (020) 7636 5601, *resmarl@radisson.com, Fax (020) 7240 0532* – rm, rest, – 200. VISA JCB.
Class : Meals a la carte 26.25/34.00 **st.** 9.75 – 15.00 – **171 rm** 195.00/230.00 **s.**, 2 suites – SB. p. 26 LU i

Mountbatten, 20 Monmouth St., WC2H 9HD, (020) 7836 4300, *Fax (020) 7240 3540*, – rm, – 90. VISA JCB. p. 37 DV o
The Ad-Lib : Meals a la carte 34.70/35.00 **st.** 8.25 – 15.00 – **120 rm** 240.00/310.00 **s.**, 7 suites – SB.

Grafton, 130 Tottenham Court Rd, W1P 9HP, (020) 7388 4131, *resgraf@radisson.com, Fax (020) 7387 7394* – rm, rest, – 100. VISA JCB. p. 26 KU n
Meals a la carte 17.50/31.00 **st.** 7.50 – 12.00 – **320 rm** 160.00/199.00 **s.**, 4 suites – SB.

Covent Garden, 10 Monmouth St., WC2H 9HB, (020) 7806 1000, *covent@firmdale m, Fax (020) 7806 1100,* – – 50. VISA JCB. p. 37 **DV**
Brasserie Max : **Meals** (booking essential) a la carte 26.40/32.50 **t.** – 16.50 – **56**
190.00/280.00 **s.**, 2 suites.

Thistle Bloomsbury, Bloomsbury Way, WC1A 2SD, (020) 7242 5881, *bloomsbury istle.co.uk, Fax (020) 7831 0225* – , rm, rest, – 100. VISA JCB.
Meals *(closed Saturday lunch, Sunday and Bank Holiday Mondays)* a la carte 20.25/26.9
7.50 – 12.95 – **138 rm** 170.00/250.00 **st.** – SB. p. 26 **LU**

Grange Holborn, 50-60 Southampton Row, WC1B 4AR, (020) 7242 1800, *holborn angehotels.co.uk,* , , , – , rm, – 180. JCB p. 26 **LU**
Meals *(closed lunch Saturday, Sunday and Bank Holidays)* 24.50 **st.** and a la carte 8.15 –
16.50 – **152 rm** 220.00/250.00 **st.**, 8 suites.

Montague, 15 Montague St., WC1B 5BJ, (020) 7637 1001, *sales@montague.redcar onhotels.com, Fax (020) 7637 2516,* , , , – , rm, – 120. VISA JCB p. 26 **LU**
Blue Door Bistro : **Meals** a la carte 23.15/47.50 **t.** 15.50 – 13.50 – **98 rm** 160.
180.00 **s.**, 6 suites – SB.

Posthouse Bloomsbury, Coram St., WC1N 1HT, (0870) 400 92
Fax (020) 7837 5374 – , rm, rest, – 300. VISA JCB p. 26 **LT**
Meals *closed lunch Saturday and Sunday* 10.00/25.00 **t.** and a la carte – 11.95 – **310**
129.00 **st.**, 3 suites.

Kenilworth, 97 Great Russell St., WC1B 3LB, (020) 7637 3477, *resmarl@radisson.c*
Fax (020) 7631 3133 – , rm, rest, – 65. VISA JCB. p. 26 **LU**
Meals a la carte 26.25/34.00 **st.** 8.00 – 12.00 – **187 rm** 175.00/230.00 **s.** – SB.

Blooms, 7 Montague St., WC1B 5BP, (020) 7323 1717, *blooms@mermaid.co*
Fax (020) 7636 6498, – . VISA JCB. p. 26 **LU**
Meals a la carte 17.60/26.75 **t.** – **27 rm** 130.00/205.00 **t.**

Myhotel, 11-13 Bayley St., Bedford Sq., WC1B 3HD, (020) 7667 6000, *guest-services yhotels.co.uk, Fax (020) 7667 6001,* – – 60. VISA
Meals a la carte 15.00/30.00 **st.** – 16.00 – **76 rm** 170.00/355.00 **s.** p. 26 **KU**

Bonnington in Bloomsbury, 92 Southampton Row, WC1B 4BH, (020) 7242 282
ales@bonnington_com, Fax (020) 7831 9170 – , rm, rest, – 250. VISA JCB p. 26 **LU**
Meals *(closed Sunday and Bank Holiday Mondays)* (bar lunch)/dinner 20.75 **st.** and a la c
– **215 rm** 117.00/149.00 **t.** – SB.

Academy, 17-21 Gower St., WC1E 6HG, (020) 7631 4115, *res-academy@etontownh e.com, Fax (020) 7636 3442,* – rest, . VISA JCB. p. 26 **KLU**
closed 24-26 December – ***Alchemy :*** **Meals** *(closed Saturday and Sunday)* (lu
only) 14.95/19.95 **t.** and a la carte – **49 rm** 115.00/165.00.

High Holborn, 95-96 High Holborn, WC1V 6LF, (020) 7404 3338, *Fax (020) 7404 33* . VISA JCB p. 26 **MU**
closed Christmas-New Year, Saturday lunch, Sunday and Bank Holidays – **Meals** 23.0
(lunch) and a la carte 26.00/38.00 **t.** 13.70
Spec. Roast scallops with wild mushroom ravioli. Saddle of lamb with asparagus and br
beans. Vanilla and chocolate chip cheesecake.

Pied à Terre, 34 Charlotte St., W1P 1HJ, (020) 7636 1178, *p-a-t@dircon.co*
Fax (020) 7916 1171 – . VISA JCB p. 26 **KU**
closed 1 week Christmas, 1 week New Year, last week August, Saturday lunch, Sunday Bank Holidays – **Meals** 23.00/50.00-65.00 **t.** 9.50
Spec. Poached foie gras with peas and pasta, Sauternes consommé. Dover sole in oy
and Champagne velouté. Banana Tatin with passion fruit parfait..

Incognico, 117 Shaftesbury Av., WC2H 8AD, (020) 7836 8866, *Fax (020) 7240 9525* – VISA p. 33 **GK**
closed 4 days Easter, 10 days Christmas, Sunday and Bank Holidays – **Meals** 12.5
(lunch) and a la carte 22.50/34.00 **t.**

Neal Street, 26 Neal St., WC2H 9PS, (020) 7836 8368, *Fax (020) 7240 3964* – VISA JCB p. 37 **DV**
closed 25 and 26 December, 1 January, Sunday and Bank Holidays – **Meals** - Itali
a la carte 23.00/42.00 **t.** 14.00.

The Birdcage, 110 Whitfield St., W1P 5RU, (020) 7323 9655, *Fax (020) 7323 9616* – VISA p. 26 **KU**
closed Saturday lunch and Sunday – **Meals** 19.50/38.50 **t.** 10.00.

Mon Plaisir, 21 Monmouth St., WC2H 9DD, ☎ (020) 7836 7243, *eatafrog@mon.plaisir.co.uk, Fax (020) 7240 4774* – MC AE Diners VISA JCB p. 37 **DV** a
closed 25 December, Saturday lunch, Sunday and Bank Holidays – **Meals** - French - 15.95/23.50 and a la carte 6.75.

Malabar Junction, 107 Great Russell St., WC1B 3NA, ☎ (020) 7580 5230, *Fax (020) 7436 9942* – ▤. MC AE VISA p. 26 **LU** x
closed 25-26 December **Meals** - South Indian - 20.00/35.00 **t.** and a la carte.

Passione, 10 Charlotte St., W1P 1HE, ☎ (020) 7636 2833, *lizprzybylski@lineone.net, Fax (020) 7636 2889* – MC AE Diners VISA JCB p. 26 **KU** u
closed Christmas, Saturday lunch, Sunday and Bank Holidays – **Meals** - Italian - a la carte 17.50/29.50 **t.** 9.50.

Alfred, 245 Shaftesbury Av., WC2H 8EH, ☎ (020) 7240 2566, *Fax (020) 7497 0672,* – ▤. MC AE Diners VISA p. 37 **DV** u
closed 25-26 December, Sunday, Saturday lunch and Bank Holidays – **Meals** 13.90/17.00 **t.** and a la carte 10.50.

Josephine's, 4 Charlotte St., W1P 2LP, ☎ (020) 7580 6551, *Fax (020) 7580 1514* – MC AE Diners VISA JCB p. 26 **KU** s
closed 25 December, 1 January, Good Friday and Sunday – **Meals** - Filipino - a la carte 13.70/22.80 **t.** 5.95.

Abeno, 47 Museum St., WC1A 1LY, ☎ (020) 7405 3211, *Fax (020) 7405 3212* – ▤. MC VISA JCB p. 26 **LU** e
closed 25-26 December and 1 January – **Meals** - Japanese (Okonomi-Yaki) - 7.95/11.95 **t.** (lunch) and a la carte 11.80/20.30 **t.** 5.95.

rtmouth Park – ✉ *NW5.*

Bull & Last, 168 Highgate Rd, NW5 1QS, ☎ (020) 7267 3641, *Fax (020) 7482 6366* – MC VISA
closed 25 December – **Meals** (lunch in bar) a la carte 16.00/21.75 **t.** p. 24 **EU** n

Lord Palmerston, 33 Dartmouth Park Hill, NW5 1HU, ☎ (020) 7485 1578 – MC VISA p. 24 **EU** x
closed 26 December and 1 January – **Meals** (bookings not accepted) a la carte 15.00/18.00 **t.**

ston – ✉ *WC1.*

Shaw Park Plaza, 100-110 Euston Rd, NW1 2AJ, ☎ (020) 7666 9000, *sppres@parkplazahotels.co.uk, Fax (020) 7666 9100,* – rm, ▤ – 450. MC AE Diners VISA JCB. p. 26 **LT** r
Meals 15.50/19.50 **st.** and a la carte 13.50 – 14.50 – **312 rm** 155.00/195.00 **st.**

Euston Plaza, 17-18 Upper Woburn Pl., WC1H 0HT, ☎ (020) 7943 4500, *eustonplaza@euston-plaza-hotel.co.uk, Fax (020) 7943 4501,* – rm, ▤ – 150. MC AE Diners VISA JCB. p. 26 **KLT** e
Three Crowns : **Meals** (dinner only) 18.95/50.00 **t.** and a la carte 6.95 – ***Terrace :*** **Meals** *(closed Saturday and Sunday)* 10.95/20.00 **t.** (lunch) and a la carte approx. 23.00 **t.** 6.95 – 12.50 – **150 rm** 159.00/179.00 **st.**

London Euston Travel Inn Capital, 141 Euston Rd, NW1 2AU, ☎ (020) 7554 3400, *Fax (020) 7554 3419* – rm, ▤ rest, MC AE Diners VISA. p. 26 **LT** s
Meals (grill rest.) (dinner only) – **220 rm** 69.95 **t.**

mpstead – ✉ *NW3.*

Winnington Rd, Hampstead ☎ (020) 8455 0203.

Posthouse Hampstead, 215 Haverstock Hill, NW3 4RB, ☎ (0870) 400 9037, *Fax (020) 7435 5586* – – 30. MC AE Diners VISA JCB p. 24 **ES** r
Meals – (see ***MPW Brasserie*** below) – 10.95 – **140 rm** 110.00/130.00 **st.**

Langorf without rest., 20 Frognal, NW3 6AG, ☎ (020) 7794 4483, *langorf@aol.com, Fax (020) 7435 9055* – MC AE Diners VISA. p. 24 **ES** c
31 rm 77.00/100.00 **st.**, 5 suites.

Byron's, 3a Downshire Hill, NW3 1NR, ☎ (020) 7435 3544, *Fax (020) 7431 3544* – MC AE VISA p. 24 **ES** v
closed 25-26 December – **Meals** 15.00/23.00 **t.** and dinner a la carte.

ZeNW3, 83-84 Hampstead High St., NW3 1RE, ☎ (020) 7794 7863, *Fax (020) 7794 6956* – ▤. MC AE Diners VISA JCB p. 24 **ES** a
closed 25 December – **Meals** - Chinese - 13.80/32.50 **t.** and a la carte.

Gresslin's, 13 Heath St., NW3 6TP, ☎ (020) 7794 8386, *restaurant@gresslins.co.uk, Fax (020) 7433 3282* – ▤. MC AE VISA JCB p. 24 **ES** u
closed last 2 weeks August, Sunday dinner, Monday lunch and Bank Holidays – **Meals** 17.95 **t.** and a la carte 9.25.

X **MPW Brasserie** (at Posthouse Hampstead H.), 215 Haverstock Hill, NW3 4
ℰ (020) 7435 6080, *Fax (020) 7435 5586*, – . MC AE DC VISA JCB p. 24 ES
Meals 13.50 **st.** (lunch) and a la carte 20.50/26.95 **st.**

X **New End,** 102 Heath St., NW3 1DR, ℰ (020) 7431 4423, *info@thenewend.co.*
Fax (020) 7794 7508 – MC AE VISA p. 24 ES
closed 13-27 August, 24-26 December, 1 January, Monday and lunch Tuesday – **Me**
18.50/23.50 **t.** (lunch) and a la carte 27.50/39.50 **t.** 11.95.

X **Cucina,** 45a South End Rd, NW3 2QB, ℰ (020) 7435 7814, *enquiries@cucina.uk.co*
Fax (020) 7435 7815 – . MC AE VISA p. 24 ES
closed 25-26 December, Easter Monday and Sunday dinner – **Meals** a la carte 23.00/26.5
8.95.

X **Base,** 71 Hampstead High St., NW3 1QP, ℰ (020) 7431 2224, *Fax (020) 7433 1262* – .
AE DC VISA p. 24 ES
Meals a la carte 14.00/22.00 **t.** 6.00.

The Magdala, 2A South Hill Park, NW3 2SB, ℰ (020) 7435 2503, *Fax (020) 7435 6167* –
VISA JCB p. 24 ES
closed 25 December – **Meals** (lunch in bar) a la carte 16.25/20.75 **t.** 5.00.

Hatton Garden – ✉ *EC1.*

XX **Bleeding Heart,** Bleeding Heart Yard, EC1N 8SJ, off Greville St. ℰ (020) 7242 2056, *bo*
ngs@bleedingheart.co.uk, Fax (020) 7831 1402, – MC AE DC VISA p. 27 NU
closed 24 December-4 January, Saturday, Sunday and Bank Holidays – **Meals** a la ca
23.95/28.65 **t.** 7.50.

Holborn – ✉ *WC2.*

Kingsway Hall, Great Queen St., WC2B 5BX, ℰ (020) 7309 0909, *kingswayhall@comp*
rve.com, Fax (020) 7309 9696, , – , rm, – 150. MC AE DC VISA
p. 37 EV
Harlequin : **Meals** 16.50/18.50 **st.** (dinner) and a la carte 28.00/45.00 **st.** 8.50 – 15
– **168 rm** 220.00/235.00 **st.**, 2 suites.

Drury Lane Moat House, 10 Drury Lane, High Holborn, WC2B 5RE, ℰ (020) 7208 9
Fax (020) 7831 1548, – , rm, – 60. MC AE DC VISA. p. 37 DV
Meals (dinner only) a la carte approx. 25.40 **t.** 7.95 – 13.50 – **162 rm** 173.00/194.00
1 suite.

Kentish Town – ✉ *NW5.*

The Vine, 86 Highgate Rd, NW5 1PB, ℰ (020) 7209 0038, *Fax (020) 709 3161* – MC AE
Meals a la carte 18.95/27.30 **t.** p. 10 EU

Primrose Hill – ✉ *NW1.*

XX **Odette's,** 130 Regent's Park Rd, NW1 8XL, ℰ (020) 7586 5486, *Fax (020) 7586 2575* –
AE DC VISA p. 25 HS
closed 1 week Christmas, and Sunday dinner – **Meals** 12.50 **t.** (lunch) and a la carte 19
34.75 **t.** 8.50 – (see also ***Odette's Wine Bar*** below).

X **Black Truffle,** 40 Chalcot Rd, NW1 8LS, ℰ (020) 7483 0077, *Fax (020) 7483 0088* – .
AE VISA p. 25 HIS
closed 25 December, Saturday lunch, Sunday and Bank Holidays – **Meals** - Italian - 15
18.00 **t.** (lunch) and a la carte 22.00/26.00 **t.** 9.00.

X **Odette's Wine Bar** (at Odette's), 130 Regent's Park Rd, NW1 8XL, ℰ (020) 7722 5
Fax (020) 7586 2575 – MC AE DC VISA p. 25 HS
closed 1 week Christmas and Sunday dinner – **Meals** (booking essential) 12.5
(lunch) and a la carte 15.00/23.00 **t.** 8.50.

The Queens, 49 Regent's Park Rd, NW1 8XD, ℰ (020) 7586 0408, *Fax (020) 7586 5*
– MC DC VISA p. 25 HS
Meals a la carte 12.35/20.35 **t.**

The Engineer, 65 Gloucester Av., NW1 8JH, ℰ (020) 7722 0950, *info@the-eng.c*
Fax (020) 7483 0592, – MC VISA p. 25 IS
closed 25-26 December and 1 January – **Meals** a la carte 17.25/26.00 **t.**

The Lansdowne, 90 Gloucester Av., NW1 8HX, ℰ (020) 7483 0409, *Fax (020) 7586 17*
MC VISA p. 25 IS
closed Monday – **Meals** (lunch in bar Tuesday-Friday) a la carte 19.00/25.00 **t.** 7.00.

gent's Park – NW1.

Meliá White House, Albany St., NW1 3UP, (020) 7387 1200, *melia.whitehouse@solmelia.com, Fax (020) 7388 0091*, – rm, rest, – 120. VISA JCB. p. 25 JT o
The Restaurant : Meals *(closed Sunday)* 22.75/24.75 **t.** and a la carte – ***Garden Cafe*** : Meals 11.75 **t.** and a la carte 6.75 – 13.50 – **580 rm** 163.00 **st.**, 2 suites.

Belgo Noord, 72 Chalk Farm Rd, NW1 8AN, (020) 7267 0718, *Fax (020) 7284 4842* – . VISA JCB p. 25 IS e
closed 25 December – **Meals** 19.50/25.50 **t.** (dinner) and a la carte 17.15/22.40 **t.**

iss Cottage – NW3.

Marriott Regents Park, 128 King Henry's Rd, NW3 3ST, (020) 7722 7711, *Fax (020) 7586 5822*, – rm, – 300. VISA JCB. p. 25 GS a
Meals 20.00/30.00 **st.** and a la carte 7.95 – 15.95 – **298 rm** 230.00 **s.**, 5 suites.

Swiss Cottage without rest., 4 Adamson Rd, NW3 3HP, (020) 7722 2281, *reservations@swisscottage2.demon.co.uk, Fax (020) 7483 4588* – – 35. VISA JCB.
48 rm 95.00/130.00 **st.**, 6 suites. p. 25 GS n

Bradley's, 25 Winchester Rd, NW3 3NR, (020) 7722 3457, *Fax (020) 7431 4776* – . VISA JCB p. 25 GS e
closed 1 week Christmas, 1 week Easter, last 2 weeks August, Saturday lunch and Bank Holidays – **Meals** 10.00/14.00 **t.** (lunch) and a la carte 24.50/31.00 **t.** 12.50.

Benihana, 100 Avenue Rd, NW3 3HF, (020) 7586 9508, *benihana@dircon.co.uk, Fax (020) 7586 6740* – . VISA JCB p. 25 GS o
closed 25 December – **Meals** - Japanese (Teppan-Yaki) - 8.50/14.00 **t.** and a la carte.

Globe, 100 Avenue Rd, NW3 3HF, (020) 7722 7200, *globerella@aol.com, Fax (020) 7722 2772* – . VISA p. 25 GS v
closed Saturday lunch and Monday – **Meals** 12.50/14.50 **t.** and a la carte.

Y OF LONDON.

Great Eastern, Liverpool St., EC2M 7QN, (020) 7618 5000, *sales@rgreateastern-hotel.co.uk, Fax (020) 7618 5001*, – rm, – 250. VISA
Fishmarket : Meals - Seafood - *(closed Saturday lunch and Sunday)* a la carte 22.50/41.50 **t.** – ***Miyabi*** : Meals - Japanese - *(closed Saturday and Sunday)* a la carte 19.00/33.50 **t.** – (see also ***Aurora*** below) – 19.50 – **265 rm** 225.00/260.00 **s.**, 2 suites – SB. p. 27 PU o

Travelodge without rest., 1 Harrow Pl., E1 7DB, (020) 7626 1142, *Fax (020) 7626 1105* – . VISA JCB. p. 27 PU s
142 rm 79.95 **t.**

Aurora (at Great Eastern H.), Liverpool St., EC2M 7QN, (020) 7618 7000, *restaurants@great-eastern-hotel.co.uk, Fax (020) 7618 7001* – . VISA p. 27 PU o
closed Saturday and Sunday – **Meals** a la carte 33.00/45.00 **t.** 11.50.

City Rhodes, 1 New Street Sq., EC4A 3BF, (020) 7583 1313, *Fax (020) 7353 1662* – . VISA p. 27 NU u
closed Christmas, Saturday and Sunday – **Meals** a la carte 34.50/48.00 **t.** 11.50
Spec. Lobster and broad bean salad with a white bean purée. Roast turbot with girolles and garlic mash. Bread and butter pudding.

Coq d'Argent, No.1 Poultry, EC2R 8EJ, (020) 7395 5000, *Fax (020) 7395 5050*, « Rooftop terrace » – . VISA p. 27 PV c
closed Saturday lunch, Sunday dinner and Bank Holidays – **Meals** (booking essential) a la carte 32.00/42.50 14.50.

Twentyfour, 24th floor, Tower 42, 25 Old Broad St., EC2N 1HQ, (020) 7877 2424, *Fax (020) 7877 7788*, London – . VISA JCB p. 27 PU v
closed Saturday, Sunday and Bank Holidays – **Meals** (booking essential) 22.00/28.50 **t.** (lunch) and a la carte 29.00/39.25 **t.** 10.00.

Tatsuso, 32 Broadgate Circle, EC2M 2QS, (020) 7638 5863, *Fax (020) 7638 5864* – . VISA JCB p. 27 PU u
closed Christmas, Saturday, Sunday and Bank Holidays – **Meals** - Japanese - (booking essential) 28.00/36.00 **t.** and a la carte 14.50.

1 Lombard Street (Restaurant), 1 Lombard St., EC2V 9AA, (020) 7929 6611, *js@1lombardstreet.com, Fax (020) 7929 6622* – . VISA JCB p. 27 PV r
closed 1 week Christmas, Saturday, Sunday and Bank Holidays – **Meals** 22.00/34.00 **t.** and a la carte 45.00/58.50 **t.** 17.80 – (see also ***1 Lombard Street (Brasserie)*** below)
Spec. Feuilleté of smoked haddock with quail's egg, mustard sauce. Suprême and fricassee of chicken with young leeks. Summer berries in Sauternes.

XXX **Prism,** 147 Leadenhall, EC3V 4QT, ☎ (020) 7256 3888, *Fax (020) 7256 3883* – ▤. MC AE VISA JCB p. 27 **PV**
closed Saturday, Sunday and Bank Holidays – **Meals** a la carte 31.50/43.00 **t.** 🍷 10.50.

XX **1 Lombard Street (Brasserie),** 1 Lombard St., EC2V 9AA, ☎ (020) 7929 66 *Fax (020) 7929 6622* – ▤. MC AE ⓓ VISA JCB p. 27 **PV**
closed Saturday, Sunday and Bank Holidays – **Meals** a la carte 27.50/34.00 **t.** 🍷 17.50.

XX **Brasserie Rocque,** 37 Broadgate Circle, EC2M 2QS, ☎ (020) 7638 7919, *brocque@ao m.uk, Fax (020) 7628 5899,* 🏠 – ▤. MC AE VISA p. 27 **PU**
closed Saturday, Sunday and Bank Holidays – **Meals** (lunch only) a la carte 20.95/31.9 🍷 5.00.

XX **Pacific Oriental,** first floor, 1 Bishopsgate, EC2N 3AB, ☎ (020) 7621 9988, *enquiries@ plc.co.uk, Fax (020) 7621 9911* – ▤. MC AE ⓓ VISA JCB p. 27 **PV**
closed Saturday, Sunday and Bank Holidays – **Meals** - South East Asian - a la carte 17. 28.95 **t.**

XX **Club Gascon,** 57 West Smithfield, EC1A 9DS, ☎ (020) 7796 0600, *Fax (020) 7796 060* ▤. MC VISA p. 27 **OU**
closed 25 December-7 January, Sunday, Saturday lunch and Bank Holidays – **Meals** - Fre and Gascony specialities - (booking essential) 30.00 **t.** and a la carte 14.50/26.50 **t.** 🍷 5.50

XX **Imperial City,** Royal Exchange, Cornhill, EC3V 3LL, ☎ (020) 7626 3437, *enquiries@org co.uk, Fax (020) 7338 0125* – ▤. MC AE ⓓ VISA JCB p. 27 **PV**
closed Saturday, Sunday and Bank Holidays – **Meals** - Chinese - 15.95/26.95 **t.** and a la ca

XX **Sri Siam City,** 85 London Wall, EC2M 7AD, ☎ (020) 7628 5772, *enquiries@cvgplc.cc Fax (020) 7628 3395* – ▤. MC AE ⓓ VISA JCB p. 27 **PU**
closed Saturday, Sunday and Bank Holidays – **Meals** - Thai - (booking essential) 15.95/26.5 and a la carte.

XX **Shimla Pinks,** 7 Bishopsgate Churchyard, EC2M 3TJ, ☎ (020) 7628 7888, *enquiries@c lc.co.uk, Fax (020) 7628 8282,* « Victorian former Turkish baths » – ▤. MC AE ⓓ JCB p. 27 **PU**
closed Saturday, Sunday and Bank Holidays – **Meals** - Indian - 23.95 **t.** and a la carte.

CROYDON.

Addington – ✉ *Surrey.*

⛳18, ⛳18, ⛳9 *Addington Court, Featherbed Lane* ☎ *(020) 8657 0281* **GZ** – ⛳18 *The Addington, Shirley Church Rd* ☎ *(020) 8777 1055* **GZ**.

XXX **Tezelin,** Addington Palace, Gravel Hill, CR0 5BB, ☎ (020) 8662 5060, *info@addington-p e.co.uk, Fax (020) 8662 5001,* ≤ – 🚭 P. MC AE VISA p. 14 **GZ**
closed Saturday lunch and dinner Sunday and Monday – **Meals** 19.50/25.00 and a la carte 🍷 11.00.

XX **Planet Spice,** 88 Selsdon Park Rd, CR2 8JT, ☎ (020) 8651 3300, *Fax (020) 8651 4400* P. MC AE ⓓ VISA p. 14 **GZ**
closed 25-26 December – **Meals** - Indian - a la carte 16.50/22.45 **t.**

Coulsdon – ✉ *Surrey.*

🏨 **Coulsdon Manor** 🐎, Coulsdon Court Rd, via Stoats Nest Rd, CR5 ☎ (020) 8668 0414, *coulsdonmanor@marstonhotel.co.uk, Fax (020) 8668 3118,* ≤, 🏋, ⛳18, 🎾, squash – 🛗 🚭 📺 P – 🎤 180. MC AE ⓓ VISA. 🐕
Manor House : **Meals** *(closed Saturday lunch)* 19.50/27.00 **st.** and dinner a la carte 🍷 8. ☕ 11.00 – **35 rm** 99.00/120.00 **t.** – SB.

Croydon – ✉ *Surrey.*

ℹ *Katherine St.* ☎ *(020) 8253 1009.*

🏨 **Hilton Croydon,** Waddon Way, Purley Way, CR9 4HH, ☎ (020) 8680 3 *Fax (020) 8681 6171,* 🏋, ≘s, 🏊 – 🛗, 🚭 rm, ▤ 📺 📞 ♿ P – 🎤 400. MC AE 🐕 p. 14 **FZ**
Meals a la carte 18.40/28.85 **t.** – ☕ 12.00 – **168 rm** 155.00/195.00 **st.**

🏨 **Croydon Park,** 7 Altyre Rd, CR9 5AA, ☎ (020) 8680 9200, *reservations@croydonpar el.co.uk, Fax (020) 8760 0426,* 🏋, ≘s, 🏊, squash – 🛗, 🚭 rm, ▤ 📺 📞 P – 🎤 300. ⓓ VISA p. 14 **FZ**
Oscars : **Meals** 15.95/17.95 **st.** and a la carte 🍷 13.00 – **211 rm** ☕ 108.00/128.00 **st.** – S

🏨 **Posthouse Croydon,** Purley Way, CR9 4LT, ☎ (0870) 400 9022, *Fax (020) 8681 64* 🚭 rm, ▤ rest, 📺 P – 🎤 120. MC AE ⓓ VISA JCB p. 14 **FZ**
Meals a la carte 18.35/29.15 **t.** 🍷 6.95 – ☕ 11.95 – **83 rm** 115.00 **st.** – SB.

🏨 **Travel Inn Metro,** 104 Coombe Rd, CR0 5RB, on A 212 ☎ (020) 8686 2 *Fax (020) 8686 6435,* 🚗 – 🚭 rm, 📺 ♿ P. MC AE ⓓ VISA. 🐕 p. 14 **GZ**
Meals (grill rest.) – **39 rm** 46.95 **t.**

Premier Lodge, 619 Purley Way, CR0 4RJ, (020) 8225 1909, *Fax (020) 8680 9109* – rm, TV, P. MC AE VISA. p. 14 FZ e
Meals 6.50/8.50 **t.** (lunch) and a la carte 9.35/28.45 **t.** – **82 rm** 46.00 **st.**

Mario, 299 High St., CR0 1QL, (020) 8686 5624 – MC AE VISA JCB p. 14 FZ s
closed 24-25 December, first week January, last 2 weeks August, Sunday Monday and Saturday lunch. – **Meals** - Italian - 14.50 **t.** (lunch) and a la carte 19.00/29.50 **t.** 7.95.

Tai Tung, Unit 1A, Wing Yip Centre, 550 Purley Way, CR0 4RF, (020) 8688 3668, *Fax (020) 8688 0116* – P. MC AE VISA p. 14 FZ v
closed 24 to 26 December – **Meals** - Chinese (Canton) - 15.50/25.00 **t.** and a la carte 5.95.

nderstead – *Surrey.*

Selsdon Park Hotel, Addington Rd, Sanderstead (020) 8657 8811 **GZ.**

Selsdon Park, Addington Rd, CR2 8YA, (020) 8657 8811, *Fax (020) 8651 6171*, heated, squash – rm, rest, TV P – 150. MC AE VISA. p. 14 GZ n
Meals (dancing Saturday evening) (buffet lunch Monday-Saturday) 19.95/24.95 **st.** and a la carte 7.50 – 13.95 – **200 rm** 125.00/160.00 **st.**, 4 suites – SB.

LING.

dford Park – *W4.*

Riso, 76 South Par., W4 5LF, (020) 8742 2121, *Fax (020) 8742 2121* – MC VISA
closed 1 week Easter and 1 week Christmas – **Meals** - Italian - (dinner only and Sunday lunch)/dinner 14.50/23.50 **t.**. p. 13 CV o

ling – *W5.*

West Middlesex, Greenford Rd, Southall (020) 8574 3450 **BV** – *Horsenden Hill, Woodland Rise, Greenford (020) 8902 4555* **BU.**

Jarvis International, Ealing Common, W5 3HN, (020) 8992 5399, *Fax (020) 8992 7082* – rm, rest, TV P – 200. MC AE VISA JCB p. 9 CV v
Meals a la carte 18.45/25.30 **t.** – 11.50 – **189 rm** 135.00/155.00 **st.** – SB.

Travelodge without rest., Western Av., W3 0TE, (020) 8752 1072, *Fax (020) 8752 1134* – TV P. MC AE VISA. p. 13 CV x
64 rm 69.95 **t.**

Parade, 18-19 The Mall, W5 2PJ, (020) 8810 0202, *Fax (020) 8810 0303* – MC AE VISA p. 13 CV s
closed 25 December, Sunday dinner and Bank Holidays – **Meals** 12.00/23.50 **t.** and lunch a la carte.

Maxim, 153-155 Northfield Av., W13 9QT, (020) 8567 1719, *maximrest@hotmail.com, Fax (020) 8932 0717* – MC AE VISA JCB p. 8 BV a
closed 25 to 28 December and Sunday lunch – **Meals** - Chinese (Peking) - 12.90/27.90 **t.** and a la carte.

FIELD.

Lee Valley Leisure, Picketts Lock Lane, Edmonton (020) 8803 3611 **GT.**

ield – *Middx.*

Whitewebbs, Beggars Hollow, Clay Hill (020) 8363 2951, N : 1 m. **FT.**

Royal Chace, The Ridgeway, EN2 8AR, (020) 8884 8181, *royalchace@dial.pipex.com, Fax (020) 8884 8150,* heated, – TV P – 270. MC AE VISA.
closed 25-26 December – **Meals** (bar lunch Monday to Saturday)/dinner 14.95 **st.** and a la carte 8.95 – **92 rm** 109.00/130.00 **st.** p. 10 ET a

Oak Lodge, 80 Village Rd, Bush Hill Park, EN1 2EU, (020) 8360 7082, – TV MC AE VISA JCB p. 10 FT a
Meals (lunch by arrangement)/dinner a la carte 20.90/26.90 **t.** 7.25 – **6 rm** 93.40/130.00 **st.** – SB.

dley Wood – *Herts.*

West Lodge Park, off Cockfosters Rd, EN4 0PY, (020) 8216 3900, *beales-westlodgepark@compuserve.com, Fax (020) 8216 3937,* – TV P – 80. MC AE VISA. p. 10 ET i
The Cedar **: Meals** *(closed 27 to 30 December)* 23.95/34.50 **st.** 7.75 – 12.50 – **55 rm** 99.50/160.00 **st.** – SB.

GREENWICH.

Blackheath – SE3.

Bardon Lodge, 15 Stratheden Rd, SE3 7TH, (020) 8853 7000, *bardonlodge@btclick m, Fax (020) 8858 7387,* – rest, – 30. AE VISA JCB p. 15 **HV**
Lamplight : **Meals** (dinner only) a la carte 21.50/25.50 **st.** 5.50 – **28 rm** 85. 130.00 **st.**

Chapter Two, 43-45 Montpelier Vale, SE3 0TJ, (020) 8333 2666, *fiona.chapter2@ta .com, Fax (020) 8355 8399* – . AE VISA p. 15 **HX**
Meals 18.50/22.50 **t.**.

Lawn, Lawn Terr., SE3 9LJ, (020) 7379 0724, *enquiries@one_lawn_terrace.co Fax (020) 7379 9014* – . AE VISA JCB p. 15 **HX**
closed Sunday dinner, Monday lunch and Bank Holidays – **Meals** 15.50 (lunch) and a la carte 19.50/30.50 **t.** 10.20.

Greenwich – SE10.

Pepys House, 2 Cutty Sark Gdns (0870) 6082000.

Spread Eagle, 1-2 Stockwell St., SE10 9JN, (020) 8853 2333, *goodfood@spreadeag rg, Fax (020) 8305 1666* – . AE VISA JCB p. 14 **GV**
closed 24 to 30 December – **Meals** 12.50/15.50 **t.** and a la carte 6.00.

North Pole, 131 Greenwich High Rd, SE10 8JA, (020) 8853 3020, *Fax (020) 8853 35* AE VISA JCB p. 14 **GV**
closed 25 December and Monday lunch – **Meals** 17.00 **t.** (dinner) and a la carte 21 30.00 **t.** 6.50.

Time, 7a College Approach, SE10 9HY, (020) 8305 9767, *enquiries@timerestaurant.c Fax (020) 8305 9767* – AE VISA p. 14 **GV**
closed 25 December, 1 January and Monday lunch – **Meals** 23.50 **st.** (dinner) and a la c 22.50/28.00 **st.** 6.00.

HACKNEY.

Dalston – N1.

Soulard, 113 Mortimer Rd, N1 4JY, (020) 7254 1314, *Fax (020) 7254 1314* – VISA p. 27 **PS**
closed 3 weeks August-September, Easter, 26 December-5 January, Sunday and Mond **Meals** - French - (dinner only and lunch December) 19.50 **t.**.

Hoxton – N1.

Express by Holiday Inn, 275 Old St., EC1V 9LN, (020) 7300 4300, *reservationsfc idayinnlondon.demon.co.uk, Fax (020) 7300 4400* – , rm, rest, – 80 AE VISA JCB. p. 27 **PT**
restricted opening Christmas and New Year – **Meals** *(closed Saturday)* (dinner c a la carte 16.00/23.00 **t.** 6.95 – **224 rm** 99.00 **st.**

Real Greek, 15 Hoxton Market, N1 6HG, (020) 7739 8212, *Fax (020) 7739 4910* – VISA p. 27 **PT**
closed 24 December-2 January, Sunday and Bank Holidays – **Meals** - Greek - a la c 26.40/31.90 **t.**

Stoke Newington – N16.

Mesclun, 24 Stoke Newington Church St., N16 0LU, (020) 7249 5 *Fax (020) 7275 8448* – VISA JCB p. 10 **FU**
closed 25-31 December and Sunday – **Meals** (dinner only) a la carte 16.75/21.75 **t.** 7.9

HAMMERSMITH and FULHAM.

Fulham – SW6.

La Reserve, 422-428 Fulham Rd, SW6 1DU, (020) 7385 8561, *info@la-reserve.c Fax (020) 7385 7662* – , rm, . AE VISA JCB. p. 28 **FZ**
Meals (dinner only) a la carte 15.00/19.00 **t.** – 9.50 – **43 rm** 110.00/135.00 **t.**

London Putney Bridge Travel Inn Capital, 3 Putney Bridge Approach, SW6 (020) 7471 8300, *Fax (020) 7471 8315* – , rm, rest, . AE VISA. p. 16 **AC**
Meals (grill rest.) (dinner only) – **154 rm** 69.95 **t.**

Blue Elephant, 4-6 Fulham Broadway, SW6 1AA, (020) 7385 6595, *london@bluee ant.com, Fax (020) 7386 7665* – . AE VISA p. 28 **EZ**
closed Christmas and Saturday lunch – **Meals** - Thai - (booking essential) 29.00/34.0 and a la carte 6.25.

XX **Mao Tai,** 58 New Kings Rd., Parsons Green, SW6 4LS, ✆ (020) 7731 2520, *Fax (020) 7471 8992* – ▤. MC AE ① VISA JCB p. 16 **BQ** e
closed 25 and 26 December – **Meals** - Chinese (Szechuan) - 23.70 **t.** and a la carte.

The Salisbury Tavern, 21 Sherbrooke Rd, SW6 7HX, ✆ (020) 7381 4005, *longshot@dial.pipex.com, Fax (020) 7381 1002* – ▤. MC AE VISA p. 28 **EZ** e
closed 24-27 and 31 December – **Meals** (live jazz Monday evening) a la carte 19.70/25.25 **t.**

ammersmith – ✉ *W6/W12/W14.*

XX **River Café** (Ruth Rogers/Rose Gray), Thames Wharf, Rainville Rd, W6 9HA, ✆ (020) 7381 8824, *info@rivercafe.co.uk, Fax (020) 7381 6217,* – MC AE ① VISA JCB p. 13 **DV** r
closed Christmas-New Year, Easter, Sunday dinner and Bank Holidays – **Meals** - Italian - (booking essential) a la carte 36.50/49.00 **t.**
Spec. Chargrilled squid with chilli and rocket. Tranche of turbot with capers and marjoram. Roasted grouse with quince jam, Chianti and celeriac.

XX **Rafique,** 291 King St., W6 9NH, ✆ (020) 8748 7345, *Fax (020) 8563 9679* – ▤. MC AE ① VISA JCB p. 13 **CV** i
closed Saturday lunch – **Meals** - Indian - 8.50 **t.** (lunch) and a la carte 18.95/23.85 **t.**

X **Snows on the Green,** 166 Shepherd's Bush Rd, Brook Green, W6 7PB, ✆ (020) 7603 2142, *Fax (020) 7602 7553* – ▤. MC AE ① VISA p. 13 **DV** x
closed Sunday, Saturday lunch and Bank Holidays – **Meals** 16.50 **t.** (lunch) and a la carte 17.75/28.95 **t.**

X **The Brackenbury,** 129-131 Brackenbury Rd, W6 0BQ, ✆ (020) 8748 0107, *Fax (020) 8741 0905,* – MC AE ① VISA JCB p. 13 **CV** a
closed 25 December, 1 January, Saturday lunch and Sunday dinner – **Meals** 12.50 **t.** (lunch) and a la carte 17.75/26.25 **t.**

X **Azou,** 375 King St., W6 9NJ, ✆ (020) 8536 7266, *Fax (020) 8748 1009* – ▤. MC ① VISA p. 13 **CV** u
closed lunch Saturday and Sunday – **Meals** - North African - 7.50/15.50 **t.** and a la carte.

Thatched House, 115 Dalling Rd, W6 0ET, ✆ (020) 8748 6174, *thatchedhouse@establishment.co.uk, Fax (020) 8563 2735* – MC VISA JCB p. 13 **CV** r
closed Christmas and New Year – **Meals** a la carte 14.35/21.85 **t.**

Anglesea Arms, 35 Wingate Rd, W6 0UR, ✆ (020) 8749 1291, *Fax (020) 8749 1254* – MC VISA p. 13 **CV** c
closed 24-31 December – **Meals** (bookings not accepted) a la carte 15.85/19.70 **t.** 🍷 7.75.

ympia – ✉ *W14.*

XX **Cotto,** 44 Blythe Rd, W14 0HA, ✆ (020) 7602 9333, *Fax (020) 7602 5003* – ▤. MC VISA JCB p. 28 **EZ** i
closed 1 week in summer, 25-26 December, Saturday lunch, Sunday and Bank Holidays – **Meals** 15.50 **t.** (lunch) and a la carte 18.45/27.00 **t.** 🍷 9.00.

epherd's Bush – ✉ *W12/W14.*

XX **Chinon,** 23 Richmond Way, W14 0AS, ✆ (020) 7602 5968, *johnchinon@hotmail.com, Fax (020) 7602 4082* – ▤. MC AE VISA p. 13 **DV** c
closed Sunday – **Meals** (dinner only) a la carte 19.50/33.50 **t.**

X **Wilsons,** 236 Blythe Rd, W14 0HJ, ✆ (020) 7603 7267, *haggis@wilsonsrestaurant.co.uk, Fax (020) 7602 9018* – MC VISA JCB p. 13 **DV** a
closed Christmas, Sunday and Bank Holidays – **Meals** (dinner only) 15.00 **t.** and a la carte 🍷 6.00.

Havelock Tavern, 57 Masbro Rd, W14 0LS, ✆ (020) 7603 5374, *Fax (020) 7602 1163,* – ▤ p. 13 **DV** e
closed 23-27 December and 20 August – **Meals** (bookings not accepted) a la carte approx. 20.00 **t.** 🍷 10.00.

RINGEY.

ouch End – ✉ *N8.*

XX **Les Associés,** 172 Park Rd, N8 8JT, ✆ (020) 8348 8944 – MC VISA p. 10 **EU** e
closed 2 weeks January, 2 weeks August and Monday – **Meals** - French - (dinner only and Sunday lunch)/dinner a la carte 18.80/23.60 **t.** 🍷 8.80.

X **Florians,** 4 Topsfield Par., Middle Lane, N8 8RP, ✆ (020) 8348 8348, *Fax (020) 8292 2092,* – ▤. MC VISA p. 10 **EU** c
closed 25-26 December and 1 January – **Meals** - Italian - a la carte 18.95/22.50 **t.** 🍷 6.70.

HARROW.

Harrow Weald – ✉ Middx.

Grim's Dyke, Old Redding, HA3 6SH, ☎ (020) 8385 3100, *enquiries@grimsdyke.co* *Fax (020) 8954 4560*, – rm, – 70. MC AE VISA p. 8 **BT**
Meals (residents only Saturday lunch) 22.00 **t.** and a la carte 12.00 – **44 rm** 122. 149.00 **t.** – SB.

Kenton – ✉ Middx.

Travel Inn Metro, Kenton Rd, HA3 8AT, ☎ (020) 8907 4069, *Fax (020) 8909 1604* – rm, TV P. MC AE VISA. p. 8 **BU**
Meals (grill rest.) – **70 rm** 46.95 **t.**

Pinner – ✉ Middx.

Friends, 11 High St., HA5 5PJ, ☎ (020) 8866 0286, *Fax (020) 8866 0286* – . MC AE VISA p. 8 **BU**
closed 2 weeks August, Sunday dinner and Bank Holidays – **Meals** 23.75 **t.** (d ner) and a la carte 25.40/31.15 **t.** 10.50.

HAVERING.

Romford – ✉ Essex.

18, 9 *Risebridge, Risebridge Chase, Lower Bedfords Rd* ☎ *(01708) 741429*, **JT**.

Travel Inn Metro, Mercury Gdns., RM1 3EN, ☎ (01708) 760548, *Fax (01708) 760456* – rm, TV P. MC AE VISA p. 11 **JU**
Meals (grill rest.) – **40 rm** 46.95 **t.**

HILLINGDON.

18 *Haste Hill, The Drive, Northwood* ☎ *(01923) 825224* **AU**.

Hayes – ✉ Middx.

Travel Inn Metro, 362 Uxbridge Rd, UB4 0HF, ☎ (020) 8573 7479, *Fax (020) 8569 12* rm, rest, TV P. MC AE VISA. p. 8 **AV**
Meals (grill rest.) – **62 rm** 46.95 **t.**

Heathrow Airport – ✉ Middx.

Radisson Edwardian, 140 Bath Rd, Hayes, UB3 5AW, ☎ (020) 8759 6311, *radissone rdian.com, Fax (020) 8759 4559*, , , – , rm, TV P – 550. MC AE JCB. p. 12 **AX**
Henleys : **Meals** a la carte 31.50/41.00 **st.** – ***Brasserie :*** **Meals** a la carte 17.50/25.00 s 13.50 – **442 rm** 185.00/235.00, 17 suites – SB.

Crowne Plaza London Heathrow, Stockley Rd, West Drayton, UB7 9 ☎ (01895) 445555, *Fax (01895) 445122*, , , , 9 – , rm, TV P – MC AE VISA JCB. p. 8 **AV**
Concha Grill : **Meals** 20.50 **t.** (lunch) and a la carte 19.70/37.45 **t.** 9.75 – (see also ***Sim Nico Heathrow*** below) – 16.50 – **457 rm** 175.00 **st.**, 1 suite.

Sheraton Skyline, Bath Rd, Hayes, UB3 5BP, ☎ (020) 8759 2535, *Fax (020) 8750 9* , – , rm, TV P – 500. MC AE VISA JCB. p. 12 **AX**
Colony Room : **Meals** (dinner only) a la carte 25.65/35.95 **t.** – ***Le Jardin :*** **Meals** (lu only) 25.90/32.70 **t.** and a la carte – 15.75 – **346 rm** 168.00/190.00 **st.**, 5 suites.

Hilton London Heathrow Airport, Terminal 4, TW6 3AF, ☎ (020) 8759 7755, *gm athrow@hilton.com, Fax (020) 8759 7579*, , , – , rm, TV P – MC AE VISA JCB. p. 12 **AX**
Brasserie : **Meals** 24.50 **st.** (dinner) and a la carte 27.00/35.00 **st.** 8.00 – ***Zen Orien*** **Meals** - Chinese - 30.80/36.50 **t.** and a la carte 8.00 – 16.00 – **390 rm** 230.00/270.0 5 suites – SB.

London Heathrow Marriott, Bath Rd, Hayes, UB3 5AN, ☎ (020) 8990 1 *Fax (020) 8990 1110*, , , – , rm, TV P – 540. MC AE VISA p. 12 **AX**
Tuscany : **Meals** - Italian - (dinner only) a la carte 26.95/36.40 **t.** – ***Allie's grille :*** **M** a la carte 18.30/31.40 **t.** 8.95 – 13.95 – **388 rm** 180.00 **t.**, 2 suites.

Le Meridien Heathrow, Bath Rd, West Drayton, UB7 0DU, ℘ (020) 8759 6611, *excelsior hotel@compuserve.com, Fax (020) 8759 3421,* – rm, – 700. AE VISA JCB. p. 12 **AX** x
Meals (carving rest.) 16.50/19.95 **t.** 6.95 – ***Wheeler's :*** **Meals** - Seafood - *(closed Saturday lunch, Sunday and Bank Holidays)* 24.50 **st.** and a la carte 8.95 – 14.95 – **527 rm** 120.00/180.00 **s.**, 10 suites – SB.

Posthouse Premier Heathrow, Sipson Rd, West Drayton, UB7 0JU, ℘ (0870) 400 8595, *Fax (020) 8897 8659* – rm, – 140. AE VISA JCB. p. 8 **AV** c
Sampans : **Meals** - Chinese - (dinner only) 18.95/29.95 **t.** and a la carte 8.50 – ***Carvery :*** **Meals** 19.50 **t.** 6.95 – 13.95 – **604 rm** 129.00 **st.**, 6 suites – SB.

Renaissance London Heathrow, Bath Rd, TW6 2AQ, ℘ (020) 8897 6363, *106047.3556@compuserve.com, Fax (020) 8897 1113,* – rm, – 550. AE VISA JCB. p. 12 **AX** c
Meals 17.50/20.50 **st.** and a la carte 8.50 – 12.95 – **644 rm** 169.00 **st.**, 5 suites.

Sheraton Heathrow, Colnbrook bypass, West Drayton, UB7 0HJ, ℘ (020) 8759 2424, *Fax (020) 8759 2091,* – rm, – 70. AE VISA JCB. p. 12 **AVX** a
Meals 17.95/20.50 **t.** and a la carte 10.00 – 14.25 – **426 rm** 138.00/162.00 **st.**, 5 suites.

Posthouse Heathrow, 118 Bath Rd, Hayes, UB3 5AJ, ℘ (0870) 400 9040, *Fax (020) 8564 9265* – rm, rest, – 55. AE VISA JCB.
Meals (bar lunch Saturday) (buffet lunch) 12.95/16.95 **t.** and a la carte 7.50 – 11.95 – **186 rm** 99.00/159.00 **st.** – SB. p. 12 **AX** i

Travelodge, Sipson Rd, West Drayton, UB7 0UD, ℘ (020) 8897 7775, *Fax (020) 8897 6381* – AE VISA JCB. p. 12 **AX** x
Meals (grill rest.) – **289 rm** 69.95 **t.**

Simply Nico Heathrow (at Crowne Plaza London Heathrow H.), Stockley Rd, West Drayton, UB7 9NA, ℘ (01895) 437564, *simplynico@trpplc.com, Fax (01895) 437565* – AE VISA p. 12 **AV** v
closed Christmas, Saturday lunch, Sunday and Bank Holidays – **Meals** 16.50/19.50 **t.** (lunch) and a la carte 26.00/39.50 **t.** 10.00.

enham – ✉ *Middx.*

Roberto's, 15 Long Lane, UB10 8AX, ℘ (01895) 632519 – AE VISA JCB
closed first 2 weeks August, Sunday and lunch Saturday – **Meals** - Italian - a la carte 15.00/34.00 **t.** p. 8 **AU** i

UNSLOW.

Wyke Green, Syon Lane, Isleworth ℘ *(020) 8560 8777* **BV** – *Airlinks, Southall Lane* ℘ *(020) 8561 1418* **ABV** – *Hounslow Heath, Staines Rd* ℘ *(020) 8570 5271* **BX**.

24 The Treaty Centre, High St. ℘ *(020) 8583 2929 (closed Sunday).*

swick – ✉ *W4.*

The Chiswick, 131 Chiswick High Rd, W4 2ED, ℘ (020) 8994 6887, *thechiswick@talk21.com, Fax (020) 8994 5504* – AE VISA p. 13 **CV** e
closed 25-26 December, Saturday lunch, Sunday dinner and Bank Holidays – **Meals** 12.95/15.50 **t.** and a la carte 8.00.

Grano, 162 Thames Rd, W4 3QS, ℘ (020) 8995 0120, *Fax (020) 8995 0120* – AE VISA JCB p. 13 **CV** n
closed Sunday – **Meals** - Italian - (booking essential) (dinner only) a la carte 27.00/33.75 **st.**

Springbok Café, 42 Devonshire Rd, W4 2HD, ℘ (020) 8742 3149, *pcg@springbokcafe.freeserve.co.uk, Fax (020) 8742 8541* – VISA p. 13 **CV** z
closed Sunday – **Meals** - South African - (dinner only) a la carte 17.50/22.50 **t.** 5.50.

tham – ✉ *Middx.*

St. Giles, Hounslow Rd, TW14 9AD, ℘ (020) 8817 7000, *Fax (020) 8817 7001,* – rm, – 60. AE VISA. p. 12 **AX** v
Meals - Italian - *(closed lunch Saturday and Sunday)* a la carte 17.45/27.40 **t.** – 9.95 – **268 rm** 109.00/119.00 **st.**, 17 suites.

Heston Service Area – ⊠ *Middx.*

Travelodge without rest., TW5 9NB, on M 4 (between junctions 2 and 3 westbou carriageway) ✆ (020) 8580 2000, *Fax (020) 8580 2006* – ⇆ TV ♿ P. MC AE ① VISA JCB.
145 rm 69.95 **t.** p. 12 **ABV**

Travelodge, TW5 9NA, on M 4 (between junctions 3 and 2 on eastbound carriagev ✆ (020) 8580 2122, *Fax (020) 8580 2128* – ⇆ rm, TV ♿ P. MC AE ① VISA JCB. ⚹
Meals (grill rest.) – **66 rm** 69.95 **t.** p. 12 **AV**

ISLINGTON.

Archway – ⊠ *N19.*

Paris-London Café, 5 Junction Rd, N19 5QT, ✆ (020) 7561 0330 p. 10 **EU**
closed last 2 weeks August and 1 week Christmas – **Meals** - French - 5.95/15.95 and a la carte 🍷 6.90.

St. John's, 91 Junction Rd, N19 5QU, ✆ (020) 7272 1587 – MC VISA p. 10 **EU**
closed 25 December-5 January and Monday lunch – **Meals** (bar lunch)/dinner a la c 16.50/24.50 **t.**

Canonbury – ⊠ *N1.*

Anna's Place, 90 Mildmay Park, N1 4PR, ✆ (020) 7249 9379 p. 10 **FU**
closed 1 week Christmas, Sunday and lunch Friday – **Meals** - Swedish - (booking esser 12.95 **t.** and a la carte.

Centuria, 100 St. Paul's Rd, N1 2QP, ✆ (020) 7704 2345 – MC VISA p. 10 **FU**
closed lunch Monday-Friday – **Meals** a la carte 18.00/21.00 **t.**

Clerkenwell – ⊠ *EC1.*

The Rookery without rest., 12 Peters Lane, Cowcross St., EC1M 6DS, ✆ (020) 7336 0 *reservations@rookery.co.uk, Fax (020) 7336 0932,* « Georgian town houses » – TV ✆. MC ① VISA JCB. ⚹ p. 27 **NU**
closed 25 December – **32 rm** 175.00/205.00 **s.**, 1 suite.

Maison Novelli, 29 Clerkenwell Green, EC1R 0DU, ✆ (020) 7251 6 *Fax (020) 7490 1083* – ▤. MC AE ① VISA p. 27 **NU**
closed Sunday, Saturday lunch and Bank Holidays – **Meals** a la carte 26.45/46.95 **t.** 🍷 10.

Smiths of Smithfield, Top Floor, 67-77 Charterhouse St., EC1M ✆ (020) 7236 6666, *smiths@smithfield.co.uk, Fax (020) 7236 5666,* ≤, 🏠 – |‡| ▤. MC AE VISA JCB p. 27 **NU**
closed 25-26 December and Saturday lunch – **Meals** a la carte 25.50/42.50 **t.** 🍷 6.50 –
Dining Room : **Meals** *(closed 25-26 December, Saturday lunch and Sunday)* a la c 17.50/18.50 **t.** 🍷 5.00.

Gaudi, 63 Clerkenwell Rd, EC1M 5PT, ✆ (020) 7608 3220, *gaudi@turnmills.cc Fax (020) 7250 1057* – ▤. MC AE ① VISA p. 27 **NU**
closed 24 December-3 January, Saturday, Sunday and Bank Holidays – **Meals** - Spani 10.00/15.00 **t.** (lunch) and a la carte 30.00/34.00 **t.**

19:20, 19-20 Great Sutton St., EC1V 0DR, ✆ (020) 7253 1920, *Fax (020) 7253 1925* – ▤ AE VISA JCB p. 27 **OT**
closed 24-31 December, Sunday and Saturday lunch – **Meals** 15.00 **t.** (lunch) and a la c 18.75/22.90 **t.**

Finsbury – ⊠ *WC1/EC1/EC2.*

Simply Nico, 7 Goswell Rd, EC1N 7AH, ✆ (020) 7336 7677, *simplynico@trpplc.c Fax (020) 7336 7690* – ▤. MC AE ① VISA p. 27 **OUT**
closed Christmas, Sunday and Bank Holidays – **Meals** 16.75/18.50 **t.** (lunch) and a la c 22.75/29.50 **t.** 🍷 9.00.

Café Lazeez City, 88 St. John St., EC1M 4EH, ✆ (020) 7253 2224, *Fax (020) 7253 21* ▤. MC AE ① VISA JCB p. 27 **OU**
closed Christmas, Sunday, Saturday lunch and Bank Holidays – **Meals** - North Indi a la carte 18.00/25.00 **t.**

Quality Chop House, 94 Farringdon Rd, EC1R 3EA, ✆ (020) 7837 5 *Fax (020) 7833 8748* – ⇆. MC VISA p. 26 **MT**
closed 24 December-3 January and Saturday lunch – **Meals** a la carte 22.50/35.25 **t.** 🍷 9

Moro, 34-36 Exmouth Market, EC1R 4QE, ✆ (020) 7833 8336, *Fax (020) 7833 9338* – ▤ AE ① VISA p. 27 **NT**
closed 22 December-2 January, Saturday lunch, Sunday and Bank Holidays – **Meals** a la c 18.50/27.50 **t.** 🍷 12.25.

St. John, 26 St. John St., EC1M 4AY, ✆ (020) 7251 0848, *tg@stjohnrestaurant.co.uk, Fax (020) 7251 4090,* « Converted 19C former smokehouse » – ▤. MC AE ① VISA JCB
closed Christmas-New Year, Easter weekend, Sunday and lunch Saturday – **Meals** a la carte 19.30/27.50 **t.** 9.00. p. 27 **OU** c

The Peasant, 240 St. John St., EC1V 4PH, ✆ (020) 7336 7726, *eat@thepeasant.co.uk, Fax (020) 7251 4476* – MC AE ① VISA p. 27 **NT** e
closed 24 December-2 January, Saturday lunch, Sunday and Bank Holidays – **Meals** a la carte 16.30/19.50 **t.** 5.00.

ghbury – ✉ *N7.*

Bu-San, 41-43 Holloway Rd, N7 8JP, ✆ (020) 7607 8264, *Fax (020) 7700 0961* – ▤ P. MC VISA p. 27 **NS** x
closed Christmas-New Year, lunch Saturday and Sunday and Bank Holidays – **Meals** - Korean - 6.60/14.75 **t.** and a la carte.

ington – ✉ *N1.*

Hilton London Islington, 53 Upper St., N1 0UY, ✆ (020) 7354 7700, *Fax (020) 7354 7711,* 🏠, 🏋, ≘s – |♦|, ⇹ rm, ▤ TV ✆ ♿ – 🏃 35. MC AE ① VISA. ✂ p. 27 **NS** s
Meals 18.95 **t.** and a la carte – ☐ 15.50 – **178 rm** 180.00/200.00 **st.**, 6 suites – SB.

Jurys Inn London, 60 Pentonville Rd, N1 9LA, ✆ (020) 7282 5500, *london-inn@jurysdoyle.com, Fax (020) 7282 5511* – |♦|, ⇹ rm, ▤ TV ✆ ♿. MC AE ① VISA. ✂ p. 26 **MT** e
Meals (bar lunch)/dinner a la carte 16.00/27.00 **st.** 8.00 – **230 rm** 87.00 **st.**

Frederick's, Camden Passage, N1 8EG, ✆ (020) 7359 2888, *eat@fredericks.co.uk, Fax (020) 7359 5173,* 🏠, 🏠 – ▤. MC AE ① VISA JCB p. 27 **NS** c
closed Christmas-New Year, Sunday and Bank Holidays – **Meals** 15.50 **t.** (lunch) and a la carte 25.50/31.00 **t.** 8.00.

Lola's, Mall Building, 359 Upper St., N1 0PD, ✆ (020) 7359 1932, *lolasreatuk@btinternet.com, Fax (020) 7359 2209,* « Converted former tram shed » – ▤. MC AE ① VISA
closed 25-26 December, 1 January and lunch Bank Holidays – **Meals** 15.00 **t.** (lunch) and a la carte 25.25/27.50 **t.** 8.50. p. 27 **NS** n

White Onion, 297 Upper St., N1 2TU, ✆ (020) 7359 3533, *Fax (020) 7359 3533* – ▤. MC AE VISA p. 27 **NS** r
Meals *(dinner only and Sunday lunch)* 24.50 **t.**.

Granita, 127 Upper St., N1 1PQ, ✆ (020) 7226 3222, *Fax (020) 7226 4833* – ▤. MC VISA
closed 2 weeks August, 1 week Easter, 10 days Christmas, Monday and lunch Tuesday – **Meals** 13.95 **t.** (lunch) and dinner a la carte 23.85/27.95 **t.** 10.50. p. 27 **NS** a

Euphorium, 203 Upper St., N1 1RQ, ✆ (020) 7704 6909, *Fax (020) 7226 0241,* 🏠 – MC AE VISA p. 27 **NS** e
closed Christmas and Bank Holidays – **Meals** a la carte 20.00/26.50 **t.**

The Crown, 116 Cloudesley Rd, N1 0EB, ✆ (020) 7837 7107, 🏠 – MC AE VISA
closed 25 December and Sunday dinner – **Meals** a la carte 14.20/18.00 **t.** p. 27 **NS** v

---

NSINGTON and CHELSEA *(Royal Borough of).*

elsea – ✉ *SW1/SW3/SW10.*

Hyatt Carlton Tower, 2 Cadogan Pl., SW1X 9PY, ✆ (020) 7235 1234, *ctower@hytlondon.co.uk, Fax (020) 7235 9129,* ≤, 🏋, ≘s, 🏊, 🏠, ✂ – |♦|, ⇹ rm, ▤ TV ✆ 🚗 – 🏃 250. MC AE ① VISA JCB. ✂ p. 35 **FR** n
***Rib Room*:** **Meals** a la carte 34.00/61.50 **t.** 14.00 – ***Grissini*:** **Meals** - Italian - *(closed Saturday lunch and Sunday dinner)* 21.00 **t.** (lunch) and a la carte 29.00/42.00 **t.** 14.00 – ☐ 18.50 – **191 rm** 325.00/350.00, 29 suites.

Conrad International London, Chelsea Harbour, SW10 0XG, ✆ (020) 7823 3000, *Fax (020) 7351 6525,* ≤, 🏋, ≘s, 🏊 – |♦|, ⇹ rm, ▤ TV ✆ ♿ 🚗 – 🏃 180. MC AE ① VISA JCB p. 17 **CQ** i
***Aquasia*:** **Meals** 17.00/19.00 **t.** (lunch) and a la carte 23.50/33.50 **t.** 10.00 – ☐ 21.00, **160 suites** 330.00 – SB.

Sheraton Park Tower, 101 Knightsbridge, SW1X 7RN, ✆ (020) 7235 8050, *reservation_central_london@starwoodhotels.com, Fax (020) 7235 8231,* ≤ – |♦|, ⇹ rm, ▤ TV ✆ ♿ 🚗 – 🏃 60. MC AE ① VISA. ✂ p. 35 **FQ** v
Meals – (see ***One-O-One*** below) – ☐ 19.00 – **267 rm** 288.00/368.00, 22 suites.

Capital, 22-24 Basil St., SW3 1AT, (020) 7589 5171, *reservations@capitalhotel.co* *Fax (020) 7225 0011* – 25. p. 35 ER
Meals (booking essential) 24.50/49.00-60.00 **t.** 10.50 – 16.50 – **48 rm** 180.00/350.0
Spec. Pan-fried foie gras with grilled asparagus. Fillet of lamb with herb crust , fricas printanière. Carpaccio of pineapple with Champagne velouté.

Cadogan, 75 Sloane St., SW1X 9SG, (020) 7235 7141, *info@cadogan.co* *Fax (020) 7245 0994,* – rm, rest, – 40.
Meals *(closed Saturday lunch)* 15.90/27.00 **t.** and a la carte 6.75 – 16.50 – **61** 175.00/225.00 **s.**, 4 suites – SB. p. 35 FR

Chelsea Village & Court H., Fulham Rd, SW6 1HS, (020) 7565 14 *Fax (020) 7565 1450,* « Adjacent to Chelsea Football Club » – rm, 300. p. 28 FZ
Arkles : **Meals** - Irish - *(closed Monday and dinner Sunday)* 17.00 **t.** (lunch) and ner a la carte 22.00/29.00 **t.** – ***Kings brasserie :*** **Meals** a la carte 21.00/25.00 **t.** – ***Fishn*** **Meals** - Seafood - *(closed Sunday and lunch Monday)* 14.50 **t.** and a la carte 16.25/22.00 14.00 – **288 rm** 140.00/150.00 **t.**, 3 suites – SB.

Durley House, 115 Sloane St., SW1X 9PJ, (020) 7235 5537, *durley@firmdale.c* *Fax (020) 7259 6977,* « Georgian town house », –
Meals (room service only) a la carte approx. 15.00 **t.** 15.00 – 17.00, **11 suites** 250 480.00 **s.** p. 35 FS

Cliveden Town House, 26 Cadogan Gdns., SW3 2RP, (020) 7730 6466, *reservatio* *clivedentownhouse.co.uk, Fax (020) 7730 0236,* – rm, rm, p. 35 FS
Meals (room service only) – 18.50 – **31 rm** 160.00/310.00 **s.**, 4 suites.

Millennium Knightsbridge, 17-25 Sloane St., SW1X 9NU, (020) 7235 4377, *sales* *ghtsbridge@mill-cop.com, Fax (020) 7235 3705* – rm, – 120. p. 35 FR
Meals *(closed lunch Saturday and Sunday and Bank Holidays)* 9.00/19.50 **t.** and a la c 9.50 – 15.50 – **218 rm** 225.00 **s.**, 4 suites.

Franklin, 22-28 Egerton Gdns., SW3 2DB, (020) 7584 5533, *bookings@franklinhote* *uk, Fax (020) 7584 5449,* « Tastefully furnished Victorian town house », – p. 35 DS
Meals (room service only) a la carte 19.75/37.00 **t.** 7.50 – 16.00 – **46 rm** 160 325.00 **s.**, 1 suite.

Basil Street, 8 Basil St., SW3 1AH, (020) 7581 3311, *info@thebasil.c* *Fax (020) 7581 3693* – rm, – 55. p. 35 FC
Meals 17.50/23.00 **t.** and lunch a la carte – 14.50 – **80 rm** 128.00/205.00.

Egerton House, 17-19 Egerton Terr., SW3 2BX, (020) 7589 2412, *bookings@theeg* *n.force9.net, Fax (020) 7584 6540,* « Tastefully furnished Victorian town house » – p. 35 DR
Meals (room service only) – 16.00 – **29 rm** 160.00/250.00 **s.**

Sydney House, 9-11 Sydney St., SW3 6PU, (020) 7376 7711, *sydneyhousehotel@* *ondon.com, Fax (020) 7376 4233* – p. 35 DT
Meals (room service only) – 14.10 – **21 rm** 150.00/220.00 **s.**

The Sloane, 29 Draycott Pl., SW3 2SH, (020) 7581 5757, *sloanehotel@btinternet.c* *Fax (020) 7584 1348,* « Victorian town house, antiques » –
Meals (room service only) a la carte 19.00/23.00 **s.** 7.50 – 12.00 – **12 rm** 140 225.00 **s.** p. 35 ET

The London Outpost of the Carnegie Club without rest., 69 Cadogan Gdns., 2RB, (020) 7589 7333, *londonoutpost@dialpipex.com, Fax (020) 7581 4958,* – p. 35 FS
closed 25-26 December – – 16.95 – **11 rm** 150.00/250.00.

Eleven Cadogan Gardens, 11 Cadogan Gdns., SW3 2RJ, (020) 7730 7000, *reser* *ns@numbereleven.co.uk, Fax (020) 7730 5217,* – p. 35 FS
Meals (room service only) 18.00 6.00 – 11.75 – **57 rm** 158.00/258.00 **t.**, 3 suites.

L'Hotel, 28 Basil St., SW3 1AS, (020) 7589 6286, *reservations@capitalhotel.c* *Fax (020) 7823 7826* – p. 35 ER
Le Metro : **Meals** *(closed 25 December and Bank Holidays)* a la carte 18.50/22.95 **t.** 6.50 – **12 rm** 145.00/165.00 **s.**

Chelsea Green without rest., 35 Ixworth Pl., SW3 3QX, (020) 7225 7500, *park-cor* *con.co.uk, Fax (020) 7225 7555* – – 80. p. 35 DT
15.00 – **42 rm** 150.00/180.00 **st.**, 4 suites.

Parkes without rest., 41 Beaufort Gdns., SW3 1PW, (020) 7581 9944, *reception@pa* *hotel.com, Fax (020) 7581 1999* – p. 35 ER
10.00 – **18 rm** 150.00/225.00 **s.**, 15 suites 210.00/265.00 **s.**

Sloane Square Moat House, Sloane Sq., SW1W 8EG, ✆ (020) 7896 9988, *reservations @queensmoat.co.uk, Fax (020) 7824 8381* – ▮ ⇔ TV ✆ – 🏛 40. MC AE ⓓ VISA p. 35 FST v
Meals – (see ***Simply Nico*** below) – ☕ 10.50 – **105 rm** 156.00/197.00 **st.** – SB.

Beaufort without rest., 33 Beaufort Gdns., SW3 1PP, ✆ (020) 7584 5252, *thebeaufort@n ol.co.uk, Fax (020) 7589 2834,* « English floral watercolour collection » – ▮ ⇔ ▤ TV ✆. MC AE ⓓ VISA JCB. ✂ p. 35 ER n
28 rm 165.00/295.00 **s.**

Claverley without rest., 13-14 Beaufort Gdns., SW3 1PS, ✆ (020) 7589 8541, *reservations @claverleyhotel.co.uk, Fax (020) 7584 3410* – ▮ TV. MC AE ⓓ VISA JCB. ✂ p. 35 ER o
30 rm ☕ 75.00/215.00 **st.**

Knightsbridge without rest., 12 Beaufort Gdns., SW3 1PT, ✆ (020) 7589 9271, *reception @knightsbridgehotel.co.uk, Fax (020) 7823 9692* – ▮ TV. MC AE ⓓ VISA JCB. ✂
44 rm ☕ 110.00/150.00 **st.**, 6 suites. p. 35 ER o

Gordon Ramsay, 68-69 Royal Hospital Rd, SW3 4HP, ✆ (020) 7352 4441, *Fax (020) 7352 3334* – ▤. MC AE ⓓ VISA JCB p. 35 EU c
closed 1 week Christmas, Saturday, Sunday and Bank Holidays – **Meals** (booking essential) 30.00/60.00-75.00 **t.**
Spec. Panaché of scallops with truffled cauliflower purée. Fillet of Aberdeen Angus with baby artichokes, Port wine sauce. "Three tastes" of white peach.

Aubergine, 11 Park Walk, SW10 0AJ, ✆ (020) 7352 3449, *Fax (020) 7351 1770* – ▤. MC AE ⓓ VISA JCB p. 34 CU r
closed 2 weeks August, 2 weeks Christmas-New Year, Easter, Sunday, Saturday lunch and Bank Holidays – **Meals** (booking essential) 16.00/45.00 **t.** 🍷 12.50
Spec. Warm salad of quail, foie gras and sweetbreads. Pan-fried sea bass with sweet pepper and tomato bouillon. Lemon Chiboust with passion fruit sauce.

Bibendum, Michelin House, 81 Fulham Rd, SW3 6RD, ✆ (020) 7581 5817, *manager@bibe ndum.co.uk, Fax (020) 7823 7925* – ▤. MC AE ⓓ VISA p. 35 DS s
closed 25-26 December – **Meals** 27.50 **t.** (lunch) and dinner a la carte 29.00/49.00 **t.** 🍷 7.25.

Floriana, 15 Beauchamp Pl., SW3 1NQ, ✆ (020) 7838 1500, *Fax (020) 7584 1464* – ▤. MC AE ⓓ VISA p. 35 ER c
closed 10 days Christmas, 2 weeks August, Sunday, Monday lunch and Bank Holidays – **Meals** - Italian - 10.50/19.50 **t.** (lunch) and a la carte 41.50/52.00 **t.**

Fifth Floor (at Harvey Nichols), Knightsbridge, SW1X 7RJ, ✆ (020) 7235 5250, *Fax (020) 7823 2207* – ▤. MC AE ⓓ VISA JCB p. 35 FQ a
closed 25-26 December, and dinner Sunday – **Meals** 24.50 **t.** (lunch) and dinner a la carte 32.00/44.00 **t.** 🍷 8.50.

One-O-One (at Sheraton Park Tower H.), William St., SW1X 7RN, ✆ (020) 7290 7101, *Fax (020) 7235 6196* – ▤. MC AE ⓓ VISA p. 35 FQ v
Meals - Seafood - 15.00/25.00 **st.** (lunch) and a la carte 35.00/46.00 **st.** 🍷 12.00.

Turner's, 87-89 Walton St., SW3 2HP, ✆ (020) 7584 6711, *turnerrest@aol.com, Fax (020) 7584 4441* – ▤. MC AE ⓓ VISA p. 35 ES n
closed 2 weeks August, Sunday and Bank Holidays – **Meals** 17.50/29.50 **t.** and a la carte 🍷 13.50.

Toto's, Walton House, Walton St., SW3 2JH, ✆ (020) 7589 0075, *Fax (020) 7581 9668* – ▤. MC AE ⓓ VISA JCB p. 35 ES a
closed 25 to 27 December – **Meals** - Italian - 19.50 **st.** (lunch) and a la carte 29.50/39.50 **st.** 🍷 8.50.

Chutney Mary, 535 King's Rd, SW10 0SZ, ✆ (020) 7351 3113, *Fax (020) 7351 7694* – ▤. MC AE ⓓ VISA JCB p. 28 FZ v
closed 25 December – **Meals** - Indian - 15.00 **t.** (lunch) and a la carte 20.00/30.25 **t.** 🍷 8.50.

Zaika, 257-259 Fulham Rd, SW3 6HY, ✆ (020) 7351 7823, *Fax (020) 7376 4971* – ▤. MC AE VISA p. 34 CU a
closed Saturday lunch and Bank Holidays – **Meals** - Indian - 14.95 **t.** (lunch) and a la carte 20.65/27.20 **t.**
Spec. Tava Machli (swordfish in crushed fennel). Murg Makhanwala (butter chicken). Adraki Champaen (ginger lamb chops).

Bluebird, 350 King's Rd, SW3 5UU, ✆ (020) 7559 1000, *Fax (020) 7559 1111* – ▮ ▤. MC AE ⓓ VISA p. 34 CU e
Meals 15.75 **t.** (lunch) and a la carte 20.25/47.25 **t.**

Poissonnerie de l'Avenue, 82 Sloane Av., SW3 3DZ, ✆ (020) 7589 2457, *info@poisson nerie.co.uk, Fax (020) 7581 3360* – ▤. MC AE ⓓ VISA JCB p. 35 DS u
closed 24 December-3 January, Easter Saturday, Sunday and Bank Holidays – **Meals** - French Seafood - 18.95 **t.** (lunch) and a la carte 30.00/37.00 **t.** 🍷 7.50.

English Garden, 10 Lincoln St., SW3 2TS, ✆ (020) 7584 7272, *Fax (020) 7584 1961* – ▤. MC AE ⓓ VISA JCB p. 35 ET x
closed first 2 weeks August – **Meals** 19.50 **t.** (lunch) and a la carte 28.00/37.00 **t.** 🍷 14.00.

XX **The House,** 3 Milner St., SW3 2QA, ✆ (020) 7584 3002, *Fax (020) 7581 2848* – MC AE VISA JCB p. 35 ES
closed 2 weeks August, 1 week Christmas, Saturday lunch and Sunday – **Meals** 16. 23.00 **t.** 10.50.

XX **Brompton Bay,** 96 Draycott Av., SW3 3AD, ✆ (020) 7225 2500, *Fax (020) 7225 1965* – MC AE VISA JCB p. 35 ES
closed 23 December-3 January – **Meals** a la carte 18.50/29.00 **t.** 14.00.

XX **Brasserie St. Quentin,** 243 Brompton Rd, SW3 2EP, ✆ (020) 7589 8(*Fax (020) 7584 6064* – ▤. MC AE VISA p. 35 DR
Meals - French - 15.00 **t.** (lunch) and a la carte 19.90/27.80 **t.**

XX **Benihana,** 77 King's Rd, SW3 4NX, ✆ (020) 7376 7799, *benihana@dircon.co* *Fax (020) 7376 7377* – ▤. MC AE VISA JCB p. 35 EU
closed 25 December – **Meals** - Japanese (Teppan-Yaki) - 8.50/14.00 **t.** and a la carte.

XX **Daphne's,** 112 Draycott Av., SW3 3AE, ✆ (020) 7589 4257, *Fax (020) 7581 2232* – ▤. MC VISA JCB p. 35 DS
closed 25-28 December – **Meals** - Italian - a la carte 26.50/43.50 **t.** 16.00.

XX **Caraffini,** 61-63 Lower Sloane St., SW1W 8DH, ✆ (020) 7259 0235, *info@caraffini.co* *Fax (020) 7259 0236,* – ▤. MC AE VISA p. 35 FT
closed Sunday and Bank Holidays – **Meals** - Italian - a la carte 18.45/32.85 **t.** 7.95.

XX **Vama,** 438 King's Rd, SW10 0LJ, ✆ (020) 7351 4118, *andyv@aol.com, Fax (020) 7565 8* – MC AE VISA JCB p. 29 GZ
closed 25 December and 1 January – **Meals** - Indian - 9.95/30.00 **t.** and a la carte.

XX **Le Colombier,** 145 Dovehouse St., SW3 6LB, ✆ (020) 7351 1155, *colombier@compus* *.com, Fax (020) 7351 0077,* – MC AE VISA p. 35 DT
Meals - French - 13.00/15.00 **t.** (lunch) and a la carte 20.30/32.90 **t.** 6.00.

XX **The Collection,** 264 Brompton Rd, SW3 2AS, ✆ (020) 7225 1212, *Fax (020) 7225 10* ▤. MC AE VISA JCB p. 35 DS
closed 25-26 December and Sunday – **Meals** (dinner only) a la carte 21.00/35.50 **t.**

XX **Good Earth,** 233 Brompton Rd, SW3 2EP, ✆ (020) 7584 3658, *Fax (020) 7823 8769* – MC AE VISA JCB p. 35 DF
closed 23-30 December – **Meals** - Chinese - 21.80/29.80 **t.** (dinner) and a la carte 13 22.80 **t.** 7.50.

XX **Dan's,** 119 Sydney St., SW3 6NR, ✆ (020) 7352 2718, *Fax (020) 7352 3265,* – MC VISA p. 35 DU
Meals 16.00/27.00.

XX **Jak's,** 77 Lower Sloane St., SW1W 8DA, ✆ (020) 7730 9476, *info@jaksclub.c* *Fax (020) 7823 5040* – ▤. MC VISA JCB p. 35 FT
closed Saturday and Sunday – **Meals** 15.00/20.00 **t.** 9.50.

X **Simply Nico** (at Sloane Square Moat House H.), Sloane Sq., SW1W ✆ (020) 7896 9909, *Fax (020) 7896 9908* – ▤. MC AE VISA JCB p. 35 FST
closed 25-26 December – **Meals** a la carte 24.00/29.70 **t.** 9.00.

X **Thierry's,** 342 King's Rd, SW3 5UR, ✆ (020) 7352 3365, *thierrys@trpplc.c* *Fax (020) 7352 3365* – ▤. MC AE VISA p. 34 CU
closed Christmas – **Meals** 10.00/15.00 **t.** and a la carte 9.00.

X **I Cardi,** 351 Fulham Rd, SW10 9TW, ✆ (020) 7351 2939, *Fax (020) 7376 4619* – ▤. MC VISA JCB p. 34 BU
closed 1 week Christmas, Sunday and Bank Holidays – **Meals** - Italian - 16.50/23.50 **t.** 8

X **Bibendum Oyster Bar,** Michelin House, 81 Fulham Rd, SW3 6RD, ✆ (020) 7589 148 *anager@bibendum.co.uk, Fax (020) 7823 7148* – MC AE VISA p. 35 DS
closed 1 week Christmas – **Meals** - Seafood specialities - (bookings not accepted) a la c 15.25/23.50 **t.** 6.95.

X **itsu,** 118 Draycott Av., SW3 3AE, ✆ (020) 7584 5522, *cebsanetcomuk.co* *Fax (020) 7581 8716* – ▤. MC AE VISA p. 35 DS
Meals - Japanese - (bookings not accepted) a la carte 18.00/25.00 **t.**

Admiral Codrington, 17 Mossop St., SW3 2LY, ✆ (020) 7581 0005, *londshot@dial.p com, Fax (020) 7589 2452* – MC AE VISA p. 35 ES
closed 24-27 and 31 December – **Meals** a la carte 17.40/25.20 **t.**

Chelsea Ram, 32 Burnaby St., SW10 0PL, ✆ (020) 7351 4008, *pint@chelsearam.c* *Fax (020) 7349 0885* – MC VISA p. 28 FZ
closed 25, 26 and 31 December – **Meals** (bookings not accepted) a la carte 17.85/21. 5.95.

Swag and Tails, 10-11 Fairholt St., SW7 1EG, ☎ (020) 7584 6926, *swag+tails@mway.com, Fax (020) 7581 9935* – MC AE VISA JCB p. 35 **DR r**
closed 25-26 December, 1 January and Bank Holidays – **Meals** a la carte 18.00/23.20 **t.** 11.50.

Builders Arms, 13 Britten St., SW3 3TY, ☎ (020) 7349 9040, *Fax (020) 7357 3181* – ▤. MC ⓓ VISA p. 35 **DU x**
closed 25 December – **Meals** (bookings not accepted) a la carte 14.35/22.85 **t.**

rl's Court – ✉ *SW5/SW10.*

K + K H. George without rest., 1-15 Templeton Pl., SW5 9NB, ☎ (020) 7598 8700, *hotelgeorge@kkhotels.co.uk, Fax (020) 7370 2285,* – ▤ TV P – 30. MC AE ⓓ VISA JCB. p. 28 **EZ s**
154 rm 160.00/190.00 **st.**

Twenty Nevern Square, Nevern Sq., SW5 9PD, ☎ (020) 7565 9555, *hotel@twentynevernsquare.co.uk, Fax (020) 7565 9444* – TV P. MC AE ⓓ VISA JCB. p. 28 **EZ u**
Meals *(closed Monday)* (dinner only) a la carte 26.00/40.00 **t.** – 10.00 – **20 rm** 100.00/275.00 **st.** – SB.

Henley House without rest., 30 Barkston Gdns., SW5 0EN, ☎ (020) 7370 4111, *henleyhse@aol.com, Fax (020) 7370 0026,* – TV. MC AE ⓓ VISA JCB. p. 34 **AT e**
3.40 – **21 rm** 75.00/112.00 **st.**

Amsterdam without rest., 7 and 9 Trebovir Rd, SW5 9LS, ☎ (020) 7370 2814, *reservations@amsterdam-hotel.com, Fax (020) 7244 7608,* – TV. MC AE ⓓ VISA JCB.
2.75 – **19 rm** 74.00/86.00 **st.**, 8 suites. p. 28 **EZ c**

Rushmore without rest., 11 Trebovir Rd, SW5 9LS, ☎ (020) 7370 3839, *Fax (020) 7370 0274* – TV. MC AE ⓓ VISA JCB. p. 28 **EZ c**
22 rm 65.00/82.00 **st.**

Langan's Coq d'Or, 254-260 Old Brompton Rd, SW5 9HR, ☎ (020) 7259 2599, *Fax (020) 7370 7735,* – ▤. MC AE ⓓ VISA JCB p. 34 **AU e**
closed Easter, Christmas, Monday, Sunday dinner and Bank Holidays – **Meals** 15.50 **t.** (lunch) and a la carte 19.70/24.50 **t.** 11.95.

Chezmax, 168 Ifield Rd, SW10 9AF, ☎ (020) 7835 0874, *chezmax@aol.com, Fax (020) 7244 0618* – MC AE ⓓ VISA p. 34 **AU c**
closed 25-26 December, Sunday, lunch Monday Bank Holidays – **Meals** 17.50/29.50 **t.** and lunch a la carte 6.00.

nsington – ✉ *SW7/W8/W11/W14.*

Royal Garden, 2-24 Kensington High St., W8 4PT, ☎ (020) 7937 8000, *guest@royalgdn.co.uk, Fax (020) 7937 1991,* ≤, – , rm, ▤ TV P – 600. MC AE ⓓ VISA JCB. p. 34 **AQ c**
Park Terrace : **Meals** 21.50 **st.** (dinner) and a la carte 17.75/30.25 **st.** st. – (see also ***The Tenth*** below) – 17.50 – **381 rm** 210.00/310.00 **s.**, 15 suites.

Copthorne Tara, Scarsdale Pl., W8 5SR, ☎ (020) 7937 7211, *tara.sales@mill-cop.com, Fax (020) 7937 7100* – , rm, ▤ TV P – 400. MC AE ⓓ VISA JCB. p. 28 **FY u**
Jerome K. Jerome : **Meals** (dinner only) 16.00/19.00 **st.** and a la carte 7.00 – ***Brasserie :*** **Meals** 16.00/19.00 **st.** and a la carte 7.00 – 15.00 – **824 rm** 205.00 **st.**, 10 suites.

Halcyon, 81 Holland Park Av., W11 3RZ, ☎ (020) 7727 7288, *sales@thehalcyon.com, Fax (020) 7229 8516* – ▤ TV. MC AE ⓓ VISA JCB p. 28 **EX u**
Aix en Provence : **Meals** *(closed Saturday lunch)* 20.00/35.00 **t.** and a la carte – 17.95 – **39 rm** 175.00/275.00, 3 suites – SB.

Hilton London Kensington, 179-199 Holland Park Av., W11 4UL, ☎ (020) 7603 3355, *saleskensington@hilton.com, Fax (020) 7602 9397* – , rm, ▤ TV P – 300. MC AE ⓓ VISA JCB. p. 28 **EX s**
Hiroko : **Meals** - Japanese - *(closed Monday)* 16.00/35.00 **t.** and a la carte – ***Market :*** **Meals** *closed lunch Saturday and Sunday* 19.50 **t.** (dinner) and a la carte 27.40/35.85 **t.** – 15.00 – **400 rm** 195.00 **st.** – SB.

Posthouse Kensington, Wrights Lane, W8 5SP, ☎ (0870) 400 9000, *gm1253@forte-hotels.com, Fax (020) 7937 8289,* , , , – , rm, ▤ rest, TV P – 180. MC AE ⓓ VISA JCB p. 28 **FY c**
Green's : **Meals** 9.95/16.95 **t.** and a la carte 6.95 – 11.95 – **550 rm** 119.00/179.00 **st.** – SB.

Hilton London Olympia, 380 Kensington High St., W14 8NL, ☎ (020) 7603 3333, *sales_olympia@hilton.com, Fax (020) 7603 4846,* , – , rm, ▤ TV P – 450. MC AE ⓓ VISA JCB p. 28 **EY a**
Meals (bar lunch Saturday) and a la carte 26.50/31.75 **st.** – 15.50 – **395 rm** 165.00/175.00 **st.**, 10 suites – SB.

Thistle Kensington Park, 16-32 De Vere Gdns., W8 5AG, (020) 7937 8080, *kensin n.park@thistle.co.uk, Fax (020) 7937 7616* – rm, – 120. JCB. p. 34 **BQ**
Meals 16.95 **st.** and a la carte – 13.95 – **346 rm** 170.00/251.00 **st.**, 6 suites.

The Milestone, 1-2 Kensington Court, W8 5DL, (020) 7917 1000, *guestservices@mi one.redcarnationhotels.com, Fax (020) 7917 1010,* – . JCB p. 34 **AQ**
Meals 19.00 **t.** (lunch) and a la carte 31.00/70.00 **t.** – 17.50 – **52 rm** 270.00/290.00 5 suites – SB.

Holland Court without rest., 31-33 Holland Rd, W14 8HJ, (020) 7371 11 *Fax (020) 7602 9114,* – . VISA. p. 28 **EY**
22 rm 95.00/125.00 **st.**

The Tenth (at Royal Garden H.), 2-24 Kensington High St., W8 4PT, (020) 7361 1910 Kensington Palace and Gardens – . VISA JCB p. 34 **AQ**
closed Sunday and lunch Saturday – **Meals** (live music Saturday) 17.75 (lunch) and a la carte 30.00/51.00 **st.** 7.50.

Belvedere, Holland House, off Abbotsbury Rd, W8 6LU, (020) 7602 12 *Fax (020) 7610 4382,* , « 19C orangery in park » – . VISA
Meals 17.95/38.00 **t.** and a la carte 9.25. p. 28 **EY**

Clarke's, 124 Kensington Church St., W8 4BH, (020) 7221 9225, *restaurant@sallycla com, Fax (020) 7229 4564* – . VISA p. 28 **EX**
closed 2 weeks August, 10 days Christmas, Saturday and Sunday – **Meals** (set menu onl dinner) 30.00/44.00 **st.** 8.50.

Launceston Place, 1a Launceston Pl., W8 5RL, (020) 7937 6912, *Fax (020) 7938 2* – . VISA p. 34 **BR**
closed Saturday lunch, Sunday dinner and Bank Holidays – **Meals** 15.50/18.50 (lunch) and a la carte 25.00/36.00 **t.** 7.00.

L'Anis, 1 Kensington High St., W8 5NP, (020) 7795 6533, *Fax (020) 7937 8854* – . VISA JCB p. 34 **AQ**
closed 24 December-4 January and Sunday dinner – **Meals** - Italian influences - 12 23.50 **t.** 8.75.

6 Clarendon Road, 6 Clarendon Rd, W11 3AA, (020) 7727 3330, *six@restauration emon.co.uk, Fax (020) 7221 4509* – . VISA p. 28 **EX**
closed 1 week December, Sunday and Monday – **Meals** (dinner only) a la carte 22 25.25 **t.** 7.50.

L'Escargot Doré, 2-4 Thackeray St., W8 5ET, (020) 7937 8508, *Fax (020) 7937 85* . VISA p. 34 **AQR**
closed 2 weeks August, Sunday and Bank Holidays – **Meals** - French - a la carte 28 45.30 **t.**

Memories of China, 353 Kensington High St., W8 6NW, (020) 7603 6 *Fax (020) 7603 0848* – . VISA JCB p. 28 **EY**
closed Sunday lunch – **Meals** - Chinese - (booking essential) 19.50/32.50 **t.** and a la c 11.50.

The Terrace, 33c Holland St., W8 4LX, (020) 7937 3224, *Fax (020) 7937 3323,* – VISA JCB p. 28 **EY**
closed 23 December-3 January and Sunday dinner – **Meals** (booking essential) 14 17.50 **t.** (lunch) and a la carte 25.00/31.50 **t.** 7.00.

The Ark, 122 Palace Gardens Terr., W8 4RT, (020) 7229 4024, *Fax (020) 7792 8787,* . VISA p. 36 **AZ**
closed Sunday dinner and Monday lunch – **Meals** - Italian - a la carte 23.50/29.50 **t.** 10

Phoenicia, 11-13 Abingdon Rd, W8 6AH, (020) 7937 0120, *Fax (020) 7937 7668* – VISA JCB p. 28 **EY**
Meals - Lebanese - (buffet lunch) 9.95/24.95 and a la carte 5.50.

Kensington Place, 201 Kensington Church St., W8 7LX, (020) 7727 3184, *kpr@pl estaurants.co.uk, Fax (020) 7229 2025* – . VISA JCB p. 36 **AZ**
closed 24 to 27 December and 1 January – **Meals** (booking essential) 14.50 (lunch) and a la carte 23.00/35.50 **t.** 5.50.

Cibo, 3 Russell Gdns., W14 8EZ, (020) 7371 6271, *Fax (020) 7602 1371* – JCB p. 28 **EY**
closed 1 week Christmas, Saturday lunch and Sunday dinner – **Meals** - Italian - 12.5 (lunch) and a la carte 20.00/33.25 **t.**

Malabar, 27 Uxbridge St., W8 7TQ, (020) 7727 8800, *feedback@malabar-restaurant.co.uk* – VISA p. 36 **AZ** e
closed last week August and 4 days Christmas – **Meals** - Indian - (booking essential) (buffet lunch Sunday) 17.50 **st.** and a la carte 18.65/29.75 **st.** 5.00.

Wódka, 12 St. Albans Grove, W8 5PN, (020) 7937 6513, *john@wodka.demon.co.uk, Fax (020) 7937 8621* – AE VISA p. 34 **AR** c
closed 25-26 December and lunch Saturday and Sunday – **Meals** - Polish - 13.50 **t.** (lunch) and dinner a la carte 18.30/24.90 **t.** 10.50.

rth Kensington – W2/W10/W11.

Pembridge Court, 34 Pembridge Gdns., W2 4DX, (020) 7229 9977, *reservations@pemct.co.uk, Fax (020) 7727 4982,* « Collection of antique clothing » – TV. AE VISA p. 36 **AZ** n
Meals (room service only) – **20 rm** 125.00/195.00 **st.**

Abbey Court without rest., 20 Pembridge Gdns., W2 4DU, (020) 7221 7518, *info@abbeycourthotel.co.uk, Fax (020) 7792 0858,* « Victorian town house » – TV. AE VISA JCB. p. 36 **AZ** u
8.50 **22 rm** 99.00/195.00 **st.**

Portobello, 22 Stanley Gdns., W11 2NG, (020) 7727 2777, *info@portobello-hotel.co.uk, Fax (020) 7792 9641,* « Attractive town house in Victorian terrace » – TV. AE VISA p. 28 **EV** n
closed 22 December-2 January – **Meals** a la carte approx. 25.00 – 7.50 – **24 rm** 140.00/260.00 **t.**

Chez Moi, 1 Addison Av., Holland Park, W11 4QS, (020) 7603 8267, *chezmoi-rest@hotmail.com, Fax (020) 7603 3898* – AE VISA p. 28 **EX** n
closed Sunday, Saturday lunch and Bank Holidays – **Meals** - French - 15.00 **t.** (lunch) and a la carte 21.75/34.50 **t.** 6.00.

Pharmacy, 150 Notting Hill Gate, W11 3QG, (020) 7221 2442, *pharmacyw@aol.com, Fax (020) 7243 2345* – AE VISA p. 36 **AZ** a
closed Christmas and New Year – **Meals** 17.50 **t.** (lunch) and a la carte 23.00/59.50 **t.**

Orsino, 119 Portland Rd, W11 4LN, (020) 7221 3299, *joeallen.ldn@btinternet.com, Fax (020) 7229 9414* – AE VISA p. 28 **EX** x
closed 24 and 25 December – **Meals** - Italian - (booking essential) 15.50 **t.** (lunch) and a la carte 17.00/28.00 **t.** 7.00.

Bali Sugar, 33a All Saints Rd, W11 1HE, (020) 7221 4477, *Fax (020) 7221 9955,* – AE VISA p. 24 **EU** a
closed 25-26 December, 1 January and lunch Monday – **Meals** a la carte 26.60/33.80 **t.** 8.90.

Alastair Little Lancaster Road, 136a Lancaster Rd, W11 1QU, (020) 7243 2220, *Fax (020) 7229 2991* – AE VISA JCB p. 24 **EU** e
closed Sunday and Bank Holidays – **Meals** 27.50 **t.** (dinner) and lunch a la carte 18.00/25.00 **t.** 10.00.

Wiz, 123A Clarendon Rd, W11 4JG, (020) 7229 1500, *Fax (020) 7229 8889,* – AE VISA JCB p. 24 **EV** z
closed 25-26 December, Sunday dinner and Monday lunch – **Meals** 15.50 **t.** (lunch) and a la carte 18.00/24.00 **t.** – ***Woz :*** **Meals** (dinner only) (set menu only) 29.95 **t.**

th Kensington – SW5/SW7/W8.

Millennium Gloucester, 4-18 Harrington Gdns., SW7 4LH, (020) 7373 6030, *sales.gloucester@mill_cop.com, Fax (020) 7373 0409,* – rm, TV P – 650. AE VISA JCB. p. 34 **BS** r
SW7 : **Meals** (dinner only) 15.00/25.00 **t.** and a la carte 8.00 – ***Bugis Street :*** **Meals** 7.50/15.95 **t.** and a la carte – 15.00 – **604 rm** 225.00, 6 suites – SB.

Pelham, 15 Cromwell Pl., SW7 2LA, (020) 7589 8288, *pelham@firmdale.com, Fax (020) 7584 8444,* « Tastefully furnished Victorian town house » – TV. AE VISA. p. 34 **CS** z
Kemps : **Meals** 15.00/18.00 **t.** (dinner) and a la carte 20.70/28.70 **t.** 12.50 – 15.50 – **48 rm** 145.00/235.00 **s.**, 3 suites.

Blakes, 33 Roland Gdns., SW7 3PF, (020) 7370 6701, *blakes@easynet.co.uk, Fax (020) 7373 0442,* , « Antique oriental furnishings » – , rest, TV. AE VISA JCB. p. 34 **BU** n
Meals a la carte 60.00/78.00 **t.** 16.00 – 21.00 – **45 rm** 155.00/310.00 **s.**, 5 suites.

Vanderbilt, 68-86 Cromwell Rd, SW7 5BT, (020) 7761 9000, *resvand@radisson.com, Fax (020) 7761 9003* – , rm, TV – 120. AE VISA JCB. p. 34 **BS** z
Meals 19.50/22.50 **t.** and a la carte 13.95 – 12.50 – **215 rm** 195.00/212.00.

Harrington Hall, 5-25 Harrington Gdns., SW7 4JW, ☏ (020) 7396 9696, *harringtonha ompuserve.com, Fax (020) 7396 9090,* – rm, 260. JCB. p. 34 **BST**
Wetherby's : **Meals** 18.00/19.75 **st.** and a la carte 6.75 – 15.50 – **200 rm** 198 240.00 **st.**

Millennium Bailey's, 140 Gloucester Rd, SW7 4QH, ☏ (020) 7373 6000, *baileys@mill .com, Fax (020) 7370 3760* – rm, – 460. VISA.
Olives : **Meals** (dinner only) a la carte 20.15/29.00 **t.** 7.90 – 14.95 – **212 rm** 145 240.00 **st.** p. 34 **BS**

Rembrandt, 11 Thurloe Pl., SW7 2RS, ☏ (020) 7589 8100, *rembrandt@sarova.co Fax (020) 7225 3476,* – rm, rest, – 200. VISA p. 35 **DS**
Meals (carving lunch) 12.00/17.95 **st.** and dinner a la carte 17.85/25.85 **st.** 6.95 – 1 – **195 rm** 175.00/195.00 **st.**

Swallow International (Becoming a Marriott Summer 2001), Cromwell Rd, SW5 ☏ (020) 7973 1000, *info@swallowhotels.com, Fax (020) 7244 8194,* – – 200. VISA p. 34 **AS**
– ***Blayneys :*** **Meals** (dinner only) 27.00 **t.** and a la carte – ***Hunter's :*** **Meals** (carving r 18.00 **st.** and a la carte – 13.00 – **419 rm** 155.00/250.00 **st.**, 2 suites – SB.

Jurys Kensington, 109-113 Queen's Gate, SW7 5LR, ☏ (020) 7589 6300, *kensington el@jurydoyle.com, Fax (020) 7581 1492* – rm, – 80. VISA p. 34 **CT**
closed 24 to 27 December – **Meals** (bar lunch)/dinner 15.00 **t.** and a la carte 6.00 – 14.95 – **173 rm** 190.00/210.00 **t.**

Regency, 100 Queen's Gate, SW7 5AG, ☏ (020) 7373 7878, *info@regency_london.co Fax (020) 7370 5555,* – rm, – 100. VISA JCB.
Meals *(closed lunch Saturday and Sunday)* (carving lunch) 18.50/25.00 **st.** and ner a la carte 6.00 – 13.00 – **193 rm** 154.00 **s.**, 6 suites. p. 34 **CT**

Holiday Inn Kensington, 100 Cromwell Rd, SW7 4ER, ☏ (020) 7373 2222, *info@hi uk, Fax (020) 7373 0559,* – rm, – 200. p. 34 **BS**
Meals 12.95/17.95 and a la carte 7.50 – 12.75 – **143 rm** 180.00/200.00 **st.**, 19 sui SB.

Gore, 189 Queen's Gate, SW7 5EX, ☏ (020) 7584 6601, *sales@gorehotel.c Fax (020) 7589 8127,* « Attractive decor » – rm, . VISA p. 34 **BF**
closed 24-25 December – ***Bistrot 190 :*** **Meals** (booking essential) a la carte 20.25/27.2 (see also ***The Restaurant at One Ninety*** below) – 9.50 – **53 rm** 140.00/178.00 **s.**

John Howard, 4 Queen's Gate, SW7 5EH, ☏ (020) 7808 8400, *johnhowardhotel@bt net.com, Fax (020) 7589 8403* – . VISA JCB. p. 34 **BC**
Meals *(closed Sunday)* (dinner only) 14.50 **st.** and a la carte 6.00 – 12.50 – 4 129.00/159.00 **st.**, 7 suites.

Cranley, 10-12 Bina Gdns., SW5 0LA, ☏ (020) 7373 0123, *info@thecranley. Fax (020) 7373 9497,* « Antiques » – . VISA JCB. p. 34 **B**
Meals (room service only) – 9.95 – **35 rm** 155.00/180.00 **s.**, 3 suites.

Gallery without rest., 8-10 Queensberry Pl., SW7 2EA, ☏ (020) 7915 0000, *gallery@ee uk, Fax (020) 7915 4400* – . VISA JCB. p. 34 **C**
36 rm 120.00/240.00 **s.**

Gainsborough without rest., 7-11 Queensberry Pl., SW7 2DL, ☏ (020) 7957 0000, *g orough@eeh.co.uk, Fax (020) 7957 0001* – . VISA JCB. p. 34 **C**
42 rm 67.00/145.00 **s.**, 3 suites.

Five Sumner Place without rest., 5 Sumner Pl., SW7 3EE, ☏ (020) 7584 7586, *reser ns@sumnerplace.com, Fax (020) 7823 9962* – . VISA JCB. p. 34 **C**
13 rm 82.00/130.00 **s.**

Aster House without rest., 3 Sumner Pl., SW7 3EE, ☏ (020) 7581 5888, *asterhouse@ ernet.com, Fax (020) 7584 4925,* – . VISA JCB. p. 34 **C**
12 rm 75.00/175.00 **st.**

Bombay Brasserie, Courtfield Rd, SW7 4UH, ☏ (020) 7370 4040, *bombaybrasserie com, Fax (020) 7835 1669,* « Raj-style decor, conservatory » – . VISA JCB
closed 25-27 December – **Meals** - Indian - (buffet lunch)/dinner a la carte 24.45/31 7.75. p. 34 **B**

Hilaire, 68 Old Brompton Rd, SW7 3LQ, ☏ (020) 7584 8993, *Fax (020) 7581 2949* – VISA p. 34 **C**
closed 2 weeks August, 2 weeks Christmas, Sunday, Saturday lunch and Bank Holid
Meals (booking essential) 18.50/37.50 11.50.

XX **The Restaurant at One Ninety** (at Gore H.), 190 Queen's Gate, SW7 5EU, ☎ (020) 7581 5666, *Fax (020) 7581 8172* – ▤. MC AE ① VISA p. 34 **BR n**
closed 24-25 December, Sunday and Bank Holidays – **Meals** - Seafood - (booking essential) (dinner only) a la carte 25.40/29.40 **t.** 8.95.

XX **Chives,** 204 Fulham Rd, SW10 9PG, ☎ (020) 7351 4747, *Fax (020) 7351 7646,* – MC AE VISA p. 34 **BU u**
closed Sunday and lunch Monday-Wednesday – **Meals** 23.50 **t.** 10.00.

XX **Lundum's,** 119 Old Brompton Rd, SW7 3RN, ☎ (020) 7373 7774, *Fax (020) 7373 4472,* – ▤. MC AE VISA JCB p. 34 **BT o**
closed 24 December-2 January, last 2 weeks August and Sunday dinner – **Meals** - Danish - 15.50/21.50 **t.** and a la carte.

XX **Café Lazeez,** First floor, 93-95 Old Brompton Rd, SW7 3LD, ☎ (020) 7581 9993, *cafelazeez@compuserve.com.uk, Fax (020) 7581 8200* – ▤. MC AE ① VISA JCB p. 34 **CT a**
Meals - North Indian - a la carte 13.00/24.90.

XX **Khan's of Kensington,** 3 Harrington Rd, SW7 3ES, ☎ (020) 7581 2900, *Fax (020) 7581 2900* – ▤. MC AE ① VISA p. 34 **CS e**
closed 25 December – **Meals** - Indian - 7.95/25.00 **t.** and a la carte 4.95.

XX **Cambio de Tercio,** 163 Old Brompton Rd, SW5 0LJ, ☎ (020) 7244 8970, *Fax (020) 7373 8817* – MC AE VISA p. 34 **BT z**
closed 10 days Christmas – **Meals** - Spanish - a la carte 23.50/28.50 **t.** 8.50.

XX **Pasha,** 1 Gloucester Rd, SW7 4PP, ☎ (020) 7589 7969, *Fax (020) 7581 9996* – ▤. MC AE ① VISA JCB p. 34 **BR i**
closed 25-26 December, 1 January and Sunday lunch – **Meals** - Moroccan - a la carte 21.50/29.50 **t.**

XX **Memories of India,** 18 Gloucester Rd, SW7 4RB, ☎ (020) 7589 6450, *Fax (020) 7584 4438* – ▤. MC AE ① VISA JCB p. 34 **BR s**
closed 25 December – **Meals** - Indian - a la carte approx. 10.40 **t.**

X **Star of India,** 154 Old Brompton Rd, SW5 0BE, ☎ (020) 7373 2901, *info@starofindia.co.uk, Fax (020) 7373 5664* – ▤. MC AE ① VISA JCB p. 34 **BT s**
closed 25 December, 1 January and Bank Holidays – **Meals** - Indian - a la carte 25.45/33.95 **t.**

X **Bangkok,** 9 Bute St., SW7 3EY, ☎ (020) 7584 8529 – ▤. MC VISA p. 34 **CS v**
closed Christmas-New Year, Sunday and Bank Holidays – **Meals** - Thai Bistro - a la carte 16.50/30.45 **t.** 8.50.

X **Catch,** 158 Old Brompton Rd, SW5 0BA, ☎ (020) 7370 3300, *Fax (020) 7370 3377* – ▤. MC AE ① VISA JCB p. 34 **BT i**
closed 24 December-7 January – **Meals** - Seafood - (booking essential) a la carte 24.50/28.50 **t.**

IGSTON UPON THAMES.

18 *Home Park, Hampton Wick* ☎ *(020) 8977 6645,* **BY.**

ssington – ✉ *Surrey.*

Travel Inn Metro, Leatherhead Rd, KT9 2NE, on A 243 ☎ (01372) 744060, *Fax (01372) 720889* – ⇔ rm, TV ♿ P. MC AE ① VISA. ✂ p. 12 **BZ c**
Meals (grill rest.) – **42 rm** 46.95 **t.**

gston – ✉ *Surrey.*

Kingston Lodge, Kingston Hill, KT2 7NP, ☎ (020) 8541 4481, *Fax (020) 8547 1013,* – ⇔ rm, ▤ rest, TV ♿ P – 60. MC AE ① VISA. ✂ p. 13 **CY u**
The Burnt Orange : **Meals** 8.95/20.00 **t.** and a la carte 8.95 – 10.50 – **64 rm** 150.00/180.00 **t.** – SB.

XX **Gravier's,** 9 Station Rd, Norbiton, KT2 7AA, ☎ (020) 8549 5557 – MC AE ① VISA JCB p. 13 **CY x**
closed 1 week Easter, 1 week Christmas, 2 weeks in summer, Saturday lunch, Sunday and Bank Holidays – **Meals** - French Seafood - a la carte 18.95/30.45 **t.** 6.25.

X **Ayudhya,** 14 Kingston Hill, KT3 6LY, ☎ (020) 8549 5984, *Fax (020) 8549 5984* – MC AE ① VISA p. 13 **CY z**
closed Monday and Bank Holidays – **Meals** - Thai - a la carte 16.90/33.50 **st.**

biton – ✉ *Surrey.*

X **Luca,** 85 Maple Rd, KT6 4AW, ☎ (020) 8399 2365, *Fax (020) 8390 5353* – ▤. MC VISA
closed 25-26 December, Sunday and Monday – **Meals** (dinner only and Sunday brunch)/dinner a la carte 17.40/24.50 **t.** 9.90. p. 13 **CY a**

LAMBETH.

Brixton – ✉ SW9.

Helter Skelter, 50 Atlantic Rd, SW9 8JN, ℘ (020) 7274 8600, *Fax (020) 7274 8600* – MC AE ⓓ VISA JCB p. 14 **FX**
closed 3 days Christmas and 1 January – **Meals** (dinner only and Sunday lunch)/dir a la carte 20.60/26.00 **t.**

Clapham Common – ✉ SW4.

Windmill on the Common, Clapham Common South Side, SW4 9 ℘ (020) 8673 4578, *Fax (020) 8675 1486* – rm, TV P. MC AE ⓓ VISA
Meals *(closed Sunday dinner and Bank Holidays)* (bar lunch)/dinner 16.50 **st.** and a la car
29 rm 92.00/125.00 **st.** p. 17 **DQ**

Herne Hill – ✉ SE24.

3 Monkeys, 136-140 Herne Hill, SE24 9QH, ℘ (020) 7738 5500, *Fax (020) 7738 5505* – MC AE ⓓ VISA JCB p. 14 **FX**
closed 25 December, 1 January and Monday – **Meals** - Indian - (dinner only) 14.95/18.9 and a la carte.

Kennington – ✉ SE11.

Kennington Lane, 205-209 Kennington Lane, SE11 5QS, ℘ (020) 7793 83 *Fax (020) 7793 8323*, – MC AE ⓓ VISA JCB p. 30 **MZ**
closed Sunday dinner – **Meals** 13.50/15.75 **t.** (lunch) and a la carte 17.95/27.50 **t.**

Lobster Pot, 3 Kennington Lane, SE11 4RG, ℘ (020) 7582 5556 – MC AE ⓓ JCB p. 31 **NZ**
closed 24 December-first week January, Sunday and Monday – **Meals** - French Seafo 10.00/19.50 **st.** and a la carte 7.50.

Lambeth – ✉ SE1.

Novotel London Waterloo, 113 Lambeth Rd, SE1 7LS, ℘ (020) 7793 1 *Fax (020) 7793 0202*, – rm, TV – 40. MC AE ⓓ VISA
Meals (bar lunch Saturday and Sunday) 19.95/21.95 **st.** and a la carte – 12.00 – 185 130.00/150.00 **st.**, 2 suites. p. 30 **LMY**

Streatham – ✉ SW16.

Barrow House without rest., 45 Barrow Rd, SW16 5PE, ℘ (020) 8677 1925, *barrow e@onetel.net.uk, Fax (020) 8677 1925*, « Victoriana », – . p. 14 **EY**
closed 24-26 December – **4 rm** 35.00/60.00.

Waterloo – ✉ SE1.

Channel Tunnel : Eurostar information and reservations ℘ (0990) 186186.

London Marriott H. County Hall, SE1 7PB, ℘ (020) 7928 5200, *Fax (020) 7928 5* – rm, TV – 70. MC AE ⓓ VISA JCB. p. 30 **LY**
County Hall : **Meals** 19.50 **t.** (lunch) and a la carte 27.00/37.50 **t.** – 15.95 – 195 245.00 **s.**, 5 suites.

London County Hall Travel Inn Capital, Belvedere Rd, SE1 7PB, ℘ (020) 7902 1 *Fax (020) 7902 1619* – rest, TV. MC AE ⓓ VISA. p. 30 **MX**
Meals (grill rest.) (dinner only) – **313 rm** 69.95 **t.**

Days Inn without rest., 54 Kennington Rd, SE1 7BJ, ℘ (020) 7922 1331, Rese tions (Freephone) 0800 0280400, *waterloo@premierhotel.co.uk, Fax (020) 7922 1441* TV – 35. MC AE ⓓ VISA. p. 30 **MY**
162 rm 75.00 **st.**

LONDON HEATHROW AIRPORT – *see Hillingdon, London p. 61.*

MERTON.

Colliers Wood – ✉ SW19.

Express by Holiday Inn without rest., 200 High St., SW19 2BH, on ℘ (020) 8545 7300, *Fax (020) 8545 7301* – TV – 50. MC AE ⓓ VISA J
83 rm 89.00 **st.** p. 14 **E**

Morden – ✉ Morden.

Travelodge without rest., Epsom Rd, SM4 5PH, Southwest : on A 24 ℘ (020) 8640 8 *Fax (020) 8640 8227* – TV P. MC AE ⓓ VISA JCB. p. 13 **D**
32 rm 59.95 **t.**

mbledon – ✉ *SW19.*

Cannizaro House ⛔, West Side, Wimbledon Common, SW19 4UE, ✆ (020) 8879 1464, *cannizaro.house@thistle.co.uk, Fax (020) 8879 7338,* ≤, « Part 18C country house in Cannizaro Park », – |‡|, ⅍ rm, TV ✆ P – 60. MC AE ① VISA. ⅍ p. 13 DXY x
Meals 19.95/29.75 **st.** and a la carte 15.95 – ☕ 15.50 – **43 rm** 217.00/314.00 **st.**, 2 suites – SB.

Light House, 75-77 Ridgway, SW19 4ST, ✆ (020) 8944 6338, *Fax (020) 8946 4440* – MC AE VISA p. 13 DY h
closed 1 week Christmas – **Meals** - Italian influences - a la carte 19.20/30.70 **t.**

DBRIDGE.

ℹ *Town Hall, High Rd ✆ (020) 8478 3020.*

rd – ✉ *Essex.*

18 *Wanstead Park Rd ✆ (020) 8554 2930,* **HU** – 18, 9 *Fairlop Waters, Forest Rd, Barkingside ✆ (020) 8500 9911* **JT**.

Travelodge, Beehive Lane, IG4 5DR, ✆ (020) 8550 4248, *Fax (020) 8550 4248* – ⅍ rm, TV ♿ P. MC AE ① VISA JCB. ⅍ p. 11 HU e
Meals (grill rest.) – **32 rm** 59.95 **t.**

Travel Inn Metro, Redbridge Lane East, IG4 5BG, ✆ (020) 8550 7909, *Fax (020) 8550 6214* – |‡|, ⅍ rm, ▤ rest, TV ♿ P – 40. MC AE ① VISA. ⅍ p. 11 HU i
Meals (grill rest.) – **44 rm** 46.95 **t.**

uth Woodford – ✉ *Essex.*

Ho-Ho, 20 High Rd, E18 2QL, ✆ (020) 8989 1041 – ▤. MC AE ① VISA p. 11 HU c
closed 25-27 December and lunch Saturday – **Meals** - Chinese (Peking, Szechuan) - 7.50/27.50 **st.** and a la carte.

odford – ✉ *Essex.*

9 *2 Sunset Av., Woodford Green ✆ (020) 8504 0553.*
London 13 – Brentwood 16 – Harlow 16.

County H. Epping Forest, 30 Oak Hill, Woodford Green, IG8 9NY, ✆ (020) 8787 9988, *Fax (020) 8506 0941* – |‡| ⅍, ▤ rest, TV P – 150. MC AE ① VISA p. 11 HT c
Meals *(closed Saturday lunch)* 10.95/16.95 **t.** (dinner) and a la carte 18.00/22.75 **t.** 7.00 – ☕ 9.50 – **99 rm** 95.00/115.00 **t.** – SB.

HMOND-UPON-THAMES.

nes – ✉ *SW13.*

Sonny's, 94 Church Rd, SW13 0DQ, ✆ (020) 8748 0393, *Fax (020) 8748 2698* – ▤. MC AE ① VISA p. 13 CX x
closed 25 December, Sunday dinner and Bank Holidays – **Meals** 12.00/15.00 **t.** (lunch) and a la carte 22.75/26.75 **t.**

Riva, 169 Church Rd, SW13 9HR, ✆ (020) 8748 0434, *Fax (020) 8748 0434* – MC AE VISA JCB p. 13 CX a
closed last 2 weeks August, 1 week Christmas-New Year, 1 week Easter, Saturday lunch and Bank Holidays – **Meals** - Italian - a la carte 22.50/31.50 **t.** 8.00.

t Sheen – ✉ *SW14.*

Redmond's, 170 Upper Richmond Road West, SW14 8AW, ✆ (020) 8878 1922, *Fax (020) 8878 1133* – ▤. MC VISA p. 13 CX v
closed 4 days Christmas, Saturday lunch, Sunday dinner and Bank Holidays except Good Friday – **Meals** 12.50-21.00/25.00 **t.** 7.00.

Crowther's, 481 Upper Richmond Rd West, SW14 7PU, ✆ (020) 8876 6372, *Fax (020) 8876 6372* – ▤. MC VISA JCB p. 13 CX n
closed 2 weeks August, 25-31 December, Sunday and Monday – **Meals** (booking essential) (lunch by arrangement)/dinner 19.50/24.50 **t.** 6.95.

npton Court – ✉ *Surrey.*

Carlton Mitre, Hampton Court Rd, KT8 9BN, ✆ (020) 8979 9988, *mitre@carltonhotels.co.uk, Fax (020) 8979 9777,* ≤, « Thames-side setting » – |‡| ⅍ TV P – 25. MC AE VISA
Rivers Edge : **Meals** a la carte 19.50/29.50 **t.** – ☕ 11.50 – **35 rm** 160.00/195.00 **t.**, 1 suite – SB. p. 12 BY v

Hampton Hill – ✉ *Middx.*

Monsieur Max, 133 High St., TW12 1NJ, ☏ (020) 8979 5546, *Fax (020) 8979 3747* – AE VISA p. 12 BY
closed Saturday lunch – **Meals** 18.50/26.00 **t.** 8.00
Spec. Oxtail "en gelée". Seared sea bass with lobster ravioli and Champagne velouté. Cre brûlée.

Hampton Wick – ✉ *Surrey.*

Chase Lodge, 10 Park Rd, KT1 4AS, ☏ (020) 8943 1862, *Fax (020) 8943 9363* – TV. VISA JCB p. 12 BY
Meals (lunch by arrangement) 16.00/22.00 **t.** 7.00 – **11 rm** 65.00/95.00 **t.** – SB.

Kew – ✉ *Surrey.*

The Glasshouse, 14 Station Par., TW9 3PZ, ☏ (020) 8940 6777, *Fax (020) 8940 3833* – AE VISA p. 13 CX
closed 25 December, 1 January and Sunday dinner – **Meals** 19.50/25.00 **t.** 9.50.

Richmond – ✉ *Surrey.*

18, 18 *Richmond Park, Roehampton Gate* ☏ *(020) 8876 3205* **CX** – 18 *Sudbrook Park* ☏ *(8940 1463* **CX**.
Old Town Hall, Whittaker Av. ☏ *(020) 8940 9125.*

Petersham, Nightingale Lane, TW10 6UZ, ☏ (020) 8940 7471, *enq@petershamhotel. k, Fax (020) 8939 1098,* ≤, « Working cellars », – TV P – 50. AE p. 13 CX
Meals – (see ***Nightingales*** below) – **60 rm** 130.00/180.00 **st.**, 1 suite – SB.

Richmond Gate, 158 Richmond Hill, TW10 6RP, ☏ (020) 8940 0061, *Fax (020) 8332 (* – TV P – 45. AE VISA. p. 13 CX
Gates On The Park: **Meals** *(closed Saturday lunch)* 17.25/31.00 **t.** 12.75 – **6** 145.00/172.00 **t.**, 1 suite.

Richmond Hill, Richmond Hill, TW10 6RW, ☏ (020) 8940 2247, *Fax (020) 8940 5424* – rm, rest, TV P – 200. AE VISA JCB p. 13 CX
Pembrokes: **Meals** (dancing Saturday evening) (carving lunch Sunday) 16.00/22. and a la carte 7.00 – 13.50 – **133 rm** 137.00/192.00 **st.**, 5 suites – SB.

Nightingales (at Petersham H.), Nightingale Lane, TW10 6UZ, ☏ (020) 8939 *Fax (020) 8939 1098,* ≤, – P. AE VISA p. 13 CX
Meals (residents only Sunday dinner) 19.00 **st.** (lunch) and a la carte 32.50/37.00 **st.**

Four Regions, 102-104 Kew Rd, TW9 2PQ, ☏ (020) 8940 9044, *Fax (020) 8332 6130,* AE VISA JCB p. 13 CX
Meals - Chinese - 18.00/25.00 **t.** (dinner) and a la carte 20.00/34.00 **t.**

Twickenham – ✉ *Middx.*

McClements, 2 Whitton Rd, TW1 1BJ, ☏ (020) 8744 9610, *johnmac21@aol. Fax (020) 8744 9598* – AE VISA p. 12 BX
closed Sunday – **Meals** 19.00/27.00 **t.** 8.50.

Brula, 43 Crown Rd, St. Margarets, TW1 3EJ, ☏ (020) 8892 0602, *Fax (020) 8892 0602 closed 25-26 December, 1 January, Saturday lunch, Sunday and Monday* – **Meals** (boo essential) 10.00 **t.** (lunch) and a la carte 19.00/23.00 **t.** 6.50. p. 12 BX

SOUTHWARK.

London Bridge, 6 Tooley St. ☏ *(020) 7403 8299.*

Bermondsey – ✉ *SE1.*

London Bridge, 8-18 London Bridge St., SE1 9SG, ☏ (020) 7855 2200, *sales@londo ge.hotel.co.uk, Fax (020) 7855 2233,* – rm, TV – 85. AE VISA p. 31 P
Meals – (see ***Simply Nico*** below) – 14.95 – **138 rm** 165.00/175.00 **st.**, 3 suites.

London Tower Bridge Travel Inn Capital, 159 Tower Bridge Rd, SE1 ☏ (020) 7940 3700, *Fax (020) 7940 3719* – rest, TV P. AE VISA. p. 31 P
Meals (grill rest.) (dinner only) – **195 rm** 69.95 **t.**

Le Pont de la Tour, 36d Shad Thames, Butlers Wharf, SE1 2YE, ☏ (020) 7403 *Fax (020) 7403 0267,* ≤, « Thames-side setting » – AE VISA JCB p. 31 P
closed Saturday lunch – **Meals** 28.50 **t.** (lunch) and dinner a la carte 34.00/48.00 **t.**

XXX **Bengal Clipper,** Cardamom Building, Shad Thames, Butlers Wharf, SE1 2YR, ☏ (020) 7357 9001, *clipper@bengalrestaurants.com, Fax (020) 7357 9002* – ▤. MC AE DC VISA JCB p. 31 **PX** e
closed Christmas – **Meals** - Indian - a la carte 19.40/29.95 **t.**

XX **Tentazioni,** 2 Mill St., Lloyds Wharf, SE1 2BD, ☏ (020) 7237 1100, *Fax (020) 7237 1100* – MC AE DC VISA JCB p. 14 **GV** x
closed 24 December-6 January, last week August, Sunday and lunch Saturday and Monday – **Meals** - Italian - 15.00/19.00 **t.** (lunch) and a la carte 25.00/31.00 **t.** 6.50.

XX **Simply Nico** (at London Bridge H.), 8-18 London Bridge St., SE1 9SG, ☏ (020) 7407 4536, *simplynico@trpplc.com, Fax (020) 7407 4554* – ▤. MC AE DC VISA p. 31 **PX** a
closed Christmas, Sunday and Bank Holidays – **Meals** 16.50/18.75 **t.** (lunch) and a la carte 22.00/29.50 **t.** 9.00.

X **Blue Print Café,** Design Museum, Shad Thames, Butlers Wharf, SE1 2YD, ☏ (020) 7378 7031, *Fax (020) 7357 8810*, « Thames-side setting, ≤ Tower Bridge » – MC AE DC VISA JCB p. 31 **PX** u
closed Sunday dinner – **Meals** a la carte 24.00/35.50 **t.** 13.50.

X **Butlers Wharf Chop House,** 36e Shad Thames, Butlers Wharf, SE1 2YE, ☏ (020) 7403 3403, *Fax (020) 7403 3414*, « Thames-side setting, ≤ Tower Bridge » – MC AE DC VISA JCB p. 31 **PX** n
closed 1-3 January and Sunday dinner – **Meals** a la carte 21.45/39.95 **t.** 10.95.

X **Cantina Del Ponte,** 36c Shad Thames, Butlers Wharf, SE1 2YE, ☏ (020) 7403 5403, *Fax (020) 7403 0267*, ≤, « Thames-side setting » – MC AE DC VISA JCB p. 31 **PX** c
closed Sunday dinner – **Meals** - Italian - 12.50 **t.** and a la carte.

'wich – ✉ *SE19.*

XX **Belair House,** Gallery Rd, Dulwich Village, SE21 7AB, ☏ (020) 8299 9788, *Fax (020) 8299 6793*, « Georgian summer house », – P. MC AE DC VISA JCB p. 14 **FX** e
Meals 14.50/25.95 **t.**.

:herhithe – ✉ *SE16.*

Holiday Inn Nelson Dock, 265 Rotherhithe St., Nelson Dock, SE16 1EJ, ☏ (020) 7231 1001, *Fax (020) 7231 0599*, ≤, « Thames-side setting », – rm, ▤ rest, P – 350. MC AE DC VISA JCB. p. 14 **GV** r
closed 22-29 December – ***Three Crowns*** **:** **Meals** 22.50/45.00 **t.** and dinner a la carte – ***Columbia's*** **: Meals** - Chinese - *(closed Sunday)* (dinner only) 15.95/25.00 **st.** – 13.00 – **364 rm** 140.00/160.00 **st.**, 4 suites.

thwark – ✉ *SE1.*

Mercure, 75-79 Southwark St., SE1 0JA, ☏ (020) 7902 0800, *h2814@accor_hotels.com, Fax (020) 7902 0810*, – rm – 30. MC AE DC VISA p. 31 **OX** r
The Loft **: Meals** 12.00/20.00 **st.** and a la carte 8.00 – 12.00 – **144 rm** 135.00/155.00 **st.**

Express by Holiday Inn without rest., 103-109 Southwark St., SE1 0JQ, ☏ (020) 7401 2525, *stay@expresssouthwark.co.uk, Fax (020) 7401 3322* – rm, P. MC AE DC VISA. p. 31 **OX** e
90 rm 94.00 **st.**

XX **Oxo Tower,** (8th floor), Oxo Tower Wharf, Barge House St., SE1 9PH, ☏ (020) 7803 3888, *oxo.reservations@harveynichols.co.uk, Fax (020) 7803 3838*, ≤ London skyline and River Thames, – ▤. MC AE DC VISA JCB p. 31 **NX** a
closed 25-26 December and 1 January – **Meals** 27.50 **t.** (lunch) and dinner a la carte 26.50/40.00 **t.** – (see also ***Oxo Tower Brasserie*** below).

X **Oxo Tower Brasserie,** (8th floor), Oxo Tower Wharf, Barge House St., SE1 9PH, ☏ (020) 7803 3888, *Fax (020) 7803 3838*, ≤ London skyline and River Thames, – ▤. MC AE DC VISA JCB p. 31 **NX** a
Meals a la carte 32.50/40.00 **t.**

X **Cantina Vinopolis (Brasserie),** No.1 Bank End, SE1 9BU, ☏ (020) 7940 8333, *Fax (020) 7940 8334* – MC AE DC VISA p. 31 **OX** z
closed Sunday dinner and Bank Holidays – **Meals** a la carte 16.85/26.70 **t.**

X **Livebait,** 43 The Cut, SE1 8LF, ☏ (020) 7928 7211, *Fax (020) 7928 2279* – MC AE DC VISA p. 31 **NX** c
closed Sunday – **Meals** - Seafood - 12.50/15.50 **t.** and a la carte 7.50.

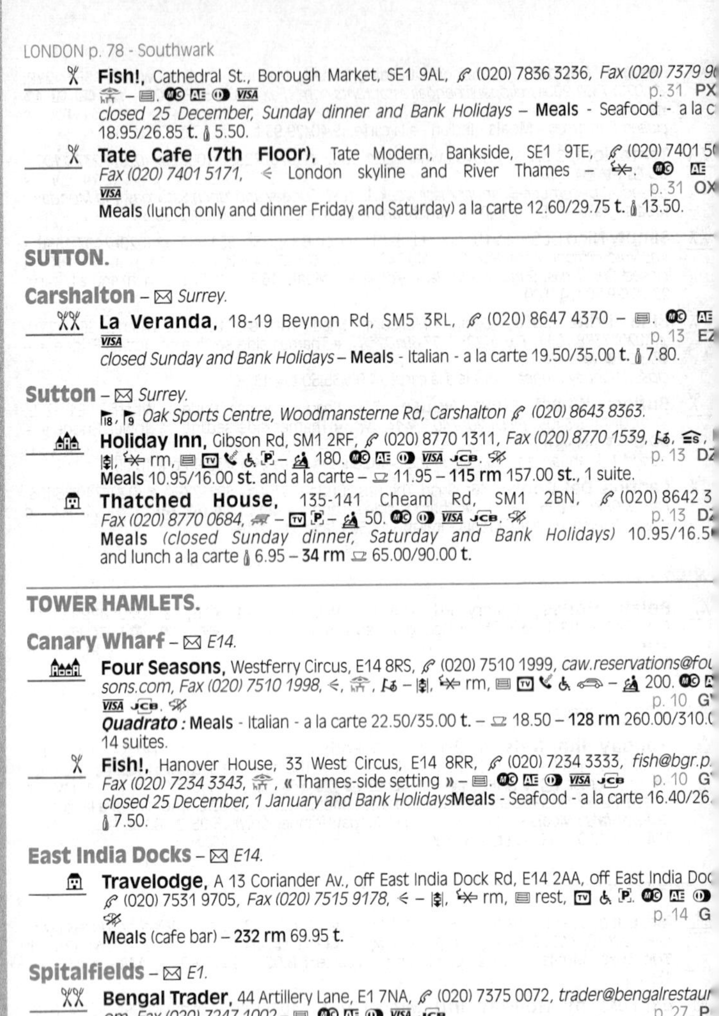

Fish!, Cathedral St., Borough Market, SE1 9AL, (020) 7836 3236, *Fax (020) 7379 9* – . p. 31 PX
closed 25 December, Sunday dinner and Bank Holidays – **Meals** - Seafood - a la c 18.95/26.85 **t.** 5.50.

Tate Cafe (7th Floor), Tate Modern, Bankside, SE1 9TE, (020) 7401 5 *Fax (020) 7401 5171,* London skyline and River Thames – . p. 31 OX
Meals (lunch only and dinner Friday and Saturday) a la carte 12.60/29.75 **t.** 13.50.

SUTTON.

Carshalton – *Surrey.*

La Veranda, 18-19 Beynon Rd, SM5 3RL, (020) 8647 4370 – . p. 13 EZ
closed Sunday and Bank Holidays – **Meals** - Italian - a la carte 19.50/35.00 **t.** 7.80.

Sutton – *Surrey.*

18, 9 *Oak Sports Centre, Woodmansterne Rd, Carshalton (020) 8643 8363.*

Holiday Inn, Gibson Rd, SM1 2RF, (020) 8770 1311, *Fax (020) 8770 1539,* rm, – 180. p. 13 DZ
Meals 10.95/16.00 **st.** and a la carte – 11.95 – **115 rm** 157.00 **st.**, 1 suite.

Thatched House, 135-141 Cheam Rd, SM1 2BN, (020) 8642 3 *Fax (020) 8770 0684,* – – 50. p. 13 D
Meals *(closed Sunday dinner, Saturday and Bank Holidays)* 10.95/16.5 and lunch a la carte 6.95 – **34 rm** 65.00/90.00 **t.**

TOWER HAMLETS.

Canary Wharf – *E14.*

Four Seasons, Westferry Circus, E14 8RS, (020) 7510 1999, *caw.reservations@fou sons.com, Fax (020) 7510 1998,* – rm, – 200. p. 10 G
Quadrato : **Meals** - Italian - a la carte 22.50/35.00 **t.** – 18.50 – **128 rm** 260.00/310.0 14 suites.

Fish!, Hanover House, 33 West Circus, E14 8RR, (020) 7234 3333, *fish@bgr.p. Fax (020) 7234 3343,* « Thames-side setting » – . p. 10 G
*closed 25 December, 1 January and Bank Holidays***Meals** - Seafood - a la carte 16.40/26. 7.50.

East India Docks – *E14.*

Travelodge, A 13 Coriander Av., off East India Dock Rd, E14 2AA, off East India Doc (020) 7531 9705, *Fax (020) 7515 9178,* – rm, rest, . p. 14 G
Meals (cafe bar) – **232 rm** 69.95 **t.**

Spitalfields – *E1.*

Bengal Trader, 44 Artillery Lane, E1 7NA, (020) 7375 0072, *trader@bengalrestaur om, Fax (020) 7247 1002* – . p. 27 P
closed Saturday, Sunday and Bank Holidays – **Meals** - Indian - 11.95/20.00 **t.** and a la ca

Whitechapel – *E1.*

Cafe Spice Namaste, 16 Prescot St., E1 8AZ, (020) 7488 9242, *Fax (020) 7481 0* . p. 14 G
closed Sunday, Saturday lunch and Bank Holidays – **Meals** - Indian - a la carte 14.70/20 6.00.

WANDSWORTH.

Battersea – *SW8/SW11.*

Travelodge without rest., 200 York Rd, SW11 3SA, (020) 7228 *Fax (020) 7228 5508* – . p. 17 C
80 rm 69.95 **t.**

Cafe Spice Namaste, 247 Lavender Hill, SW11 1JW, (020) 7738 *Fax (020) 7738 1666* – rest. p. 17 C
closed Monday and Bank Holidays – **Meals** - Indian - (dinner only and buffet Su lunch)/dinner a la carte 14.70/20.00 **t.**

XX **Chada,** 208-210 Battersea Park Rd, SW11 4ND, ✆ (020) 7622 2209, *Fax (020) 7924 2178* – ▤. MC AE ⓓ VISA JCB p. 17 **CQ** x
closed Sunday and Bank Holidays – **Meals** - Thai - (dinner only) a la carte 11.65/30.15 **t.**

X **Metrogusto,** 153 Battersea Park Rd, SW8 4BX, ✆ (020) 7720 0204, *Fax (020) 7720 0888* – MC VISA JCB p. 17 **DQ** r
closed Sunday and Bank Holidays – **Meals** - Italian - a la carte 18.00/26.00 **t.**

X **The Stepping Stone,** 123 Queenstown Rd, SW8 3RH, ✆ (020) 7622 0555, *thesteppingstone@aol.com, Fax (020) 7622 4230* – ▤. MC VISA p. 17 **DQ** c
closed 5 days Christmas, Saturday lunch, Sunday dinner and Bank Holidays – **Meals** 15.00 **t.** (lunch) and a la carte 19.00/27.00 **t.** 🌢 10.00.

X **Ransome's Dock,** 35-37 Parkgate Rd, SW11 4NP, ✆ (020) 7223 1611, *martinlam@compuserve.com, Fax (020) 7924 2614,* – MC AE ⓓ VISA JCB p. 29 **HZ** c
closed Christmas, August Bank Holiday and Sunday dinner – **Meals** a la carte 19.00/32.20 **t.** 🌢 6.50.

Duke of Cambridge, 228 Battersea Bridge Rd, SW11 3AA, ✆ (020) 7223 5662, *Fax (020) 7801 9684,* – MC ⓓ VISA p. 17 **CQ** a
Meals a la carte 13.85/19.35 **t.**

:ney – ✉ *SW15.*

XX **Putney Bridge,** Lower Richmond Rd, SW15 1LB, ✆ (020) 8780 1811, *Fax (020) 8780 1211,* ≤, « Thames-side setting » – ▤. MC AE ⓓ VISA JCB p. 16 **AQ** u
closed Christmas-New Year, Sunday dinner and Monday – **Meals** 18.50/39.50-45.00 **t.** 🌢 10.00
Spec. Scottish lobster with sweet spices. Roast duck "in two services". Valhrona chocolate moelleux with almond milk sorbet.

X **The Phoenix,** Pentlow St., SW15 1LY, ✆ (020) 8780 3131, *Fax (020) 8780 1114,* – ▤. MC AE ⓓ VISA p. 16 **AQ** s
closed Bank Holidays – **Meals** 15.00/18.50 **t.** (lunch) and a la carte 18.50/30.00 **t.**

X **Del Buongustaio,** 283-285 Putney Bridge Rd, SW15 2PT, ✆ (020) 8780 9361, *Fax (020) 8780 9361* – ▤. MC AE VISA JCB p. 16 **AQ** e
closed Sunday – **Meals** - Italian - 12.95/15.95 **t.** and a la carte 🌢 9.60.

X **Enoteca Turi,** 28 Putney High St., SW15 1SQ, ✆ (020) 8785 4449, *Fax (020) 8785 4449* – MC AE ⓓ VISA p. 16 **AQ** n
closed 25-30 December, Sunday and lunch Bank Holidays – **Meals** - Italian - a la carte 23.15/28.40 **t.** 🌢 5.25.

X **The Cookhouse,** 56 Lower Richmond Rd, SW15 1JT, ✆ (020) 8785 2300, *info@the_cookhouse.com* – ▤. MC AE ⓓ VISA p. 16 **AQ** a
closed Sunday and Monday – **Meals** (dinner only and lunch Saturday and Sunday) a la carte 19.00/25.50 **t.**

Coat and Badge, 8 Lacy Rd, SW15 1NL, ✆ (020) 8788 4900, *Fax (020) 8780 5733,* – MC ⓓ VISA p. 16 **AQ** r
Meals (bookings not accepted) a la carte 13.40/20.35 **t.** 🌢 4.50.

thfields – ✉ *SW18.*

X **Sarkhel's,** 199 Replingham Rd, SW18 5LY, ✆ (020) 8870 1483, *veronica@sarkhels.co.uk, Fax (020) 8874 6603* – ▤. MC AE VISA p. 16 **BR** e
closed 1 week August-September, 25-26 December and Monday – **Meals** - Indian - (dinner only and lunch Friday-Sunday) 9.95/12.00 **t.** and a la carte 10.95/23.95 **t.**

ting – ✉ *SW17.*

X **Kastoori,** 188 Upper Tooting Rd, SW17 7EJ, ✆ (020) 8767 7027 – ▤. MC VISA
closed 25 December, 1 week mid January and lunch Monday and Tuesday – **Meals** - Indian Vegetarian - a la carte 12.10/15.45 **t.** p. 17 **CR** v

X **Oh Boy,** 843 Garratt Lane, SW17 0PG, ✆ (020) 8947 9760 – ▤. MC AE ⓓ VISA JCB p. 17 **CR** c
closed Monday – **Meals** - Thai - (dinner only) a la carte 11.75/13.50 **t.**

ıdsworth – ✉ *SW12/SW17/SW18.*

X **Chez Bruce** (Poole), 2 Bellevue Rd, SW17 7EG, ✆ (020) 8672 0114, *Fax (020) 8767 6648* – ▤. MC AE ⓓ VISA p. 17 **CR** e
closed 24-31 December, Sunday dinner and Bank Holidays – **Meals** (booking essential) 21.50/27.50 **t.**
Spec. Tartare of salmon with smoked salmon mousse. Roast rump of lamb à la niçoise. Coconut rice pudding with mango and raspberries.

X **Ditto,** 55-57 East Hill, SW18 2QE, ✆ (020) 8877 0110, *christian-gilles@ditto1.fsnet.cc* *Fax (020) 8875 0110* – MC VISA JCB p. 16 BQ
closed 25-27 December, 1 January and Saturday lunch – **Meals** 18.50 **t.** and a la carte ₰ 9

X **Bombay Bicycle Club,** 95 Nightingale Lane, SW12 8NX, ✆ (020) 8673 6 *Fax (020) 8673 9100* – MC AE ① VISA p. 17 DR
closed Sunday and Bank Holidays – **Meals** - Indian - (dinner only) a la carte 25.00/27.5 ₰ 8.50.

X **Fish!,** 419 Queenstown Rd, SW8, ✆ (020) 7234 3333, *fish@bgr.plc.uk, Fax (020) 7234 3* – ▤. MC AE ① VISA JCB p. 17 DC
Meals - Seafood - a la carte 15.80/30.80 **t.** ₰ 7.50.

WESTMINSTER (City of).

Bayswater and Maida Vale – ✉ *W2/W9.*

Royal Lancaster, Lancaster Terr., W2 2TY, ✆ (020) 7262 6737, *sales@royallancaster.c* *Fax (020) 7724 3191,* ≤ – |‡|, ⇹ rm, ▤ TV ✆ ♿ P – 🏛 1400. MC AE ① VISA JCB. ✻
Park : **Meals** *(closed Saturday lunch, Sunday and Bank Holidays)* 23.50 **t.** and a la c ₰ 13.00 – ***Pavement Cafe :*** **Meals** a la carte 19.10/26.50 **t.** ₰ 8.00 – (see also ***Nipa*** belo ☕ 15.00 – **394 rm** 230.00/305.00 **s.**, 22 suites. p. 37 DZ

Hilton London Metropole, Edgware Rd, W2 1JU, ✆ (020) 7402 4 *Fax (020) 7724 8866,* ≤, Lδ, ≘s, ☒ – |‡|, ⇹ rm, ▤ TV – 🏛 1200. MC AE ① VISA JCB. ✻
Meals (buffet rest.) 15.00/25.00 – (see also ***Aspects*** below) – ☕ 16.95 – **104** 210.00 **st.**, 25 suites – SB. p. 25 GU

The Hempel ⊗, 31-35 Craven Hill Gdns., W2 3EA, ✆ (020) 7298 9000, *hotel@the-he .co.uk, Fax (020) 7402 4666,* « Minimalist », ⇁ – |‡| ▤ TV ✆ ♿ P – 🏛 40. MC AE ① JCB. ✻ p. 36 CZ
I-Thai : **Meals** - Thai-Italian - a la carte 45.15/62.70 **st.** – ☕ 21.50 – **41 rm** 255.00 **s.**, 6 s. – SB.

Thistle Hyde Park, Bayswater Rd, 90-92 Lancaster Gate, W2 3NR, ✆ (020) 7262 2 *Fax (020) 7262 2147* – |‡|, ⇹ rm, ▤ TV ✆ P – 🏛 30. MC AE ① VISA JCB. ✻ p. 36 C
Meals (dinner only) a la carte 16.75/24.00 **t.** ₰ 7.00 – ☕ 15.95 – **52 rm** 236.00/28 2 suites – SB.

Hilton London Hyde Park, 129 Bayswater Rd, W2 4RJ, ✆ (020) 7221 2 *Fax (020) 7229 0557* – |‡|, ⇹ rm, ▤ TV ✆ – 🏛 90. MC AE ① VISA JCB. ✻ p. 36 B
Meals (bar lunch)/dinner a la carte 18.85/31.85 **t.** – ☕ 12.95 – **128 rm** 120.00/140. 1 suite.

Jarvis International Hyde Park, 150 Bayswater Rd, W2 4RT, ✆ (020) 7229 1212, *epark@jarvis.co.uk, Fax (020) 7229 2623* – |‡|, ⇹ rm, ▤ rest, TV ✆ P – 🏛 100. MC VISA p. 36 B
Meals (carving rest.) 18.00/25.00 **t.** and a la carte – ☕ 10.50 – **212 rm** 145.00/165.0 1 suite – SB.

Mornington without rest., 12 Lancaster Gate, W2 3LG, ✆ (020) 7262 7361, *london@ nington.co.uk, Fax (020) 7706 1028* – |‡| ⇹ TV. MC AE ① VISA JCB. ✻ p. 37 D
66 rm ☕ 115.00/160.00 **st.**

Commodore, 50 Lancaster Gate, W2 3NA, ✆ (020) 7402 5291, *reservations@comm e-hotel.com, Fax (020) 7262 1088* – |‡|, ⇹ rm, TV ✆. MC AE ① VISA. ✻ p. 36 C
Meals - Spanish - *(closed Sunday)* a la carte 11.25/25.50 **st.** – ☕ 12.50 – **90 rm** 11 135.00 **st.**

Miller's without rest., 111A Westbourne Grove, W2 4UW, ✆ (020) 7243 1024, *enqu millersuk.com, Fax (020) 7243 1064,* « Antique furnishings » – TV. MC AE VISA. ✻
closed 24-27 December – **8 rm** 140.00/160.00. p. 36 A

Byron without rest., 36-38 Queensborough Terr., W2 3SH, ✆ (020) 7243 0987, *byror ricornhotels.co.uk, Fax (020) 7792 1957* – |‡| ▤ TV. MC AE ① VISA JCB. ✻ p. 36 C
44 rm ☕ 78.00/120.00 **st.**, 1 suite.

Delmere, 130 Sussex Gdns., W2 1UB, ✆ (020) 7706 3344, *delmerehotel@compuser m, Fax (020) 7262 1863* – |‡|, ⇹ rm, TV ✆. MC AE ① VISA JCB. ✻ p. 37 D
Meals *(closed Sunday and Bank Holidays)* (dinner only) a la carte 14.50/20.00 **t.** ₰ 5.50 6.00 – **36 rm** 84.00/105.00 **st.**

Comfort Inn without rest., 18-19 Craven Hill Gdns., W2 3EE, ✆ (020) 7262 6644, *cor nn_hydepark@compuserve.com, Fax (020) 7262 0673* – |‡| ⇹ TV. MC AE ① VISA. ✻
☕ 4.50 – **60 rm** 87.00/104.00 **st.** p. 36 C

XX **Aspects** (at Hilton London Metropole H.), Edgware Rd, W2 1JU, ✆ (020) 7402 *Fax (020) 7724 8866,* ≤ London – ▤. MC AE ① VISA JCB p. 25 G
closed Sunday dinner – **Meals** 15.00/25.00 **st.** and a la carte ₰ 7.00.

Amandier, 26 Sussex Pl., W2 2TH, ℘ (020) 7262 6073, *Fax (020) 7723 8395* – MC AE D VISA JCB p. 37 DZ r
closed 24-25 December, Sunday, Saturday lunch and Bank Holidays – **Meals** - French - 15.00/29.50 **t.** and a la carte 12.50 – (see also ***Bistro Daniel*** below).

Nipa (at Royal Lancaster H.), Lancaster Terr., W2 2TY, ℘ (020) 7262 6737, *Fax (020) 7724 3191* – P. MC AE D VISA JCB p. 37 DZ e
Meals - Thai - 23.00/26.00 **t** and a la carte.

Al San Vincenzo, 30 Connaught St., W2 2AE, ℘ (020) 7262 9623 – MC VISA p. 37 EZ o
closed Saturday lunch and Sunday – **Meals** - Italian - (booking essential) 31.00 **t.** 8.50.

Poons, Unit 205, Whiteleys, Queensway, W2 4YN, ℘ (020) 7792 2884, *Fax (020) 8458 0968* – . MC AE D VISA JCB p. 36 BZ x
closed 24-26 December – **Meals** - Chinese - 16.00/22.00 **t.** and a la carte 13.00.

Jason's, Blomfield Rd, Little Venice, W9 2PD, ℘ (020) 7286 6752, *enquiries@jasons.co.uk, Fax (020) 7266 4332,* , « Canalside setting » – MC AE D VISA JCB p. 24 FU c
closed 25 December-2 January and Sunday dinner – **Meals** - Seafood - 17.95/21.95 **t.** and a la carte 12.50.

Assaggi, 39 Chepstow Pl., (above Chepstow pub), W2 4TS, ℘ (020) 7792 5501 – MC AE D VISA JCB p. 36 AZ c
closed 24 December-8 January, Sunday and Bank Holidays – **Meals** - Italian - a la carte approx. 31.40 **t.**

The Vale, 99 Chippenham Rd, W9 2AB, ℘ (020) 7266 0990, *Fax (020) 7286 7224* – . MC D VISA p. 24 ET z
closed 1 week Christmas, last weekend August and lunch Saturday and Monday – **Meals** 11.50/15.00 **t.** and a la carte 19.00/24.00 **t.** 5.50.

Livebait, 175 Westbourne Grove, W11 2SB, ℘ (020) 7727 4321, *Fax (020) 7792 3655* – . MC AE D VISA JCB p. 36 AZ x
closed 25-26 December – **Meals** - Seafood - 12.95/15.50 **st.** and a la carte 12.25.

L'Accento, 16 Garway Rd, W2 4NH, ℘ (020) 7243 2201, *laccentorest@aol.com, Fax (020) 7243 2201,* – MC AE VISA JCB p. 36 BZ a
closed August, Christmas and Bank Holidays – **Meals** - Italian - 16.50 and a la carte 21.00/26.00 8.50.

Green Olive, 5 Warwick Pl., W9 2PX, ℘ (020) 7289 2469, *Fax (020) 7289 4178* – MC AE VISA p. 24 FU a
closed 25-26 December, Saturday lunch and Bank Holidays – **Meals** - Italian - 16.00/19.00 (lunch) and a la carte 24.50/30.50 9.00.

Bistro Daniel (at Amandier), 26 Sussex Pl., W2 2TH, ℘ (020) 7262 6073, *Fax (020) 7723 8395* – MC AE VISA JCB p. 37 DZ r
closed 24-25 December, Saturday lunch, Sunday and Bank Holidays – **Meals** - French - 9.95/12.95 **t.** (lunch) and a la carte 17.80/24.45 **t.** 8.95.

The Chepstow, 39 Chepstow Pl., W2 4TS, ℘ (020) 7229 0323, *Fax (020) 7229 0323* – MC D VISA JCB p. 36 AZ c
closed Christmas – **Meals** a la carte 17.50/28.15 **st.**

gravia – ✉ *SW1.*

The Lanesborough, Hyde Park Corner, SW1X 7TA, ℘ (020) 7259 5599, *reservations@lanesborough.co.uk, Fax (020) 7259 5606,* – , rm, TV P – 90. MC AE D VISA. p. 29 IY a
***The Conservatory*:** **Meals** 26.50/39.00 **st.** and a la carte 17.50 – 24.00 – **86 rm** 265.00/450.00 **s.**, 9 suites.

The Berkeley, Wilton Pl., SW1X 7RL, ℘ (020) 7235 6000, *info@theberkeley.co.uk, Fax (020) 7235 4330,* « Rooftop », , – , rm, TV – 220. MC AE D VISA JCB. p. 35 FQ e
Meals – (see ***La Tante Claire*** and ***Vong*** below) – 22.50 – **140 rm** 310.00/575.00 **s.**, 28 suites.

The Halkin, 5 Halkin St., SW1X 7DJ, ℘ (020) 7333 1000, *sales@halkin.co.uk, Fax (020) 7333 1100,* « Contemporary interior design » – , rm, TV P – 25. MC AE D VISA JCB. p. 36 AV a
***Stefano Cavallini Restaurant at The Halkin*:** **Meals** - Italian - *(closed lunch Saturday and Sunday)* (booking essential) 25.00/55.00 **t.** and a la carte 44.50/80.00 **t.** 11.50 – 18.00 – **37 rm** 285.00/360.00 **s.**, 4 suites
Spec. Duck ravioli with savoy cabbage and foie gras. Fillet of sea bass with tomatoes, olives and capers. Saffron risotto.

Sheraton Belgravia, 20 Chesham Pl., SW1X 8HQ, ℘ (020) 7235 6040, *reservations_central_london@starwoodhotels.com, Fax (020) 7259 6243* – , rm, TV P – 25. MC AE D VISA. p. 35 FR u
***Mulberry*:** **Meals** *(closed Saturday lunch)* 10.00/20.00 **st.** (lunch) and dinner a la carte 25.00/35.00 **st.** 20.00 – 17.50 – **82 rm** 264.00/332.00, 7 suites.

The Lowndes, 21 Lowndes St., SW1X 9ES, ✆ (020) 7823 1234, *lowndes@hyattintl.co* *Fax (020) 7235 1154*, – |⇅|, ⇔ rm, ▤ TV – 25. MC AE D VISA JCB. p. 35 FR
***Brasserie 21*: Meals** 18.00 **st.** (lunch) and a la carte 25.50/42.50 **st.** – ▭ 15.50 – **77** 240.00/270.00 **s.**, 1 suite.

Diplomat without rest., 2 Chesham St., SW1X 8DT, ✆ (020) 7235 1544, *diplomat.hote tinternet.com, Fax (020) 7259 6153* – |⇅| TV. MC AE D VISA JCB. p. 35 FR
26 rm ▭ 90.00/160.00 **st.**

La Tante Claire (Koffmann) (at The Berkeley H.), Wilton Pl., SW1X 7RL, ✆ (020) 7823 20 *Fax (020) 7823 2001* – ▤. MC AE D VISA p. 35 FQ
closed Saturday lunch, Sunday and Bank Holidays – **Meals** - French - (booking essen 28.00 **t.** (lunch) and a la carte 61.00/76.00 **t.** 🍷 13.00
Spec. Bouillon de poule, petits raviolis de langoustine. Pied de cochon "classique Ta Claire". Soufflé à la pistache.

Zafferano (Locatelli), 15 Lowndes St., SW1X 9EY, ✆ (020) 7235 5800, *Fax (020) 7235 1* – ▤. MC AE D VISA p. 35 FR
closed Easter, Christmas and Bank Holidays – **Meals** - Italian - 18.50/39.50 **t.**
Spec. Sea bream with balsamic vinaigrette. Rabbit with polenta and Parma ham. P ribbons with broad beans and rocket.

Vong (at The Berkeley H.), Wilton Pl., SW1X 7RL, ✆ (020) 7235 1010, *Fax (020) 7235 10* ▤. MC AE D VISA JCB p. 35 FQ
closed Christmas and Bank Holidays – **Meals** - French-Thai - (booking essential) 23 54.00 **st.** and a la carte.

Noura Brasserie, 16 Hobart Pl., SW1W 0HH, ✆ (020) 7235 9444, *Fax (020) 7235 92* ▤. MC AE D VISA JCB p. 36 AX
Meals - Lebanese - 12.50/28.50 **t.** and a la carte.

Al Bustan, 27 Motcomb St., SW1X 8JU, ✆ (020) 7235 8277, *Fax (020) 7235 1668* – ▤ AE D VISA p. 35 FR
Meals - Lebanese - 13.00 **t.** (lunch) and a la carte 26.40/33.00 **t.**

Hyde Park and Knightsbridge – ✉ *SW1/SW7.*

Mandarin Oriental Hyde Park, 66 Knightsbridge, SW1X 7LA, ✆ (020) 7235 2 *Fax (020) 7235 4552*, <, Fø, ≘s – |⇅|, ⇔ rm, ▤ TV ♿ – 220. MC AE D p. 35 FC
Cafe on the Park* : Meals** a la carte 18.50/27.00 **t.** 🍷 14.00 – (see also ***Foliage below) 19.00 – **177 rm** 295.00/495.00 **s.**, 23 suites.

Knightsbridge Green without rest., 159 Knightsbridge, SW1X 7PD, ✆ (020) 7584 6 *thekghotel@aol.com, Fax (020) 7225 1635* – |⇅| ⇔ ▤ TV. MC AE D VISA. p. 35 EC
▭ 9.50 – **16 rm** 105.00/140.00 **st.**, 12 suites 165.00 **st.**

Foliage (at Mandarin Oriental Hyde Park H.), 66 Knightsbridge, SW1X ✆ (020) 7235 2000, *Fax (020) 7235 4552* – ▤. MC AE D VISA p. 35 FC
closed Saturday lunch and Sunday – **Meals** 19.00/32.50 **t.** 🍷 14.00.

Isola, 145 Knightsbridge, SW1X 7PA, ✆ (020) 7838 1044, *Fax (020) 7838 1099* – ▤. D VISA p. 35 EC
closed Bank Holidays – **Meals** - Italian - *(closed Sunday)* (dinner only) a la carte 31.50/41. – ***Osteria d'Isola*** *(✆ (020) 7838 1055)* **: Meals** 14.50 **t.** and a la carte.

Mr. Chow, 151 Knightsbridge, SW1X 7PA, ✆ (020) 7589 7347, *Fax (020) 7584 5780* MC AE D VISA JCB p. 35 EC
closed 24-26 December and 1 January – **Meals** - Chinese - 9.50 **t.** (lunch) and a la 27.75/33.00 **t.**

Mayfair – ✉ *W1.*

Dorchester, Park Lane, W1A 2HJ, ✆ (020) 7629 8888, *info@dorchesterhotel. Fax (020) 7409 0114*, Fø, ≘s – |⇅|, ⇔ rm, ▤ TV ♿ – 550. MC AE D VISA p. 32 BI
Meals – (see ***The Oriental*** and ***Grill Room*** below) – ▭ 20.50 – **201 rm** 285.00/345. 47 suites – SB.

Claridge's, Brook St., W1A 2JQ, ✆ (020) 7629 8860, *info@claridges.c Fax (020) 7499 2210*, Fø – |⇅|, ⇔ rm, ▤ TV ♿ – 200. MC AE D VISA p. 32 B
***Restaurant* : Meals** (live music and dancing Saturday evening) 28.75/35.00 **t.** and a la 46.75/64.00 **t.** 🍷 11.00 – ▭ 16.00 – **137 rm** 295.00/475.00, 60 suites.

Le Meridien Piccadilly, 21 Piccadilly, W1V 0BH, ✆ (0870) 400 8400, *lmpicc@forte-s.com, Fax (020) 7437 3574*, Fø, ≘s, ⊠, squash – |⇅|, ⇔ rm, ▤ TV ♿ – 250. MC VISA JCB p. 33 EI
Meals – (see ***The Oak Room Marco Pierre White*** and ***Terrace*** below) – ▭ 18.50 – 24 285.00/355.00, 18 suites.

Le Meridien Grosvenor House, Park Lane, W1K 7TN, (020) 7499 6363, *grosvenor.reservations@forte-hotels.com, Fax (020) 7493 3341,* – rm, – 1500. VISA JCB. p. 32 **AM** a
La Terrazza : **Meals** a la carte 33.50/37.75 **t.** 10.00 – 19.50 – **373 rm** 320.00/395.00 **s.,** 74 suites – SB.

Four Seasons, Hamilton Pl., Park Lane, W1A 1AZ, (020) 7499 0888, *Fax (020) 7493 1895,* – rm, – 500. VISA JCB. p. 32 **BP** a
Lanes : **Meals** 35.00/33.00 **st.** and a la carte 8.00 – 20.50 – **185 rm** 270.00/325.00 **s.,** 35 suites.

London Hilton, 22 Park Lane, W1Y 4BE, (020) 7493 8000, *email.park-lane@hilton.com, Fax (020) 7208 4146,* « Panoramic of London », – rm, – 1000. VISA JCB. p. 32 **BP** e
Trader Vics *((020) 7208 4113)* **: Meals** (dinner only) 16.00 **t.** and a la carte – ***Park Brasserie :*** **Meals** 21.50/24.50 **t.** and a la carte 7.75 – (see also ***Windows*** below) – 19.50 – **396 rm** 315.00 **s.,** 53 suites.

Connaught, Carlos Pl., W1K 2AL, (020) 7499 7070, *info@the_connaught.co.uk, Fax (020) 7495 3262* – VISA JCB. p. 32 **BM** e
The Restaurant : **Meals** (booking essential) 28.50/58.00 **t.** and a la carte 30.80/62.00 **t.** 15.00 – ***Grill Room :*** **Meals** *(closed Saturday lunch)* (booking essential) 28.50/58.00 **t.** and a la carte 30.80/62.00 **t.** – 21.00 – **66 rm** 300.00/425.00 **s.,** 24 suites – SB
Spec. Terrine Connaught. Homard d'Ecosse, "Reine Elizabeth". Sherry trifle "Wally Ladd".

Brown's, Albemarle St., W1X 4BP, (020) 7493 6020, *reservations@brownshotel.com, Fax (020) 7493 9381* – – 70. VISA JCB. p. 33 **DM** e
Meals – (see ***1837*** below) – 19.00 – **112 rm** 305.00/380.00, 6 suites.

Inter-Continental, 1 Hamilton Pl., Hyde Park Corner, W1V 0QY, (020) 7409 3131, *london@interconti.com, Fax (020) 7493 3476,* – rm, – 1000. VISA JCB. p. 32 **BP** o
Meals 25.10/29.50 **t.** and a la carte 10.00 – (see also ***Le Soufflé*** below) – 20.00 – **418 rm** 305.00/355.00 **s.,** 40 suites.

47 Park Street, 47 Park St., W1Y 4EB, (020) 7491 7282, *reservations@47parkstreet.com, Fax (020) 7491 7281* – VISA. p. 32 **AM** c
Meals (room service) – (see also ***Le Gavroche*** below) – 24.50, **52 suites** 295.00/565.00 **s.**

Millennium Britannia Mayfair, Grosvenor Sq., W1K 2HP, (020) 7629 9400, *salesbritannia@mill_cop.com, Fax (020) 7629 7736,* – rm, – 770. VISA JCB. p. 32 **BM** x
Meals *(closed Saturday lunch)* 22.50 **t.** (lunch) and a la carte 31.00/42.00 **t.** – (see also ***Shogun*** below) – 17.50 – **342 rm** 175.00/255.00, 6 suites – SB.

May Fair Inter-Continental, Stratton St., W1A 2AN, (020) 7629 7777, *mayfair@interconti.com, Fax (020) 7629 1459,* – rm, – 300. VISA JCB. p. 33 **DN** z
May Fair Café *((020) 7915 2842)* **: Meals** (lunch only) 16.00 **t.** and a la carte – ***Opus 70 :*** **Meals** 20.00 **t.** (lunch) and a la carte 29.50/34.50 **t.** 7.00 – 17.50 – **278 rm** 315.00, 12 suites – SB.

Park Lane, Piccadilly, W1Y 8BX, (020) 7499 6321, *reservation_central_london@starwoodhotels.com, Fax (020) 7499 1965,* – rm, – 300. VISA. p. 32 **CP** x
Citrus *((020) 7290 7364)* **: Meals** 15.00/25.00 **st.** (lunch) and a la carte 24.00/36.00 **st.** 13.00 – 18.50 – **285 rm** 246.00/304.00, 20 suites.

Westbury, Bond St., W1A 4UH, (020) 7629 7755, *westburyhotel@compuserve.com, Fax (020) 7495 1163* – rm, – 120. VISA JCB. p. 33 **DM** a
Meals 16.50/21.50 **st.** and a la carte – 16.75 – **225 rm** 225.00/260.00 **s.,** 19 suites – SB.

The Metropolitan, Old Park Lane, W1Y 4LB, (020) 7447 1000, *sales@metropolitan.co.uk, Fax (020) 7447 1100,* « Contemporary interior design », – rm, VISA JCB. p. 32 **BP** c
Met Bar : **Meals** (residents and members only) (restricted menu) a la carte approx. 25.00 **st.** 14.00 – (see also ***Nobu*** below) – 20.00 – **152 rm** 240.00/545.00 **s.,** 3 suites.

Athenaeum, 116 Piccadilly, W1V 0BJ, (020) 7499 3464, *info@athenaeumhotel.com, Fax (020) 7493 1860,* – rm, – 55. VISA JCB.
Bulloch's at 116 : **Meals** *(closed lunch Saturday and Sunday)* 20.00 **st.** (lunch) and a la carte 35.45/42.95 **st.** – 18.50 – **124 rm** 240.00/310.00, 33 suites. p. 32 **CP** s

London Marriott Grosvenor Square, Duke St., Grosvenor Sq., W1A 4AW, (020) 7493 1232, *sales@londonmarriott.co.uk, Fax (020) 7491 3201,* – rm, – 600. VISA JCB. p. 32 **BL** a
Diplomat : **Meals** *(closed Saturday lunch)* a la carte 24.70/37.45 **t.** 12.75 – 14.95 – **209 rm** 205.00/255.00 **s.,** 12 suites.

Washington Mayfair, 5-7 Curzon St., W1Y 8DT, ✆ (020) 7499 7000, *reemesenger@mpuserve.com, Fax (020) 7495 6172* – |‡|, ✂ rm, ▤ TV ✆ – 🏠 80. MC AE ⓓ VISA JCB ✂ p. 32 CN
Meals 13.95 **st.** and a la carte 🍷 7.50 – ☕ 13.95 – **168 rm** 195.00 **s.**, 5 suites.

Chesterfield, 35 Charles St., W1X 8LX, ✆ (020) 7491 2622, *reservations@chesterfield.carnationhotels.com, Fax (020) 7491 4793* – |‡|, ✂ rm, ▤ TV ✆ – 🏠 110. MC AE ⓓ VISA
Meals *(closed Saturday lunch)* 15.50/19.50 **t.** and a la carte 🍷 7.50 – ☕ 16.00 – **106** 195.00/215.00 **s.**, 4 suites – SB. p. 32 CN

Holiday Inn Mayfair, 3 Berkeley St., W1X 6NE, ✆ (020) 7493 8282, *himayfair@easyn o.uk, Fax (020) 7629 2827,* Ⅎ₆ – |‡|, ✂ rm, ▤ TV ✆ – 🏠 60. MC AE ⓓ VISA JCB ✂ p. 33 DN
Meals a la carte 19.95/30.95 **st.** – ☕ 13.95 – **182 rm** 230.00 **st.**, 4 suites.

Flemings, Half Moon St., W1Y 7RA, ✆ (020) 7499 2964, *sales@flemings_mayfair.co. Fax (020) 7629 4063* – |‡|, ✂ rm, ▤ TV ✆ – 🏠 50. MC AE ⓓ VISA JCB ✂ p. 32 CN
Meals 19.95/23.95 **st.** and a la carte 🍷 9.00 – ☕ 16.50 – **120 rm** 165.00/195.00 **s.**, 10 suit

Hilton London Green Park, Half Moon St., W1Y 8BP, ✆ (020) 7629 7522, *greenpark tel@btinternet.com, Fax (020) 7491 8971* – |‡|, ✂ rm, ▤ TV ✆ – 🏠 130. MC AE ⓓ VISA JCB ✂ p. 32 CN
Meals *(closed Saturday lunch)* a la carte 21.20/30.20 **st.** 🍷 6.00 – ☕ 13.95 – **161 rm** 190. 210.00.

Hilton London Mews, 2 Stanhope Row, W1Y 7HE, ✆ (020) 7493 7222, *lonmwtw.gm ilton.com, Fax (020) 7629 9423* – |‡|, ✂ rm, ▤ TV ✆ – 🏠 50. MC AE ⓓ VISA JCB
Meals (dinner only) a la carte 16.65/24.40 **t.** 🍷 15.00 – ☕ 15.50 – **72 rm** 205.00/265.00 s SB. p. 32 BP

XXXXX ✿ **The Oak Room Marco Pierre White** (at Le Meridien Piccadilly H.), 21 Piccadilly, W 0BH, ✆ (020) 7437 0202, *Fax (020) 7851 3141* – ▤. MC AE ⓓ VISA p. 33 EM
closed Saturday lunch, Sunday and Bank Holidays – **Meals** (booking essential) 28.00/38. 48.00 **t.** 🍷 12.50
Spec. Vinaigrette of rabbit printanière. Fillet of beef à la ficelle, sauce rémoulade. Pru and Armagnac soufflé.

XXXX ✿✿ **Le Gavroche** (Roux), 43 Upper Brook St., W1K 7QR, ✆ (020) 7408 0881, *gavroche@cv m.net, Fax (020) 7409 0939* – ▤. MC AE ⓓ VISA JCB p. 32 AM
closed Christmas-New Year, Saturday, Sunday and Bank Holidays – **Meals** - French - (bo ing essential) 38.50 **t.** (lunch) and a la carte 55.40/88.40 **t.** 🍷 15.00
Spec. Foie gras chaud et pastilla de canard à la cannelle. Râble de lapin et galette parmesan. Le palet au chocolat amer et praline croustillant.

XXXX **The Oriental** (at Dorchester H.), Park Lane, W1A 2HJ, ✆ (020) 7317 63 *Fax (020) 7317 6464* – ▤. MC AE ⓓ VISA JCB p. 32 BN
closed 25 December, August, Saturday lunch and Sunday – **Meals** - Chinese (Canto 25.00/43.00 **st.** and a la carte 43.50/66.00 **st.** 🍷 12.00.

XXXX **Grill Room** (at Dorchester H.), Park Lane, W1A 2HJ, ✆ (020) 7317 63 *Fax (020) 7317 6464* – ▤. MC AE ⓓ VISA JCB p. 32 BN
Meals - English - 32.50/39.50 **st.** and a la carte 41.00/62.00 **st.** 🍷 12.00.

XXXX **1837** (at Brown's H.), Albemarle St., W1X 4BP, ✆ (020) 7408 1837, *brownshotel@ukbusi s.com, Fax (020) 7493 9381* – ▤. MC AE ⓓ VISA JCB p. 33 DM
closed Saturday lunch and Sunday – **Meals** 23.00/45.00 **t.** and a la carte.

XXXX **Windows** (at London Hilton H.), 22 Park Lane, W1Y 4BE, ✆ (020) 7208 40 *Fax (020) 7208 4147,* « Panoramic ≤ of London » – ▤. MC AE ⓓ VISA JCB p. 32 BP
closed Saturday lunch and Sunday dinner – **Meals** 36.50 **t.** (lunch) and dinner a la ca 36.00/60.00 **t.** 🍷 13.00.

XXX ✿✿ **The Square** (Howard), 6-10 Bruton St., W1J 6PU, ✆ (020) 7495 7100, *squarethe@aol.c , Fax (020) 7495 7150* – ▤. MC AE ⓓ VISA JCB p. 32 CM
closed 25-26 December, 1 January, lunch Saturday, Sunday and Bank Holidays – **Me** 25.00/50.00-70.00 **t.** 🍷 9.00
Spec. Lasagne of crab with mousseline of scallops and basil. Herb crusted saddle of lar shallot purée and rosemary. "Brillat Savarin" cheesecake with strawberries and Champag

XXX ✿ **Mirabelle,** 56 Curzon St., W1J 8PA, ✆ (020) 7499 4636, *Fax (020) 7499 5449,* 🍴 – ▤. AE ⓓ VISA p. 32 CN
Meals 17.95 **t.** (lunch) and a la carte 32.50/43.50 **t.** 🍷 11.00
Spec. Vinaigrette of rabbit en gelée. Bresse pigeon with foie gras en chou vert. Choco and almond parfait.

XXX **Terrace** (at Le Meridien Piccadilly H.), 21 Piccadilly, W1V 0BH, ✆ (020) 7851 30 *Fax (020) 7851 3090* – ▤. MC AE ⓓ VISA JCB p. 33 EM
Meals a la carte 30.00/40.50 **t.** 🍷 14.00.

XXX **Sartoria,** 20 Savile Row, W1X 1AE, ☎ (020) 7534 7000, *Fax (020) 7534 7070* – ▤. MC AE Diners VISA JCB p. 33 **DL** c
closed 24-26 December, 1 January and Sunday lunch – **Meals** - Italian - a la carte 30.50/38.50 **t.**

XXX **Firebird,** 23 Conduit St., W1S 2XS, ☎ (020) 7493 7011, *Fax (020) 7493 7088* – ▤. MC AE VISA p. 33 **DL** x
closed 2 weeks August, 25-26 December, Sunday and Bank Holidays – **Meals** - Tsarist Russian - 18.95 **t.** (lunch) and a la carte 29.50/48.00 **t.** 12.00.

XXX **Scotts,** 20 Mount St., W1Y 6HE, ☎ (020) 7629 5248, *Fax (020) 7499 8246* – ▤. MC AE Diners VISA p. 32 **BM** a
closed 25 December – **Meals** - Seafood - 26.50 **t.** (lunch) and dinner a la carte 27.75/42.20 **t.**

XXX **Morton's - The Restaurant,** 28 Berkeley Sq., W1X 5HA, ☎ (020) 7493 7171, *Fax (020) 7495 3160* – MC AE Diners VISA JCB p. 32 **CM** a
closed Christmas-31 December, Sunday, Saturday lunch and Bank Holidays – **Meals** a la carte 29.90/38.55 **st.** 14.00.

XXX **Le Soufflé** (at Inter-Continental H.), 1 Hamilton Pl., Hyde Park Corner, W1V 0QY, ☎ (020) 7318 8577, *Fax (020) 7409 7460* – ▤ 🚗. MC AE Diners VISA p. 32 **BP** o
closed Monday, Saturday lunch and Sunday dinner – **Meals** 30.50/41.00 **t.** and a la carte 13.00.

XXX **Kaspia,** 18-18A Bruton Pl., W1X 7AA, ☎ (020) 7493 2612, *Fax (020) 7408 1627* – ▤. MC AE Diners VISA p. 32 **CM** i
closed 25-27 December, 1-3 January, 15 days August, Sunday and Bank Holidays – **Meals** - Caviar specialities - 18.00/30.00 **t.** and a la carte 11.50.

XX **Cassia Oriental,** 12 Berkeley Sq., W1X 5HG, ☎ (020) 7629 8886, *Fax (020) 7491 8883* – ▤. MC AE Diners VISA p. 32 **CM** z
closed 25-26 December, 1 January, Sunday and Bank Holidays – **Meals** - South East Asian - 22.00 **t.** (dinner) and a la carte 18.50/28.50 **t.**

XX **Greenhouse,** 27a Hay's Mews, W1X 7RJ, ☎ (020) 7499 3331, *Fax (020) 7499 5368* – ▤. MC AE Diners VISA JCB p. 32 **BN** e
closed Christmas-New Year, Saturday lunch and Bank Holidays – **Meals** a la carte 30.00/41.00 **t.** 6.60.

XX **Noble Rot,** 3-5 Mill St., W1R 9TF, ☎ (020) 7629 8877, *noble@noblerot.com, Fax (020) 7629 8878* – ▤. MC AE Diners VISA p. 33 **DL** r
closed 25-26 December, 1 January, Easter Bank Holidays and Sunday – **Meals** a la carte approx. 32.00 **t.**

XX ✿ **Tamarind,** 20 Queen St., W1X 7PJ, ☎ (020) 7629 3561, *tamarind.restaurant@virgin.net, Fax (020) 7499 5034* – ▤. MC AE Diners VISA JCB p. 32 **CN** e
closed lunch Saturday and Bank Holidays – **Meals** - Indian - 14.95/28.50 **t.** and a la carte 24.00/41.00 **t.** 15.00
Spec. Bhalla Papri Chaat (lentil dumplings). Jhinga Khyber (prawns in ginger). Hari Machchi (John Dory with crispy spinach).

XX **Alloro,** 19-20 Dover St., W1X 3PB, ☎ (020) 7495 4768, *Fax (020) 7629 5348* – ▤. MC AE Diners VISA p. 33 **DM** r
closed Sunday and Bank Holidays – **Meals** - Italian - 18.00/28.00 **t.** and a la carte.

XX ✿ **Nobu** (at The Metropolitan H.), 19 Old Park Lane, W1Y 4LB, ☎ (020) 7447 4747, *Fax (020) 7447 4749*, ≤ – ▤. MC AE Diners VISA p. 32 **BP** c
closed 25-26 December and Saturday lunch – **Meals** - New style Japanese with South American influences - (booking essential) 23.50 **t.** (lunch) and a la carte 55.00/85.00 **t.** 15.00
Spec. Yellow tail jalepeño. Black cod with miso. Sashimi salad.

XX **Chor Bizarre,** 16 Albemarle St., W1X 3HA, ☎ (020) 7629 9802, *Fax (020) 7493 7756*, « Authentic Indian decor and furnishings » – ▤. MC AE Diners VISA JCB p. 33 **DM** s
Meals - Indian - a la carte 14.00/29.00 **st.** 11.00.

XX **Yatra,** 34 Dover St., W1X 3RA, ☎ (020) 7493 0200, *Fax (020) 7408 2069* – ▤. MC AE VISA JCB p. 33 **DM** o
closed Sunday and lunch Saturday – **Meals** - Indian - 14.50/23.50 **t.** and a la carte 6.50.

XX **L'Odéon,** 65 Regent St., W1R 7HH, ☎ (020) 7287 1400, *lodeon@lodeon-rest-bar.demon.co.uk, Fax (020) 7287 1300* – ▤. MC AE Diners VISA JCB p. 33 **EM** r
closed Sunday and Bank Holidays – **Meals** 14.50/19.50 **t.** (lunch) and a la carte 24.50/41.00 **t.** 12.50.

XX **Bentley's,** 11-15 Swallow St., W1B 4DG, ☎ (020) 7734 4756, *Fax (020) 7287 2972* – ▤. MC AE Diners VISA JCB p. 33 **EM** i
closed 25-26 December – **Meals** - Seafood - 14.75/19.50 **t.** and a la carte.

XXX **Langan's Brasserie,** Stratton St., W1X 5FD, ☎ (020) 7491 8822, *Fax (020) 7493 830.*
▤. MC AE ⓓ VISA JCB p. 33 **DN**
closed Christmas, Easter, Sunday, Saturday lunch and Bank Holidays – **Meals** a la ca
24.75/32.95 **t.** 🌡 8.50.

XXX **Marquis,** 121A Mount St., W1Y 5HB, ☎ (020) 7499 1256, *Fax (020) 7493 4460* – MC AE
VISA JCB p. 32 **BM**
closed 24 December-2 January, last 2 weeks August, Saturday, Sunday and Bank Holiday
Meals 17.50 **t.** and a la carte 🌡 6.50.

XXX **Kai,** 65 South Audley St., W1Y 5FD, ☎ (020) 7493 8988, *kai@kaimayfair.co.*
Fax (020) 7493 1456 – ▤. MC AE ⓓ VISA JCB p. 32 **BM**
closed 25-26 December and 1 January – **Meals** - Chinese - a la carte 25.00/50.00 **t.** 🌡 15.

XXX **Teca,** 54 Brooks Mews, W1Y 2NY, ☎ (020) 7495 4774, *Fax (020) 7491 3545* – MC AE ⓓ V
closed 25 December, 1 January, Sunday, Saturday lunch and Bank Holidays – **Meals** - Italia
16.00/23.50 **t.** 🌡 9.00. p. 32 **CL**

XXX **Hush,** 8 Lancashire Court, Brook St., W1S 1EY, ☎ (020) 7659 1500, *steamroller@hush.*
uk, Fax (020) 7659 1501 – |$|, ▤. MC AE VISA JCB p. 32 **CL**
closed Sunday and Bank Holidays – ***hush down*** 🏠 **:** **Meals** a la carte 29.50/38.00 **t.** – ***hu***
***up* :** **Meals** *(closed Saturday lunch)* (booking essential) 25.00 **t.** (lunch) and a la carte 39.
46.50 **t.**.

XXX **Shogun** (at Millennium Britannia Mayfair H.), Adams Row, W1Y 5DF, ☎ (020) 7493 1255
itannia.res@mill_cop, Fax (020) 7493 1255 – ▤. MC AE ⓓ VISA p. 32 **BM**
closed Monday – **Meals** - Japanese - (dinner only) a la carte approx. 14.50 **t.**

XXX **Momo,** 25 Heddon St., W1B 4BX, ☎ (020) 7434 4040, *Fax (020) 7287 0404* – ▤. MC AE
VISA p. 33 **EM**
closed Christmas – **Meals** - Moroccan - 12.00/15.50 **t.** (lunch) and a la carte 21.50/34.00

XXX **Nicole's** (at Nicole Farhi), 158 New Bond St., W1V 9PA, ☎ (020) 7499 84
Fax (020) 7409 0381 – ▤. MC AE ⓓ VISA JCB p. 33 **DM**
closed Saturday dinner, Sunday and Bank Holidays – **Meals** a la carte 29.75/35.75 **t.** 🌡 11.

X **Veeraswamy,** Victory House, 99 Regent St., W1B 4RS, entrance on Swallow
☎ (020) 7734 1401, *Fax (020) 7439 8434* – ▤. MC AE ⓓ VISA JCB p. 33 **EM**
closed dinner 25 December – **Meals** - Indian - 14.00 **t.** (lunch) and a la carte 19.25/27.5
🌡 8.50.

X **The Cafe** (at Sotheby's), 34-35 New Bond St., W1A 2AA, ☎ (020) 7293 50
Fax (020) 7293 5920 – ⊭. MC AE ⓓ VISA p. 33 **DL**
closed 2 weeks August, 2 weeks Christmas, Saturday and Sunday – **Meals** (booking ess
tial) (lunch only) a la carte 18.95/25.40 **st.**

X **Zinc Bar & Grill,** 21 Heddon St., W1R 7LF, ☎ (020) 7255 8899, *Fax (020) 7255 8888* – MC
ⓓ VISA JCB p. 33 **EM**
closed 25-26 December, Sunday and Bank Holidays – **Meals** 14.50 **t.** (lunch) and a la ca
16.95/29.25 **t.**

Regent's Park and Marylebone – ✉ *NW1/NW6/NW8/W1.*

🏨 **Landmark London,** 222 Marylebone Rd, NW1 6JQ, ☎ (020) 7631 8000, *reservations*
elandmark.co.uk, Fax (020) 7631 8080, « Victorian Gothic architecture, atrium and wir
garden », Fδ, ≘s, 🏊 – |$|, ⊭ rm, ▤ TV ☎ ♿ 🚗 – 🏛 350. MC AE ⓓ VISA JCB. ✂
Winter Garden* :** **Meals** 22.50 **t.** and a la carte – (see also ***John Burton-Race below) –
17.95 – **290 rm** 285.00/305.00 **s.**, 9 suites. p. 25 **HU**

🏨 **Churchill Inter-Continental London,** 30 Portman Sq., W1A 4ZX, ☎ (020) 7486 58
churchill@interconti.com, Fax (020) 7486 1255, 🎾 – |$|, ⊭ rm, ▤ TV ☎ ♿ – 🏛 300. MC
ⓓ VISA JCB. ✂ p. 32 **AJ**
***Clementine's* :** **Meals** *(closed Saturday lunch)* 19.00/24.00 **st.** and a la carte – ☕ 18.7
401 rm 300.00 **s.**, 40 suites.

🏨 **Langham Hilton,** 1c Portland Pl., Regent St., W1N 4JA, ☎ (020) 7636 1000, *langham*
ton.com, Fax (020) 7323 2340 – |$|, ⊭ rm, ▤ TV ☎ ♿ – 🏛 250. MC AE ⓓ VISA J
✂ p. 25 **JU**
***Memories* :** **Meals** 32.00 **t.** (lunch) and a la carte 30.00/53.25 **t.** 🌡 10.50 – ***Tsar's* :** **Mea**
Russian - *(closed Sunday)* a la carte 25.00/31.00 **t.** 🌡 10.50 – ☕ 19.75 – **379 rm** 295.0
18 suites.

🏨 **Selfridge Thistle,** Orchard St., W1H 0JS, ☎ (020) 7408 2080, *selfridgehotel@cax.com*
nk.co.uk, Fax (020) 7629 8849 – |$|, ⊭ rm, ▤ TV – 🏛 250. MC AE ⓓ VISA JCB. ✂
***Fletchers* :** **Meals** (dinner only) 18.50 **t.** and a la carte – ***Orchard Terrace* :** **Meals** (lu
only) 15.00 **t.** and a la carte – **290 rm** ☕ 202.00/247.00 **t.**, 4 suites. p. 32 **AK**

🏨 **Sanderson,** 50 Berners St., W1P 3NG, ☎ (020) 7300 1400, *reservation@sanderson.sch*
erhotels.com, Fax (020) 7300 1401, 🏠, « Contemporary interior », Fδ – |$|, ⊭ rm, ▤
☎. MC AE ⓓ VISA JCB. ✂ p. 33 **EJ**
***Spoon+* :** **Meals** 45.00/70.00 **t.** and a la carte 🌡 33.00 – ☕ 19.00 – **150 rm** 270.00/295.0

Charlotte Street, 15 Charlotte St., W1P 1HB, ☎ (020) 7806 2000, *charlotte@firmdale.com, Fax (020) 7806 2002,* « Modern English interior », – |‡|, ▤ TV ☎. MC AE VISA JCB. ✂ p. 26 KU v
Oscar : Meals *(closed Sunday)* a la carte 24.50/35.50 **t.** – ☕ 16.50 – **44 rm** 175.00/280.00 **s.**, 8 suites.

The Leonard, 15 Seymour St., W1H 5AA, ☎ (020) 7935 2010, *theleonard@dial.pipex.com, Fax (020) 7935 6700,* « Attractively furnished Georgian town houses », – |‡| ▤ TV ☎. MC AE ⓓ VISA JCB. ✂ p. 32 AK n
Meals (room service only) – ☕ 17.00 – **9 rm** 180.00/200.00 **s.**, **20 suites** 250.00/500.00 **s.**

Radisson SAS Portman, 22 Portman Sq., W1H 9BG, ☎ (020) 7208 6000, *sales@lonza.rdsas.com, Fax (020) 7208 6001,* – |‡|, rm, ▤ TV ☎ – 650. MC AE ⓓ VISA JCB. ✂ p. 32 AJ o
Portman Corner : Meals (buffet lunch)/dinner 12.00/20.00 **t.** (dinner) and a la carte approx. 23.50 **t.** 11.50 – ☕ 17.50 – **265 rm** 190.00/200.00, 7 suites – SB.

Montcalm, Great Cumberland Pl., W1A 2LF, ☎ (020) 7402 4288, *montcalm@montcalm.co.uk, Fax (020) 7724 9180* – |‡|, rm, ▤ TV ☎ – 80. MC AE ⓓ VISA JCB p. 37 EZ x
Meals – (see ***The Crescent*** below) – ☕ 17.95 – **110 rm** 220.00/330.00 **s.**, 10 suites.

Jarvis International Regents Park, 18 Lodge Rd, NW8 7JT, ☎ (020) 7722 7722, *regentspark@jarvis.co.uk, Fax (020) 7483 2408* – |‡|, rm, ▤ TV P – 150. MC AE ⓓ VISA JCB. ✂ p. 25 GT v
Minsky's : Meals 19.50/20.95 **t.** and a la carte 7.25 – ***Kashinoki*** : Meals - Japanese - *(closed Monday)* 18.00/32.00 **st.** and a la carte 9.00 – ☕ 16.50 – **376 rm** 199.00 **st.**, 1 suite.

Clifton Ford, 47 Welbeck St., W1M 8DN, ☎ (020) 7486 6600, *cliftonford-hotel@jurysdoyle.com, Fax (020) 7486 7492* – |‡| ▤ TV ☎ & – 150. MC AE ⓓ VISA JCB. ✂ p. 32 BH a
closed 25-26 December – **Meals** a la carte 17.25/28.75 **st.** 10.00 – ☕ 12.95 – **184 rm** 205.00/215.00 **t.**, 2 suites.

Berners, 10 Berners St., W1A 3BE, ☎ (020) 7666 2000, *berners@berners.co.uk, Fax (020) 7666 2001* – |‡|, rm, ▤ rest, TV & – 150. MC AE ⓓ VISA JCB. ✂
Meals (carving lunch) a la carte 22.00/33.45 **t.** 7.95 – ☕ 15.95 – **214 rm** 170.00/250.00 **st.**, 3 suites. p. 33 EJ r

London Marriott Marble Arch, 134 George St., W1H 6DN, ☎ (020) 7723 1277, *Fax (020) 7402 0666,* – |‡|, rm, ▤ TV ☎ & P – 150. MC AE ⓓ VISA. ✂
Meals *(closed lunch Saturday and Sunday)* 19.95 **t.** and a la carte 8.45 – ☕ 15.95 – **240 rm** 140.00 **s.** p. 37 EZ i

Posthouse Regent's Park, Carburton St., W1W 5EE, ☎ (0870) 400 9111, *Fax (020) 7387 2806* – |‡|, rm, ▤ rest, TV – 350. MC AE ⓓ VISA JCB. ✂ p. 25 JU i
Meals 13.60/16.25 **t.** and a la carte 6.95 – ☕ 11.95 – **326 rm** 149.00/169.00 **st.** – SB.

Berkshire, 350 Oxford St., W1N 0BY, ☎ (020) 7629 7474, *resberk@radisson.com, Fax (020) 7629 8156* – |‡|, rm, ▤ TV ☎ – 40. MC AE ⓓ VISA JCB. ✂ p. 32 BK n
Meals a la carte 27.50/35.00 **st.** 8.00 – ☕ 15.00 – **145 rm** 240.00/310.00 **s.**, 2 suites – SB.

Dorset Square, 39-40 Dorset Sq., NW1 6QN, ☎ (020) 7723 7874, *dorset@firmdale.com, Fax (020) 7724 3328,* « Attractively furnished Regency town houses », – |‡| ▤ TV ☎. MC AE VISA JCB. ✂ p. 25 HU s
The Potting Shed : **Meals** *(closed Saturday lunch and Sunday)* 16.95/22.50 **t.** and a la carte 12.00 – ☕ 14.00 – **38 rm** 98.00/240.00 **s.**

Durrants, 26-32 George St., W1H 5BJ, ☎ (020) 7935 8131, *enquiries@durrants.co.uk, Fax (020) 7487 3510,* « Converted Georgian houses with Regency façade » – |‡|, ▤ rest, TV – 100. MC AE VISA. ✂ p. 32 AH e
Meals 17.50/19.50 **t.** and a la carte 9.50 – ☕ 13.50 – **88 rm** 97.50/140.00 **st.**, 4 suites.

Jarvis Marylebone, Harewood Row, NW1 6SE, ☎ (020) 7262 2707, *Fax (020) 7262 2975* – |‡|, rm, ▤ rest, TV ☎. MC AE ⓓ VISA. ✂ p. 25 HU x
closed 23-26 December – **Meals** (bar lunch)/dinner a la carte approx. 19.00 **t.** – ☕ 10.75 – **92 rm** 125.00/165.00 **st.**

Hart House without rest., 51 Gloucester Pl., W1U 8JF, ☎ (020) 7935 2288, *Fax (020) 7935 8516* – TV. MC AE VISA. ✂ p. 32 AH a
15 rm ☕ 70.00/98.00 **st.**

John Burton-Race (at Landmark London H.), 222 Marylebone Rd, NW1 6JQ, ☎ (020) 7723 7800, *jbrthelandmark@btconnect.co.uk, Fax (020) 7723 4700* – ▤. MC AE ⓓ VISA p. 25 HU a
closed Saturday lunch and Sunday dinner – **Meals** - French - 28.00/45.00 **t.** and a la carte 62.00/84.00 **t.** 15.00
Spec. Ravioli of langoustine, truffle scented potato, Madeira jus. Roast poussin with foie gras, baby spinach and Sauternes sauce. Plate of chocolate desserts.

XXX **Orrery,** 55 Marylebone High St., W1M 3AE, ☎ (020) 7616 8000, *Fax (020) 7616 80*
« Converted 19C stables, contemporary interior » – |‡|. MC AE D VISA JCB p. 25 **IU**
✿ *closed 25 December and 1-3 January* – **Meals** (booking essential) 23.50 (lunch) and a la carte 32.50/48.50 **t.** 🌢 19.50
Spec. Cannelloni of lobster with vine tomatoes. Fillet of beef with artichoke, parsley oil a Burgundy jus. Millefeuille of strawberries and green peppercorns.

XX **The Crescent** (at Montcalm H.), Great Cumberland Pl., W1A 2LF, ☎ (020) 7402 4288, *re rvations@montcalm.co.uk, Fax (020) 7724 9180* – ▤. MC AE D VISA JCB p. 37 **EZ**
closed lunch Saturday and Sunday – **Meals** 20.00/25.00 **st.**.

XX **Nico Central,** 35 Great Portland St., W1N 5DD, ☎ (020) 7436 8846, *Fax (020) 7436 345*
▤. MC AE D VISA p. 33 **DJ**
closed Christmas, Sunday and Bank Holidays – **Meals** 14.50/18.50 **t.** (lunch) and a la ca 26.00/33.00 **t.** 🌢 10.00.

XX **Ozer,** 4-5 Langham Pl., Regent St., W1N 7DD, ☎ (020) 7323 0505, *res@ozer.co.*
Fax (020) 7323 0111 – ▤. MC AE D VISA p. 25 **JU**
closed 25-26 December – **Meals** - Turkish - 17.95 **t.** (lunch) and dinner a la carte 20.C 33.00 **t.**

XX **Rasa Samudra,** 5 Charlotte St., W1P 1HD, ☎ (020) 7637 0222, *Fax (020) 7637 0224* –
MC AE D VISA JCB p. 26 **KU**
closed 24-31 December – **Meals** - Indian Seafood and Vegetarian - a la carte 12.75/23.95 🌢 8.50.

XX **La Porte des Indes,** 32 Bryanston St., W1H 7AE, ☎ (020) 7224 0055, *pilondon@aol.co*
Fax (020) 7224 1144 – ▤. MC AE D VISA JCB p. 32 **AK**
closed 25-26 December, 1 January and Saturday lunch – **Meals** - Indian - 29.00/33.00 and a la carte.

XX **Rosmarino,** 1 Blenheim Terr., NW8 0EH, ☎ (020) 7328 5014, *Fax (020) 7625 2639*,
▤. MC AE VISA p. 24 **FS**
closed 1 week Christmas – **Meals** - Italian - 19.00/24.00 **t.** 🌢 7.25.

XX **Stephen Bull,** 5-7 Blandford St., W1U 3DB, ☎ (020) 7486 9696, *sbull@compuserve.co*
Fax (020) 7490 3128 – ▤. MC AE D VISA p. 32 **BH**
closed 1 week Christmas, Saturday dinner, Sunday and Bank Holidays – **Meals** a la ca 18.40/26.50 **t.** 🌢 6.00.

XX **Levant,** Jason Court, 76 Wigmore St., W1H 9DQ, ☎ (020) 7224 1111, *Fax (020) 7486 121*
▤. MC AE D VISA JCB p. 32 **BJ**
closed Saturday lunch, Sunday and Bank Holidays – **Meals** - Eastern Mediterranean 12.50/15.50 **t.** (lunch) and a la carte approx. 24.00 **t.** 🌢 8.00.

XX **Caldesi,** 15-17 Marylebone Lane, W1M 5FE, ☎ (020) 7935 9226, *Fax (020) 7935 9228* –
MC AE D VISA JCB p. 32 **BJ**
closed Saturday lunch, Sunday and Bank Holidays – **Meals** - Italian - a la carte 18.50/28.0

XX **Bertorelli's,** (first floor), 19-23 Charlotte St., W1P 1HP, ☎ (020) 7636 41
Fax (020) 7467 8902 – ▤. MC AE D VISA p. 26 **KU**
closed 25 December, Easter and Sunday – **Meals** - Italian - a la carte 18.35/25.65 **t.**

XX **Asuka,** Berkeley Arcade, 209a Baker St., NW1 6AB, ☎ (020) 7486 5026, *Fax (020) 7224 1*
– MC AE VISA JCB p. 25 **HU**
closed Sunday, Saturday lunch and Bank Holidays – **Meals** - Japanese - 14.50/23.90 and a la carte.

XX **L'Aventure,** 3 Blenheim Terr., NW8 0EH, ☎ (020) 7624 6232, *Fax (020) 7625 5548*,
MC AE VISA p. 24 **FS**
closed 1-15 January, Sunday except Easter and lunch Saturday – **Meals** - French - 18. 27.50 **t.** and lunch a la carte 🌢 7.50.

X **Mash,** 19-21 Great Portland St., W1M JD8, ☎ (020) 7637 5555, *Fax (020) 7637 7333* –
MC AE D VISA p. 33 **DJ**
closed Sunday dinner and Bank Holidays – **Meals** (booking essential) a la carte 22. 33.00 **t.**

X **Purple Sage,** 92 Wigmore St., WIH 9DR, ☎ (020) 7486 1912, *Fax (020) 7486 1913* – ▤.
AE VISA JCB p. 32 **BJ**
closed 25-26 December, Easter, Saturday lunch and Sunday – **Meals** - Italian - 15.5C (lunch) and a la carte 16.00/25.50 **t.**

X **Ibla,** 89 Marylebone High St., W1M 3DE, ☎ (020) 7224 3799, *ibla@ibla.co.*
Fax (020) 7486 1370 – MC AE VISA JCB p. 25 **IU**
closed 1 week Christmas, Sunday and Bank Holidays – **Meals** - Italian - 18.00/27.0 🌢 13.00.

X **Villandry,** 170 Great Portland St., W1N 5TB, ☎ (020) 7631 3131, *Fax (020) 7631 3030* –
▤. MC AE VISA p. 25 **JU**
closed 25 December, 1 January, Sunday dinner and Bank Holidays – **Meals** 15.00/25.00 (lunch) and a la carte 24.00/27.00 **st.**

Union Café, 96 Marylebone Lane, W1M 5FP, ☎ (020) 7486 4860, *Fax (020) 7486 4860* – MC AE VISA JCB p. 32 **BH c**
closed Christmas, New Year, Sunday and Bank Holidays – **Meals** a la carte 20.50/26.50 **t.** 4.00.

Chada Chada, 16-17 Picton Pl., W1M 5DE, ☎ (020) 7935 8212, *Fax (020) 7924 2178* – ▤. MC AE D VISA JCB p. 32 **BJ i**
closed Sunday and Bank Holidays – **Meals** - Thai - a la carte 10.95/29.45 **t.**

R K Stanleys, 6 Little Portland St., W1N 5NG, ☎ (020) 7462 0099, *fred@rkstanleys.co.uk, Fax (020) 7462 0088* – ▤. MC AE D VISA p. 25 **JU a**
closed Sunday – **Meals** - specialising in sausages - a la carte 14.25/20.45 **t.**

The Salt House, 63 Abbey Rd, NW8 0AE, ☎ (020) 7328 6626, *Fax (020) 7625 9168,* – ▤. MC AE VISA p. 24 **FS z**
closed Monday lunch – **Meals** (booking essential) 9.75 **t.** (lunch) and a la carte 14.65/23.70 **t.**

St. James's – ✉ *W1/SW1/WC2.*

Ritz, 150 Piccadilly, W1J 9BR, ☎ (020) 7493 8181, *enquire@theritzhotel.co.uk, Fax (020) 7493 2687,* – , rm, ▤ TV – 50. MC AE D VISA JCB. p. 33 **DN a**
Meals – (see ***The Restaurant*** below) – 22.50 – **115 rm** 295.00/385.00, 18 suites – SB.

Dukes, 35 St. James's Pl., SW1A 1NY, ☎ (020) 7491 4840, *enquiries@dukeshotel.co.uk, Fax (020) 7493 1264,* – , rest, ▤ TV – 50. MC AE D VISA JCB.
Meals *(closed lunch Saturday)* (residents only) 19.50 **t.** (lunch) and dinner a la carte 32.50/39.00 **t.** 9.00 – 14.75 – **82 rm** 195.00/260.00 **s.**, 7 suites. p. 33 **EP x**

Stafford, 16-18 St. James's Pl., SW1A 1NJ, ☎ (020) 7493 0111, *info@thestaffordhotel.co.uk, Fax (020) 7493 7121* – ▤ TV – 40. MC AE D VISA JCB p. 33 **DN u**
Meals a la carte 32.00/50.00 **t.** – 16.00 – **75 rm** 260.00 **s.**, 6 suites.

Cavendish, 81 Jermyn St., SW1Y 6JF, ☎ (020) 7930 2111, *guests@cavendishstjames.co.uk, Fax (020) 7839 2125* – , rm, ▤ rest, TV – 80. MC AE D VISA JCB.
Meals *(closed lunch Saturday and Sunday)* 21.50 **t.** (lunch) and a la carte 26.00/38.00 **t.** 9.95 – 14.95 – **249 rm** 175.00/195.00 **st.**, 2 suites – SB. p. 33 **EN i**

22 Jermyn Street, 22 Jermyn St., SW1Y 6HL, ☎ (020) 7734 2353, *office@22jermyn.com, Fax (020) 7734 0750* – ▤ TV . MC AE D VISA JCB. p. 33 **FM e**
Meals (room service only) – 17.00 – **5 rm** 205.00 **s.**, **13 suites** 290.00/325.00 **s.**

Pastoria, 3-6 St. Martin's St., off Leicester Sq., WC2H 7HL, ☎ (020) 7930 8641, *Fax (020) 7925 0551,* – , rm, ▤ rest, TV – 60. MC AE D VISA JCB. p. 33 **GM v**
Meals a la carte 28.45/39.95 **st.** 8.75 – 12.00 – **58 rm** 195.00/229.00 **s.** – SB.

Trafalgar Square Thistle, Whitcomb St., WC2H 7HG, ☎ (020) 7930 4477, *trafalgar.square@thistle.co.uk, Fax (020) 7925 2149* – , rm, ▤ rest, TV . MC AE D VISA JCB. p. 33 **GM r**
Meals 10.50/14.50 **st.** and a la carte 7.95 – 14.50 – **124 rm** 160.00/216.00 **st.**

Piccadilly Thistle without rest., 39 Coventry St., W1V 7FH, ☎ (020) 7930 4033, *Fax (020) 7925 2586* – TV. MC AE D VISA JCB. p. 33 **FGM a**
14.50 – **91 rm** 187.00/223.00 **t.**

The Restaurant (at Ritz H.), 150 Piccadilly, W1V 9DG, ☎ (020) 7493 8181, *Fax (020) 7493 2687,* , « Elegant restaurant in Louis XVI style » – ▤. MC AE D VISA JCB
Meals (dancing Friday and Saturday evenings) 35.00/43.00-59.00 **st.** and a la carte 46.00/53.50 **st.** 13.00. p. 33 **DN a**

Pétrus, 33 St. James's St., SW1A 1HD, ☎ (020) 7930 4272, *Fax (020) 7930 9702* – ▤. MC AE D VISA JCB p. 33 **EN v**
closed 1 week Christmas, Sunday, Saturday lunch and Bank Holidays – **Meals** (booking essential) 24.00/40.00-50.00 **t.** 13.00
Spec. Ravioli of quail with foie gras velouté. Braised halibut with caramelised orange chicory, Sauternes sauce. Iced coconut cream, warm chocolate sauce.

L'Oranger, 5 St. James's St., SW1A 1EF, ☎ (020) 7839 3774, *Fax (020) 7839 4330* – ▤. MC AE D VISA JCB p. 33 **EP a**
closed Christmas-New Year, Saturday lunch, Sunday and Bank Holidays – **Meals** 24.50/37.00 **st.** 18.00
Spec. Salt cod and potato tart with shallots. Magret of duck, fondant potato and foie gras sauce. Roast monkfish tail with spinach and antiboise sauce.

Orient, 160 Piccadilly (1st floor), W1V 9DF, ☎ (020) 7499 6888, *Fax (020) 7659 9300* – ▤. MC AE VISA p. 33 **DN i**
closed Saturday lunch and Sunday – **Meals** - Chinese - a la carte 30.00/65.00 **st.**

XXX **Suntory,** 72-73 St. James's St., SW1A 1PH, ☎ (020) 7409 0201, *Fax (020) 7499 0208* – MC AE (D) VISA JCB p. 33 EP
closed Easter, Christmas-New Year, Sunday lunch and Bank Holidays – **Meals** - Japanese 17.00/50.00 **st.** and a la carte 16.00.

XX **Quaglino's,** 16 Bury St., SW1Y 6AL, ☎ (020) 7930 6767, *Fax (020) 7839 2866* – MC AE VISA p. 33 EN
closed 25 December – **Meals** (booking essential) 15.00 **t.** (lunch) and a la carte 22.0 43.00 **t.**

XX **Criterion Brasserie Marco Pierre White,** 224 Piccadilly, W1J 9H ☎ (020) 7930 0488, *Fax (020) 7930 8380,* « 19C neo-Byzantine decor » – ▤. MC AE (D) JCB p. 33 FM
closed 25-26 December and Sunday lunch – **Meals** 17.95 **t.** (lunch) and a la carte 28.7 49.75 **t.** 11.00.

XX **Le Caprice,** Arlington House, Arlington St., SW1A 1RT, ☎ (020) 7629 22 *Fax (020) 7493 9040* – ▤. MC AE (D) VISA JCB p. 33 DN
closed dinner 24-26 and 31 December, 1 January and August Bank Holiday – **Mea** a la carte 26.25/44.40 **t.** 9.25.

XX **Café de Nikolaj,** 161 Piccadilly, W1V 9DF, ☎ (020) 7409 0445, *Fax (020) 7493 1667* – MC AE (D) VISA JCB p. 33 DN
closed 5 January-5 February – **Meals** - caviar specialities - 22.50/24.50 **t.** and a la car 12.00.

XX **Che,** 23 St. James's St., SW1A 1HE, ☎ (020) 7747 9380, *Fax (020) 7747 9389* – |‡| ▤. MC (D) VISA p. 33 EN
closed 25 December, 1 January, Saturday lunch and Sunday – **Meals** 15.50/17.95 (lunch) and a la carte 23.00/31.00 **t.**

XX **The Avenue,** 7-9 St. James's St., SW1A 1EE, ☎ (020) 7321 2111, *Fax (020) 7321 2500* – MC AE (D) VISA p. 33 EP
closed 24-26 December – **Meals** 19.50 **t.** (lunch) and dinner a la carte 26.00/31.75 **t.**

XX **Matsuri,** 15 Bury St., SW1Y 6AL, ☎ (020) 7839 1101, *Fax (020) 7930 7010* – ▤. MC AE VISA JCB p. 33 EN
closed Sunday and Bank Holidays – **Meals** - Japanese (Teppan-Yaki, Sushi) - 20.00/70.00 and a la carte 12.00.

X **Al Duca,** 4-5 Duke of York St., SW1Y 6LA, ☎ (020) 7839 3090, *Fax (020) 7839 4050* – ▤. AE VISA JCB p. 33 EN
closed Sunday – **Meals** - Italian - 18.50/21.00 **t.** 12.50.

X **China House,** 160 Piccadilly, W1V 9DF, ☎ (020) 7499 6996, *chinahouse@chinahouse.co k, Fax (020) 7499 7779,* « Former bank » – MC AE VISA p. 33 DN
Meals - Chinese - a la carte 13.00/16.00 **t.**

Soho – ✉ *W1/WC2.*

Hampshire, Leicester Sq., WC2H 7LH, ☎ (020) 7839 9399, *Fax (020) 7930 8122,* |‡|, ⇶ rm, ▤ TV ☎ – 100. MC AE (D) VISA JCB. p. 33 GM
The Apex : **Meals** a la carte 29.95/39.95 **st.** 12.25 – 15.00 – **119 rm** 305.00/399.00 5 suites – SB.

Hazlitt's without rest., 6 Frith St., W1V 5TZ, ☎ (020) 7434 1771, *reservations@hazlitts. uk, Fax (020) 7439 1524,* « Early 18C town houses » – TV ☎. MC AE (D) VISA JCB
closed 24-25 December – **22 rm** 140.00/175.00 **s.**, 1 suite. p. 33 FK

XXX **L'Escargot,** 48 Greek St., W1V 5LQ, ☎ (020) 7437 2679, *Fax (020) 7437 0790* – ▤. MC (D) VISA JCB p. 33 GK
Ground Floor : **Meals** *(closed 25-26 December, 1 January, Sunday and Saturday lun* 17.95 **t.** (lunch) and a la carte 22.65/31.65 **t.** 15.00 – ***Picasso Room*** « Collection of lim ed edition Picasso art » **: Meals** *(closed 25-26 December, 1 January, August, Sunc Monday, Saturday lunch and Bank Holidays)* 29.50/42.00 **t.** 12.00
Spec. "Escargot" tartlet. Roast fillet of sea bass, velouté of crab, beignet of oyste Chocolate truffle cake.

XXX **Quo Vadis,** 26-29 Dean St., W1V 6LL, ☎ (020) 7437 9585, *Fax (020) 7734 7593* – ▤. MC (D) VISA p. 33 FK
closed 24-26 December, 1 January, Sunday and Saturday lunch – **Meals** 17.95 (lunch) and a la carte 28.50/40.00 **t.** 8.50.

XX **Richard Corrigan at Lindsay House,** 21 Romilly St., W1V 5TG, ☎ (020) 7439 04 *Fax (020) 7437 7349* – ▤. MC AE (D) VISA JCB p. 33 GL
closed 23 December-2 January, last week August, first week September, Sunday a Saturday lunch – **Meals** 23.00/44.00 **t.** 15.00
Spec. Ballottine of duck foie gras with celeriac cream. Saddle of rabbit with black pudd and mustard juices. Mango with rhubarb compote and vanilla ice cream.

XX **Teatro,** 93-107 Shaftesbury Av., W1V 8BT, ☎ (020) 7494 3040, *Fax (020) 7494 3050* – ▤. MC AE ① VISA JCB p. 33 **GL** e
closed 1 week Christmas, Sunday, Bank Holiday Monday and Saturday lunch – **Meals** 18.00 **t.** (lunch) and dinner a la carte 23.75/40.00 **t.** 🍷 6.75.

XX **The Sugar Club,** 21 Warwick St., W1R 5RB, ☎ (020) 7437 7776, *Fax (020) 7437 7778* – ⇔. MC AE ① VISA p. 33 **EL** r
closed 25-26 December and 1 January – **Meals** a la carte 29.40/42.50 **t.** 🍷 8.75.

XX **Circus,** 1 Upper James St., W1F 4DF, ☎ (020) 7534 4000, *circus@egami.co.uk, Fax (020) 7534 4010* – ▤. MC AE ① VISA p. 33 **EL** e
closed 25-26 December, Easter Monday, Sunday and lunch Saturday and Bank Holidays – **Meals** 12.50 **t.** (lunch) and dinner a la carte 24.20/32.75 **t.** 🍷 7.25.

XX **Seven,** One Leicester Sq., WC2H 7NO, ☎ (020) 7909 1177, *Fax (020) 7909 1178*, ≤ London skyline, 斧 – |‡|. MC AE VISA p. 33 **GM** e
closed Sunday and Saturday lunch – **Meals** 14.50/17.50 **t.** (lunch) and a la carte 24.00/46.00 **t.**

X **Il Forno,** 63-64 Frith St., W1V 5TA, ☎ (020) 7734 4545, *Fax (020) 7287 8624* – ▤. MC AE VISA JCB p. 33 **FJK** n
closed Christmas, New Year, lunch Saturday and Sunday and Bank Holidays – **Meals** - Italian - a la carte 15.00/25.00 **st.** 🍷 7.50.

XX **Mezzo,** Lower ground floor, 100 Wardour St., W1F 0TN, ☎ (020) 7314 4000, *Fax (020) 7314 4040* – ▤. MC AE ① VISA JCB p. 33 **FK** a
closed 25-26 December and lunch Monday, Tuesday and Saturday – **Meals** 15.50 **t.** (lunch) and a la carte 19.50/32.50 **t.**

XX **Soho Soho,** First floor, 11-13 Frith St., W1V 5TS, ☎ (020) 7494 3491, *Fax (020) 7437 3091*, 斧 – ▤. MC AE ① VISA p. 33 **FK** s
closed Good Friday, 25 December and Sunday – **Meals** a la carte 22.90/29.45 **t.**

XX **The Lexington,** 45 Lexington St., W1R 3LG, ☎ (020) 7434 3401, *Fax (020) 7287 2997* – ▤. MC AE ① VISA JCB p. 33 **EK** e
closed Sunday, Saturday lunch and Bank Holidays – **Meals** a la carte 17.00/23.50 **t.**

X **Alastair Little,** 49 Frith St., W1V 5TE, ☎ (020) 7734 5183, *Fax (020) 7734 5206* – ▤. MC AE ① VISA JCB p. 33 **FK** o
closed 25-26 December, 1 January, Sunday, Saturday lunch and Bank Holidays – **Meals** (booking essential) 25.00/33.00 **t.** 🍷 7.00.

X **Sugar Reef,** 42-44 Great Windmill St., W1V 7PA, ☎ (020) 7851 0800 – ▤. MC AE ① VISA
closed 25 December, Sunday, Saturday lunch and Bank Holidays – **Meals** 14.95 **t.** (lunch) and a la carte 21.95/39.95 **t.** p. 33 **FLM** r

X **Vasco and Piero's Pavilion,** 15 Poland St., W1V 3DE, ☎ (020) 7437 8774, *Fax (020) 7437 0467* – ▤. MC AE ① VISA JCB p. 33 **EJK** i
closed 25-26 December, Sunday, Saturday lunch and Bank Holidays – **Meals** - Italian - (lunch booking essential) 18.50 **t.** (dinner) and lunch a la carte 25.00/31.00 **t.** 🍷 5.50.

X **Sri Siam,** 16 Old Compton St., W1V 5PE, ☎ (020) 7434 3544, *Fax (020) 7287 1311* – ▤. MC AE ① VISA JCB p. 33 **GK** r
closed 25-26 December, 1 January and Sunday lunch – **Meals** - Thai - 14.00/27.95 **t.** and a la carte.

X **Aurora,** 49 Lexington St., W1F 9AP, ☎ (020) 7494 0514, *Fax (020) 7494 4357*, 斧 – MC VISA JCB p. 33 **EK** e
closed Christmas-New Year, Easter, Sunday and Bank Holidays – **Meals** (booking essential) a la carte approx. 21.00 **t.**

X **Soho Spice,** 124-126 Wardour St., W1V 3LA, ☎ (020) 7434 0808, *info@sohospice.co.uk, Fax (020) 7434 0799* – ⇔ ▤. MC AE VISA p. 33 **FJ** e
closed 25 December – **Meals** - Indian - (bookings not accepted) 7.50/15.95 **t.** and a la carte.

X **Fung Shing,** 15 Lisle St., WC2H 7BE, ☎ (020) 7734 0284, *Fax (020) 7734 0284* – ▤. MC AE ① VISA p. 33 **GL** a
closed 24-26 December and lunch Bank Holidays – **Meals** - Chinese (Canton) - 16.00/30.00 **t.** and a la carte 🍷 6.00.

X **Saigon,** 45 Frith St., W1V 5TE, ☎ (020) 7437 7109, *Fax (020) 7734 1668* – ▤. MC AE ① VISA p. 33 **FGK** x
closed Christmas, Easter, 25-26 December, Sunday and Bank Holidays – **Meals** - Vietnamese - a la carte approx. 16.55 **t.**

rand and Covent Garden – ✉ *WC2.*

Savoy, Strand, WC2R 0EU, ☎ (020) 7836 4343, *info@thesavoy.co.uk, Fax (020) 7240 6040*, Lö, ≘, ◙ – |‡|, ⇔ rm, ▤ TV ☎ ⇔ – 🔏 500. MC AE ① VISA JCB. ✈
***River*:** Meals 29.75/44.50 **t.** and a la carte 43.00/65.50 **t.** 🍷 10.00 – ***Grill*:** Meals *(closed August, Sunday, Saturday lunch and Bank Holidays)* a la carte 35.00/67.50 **t.** – ☕ 22.00 – **159 rm** 280.00/370.00 **s.**, 48 suites – SB. p. 37 **DEY** a

Le Meridien Waldorf, Aldwych, WC2B 4DD, ✆ (0870) 400 8484, *Fax (020) 7836 7244* – |‡|, ⇹ rm, ▤ rm, TV ✆ – 450. MC AE ① VISA JCB. ✻ p. 33 **EX**
Palm Court : Meals *(closed Sunday and Lunch Saturday)* 16.95 **t.** and a la carte 12.00 – ***Spices :*** Meals a la carte 15.50/24.20 **t.** 12.00 – ⊒ 18.00 – **286 rm** 240.00/270.00 6 suites.

Swissôtel London, The Howard, Temple Pl., WC2R 2PR, ✆ (020) 7836 3555, *email @swissotel.com, Fax (020) 7300 0234,* ←, ☂ – |‡|, ⇹ rm, ▤ TV ✆ 🚗 – 150. MC AE ① VISA JCB. ✻ p. 33 **EX**
Meals 26.00/35.00 **st.** and a la carte 9.00 – ⊒ 23.50 – **127 rm** 265.00 **s.**, 8 suites.

One Aldwych, 1 Aldwych, WC2B 4BZ, ✆ (020) 7300 1000, *sales@onealdwych.co.uk, Fax (020) 7300 1001,* « Contemporary interior », 🏋, ≘s, ⊠ – |‡|, ⇹ rm, ▤ TV ✆ ♿ – 100. MC AE ① VISA JCB. ✻ p. 33 **EX**
Indigo : Meals a la carte 23.25/30.25 **t.** 7.50 – (see also ***Axis*** below) – ⊒ 17.50 – **96 rm** 275.00/335.00 **s.**, 9 suites.

St. Martins Lane, 45 St. Martin's Lane, WC2N 4HX, ✆ (020) 7300 5500, *stmartinslane@mpuserve.com, Fax (020) 7300 5515,* ☂, « Contemporary interior », 🏋 – |‡| ▤ TV ✆ 🚗 MC AE ① VISA JCB. ✻ p. 37 **DY**
Asia de Cuba : Meals - Asian - a la carte approx. 35.00 **t.** 10.00 – ***Saint M's :*** Meals a la carte approx. 40.00 **t.** 12.00 – ***Seabar :*** Meals - Seafood - *(closed Sunday)* (dinner only) a la carte approx. 40.00 **t.** 10.50 – ⊒ 17.50 – **200 rm** 255.00/275.00 **s.**, 4 suites.

XXX **Ivy,** 1 West St., WC2H 9NE, ✆ (020) 7836 4751, *Fax (020) 7240 9333* – ▤. MC AE ① VISA JCB p. 33 **GK**
closed dinner 24-26 and 31 December, 1 January and August Bank Holiday – **Meals** a la carte 25.75/46.25 **t.** 9.25.

XXX **Axis,** 1 Aldwych, WC2B 4BZ, ✆ (020) 7300 0300, *sales@onealdwych.co.uk, Fax (020) 7300 0301* – ▤. MC AE ① VISA JCB p. 37 **EX**
closed Sunday, Saturday lunch and Bank Holidays – **Meals** 23.75 **t.** (lunch) and a la carte 25.90/30.25 **t.** 10.00.

XX **J. Sheekey,** 28-32 St. Martin's Court, WC2N 4AL, ✆ (020) 7240 2565, *Fax (020) 7240 81..* – ▤. MC AE ① VISA JCB p. 37 **DX**
closed dinner 24 to 26 December, 1 January, Easter Monday, 1 May and August Bank Holiday – **Meals** - Seafood - (booking essential) a la carte 22.00/64.25 9.75.

XX **Rules,** 35 Maiden Lane, WC2E 7LB, ✆ (020) 7836 5314, *Fax (020) 7497 1081,* « London's oldest restaurant with collection of antique cartoons, drawings and paintings » – ⇹. MC AE ① VISA JCB p. 37 **DX**
closed 4 days Christmas – **Meals** - English - a la carte 29.40/34.40 **t.**

XX **The Admiralty,** Somerset House, The Strand, WC2R 1LA, ✆ (020) 7845 464.. *Fax (020) 7845 4647* – ⇹. MC AE ① VISA p. 37 **EY**
Meals - French - (booking essential) a la carte 28.00/41.50 **t.**

XX **Bank,** 1 Kingsway, Aldwych, WC2B 6UA, ✆ (020) 7234 3344, *bank@bgr.plc.uk, Fax (020) 7234 3343* – ▤. MC AE ① VISA p. 37 **EX**
closed 25 December, and Bank Holidays – **Meals** 17.50 **t.** (lunch) and a la carte 21.00/31.00 **t.**

X **Le Café du Jardin,** 28 Wellington St., WC2E 7BD, ✆ (020) 7836 876.. *Fax (020) 7836 4123* – ▤. MC AE ① VISA p. 37 **EX**
closed 25 December – **Meals** 13.50 **t.** (lunch) and a la carte 24.50/29.00 **t.** 7.50.

X **Livebait,** 21 Wellington St., WC2E 7DN, ✆ (020) 7836 7161, *Fax (020) 7836 7141* – MC ① VISA p. 37 **EX**
closed Sunday – **Meals** - Seafood - 12.50/15.50 **t.** and a la carte 7.50.

Victoria – ✉ *SW1.*

Victoria Station Forecourt.

Royal Horseguards Thistle, 2 Whitehall Court, SW1A 2EJ, ✆ (020) 7839 3400, *royalhorseguards@thistle.co.uk, Fax (020) 7925 2263,* ☂, 🏋 – |‡|, ⇹ rm, ▤ TV ✆ – 200. MC ① VISA JCB. ✻ p. 30 **LX**
One Twenty One Two : Meals *closed Sunday and lunch Saturday* 18.50/30.00 and a la carte – ⊒ 14.95 – **277 rm** 252.00/273.00 **st.**, 3 suites – SB.

Crowne Plaza London St. James, 45 Buckingham Gate, SW1E 6A.., ✆ (020) 7834 6655, *sales.sjc@stjamescourt.co.uk, Fax (020) 7630 7587,* 🏋, ≘s – |‡|, ⇹ rm, ▤ TV ✆ – 180. MC AE ① VISA JCB. ✻ p. 36 **CX**
Café Mediterranée : Meals *closed Sunday* 15.00/30.00 **t.** and a la carte 7.50 – (see also ***Quilon*** and ***Zander*** below) – ⊒ 14.00 – **322 rm** 130.00/205.00 **s.**, 20 suites.

Hilton London St. Ermin's, Caxton St., SW1H 0QW, ✆ (020) 7222 78.. *Fax (020) 7222 6914* – |‡|, ⇹ rm, ▤ rest, TV – 250. MC AE ① VISA JCB. ✻
Cloisters Brasserie : Meals *(closed lunch Saturday and Sunday)* (carving lunch) 19.75 and a la carte – ⊒ 14.95 – **283 rm** 230.00/254.00 **st.**, 7 suites – SB. p. 36 **CX**

The Goring, 15 Beeston Pl., Grosvenor Gdns., SW1W 0JW, (020) 7396 9000, *reception@goringhotel.co.uk, Fax (020) 7834 4393* – – 50. VISA. p. 36 BX a
Meals 25.00/38.00 **st.** 9.00 – 16.50 – **68 rm** 185.00/225.00 **s.**, 6 suites.

Thistle Victoria, 101 Buckingham Palace Rd, SW1W 0SJ, (020) 7834 9494, *victoria@thistle.co.uk, Fax (020) 7630 1978* – rm, – 200. VISA JCB. p. 36 BX e
Meals (carving lunch)/dinner 18.50 **t.** (lunch) and a la carte 26.90/43.90 **t.** 8.00 – 13.95 – **361 rm** 168.00/217.00 **st.**, 3 suites – SB.

Rubens, 39 Buckingham Palace Rd, SW1W 0PS, (020) 7834 6600, *reservations@rubens.redcarnationhotels.com, Fax (020) 7828 5401* – rm, – 75. VISA JCB. p. 36 BX n
Meals *(closed Saturday lunch)* (carving lunch) 16.95 **t.** (lunch) and a la carte approx. 17.40 **t.** 11.50 – ***The Library*** **: Meals** (dinner only) a la carte approx. 34.40 **st.** – 15.00 – **172 rm** 150.00/210.00 **s.**, 2 suites.

Thistle Westminster, 49 Buckingham Palace Rd, SW1W 0QT, (020) 7834 1821, *westminster@thistle.co.uk, Fax (020) 7931 7542* – rm, – 180. VISA JCB. p. 36 BX z
Meals 11.25/13.25 **st.** – 13.95 – **134 rm** 190.00/214.00 **st.** – SB.

Dolphin Square, Dolphin Sq., Chichester St., SW1V 3LX, (020) 7834 3800, *reservations@dolphinsquarehotel.co.uk, Fax (020) 7798 8735*, , , , , , squash – , rest, – 50. VISA. p. 30 KZ a
Meals 13.95 **st.** and a la carte – (see also ***Rhodes in the Square*** below) – 12.50 – **48 rm** 140.00/165.00 **st.**, **117 suites** 195.00 **st.**

41, 41 Buckingham Palace Rd, SW1W 0PS, (020) 7300 0041, *41club@redcarnationhotels.com, Fax (020) 7300 0141* – rm, . VISA. p. 36 BX n
Meals (residents only) – **16 rm** (fully inclusive) 325.00 **s.**, 4 suites.

Rochester, 69 Vincent Sq., SW1P 2PA, (020) 7828 6611, *rochester@grangehotels.co.uk, Fax (020) 7233 6724* – rest, – 70. VISA JCB. p. 36 CY e
Meals *(closed lunch Saturday, Sunday and Bank Holidays)* 24.50 **st.** and a la carte 8.45 – 15.00 – **76 rm** 160.00/180.00 **st.**

Tophams Belgravia, 28 Ebury St., SW1W 0LU, (020) 7730 8147, *tophamsbelgravia@compuserve.com, Fax (020) 7823 5966* – – 30. VISA JCB. p. 36 AX e
closed 24 December-early January – **Meals** *(closed Sunday, Saturday lunch and Bank Holidays)* 9.50 **st.** (lunch) and a la carte 16.00/21.50 **st.** 4.90 – **39 rm** 115.00/170.00 **st.**

Winchester without rest., 17 Belgrave Rd, SW1V 1RB, (020) 7828 2972, *Fax (020) 7828 5191* – . p. 36 BY s
18 rm 85.00/110.00.

Rhodes in the Square (at Dolphin Square H.), Dolphin Sq., Chichester St., SW1V 3LX, (020) 7798 6767, *Fax (020) 7798 5685* – . VISA p. 30 KZ a
closed Saturday lunch, Sunday and Monday – **Meals** 19.50/31.00 **t.**
Spec. Pan-fried white pudding sausage with cabbage and bacon. Steamed skate with white crab and clam soup. Raspberry red wine jelly.

Quilon (at Crowne Plaza London St. James H.), 45 Buckingham Gate, SW1 6AF, (020) 7821 1899, *Fax (020) 7828 5802* – . VISA p. 36 CX i
closed Sunday and Saturday lunch – **Meals** - Indian - 12.50/15.95 **t.** (lunch) and dinner a la carte 20.95/28.85 **t.**

L'Incontro, 87 Pimlico Rd, SW1W 8PH, (020) 7730 6327, *Fax (020) 7730 5062* – . VISA JCB p. 35 FT u
closed 25-26 December, Easter and lunch Saturday and Sunday – **Meals** - Italian - 18.50 **t.** (lunch) and a la carte 29.50/50.50 **t.** 12.50.

Santini, 29 Ebury St., SW1W 0NZ, (020) 7730 4094, *Fax (020) 7730 0544* – . VISA JCB p. 36 ABX v
closed 25-26 December, Easter and lunch Saturday and Sunday – **Meals** - Italian - 19.75 **t.** (lunch) and a la carte 30.00/45.25 **t.** 11.00.

Shepherd's, Marsham Court, Marsham St., SW1P 4LA, (020) 7834 9552, *Fax (020) 7233 6047* – . VISA JCB p. 30 LZ z
closed Christmas, Easter, Saturday, Sunday and Bank Holidays – **Meals** - English - (booking essential) 25.50 **t.**.

Roussillon, 16 St. Barnabas St., SW1W 8PB, (020) 7730 5550, *alexis@roussillon.co.uk, Fax (020) 7824 8617* – . VISA JCB p. 29 IZ c
closed 25-26 December, New Year, Saturday lunch and Bank Holidays – **Meals** 18.00/35.00-50.00 **t.**
Spec. Bembridge lobster with wild garlic leaves. Shedbush Farm lamb rubbed with mint. Spicy goose egg soufflé, maple infusion.

XX **Zander,** 45 Buckingham Gate, SW1E 6BS, ✆ (020) 7378 3838, *zander@bgr.plc.u* *Fax (020) 7630 5665* – ▤. MC AE ⓓ VISA p. 36 **CX**
Meals 12.50 **t.** (lunch) and a la carte 27.00/32.00 **t.** ⓘ 9.60.

XX **Il Convivio,** 143 Ebury St., SW1W 9QN, ✆ (020) 7730 4099, *Fax (020) 7730 4103* – ▤. AE ⓓ VISA JCB p. 36 **AY**
closed 2 weeks mid August, 2 weeks Christmas and Sunday – **Meals** - Italian - 20.00/35.00

XX **Simply Nico,** 48a Rochester Row, SW1P 1JU, ✆ (020) 7630 8061, *Fax (020) 7828 854* ▤. MC AE ⓓ VISA p. 36 **CY**
closed 25-26 December, Easter, Saturday lunch, Sunday and Bank Holidays – **Meals** (booki essential) 23.50/25.50 **t.** ⓘ 9.00.

XX **Tate Britain,** Tate Gallery, Millbank, SW1P 4RG, ✆ (020) 7887 8825, *information@tate.o uk, Fax (020) 7887 8902,* « Rex Whistler murals » – ▤. MC AE ⓓ VISA p. 30 **LZ**
Meals (booking essential) (lunch only) 16.75/19.50 **t.** and a la carte ⓘ 12.00.

XX **The Atrium,** 4 Millbank (lower ground floor), SW1P 3JA, ✆ (020) 7233 00 *Fax (020) 7233 0010* – ▤. MC AE ⓓ VISA p. 30 **LY**
closed Christmas, New Year, Easter, Saturday, Sunday and Bank Holidays – **Meals** a la ca 17.70/28.65 **t.**

XX **Ken Lo's Memories of China,** 67-69 Ebury St., SW1W 0NZ, ✆ (020) 7730 77 *Fax (020) 7730 2992* – ▤. MC AE ⓓ VISA JCB p. 36 **AY**
closed 23 December-1 January, Sunday lunch and Bank Holidays – **Meals** - Chines 19.50/27.50 **t.** and a la carte.

X **Olivo,** 21 Eccleston St., SW1W 9LX, ✆ (020) 7730 2505, *Fax (020) 7824 8190* – ▤. MC AE V
closed lunch Saturday and Sunday and Bank Holidays – **Meals** - Italian - 17.00 (lunch) and dinner a la carte 22.50/28.00 **t.** ⓘ 7.50. p. 36 **AY**

X **La Poule au Pot,** 231 Ebury St., SW1W 8UT, ✆ (020) 7730 7763, *Fax (020) 7259 9651,* – ▤. MC AE ⓓ VISA JCB p. 29 **IZ**
Meals - French - 16.00 **t.** (lunch) and a la carte 24.25/34.25 **t.** ⓘ 5.75.

X **Justin de Blank - brasserie,** 50-52 Buckingham Palace Rd, SW1W 0 ✆ (020) 7828 4111, *Fax (020) 7828 3666,* ☂. MC AE VISA p. 36 **BX**
closed 25 December-2 January and dinner Saturday and Sunday – **Meals** 15.50/22.50 and a la carte ⓘ 7.75.

NGBRIDGE *Warks. – see Warwick.*

NG CRENDON *Bucks.* 403 404 R 28 – *pop. 2 505* – ✉ *Aylesbury.*
London 50 – Aylesbury 11 – Oxford 15.

X **Angel Inn** with rm, Bicester Rd, HP18 9EE, ✆ (01844) 208268, *Fax (01844) 202497*, « Part 16C » – rm, TV P. MO VISA.
Meals *(closed Sunday dinner)* 14.95 **t.** (lunch) and a la carte 19.25/32.25 **t.** – 5.00 – **3 rm** 55.00/65.00 **t.**

NG MELFORD *Suffolk* 404 W 27 *Great Britain G.* – *pop. 2 808.*
See : *Melford Hall★ AC.*
London 62 – Cambridge 34 – Colchester 18 – Ipswich 24.

Bull, Hall St., CO10 9JG, ✆ (01787) 378494, *Fax (01787) 880307*, « Part 15C coaching inn » – rm, TV P – 60. MO AE ① VISA JCB
Meals 10.95/21.95 **t.** and dinner a la carte 5.95 – **25 rm** 70.00/120.00 **t.** – SB.

Black Lion, The Green, CO10 9DN, ✆ (01787) 312356, *Fax (01787) 374557*, – rest, TV P. MO AE VISA
Meals 27.95 **t.** and a la carte – **8 rm** 71.00/101.00 **t.**, 1 suite – SB.

George and Dragon, Hall St., CO10 9JB, ✆ (01787) 371285, *geodrg@globalnet.co.uk, Fax (01787) 312428*, – rest, TV P – 30. MO VISA
Meals a la carte 11.85/17.95 **st.** 4.95 – **8 rm** 35.00/60.00 **st.**

XXX **Chimneys,** Hall St., CO10 9JR, ✆ (01787) 379806, *Fax (01787) 312294*, « Part 16C cottage », – MO VISA
closed 25 December and Sunday – **Meals** 18.50 **st.** and a la carte.

X **Scutchers,** Westgate St., CO10 9DP, on A 1092 ✆ (07000) 728824, *Fax (07000) 785443*, « Former medieval hall house », – MO AE VISA
closed 1-10 January, Sunday and Monday – **Meals** a la carte 20.60/25.00 **t.**

NGRIDGE *Lancs.* 402 M 22 – *pop. 7 351.*
London 241 – Blackburn 12 – Burnley 18.

XXX **Paul Heathcote's,** 104-106 Higher Rd, PR3 3SY, Northeast : ½ m. by B 5269 following signs for Jeffrey Hill ✆ (01772) 784969, *longridge@heathcotes.co.uk, Fax (01772) 785713* – . MO AE ① VISA JCB
closed 1 January, Monday and Tuesday (except December) and Saturday lunch – **Meals** 16.50 **t.** (lunch) and dinner a la carte 29.00/52.50 **t.** 8.00
Spec. Hash brown of black pudding and cheese, seared scallops and apple sauce. Breast of duck with wilted greens and orange dressing. Rhubarb and elderflower crumble soufflé.

NG SUTTON *Lincs.* 404 U 25 – *pop. 4 185.*
London 100 – Lincoln 51 – Leicester 67 – Norwich 54.

Travelodge, Wisbech Rd, PE12 9AG, Southeast : 1 m. at junction of A 17 with A 1101 ✆ (01406) 362230 – rm, TV & P. MO AE ① VISA JCB.
Meals (grill rest.) – **40 rm** 39.95 **t.**

NGTOWN *Cumbria* 401 402 L 18.
74 Swan St. ✆ (01228) 792835.
London 326 – Carlisle 9 – Newcastle upon Tyne 61.

Bessiestown Farm , Catlowdy, CA6 5QP, Northeast : 8 m. by Netherby St. on B 6318 ✆ (01228) 577219, *bestbb2000@cs.com, Fax (01228) 577019*, « Working farm », , , – TV P. MO VISA.
Meals (by arrangement) 12.50 **s.** 5.00 – **4 rm** 33.00/50.00.

Particularly pleasant hotels and restaurants are shown in the Guide by a **red symbol**.

Please send us the names of anywhere you have enjoyed your stay.

Your **Michelin Guide** will be even better.

... ,

XXXXX ... X,

LOOE *Cornwall* 403 G 32 *The West Country G. – pop. 5 022.*

See : *Town★ – Monkey Sanctuary★ AC.*

Bin Down ☏ (01503) 240239 – Whitsand Bay Hotel, Portwrinkle, Torpoint ☏ (015 230470.

The Guildhall, Fore St. ☏ (01503) 262072 (restricted opening in winter).

London 264 – Plymouth 23 – Truro 39.

Klymiarven, Barbican Hill, East Looe, PL13 1BH, East : 2 m. by A 387 off B 3253 access from town on foot ☏ (01503) 262333, *klymiarven@cwcom.net, Fax (01503) 2623* ← Looe and harbour, – TV P. VISA JCB
closed 4 January-1 March – **Meals** 10.95/14.95 **st.** and dinner a la carte 6.50 – **14** 59.00/98.00 **st.** – SB.

Commonwood Manor, St. Martins Rd, East Looe, PL13 1LP, Northeast : ½ m. b 387 on B 3253 ☏ (01503) 262929, *commonwood@compuserve.com, Fax (01503) 2626* ← Looe Valley, heated, – TV P. AE VISA JCB
closed January-March – **Meals** (restricted menu) 9.50/12.50 **st.** 5.35 – **11 rm** 39.(78.00 **st.**

Bucklawren Farm, St. Martin-by-Looe, PL13 1NZ, Northeast : 3 ½ m. by A 387 an 3253 turning right onto single track road signposted to monkey sanctu ☏ (01503) 240738, *bucklawren@compuserve.com, Fax (01503) 240481*, ←, « Work farm », – TV P. VISA.
March-November – **Meals** (by arrangement) 11.00 **st.** 4.00 – **6 rm** 27.50/46.00 **st.**

Coombe Farm, Widegates, PL13 1QN, Northeast : 3 ½ m. on B 32 ☏ (01503) 240223, *coombe-farm@hotmail.com, Fax (01503) 240895*, ← countrysi heated, – TV P. AE VISA.
27 February-7 November – **Meals** (by arrangement) 17.50 **st.** 4.00 – **10 rm** 35.(70.00 **st.** – SB.

Trawlers, Buller Quay, East Looe, PL13 1AH, ☏ (01503) 263593 – . AE VISA
closed January-13 February, Monday September-May and Sunday – **Meals** (dinner o 18.00/20.00 **t.** and a la carte 6.00.

at Talland Bay *Southwest : 4 m. by A 387 – ✉ Looe.*

Talland Bay, PL13 2JB, ☏ (01503) 272667, *tallandbay@aol.com, Fax (01503) 2729* ←, « Country house atmosphere », heated, – rest, TV P. AE VISA.
closed January-mid February – **Meals** 12.50/22.00 **t.** and dinner a la carte 6.60 – **20 rm** (dinner included) 76.00/172.00 **t.**, 1 suite – SB.

at Pelynt *Northwest : 4 m. by A 387 on B 3359 – ✉ Looe.*

Jubilee Inn, Pelynt, PL13 2JZ, ☏ (01503) 220312, *Fax (01503) 220920*, « Part 16C » – P. VISA JCB
Meals a la carte 11.30/24.75 **t.** 5.50 – **9 rm** 38.50/65.00 **t.** – SB.

LORTON *Cumbria* 402 K 20 – *see Cockermouth.*

LOUGHBOROUGH *Leics.* 402 403 404 Q 25 – *pop. 46 867.*

Lingdale, Joe Moore's Lane, Woodhouse Eaves ☏ (01509) 890703.

Town Hall, Market Pl. ☏ (01509) 218113.

London 117 – Birmingham 41 – Leicester 11 – Nottingham 15.

Quality, New Ashby Rd, LE11 4EX, West : 2 m. on A 512 ☏ (01509) 211800, *admin@gb6 u_net.com, Fax (01509) 211868*, , , – rm, rest, TV P – 225. AE VISA JCB
Meals (dinner only) 14.50/22.00 **st.** and a la carte 6.50 – 9.75 – **94 rm** 83.00/108.00

Garendon Park, 92 Leicester Rd, LE11 2AQ, Southeast : ½ m. on A 6 ☏ (01509) 23655 *nfo@garendonparkhotel.co.uk., Fax (01509) 265559* – TV. VISA JCB.
Meals 11.50 **st.** 4.50 – **9 rm** 25.00/50.00 **st.** – SB.

Charnwood Lodge, 136 Leicester Rd, LE11 2AQ, Southeast : ¾ m. on ☏ (01509) 211120, *charnwoodlodge@charwat.freeserve.co.uk, Fax (01509) 21112* rm, TV P. VISA JCB.
Meals (by arrangement) 10.50 **st.** 4.50 – **8 rm** 35.00/55.00 **st.**

The Old Manor with rm, 11-14 Sparrow Hill, LE11 1BT, off Baxter Gate ☏ (01509) 2112 *bookings@oldmanor.com, Fax (01509) 211128*, « Part 15C » – TV. AE VISA
Meals (dinner only) 32.50 **st.** – 10.50 – **8 rm** 87.50/140.00 **st.**

at Burton-on-the-Wolds *East : 3 ¾ m. by A 60 on B 676 – ✉ Loughborough.*

Lang's, Horse Leys Farm, LE12 5TQ, East : 1 m. on B 676 ☏ (01509) 8809 *Fax (01509) 880980* – P. VISA JCB
closed 1 week in summer, 2 weeks in winter, Monday and Sunday dinner – **Meals** (li lunch) a la carte 20.75/26.50 **t.** 9.75.

Quorndon *Southeast : 3 m. by A 6 – ✉ Loughborough.*

Quorn Country H., 66 Leicester Rd, LE12 8BB, ☎ (01509) 415050, *Fax (01509) 415557,* – rm, rm, TV P – 120. MC AE VISA
Shires : **Meals** 18.00/22.50 **t.** and a la carte 12.75 – ***Orangery :*** **Meals** 13.00/22.50 **t.** and a la carte 12.75 – 8.95 – **21 rm** 102.00/115.00 **t.**, 2 suites – SB.

Quorn Grange, 88 Wood Lane, LE12 8DB, Southeast : ¾ m. ☎ (01509) 412167, *Fax (01509) 415621,* – TV P – 100. MC AE VISA JCB.
closed 26-28 December – **Meals** *(closed Saturday lunch)* 12.00/26.50 **st.** 8.50 – **38 rm** 83.00/103.00 **st.**

UGHTON *Essex* 404 U 29.
Loughton, Clays Lane, Debden Green ☎ (020) 8502 2923.
London 15 – Cambridge 44 – Ipswich 66 – Luton 30 – Southend-on-Sea 35.

Ne'als Brasserie, 241 High Rd, IG10 1AD, ☎ (020) 8508 3443 – . MC VISA JCB
closed Sunday dinner and Monday – **Meals** 12.95 **t.** (lunch) and a la carte 23.90/31.45 **t.** 6.50.

In this guide

a symbol or a character, printed in red or **black**, in **bold** or light type, does not have the same meaning.
Pay particular attention to the explanatory pages.

UTH *Lincs.* 402 404 U 23 – *pop. 14 248.*
The New Market Hall, off Cornmarket ☎ (01507) 609289.
London 156 – Boston 34 – Great Grimsby 17 – Lincoln 26.

Kenwick Park , LN11 8NR, Southeast : 2 ¼ m. by B 1520 on A 157 ☎ (01507) 608806, *enquiries@kenwick-park.co.uk, Fax (01507) 608027,* , , , , , , , , squash – TV P – 30. MC AE VISA.
Meals 18.50/21.95 **st.** and a la carte 7.50 – **34 rm** 79.50/120.00 **st.** – SB.

Brackenborough Arms, Cordeaux Corner, Brackenborough, LN11 0SZ, North : 2 m. by A 16 ☎ (01507) 609169, *info@brackenborough.co.uk, Fax (01507) 609413* – rm, TV P – 55. MC AE VISA JCB.
closed 25-26 December – **Meals** *(closed Monday lunch)* a la carte 16.85/24.45 **t.** 6.25 – **24 rm** 62.00/105.00 **t.** – SB.

The Beaumont, 66 Victoria Rd, LN11 0BX, by Eastgate off Ramsgate Rd ☎ (01507) 605005, *enquiries@thebeaumont.freeserve.co.uk, Fax (01507) 607768* – TV P. MC AE VISA
Meals *(closed Sunday)* 14.95 **st.** and a la carte 5.00 – **16 rm** 55.00/80.00 **st.**

WER ODDINGTON *Glos.* 403 404 P 28 – *see Stow-on-the-Wold.*

WER SLAUGHTER *Glos.* 403 404 O 28 – *see Bourton-on-the-Water.*

WER WIELD *Hants.* – *see Four Marks.*

WESTOFT *Suffolk* 404 **Z 26** *Great Britain G.* – *pop. 62 907.*
Env. : *The Broads*★.
Rookery Park, Carlton Colville ☎ (01502) 560380.
East Point Pavillion, Royal Plain ☎ (01502) 533600.
London 116 – Ipswich 43 – Norwich 30.

Travel Inn, 249 Yarmouth Rd, NR32 4AA, North : 2 ½ m. on A 12 ☎ (01502) 572441 – rm, TV P. MC AE VISA.
Meals (grill rest.) – **41 rm** 40.95 **t.**

Oulton Broad *West : 2 m. by A 146 – ✉ Lowestoft.*

Ivy House Farm , Ivy Lane, NR33 8HY, Southwest : 1 ½ m. by A 146 ☎ (01502) 501353, *admin@ivyhousefarm.co.uk, Fax (01502) 501539,* , – TV P – 50. MC AE VISA
Meals – (see ***The Crooked Barn*** below) – **19 rm** 69.00/109.00 **t.**

The Crooked Barn (at Ivy House Farm), Ivy Lane, NR33 8HY, Southwest : 1 ½ m. by A 146 ☎ (01502) 501353, *admin@ivyhousefarm.co.uk, Fax (01502) 501539,* , « Part 18C thatched converted barn » – P. MC AE VISA
Meals a la carte 21.25/32.85 **t.** 7.95.

LOW FELL *Tyne and Wear – see Gateshead.*

LOW LAITHE *N. Yorks. – see Pateley Bridge.*

LUDLOW *Shrops.* 403 L 26 *Great Britain G. – pop. 9 040.*

See : *Town★ – Castle★* **AC** *– Feathers Hotel★ – St. Laurence's Parish Church★ (Misericords★).*

Exc. : *Stokesay Castle★* **AC**, *NW : 6½ m. by A 49.*

Castle St. ☎ (01584) 875053.

London 162 – Birmingham 39 – Hereford 24 – Shrewsbury 29.

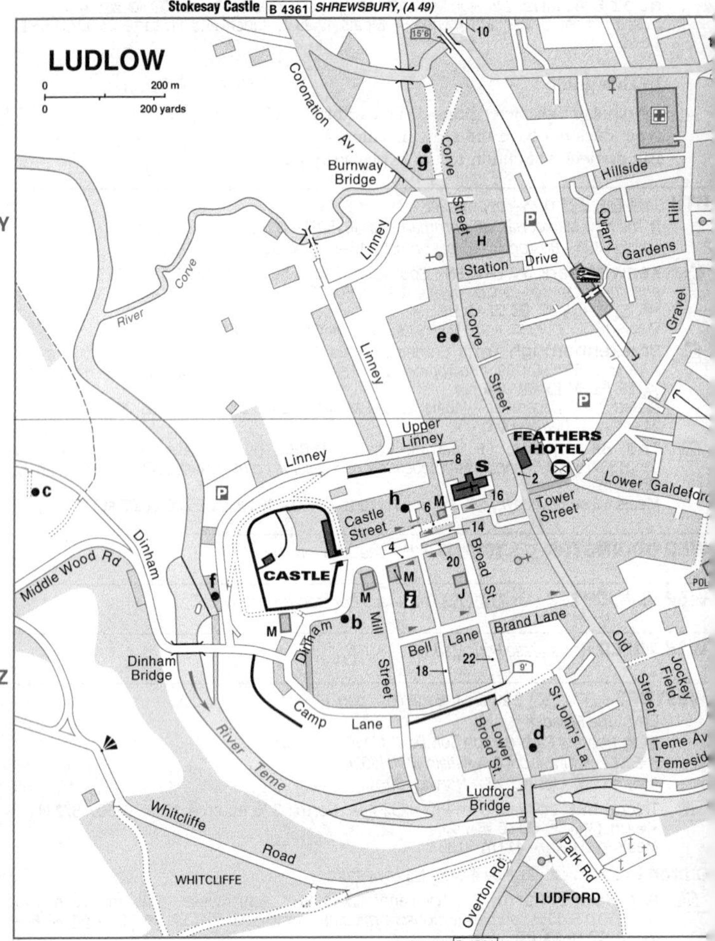

Dinham Hall, Dinham, SY8 1EJ, (01584) 876464, *Fax (01584) 876019*, – rest, Z b
Meals a la carte approx. 26.00 **t.** 9.15 – **14 rm** 65.00/160.00 **t.** – SB.

Overton Grange, Hereford Rd, SY8 4AD, South : 1 ¾ m. by B 4361 (01584) 873500, *Fax (01584) 873524*, – rest, – 100.
Les Marches : **Meals** *(closed Saturday lunch and Sunday dinner)* (booking essential to non-residents) 25.00/32.50 **t.** 7.50 – **12 rm** 60.00/120.00 **t.**, 2 suites – SB.

Cliffe, Dinham, SY8 2JE, West : ½ m. via Dinham Bridge (01584) 872063, *cliffhotel@lineone.net, Fax (01584) 873991*, – Z c
closed 24-26 December – **Meals** (booking essential) (bar lunch Monday to Saturday)/dinner 14.95 **st.** – **9 rm** 35.00/70.00 **st.** – SB.

Number Twenty Eight without rest., 28 Lower Broad St., SY8 1PQ, (01584) 876996, *ross.no28@btinternet.com, Fax (01584) 876860*, – Z d
6 rm 70.00/90.00 **st.**

Hibiscus (Bosi), 17 Corve St., SY8 1DA, (01584) 872325, *Fax (01584) 874024* – Y e
closed 25 December, 1 week in spring, Sunday and Monday lunch – **Meals** (booking essential) 19.50/32.50 **t.** 8.00
Spec. Scallops with Thai curry and celeriac. John Dory with girolles. Chocolate fondant with star anise.

Mr. Underhill's at Dinham Weir (Bradley) with rm, Dinham Bridge, SY8 1EH, (01584) 874431, *Fax (01584) 874431*, « Riverside setting », – Z f
closed 1 week January – **Meals** *(closed Tuesday dinner)* (set menu only) (booking essential) (lunch by arrangement) 25.00/34.00 **t.** 7.00 – **6 rm** 70.00/125.00 **t.**
Spec. Confit of chicken livers with bacon, broad bean cream. Fillet of beef with parsley, shallots and vegetable latkes. Rice pudding with apricot compote.

Merchant House (Hill), Lower Corve St., SY8 1DU, (01584) 875438, *Fax (01584) 876927*, « Jacobean house » – Y g
closed 1 week spring, 1 week Christmas, Sunday and Monday – **Meals** (dinner only and lunch Friday and Saturday) 31.00 **st.** 10.00
Spec. Steamed lobster with chick pea, coriander and olive oil sauce. Saddle of venison with goat's cheese gnocchi. Caramel and apple tart with caramel ice cream.

Courtyard, 2 Quality Sq., SY8 1AR, (01584) 878080 – Z h
closed 25-26 December, 1 January, 1 May, Sunday and dinner Monday to Wednesday – **Meals** (light lunch) 11.40/25.95 **t.** and a la carte 9.50.

Woofferton *South : 4 m. by B 4361 and A 49* – Z – *Ludlow.*

Travelodge, SY8 4AL, (01584) 711695, *Fax (01584) 711695* – rm,
Meals (grill rest.) – **32 rm** 39.95 **t.**

Brimfield *South : 4½ m. by B 4361 and A 49* – Z – *Ludlow.*

The Marcle, SY8 4NE, (01584) 711459, *marcle@supanet.com, Fax (01584) 711459*, « 16C cottage », –
closed December and January – **Meals** (by arrangement) 19.50 **s.** – **3 rm** 40.00/60.00 **s.**

Roebuck Inn with rm, SY8 4NE, (01584) 711230, *roebuckinn@demon.co.uk, Fax (01584) 711654*, –
Meals a la carte 21.95/29.40 **t.** 6.95 – **3 rm** 45.00/65.00 **t.**

Bromfield *Northwest : 2½ m. on A 49* – *Ludlow.*

The Cookhouse (Restaurant), SY8 2JR, (01584) 856565, *Fax (01584) 856661*, –
Meals 12.25/25.00 **t.** and dinner a la carte.

LUTON *Luton* 404 S 28 *Great Britain G. – pop. 171 671.*
See : *Luton Hoo★ (Wernher Collection★★) AC* X.
Stockwood Park, London Rd ℘ *(01582) 413704,* X – 18, 9 *South Beds, Warden Hill Rd (01582) 591209.*
Luton International Airport : ℘ *(01582) 405100, E : 1 ½ m.* X – **Terminal** : Luton Bus Station.
The Bus Station, Bute St. ℘ *(01582) 401579.*
London 35 – Cambridge 36 – Ipswich 93 – Oxford 45 – Southend-on-Sea 63.

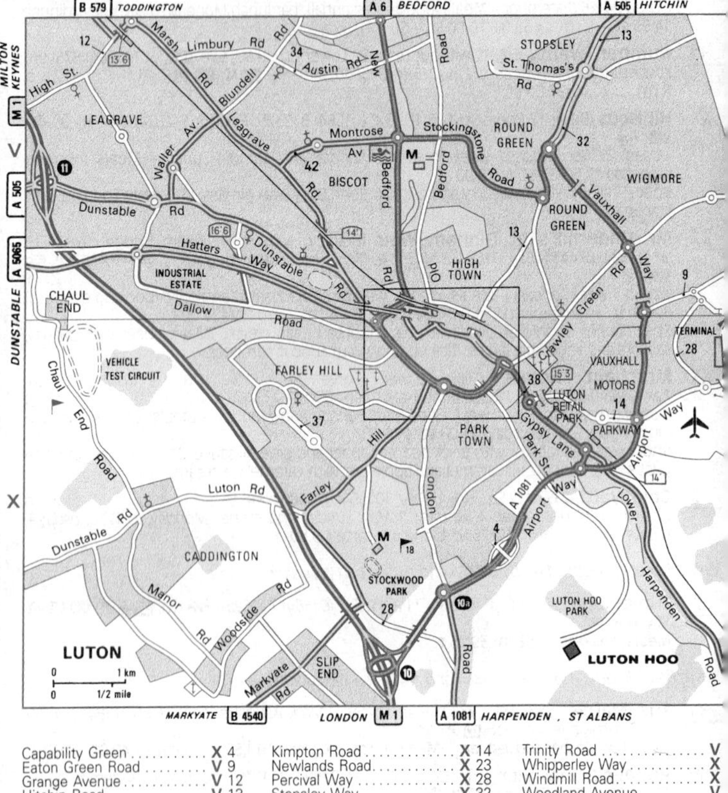

Thistle Luton, Arndale Centre, LU1 2TR, ℘ (01582) 734199, *luton@thistle.co.uk*, *Fax (01582) 402528* – |≡|, ⇔ rm, TV ♿ P – 🏛 300. MC AE ① VISA JCB. ✻ Y
Meals 15.50/17.50 and a la carte – ☐ 10.95 – **151 rm** 102.00/142.00 **st.**, 1 suite – SB.

ⅩBOROUGH *Somerset* 403 J 30 – *pop. 201* – ✉ *Watchet.*
London 205 – Exeter 42 – Minehead 9 – Taunton 25.

Royal Oak of Luxborough with rm, Exmoor National Park, TA23 0SH, ✆ (01984) 640319, *royaloakof.luxborough@virgin.net*, « Part 14C inn », – P. MC VISA
Meals a la carte 11.95/19.50 **st.** – **13 rm** 45.00/65.00 **st.** – SB.

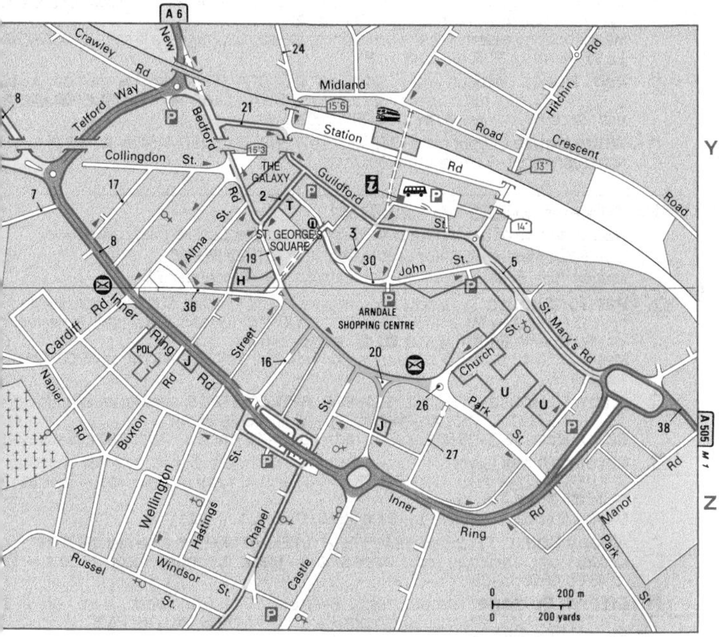

DFORD *Devon* 403 H 32 *The West Country G.* – *pop. 1 734* – ✉ *Okehampton.*
See : *Village★★.*
Env. : *Dartmoor National Park★★.*
London 234 – Exeter 33 – Plymouth 25.

Moor View House, Vale Down, EX20 4BB, Northeast : 1 ½ m. on A 386 ✆ (01822) 820220, *Fax (01822) 820220*, – TV P
Meals (by arrangement) 20.00 **st.** 5.00 – **4 rm** 50.00/70.00 **st.** – SB.

Dartmoor Inn, EX20 4AY, East : 1 m. on A 386 ✆ (01822) 820221, *Fax (01822) 820494* – P. MC VISA JCB
closed 24-26 and 31 December, 1 January, Monday, Sunday dinner and Bank Holidays – **Meals** 15.00/21.50 **t.** and a la carte 8.25.

ME REGIS *Dorset* 403 L 31 *The West Country G.* – *pop. 3 566.*
See : *Town★ – The Cobb★.*
18 *Timber Hill ✆ (01297) 442963.*
Guildhall Cottage, Church St. ✆ (01297) 442138.
London 160 – Dorchester 25 – Exeter 31 – Taunton 27.

Alexandra, Pound St., DT7 3HZ, ℘ (01297) 442010, *alexandra@lymeregis.co.u* *Fax (01297) 443229*, ←, – TV P. MC AE VISA. *closed January and Christmas* – **Meals** 13.25/22.75 **t.** 7.00 – **27 rm** 55.00/125.00 **t.** SB.

Victoria, Uplyme Rd, DT7 3LP, ℘ (01297) 444801, *info@vichotel.co.u* *Fax (01297) 442949* – rest, TV P. MC VISA. **Meals** (booking essential) (bar lunch Monday to Saturday)/dinner a la carte 11.45/20.20 6.95 – **6 rm** 32.50/60.00 **st.** – SB.

Red House without rest., Sidmouth Rd, DT7 3ES, West : 3/4 m. on A 30 ℘ (01297) 442055, *red.house@virgin.net, Fax (01297) 442055*, – TV P. MC VISA. *mid March-November* – **3 rm** 35.00/54.00 **s.**

White House without rest., 47 Silver St., DT7 3HR, ℘ (01297) 443420, ← – TV P *April-September* – **7 rm** 28.00/50.00 **st.**

LYMINGTON *Hants.* 403 404 P 31 – *pop. 13 508.*

to the Isle of Wight (Yarmouth) (Wightlink Ltd) frequent services daily (30 mn).

St. Barbe Museum & Visitor Centre, New St. ℘ (01590) 689000.

London 103 – Bournemouth 18 – Southampton 19 – Winchester 32.

Passford House, Mount Pleasant Lane, Mount Pleasant, SO41 8LS, Northwest : 2 by A 337 and Sway Rd ℘ (01590) 682398, *Fax (01590) 683494*, ←, , , heated, , , – TV P – 100. MC AE VISA **Meals** 28.50 **t.** (dinner) and a la carte 24.75/34.25 **t** 14.50 – **49 rm** 85.00/180.00 1 suite – SB.

Stanwell House, 15 High St., SO41 9AA, ℘ (01590) 677123, *sales@stanwellhousehote o.uk, Fax (01590) 677756*, – rm, TV – 40. MC AE VISA ***Bistro :*** **Meals** 12.00/25.00 **t.** and a la carte 9.95 – **25 rm** 55.00/105.00 **t.**, 5 suites –

Gordleton Mill, Silver St., Hordle, SO41 6DJ, Northwest : 3 1/2 m. by A 337 and Sway ℘ (01590) 682219, *Fax (01590) 683073*, , « Part 17C water mill, gardens » – , re TV P. MC AE VISA JCB. **Meals** a la carte 15.70/26.85 **t.** – **8 rm** 60.00/85.00 **t.**, 1 suite – SB.

Albany House, 3 Highfield, SO41 9GB, ℘ (01590) 671900, – rest, TV P. *closed 5 days Christmas and 1 week winter* – **Meals** (by arrangement) 17.50 **s.** – **3 r** 45.00/66.00 **s.** – SB.

Efford Cottage without rest., Everton, SO41 0JD, West : 2 m. on A 3 ℘ (01590) 642315, *effcottage@aol.com, Fax (01590) 641030*, – TV P **3 rm** 50.00/60.00 **s.**

Limpets, 9 Gosport St., SO41 9BG, ℘ (01590) 675595, *Fax (01590) 675595* – MC VISA *closed Sunday and Monday* – **Meals** 14.00/22.00 **t.** and a la carte 6.50.

at East End *Northeast : 4 1/4 m. by B 3054 off South Baddesley rd* – ✉ *Lymington.*

East End Arms, Main Rd, SO41 5SY, ℘ (01590) 626223, *jennie@eastendarms.co.* *Fax (01590) 626223*, – MC VISA JCB *closed 1 January, Sunday dinner and Monday* – **Meals** a la carte 13.75/19.75 **t.**

LYMM *Ches.* 402 403 404 M 23 – *pop. 2 583.*

London 197 – Chester 26 – Liverpool 29 – Manchester 15.

Lymm, Whitbarrow Rd, WA13 9AQ, via Brookfield Rd ℘ (01925) 7522 *Fax (01925) 756035*, – TV P – 120. MC AE VISA. **Meals** (bar lunch Monday to Saturday)/dinner 18.00 **st.** and a la carte – 10.50 – **63 r** 77.00/87.00 **st.** – SB.

LYMPSTONE *Devon* 403 J 32 – *see Exmouth.*

LYNDHURST *Hants.* 403 404 P 31 *Great Britain G.* – *pop. 2 381.*

Env. : *New Forest★★ (Bolderwood Ornamental Drive★★, Rhinefield Ornamental Drive★★)*

18, 9 *Dibden Golf Centre, Main Rd ℘ (023) 8084 5596* – 18 *New Forest, Southampton ℘ (023) 8028 2752.*

New Forest Museum & Visitor Centre, Main Car Park ℘ (01590) 689000.

London 95 – Bournemouth 20 – Southampton 10 – Winchester 23.

Crown, 9 High St., SO43 7NF, ℘ (023) 8028 2922, *Fax (023) 8028 2751*, – , re TV P – 70. MC AE VISA. **Meals** (bar lunch Monday to Saturday)/dinner 19.00 **st.** and a la carte 7.65 – **38** 83.00/135.00 **st.**, 1 suite – SB.

Beaulieu, Beaulieu Rd, SO42 7YQ, Southeast : 3 1/2 m. on B 3056 ☎ (023) 8029 3344, *info@carehotels.co.uk, Fax (023) 8029 2729,* ⛆, – rest, TV P – 40. MC AE VISA
Meals (dinner only) 21.50 **t.** 17.95 – **17 rm** 77.50/130.00 **st.**, 1 suite – SB.

Ormonde House, Southampton Rd, SO43 7BT, ☎ (023) 8028 2806, *info@ormondehouse.co.uk, Fax (023) 8028 2004,* – TV P. MC AE VISA JCB
closed 1 week Christmas – **Meals** (by arrangement) (residents only) (dinner only) 16.00 **st.** – **19 rm** 26.00/86.00 **st.** – SB.

Whitemoor House, Southampton Rd, SO43 7BU, ☎ (023) 8028 2186, *Fax (023) 8028 2186* – TV P. MC VISA JCB
closed 25-26 December and 1 January – **Meals** (by arrangement) 12.50 **st.** 5.00 – **8 rm** 30.00/60.00 **st.** – SB.

XXX **Le Poussin at Parkhill** (Aitken) with rm, Beaulieu Rd, SO43 7FZ, Southeast : 1 1/4 m. on B 3056 ☎ (023) 8028 2944, *sales@lepoussinatparkhill.co.uk, Fax (023) 8028 3268,* ≤, « Tastefully furnished country house », ⛆ heated, – TV P – 50. MC AE VISA.
Meals 15.00/37.00 **t.** 7.50 – 10.00 – **18 rm** 79.00/125.00 **t.**, 2 suites – SB
Spec. Terrine of roast poussin, foie gras and prunes. Tomato "Tarte Tatin" with sea bass. New Forest venison with prosciutto and wild fungi.

'NMOUTH *Devon* 403 I 30 – *see Lynton.*

'NTON *Devon* 403 I 30 *The West Country G. – pop. 1 870 (inc. Lynmouth).*

See : *Town★ (≤★).*

Env. : *Valley of the Rocks★, W : 1 m. – Watersmeet★, E : 1 1/2 m. by A 39.*

Exc. : *Exmoor National Park★★ – Doone Valley★, SE : 7 1/2 m. by A 39 (access from Oare on foot).*

Town Hall, Lee Rd ☎ (01598) 752225.

London 206 – Exeter 59 – Taunton 44.

Lynton Cottage, North Walk Hill, EX35 6ED, ☎ (01598) 752342, *lyntoncot@aol.com, Fax (01598) 752597,* ≤ bay and Countisbury Hill, – rest, TV P. MC AE VISA.
closed December and January – **Meals** (light lunch)/dinner 25.00 **st.** – **17 rm** 41.00/118.00 **st.** – SB.

Hewitt's, North Walk, EX35 6HJ, ☎ (01598) 752293, *hewitts.hotel@talk21.com, Fax (01598) 752489,* ≤ bay and Countisbury Hill, « Victorian house in wooded cliffside setting », – TV P. MC VISA JCB
closed 15 December-15 January – **Meals** *(closed Tuesday)* (booking essential) 12.50/28.50 **s.** and a la carte 7.50 – 12.50 – **10 rm** 40.00/120.00 **s.** – SB.

Victoria Lodge, 30-31 Lee Rd, EX35 6BS, ☎ (01598) 753203, *info@victorialodge.co.uk, Fax (01598) 753203,* – TV P. MC VISA.
closed November- February and restricted opening February- March – **Meals** *(closed Monday to Wednesday)* (dinner only) 18.50 **st.** – **9 rm** 35.00/72.00 **st.**

Highcliffe House, Sinai Hill, EX35 6AR, ☎ (01598) 752235, *Fax (01598) 752235,* ≤ bay and Countisbury Hill, « Victorian residence, antiques », – TV P. MC VISA.
Meals (booking essential to non-residents) (dinner only) 18.00 **t.** – **6 rm** 40.00/70.00 **t.** – SB.

Seawood, North Walk, EX35 6HJ, ☎ (01598) 752272, *Fax (01598) 752272,* ≤ bay and headland – rest, TV P
April-October – **Meals** (dinner only) 16.00 **st.** 3.95 – **12 rm** 29.00/60.00 **st.** – SB.

Chough's Nest, North Walk, EX35 6HJ, ☎ (01598) 753315, *Fax (01598) 763529,* ≤ bay and Countisbury Hill – TV P. MC VISA JCB.
closed December and January – **Meals** (dinner only) 19.00 **t.** – **10 rm** (dinner included) 30.00/92.00 **t.**

Longmead House, 9 Longmead, EX35 6DQ, ☎ (01598) 752523, *info@longmeadhouse.co.uk, Fax (01598) 752523,* – TV P. MC VISA JCB.
April-October – **Meals** (by arrangement) 13.95 **st.** – **7 rm** 22.50/45.00 **st.** – SB.

Rockvale, Lee Rd, EX35 6HW, off Lee Rd ☎ (01598) 752279, *judithwoodland@rockvale.fsbusiness.co.uk,* ≤ – TV P. MC VISA JCB.
March-October – **Meals** (by arrangement) 16.00 **st.** 5.50 – **8 rm** 24.00/52.00 **st.** – SB.

Lynmouth.

Tors, EX35 6NA, ☎ (01598) 753236, *torshotel@torslynmouth.co.uk, Fax (01598) 752544,* ≤ Lynmouth and bay, ⛆ heated, – TV P – 80. MC AE VISA
closed 4 January-6 March – **Meals** (bar lunch Monday to Saturday)/dinner 23.00 **st.** and a la carte 6.50 – **33 rm** 40.00/140.00 **st.** – SB.

ENGLAND

Rising Sun, Harbourside, EX35 6EQ, ☎ (01598) 753223, *risingsunlynmouth@easynet.co.uk, Fax (01598) 753480*, ≤, « Part 14C thatched inn », – ✈ TV. MC AE D VISA JCB.
Meals – (see *The Restaurant* below) – **15 rm** ☐ 63.00/126.00 **t.**, 1 suite – SB.

Heatherville, Tors Park, EX35 6NB, by Tors Rd ☎ (01598) 752327, ≤ – ✈ rest, P. MC AE VISA JCB
April-October – **Meals** 17.50 **st.** – **7 rm** ☐ 25.00/56.00 **st.** – SB.

The Restaurant (at Rising Sun H.), Harbourside, EX35 6EQ, ☎ (01598) 75322 *Fax (01598) 753480*, « Part 14C thatched inn », – ✈. MC AE D VISA JCB
Meals (booking essential) (bar lunch)/dinner 27.50/35.00 **t.** and a la carte 8.95.

at Martinhoe *West : 4¼ m. via Coast rd (toll) – ✉ Barnstaple.*

Old Rectory, EX31 4QT, ☎ (01598) 763368, *reception@oldrectoryhotel.co.uk Fax (01598) 763567*, – ✈ TV P. MC VISA JCB.
March-November – **Meals** (dinner only) 27.50 **st.** 8.00 – **9 rm** ☐ (dinner include 72.00/144.00 **st.** – SB.

LYTHAM *Lancs.* 402 L 22.
Lytham Green Drive, Ballam Rd ☎ (01253) 734782.
London 239 – Blackpool 7 – Liverpool 50 – Preston 12.

Clifton Arms, West Beach, FY8 5QJ, ☎ (01253) 739898, *Fax (01253) 730657*, ≤ – TV – 150. MC AE D VISA.
Meals 25.00 **t.** (dinner) and a la carte 12.25/42.50 **t.** 9.50 – **46 rm** ☐ 89.50/130.00 2 suites – SB.

Premier Lodge, Church Rd, FY8 5LH, ☎ (0870) 7001424, *Fax (0870) 7001425* – ✈ MC AE D VISA.
Meals (grill rest.) – **21 rm** 46.00 **t.**

The Brasserie, 9 Clifton St., FY8 5EP, ☎ (01253) 794000, *Fax (01253) 795255* – MC AE VISA JCB
closed 25-26 December, Sunday and Monday – **Meals** (dinner only) 12.95/15.95 and a la carte 7.95.

Le Grand Londres (GREATER LONDON) est composé de la City et de 32 arrondissements administratifs (Borough) eux-mêmes divisés en quartiers ou en villages ayant conservé leur caractère propre (Area).

LYTHAM ST. ANNE'S *Lancs.* 402 L 22 – *pop. 40 866.*
Fairhaven, Lytham Hall Park, Ansdell ☎ (01253) 736741 – St. Annes Old Links, Highbu Rd ☎ (01253) 723597.
290 Clifton Drive South ☎ (01253) 725610.
London 237 – Blackpool 7 – Liverpool 44 – Preston 13.

Dalmeny, 19-33 South Promenade, FY8 1LX, ☎ (01253) 712236, *info@dalmenyhotel.co, Fax (01253) 724447*, ≤, squash – TV P – 200. MC AE D VISA.
closed 24 to 26 December – ***Atrium* : Meals** *(closed Saturday lunch and Sunday dinn* 12.50 **t.** (lunch) and a la carte 21.75/34.25 **t.** – **111 rm** ☐ 79.00/130.00 **t.**

The Grand, South Promenade, FY8 1NB, ☎ (01253) 721288, *book@the-grand.co.u Fax (01253) 714459*, ≤ – ✈ rm, TV P – 140. MC AE VISA.
closed 24 to 26 December – ***The Bistro* : Meals** (bar lunch Monday to Saturday)/dinr 15.00/20.50 **st.** and a la carte 6.95 – **40 rm** ☐ 76.50/113.00 **st.** – SB.

Glendower, North Promenade, FY8 2NQ, ☎ (01253) 723241, *glendower@bestwesterr o.uk, Fax (01253) 640069*, ≤, ✈ rest, TV P – 150. MC AE D VISA
closed 24 to 26 December – **Meals** (bar lunch)/dinner 17.00/25.00 **t.** 5.00 – **58 r** ☐ 42.00/80.00 **t.** – SB.

Bedford, 307-311 Clifton Drive South, FY8 1HN, ☎ (01253) 724636, *reservations@bedf dhotel.com, Fax (01253) 729244*, – ✈ rest, TV P – 120. MC AE D VISA JC
Meals 6.95/17.50 **t.** and a la carte 4.95 – **36 rm** ☐ 45.00/75.00 **t.** – SB.

MACCLESFIELD *Ches.* 402 403 404 N 24 – *pop. 50 270.*
The Tytherington Club ☎ (01625) 506000 – Shrigley Hall, Shrigley Park, Pott Shrig ☎ (01625) 575757.
Town Hall ☎ (01625) 504114.
London 186 – Chester 38 – Manchester 18 – Stoke-on-Trent 21.

Sutton Hall ⚘, Bullocks Lane, Sutton, SK11 0HE, Southeast : 2 m. by A 523 ✆ (01260) 253211, *Fax (01260) 252538*, – TV P. MC AE VISA
Meals 13.95/23.95 **st.** and a la carte 5.55 – **10 rm** 75.00/90.00 **st.**

Premier Lodge, Congleton Rd, Gawsworth, SK11 7XD, Southwest : 2 m. by A 537 on A 536 ✆ (0870) 7001466, *Fax (0870) 7001467* – rm, TV P. MC AE VISA.
Meals (grill rest.) a la carte approx. 10.35 **st.** – 6.00 – **28 rm** 46.00 **st.**

Travel Inn, Tytherington Business Park, Springwood Way, SK10 2XA, Northeast : 2 ½ m. by A 523 ✆ (01625) 427809, *Fax (01625) 422874* – rm, rest, TV P. MC AE VISA
Meals (grill rest.) – **40 rm** 40.95 **t.**

Adlington *North : 5 m. on A 523 – ✉ Macclesfield.*

Travelodge, London Road South, SK12 4NA, on A 523 ✆ (01625) 875292 – rm, TV P. MC AE VISA JCB.
Meals (grill rest.) – **32 rm** 39.95 **t.**

Bollington *Northeast : 3½ m. by A 523 on B 5090 – ✉ Macclesfield.*

Mauro's, 88 Palmerston St., SK10 5PW, ✆ (01625) 573898, *Fax (01625) 572800* – MC AE VISA JCB
closed 25-26 December, Sunday and Monday – **Meals** - Italian - 11.30 **t.** (lunch) and a la carte 14.65/25.00 **t.** 6.00.

Beasdales, 22 Old Market Pl., High St., SK10 5PH, ✆ (01625) 575058 – . MC VISA
closed 2 weeks August, Sunday and Monday – **Meals** - Bistro - (dinner only) a la carte 14.85/24.40 **t.**

Pott Shrigley *Northeast : 4¾ m. by A 523 on B 5090 – ✉ Macclesfield.*

Shrigley Hall ⚘, Shrigley Park, SK10 5SB, North : ¼ m. ✆ (01625) 575757, *shrigleyhall@paramount-hotels.co.uk, Fax (01625) 573323,* « Part 19C country house in park », ₣₆, , , 18, – , rm, TV P – 300. MC AE VISA
Oakridge : **Meals** (dinner only) 24.00/40.00 **t.** and a la carte 6.50 – **148 rm** 120.00/200.00 **t.** – SB.

ACKWORTH *Derbs.* 402 403 404 P 25 – *see Derby.*

ADINGLEY *Cambs.* 404 U 27 – *see Cambridge.*

ADLEY *Herefordshire* 403 L 27 – *see Hereford.*

AGHAM DOWN *E. Sussex – see Hailsham.*

AIDENCOMBE *Devon* 403 J 32 – *see Torquay.*

AIDENHEAD *Windsor & Maidenhead* 404 R 29 – *pop. 59 605.*

18 Bird Hills, Drift Rd, Hawthorn Hill ✆ (01628) 771030 – 18 Shoppenhangers Rd ✆ (01628) 624693 X.

to Marlow, Cookham and Windsor (Salter Bros. Ltd) (summer only).

The Library, St. Ives Rd ✆ (01628) 781110.

London 33 – Oxford 32 – Reading 13.

Plan on next page

Holiday Inn Maidenhead, Manor Lane, SL6 2RA, off Shoppenhangers Rd ✆ (01628) 506000, *janethomas@basshotels.com, Fax (01628) 506001,* ₣₆, , , , squash – , rm, rest, TV P – 400. MC AE VISA JCB X n
The Dining Room : **Meals** (carving rest.) a la carte 18.50/21.50 **st.** 10.00 – ***Borders Brasserie :*** **Meals** (lunch booking essential) a la carte 20.00/25.00 **st.** 10.00 – 13.50 – **187 rm** 175.00 **st.**, 2 suites – SB.

Fredrick's, Shoppenhangers Rd, SL6 2PZ, ✆ (01628) 581000, *reservations@fredricks-hotel.co.uk, Fax (01628) 771054,* – TV P – 150. MC AE VISA JCB. X c
closed Christmas and New Year – **Meals** – (see ***Fredrick's*** below) – **36 rm** 185.00/240.00 **t.**, 1 suite – SB.

Walton Cottage, Marlow Rd, SL6 7LT, ✆ (01628) 624394, *res@walcothotel.co.uk, Fax (01628) 773851* – , rest, TV P – 70. MC AE VISA JCB. Y e
closed 24 December-5 January – **Meals** *(closed Friday to Sunday and Bank Holidays)* (dinner only) 17.95 **st.** 8.50 – **66 rm** 98.00/135.00 **st.**, 3 suites.

ENGLAND

MAIDENHEAD

Street	Square	No.
Bad Godesberg Way	Y	2
Belmont Park Avenue	V	3
Blackamoor Lane	V	5
Boyn Hill Avenue	Z	6
Braywick Road	Z	7
Bridge Street	Y	9
College Road	V	13
Cookham Road	Y	14
Crescent (The)	Y	15
Ferry Road	X	17
Frascati Way	YZ	18
Furze Platt Road	V	20
Grenfell Place	Z	21
Gringer Hill	V	22
Harrow Lane	V	24
High Street	Y	
High Street BRAY-ON-THAMES	X	25
King's Grove	Z	27
Linden Avenue	V	28
Lower Cookham Road	V	29
Manor Lane	X	31
Market Street	Y	32
Nicholson's Walk Shopping Centre	YZ	
Norreys Drive	X	35
Oldfield Road	V	36
Ray Street	V	38
Ray Mill Rd West	V	39
St. Ives Road	Y	41
St. Mark's Road	V	42
Stafferton Way	Z	43
Upper Bray Road	X	45

For business or tourist interest:
MICHELIN Red Guide EUROPE.

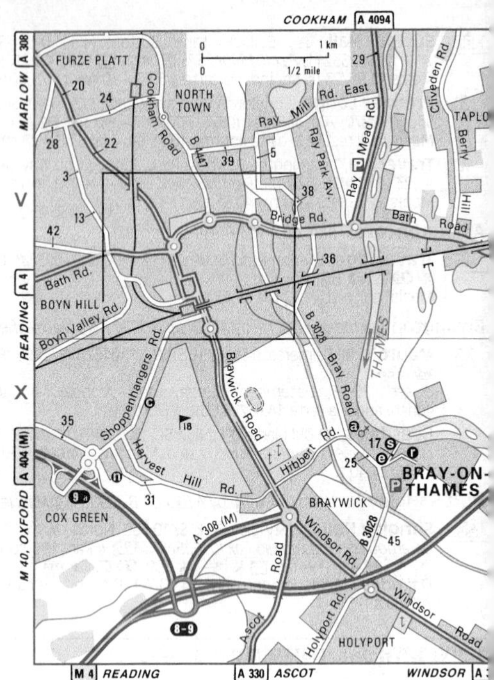

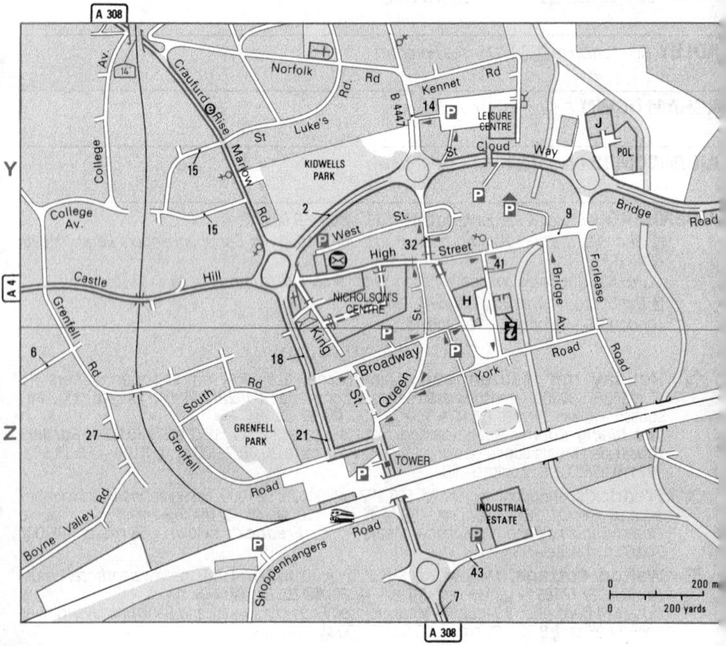

A 308
Y
Z
A 4
Craufurd Rise
Marlow Rd
College Av.
College
Norfolk Rd
St Luke's Rd.
Kennet Rd
B 4447
LEISURE CENTRE
St Cloud Way
KIDWELLS PARK
POL.
Bridge Road
West St.
High Street
Castle Hill
NICHOLSON'S CENTRE
King St.
Bridge Av.
Forlease Road
Grenfell Rd
Broadway
Queen St.
York Road
South Rd
GRENFELL PARK
Grenfell Road
TOWER
Boyne Valley Rd
Shoppenhangers Road
INDUSTRIAL ESTATE
200 m
200 yards
A 308

XXX **Fredrick's** (at Fredrick's H.), Shoppenhangers Rd, SL6 2PZ, ☎ (01628) 581000, *reservations@fredricks-hotel.co.uk, Fax (01628) 771054,* – P. MC AE VISA JCB X C
closed Christmas, New Year and Saturday lunch – **Meals** 27.50/37.50 **t.** and a la carte 9.00.

ENGLAND

MAIDEN NEWTON *Dorset* 403 404 M 31.

London 144 – Exeter 55 – Taunton 37 – Weymouth 16.

XX **Le Petit Canard,** Dorchester Rd, DT2 0BE, ☎ (01300) 320536, *craigs@lepetitcanard.freeserve.co.uk, Fax (01300) 321286* – . MC AE VISA
closed Sunday and Monday – **Meals** (dinner only) 25.50 **t.** 8.95.

MAIDSTONE *Kent* 404 V 30 *Great Britain G. – pop. 90 878.*

Env. : *Leeds Castle★ AC, SE : 4½ m. by A 20 and B 2163.*

Tudor Park Hotel, Ashford Rd, Bearsted ☎ (01622) 734334 – Cobtree Manor Park, Chatham Rd, Boxley ☎ (01622) 753276.

The Gatehouse, Palace Gdns., Mill St. ☎ (01622) 602169 – Motorway Service Area, junction 8, M 20, Hollingbourne ☎ (01622) 739029.

London 36 – Brighton 64 – Cambridge 84 – Colchester 72 – Croydon 36 – Dover 45 – Southend-on-Sea 49.

Hilton Maidstone, Bearsted Rd, ME14 5AA, Northeast : 1 ½ m. by A 249 ☎ (01622) 734322, *reservations@hilton.com, Fax (01622) 734600,* – , rest, P – 200. MC AE VISA
Meals *(closed Saturday lunch)* 13.95/19.95 **st.** and dinner a la carte 5.75 – 10.50 – **145 rm** 114.00 **st.**, 1 suite – SB.

Travel Inn, Allington Lock, Sandling, ME14 3AS, North : 2 ¼ m. by A 229 off Aylesford rd ☎ (01622) 717251, *Fax (01622) 715159,* – rm, rest, P. MC AE VISA.
Meals (grill rest.) – **40 rm** 40.95 **t.**

Travel Inn, London Rd, ME16 0HG, Northwest : 2 m. on A 20 ☎ (01622) 752515, *Fax (01622) 672469* – rm, P. MC AE VISA.
Meals (grill rest.) – **40 rm** 40.95 **t.**

XX **Waterside,** St. Faith's St., ME14 1LJ, ☎ (01622) 691248, *Fax (01622) 690909,* « Part 15C » – MC AE VISA
closed Sunday dinner, Monday lunch and Bank Holidays – **Meals** a la carte 25.95/33.40 **st.** 10.00.

at Bearsted *East : 3 m. by A 249 off A 20 – Maidstone.*

Marriott Tudor Park H. & Country Club, Ashford Rd, ME14 4NQ, on A 20 ☎ (01622) 734334, *Fax (01622) 735360,* – P – 250. MC AE VISA.
Fairviews : **Meals** 15.95/22.50 **st.** (lunch) and dinner a la carte 18.95/26.50 **st.** 8.25 – ***LongWeekend :*** **Meals** a la carte 14.00/21.25 **st.** 7.75 – 10.95 – **119 rm** 90.00/114.00 **st.**, 1 suite.

XX **Soufflé Restaurant on the Green,** The Green, ME14 4DN, ☎ (01622) 737065, *Fax (01622) 737065,* – P. MC AE VISA JCB
closed Saturday lunch, Sunday dinner and Monday – **Meals** 13.50/16.50 **t.** (lunch) a la carte 29.00/33.50 **t.** 10.50.

at Wateringbury *Southwest : 4½ m. on A 26 – Maidstone.*

Premier Lodge, Tonbridge Rd, ME18 5NS, ☎ (0870) 7001560, *Fax (0870) 7001561,* – rm, P – 25. MC AE VISA.
Meals (grill rest.) – 6.00 – **38 rm** 46.00 **st.**

at Larkfield *Northwest : 3 ¼ m. on A 20 – Maidstone.*

Larkfield Priory, London Rd, ME20 6HJ, ☎ (01732) 846858, *Fax (01732) 846786* – P – 80. MC AE VISA
Meals (bar lunch Monday to Saturday)/dinner 17.00/20.00 **st.** 7.25 – 9.75 – **52 rm** 80.00/90.00 **st.** – SB.

MAIDSTONE SERVICE AREA *Kent* 404 V 30 – *Maidstone.*

Travel Inn without rest., Hollingbourne, ME17 1SS, at junction 8 of M 20 ☎ (01622) 631100, *Fax (01622) 739535* – P. MC AE VISA.
closed Christmas and New Year – **58 rm** 40.95.

The Guide is updated annually so renew your Guide every year.

MALDON *Essex* 404 W 28 – *pop. 15 841.*

Forrester Park, Beckingham Rd, Great Totham ℘ (01621) 891406 – , Bunsay Downs, Little Baddow Rd, Woodham Walter ℘ (01245) 412648.

Coach Lane ℘ (01621) 856503.

London 42 – Chelmsford 9 – Colchester 17.

Blue Boar, Silver St., CM9 4QE, ℘ (01621) 852681, *Fax (01621) 856202* – rm, 30. VISA
Meals 12.50/15.00 and a la carte 5.95 – **29 rm** 65.00/95.00 **st.** – SB.

Chigborough Lodge, Chigborough Rd, Heybridge, CM9 4RE, Northeast : 2 ½ m. by B 1026 ℘ (01621) 853590 – VISA
closed 2 weeks in summer, 2 weeks in winter, Monday, Tuesday, Saturday lunch and Sunday dinner – **Meals** (booking essential) a la carte 19.25/24.25 **t.** 6.90.

at Tolleshunt Knights *Northeast : 7 m. by B 1026 – ✉ Maldon.*

Five Lakes H. Golf Country Club & Spa, Colchester Rd, Tolleshunt Knights, CM9 8HX, Southeast : 1 ¼ m. by B 1026 ℘ (01621) 868888, *enquiries@fivelake.co.uk*, *Fax (01621) 869696*, , , , , , , , squash – , rest, – 250. VISA
Camelot : **Meals** *(closed Sunday and Monday)* (dinner only) 24.50 **t.** and a la carte 13.00
Bejerano's Brasserie : **Meals** 18.50 **t.** (dinner) and a la carte 13.00/19.60 **t.** 13.00 – 9.50 – **110 rm** 90.00/142.00 **st.**, 4 suites – SB.

MALMESBURY *Wilts.* 403 404 N 29 *The West Country G. – pop. 4 218.*

See : *Town★ – Market Cross★★ – Abbey★.*

Town Hall, Market Lane ℘ (01666) 823748.

London 108 – Bristol 28 – Gloucester 24 – Swindon 19.

Old Bell, Abbey Row, SN16 0AG, ℘ (01666) 822344, *info@oldbellhotel.com*, *Fax (01666) 825145*, « Part 13C former abbots hostel », – – 35. JCB
Meals – (see ***The Restaurant*** below) – **29 rm** 75.00/95.00 **st.**, 2 suites – SB.

Knoll House, Swindon Rd, SN16 9LU, on B 4042 ℘ (01666) 823114, *Fax (01666) 8238*, heated, – rest, VISA JCB
Meals (dinner only) a la carte 17.40/25.25 **t.** 6.00 – **22 rm** 70.00/95.00 **st.** – SB.

The Restaurant (at Old Bell H.), Abbey Row, SN16 0AG, ℘ (01666) 8223, *Fax (01666) 825145*, – VISA JCB
Meals (booking essential) 11.75/19.75 **st.** and a la carte 10.50.

at Crudwell *North : 4 m. on A 429 – ✉ Malmesbury.*

Mayfield House, SN16 9EW, on A 429 ℘ (01666) 577409, *mayfield@callnetuk.com*, *Fax (01666) 577977*, – rest, – 30. VISA
Meals (bar lunch Monday to Saturday)/dinner 17.95/22.95 **st.** 5.25 – **24 rm** 56.00/79.00 **st.** – SB.

MALPAS *Ches.* 402 403 L 24 – *pop. 3 684.*

London 177 – Birmingham 60 – Chester 15 – Shrewsbury 26 – Stoke-on-Trent 30.

Tilston Lodge without rest., Tilston, SY14 7DR, Northwest : 3 m. on Tilston ℘ (01829) 250223, *Fax (01829) 250223*, « Rare breed farm animals », , –
3 rm 45.00/72.00 **st.**

MALVERN *Worcs.* 403 404 N 27 – *see Great Malvern.*

MALVERN WELLS *Worcs.* 403 404 N 27 – *see Great Malvern.*

In alta stagione, *e soprattutto nelle stazioni turistiche, è prudente prenotare con un certo anticipo. Avvertite immediatamente l'albergatore se non potete più occupare la camera prenotata.*

Se scrivete ad un albergo all'estero, allegate alla vostra lettera un tagliando-risposta internazionale (disponibile presso gli uffici postali).

MAN (Isle of) 402 FG 21 *Great Britain G. – pop. 71 714.*

See : *Laxey Wheel★★ – Snaefell★ (✻★★★) – Cregneash Folk Museum★.*

from Douglas to Belfast (Isle of Man Steam Packet Co. Ltd) (summer only) (2 h 45 mn) – from Douglas to Republic of Ireland (Dublin) (Isle of Man Steam Packet Co. Ltd) (2 h 45 mn) – from Douglas to Heysham (Isle of Man Steam Packet Co.) (3 h 30 mn) – from Douglas to Liverpool (Isle of Man Steam Packet Co. Ltd) (2 h 30 mn/4 h).

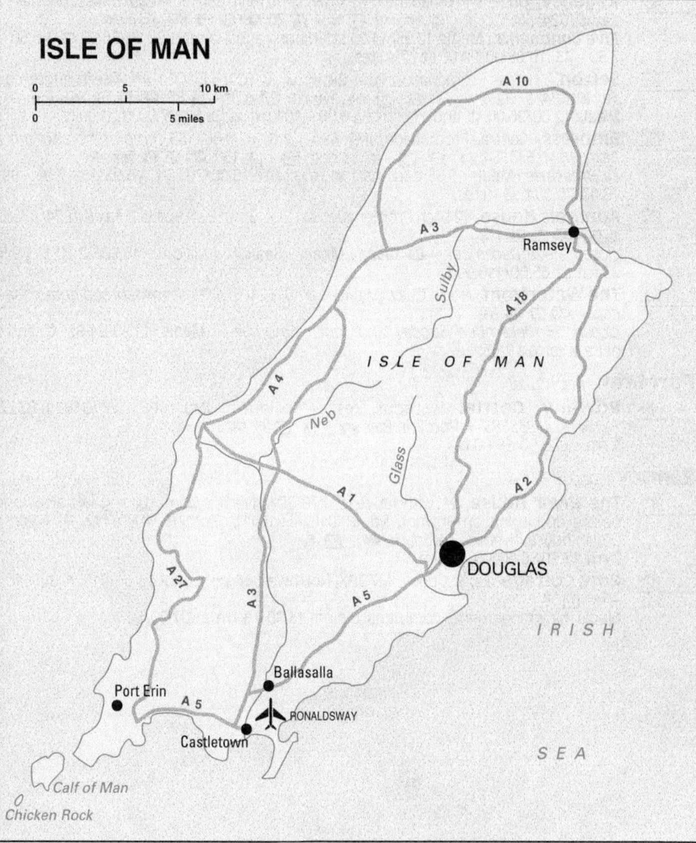

Ballasalla.

XX **Haworths,** Main Rd, IM9 2DA, ☎ (01624) 822940 – MC VISA
closed Sunday, Monday and Saturday lunch – **Meals** 14.00/25.00 **t.** 9.00.

Castletown – *pop. 2 958.*

Douglas 10.

XX **Chablis Cellar,** 21 Bank St., IM9 1AT, ☎ (01624) 823527, *adrian.chablis@virgin.net, Fax (01624) 824165* – P. MC AE VISA
closed 2 weeks January – **Meals** 13.45/36.00 **st.** and a la carte 7.25.

Douglas – *pop. 23 487.*

Douglas Municipal, Pulrose Park ☎ (01624) 675952 – King Edward Bay, Groudle Rd, Onchan ☎ (01624) 620430.

Ronaldsway Airport : ☎ (01624) 821600, SW : 7 m. – **Terminal** : *Coach service from Lord St.*

Sea Terminal Building ☎ (01624) 686766.

ENGLAND

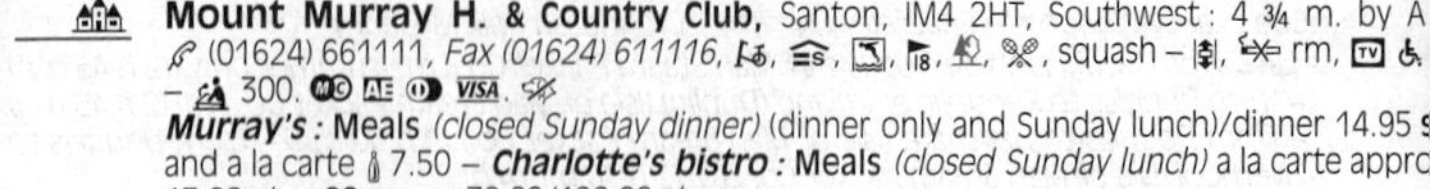

Mount Murray H. & Country Club, Santon, IM4 2HT, Southwest : 4 ¾ m. by A
(01624) 661111, *Fax (01624) 611116,* squash – rm,
– 300.
Murray's : Meals *(closed Sunday dinner)* (dinner only and Sunday lunch)/dinner 14.95 s
and a la carte 7.50 – ***Charlotte's bistro :*** Meals *(closed Sunday lunch)* a la carte appro
13.00 **st.** – **90 rm** 79.00/129.00 **st.**

Regency, Queens Promenade, IM2 4NN, (01624) 680680, *regency@securemail-l.ne*
Fax (01624) 680690, – rm, – 70.
Five Continents : Meals 12.95/14.95 **st.** (dinner) and a la carte 17.90/26.00 **st.** 6.50 –
7.50 – **43 rm** 65.00/90.00 **st.**, 2 suites.

Sefton, Harris Promenade, IM1 2RW, (01624) 645500, *info@seftonhotel.co.in*
Fax (01624) 676004, – rm, – 80.
Meals 12.00/26.00 **st.** and a la carte 6.00 – **101 rm** 68.00/97.00 **st.**, 1 suite.

Empress, Central Promenade, IM2 4RA, (01624) 661155, *empresshotel@manx.ne*
Fax (01624) 673554, – rest, – 150.
La Brasserie : Meals 15.95 **t.** (dinner) and a la carte 18.00/20.75 **t.** 6.95 – 7.95 – **99 r**
70.00/75.00 **t.**, 3 suites.

Admirals House, 12 Loch Promenade, IM1 2LX, (01624) 629551, *Fax (01624) 675021*
closed 25-28 December – ***La Tasca :*** Meals - Spanish - a la carte 14.90/22.20 **t.** 9.50
23 rm 65.00/110.00 **t.**

The Waterfront, North Quay, IM1 4LH, (01624) 673222, *jean@fabfood.enterprise-p*
com –
closed 25 December, Sunday and lunch Saturday – **Meals** 12.95/21.95 **t.** and di
ner a la carte 7.65.

Port Erin – *pop. 3 218.*

Rowany Cottier without rest., Spaldrick, IM9 6PE, (01624) 83228
Fax (01624) 835685, Port Erin Bay, –
5 rm 35.00/58.00 **t.**

Ramsey – *pop. 6 874.*

The River House without rest., IM8 3DA, North : ¼ m. turning left after brid
before Bridge Inn on Bowring Rd (01624) 816412, *Fax (01624) 816412,* « Part G
orgian house, riverside setting », –
2 rm 39.50/87.00, 1 suite.

Rose Cottage , St. Judes, IM7 3BX, Northwest : 4 ½ m. off A 13 (01624) 880610,
–
Meals (by arrangement) (communal dining) 13.00 – **3 rm** 27.00/54.00.

MANCHESTER

Gtr. Manchester 402 403 404 N 23 *Great Britain G. – pop. 402 889*

London 202 – Birmingham 86 – Glasgow 221 – Leeds 43 – Liverpool 35 – Nottingham 72.

TOURIST INFORMATION

Manchester Visitor Centre, Town Hall Extension, Lloyd St. ℘ (0161) 234 3157.

Manchester Airport, International Arrivals Hall, Terminal 1 ℘ (0161) 436 3344 – Manchester Airport, International Arrivals Hall, Terminal 2 ℘ (061) 489 6412.

PRACTICAL INFORMATION

18 *Heaton Park, Prestwich ℘ (0161) 654 9899,* **ABV**.

18 *Houldsworth Park, Houldsworth St., Reddish, Stockport ℘ (0161) 442 9611.*

18 *Chorlton-cum-Hardy, Barlow Hall, Barlow Hall Rd ℘ (0161) 881 3139.*

18 *William Wroe, Pennybridge Lane, Flixton ℘ (0161) 748 8680.*

Manchester International Airport : ℘ (0161) 489 3000, S : 10 m. by A 5103 – **AX** – and M 56 – **Terminal** : *Coach service from Victoria Station.*

SIGHTS

See : *City★ - Castlefield Heritage Park★* **CZ** – *Town Hall★* **CZ** – *City Art Gallery★* **CZ M2** – *Cathedral★ (stalls and canopies★)* **CY** – *Museum of Science and Industry★* **CZ** M.

Env. : *Whitworth Art Gallery★, S : 1½ m.*

Exc. : *Quarry Bank Mill★, S : 10 m. off B 5166, exit 5 from M 56.*

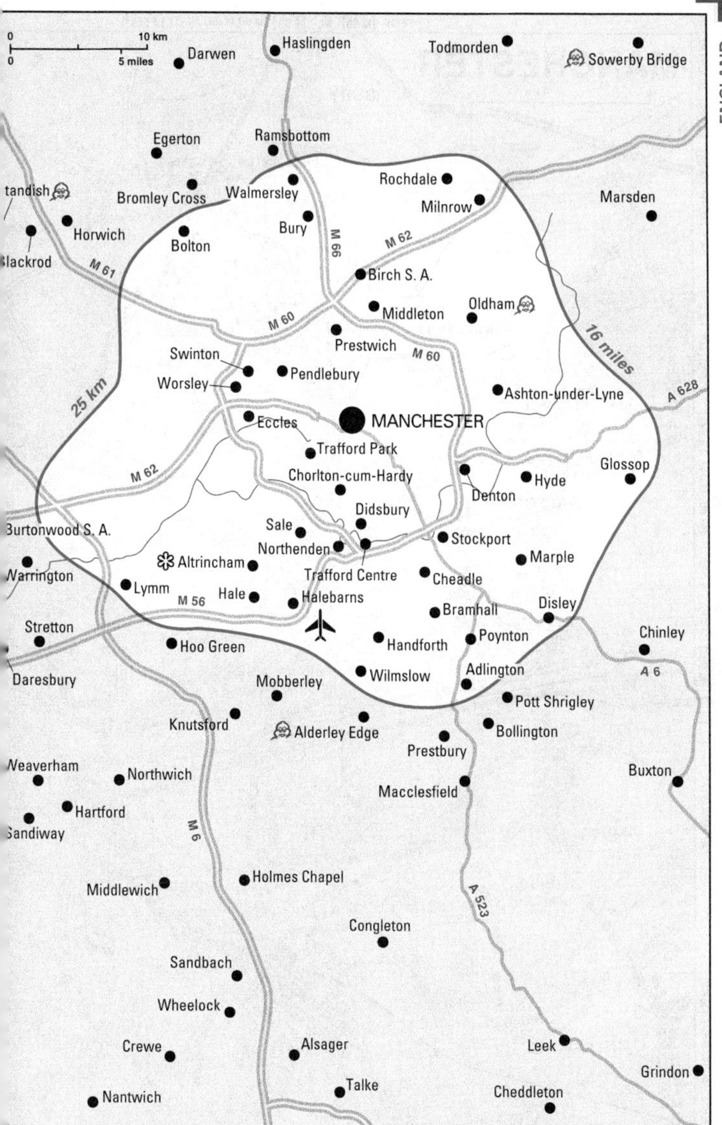

En saison, *surtout dans les stations fréquentées,*
il est prudent de retenir à l'avance.
Cependant, si vous ne pouvez pas occuper la chambre
que vous avez retenue, prévenez immédiatement l'hôtelier.

Si vous écrivez à un hôtel à l'étranger, joignez à votre lettre
un coupon-réponse international (disponible dans les bureaux de poste).

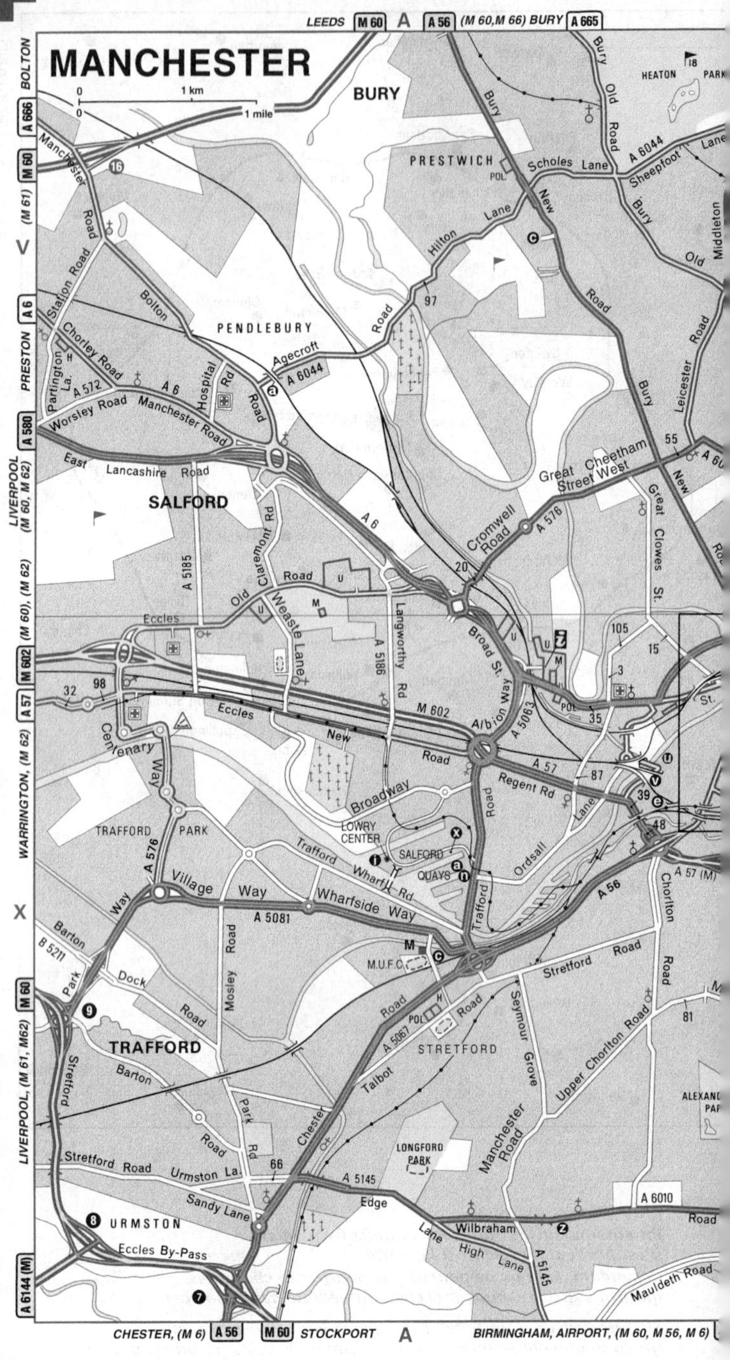
MANCHESTER
LEEDS
M 60
A
A 56
(M 60, M 66) BURY
A 665
BOLTON
A 666
M 60
(M 61)
V
A 6
PRESTON
A 580
LIVERPOOL (M 60, M 62)
(M 60), (M 62)
M 602
A 57
WARRINGTON, (M 62)
X
M 60
LIVERPOOL, (M 61, M62)
A 6144 (M)
CHESTER, (M 6)
A 56
M 60
STOCKPORT
A
BIRMINGHAM, AIRPORT, (M 60, M 56, M 6)
BURY
PRESTWICH
PENDLEBURY
SALFORD
TRAFFORD PARK
TRAFFORD
STRETFORD
URMSTON
HEATON PARK
LOWRY CENTER
SALFORD QUAYS
M.U.F.C.
LONGFORD PARK
Scholes Lane
Sheepfoot Lane
Bury Old Road
Bury New Road
Hilton Lane
Agecroft Road
Bolton Road
Station Road
Chorley Road
Worsley Road
Manchester Road
Hospital Rd
East Lancashire Road
Great Cheetham Street West
Cromwell Road
Great Clowes St.
Old Road
Claremont Rd
Weaste Lane
Langworthy Rd
Broad St.
Albion Way
Eccles New Road
Regent Rd
Ordsall Lane
Broadway
Trafford Wharf Rd
Trafford Road
Centenary Way
Village Way
Wharfside Way
Barton Dock Road
Mosley Road
Stretford Road
Chorlton Road
Upper Chorlton Road
Seymour Grove
Talbot Road
Chester Road
Manchester Road
Barton Road
Park Rd
Urmston La.
Sandy Lane
Edge Lane
Wilbraham Road
High Lane
Mauldeth Road
Eccles By-Pass
Partington La.
Leicester Road
Middleton Old Road
A 6044
A 572
A 5185
A 5186
A 5063
A 576
A 5081
A 5067
A 5145
A 6010
B 5211
A 57 (M)
1 km
1 mile
ALEXANDRA PARK

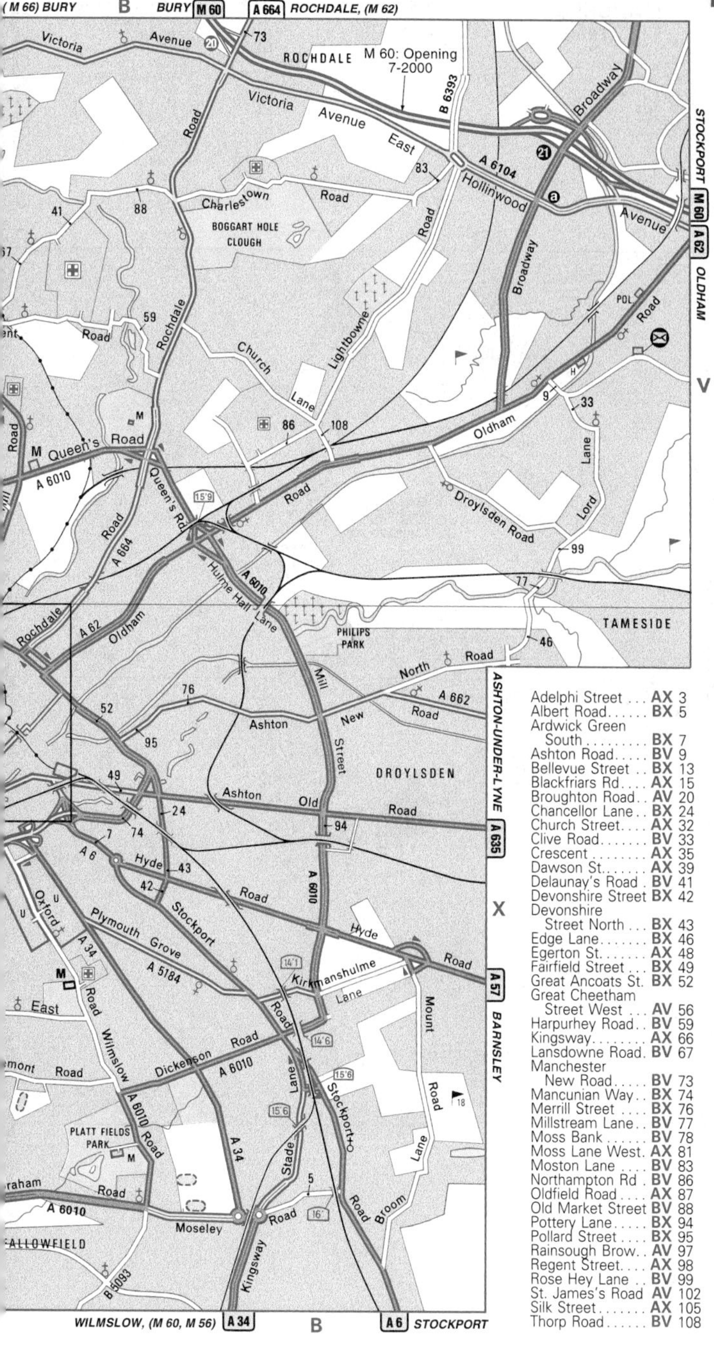
(M 66) BURY
B
BURY M 60
A 664 ROCHDALE, (M 62)
M 60: Opening
7-2000
ROCHDALE
Victoria Avenue
Victoria Avenue East
A 6104
Hollinwood Avenue
Broadway
B 6393
Charlestown Road
BOGGART HOLE
CLOUGH
Rochdale Road
Church Lane
Lightbowne Road
Queen's Road
Queen's Rd
A 6010
A 664
A 62
Oldham Road
Droylsden Road
Lord Lane
Hulme Hall Lane
Mill Street
North Road
A 662
Ashton New Road
Ashton Old Road
PHILIPS
PARK
TAMESIDE
DROYLSDEN
STOCKPORT M 60
A 62 OLDHAM
ASHTON-UNDER-LYNE A 635
A 57 BARNSLEY
V
X
A 6
Hyde Road
Stockport Road
Plymouth Grove
A 5184
Oxford Road
A 34
Kirkmanshulme Lane
Mount Road
Broom Lane
Dickenson Road
Wilmslow Road
A 6010 Road
Stade Lane
Stockport Road
PLATT FIELDS
PARK
Moseley Road
Kingsway
FALLOWFIELD
B 5093
WILMSLOW, (M 60, M 56) A 34
A 6 STOCKPORT

MANCHESTER
CENTRE

GREEN TOURIST GUIDES
Picturesque scenery, buildings
Attractive routes
Touring programmes
Plans of towns and buildings.

Crowne Plaza Midland, Peter St., M60 2DS, (0161) 236 3333, *Fax (0161) 932 4100*, squash – rm, – 450. VISA JCB CZ x
Trafford Room : **Meals** *(closed dinner Monday and Tuesday)* (carving rest.) 16.50/24.95 **st.** and a la carte 10.25 – (see also ***The French Restaurant*** and ***Nico Central*** below) – 14.50 – **289 rm** 155.00 **t.**, 14 suites – SB.

Le Meridien Victoria and Albert, Water St., M3 4JQ, (0161) 832 1188, *gm1452@forte-hotels.com, Fax (0161) 834 2484*, « Converted 19C warehouse, television themed interior », – rm, – 250. VISA AX u
Cafe Maigret : **Meals** a la carte 15.25/26.15 **st.** 8.50 – 13.50 – **154 rm** 165.00 **st.**, 4 suites – SB.

Renaissance, Blackfriars St., Deansgate, M3 2EQ, (0161) 835 2555, *manchester.sales@renaissancehotels.com, Fax (0161) 835 3077* – rm, – 400. VISA CY v
Meals a la carte 22.50/28.50 **st.** 7.50 – 11.50 – **196 rm** 115.00 **st.**, 4 suites.

Palace, Oxford St., M60 7HA, (0161) 288 1111, *Fax (0161) 288 2222*, « Victorian Gothic architecture, former Refuge Assurance building » – – 850. VISA
Waterhouses : **Meals** 12.90/35.00 **st.** and a la carte 8.75 – 11.95 – **241 rm** 144.00/160.00 **st.**, 11 suites – SB. CZ s

Malmaison, Piccadilly, M1 3AQ, (0161) 278 1000, *manchester@malmaison.com, Fax (0161) 278 1002*, « Contemporary interior », – rm, – 48. VISA JCB CZ u
Brasserie : **Meals** 11.95/12.95 **t.** and a la carte 10.95 – 10.75 – **104 rm** 110.00 **st.**, 8 suites.

Copthorne Manchester, Clippers Quay, Salford Quays, M5 2XP, (0161) 873 7321, *manchester@mill-cop.com, Fax (0161) 873 7318*, – rm, rest, – 150. VISA AX n
Chandlers : **Meals** (bar lunch Saturday and Sunday) 31.50 **st.** – 13.50 – **166 rm** 145.00/180.00 **st.** – SB.

Castlefield, Liverpool Rd, M3 4JR, (0161) 832 7073, *info@yclub.ivnet.com, Fax (0161) 837 3534*, – rest, – 60. VISA AX v
closed 25 and 26 December – **Meals** (bar lunch)/dinner a la carte 11.35/20.80 **st.** 3.45 – **48 rm** 78.00/84.00 **st.** – SB.

Jurys Inn, 56 Great Bridgewater St., M1 5LE, (0161) 953 8888, *manchester-inn@jurysdoyle.com, Fax (0161) 953 9090* – rm, – 50. VISA JCB
closed 24 to 27 December – **Meals** (bar lunch)/dinner a la carte 16.00/27.00 **st.** 8.00 – **265 rm** 62.00 **t.** CZ i

Premier Lodge, 7-11 Lower Mosley St., M2 3DW, (0870) 7001476, *Fax (0870) 7001477*, – rm, – 50. VISA CZ v
Meals (grill rest.) – 6.00 – **147 rm** 46.00 **t.**

Travelodge, Townbury House, Blackfriars St., M3 5AB, (0161) 834 9476, *Fax (0161) 839 5181* – rm, rest, . VISA CY a
Meals (cafe bar) – **160 rm** 49.95 **t.**

Express by Holiday Inn without rest., Waterfront Quay, Salford Quays, M5 2XW, (0161) 868 1000, *Fax (0161) 868 1068* – . VISA AX a
120 rm 58.00 **st.**

Travel Inn, Basin 8, The Quays, Salford Quays, M5 4SQ, (0161) 872 4026, *Fax (0161) 876 0094* – rm, . VISA AX x
Meals (grill rest.) – **52 rm** 40.95 **t.**

The French Restaurant (at Crowne Plaza Midland H.), Peter St., M60 2DS, (0161) 236 3333 – . VISA JCB CZ x
closedSunday – **Meals** (dinner only) 29.00/38.00 **st.** and a la carte 13.50.

Simply Heathcotes, Jackson Row, M2 5WD, (0161) 835 3536, *manchester@simply.co.uk, Fax (0161) 835 3534* – . VISA CZ c
closed 25-26 December, 1 January and Bank Holiday Monday – **Meals** 12.50/14.50 **t.** (lunch) and a la carte 23.00/25.00 **t.** 6.75.

Nico Central (at Crowne Plaza Midland H.), 2 Mount St., M60 2DS, (0161) 236 6488, *Fax (0161) 236 8897* – . VISA JCB CZ x
closed lunch Saturday and Sunday and Bank Holidays – **Meals** 14.95 **t.** (lunch) and a la carte 21.50/28.90 **t.** 9.00.

The Lincoln, 1 Lincoln Sq., M2 5LN, (0161) 834 9000, *Fax (0161) 834 9555* – . VISA CZ a
closed 25 December, 1 January, Saturday lunch and Bank Holidays – **Meals** 14.50/16.95 **t.** (lunch) and a la carte 22.40/38.40 **t.** 15.00.

Steven Saunders at The Lowry, Pier 8, Salford Quays, M5 2AZ, (0161) 876 2121, *stevensaunders@thelowry.com, Fax (0161) 876 2021* – . VISA AX i
Meals a la carte 13.00/24.00 **t.**

ENGLAND

XX **Yang Sing,** 34 Princess St., M1 4JY, ✆ (0161) 236 9438, *info@yang.sing.*
Fax (0161) 236 5934 – ▤. MC AE VISA CZ
closed 25 December – **Meals** - Chinese - a la carte 16.50/25.00 **st.**

XX **Barça,** Arches 8-9, Catalan Sq., Castlefield, M3 4WD, ✆ (0161) 839 70
Fax (0161) 839 7022, « Converted Victorian railway arches » – MC AE VISA JCB AX
closed Saturday lunch and Sunday – **Meals** a la carte 22.00/28.00 ⅓ 7.95.

XX **Giulio's Terrazza,** 14 Nicholas St., M1 4EJ, ✆ (0161) 236 4033, *Fax (0161) 228 6501* –
MC AE ⓓ VISA JCB CZ
closed 25 December and Sunday – **Meals** - Italian - 9.50/12.00 **t.** and a la carte ⅓ 6.50.

XX **Koreana,** Kings House, 40a King St. West, M3 2WY, ✆ (0161) 832 4330, *113036.1764@*
mpuserve.com, Fax (0161) 832 2293 – MC AE ⓓ VISA CZ
closed 1 week Christmas, Sunday and lunch Saturday and Bank Holidays – **Meals** - Korea
a la carte 12.40/26.00 **t.**

XX **Royal Orchid,** 36 Charlotte St., M1 4FD, ✆ (0161) 236 5183, *muaythai@iamtf.o*
Fax (0161) 236 8830 – MC AE ⓓ VISA CZ
closed 25 December and Sunday lunch – **Meals** - Thai - 7.50/20.00 **st.** and a la carte.

X **Market,** 104 High St., M4 1HQ, ✆ (0161) 834 3743, *marketrestaurant@btinternet.cc*
Fax (0161) 834 3743 – MC AE ⓓ VISA JCB CY
closed August, 1 week Easter, 1 week Christmas and Sunday-Tuesday – **Meals** (dinner or
a la carte 17.85/26.35 **t.** ⅓ 5.95.

at Northenden *South : 5¼ m. by A 5103* – **AX** – ✉ *Manchester.*

Posthouse Manchester, Palatine Rd, M22 4FH, ✆ (0870) 400 90
Fax (0161) 946 0139 – ⎮‡⎮, ✈ rm, TV P – 🏛 150. MC AE ⓓ VISA
Meals 15.00 **t.** and a la carte – ☕ 11.95 – **190 rm** 69.00 **st.** – SB.

at Didsbury *South : 5½ m. by A 5103* – **AX** – *on A 5145* – ✉ *Manchester.*

Eleven Didsbury Park without rest., 11 Didsbury Park, M20 5LH, ✆ (0161) 448 7711
nquiries@elevendidsburypark.com, Fax (0161) 448 8282, « Contemporary interior »,
✈ TV ✆ P. MC AE ⓓ VISA. ✂
☕ 9.50 **14 rm** 109.50/155.50 **st.**

at Trafford Centre *Southeast : 6½ m. by A 34* – **BX** – ✉ *Manchester.*

Travel Inn, Wilderspool Wood, M17 8NN, ✆ (0161) 747 8850, *Fax (0161) 747 4763* –
✈ rm, TV ♿ P. MC AE ⓓ VISA. ✂
Meals (grill rest.) – **59 rm** 40.95 **t.**

at Manchester Airport *South : 9 m. by A 5103* – **AX** – *off M 56* – ✉ *Manchester.*

Radisson SAS, Chicago Av., M90 3RA, ✆ (0161) 490 5000, *sales@manzq.rdsas.cc*
Fax (0161) 490 5100 – ✈ ▤ TV ✆ ♿ P – 🏛 400. MC AE ⓓ VISA JCB. ✂
Phileas Fogg : **Meals** 16.00/26.00 **t.** ⅓ 9.00 – ☕ 13.00 – **352 rm** 155.00/170.00 **st.**, 8 sui
– SB.

Hilton Manchester Airport, Outwood Lane (Terminal One), M90 4
✆ (0161) 435 3000, *manhitw@hilton.com, Fax (0161) 435 3040,* Fø, ≘s, 🏊 – ⎮‡⎮, ✈ rm,
TV ✆ ♿ P – 🏛 300. MC AE ⓓ VISA
Meals *(closed Saturday lunch)* 21.00 **st.** and a la carte ⅓ 3.95 – ***Portico :*** **Meals** *(clo*
Sunday) (dinner only) 30.00 **t.** ⅓ 8.50 – ☕ 14.50 – **222 rm** 150.00 **st.**, 1 suite – SB.

Posthouse Manchester Airport, Outwood Lane (Terminal One), M90 3
✆ (0161) 437 5811, *Fax (0161) 436 2340,* Fø, ≘s, 🏊 – ⎮‡⎮, ✈ rm, ▤ TV ✆ P – 🏛 75. MC
ⓓ VISA JCB. ✂
Meals *(closed Saturday lunch)* a la carte 22.85/27.95 **t.** ⅓ 7.95 – ☕ 13.95 – **295 rm** 99.00
– SB.

Etrop Grange, Thorley Lane, M90 4EG, ✆ (0161) 499 0500, *etropgrange@corushotels*
m, Fax (0161) 499 0790 – ✈ rm, TV ✆ P – 🏛 40. MC AE ⓓ VISA JCB
Meals – (see ***The Restaurant*** below) – ☕ 12.50 – **62 rm** 121.00/142.00 **st.**, 2 suites – S

Holiday Inn Garden Court, Outwood Lane, (Terminal One), M90 4
✆ (0161) 498 0333, *reservations@mchap.co.uk, Fax (0161) 498 0222* – ⎮‡⎮, ✈ rm, TV ♿
MC AE ⓓ VISA JCB. ✂
Meals (bar lunch)/dinner 14.95 **st.** and a la carte ⅓ 5.25 – ☕ 7.95 – **226 rm** 69.50/99.50 s
SB.

Travel Inn, Finney Lane, Heald Green, SK8 2QH, East : 2 m. by B 5166 ✆ (0161) 499 19
Fax (0161) 437 4910 – ✈ rm, TV ♿ P – 🏛 70. MC AE ⓓ VISA. ✂
Meals (grill rest.) – **60 rm** 40.95 **t.**

ENGLAND

XXX **Moss Nook,** Ringway Rd, Moss Nook, M22 5WD, ✆ (0161) 437 4778, *Fax (0161) 498 8089* – P. MC AE VISA
closed 2 weeks Christmas-New Year, Saturday lunch, Sunday and Monday – **Meals** 18.50/31.50 **t.** and a la carte 10.90.

XX **The Restaurant** (at Etrop Grange H.), Thorley Lane, M90 4EG, ✆ (0161) 499 0500, *etropgrange@corushotels.com, Fax (0161) 499 0790* – P. MC AE VISA JCB
closed Saturday lunch – **Meals** 28.95 **st.** (dinner) and lunch a la carte 16.85/27.50 **st.** 9.95.

at Trafford Park *Southwest : 2 m. by A 56 and A 5081 – ✉ Manchester.*

Quality H. Manchester, Waters Reach, M17 1WS, ✆ (0161) 873 8899, *info@qualitymanchester.co.uk, Fax (0161) 872 6556* – rm, TV P. MC AE VISA JCB. AX c
Meals – (see ***Rhodes & Co.*** below) – 10.00 – **111 rm** 75.00/98.50 **st.**

X **Rhodes & Co.,** Waters Reach, M17 1WS, ✆ (0161) 868 1900, *Fax (0161) 868 1901* – P. MC AE VISA AX i
closed lunch Saturday and Sunday – **Meals** 11.50 **t.** (lunch) and a la carte 14.80/26.95 **t.** 10.00.

Chorlton-Cum-Hardy *Southwest : 5 m. by A 5103 on A 6010 – ✉ Manchester.*

Abbey Lodge without rest., 501 Wilbraham Rd, M21 0UJ, ✆ (0161) 862 9266, *Fax (0161) 862 9266,* – TV P. AX z
closed 20 December-2 January – **4 rm** 40.00/50.00 **s.**

Eccles *West : 4 m. by M 602 –* **AX** *– ✉ Manchester.*

Highbury, 113 Monton Rd, M30 9HQ, Northwest : 1 ¼ m. by A 576 on B 5229 ✆ (0161) 787 8545, *Fax (0161) 787 9023* – rest, TV P. MC AE VISA.
closed 1 week Christmas – **Meals** (dinner only) 7.50/12.00 **st.** 3.75 – **16 rm** 38.00/46.00 **st.**

Worsley *West : 7¼ m. by M 602 –* **AV** *– and M 60 (eastbound) on A 572 – ✉ Manchester.*

Marriott Manchester Hotel & Country Club, Worsley Park, M28 2QT, on A 575 ✆ (0161) 975 2000, *Fax (0161) 799 6341,* 18, – rm, rest, TV P – 250. MC AE VISA JCB
Brindley's : **Meals** *(closed Saturday lunch)* 17.50/22.50 **t.** and dinner a la carte 11.95 – 11.95 – **154 rm** 109.00 **t.**, 5 suites – SB.

Novotel Manchester West, Worsley Brow, M28 2YA, at junction 13 of M 62 ✆ (0161) 799 3535, *Fax (0161) 703 8207,* heated – rm, rest, TV P – 220. MC AE VISA JCB
Meals 16.50 **t.** and a la carte – 9.50 – **119 rm** 72.00 **t.** – SB.

XX **Tung Fong,** 2 Worsley Rd, M28 4NL, on A 572 ✆ (0161) 794 5331, *Fax (0161) 727 9598* – . MC AE VISA
Meals - Chinese (Peking) - (dinner only) 18.00/29.50 **st.** and a la carte 5.50.

Pendlebury *Northwest : 4 m. by A 6 on A 666 – ✉ Manchester.*

Premier Lodge, 219 Bolton Rd, M27 8TG, ✆ (0870) 7001470, *Fax (0870) 7001471* – TV P. MC AE VISA. AV a
Meals (grill rest.) – **31 rm** 46.00 **t.**

Swinton *Northwest : 4 m. by A 580 –* **AV** *– and A 572 on B 5231 – ✉ Manchester.*

Premier Lodge, East Lancs Rd, M27 0AA, Southwest : ½ m. on A 580 ✆ (0870) 7001472, *Fax (0870) 7001473* – rm, TV P. MC AE VISA.
Meals (grill rest.) a la carte 8.95/17.85 **st.** – 6.00 – **27 rm** 46.00 **st.**

MANCHESTER AIRPORT *Gtr. Manchester* 402 403 404 N 23 – *see Manchester.*

MANGOTSFIELD *Bristol* 403 404 M 29 – *see Bristol.*

MANNINGTREE *Essex* 404 X 28 – *pop. 5 043 – ✉ Colchester.*
London 67 – Colchester 10 – Ipswich 12.

X **Stour Bay Cafe,** 39-43 High St., CO11 1AH, ✆ (01206) 396687, *mark@stourbaycafe.co.uk, Fax (01206) 395462* – MC AE VISA
closed 3 weeks January, Sunday, Monday and Saturday lunch – **Meals** 8.50/13.50 **t.** and dinner a la carte 6.95.

Les prix — Pour toutes précisions sur les prix indiqués dans ce guide, reportez-vous aux pages de l'introduction.

MANSFIELD *Notts.* 402 403 404 Q 24.
18 Sherwood Forest, Eakring Rd ☎ (01623) 626689.
London 145 – Derby 24 – Nottingham 16 – Sheffield 30.

Stoneleigh, Crow Hill Drive, NG19 7AE, off A 617 ☎ (01623) 650692, *julie@stoneleigh-breeserve.co.uk*, « Victorian Gothic house », – TV P.
closed 25 December and 1 January – **Meals** (by arrangement) 25.00 **s.** – **3 rm** 40.0 75.00 **s.** – SB.

MARAZION *Cornwall* 403 D 33 *The West Country G.* – *pop. 1 381* – ✉ *Penzance.*
Env. : *St. Michael's Mount★★ (≤★★) – Ludgvan★ (Church★) N : 2 m. by A 30 – Chysaus Village★, N : 2 m. by A 30 – Gulval★ (Church★) W : 2½ m – Prussia Cove★, SE : 5½ m. by A and minor rd.*
9 Praa Sands, Penzance ☎ (01736) 763445.
London 318 – Penzance 3 – Truro 26.

Ennys without rest., Trewhella Lane, St. Hilary, TR20 9BZ, East : 2 ½ m. by Turnpike on B 3280 ☎ (01736) 740262, *ennys@zetnet.co.uk, Fax (01736) 740055*, « 17C mar house, working farm », heated, – TV P. VISA.
13 February-October – **5 rm** 40.00/70.00 **st.**

at Perranuthnoe *Southeast : 1 ¾ m. by A 394* – ✉ *Penzance.*

Ednovean Farm without rest., TR20 9LZ, ☎ (01736) 711883, *Fax (01736) 710480*, « Converted 17C barn », – TV P.
closed 2 weeks Christmas – **2 rm** 50.00/65.00 **s.**, 1 suite.

MARCH *Cambs.* 402 404 U 26 – *pop. 16 221.*
9 Frogs Abbey, Grange Rd ☎ (01354) 652364.
London 93 – Cambridge 34 – Norwich 63.

Olde Griffin, High St., PE15 9JS, ☎ (01354) 652517, *griffhotel@aol.cc Fax (01354) 650086* – TV P – 100. AE VISA JCB.
Meals (barlunch)/dinner a la carte 11.65/20.65 **st.** – **20 rm** 45.00/59.50 **st.** – SB.

MARDEN *Herefordshire – see Hereford.*

MARGARETTING *Essex* 404 V 28 – *see Chelmsford.*

MARGATE *Kent* 404 Y 29.
22 High st. (01843) 220241.
London 74 – Canterbury 17 – Dover 21 – Maidstone 43.

Travel Inn, Station Green, Station Rd, CT9 5AF, ☎ (01843) 299280, *Fax (01843) 22145* rm, rest, TV P. AE VISA.
Meals (grill rest.) – **44 rm** 40.95 **t.**

MARKET BOSWORTH *Leics.* 402 403 404 P 26 – *pop. 2 019* – ✉ *Nuneaton.*
London 109 – Birmingham 30 – Coventry 23 – Leicester 22.

Softleys, Market Pl., CV13 0JS, ☎ (01455) 290464, *Fax (01455) 290464* – TV. AE VISA.
closed 25-26 December – **Meals** *(closed Monday lunch and Sunday)* 12.50 **t.** and a la ca 6.75 – **4 rm** 50.00/60.00 **t.**

MARKET HARBOROUGH *Leics.* 404 R 26 – *pop. 16 563.*
18 Great Oxendon Rd ☎ (01858) 463684.
Council Offices, Adam and Eve St. ☎ (01858) 821270.
London 88 – Birmingham 47 – Leicester 15 – Northampton 17.

The Angel, High St., LE16 7NL, ☎ (01858) 462702, *angel@menzies_hotels.co Fax (01858) 410464* – , rest, TV P – 25. AE VISA
Meals a la carte 11.75/20.95 **t.** – **37 rm** 71.25/92.50 **t.** – SB.

at Marston Trussell *(Northants.) West : 3½ m. by A 4304* – ✉ *Market Harborough.*

The Sun Inn, Main St., LE16 9TY, ☎ (01858) 465531, *manager@suninn.fsbusiness.cc Fax (01858) 433155* – TV P – 80. AE VISA.
Meals (bar lunch)/dinner a la carte 17.40/20.40 **t.** – **20 rm** 69.00 **t.**

ARKET RASEN *Lincs.* 402 404 T 23 – *pop. 2 948.*

London 156 – Boston 41 – Great Grimsby 19 – Lincoln 16.

Bleasby House without rest., Legsby, LN8 3QN, Southeast : 4 ¼ m. by B 1202 *(01673) 842383, Fax (01673) 844808,* « Working farm », – *closed 1 week Christmas* – **3 rm** 20.00/44.00 **st.**

ARKFIELD *Leics.* 402 403 404 Q 25 – *pop. 3 897.*

London 113 – Birmingham 45 – Leicester 6 – Nottingham 24.

Field Head, Markfield Lane, LE67 9PS, on B 5327 (01530) 245454, *fieldhead.hotel@virgin.net, Fax (01530) 243740* – – 50.
Meals a la carte 11.30/18.95 **t.** – **28 rm** 74.00/90.00 **t.** – SB.

Travelodge, Littleshaw Lane, LE67 0PP, Northwest : 1 m. on A 50 at junction 22 of M 1 (01530) 244777, *Fax (01530) 244580* – .
Meals (grill rest.) – **40 rm** 49.95 **t.**

ARKHAM MOOR *Notts.* 403 – ✉ *Retford.*

London 143 – Lincoln 18 – Nottingham 28 – Sheffield 27.

Travelodge, DN22 0QU, on A 1 (northbound carriageway) (01777) 838091, *Fax (01777) 838091* – rm, rest, .
Meals (grill rest.) – **40 rm** 29.95 **t.**

ARKINGTON *N. Yorks.* 402 P 21 – *see Ripon.*

ARKS TEY *Essex* 404 W 28 – *see Colchester.*

ARLBOROUGH *Wilts.* 403 404 O 29 *The West Country G.* – *pop. 6 788.*

See : *Town★.*

Env. : *Savernake Forest★★ (Grand Avenue★★★), SE : 2 m. by A 4 – Whitehorse (≤★), NW : 5 m – West Kennett Long Barrow★, Silbury Hill★, W : 6 m. by A 4.*

Exc. : *Ridgeway Path★★ – Avebury★★ (The Stones★, Church★), W : 7 m. by A 4 – Crofton Beam Engines★* **AC**, *SE : 9 m. by A 346 – Wilton Windmill★* **AC**, *SE : 9 m. by A 346, A 338 and minor rd.*

The Common (01672) 512147.

George Lane Car Park (01672) 513989.

London 84 – Bristol 47 – Southampton 40 – Swindon 12.

Ivy House, High St., SN8 1HJ, (01672) 515333, *ivy.house@btconnect.com, Fax (01672) 515338* – rest, – 50.
Scotts : **Meals** 12.95 **t.** (lunch) and a la carte 22.95/27.20 **t.** 8.00 – **30 rm** 69.00/115.00 **t.** – SB.

Coles, 27 Kingsbury Hill, SN8 1JA, (01672) 515004, *Fax (01672) 841504* – *closed Sunday and Bank Holidays* – **Meals** a la carte 13.75/24.50 **t.** 4.75.

ARLOW *Bucks.* 404 R 29 – *pop. 17 771.*

to Henley-on-Thames (Salter Bros. Ltd) (summer only) – to Maidenhead, Cookham and Windsor (Salter Bros. Ltd) (summer only).

31 High St. (01628) 483597.

London 35 – Aylesbury 22 – Oxford 29 – Reading 14.

Danesfield House, Henley Rd, SL7 2EY, Southwest : 2 ½ m. on A 4155 (01628) 891010, *sales@danesfieldhouse.co.uk, Fax (01628) 890408,* « Italian Renaissance style mansion ≤ terraced gardens and River Thames », heated, – rest, rest, – 80.
Oak Room : **Meals** 22.50/35.50 **st.** and a la carte 10.00 – ***Orangery :*** **Meals** a la carte 23.15/26.25 **st.** 10.00 – **86 rm** 155.00/205.00 **st.**, 1 suite.

Compleat Angler, Marlow Bridge, Bisham Rd, SL7 1RG, (01628) 484444, *heritagehotels-marlow.compleat-angler@forte-hotels.com, Fax (01628) 486388,* ≤ River Thames, « Riverside setting », – – 120.
Riverside : **Meals** 21.50/34.50 **t.** and a la carte – ***Waltons brasserie :*** **Meals** a la carte 33.95/62.10 **t.** 11.50 – 15.50 – **61 rm** 235.00/240.00 **t.**, 3 suites – SB.

Country House without rest., Bisham Rd, SL7 1RP, (01628) 890606, *Fax (01628) 890983,* – . *closed 2 weeks Christmas* – **11 rm** 80.00/109.00 **st.**

ENGLAND

Holly Tree House without rest., Burford Close, Marlow Bottom, SL7 3NF, North : 2 m. A 4155 and Wycombe Rd, off Marlow Bottom ☎ (01628) 891110, *Fax (01628) 4812* heated, – TV P. MC AE VISA JCB.
5 rm 64.50/79.50 **st.**

Royal Oak, Frieth Rd, Bovingdon Green, SL7 2JF, West : 1 ¼ m. by A 41 ☎ (01628) 488611, *Fax (01628) 478680*, – P. MC AE VISA JCB
Meals a la carte 16.00/22.25 **t.**

MARPLE *Gtr. Manchester* 402 403 404 N 23 – *pop. 19 829.*
London 190 – Chesterfield 35 – Manchester 11.

Springfield without rest., 99 Station Rd, SK6 6PA, ☎ (0161) 449 07 *Fax (0161) 449 0766*, – TV P. MC AE VISA.
7 rm 40.00/55.00 **st.**

MARSDEN *W. Yorks.* 402 404 O 23 – *pop. 3 873* – ✉ *Huddersfield.*
London 195 – Leeds 22 – Manchester 18 – Sheffield 30.

Olive Branch with rm, Manchester Rd, HD7 6LU, Northeast : 1 m. on A ☎ (01484) 844487, *reservations@olivebranch.uk.com, Fax (01484) 841549* – TV P. MC VISA JCB
closed 2 weeks January and 1 week August – **Meals** *(closed lunch Monday, Tuesday a Saturday)* 14.95 **t.** (lunch) and a la carte 21.15/27.80 **t.** 6.95 – **3 rm** 40.00/50.00 **st.** –

Les prix

Pour toutes précisions sur les prix indiqués dans ce guide, reportez-vous aux pages de l'introduction.

MARSH BENHAM *West Berks. – see Newbury.*

MARSTON MORETAINE *Beds.* 404 S 27 – *see Bedford.*

MARSTON TRUSSELL *Northants.* 404 R 26 – *see Market Harborough.*

MARTINHOE *Devon – see Lynton.*

MARTOCK *Somerset* 403 L 31 *The West Country G. – pop. 4 051.*
See : *Village★ – All Saints★★.*
Env. : *Montacute House★★* **AC**, *SE : 4 m. – Muchelney★★ (Parish Church★★), NW : 4½ m B 3165 – Ham Hill (≤★★), S : 2 m. by minor roads.*
Exc. : *Martock★ – Barrington Court★* **AC**, *SW : 7½ m. by B 3165 and A 303.*
London 148 – Taunton 19 – Yeovil 6.

Hollies, Bower Hinton, TA12 6LG, South : 1 m. on B 3165 ☎ (01935) 822232, *theholliesh l@ukonline.co, Fax (01935) 822249*, – TV P – 175. MC AE VISA JCB.
Meals *(closed Saturday lunch)* (dinner only) a la carte 20.00/30.00 **st.** 5.50 – **29** 65.00/80.00 **st.**, 2 suites.

MARTON *Lincs.* 402 404 R 24 – *pop. 508.*
London 155 – Doncaster 27 – Lincoln 14 – Nottingham 40.

Black Swan without rest., 21 High St., DN21 5AH, ☎ (01427) 718878, *info/reservatio blackswan-marton.co.uk, Fax (01427) 718878*, – TV P. MC VISA.
8 rm 30.00/60.00 **s.**

MASHAM *N. Yorks.* 402 P 21 – *pop. 1 171* – ✉ *Ripon.*
London 231 – Leeds 38 – Middlesbrough 37 – York 32.

King's Head, Market Pl., HG4 4EF, ☎ (01765) 689295, *Fax (01765) 689070*, « 18C » – MC AE VISA JCB
Meals a la carte 12.75/24.75 **t.** – 6.95 – **10 rm** 47.00/75.00 **t.** – SB.

Floodlite, 7Silver St., HG4 4DX, ☎ (01765) 689000 – MC AE VISA
closed 2 weeks January-February, 1 week October, Monday, Sunday dinner and lu Tuesday-Thursday – **Meals** 12.50/15.00 **t.** and a la carte 5.50.

ATFEN *Northd.* 401 402 O 18 – *pop. 500.*
London 309 – Carlisle 42 – Newcastle upon Tyne 24.

Matfen Hall ⛰, NE20 0RH, ✆ (01661) 886500, *info@matfenhall.com, Fax (01661) 886055,* ≤, « Early 19C country mansion », 18, – 100.
Library : Meals (dinner only and Sunday lunch) 19.50/28.00 **st.** – **30 rm** 88.00/216.00 **st.** – SB.

ATLOCK *Derbs.* 402 403 404 P 24 *Great Britain G.* – *pop. 14 680.*
Exc. : *Hardwick Hall** AC, E : 12½ m. by A 615 and B 6014.*
The Pavilion ✆ (01629) 55082 – Crown Sq. ✆ (01629) 583388.
London 153 – Derby 17 – Manchester 46 – Nottingham 24 – Sheffield 24.

Riber Hall ⛰, Riber Village, DE4 5JU, Southeast : 3 m. by A 615 ✆ (01629) 582795, *info@riber_hall.co.uk, Fax (01629) 580475,* « Part Elizabethan manor house », –
Meals 16.00/34.00 **t.** 7.95 – 8.00 – **14 rm** 85.00/165.00 **t.** – SB.

New Bath, New Bath Rd, Matlock Bath, DE4 3PX, South : 1½ m. on A 6 ✆ (01629) 583275, *heritagehotels_bath.matlock.new_bath@forte-hotels.com, Fax (01629) 580268,* heated, – – 130.
Meals *(closed Saturday lunch)* a la carte 12.85/21.85 **t.** 8.70 – 10.95 – **55 rm** 85.00/135.00 **st.** – SB.

The Guide is updated annually so renew your Guide every year.

AWDESLEY *Lancs.* 402 L 23 – *pop. 1 750* – ✉ *Ormskirk.*
London 217 – Liverpool 26 – Manchester 28 – Preston 15.

Mawdesley's Eating House and H., Hall Lane, L40 2QZ, North : ½ m. ✆ (01704) 822552, *mawdsleeh@aol.com, Fax (01704) 822096,* – – 50.
closed 25 and 26 December – **Meals** (grill rest.) 10.50 **t.** and dinner a la carte 5.00 – **56 rm** 45.00/55.00 **t.** – SB.

AWNAN SMITH *Cornwall* 403 E 33 – *see Falmouth.*

EADOW HEAD *S. Yorks.* – *see Sheffield.*

EDWAY SERVICE AREA *Medway* 404 V 29/30 – ✉ *Gillingham.*
London 39 – Canterbury 22 – Maidstone 11.

Travelodge without rest., ME8 8PQ, on M 2 between junctions 4 and 5 (westbound carriageway) ✆ (01634) 236903, *Fax (01634) 263187* –
58 rm 49.95 **t.**

ELBOURN *Cambs.* 404 U 27 – *pop. 4 006* – ✉ *Royston (Herts.).*
London 44 – Cambridge 10.

Melbourn Bury ⛰, Royston Rd, SG8 6DE, Southwest : ¾ m. ✆ (01763) 261151, *melbournbury@biztobiz.co.uk, Fax (01763) 262375,* ≤, « Country house of Tudor origin », –
closed Easter, 2 weeks in summer and Christmas-2 January – **Meals** *(closed Sunday)* (booking essential) (residents only) (communal dining) (dinner only) 18.50 **st.** 7.50 – **3 rm** 60.00/100.00 **st.**

Chiswick House without rest., 3 Chiswick End, SG8 6LZ, Northwest : 1 m. by Meldreth rd, off Whitecroft Rd ✆ (01763) 260242, « Part 14C timbered former farmhouse », –
closed December and January – **6 rm** 38.00/45.00.

Pink Geranium, 25 Station Rd, SG8 6DX, ✆ (01763) 260215, *lawrence@pinkgeranium.co.uk, Fax (01763) 262110,* –
Meals 16.00/30.00 **t.** and a la carte 7.00.

Sheene Mill with rm, Station Rd, SG8 6DX, ✆ (01763) 261393, *Fax (01763) 261376,* ≤, « Restored 17C water mill », – rm,
closed 26 December and 1 January – **Meals** *(closed Sunday dinner)* 14.00/18.50 **t.** (lunch) and a la carte 23.00/31.00 **t.** 7.00 – **9 rm** 65.00/110.00 **t.**

MELKSHAM *Wilts.* 403 404 N 29 *The West Country G. – pop. 13 074.*

Env.: *Corsham Court** AC, NW : 4½ m. by A 365 and B 3353 – Lacock** (Lacock Abbe AC, High Street*, St. Cyriac*, Fox Talbot Museum of Photography* AC) N : 3½ m. b 350.*

Church St. ☎ (01225) 707424.

London 113 – Bristol 25 – Salisbury 35 – Swindon 28.

Beechfield House, Beanacre, SN12 7PU, North : 1 m. on A 350 ☎ (01225) 7037 *Fax (01225) 790118,* ≤, « Late Victorian country house, gardens », heated, – TV P – 25. MC AE VISA.
closed 26 December-2 January – **Meals** 14.95 **t.** (lunch) and a la carte 18.25/27.25 **t.** 6 – **21 rm** 85.00/175.00 **t.** – SB.

Shurnhold House without rest., Shurnhold, SN12 8DG, Northwest : 1 m. on A ☎ (01225) 790555, *susan.tanir@shurnholdhouse.com, Fax (01225) 793147,* « Jacobean r nor house, gardens » – TV P. MC AE VISA.
7.50 – **4 rm** 55.00/98.00 **s.**

Sandridge Park, Sandridge Hill, SN12 7QU, East : 2 m. on A 3102 ☎ (01225) 7068 *annettehoogeweegen@compuserve.com, Fax (01225) 702838,* ≤, « Early Victorian m sion », – rm, TV P. MC VISA JCB.
closed 3 days Christmas – **Meals** (booking essential) (communal dining) 25.00 **s.** – 4 60.00/80.00 **s.** – SB.

at Whitley *Northwest : 2 m. by A 365 on B 3353 – ✉ Melksham.*

Pear Tree Inn, Top Lane, SN12 8QX, by First Lane ☎ (01225) 709131, *Fax (01225) 7022* – P. MC VISA
closed 26-27 December and 1 January – **Meals** (booking essential) 11.50 (lunch) and a la carte 20.50/26.55 **st.** 6.95.

MELLOR *Lancs. – see Blackburn.*

MELTON MOWBRAY *Leics.* 402 404 R 25 – *pop. 24 348.*

Waltham Rd, Thorpe Arnold ☎ (01664) 562118.

Melton Carnegie Museum, Thorpe End ☎ (01664) 480992.

London 113 – Leicester 15 – Northampton 45 – Nottingham 18.

Stapleford Park, LE14 2EF, East : 5 m. by B 676 on Stapleford rd ☎ (01572) 7875 *reservations@stapleford.co.uk, Fax (01572) 787651,* ≤, « Part 16C and 19C mansion park », – TV P – 200. MC AE VISA
Meals (booking essential to non-residents) (light lunch Monday to Saturday)/dinner 44.0 – **50 rm** 175.00/360.00, 1 suite.

Quorn Lodge, 46 Asfordby Rd, LE13 0HR, West : ½ m. on A 6006 ☎ (01664) 566660, *q nlodge@aol.com, Fax (01664) 480660* – TV P – 80. MC AE VISA.
Meals *(closed Sunday dinner)* 9.95/15.75 **t.** and a la carte 6.95 – **19 rm** 52.95/75.00 SB.

MEMBURY *Devon – see Axminster.*

MEMBURY SERVICE AREA *Newbury* 403 404 P 29 – ✉ *Newbury.*

Days Inn, Membury, Lambourn Woodlands, RG16 7TZ, M 4 between junctions 14 an (westbound carriageway) ☎ (01488) 72336, Reservations (Freephone) 0800 0280 *Fax (01488) 72336* – rm, TV P. MC AE VISA JCB
Meals (grill rest.) a la carte 9.65/13.90 **st.** – 5.95 – **38 rm** 49.00/54.00 **t.**

MENDLESHAM GREEN *Suffolk* 404 W 27 – *see Stowmarket.*

MERIDEN *W. Mids.* 403 404 P 26 – *see Coventry.*

Particularly pleasant hotels and restaurants are shown in the Guide by a red symbol.
Please send us the names of anywhere you have enjoyed your stay.
Your **Michelin Guide** will be even better.

EVAGISSEY *Cornwall* 403 F 33 *The West Country G. – pop. 2 272.*

See : *Town*★★.

Env. : *NW : Lost Gardens of Heligan*★.

London 287 – Newquay 21 – Plymouth 44 – Truro 20.

Kerryanna, Treleaven Farm, PL26 6RZ, (01726) 843558, *linda.hennah@talk21.com, Fax (01726) 843558*, heated, – rest, TV P. VISA.
March-October – **Meals** (by arrangement) 12.50 **st.** 4.50 – **6 rm** 54.00 **st.** – SB.

EYSEY HAMPTON *Glos.* 403 404 O 28 – *Cirencester.*

London 101 – Bristol 44 – Gloucester 26 – Oxford 29.

Masons Arms with rm, High St., GL7 5JT, (01285) 850164, *jane@themasonsarms.freeserve.co.uk, Fax (01285) 850164*, « Part 17C inn » – rest, TV. VISA JCB.
Meals *(closed Sunday dinner November-March)* a la carte 14.35/19.80 **t.** 6.95 – **9 rm** 38.00/68.00 **t.**

ICHAELWOOD SERVICE AREA *Glos.* 403 M29 – *Dursley.*

Days Inn without rest., Lower Wick, GL11 5DD, M 5 between junctions 13 and 14 (northbound carriageway) (01454) 261513, Reservations (Freephone) 0800 0280400, *Fax (01454) 261513* – TV P. AE VISA JCB
7.45 **40 rm** 45.00/50.00 **t.**

Le Guide change, changez de **guide Michelin** *tous les ans.*

CKLEHAM *Surrey* 404 (42) – *pop. 484.*

London 21 – Brighton 32 – Guildford 14 – Worthing 34.

The King William IV, Byttom Hill, RH5 6EL, North : ½ m. by A 24 (01372) 372590, – VISA
closed 25 December and 31 January – **Meals** a la carte approx. 18.50 6.75.

CKLEOVER *Derbs.* 402 403 404 P 25 – *see Derby.*

CKLETON *Glos.* 403 404 O 27 – *see Chipping Campden.*

DDLEHAM *N. Yorks.* 402 O 21 – *pop. 754.*

London 233 – Kendal 45 – Leeds 47 – York 45.

Miller's House, Market Pl., DL8 4NR, (01969) 622630, *hotel@millerhouse.demon.co.uk, Fax (01969) 623570*, « 18C » – TV P. VISA.
closed 25 December and January-mid February – **Meals** (dinner only) 19.50 **st.** 8.50 – **7 rm** (dinner included) 59.00/132.00 **st.** – SB.

Waterford House, 19 Kirkgate, DL8 4PG, (01969) 622090, *Fax (01969) 624020*, « Part 17C house, antiques », – rest, TV P. VISA JCB
Number 19 : **Meals** (lunch by arrangement) 19.50/29.50 **st.** and a la carte 7.50 – **5 rm** 50.00/90.00 **st.**

Carlton-in-Coverdale *Southwest : 4½ m. on Coverdale Rd* – *Leyburn.*

Abbots Thorn, DL8 4AY, (01969) 640620, *abbots.thorn@virgin.net, Fax (01969) 640304*, – TV
Meals (by arrangement) (communal dining) 12.00 – **3 rm** 30.00/50.00.

Foresters Arms with rm, DL8 4BB, (01969) 640272, *Fax (01969) 640272* – TV P. VISA.
closed 3 weeks January – **Meals** - Seafood specialities - *(closed Monday, Sunday dinner and Tuesday lunch)* (lunch in bar) a la carte 19.95/31.70 10.40 – **3 rm** 40.00/75.00 **t.**

DDLESBROUGH *Middlesbrough* 402 Q 20 – *pop. 147 430.*

Middlesbrough Municipal, Ladgate Lane (01642) 315533 – Brass Castle Lane, Marton (01642) 311515.

Cleveland Transporter Bridge (toll) **BY**.

Teesside Airport : (01325) 332811, SW : 13 m. by A 66 – **AZ** *– and A 19 on A 67.*

99-101 Abert Rd (01642) 243425.

London 246 – Kingston-upon-Hull 89 – Leeds 66 – Newcastle upon Tyne 41.

MIDDLESBROUGH

Street	Grid	No.
Albert Road	BY	2
Ayresome Green Lane	AZ	3
Bridge Street West	AY	4
Bright Street	BY	5
Clairville Road	BZ	6
Cleveland Centre	ABY	
Cleveland Street	BY	7
Corporation Road	BY	8
Devonshire Road	AZ	10
Dundas Street	ABY	12
Eastbourne Road	AZ	14
Ferry Road	BY	15
Finsbury Street	AZ	16
Grange Road	ABY	17
Gresham Road	AZ	18
Hartington Road	AY	19
Hill Street Centre	AY	
Linthorpe Road	AY	
Longford Street	AZ	22
Newport Road	AY	
Ormesby Road	BZ	24
Princes Road	AZ	26
St. Barnabas Road	AZ	27
Saltersgill Avenue	BZ	28
Sussex Street	AY	30
Tees Bridge Approach Road	AZ	
West Terrace	BZ	
Westbourne Grove	BZ	
Wilson Street	AY	
Woodlands Road	BZ	
Zetland Street	ABY	

Baltimore, 250 Marton Rd, TS4 2EZ, ☎ (01642) 224111, *info@lincoln-group.c*
Fax (01642) 226156 – TV P – 25. MC AE ① VISA JCB BZ
Meals 15.00 **st.** (lunch) and a la carte 16.40/28.00 **st.** 6.75 – 9.50 – **30 rm** 53
95.00 **st.**, 1 suite.

Grey House without rest., 79 Cambridge Rd, TS5 5NL, ☎ (01642) 817 AZ
Fax (01642) 817485, – rm, TV P. MC VISA
10 rm 40.00/60.00 **s.**

The Purple Onion, 80 Corporation Rd, TS1 2RF, ☎ (01642) 222250, *Fax (01642) 24*
– . MC VISA BY
closed 25 December – **Meals** - Brasserie - (booking essential) a la carte 16.50/31.
5.95.

IDDLETON *Gtr. Manchester* 402 403 404 N 23 – *pop. 45 729.*
London 210 – Manchester 6 – Leeds 38 – Liverpool 35.

Premier Lodge, 818 Manchester Old Rd, Rhodes, M24 4RF, ☎ (0870) 7001474, *Fax (0870) 7001475* – TV ☎ ♿ P. MC AE ⓓ VISA. ✻
Meals 10.95 **t.** and a la carte – ☕ 6.00 – **42 rm** 42.00.

DDLETON *N. Yorks. – see Pickering.*

DDLETON STONEY *Oxon.* 403 404 Q 28 – *pop. 304.*
London 66 – Northampton 30 – Oxford 12.

Jersey Arms, OX6 8SE, ☎ (01869) 343234, *jerseyarms@bestwestern.co.uk, Fax (01869) 343565,* – ⇔ rest, TV P. MC AE ⓓ VISA JCB. ✻
Meals a la carte 16.00/26.00 **t.** – **17 rm** ☕ 79.00/92.00 **t.**, 3 suites – SB.

DDLE WALLOP *Hants.* 403 404 P 30 – ✉ *Stockbridge.*
London 80 – Salisbury 11 – Southampton 21.

Fifehead Manor, SO20 8EG, on A 343 ☎ (01264) 781565, *Fax (01264) 781400,* « Part 16C manor house », – ⇔ rest, TV P – 🏃 30. MC AE VISA JCB. ✻
Meals 14.25/27.50 **t.** and a la carte 🍷 8.25 – **17 rm** ☕ 80.00/150.00 **t.** – SB.

DDLEWICH *Ches.* 402 403 404 M 24.
London 180 – Manchester 29 – Chester 21 – Liverpool 21 – Stoke-on-Trent 58.

Travelodge, Holmes Chapel Rd, CW10 0NZ, East : ½ m. on A 54 ☎ (01606) 738229, *Fax (01606) 738229* – ⇔ rm, TV ♿ P. MC AE ⓓ VISA JCB
Meals (grill rest.) – **32 rm** 49.95 **t.**

DDLE WINTERSLOW *Wilts. – see Salisbury.*

DGLEY *W. Yorks.* 402 P 22 – *see Wakefield.*

DHURST *W. Sussex* 404 R 31 – *pop. 6 451.*
ℹ *North St. ☎ (01730) 817322.*
London 57 – Brighton 38 – Chichester 12 – Southampton 41.

Spread Eagle, South St., GU29 9NH, ☎ (01730) 816911, *spreadeagle@hshotels, Fax (01730) 815668,* « 15C hostelry, antique furnishings », Fá, ≘s, 🏊 – ⇔ rest, TV P – 🏃 50. MC AE ⓓ VISA
Meals 18.50/45.00 **t.** and a la carte 🍷 9.95 – **37 rm** ☕ 80.00/210.00 **t.**, 2 suites – SB.

Angel, North St., GU29 9DN, ☎ (01730) 812421, *theangel@hshotels.co.uk, Fax (01730) 815928,* « 16C coaching inn », – ⇔ TV ♿ P – 🏃 60. MC AE ⓓ VISA
Brasserie : **Meals** (lunch booking essential) 9.75 **t.** (lunch) and a la carte 19.00/30.70 **t.** – ☕ 5.00 – **28 rm** 90.00/180.00 **t.** – SB.

Maxine's, Red Lion St., GU29 9PB, ☎ (01730) 816271, *maxines@lineone.net,* « 15C timbered cottage » – ⇔. MC AE VISA
closed 2 weeks January, 1 week in autumn, Monday, Tuesday and Sunday dinner – **Meals** 16.95 **st.** (lunch) and a la carte 19.40/25.40 **st.** 🍷 5.95.

at Bepton *Southwest : 2½ m. by A 286 on Bepton rd – ✉ Midhurst.*

Park House , Bepton, GU29 0JB, ℘ (01730) 812880, *reservations@parkhouse.c* *Fax (01730) 815643*, heated, , – rest, – 70.
Meals (booking essential) 15.00/27.00 **t.** – **16 rm** 85.00/150.00 **st.**, 1 suite – SB.

at Stedham *West : 2 m. by A 272 – ✉ Midhurst.*

Nava Thai at Hamilton Arms, School Lane, GU29 0NZ, ℘ (01730) 812 *Fax (01730) 817459* –
closed Monday except Bank Holidays – **Meals** - Thai - 19.50 **t.** (dinner) and a la carte 15 20.95 **t.** 4.95.

at Trotton *West : 3¼ m. on A 272 – ✉ Petersfield (Hants.).*

Southdowns Country , GU31 5JN, South : 1 m. ℘ (01730) 821521, *reception@s hdownhotel.freeserve.co.uk, Fax (01730) 821790*, , , , – , rest, 100.
Meals 9.95/25.00 **t.** and a la carte 6.50 – **20 rm** 75.00/99.00 **t.** – SB.

at Elsted Marsh *Southwest : 4 m. by A 272 on Elsted rd – ✉ Midhurst.*

Elsted Inn with rm, GU29 0JT, ℘ (01730) 813662, *Fax (01730) 813662*, – rm,
closed 25 December – **Meals** (booking essential) a la carte 16.50/21.20 **t.** 7.50 – 4
37.00/60.00 **t.**

at Elsted *Southwest : 5 m. by A 272 on Elsted rd – ✉ Midhurst.*

Three Horseshoes, GU29 0JY, ℘ (01730) 825746, « 16C drovers inn » –
Meals *(closed Sunday dinner in winter)* a la carte 15.00/22.00 **t.**

MIDSOMER NORTON *Bath & North East Somerset* 403 M 30 – ✉ *Bath.*

Fosseway C.C., Charlton Lane ℘ (01761) 412214.
London 129 – Bath 10 – Bristol 15 – Wells 8.

Centurion, Charlton Lane, BA3 4BD, Southeast : 1 m. by B 3355, Charlton Rd Fosseway ℘ (01761) 417711, *centurion@centurionhotel.demon.co.uk, Fax (01761) 418* <, , , , , – rest, – 180.
closed 24-27 December – **Meals** *(closed Saturday lunch)* 15.00/17.50 **t.** 6.50 – 4
62.00/72.00 **t.** – SB.

MILBORNE PORT *Dorset* 403 404 M 31 – *see Sherborne.*

MILDENHALL *Suffolk* 404 V 26 – *pop. 12 827.*

London 72 – Cambridge 24 – Ipswich 37 – Norwich 45.

Riverside, Mill St., IP28 7DP, ℘ (01638) 717274, *cameronhotels@riversidehotel.frees co.uk, Fax (01638) 715997*, , – – 60.
Meals 14.00/35.00 **st.** and a la carte 7.00 – **30 rm** 62.00/88.00 **st.** – SB.

ILFORD-ON-SEA *Hants.* 403 404 P 31 – *pop. 4 434* – ✉ *Lymington.*
London 109 – Bournemouth 15 – Southampton 24 – Winchester 37.

Westover Hall, Park Lane, SO41 0PT, ✆ (01590) 643044, *westoverhallhotel@barclays.net, Fax (01590) 644490*, ≤ Christchurch Bay, Isle of Wight and The Needles, « Victorian mansion built by Arnold Mitchell », – rest, TV P. MC AE VISA JCB
Meals 21.50/27.50 **st.** 5.95 – **14 rm** 65.00/140.00 **st.** – SB.

South Lawn, Lymington Rd, SO41 0RF, ✆ (01590) 643911, *enquiries@southlawn.co.uk, Fax (01590) 644820*, – TV P. MC VISA.
closed late December-late January – **Meals** *(closed Monday lunch)* 22.00/29.00 **t.** (dinner) and a la carte 13.50/22.50 **t.** 7.00 – **24 rm** 65.00/130.00 **t.** – SB.

Rouille, 69-71 High St., SO41 0QG, ✆ (01590) 642340, *rouille@ukonline.co.uk, Fax (01590) 642340* – . MC AE VISA
closed 2 weeks January, Sunday and Monday – **Meals** 12.95/24.95 **st.** 10.00.

LNROW *Gtr. Manchester* 402 404 N 23 – *see Rochdale.*

LTON ERNEST *Beds.* 404 S 27 – *see Bedford.*

La Grande Londra (GREATER LONDON) è composta dalla City e da 32 distretti amministrativi (Borough) divisi a loro volta in quartieri o villaggi che hanno conservato il loro proprio carattere (Area).

LTON KEYNES *Milton Keynes* 404 R 27 – *pop. 156 148.*
18 Abbey Hill, Monks Way, Two Mile Ash ✆ (01908) 563845 **AV** – *18 Windmill Hill, Tattenhoe Lane, Bletchley ✆ (01908) 648149* **BX** – *18, 9 Wavendon Golf Centre, Lower End Rd, Wavendon ✆ (01908) 281811* **CV**.
Theatre Sq., 890 Midsummer Boulevard ✆ (01908) 558300 **FY**.
London 56 – Birmingham 72 – Bedford 16 – Northampton 18 – Oxford 37.

Plans on following pages

Posthouse Milton Keynes, 500 Saxon Gate West, Central Milton Keynes, MK9 2HQ, ✆ (0870) 400 9057, *Fax (01908) 674714*, – rm, TV P – 150. MC AE VISA JCB. EYZ a
Meals *(closed Saturday lunch)* 15.00 **t.** (dinner) and a la carte 22.70/28.10 **t.** 6.95 – 11.95 – **151 rm** 129.00 **st.**, 2 suites – SB.

Hilton Milton Keynes, Timbold Drive, Kents Hill Park, MK7 6HL, Southeast : 4 m. by B 4034 and A 421 off Brickhill St. (V10) ✆ (01908) 694433, *Fax (01908) 695533*, – , rest, TV P – 320. MC AE VISA JCB. CVX d
Britisserie : **Meals** 12.50/17.00 **st.** and dinner a la carte – 11.50 – **138 rm** 145.00/205.00 **st.** – SB.

Courtyard by Marriott Milton Keynes, London Rd, MK16 0JA, Northeast : 4 ¼ m. on A 509 ✆ (01908) 613688, *Fax (01908) 617335*, – , rest, TV P – 200. MC AE VISA. CV r
Meals a la carte 22.95/29.95 **st.** – 10.00 – **49 rm** 95.00/145.00 **st.** – SB.

Quality, Monks Way, Two Mile Ash, MK8 8LY, Northwest : 2 m. by A 509 and A 5 at junction with A 422 ✆ (01908) 561666, *admin@gb616.u-net.com, Fax (01908) 568303*, – rm, rest, TV P – 150. MC AE VISA JCB. AV e
Meals *(closed Saturday lunch)* (carving rest.) 16.00 **st.** (dinner) and a la carte 15.65/24.95 **st.** 5.75 – 9.75 – **88 rm** 105.00/125.00 **st.** – SB.

Shenley Church Inn, Burchard Cres., Shenley Church End, MK5 6HQ, Southwest : 2 m. by A 509 and Portway (H5) off Watling St. (V4) ✆ (01908) 505467, *Fax (01908) 340002* – , rest, TV P – 100. MC VISA. BVX f
Meals (carving rest.) a la carte 11.65/15.65 **t.** – **50 rm** 74.95 **t.** – SB.

Premier Lodge, Shirwell Cres., Furzton, MK4 1GA, South : 3 m. by A 509 and Portway (H 5) off Watling St. (V 4) ✆ (01908) 520200, *Fax (01908) 521230* – rm, rest, TV P. MC AE VISA. BX g
Meals (grill rest.) – 6.00 – **120 rm** 49.50 **t.**

Premier Lodge, Bletcham Way (H10), MK7 8HP, Southeast : 5 ½ m. by A 509 and A 5, taking 2nd junction left signposted Milton Keynes (South and East) ✆ (01908) 366188, *Fax (01908) 366603*, « Windmill feature, lakeside setting » – rm, TV P. MC AE VISA. CX h
Meals (in bar) a la carte 10.50/15.50 **st.** – 6.00 – **40 rm** 49.50 **st.**

MILTON KEYNES

Buckingham Road . . . . BX
London Road . . . . CUV
Manor Road CX
Marsh End Road . . . . CU
Newport Road . . . . BV
Northampton Road . . . . AU
Stoke Road CX
Stratford Road . . . . AV
Whaddon Way . . . . BX
Wolverton Road . . . . BU

« VERTICAL » ROADS

V1 Snelshall Street . . . . BX
V2 Tattenhoe Street . . . . ABX
V3 Fulmer Street . . . . ABX
V4 Watling Street . . . . AV, BX
V5 Great Monks Street . . . . AV
V6 Grafton Street . . . . BVX
V7 Saxon Street . . . . BVX
V8 Marlborough Street . . . . BV, CX
V9 Overstreet . . . . BV
V10 Brickhill Street . . . . BU, CX
V11 Tongwell Street CVX

« HORIZONTAL » ROADS

H1 Ridgeway . . . . AV
H2 Millers Way . . . . AV
H3 Monks Way . . . . ABV
H4 Dansteed Way . . . . ABV
H5 Portway . . . . BCV
H6 Childs Way . . . . BX, CV
H7 Chaffron Way . . . . BX, CV
H8 Standing Way . . . . BX, CV
H9 Groveway CVX
H10 Bletcham Way CX

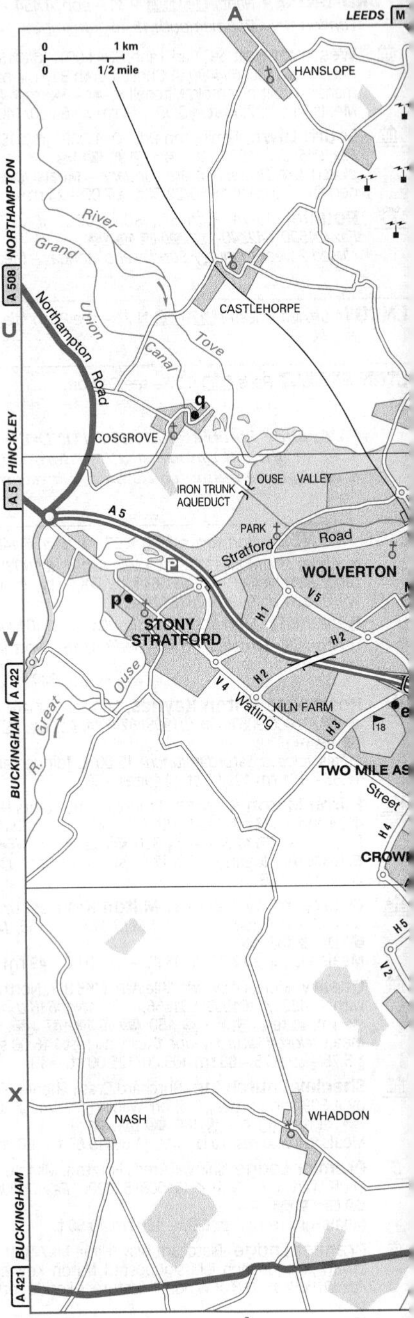

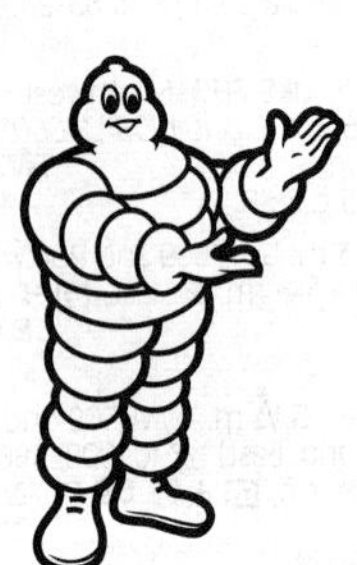

A
LEEDS
0 1 km
0 1/2 mile
HANSLOPE
NORTHAMPTON
A 508
River
Grand
Union
Canal
Tove
CASTLEHORPE
U
Northampton Road
q
COSGROVE
HINCKLEY
A 5
OUSE VALLEY
IRON TRUNK AQUEDUCT
PARK
Stratford Road
WOLVERTON
A 5
V5
H1
p
STONY STRATFORD
V
H2
A 422
Ouse
V4
Watling
KILN FARM
H3
e
BUCKINGHAM
R. Great
TWO MILE AS
Street
H4
CROW
H5
V2
X
NASH
WHADDON
BUCKINGHAM
A 421
A

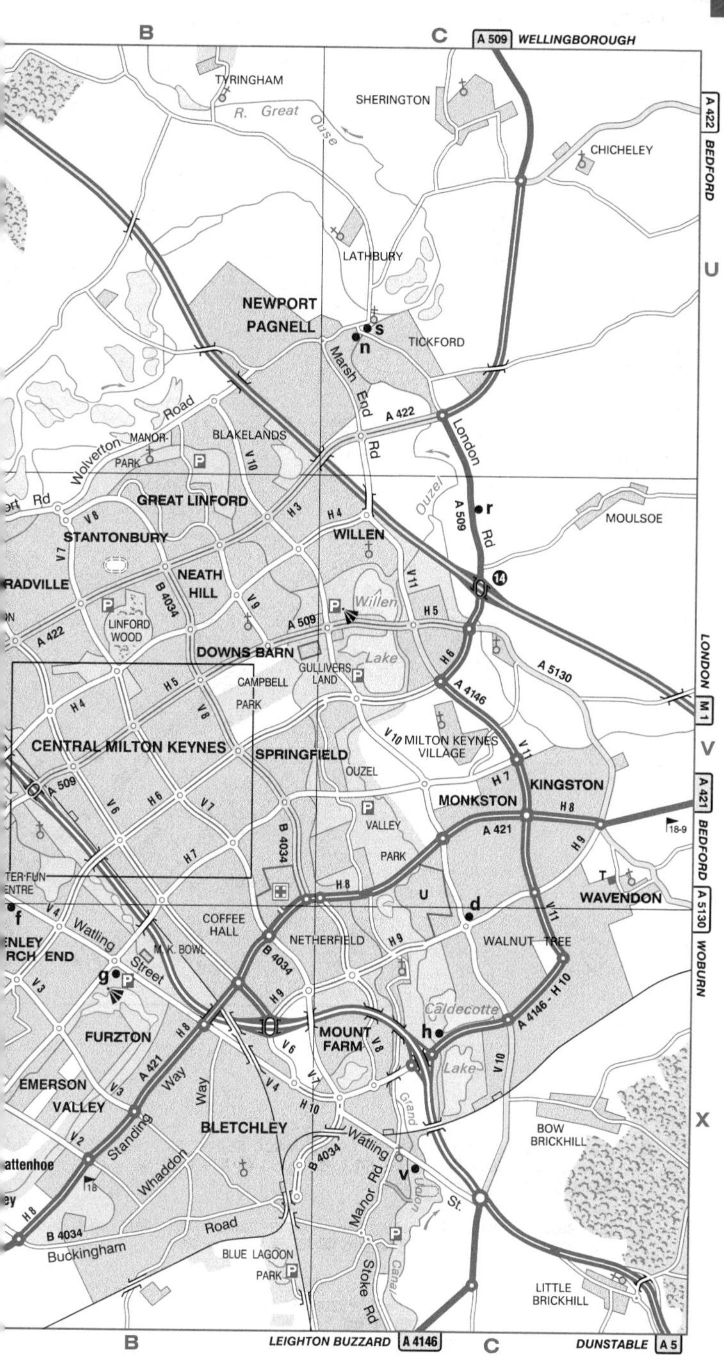

B
C
A 509 WELLINGBOROUGH
TYRINGHAM
SHERINGTON
R. Great Ouse
A 422 BEDFORD
CHICHELEY
LATHBURY
U
NEWPORT PAGNELL
TICKFORD
Marsh End Rd
A 422
London Rd
A 509
Wolverton Road
MANOR PARK
BLAKELANDS
V 10
GREAT LINFORD
STANTONBURY
H 3
H 4
WILLEN
Ouzel
MOULSOE
NEATH HILL
B 4034
V 11
V 9
Willen Lake
H 5
A 509
A 422
LINFORD WOOD
DOWNS BARN
GULLIVERS LAND
CAMPBELL PARK
H 6
A 5130
LONDON M 1
A 4146
H 4
H 5
V 8
CENTRAL MILTON KEYNES
SPRINGFIELD
V 10 MILTON KEYNES VILLAGE
OUZEL
V
H 7
KINGSTON
MONKSTON
H 8
A 421 BEDFORD
A 509
V 6
H 6
V 7
B 4034
VALLEY PARK
A 421
18-9
H 9
H 7
H 8
U
d
WAVENDON
A 5130 WOBURN
COFFEE HALL
NETHERFIELD
H 9
WALNUT TREE
V 11
Watling Street
M. K. BOWL
B 4034
H 9
A 4146 - H 10
Caldecotte Lake
FURZTON
H 8
MOUNT FARM
V 6
V 8
h
V 10
EMERSON VALLEY
A 421
V 3
Way
Way
V 4
V 7
Grand
H 10
X
BOW BRICKHILL
BLETCHLEY
Standing
Watling
B 4034
Manor Rd
Whaddon
V 2
18
H 8
B 4034
Buckingham Road
Ouzel
St.
BLUE LAGOON PARK
Stoke Rd
Canal
LITTLE BRICKHILL
B
LEIGHTON BUZZARD A 4146
C
DUNSTABLE A 5

MILTON KEYNES

Avebury Boulevard .... **EFY**
Boundary (The)............... **FZ** 3
Boycott Avenue.............. **EZ** 4
Bradwell Common
  Boulevard................ **DEY**
Bradwell Road............... **DZ**
Brearley Avenue .... **EFZ**
Brill Place .... **DY**
Burnham Drive .... **DY**
Century Avenue............. **EFZ**
Chaffron Way (H7)........... **FZ**
Childs Way (H6) .... **EFZ**
Conniburrow Boulevard .... **EY**
Dansteed Way (H4) .... **DY**
Deltic Avenue .... **DY** 6
Dexter Avenue............... **FZ** 7
Elder Gate .... **DZ** 9
Evans Gate.................. **EZ**
Fishermead Boulevard .... **FZ**
Food Centre .... **FY**
Fulwoods Drive .... **FZ** 10
Gibsons Green............... **DY**
Glovers Lane .... **DY** 12
Grafton Street (V6).......... **DYZ**
Ibstone Avenue .... **DEY** 13
Kirkstall Place................ **EZ**
Leys Road .... **DZ**
Loughton Road .... **DY**
Main Shopping Centre....... **EFY**
Mallow Gate.................. **EY** 15
Marlborough Street (V8) ...... **FY**
Mayditch Place .... **DY**
Midsummer Boulevard ...... **EFY**
Oldbrook Boulevard .... **EFZ**
Patriot Drive................. **DY** 16
Pitcher Lane.................. **DZ**
Portway (H5) .... **EFY**
Precedent Drive .... **DY** 18
Quinton Drive .... **DY**
Saxon Gate (V7) .... **EY**
Saxon Street (V7)......... **EY, FZ**
Secklow Gate................. **FY**
Silbury Boulevard .... **EFY**
Walgrave Drive .... **DY** 19
Witan Gate .... **EZ**

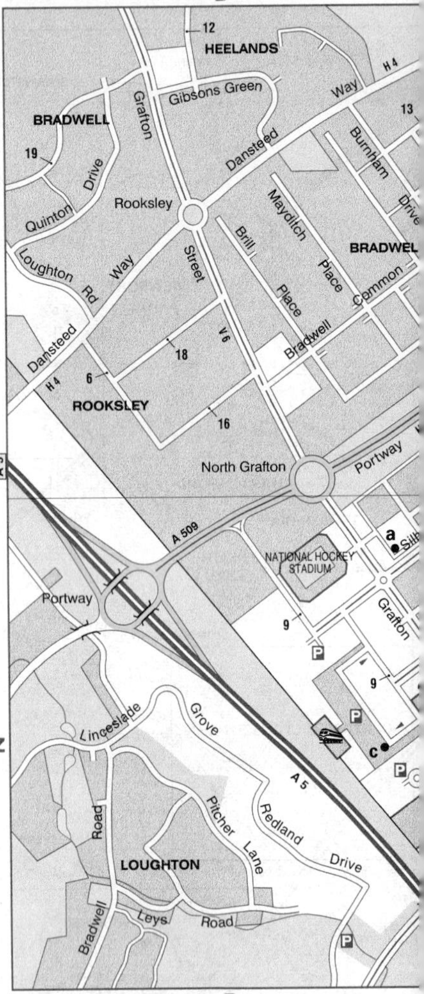

[hotel] **Travel Inn,** Secklow Gate West, Central Milton Keynes, MK9 3BZ, ☎ (01908) 663
Fax (01908) 607481 – ⇔, ▤ rest, TV ♿ **P** – 🏛 50. MC AE ① VISA. ✕ F
Meals (grill rest.) – **38 rm** 40.95 **t.**

[hotel] **Travelodge** without rest., 199 Grafton Gate, MK9 1AL, ☎ (01908) 241
Fax (01908) 241737 – ▮ ⇔ TV ☎ ♿ **P**. MC AE ① VISA JCB. ✕ D
80 rm 59.95 **t.**

XX **Jaipur,** Elder House, 502 Eldergate, Station Sq., MK9 1LR, ☎ (01908) 669
Fax (01908) 694464 – ▤. MC AE ① VISA D
closed 25 December – **Meals** - Indian - (buffet lunch Sunday) a la carte 17.15/28.90 **t.**

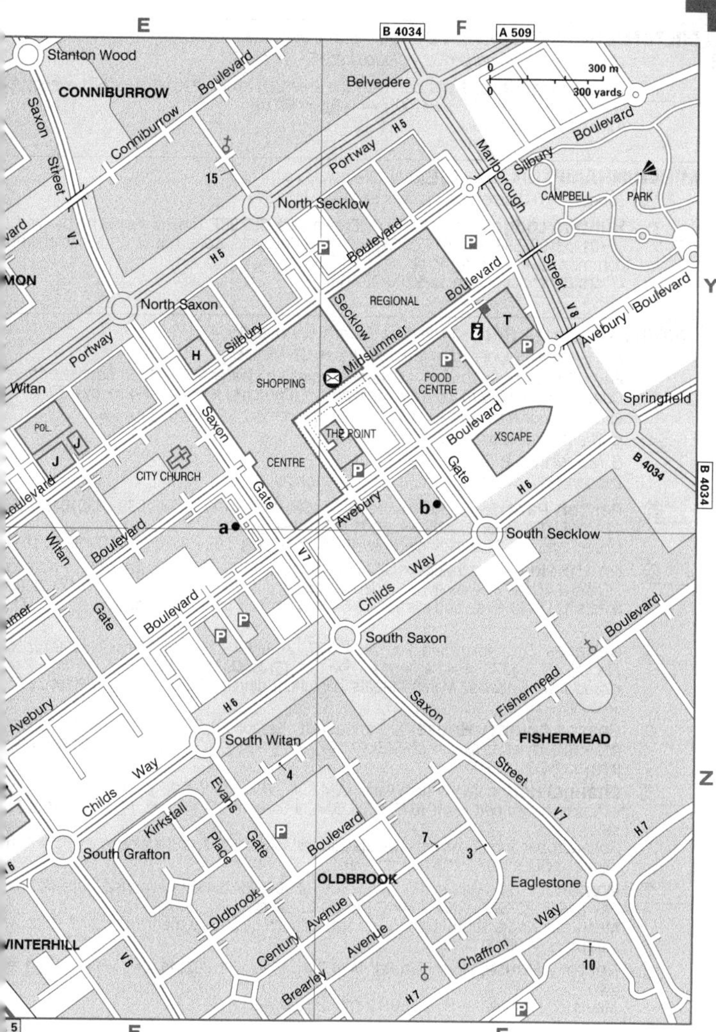

ewton Longville *Southwest : 6 m. by A 421* – **AX** – ✉ *Milton Keynes.*

Crooked Billet, MK17 0DF, ☎ (01908) 373936, *johngilchrist@the-crooked-billet-pub.co.uk, Fax (01908) 631979,* – P. MC AE VISA
closed Sunday dinner and Monday – **Meals** a la carte 12.50/27.00 **t.** 8.00.

MILTON-UNDER-WYCHWOOD *Oxon. – pop. 2 030.*
London 83 – Birmingham 52 – Gloucester 35 – Oxford 27.

Hillborough House without rest., The Green, OX7 6JH, ☏ (01993) 830501, *wendy.jo@lineone.net, Fax (01993) 832005,* – TV P. MC VISA
4 rm 28.00/50.00.

MINCHINHAMPTON *Glos.* 403 404 N 28 – *pop. 3 201.*
London 115 – Bristol 26 – Gloucester 11 – Oxford 51.

Hunters Lodge without rest., Dr Brown's Rd, GL6 9BT, Northwest : ½ m. by West ☏ (01453) 883588, *Fax (01453) 731449,* ←, « Cotswold stone house on Minchinhamp common », – TV P.
closed Christmas – **3 rm** 30.00/48.00.

MINEHEAD *Somerset* 403 J 30 *The West Country G. – pop. 9 904.*
See : *Town★ - Higher Town (Church Steps★, St. Michael's★).*
Env. : *Dunster★★ - Castle★★* **AC** *(upper rooms ←★) Water Mill★* **AC**, *St. George's Churc Dovecote★, SE : 2½ m. by A 39 – Selworthy★ (Church★, ←★★) W : 4½ m. by A 39.*
Exc. : *Exmoor National Park★★ – Cleeve Abbey★★* **AC**, *SE : 6½ m. by A 39.*
The Warren, Warren Rd ☏ (01643) 702057.
17 Friday St. ☏ (01643) 702624.
London 187 – Bristol 64 – Exeter 43 – Taunton 25.

Periton Park, Middlecombe, TA24 8SN, West : 1 ½ m. by A 39 ☏ (01643) 7068 *Fax (01643) 706885,* ←, – TV P. MC AE VISA JCB
closed January – **Meals** (dinner only) 19.50/23.50 **st.** 5.85 – **8 rm** 54.00/99.00 **st.** –

Northfield, Northfield Rd, TA24 5PU, ☏ (01643) 705155, *sales@northfield-hotel.c, Fax (01643) 707715,* ← bay, « Gardens », – rest, TV P – 70. MC AE VISA
Meals 12.95/18.95 **st.** and a la carte 6.75 – **28 rm** (dinner included) 56.00/112.00 s SB.

Benares, Northfield Rd, TA24 5PT, ☏ (01643) 704911, *pmas213508@aol.c Fax (01643) 706373,* ←, « Gardens » – rest, TV P. MC AE VISA JCB
closed 2 November-25 March – **Meals** (bar lunch)/dinner 22.50 **st.** 5.50 – **19 rm** 53 94.00 **st.** – SB.

Beacon Country House without rest., Beacon Rd, TA24 5SD, ☏ (01643) 703476 *acon@globalnet.co.uk, Fax (01643) 707007,* ←, – rest, TV P. MC VISA JCB
9 rm 86.00/136.00 **st.**

Channel House, Church Path, TA24 5QG, off Northfield Rd ☏ (01643) 703229, *ch el.house@virgin.net, Fax (01643) 708925,* ←, « Gardens » – rest, TV P. MC VISA
April-October and Christmas – **Meals** (dinner only) 21.00 **t.** and a la carte 6.50 – **8 rm** (dinner included) 87.00/134.00 **st.** – SB.

Wyndcott, Martlet Rd, TA24 5QE, ☏ (01643) 704522, *mineheadhotel@msn.c Fax (01643) 707577,* ←, – TV P. MC AE VISA
Meals (booking essential to non-residents) (lunch by arrangement)/dinner 19.95 **st.** – **9 rm** 34.00/80.00 **st.**

Rectory House, Northfield Rd, TA24 5QH, ☏ (01643) 702611, – rest, TV P VISA
Meals (dinner only) 21.50 8.50 – **7 rm** 30.00/60.00.

MINSTERLEY *Shrops.* 402 403 L 26 – *pop. 1 397.*
London 174 – Birmingham 57 – Hereford 55 – Shrewsbury 10.

Cricklewood Cottage without rest., Plox Green, SY5 0HT, Southwest : 1 m. on A ☏ (01743) 791229, – P.
3 rm 39.00/52.00.

MOBBERLEY *Ches.* 402 403 404 N 24 – *see Knutsford.*

MONK FRYSTON *N. Yorks.* 402 Q 22 – *pop. 722 –* ✉ *Lumby.*
London 190 – Kingston-upon-Hull 42 – Leeds 13 – York 20.

Monk Fryston Hall, LS25 5DU, ☏ (01977) 682369, *reception@monkfryston-hotel. Fax (01977) 683544,* « Part 16C and 17C manor house, extensive ornamental gardens – rest, TV P – 70. MC AE VISA JCB
Meals 16.25/23.25 **t.** 7.50 – **28 rm** 81.00/112.00 **t.** – SB.

ONKTON COMBE *Bath & North East Somerset – see Bath.*

ONKTON FARLEIGH *Wilts.* 403 404 N 29 – *see Bradford-on-Avon.*

ORCOTT SERVICE AREA *Rutland – see Uppingham.*

ORECAMBE *Lancs.* 402 L 21 – *pop. 46 657.*

Bare (01524) 418050 – Heysham, Trumacar Park, Middleton Rd (01524) 851011.
Old Station Buildings, Marine Rd Central (01524) 582808.
London 248 – Blackpool 29 – Carlisle 66 – Lancaster 4.

Strathmore, Marine Rd, East Promenade, LA4 5AP, (01524) 421234, *info@strathmore-hotel.co.uk, Fax (01524) 414242,* – – 200. MC AE VISA JCB.
Meals 7.50/17.50 **t.** and dinner a la carte 7.50 – **50 rm** 50.00/95.00 **t.** – SB.

ORETON *Mersey.* 402 403 K 23 – *pop. 12 053.*

London 225 – Birkenhead 4 – Liverpool 6.

Lee Ho, 304-308 Hoylake Rd, L46 6DE, West : ¼ m. on A 553 (0151) 677 6440 – . MC AE VISA
closed 25-26 December, Sunday, Monday and Bank Holidays – **Meals** - Chinese - (dinner only) 17.50/25.00 **t.** and a la carte **st.** 4.95.

ORETONHAMPSTEAD *Devon* 403 I 32 *The West Country G. – pop. 1 380 – Newton Abbot.*

Env. : *Dartmoor National Park★★.*
Manor House Hotel (01647) 440998.
London 213 – Exeter 13 – Plymouth 30.

Manor House , TQ13 8RE, Southwest : 2 m. on B 3212 (01647) 440355, *manor.house@principalhotels.co.uk, Fax (01647) 440961,* , « Part 19C », , , , , – , rest, – 120. MC AE VISA.
Meals 12.50/23.00 **st.** and dinner a la carte – **90 rm** (dinner included) 79.00/138.00 **st.** – SB.

Great Slocombe Farm , TQ13 8QF, Northwest : 1 ½ m. by A 382 (01647) 440595, *hmerchant@slocombe.freeserve.co.uk, Fax (01647) 440595,* « Working farm », –
Meals (by arrangement) 13.00 – **3 rm** 30.00/46.00 **s.**

Moorcote without rest., TQ13 8LS, Northwest : ¼ m. on A 382 (01647) 440966, *moorcote@smartone.co.uk,* – .
March-October – **5 rm** 25.00/42.00.

RETON-IN-MARSH *Glos.* 403 404 O 28 *Great Britain G. – pop. 1 895.*

Env. : *Chastleton House★★, SE : 5 m. by A 44.*
London 86 – Birmingham 40 – Gloucester 31 – Oxford 29.

Manor House, High St., GL56 0LJ, (01608) 650501, *Fax (01608) 651481,* « Part 16C manor house », , – , rest, – 75. MC AE VISA JCB
Meals 9.50/30.00 **t.** and dinner a la carte 8.50 – **38 rm** 75.00/98.00, 2 suites – SB.

Treetops without rest., London Rd, GL56 0HE, (01608) 651036, *treetops.1@talk21.com, Fax (01608) 651036,* – . MC VISA JCB
6 rm 30.00/47.00 **s.**

Marsh Goose, High St., GL56 0AX, (01608) 653500, *manager@marshgoose.com, Fax (01608) 653510* – . MC AE VISA JCB
closed Tuesday lunch, Sunday dinner and Monday – **Meals** 17.00/30.00 **t.**.

Annies, 3 Oxford St., GL56 0LA, (01608) 651981, *anniesrest@easicom.com, Fax (01608) 651981* – MC AE VISA
closed 1 week late January, 1 week early November and Sunday – **Meals** (dinner only) a la carte 22.80/32.55 **st.** 6.25.

Bourton on the Hill *West : 1 ¾ m. on A 44 – Moreton-in-Marsh.*

Horse and Groom with rm, GL56 9AQ, (01386) 700413, *Fax (01386) 701579,* « 18C inn », – rm, . MC VISA.
closed 25 December and 1 week January – **Meals** *(closed Monday and dinner Sunday)* a la carte 13.80/22.10 **t.** – **5 rm** 60.00/75.00 **st.**

MORPETH *Northd.* 401 402 O 18 – *pop. 14 393.*

The Common ✆ *(01670) 504942.*

The Chantry, Bridge St. ✆ *(01670) 511323.*

London 301 – Edinburgh 93 – Newcastle upon Tyne 15.

Linden Hall, Longhorsley, NE65 8XF, Northwest : 7 ½ m. by A 192 on A 6 ✆ (01670) 500000, *stay@lindenhall.co.uk, Fax (01670) 500001*, ←, « Country house in tensive grounds », Ls, ▣, 18, ⛯, ♘ – |‡|, ⇔ rest, TV & P – 300. MC AE O VISA
Meals 15.50/24.50 **st.** 9.00 – **49 rm** ⊐ 69.50/99.00 **st.**, 1 suite – SB.

at Eshott *North : 6 m. by A 1 – ✉ Morpeth.*

Eshott Hall, NE65 9EP, 1 m. on Eshott rd ✆ (01670) 787777, *eshott@btinternet.co Fax (01670) 786000*, « Georgian mansion », ⛯, ♘ – P. MC AE O VISA JCB
closed Christmas and New Year – **Meals** (by arrangement) (communal dining) 17.50 4.50 – **7 rm** ⊐ 45.00/96.00 **st.**

MORSTON *Norfolk – see Blakeney.*

MORTEHOE *Devon* 403 H 30 – *see Woolacombe.*

MOTCOMBE *Dorset* 403 404 N 30 – *see Shaftesbury.*

MOULSFORD *Oxon.* 403 404 Q 29 *The West Country G.* – *pop. 491.*

Exc. : *Ridgeway Path*★★.

London 58 – Oxford 17 – Reading 13 – Swindon 37.

XXX **Beetle and Wedge** with rm, Ferry Lane, OX10 9JF, ✆ (01491) 6513 *Fax (01491) 651376*, ←, « Thames-side setting », ⛯, ⛯ – ⚓ ⇔ TV P. MC AE O VISA
The Dining Room : **Meals** *(closed Sunday dinner and Monday)* (booking essential) a la c 34.25/38.50 **t.** 6.75 – (see also ***The Boathouse*** below) – **10 rm** ⊐ 95.00/165.00 **t.** – S

X **The Boathouse** (at Beetle and Wedge), Ferry Lane, OX10 9JF, ✆ (01491) 6513 *Fax (01491) 651376*, ←, ⛯, « Thames-side setting », ⛯ – ⚓ P. MC AE O VISA JCB
Meals (booking essential) a la carte 21.25/31.00 **t.** 6.50.

MOULTON *N. Yorks.* 402 P 20 – *pop. 197 – ✉ Richmond.*

London 243 – Leeds 53 – Middlesbrough 25 – Newcastle upon Tyne 43.

XX **Black Bull Inn**, DL10 6QJ, ✆ (01325) 377289, *sarah@blackbullinn.demon.co Fax (01325) 377422*, « Brighton Belle Pullman coach » – P. MC AE O VISA
closed 24 to 26 December and Sunday dinner – **Meals** - Seafood specialities - 15.5 (lunch) and a la carte 21.20/31.20 **t.** 6.50.

MOUSEHOLE *Cornwall* 403 D 33 *The West Country G.* – ✉ *Penzance.*

See : *Village*★.

Env. : *Penwith*★★ – *Lamorna (The Merry Maidens and The Pipers Standing Stone*★ *) SW : by B 3315.*

Exc. : *Land's End*★ *(cliff scenery*★★★ *) W : 9 m. by B 3315.*

London 321 – Penzance 3 – Truro 29.

The Old Coastguard, The Parade, TR18 6PR, ✆ (01736) 731222, *bookings@oldcoastguardhotel.co.uk, Fax (01736) 731720*, ←, ⛯ – ⇔ TV P. MC AE VISA
Meals 23.00 **st.** (dinner) and a la carte 16.00/24.00 **st.** 5.00 – **21 rm** ⊐ 32.00/80.00 **t.** -

MUCH WENLOCK *Shrops.* 402 403 M26 *Great Britain G.* – *pop. 1 921.*

See : *Priory*★ *AC.*

Env. : *Ironbridge Gorge Museum*★★ *AC (The Iron Bridge*★★ *- Coalport China Museum Blists Hill Open Air Museum*★★ *– Museum of the River and Visitor Centre*★ *) NE : 4½ m. 4169 and B 4380.*

The Museum, High St. ✆ *(01952) 727679 (summer only).*

London 154 – Birmingham 34 – Shrewsbury 12 – Worcester 37.

Raven, Barrow St., TF13 6EN, ✆ (01952) 727251, *Fax (01952) 728416*, ⛯ – ⇔ rest, MC AE O VISA JCB. ⛯
closed 25 December – **Meals** 15.00 **t.** (lunch) and a la carte 21.25/25.25 **t.** 7.50 – 1 ⊐ 65.00/95.00 **t.** – SB.

JDEFORD *Dorset* 403 404 O 31 – *see Christchurch.*

JLLION *Cornwall* 403 E 33 *The West Country G. – pop. 2 040 –* ✉ *Helston.*

See : *Mullion Cove★★ (Church★) – Lizard Peninsula★.*

Env. : *Kynance Cove★★, S : 5 m. – Cury★ (Church★), N : 2 m. by minor roads.*

Exc. : *Helston (The Flora Day Furry Dance★★) (May), N : 7 ½ m. by A 3083 – Culdrose (Flambards Village Theme Park★) AC, N : 6 m. by A 3083 – Wendron (Poldark Mine★), N : 9½ m. by A 3083 and B 3297.*

London 323 – Falmouth 21 – Penzance 21 – Truro 26.

Polurrian, TR12 7EN, Southwest : ½ m. ☎ (01326) 240421, *polurotel@aol.com, Fax (01326) 240083,* ≤ Mounts Bay, heated, squash – rest, – 150. MC AE VISA JCB
Meals (bar lunch Monday to Saturday)/dinner 22.50 **t.** and a la carte 8.95 – **38 rm** (dinner included) 95.00/190.00 **t.**, 1 suite – SB.

Mullion Cove, TR12 7EP, Southwest : 1 m. by B 3296 ☎ (01326) 240328, *mullioncove@btinternet.com, Fax (01326) 240998,* ≤ Mullion Cove and Mount's Bay, – rest, MC AE VISA JCB
Meals (bar lunch)/dinner 19.50 **st.** – **30 rm** (dinner included) 75.00/160.00 **st.** – SB.

INGRISDALE *Cumbria* 401 402 L 19 20 *– pop. 330 –* ✉ *Penrith.*

London 301 – Carlisle 33 – Keswick 8.5 – Penrith 13.

Mosedale House, Mosedale, CA11 0XQ, North : 1 m. by Mosedale rd ☎ (017687) 79371, *colin.smith2@ukonline.co.uk* –
closed 25 and 26 December and restricted opening in winter – **Meals** (by arrangement) 13.75/14.50 **s.** 5.55 – **7 rm** 25.50/51.00 **s.**

'LOR BRIDGE *Cornwall* 403 E 33 – *see Falmouth.*

ILSWORTH *Glos.* 403 404 N 28 *– pop. 5 242.*

London 120 – Bristol 30 – Swindon 41.

Egypt Mill, GL6 0AE, ☎ (01453) 833449, *Fax (01453) 836098,* « Part 16C converted riverside mill », – – 100. MC AE VISA.
Restaurant : Meals (dinner only) a la carte 17.50/24.60 **st.** – ***Cellar Bistro :*** Meals a la carte 15.45/23.45 **st.** – **16 rm** 50.00/95.00 **st.**

Aaron Farm, Nympsfield Rd, GL6 0ET, West : ¾ m. by Spring Hill ☎ (01453) 833598, *aaronfarm@aol.com, Fax (01453) 833626* –
Meals (by arrangement) 14.00 **st.** – **3 rm** 30.00/42.00 **s.**

Waterman's, Old Market, GL6 0BX, ☎ (01453) 832808, – MC AE VISA
closed Sunday and Monday – **Meals** (dinner only and Saturday lunch)/dinner a la carte 19.60/26.75 **t.** 4.95.

NTWICH *Ches.* 402 403 404 M 24 *– pop. 11 695.*

Alvaston Hall, Middlewich Rd ☎ (01270) 624321.

Church House, Church Walk ☎ (01270) 610983.

London 176 – Chester 20 – Liverpool 45 – Stoke-on-Trent 17.

Rookery Hall, Worleston, CW5 6DQ, North : 2 ½ m. by A 51 on B 5074 ☎ (01270) 610016, *Fax (01270) 626027,* ≤, « Part 19C country house », – rest, – 70. MC AE VISA
Meals *(closed Saturday lunch)* (booking essential) 37.50/39.50 **st.** (dinner) and lunch a la carte 17.00/21.00 **st.** – **43 rm** 95.00/110.00 **st.**, 2 suites.

Premier Lodge, 221 Crewe Rd, CW5 6NE, Northeast : 1 ¼ m. on A 534 ☎ (0870) 7001496, *Fax (0870) 7001497* – MC AE VISA.
Meals (grill rest.) – **37 rm** 46.00 **t.**

Oakland House without rest., 252 Newcastle Rd, Blakelow, Shavington, CW5 7ET, East : 2 ½ m. by A 51 on A 500 ☎ (01270) 567134, *Fax (01270) 651752,* – MC VISA JCB
5 rm 34.00/45.00 **st.**

The Limes without rest., 5 Park Rd, CW5 7AQ, ☎ (01270) 624081, *Fax (01270) 624081,* –
March-November **3 rm** 40.00/50.00 **s.**

'IONAL EXHIBITION CENTRE *W. Mids.* 403 404 O 26 – *see Birmingham.*

NAWTON *N. Yorks. – see Helmsley.*

NAYLAND *Suffolk* 404 W 28.
London 64 – Bury St. Edmunds 24 – Cambridge 54 – Colchester 6 – Ipswich 19.

Gladwins Farm, Harpers Hill, CO6 4NU, Northwest : ½ m. on A
(01206) 262261, *gladwinsfarm@compuserve.com, Fax (01206) 263001*, – TV P. MO VISA.
closed Christmas-New Year – **Meals** (by arrangement) 20.00 **st.** – **3 rm** 25.00/58.00

White Hart Inn with rm, High St., CO6 4JF, (01206) 263382, *nayhart@aol.c*
Fax (01206) 263638, « Part 16C former coaching inn » – rm, TV P. MO AE
JCB.
closed 26 December-4 January – **Meals** *(closed Monday except Bank Holidays)* (book
essential) 18.00/23.00 **t.** (lunch) and a la carte 17.50/29.50 **t.** 9.00 – **6 rm** 66
71.50 **st.** – SB.

NEAR SAWREY *Cumbria* 402 L 20 – *see Hawkshead.*

NEEDHAM MARKET *Suffolk* 404 X 27 – *pop. 4 312.*
London 77 – Cambridge 47 – Ipswich 8.5 – Norwich 38.

Travelodge, Beacon Hill Service Area, IP6 8NY, Southeast : 1 ¾ m. by B 1078, at junc
of A 14 with A 140 (01449) 721640, *Fax (01449) 721640* – rm, TV P. MO AE
JCB.
Meals (grill rest.) – **40 rm** 39.95 **t.**

Pipps Ford, Norwich Rd roundabout, IP6 8LJ, Southeast : 1 ¾ m. by B 1078 at junctio
A 14 with A 140 (01449) 760208, *pippsford@aol.com, Fax (01449) 760561*, « Elizabet
farmhouse », – P. MO VISA.
closed 2 weeks Christmas-New Year – **Meals** (by arrangement) (communal dining) 2
7.50 – **7 rm** 47.50/75.00.

Les prix — Pour toutes précisions sur les prix indiqués dans ce guide, reportez-vous aux pages de l'introduction.

NETTLETON SHRUB *Wilts.* 403 404 N 29 – *see Castle Combe.*

NEWARK-ON-TRENT *Notts.* 402 404 R 24 *Great Britain G.* – *pop. 35 129.*
See : *St. Mary Magdalene*★.
18 *Kelwick, Coddington (01636) 626241.*
London 127 – Lincoln 16 – Nottingham 20 – Sheffield 42.

Grange, 73 London Rd, NG24 1RZ, South : ½ m. on Grantham rd (A 1) (01636) 703
Fax (01636) 702328, – TV P. MO AE VISA JCB.
closed 24 December-1 January – **Meals** (lunch by arrangement)/dinner 12.9
and a la carte 4.50 – **15 rm** 44.95/72.95 **t.** – SB.

Travel Inn, Lincoln Rd, NG24 2DB, Northwest : 1 ½ m. at A1/A46 roundab
(01636) 640690, *Fax (01636) 605135* – rm, TV P. MO AE VISA.
Meals (grill rest.) – **40 rm** 40.95 **t.**

at North Muskham *North : 4½ m. by A 46 and A 1 – Newark-on-Trent.*

Travelodge, NG23 6HT, North : ½ m. on A 1 (southbound carriage
(01636) 703635, *Fax (01636) 703635* – rm, TV P. MO AE VISA JCB.
Meals (grill rest.) – **30 rm** 39.95 **t.**

at Caunton *Northwest : 4½ m. by A 616 – Newark-on-Trent.*

Caunton Beck, Main St., NG23 6AB, (01636) 636793, *Fax (01636) 636828*, – P
AE VISA JCB
Meals a la carte 14.75/24.75 **st.** 8.65.

NEWBURGH *Lancs.* 402 L 23.
London 217 – Liverpool 23 – Manchester 39 – Preston 20 – Southport 13.

Red Lion, Ash Brow, WN8 7NG, on A 5209 (01257) 462336, *Fax (01257) 462827* – TV
45. MO AE VISA JCB
Meals (in bar) a la carte 10.95/18.85 **st.** 5.95 – 4.95 – **13 rm** 39.50/44.50 **st.**

NEWBURY

A — A 34 OXFORD

V — X

A 4 READING — A 339 BASINGSTOKE

A 343 ANDOVER — A 34 WINCHESTER — A

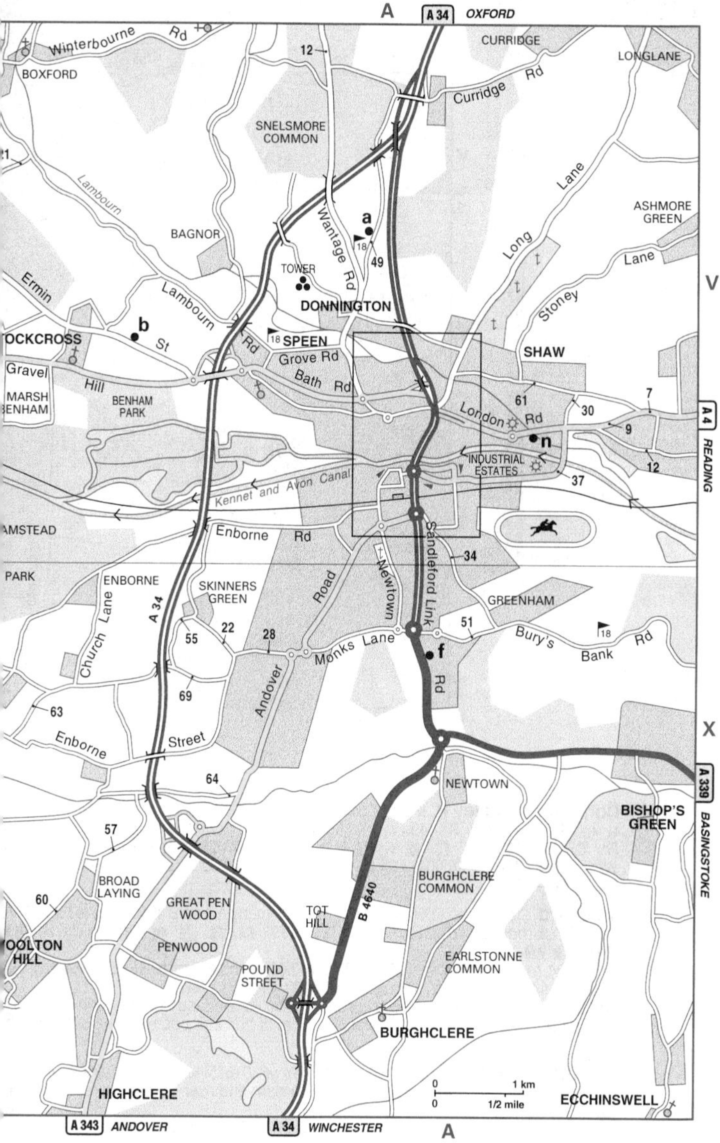

NEWBURY *Newbury* 403 404 Q 29 – *pop. 33 273.*

Newbury and Crookham, Bury's Bank Rd, Greenham Common ☎ (01635) 40035 **AX**

Donnington Valley, Old Oxford Rd ☎ (01635) 32488 **AV**.

The Wharf ☎ (01635) 30267.

London 67 – Bristol 66 – Oxford 28 – Reading 17 – Southampton 38.

NEWBURY

Almond Avenue . . . . **BY** 3
Andover Road. . . . . **BZ** 4
Bartholomew Street . . . . **BZ** 6
Bone Lane. . . . . **BZ** 10
Carnegie Road . . . . **BZ** 13
Castle Grove. . . . . **BY** 15
Cheap Street. . . . . **BZ** 16
Chesterfield Road . . . . . . **BZ** 18
Craven Road . . . . **BZ** 24
Dolman Road . . . . **BY** 25
Donnington Link. . . . . **BY** 27
Greenham Hill. . . . . **BZ** 31
Greenham Road. . . . . **BZ** 33
Hambridge Road . . . . **BZ** 36
Kennett Shopping Centre . . . . **BZ**
Kiln Road. . . . . **BY** 40
Kings Road . . . . **BZ**
London Road . . . . **BY**
Love Lane. . . . . **BY**
Maple Crescent . . . . **BY** 43
Market Street . . . . **BZ** 45
Mill Lane . . . . **BZ**
New Road. . . . . **BZ** 46
Newtown Road . . . . **BZ** 48
Northbrook Street. . . . . . **BYZ**
Northcroft Lane . . . . **BZ**
Old Bath Road . . . . **BY**
Oxford Road. . . . . **BY**
Park Way . . . . **BYZ** 50
Pound Street. . . . . **BZ**
Queens Road . . . . **BZ**
Racecourse Road. . . . . **BZ**
Rockingham Road . . . . **BZ** 52
St. Johns Road. . . . . **BZ**
Sandleford Link . . . . **BZ** 54
Shaw Hill. . . . . **BY**
Shaw Road. . . . . **BY**
Station Road . . . . **BZ**
Strawberry Hill . . . . **BY** 58
West Street. . . . . **BZ** 66
Western Avenue . . . . **BY**
Wharf Street. . . . . **BZ** 67

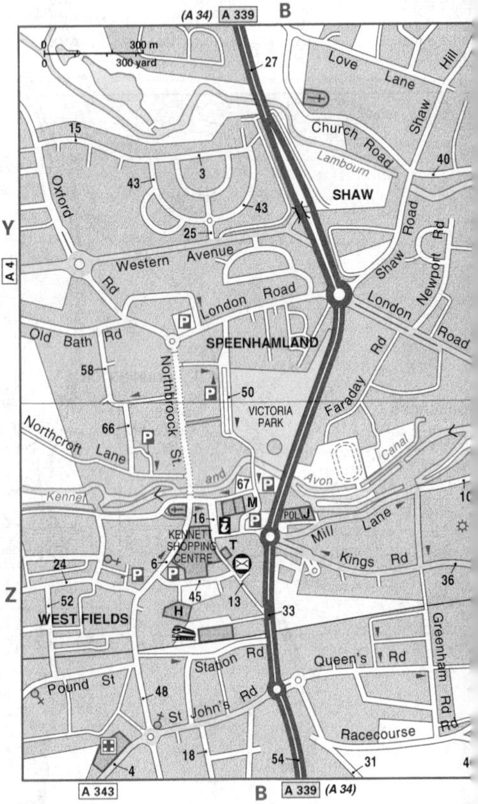

There is no paid advertising in this Guide.

Donnington Valley H. & Golf Course, Old Oxford Rd, Donnington, RG14 3AG, North : ¾ m. by A 4 off B 4494 ☎ (01635) 551199, *general@donningtonvalley.co* *Fax (01635) 551123*, – – 140. AE VISA JCB AV
Winepress : **Meals** 18.00/35.00 **st.** and a la carte 9.00 – 13.50 – **58 rm** 129. 250.00 **st.** – SB.

Vineyard, Stockcross, RG20 8JU, Northwest : 2 m. by A 4 on B 4000 ☎ (01635) 52877 *servations@thevineyard.co.uk, Fax (01635) 528398*, , , – , rm, AE VISA, AV
closed 24 to 30 December – **Meals** 22.00/42.00 **t.** and a la carte 36.25/48.50 **t.** 13.5
20 rm 146.00/205.00 **s.**, 13 suites 258.00/458.00 **s.** – SB
Spec. Breast of guinea fowl with prunes, baby carrots and turnips. Loin of lamb fondant potato, Madeira and rosemary jus. Fillet of brill with potato purée, red wine sh jus.

Newbury Manor , London Rd, RG14 2BY, ☎ (01635) 528838, *enquires@newbury nor-hotel.co.uk, Fax (01635) 523406*, , « Gardens and river » – , rest, 50. AE VISA AV
Meals 16.50/25.00 **t.** and a la carte – **32 rm** 145.00/195.00 **st.**, 1 suite – SB.

ENGLAND

Jarvis Elcot Park H. and Country Club, RG20 8NJ, West : 5 m. by A 4 (01488) 658100, *Fax (01488) 658288*, ≤, , , , , , – rm, rest, – 110.
Meals *(closed Saturday lunch)* 18.00 **t.** and a la carte 6.95 – 11.50 – **75 rm** 113.00/150.00 **t.** – SB.

Hilton Newbury North, Oxford Rd, RG20 8XY, North : 3 ¼ m. on A 34 at junction 13 of M 4 (01635) 247010, *Fax (01635) 247077*, , , – rm, – 80.
Meals *(closed Saturday lunch)* (carving lunch) 9.95/19.95 **t.** – 12.95 – **109 rm** 146.00/166.00 **t.** – SB.

Hilton Newbury Centre, Pinchington Lane, RG14 7HL, South : 2 m. by A 339 (01635) 529000, *Fax (01635) 529337*, , , – rm, rest, – 200.
AX f
Meals (bar lunch Saturday) 10.25/15.75 **t.** and dinner a la carte 5.90 – 12.75 – **109 rm** 114.00/167.00 **st.** – SB.

Hamstead Marshall *Southwest : 5½ m. by A 4* – **AV** – *Newbury.*

White Hart Inn, Kintbury Rd, RG20 0HW, (01488) 658201, *Fax (01488) 657192*, , – .
closed 25-26 December and 1 January – **Meals** - Italian - *(closed Sunday)* a la carte 14.50/24.50 **t.** 5.50 – **6 rm** 60.00/90.00 **t.**

Marsh Benham *West : 3½ m. by A 4* – **AV** – *Newbury.*

The Red House, RG20 8LY, (01635) 582017, *redhouse@ukonline.co.uk*, *Fax (01635) 581621*, « Thatched inn », – .
closed Sunday dinner and Monday – **Meals** a la carte 23.50/27.00 **t.** 9.50.

WBY BRIDGE *Cumbria* 402 L 21 *Great Britain G.* – *Ulverston.*
Env. : *Lake Windermere*★★.
London 270 – Kendal 16 – Lancaster 27.

Lakeside, Lakeside, LA12 8AT, Northeast : 1 m. on Hawkshead rd (015395) 31207, *sales@lakesidehotel.co.uk*, *Fax (015395) 31699*, ≤, « Lakeside setting », , – – 100.
Meals (bar lunch Monday to Saturday)/dinner 35.00/41.00 **st.** 9.95 – **77 rm** 120.00/205.00 **st.**, 3 suites – SB.

Swan, LA12 8NB, (015395) 31681, *swanhotel@aol.com*, *Fax (015395) 31917*, ≤, , , , , – , rest, – 140. .
Meals (bar lunch Monday to Saturday)/dinner 22.00 **t.** and a la carte 5.25 – **55 rm** 85.00/140.00 **t.** – SB.

Whitewater, The Lakeland Village, LA12 8PX, Southwest : 1 ½ m. by A 590 (015395) 31133, *Fax (015395) 31881*, , , , , squash – – 70. .
closed 2-4 January – **Meals** (bar lunch Monday to Saturday)/dinner 20.00/23.50 **st.** and a la carte 8.50 – **35 rm** 80.00/140.00 **st.** – SB.

Cartmell Fell *Northeast : 3¼ m. by A 590 off A 592* – *Grange-over-Sands.*

Lightwood Farmhouse , LA11 6NP, (015395) 31454, *Fax (015395) 31454*, ≤, – . .
closed mid December-mid February – **Meals** (by arrangement) 14.00 **s.** 5.00 – **4 rm** 35.00/56.00 **s.** – SB.

WBY WISKE *N. Yorks.* 402 P 21 – *see Northallerton.*

WCASTLE AIRPORT *Tyne and Wear* 401 402 O 19 – *see Newcastle upon Tyne.*

NEWCASTLE-UNDER-LYME *Staffs.* 402 403 404 N 24 *Great Britain G. – pop. 73 731.*

EXC. : *Wedgwood Visitor's Centre★ AC, SE : 6½ m. by A 34 Z.*

Keele Golf Centre, Keele Rd ☎ (01782) 717417.

Newcastle Library, Ironmarket ☎ (01782) 297313.

London 161 – Birmingham 46 – Liverpool 56 – Manchester 43.

Plan of Built up Area : see Stoke-on-Trent

NEWCASTLE-UNDER-LYME CENTRE

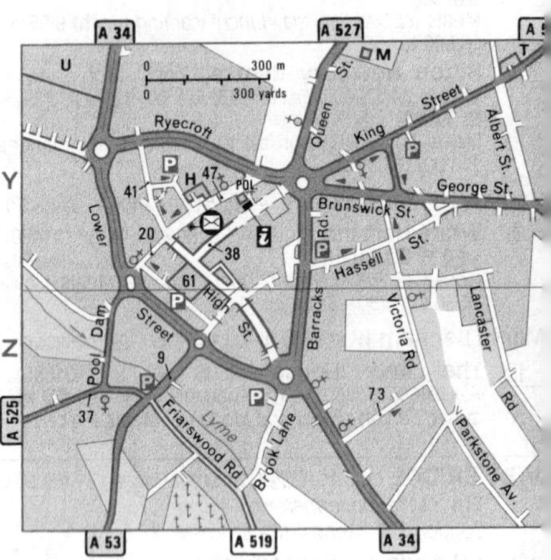

Posthouse Stoke-on-Trent, Clayton Rd, Clayton, ST5 4DL, South : 2 m. on A ☎ (0870) 400 9077, *Fax (01782) 717138,* ⅼ, ≘s, ▣, ⇌ – ⅹ rm, TV P – 🏛 70. MC AE VISA JCB on Stoke-on-Trent town plan V
Meals 15.00 **t.** (dinner) and a la carte 18.85/28.35 **t.** 6.95 – ☐ 11.95 – **119 rm** 69 89.00 **st.** – SB.

Clayton Lodge, Clayton Rd, Clayton, ST5 4AF, South : 1 ¼ m. on A ☎ (01782) 613093, *Fax (01782) 711896* – ⅹ rm, TV P – 🏛 280. MC AE ① JCB on Stoke-on-Trent town plan V
Meals a la carte 15.70/21.50 **st.** – ☐ 9.95 – **50 rm** 85.00/95.00 **st.** – SB.

Bauhinia, Parklands, ST4 6NW, ☎ (01782) 719709 – ▤ P. MC AE VISA JCB
closed 25-26 December, lunch Sunday and Bank Holidays – **Meals** - Chinese - 5.95/18.4 and a la carte 5.35. on Stoke-on-Trent town plan V

NEWCASTLE UPON TYNE

Tyne and Wear 401 402 O 19 *Great Britain G. – pop. 189 150.*

London 276 – Edinburgh 105 – Leeds 95.

TOURIST INFORMATION

City Library, Princess Sq. ☎ (0191) 261 0610.
Main Concourse, Central Station ☎ (0191) 230 0030.
132 Grainger St. ☎ (0191) 277 8000.

PRACTICAL INFORMATION

18 *Broadway East, Gosforth ☎ (0191) 285 6710,* **BV**.
18 *City of Newcastle, Three Mile Bridge, Gosforth ☎ (0191) 285 1775.*
18 *Wallsend, Rheydt Av., Bigges Main ☎ (0191) 262 1973, NE : by A 1058* **BV**.
18 *Whickham, Hollinside Park Fellside Rd ☎ (0191) 488 7309.*
Tyne Tunnel (toll).
Newcastle Airport : ☎ (0191) 286 0966, NW : 5 m. by A 696 **AV**.
Terminal : *Bus Assembly : Central Station Forecourt.*
to Norway (Bergen, Haugesund and Stavanger) (Fjord Line) (26 h) – to Sweden (Gothenburg) (via Kristiansand, Norway) (Scandinavian Seaways) weekly (22 h) – to The Netherlands (Amsterdam) (Scandinavian Seaways) daily (14 h).

SIGHTS

See : *City★★ – Grey Street★* CZ – *Quayside★* CZ : *Composition★, All Saints Church★ (interior★) – Castle Keep★ AC* CZ – *Laing Art Gallery and Museum★ AC* CY **M1** – *Museum of Antiquities★* CY **M2**.

Env. : *Hadrian's Wall★★, W : by A 69* AV.

Exc. : *Beamish : North of England Open-Air Museum★★ AC, SW : 7 m. by A 692 and A 6076* AX – *Seaton Delaval Hall★ AC, NE : 11 m. by A 189 –* BV *– and A 190.*

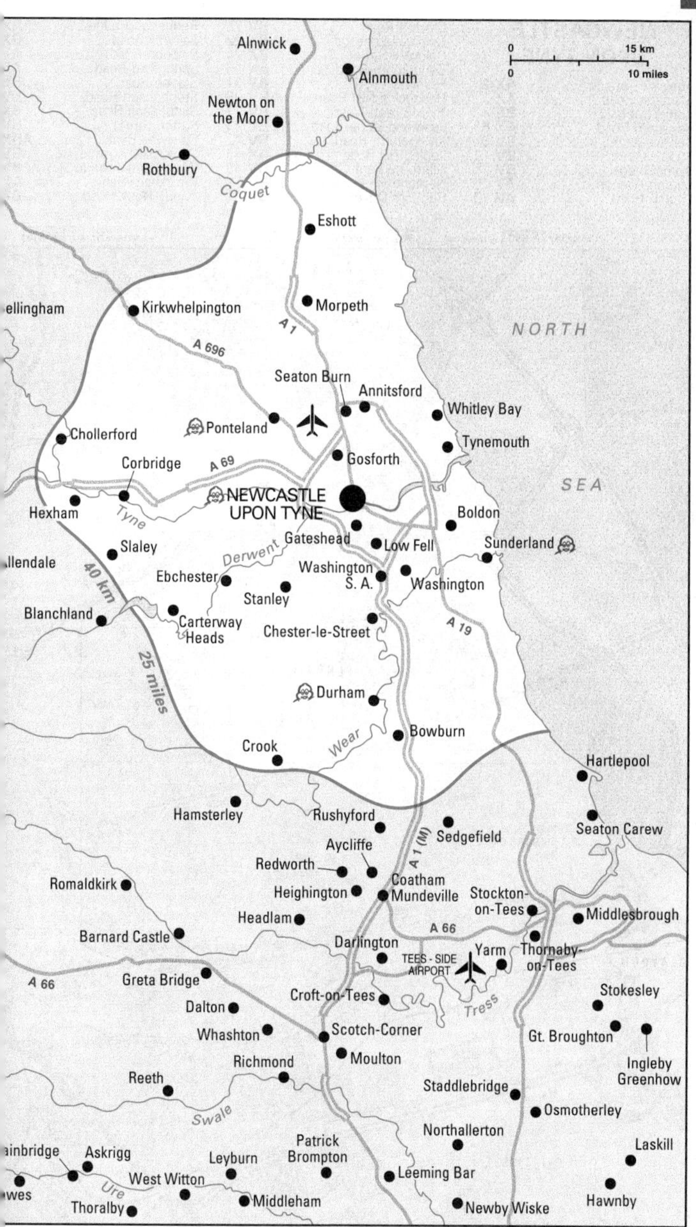

Wenn Sie ein ruhiges Hotel suchen, benutzen Sie zuerst die Karte in der Einleitung oder wählen Sie im Text ein Hotel mit dem Zeichen oder .

NEWCASTLE UPON TYNE

Adelaide Terrace . . . . **AX** 2
Atkinson Road . . . . **AX** 3
Bath Street . . . . **BX** 4
Bensham Road . . . . **AX** 6
Benton Bank. . . . . **BV** 8
Buddle Street . . . . **BV** 13
Byker Bridge. . . . . **BV** 15
Church Avenue. . . . . **AV** 16
Church Road. . . . . **AV** 18
Clayton Road . . . . **BV** 21
Coldwell Lane. . . . . **BX** 22
Coldwell Street . . . . **BX** 24
Condercum Road. . . . . **AX** 26
Fossway . . . . **BV** 31
Haddrick's Mill Road. . . . . **BV** 36
High Street West. . . . . **BV** 37
Jesmond Dene Road . . . . . **BV** 39
Killingworth Road. . . . . **BV** 42
Lobley Hill Road. . . . . **AX** 45
Matthew Bank . . . . **BV** 49
Neptune Road . . . . **BV** 51
Red Hall Drive . . . . **BV** 61
Redheugh Bridge. . . . . **AX**
Saltwell Road . . . . **BX**
Shipdon Road. . . . . **AX**
Springfield Road. . . . . **AV**
Station Road . . . . **BX**
Stephenson Road . . . . **BV**
Sunderland Road . . . . **BX**
Sutton Street . . . . **BV**
Swalwell Bank. . . . . **ABX**
Waverdale Avenue . . . . **BV**
West Farm Avenue . . . . **BV**
Whickham Bank. . . . . **AX**
Windy Nook Road . . . . **BX**

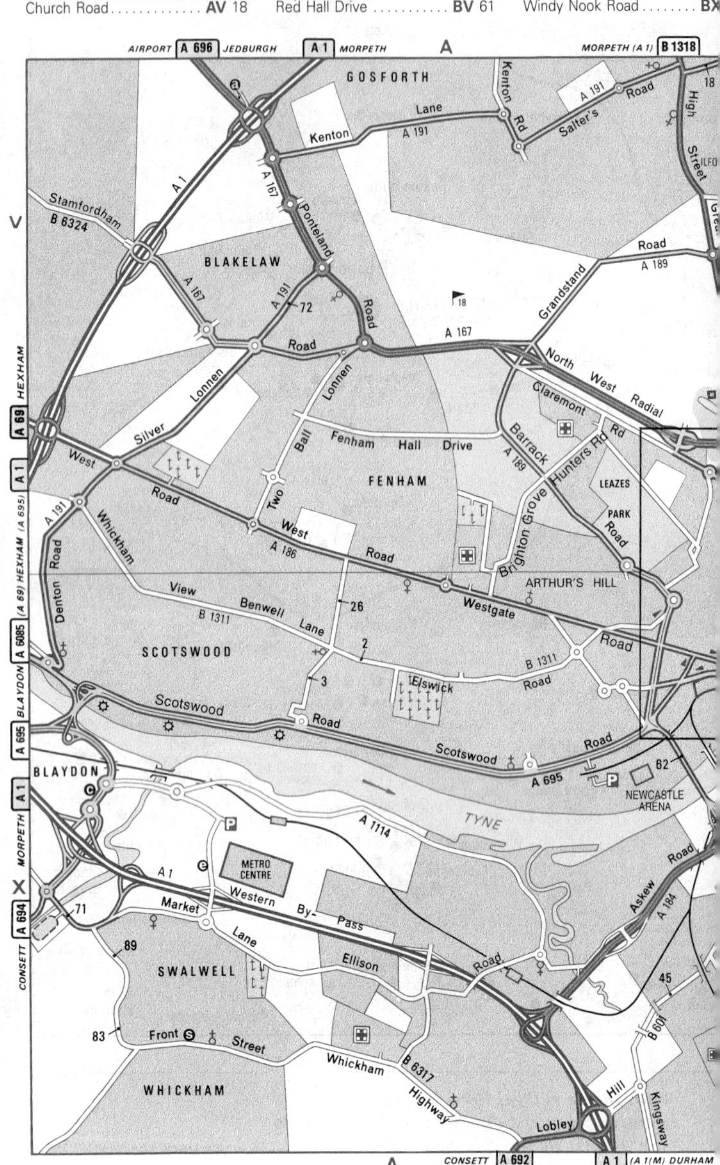

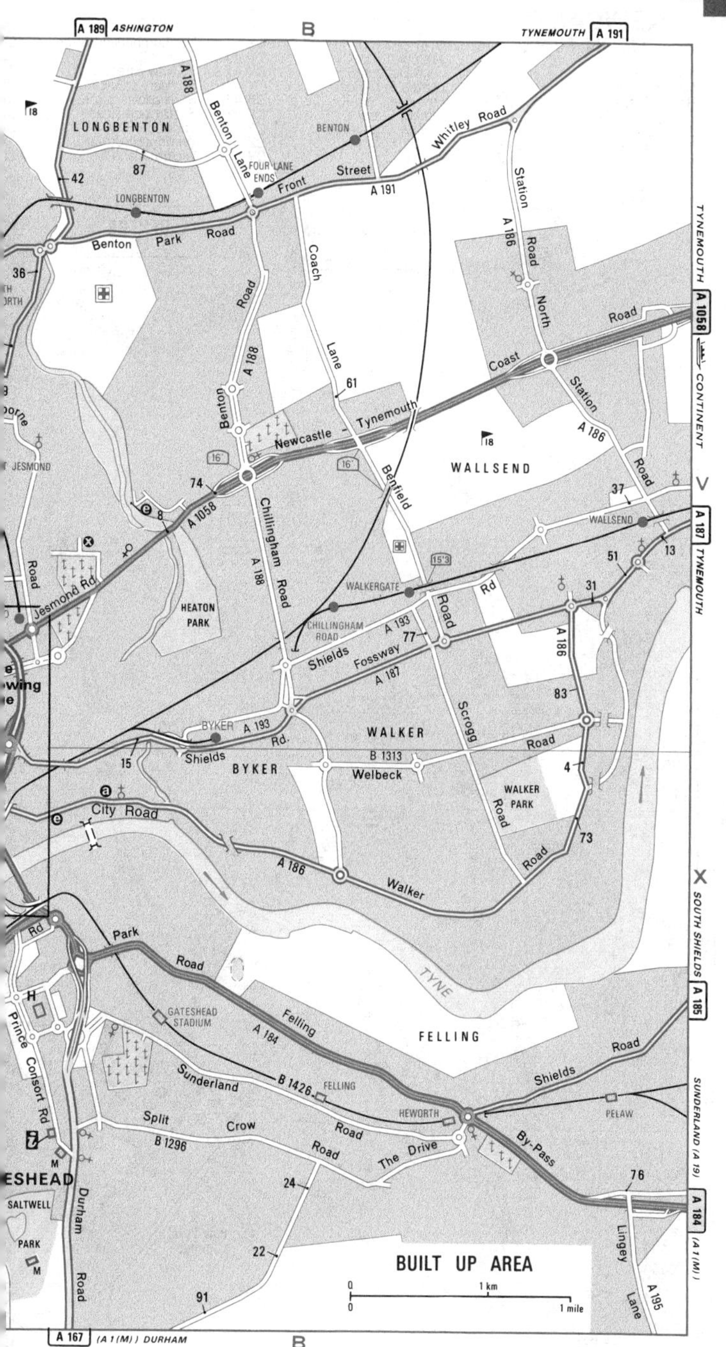

A 189 ASHINGTON
B
TYNEMOUTH A 191
LONGBENTON
BENTON
FOUR LANE ENDS
Front Street
Whitley Road
A 191
LONGBENTON
Benton Park Road
Coach Lane
Station Road
North
A 186
TYNEMOUTH
A 1058
CONTINENT
Coast Road
Newcastle - Tynemouth
WALLSEND
Benfield
Benton Road
A 188
JESMOND
Jesmond Rd
A 1058
HEATON PARK
Chillingham Road
A 188
WALKERGATE
CHILLINGHAM ROAD
Shields
Fossway
A 193
A 187
Road
Rd
A 187
TYNEMOUTH
WALLSEND
BYKER
A 193
Shields Rd.
WALKER
BYKER
Welbeck
B 1313
Road
Scrogg Road
WALKER PARK
City Road
A 186
Walker Road
TYNE
SOUTH SHIELDS
A 185
Park Road
Felling
A 184
GATESHEAD STADIUM
FELLING
Sunderland
B 1426
FELLING
HEWORTH
PELAW
Shields Road
SUNDERLAND (A 19)
By-Pass
Prince Consort Rd
Split Crow Road
B 1296
Road
The Drive
ESHEAD
SALTWELL PARK
Durham Road
BUILT UP AREA
1 km
1 mile
Lingey Lane
A 195
A 184
(A 1(M))
A 167
(A 1(M)) DURHAM
B

NEWCASTLE UPON TYNE

Street	Grid	No.
Blackett Street	CY	
Bridge Street	CZ	10
Broad Chare	CZ	12
Collingwood Street	CZ	25
Eldon Square Shopping Centre	CYZ	
Forth Street	CZ	30
George Street	CZ	32
Great North Road	CY	33
Grey Street	CZ	
Jesmond Road	CY	40
John Dobson Street	CY	41
Leazes Park Road	CY	43
Low Friar Street	CZ	46
Market Street	CZ	47
Mosley Street	CZ	50
Neville Street	CZ	52
New Bridge St. West	CY	53
Newgate Street	CZ	
Northumberland Street	CY	
Pilgrim Street	CZ	
Railway Street	CZ	
St. Mary's Place	CY	
St. Nicholas Street	CZ	
Scotswood Road	CZ	
Thornton Street	CZ	
Wellington Street	CY	
Westmorland Rd	CZ	

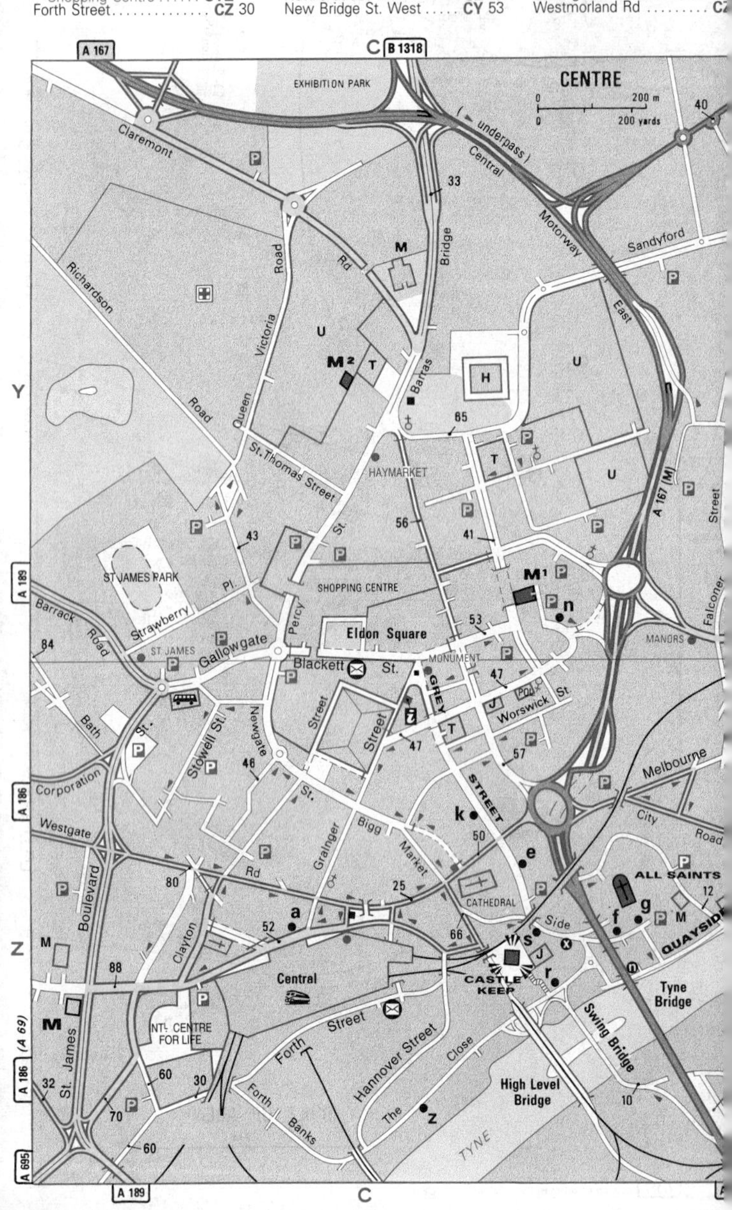

ENGLAND

Copthorne Newcastle, The Close, Quayside, NE1 3RT, ☎ (0191) 222 0333, *sales.newcastle@mill-cop.com, Fax (0191) 230 1111*, ≤, Fð, ≘s, ⊡ – |‡|, ⇹ rm, ▤ rest, TV ☎ ♿ P – 🏛 200. MC AE ⓓ VISA JCB CZ z
Le Rivage **: Meals** *(closed Sunday)* (dinner only) a la carte 30.85/32.85 **t.** – ***Harry's*** **: Meals** *(closed Saturday lunch)* 15.95 **t.** (dinner) and a la carte 16.00/28.70 **t.** – ☕ 13.50 – **156 rm** 155.00/360.00 **t.** – SB.

Vermont, Castle Garth (off St. Nicholas St.), NE1 1RQ, ☎ (0191) 233 1010, *info@vermont-hotel.co.uk, Fax (0191) 233 1234*, ≤, Fð – |‡|, ⇹ rm, TV ☎ ♿ P – 🏛 200. MC AE ⓓ VISA JCB
The Bridge **: Meals** 15.50/18.50 **st.** and a la carte 🍷 6.50 – (see also ***Blue Room*** below) – ☕ 12.50 – **95 rm** 145.00/165.00 **st.**, 6 suites – SB. CZ s

Malmaison, Quayside, NE1 3DX, ☎ (0191) 245 5000, *newcastle@malmaison.com, Fax (0191) 245 0566*, « Contemporary interior », Fð, ≘s – |‡| ⇹, ▤ rest, TV ☎ ♿ P – 🏛 60. MC AE ⓓ VISA. ✗ BX e
Meals 9.95/11.95 **t.** (lunch) and a la carte 20.10/27.80 **st.** 🍷 10.95 – ☕ 10.50 – **112 rm** 105.00 **t.**, 4 suites – SB.

Imperial Swallow, Jesmond Rd, NE2 1PR, ☎ (0191) 281 5511, *jesmond@swallow-hotels.co.uk, Fax (0191) 281 8472*, Fð, ≘s, ⊡ – |‡|, ⇹ rm, ▤ rest, TV P – 🏛 150. MC AE ⓓ VISA
Meals *(closed Saturday lunch)* 9.50/19.50 **st.** and a la carte 🍷 7.50 – **122 rm** ☕ 90.00/125.00 **st.** – SB. CY e

Posthouse Newcastle upon Tyne, 1 New Bridge Street West, NE1 8BS, ☎ (0870) 400 9058, *sales.phntune@btclick.com, Fax (0191) 261 8529*, Fð, ≘s, ⊡ – |‡|, ⇹ rm, ▤ rest, TV ♿ P – 🏛 400. MC AE ⓓ VISA JCB CY n
Meals a la carte approx. 20.00 **t.** 🍷 8.50 – ☕ 13.95 – **172 rm** 99.00/109.00 **st.** – SB.

Novotel, Ponteland Rd, Kenton, NE3 3HZ, at junction of A 1(M) with A 696 ☎ (0191) 214 0303, *h1118@accor-hotels.com, Fax (0191) 214 0633*, ≘s, ⊡ – |‡|, ⇹ rm, ▤ rest, TV ☎ ♿ P – 🏛 220. MC AE ⓓ VISA. ✗ AV a
Meals 9.95/15.95 **st.** and a la carte 🍷 10.00 – ☕ 9.50 – **126 rm** 75.00 **st.** – SB.

Thistle Newcastle, Neville St., NE99 1AH, ☎ (0191) 232 2471, *newcastle@thistle.co.uk, Fax (0191) 232 1285* – |‡|, ⇹ rm, TV P – 🏛 130. MC AE ⓓ VISA. ✗ CZ a
Meals (bar lunch Saturday) 10.00/31.00 **st.** and a la carte 🍷 7.25 – ☕ 12.50 – **115 rm** 110.00/140.00 **st.** – SB.

Bank Top Toby, Ponteland Rd, Kenton, NE3 3TY, at junction of A 1(M) with A 696 ☎ (0191) 214 0877, *Fax (0191) 214 1922* – ⇹, ▤ rest, TV ♿ P – 🏛 50. MC VISA. ✗
Meals (grill rest.) a la carte 8.35/12.15 **t.** – **30 rm** ☕ 49.95 **t.** – SB. AV a

Waterside, 48-52 Sandhill, Quayside, NE1 3JF, ☎ (0191) 230 0111, *enquiries@watersidehotel.com, Fax (0191) 230 1615* – |‡| TV ☎. MC AE ⓓ VISA JCB. ✗ CZ r
Meals *(closed Sunday)* a la carte 15.40/23.15 **t.** 🍷 4.50 – ☕ 9.95 – **36 rm** 62.00/88.00 **st.**

Premier Lodge, Exchange Buildings, The Quayside, NE1 3DW, ☎ (0870) 7001504, *Fax (0870) 7001505* – |‡|, ⇹ rm, TV ☎ ♿ 🚗 – 🏛 35. MC AE ⓓ VISA JCB. ✗ CZ n
Meals (dinner only) a la carte approx. 11.15 **t.** – ☕ 6.00 – **136 rm** 49.50 **st.** – SB.

Travelodge, Whitemare Pool, NE10 8YB, Southeast : 4 m. at junction of A 194 with A 184 ☎ (0191) 438 3333, *Fax (0191) 438 3333* – ⇹ rm, TV ♿ P. MC AE ⓓ VISA JCB. ✗
Meals (grill rest.) – **71 rm** 49.95 **t.**

Travel Inn Metro, City Rd, Quayside, NE2 2AQ, ☎ (0191) 232 6533, *Fax (0191) 232 6557* – |‡|, ⇹ rm, ▤ rest, TV ♿ P. MC AE ⓓ VISA BX a
Meals (grill rest.) (dinner only) – **81 rm** 46.95 **t.**

Blue Room (at Vermont H.), Castle Garth (off St. Nicholas St.), NE1 1RQ, ☎ (0191) 233 1010, *info@vermont-hotel.co.uk, Fax (0191) 233 1234* – ▤ P. MC AE ⓓ VISA JCB CZ s
closed 2 weeks August, Sunday and Monday – **Meals** (dinner only) a la carte 33.00/42.00 **st.** 🍷 7.50.

Fisherman's Lodge, Jesmond Dene, Jesmond, NE7 7BQ, ☎ (0191) 281 3281, *Fax (0191) 281 6410*, « Victorian country house in wooded valley » – ⇹ P. MC AE VISA
closed Saturday lunch, Sunday and Bank Holidays – **Meals** 19.50/34.50 **t.** and a la carte 🍷 8.20. BV e

Vujon, 29 Queen St., Quayside, NE1 3UG, ☎ (0191) 221 0601, *mataj@vujon.demon.co.uk, Fax (0191) 221 0602* – ▤. MC AE ⓓ VISA CZ g
closed Sunday lunch – **Meals** - Indian - 14.50/22.00 **t.** a la carte.

Leela's, 20 Dean St., NE1 1PG, ☎ (0191) 230 1261 – ⇹. MC AE ⓓ VISA CZ e
closed Sunday and Bank Holidays – **Meals** - South Indian - 9.95 **t.** (lunch) and a la carte 14.75/22.90 **t.** 🍷 8.50.

Treacle Moon, 5-7 The Side, Quayside, NE1 3JE, ☎ (0191) 232 5537, *Fax (0191) 221 1745* – ⇹ ▤. MC AE VISA JCB CZ x
closed Christmas, New Year, Saturday lunch and Sunday – **Meals** (booking essential) 12.95 **t.** (lunch) and a la carte 21.85/34.20 **t.** 🍷 14.95.

ENGLAND

Café 21, 21 Queen St., Princes Wharf, Quayside, NE1 3UG, (0191) 222 07 *Fax (0191) 221 0761* – MC AE VISA CZ
closed 25-26 December, 1 January, Sunday and Bank Holidays – **Meals** 14.50 (lunch) and a la carte 15.50/26.00 **t.** 8.30.

The Metropolitan, 35 Grey St., NE1 6EE, (0191) 230 2306, *info@metropolitanbrasses.co.uk, Fax (0191) 230 2307* – MC AE VISA CZ
closed 25-26 December, 1 January and Sunday – **Meals** 13.90/20.90 **t.** and a la carte **t.**

at Gosforth *North : 4 ¾ m. by B 1318 – AV – Tyneside.*

Newcastle Marriott H. Gosforth Park, High Gosforth Park, NE3 5HN, on B 1 (0191) 236 4111, *Fax (0191) 236 8192*, squash – rest, – 600. MC AE VISA
Brandling : **Meals** 10.00/40.00 **t.** and a la carte 7.75 – ***Conservatory :*** **Meals** (dinner only) 17.50 **t.** and a la carte 7.75 – 11.95 – **174 rm** 95.00 **st.**, 4 suites – SB.

at Seaton Burn *North : 8 m. by B 1318 – AV – Newcastle upon Tyne.*

Holiday Inn, Great North Rd, NE13 6BP, North : ¾ m. at junction with (0191) 201 9988, *reunhi@queensmoat.co.uk, Fax (0191) 236 8091*, – 400. MC AE VISA JCB
Meals *(closed Saturday lunch)* 12.00/18.50 **st.** and dinner a la carte 6.50 – 11.5 **150 rm** 103.00/125.00 **t.** – SB.

Travelodge, Fisher Lane, NE13 6EP, North : ¾ m. at junction with A 1 (0191) 217 0 *Fax (0191) 217 0107* – rm, rest, MC AE VISA JCB.
Meals (grill rest.) – **40 rm** 39.95 **t.**

Horton Grange with rm, NE13 6BU, Northwest : 3 ½ m. by Blagdon rd on Pontelan (01661) 860686, *andrew@horton_grange.co.uk, Fax (01661) 860308*, – rest, MC AE VISA JCB.
closed Christmas and New Year – **Meals** (booking essential) (dinner only) 25.00/36.0 5.50 – **9 rm** 59.00/95.00 **t.** – SB.

at Annitsford (Northd.) *Northeast : 7 m. by B 1318 and A 189 – Newcastle upon Tyne.*

Travel Inn, Moor Farm Industrial Estate, NE23 7RG, at junction of A 19 and A (0191) 250 2770, *Fax (0191) 250 2216* – rm, rest, MC AE VISA.
Meals (grill rest.) – **40 rm** 40.95 **t.** AX

at Newcastle Airport *Northwest : 6 ¾ m. by A 167 off A 696 – AV – Newcastle upon Tyne*

Travel Inn Metro, Ponteland Rd, Prestwick, NE20 9DB, (01661) 825 *Fax (01661) 824940*, « Aeronautical themed restaurant » – – 30. VISA.
Meals (grill rest.) – **86 rm** 46.95 **t.**

at Ponteland *Northwest : 8¼ m. by A 167 on A 696 – AV – Newcastle upon Tyne.*

Café 21, 35 Broadway, Darras Hall Estate, NE20 9PW, Southwest : 1 ½ m. by B 6323 Darras Hall Estate rd (01661) 820357, *Fax (01661) 820357* – MC AE VISA
closed Sunday and Bank Holidays – **Meals** - Bistro - (booking essential) (dinner only Saturday lunch) 13.00 **t.** and a la carte 15.00/28.50 **t.** 7.00.

NEWENT *Glos.* 403 404 M 28 – *pop. 4 111.*
7 Church St. (01531) 822468.
London 109 – Gloucester 10 – Hereford 22 – Newport 44.

at Clifford's Mesne *Southwest : 3 m. by B 4216 – Newent.*

Yew Tree with rm, GL18 1JS, on Glasshouse rd (01531) 820719, – VISA
Meals *(closed Monday)* 22.50 **t.** – **2 rm** 60.00 **st.**

NEWHAVEN *E. Sussex* 404 U 31 – *pop. 11 208.*
to France (Dieppe) (Hoverspeed Ltd) 2-6 daily (2 h).
London 63 – Brighton 9 – Eastbourne 14 – Lewes 7.

Travel Inn, Avis Rd, BN9 0AG, East : ½ m. on A 259 (01273) 612356, *Fax (01273) 61* – rm, MC AE VISA
Meals (grill rest.) – **40 rm** 40.95 **t.**

Si vous cherchez un hôtel tranquille,
consultez d'abord les cartes de l'introduction
ou repérez dans le texte les établissements indiqués avec le signe ou

WICK *E. Sussex* 404 U 31 – *pop. 2 445.*
London 57 – Brighton 14 – Eastbourne 20 – Hastings 34 – Maidstone 30.

Newick Park, BN8 4SB, Southeast : 1 ½ m. following signs for Newick Park ☎ (01825) 723633, *bookings@newickpark.co.uk, Fax (01825) 723969*, ≤, « Georgian house, extensive grounds », heated, – TV P. VISA JCB
Meals (booking essential to non-residents) 19.50/27.50 **t.** and dinner a la carte 9.75 – **15 rm** 95.00/235.00 **t.**, 1 suite – SB.

WINGTON *Kent* 404 V/W 29 – *pop. 2 454.*
London 40 – Canterbury 20 – Maidstone 13.

Newington Manor, Callaways Lane, ME9 7LU, ☎ (01795) 842053, *Fax (01795) 844273*, « Part 14C and 16C manor house », – TV P. AE VISA.
closed 25-26 December and 1 January – **Meals** *(closed Friday-Sunday)* (lunch by arrangement)/dinner 23.25 **st.** 6.50 – 5.50 – **12 rm** 68.00/98.00 **st.**

WLYN *Cornwall* 403 D 33 – *see Penzance.*

WMARKET *Suffolk* 404 V 27 – *pop. 16 498.*
Links, Cambridge Rd ☎ (01638) 663000.
Palace House, Palace St. ☎ (01638) 667200.
London 64 – Cambridge 13 – Ipswich 40 – Norwich 48.

Bedford Lodge, Bury Rd, CB8 7BX, Northeast : ½ m. on A 1304 ☎ (01638) 663175, *Fax (01638) 667391*, – rm, TV P – 200. AE VISA JCB
closed 25-29 December – ***Orangery*** **: Meals** 21.50 **st.** (dinner) and lunch a la carte 15.00/21.50 **st.** 10.00 – **50 rm** 140.00/160.00 **st.**, 6 suites – SB.

Heath Court, Moulton Rd, CB8 8DY, ☎ (01638) 667171, *quality@heathcourt.hotel.co.uk, Fax (01638) 666533* – rm, TV P – 120. AE VISA
Meals (grill rest.) (bar lunch Saturday) 15.00/18.00 **st.** and a la carte 6.50 – **41 rm** 78.00/175.00 **st.** – SB.

Rutland Arms, High St., CB8 8NB, ☎ (01638) 664251, *Fax (01638) 666298*, – rm, TV P – 80. AE VISA.
Meals 10.95/16.50 **st.** and a la carte 8.00 – 8.95 – **46 rm** 68.50/78.50 **st.** – SB.

Brasserie 22, 160 High St., CB8 9AQ, ☎ (01638) 660646, *Fax (01638) 600083* – AE VISA JCB
closed 1 week Christmas and New Year, Sunday and Monday – **Meals** 9.95/20.50 **t.** and a la carte 7.95.

ix Mile Bottom *(Cambs.) Southwest : 6 m. on A 1304 – ✉ Newmarket.*

Swynford Paddocks, CB8 0UE, ☎ (01638) 570234, *sales@swynfordpaddocks.com, Fax (01638) 570283*, ≤, – rest, TV P – 25. AE VISA
Meals *(closed Saturday lunch)* 24.50/31.50 **t.** 7.25 – **15 rm** 150.00/210.00 **t.** – SB.

WMILLERDAM *W. Yorks. – see Wakefield.*

W MILTON *Hants.* 403 404 P 31 – *pop. 24 324 (inc. Barton-on-Sea).*
18, 9 Barton-on-Sea, Milford Rd ☎ (01425) 615308.
London 106 – Bournemouth 12 – Southampton 21 – Winchester 34.

Chewton Glen, Christchurch Rd, BH25 6QS, West : 2 m. by A 337 and Ringwood Rd on Chewton Farm Rd ☎ (01425) 275341, *reservations@chewtonglen.com, Fax (01425) 272310*, ≤, « Gardens », heated, 9, indoor/outdoor – rest, rest, TV P – 120. AE VISA.
Marryat Room and Conservatory **: Meals** 47.50/60.00 **t.** 10.50 – 17.50 – **45 rm** 235.00/360.00 **t.**, 13 suites 360.00/635.00 **t.**
Spec. Double baked Emmental soufflé. Braised fillet of sea bass with shiitake mushrooms and beansprouts. Chocolate fondant, vanilla ice cream.

WPORT *Wrekin* 402 403 404 M 25 *Great Britain G.* – *pop. 10 964.*
Exc. : *Weston Park★★, SE : 6½ m. by A 41 and A 5.*
London 150 – Birmingham 33 – Shrewsbury 18 – Stoke-on-Trent 21.

Royal Victoria, St. Mary's St., TF10 7AB, ☎ (01952) 820331, *info@royal-victoria.co.uk, Fax (01952) 820209* – TV P – 140. AE VISA
Meals *(closed Sunday dinner)* a la carte 12.45/16.65 **t.** – **24 rm** 44.00/59.00 **t.** – SB.

NEWPORT PAGNELL *Milton Keynes* 404 R 27 – *pop.* 12 285.
London 57 – Bedford 13 – Luton 21 – Northampton 15.

Plan : see Milton Keynes

Swan Revived, High St., MK16 8AR, ☎ (01908) 610565, *swanrevived@btinternet.co* *Fax (01908) 210995* – |‡| TV P – 🏠 70. MO AE ① VISA CU
Meals *(closed Saturday lunch)* a la carte 15.50/24.50 **t.** 🍷 6.25 – **40 rm** ☕ 74.00/80.00 2 suites – SB.

Robinsons, 18-20 St. John St., MK16 8HJ, ☎ (01908) 611400, *robinsons.n.p@fsbdial.c* *k, Fax (01908) 216900* – MO AE ① VISA CU
closed 1 week August, 26 December-1 January, Saturday lunch, Sunday and Bank Holi Monday – **Meals** 13.50 **t.** (lunch) and a la carte 20.90/26.40 **t.** 🍷 7.00.

Remember the speed limits that apply in the United Kingdom, unless otherwise signposted.
- 60 mph on single carriageway roads
- 70 mph on dual carriageway roads and motorways

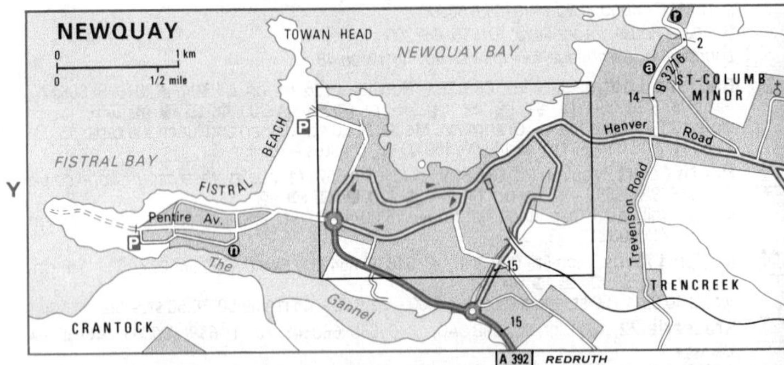

Z

Alexandra Road	Y 2	Fore Street	Z	Marcus Hill	
Bank Street	Z 3	Higher Tower Road	Z 9	Porth Way	
Beacon Road	Z 5	Hope Terrace	Z 10	Trevemper Road	
Berry Road	Z 6	Jubilee Street	Z 12	St. Georges Road	
East Street	Z 8			St. John's Road	

WQUAY *Cornwall* 403 E 32 *The West Country G. – pop. 17 390.*

Env. : *Penhale Point and Kelsey Head★ (≤★★), SW : by A 3075* Y – *Trerice★* AC, *SE : 3½ m. by A 392* – Y – *and A 3058.*

Exc. : *St. Agnes – St. Agnes Beacon★★ (✳★★), SW : 12½ m. by A 3075* – Y – *and B 3285.*

18 *Tower Rd* ☎ *(01637) 872091*, Z – 9 *Treloy* ☎ *(01637) 878554* – 18 *Merlin, Mawgan Porth* ☎ *(01841) 540222.*

✈ *Newquay Airport :* ☎ *(01637) 860551* Y.

ℹ *Municipal Offices, Marcus Hill* ☎ *(01637) 854020.*

London 291 – Exeter 83 – Penzance 34 – Plymouth 48 – Truro 14.

Plan opposite

The Bristol, Narrowcliff, TR7 2PQ, ☎ (01637) 875181, *info@hotelbristol.co.uk, Fax (01637) 879347*, ≤, ≘s, ⛆ – |≑| TV P – 🏛 200. MC AE ⓓ VISA JCB Z r
closed 2 weeks January – **Meals** 12.50/19.95 **st.** and dinner a la carte 🍷 6.50 – ☕ 9.50 – **73 rm** 53.00/106.00 **st.**, 1 suite – SB.

Trebarwith, Trebarwith Cres., TR7 1BZ, ☎ (01637) 872288, *enquiry@trebarwith-hotel.co.uk, Fax (01637) 875431*, ≤ bay and coast, ≘s, ⛆, 🌳 – ⚡ rest, TV P. MC VISA JCB. ✗ Z a
April-October – **Meals** (bar lunch)/dinner 14.00/25.00 **st.** and a la carte 🍷 6.00 – **41 rm** ☕ (dinner included) 59.00/118.00 **st.** – SB.

Kilbirnie, Narrowcliff, TR7 2RS, ☎ (01637) 875155, *enquirykilbirnie@aol.com, Fax (01637) 850769*, ≘s, ⛆ heated, ⛆ – |≑| TV P – 🏛 200. MC AE ⓓ VISA JCB. ✗ Z e
Meals (bar lunch)/dinner 14.00/20.50 **t.** 🍷 4.00 – **66 rm** ☕ 38.00/76.00 **t.** – SB.

Trenance Lodge, 83 Trenance Rd, TR7 2HW, ☎ (01637) 876702, *info@trenance-lodge.co.uk, Fax (01637) 872034*, ⛆ heated, 🌳 – ⚡ TV P. MC VISA. ✗ Z u
Meals (lunch by arrangement)/dinner 17.50/21.50 **t.** and a la carte – **5 rm** ☕ 30.00/60.00 **s.** – SB.

Whipsiderry, Trevelgue Rd, Porth, TR7 3LY, Northeast : 2 m. by A 392 off B 3276 ☎ (01637) 874777, *whipsiderry@cornwall_net, Fax (01637) 874777*, ≤, ≘s, ⛆ heated, 🌳 – ⚡ rest, TV P. MC AE VISA
April-October and Christmas – **Meals** (bar lunch)/dinner 15.00/21.00 **t.** 🍷 5.95 – **20 rm** ☕ (dinner included) 49.00/98.00 **st.**

Windward, Alexandra Rd, Porth Bay, TR7 3NB, ☎ (01637) 873185, *caswind@aol.com, Fax (01637) 852436* – ⚡ rest, TV P. MC AE VISA. ✗ Y r
closed Christmas and restricted opening in winter – **Meals** (residents only) (dinner only) 10.00 **st.** and a la carte 🍷 5.50 – **14 rm** ☕ 38.00/62.00 **st.**

Corisande Manor 🐦, Riverside Av., Pentire, TR7 1PL, ☎ (01637) 872042, *relax@corisande.com, Fax (01637) 874557*, ≤ Gannel Estuary, 🌳 – ⚡ rest, TV P. MC AE VISA. ✗ Y n
Meals (dinner only) 21.50 **st.** 🍷 5.50 – **9 rm** ☕ 75.00/139.00 **st.** – SB.

Porth Veor Manor, Porth Way, TR7 3LW, ☎ (01637) 873274, *info@porthveor.co.uk, Fax (01637) 851690*, 🌳 – ⚡ rest, TV P. MC AE VISA JCB Y a
Meals (lunch by arrangement)/dinner 12.95 **st.** and a la carte 🍷 5.95 – **22 rm** ☕ (dinner included) 52.50/95.00 **t.** – SB.

Philadelphia without rest., 19 Eliot Gdns., TR7 2QF, ☎ (01637) 877747, *stay@thephiladelphia.co.uk, Fax (01637) 876860* – ⚡ TV P. MC VISA. ✗ Z n
7 rm ☕ 30.00/54.00 **s.**

Wheal Treasure, 72 Edgcumbe Av., TR7 2NN, ☎ (01637) 874136 – ⚡ TV P. ✗ Z z
May-September – **Meals** (by arrangement) 8.00 – **12 rm** ☕ 30.00/56.00 **st.**

Chynoweth Lodge, 1 Eliot Gdns., TR7 2QE, ☎ (01637) 876684, *dee@chynowethlodge.co.uk, Fax (01637) 876684*, 🌳 – ⚡ TV P Z v
closed November and December – **Meals** (by arrangement) 7.00 **s.** – **9 rm** ☕ 20.00/40.00 **s.**

rantock *Southwest : 4 m. by A 3075* – Y – ✉ *Newquay.*

Crantock Bay 🐦, West Pentire, TR8 5SE, West : ¾ m. ☎ (01637) 830229, *stay@crantockbayhotel.co.uk, Fax (01637) 831111*, ≤ Crantock Bay, Ⅰ6, ≘s, ⛆, 🌳, 🎾 – ⚡ rest, TV P. MC AE ⓓ VISA JCB
closed December and January except New Year and restricted opening February, March and November – **Meals** (buffet lunch)/dinner 17.95 **t.** 🍷 5.50 – **33 rm** ☕ (dinner included) 53.50/107.50 **t.** – SB.

V ROMNEY *Kent* 404 W 31.

London 71 – Brighton 60 – Folkestone 17 – Maidstone 36.

Romney Bay House 🐦, Coast Rd, Littlestone, TN28 8QY, East : 2 ¼ m. off B 2071 ☎ (01797) 364747, *Fax (01797) 367156*, ≤, « Beachside house designed by Sir Clough Williams-Ellis », 🌳, 🎾 – ⚡ TV P. MC ⓓ VISA. ✗
closed 3 weeks mid June and 1 week Christmas – **Meals** (booking essential to non-residents) (dinner only) (set menu only) 29.50 **t.** – **10 rm** ☕ 55.00/130.00 **t.** – SB.

NEWTON LONGVILLE *Bucks.* 404 R 28 – *see Milton Keynes.*

NEWTON ON THE MOOR *Northd.* 401 402 O 17 – *see Alnwick.*

NEWTON POPPLEFORD *Devon* 403 K 31 – *pop. 1 765 (inc. Harpford) – ✉ Ottery St. Mary.*
London 208 – Exeter 10 – Sidmouth 4.

Coach House ⊗, Southerton, EX11 1SE, North : 1 m. by Venn Ottery
✆ (01395) 568577, *southerton@fsbdial.co.uk, Fax (01395) 568946,* – ⊁ TV P
Meals (by arrangement) 14.00 **st.** 5.00 – **6 rm** 42.00/88.00 **st.**

NEWTON SOLNEY *Derbs.* 402 403 404 P 25 – *see Burton-upon-Trent (Staffs.).*

NITON *I.O.W.* 403 404 Q 32 – *see Wight (Isle of).*

NOMANSLAND *Wilts.* 403 404 P 31 – ✉ *Salisbury.*
London 96 – Bournemouth 26 – Salisbury 13 – Southampton 14 – Winchester 25.

Les Mirabelles, Forest Edge Rd, SP5 2BN, ✆ (01794) 390205, *Fax (01794) 390106,*
MC AE VISA
closed first 2 weeks January, 27 May-5 June, Sunday dinner and Monday – **Meals** - Fren
a la carte 16.60/23.80 **t.** 11.00.

NORMAN CROSS *Peterborough* 404 T 26 – *see Peterborough.*

NORMANTON PARK *Rutland – see Stamford.*

NORTHALLERTON *N. Yorks.* 402 P 20 – *pop. 13 774.*
ℹ *The Applegarth Car Park ✆ (01609) 776864.*
London 238 – Leeds 48 – Middlesbrough 24 – York 33.

at Staddlebridge *Northeast : 7½ m. by A 684 on A 19 at junction with A 172 – ✉ Northallert*

The Tontine, DL6 3JB, on southbound carriageway (A 19) ✆ (01609) 882
Fax (01609) 882660 – ▤ rm, TV P. MC AE VISA
closed 25-26 December and 1 January – **Meals** – (see ***McCoys Bistro*** below) – 6
75.00/90.00 **t.**

McCoys Bistro (at The Tontine H.), DL6 3JB, on southbound carriageway (A
✆ (01609) 882671, *Fax (01609) 882660* – P. MC AE VISA
closed 25-26 December and 1 January – **Meals** - Brasserie - (booking essential) 13.5
(lunch) and a la carte 23.85/32.25 **t.** 9.95.

at Newby Wiske *South : 2½ m. by A 167 – ✉ Northallerton.*

Solberge Hall ⊗, DL7 9ER, Northwest : 1 ¼ m. on Warlaby rd ✆ (01609) 779
Fax (01609) 780472, ≤, – ⊁ rest, TV P – 100. MC AE VISA
Meals 9.00/13.00 **st.** (lunch) and dinner a la carte 9.00/22.50 **st.** 6.95 – **23 rm** 75
110.00 **st.**, 1 suite – SB.

NORTHAMPTON *Northants.* 404 R 27 *Great Britain G. – pop. 179 596.*
Exc. : *All Saints, Brixworth*★, *N : 7 m. on A 508* **Y**.
18, 9 *Delapre, Eagle Dr., Nene Valley Way ✆ (01604) 764036* **Z** – 18 *Collingtree*
Windingbrook Lane ✆ (01604) 700000.
ℹ *Mr Grant's House, St. Giles Sq. ✆ (01604) 622677.*
London 69 – Cambridge 53 – Coventry 34 – Leicester 42 – Luton 35 – Oxford 41.

Plan opposite

Northampton Marriott, Eagle Drive, NN4 7HW, Southeast : 2 m. by A 428 off
✆ (01604) 768700, *Fax (01604) 769011,* – ⊁ rm, ▤ rest, TV
220. MC AE VISA.
La Fontana : **Meals** - Italian - 14.75/35.00 **st.** and a la carte 8.25 – 9.75 – **11**
95.00 **st.**, 2 suites – SB.

Hilton Northampton, 100 Watering Lane, Collingtree, NN4 0XW, South : 3 m. on A
✆ (01604) 700666, *Fax (01604) 702850,* – ⊁ rm, ▤ rest, TV
300. MC AE VISA
Meals (carving lunch) (bar lunch Saturday) 14.50/19.95 **st.** and dinner a la carte – 10
136 rm 150.00/170.00 **st.**, 3 suites – SB.

ORTHAMPTON

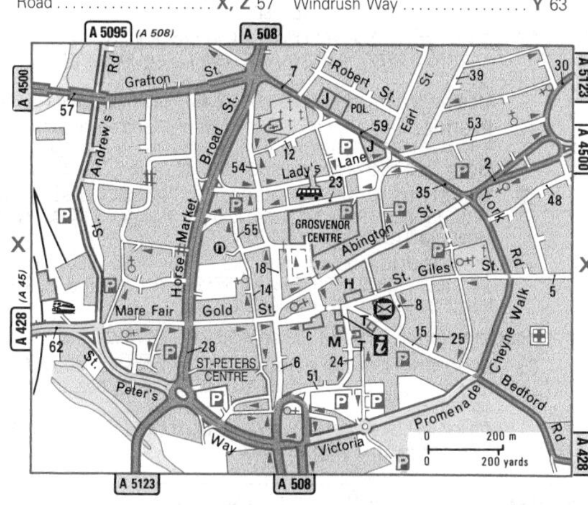

LEICESTER A 5199
A 508 MARKET HARBOROUGH
KETTERING A 43
Holly Lodge Drive
Red House Road
MOULTON PARK
Talavera Way
(A 45)
Welford Road
Harborough Rd
Boughton Green Rd
KINGSTHORPE
A 5123 Road
Booth Lane
Lumbertubs Way
WESTON FAVELL CENTRE
WELLINGBOROUGH
A 4500
Mill Lane
Kingsthorpe Rd
Balfour Rd
Kingsley Rd
Kettering Road
WESTON FAVELL
Y
Harlestone
DALLINGTON
A 508
ABINGTON PARK
A 45
WELLINGBOROUGH
DUSTON
A 428
Road
Wellingborough
A 4500 Billing Road
Billing Rd East
Way
A 4500
Weedon Rd
Valley
Nene
Z
Upton Way
A 45
Grand Union Canal
Bedford
A 428
A 428
BEDFORD
Rd
Rd
Road
BRACKMILLS
Way
Danes Camp Way
Towcester
FAR COTTON
London
A 45 Valley
GREAT HOUGHTON
High St.
Mere Way
Nene
HARDINGSTONE
B 526
1 km
1 mile
A 43 OXFORD
A 508 (M 1), MILTON KEYNES

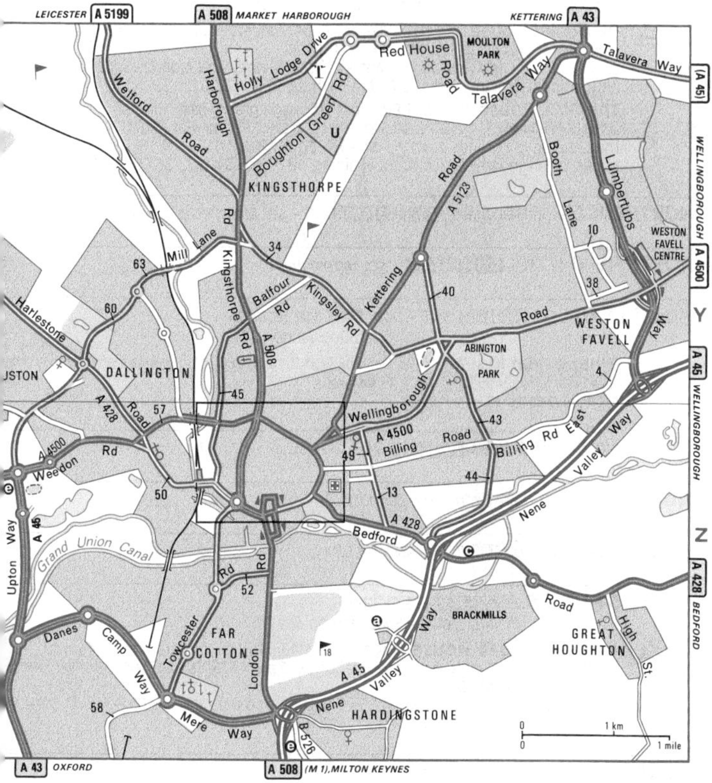

ENGLAND

Northampton Moat House, Silver St., NN1 2TA, (01604) 7399
Fax (01604) 230614, – rm, – 600. AE VISA JCB
Meals (buffet lunch) (bar lunch Saturday) 8.50/32.00 **st.** and a la carte 6.00 – 11.5
145 rm 110.00/120.00 **st.** – SB. X

Courtyard by Marriott, Bedford Rd, NN4 7YF, Southeast : 1 ½ m. on A
(01604) 22777, *Fax (01604) 35454,* – 40. AE VISA
Z
Meals a la carte 11.60/24.20 **st.** 7.45 – 10.00 – **104 rm** 80.00/90.00 **t.** – SB.

Premier Lodge, London Road West, Wootton, NN4 0JJ, South : 1 ½ m. by A 508 o
526 (01604) 762468, *Fax (01604) 706191* – rm, – 90. AE VISA.
Meals (grill rest.) a la carte 8.95/15.35 **st.** – 6.00 – **20 rm** 46.00 **st.** Z

Travel Inn, Harpole Turn, Weedon Rd, NN7 4DD, West : 3 ¾ m. on A 45 (01604) 832
Fax (01604) 831807 – , rest, – 60. AE VISA.
Meals (grill rest.) – **51 rm** 40.95 **t.**

Travelodge, Upton Way (Ring Rd), NN5 6EG, Southwest : 1 ¾ m. by A
(01604) 758395, *Fax (01604) 758395* – rm, AE VISA JCB. Z
Meals (grill rest.) – **62 rm** 49.95 **t.**

at Spratton *North : 7 m. by A 508 off A 50* – **Y** – *Northampton.*

Broomhill Country House, Holdenby Rd, NN6 8LD, Southwest : 1 m. on Holde
rd (01604) 845959, *Fax (01604) 845834,* heated, – rest,
VISA.
closed 26 December-January – **Meals** *(closed Sunday dinner)* 14.95/21.00 **t.** and a la c
7.70 – **13 rm** 70.00/90.00 **t.**

NORTH BOVEY *Devon* 403 I 32 *The West Country G.* – *pop. 254* – *Newton Abbot.*
Env. : *Dartmoor National Park*★★.
London 214 – *Exeter 13* – *Plymouth 34* – *Torquay 21.*

Blackaller House, TQ13 8QY, (01647) 440322, *peter@blackaller.fsbusiness.co*
Fax (01647) 441131, – rest,
closed January and February – **Meals** *(closed Sunday and Monday)* (booking essentia
non-residents) (dinner only) 23.00 **t.** – **5 rm** 33.00/80.00 **t.** – SB.

The Gate House, TQ13 8RB, just off village green, past "Ring of Bells" public ho
(01647) 440479, *gatehouseondartmoor@talk21.com, Fax (01647) 440479,* «
thatched Devon hallhouse », –
Meals (by arrangement) (communal dining) 18.00 **s.** – **3 rm** 36.00/58.00.

NORTHENDEN *Gtr. Manchester* 402 403 404 N 23 – *see Manchester.*

NORTHFIELD *W. Mids.* 403 ㉒ 404 ⑳ – *see Birmingham.*

NORTHLEACH *Glos.* 403 404 O 28 – *pop. 1 462 (inc. Eastington).*
London 88 – *Gloucester 18* – *Oxford 30* – *Swindon 24.*

Wheatsheaf Inn, West End, GL54 3EZ, (01451) 860244, *wheatsheaf@establishme*
d.uk, Fax (01451) 861037, – VISA
Meals a la carte 14.95/18.95 **t.**

NORTH MUSKHAM *Notts.* 402 404 R 24 – *see Newark-on-Trent.*

NORTH NEWINGTON *Oxon.* – *see Banbury.*

NORTHREPPS *Norfolk* 404 Y 25 – *see Cromer.*

NORTH STIFFORD *Essex* 404 ㊹ – *Grays.*
London 22 – *Chelmsford 24* – *Southend-on-Sea 20.*

Lakeside Moat House, High Rd, RM16 5UE, at junction of A 13 with A
(01708) 719988, *cblak@queensmoat.co.uk, Fax (01375) 390426,* – rm
– 150. AE VISA
Meals *(closed Saturday lunch)* 17.95/35.00 **st.** and a la carte 7.00 – 11.50 – 97
103.00/125.00 **s.** – SB.

NORTH STOKE *Oxon.* – *see Wallingford.*

RTH WALSHAM *Norfolk* 403 404 Y 25 *Great Britain G. – pop. 9 534.*
Exc. : *Blicking Hall★★ AC, W : 8½ m. by B 1145, A 140 and B 1354.*
London 125 – Norwich 16.

Beechwood, 20 Cromer Rd, NR28 0HD, ☎ (01692) 403231, *Fax (01692) 407284,* – TV P. MC VISA
Meals *(closed Saturday lunch)* 12.00/24.00 **t.** 12.50 – **10 rm** 60.00/94.00 **t.** – SB.

RTHWICH *Ches.* 402 403 404 M 24 – *pop. 4 243.*
London 188 – Chester 19 – Liverpool 29 – Manchester 25.

Premier Lodge, London Rd, Leftwich, CW9 8EG, South : 1 ½ m. on A 533 ☎ (01606) 45524, *Fax (01606) 330350,* – rm, TV P – 35. MC AE VISA.
closed 25 December – **Meals** (grill rest.) a la carte 8.75/19.35 **t.** – 6.00 – **32 rm** 42.00 **st.**

RTH WOODCHESTER *Glos.* 403 404 N 28 – *see Stroud.*

RTON *Shrops. – see Telford.*

RTON ST. PHILIP *Somerset* 403 404 N 30 – *pop. 820* – ✉ *Bath.*
London 113 – Bristol 22 – Southampton 55 – Swindon 40.

George Inn, High St., BA3 6LH, ☎ (01373) 834224, *georgeinnsp@aol.com, Fax (01373) 834861,* « Historic 15C inn », – rest, TV P. MC AE VISA
Meals a la carte 15.85/23.85 **t.** – **8 rm** 60.00/90.00 **t.**

Bath Lodge, BA3 6NH, East : 1 ¼ m. by A 366 on A 36 ☎ (01225) 723040, *walker@bathlodge.demon.co.uk, Fax (01225) 723737,* « Castellated former gatehouse », – TV P. MC AE VISA.
Meals *(closed Sunday-Thursday)* (dinner only) 26.50 **st.** – **8 rm** 50.00/105.00 **st.** – SB.

Monmouth Lodge without rest., BA3 6LH, on B 3110 ☎ (01373) 834367, – TV P. MC VISA.
closed 20 December-10 January – **3 rm** 50.00/70.00.

The Plaine without rest., BA3 6LT, ☎ (01373) 834723, *theplaine@easynet.co.uk, Fax (01373) 834101,* « 16C cottages » – TV P. MC VISA.
closed 24 to 26 December – **3 rm** 50.00/70.00 **s.**

RWICH *Norfolk* 404 Y 26 *Great Britain G. – pop. 171 304.*
See : *City★★ - Cathedral★★* **Y** – *Castle (Museum and Art Gallery★ AC)* **Z** – *Market Place★* **Z.**
Env. : *Sainsbury Centre for Visual Arts★ AC, W : 3 m. by B 1108* **X.**
Exc. : *Blicking Hall★★ AC, N : 11 m. by A 140* – **V** – *and B 1354 – NE : The Broads★.*
18 *Royal Norwich, Drayton High Rd, Hellesdon ☎ (01603) 425712,* **V** – 18 *Sprowston Park, Wroxham Rd ☎ (01603) 410657* – 18 *Costessy Park, Costessey ☎ (01603) 746333* – 18 *Bawburgh, Glen Lodge, Marlingford Rd ☎ (01603) 740404.*
Norwich Airport : ☎ (01603) 411923, N : 3½ m. by A 140 **V.**
The Guildhall, Gaol Hill ☎ (01603) 666071.
London 109 – Kingston-upon-Hull 148 – Leicester 117 – Nottingham 120.

Plans on following pages

Marriott Sprowston Manor H. & Country Club, Wroxham Rd, NR7 8RP, Northeast : 3 ¼ m. on A 1151 ☎ (01603) 410871, *Fax (01603) 423911,* 18, – rest, TV P – 120. MC AE VISA.
Meals 16.50/22.00 **st.** and a la carte – 9.95 – **93 rm** 99.00 **st.**, 1 suite – SB.

Dunston Hall H. Golf & Country Club, Ipswich Rd, NR14 8PQ, South : 4 m. on A 140 ☎ (01508) 470444, *dhreception@devere-hotels.com, Fax (01508) 470689,* 18, – rest, TV P – 300. MC AE VISA JCB.
Meals (carving rest.) a la carte 22.20/28.55 **t.** – ***La Fontaine :*** **Meals** *(closed Sunday)* (dinner only) 26.50 **t.** and a la carte – **128 rm** 105.00/150.00 **st.**, 2 suites.

Swallow Nelson, Prince of Wales Rd, NR1 1DX, ☎ (01603) 760260, *info@swallowhotels.com, Fax (01603) 620008,* – rm, rest, TV P – 90. MC AE VISA JCB Z a
Trafalgar : **Meals** (dinner only and Sunday lunch)/dinner 16.50/18.00 **st.** and a la carte 6.75 – ***Quarter-deck :*** **Meals** a la carte 10.30/17.65 **st.** 6.75 – **132 rm** 95.00/130.00 **st.** – SB.

Posthouse Norwich, Ipswich Rd, NR4 6EP, South : 2 ¼ m. on A 140 ☎ (0870) 400 9060, *gm1161@forte-hotels.com, Fax (01603) 506400,* – rm, TV P – 100. MC AE VISA
Meals a la carte 20.35/29.15 **t.** 6.95 – 11.95 – **120 rm** 69.00/89.00 **st.** – SB.

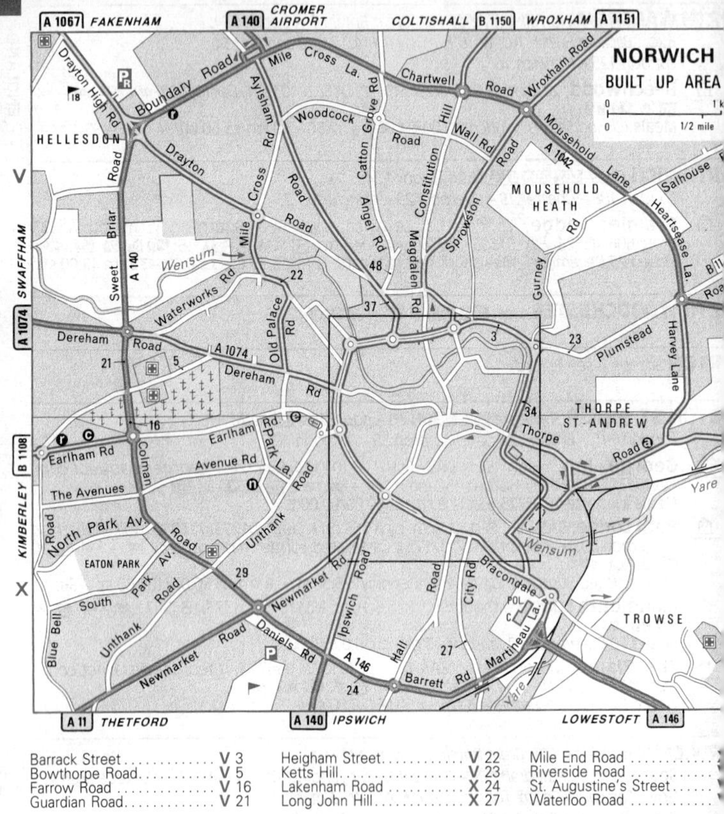

Barrack Street . . . . V 3	Heigham Street. . . . . V 22	Mile End Road . . . .
Bowthorpe Road. . . . . V 5	Ketts Hill. . . . . V 23	Riverside Road . . . .
Farrow Road . . . . V 16	Lakenham Road . . . . X 24	St. Augustine's Street. . . . . .
Guardian Road. . . . . V 21	Long John Hill. . . . . X 27	Waterloo Road . . . .

Beeches, 2-6 Earlham Rd, NR2 3DB, ℘ (01603) 621167, *reception@beeches.co* *Fax (01603) 620151,* « Victorian gardens » – ⇔ TV ♿ P. MC AE ① VISA JCB. ✻ VX
closed 23-30 December – **Meals** (dinner only) 14.95 **st.** and a la carte – **36 rm** ☕ 59 88.00 **st.** – SB.

Annesley House, 6 Newmarket Rd, NR2 2LA, ℘ (01603) 624553, *Fax (01603) 62157* – ⇔ rest, TV P. – 🔆 25. MC AE ① VISA JCB. ✻
closed Christmas and New Year – **Meals** (dinner only) a la carte 17.65/24.85 **t.** 🍷 6. **26 rm** ☕ 67.50/92.50 **t.** – SB.

Jarvis International, 121 Boundary Rd, NR3 2BA, on A 140 ℘ (01603) 787 *Fax (01603) 400466,* F5, ≘s, ⛶ – ⇔ rm, ▤ rest, TV ♿ P. – 🔆 300. MC AE VISA
Meals *(closed lunch Saturday and Bank Holidays)* 15.50 **st.** (dinner) and a la carte 15 21.50 **st.** – ☕ 9.95 – **107 rm** 89.00/139.00 **st.** – SB.

Quality H. Norwich, 2 Barnard Rd, Bowthorpe, NR5 9JB, West : 3 ½ m. on A ℘ (01603) 741161, *admin@gb619.u-net.com, Fax (01603) 741500,* F5, ≘s, ⛶ – ⇔ rm ♿ P. – 🔆 200. MC AE ① VISA JCB
Meals (carving rest.) 14.50 **t.** and dinner a la carte 🍷 4.95 – ☕ 9.75 – **80 rm** 75.00/85.00 SB.

Catton Old Hall, Lodge Lane, Old Catton, NR6 7HG, North : 3 ¼ m. by Catton Grov and St. Faiths Rd ℘ (01603) 419379, *enquiries@cattonhall.co.uk, Fax (01603) 400339,* « farmhouse », ⚘ – TV P. MC AE ① VISA. ✻
Meals *(closed Sunday)* (booking essential) (residents only) (dinner only) 21.00 **st.** 🍷 5. **7 rm** ☕ 55.00/90.00 **st.**

NORWICH

k Plain . . . . . . Y 2
nel Street . . . . . . Z 4
tle Mall
hopping Centre . . . . . . Z
tle Meadow . . . . . . Z 6
le Market Street . . . . . . Z 7
pel Field North . . . . . . Z 9
Charing Cross . . . . . . Y 10
Colegate . . . . . . Y 14
Elm Hill . . . . . . Y
Exchange Street . . . . . . YZ 15
Gentleman's Walk . . . . . . Z 17
Grapes Hill . . . . . . Y 19
London Street . . . . . . YZ 26
Market Avenue . . . . . . Z 28
Rampant Horse Street . . . . . . Z 32
Red Lion Street . . . . . . Z 33
St. Andrew's Street . . . . . . Y 36
St. George Street . . . . . . Y 38
St. Stephen's Street . . . . . . Z
Thorn Lane . . . . . . Z 42
Timber Hill . . . . . . Z 43
Tombland . . . . . . Y 45
Upper King Street . . . . . . Y 46
Wensum Street . . . . . . Y 49
Westlegate . . . . . . Z 50
Whitefriars . . . . . . Y 51

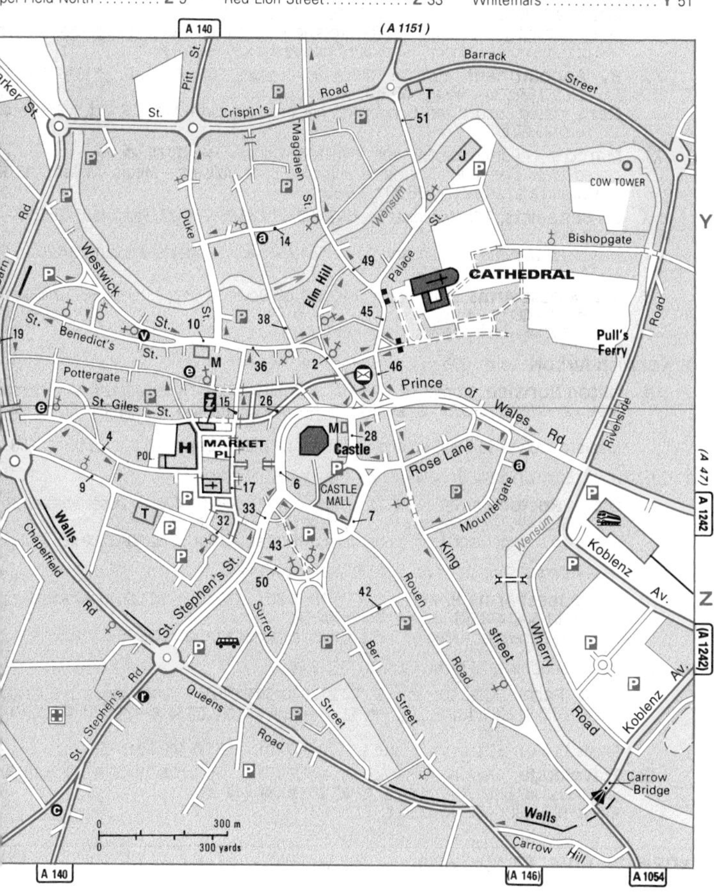

Travel Inn, Longwater Interchange, New Costessey, NR5 0TL, Northwest : 5 ¼ m. on A 1074 (junction with A 47) ☎ (01603) 749140, *Fax (01603) 749 1219* – ⇔ rm, TV ♿ P. MC AE ⓓ VISA
Meals (grill rest.) – **40 rm** 40.95 **t.**

The Gables without rest., 527 Earlham Rd, NR4 7HN, ☎ (01603) 456666, *Fax (01603) 250320*, – ⇔ TV P. MC VISA JCB. ⅌ X c
closed 20 December-2 January – **11 rm** 40.00/63.50 **st.**

Cumberland, 212-216 Thorpe Rd, NR1 1TJ, ☎ (01603) 434550, *cumberland@paston.co.uk, Fax (01603) 433355* – ⇔ rest, TV P – 60. MC AE ⓓ VISA JCB. ⅌ X a
Meals *(closed Saturday and Sunday lunch)* (booking essential) 9.95/24.95 **st.** and dinner a la carte 5.95 – **25 rm** 49.95/90.00 **st.** – SB.

Arbor Linden Lodge without rest., 557 Earlham Rd, NR4 7HW, ☎ (01603) 451303, *Fax (01603) 250641*, – ⇔ TV P. MC VISA X r
closed 2 weeks Christmas-New Year – **6 rm** 30.00/50.00 **s.**

Kingsley Lodge without rest., 3 Kingsley Rd, NR1 3RB, ☎ (01603) 615819, *kingsley@p on.co.uk, Fax (01603) 615819* – ⇆ TV. ✻ Z
closed January and Christmas – **3 rm** ☐ 30.00/44.00.

Adlard's, 79 Upper St. Giles St., NR2 1AB, ☎ (01603) 633522, *info@adlards.co. Fax (01603) 617733* – ▤. MC AE ◑ VISA JCB Z
closed 1 week Christmas, Monday lunch, Sunday and Bank Holidays except Good Frida
Meals 19.00 **t.** (lunch) and a la carte 33.00/37.50 **t.** 9.50
Spec. Smoked duck salad with truffle dressing. Roast turbot with wild mushroom casser and pomme purée. Banana "Tarte Tatin" with vanilla ice cream.

By Appointment with rm, 25-29 St. Georges St., NR3 1AB, ☎ (01603) 6307 *Fax (01603) 630730* – ⇆ TV. MC VISA. ✻ Y
Meals *(closed Sunday and Monday)* (dinner only) a la carte 23.65/26.40 **t.** 6.95 – 4 ☐ 70.00/95.00 **t.**

Marco's, 17 Pottergate, NR2 1DS, ☎ (01603) 624044 – ⇆. MC AE ◑ VISA Y
closed 25-26 December, Sunday, Monday and Bank Holidays – **Meals** - Italian - 15.0((lunch) and a la carte 21.50/28.90 **t.** 6.80.

St. Benedicts, 9 St. Benedicts St., NR2 4PE, ☎ (01603) 765377, *Fax (01603) 765377* – AE ◑ VISA Y
closed 25 December-2 January, Sunday and Monday – **Meals** a la carte 14.20/20.9 6.50.

Mad Moose Arms, 2 Warwick St., NR2 3LB, off Dover St. ☎ (01603) 627687, *mail@ani inns.co.uk* – MC AE ◑ VISA X
closed 25 December – **Meals** a la carte 16.50/23.00 **t.** 4.95.

at Norwich Airport *North : 3½ m. by A 140 – V – ✉ Norwich.*

Hilton Norwich, Cromer Rd, NR6 6JA, ☎ (01603) 410544, *reservations@norwich.stak o.uk, Fax (01603) 789935*, Fø, ≘s, ▢ – ▮ ⇆, ▤ rest, TV ☏ ♿ P – 🏛 450. MC AE ◑ ✻
Meals (carvery) 9.95/15.95 **st.** and a la carte – ☐ 9.95 – **121 rm** 105.00/170.00 **st.** – SB.

at Caistor St. Edmund *South : 4¼ m. by A 140 – X – ✉ Norwich.*

Old Rectory ⑤, NR14 8QS, ☎ (01508) 492490, *pusey@paston.co Fax (01508) 495172*, « Georgian rectory », ⛪, ♧ – ⇆ TV P. VISA
Meals (by arrangement) (communal dining) 18.00 **st.** – **3 rm** ☐ 32.00/60.00 **st.**

at Stoke Holy Cross *South : 5¾ m. by A 140 – X – ✉ Norwich.*

Wildebeest Arms, 82-86 Norwich Rd, NR14 8QJ, ☎ (01508) 492497, *mail@animalinn .uk, Fax (01508) 494353*, ⛪ – P. MC AE ◑ VISA
closed 25 December – **Meals** 12.95 **t.** (lunch) and a la carte 19.15/28.25 **t.** 5.95.

at Hethersett *Southwest : 6 m. by A 11 – X – ✉ Norwich.*

Park Farm, NR9 3DL, on B 1172 ☎ (01603) 810264, *enq@parkfarm-hotel.co Fax (01603) 812104*, Fø, ≘s, ▢, ⛪, ♧ – ⇆ rest, ▤ rest, TV ☏ P – 🏛 120. MC AE ◑ ✻
Meals 13.75/20.50 **t.** and a la carte 10.70 – **47 rm** ☐ 75.00/140.00 **t.** – SB.

Travelodge, Thickthorn Service Area, NR9 3AU, at junction of A 11 with A ☎ (01603) 457549 – ⇆ rm, TV ♿ P. MC AE ◑ VISA JCB. ✻
Meals (grill rest.) – **62 rm** 49.95 **t.**

NORWICH AIRPORT *Norfolk* 404 X 25 – *see Norwich.*

NOTTINGHAM *Nottingham* 402 403 404 Q 25 *Great Britain G.* – *pop. 270 222.*

See : *Castle Museum★ (alabasters★) AC,* **CZ M.**
Env. : *Wollaton Hall★ AC, W : 2½ m. by Ilkeston Rd, A 609* **AZ M.**
Exc. : *Southwell Minster★★, NE : 14 m. by A 612* **BZ** – *Newstead Abbey★ AC, N : 11 m. 60, A 611 -* **AY** *- and B 683 – Mr. Straw's House★, Worksop, N : 20 m. signed from B 6 (past Bassetlaw Hospital) – St. Mary Magdalene★, Newark-on-Trent, NE : 20 m. by A 612*
▶18 *Bulwell Forest, Hucknall Rd ☎ (0115) 977 0576,* **AY** – ▶18 *Wollaton Park ☎ (0115) 978 7.* **AZ** – ▶18 *Mapperley, Central Av., Plains Rd ☎ (0115) 955 6672,* **BY** – ▶18 *Nottingham Lawton Dr., Bulwell ☎ (0115) 927 8021* – ▶18 *Beeston Fields, Beeston ☎ (0115) 925 7062 Ruddington Grange, Wilford Rd, Ruddington ☎ (0115) 984 6141,* **BZ** – ▶9, ▶9 *Edwalto (0115) 923 4775,* **BZ** – ▶9, ▶9, ▶9 *Cotgrave Place G & C.C., Stragglethorpe ☎ (0115) 933 3.*
✈ *East Midlands Airport, Castle Donington : ☎ (01332) 852852 SW : 15 m. by A 453 A.*
ℹ *1-4 Smithy Row ☎ (0115) 915 5330 – at West Bridgford : County Hall, Loughboroug ☎ (0115) 977 3558.*
London 135 – Birmingham 50 – Leeds 74 – Manchester 72.

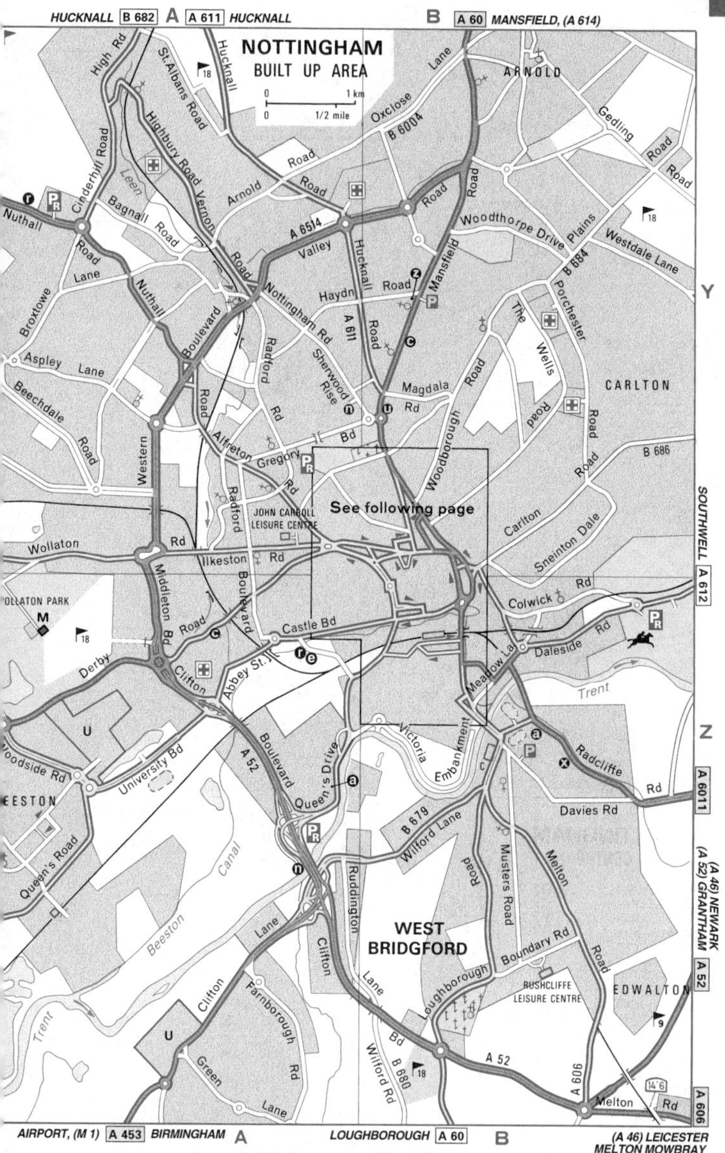

Posthouse Nottingham City, St. James's St., NG1 6BN, ✆ (0870) 400 9061, *gm1764@posthouse_hotels.com, Fax (0115) 948 4366* – |♦|, ⇔ rm, ▤ TV – 600. MC AE ⊕ VISA JCB CY a
– **Meals** 15.00 **st.** and a la carte 6.95 – 11.95 – **159 rm** 89.00 **st.**, 1 suite – SB.

Nottingham Gateway, Nuthall Rd, NG8 6AZ, ✆ (0115) 979 4949, *nottinghamgateway@btinternet.com, Fax (0115) 979 4744* – |♦|, ⇔ rm, ▤ rest, TV ♿ P – 250. MC AE ⊕ VISA. ✈ AY r
Meals (carving rest.) 6.95/15.50 **st.** and a la carte 6.95 – 8.50 – **107 rm** 75.00/80.00 **st.** – SB.

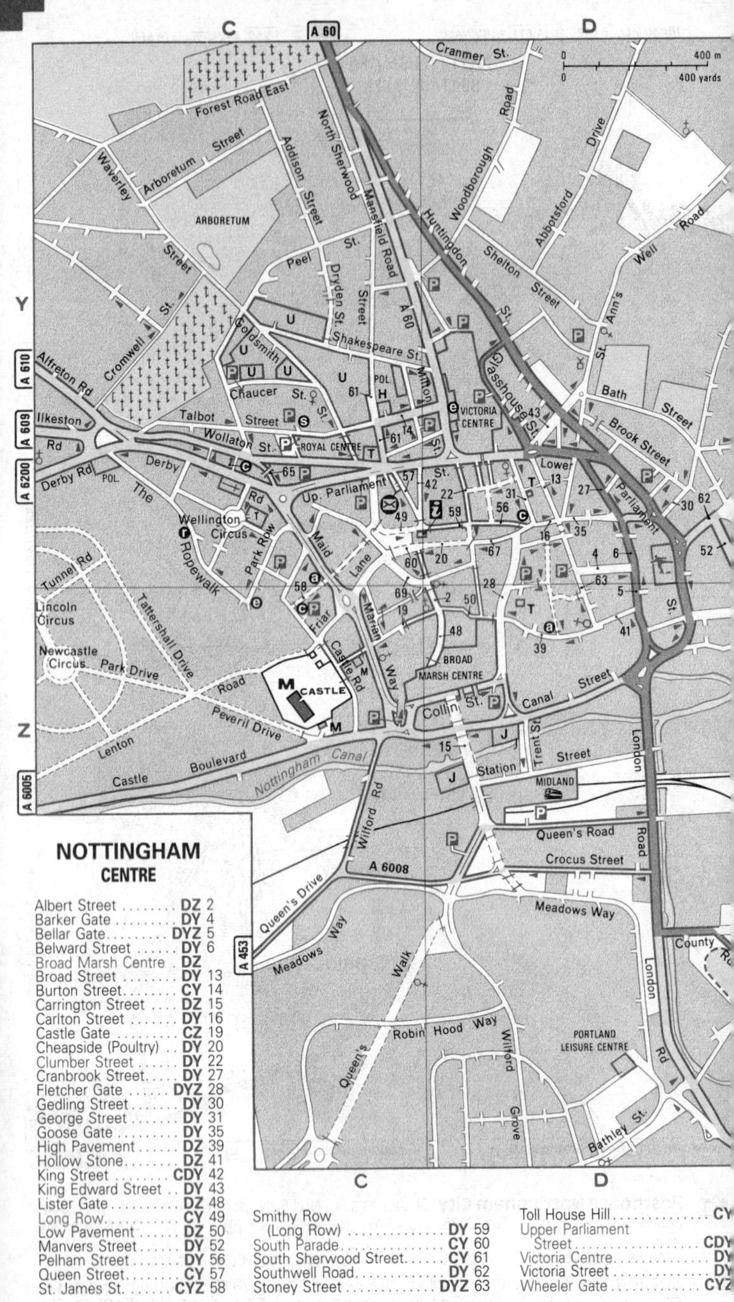

NOTTINGHAM
CENTRE

Albert Street .... **DZ** 2
Barker Gate .... **DY** 4
Bellar Gate........ **DYZ** 5
Belward Street ...... **DY** 6
Broad Marsh Centre . **DZ**
Broad Street .... **DY** 13
Burton Street........ **CY** 14
Carrington Street .... **DZ** 15
Carlton Street .... **DY** 16
Castle Gate .... **CZ** 19
Cheapside (Poultry) .. **DY** 20
Clumber Street ...... **DY** 22
Cranbrook Street..... **DY** 27
Fletcher Gate ...... **DYZ** 28
Gedling Street .... **DY** 30
George Street .... **DY** 31
Goose Gate .... **DY** 35
High Pavement...... **DZ** 39
Hollow Stone........ **DZ** 41
King Street .... **CDY** 42
King Edward Street .. **DY** 43
Lister Gate .... **DZ** 48
Long Row........... **CY** 49
Low Pavement ...... **DZ** 50
Manvers Street...... **DY** 52
Pelham Street....... **DY** 56
Queen Street........ **CY** 57
St. James St. ...... **CYZ** 58

Smithy Row
(Long Row) .... **DY** 59
South Parade............. **CY** 60
South Sherwood Street...... **CY** 61
Southwell Road............ **DY** 62
Stoney Street .... **DYZ** 63

Toll House Hill.............. **CY**
Upper Parliament
Street .... **CDY**
Victoria Centre............. **DY**
Victoria Street .... **DY**
Wheeler Gate .... **CYZ**

If you find you cannot take up a hotel booking you have made, please let the hotel know immediately.

Nottingham Moat House, 296 Mansfield Rd, NG5 2BT, ☎ (0115) 935 9988, *revnhm@queensmoat.co.uk, Fax (0115) 969 1506* – ‖, rm, rest, – 180. VISA
Meals (grill rest.) 11.90/16.00 **st.** 6.00 – 10.50 – **169 rm** 103.00/125.00 **st.**, 3 suites – SB. BY u

Hilton Nottingham, Milton St., NG1 3PZ, ☎ (0115) 934 9700, *rm_nottingham@hilton.com, Fax (0115) 934 9701,* – rest, – 200. VISA JCB. DY e
***Bar Bacoa :* Meals** 5.45/25.00 **st.** and a la carte – 14.50 – **175 rm** 130.00 **st.**, 2 suites – SB.

Rutland Square, St. James's St., NG1 6FJ, ☎ (0115) 941 1114, *rutlandsquare@zoffanyhotels.co.uk, Fax (0115) 941 0014* – rm, rest, – 200. VISA. CZ c
Meals (bar lunch)/dinner 14.95 **st.** and a la carte – 9.95 – **104 rm** 87.00/100.00 **st.**, 1 suite.

Lace Market, 29-31 High Pavement, The Lace Market, NG1 1HE, ☎ (0115) 852 3232, *admin@lacemarkethotel.co.uk, Fax (0115) 852 3223,* « Contemporary interior » – – 35. VISA DZ a
Meals – (see ***Merchants*** below) – 10.95 – **29 rm** 89.00/110.00 **st.**

Welbeck, Talbot St., NG1 5GS, ☎ (0115) 841 1000, *info@welbeck-hotel.co.uk, Fax (0115) 841 1001* – rm, – 60. VISA. CY s
closed Christmas and New Year – **Meals** *(closed Sunday dinner to non-residents)* 11.00 **st.** (dinner) and a la carte 9.45/19.85 **st.** – 8.50 – **96 rm** 95.00 **st.**

Strathdon, 44 Derby Rd, NG1 5FT, ☎ (0115) 941 8501, *info@strathdon-hotel-nottingham.com, Fax (0115) 948 3725* – rm, rest, – 120. VISA JCB. CY c
Meals 16.50 **t.** (dinner) and a la carte 18.10/30.00 **t.** 6.50 – 11.50 – **68 rm** 95.00/135.00 **st.** – SB.

Holiday Inn Garden Court, Castle Marina Park, off Castle Boulevard, NG7 1GX, ☎ (0115) 993 5000, *holidayinn.nottingham@zoom.co.uk, Fax (0115) 993 4000* – rm, rest, – 45. VISA JCB AZ e
Meals *(closed lunch Saturday and Sunday)* (bar lunch Monday to Friday)/dinner a la carte approx. 18.00 **st.** – 10.50 – **130 rm** 93.00 **st.** – SB.

Woodville, 340 Mansfield Rd, NG5 2EF, ☎ (0115) 960 6436, *info@woodvillehotel.co.uk, Fax (0115) 985 6846* – rest, – 90. VISA JCB BY c
Meals *(closed Sunday)* (bar lunch)/dinner 12.95 **st.** and a la carte – **43 rm** 52.50/62.50 **t.** – SB.

Novotel, Bostock Lane, Long Eaton, NG10 4EP, Southwest : 7 m. by A 52 following signs for M 1, taking Long Eaton rd off roundabout at junction 25 of M 1 ☎ (0115) 946 5111, *mso7@accor.hotels.com, Fax (0115) 946 5900,* heated, – rm, – 200. VISA
Meals 12.50/14.95 **t.** and a la carte 3.85 – 9.25 – **108 rm** 65.00 **st.**

Jarvis Nottingham, Bostock Lane, Long Eaton, NG10 5NL, Southwest : 7 m. by A 52 following signs for M 1, taking Long Eaton rd off roundabout at junction 25 of M 1 ☎ (0115) 946 0000, *Fax (0115) 946 0726* – rm, – 60. VISA JCB
closed 24-26 December – **Meals** (grill rest.) a la carte 12.95/29.40 **t.** – 7.00 – **101 rm** 65.00 **t.** – SB.

Morgans without rest., The Townhouse, 34 The Ropewalk, The Park, NG1 5DW, ☎ (0115) 957 0017, *info@morgans34.com, Fax (0115) 957 0018,* « Part Georgian town house, contemporary interior » – VISA JCB. CY r
closed 2 weeks in summer and 1 week Christmas – **5 rm** 95.00/135.00 **st.**

Greenwood Lodge City, Third Av., Sherwood Rise, NG7 6JH, ☎ (0115) 962 1206, *coolspratt@aol.com, Fax (0115) 962 1206,* – VISA JCB. AY n
Meals *(closed Saturday and Sunday)* (residents only) (dinner only) 15.00/20.00 **s.** 5.00 – **6 rm** 36.00/65.00.

Lucieville St. James, 349 Derby Rd, NG7 2DZ, ☎ (0115) 978 7389, *lucieville@aol.com, Fax (0115) 979 0346,* – VISA. AZ c
Meals (residents only) (dinner only) 19.50/25.75 **st.** – 7.50 – **6 rm** 60.00/95.00 **t.**

Travel Inn Metro, Castle Marina Park, off Castle Boulevard, NG2 2DG, ☎ (0115) 947 3419, *Fax (0115) 958 2362* – VISA. AZ r
Meals (grill rest.) – **38 rm** 46.95 **t.**

Travelodge, Riverside Park, Queens Dr., NG2 1RT, ☎ (0115) 850934, *Fax (0115) 986 0467* – rm, VISA JCB. AZ a
Meals (grill rest.) – **61 rm** 49.95 **t.**

Travel Inn, Phoenix Centre, Millenium Way West, NG8 6AS, Northwest : 4 m. on A 610 ☎ (0115) 951 9971, *Fax (0115) 977 0113* – rm, rest, VISA.
Meals (grill rest.) – **86 rm** 40.95 **t.**

XX **Restaurant des Clos** with rm, Old Lenton Lane, NG7 2SA, ✆ (0115) 986 656 *Fax (0115) 986 0343*, – TV P. MC AE VISA. AZ
closed Saturday lunch, Sunday and Bank Holidays – **Meals** 14.95/35.00 **t.** 9.00 – 9.50 **6 rm** 75.00/85.00 **t.**, 2 suites – SB.

XX **Merchants** (at Lace Market H.), 29-31 High Pavement, The Lace Market, NG1 1H ✆ (0115) 852 3232, *Fax (0115) 852 3223* –. MC AE VISA DZ
closed 25 December, Saturday lunch and Sunday dinner – **Meals** 12.50/16.50 (lunch) and a la carte 25.50/29.00 **t.**

XX **Hart's,** Standard Court, Park Row, NG1 6GN, ✆ (0115) 911 0666, *enquiries@hartsnotting am.co.uk, Fax (0115) 911 0611*, – MC AE VISA CZ
Meals 9.90/13.40 **t.** (lunch) and a la carte 23.75/27.00 **t.**

XX **Sonny's,** 3 Carlton St., NG1 1NL, ✆ (0115) 947 3041, *Fax (0115) 950 7776* –. MC AE VISA DY
closed Bank Holidays – **Meals** a la carte 23.00/26.95 **t.**

XX **Saagar,** 473 Mansfield Rd, Sherwood, NG5 2DR, ✆ (0115) 962 2014 –. MC AE V JCB BY
closed 25 December and Sunday lunch – **Meals** - Indian - a la carte 13.60/22.80 **t.**

at West Bridgford *Southeast : 2 m. on A 52 – ✉ Nottingham.*

Windsor Lodge, 116 Radcliffe Rd, NG2 5HG, ✆ (0115) 952 8528, *windsor@bt.internet. m, Fax (0115) 952 0020* – TV P – 40. MC AE VISA BZ
closed 25 and 26 December – **Meals** *(closed Saturday and Sunday)* (residents only) (dinn only) 11.75 **st.** 3.50 – **48 rm** 52.00/59.00 **st.**

Swans, 84-90 Radcliffe Rd, NG2 5HH, ✆ (0115) 981 4042, *swanshotel@aol.co. Fax (0115) 945 5745* – TV P – 50. MC AE VISA. BZ
Meals 13.95/20.00 **st.** and a la carte 6.75 – **30 rm** 53.00/68.00 **st.**, 1 suite.

at Plumtree *Southeast : 5 ¾ m. by A 60 – BZ – off A 606 – ✉ Nottingham.*

X **Perkins,** Old Railway Station, Station Rd, NG12 5NA, ✆ (0115) 937 3695, *perkinsrestaura @supanet.com, Fax (0115) 937 6405*, – P. MC AE VISA JCB
closed 1 week Christmas, Sunday dinner and Monday – **Meals** a la carte 18.75/23.45 7.50.

at Beeston *Southwest : 4 ¼ m. on A 6005 – AZ – ✉ Nottingham.*

Village H. & Leisure Club, Brailsford Way, Chilwell Meadows, NG9 6DL, Southwest : 2 ¾ by A 6005 ✆ (0115) 946 4422, *Fax (0115) 946 4428*, , , , squash – , rest, P – 220. MC AE VISA.
Meals (grill rest.) 12.95 **t.** and a la carte – **92 rm** 89.00/129.00 **t.**

at Risley (Derbs.) *Southwest : 7½ m. by A 52 – AZ – on B 5010 – ✉ Derby.*

Risley Hall, Derby Rd, DE72 3SS, ✆ (0115) 939 9000, *Fax (0115) 939 7766*, « Victori manor house », , , , – , rest, TV P – 150. MC AE VISA.
Meals *(closed Sunday dinner)* 9.95/22.50 **t.** and a la carte 9.95 – 9.50 – **16 rm** 85.0 115.00 **t.** – SB.

at Sandiacre *(Derbs.) Southwest : 7½ m. by A 52 – AZ – on B 5010 – ✉ Nottingham.*

Posthouse Nottingham/Derby, Bostocks Lane, NG10 5NJ, Southwest : ¾ m. junction 25 of M 1 ✆ (0870) 400 9062, *gm1163@forte-hotels.com, Fax (0115) 949 046* rm, rest, TV P – 50. MC AE VISA JCB
Meals a la carte 16.85/28.45 **t.** 6.95 – 11.95 – **93 rm** 89.00 **st.** – SB.

NUNEATON *Warks.* 403 404 P 26 – *pop. 66 715.*

Purley Chase, Pipers Lane, Ridge Lane ✆ (024) 7639 3118.
Nuneaton Library, Church St. ✆ (024) 7638 4027.
London 107 – Birmingham 25 – Coventry 10 – Leicester 18.

Travel Inn, Coventry Rd, CV10 7PJ, South : 2 ½ m. by A 444 on B 4113 ✆ (024) 7634 35 *Fax (024) 7632 7156*, – rm, rest, TV P – 30. MC AE VISA.
Meals (grill rest.) – **48 rm** 40.95 **t.**

Travelodge without rest., CV10 7TF, South : 1 ½ m. on A 444 (southbound carriagew ✆ (024) 7638 2541, *Fax (024) 7638 2541* – TV P. MC AE VISA JCB.
40 rm 39.95 **t.**

Travelodge, St. Nicholas Park Drive, CV11 6EN, Northeast : 1 ½ m. by A 47 (Hinkley ✆ (024) 7635 3885, *Fax (024) 7635 3885* – rm, TV P. MC AE VISA JCB.
Meals (grill rest.) – **28 rm** 39.95 **t.**

Sibson *(Leics.) North : 7 m. on A 444 – ✉ Nuneaton.*

Millers', Twycross Rd, CV13 6LB, ☎ (01827) 880223, *Fax (01827) 880223* – TV P – 50. MC AE ⊕ VISA JCB
Meals *(closed Saturday lunch and Sunday dinner)* 12.95 **st.** and a la carte 5.50 – **40 rm** 49.50/57.50 **st.** – SB.

JNNINGTON *N. Yorks.* 402 Q 21 – *see Helmsley.*

AKHAM *Rutland* 402 404 R 25 – *pop. 8 691.*
Flore's House, 34 High St. ☎ (01572) 724329.
London 103 – Leicester 26 – Northampton 35 – Nottingham 28.

Barnsdale Lodge, The Avenue, Rutland Water, LE15 8AH, East : 2 ½ m. on A 606 ☎ (01572) 724678, *barnsdale.lodge@btconnect.com, Fax (01572) 724961,* « Converted part 17C farmhouse », – TV P – 300. MC AE ⊕ VISA
Meals a la carte approx. 19.85 **t.** 6.95 – **45 rm** 65.00/109.50 **t.** – SB.

Whipper-In, Market Pl., LE15 6DT, ☎ (01572) 756971, *whipper.in@lineone.net, Fax (01572) 757759,* « Part 17C former coaching inn » – rest, TV – 60. MC AE ⊕ VISA JCB.
The George : **Meals** 12.95/18.50 **t.** and dinner a la carte – ***No. 5*** *(☎ (01572) 740774)* **: Meals** a la carte 11.95/19.65 **t.** – **24 rm** 69.00/94.00 **t.** – SB.

Serpentine House without rest., Lodge Gdns., LE15 6EP, East : ¾ m. by B 668, Vicarage Rd and St. Albans Cl., bearing right into Lodge Gdns., entrance is on right hand bend ☎ (01572) 757878, *jenny.dryden@freeuk.com,* – TV P.
3 rm 30.00/55.00 **s.**

Lord Nelson's House H. and Nicks Restaurant with rm, Market Pl., LE15 6DT, ☎ (01572) 723199, *nelsons-house@compuserve.com, Fax (01572) 723199,* « 17C town house » – rm, TV. MC VISA.
closed 2 weeks late July and 24 December-9 January – **Meals** *(closed Sunday and Monday)* a la carte 22.40/29.40 **t.** 7.50 – **4 rm** 65.00/90.00 **st.**

The Admiral Hornblower with rm, 64 High St., LE15 6AS, ☎ (01572) 723004, *david@hornblowerhotel.co.uk, Fax (01572) 722325,* , – TV. MC VISA.
closed 25 December – **Meals** a la carte 15.95/28.50 **st.** – **6 rm** 49.50/95.00 **st.**

Hambleton *East : 3 m. by A 606 – ✉ Oakham.*

Hambleton Hall , LE15 8TH, ☎ (01572) 756991, *hotel@hambletonhall.com, Fax (01572) 724721,* « Victorian country house, ← Rutland Water », heated, , , – , rest, TV P. MC AE VISA
Meals 21.50/35.00 **st.** and a la carte 47.00/58.50 **st.** – 12.00 – **16 rm** 165.00/320.00 **st.**, 1 suite
Spec. Pan-fried foie gras with marinated aubergine. Assiette of rabbit, grain mustard and red wine sauce. Selection of sorbets.

Finch's Arms with rm, Oakham Rd, LE15 8TL, ☎ (01572) 756575, *Fax (01572) 771142,* ←, , – TV P. MC VISA.
Meals 9.95 **t.** (lunch) and a la carte 15.40/19.50 **t.** – **6 rm** 55.00/65.00 **t.** – SB.

KLEY *Hants.* 403 404 Q 30 – *see Basingstoke.*

ORNE *Dorset* 403 404 M 31 – *see Sherborne.*

KHAM *Surrey* 404 S 30 – *pop. 407 – ✉ Ripley.*
London 27 – Guildford 9.

The Hautboy , Ockham Lane, GU23 6NP, ☎ (01483) 225355, *Fax (01483) 211176,* – , rest, TV P. MC AE ⊕ VISA.
Oboe : **Meals** *(restricted opening Saturday)* a la carte 14.00/26.00 **t.** 13.00 – (see also ***The Chapel*** below) – 7.50 – **5 rm** 98.00/125.00 **st.** – SB.

The Chapel (at The Hautboy H.), Ockham Lane, GU23 6NP, ☎ (01483) 225355, *Fax (01483) 211176,* – P. MC AE ⊕ VISA
closed Sunday to Tuesday – **Meals** (dinner only) 38.50/42.00 **t.** 12.00.

es prix — Pour toutes précisions sur les prix indiqués dans ce guide, reportez-vous aux pages de l'introduction.

OCKLEY *Surrey* 404 S 30.

Gatton Manor Hotel G. & C.C., Standon Lane (01306) 627555.
London 31 – Brighton 32 – Guildford 23 – Lewes 36 – Worthing 29.

Bryce's, The Old School House, RH5 5TH, (01306) 627430, *bryces.fish@virgin.n* *Fax (01306) 628274* – P. MC VISA
closed 25-26 December, 1-2 January and Sunday dinner November-February – **Meal** Seafood - 20.45/24.00 **st.** 5.25.

ODDINGLEY *Worcs.* 403 404 N 27 – *see Droitwich.*

ODIHAM *Hants.* 404 R 30 – *pop. 3 531* – *Hook.*
London 51 – Reading 16 – Winchester 25.

George, 100 High St., RG29 1LP, (01256) 702081, *Fax (01256) 704213,* « 15C inn » rm, TV P. MC AE D VISA
Cromwell's : Meals *(closed Sunday dinner)* 15.95/18.95 **t.** and a la carte 5.95 – ***Ne door at the George :*** Meals a la carte 15.70/20.40 **t.** 5.95 – **28 rm** 80.00/90.00 **t.**

Grapevine, 121 High St., RG29 1LA, (01256) 701122, *Fax (01256) 704662* – . MC AE VISA
closed 1 week Christmas-New Year, Sunday, Saturday lunch and Bank Holidays – **Me** 12.95 **t.** (lunch) and a la carte 17.75/25.80 **t.** 5.75.

OKEHAMPTON *Devon* 403 H 31 *The West Country G.* – *pop. 4 841.*
Exc. : *S : Dartmoor National Park★★ – Lydford★★, S : 8 m. by B 3260 and A 386.*
Okehampton (01837) 52113 – , , Ashbury, Fowley Cross (01837) 55453.
3 West St. (01837) 53020 (restricted opening in winter).
London 226 – Exeter 25 – Plymouth 32.

Travelodge, Sourton Cross, EX20 4LY, Southwest : 4 ½ m. by B 3260 and A 30 on A 3 (01837) 52124, *Fax (01837) 52124* – rm, rest, TV P. MC AE D VISA JCB.
Meals (grill rest.) – **42 rm** 39.95 **t.**

Travelodge, Whiddon Down, EX20 2QT, East : 7 ¾ m. by A 30 on A 382 (01647) 2316 *Fax (01647) 231626* – rm, rest, TV P. MC AE D VISA JCB.
Meals (grill rest.) – **40 rm** 39.95 **t.**

OLD BURGHCLERE *Hants.* 404 Q 29 – *Newbury.*
London 77 – Bristol 76 – Newbury 10 – Reading 27 – Southampton 28.

Dew Pond, RG20 9LH, (01635) 278408, *Fax (01635) 278408,* ← – P. MC AE D JCB
closed 2 weeks August, 2 weeks Christmas-New Year, Sunday and Monday – Meals (din only) 25.00/31.00 **t.** 7.50.

OLDBURY *W. Mids.* 402 403 404 N 26 – *see Birmingham.*

OLDHAM *Gtr. Manchester* 402 404 N 23 – *pop. 103 931.*
Crompton and Royton, High Barn, Royton (0161) 624 2154 – Werneth, Green La Garden Suburb (0161) 624 1190 – Lees New Rd (0161) 624 4986.
11 Albion St. (0161) 627 1024.
London 212 – Leeds 36 – Manchester 7 – Sheffield 38.

Plan : see Manchester

Smokies Park, Ashton Rd, Bardsley, OL8 3HX, South : 2 ¾ m. on A (0161) 785 5000, *reservations@smokies.co.uk, Fax (0161) 785 5010,* – rm, P – 110. MC AE D VISA JCB.
Meals *(closed lunch Saturday and Bank Holidays)* (dancing Friday and Saturday evenir (buffet lunch) 5.95/16.95 **st.** and a la carte 6.00 – **73 rm** 70.00/100.00 **st.** – SB.

Avant, Windsor Rd, off Manchester St., OL8 4AS, (0161) 627 5500, *avant@menzies_h ls.co.uk, Fax (0161) 627 5896* – , rm, rest, TV P – 250. MC AE D VISA JCB
Meals *(closed Saturday lunch)* 10.00/17.00 **t.** and dinner a la carte 7.95 – 10.9 **101 rm** 85.50/105.00 **t.**, 2 suites – SB.

Pennine Way, Manchester St., OL8 1UZ, (0161) 624 0555, *reservations@penninew otel.co.uk, Fax (0161) 627 2031,* – TV P – 320. MC AE D VISA
Meals (bar lunch)/dinner 14.95/18.95 **st.** and a la carte 7.95 – **130 rm** 75.00/95.00 s SB.

Travel Inn, The Broadway, Chadderton, OL9 8DW, Southwest : 3 ½ m. by A 62 on A 6104 at junction with A 663 ☎ (0161) 681 1373, *Fax (0161) 682 7974* – rm, rest, TV, P. MC AE VISA. BV a
Meals (grill rest.) – **40 rm** 40.95 **t.**

White Hart Inn with rm, 51 Stockport Rd, Lydgate, OL4 4JJ, East : 3 m. by A 669 on A 6050 ☎ (01457) 872566, *charles@thewhitehart.co.uk, Fax (01457) 875190* – TV P. MC AE VISA
Meals *(closed Sunday dinner and Monday)* (dinner only and Sunday lunch)/dinner a la carte 16.50/24.75 **t.** 8.50 – (see also ***Brasserie*** below) – **12 rm** 62.50/90.00 **t.**

Brasserie (at White Hart Inn), 51 Stockport Rd, Lydgate, OL4 4JJ, East : 3 m. by A 669 on A 6050 ☎ (01457) 872566, *charles@thewhitehart.co.uk, Fax (01457) 875190* – P. MC AE VISA
Meals (booking essential) 12.50 **t.** (lunch) and a la carte 13.75/26.15 **t.** 8.50.

D SODBURY *South Gloucestershire* 403 404 M 29 – ✉ *Bristol.*
18, 9 *Chipping Sodbury ☎ (01454) 312024.*
London 110 – Bristol 14 – Gloucester 30 – Swindon 29.

Dornden, 15 Church Lane, BS37 6NB, ☎ (01454) 313325, *Fax (01454) 312263*, – TV P.
closed 3 weeks late September-October, Christmas and New Year – **Meals** (by arrangement) 12.00 **t.** – **9 rm** 29.00/58.00 **t.**

TON *W. Mids.* 402 ㉒ 403 ⑩ 404 ⑳ – *see Solihull.*

IBERSLEY *Worcs.* 403 404 N 27 – *pop. 2 089.*
London 148 – Birmingham 42 – Leominster 33.

Greenlands without rest., Uphampton, WR9 0JP, Northwest : 1 ½ m. by A 449 turning left at the Reindeer pub ☎ (01905) 620873, «16C cottage», – TV P. – **3 rm** 20.00/44.00 **st.**

The Venture In, Main St., WR9 0EW, ☎ (01905) 620552, « 15C » – P. MC VISA
closed 2 weeks in summer, 2 weeks in winter, 25 December, Sunday dinner, Monday and Bank Holidays – **Meals** 16.95/26.95 **t.** 6.50.

Kings Arms, Main Rd, WR9 0EW, ☎ (01905) 620142, *Fax (01905) 620142*, « 15C inn » – P. MC AE VISA
closed 25 December – **Meals** a la carte 15.90/25.00 **t.** 5.00.

INELEY *Staffs..*
London 158 – Birmingham 50 – Chester 28 – Shrewsbury 31 – Stoke-on-Trent 9.

Wheatsheaf Inn with rm, Barhill Rd, CW3 9QF, ☎ (01782) 751581, *wheatsheaf@pernickety.co.uk, Fax (01782) 751499,* « Part 18C » – rest, TV P – 55. MC AE VISA JCB
Meals *(closed Sunday dinner)* a la carte 15.85/22.85 **t.** – **6 rm** 50.00/65.00 **t.**

FORD *Suffolk* 404 Y 27 – *pop. 1 153* – ✉ *Woodbridge.*
London 103 – Ipswich 22 – Norwich 52.

The Trinity (at Crown and Castle H.), IP12 2LJ, ☎ (01394) 450205, *david.watson@btinternet.com, Fax (01394) 450176,* – P. MC VISA
Meals (booking essential) a la carte 19.00/25.50 **t.** 6.80.

MOTHERLEY *N. Yorks.* 402 Q 20 – *pop. 1 217* – ✉ *Northallerton.*
London 245 – Darlington 25 – Leeds 49 – Middlesbrough 20 – York 36.

The 3 Tuns with rm, 9 South End, DL6 3BN, ☎ (01609) 883301, *peter.holligon@steelriver.co.uk, Fax (01609) 883988,* – TV P. MC VISA.
Meals a la carte 16.15/25.00 **t.** – **2 rm** 55.00/75.00 **t.**

Golden Lion, 6 West End, DL6 3AA, ☎ (01609) 883526, *Fax (01609) 883168* – MC VISA
Meals a la carte 12.50/21.65 **t.** 8.50.

WESTRY *Shrops.* 402 403 K 25 – *pop. 15 612.*
18 *Aston Park ☎ (01691) 610221* – 18 *Llanymynech, Pant ☎ (01691) 830542.*
Mile End Services ☎ (01691) 662488 – The Heritage Centre, 2 Church Terr. ☎ (01691) 662753.
London 182 – Chester 28 – Shrewsbury 18.

ENGLAND

Wynnstay, Church St., SY11 2SZ, ✆ (01691) 655261, *info@wynnstayhotel.cc* *Fax (01691) 670606,* – rm, rest, – 250. MC AE VISA
The Italian : **Meals** *(closed Sunday dinner)* 10.50/16.95 **st.** and dinner a la carte 6.00 – 8.95 – **28 rm** 74.00/95.00 **st.**, 1 suite – SB.

Travelodge, Mile End Service Area, SY11 4JA, Southeast : 1 ¼ m. at junction of A 5 wit 483 ✆ (01691) 658178 – rm, MC AE VISA JCB.
Meals (grill rest.) – **40 rm** 39.95 **t.**

Sebastian's with rm, 45 Willow St., SY11 1AQ, ✆ (01691) 655444, *sebastians.rest@virg net, Fax (01691) 653452* – MC AE VISA JCB.
closed 25-26 December and 1 January – **Meals** - French - *(closed Sunday and Monc* (dinner only) 22.50/27.00 **t.** 6.00 – 8.95 – **7 rm** 45.00/60.00 **st.**

at Rhydycroesau *West : 3 ¼ m. on B 4580 – Oswestry.*

Pen-Y-Dyffryn Country H., SY10 7JD, Southeast : ¼ m. by B 4! ✆ (01691) 653700, *stay@peny.co.uk, Fax (01691) 650066,* – rest, MC VISA JCB
closed 20 December-20 January – **Meals** (booking essential to non-residents) (dinner o 21.00/25.00 **t.** 6.00 – **10 rm** 64.00/86.00 **t.** – SB.

OTLEY *W. Yorks.* 402 O 22 – *pop. 13 596.*
West Busk Lane ✆ (01943) 465329.
8 Boroughgate ✆ (0113) 247 7707.
London 216 – Harrogate 14 – Leeds 12 – York 28.

Chevin Lodge, York Gate, LS21 3NU, South : 2 m. by B 6451 off East Chevin ✆ (01943) 467818, *reception@chevinlodge.co.uk, Fax (01943) 850335,* « Pine lodge vill in extensive woodland », – rest, – 120. MC AE
Meals 13.50/19.50 **st.** and a la carte – **46 rm** 95.00/110.00 **st.**, 4 suites – SB.

In alta stagione, e soprattutto nelle stazioni turistiche, è prudente prenotare con un certo anticipo. Avvertite immediatamente l'albergatore se non potete più occupare la camera prenotata.

Se scrivete ad un albergo all'estero, allegate alla vostra lettera un tagliando-risposta internazionale (disponibile presso gli uffici postali).

OTTERY ST. MARY *Devon* 403 K 31.
10b Broad St. ✆ (01404) 813964 (restricted opening in winter).
London 171 – Exeter 15 – Southampton 87 – Taunton 13.

Normandy House, 5 Cornhill, EX11 1DW, ✆ (01404) 811088, *Fax (01404) 811023,* « orgian town house », – MC VISA JCB.
closed 24-31 December – **Meals** a la carte 13.40/16.85 **st.** 4.95 – **5 rm** 29.95/55.00

OULTON BROAD *Suffolk* 404 Z 26 – *see Lowestoft.*

OUNDLE *Northants.* 404 S 26 – *pop. 3 996 – Peterborough.*
Benefield Rd ✆ (01832) 273267.
14 West St. ✆ (01832) 274333.
London 89 – Leicester 37 – Northampton 30.

Castle Farm, Fotheringhay, PE8 5HZ, North : 3 ¾ m. by A 427 off A ✆ (01832) 226200, *Fax (01832) 226200,* « Riverside garden », – rm,
Meals (by arrangement) 13.50 – **6 rm** 33.00/54.00 **st.**

The Falcon Inn, Fotheringhay, PE8 5HZ, North : 3 ¾ m. by A 427 off A ✆ (01832) 226254, *Fax (01832) 226046,* – MC AE VISA
closed Monday lunch October-November and January-February – **Meals** 13.50 (lunch) and a la carte 17.40/22.50 **st.** 6.00.

OUTLANE *W. Yorks.* – *see Huddersfield.*

OVERSTRAND *Norfolk* 404 Y 25 – *see Cromer.*

XFORD *Oxon.* 403 404 Q 28 *Great Britain G.* – *pop. 118 795.*

See : *City★★★ - Christ Church★★ (Hall★★* **AC**, *Tom Quad★, Tom Tower★, Cathedral★* **AC** *- Choir Roof★)* **BZ** *– Merton College★★* **AC BZ** *- Magdalen College★★* **BZ** *– Ashmolean Museum★★* **BY M1** *– Bodleian Library★★ (Ceiling★★, Lierne Vaulting★)* **AC BZ A1** *– St. John's College★* **BY** *- The Queen's College★* **BZ** *– Lincoln College★* **BZ** *- Trinity College (Chapel★)* **BY** *– New College (Chapel★)* **AC, BZ** *– Radcliffe Camera★* **BZ P1** *– Sheldonian Theatre★* **AC, BZ T** *– University Museum★* **BY M4** *– Pitt Rivers Museum★* **BY M3.**

Env. : *Iffley Church★* **AZ A.**

Exc. : *Woodstock : Blenheim Palace★★★ (The Grounds★★★)* **AC**, *NW : 8 m. by A 4144 and A 34* **AY**.

Swinford Bridge (toll).

to Abingdon Bridge (Salter Bros. Ltd) (summer only).

The Old School, Gloucester Green (01865) 726871.

London 59 – Birmingham 63 – Brighton 105 – Bristol 73 – Cardiff 107 – Coventry 54 – Southampton 64.

Plans on following pages

Randolph, Beaumont St., OX1 2LN, (01865) 247481, *heritagehotels-oxford.randolph@forte.hotel.com, Fax (01865) 791678* – – 250. VISA JCB BY n
Spires : **Meals** 9.95/25.95 **st.** and a la carte 8.00 – 14.95 – **114 rm** 150.00/190.00 **st.**, 5 suites – SB.

Old Bank, 92-94 High St., OX1 4BN, (01865) 799599, *info@oldbank-hotel.co.uk, Fax (01865) 799598,* « Contemporary interior » – VISA JCB. BZ s
closed 24-27 December – ***Quod :*** **Meals** a la carte 14.95/21.55 **t.** – 7.95 – **43 rm** 135.00/255.00 **t.**, 1 suite.

Oxford Spires, Abingdon Rd, OX1 4PS, (01865) 324324, *enquiries@four-pillars.co.uk, Fax (01865) 324325,* – rm, – 230. VISA AZ e
Deacons : **Meals** 12.50/36.00 **st.** and a la carte 6.95 – 12.75 – **103 rm** 139.00/169.00, 12 suites – SB.

Old Parsonage, 1 Banbury Rd, OX2 6NN, (01865) 310210, *info@oldparsonage-hotel.co.uk, Fax (01865) 311262,* « Part 17C house », – VISA JCB. BY e
closed 24-28 December – **Meals** (room service and meals in bar only) a la carte 18.00/23.00 **t.** 13.00 – **30 rm** 100.00/200.00 **t.**

Cotswold Lodge, 66a Banbury Rd, OX2 6JP, (01865) 512121, *Fax (01865) 512490* – – 100. VISA JCB. AY x
Meals 17.50/39.50 **t.** and a la carte 8.95 – **47 rm** 125.00/175.00 **t.**, 2 suites – SB.

Eastgate, Merton St., OX1 4BE, (0870) 4008201, *heritagehotels-oxford.eastgate@forte-hotels.com, Fax (01865) 791681* – rm, VISA JCB BZ c
Cafe Boheme : **Meals** a la carte 17.85/32.40 **t.** 6.95 – 9.95 – **64 rm** 115.00/190.00 **t.** – SB.

Bath Place without rest., 4-5 Bath Pl., OX1 3SU, (01865) 791812, *bathplace@compuserve.com, Fax (01865) 791834,* « 17C Flemish weavers cottages » – VISA JCB. BY a
closed 2 weeks Christmas and New Year – **11 rm** 100.00/150.00 **t.**, 2 suites.

Marlborough House without rest., 321 Woodstock Rd, OX2 7NY, (01865) 311321, *enquiries@marlbhouse.win_uk.net, Fax (01865) 515329* – VISA JCB. AY v
16 rm 70.00/81.00 **st.**

Burlington House without rest., 374 Banbury Rd, OX2 7PP, (01865) 513513, *stay@burlington-house.co.uk, Fax (01865) 311785* – VISA. AY a
closed 17 December-2 January – **11 rm** 50.00/75.00 **st.**

Cotswold House without rest., 363 Banbury Rd, OX2 7PL, (01865) 310558, *Fax (01865) 310558* – VISA JCB. AY c
7 rm 45.00/72.00 **st.**

Chestnuts without rest., 45 Davenant Rd, OX2 8BU, (01865) 553375, *Fax (01865) 553375* – AY s
closed 22 December-7 January – **5 rm** 44.00/75.00 **st.**

Pine Castle without rest., 290-292 Iffley Rd, OX4 4AE, (01865) 241497, *stay@pinecastle.co.uk, Fax (01865) 727230* – VISA JCB. AZ r
closed 23-31 December – **8 rm** 60.00/74.00 **st.**

Gee's, 61 Banbury Rd, OX2 6PE, (01865) 553540, *info@gees-restaurant.co.uk, Fax (01865) 310308,* « Conservatory » – VISA JCB AY r
closed 25 December – **Meals** a la carte 22.10/29.85 **t.**

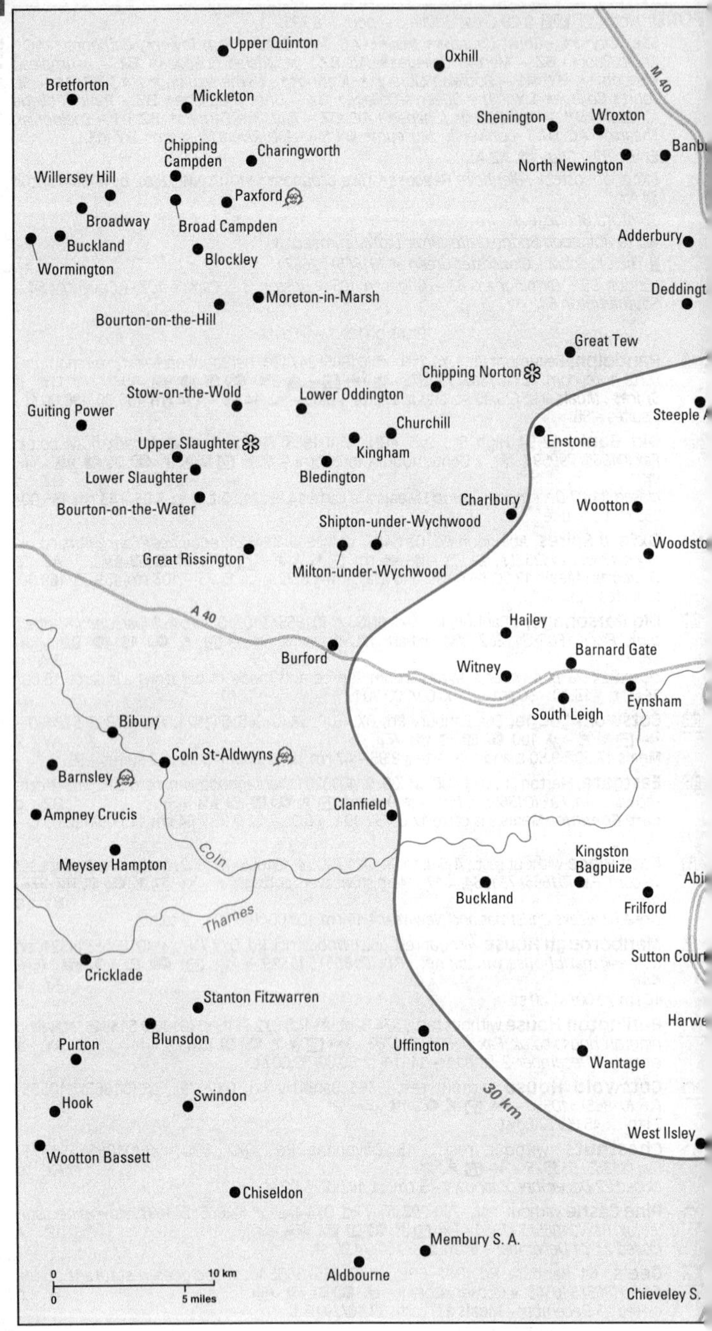
Upper Quinton
Oxhill
M 40
Bretforton
Mickleton
Shenington
Wroxton
Banb
Chipping Campden
Charingworth
North Newington
Willersey Hill
Paxford
Broadway
Broad Campden
Buckland
Adderbury
Wormington
Blockley
Deddingt
Moreton-in-Marsh
Bourton-on-the-Hill
Great Tew
Chipping Norton
Stow-on-the-Wold
Lower Oddington
Guiting Power
Steeple
Churchill
Upper Slaughter
Enstone
Kingham
Lower Slaughter
Bledington
Bourton-on-the-Water
Charlbury
Wootton
Shipton-under-Wychwood
Woodsto
Great Rissington
Milton-under-Wychwood
A 40
Hailey
Burford
Barnard Gate
Witney
South Leigh
Eynsham
Bibury
Coln St-Aldwyns
Barnsley
Clanfield
Ampney Crucis
Kingston Bagpuize
Coln
Meysey Hampton
Abi
Buckland
Frilford
Thames
Sutton Cour
Cricklade
Stanton Fitzwarren
Harwe
Blunsdon
Purton
Uffington
Wantage
30 km
Hook
Swindon
West Ilsley
Wootton Bassett
Chiseldon
Membury S. A.
Aldbourne
0
10 km
0
5 miles
Chieveley S.

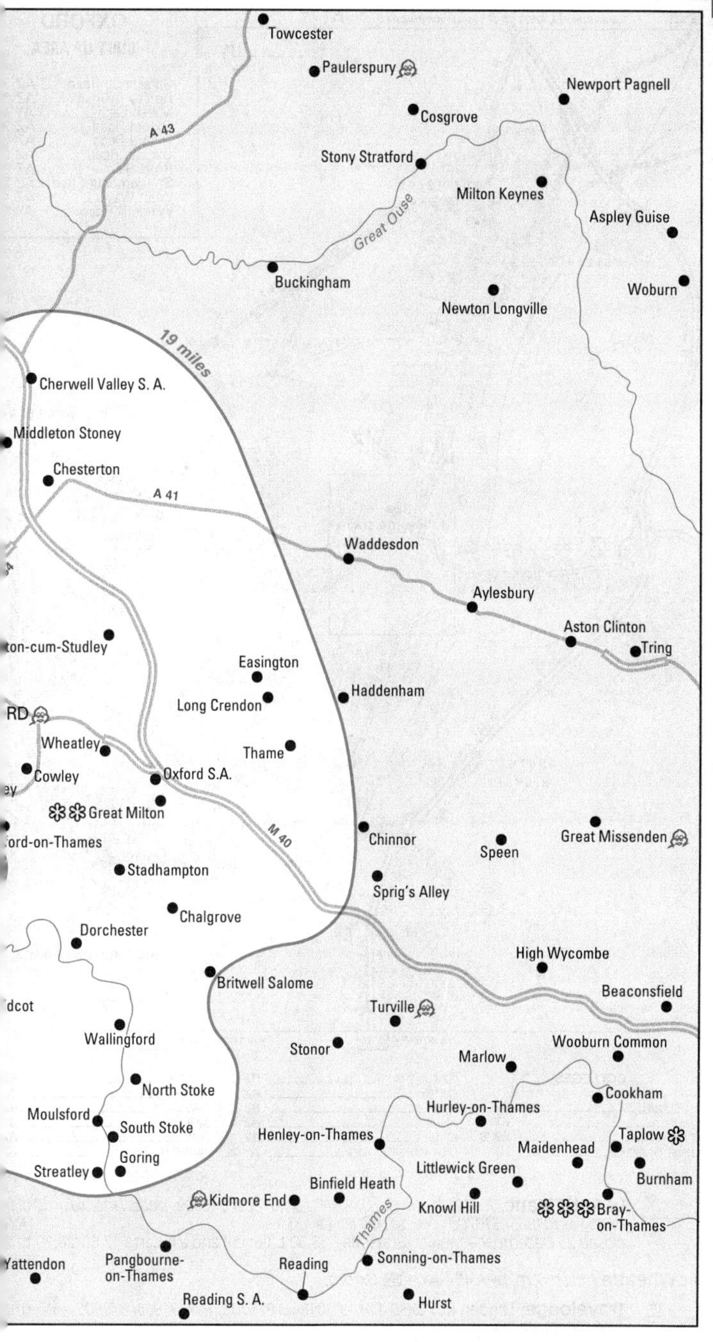

Towcester
Paulerspury
Newport Pagnell
Cosgrove
A 43
Stony Stratford
Milton Keynes
Aspley Guise
Great Ouse
Buckingham
Woburn
Newton Longville
19 miles
Cherwell Valley S. A.
Middleton Stoney
Chesterton
A 41
Waddesdon
Aylesbury
Aston Clinton
Tring
ton-cum-Studley
Easington
Haddenham
Long Crendon
RD
Wheatley
Thame
Cowley
Oxford S.A.
Great Milton
M 40
Chinnor
Great Missenden
Speen
ford-on-Thames
Stadhampton
Sprig's Alley
Chalgrove
Dorchester
High Wycombe
Britwell Salome
Beaconsfield
dcot
Turville
Wallingford
Stonor
Wooburn Common
Marlow
North Stoke
Cookham
Hurley-on-Thames
Moulsford
South Stoke
Henley-on-Thames
Taplow
Maidenhead
Goring
Littlewick Green
Burnham
Streatley
Binfield Heath
Kidmore End
Knowl Hill
Bray-on-Thames
Thames
Yattendon
Pangbourne-on-Thames
Reading
Sonning-on-Thames
Reading S. A.
Hurst

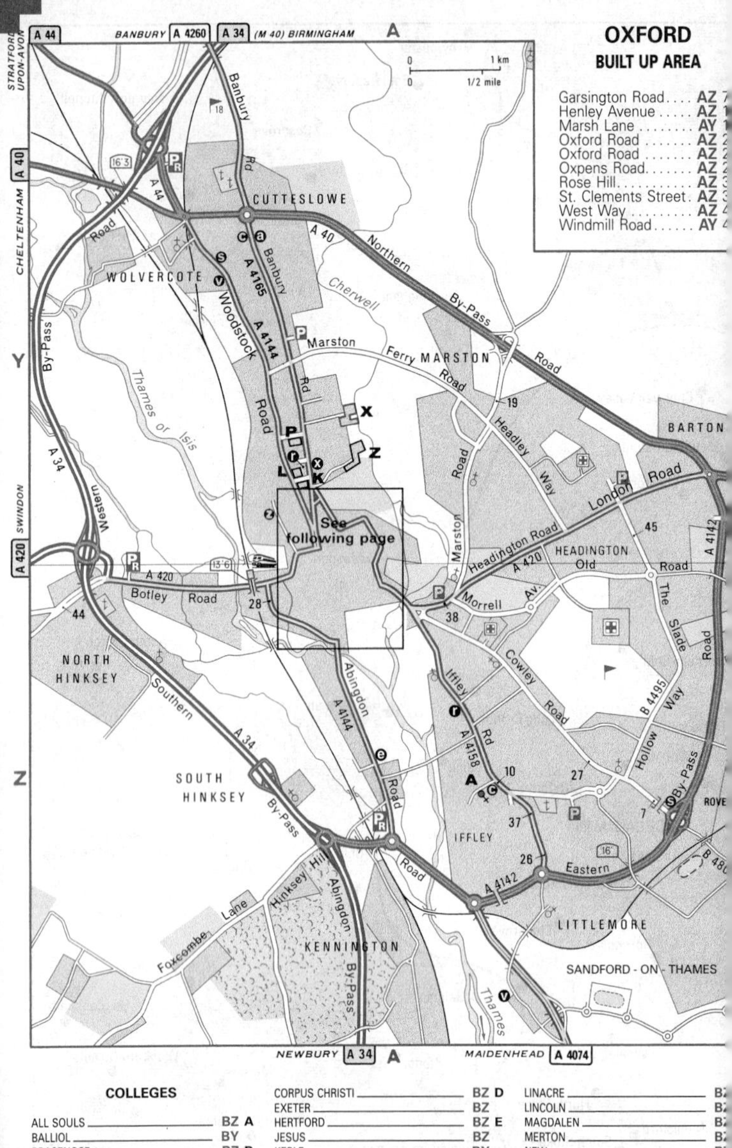

COLLEGES

ALL SOULS	BZ A	CORPUS CHRISTI	BZ D	LINACRE	B
BALLIOL	BY	EXETER	BZ	LINCOLN	B
BRASENOSE	BZ B	HERTFORD	BZ E	MAGDALEN	B
CHRIST CHURCH	BZ	JESUS	BZ	MERTON	B
		KEBLE	BY	NEW	B
		LADY MARGARET HALL	AY Z	NUFFIELD	B

Le Petit Blanc, 71-72 Walton St., OX2 6AG, ☎ (01865) 510999, *petitblanc.oxford@blan o.uk, Fax (01865) 510700* – ⅙. ▤. MC AE ⓓ VISA AY
closed 25 December – **Meals** - Brasserie - 15.00 **t.** (lunch) and a la carte 17.50/28.20 **t.**

at Wheatley *East : 7 m. by A 40* – **AY** – ✉ *Oxford.*

Travelodge, London Rd, OX33 1JH, ☎ (01865) 875705, *Fax (01865) 875905* – ⅙ rm, ♿ P. MC AE ⓓ VISA JCB. ✂
Meals (grill rest.) – **36 rm** 59.95 **t.**

OXFORD

COLLEGES (CONTINUED)

Iffley *Southeast : 2 m. by A 4158 – ✉ Oxford.*

Hawkwell House, Church Way, OX4 4DZ, ✆ (01865) 749988, *Fax (01865) 748525,* –
, rest, TV ✆ P – 200. MC AE VISA JCB. AZ c
Meals 18.95 **t.** and a la carte 6.95 – 11.75 **51 rm** 105.00/115.00 **t.** – SB.

ENGLAND

at Cowley *Southeast : 2½ m. by B 480 – ✉ Oxford.*

Travel Inn, Garsington Rd, OX4 2JZ, ✆ (01865) 779230, *Fax (01865) 775887* – |♦|, ⇔ rr
TV ♿ P. MC AE ① VISA. ✻ AZ
Meals (grill rest.) – **121 rm** 40.95 **t.**

at Sandford-on-Thames *Southeast : 5 m. by A 4158 – ✉ Oxford.*

Oxford Thames Four Pillars, Henley Rd, OX4 4GX, ✆ (01865) 334444, *enquiries@fo-pillars.co.uk, Fax (01865) 334400,* « Thames-side setting », Ƒ6, ≘s, ▢, ↘, ⚘, ♨, ✗ – ⇔ rm, ▤ rest, TV ♿ P – 🎪 200. MC AE ① VISA AZ
The River Room : **Meals** 12.50/36.00 **st.** and a la carte 🍷 6.95 – ☐ 12.75 – **60 rm** 139.0 169.00 **st.** – SB.

at Great Milton *Southeast : 12 m. by A 40 off A 329 – AY – ✉ Oxford.*

Le Manoir aux Quat' Saisons (Blanc) ⚘, Church Rd, OX44 7PD, ✆ (01844) 278881, *manoir@blanc.co.uk, Fax (01844) 278847,* ≤, « Part 15C and 16C manor house, gardens
✿✿ ♨ – ⇔ rest, ▤ rest, TV ✆ P – 🎪 50. MC AE ① VISA JCB. ✻
Meals - French - 35.00 **st.** (lunch weekdays only) and a la carte 67.00/84.00 **t.** 🍷 15.00 – 10.00 – **27 rm** 230.00/495.00 **st.**, 7 suites 475.00/650.00 **st.** – SB
Spec. Pan-fried lamb sweetbreads with morels, Gewürztraminer sauce. Pan-fried squ and red mullet fillets, salt cod brandade, sea urchin jus. Poached peach with figs filled w Port ice cream.

at Kingston Bagpuize *Southwest : 10 m. by A 420 – AY – off A 415 – ✉ Oxford.*

Fallowfields Country House ⚘, Faringdon Rd, OX13 5BH, ✆ (01865) 820416, *stay allowfields.com, Fax (01865) 821275,* ⛱, ⚘ – ⇔ TV ✆ P. MC AE VISA
Meals 19.50/28.50 **t.** and a la carte 🍷 7.50 – **10 rm** ☐ 113.00/165.00 **t.** – SB.

Benutzen Sie die Grünen Michelin-Reiseführer wenn Sie eine Stadt oder Region kennenlernen wollen.

OXFORD SERVICE AREA *Oxon. – ✉ Oxford.*

Days Inn without rest., Waterstock, OX33 1JN, at junction 8a of M ✆ (01865) 877000, Reservations (Freephone) 0800 0280400, *Fax (01865) 877016* – ⇔
♿ P. MC AE ① VISA JCB
☐ 7.45 – **59 rm** 59.00/64.00 **t.**

OXHILL *Warks.* 403 404 P 27 – *pop. 303 – ✉ Stratford-upon-Avon.*
London 85 – Birmingham 32 – Oxford 25.

Nolands Farm ⚘, CV35 0RJ, on A 422 ✆ (01926) 640309, *inthecountry@nolandsfarm o.uk, Fax (01926) 641662,* ↘, ⚘ – ⇔ TV P. MC VISA. ✻
Meals (by arrangement) 16.95 **st.** 🍷 3.50 – **8 rm** ☐ 35.00/52.00 **st.**

PADIHAM *Lancs.* 402 N 22.
London 232 – Burnley 4 – Manchester 26 – Preston 22.

Red Rock Inn, Sabden Rd., Northtown, BB12 9AD, Northwest : 1 m. by A 6068 a Sabden Rd ✆ (01282) 771476 – P. MC VISA JCB
closed Monday except Bank Holiday lunch – **Meals** a la carte 17.50/22.00 **t.**

PADSTOW *Cornwall* 403 F 32 *The West Country G. – pop. 2 855.*
See : *Town★ – Prideaux Place★.*
Env. : *Trevone (Cornwall Coast Path★★) W : 3 m. by B 3276 – Trevose Head★ (≤★★) W : 6 by B 3276.*
Exc. : *Bedruthan Steps★, SW : 7 m. by B 3276 – Pencarrow★, SE : 11 m. by A 389.*
18, 9, 9 *Trevose, Constantine Bay ✆ (01841) 520208.*
Red Brick Building, North Quay ✆ (01841) 533449.
London 288 – Exeter 78 – Plymouth 45 – Truro 23.

The Metropole, Station Rd, PL28 8DB, ✆ (01841) 532486, *heritagehotels-padstowmetropole@forte-hotels.com, Fax (01841) 532867,* ≤ Camel Estuary, ⛱ heated, ⚘ – |♦| ⇔ TV MC AE ① VISA JCB. ✻
Meals (bar lunch Monday to Saturday)/dinner 23.00 **t.** and a la carte 23.45/33.00 **t.** 🍷 8.5 ☐ 12.95 – **50 rm** 85.00/170.00 **t.** – SB.

ENGLAND

Cross House without rest., Church St., PL28 8BG, (01841) 532391, *info@crosshouse.co.uk, Fax (01841) 533633* – TV P. MC VISA.
9 rm 50.00/120.00 t.

St. Petroc's, 4 New St., PL28 8EA, (01841) 532700, *seafoodpadstow@cs.com, Fax (01841) 532942,* – rm, TV P. MC VISA JCB
closed 2 weeks January and 1 week Christmas – ***St. Petrocs Bistro :*** Meals *(closed Monday)* (booking essential) a la carte 21.25/25.25 **t.** 8.00 – **13 rm** 45.00/140.00 **t.** – SB.

Dower House, Fentonluna Lane, PL28 8BA, (01841) 532317, *dower@btinternet.com, Fax (01841) 532667* – TV P. MC VISA
closed December and January – **Meals** *(closed Tuesday and Thursday dinner)* a la carte approx. 16.00 **t.** 5.00 – **6 rm** 50.00/88.00 **st.**

Old Custom House Inn, South Quay, PL28 8ED, (01841) 532359, *Fax (01841) 533372,* ≤ Camel Estuary and harbour – rest., rest., TV. MC AE VISA JCB
closed 25 December – **Meals** a la carte 18.40/25.00 **t.** – **24 rm** 86.00/145.00 **t.**

Rick Stein's Café, 10 Middle St., PL28 8AP, (01841) 532777, *Fax (01841) 532942,* – rm, TV. MC VISA JCB
closed 1 May and 25, 26 and 31 December – **Meals** *(closed Sunday)* (light lunch)/dinner 18.00 **t.** and a la carte – **3 rm** 65.00/85.00 **st.**

Woodlands without rest., Treator, PL28 8RU, West : 1 ¼ m. by A 389 on B 3276 (01841) 532426, *Fax (01841) 532426,* ≤, – TV P
April-October – **9 rm** 30.00/64.00 **s.**

Treverbyn House without rest., Station Rd, PL28 8AD, (01841) 532855, *Fax (01841) 532855,* ≤, – rm, TV P.
closed Christmas and New Year – **5 rm** 54.00/80.00 **st.**

The Seafood with rm, Riverside, PL28 8BY, (01841) 532700, *seafoodpadstow@cs.com, Fax (01841) 532942,* « Converted granary overlooking quayside and Camel Estuary » – rest., rest., TV P. MC VISA JCB
closed 1 week Christmas – **Meals** - Seafood - (booking essential) 31.50/37.00 **t.** and a la carte 33.25/52.25 **t.** 8.00 – **13 rm** 90.00/150.00 **t.** – SB.

Brocks, The Strand, PL28 8AJ, (01841) 532565, *brockx@compuserve.com, Fax (01841) 533199* – . MC VISA
closed 5 January-5 February, Sunday and Monday except in summer – **Meals** 19.50/24.50 **t.** (dinner) and a la carte 28.20/35.50 **t.** 5.50.

Margot's, 11 Duke St., PL28 8AB, (01841) 533441, *oliveradrian@hotmail.com* – . MC AE VISA JCB
closed January, Monday and Tuesday and restricted opening November-December – **Meals** (dinner booking essential) (light lunch)/dinner 24.95 **t.** 5.95.

at Little Petherick *South : 3 m. on A 389* – *Wadebridge.*

Molesworth Manor without rest., PL27 7QT, (01841) 540292, ≤, « Part 17C and 19C rectory », – P.
closed November and December – **10 rm** 25.00/70.00 **st.**

Old Mill Country House without rest., PL27 7QT, (01841) 540388, « Part 16C corn mill », – P. MC VISA.
April-October – **4 rm** 42.00/64.00 **st.**

at St. Issey *South : 3½ m. on A 389* – *Wadebridge.*

Olde Treodore House without rest., PL27 7QS, North : ¼ m. off A 389 (01841) 540291, ≤, – TV P.
closed 25 and 31 December – **3 rm** 35.00/52.00 **t.**

at Constantine Bay *Southwest : 4 m. by B 3276* – *Padstow.*

Treglos , PL28 8JH, (01841) 520727, *treglos-hotel@demon.co.uk, Fax (01841) 521163,* ≤, , – , rest., rest., TV P. MC VISA
15 March-6 November – **Meals** 10.00/36.00 **t.** and a la carte 10.00 – **41 rm** (dinner included) 74.50/149.00 **st.**, 3 suites – SB.

PADWORTH *Newbury* 403 404 Q 29 – *pop. 545* – *Reading.*
London 58 – *Basingstoke 12* – *Reading 10.*

Courtyard by Marriott Reading, Bath Rd, RG7 5HT, on A 4 (01189) 714411, *Fax (01189) 714442,* – TV P – 180. MC AE VISA.
Meals (bar lunch Saturday) a la carte 17.65/22.20 **st.** 7.45 – **50 rm** 99.00/110.00 **st.** – SB.

PAIGNTON *Torbay* 403 J 32 *The West Country G.* – *pop. 42 989.*

See : *Torbay*★ - *Kirkham House*★ **AC Y B**.

Env. : *Paignton Zoo*★★ **AC**, *SW : 1/2 m. by A 3022* **AY** *(see Plan of Torbay)* – *Cockington*★, N
3 m. by A 3022 and minor roads.

The Esplanade ✆ *(01803) 558383.*

London 226 – Exeter 26 – Plymouth 29.

Plan of Built up Area : see Torbay

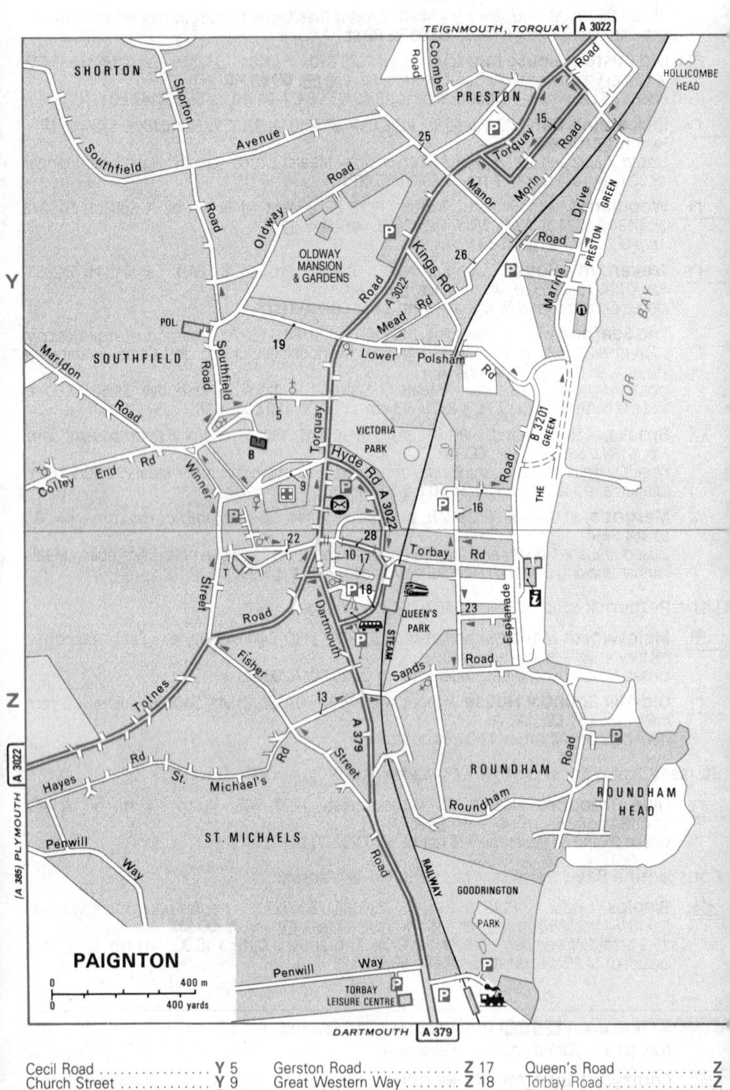

Cecil Road . . . . Y 5
Church Street . . . . Y 9
Commercial Road . . . . Z 10
Elmsleigh Road . . . . Z 13
Eugene Road . . . . Y 15
Garfield Road . . . . Y 16

Gerston Road . . . . Z 17
Great Western Way . . . . Z 18
Higher Polsham
Road . . . . Y 19
Hyde Road . . . . Y
Palace Avenue . . . . Z 22

Queen's Road . . . . Z
Torbay Road . . . . Z
Torquay Road . . . . Y
Upper Manor Road . . . . Y
Upper Morin Road . . . . Y
Victoria Road . . . . Z

Redcliffe, 4 Marine Drive, TQ3 2NL, ☎ (01803) 526397, *redclfe@aol.com, Fax (01803) 528030,* ≤ Torbay, heated, – rest, – 200. Y n
Meals (bar lunch Monday to Saturday)/dinner 16.75/17.50 **t.** and a la carte 6.00 – **65 rm** 45.00/100.00 **t.**

ENGLAND

PAINSWICK *Glos.* 403 404 N 28 *Great Britain G. – pop. 1 628.*
See : *Town*★.
London 107 – Bristol 35 – Cheltenham 10 – Gloucester 7.

Painswick, Kemps Lane, GL6 6YB, Southeast : ½ m. by Bisley St., St. Marys St. and Tibbiwell Lane ☎ (01452) 812160, *reservations@painswickhotel.com, Fax (01452) 814059,* « Part 18C Palladian house », – . MC AE VISA JCB
Meals 13.00/26.00 **st.** and dinner a la carte 7.50 – **19 rm** 85.00/185.00 **st.** – SB.

Cardynham House without rest., The Cross, GL6 6XX, ☎ (01452) 814006, *info@cardynham.co.uk, Fax (01452) 812321,* « Part 15C » – . MC VISA JCB.
9 rm 47.00/69.00 **st.**

PAINTER'S FORSTAL *Kent – see Faversham.*

PANGBOURNE-ON-THAMES *Newbury* 403 404 Q 29 – ✉ *Reading.*
London 53 – Basingstoke 18 – Newbury 16 – Oxford 22 – Reading 6.

Copper Inn, Church Rd, RG8 7AR, ☎ (01189) 842244, *Fax (01189) 845542,* , – – 60. MC AE VISA.
Meals a la carte 20.20/27.20 **t.** 8.95 – 10.00 – **22 rm** 85.00/130.00 **t.** – SB.

PARBOLD *Lancs.* 402 L 23 *Great Britain G. – pop. 2 872 –* ✉ *Wigan.*
Env. : *Rufford Old Hall*★ *(Great Hall*★*) AC, NW : 4 m. by B 5246.*
London 212 – Liverpool 25 – Manchester 24 – Preston 19.

High Moor Inn, High Moor Lane, WN6 9QA, Northeast : 3 m. by B 5246 and Chorley Rd ☎ (01257) 252364, *Fax (01257) 255120* – . MC AE VISA
closed 26 December, Monday and Saturday lunch – **Meals** 12.50 **t.** (lunch) and a la carte 20.50/28.00 **t.**

PARKGATE *Mersey.* 402 403 K 24.
London 212 – Birkenhead 10 – Chester 16 – Liverpool 12.

Marsh Cat, 1 Mostyn Sq., CH64 6SL, ☎ (0151) 336 1963 – MC AE VISA
Meals a la carte 19.95/24.40 **t.**

PARKHAM *Devon* 403 H 31 – ✉ *Bideford.*
London 229 – Barnstaple 14 – Exeter 87 – Plymouth 58.

Penhaven Country House, Rectory Lane, EX39 5PL, ☎ (01237) 451711, *reservations@penhaven.co.uk, Fax (01237) 451878,* , – rest, . MC AE VISA
Meals (dinner only and Sunday lunch)/dinner 17.00 **st.** and a la carte 8.50 – **12 rm** (dinner included) 69.95/150.00 **st.** – SB.

PATCHWAY *South Gloucestershire* 403 404 M 29 – *see Bristol.*

PATELEY BRIDGE *N. Yorks.* 402 O 21 *Great Britain G. – pop. 2 504 –* ✉ *Harrogate.*
Exc. : *Fountains Abbey*★★★ *AC - Studley Royal*★★ *AC (≤*★ *from Anne Boleyn's Seat) - Fountains Hall (Façade*★*), NE : 8½ m. by B 6265.*
14 High St. ☎ (01423) 711147 (summer only).
London 225 – Leeds 28 – Middlesbrough 46 – York 32.

Grassfields Country House, Low Wath Rd, HG3 5HL, ☎ (01423) 711412, *Fax (01423) 712844,* , « Part 18C », – rest, – 60. MC VISA
Meals *(closed Monday lunch)* 18.95 **st.** (dinner) and a la carte 13.00/18.95 **st.** – **9 rm** 31.50/75.00 **st.** – SB.

Knottside Farm, The Knott, HG3 5DQ, Southeast : 1 m. by A 6165 ☎ (01423) 712927, *Fax (01423) 712927,* ≤, « 17C », –
Meals (by arrangement) (unlicensed) 18.00 – **3 rm** 40.00/60.00 – SB.

at Low Laithe *Southeast : 2 ¾ m. on B 6165 – ✉ Harrogate.*

XX **Dusty Miller,** Main Rd, Summerbridge, HG3 4BU, ✆ (01423) 780837 – P. MC AE VISA
closed 25-26 December and 1 January – **Meals** (dinner only) (by arrangement Sunday an Monday) 24.00 **t.** and a la carte 25.30/35.40 **t.** 12.90.

X **Carters Knox Manor** with rm, Summer Bridge, HG3 4DQ, ✆ (01423) 780607 – rm TV P. MC VISA
accommodation closed 25 December – **Meals** 12.50/14.50 **t.** and a la carte 4.95 – **4 r** 45.00/66.00 **t.** – SB.

at Summerbridge *Southeast : 3 ¾ m. on B 6165 – ✉ Harrogate.*

North Pasture Farm, Brimham Rocks, HG3 4DW, Northeast : 2 ¾ m. by Hartwi Bank Rd ✆ (01423) 711470, *Fax (01423) 711470*, ≤, « Part 14C and 17C farmhouse, worki farm », – P.
March-November – **Meals** 13.50 **st.** – **3 rm** 45.00 **st.**

at Wath-in-Nidderdale *Northwest : 2 ¼ m. by Low Wath Rd – ✉ Harrogate.*

XX **Sportsman's Arms** with rm, HG3 5PP, ✆ (01423) 711306, *Fax (01423) 71252* « Part 17C », – TV P. MC VISA.
closed 25 December – **Meals** (booking essential to non-residents) a la carte 15.00/25.00 7.00 – **13 rm** 50.00/90.00 **st.** – SB.

at Ramsgill-in-Nidderdale *Northwest : 5 m. by Low Wath Rd – ✉ Harrogate.*

XX **Yorke Arms** with rm, HG3 5RL, ✆ (01423) 755243, *enquiries@yorke-arms.co.* *Fax (01423) 755330*, « Part 17C former shooting lodge », – TV P. MC AE VI
Meals *(closed Sunday dinner to non-residents)* a la carte 20.65/30.00 **t.** 7.00 – **13 r** 85.00/200.00 **t.**

PATRICK BROMPTON *N. Yorks.* 402 P 21 – ✉ *Bedale.*
London 242 – Newcastle upon Tyne 58 – York 43.

Elmfield House, Arrathorne, DL8 1NE, Northwest : 2 ¼ m. by A 684 on Richmond ✆ (01677) 450558, *stay@elmfieldhouse.freeserve.co.uk*, *Fax (01677) 450557*, rest, TV P. MC VISA.
Meals (residents only) (dinner only) 12.00 **st.** 4.50 – **9 rm** 35.00/60.00 **st.** – SB.

PAULERSPURY *Northants.* 403 404 R 27 – *see Towcester.*

PAXFORD *Glos.* 403 404 O 27 – *see Chipping Campden.*

PAYHEMBURY *Devon – see Honiton.*

PEASMARSH *E. Sussex* 404 W 31 – *see Rye.*

PELYNT *Cornwall* 403 G 32 – *see Looe.*

PEMBROKE BAY *Guernsey (Channel Islands)* 403 P 33 and 230 ⑩ – *see Channel Islands.*

PEMBURY *Kent* 404 U 30 – *see Royal Tunbridge Wells.*

PENDLEBURY *Gtr. Manchester* 402 403 404 N 23 – *see Manchester.*

PENRITH *Cumbria* 401 402 L 19 – *pop. 12 049.*
18 *Salkeld Rd ✆ (01768) 891919.*
Robinsons School, Middlegate ✆ (01768) 867466.
London 290 – Carlisle 24 – Kendal 31 – Lancaster 48.

North Lakes, Ullswater Rd, CA11 8QT, South : 1 m. by A 592 at junction 40 of M ✆ (01768) 868111, *nlakes@shireinns.co.uk*, *Fax (01768) 868291*, squash – TV P – 200. MC AE VISA
Meals (bar lunch Saturday) a la carte 26.00/38.00 **st.** – **84 rm** 102.00/122.00 **st.** – SB.

Travelodge, Redhills, CA11 0DT, Southwest : 1 1/2 m. by A 592 on A 66 ☎ (01768) 866958 – ⇔ rm, TV ♿ P. MC AE ⊕ VISA JCB. ✻
Meals (grill rest.) – **40 rm** 49.95 **t.**

A Bit on the Side, Brunswick Sq., CA11 7LG, ☎ (01768) 892526 – ⇔. MC VISA
closed 2 weeks in spring, 25 December, Monday and lunch Saturday-Tuesday – **Meals** 8.95/10.95 **t.** (lunch) and dinner a la carte 17.95/24.60 **t.**

at Temple Sowerby *East : 6 3/4 m. on A 66 – ✉ Penrith.*

Temple Sowerby House, CA10 1RZ, ☎ (01768) 361578, *stay@temple-sowerby.com, Fax (01768) 361958,* « Early 18C farmhouse with Georgian additions », ⛲ – ⇔ rest, TV P. MC AE VISA. ✻
Meals (dinner only) a la carte 24.25/31.95 **st.** 🍷 7.25 – **13 rm** ☐ 68.00/110.00 **st.** – SB.

PENZANCE *Cornwall* 403 D 33 *The West Country G. – pop. 20 284.*

See : *Town*★ - *Outlook*★★★ – *Western Promenade* (≤★★★) YZ – *National Lighthouse Centre*★ *AC* Y – *Chapel St.*★ Y – *Maritime Museum*★ *AC* Y **M1**.

Env. : *St. Buryan*★★ *(church tower*★★*), SW : 5 m. by A 30 and B 3283 – Penwith*★★ – *Trengwainton Garden*★★, *NW : 2 m. – Sancreed - Church*★★ *(Celtic Crosses*★★*) - Carn Euny*★, *W : 3 1/2 m. by A 30* Z – *St. Michael's Mount*★★ (≤★★), *E : 4 m. by B 3311* – Y – *and A 30 – Gulval*★ *(Church*★*), NE : 1 m. – Ludgvan*★ *(Church*★*), NE : 3 1/2 m. by A 30 – Chysauster Village*★, *N : 3 1/2 m. by A 30, B 3311 and minor rd – Newlyn*★ *- Pilchard Works*★, *SW : 1 1/2 m. by B 3315* Z – *Lanyon Quoit*★, *NW : 3 1/2 m. by St. Clare Street – Men-an-Tol*★, *NW : 5 m. by B 3312 – Madron Church*★, *NW : 1 1/2 m. by St. Clare Street* Y.

Exc. : *Morvah* (≤★★), *NW : 6 1/2 m. by St. Clare Street* Y – *Zennor (Church*★*), NW : 6 m. by B 3311* Y – *Prussia Cove*★, *E : 8 m. by B 3311* – Y – *and A 394 – Land's End*★ *(cliff scenery*★★★*), SW : 10 m. by A 30* Z – *Porthcurno*★, *SW : 8 1/2 m. by A 30, B 3283 and minor rd.*

Access to the Isles of Scilly by helicopter, British International Heliport (01736) 363871, Fax (01736) 364293.

⛴ *to the Isles of Scilly (Hugh Town) (Isles of Scilly Steamship Co. Ltd) (summer only) (approx. 2 h 40 mn).*

ℹ *Station Rd* ☎ *(01736) 362207 – London 319 – Exeter 113 – Plymouth 77 – Taunton 155.*

Plan on next page

Abbey, Abbey St., TR18 4AR, ☎ (01736) 366906, *gly@abbeyhotel.fsnet.co.uk, Fax (01736) 351163,* « Attractively furnished 17C house », ⛲ – ⇔ rest, TV P. MC AE VISA
closed 22-27 December – **Meals** (booking essential) (dinner only) 25.00 **t.** 🍷 7.00 – **6 rm** ☐ 75.00/155.00 **t.**, 1 suite – SB. Y u

Beachfield, The Promenade, TR18 4NW, ☎ (01736) 362067, *office@beachfield.co.uk, Fax (01736) 331100,* ≤ – TV. MC AE VISA JCB Z a
closed 1 week Christmas – **Meals** (bar lunch)/dinner 14.95 **st.** and a la carte 🍷 5.00 – **18 rm** ☐ 44.50/99.00 **st.**

Tarbert, 11 Clarence St., TR18 2NU, ☎ (01736) 363758, *reception@tarbert-hotel.co.uk, Fax (01736) 331336* – ⇔ rest, TV. MC AE VISA JCB. ✻ Y i
closed 21 December-31 January – **Meals** (dinner only) a la carte approx. 21.00 **st.** 🍷 4.50 – **12 rm** ☐ 36.00/80.00 **st.** – SB.

Estoril without rest., 46 Morrab Rd, TR18 4EX, ☎ (01736) 362468, *estoril@aol.com, Fax (01736) 367471* – ⇔ TV. MC VISA. ✻ Y o
closed Christmas and New Year – **9 rm** ☐ 30.00/60.00 **st.**

Chy-An-Mor without rest., 15 Regent Terr., TR18 4DW, ☎ (01736) 363441, *Fax (01736) 363441,* ≤, ⛲ – ⇔ TV P. ✻ Y e
closed December – **10 rm** ☐ 34.00/60.00 **t.**

Harris's, 46 New St., TR18 2LZ, ☎ (01736) 364408, *Fax (01736) 333273* – ⇔. MC AE VISA
closed 3 weeks in winter, 25-26 December, 1 January, Sunday and Monday in winter – **Meals** a la carte 24.85/38.95 **t.** 🍷 7.50. Y a

The Summer House with rm, Cornwall Terr., TR18 4HL, ☎ (01736) 363744, *summerhouse@dial.pipex.com, Fax (01736) 360959,* ⛲ – ⇔ TV P. MC VISA JCB Z s
29 March-25 December – **Meals** *(closed Tuesday and Wednesday to non-residents except July-September and Sunday-Monday)* (dinner only) 21.50 **st.** 🍷 6.00 – **5 rm** ☐ 50.00/85.00 **st.** – SB.

at Newlyn *Southwest : 1 1/2 m. on B 3315* – Z – *✉ Penzance.*

Higher Faugan 🐦, TR18 5NS, Southwest : 3/4 m. on B 3315 ☎ (01736) 362076, *hfhotel@tesco.net, Fax (01736) 351648,* 🏊 heated, ⛲, 🎾, ✂ – ⇔ rest, TV P. MC AE ⊕ VISA
Meals (bar lunch)/dinner 17.50 **st.** 🍷 5.10 – **11 rm** ☐ 70.00/120.00 **t.** – SB.

at Drift *Southwest : 2 1/2 m. on A 30* – Z – *✉ Penzance.*

Rose Farm 🐦 without rest., Chyenhal, Buryas Bridge, TR19 6AN, Southwest : 3/4 m. on Chyenhal rd ☎ (01736) 731808, *Fax (01736) 731808,* « Working farm », ⛲ – TV P. ✻
closed 24 and 25 December – **3 rm** ☐ 30.00/44.00 **st.**

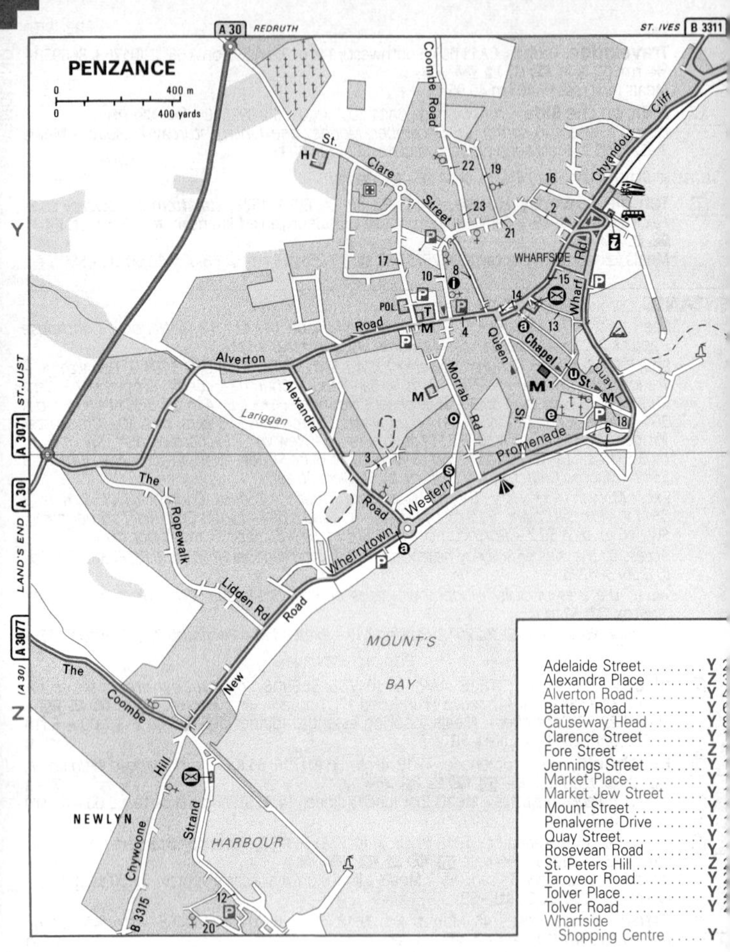

Questa guida non è un repertorio di tutti gli alberghi e ristoranti, nè comprende tutti i buoni alberghi e ristoranti di Gran Bretagna ed Irlanda.
Nell'intento di tornare utili a tutti i turisti, siamo indotti ad indicare esercizi di tutte le classi ed a citarne soltanto un certo numero di ognuna.

PERRANUTHNOE *Cornwall* 403 D 33 – *see Marazion.*

PETERBOROUGH *Peterborough* 402 404 T 26 *Great Britain G. – pop. 134 788.*

See : *Cathedral*★★ *AC* Y.

Thorpe Wood, Nene Parkway ☎ *(01733) 267701*, **BX** – *Peterborough Milton, Mil Ferry* ☎ *(01733) 380204*, **BX** – *Orton Meadows, Ham Lane* ☎ *(01733) 237478*, **BX**.

3 Minster Par. ☎ *(01733) 452336.*

London 85 – Cambridge 35 – Leicester 41 – Lincoln 51.

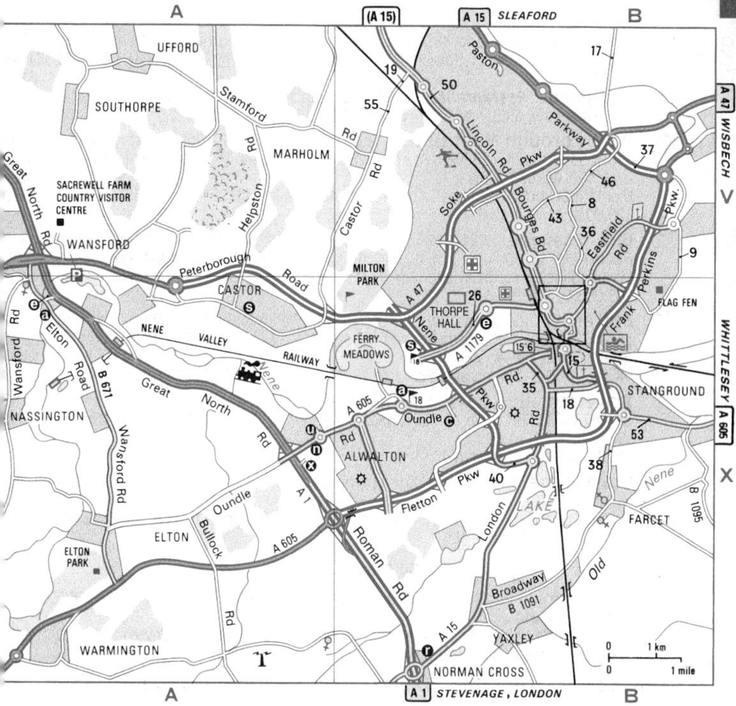

A
(A 15)
A 15 SLEAFORD
B
UFFORD
SOUTHORPE
Stamford Rd
MARHOLM
Paston Parkway
17
19
50
55
A 47 WISBECH
V
37
46
Lincoln Rd
Pkw
Soke
Bourges Bd
43
8
36
Eastfield Rd
Frank Perkins Pkw.
9
SACREWELL FARM COUNTRY VISITOR CENTRE
Great North Rd
Helpston Rd
Castor Rd
WANSFORD
Peterborough Road
CASTOR
MILTON PARK
A 47
26
THORPE HALL
FLAG FEN
WHITTLESEY
Nene
Elton Road
Wansford Rd
NENE VALLEY RAILWAY
FERRY MEADOWS
A 1179
15'6
15
B 671
Great North Rd
Nene
A 605
Oundle
Rd.
35
18
STANGROUND
A 605
NASSINGTON
Oundle Rd
ALWALTON
Pkw
Rd
53
38
X
Wansford Rd
Oundle
A 1
Fletton Pkw
40
Nene
B 1095
ELTON
Bullock Rd
A 605
Roman Rd
London Rd
LAKE
FARCET
ELTON PARK
Broadway
B 1091
Old
A 15
YAXLEY
WARMINGTON
NORMAN CROSS
0 1 km
0 1 mile
A
A 1 STEVENAGE, LONDON
B

PETERBOROUGH

idge Street . . . . Z
attle Market Road . . . . Y 2
hurch Street . . . . YZ
ty Road . . . . Y 3
owgate . . . . Y 5
oss Street . . . . Z 6
ogsthorpe Road . . . . BV 8
dgerley Drain Road . . . . . BV 9
nbankment Road . . . . Z 12
xchange Street . . . . Y 13
etton Avenue . . . . BX 15
eneva Street . . . . Y 16
untons Road . . . . BV 17
gh Street . . . . BX 18
urn Road . . . . BV 19
ng Causeway . . . . Y 25
ngthorpe
Parkway . . . . BX 26
arket Way . . . . Y 28
dgate . . . . Y 29
ew Road . . . . Y 34
ew Road . . . . BX 35
rk Road . . . . BV 36
ston Parkway . . . . BV 37
eterborough Road . . . . . . BX 38
orpres Way . . . . BX 40
ueensgate
Shopping Centre . . . . Y
vergate . . . . Z 42
vergate
Shopping Centre . . . . Z
Paul's Road . . . . BV 43
orpe Road . . . . Y 45
elland Road . . . . BV 46
entworth Street . . . . Z 48
errington
Parkway . . . . BV 50
heelyard . . . . Y 52
hittlesey Road . . . . BX 53
oodcroft Road . . . . BV 55

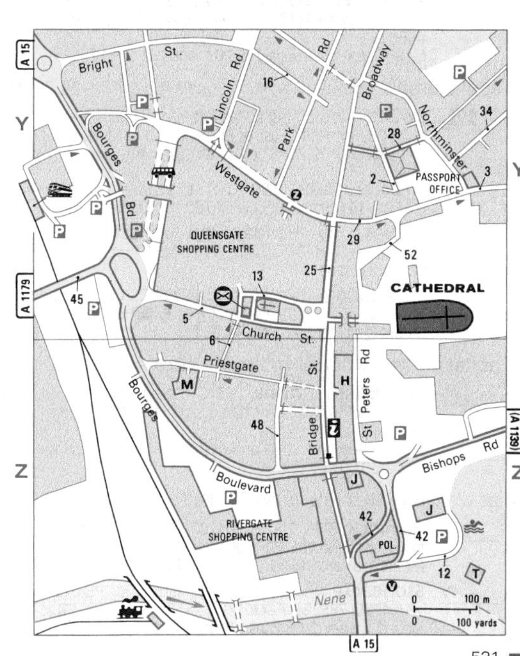

ENGLAND

Orton Hall, The Village, Orton Longueville, PE2 7DN, Southwest : 2 ½ m. by Oundle Rd 605) ☎ (01733) 391111, *Fax (01733) 231912*, – rm, TV P – 120. MC AE VISA JCB BX
The Huntly Restaurant: Meals (bar lunch Monday to Saturday)/dinner 21.95 and a la carte 6.45 – 9.85 – **63 rm** 75.00/130.00 **st.** – SB.

Peterborough Moat House, Thorpe Wood, PE3 6SG, Southwest : 2 ¼ m. at roun about 33 ☎ (01733) 289988, *Fax (01733) 262737*, – rm, rest, TV P – 400. MC AE VISA BX
Meals (bar lunch Saturday) a la carte 15.40/25.40 **t.** 6.95 – 11.50 – **133 rm** 103.0 120.00 **st.**

Bull, Westgate, PE1 1RB, ☎ (01733) 561364, *info@bull-hotel-peterborough.co Fax (01733) 557304* – rm, rest, TV P – 400. MC AE VISA JCB. Y
Meals (dancing Saturday evening) 17.95 **t.** and a la carte 8.25 – 10.50 – **117 rm** 85.0 105.00 **st.**, 1 suite – SB.

Butterfly, Thorpe Meadows, off Longthorpe Parkway, PE3 6GA, West : 1 m. by Thorpe ☎ (01733) 564240, *peterbutterfly@lineone.net, Fax (01733) 565538* – rm, TV P 80. MC AE VISA JCB BX
Meals 17.50 **t.** (dinner) and a la carte 15.95/26.95 **t.** – 8.50 – **70 rm** 69.50/95.00 **t.** – SB

Travel Inn, Ham Lane, Orton Meadows, PE2 0UU, Southwest : 3 ½ m. by Oundle Rd (A 60 ☎ (01733) 235794, *Fax (01733) 391055* – rm, rest, TV P. MC AE VIS BX
Meals (grill rest.) – **40 rm** 40.95 **t.**

Grain Barge, The Quayside, Embankment Rd, PE1 1EG, ☎ (01733) 311967 – . MC AE VISA JCB Z
closed 25 and 26 December – **Meals** - Chinese (Peking) - (buffet lunch Sunday) 14.8 21.00 **st.** and a la carte **st.**

at Eye *Northeast : 4 m. by A 47* – **BV** – *Peterborough.*

I Toscanini, 2 Peterborough Rd, PE6 7YB, ☎ (01733) 223221, *Fax (01733) 755355*, P. MC AE VISA
closed Sunday and Monday – **Meals** - Italian - (live music Thursday to Saturday evenin 9.95 **t.** (lunch) and a la carte 22.00/30.40 **t.** 6.00.

at Norman Cross *South : 5 ¾ m. on A 15 at junction with A 1(M)* – *Peterborough.*

Posthouse Peterborough, Great North Rd, PE7 3TB, ☎ (0870) 400 9063, *fc1428@fc e-hotels.com, Fax (01733) 244455*, – rm, rest, TV P – 50. MC AE VISA BX
Meals *(closed Saturday)* 15.00 **t.** and a la carte 7.95 – 11.95 – **96 rm** 69.00 **t.** – SB.

at Alwalton *Southwest : 5 ¾ m. on Oundle Rd (A 605)* – *Peterborough.*

Swallow (becoming a Marriott spring 2001), Peterborough Business Park, Lynch Woo PE2 6GB, (opposite East of England Showground) ☎ (01733) 371111, *info@swallowhotel om, Fax (01733) 236725*, – , rest, TV P – 300. MC AE V JCB AX
Emperor: Meals 18.50/25.00 **st.** 6.50 – ***Laurels:*** Meals 15.50/18.50 **st.** and a la car 6.50 – **161 rm** 115.00/140.00 **st.**, 2 suites – SB.

Express by Holiday Inn without rest., East of England Way, PE2 6H ☎ (01733) 284450, *Fax (01733) 284451* – TV P – 30. MC AE VISA.
80 rm 58.00 **st.** AX

Travelodge, Great North Rd, PE7 3UR, A 1 (southbound carriageway) ☎ (01733) 2311 *Fax (01733) 231109* – rm, TV P. MC AE VISA JCB. AX
Meals (grill rest.) – **32 rm** 49.95 **t.**

at Castor *West : 5 m. by A 1179 and A 1260 off A 47* – *Peterborough.*

Fitzwilliam Arms, 34 Peterborough Rd, PE5 7AX, ☎ (01733) 3802 *Fax (01733) 380116*, « Characterful thatched inn », – P. MC AE VISA JC AX
Meals - Seafood, steak and oyster specialities - (bookings not accepted at dinner) a la car 12.00/39.00 **st.**

at Wansford *West : 8½ m. by A 47* – *Peterborough.*

Haycock, PE8 6JA, ☎ (01780) 782223, *Fax (01780) 783031*, « Part 17C coachi inn », – rm, TV P – 150. MC AE VISA AX
Meals a la carte 16.85/30.25 **st.** – **50 rm** 75.00/130.00 **st.** – SB.

Stoneacre without rest., Elton Rd, PE8 6JT, South : ½ m. on unmarked dr ☎ (01780) 783283, *Fax (01780) 783283*, – TV P AX
closed 1 week Christmas – **5 rm** 34.00/50.00 **st.**

ETERSFIELD *Hants.* 404 R 30.
London 60 – Brighton 45 – Portsmouth 21 – Southampton 34.

Langrish House, Langrish, GU32 1RN, West : 3 ½ m. by A 272 (01730) 266941, *Fax (01730) 260543*, – – 60. *closed 28-29 December and 1-8 January* – **Meals** *(closed Sunday dinner)* (lunch by arrangement)/dinner 19.95/24.95 **t.** 10.90 – **14 rm** 82.00/120.00 **t.** – SB.

JSW, 1 Heath Rd, GU31 4JE, (01730) 262030 – *closed first 2 weeks January, Sunday and Monday* – **Meals** 15.00/25.00 **t.** 7.50.

ETERSTOW *Herefordshire* 403 404 M 28 – *see Ross-on-Wye.*

ETWORTH *W. Sussex* 404 S 31 *Great Britain G.* – *pop. 2 156.*
See : *Petworth House★★ AC.*
Osiers, London Rd (01798) 344097.
London 54 – Brighton 31 – Portsmouth 33.

Old Railway Station without rest., GU28 0JF, South : 1 ½ m. off A 285 (01798) 342346, *mlr@old-station.co.uk, Fax (01798) 342346,* « Converted late 19C station and restored Pullman coaches », – . **6 rm** 65.00/94.00 **st.**

Soanes, Grove Lane, GU28 0HY, South : ½ m. by High St. and Pulborough rd (01798) 343659, *Fax (01798) 343659,* – *closed Sunday, Monday and 2 weeks January* – **Meals** (dinner only) a la carte 28.85/42.90 **t.** 10.50.

Horse Guards Inn with rm, Upperton Rd, Tillington, GU28 9AF, West : 1 ½ m. by A 272 (01798) 342332, *mail@horseguardsinn.co.uk, Fax (01798) 344351,* – rm, . **Meals** (booking essential) a la carte 18.60/27.95 **t.** 8.50 – **3 rm** 60.00/82.00 **t.**

Sutton *South : 5 m. by A 283 – Pulborough.*

White Horse Inn with rm, The Street, RH20 1PS, (01798) 869221, *Fax (01798) 869291,* – **Meals** a la carte 15.15/24.65 **t.** – **6 rm** 65.00 **t.**

Halfway Bridge *West : 3 m. on A 272 – Petworth.*

The Halfway Bridge Inn, GU28 9BP, (01798) 861281, *mail@thesussexpub.co.uk, Fax (01798) 861878,* « 17C coaching inn », – *closed 25 December and Sunday dinner in winter* – **Meals** a la carte 12.95/19.50 **t.** 7.95.

Lickfold *Northwest : 6 m. by A 272 – Petworth.*

Lickfold Inn, GU28 9EY, (01798) 861285, *sam@timoko.co.uk, Fax (01798) 861342,* « 15C inn », – **Meals** a la carte 23.70/27.25 **t.** 11.50.

CKERING *N. Yorks.* 402 R 21 – *pop. 5 914.*
Eastgate Car Park (01751) 473791.
London 237 – Middlesbrough 43 – Scarborough 19 – York 25.

White Swan, Market Pl., YO18 7AA, (01751) 472288, *welcome@white-swan.co.uk, Fax (01751) 475554* – **Meals** a la carte 14.00/23.45 **t.** 10.95 – **11 rm** 60.00/90.00 **t.**, 1 suite – SB.

Burgate House, 17 Burgate, YO18 7AU, (01751) 473463, *burgate.house@btinternet.com, Fax (01751) 473463,* « Part 17C » – rest, . *closed Christmas* – **Meals** (booking essential) 15.00 4.00 – **7 rm** 37.00/60.00 **s.** – SB.

Bramwood, 19 Hall Garth, YO18 7AW, (01751) 474066, – . *closed 2 weeks in winter* – **Meals** (by arrangement) 13.00 **s.** – **8 rm** 25.00/48.00 **s.**

Old Manse, Middleton Rd, YO18 8AL, (01751) 476484, *Fax (01751) 477124,* – . **Meals** 17.50 **st.** – **8 rm** 26.00/52.00 **st.** – SB.

Thornton-le-Dale *East : 2 m. by A 170 – Pickering.*

New Inn with rm, YO18 7LF, (01751) 474226, *newinntld@aol.com, Fax (01751) 477715,* « 18C » – . **Meals** a la carte 13.70/18.70 **st.** – **6 rm** 39.00/66.00 **t.**

ENGLAND

at Middleton *Northwest : 1½ m. on A 170 – ✉ Pickering.*

Cottage Leas ⚲, Nova Lane, YO18 8PN, North : 1 m. via Church Lane ☎ (01751) 47212 *reservations@cottleashotel.fsbusiness.co.uk, Fax (01751) 474930,* ≤, – TV P. MC V JCB
closed 9-17 November and accommodation closed 24-26 December – **Meals** (dinner or and Sunday lunch)/dinner 14.50 **st.** and a la carte 4.75 – **11 rm** 44.50/79.00 **st.** – SB.

Sunnyside without rest., Carr Lane, YO18 8PD, ☎ (01751) 476104, *Fax (01751) 4761(* – TV
closed January and December – **3 rm** 29.00/48.00 **t.**

at Sinnington *Northwest : 4 m. by A 170 – ✉ York.*

Fox and Hounds, Main St., YO62 6SQ, ☎ (01751) 431577, *foxhoundsinn@easynet.co. Fax (01751) 432791,* – TV P. MC AE VISA
Meals a la carte 17.35/24.65 **t.** 6.60 – **10 rm** 44.00/100.00 **t.**

at Cropton *Northwest : 4¾ m. by A 170 – ✉ Pickering.*

Burr Bank ⚲, YO18 8HL, North : ¼ m. ☎ (01751) 417777, *baub@burrbank.cor Fax (01751) 417789,* , – TV P.
Meals (by arrangement) 16.00 **st.** 4.00 – **3 rm** 27.00/54.00 **st.**

The New Inn with rm, YO18 8HH, ☎ (01751) 417330, *Fax (01751) 417310,* « Home Cropton brewery » – TV P. MC VISA.
Meals a la carte 13.00/20.00 **st.** 5.95 – **9 rm** 35.00/70.00 **st.**

Le Grand Londres (GREATER LONDON) est composé de la City et de 32 arrondissements administratifs (Borough) eux-mêmes divisés en quartiers ou en villages ayant conservé leur caractère propre (Area).

PICKHILL *N. Yorks.* 402 P 21 – *pop. 412* – ✉ *Thirsk.*
London 229 – Leeds 41 – Middlesbrough 30 – York 34.

Nags Head Country Inn, YO7 4JG, ☎ (01845) 567391, *reservations@nagsheadpickh reeserve.co.uk, Fax (01845) 567212,* – TV P – 30. MC VISA JCB
closed 25 December – **Meals** 13.95/16.00 **st.** and a la carte 5.95 – **15 rm** 40.(60.00 **st.**

PILLING *Lancs.* 402 L 22 – *pop. 2 204* – ✉ *Preston.*
London 243 – Blackpool 11 – Burnley 43 – Manchester 49.

Springfield House ⚲, Wheel Lane, PR3 6HL, ☎ (01253) 790301, *recep@springfieldh sehotel.co.uk, Fax (01253) 790907,* « Georgian house », – rest, TV P. MC AE VISA
Meals *(closed lunch Monday and Saturday)* 9.50/12.45 **t.** 5.50 – **8 rm** 40.00/65.00 t SB.

PLUCKLEY *Kent* 404 W 30 – *pop. 883.*
London 53 – Folkestone 25 – Maidstone 18.

Elvey Farm Country H. ⚲ without rest., TN27 0SU, West : 2 m. by Smarden rd a Marley Farm rd, off Mundy Bois rd ☎ (01233) 840442, *Fax (01233) 840726,* ≤, « Convert oast house and barn », – TV P. MC VISA JCB
– **9 rm** 55.50/65.50 **t.**

Dering Arms, Station Rd, TN27 0RR, South : 1½ m. on Bethersden rd ☎ (01233) 8403 *Fax (01233) 840498,* « Mid 19C former hunting lodge », – P. MC AE VISA
closed 26 to 29 December, Sunday dinner and Monday – **Meals** a la carte 17.10/25.5 5.45.

PLUMTREE *Notts.* – *see Nottingham.*

PLUSH *Dorset.*
London 142 – Bournemouth 35 – Salisbury 44 – Taunton 52 – Weymouth 15 – Yeovil 23.

Brace of Pheasants, DT2 7RQ, ☎ (01300) 348357, *geoffreyknights@braceofpheasa freeserve.co.uk,* , « 16C thatched inn », – rest, P. MC VISA JCB
closed 25 December – **Meals** a la carte 12.80/22.65 **t.** 6.00.

PLYMOUTH *Plymouth* 403 H 32 *The West Country G. – pop. 245 295.*

See : *Town*★ – *Smeaton's Tower* (≤★★) AC BZ A – *Plymouth Dome*★ AC BZ – *Royal Citadel (ramparts* ≤★★) AC BZ – *City Museum and Art Gallery*★ BZ M.

Env. : *Saltram House*★★ AC, E : 3½ m. BY A – *Tamar River*★★ – *Anthony House*★ AC, W : 5 m. by A 374 – *Mount Edgcumbe* (≤★) AC, SW : 2 m. by passenger ferry from Stonehouse AZ.

Exc. : NE : *Dartmoor National Park*★★ – *Buckland Abbey*★★ AC, N : 7½ m. by A 386 ABY.

18 *Staddon Heights, Plymstock* ☎ (01752) 402475 – 9 *Elfordleigh Hotel G & C.C., Colebrook, Plympton* ☎ (01752) 336428.

Tamar Bridge (toll) AY.

✈ *Plymouth City (Roborough) Airport* : ☎ (01752) 204090, N : 3½ m. by A 386 ABY.

⛴ *to France (Roscoff) (Brittany Ferries) 1-3 daily (6 h) – to Spain (Santander) (Brittany Ferries) 2 weekly (approx. 24 h) – to Spain (Bilbao) (P & O Portsmouth) 2 weekly (approx. 30 h) – to France (St. Malo) (Brittany Ferries) (winter only) (8 h).*

ℹ *Island House, 9 The Barbican* ☎ (01752) 304849 – *Plymouth Discovery Centre, Crabtree* ☎ (01752) 266030.

London 242 – Bristol 124 – Southampton 161.

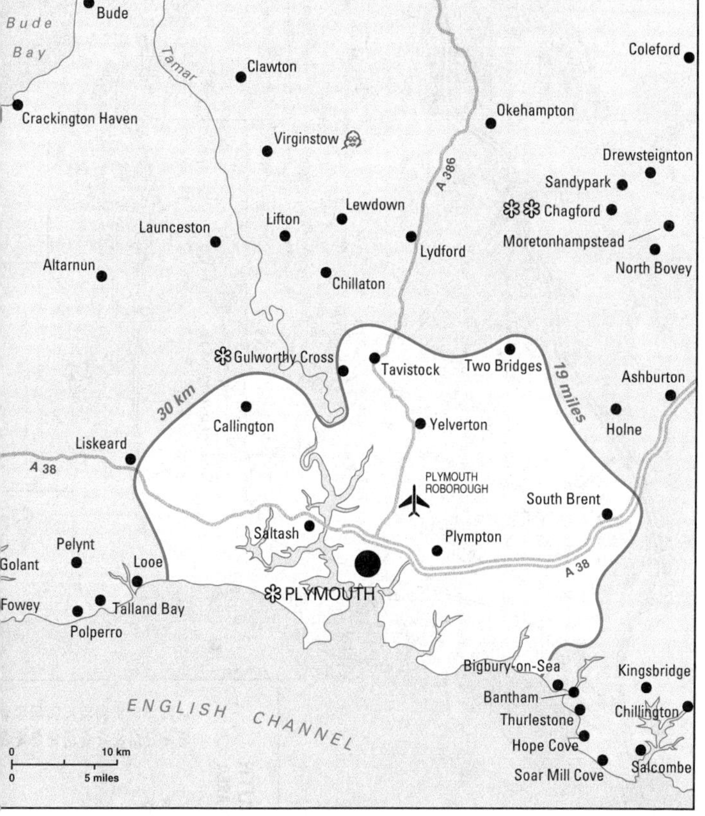

Plymouth Hoe Moat House, Armada Way, PL1 2HJ, ☎ (01752) 639988, *smplm@queensmoat.co.uk, Fax (01752) 673816,* ≤ city and Plymouth Sound, ⛾, ≘s, 🏊 – |♦| ⇆, ▤ rest, TV ♿ 🚗 – 🎪 400. MC AE ⓓ VISA. ✂ BZ s
Blue Riband : Meals 12.95/18.00 st. and dinner a la carte 🍷 6.90 – ☕ 11.50 – 210 rm 140.00/155.00 st.

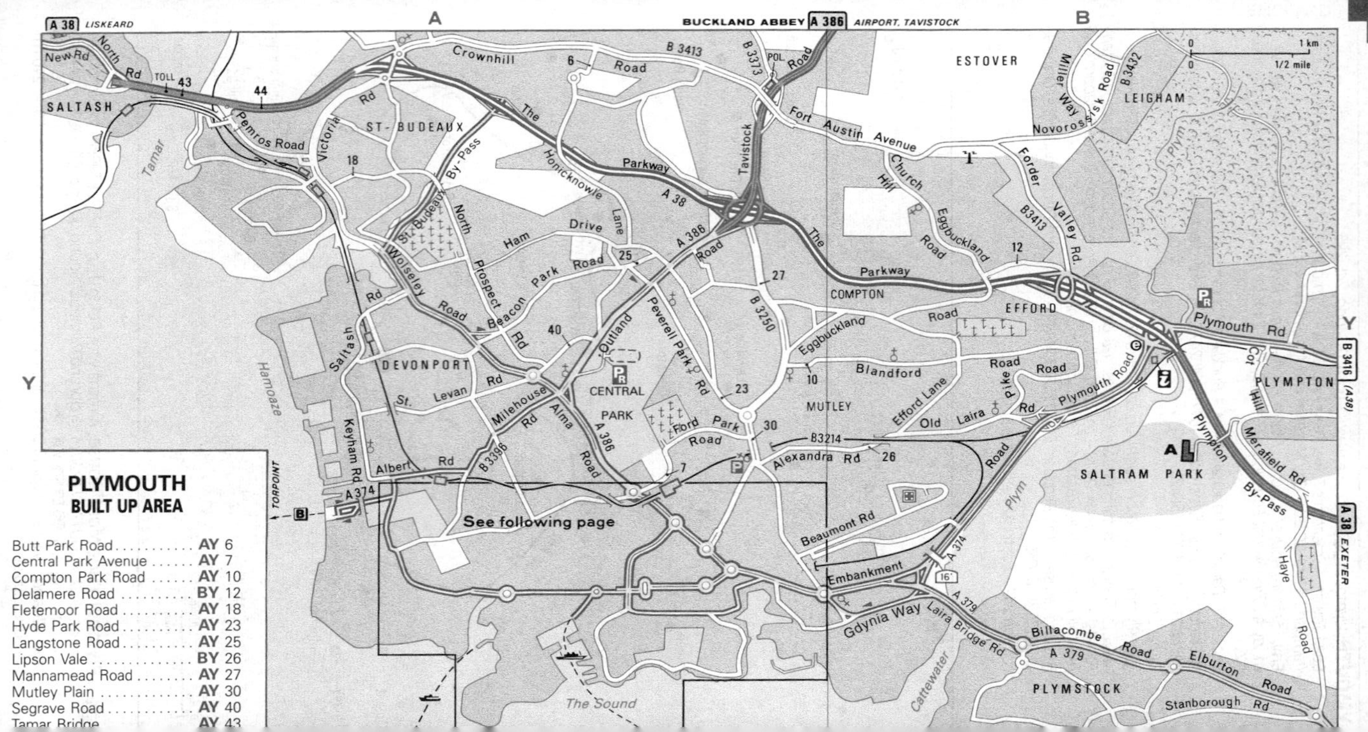

PLYMOUTH
BUILT UP AREA

Butt Park Road	AY 6
Central Park Avenue	AY 7
Compton Park Road	AY 10
Delamere Road	BY 12
Fletemoor Road	AY 18
Hyde Park Road	AY 23
Langstone Road	AY 25
Lipson Vale	BY 26
Mannamead Road	AY 27
Mutley Plain	AY 30
Segrave Road	AY 40
Tamar Bridge	AY 43

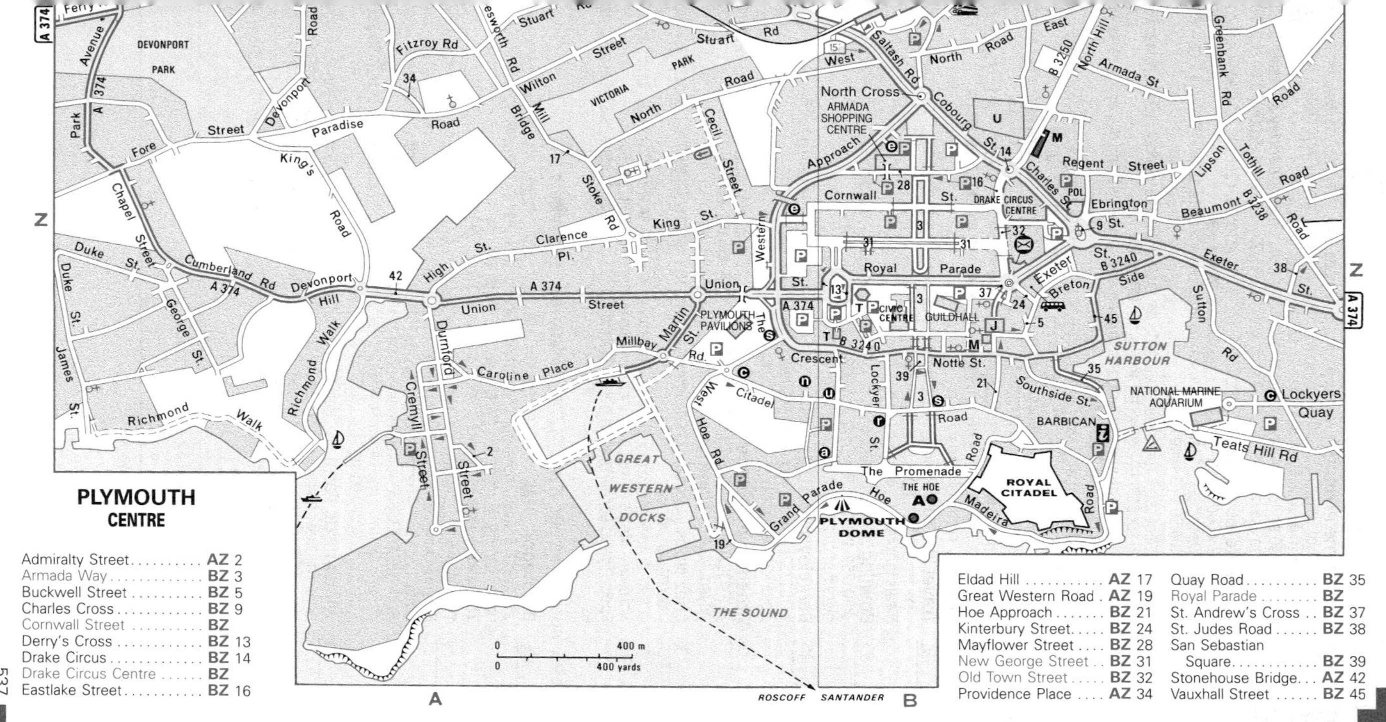

Admiralty Street	AZ	2
Armada Way	BZ	3
Buckwell Street	BZ	5
Charles Cross	BZ	9
Cornwall Street	BZ	
Derry's Cross	BZ	13
Drake Circus	BZ	14
Drake Circus Centre	BZ	
Eastlake Street	BZ	16
Eldad Hill	AZ	17
Great Western Road	AZ	19
Hoe Approach	BZ	21
Kinterbury Street	BZ	24
Mayflower Street	BZ	28
New George Street	BZ	31
Old Town Street	BZ	32
Providence Place	AZ	34
Quay Road	BZ	35
Royal Parade	BZ	
St. Andrew's Cross	BZ	37
St. Judes Road	BZ	38
San Sebastian Square	BZ	39
Stonehouse Bridge	AZ	42
Vauxhall Street	BZ	45

ENGLAND

Copthorne Plymouth, Armada Centre, Armada Way, PL1 1AR, (via Western Appro southbound) ☎ (01752) 224161, *sales.plymouth@mill-cop.com, Fax (01752) 670688,* – rm, rest, 150. *VISA* JCB. BZ
Meals 18.50 **st.** (dinner) and a la carte 18.50/28.00 **st.** 6.00 – ***Bentley's :*** **Meals** 18.50 (dinner) and a la carte 18.50/28.00 **st.** 6.00 – 11.50 – **135 rm** 115.00/170.00 **st.** – SB

The Duke of Cornwall, Millbay Rd, PL1 3LG, ☎ (01752) 266256, *duke@bhere.co Fax (01752) 600062* – 300. *VISA*. AZ
closed 26 December – **Meals** (bar lunch)/dinner and a la carte 15.00/23.00 **t.** 7.00 – **69** 84.50/104.50 **t.**, 3 suites – SB.

Grand, Elliot St., The Hoe, PL1 2PT, ☎ (01752) 661195, *info@plymouthgrand.c Fax (01752) 600653,* ≤ – 70. *VISA*. BZ
Meals (bar lunch Saturday) (dancing Saturday evening) 19.95 **st.** and dinner a la carte 6 – **77 rm** 82.00/160.00 **st.** – SB.

New Continental, Millbay Rd, PL1 3LD, ☎ (01752) 220782, *newconti@aol.c Fax (01752) 227013,* – rm, – 400. *VISA* AZ
closed 24 December-4 January – **Meals** (bar lunch Monday to Thursday and Saturd dinner 14.50/16.25 **t.** and a la carte 6.75 – **99 rm** 83.00/160.00 **t.** – SB.

Travel Inn Metro, 1 Lockyers Quay, Coxside, PL4 0DX, ☎ (01752) 254 *Fax (01752) 663872,* – rm, rest, – 30. *VISA*. BZ
Meals (grill rest.) – **40 rm** 46.95 **t.**

Travel Inn, 300 Plymouth Rd, Crabtree, PL3 6RW, ☎ (01752) 600660, *Fax (01752) 600* – rm, rest, – 30. *VISA*. BY
Meals (grill rest.) – **40 rm** 40.95 **t.**

Bowling Green without rest., 9-10 Osborne Pl., Lockyer St., The Hoe, PL1 2 ☎ (01752) 209090, *Fax (01752) 209092* – . *VISA* BZ
closed 24 to 28 December – **12 rm** 38.00/52.00 **st.**

Berkeley's of St. James without rest., 4 St. James Place East, The Hoe, PL1 3 ☎ (01752) 221654, *Fax (01752) 221654* – . *VISA* JCB. AZ
closed 22 December-1 January – **5 rm** 28.00/55.00.

Athenaeum Lodge without rest., 4 Athenaeum St., The Hoe, PL1 2 ☎ (01752) 665005, *Fax (01752) 665005* – . *VISA* JCB. BZ
closed 24 December-2 January – **9 rm** 25.00/42.00 **s.**

Chez Nous (Marchal), 13 Frankfort Gate, PL1 1QA, ☎ (01752) 266793, *Fax (01752) 266* – *VISA*. AZ
closed 3 weeks February, 3 weeks September, Sunday, Monday, Saturday lunch and B Holidays – **Meals** - French - (lunch booking essential) 33.50 **t.** 9.50
Spec. Pigeon et foie gras en gelée. Sauté de ris d'agneau au Madère. Sables aux framb es.

at Plympton *Northeast : 5 m. by A 374 on B 3416* – **BY** – ✉ *Plymouth.*

Boringdon Hall , Boringdon Hill, PL7 4DP, North : 1 ½ m. by Glen ☎ (01752) 344455, *hotel@boringdon.fsbusiness.co.uk, Fax (01752) 346578,* « Part 16C nor », – – 150. *VISA*.
The Gallery : **Meals** (dinner only) 23.00 **st.** – **40 rm** 70.00/140.00 **t.**

The Barn , Hemerdon, PL7 5BU, Northeast : 2 ½ m. by Glen Rd following signs Newnham industrial estate then Hemerdon, turning left beside telephone box after Mi Arms in Hemerdon ☎ (01752) 347016, *frances@tagert.freeserve.cc Fax (01752) 335670,* « Converted 19C barn », – .
closed Christmas and New Year – **Meals** (by arrangement) (communal dining) 21.50 5. **3 rm** 35.00/70.00 **st.**

Windwhistle Farm , Hemerdon, PL7 5BU, Northeast : 2 ½ m. by Glen Rd follov signs for Newnham industrial estate then Hemerdon, turning left beside telephone after Miners Arms in Hemerdon ☎ (01752) 340600, *admin@windwhistlefarm.fq.cc Fax (01752) 340600,* – .
closed 25 December – **Meals** (by arrangement) (communal dining) 15.00 **st.** – 4 30.00/50.00 **st.**

PLYMPTON *Plymouth* 403 H 32 – *see Plymouth.*

PODIMORE *Somerset* – *see Yeovil.*

When looking for a quiet hotel
use the maps found in the introduction
or look for establishments with the sign or .

POLPERRO *Cornwall* 403 G 33 *The West Country G.* – ✉ *Looe.*
See : *Village*★.
London 271 – Plymouth 28.

Trenderway Farm without rest., Pelynt, PL13 2LY, Northeast : 2 m. by A 387 ☎ (01503) 272214, *trenderwayfarm@hotmail.com, Fax (01503) 272991*, ≤, « 16C farmhouse, working farm », ⚘, – ⚘ TV P. MC VISA. ⚘
closed Christmas and New Year – **4 rm** ☐ 40.00/70.00 **s.**

The Kitchen, The Coombes, PL13 2RQ, ☎ (01503) 272780 – ⚘. MC VISA
April-September – **Meals** (dinner only) a la carte 18.00/24.00 **t.** 6.50.

PONTEFRACT *N. Yorks.* 402 Q 22.
London 194 – Leeds 16 – Manchester 53 – Nottingham 64 – Sheffield 29 – York 25.

Travel Inn, Knottingley Rd, Knottingley, WF11 0BU, Northeast : 2 ½ m. on A 645 ☎ (01977) 607946, *Fax (01977) 607954* – ⚘ rm, ▤ rest, TV ♿ P. MC AE VISA
Meals (grill rest.) – **40 rm** 40.95 **t.**

PONTELAND *Tyne and Wear* 401 402 O 19 – *see Newcastle upon Tyne.*

POOLE *Poole* 403 404 O 31 *The West Country G.* – *pop. 133 050.*
See : *Town*★ *(Waterfront* **M1** *, Scaplen's Court* **M2** *).*
Env. : *Compton Acres*★★, *(English Garden* ≤★★★*) AC, SE : 3 m. by B 3369* **BX** *(on Bournemouth town plan) – Brownsea Island*★ *(Baden-Powell Stone* ≤★★*) AC, by boat from Poole Quay or Sandbanks* **BX** *(on Bournemouth town plan).*
18 *Parkstone, Links Rd* ☎ *(01202) 707138* – 18 *The Bulbury Club, Bulberry Lane, Lytchett Matravers* ☎ *(01929) 459574.*
to France (Cherbourg) (Brittany Ferries) 1-2 daily (4 h 15 mn) day (5 h 45 mn) night – to France (St. Malo) (Brittany Ferries) (winter only) 4 weekly (8 h) – to France (St. Malo) (Condor Ferries Ltd).
Waterfront Museum, High St. ☎ *(01202) 253253.*
London 116 – Bournemouth 4 – Dorchester 23 – Weymouth 28.

Plan of Built up Area : see Bournemouth

Haven, Banks Rd, Sandbanks, BH13 7QL, Southeast : 4 ¼ m. on B 3369 ☎ (01202) 707333, *Fax (01202) 708796*, ≤ Ferry, Old Harry Rocks and Poole Bay, ⚘, ⚘, ⚘, heated, ⚘, ⚘ – ⚘, ⚘ rest, ▤ rest, TV ☎ P – 160. MC AE VISA. ⚘
Seaview : **Meals** 15.00/24.50 **t.** and dinner a la carte 6.25 – ***La Roche :*** **Meals** *(closed Sunday)* (dinner only) a la carte 32.20/35.00 **t.** 6.25 – ***Brasserie :*** **Meals** *(closed in winter)* (dinner only) a la carte 18.00/25.00 **t.** 6.25 – **92 rm** ☐ (dinner included) ☐ 82.00/300.00 **t.**, 2 suites – SB. on Bournemouth town plan **BX c**

Salterns, 38 Salterns Way, Lilliput, BH14 8JR, ☎ (01202) 707321, *Fax (01202) 707488*, ≤, ⚘, « Harbourside setting », ⚘ – ⚘ rm, ▤ rest, TV P – 80. MC AE VISA. ⚘ on Bournemouth town plan **BX e**
Waterside : **Meals** 20.00/25.00 **t.** and a la carte 8.50 – ***Shellies Bistro :*** **Meals** a la carte 20.00/24.00 **t.** 7.50 – ☐ 12.50 – **20 rm** 86.00/140.00 **t.** – SB.

Mansion House, 7-11 Thames St., BH15 1JN, off Poole Quay ☎ (01202) 685666, *enquiries@themansionhouse.co.uk, Fax (01202) 665709*, « 18C town house » – ▤ rest, TV P – 40. MC AE VISA JCB. ⚘ **a**
Benjamin's : **Meals** *(closed Sunday dinner lunch Saturday and Bank Holiday Mondays)* 14.95/24.00 **t.** and a la carte 8.50 – ***JJ's Bistro :*** **Meals** *(closed Sunday lunch and Monday)* (residents only) 14.45/19.45 **t.** (dinner) and lunch a la carte 13.45/20.75 **t.** 7.00 – **32 rm** ☐ 90.00/130.00 **st.** – SB.

Thistle Poole, The Quay, BH15 1HD, ☎ (01202) 666800, *poole@thistle.co.uk, Fax (01202) 684470*, ≤ – ⚘, ⚘ rm, TV P – 60. MC AE VISA JCB **e**
Meals *(closed lunch in July and August)* a la carte 16.65/27.05 **st.** 7.50 – ☐ 11.75 – **70 rm** 120.00/140.00 **st.** – SB.

Arndale Court, 62-66 Wimborne Rd, BH15 2BY, ☎ (01202) 683746, *Fax (01202) 668838* – TV P – 30. MC AE VISA. ⚘ on Bournemouth town plan **ABX r**
Meals (in bar Monday to Saturday lunch and Sunday dinner)/dinner and a la carte 17.25/20.70 **st.** 5.95 – **32 rm** ☐ 61.00/70.00 **st.**

Travel Inn, Holesbay Rd, BH15 2BD, ☎ (01202) 669944, *Fax (01202) 669954* – ⚘ rm, TV ♿ P. MC AE VISA. ⚘ **r**
Meals (grill rest.) – **40 rm** 40.95 **t.**

POOLE

Church Street 3
Dolphin
  Shopping Centre
Emerson Road 4
Falkland Sq. 6
Fishermans Rd 7
Furnell Rd. 8
High Street
Holes Bay Rd. 10
Labrador Drive 12
Longfleet Rd 13
Market St. . . . .
New Orchard . . . .
New Street. . . . .
Serpentine Rd . . . .
Thames St. . . . .
Towngate Bridge . . . .
Westons Lane . . . .

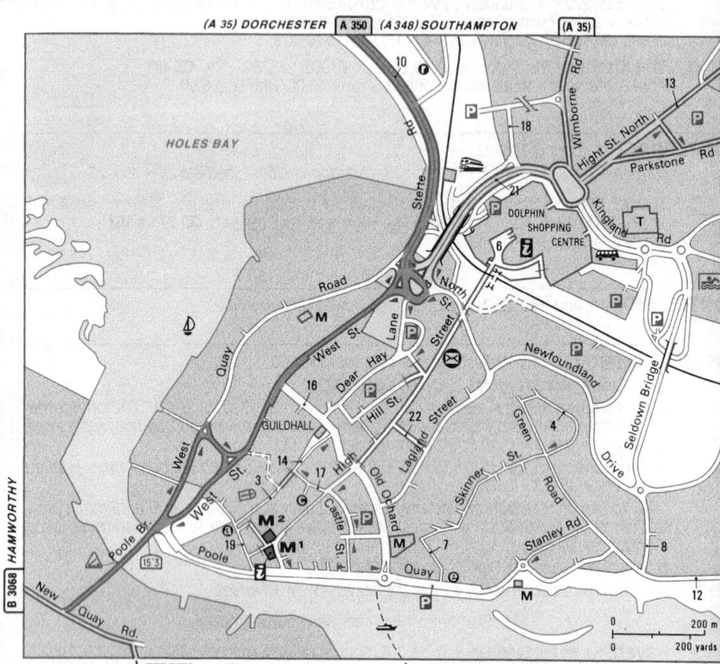

XX **John B's,** 20 High St., Old Town, BH15 1BP, ☏ (01202) 672440, *mark@markroberts.co*
Fax (01202) 672440 – MO AE ① VISA
closed Sunday and Saturday lunch, except dinner Bank Holidays – **Meals** a la carte 22.
29.65 **t.** 7.60.

X **Isabel's,** 32 Station Rd, Lower Parkstone, BH14 8UD, ☏ (01202) 7478
Fax (01202) 747885 – MO AE ① VISA on Bournemouth town plan **BX**
closed 26-27 December, 1-2 January, Sunday and Monday – **Meals** (dinner only) a la ca
14.60/27.20 **t.**

POOLEY BRIDGE *Cumbria* 401 402 L 20 – *see Ullswater.*

PORLOCK *Somerset* 403 J 30 *The West Country G.* – *pop. 1 395 (inc. Oare)* – ✉ *Minehead.*

See : *Village★ – Porlock Hill (≤★★) – St. Dubricius Church★.*

Env. : *Dunkery Beacon★★★ (≤★★★), S : 5 ½ m. – Exmoor National Park★★ – Selwort (≤★★, Church★), E : 2 m. by A 39 and minor rd – Luccombe★ (Church★), E : 3 m. by A 3 Culbone★ (St. Beuno), W : 3½ m. by B 3225, 1½ m. on foot – Doone Valley★, W : 6 m. b 39, access from Oare on foot.*

London 190 – Bristol 67 – Exeter 46 – Taunton 28.

Oaks, TA24 8ES, ☏ (01643) 862265, *oakshotel@aol.com, Fax (01643) 863131,* ≤ Porl Bay, – TV P. MO AE VISA
April-October and Christmas – **Meals** (booking essential to non-residents) (dinner o 26.00 **st.** 4.50 – **9 rm** 57.50/95.00 **st.** – SB.

Bales Mead without rest., West Porlock, TA24 8NX, Northwest : 1 m. on B 3
☏ (01643) 862565, *Fax (01643) 862544,* ≤, – TV P.
closed December and January – **3 rm** 46.00/68.00 **st.**

ORT ERIN *Isle of Man* 402 F 21 – *see Man (Isle of).*

ORTINSCALE *Cumbria – see Keswick.*

ORT ISAAC *Cornwall* 403 F 32 *The West Country G.*

Env. : *St. Endellion (church★★), S : 2½ m. by B 3267 on B 3314 – St. Kew★ (church★), SE : 3 m. by B 3267, B 3314 and minor roads.*

Exc. : *Pencarrow★, SE : 12 m. by B 3267, B 3314 and A 389.*

London 266 – Newquay 24 – Tintagel 14 – Truro 32.

Port Gaverne, Port Gaverne, PL29 3SQ, South : ½ m. ✆ (01208) 880244, *pghotel@telinco.co.uk, Fax (01208) 880151,* « Retaining 17C features » – rest, TV P. MC AE VISA JCB
closed 6 January-16 February – **Meals** (bar lunch Monday-Saturday)/dinner a la carte 21.40/28.95 **t.** 4.90 – **16 rm** (dinner included) 60.00/120.00 **t.** – SB.

Castle Rock, 4 New Rd, PL29 3SB, ✆ (01208) 880300, *castlerock@talk21.com, Fax (01208) 880219,* ≤ Port Isaac Bay and Tintagel Head, – rest, TV P. MC VISA
closed 3 January-1 February – **Meals** (bar lunch)/dinner and a la carte 14.75/29.20 **t.** 5.00 – **17 rm** 30.00/84.00 **t.** – SB.

Slipway, Harbour Front, PL29 3RH, ✆ (01208) 880264, *slipwayhotel@portisaac.com, Fax (01208) 880264,* , « Part 16C inn » – MC AE VISA JCB
closed 6 weeks January-February – **Meals** *(restricted opening in winter)* (bar lunch)/dinner a la carte 15.25/24.75 **t.** 5.25.

ORTLOE *Cornwall* 403 F 33 – ✉ *Truro.*

London 296 – St. Austell 15 – Truro 15.

Lugger, TR2 5RD, ✆ (01872) 501322, *Fax (01872) 501691,* ≤, – rest, TV P. MC AE VISA JCB.
mid March-early October – **Meals** (bar lunch Monday to Saturday)/dinner 25.00 **t.** 8.00 – **18 rm** (dinner included) 79.00/158.00 **t.** – SB.

Tregain, The Post Office, TR2 5QU, ✆ (01872) 501252 – . MC VISA
closed November-March and Sunday dinner except Bank Holidays – **Meals** (light lunch) (dinner booking essential) a la carte 21.50/27.50 **t.** 6.50.

ORTREATH *Cornwall* 403 E 33 – *pop. 1 251.*

London 309 – Falmouth 20 – Penzance 23 – Truro 14.

Tabb's, Tregea Terr., TR16 4LD, ✆ (01209) 842488, *Fax (01209) 842488* – MC VISA JCB
closed 2 weeks January, 2 weeks November and Tuesday – **Meals** (dinner only and Sunday lunch)/dinner 15.00 and a la carte 9.50.

ORTSCATHO *Cornwall* 403 F 33 *The West Country G.* – ✉ *Truro.*

Env. : *St. Just-in-Roseland Church★★, W : 4 m. by A 3078 – St. Anthony-in-Roseland (≤★★) S : 3½ m.*

London 298 – Plymouth 55 – Truro 16.

Roseland House , Rosevine, TR2 5EW, North : 2 m. by A 3078 ✆ (01872) 580644, *anthony-hindley@btinternet.com, Fax (01872) 580801,* ≤ Gerrans Bay, – TV P. MC AE VISA.
closed Christmas and New Year and restricted opening November-January – **Meals** (booking essential) (bar lunch)/dinner 23.00/25.00 **t.** 9.00 – **10 rm** (dinner included) 105.00/150.00 **t.** – SB.

Rosevine, Rosevine, TR2 5EW, North : 2 m. by A 3078 ✆ (01872) 580206, *info@makepeacehotels.co.uk, Fax (01872) 580230,* , – rest, TV P. MC AE VISA
closed November-February except Christmas – **Meals** 12.00/40.00 **t.** and a la carte 12.00 – **17 rm** 130.00/200.00 **st.** – SB.

Bitte beachten Sie die Geschwindigkeitsbeschränkungen in Großbritannien
- 60 mph (= 96 km/h) außerhalb geschlossener Ortschaften
- 70 mph (= 112 km/h) auf Straßen mit getrennten Fahrbahnen und Autobahnen.

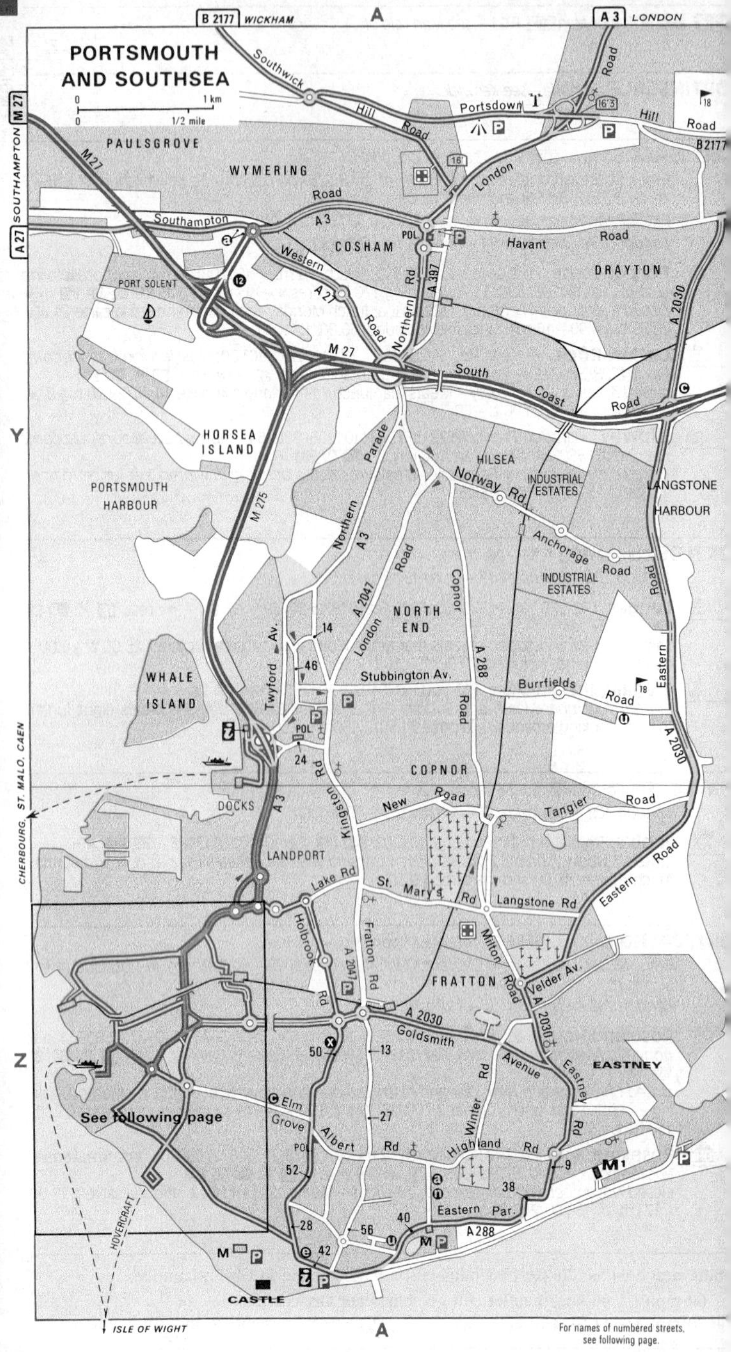
PORTSMOUTH
AND SOUTHSEA
0 1 km
0 1/2 mile
A
B 2177 WICKHAM
A 3 LONDON
M 27
SOUTHAMPTON
A 27
Y
Z
Southwick Hill Road
Portsdown Hill Road
B 2177
PAULSGROVE
WYMERING
Southampton Road
A 3
Western Road
A 27
COSHAM
POL
London Road
Havant Road
DRAYTON
A 397
Northern Rd
PORT SOLENT
M 27
South Coast Road
A 2030
HORSEA ISLAND
PORTSMOUTH HARBOUR
M 275
HILSEA
Norway Rd
INDUSTRIAL ESTATES
LANGSTONE HARBOUR
Anchorage Road
Northern Parade
A 3
A 2047
London Road
NORTH END
Copnor Road
A 288
Eastern Road
WHALE ISLAND
Twyford Av.
Stubbington Av.
Burrfields Road
A 2030
CHERBOURG, ST. MALO, CAEN
POL
Kingston Rd
COPNOR
DOCKS
New Road
Tangier Road
Eastern Road
LANDPORT
Lake Rd
St. Mary's Rd
Langstone Rd
Holbrook Rd
Fratton Rd
A 2047
Milton Road
FRATTON
Velder Av.
A 2030
Goldsmith Avenue
Winter Rd
EASTNEY
Eastney Rd
Elm Grove
See following page
Albert Rd
Highland Rd
POL
Eastern Par.
A 288
HOVERCRAFT
CASTLE
ISLE OF WIGHT
14
46
24
50
13
27
52
28
56
40
42
38
9
M1
M
For names of numbered streets, see following page.

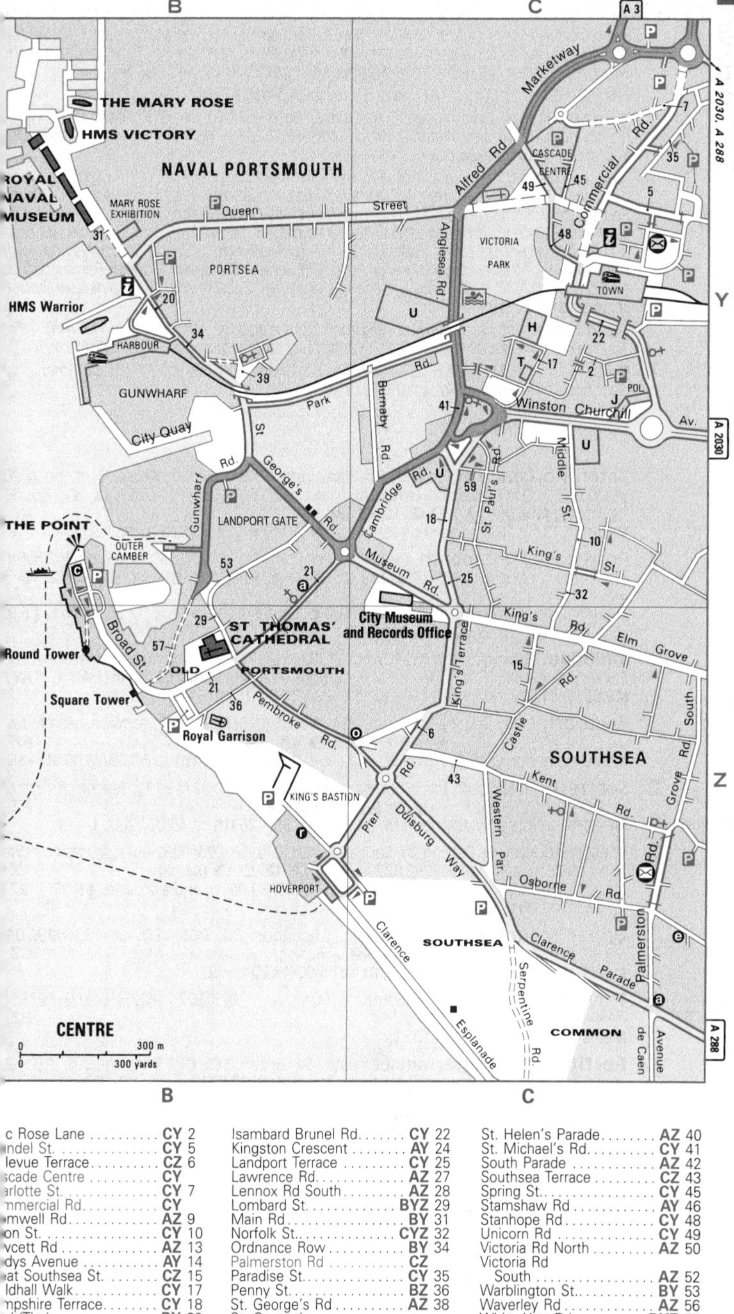

c Rose Lane .... **CY** 2	Isambard Brunel Rd....... **CY** 22	St. Helen's Parade........ **AZ** 40
ındel St. .... **CY** 5	Kingston Crescent .... **AY** 24	St. Michael's Rd.......... **CY** 41
llevue Terrace.......... **CZ** 6	Landport Terrace .... **CY** 25	South Parade .... **AZ** 42
scade Centre .... **CY**	Lawrence Rd.............. **AZ** 27	Southsea Terrace .... **CZ** 43
arlotte St. .... **CY** 7	Lennox Rd South.......... **AZ** 28	Spring St................. **CY** 45
mmercial Rd............ **CY**	Lombard St.............. **BYZ** 29	Stamshaw Rd .... **AY** 46
omwell Rd............. **AZ** 9	Main Rd.................. **BY** 31	Stanhope Rd.............. **CY** 48
on St. .... **CY** 10	Norfolk St.............. **CYZ** 32	Unicorn Rd .... **CY** 49
vcett Rd .... **AZ** 13	Ordnance Row .... **BY** 34	Victoria Rd North .... **AZ** 50
dys Avenue .... **AY** 14	Palmerston Rd .... **CZ**	Victoria Rd South .... **AZ** 52
eat Southsea St. .... **CZ** 15	Paradise St.............. **CY** 35	Warblington St........... **BY** 53
ldhall Walk............ **CY** 17	Penny St................. **BZ** 36	Waverley Rd .... **AZ** 56
mpshire Terrace........ **CY** 18	St. George's Rd .... **AZ** 38	White Hart Rd .... **BYZ** 57
d (The) .... **BY** 20	St. George's Square .... **BY** 39	Wiltshire St. .... **CY** 59
h St.................. **BYZ** 21		

PORTSMOUTH and SOUTHSEA *Portsmouth* **403** **404** Q 31 *Great Britain G. – pop. 174 690*

See : *City★ – Naval Portsmouth* **BY** : *H.M.S. Victory★★★ AC, The Mary Rose★★, Royal Na Museum★★ AC – Old Portsmouth★* **BYZ** : *The Point (≤★★) - St. Thomas Cathedral★ Southsea (Castle★ AC)* **AZ** *– Royal Marines Museum, Eastney★ AC,* **AZ M1.**

Env. : *Portchester Castle★ AC, NW : 5½ m. by A 3 and A 27* **AY**.

18 Great Salterns, Portsmouth Golf Centre, Burrfields Rd ✆ (023) 9266 4549 **AY** *– Crookhorn Lane, Widley, Waterlooville ✆ (023) 9237 2210 – 18 Southwick Park, Pinsley Dri Southwick ✆ (023) 9238 0131.*

to France (Cherbourg) (P & O Portsmouth) 3-4 daily (5 h) day, (7 h) night – to Fran (Le Havre) (P & O Portsmouth) 3 daily (5 h 30 mn/7 h 30 mn) – to France (St. Malo) (Britta Ferries) daily (8 h 45 mn) day (10 h 45 mn) night – to France (Caen) (Brittany Ferries) 2-3 da (6 h) – to France (Cherbourg) (P & O Portsmouth) 2-3 daily (2 h 45 mn) – to Spain (Bilbao) & O European Ferries Ltd) 1-2 weekly (35 h) – to Spain (Santander) (Brittany Ferries) (win only) (30 h) – to Guernsey (St. Peter Port) and Jersey (St. Helier) (Condor Ferries Ltd) da except Sunday (10 h 30 mn) – to the Isle of Wight (Fishbourne) (Wightlink Ltd) freque services daily (35 mn).

to the Isle of Wight (Ryde) (Wightlink Ltd) frequent services daily (15 mn) – fro Southsea to the Isle of Wight (Ryde) (Hovertravel Ltd) frequent services daily (10 mn).

The Hard ✆ (023) 9282 6722 – Clarence Esplanade ✆ (023) 9283 2464 (summer only Central Library, Guildhall Sq. ✆ (023) 9283 8382.

London 78 – Brighton 48 – Salisbury 44 – Southampton 21.

Plan on preceding page

Hilton Portsmouth, Eastern Rd, Farlington, PO6 1UN, Northeast : 5 m. on A 2C ✆ (023) 9221 9111, *sales-portsmouth@hilton.com, Fax (023) 9221 0762,* – rm, – 230. MC AE DC VISA. AY
Meals 14.75/18.50 **t.** and a la carte – 12.45 – **119 rm** 99.00/129.00 **st.** – SB.

Posthouse Portsmouth, Pembroke Rd, PO1 2TA, ✆ (0870) 4009065, *gm1429@for hotels.com, Fax (023) 9275 6715,* – – 250. MC AE DC JCB CZ
Meals *(closed Saturday lunch)* 15.00/18.00 **t.** (dinner) and a la carte 17.85/31.00 **t.** 6.9 11.95 – **167 rm** 89.00/119.00 **st.** – SB.

Innlodge, Burrfields Rd, PO3 5HH, ✆ (023) 9265 0510, *innlodge@bestwestern.co. Fax (023) 9269 3458,* – rm, rest, – 150. MC AE DC VISA. AY
Meals (grill rest.) a la carte 11.95/20.15 **t.** – 8.50 – **74 rm** 54.00/64.00 **t.**

Beaufort, 71 Festing Rd, Southsea, PO4 0NQ, ✆ (023) 9282 3707, *enq@beauforthotel. uk, Fax (023) 9287 0270* – . MC AE DC VISA JCB. AZ
Meals (dinner only) 16.95/18.95 **st.** and a la carte 4.95 – **20 rm** 50.00/78.00 **st.** – SB.

Seacrest, 11-12 South Par., Southsea, PO5 2JB, ✆ (023) 9273 3192, *seacrest@mcmail m, Fax (023) 9283 2523,* ≤ – . MC AE VISA JCB AZ
Meals (residents only) (dinner only) 14.95 **t.** 3.95 – **26 rm** 45.00/75.00 **t.** – SB.

Westfield Hall, 65 Festing Rd, Southsea, PO4 0NQ, ✆ (023) 9282 6971, *jdanie@westfie hall-hotel.co.uk, Fax (023) 9287 0200* – . MC AE DC VISA. AZ
closed Christmas – **Meals** (dinner only) 18.95/20.95 **t.** and a la carte 5.95 – **27** 48.00/75.00 **t.**

Upper Mount House, The Vale, Clarendon Rd, PO5 2EQ, ✆ (023) 9282 04 *Fax (023) 9282 0456* – . MC VISA JCB. CZ
Meals (dinner only) 12.50 **st.** – **12 rm** 35.00/48.00 **t.** – SB.

Travel Inn, Long Curtain Rd, Southsea, PO4 3AA, ✆ (023) 9273 4622, *Fax (023) 9273 5* – rm, . MC AE DC VISA. BZ
Meals (grill rest.) – **40 rm** 40.95 **t.**

Fortitude Cottage without rest., 51 Broad St., Old Portsmouth, PO1 2 ✆ (023) 9282 3748, *fortcott@aol.com, Fax (023) 9282 3748* – . MC AE VISA J BY
closed 24 to 26 December – **3 rm** 35.00/50.00 **st.**

Glencoe without rest., 64 Whitwell Rd, Southsea, PO4 0QS, ✆ (023) 9273 74 *Fax (023) 9273 7413* – . MC VISA. AZ
7 rm 20.00/40.00 **st.**

Hamilton House without rest., 95 Victoria Road North, PO5 1PS, ✆ (023) 9282 3502, *dra@hamiltonhouse.co.uk, Fax (023) 9282 3502* – . MC VISA. AZ
9 rm 25.00/48.00 **s.**

Tang's, 127 Elm Grove, Southsea, PO5 1LJ, ✆ (023) 9282 2722, *Fax (023) 9283 8323* – MC AE DC VISA AZ
closed 25-26 December – **Meals** - Chinese - (dinner only) 15.00/25.00 **t.** and a la ca 4.50.

Bistro Montparnasse, 103 Palmerston Rd, Southsea, PO5 3PS, (023) 9281 6754 – MC VISA JCB CZ a
closed 2 weeks early March, 2 weeks early October, 25-26 December, Sunday and Monday – **Meals** 15.00/23.50 **t.** 6.50.

Lemon Sole, 123 High St., Old Portsmouth, PO1 2HW, (023) 9281 1303, *bestfishes@lemonsole.co.uk, Fax (023) 9281 1345* – MC AE VISA JCB BY a
closed Sunday – **Meals** - Seafood - a la carte 13.65/19.85 **t.** 5.95.

Cosham *North : 4½ m. by A 3 and M 275 on A 27 – Portsmouth.*

Portsmouth Marriott, North Harbour, PO6 4SH, (023) 9238 3151, *Fax (023) 9238 8701,* rm, – 300. MC AE VISA
Meals 14.00/21.50 **t.** (dinner) and a la carte 17.65/29.85 **t.** 7.75 – 12.50 – **172 rm** 89.00 **st.** – SB. AY a

Travel Inn, 1 Southampton Rd, North Harbour, PO6 4SA, (023) 9232 1122, *Fax (023) 9232 4895* – rm, MC AE VISA. AY a
Meals (grill rest.) – **64 rm** 40.95 **t.**

POTT SHRIGLEY *Ches. – see Macclesfield.*

POYNTON *Ches.* 402 403 N 23 – *pop. 14 768.*

London 193 – Chester 44 – Manchester 12 – Stoke-on-Trent 28.

The Spinney without rest., 59-61 Chester Rd, SK12 1HB, West : ¼ m. on A 5149 (01625) 871397, *Fax (01625) 872143,* – MC AE VISA JCB
closed 2 weeks Christmas-New Year – **13 rm** 54.00/69.00 **st.**

PRESTBURY *Ches.* 402 403 404 N 24 – *pop. 3 346.*

Mottram Hall Hotel, Wilmslow Rd, Mottram St. Andrews (01625) 828135.

London 184 – Liverpool 43 – Manchester 17 – Stoke-on-Trent 25.

De Vere Mottram Hall, Wilmslow Rd, Mottram St. Andrew, SK10 4QT, Northwest : 2 ¼ m. on A 538 (01625) 828135, *dmh.sales@devere-hotels.com, Fax (01625) 829284,* « Part 18C mansion », squash – – 275. MC AE VISA.
Meals (dancing Friday and Saturday evenings) (bar lunch Saturday) 26.00 **st.** – **129 rm** 145.00/170.00 **st.**, 3 suites – SB.

White House Manor, The Village, SK10 4HP, (01625) 829376, *stay@cheshire-white-house.com, Fax (01625) 828627,* – MC AE VISA.
closed 25-26 December – **Meals** – (room service or see ***White House*** below) – 8.50 – **11 rm** 70.00/120.00 **t.**

The Bridge, The Village, SK10 4DQ, (01625) 829326, *Fax (01625) 827557,* – – 100. MC AE VISA JCB.
Meals *(closed Sunday dinner)* 9.25/14.75 **t.** and a la carte 7.00 – 8.50 – **23 rm** 45.00/145.00 **st.** – SB.

White House, The Village, SK10 4DG, (01625) 829376, *stay@cheshire-white-house.com, Fax (01625) 828627* – MC AE VISA
closed 25 December, Monday lunch and Sunday dinner – **Meals** 13.95/17.95 **t.** and a la carte 8.25.

PRESTON *Lancs.* 402 L 22 – *pop. 177 660.*

Fulwood Hall Lane, Fulwood (01772) 700011 – Ingol, Tanterton Hall Rd (01772) 734556 – Aston & Lea, Tudor Av., Blackpool Rd (01772) 726480 – Penwortham, Blundell Lane (01772) 744630.

The Guildhall, Lancaster Rd (01772) 253731.

London 226 – Blackpool 18 – Burnley 22 – Liverpool 30 – Manchester 34 – Stoke-on-Trent 65.

Posthouse Preston, The Ringway, PR1 3AU, (0870) 400 9066, *gm1430@forte-hotels.com, Fax (01772) 201923* – rm, – 120. MC AE VISA JCB
Meals 12.50 **t.** (dinner) and a la carte 22.00/28.00 **t.** 8.95 – 11.95 – **119 rm** 69.00/109.00 **st.** – SB.

Tulketh, 209 Tulketh Rd, PR2 1ES, Northwest : 2 ¼ m. by A 6 off A 5085 (01772) 726250, *Fax (01772) 723743* – MC AE VISA JCB.
closed Christmas and New Year – **Meals** *(closed Friday to Sunday)* (dinner only) a la carte 7.75/13.25 **st.** 2.60 – **12 rm** 37.50/49.50 **st.**

ENGLAND

Claremont, 516 Blackpool Rd, Ashton, PR2 1HY, Northwest : 2 m. by A 6 on A 5C
(01772) 729738, *claremonthotel@btinternet.com, Fax (01772) 726274*, – rest,
P. MC AE D VISA
Meals (lunch by arrangement)/dinner 11.95 **st.** and a la carte 5.50 – **14 rm** 38.5
65.00 **st.**

Travel Inn, Bluebell Way, Preston East Link Rd, PR2 5RU, Northeast : 3 ¼ by B 62
(Longridge rd) off B 6242 (Preston East) (01772) 651580, *Fax (01772) 651619* –
rest, TV P – 25. MC AE D VISA.
Meals (grill rest.) – **65 rm** 40.95 **t.**

Heathcotes Brasserie, 23 Winckley Sq., PR1 3JJ, (01772) 252732, *preston@simply
athcotes.co.uk, Fax (01772) 203433* – . MC AE D VISA JCB
closed 25-26 December, 1 January and Bank Holidays – **Meals** 12.50 **t.** and a la ca
20.00/22.25 **t.**

at Broughton *North : 3 m. on A 6 – Preston.*

Preston Marriott, 418 Garstang Rd, PR3 5JB, (01772) 864087, *Fax (01772) 8617*
, , , – TV P – 200. MC AE D VISA JCB.
Meals (dinner only) 23.50 **st.** and a la carte 8.00 – 12.50 – **149 rm** 81.00 **st.**, 1 suit
SB.

Ibis without rest., Garstang Rd, PR3 5JE, South : ¾ m. off A 6 (01772) 8618
Fax (01772) 861900 – TV P – 40. MC AE D VISA
82 rm 49.50 **st.**

Burlingtons, 502 Garstang Rd, PR3 5HE, (01772) 863424, *Fax (01772) 866424* – P.
AE VISA
Meals 5.95/10.00 **st.** and a la carte 3.95.

at Samlesbury *East : 2½ m. by A 59 – Preston.*

Tickled Trout, Preston New Rd, PR5 0UJ, West : 1 m. on A 59 (01772) 8776
Fax (01772) 877463, , , – TV P – 150. MC AE D VISA
Meals *(closed Saturday lunch)* 18.95 **t.** (dinner) and a la carte 19.40/26.40 **t.** 7.95 – **72**
79.00/95.00 **st.** – SB.

Swallow, Preston New Rd, PR5 0UL, East : 1 m. at junction of A 59 with A
(01772) 877351, *info@swallowhotels.com, Fax (01772) 877424*, , , –
rest, TV P – 250. MC AE D VISA JCB.
Meals *(closed Saturday lunch)* 12.95/19.00 **st.** and dinner a la carte 9.00 – **78**
79.00/125.00 **st.** – SB.

Campions, Cuerdale Lane, PR5 0UY, East : 1 m. by A 59 on B 6230 (01772) 8776
Fax (01772) 877197 – P. MC AE VISA JCB
Meals *(closed dinner 25 December)* 8.95 **t.** (lunch) and a la carte 15.65/23.50 **t.**

at Walton le Dale *Southeast : 2 m. by A 6, A 675, B 6230 (Bamber Bridge rd) on B 625*
Preston.

The Vineyard, Cinnamon Hill, PR5 4JN, (01772) 254646, *Fax (01772) 258967* – TV
100. MC AE D VISA.
Meals (grill rest.) 10.00 **st.** and a la carte 4.50 – 6.25 – **16 rm** 49.50 **st.** – SB.

at Bamber Bridge *South : 5 m. by A 6 on B 6258 – Preston.*

Novotel, Reedfield Place, Walton Summit, PR5 8AA, Southeast : ¾ m. by A 6 at junctior
of M 6 (01772) 313331, *h0838@accor-hotels.com, Fax (01772) 627868*, heated,
, rm, rest, TV P – 180. MC AE D VISA
Meals 11.00/13.95 **st.** and a la carte – 8.50 – **98 rm** 55.00 **st.** – SB.

Premier Lodge, Lobstock Lane, PR5 6BA, South : ½ m. on A 6 (0870) 70015
Fax (0870) 7001513 – rm, TV P. MC AE D VISA.
Meals (grill rest.) a la carte 10.00/20.40 **st.** – 6.00 – **40 rm** 42.00 **t.**

at Lea *West : 3½ m. on A 583 – Preston.*

Travel Inn, Blackpool Rd, PR4 0XL, on A 583 (01772) 720476, *Fax (01772) 7299*
rm, rest, TV P. MC AE D VISA.
Meals (grill rest.) – **38 rm** 40.95 **t.**

Remember the speed limits that apply in the United Kingdom, unless otherwise signposted.

- 60 mph on single carriageway roads
- 70 mph on dual carriageway roads and motorways

ESTWICH *Gtr. Manchester* 402 403 404 N 23 – *pop. 31 801* – ✉ *Manchester.*
London 205 – Leeds 40 – Liverpool 30 – Manchester 5.

Plan : see Manchester

Village H & Leisure Club, George St., M25 9WS, South : 1 ¾ m. by A 56 ☎ (0161) 798 8905, *Fax (0161) 773 5562*, squash – rest, – 150. AE VISA JCB. AV c
Meals (grill rest.) 8.50/15.00 **st.** and a la carte – **39 rm** 69.00/84.00 **st.**, 1 suite.

Travel Inn, Bury New Rd, M25 3AJ, Northwest : ½ m. on A 56 ☎ (0161) 798 0827, *Fax (0161) 773 8099* – rm, TV P. AE VISA.
Meals (grill rest.) – **60 rm** 40.95 **t.**

IDDY *Somerset* 403 L 30 – *see Wells.*

CKRUP *Glos. – see Tewkesbury.*

DDINGTON *Ches.* 402 403 K 24 – *see Chester.*

DSEY *W. Yorks.* 402 P 22 – *see Leeds.*

LBOROUGH *W. Sussex* 404 S 31 – *pop. 3 497.*
18, 9 West Chiltington, Broadford Bridge Rd ☎ (01798) 813574.
London 49 – Brighton 25 – Guildford 25 – Portsmouth 35.

Chequers, Old Rectory Lane, RH20 1AD, Northeast : ¼ m. on A 29 ☎ (01798) 872486, *chequers@btinternet.com, Fax (01798) 872715*, – TV P. AE VISA JCB
Meals (light lunch)/dinner 25.00 **t.** 7.50 – **11 rm** 49.50/95.00 **t.** – SB.

PULENTE *Jersey (Channel Islands)* 403 P 33 and 230 ⑪ – *see Channel Islands.*

LHAM MARKET *Norfolk* 404 X 26 – *pop. 919* – ✉ *Diss.*
London 106 – Cambridge 58 – Ipswich 29 – Norwich 16.

Old Bakery, Church Walk, IP21 4SJ, ☎ (01379) 676492, *Fax (01379) 676492*, « Part 16C timbered house », – TV.
closed Christmas and New Year – **Meals** (by arrangement) 16.00 **st.** – **3 rm** 48.00/54.00 **st.** – SB.

RFLEET *Essex* 404 ㊹.
Dartford Tunnel and Bridge (toll).
London 16 – Hastings 56 – Maidstone 26 – Southend-on-Sea 24.

Travel Inn, High St., RM16 1QA, ☎ (01708) 865432, *Fax (01708) 860852* – rm, TV P. AE VISA.
Meals (grill rest.) – **30 rm** 40.95 **t.**

RTON *Wilts.* 403 404 O 29 – *pop. 3 879* – ✉ *Swindon.*
London 94 – Bristol 41 – Gloucester 31 – Oxford 38 – Swindon 5.

Pear Tree at Purton, Church End, SN5 4ED, South : ½ m. by Church St. on Lydiard Millicent rd ☎ (01793) 772100, *res@peartreepurton.co.uk, Fax (01793) 772369*, « Conservatory restaurant », – TV P – 60. AE VISA JCB
closed 26 to 30 December – **Meals** *(closed Saturday lunch)* 12.50/29.50 **st.** 6.00 – **16 rm** 110.00/130.00 **st.**, 2 suites.

ORNDON *Leics.* 402 403 404 Q 25 – *see Loughborough.*

INHILL *Mersey.* 402 ㉝ 403 ⑬ – *see St. Helens.*

MSBOTTOM *Gtr. Manchester* 402 N 23 – *pop. 17 318.*
London 223 – Blackpool 39 – Burnley 12 – Leeds 46 – Manchester 13 – Liverpool 39.

Ramsons, 18 Market Pl., BL0 9HT, ☎ (01706) 825070, *rammy.vics@which.net, Fax (01706) 822005* – VISA
closed Sunday dinner, Monday and Tuesday – **Meals** 9.95 **t.** (lunch) and a la carte 14.45/26.40 **t.** 5.25.

RAMSEY *Isle of Man* 402 G 21 – *see Man (Isle of).*

RAMSGATE *Kent* 404 Y 30 – *pop. 37 895.*
19-21 Harbour St. (01843) 583333.
London 77 – Dover 19 – Maidstone 45 – Margate 4.5.

Jarvis Marina, Harbour Par., CT11 8LJ, (01843) 588276, *Fax (01843) 586866,* ←, – rest, – 120. VISA.
Meals (bar lunch Monday to Saturday)/dinner a la carte 16.15/23.70 **t.** 6.85 – 8.9
58 rm 85.00/120.00 **t.** – SB.

RAMSGILL-IN-NIDDERDALE *N. Yorks.* 402 O 21 – *see Pateley Bridge.*

RASKELF *N. Yorks.* 402 Q 21 – *see Easingwold.*

RAVENSTONEDALE *Cumbria* 402 M 20 – *pop. 886* – *Kirkby Stephen.*
London 280 – Carlisle 43 – Kendal 19 – Kirkby Stephen 5.

Black Swan, CA17 4NG, (015396) 23204, *reservations@blackswanhotel.c*
Fax (015396) 23604, – rest, VISA
Meals 8.00/25.00 **t.** and a la carte 6.00 – **16 rm** 48.00/80.00 **t.** – SB.

READING *Reading* 403 404 Q 29 – *pop. 213 474.*
Calcot Park, Bath Rd, Calcot (0118) 942 7124.
Whitchurch Bridge (toll).
to Henley-on-Thames (Salter Bros. Ltd) (summer only).
Town Hall, Blagrave St. (0118) 956 6226.
London 43 – Brighton 79 – Bristol 78 – Croydon 47 – Luton 62 – Oxford 28 – Portsmout
– Southampton 46.

Plan opposite

Holiday Inn Reading, Caversham Bridge, Richfield Av., RG1 8BD, (01189) 259988,
hi@queensmoat.co.uk, Fax (01189) 391665, ←, « Thames-side setting », –
rm, rest, – 250. VISA JCB.
Meals *(closed Saturday lunch)* 17.95 **st.** and dinner a la carte 7.25 – 11.50 – **110**
140.00 **st.**, 2 suites.

Renaissance Reading, Oxford Rd, RG1 7RH, (01189) 586222, *Fax (01189) 597*
– , rm, – 220. VISA JCB.
Meals (restricted menu Sunday dinner) 14.50/22.50 **st.** and dinner a la carte 6.95 –
10.95 – **195 rm** 128.00 **st.**, 1 suite.

Millennium Madejski, Madejski Stadium, RG2 0FL, (0118) 9253500, *sales.reading*
ll-cop.com, Fax (0118) 9253501, « Adjacent to Madejski sports stadium », –
rm, VISA JCB
***Cilantro* : Meals** (dinner only) 32.00 **st.** 8.75 – ***Le Café* : Meals** *(closed Saturday lu*
18.95 **st.** (dinner) and a la carte 20.20/28.45 **st.** 8.75 – 12.95 – **132 rm** 180.0
8 suites – SB.

Posthouse Reading, 500 Basingstoke Rd, RG2 0SL, South : 2 ½ m. on A
(0870) 400 9067, *Fax (01189) 311958,* – rm, rest, – 100
VISA JCB.
Meals *(closed lunch Saturday and Bank Holidays)* a la carte 18.85/27.15 **t.** 8.95 – 1
– **202 rm** 129.00 **st.** – SB.

Rainbow Corner, 132-138 Caversham Rd, RG1 8AY, (01189) 588140, *info@rainbo*
tel.co.uk, Fax (01189) 586500 – rest, rest, VISA
Meals *(closed dinner Friday and Sunday)* (dinner only) 11.95 **st.** and a la carte 4.00 –
5.95 – **24 rm** 70.00/90.00 **st.**

Travelodge without rest., 387 Basingstoke Rd, RG2 0JE, South : 2 m. on A
(01189) 750618, *Fax (01189) 751303* – VISA JCB.
36 rm 59.95 **t.**

Old Siam, King's Walk, King St., RG1 2HG, (01189) 512600, *renaissance@btinternet.c*
Fax (01189) 596300 – VISA JCB
closed 2 weeks Christmas, Sunday and Bank Holidays – **Meals** - Thai - 14.50/22.0
and a la carte.

at Kidmore End *North : 5 m. by A 4155 – X – off B 481 – Reading.*

New Inn, RG4 9AU, (01189) 724733, « 16C », – VISA
closed Sunday dinner and Monday – **Meals** (booking essential) a la carte 18.70/25.
6.75.

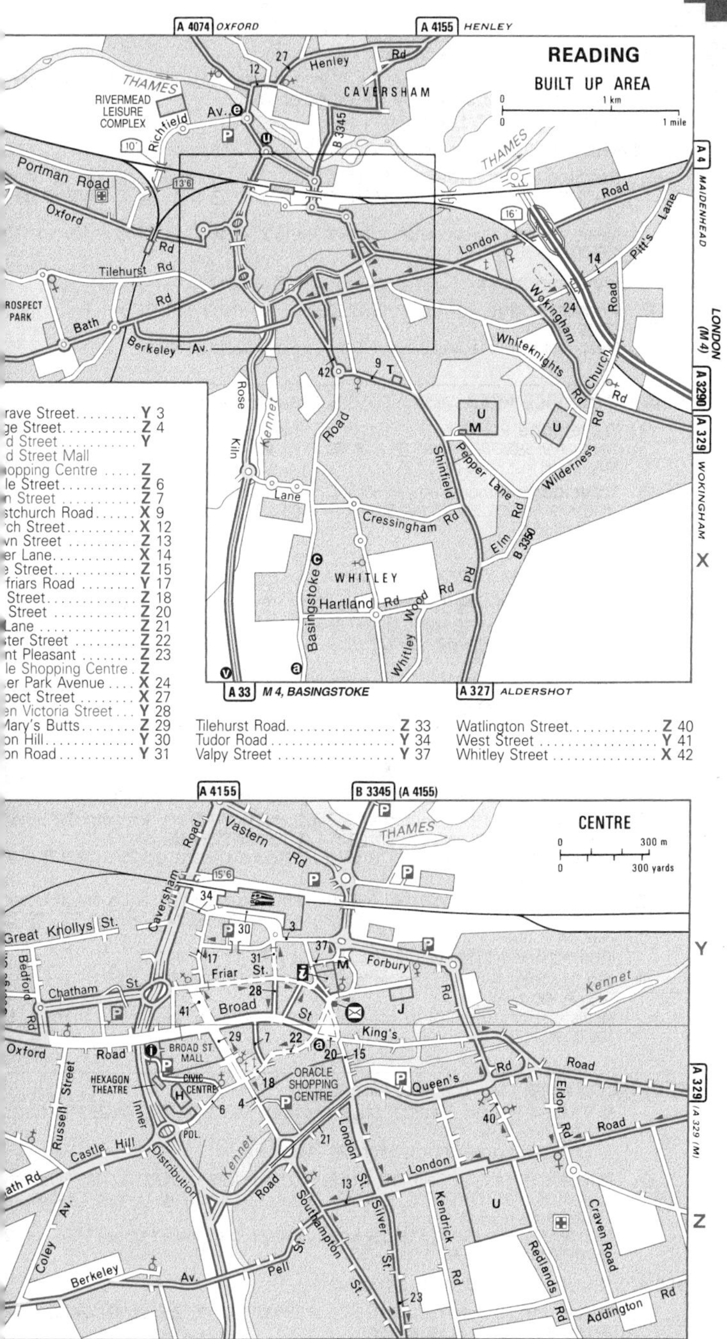

rave Street . . . . Y 3
ge Street . . . . Z 4
d Street . . . . Y
d Street Mall
opping Centre . . . . . Z
le Street . . . . Z 6
n Street . . . . Z 7
stchurch Road . . . . . . X 9
ch Street . . . . X 12
vn Street . . . . Z 13
er Lane . . . . X 14
e Street . . . . Z 15
friars Road . . . . Y 17
Street . . . . Z 18
Street . . . . Z 20
Lane . . . . Z 21
ster Street . . . . Z 22
nt Pleasant . . . . Z 23
le Shopping Centre . Z
er Park Avenue . . . . X 24
pect Street . . . . X 27
en Victoria Street . . . Y 28
Mary's Butts . . . . Z 29
on Hill . . . . Y 30
on Road . . . . Y 31
Tilehurst Road . . . . Z 33
Tudor Road . . . . Y 34
Valpy Street . . . . Y 37
Watlington Street . . . . Z 40
West Street . . . . Y 41
Whitley Street . . . . X 42

ENGLAND

at Hurst *East : 5 m. by A 329 – X – on B 3030 – ✉ Reading.*

XX **Castle,** Church Hill, RG10 0SJ, ☎ (01189) 340034, *info@castlerestaurant.cc* *Fax (01189) 340334,* « 16C », – ⅓ P. MO AE O VISA
Meals 17.95/33.00 **t.** 12.00.

at Sindlesham *Southeast : 5 m. by A 329 on B 3030 – X – ✉ Wokingham.*

Reading Moat House, Mill Lane, RG41 5DF, Northwest : ½ m. by Mole ☎ (01189) 499988, *Fax (01189) 666530,* – | TV P – 80. MO AE O VISA
Meals *(closed Saturday lunch)* a la carte 18.15/25.45 **st.** – 11.50 – **100 rm** 140 155.00 **st.** – SB.

at Grazeley Green *Southwest : 5½ m. by A 33 – X – ✉ Reading.*

Premier Lodge, RG7 1LS, ☎ (0870) 7001500, *Fax (0870) 7001501,* – rm, TV
MO AE VISA.
Meals (grill rest.) a la carte 8.95/16.35 **t.** – 6.00 – **32 rm** 49.50 **st.**

READING SERVICE AREA *Newbury* 403 404 Q 29 – ✉ *Reading.*

Travelodge, RG30 3UQ, M 4 westbound between junctions 11 and 12 ☎ (01189) 566 *Fax (01189) 582350* – rm, TV P. MO AE O VISA JCB.
Meals (grill rest.) – **40 rm** 59.95 **t.**

Travelodge without rest., RG30 3UQ, M 4 eastbound between junctions 11 and ☎ (01189) 566966, *Fax (01189) 508427* – TV P. MO AE O VISA JCB.
90 rm 49.95 **t.**

Groß-London (GREATER LONDON) besteht aus der City und 32 Verwaltungsbezirken (Borough). Diese sind wiederum in kleinere Bezirke (Area) unterteilt, deren Mittelpunkt ehemalige Dörfer oder Stadtviertel sind, die oft ihren eigenen Charakter bewahrt haben.

REDDITCH *Worcs.* 403 404 O 27 – *pop. 73 372.*

18 Abbey Park G & C.C., Dagnell End Rd ☎ (01527) 63918 – 18 Lower Grinsty, Green Callow Hill ☎ (01527) 543309 – 9 Pitcheroak, Plymouth Rd ☎ (01527) 541054.
Civic Square, Alcester St. ☎ (01527) 60806.
London 111 – Birmingham 15 – Cheltenham 33 – Stratford-upon-Avon 15.

Quality , Pool Bank, Southcrest, B97 4JS, ☎ (01527) 541511, *admin@gb646.u-net.* , *Fax (01527) 402600,* – rm, TV P – 100. MO AE O VISA.
Meals *(closed Saturday lunch)* 11.50/16.50 **st.** and a la carte 5.25 – 9.75 – 7 75.00/90.00 **st.** – SB.

Premier Lodge, Birchfield Rd, B97 6PX, West : 4 ¾ m. by A 441 and A 448 off Tardeb rd ☎ (0870) 7001320, *Fax (0870) 7001321,* – rm, TV P – 150. MO AE JCB.
Meals (grill rest.) a la carte 9.15/18.85 **st.** – 6.00 – **33 rm** 46.00 **st.**

Old Rectory , Ipsley Lane, Ipsley, B98 0AP, ☎ (01527) 523000, *Fax (01527) 51700* – P. MO AE O VISA.
Meals (booking essential to non-residents) (dinner only) 18.50 **st.** – **10 rm** 6 100.00 **st.** – SB.

REDHILL *Surrey* 404 T 30 – *pop. 47 602 (inc. Reigate).*

18 Redhill & Reigate, Clarence Lodge, Pendleton Rd ☎ (01737) 244626 – 9 Canac ☎ (01737) 770204.
London 22 – Brighton 31 – Guildford 20 – Maidstone 34.

Nutfield Priory, Nutfield, RH1 4EN, East : 2 m. on A 25 ☎ (01737) 824400, *nutprior .com.uk, Fax (01737) 823321,* , squash – |, rest, TV P –
MO AE O VISA JCB.
Cloisters : Meals *(closed Saturday lunch)* 16.00/29.50 **st.** and a la carte 9.00 – 12
59 rm 105.00/155.00 **st.**, 1 suite – SB.

at Salfords *South : 2½ m. on A 23 – ✉ Redhill.*

Travel Inn, Brighton Rd, RH1 5BT, ☎ (01737) 767277, *Fax (01737) 778099* – rest, TV P. MO AE O VISA.
Meals (grill rest.) – **48 rm** 40.95 **t.**

DMILE *Leics. – pop. 697.*
London 140 – Leicester 20 – Lincoln 37 – Nottingham 17 – Sheffield 52.

XX **The Peacock Inn** with rm, Church Corner, NG13 0GA, ☎ (01949) 842554, *peacock@pernickety.co.uk, Fax (01949) 843746,* , « Part 17C » – ⇔ rm, TV ☎ P. MO AE ① VISA JCB. ⚘
Meals a la carte 13.95/34.40 **t.** – **10 rm** ☐ 65.00/80.00 **t.** – SB.

The Peacock Inn, Church Corner, NG13 0GA, ☎ (01949) 842554, *peacock@pernickety.co.uk, Fax (01949) 843746,* , « Part 17C » – ⇔ P. MO AE ① VISA JCB
Meals 7.95/17.95 **t.** and a la carte.

DWORTH *Durham – see Darlington.*

EPHAM *Norfolk* 404 X 25 – *pop. 2 405* – ✉ *Norwich.*
London 125 – Cromer 26 – King's Lynn 34 – Norwich 14.

Westwood Barn ⚘ without rest., Crabgate Lane South, Wood Dalling, NR11 6SW, North : 3 m. by Station Rd and Wood Dalling Rd ☎ (01263) 584108, ≤, « Converted barn », – ⇔ TV P. ⚘
3 rm ☐ 35.00/52.00 **st.**

ETH *N. Yorks.* 402 O 20 – *pop. 939* – ✉ *Richmond.*
The Literary Institute, The Green ☎ (01748) 884059.
London 253 – Leeds 53 – Middlesbrough 36.

Burgoyne, On The Green, DL11 6SN, ☎ (01748) 884292, *Fax (01748) 884292,* ≤, – ⇔ TV ♿ P. MO VISA
closed 2 January-14 February – **Meals** (dinner only) 24.50 **t.** 6.00 – **8 rm** ☐ 70.00/140.00 **t.** – SB.

Arkleside, DL11 6SG, Northeast corner of the green ☎ (01748) 884200, *info@arklesidehotel.co.uk, Fax (01748) 884200,* ≤, – ⇔ TV P. MO VISA
closed 2 January-12 February – **Meals** (dinner only) 20.00 **t.** 9.50 – **8 rm** ☐ 45.00/70.00 **t.**, 1 suite – SB.

GATE *Surrey* 404 T 30 – *pop. 47 602 (inc. Redhill).*
London 26 – Brighton 33 – Guildford 20 – Maidstone 38.

Bridge House, Reigate Hill, RH2 9RP, North : 1 ¼ m. on A 217 ☎ (01737) 246801, *Fax (01737) 223756,* ≤ – TV P – 100. MO AE ① VISA. ⚘
Meals *(closed Saturday lunch, Bank Holidays and restricted opening 27 December-3 January)* (dancing Friday and Saturday evening) 23.50 **t.** and a la carte 12.00 – ☐ 12.00 – **39 rm** 61.00/136.00 **t.**

Cranleigh, 41 West St., RH2 9BL, ☎ (01737) 223417, *cranleighhotel@tinyworld.co.uk, Fax (01737) 223734,* heated, – TV P. MO AE ① VISA JCB. ⚘
closed 10 days Christmas – **Meals** *(closed Friday to Sunday)* (dinner only) a la carte 16.00/27.00 **st.** 5.00 – **9 rm** ☐ 80.00/99.00 **st.**

XX **The Dining Room,** 59a High St., RH2 9AE, ☎ (01737) 226650 – ⇔ ▤. MO AE ① VISA
closed Easter, 2 weeks August, Christmas, New Year, Saturday lunch, Sunday dinner and Bank Holidays – **Meals** 13.50/16.95 **t.** and a la carte 9.50.

X **La Barbe,** 71 Bell St., RH2 7AN, ☎ (01737) 241966, *restaurant@labarbe.co.uk, Fax (01737) 226387* – MO AE VISA
closed Saturday lunch, Sunday and Bank Holidays – **Meals** - French - 19.95/26.45 **st.** 9.95.

TFORD *Notts.* 402 403 404 R 24 – *pop. 20 679.*
Amcott House, 40 Grove St. (01777) 860780.
London 148 – Lincoln 23 – Nottingham 31 – Sheffield 27.

The Barns ⚘ without rest., Morton Farm, Babworth, DN22 8HA, Southwest : 2 ¼ m. by A 6420 ☎ (01777) 706336, *harry@thebarns.co.uk, Fax (01777) 709773,* – ⇔ TV P. MO VISA JCB. ⚘
closed Christmas – **6 rm** ☐ 33.00/48.00 **st.**

YDYCROESAU *Shrops.* 402 403 K 25 – *see Oswestry.*

s prix — Pour toutes précisions sur les prix indiqués dans ce guide, reportez-vous aux pages de l'introduction.

ENGLAND

RIBCHESTER *Lancs.* 402 M 22 – *pop. 1 654.*

London 234 – Blackburn 13 – Blackpool 26 – Burnley 19 – Lancaster 27.

Burlingtons, Blackburn Rd, PR3 3ZQ, ℘ (01254) 878208, *Fax (01254) 878138* – MC AE
Meals 5.95/10.00 **st.** and a la carte 3.95.

Stonebridge Bistro, 19 Blackburn Rd, PR3 3ZP, ℘ (01254) 878664, *Fax (01254) 878*
– P. MC AE VISA
closed Saturday lunch and Monday – **Meals** 12.50/19.50 **st.** and a la carte 7.50.

RICHMOND *N. Yorks.* 402 O 20 *Great Britain G.* – *pop. 7 862.*

See : *Town★ – Castle★ AC – Georgian Theatre Royal and Museum★.*

Exc. : *Josephine and John Bowes Museum★, Barnard Castle, NW : 15 m. by B 6274, A and minor rd (right) – Raby Castle★, NE : 6 m. of Barnard Castle by A 688.*

Bend Hagg ℘ (01748) 825319 – Catterick, Leyburn Rd ℘ (01748) 833268.

Friary Gardens, Victoria Rd ℘ (01748) 850252.

London 243 – Leeds 53 – Middlesbrough 26 – Newcastle upon Tyne 44.

King's Head, Market Pl., DL10 4HS, ℘ (01748) 850220, *res@kingsheadrichmond.cc*
Fax (01748) 850635 – TV P – 150. MC AE VISA JCB
Meals (bar lunch Monday to Saturday)/dinner 19.50 **t.** 6.80 – **30 rm** 65.00/115.00
SB.

West End without rest., 45 Reeth Rd., DL10 4EX, West : ½ m. on A 6
℘ (01748) 824783, *westend@richmond.org,* – TV P
closed 2 weeks Christmas and New Year – **5 rm** 22.00/44.00.

The Old Brewery without rest., 29 The Green, DL10 4RG, via Victoria Rd off Craveng
℘ (01748) 822460, *Fax (01748) 825561,* – TV. MC VISA JCB.
closed December and January – **5 rm** 30.00/46.00.

at Whashton *Northwest : 4½ m. by Ravensworth rd* – ✉ *Richmond.*

Whashton Springs Farm without rest., DL11 7JS, South : 1 ½ m. on Richmon
℘ (01748) 822884, *Fax (01748) 826285,* « Working farm », – TV P. VISA JCB.
closed Christmas-6 January – **8 rm** 28.00/48.00 **s.**

The Hack and Spade, DL11 7JL, ℘ (01748) 823721 – P. MC VISA
closed 2 weeks January, Sunday dinner and Monday – **Meals** (dinner only and Sunday lu
a la carte 15.40/23.00 **t.**

at Dalton *Northwest : 6 ¾ m. by Ravensworth rd and Gayles rd* – ✉ *Richmond.*

The Travellers Rest, DL11 7HU, ℘ (01833) 621225, *travs@fsmail.net* – P. MC VISA
closed Sunday – **Meals** (dinner only) a la carte 16.40/22.50 **t.** 4.95.

RIDGEWAY *Derbs.* – *see Sheffield (S. Yorks.).*

RINGWOOD *Hants.* 403 404 O 31 – *pop. 11 959.*

The Furlong ℘ (01425) 470896 (summer only).

London 102 – Bournemouth 11 – Salisbury 17 – Southampton 20.

Moortown Lodge, 244 Christchurch Rd, BH24 3AS, South : 1 m. on B 3
℘ (01425) 471404, *hotel@burrows-jones.freeserve.co.uk, Fax (01425) 476052* – TV
MC AE VISA.
closed Christmas-mid January – **Meals** *(closed Sunday to non-residents)* (dinner
19.95/22.95 **t.** 6.95 – **6 rm** 55.00/90.00 **t.** – SB.

RIPLEY *N. Yorks.* 402 P 21 – *pop. 193* – ✉ *Harrogate.*

London 213 – Bradford 21 – Leeds 18 – Newcastle upon Tyne 79.

The Boar's Head, HG3 3AY, ℘ (01423) 771888, *reservations@boarsheadripley.c*
Fax (01423) 771509, « 18C coaching inn within estate village of Ripley Castle »,
rm, TV P. MC AE VISA JCB
The Restaurant : Meals 14.00/30.00 **t.** 6.00 – ***The Bistro :*** Meals 10.00/12.
and a la carte – **25 rm** 95.00/135.00 **st.** – SB.

at Burnt Yates *West : 2 ¾ m. on B 6165* – ✉ *Harrogate.*

Bay Horse Inn, HG3 3EJ, on B 6165 ℘ (01423) 770230, *enquiries@bayhorseinn.c*
Fax (01423) 771894, – TV P. MC VISA.
closed Christmas – **Meals** (bar lunch Monday to Saturday)/dinner a la carte 13.15/24.9
– **16 rm** 45.00/60.00 – SB.

High Winsley Cottage ⑤, HG3 3EP, Northwest : 1 m. by Brimham Rocks rd ☎ (01423) 770662, ←, – ⅹ P. ✻
closed January-February – **Meals** (by arrangement) (communal dining) 13.50 – **4 rm** 38.00/56.00.

PLEY *Surrey* 404 S 30 – *pop. 1 697.*
London 28 – Guildford 6.

Michels', 13 High St., GU23 6AQ, ☎ (01483) 224777, *Fax (01483) 222940*, – MO AE VISA
closed 2 weeks January, Saturday lunch, Sunday dinner and Monday – **Meals** 21.00/30.00 **t.** and a la carte 4.50.

PON *N. Yorks.* 402 P 21 *Great Britain G.* – *pop. 13 806.*
See : *Town★ - Cathedral★ (Saxon Crypt★★) AC.*
Env. : *Fountains Abbey★★★ AC :- Studley Royal★★ AC (←★ from Anne Boleyn's Seat) - Fountains Hall (Façade★), SW : 2½ m. by B 6265 – Newby Hall (Tapestries★) AC, SE : 3½ m. by B 6265.*
Ripon City, Palace Rd ☎ (01765) 603640.
Minster Rd ☎ (01765) 604625 (summer only).
London 222 – Leeds 26 – Middlesbrough 35 – York 23.

Ripon Spa, Park St., HG4 2BU, ☎ (01765) 602172, *spahotel@branco.co.uk*, *Fax (01765) 690770*, – |♦|, rest, TV P – 150. MO AE ① VISA JCB
Meals 13.75/18.50 **st.** and a la carte 7.00 – **40 rm** 73.00/102.00 **st.** – SB.

The Gallery (at The Outside Inn), 2-4 Skellbank, HG4 2PT, ☎ (01765) 602600, *Fax (01765) 690736*, – MO AE ① VISA JCB
Meals a la carte 11.65/29.15 **t.** 4.60.

Aldfield *Southwest : 3¾ m. by B 6265* – ✉ *Ripon.*

Bay Tree Farm ⑤, HG4 3BE, ☎ (01765) 620394, *Fax (01765) 620394*, – ⅹ TV P. MO VISA
Meals (by arrangement) (communal dining) 14.00 **t.** 4.00 – **6 rm** 30.00/50.00 **st.**

Wormald Green *South : 4¼ m. on A 61* – ✉ *Ripon.*

Newboulds (at George H.) with rm, HG3 3PR, ☎ (01765) 677214, *info@hotelgeorge.co.uk*, *Fax (01765) 676201* – ⅹ TV P. MO VISA JCB
Meals (dinner only Thursday-Saturday) 35.00/45.00 **t.** and a la carte 9.95 – **5 rm** 50.00/80.00 **t.**

Olives (at George H.), HG3 3PR, ☎ (01765) 677214, *Fax (01765) 676201* – P. MO VISA JCB
Meals 7.95/16.00 **t.** and a la carte 19.00/39.00 **t.** 7.95.

Markington *Southwest : 5 m. by A 61* – ✉ *Harrogate.*

Hob Green ⑤, HG3 3PJ, Southwest : ½ m. ☎ (01423) 770031, *hobgreen.hotel@virgin.net*, *Fax (01423) 771589*, ←, « Country house in extensive parkland », – TV P. MO AE ① VISA
Meals 9.95/23.50 **t.** and dinner a la carte 7.75 – **11 rm** 85.00/105.00 **t.**, 1 suite – SB.

LEY *Notts. – see Nottingham.*

ADE *Northants.* 404 R 27 – *pop. 2 239.*
London 66 – Coventry 36 – Northampton 5.5.

Roade House with rm, 16 High St., NN7 2NW, ☎ (01604) 863372, *info@roadehousehotel.demon.co.uk*, *Fax (01604) 862421* – ⅹ, rest, TV ☎ P. MO AE VISA. ✻
closed 1 week Christmas-New Year, lunch Saturday and Monday and Sunday dinner – **Meals** 15.00/20.00 **st.** (lunch) and dinner a la carte 23.50/31.50 **st.** 9.00 – **9 rm** 70.00/80.00 **st.** – SB.

CHDALE *Gtr. Manchester* 402 N 23 – *pop. 94 313.*
Edenfield Rd, Bagslate ☎ (01706) 646024 – Marland, Springfield Park, Bolton Rd ☎ (01706) 649801 – 18, 9 Castle Hawk, Chadwick Lane, Castleton ☎ (01706) 640841.
The Clock Tower, Town Hall ☎ (01706) 356592.
London 224 – Blackpool 40 – Burnley 11 – Leeds 45 – Manchester 12 – Liverpool 40.

Royal Toby Lodge, Manchester Rd, Castleton, OL11 3HF, Southwest : 2 m. by A 58 on A 664 ☎ (01706) 861861, *Fax (01706) 868428*, – |♦|, rest, TV ☎ & P. MO AE ① VISA
Meals 8.95/10.95 **st.** and a la carte 8.95 – ***Fallen Angel* : Meals** - Italian - (dinner only) a la carte 12.00/26.45 **st.** 9.50 – **44 rm** 77.50/92.50 **st.** – SB.

ENGLAND

Castleton, Manchester Rd, Castleton, OL11 2XX, Southwest : 3 m. by A 58 on A 6
(01706) 357888, *Fax (01706) 525757*, – TV P. MO AE VISA JCB
Meals (dinner only and Sunday lunch)/dinner 10.95 **t.** and a la carte 5.95 – **13**
60.00/70.00 **t.** – SB.

Nutters, Edenfield Rd, Cheesden, Norden, OL12 7TY, West : 5 m. on A 6
(01706) 650167, *Fax (01706) 650167*, – P. MO AE VISA
closed 2 weeks August and Tuesday – **Meals** 29.95 **t.** (dinner) and a la carte 22.25/30.20

After Eight, 2 Edenfield Rd, OL11 5AA, West : 1 m. on A 680 (01706) 646432, *ataylo ompuserve.com, Fax (01706) 646432* – . MO AE VISA
closed 1 week in summer, 25 December, 1 January, Sunday and Monday – **Meals** (din only) a la carte 19.65/25.00 **t.** 6.90.

at Milnrow *Southeast : 3 m. by A 640* – *Rochdale.*

Travel Inn, Newhey Rd, OL16 4JF, (01706) 299999, *Fax (01706) 299074* – rest, TV P. MO AE VISA.
Meals (grill rest.) – **40 rm** 40.95 **t.**

ROCHESTER *Medway* 404 V 29 *Great Britain G.* – *pop. 23 971* – *Chatham.*
See : *Castle★ AC* – *Cathedral★ AC.*
Env. : *The Historic Dockyard★, Chatham, NE : 2 m. of the Cathedral.*
Exc. : *Leeds Castle★, SE : 11 m. by A 229 and M 20.*
95 High St. (01634) 843666.
London 30 – *Dover 45* – *Maidstone 8* – *Margate 46.*

Bridgewood Manor, Bridgewood Roundabout, ME5 9AX, Southeast : 3 m. by A 2 ar 229 on Walderslade rd (01634) 201333, *bridgewoodmanor@marstonhotels.c Fax (01634) 201330*, – rest, TV P – 200. MO AE VISA
Squires : **Meals** 19.50/27.00 **st.** and dinner a la carte – 11.00 – **96 rm** 99.00/120.0 4 suites – SB.

Posthouse Rochester, Maidstone Rd, ME5 9SF, Southeast : 2 ½ m. by A 2 on A (0870) 400 9069, *gm1431@forte-hotels.com, Fax (01634) 684512*, – rm, TV P – 110. MO AE VISA
Meals a la carte 16.20/22.60 **st.** 6.95 – 11.95 – **145 rm** 79.00 **st.** – SB.

ROCHFORD *Essex* 404 W 29 – *pop. 15 081.*
Rochford Hundred, Rochford Hall, Hall Rd (01702) 544302.
London 46 – *Chelmsford 19* – *Colchester 39* – *Southend-on-Sea 3.*

Renouf, Bradley Way, SS4 1BU, (01702) 541334, *Fax (01702) 549563*, – rest, TV P – 30. MO AE VISA
closed 26 to 30 December – **Meals** (residents only Sunday dinner and Bank Holid 15.50/30.00 **t.** 6.30 – 3.00 – **23 rm** 59.50/99.50 **t.**

ROCK *Cornwall* 403 F 32 *The West Country G.* – *pop. 4 593* – *Wadebridge.*
Exc. : *Pencarrow★, SE : 8½ m. by B 3314 and A 389.*
London 266 – *Newquay 24* – *Tintagel 14* – *Truro 32.*

St. Enodoc, PL27 6LA, (01208) 863394, *enodoc@aol.com, Fax (01208) 863970*, heated, squash – rm, TV P. MO AE VISA.
closed 7 December-mid February – ***Porthilly Grill :*** **Meals** (light lunch)/dinner a la c 22.00/32.00 **st.** – 6.00 – **15 rm** 95.00/145.00 **st.**, 3 suites – SB.

LA ROCQUE *Jersey (Channel Islands)* 230 ⑪ – *see Channel Islands.*

ROGATE *W. Sussex* 404 R 30 – *pop. 1 785* – *Petersfield (Hants.).*
London 63 – *Brighton 42* – *Guildford 29* – *Portsmouth 23* – *Southampton 36.*

Mizzards Farm without rest., GU31 5HS, Southwest : 1 m. by Hartinc (01730) 821656, *Fax (01730) 821655*, « 17C farmhouse », heated, – P.
closed Christmas and New Year – **3 rm** 40.00/68.00.

ROMALDKIRK *Durham* 402 N 20 – *see Barnard Castle.*

The Guide is updated annually so renew your Guide every year.

MSEY *Hants.* 403 404 P 31 *Great Britain G. – pop. 17 032.*

See : *Abbey★ (interior★★).*

Env. : *Broadlands★ AC, S : 1 m.*

18 Dunwood Manor, Danes Rd, Awbridge ✆ (023) 8073 2218 – 18 Nursling ✆ (023) 8073 2218 – 18, 9 Wellow, Ryedown Lane, East Wellow ✆ (01794) 322872.

13 Church St. ✆ (01794) 512987.

London 82 – Bournemouth 28 – Salisbury 16 – Southampton 8 – Winchester 10.

White Horse, Market Pl., SO51 8ZJ, ✆ (0870) 400 8123, *Fax (01794) 517485* – rm, TV P – 30. MC AE VISA JCB
Meals 14.00/25.00 **t.** 8.40 – 11.85 – **33 rm** 70.00/110.00 **st.** – SB.

Ranvilles Farm House without rest., Ower, SO51 6AA, Southwest : 2 m. on A 3090 (southbound carriageway) ✆ (023) 80814481, *Fax (023) 80814481*, « Part 16C farmhouse », – TV P
closed 24, 25 and 31 December and 1 January – **3 rm** 35.00/55.00 **st.**

Highfield House, Newtown Rd, Awbridge, SO51 0GG, Northwest : 3 ½ m. by A 3090 (old A 31) and A 27 ✆ (01794) 340727, *Fax (01794) 341450*, – TV P.
Meals (by arrangement) (communal dining) 15.00 **s.** – **3 rm** 50.00/55.00 **s.**

Old Manor House, 21 Palmerston St., SO51 8GF, ✆ (01794) 517353, *Fax (01794) 513855*, « Timbered 16C house » – P. MC AE VISA
closed 24-31 December, Sunday dinner and Monday – **Meals** (booking essential) a la carte 23.50/31.50 **t.** 6.00.

East Tytherley *Northwest : 6 m. by A 3057 off B 3084 – ✉ Romsey.*

Star Inn with rm, SO51 0LW, ✆ (01794) 340225, *info@starinn-uk.com*, , – TV P. MC VISA
closed 26 December – **Meals** a la carte 12.45/22.50 **t.** – **3 rm** 45.00/60.00 **t.**

SEDALE ABBEY *N. Yorks.* 402 R 20 *Great Britain G. – pop. 332 (Rosedale) – ✉ Pickering.*

Env. : *★ on road to Hutton-le-Hole.*

London 247 – Middlesbrough 27 – Scarborough 25 – York 36.

Milburn Arms, YO18 8RA, ✆ (01751) 417312, *info@milburnarms.com*, *Fax (01751) 417312*, – rest, TV P. MC VISA
Priory : **Meals** *(closed Sunday dinner)* (bar lunch Monday to Saturday)/dinner a la carte 19.70/27.00 **t.** 5.95 – **11 rm** 45.50/80.00 **t.** – SB.

SS-ON-WYE *Herefordshire* 403 404 M 28 *Great Britain G. – pop. 9 606.*

See : *Market House★ – Yat Rock (★).*

Env. : *SW : Wye Valley★ – Goodrich Castle★ AC, SW : 3½ m. by A 40.*

Swan House, Edde Cross St. ✆ (01989) 562768.

London 118 – Gloucester 15 – Hereford 15 – Newport 35.

The Chase, Gloucester Rd, HR9 5LH, ✆ (01989) 763161, *info@chasehotel.co.uk*, *Fax (01989) 768330*, – TV P – 250. MC VISA.
Meals 17.00 **st.** and dinner a la carte 6.50 – **36 rm** 60.00/100.00 **t.** – SB.

Royal, Palace Pound, HR9 5HZ, ✆ (01989) 565105, *Fax (01989) 768058*, , – TV P – 80. MC AE VISA
Meals (bar lunch Monday to Saturday)/dinner 16.95 **st.** and a la carte 5.95 – **42 rm** 55.00/116.00 **st.** – SB.

Travel Inn, Ledbury Rd, HR9 7QJ, Northeast : 1 ½ m. by A 40 at junction with A 449 and M 50 ✆ (01989) 563861, *Fax (01989) 566124* – rm, TV P. MC AE VISA.
Meals (grill rest.) – **43 rm** 40.95 **t.**

China Boy Jo, 27 Gloucester Rd, HR9 5LE, ✆ (01989) 563533, *Fax (01989) 563533* – MC VISA
closed 25-26 December, Monday and Tuesday lunch except Bank Holidays – **Meals** - Chinese - a la carte 10.00/28.80 **t.**

Le Faisan Doré Brasserie, 52 Edde Cross St., HR9 7BZ, ✆ (01989) 565751, *Fax (01989) 763069* – . MC AE VISA
closed first week June, 24 December-3 January, Sunday, Monday and restricted opening January-February – **Meals** (dinner only) 18.70/25.00 **t.** 6.50.

erne Bridge *South : 3 ¾ m. on B 4234 – ✉ Ross-on-Wye.*

Lumleys without rest., HR9 5QT, ✆ (01600) 890040, *helen@lumleys.force9.co*, – TV P
3 rm 30.00/50.00 **st.**

ENGLAND

at Glewstone *Southwest : 3 1/4 m. by A 40 – ✉ Ross-on-Wye.*

Glewstone Court, HR9 6AW, ✆ (01989) 770367, *glewstone@aol.c Fax (01989) 770282,* ≤, « Part Georgian and Victorian country house », – TV P. MC VISA JCB
closed 25-27 December – **Meals** (bar lunch Monday to Saturday)/dinner 26.00 **st.** 5.0
7 rm 45.00/105.00 **st.** – SB.

at Peterstow *West : 2 1/2 m. on A 49 – ✉ Ross-on-Wye.*

Pengethley Manor, HR9 6LL, Northwest : 1 1/2 m. on A 49 ✆ (01989) 730211, *reservations@pengethleymanor.co.uk, Fax (01989) 730238,* ≤, heated, – TV – 50. MC AE VISA
Meals a la carte 27.00/35.00 **st.** 8.50 – **22 rm** 75.00/120.00 **st.**, 3 suites – SB.

ROSTHWAITE *Cumbria* 402 K 20 – *see Keswick.*

ROTHBURY *Northd.* 401 402 O 18 *Great Britain G. – pop. 1 805 – ✉ Morpeth.*
See : *Cragside House★ (interior★) AC.*
National Park Information Centre, Church House, Church St. ✆ (01669) 620887 (November-March weekends only).
London 311 – Edinburgh 84 – Newcastle upon Tyne 29.

Orchard without rest., High St., NE65 7TL, ✆ (01669) 620684, *jpickard@orchardguesthouse.co.uk,* – TV.
closed 17 December-3 January – **6 rm** 30.00/50.00 **s.**

ROTHERHAM *S. Yorks.* 402 403 404 P 23 – *pop. 121 380.*
Thrybergh Park ✆ (01709) 850466 – Grange Park, Upper Wortley Rd, Kimberworth (01709) 558884 – Phoenix, Pavilion Lane, Brinsworth ✆ (01709) 363788.
Central Library, Walker Pl. ✆ (01709) 835904.
London 166 – Kingston-upon-Hull 61 – Leeds 36 – Sheffield 6.

Swallow (becoming a Marriott spring 2001), West Bawtry Rd, S60 4NA, South : 2 1/4 m A 630 ✆ (01709) 830630, *info@swallowhotels.com, Fax (01709) 830549,* – rest, TV P – 300. MC AE VISA JCB
Meals (bar lunch Saturday) (carvery lunch) 10.95/19.75 **st.** 8.00 – **98 rm** 95 120.00 **st.**, 2 suites – SB.

Elton, Main St., Bramley, S66 2SF, East : 4 1/4 m. by A 6021, A 631 and Cross ✆ (01709) 545681, *bestwestern.eltonhotel@btinternet.com, Fax (01709) 549100* – TV P – 50. MC AE VISA JCB
Meals 12.50/20.00 **st.** and a la carte 6.50 – 9.35 – **29 rm** 56.00/80.00 **st.** – SB.

Ibis without rest., Moorhead Way, Bramley, S66 1YY, East : 4 1/2 m. by A 6021 off A 63 junction 1 of M 18 ✆ (01709) 730333, *Fax (01709) 730444* – TV P – 40. VISA
86 rm 45.00 **st.**

Travel Inn, Bawtry Rd, S65 3JB, East : 2 m. by A 6021 on A 631 ✆ (01709) 543 *Fax (01709) 531546* – rm, rest, TV P. MC AE VISA.
Meals (grill rest.) – **37 rm** 40.95 **t.**

ROTHERWICK *Hants. – see Hook.*

ROTHLEY *Leics.* 402 403 404 Q 25 – *see Leicester.*

ROUGHAM GREEN *Suffolk – see Bury St. Edmunds.*

ROWDE *Wilts.* 403 404 N 29 – *see Devizes.*

ROWNHAMS SERVICE AREA *Hants.* 403 404 P 31 – ✉ *Southampton.*
M 27 Services (westbound) ✆ (023) 8073 0345.

Travel Inn without rest., SO16 8AP, M 27 between junctions 3 and 4 (westbound carriageway) ✆ (023) 8074 1144, *Fax (023) 8074 0204* – TV P. MC AE VISA.
closed Christmas and New Year – **40 rm** 40.95.

WSLEY *Derbs.* 402 403 404 P 24 *Great Britain G. – pop. 451 – ✉ Matlock.*
Env. : *Chatsworth*★★★ *(Park and Garden*★★★*)* **AC**, *N : by B 6012.*
London 157 – Derby 23 – Manchester 40 – Nottingham 30.

East Lodge, DE4 2EF, ☎ (01629) 734474, *info@eastlodge.com, Fax (01629) 733949,* – rest, TV P. MC AE VISA.
Meals 12.95/25.95 **t.** and dinner a la carte 8.00 – **15 rm** 75.00/125.00 **t.** – SB.

The Peacock, Bakewell Rd, DE4 2EB, ☎ (01629) 733518, *Fax (01629) 732671,* « 17C stone house, antiques », – rest, TV P. MC AE VISA
Meals 13.50/26.00 **t.** and dinner a la carte 6.95 – 9.50 – **16 rm** 95.00/110.00 **t.** – SB.

WTON *Ches.* 402 403 L 24 – *see Chester.*

YAL LEAMINGTON SPA *Warks.* 403 404 P 27 – *pop. 55 396.*
18 *Leamington and County, Golf Lane, Whitnash ☎ (01926) 425961 (on plan of Warwick).*
The Royal Pump Rooms, The Parade ☎ (01926) 742762.
London 99 – Birmingham 23 – Coventry 9 – Warwick 3.

ROYAL LEAMINGTON SPA

aïde Road V
ue Road . . . . V 2
Street . . . . V 3
ıchamp Avenue . . . . U
ıchamp Hill . . . . U 4
wood Street . . . . U 6
don Parade . . . . U 10
ch Hill . . . . UV 16
ndon Avenue . . . . U
ndon Place . . . . U 18
Street . . . . UV
ilton Terrace . . . . V 21
Street . . . . V 22
Walk . . . . U
worth Road . . . . U
Terrace V
ester Street . . . . U
gton Avenue . . . . U
gton Road . . . . U
er Avenue . . . . V 28
bold Terrace . . . . V 30
umberland Road . . . . U 33
Warwick Road V
de . . . . UV
y Terrace . . . . V 37
ord Road V
nt Grove . . . . UV 40
nt Street . . . . UV
Priors
opping Centre . . . . U
y Road . . . . U
ell Terrace V
cer Street . . . . V 44
brook Road . . . . V 47
ria Terrace . . . . V 49
vick Street . . . . U
s Road . . . . UV

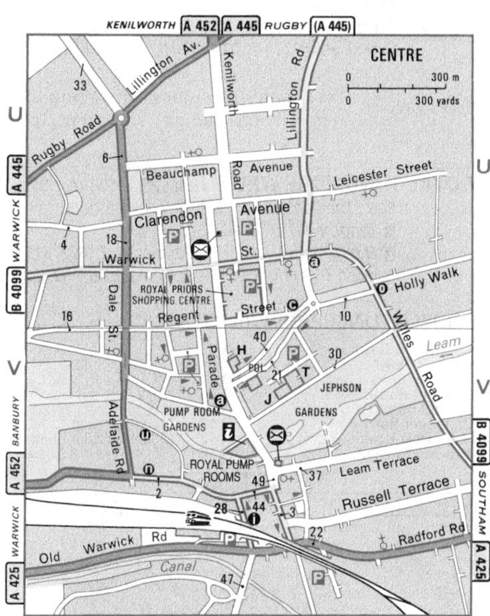

Mallory Court, Harbury Lane, Bishop's Tachbrook, CV33 9QB, South : 2 ¼ m. by B 4087 (Tachbrook Rd) ☎ (01926) 330214, *reception@mallory.co.uk, Fax (01926) 451714,* « Part Edwardian country house in Lutyens style, extensive landscaped gardens », – rest, TV P. MC AE VISA.
closed 1-5 January – **Meals** (booking essential) 25.00/39.50 **t.** and a la carte 41.50/57.50 **t.** 13.00 – 10.00 – **18 rm** 175.00/295.00 **st.** – SB.

Courtyard by Marriott, Olympus Av., Tachbrook Park, CV34 6RJ, Southwest : 1 ½ m. by A 452 ☎ (01926) 425522, *Fax (01926) 881322,* – rm, rest, TV P – 70. MC AE VISA *on Warwick town plan* Z v
Meals *(closed Sunday lunch)* a la carte 14.00/21.00 **st.** 8.00 – 10.00 – **95 rm** 83.00 **st.**

The Angel, 143 Regent St., CV32 4NZ, ☎ (01926) 881296, *Fax (01926) 881296* – TV P – 40. MC AE VISA. U c
Meals (bar lunch Monday to Saturday)/dinner 14.50 **t.** and a la carte 4.50 – **48 rm** 60.00/75.00 **t.**

Leamington H. & Bistro, 64 Upper Holly Walk, CV32 4JL, ☎ (01926) 883777, *Fax (01926) 330467,* – TV P – 40. MC AE VISA. U o
Meals 12.00/14.95 **t.** and a la carte 5.80 – 6.75 – **30 rm** 68.00/80.00 **t.** – SB.

Lansdowne, 87 Clarendon St., CV32 4PF, ✆ (01926) 450505, *Fax (01926) 42131.* ⇜ rest, TV ✆ P. MC VISA. ✗ U
closed 24-25 and 31 December – **Meals** *(closed Sunday dinner to non-residents)* (din only) 18.95 **st.** ₿ 5.95 – **14 rm** ⊐ 52.95/68.00 **st.** – SB.

Adams, 22 Avenue Rd, CV31 3PQ, ✆ (01926) 450742, *Fax (01926) 313110,* – TV P. AE ⓓ VISA. ✗ V
Meals *(closed Saturday and Sunday)* 18.50/30.00 **t.** and dinner a la carte ₿ 9.80 – 14 ⊐ 66.00/70.00 **t.** – SB.

York House, 9 York Rd, CV31 3PR, ✆ (01926) 424671, *Fax (01926) 832272* – ⇜ TV. MC ⓓ VISA. ✗ V
closed 24 December-31 January – **Meals** (by arrangement) 15.00 **t.** – **8 rm** ⊐ 26. 56.00 **t.** – SB.

XX **Amor's,** 15 Dormer Pl., CV32 5AA, ✆ (01926) 778744, *Fax (01926) 778744* – MC VISA
closed 25 to 30 December, Sunday and Bank Holidays – **Meals** 11.95/27.50 **t.** and a la c ₿ 7.95. V

XX **The Emperors,** Bath Pl., CV31 3BP, ✆ (01926) 313030, *Fax (01926) 435966* – ▤. MC ⓓ VISA. ✗ V
closed 25-26 December and 1 January – **Meals** - Chinese (Peking and Cantonese) - a la c 15.00/24.90 **st.** ₿ 4.75.

X **Solo,** 23 Dormer Pl., CV32 5AA, ✆ (01926) 422422 – ⇜. MC VISA V
closed 24 December to 3 January and Sunday – **Meals** 18.00 **t.** and a la carte 15.95/26.4

Les prix — Pour toutes précisions sur les prix indiqués dans ce guide, reportez-vous aux pages de l'introduction.

ROYAL TUNBRIDGE WELLS *Kent* 404 U 30 *Great Britain G. – pop. 60 272.*

See : *The Pantiles*★ B 26 – *Calverley Park*★ B.
Langton Rd ✆ (01892) 523034 A.
The Old Fish Market, The Pantiles ✆ (01892) 515675.
London 36 – Brighton 33 – Folkestone 46 – Hastings 27 – Maidstone 18.

ROYAL TUNBRIDGE WELLS

Benhall Mill Road .... A 3
Bishop's Down .... A 4
Calverley Road .... B
Crescent Road .... B 9
Fir Tree Road .... A 10
Grosvenor Road .... B 12
Hall's Hole Road .... A 13
High Rocks Lane .... A 16
High Street .... B 14
Hungershall Park Road .... A 17
Lansdowne Road .... B 18
Lower Green Road .... A 20
Major York's Road .... A 21
Monson Road .... B 22
Mount Ephraim .... A 23
Mount Ephraim Road .... B 24
Mount Pleasant Road .... B 25
Pantiles (The) ....
Prospect Road ....
Royal Victoria Place Shopping Centre ....
Rusthall Road ....
St. John's Road ....
Tea Garden Lane ....
Vale Road ....
Victoria Road ....
Warwick Park ....

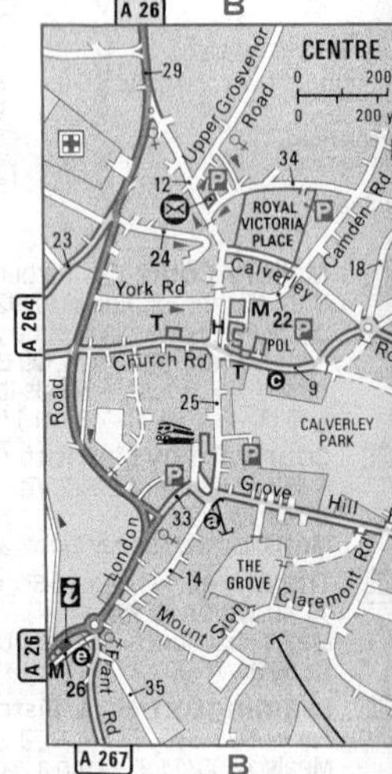

Hotel du Vin, Crescent Rd, TN1 2LY, ✆ (01892) 526455, *reception@tunbridgewells.hotelduvin.co.uk, Fax (01892) 512044,* ≤, « Georgian house, contemporary wine themed interior », – |‡| TV P – 80. MC AE VISA JCB. B c
Meals – (see ***Bistro*** below) – ▭ 10.50 – **31 rm** 75.00/139.00 **t.**, 1 suite.

Spa, Mount Ephraim, TN4 8XJ, ✆ (01892) 520331, *info@spahotel.co.uk, Fax (01892) 510575,* ≘s, – |‡| TV ♿ P – 350. MC AE VISA. A v
Meals *(closed Saturday lunch)* 18.50/30.00 **st.** and a la carte 9.50 – ▭ 10.25 – **68 rm** 82.00/155.00 **st.**, 3 suites – SB.

Danehurst without rest., 41 Lower Green Rd, Rusthall, TN4 8TW, West : 1 ¾ m. by A 264 ✆ (01892) 527739, *danehurst@zoom.co.uk, Fax (01892) 514804,* – TV P. MC AE VISA. A e
closed last week August, Christmas and New Year – **4 rm** ▭ 45.00/80.00.

Signor Franco, 5a High St., TN1 1UL, ✆ (01892) 549199, *Fax (01892) 541378* – ▤. MC VISA JCB B a
closed Sunday and Bank Holidays – **Meals** - Italian - a la carte 19.90/32.60 **t.** 6.60.

Bistro (at Hotel du Vin), TN1 2LY, ✆ (01892) 526455, *Fax (01892) 512044,* – P. MC AE VISA JCB B c
Meals (booking essential) a la carte 23.45/26.50 **t.**

The Tagore, 4 Nevill St., TN2 5SA, ✆ (01892) 615100, *thetagore-i@hotmail.com, Fax (01892) 549877* – MC AE VISA JCB B e
closed 25-26 December – **Meals** - Indian - (booking essential) 14.95 **t.** and a la carte.

Pembury *Northeast : 4 m. by A 264 off B 2015* – **A** – ✉ *Royal Tunbridge Wells.*

Jarvis International, 8 Tonbridge Rd, TN2 4QL, ✆ (01892) 823567, *Fax (01892) 823931,* ≘s, – TV ♿ P – 180. MC AE VISA.
Meals (bar lunch Saturday) 17.95/23.45 **t.** (dinner) and a la carte 23.15/30.90 **t.** 7.95 – ▭ 9.95 – **82 rm** 99.00/109.00 **st.**, 2 suites – SB.

Frant *South : 2½ m. on A 267* – **A** – ✉ *Royal Tunbridge Wells.*

Old Parsonage without rest., Church Lane, TN3 9DX, ✆ (01892) 750773, *oldparson@aol.com, Fax (01892) 750773,* ≤, « Georgian rectory », – TV P. MC VISA
closed 25-26 December – **4 rm** ▭ 59.00/77.00 **st.**

Langton Green *West : 2 m. on A 264* – **A** – ✉ *Royal Tunbridge Wells.*

The Hare, Langton Rd, TN3 0JA, ✆ (01892) 862419, *Fax (01892) 861275,* – P. MC AE VISA
Meals a la carte 15.20/23.85 **t.** 5.00.

ZEL BAY *Jersey (Channel Islands)* **403** P 33 and **230** ⑪ – *see Channel Islands.*

AN-HIGH-LANES *Cornwall* **403** F 33 – *see Veryan.*

CKHALL *Herefordshire* – *see Hereford.*

GBY *Warks.* **403** **404** Q 26 – *pop. 61 106.*

Whitefields Hotel, Coventry Rd, Thurlaston ✆ (01788) 815555 – Clifton Rd ✆ (01788) 544637.

The Library, Little Elborow St. ✆ (01788) 571813 – 4-5 Lawrence Sheriff St. ✆ (01788) 534970.

London 88 – Birmingham 33 – Leicester 21 – Northampton 20 – Warwick 17.

Brownsover Hall, Brownsover Lane, CV21 1HU, North : 2 m. by A 426 and Brownsover Rd ✆ (01788) 546100, *reservations@corushotels.com, Fax (01788) 579241,* « 19C Gothic style hall », – TV P – 70. MC AE VISA
Meals 16.95 **st.** and a la carte 5.95 – ▭ 9.75 – **47 rm** 105.00/145.00 **st.** – SB.

Rugby Grosvenor, 81-87 Clifton Rd, CV21 3QQ, on B 5414 ✆ (01788) 535686, *mail@therugbygrosvenorhotel.freeserve.co.uk, Fax (01788) 541297,* ≘s, – TV P – 35. MC AE VISA.
Meals *(closed Sunday dinner)* 14.50/18.95 **t.** – ▭ 6.50 – **26 rm** 74.50/84.50 **t.** – SB.

Travelodge, London Rd, Thurlaston, CV23 9LG, Southwest : 4 ¼ m. by A 4071 at junction with A 45 ✆ (01788) 521538, *Fax (01788) 521538* – rm, TV ♿ P. MC AE VISA JCB.
Meals (grill rest.) – **40 rm** 39.95 **t.**

ENGLAND

at Crick *Southeast : 6 m. on A 428.*

Posthouse Rugby/Northampton, NN6 7XR, West : ½ m. on A
(0870) 400 9059, Fax (01788) 823955, – rm, – 180. VISA
Meals *(closed Saturday lunch)* 15.00 **t.** and a la carte 8.50 – 11.95 – **88 rm** 89.00 s
SB.

Express by Holiday Inn without rest., Parklands, NN6 7EX, West : 1 ¼ m. on A
(01788) 824331, *daventry@premierhotel.co.uk, Fax (01788) 824332* –
35. VISA JCB.
110 rm 49.50/69.00 **t.**

RUGELEY *Staffs.* 402 403 404 O 25 – *pop. 22 975.*
London 134 – Birmingham 31 – Derby 29 – Stoke-on-Trent 22.

Travelodge, Western Springs Rd, WS15 2AS, at junction of A 51 with A
(01889) 570096, *Fax (01889) 570096* – rm, . VISA JCB.
Meals (grill rest.) – **32 rm** 39.95 **t.**

RUMWELL *Somerset – see Taunton.*

RUNCORN *Ches.* 402 403 L 23 – *pop. 64 154.*
Clifton Rd (01928) 572093.
London 202 – Liverpool 17 – Manchester 29.

Posthouse Warrington/Runcorn, Wood Lane, Beechwood, WA7 3HA, Southeast
m. off junction 12 of M 56 (0870) 400 9070, *Fax (01928) 714611,* –
rm, – 500. VISA
Meals a la carte 17.15/23.85 **t.** 7.50 – 11.95 – **150 rm** 79.00 **t.** – SB.

Travel Inn, Chester Rd, Preston Brook, WA7 3BB, Southeast : 6 m. by A 533 on A
(01928) 716829, *Fax (01928) 719852* – rm, rest, – 40. VISA
Meals (grill rest.) – **40 rm** 40.95 **t.**

RUSHDEN *Northants.* 404 S 27 – *pop. 23 854.*
London 74 – Cambridge 42 – Northampton 14 – Peterborough 25.

Travelodge, NN10 9EP, on A 45 (eastbound carriageway) (01933) 357C
Fax (01933) 411325 – rm, . VISA JCB.
Meals (grill rest.) – **40 rm** 39.95 **t.**

RUSHLAKE GREEN *E. Sussex* 404 U 31 – *Heathfield.*
London 54 – Brighton 26 – Eastbourne 13.

Stone House , TN21 9QJ, Northeast corner of the green (01435) 830§
Fax (01435) 830726, , « Part 15C, part Georgian country house, antiques », ,
. VISA.
closed 23 December-1 January – **Meals** (residents only) (dinner only) 24.95 **st.** 6.75 – 6
85.00/195.00 **st.**, 1 suite – SB.

RUSHYFORD *Durham* 401 402 P 20.
London 269 – Carlisle 82 – Middlesbrough 14 – Newcastle upon Tyne 26 – Sunderland 2

Swallow Eden Arms, DL17 0LL, (01388) 720541, *info@swallowhotels.c*
Fax (01388) 721871, – rm, – 100. VISA JCB.
Meals (light lunch)/dinner 18.50/22.00 **st.** 8.00 – **45 rm** 85.00/140.00 **st.** – SB.

RYDE *I.O.W.* 403 404 Q 31 – *see Wight (Isle of).*

RYE *E. Sussex* 404 W 31 *Great Britain G.* – *pop. 3 708.*
See : *Old Town★★ : Mermaid Street★, St. Mary's Church (≤★).*
The Heritage Centre, Strand Quay (01797) 226696.
London 61 – Brighton 49 – Folkestone 27 – Maidstone 33.

Mermaid Inn, Mermaid St., TN31 7EY, ✆ (01797) 223065, *mermaidinnrye@btclick.com, Fax (01797) 225069,* « Historic 15C inn » – ⇆ rest, TV P. MO AE ① VISA JCB. ⚘
Meals 17.00/35.00 **t.** and a la carte 7.20 – **31 rm** ☐ 70.00/160.00 **st.** – SB.

Rye Lodge, Hilders Cliff, TN31 7LD, ✆ (01797) 223838, *info@ryelodge.co.uk, Fax (01797) 223585,* ≘s, ☐ – ⇆ rest, TV P. MO AE ① VISA JCB
Meals (dinner only) 22.50 **st.** and a la carte 7.50 – **20 rm** ☐ 65.00/150.00 **st.** – SB.

George, High St., TN31 7JP, ✆ (01797) 222114, *Fax (01797) 224065* – ⇆ TV – 🏛 80. MO AE VISA
Meals 15.50/16.85 **st.** (dinner) and lunch a la carte 10.15/13.70 **st.** – **21 rm** ☐ 85.00/120.00 **t.** – SB.

Jeake's House without rest., Mermaid St., TN31 7ET, ✆ (01797) 222828, *jeakeshouse@btinternet.com, Fax (01797) 222623,* « Part 17C » – TV P. MO VISA
12 rm ☐ 28.50/93.00 **st.**

King Charles II without rest., 4 High St., TN31 7JE, ✆ (01797) 224954, « Medieval house » – ⇆ TV. MO VISA
3 rm 55.00/85.00 **st.**

Old Vicarage without rest., 66 Church Sq., TN31 7HF, ✆ (01797) 222119, *oldvicaragerye@tesco.net, Fax (01797) 227466,* « Part 14C », ⛱ – ⇆ TV P. ⚘
closed 24 to 27 December – **5 rm** ☐ 58.00/78.00 **st.**

Little Orchard House without rest., West St., TN31 7ES, ✆ (01797) 223831, *Fax (01797) 223831,* ⛱ – ⇆ TV. MO VISA JCB. ⚘
3 rm ☐ 50.00/84.00 **st.**

Flushing Inn, 4 Market St., TN31 7LA, ✆ (01797) 223292, *j.e.flynn@talk21.com,* « 15C inn with 16C mural » – ⇆. MO AE ① VISA
closed first 2 weeks January, Monday dinner and Tuesday – **Meals** - Seafood - 16.00/31.00 **t.** and a la carte 5.50.

Landgate Bistro, 5-6 Landgate, TN31 7LH, ✆ (01797) 222829 – MO AE ① VISA JCB
closed 1 week in summer, 2 weeks Christmas, Sunday and Monday – **Meals** (dinner only) a la carte 16.80/24.40 **st.** 4.50.

Peasmarsh *Northwest : 4 m. on A 268 – ✉ Rye.*

Flackley Ash, London Rd, TN31 6YH, on A 268 ✆ (01797) 230651, *flackleyash@marstonhotels.co.uk, Fax (01797) 230510,* Fǝ, ≘s, ☐, ⛱ – ⇆ rest, TV ♿ P – 🏛 100. MO AE ① VISA JCB
Meals (bar lunch Monday to Saturday)/dinner 22.50/30.00 **st.** 10.95 – **43 rm** ☐ 77.00/149.00 **st.**, 2 suites – SB.

LSTONE *N. Yorks.* 402 N 21 – *see Skipton.*

TON ON DUNSMORE *W. Mids.* 403 404 P 28 – *see Coventry.*

FFRON WALDEN *Essex* 404 U 27 *Great Britain G. – pop. 13 201.*
See : *Audley End★★ AC.*
1 Market Pl., Market Sq. ✆ (01799) 510444.
London 46 – Cambridge 15 – Chelmsford 25.

Littlebury Green *West : 4½ m. by B 1383 – ✉ Saffron Walden.*

Elmdon Lee, CB11 4XB, ✆ (01763) 838237, *dianaduke@barclays.net, Fax (01763) 838237,* ⛱ – TV P. MO ① VISA. ⚘
closed 25 December – **Meals** (by arrangement) (communal dining) 25.00 **s.** – **4 rm** ☐ 35.00/70.00 **s.**

Elmdon *West : 7½ m. by B 1052 and B 1383 off B 1039 – ✉ Saffron Walden.*

Elmdon Bury ⛰, CB11 4NF, ✆ (01763) 838220, *elmdonbury@yahoo.com, Fax (01763) 838504,* ☐, ⛱, ⚘, ⚘ – ⇆ rm, P. ⚘
closed 20 December-30 January – **Meals** (by arrangement) (communal dining) 20.00 **t.** – **3 rm** ☐ 30.00/55.00 **t.**

AGNES *Cornwall* 403 E 33 *The West Country G. – pop. 2 899.*
See : *St. Agnes Beacon★★ (✻★★).*
Env. : *Portreath★, SW : 5½ m.*
18 Perranporth, Budnic Hill ✆ (01872) 572454.
London 302 – Newquay 12 – Penzance 26 – Truro 9.

ENGLAND

Rose-in-Vale Country House , Mithian, TR5 0QD, East : 2 m. by B 32
(01872) 552202, *reception@rose-in-vale-hotel.co.uk*, *Fax (01872) 552700*, , heate
 – rest, TV P. MC AE O VISA
closed January and February – **Meals** (bar lunch Monday to Saturday)/dinner 15.0
22.95 **st.** and a la carte 5.10 – **18 rm** 51.50/131.00 **st.** – SB.

ST. ALBANS *Herts.* 404 T 28 *Great Britain G. – pop. 80 376.*

See : *City★ - Cathedral★ – Verulamium★ (Museum★ AC).*

Env. : *Hatfield House★★ AC, E : 6 m. by A 1057.*

Batchwood Hall, Batchwood Dr. (01727) 833349 – 18, 9 Redbourn, Kinsbourne Gre Lane (01582) 793493.

Town Hall, Market Pl. (01727) 864511.

London 27 – Cambridge 41 – Luton 10.

Sopwell House , Cottonmill Lane, AL1 2HQ, Southeast : 1 ½ m. by A 1081 and M
House Lane (01727) 864477, *enquiries@sopwellhouse.co.uk*, *Fax (01727) 844741*, ,
, , , – TV P – 400. MC AE O VISA
Magnolia Conservatory : **Meals** 24.50 **t.** and a la carte – ***Bejerano's Brasserie :*** **Me**
a la carte 13.70/22.75 **st.** – **136 rm** 135.00/175.00 **st.**, 2 suites – SB.

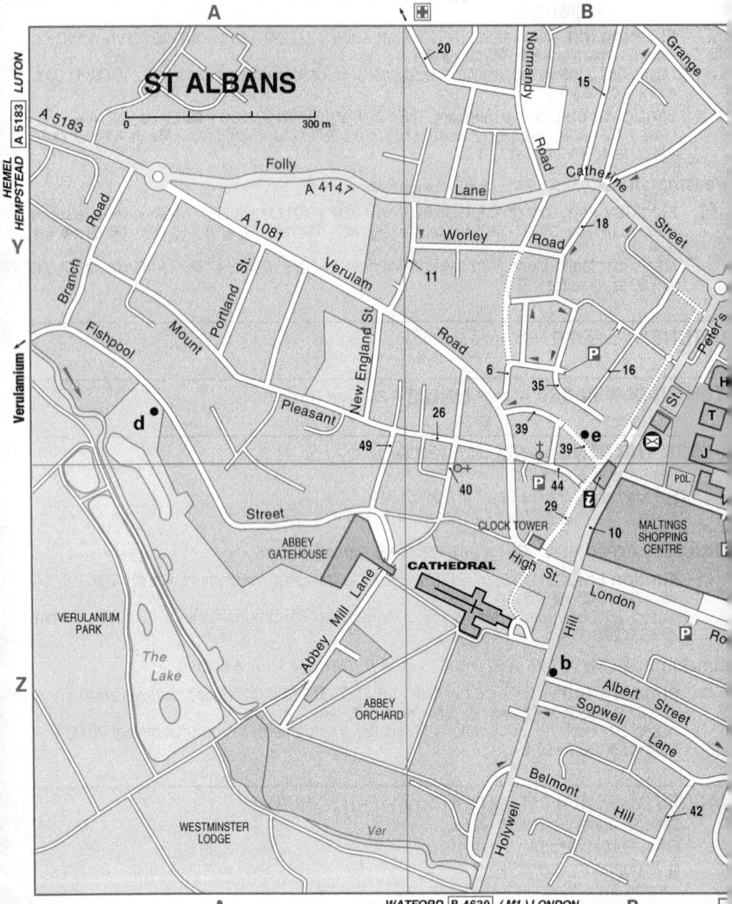

St Michael's Manor; 'St Michael's Village', Fishpool St., AL3 4RY, ✆ (01727) 864444, *smmanor@globalnet.co.uk, Fax (01727) 848909,* ≤, « Part 16C, part William and Mary manor house, lake and gardens » – ⇜ rm, TV P. MC AE VISA JCB. ✗
Meals 19.50/31.50 **t.** 9.00 – **22 rm** 110.00/295.00 **t.**, 1 suite – SB.

Thistle St. Albans, Watford Rd, AL2 3DS, Southwest : 2 ½ m. at junction of A 405 with B 4630 ✆ (01727) 854252, *stalbans@thistle.co.uk, Fax (01727) 841906,* Lø, ≘s, ◻ – ⇜ rm, ▤ rest, TV P – 🎭 50. MC AE ⓓ VISA. ✗
Restaurant : Meals *(closed lunch Saturday and Bank Holidays)* 21.50/26.00 **t.** and a la carte 12.50 – ***Carvery :*** Meals *(closed Sunday dinner)* 16.50 **t.** and a la carte 8.00 – 11.50 – **109 rm** 130.00/140.00 **st.**, 2 suites – SB.

Pré, Redbourn Rd, AL3 6JZ, Northwest : 1 ¼ m. on A 5183 ✆ (01727) 855259, *Fax (01727) 852239,* 🛋 – ⇜ rest, TV P. MC AE VISA
accommodation closed 24-25 December – **Meals** *(closed dinner 25 December)* (grill rest.) a la carte 11.20/18.40 **t.** 5.95 – **11 rm** 55.00/65.00 **t.**

Comfort, Ryder House, Holywell Hill, AL1 1HG, ✆ (01727) 848849, *admin@gbossu.net.com, Fax (01727) 812210* – |♦|, ⇜ rm, ▤ rest, TV ✆ ♿ P – 🎭 35. MC AE ⓓ VISA JCB. ✗
Meals (dinner only) 15.00/20.00 **t.** and a la carte 6.00 – 8.50 – **60 rm** 65.00 **t.** – SB.

Nonna Rosa, 3 Manor Rd, AL1 3ST, ✆ (01727) 853613, *Fax (01727) 831700,* 🛋 – ⇜ rest, TV P. MC AE ⓓ VISA. ✗
Meals (booking essential) (dinner only) a la carte approx. 12.00 **t.** 6.00 – **10 rm** 37.00/65.00 **st.**

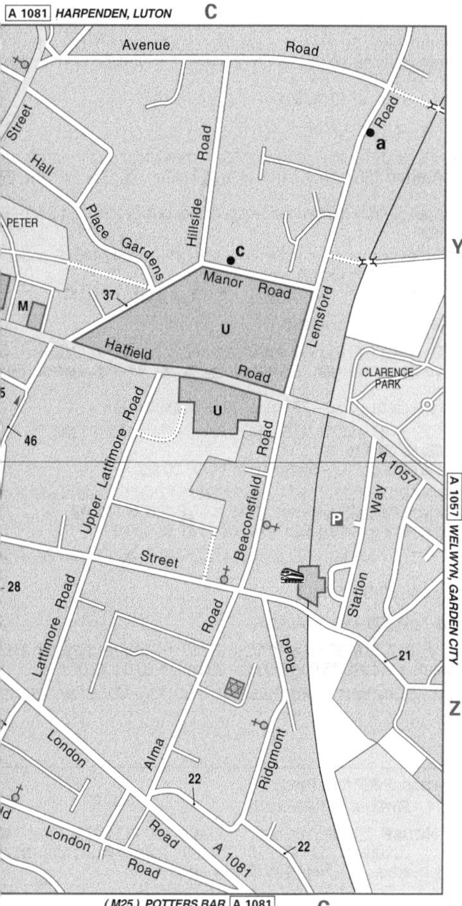

Ardmore House, 54 Lemsford Rd, AL1 3PR, (01727) 859313, *info@ardmorehouse.el.altodigital.com, Fax (01727) 859313,* – rm, TV P. MC AE VISA.
Meals (dinner only) 10.00/25.00 **t.** – **40 rm** 52.50/95.00 **t.**

Sukiyaki, 6 Spencer St., AL3 5EG, (01727) 865009 – MC AE VISA JCB
closed 2 weeks in summer, 1 week Christmas, Sunday and Monday – **Meals** - Japanes 9.50/23.50 **st.** and a la carte 14.00/17.20 **st.** 6.50.

ST. ANNE *Alderney (Channel Islands)* 403 Q 33 and 230 ⑨ – *see Channel Islands.*

ST. AUBIN *Jersey (Channel Islands)* 403 P 33 and 230 ⑪ – *see Channel Islands.*

ST. AUSTELL *Cornwall* 403 F 32 *The West Country G.* – *pop. 21 622.*

See : *Holy Trinity Church★.*

Env. : *St. Austell Bay★★ (Gribbin Head★★) E : by A 390 and A 3082 – Carthew : Wheal Mar China Clay Heritage Centre★★* **AC**, *N : 2 m. by A 391 – Mevagissey★★ - Lost Gardens Heligan★, S : 5 m. by B 3273 – Charlestown★, SE : 2 m. by A 390.*

Exc. : *Trewithen★★★* **AC**, *NE : 7 m. by A 390 – Lanhydrock★★, NE : 11 m. by A 390 an 3269 – Polkerris★, E : 7 m. by A 390 and A 3082.*

18 *Carlyon Bay* *(01726) 814250.*

London 281 – Newquay 16 – Plymouth 38 – Truro 14.

Poltarrow Farm without rest., St. Mewan, PL26 7DR, Southwest : 1 ¾ m. by A (01726) 67111, *enquire@poltarrow.co.uk, Fax (01726) 67111,* « Working farm », – TV P. MC VISA.
closed Christmas-New Year – **5 rm** 30.00/50.00.

at Tregrehan *East : 2½ m. by A 390 –* ✉ *St. Austell.*

Boscundle Manor, PL25 3RL, (01726) 813557, *stay@boscundlemanor.co Fax (01726) 814997,* « Converted 18C manor, gardens », heated, – rest, TV MC AE VISA JCB
April-October – **Meals** *(closed Sunday to non-residents)* (dinner only) 22.50 **st.** 5.50 – 8 75.00/130.00 **st.**, 2 suites.

Anchorage House, Nettles Corner, Boscundle, PL25 3RH, (01726) 814071, *enquir nchoragehouse.co.uk,* – TV P. MC VISA.
Meals (by arrangement) (communal dining) 25.00 **st.** – **3 rm** 42.00/68.00 **st.**

at Carlyon Bay *East : 2½ m. by A 3601 –* ✉ *St. Austell.*

Carlyon Bay, PL25 3RD, (01726) 812304, *info@carlyonbay.co.uk, Fax (01726) 814* Carlyon Bay, « Extensive gardens », s, heated, 18, – , rest, TV 65. MC AE VISA.
Meals 12.00/24.00 **t.** and a la carte 7.50 – **73 rm** 79.00/240.00 – SB.

Cliff Head, Sea Rd, PL25 3RB, (01726) 812345, *Fax (01726) 815511,* s, rest, TV P – 230. MC AE VISA.
Meals 7.95/19.95 **t.** and a la carte 5.95 – **55 rm** 41.00/92.00 **st.**

Porth Avallen, Sea Rd, PL25 3SG, (01726) 812802, *nmarks@aol.c Fax (01726) 817097,* Carlyon Bay, – TV P – 100. MC AE VISA.
Meals 9.25/18.50 **t.** and dinner a la carte 5.25 – **24 rm** 61.50/105.00 **t.** – SB.

Wheal Lodge without rest., 91 Sea Rd, PL25 3SH, (01726) 815543, *Fax (01726) 815* – TV P. MC VISA.
closed Christmas – **6 rm** 46.00/80.00 **st.**

at Charlestown *Southeast : 2 m. by A 390 –* ✉ *St. Austell.*

Pier House, PL25 3NJ, (01726) 67955, *Fax (01726) 69246,* – rest, TV. MC VISA.
closed 25 December – **Meals** a la carte 15.00/25.05 **t.** – **26 rm** 40.00/75.00 **t.**

T' Gallants without rest., 6 Charlestown Rd, PL25 3NJ, (01726) 70203, – TV P. VISA.
8 rm 30.00/48.00 **st.**

ST. BLAZEY *Cornwall* 403 F 32 – *pop. 8 837 (inc. Par).*

London 276 – Newquay 21 – Plymouth 33 – Truro 19.

Nanscawen Manor House without rest., Prideaux Rd, PL24 2SR, West : ¾ following signs for Luxulyan (01726) 814488, *keith@nanscawen.c Fax (01726) 814488,* , heated, – TV P. MC VISA.
3 rm 40.00/84.00 **s.**

BRELADE'S BAY *Jersey (Channel Islands)* 403 P 33 and 230 ⑪ – *see Channel Islands.*

HELENS *Mersey.* 402 403 L 23 – *pop. 106 293.*

Sherdley Park Municipal, Sherdley Park (01744) 813149.
London 207 – Liverpool 16 – Manchester 27.

Hilton St. Helens, Linkway West, WA10 1NG, (01744) 453444, *reservations@sthelens.stakis.co.uk, Fax (01744) 454655,* rm, – 200. AE VISA JCB
The Pyramid : **Meals** *(closed Saturday lunch)* 12.95/25.00 **st.** and a la carte 5.95 – 10.95 – **81 rm** 125.00 **st.**, 3 suites – SB.

Premier Lodge, East Lancashire Rd, WA11 7LX, North : 1 ¾ m. at junction of A 580 with A 571 (0870) 7001544, *Fax (0870) 7001545* – rm, – 80. AE VISA.
Meals (grill rest.) a la carte 9.85/18.15 **st.** 7.95 – 6.00 – **43 rm** 46.00 **st.** – SB.

Rainhill *Southwest : 3½ m. by A 58 and B 5413 – St. Helens.*

Premier Lodge, 804 Warrington Rd, L35 6PE, Southeast : 1 m. on A 57 (0870) 7001430, *Fax (0870) 7001431,* – AE VISA.
Meals (grill rest.) – **34 rm** 46.00 **t.**

HELIER *Jersey (Channel Islands)* 403 P 33 and 230 ⑪ – *see Channel Islands.*

ISSEY *Cornwall* 403 F 32 – *see Padstow.*

Die im **Michelin-Führer**
verwendeten Zeichen und Symbole haben
- **fett** oder dünn gedruckt, rot oder **schwarz** -
jeweils eine andere Bedeutung.
Lesen Sie daher die Erklärungen aufmerksam durch.

IVES *Cambs.* 404 T 27 – *pop. 15 312 – Huntingdon.*
London 75 – Cambridge 14 – Huntingdon 6.

Dolphin, Bridge Foot, London Rd, PE27 5EP, (01480) 466966, *Fax (01480) 495597* – – 150. AE VISA.
Meals (bar lunch Monday to Saturday)/dinner 16.50 **t.** and a la carte 8.00 – **67 rm** 70.00/110.00 **t.** – SB.

Slepe Hall, Ramsey Rd, PE27 5RB, (01480) 463122, *mail@slepehall.co.uk, Fax (01480) 300706* – rest, – 40. AE VISA.
closed 4 days Christmas-New Year – **Meals** 15.50/17.50 **st.** 4.95 – **16 rm** 75.00/100.00 **st.**

Oliver's Lodge, Needingworth Rd, PE17 4JP, (01480) 463252, *reception@oliverslodge.co.uk, Fax (01480) 461150,* – rest, – 65. AE VISA JCB
Meals a la carte 18.50/24.00 **st.** 4.75 – **17 rm** 72.00/90.00 **st.** – SB.

Holywell *East : 3 m. by A 1123 – Huntingdon.*

Old Ferryboat Inn, PE17 3TG, (01480) 463227, *Fax (01480) 463227,* – rm, AE VISA JCB.
Meals a la carte 10.70/16.90 **t.** – **7 rm** 50.00/70.00 **t.**

IVES *Cornwall* 403 D 33 *The West Country G.* – *pop. 10 092.*
See : *Town★★ - Barbara Hepworth Museum★★* AC Y **M1** – *Tate St. Ives★★ (≤★★) - St. Nicholas Chapel (≤★★)* Y – *Parish Church★* Y **A**.
Env. : *S : Penwith★★* Y.
Exc. : *St. Michael's Mount★★ (≤★★) S : 10 m. by B 3306* – Y – *B 3311, B 3309 and A 30.*
Tregenna Castle Hotel (01736) 795254 ext: 121 Y – *West Cornwall, Lelant (01736) 753401.*
The Guildhall, Street-an-Pol (01736) 796297.
London 319 – Penzance 10 – Truro 25.

Plan on next page

Porthminster, The Terrace, TR26 2BN, (01736) 795221, *reception@porthminster-hotel.co.uk, Fax (01736) 797043,* ≤, heated, – AE VISA JCB — Y s
closed 2-12 January **Meals** (bar lunch Monday to Saturday)/dinner 15.00/20.00 **t.** and a la carte 4.95 – **43 rm** (dinner included) 51.00/149.00 **st.** – SB.

Blue Hayes without rest., Trelyon Av., TR26 2AD, (01736) 797129, ≤, – VISA JCB. — Y c
April-October – – **9 rm** 34.00/95.00 **st.**

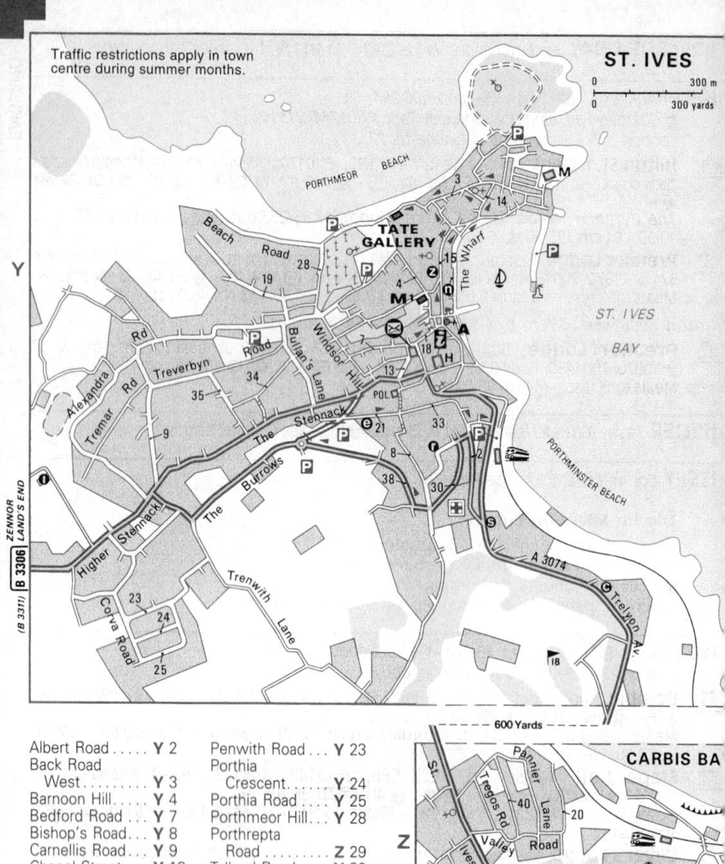

Albert Road	Y 2	Penwith Road	Y 23
Back Road West	Y 3	Porthia Crescent	Y 24
Barnoon Hill	Y 4	Porthia Road	Y 25
Bedford Road	Y 7	Porthmeor Hill	Y 28
Bishop's Road	Y 8	Porthrepta Road	Z 29
Carnellis Road	Y 9	Talland Road	Y 30
Chapel Street	Y 13	Tregenna Terrace	Y 33
Fish Street	Y 14	Trelawney Road	Y 34
Fore Street	Y 15	Trerice Road	Y 35
High Street	Y 18	Trewidden Road	Y 38
Orange Lane	Y 19	Wheal Whidden	Z 40
Parc Owles	Z 20		
Park Av.	Y 21		

Old Vicarage without rest., Parc-an-Creet, TR26 2ES, ☎ (01736) 796124, *holidays@oldvicaragehotel.freeserve.co,.uk, Fax (01736) 796124*, – **TV** **P**. **MC** **VISA** **JCB** Y
March-October – **8 rm** 27.00/52.00.

Trewinnard, 4 Parc Av., TR26 2DN, ☎ (01736) 794168, *trewinnard@cwcom..., Fax (01736) 798161*, – **TV** **P**. **MC** **VISA** **JCB**. Y
April-October – **Meals** (by arrangement) a la carte 11.65/19.15 **st.** 3.05 – **7 rm** 32.../64.00 **st.**

The Pondarosa, 10 Porthminster Terr., TR26 2DQ, ☎ (01736) 795875, *pondarosa-hot...talk21.com, Fax (01736) 797811* – **TV** **P**. **MC** **VISA**. Y
Meals (by arrangement) 14.00 **st.** – **9 rm** 25.00/46.00 **st.** – SB.

Russets, 18a Fore St., TR26 1AB, ☎ (01736) 794700, *russets@manutd.c... Fax (01736) 794700* – . **MC** **AE** **VISA** Y
Meals (dinner only and lunch 25 December) a la carte 18.55/25.90 **t.** 5.85.

Alfresco, Wharf Rd, TR26 1LF, ☎ (01736) 793737, *m.gill@which.net, Fax (01736) 7968...* **MC** **VISA** Y
Meals a la carte 19.10/27.65 **t.** 6.50.

:arbis Bay South : 1 3/4 m. on A 3074 – ✉ St. Ives.

Boskerris, Boskerris Rd, TR26 2NQ, ☎ (01736) 795295, *boskerris.hotel@btinternet.com*, *Fax (01736) 798632*, ≤, heated, – rest, TV P. MC AE VISA. Z x
Easter-October – **Meals** (bar lunch)/dinner 21.00/25.00 **t.** 5.00 – **16 rm** (dinner included) 75.00/144.00 **t.** – SB.

ENGLAND

JUST *Cornwall* 403 C 33 *The West Country G. – pop. 2 092.*
See : *Church*★.
Env. : *Penwith*★★ – *Sancreed* – *Church*★★ *(Celtic Crosses*★★*), SE : 3 m. by A 3071 – St. Buryan*★★ *(Church Tower*★★*), SE : 5 1/2 m. by B 3306 and A 30 – Land's End*★ *(cliff scenery*★★★*), S : 5 1/2 m. by B 3306 and A 30 – Cape Cornwall*★ *(≤*★★*), W : 1 1/2 m. – Morvah (≤*★★*), NE : 4 1/2 m. by B 3306 – Geevor Tin Mine*★ **AC**, *N : 3 m. by B 3306 – Carn Euny*★, *SE : 3 m. by A 3071 – Wayside Cross*★ – *Sennen Cove*★ *(≤*★*), S : 5 1/2 m. by B 3306 and A 30.*
Exc. : *Porthcurno*★, *S : 9 1/2 m. by B 3306, A 30 and B 3315.*
18 *Cape Cornwall G & C.C.* ☎ *(01736) 788611.*
London 325 – Penzance 7.5 – Truro 35.

Boscean Country ⛰, TR19 7QP, Northwest : 1/2 m. by Boswedden Rd ☎ (01736) 788748, *boscean@aol.com*, *Fax (01736) 788748*, ≤, – P. MC VISA JCB.
Meals (dinner only) (residents only) 13.00 **t.** – **12 rm** 28.00/44.00 **t.** – SB.

KEVERNE *Cornwall* 403 E 33 – *pop. 1 843.*
London 302 – Penzance 26 – Truro 28.

Valley View House, Porthallow Cove, TR12 6PN, Northeast : 2 1/2 m. ☎ (01326) 280370, *hawthorne@valleyviewhouse.freeserve.co.uk*, *Fax (01326) 280370* – TV.
Meals (by arrangement) 11.95 **st.** – **3 rm** 19.00/42.00 **st.** – SB.

LAWRENCE *I.O.W.* 403 404 Q 32 – *see Wight (Isle of).*

LAWRENCE *Jersey (Channel Islands)* 403 P 33 and 230 ⑪ – *see Channel Islands.*

LEONARDS *E. Sussex* 404 V 31 – *see Hastings and St. Leonards.*

MARGARET'S AT CLIFFE *Kent* 404 Y 30 – *see Dover.*

MARTIN *Guernsey (Channel Islands)* 403 P 33 and 230 ⑩ – *see Channel Islands.*

MARTIN'S *Cornwall* 403 ㉚ – *see Scilly (Isles of).*

MARY'S *Cornwall* 403 ㉚ – *see Scilly (Isles of).*

MAWES *Cornwall* 403 E 33 *The West Country G.* – ✉ *Truro.*
See : *Town*★ - *Castle*★ **AC** *(≤*★*).*
Env. : *St. Just-in-Roseland Church*★★, *N : 2 1/2 m. by A 3078.*
London 299 – Plymouth 56 – Truro 18.

Tresanton ⛰, 27 Lower Castle Rd, TR2 5DR, ☎ (01326) 270055, *info@tresanton.com*, *Fax (01326) 270053*, ≤ St. Mawes bay, St. Anthony's head and lighthouse, – TV P – 50. MC AE VISA.
closed 5 January-mid February – **Meals** (booking essential to non-residents) 20.00/33.00 **st.** and dinner a la carte 9.00 – **24 rm** 187.00/220.00 **st.**, 2 suites.

Idle Rocks, Harbourside, 1 Tredenham Rd, TR2 5AN, ☎ (01326) 270771, *idlerocks@talk21.com*, *Fax (01326) 270062*, ≤ harbour and estuary – rest, TV. MC AE VISA
Meals (brasserie lunch)/dinner 27.95 **st.** 8.95 – **28 rm** (dinner included) 84.00/114.00 **t.** – SB.

Rising Sun, The Square, TR2 5DJ, ☎ (01326) 270233, *Fax (01326) 270198* – TV P. MC AE VISA
Meals (bar lunch Monday to Saturday)/dinner 24.50 **t.** 6.75 – **8 rm** 59.50/119.00 **t.**

ST. MICHAELS-ON-WYRE *Lancs.* 402 L 22.
London 235 – Blackpool 24 – Burnley 35 – Manchester 43.

Compton House without rest., Garstang Rd, PR3 0TE, ☎ (01995) 6793
Fax (01995) 679378, – TV P. VISA.
closed 23 December-5 January – **3 rm** 30.00/40.00.

ST. PETER *Jersey (Channel Islands)* 403 P 33 and 230 ⑪ – *see Channel Islands.*

ST. PETER IN THE WOOD *Guernsey (Channel Islands)* 403 P 33 and 230 ⑨ – *see Cha Islands.*

ST. PETER PORT *Guernsey (Channel Islands)* 403 P 33 and 230 ⑩ – *see Channel Islands.*

ST. SAVIOUR *Guernsey (Channel Islands)* 403 P 33 and 230 ⑨ – *see Channel Islands.*

ST. SAVIOUR *Jersey (Channel Islands)* 403 P 33 and 230 ⑪ – *see Channel Islands.*

SALCOMBE *Devon* 403 I 33 *The West Country G. – pop. 2 189.*
Env. : *Sharpitor (Overbecks Museum and Garden★) (≤★★)* **AC**, *S : 2 m. by South Sands Z*
Exc. : *Prawle Point (≤★★★) E : 16 m. around coast by A 381 –* **Y** *– and A 379.*
Council Hall, Market St. ☎ (01548) 843927.
London 243 – Exeter 43 – Plymouth 27 – Torquay 28.

SALCOMBE

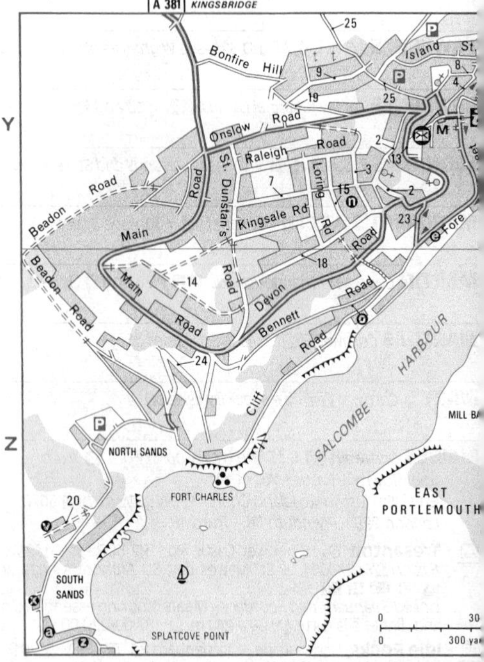

Town plans
roads most used
by traffic and those
on which guide listed
hotels and restaurants
stand are fully drawn;
the beginning only
of lesser roads
is indicated.

Tides Reach, South Sands, TQ8 8LJ, ☎ (01548) 843466, *enquiry@tidesreach.c*
Fax (01548) 843954, ≤ estuary, squash – rest, TV P. AE JCB
Meals (bar lunch)/dinner 30.00 **st.** 7.25 – **35 rm** (dinner included) 98.00/220.00 SB.

Marine, Cliff Rd, TQ8 8JH, ☎ (01548) 844444, *marine@menzies-hotels.co.uk, Fax (01548) 843109,* ≤ estuary, ⛱, ≘s, 🏊 – |¢| ⚓ ⇎ TV P. MO AE ① VISA JCB Y e
Meals (terrace lunch)/dinner 27.50 **st.** – **50 rm** ☐ (dinner included) 80.00/230.00 **st.**, 1 suite – SB.

South Sands, South Sands, TQ8 8LL, ☎ (01548) 843741, *enquire@southsands.com, Fax (01548) 842112,* ≤, 🏊 – ⚓, ⇎ rest, TV P. MO AE VISA JCB Z a
April-October – **Meals** (bar lunch)/dinner 18.00/24.00 **st.** 6.95 – **30 rm** ☐ (dinner included) 83.00/170.00 **st.** – SB.

Bolt Head, South Sands, TQ8 8LL, ☎ (01548) 843751, *info@bolthead-salcombe.co.uk, Fax (01548) 843061,* ≤ estuary, 🏊 heated – TV P. MO AE ① VISA Z z
11 March-October – **Meals** 14.50/39.00 **st.** – **28 rm** 85.00/210.00 **st.** – SB.

Grafton Towers, Moult Rd, TQ8 8LG, ☎ (01548) 842882, *graftontowers.salcombe@virgin.net, Fax (01548) 842857,* ≤ estuary, 🌳 – ⇎ rest, TV P. MO VISA Z v
April-October – **Meals** (dinner only) 17.50 **t.** 4.50 – **12 rm** ☐ 55.00/91.00 **t.** – SB.

Lyndhurst without rest., Bonaventure Rd, TQ8 8BG, ☎ (01548) 842481, *lyndnet.sale@tesco.net, Fax (01548) 842481,* ≤ – ⇎ TV P. MO VISA JCB. ✗ Y n
restricted opening in winter – **8 rm** ☐ 50.00/60.00 **s.**

Soar Mill Cove *Southwest : 4¼ m. by A 381 via Malborough village* – Y – ✉ *Salcombe.*

Soar Mill Cove ⛱, TQ7 3DS, ☎ (01548) 561566, *info@makepeacehotel.co.uk, Fax (01548) 561223,* ≤, 🏊 heated, 🏊, 🌳, ✗ – ⇎ TV P. MO AE VISA JCB
closed January – **Meals** (booking essential to non-residents) (light lunch)/dinner 29.00/34.00 **st.** – **21 rm** ☐ (dinner included) 147.00/252.00 **st.** – SB.

Hope Cove *West : 4 m. by A 381 via Malborough village* – Y – ✉ *Kingsbridge.*

Lantern Lodge ⛱, TQ7 3HE, by Grand View Rd ☎ (01548) 561280, *Fax (01548) 561736,* ≤, ≘s, 🏊, 🌳 – ⇎ rest, TV P. MO VISA JCB. ✗
March-November – **Meals** (bar lunch)/dinner 17.00 **t.** 4.95 – **14 rm** ☐ (dinner included) 66.00/136.00 **t.** – SB.

When visiting the West Country,
use the Michelin Green Guide **"The West Country of England".**
- *Detailed descriptions of places of interest*
- *Touring programmes by county*
- *Maps and street plans*
- *The history of the region*
- *Photographs and drawings of monuments, beauty spots, houses...*

E *Gtr. Manchester* 402 403 404 N 23 – *pop. 56 052* – ✉ *Manchester.*
18 Sale Lodge, Golf Rd ☎ (0161) 973 3404.
London 212 – Liverpool 36 – Manchester 6 – Sheffield 43.

Belmore, 143 Brooklands Rd, M33 3QN, ☎ (0161) 973 2538, *belmore_hotel@hotmail.com, Fax (0161) 973 2665,* 🌳 – ⇎ TV ☎ P – 🏛 80. MO AE ① VISA
***Classic :* Meals** *(closed Saturday lunch and Sunday dinner)* (booking essential to non-residents) 9.95/35.00 **t.** (dinner) and a la carte 6.50 – ***Cada's :* Meals** (dinner only and Saturday lunch and Sunday)/dinner 25.00/35.00 **t.** and a la carte 6.50 – **21 rm** ☐ 100.00/150.00 **t.**, 2 suites.

Amblehurst, 44 Washway Rd, M33 7QZ, on A 56 ☎ (0161) 973 8800, *amblehurst@aol.com, Fax (0161) 905 1697,* 🌳 – ⇎ rm, ▤ rest, TV ♿ P. MO AE ① VISA. ✗
Meals *(closed Saturday lunch and Sunday dinner)* 9.95/13.95 **t.** and dinner a la carte 6.50 – **64 rm** ☐ 75.00/85.00 **st.**

Cornerstones, 230 Washway Rd, M33 4RA, ☎ (0161) 283 6909, *cornerstones.hotel@virgin.net, Fax (0161) 283 6909,* 🌳 – ⇎ TV ☎ P. MO VISA JCB. ✗
closed Christmas-New Year – **Meals** *(closed Friday to Sunday)* (residents only) (dinner only) 15.00 5.50 – ☐ 5.00 – **9 rm** 35.00/50.00 – SB.

Travel Inn, Carrington Lane, Ashton-upon-Mersey, M33 5BL, Northwest : 1 ½ m. by B 5166 on A 6144 ☎ (0161) 962 8113, *Fax (0161) 905 1742* – ⇎ rm, TV ♿ P – 🏛 40. MO AE ① VISA. ✗
Meals (grill rest.) – **40 rm** 40.95 **t.**

FORDS *Surrey* 404 T 30 – *see Redhill.*

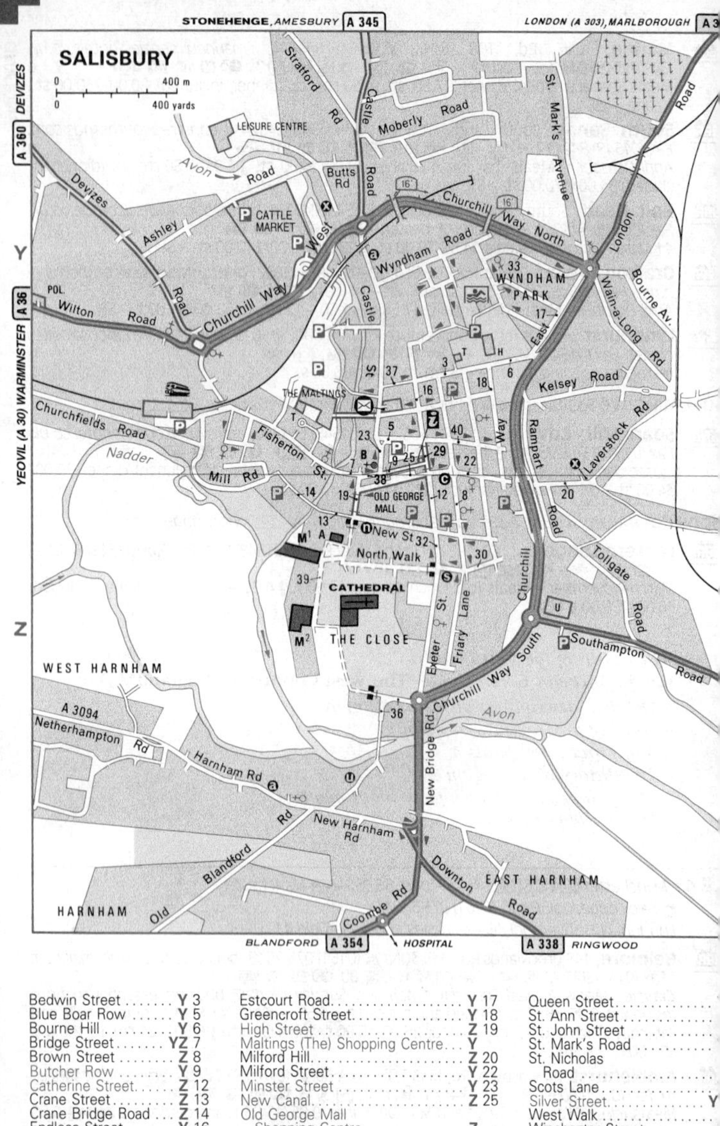

Bedwin Street .... Y 3	Estcourt Road.................. Y 17	Queen Street...............
Blue Boar Row ...... Y 5	Greencroft Street............... Y 18	St. Ann Street ....
Bourne Hill .... Y 6	High Street .... Z 19	St. John Street ....
Bridge Street........ YZ 7	Maltings (The) Shopping Centre... Y	St. Mark's Road ....
Brown Street .... Z 8	Milford Hill..................... Z 20	St. Nicholas Road..........
Butcher Row .... Y 9	Milford Street................... Y 22	Scots Lane.................
Catherine Street...... Z 12	Minster Street .... Y 23	Silver Street.............. Y
Crane Street......... Z 13	New Canal...................... Z 25	West Walk..................
Crane Bridge Road ... Z 14	Old George Mall Shopping Centre .... Z	Winchester Street ....
Endless Street....... Y 16		

When travelling for business or pleasure
in **England, Wales, Scotland** *and* **Ireland***:*

- use the series of five maps (nos 401, 402, 403, 404 and 923) at a scale of 1:400 000
- they are the perfect complement to this Guide

LISBURY *Wilts.* 403 404 O 30 *The West Country G. – pop. 39 268.*

See : *City★★ – Cathedral★★★* **AC Z** – *Salisbury and South Wiltshire Museum★* **AC Z M2** – *Close★* **Z** : *Mompesson House★* **AC Z A** – *Sarum St. Thomas Church★* **Y B** – *Royal Gloucestershire, Berkshire and Wiltshire Regiment Museum★.*

Env. : *Wilton Village★ (Wilton House★★* **AC**, *Wilton Carpet Factory★* **AC**), *W : 3 m. by A 30* **Y** – *Old Sarum★* **AC**, *N : 2 m. by A 345* **Y** – *Woodford (Heale House Garden★)* **AC**, *NW : 4½ m. by Stratford Rd* **Y**.

Exc. : *Stonehenge★★★* **AC**, *NW : 10 m. by A 345* – **Y** – *and A 303 – Wardour Castle★* **AC**, *W : 15 m. by A 30* **Y**.

18, 9 Salisbury & South Wilts., Netherhampton ☎ (01722) 742645 – 18 High Post, Great Durnford ☎ (01722) 782356.

Fish Row ☎ (01722) 334956.

London 91 – Bournemouth 28 – Bristol 53 – Southampton 23.

Plan opposite

White Hart, 1 St. John's St., SP1 2SD, ☎ (0870) 400 8125, *Fax (01722) 412761* – 80. MC AE VISA JCB Z s
Meals (bar lunch Saturday) 7.95/24.95 **t.** and dinner a la carte 8.95 – **68 rm** 94.85/134.70 **t.** – SB.

Red Lion, 4 Milford St., SP1 2AN, ☎ (01722) 323334, *reception@the-redlion.co.uk, Fax (01722) 325756* – 100. MC AE VISA JCB. Z c
Meals 11.95/35.50 **t.** and dinner a la carte 7.95 – 9.50 – **53 rm** 84.00/119.50 **st.** – SB.

Milford Hall, 206 Castle St., SP1 3TE, ☎ (01722) 417411, *milfordhallhotel@cs.com, Fax (01722) 419444* – 25. MC AE VISA Y a
Meals a la carte 12.50/25.60 **t.** 8.95 – **35 rm** 85.00/135.00 **st.** – SB.

Cricket Field House, Wilton Rd, SP2 9NS, West : 1 ¼ m. on A 36 ☎ (01722) 322595, *cricketfieldcottage@btinternet.com, Fax (01722) 322595* – MC VISA JCB.
Meals *(closed Sunday and Monday)* (dinner only) 12.50/21.00 **st.** – **14 rm** 40.00/65.00 **st.** – SB.

Travel Inn, Pearce Way, Bishopdown, SP1 3YU, Northeast : 2 ½ m. on A 338 ☎ (01722) 339836, *Fax (01722) 337889* – rm, MC AE VISA.
Meals (grill rest.) – **40 rm** 40.95 **t.**

Old House without rest., 161 Wilton Rd, SP2 7JQ, West : 1 m. on A 36 ☎ (01722) 333433, *Fax (01722) 335551*, –
6 rm 30.00/70.00 **st.**, 1 suite.

Stratford Lodge, 4 Park Lane, SP1 3NP, off Castle Rd ☎ (01722) 325177, *strlodge@interalpha.co.uk, Fax (01722) 325177*, – MC AE VISA JCB.
closed 23 December-1 January – **Meals** (by arrangement) 18.00 **t.** 5.50 – **8 rm** 45.00/65.00 **t.** – SB.

Glen Lyn, 6 Bellamy Lane, Milford Hill, SP1 2SP, ☎ (01722) 327880, *glen.lyn@btinternet.com, Fax (01722) 327880*, – MC AE VISA JCB. YZ x
Meals (by arrangement) 17.00 **st.** 3.00 **7 rm** 32.00/57.50 **st.**

Malvern without rest., 31 Hulse Rd, SP1 3LU, ☎ (01722) 327995, *Fax (01722) 327995*, – Y x
3 rm 35.00/45.00 **st.**

LXIX, 69 New St., SP1 2PH, ☎ (01722) 340000, *Fax (01722) 340000* – MC AE VISA
closed Christmas, New Year, Saturday lunch and Sunday – **Meals** 20.00 **t.** (lunch) and dinner a la carte 22.50/34.50 **t.** 7.50. Z n

Middle Winterslow *Northeast : 6½ m. by A 30* – **Y** – ✉ *Salisbury.*

Beadles, Middleton, SP5 1QS, ☎ (01980) 862922, *winterbead@aol.com, Fax (01980) 862922*, – MC VISA.
Meals (by arrangement) (communal dining) 21.50 **st.** – **3 rm** 45.00/60.00 **st.**

Whiteparish *Southeast : 7½ m. by A 36* – **Z** – *on A 27* – ✉ *Salisbury.*

Brickworth Farmhouse without rest., Brickworth Lane, SP5 2QE, Northwest : 1 ½ m. off A 36 ☎ (01794) 884663, *Fax (01794) 884186*, « Georgian farmhouse », –
closed 22 December-3 January – **4 rm** 25.00/48.00.

Newton Farmhouse, Southampton Rd, SP5 2QL, Southwest : 1 ½ m. on A 36 ☎ (01794) 884416, *reservations@newtonfarmhouse.co.uk*, , –
Meals (by arrangement) 16.00 – **8 rm** 30.00/50.00 **s.**

Downton *South : 6 m. by A 338* – **Z** – *on B 3080* – ✉ *Salisbury.*

Warren without rest., 15 High St., SP5 3PG, ☎ (01725) 510263, –
closed 21 December-6 January – **4 rm** 36.00/50.00 **s.**

ENGLAND

at Woodfalls *South : 7 ¾ m. by A 338 – Z – on B 3080 – ✉ Salisbury.*

Woodfalls Inn, The Ridge, SP5 2LN, ✆ (01725) 513222, *woodfallsi@aol.co* *Fax (01725) 513220* – ⇔ TV P – 100. MC AE VISA JCB
Meals 12.50/20.00 **st.** – **10 rm** 49.95/90.00 **st.** – SB.

at Harnham *Southwest : 1½ m. by A 3094 – ✉ Salisbury.*

Rose & Crown, Harnham Rd, SP2 8JQ, ✆ (01722) 399955, *Fax (01722) 339816*, ≤, « Part 13C inn, riverside setting », – ⇔ TV & P – 80. MC AE VISA Z
Meals 7.95/19.50 **st.** and a la carte 6.75 – 9.50 – **28 rm** 105.00/145.00 **st.** – SB.

Grasmere House, 70 Harnham Rd, SP2 8JN, ✆ (01722) 338388, *Fax (01722) 333710*, – ⇔ rm, TV & P – 80. MC AE VISA JCB. Z
Meals 12.50/24.50 **st.** and a la carte 7.50 – **20 rm** 65.50/150.00 **st.** – SB.

at Teffont *West : 10¼ m. by A 36 – Y – and A 30 on B 3089 – ✉ Salisbury.*

Howard's House , Teffont Evias, SP3 5RJ, ✆ (01722) 716392, *paul.firmin@virgin.* *Fax (01722) 716820*, « Part 17C former dower house », – ⇔ rest, TV P. MC AE V
closed Christmas – **Meals** (booking essential to non-residents) (dinner only and Sun lunch)/dinner 19.95 **t.** and a la carte 26.65/33.70 **t.** 9.95 – **9 rm** 75.00/145.00 **t.**

at Stapleford *Northwest : 7 m. by A 36 – Y – on B 3083 – ✉ Salisbury.*

Elm Tree Cottage without rest., Chain Hill, SP3 4LH, ✆ (01722) 790507, *jaw.sykes@vi* *.net*, – ⇔ TV P.
restricted opening in winter – **3 rm** 32.00/50.00 **s.**

at Little Langford *Northwest : 8 m. by A 36 – Y – and Great Wishford rd – ✉ Salisbury.*

Little Langford Farmhouse without rest., SP3 4NR, ✆ (01722) 790205, *bandb@li angford.co.uk, Fax (01722) 790086*, ≤, « Working farm », – ⇔ TV P.
restricted opening in winter – **3 rm** 42.00/52.00 **st.**

Le Grand Londres (GREATER LONDON) est composé de la City et de 32 arrondissements administratifs (Borough) eux-mêmes divisés en quartiers ou en villages ayant conservé leur caractère propre (Area).

SALTASH *Cornwall* 403 H 32 *The West Country G. – pop. 14 139.*
Env. : *Tamar River★★.*
Exc. : *St. Germans Church★, SW : 7 m. by A 38 and B 3249.*
18, 18 *St. Mellion G & C.C. ✆ (01579) 351351 –* 18 *China Fleet C.C. ✆ (01752) 848668.*
London 246 – Exeter 38 – Plymouth 7 – Truro 49.

Travelodge, Callington Rd, Carkeel, PL12 6LF, Northwest : 1 ½ m. by A 388 on A 3 Saltash Service Area ✆ (01752) 848414, *Fax (01752) 849028* – ⇔, rest, TV & P – MC AE VISA JCB.
Meals (grill rest.) – **31 rm** 49.95 **t.**

SALTFORD *Bath & North East Somerset* 403 404 M 29 – *see Bristol.*

SAMLESBURY *Lancs.* 402 M 22 – *see Preston.*

SAMPFORD PEVERELL *Devon* 403 J 31 *The West Country G. – pop. 1 091 – ✉ Tiverton.*
Env. : *Uffculme (Coldharbour Mill★★), SE : 3 m. by A 373, A 38 and minor roads.*
Exc. : *Knightshayes Court★, W : 7 m. by A 373 and minor roads.*
London 184 – Barnstaple 34 – Exeter 20 – Taunton 19.

Parkway House, EX16 7BJ, ✆ (01884) 820255, *Fax (01884) 820780*, – TV P – MC AE VISA.
Meals a la carte 13.25/18.85 **t.** – **10 rm** 37.50/55.00 **t.** – SB.

SAMPFORD PEVERELL SERVICE AREA *Devon* 403 J 31 – ✉ *Tiverton.*
London 184 – Barnstaple 34 – Exeter 20 – Taunton 19.

Travelodge, EX16 7HD, M 5 junction 27 ✆ (01884) 821087 – ⇔ rm, rest, TV & P AE VISA JCB.
Meals (grill rest.) – **40 rm** 39.95 **t.**

NDBACH *Ches.* 402 403 404 M 24 – *pop. 15 839.*

Malkins Bank ☎ *(01270) 765931.*

London 177 – Liverpool 44 – Manchester 28 – Stoke-on-Trent 16.

Chimney House, Congleton Rd, CW11 4ST, East : 1 ½ m. on A 534 ☎ (01270) 764141, *Fax (01270) 768916*, – rest, TV P – 100. MC AE VISA.
Meals 12.00/22.00 **st.** and a la carte 7.95 – 9.75 – **49 rm** 80.00/90.00 **st.** – SB.

Old Hall, High St., CW11 1AL, ☎ (01270) 761221, *Fax (01270) 762551*, « 17C coaching inn », – rest, TV P – 30. MC AE VISA
Meals 10.00/15.00 **st.** and a la carte – **14 rm** 55.00/85.00 **st.** – SB.

Saxon Cross, Holmes Chapel Rd, CW11 1SE, East : 1 ¼ m. by A 534 ☎ (01270) 763281, *Fax (01270) 768723* – TV P – 120. MC AE VISA JCB
Meals *(closed Sunday dinner)* (lunch by arrangement)/dinner 12.00/16.00 **t.** – **52 rm** 45.00/57.00 **t.**

Wheelock *South : 1½ m. by A 534 – ✉ Sandbach.*

Grove House with rm, Mill Lane, CW11 4RD, ☎ (01270) 762582, *grovehousehotel@supanet.com, Fax (01270) 759465* – rest, TV P. MC AE VISA JCB.
closed Bank Holidays – **Meals** *(closed Sunday dinner)* (dinner only and Sunday lunch)/dinner a la carte 14.00/27.20 **t.** 6.95 – **8 rm** 47.50/85.00 **t.**

NDFORD-ON-THAMES *Oxon. – see Oxford.*

NDGATE *Kent* 404 X 30 – *see Folkestone.*

NDIACRE *Derbs.* 402 403 404 Q 25 – *see Nottingham (Notts.).*

NDIWAY *Ches.* 402 403 404 M 24 – ✉ *Northwich.*

London 191 – Liverpool 34 – Manchester 22 – Stoke-on-Trent 26.

Nunsmere Hall , Tarporley Rd, CW8 2ES, Southwest : 1 ½ m. by A 556 on A 49 ☎ (01606) 889100, *reservations@nunsmere.co.uk, Fax (01606) 889055*, ←, , « Part Victorian house on wooded peninsula », , – TV P – 50. MC AE VISA.
Crystal : Meals 22.50 **t.** (lunch) and dinner a la carte 25.95/36.50 **t.** – 15.00 – **36 rm** 117.50/325.00 **st.**

NDWICH *Kent* 404 Y 30 *Great Britain G. – pop. 4 164.*

See : *Town*★.

Guildhall ☎ *(01304) 613565.*

London 72 – Canterbury 13 – Dover 12 – Maidstone 41 – Margate 9.

Bell, The Quay, CT13 9EF, ☎ (01304) 613388, *hotel@princes-leisure.co.uk, Fax (01304) 615308* – TV P – 150. MC AE VISA JCB.
Meals 11.95/17.50 **t.** and a la carte 5.70 – **33 rm** 75.00/150.00 **t.** – SB.

George & Dragon Inn, 24 Fisher St., CT13 9EG, ☎ (01304) 613106, – MC AE VISA
Meals a la carte 13.40/25.40 **t.** 5.95.

NDY *Beds.* 404 T 27 – *pop. 8 554.*

A1, Sandy Roundabout, Girtford Bridge, London Rd ☎ *(01767) 682728.*

London 49 – Bedford 8 – Cambridge 24 – Peterborough 35.

Holiday Inn Garden Court, Girtford Bridge, London Rd, SG19 1DH, West : ¾ m. by B 1042 at junction of A 1 with A 603 ☎ (01767) 692220, *qamar@holidayinns.co.uk, Fax (01767) 680452* – rm, TV P – 140. MC AE VISA.
Meals (dinner only and Sunday lunch)/dinner 15.00 **st.** and a la carte 6.50 – 7.50 – **57 rm** 69.00 **st.** – SB.

Highfield Farm without rest., Great North Rd, SG19 2AQ, North : 2 m. by B 1042 on A 1 (southbound carriageway) ☎ (01767) 682332, *margaret@highfield-farm.co.uk, Fax (01767) 692503*, « Working farm », , – P. MC VISA
6 rm 35.00/60.00 **st.**

NDYPARK *Devon* 403 I 31 – *see Chagford.*

RK 403 P 33 and 230 ⑩ – *see Channel Islands.*

SAUNTON *Devon* 403 H 30 – ✉ *Braunton.*

Env. : *Braunton★ – St. Brannock's Church★, E : 2½ m. on B 3231 – Braunton Burrows★, ½ m. on B 3231.*

18, 18 *Saunton, Braunton ☎ (01271) 812436.*

London 230 – Barnstaple 8 – Exeter 48.

Saunton Sands, EX33 1LQ, ☎ (01271) 890212, *sauntonsands@btinternet.co*
Fax (01271) 890145, ≤ Saunton Sands, heated, squash –
125. *VISA.*
Meals 10.50/22.50 **t.** and a la carte 7.00 – **92 rm** 79.00/286.00 **t.** – SB.

Preston House, EX33 1LG, ☎ (01271) 890472, *prestonhouse-saunton@zoom.co.*
Fax (01271) 890555, ≤ Saunton Sands, heated, – TV P. *VISA.*
closed 21 December-5 February – **Meals** (dinner only) 23.95/27.95 **st.** 9.95 – **12**
60.00/140.00 **st.** – SB.

SAWBRIDGEWORTH *Herts.* 404 U 28 – *pop. 9 432.*

London 26 – Cambridge 32 – Chelmsford 17.

Goose Fat & Garlic, 52 Bell St., CM21 9AN, ☎ (01279) 722554, *lwootton@goosefatand lic.co.uk, Fax (01279) 600766* – *VISA*
closed 1 week Christmas, Sunday dinner and Saturday lunch – **Meals** a la carte 22. 30.00 **t.**

SAWLEY *Lancs.* 402 M 22 – *pop. 237.*

London 242 – Blackpool 39 – Leeds 44 – Liverpool 54.

Spread Eagle, BB7 4NH, ☎ (01200) 441202, *enquiries@spreadeagle.fsnet.co.*
Fax (01200) 441973 – TV P. *VISA*
Meals a la carte 16.45/24.15 **t.** 8.00.

SAXTON *N. Yorks.* – *see Tadcaster.*

SCALBY *N. Yorks.* 402 S 21 – *see Scarborough.*

SCARBOROUGH *N. Yorks.* 402 S 21 *Great Britain G.* – *pop. 38 809.*

Exc. : *Robin Hood's Bay★, N : 16 m. on A 171 and minor rd to the right (signposted Whitby Abbey★, N : 21 m. on A 171 – Sledmere House★, S : 21 m. on A 645, B 1249 an 1253 (right).*

18 *Scarborough North Cliff, North Cliff Av., Burniston Rd ☎ (01723) 360786, NW : 2 m. b 165 Y* – 18 *Scarborough South Cliff, Deepdale Av., off Filey Rd ☎ (01723) 360522, S : 1 m A 165 Z.*

Unit 3, Pavilion House, Valley Bridge Rd ☎ (01723) 373333.

London 253 – Kingston-upon-Hull 47 – Leeds 67 – Middlesbrough 52.

Plan opposite

Beiderbecke's, 1-3 The Crescent, YO11 2PW, ☎ (01723) 365766, *info@beiderbecke m, Fax (01723) 367433* – rest, TV. *VISA.* Z
Meals – (see ***Marmalade's*** below) – **27 rm** 55.00/130.00 **t.** – SB.

The Crown, 7-11 Esplanade, YO11 2AG, ☎ (01723) 373491, *roomsales@scarborough .com, Fax (01723) 362271,* ≤ – TV – 160. *VISA* JCB Z
Meals (bar lunch Monday to Saturday)/dinner 16.95 **t.** and a la carte 5.85 – **82** 45.00/70.00 **st.**, 1 suite – SB.

Palm Court, St. Nicholas Cliff, YO11 2ES, ☎ (01723) 368161, *Fax (01723) 371547,* TV – 150. *VISA.* Z
Meals (dancing Saturday evening) (bar lunch Monday to Saturday)/dinner 13.5 and a la carte 5.50 – **45 rm** 41.00/86.00 **t.** – SB.

The Mount, Cliff Bridge Terr., YO11 2HA, ☎ (01723) 360961, *Fax (01723) 375850,* ≤ TV. *VISA* Z
Meals (dinner only and Sunday lunch)/dinner 16.50/22.50 **st.** 5.95 – **50 rm** 45 86.00 **st.** – SB.

Ox Pasture Hall , Lady Edith's Drive, Raincliffe Woods, YO12 5TD, West : 3 ¼ m. 171 following signs for Raincliffe Woods ☎ (01723) 365295, *hawksmoor@oxpasture.fre ve.co.uk, Fax (01723) 355156,* ≤, « Part 17C », – rest, TV P. *VISA*
Meals (dinner only and Sunday lunch)/dinner 16.50 **t.** and a la carte 6.75 – **23** 34.50/127.00 **t.** – SB.

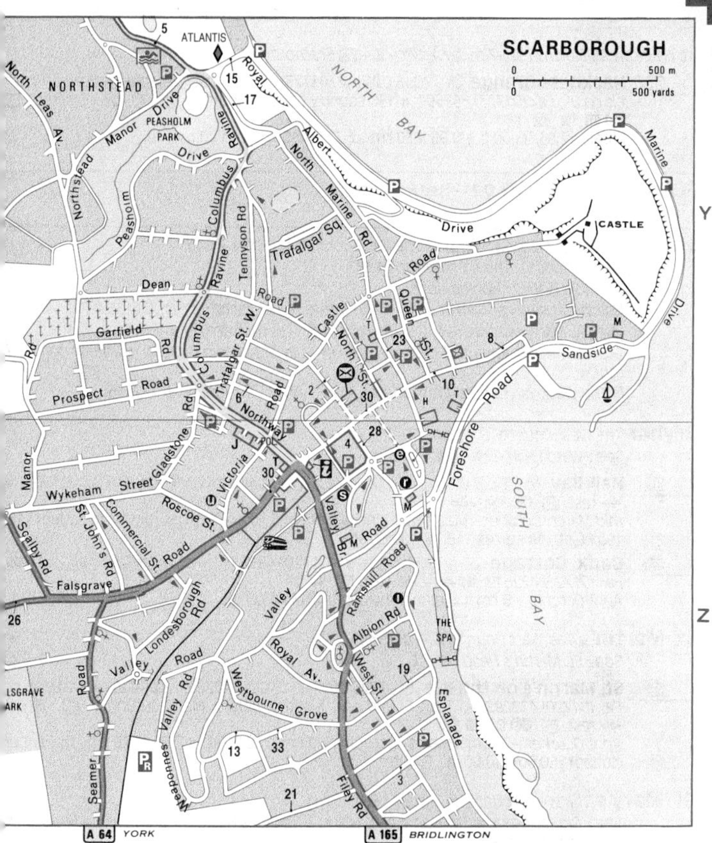

Old Mill, Mill St., YO11 1SZ, by Victoria Rd ✆ (01723) 372735, *info@windmill-hotel.co.uk, Fax (01723) 372735,* « Restored 18C windmill, toy museum » – rest., TV P. MC VISA. Z u
closed January and December – **Meals** (by arrangement) (residents only) (dinner only) 12.50 **st.** – **12 rm** 35.00/50.00 **st.**

Marmalade's (at Beiderbecke's H.), 1-3 The Crescent, YO11 2PN, ✆ (01723) 365766, *Fax (01723) 367433* – rest. MC AE VISA Z s
Meals *(closed Sunday dinner)* (live jazz music Thurday-Saturday dinner and Sunday lunch) 15.90 **t.** and a la carte 7.00.

calby *Northwest : 3 m. by A 171* – **Z** – *Scarborough.*

Wrea Head Country House, Barmoor Lane, YO13 0PB, North : 1 m. by A 171 on Barmoor Lane ✆ (01723) 378211, *wreahead@englishrosehotels.co.uk, Fax (01723) 355936,* « Victorian country house », – rest, TV P – 30. MC AE VISA.
Meals 12.95/25.00 **t.** 14.95 – **19 rm** 75.00/140.00 **t.**, 1 suite – SB.

at Hackness *Northwest : 7 m. by A 171 – Z – ✉ Scarborough.*

Hackness Grange ⛰, YO13 0JW, ☎ (01723) 882345, *hacknessgrange@englishroseels.co.uk, Fax (01723) 882391,* « 18C country house, gardens », ▣, ⛳, 🎾 – ⇌ rest, 📺 MC AE ① VISA. ✻
Meals 12.95/25.00 **t.** 🍷 8.95 – **30 rm** ☕ 75.50/159.00 **t.**, 1 suite – SB.

SCAWTON *N. Yorks.* 402 Q 21 – *see Helmsley.*

SCILLY (Isles of) *Cornwall* 403 ㉚ *The West Country G. – pop. 2 048.*

See : *Islands★ - The Archipelago (≤★★★).*

Env. : *St. Agnes : Horsepoint★.*

Helicopter service from St. Mary's and Tresco to Penzance : ☎ (01736) 363871.

✈ *St. Mary's Airport : ☎ (01720) 422677, E : 1½ m. from Hugh Town.*

⛴ *from Hugh Town to Penzance (Isles of Scilly Steamship Co. Ltd) (summer only) (2 h mn).*

ℹ *The Wesleyan Centre, Well Lane, St. Mary's ☎ (01720) (Scillonia) 422536.*

Bryher *The West Country G. – pop. 78 – ✉ Scillonia.*

See : *Watch Hill (≤★) – Hell Bay★.*

Hell Bay ⛰, TR23 0PR, ☎ (01720) 422947, *hellbay@aol.com, Fax (01720) 423004,* ≤ ⇌ rest, 📺. MC VISA JCB. ✻
mid March-October – **Meals** (bar lunch)/dinner 26.50 **t.** – **3 rm** ☕ (dinner included) 118 190.00 **st.**, **14 suites** 118.75/190.00 **st.**

Bank Cottage ⛰, TR23 0PR, ☎ (01720) 422612, *maemace@patrol.i-way.co Fax (01720) 422612,* ≤, 🌳 – ⇌ rest, 📺. ✻
April-October – **5 rm** ☕ (dinner included) 40.00/93.00 **st.**

St. Martin's *The West Country G. – pop. 113.*

See : *St. Martin's Head (≤★★).*

St. Martin's on the Isle ⛰, TR25 0QW, ☎ (01720) 422092, *stay@stmartinshotel.co Fax (01720) 422298,* ≤ Tean Sound and islands, « Idyllic island setting », ▣, 🌳, ⇌ rest, 📺. MC AE ① VISA
April-October – ***Tean*** : **Meals** (bar lunch)/dinner 30.00 **st.** 🍷 7.25 – **28 rm** ☕ (dinner included) 250.00/310.00 **st.**, 2 suites.

St. Mary's *The West Country G. – pop. 1 607.*

See : *Gig racing★★ – Garrison Walk★ (≤★★) – Peninnis Head★ – Hugh Town - Museum★*

⛳9 ☎ *(01720) 422692.*

Star Castle ⛰, TR21 0JA, ☎ (01720) 422317, *reception@starcastlescilly.demon.co Fax (01720) 422343,* ≤, « Elizabethan fortress », ▣, 🌳, 🎾 – ⇌ rest, 📺 P. MC VISA
March-October – **Meals** (bar lunch)/dinner 22.00/32.00 **st.** 🍷 6.00 – **30 rm** ☕ (dinner included) 72.00/195.00 **st.**, 4 suites – SB.

Atlantic, Hugh St., Hugh Town, TR21 0PL, ☎ (01720) 422417, *atlantichotel@btinterne m, Fax (01720) 423009,* ≤ St. Mary's Harbour – ⇌ 📺. MC VISA
14 February-10 November – **Meals** (dinner only) 15.00/25.00 **st.** 🍷 6.50 – **24 rm** ☕ (dinner included) 84.00/180.00 **st.** – SB.

Carnwethers Country House ⛰, Pelistry Bay, TR21 0NX, ☎ (01720) 422 *Fax (01720) 422415,* ≘s, ⛱ heated, 🌳 – ⇌ 📺
May-September – **Meals** 🍷 3.00 – **9 rm** ☕ (dinner included) 58.00/116.00 **st.** – SB.

Crebinick House without rest., Church St., TR21 0JT, ☎ (01720) 422 *Fax (01720) 422968* – ⇌. ✻
April-October – **6 rm** ☕ 64.00.

Evergreen Cottage without rest., Parade, High Town, TR21 0LP, ☎ (01720) 4227 ⇌
closed 24 December-3 January – **5 rm** ☕ 28.50/57.00 **st.**

Tresco *The West Country G. – pop. 167 – ✉ New Grimsby.*

See : *Island★ - Abbey Gardens★★ AC (Lighthouse Way ≤★★).*

The Island ⛰, Old Grimsby, TR24 0PU, ☎ (01720) 422883, *islandhotel@tresco.co Fax (01720) 423008,* ≤ St. Martin's and islands, « Idyllic island setting, sub-tropical dens », ⛱ heated, ⛳, 🎾 – 📺. MC ① VISA. ✻
April-September – **Meals** (bar lunch)/dinner 33.00 **t.** and a la carte 20.90/61.90 **t.** 🍷 9. **46 rm** ☕ (dinner included) 120.00/270.00 **t.**, 2 suites.

New Inn, TR24 0QQ, (01720) 422844, *newinn@tresco.co.uk, Fax (01720) 423200,* ≤, heated, – rest, . VISA JCB.
Meals (booking essential) (bar lunch)/dinner 24.50 **t.** 6.95 – **14 rm** (dinner included) 92.00/184.00 **t.** – SB.

OTCH CORNER *N. Yorks.* 402 P 20 – *Richmond.*
London 235 – Carlisle 70 – Middlesbrough 25 – Newcastle upon Tyne 43.

Quality H. Scotch Corner, DL10 6NR, (01748) 850900, *admin@gb609.u_net.com, Fax (01748) 825417,* , , – , rm, – 350. AE VISA JCB
Meals 9.95/30.00 **st.** and a la carte 5.75 – 9.95 – **90 rm** 75.00/87.50 **st.** – SB.

Travelodge, Middleton Tyas Lane, D10 6PQ, (01325) 377719, *Fax (01325) 377890* – rm, rest, . AE VISA JCB.
Meals (grill rest.) – **50 rm** 39.95 **t.**

Travelodge, Skeeby, DL10 5EQ, South : 1 m. on A 1 (northbound carriageway) (01748) 823768, *Fax (01748) 823768* – rm, rest, . AE VISA JCB.
Meals (grill rest.) – **40 rm** 39.95 **t.**

UNTHORPE *North Lincolnshire* 402 S 23 – *pop. 75 982.*
18 Ashby Decoy, Burringham Rd (01724) 842913 – 9 Kingsway (01724) 840945 – 9, 9 Grange Park, Butterwick Rd, Messingham (01724) 762945.
Humberside Airport : (01652) 688456, E : 15 m. by A 18.
London 167 – Leeds 54 – Lincoln 30 – Sheffield 45.

Forest Pines, Ermine St., Broughton, DN20 0AQ, Southeast : 5 m. by A 1029 off A 18 (01652) 650770, *enquiries@briggatelodgeinn.co.uk, Fax (01652) 650495,* , , , 18, 9 – – 250. AE VISA.
Meals 12.75/29.50 **st.** 6.95 – **84 rm** 90.00/100.00 **st.**, 2 suites.

Travel Inn, Lakeside Retail Park, Lakeside Parkway, DN16 3NA, Southeast : 2 ½ m. off A 1029 at junction with A 18 (01724) 870030, *Fax (01724) 851809* – rm, rest, . AE VISA.
Meals (grill rest.) – **40 rm** 40.95 **t.**

AFORD *E. Sussex* 404 U 31 – *pop. 19 622.*
18 Seaford Head, Southdown Rd (01323) 890139 – 18 East Blatchington (01323) 892442.
25 Clinton Pl. (01323) 897426.
London 65 – Brighton 14 – Folkestone 64.

Westdean *East : 3 ¼ m by A 259.*

Old Parsonage without rest., BN25 4AL, (01323) 870432, *raymondj.woodhams@virgin.net, Fax (01323) 870432,* « 13C King John house », – .
closed Christmas-New Year – **3 rm** 65.00/80.00.

AHOUSES *Northd.* 401 402 P 17 *Great Britain G.*
Env. : *Farne Islands* (by boat from harbour).*
18 Beadnell Rd (01665) 720794.
Car Park, Seafield Rd (01665) 720884 (Easter-October).
London 328 – Edinburgh 80 – Newcastle upon Tyne 46.

Olde Ship, 9 Main St., NE68 7RD, (01665) 720200, *theoldeship@seahouses.co.uk, Fax (01665) 721383,* « Nautical memorabilia » – rest, . VISA JCB.
closed December and January – **Meals** (bar lunch)/dinner 14.00/16.00 **t.** 5.75 – **12 rm** 40.00/80.00 **t.**, 4 suites – SB.

ATON BURN *Tyne and Wear* 402 P 18 – *see Newcastle upon Tyne.*

ATON CAREW *Hartlepool* 402 Q 20 – *see Hartlepool.*

AVIEW *I.O.W.* 403 404 Q 31 – *see Wight (Isle of).*

es prix — Pour toutes précisions sur les prix indiqués dans ce guide, reportez-vous aux pages de l'introduction.

SEAVINGTON ST. MARY *Somerset* 403 L 31 *The West Country G.* – *pop. 367* – ✉ *Ilminster.*
Env. : *Ilminster★ - Minster★★, W : 2 m.*
London 142 – Taunton 14 – Yeovil 11.

Pheasant, Water St., TA19 0QH, ☎ (01460) 240502, *Fax (01460) 242388*, – rest, P. MO AE VISA
Meals *(closed Sunday dinner)* (dinner only and Sunday lunch)/dinner a la carte 21.-31.95 **t.** 7.00 – **6 rm** 70.00/90.00 **st.**, 2 suites – SB.

SEDGEFIELD *Durham* 401 402 P 20 – *pop. 90 530.*
London 270 – Carlisle 83 – Middlesbrough 15 – Newcastle upon Tyne 27 – Sunderland 2

Travelodge, A 689 Roundabout, TS21 2JX, Southeast : ¾ m. on A 689 ☎ (01740) 6233
Fax (01740) 623399 – rm, TV P. MO AE VISA JCB.
Meals (grill rest.) – **40 rm** 39.95 **t.**

Ministers, Lambton House, 8 Church View, TS21 2AY, ☎ (01740) 6222
Fax (01740) 622201. MO AE VISA JCB
closed first 2 weeks January, 25-26 December, Monday, Saturday lunch and Sunday dinn
Meals 11.95/22.50 **st.** and a la carte 7.20.

SEDGEMOOR SERVICE AREA *Somerset* 403 L 30.
Somerset Visitor Centre, M 5 (southbound) ☎ (01934) 750833.

Days Inn without rest., BS21 0JL, M 5 (northbound carriageway) between junctions and 21 ☎ (01934) 750831, Reservations (Freephone) 0800 0280400, *Fax (01934) 75080*
TV P. MO AE VISA
7.45 **40 rm** 45.00/50.00 **t.**

SEDLESCOMBE *E. Sussex* 404 V 31 – *pop. 1 631 (inc. Whatlington)* – ✉ *Battle.*
London 56 – Hastings 7 – Lewes 26 – Maidstone 27.

Brickwall, The Green, TN33 0QA, ☎ (01424) 870253, *reception@brickwallhotel.totalse co.uk, Fax (01424) 870785*, heated, – TV P. MO AE VISA JCB
Meals 17.50/23.50 **t.** (dinner) and lunch a la carte 17.75/26.25 **t.** 7.00 – **26 rm** 60.-95.00 **t.** – SB.

SELBY *N. Yorks.* 402 Q 22 *Great Britain G.* – *pop. 12 600.*
See : *Abbey Church★.*
Park St. ☎ (01757) 703263.
London 201 – Doncaster 21 – Kingston-upon-Hull 37 – Leeds 22 – York 14.

Barff Lodge without rest., Mill Lane, Brayton, YO8 9LB, Southwest : 2 ¾ m. by A 19 Gateforth rd ☎ (01757) 213030, *barfflodge@aol.com, Fax (01757) 212313*, – TV MO VISA.
4 rm 28.00/40.00 **st.**

SELSIDE *Cumbria – see Kendal.*

SEMINGTON *Wilts.* 403 404 N 29 – *see Trowbridge.*

SETTLE *N. Yorks.* 402 N 21 – *pop. 3 082.*
Giggleswick ☎ (01729) 825288.
Town Hall, Cheapside ☎ (01729) 825192.
London 238 – Bradford 34 – Kendal 30 – Leeds 41.

Falcon Manor, Skipton Rd, BD24 9BD, ☎ (01729) 823814, *falconm@netcomuk.co Fax (01729) 822087*, – rest, TV P. – 50. MO AE VISA JCB
Meals (bar lunch Monday to Saturday)/dinner 19.75 **st.** 8.00 – **19 rm** 60.00/120.0C – SB.

SEVENOAKS *Kent* 404 U 30 *Great Britain G.* – *pop. 24 489.*
Env. : *Knole★★ AC, SE : ½ m. – Ightham Mote★ AC, E : 5 m. by A 25.*
Woodlands Manor, Tinkerpot Lane ☎ (01959) 523805 – Darenth Valley, Station Shoreham ☎ (01959) 522944.
Buckhurst Lane ☎ (01732) 450305.
London 26 – Guildford 40 – Maidstone 17.

Royal Oak, Upper High St., TN13 1HY, ☎ (01732) 451109, *roak@brook-hotels.co.uk, Fax (01732) 740187* – ▤ rest, TV P – 35. MC AE D VISA
No 5 Restaurant : Meals 14.95/21.95 **st.** and a la carte – **36 rm** ☕ 90.00/110.00 **st.** – SB.

Sun Do, 61 High St., TN13 1JF, ☎ (01732) 453299, *Fax (01732) 461289* – ▤. MC AE D VISA JCB
closed 25-26 December – **Meals** - Chinese - 6.50/15.00 **st.** and a la carte.

Ivy Hatch *East : 4 ¾ m. by A 25 on Coach Rd* – ✉ *Sevenoaks.*

The Plough, High Cross Rd, TN15 0NL, ☎ (01732) 810268, *the.plough@btinternet.com, Fax (01732) 810268,* – ▤ P. VISA
closed Sunday dinner – **Meals** a la carte 14.45/26.20 **t.** 9.50.

SEVERN VIEW SERVICE AREA *South Gloucestershire* 403 404 M 29 – ✉ *Bristol.*
Severn Bridge (toll).

Travelodge without rest., BS12 3BH, M 48 junction 1 ☎ (01454) 633199, *Fax (01454) 632482* – TV P. MC AE D VISA JCB.
51 rm 59.95 **t.**

SHAFTESBURY *Dorset* 403 404 N 30 *The West Country G.* – *pop. 6 203.*
See : *Gold Hill★ (≤★) – Local History Museum★ AC.*
Env. : *Wardour Castle★ AC, NE : 5 m.*
8 Bell St. ☎ *(01747) 853514.*
London 115 – Bournemouth 31 – Bristol 47 – Dorchester 29 – Salisbury 20.

Royal Chase, Royal Chase Roundabout, SP7 8DB, Southeast : at junction of A 30 with A 350 ☎ (01747) 853355, *royalchasehotel@btinternet.com, Fax (01747) 851969,* – TV P – 130. MC AE D VISA
Meals 21.00 **t.** 9.00 – ☕ 8.50 – **32 rm** 84.50/115.00 **st.** – SB.

Paynes Place Barn without rest., New Rd, SP7 8QL, Northwest : ½ m. off B 3081 ☎ (01747) 855016, *xstal@globalnet.co.uk, Fax (01747) 855016,* ≤ Vale of Blackmore, – TV P.
3 rm ☕ 44.00/56.00 **st.**

La Fleur de Lys, 25 Salisbury St., SP7 8EL, ☎ (01747) 853717, *Fax (01747) 853717,* – MC AE VISA JCB
closed 2 weeks January, Sunday dinner, Monday lunch and Monday October-March – **Meals** 25.50 **t.** (dinner) and a la carte 26.00/33.00 **t.** 10.00.

Wayfarers, Sherborne Causeway, SP7 9PX, West : 2 ½ m. on A 30 ☎ (01747) 852821, *Fax (01747) 852821* – P. MC AE D VISA
closed 26 December-third week January, Monday, Saturday lunch and Sunday dinner – **Meals** a la carte 15.95/29.50 **t.** 6.50.

Compton Abbas *South : 4 m. on A 350* – ✉ *Shaftesbury.*

Old Forge without rest., Chapel Hill, SP7 0NQ, ☎ (01747) 811881, *theoldforge@kerridge.virgin.net, Fax (01747) 811881,* « Thatched cottage and converted wheelwrights », – TV P
3 rm ☕ 40.00/65.00 **st.**

Motcombe *Northwest : 2½ m. by B 3081* – ✉ *Shaftesbury.*

Coppleridge Inn , SP7 9HW, North : 1 m. on Mere rd ☎ (01747) 851980, *thecoppleridgeinn@btinternet.com, Fax (01747) 851858,* – TV P – 50. MC AE D VISA
Meals 11.00 **t.** and a la carte 5.75 – **10 rm** ☕ 42.50/75.00 **t.** – SB.

SHALDON *Devon* 403 J 32 – *see Teignmouth.*

SHANKLIN *I.O.W.* 403 404 Q 32 – *see Wight (Isle of).*

SHEDFIELD *Hants.* 403 404 Q 31 – *pop. 3 558* – ✉ *Southampton.*
18, 9 *Marriott Meon Valley Hotel, Sandy Lane, off A 334* ☎ *(01329) 833455.*
London 75 – Portsmouth 13 – Southampton 10.

Marriott Meon Valley H. & Country Club, Sandy Lane, SO32 2HQ, off A 334 ☎ (01329) 833455, *Fax (01329) 834411,* 18, – ▤ rest, TV P – 80. MC AE VISA.
Treetops : Meals (dinner only and Sunday lunch)/dinner 27.50 **t.** – ***The Long Weekend :*** Meals a la carte 12.45/21.45 **t.** – ☕ 12.50 – **112 rm** 90.00/114.00 **t.**

SHEFFIELD
BUILT UP AREA

Barrow Road . . . . BY 4
Bawtry Road . . . . BY 5
Bradfield Road . . . . AY 7
Brocco Bank. . . . . AZ 8
Broughton Lane . . . . BY 10
Burngreave Road . . . . AY 12
Handsworth Road . . . . BZ 24
Holywell Road . . . . BY 29
Main Road. . . . . BZ 32
Meadow Hall Road . . . . BY 33
Meadowhall Shopping Centre . . . . BY
Middlewood Road . . . . AY
Newhall Road. . . . . BY
Westbourne Road. . . . . AZ
Western Bank . . . . AZ
Whitham Road. . . . . AZ
Woodbourn Road . . . . BYZ
Woodhouse Road . . . . BZ

Ne confondez pas :

Confort des hôtels : ... ,
Confort des restaurants : XXXXX ..... X,
Qualité de la table : ✿✿✿, ✿✿, ✿, Meals

SHEFFIELD
CENTRE

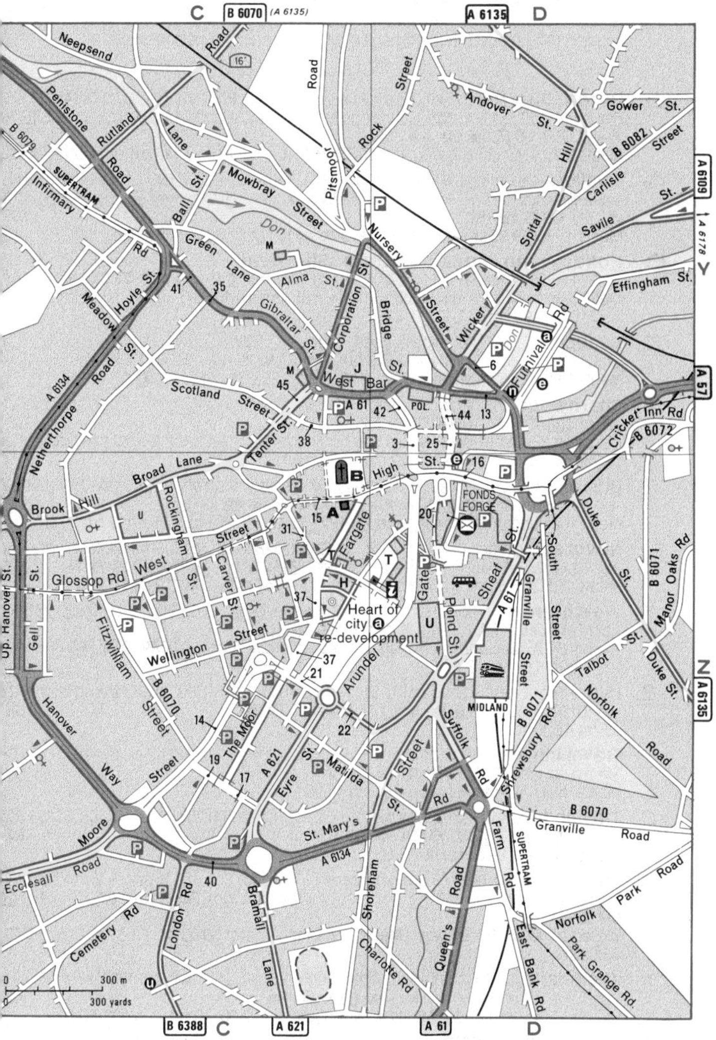

confondete :

Confort degli alberghi : 🏨🏨🏨🏨🏨 ... 🏨, ⌂
Confort dei ristoranti : XXXXX ..... X, 🍺
Qualità della tavola : ✿✿✿, ✿✿, ✿, Meals ☺

ENGLAND

SHEFFIELD *S. Yorks.* 402 403 404 P 23 *Great Britain G. – pop. 431 607.*

See : *Cutlers' Hall*★ **CZ A** – *Cathedral Church of SS. Peter and Paul* **CZ B** : *Shrewsb… Chapel (Tomb*★*).*

Tinsley Park, High Hazel Park, Darnall ☎ *(0114) 203 7435* **BY** – *Beauchief Munici… Abbey Lane* ☎ *(0114) 236 7274* **AZ** – *Birley Wood, Birley Lane* ☎ *(0114) 264 7262* **BZ** – *Concord Park, Shiregreen Lane* ☎ *(0114) 257 7378* **BY** – *Hillsborough, Worrall Rd (0114) 234 3608* **AY** – *Abbeydale, Twentywell Lane, Dore* ☎ *(0114) 236 0763* **AZ** – *L… Hall, Hemsworth Rd, Norton* ☎ *(0114) 255 4402* **AZ**.

Peace Gdns. ☎ *(0114) 273 4671.*

London 174 – Leeds 36 – Liverpool 80 – Manchester 41 – Nottingham 44.

Plans on preceding pages

Hilton Sheffield, Victoria Quays, Furnival Rd, S4 7YA, ☎ (0114) 252 55… *Fax (0114) 252 5511*, ≤, « Canalside setting », – rm, rest, – 260. MC AE VISA JCB. **DY**
Meals 8.95 **t.** (lunch) and a la carte 20.85/23.95 **t.** – 10.50 – **128 rm** 115.00/135.00 **st.**

Swallow (becoming a Marriott spring 2001), Kenwood Rd, S7 1NQ, ☎ (0114) 258 3811, *o@swallowhotels.com, Fax (0114) 250 0138*, – 200. MC AE VISA **AZ**
Meals 13.95/19.95 **st.** and dinner a la carte – **116 rm** 80.00/165.00 **st.** – SB.

Holiday Inn Royal Victoria Sheffield, Victoria Station Rd, S4 7… ☎ (0114) 276 8822, *Fax (0114) 272 4519* – rm, – 400. MC AE VISA JCB. **DY**
Meals (carvery lunch) (bar lunch Saturday and Sunday) 10.00/21.95 **st.** and a la carte 6… – 10.50 – **99 rm** 110.00, 1 suite.

Beauchief, 161 Abbeydale Road South, S7 2QW, Southwest : 3 ½ m. on A 6… ☎ (0114) 262 0500, *Fax (0114) 235 0197* – – 100. MC AE VISA
Meals 9.95/19.95 **st.** and a la carte 7.95 – 9.95 – **50 rm** 85.00/95.00 **st.** – SB.

Charnwood, 10 Sharrow Lane, S11 8AA, ☎ (0114) 258 9411, *Fax (0114) 255 510…* rm, – 100. MC AE VISA. **CZ**
closed 24-31 December – **Meals** *(closed Sunday and Bank Holiday Monday)* (dinner o… 15.25 **t.** and a la carte 5.00 – **22 rm** 75.00/90.00 **t.** – SB.

Bristol, Blonk St., S1 2AU, ☎ (0114) 220 4000, *sheffield@bhg.co.uk, Fax (0114) 220 3…* ≤ – rm, rest, – 40. MC AE VISA **DY**
Meals (bar lunch)/dinner a la carte 15.90/21.95 **st.** 5.45 – 7.95 – **112 rm** 59.00 **st.**

Novotel, Arundel Gate, S1 2PR, ☎ (0114) 278 1781, *h1348-gm@accor-hotels.c… Fax (0114) 278 7744*, – rm, rest, – 200. MC AE VISA **DZ**
Meals 13.50/16.50 **st.** and a la carte – 9.75 – **144 rm** 79.00/109.00 **st.** – SB.

Westbourne House, 25 Westbourne Rd, S10 2QQ, ☎ (0114) 266 01… *Fax (0114) 266 7778*, – . MC AE VISA. **AZ**
closed 24-26 December – **Meals** *(closed Saturday lunch)* 9.00/30.00 **t.** 8.00 – **10** 40.00/75.00 **st.** – SB.

Ibis without rest., Shude Hill, S1 2AR, ☎ (0114) 241 9600, *h2891@accor-hotels.c… Fax (0114) 241 9610* – . MC AE VISA **DZ**
95 rm 42.00 **st.**

Travel Inn, Attercliffe Common Rd, S9 2LU, ☎ (0114) 242 2802, *Fax (0114) 242 3703* – rm, rest, . MC AE VISA. **BY**
Meals (grill rest.) (dinner only) – **61 rm** 40.95 **t.**

Travelodge, 340 Prince of Wales Rd, S2 1FF, ☎ (0114) 253 0935, *Fax (0114) 253 09…* rm, – 80. MC AE VISA JCB. **BZ**
Meals (grill rest.) – **60 rm** 49.95 **t.**

The Cooke House, 78 Brookhouse Hill, Fulwood, S10 3TB, West : 3 ½ m. by A 57 Fulwood Rd ☎ (0114) 230 8186, *thecookehouse@aol.com, Fax (0114) 263 0241* – MC AE VISA.
closed 24 to 31 December – **Meals** (by arrangement) 30.00 **st.** 7.50 – **3 rm** 50 65.00 **st.**

The Briary, 12 Moncrieffe Rd, Nether Edge, S7 1HR, ☎ (0144) 255 1951, *briary@briar… co.uk, Fax (0114) 221 7716*, – . MC VISA **AZ**
closed 22-29 December – **Meals** (by arrangement) 22.00 – **6 rm** 37.00/60.00 **s.**

XX **Smith's of Sheffield,** 34 Sandygate Rd, S10 5RY, West : 2 ¼ m. by A 57, turning lef… Crosspool Tavern ☎ (0114) 266 6096 – MC AE VISA
Meals (booking essential) (dinner only and Sunday lunch) 17.50 **t.** and a la carte 22… 28.50 **t.** 5.00.

XX **Rafters,** 220 Oakbrook Rd, Nether Green, S11 7ED, Southwest : 2 ½ m. by A 625 Fulwood rd, turning left at roundabout ☎ (0114) 230 4819, *Fax (0114) 230 4819* – AE
closed 2 weeks August, 1 week January, Sunday and Tuesday – **Meals** (dinner only) 23.9… 9.50.

XX **Carriages,** 289 Abbeydale Road South, S17 3LB, Southwest : 4 m. on A 621 ✆ (0114) 235 0101 – P. MO VISA
closed 2 weeks January, Sunday dinner and Monday – **Meals** (dinner only and Sunday lunch)/dinner a la carte 22.50/28.95 **t.** 7.50.

X **Nonna's,** 539-541 Ecclesall Rd, S11 8PR, ✆ (0114) 268 6166, *nonnas@iname.com, Fax (0114) 266 6122* – MO VISA AZ e
closed 1 week Christmas – **Meals** - Italian - (lunch bookings not accepted) 10.95/14.95 **t.** and a la carte 5.50.

Grenoside *North : 4½ m. on A 61* – **AY** – ✉ *Sheffield.*

Whitley Hall, Elliott Lane, S35 8NR, East : 1 m. off Whitley Lane ✆ (0114) 245 4444, *reservations@whitleyhall.com, Fax (0114) 245 5414,* « Part 16C Elizabethan manor house », – rest, TV P – 70. MO AE VISA.
closed 24-25 December, 1 January and Bank Holiday Monday – **Meals** *(closed Saturday lunch)* 12.00/23.00 **t.** and a la carte 9.00 – **19 rm** 72.00/166.00 **t.**

Holme Lane Farm without rest., 38 Halifax Rd, S35 8PB, on A 61 ✆ (0114) 246 8858, *Fax (0114) 246 8858,* – TV P. MO VISA.
7 rm 28.00/48.00 **s.**

Chapeltown *North : 6 m. on A 6135* – **AY** – ✉ *Sheffield.*

XX **Greenhead House,** 84 Burncross Rd, S35 1SF, ✆ (0114) 246 9004, *allengreenhead@hotmail.com, Fax (0114) 246 9004* – P. MO AE VISA
closed 2 weeks Easter, 2 weeks August, 1 week Christmas, Sunday to Tuesday and lunch Wednesday and Saturday – **Meals** (booking essential) 27.75/33.00 **t.** (dinner) and lunch a la carte approx. 14.00 **t.** 7.50.

Ridgeway *(Derbs.) Southeast : 6 ¾ m. by A 6135 (signed Manor Park) on B 6054 turning right at Ridgeway Arms* – **BZ** – ✉ *Sheffield.*

XXX **Old Vicarage** (Tessa Bramley), Ridgeway Moor, S12 3XW, on Marsh Lane rd ✆ (0114) 247 5814, *eat@theoldvicarage.co.uk, Fax (0114) 247 7079,* – P. MO AE VISA JCB
closed 26 and 31 December, 1 January, Sunday dinner and Monday – **Meals** (lunch by arrangement) 30.00/43.00 **t.** 9.00
Spec. Seared scallops with sevruga caviar, vanilla bisque. Pot-roasted guinea fowl with truffles and ribbon noodles. Pecan and orange pudding with butterscotch sauce.

Meadow Head *South : 5¼ m. on A 61* – **AZ** – ✉ *Sheffield.*

Sheffield Moat House, Chesterfield Rd South, S8 8BW, ✆ (0114) 282 9988, *gmshf@queensmoat.co.uk, Fax (0114) 237 8140,* – rest, TV P – 500. MO AE VISA
Meals *(closed Saturday lunch)* a la carte 17.50/21.50 **st.** 5.85 – 10.50 – **93 rm** 110.00/120.00 **st.**, 2 suites – SB.

SHEFFORD *Beds.* 404 S 27 – *pop. 3 319.*

London 48 – Bedford 10 – Luton 16 – Northampton 37.

The Black Horse with rm, Ireland, SG17 5QL, Northwest : 1 ¾ m. by Northbridge St. and B 658 on Ireland rd ✆ (01462) 811398, *etaverns@aol.com, Fax (01462) 817238,* « Part 18C » – TV P. MO AE VISA
Meals a la carte 18.40/26.85 **t.** – **2 rm** 49.95.

SHELLEY *W. Yorks.* 402 404 O 23 – *see Huddersfield.*

SHENINGTON *Oxon.* – *see Banbury.*

SHEPTON MALLET *Somerset* 403 404 M 30 *The West Country G.* – *pop. 7 581.*

See : *Town★ - SS. Peter and Paul's Church★.*

Env. : *Downside Abbey★ (Abbey Church★) N : 5½ m. by A 37 and A 367.*

Exc. : *Longleat House★★★ AC, E : 15 m. by A 361 and B 3092 – Wells★★ - Cathedral★★★, Vicars' Close★, Bishop's Palace★ AC (≤★★) W : 6 m. by A 371 – Wookey Hole★ (Caves★ AC, Papermill★) W : 6 ½ m. by B 371 – Glastonbury★★ - Abbey★★ (Abbot's Kitchen★) AC, St. John the Baptist★★, Somerset Rural Life Museum★ AC – Glastonbury Tor★ (≤★★★) SW : 9 m. by B 3136 and A 361 - Nunney★, E : 8½ m. by A 361.*

18 *The Mendip, Gurney Slade ✆ (01749) 840570.*

London 127 – Bristol 20 – Southampton 63 – Taunton 31.

ENGLAND

Charlton House, BA4 4PR, East : 1 m. on A 361 (Frome rd) ✆ (01749) 342008, *enquiry harltonhouse.com, Fax (01749) 346362*, « Part Georgian country house », – rest, TV P. AE VISA JCB.
Mulberry : Meals 18.50/38.00-55.00 **t.** and a la carte 38.00/49.00 **t.** 10.00 – 7.50
16 rm 105.00/300.00 **st.** – SB
Spec. Croustade of duck confit with truffle oil dressing. Breast of chicken with fennel, bla olive and caperberry salsa. Walnut and mascarpone mousse, bitter chocolate sorbet.

The Shrubbery, Commercial Rd, BA4 5BU, ✆ (01749) 346671, *Fax (01749) 346581*, rest, TV P. AE VISA
Meals *(closed Sunday dinner)* 11.50/16.95 **t.** and a la carte 6.95 – **11 rm** 45.00/75.00 – SB.

Bowlish House, Wells Rd, BA4 5JD, West : ½ m. on A 371 ✆ (01749) 3420 *Fax (01749) 342022*, – TV P. AE VISA JCB
closed 2 weeks in winter – **Meals** *(closed Sunday and Monday)* (booking essential) (dinn only) 24.95 **t.** 5.50 – 5.00 – **3 rm** 55.00/65.00.

SHERBORNE *Dorset* 403 404 M 31 *The West Country G.* – *pop. 7 606.*

See : *Town★ - Abbey★★ – Castle★* **AC.**
Env. : *Sandford Orcas Manor House★* **AC**, *NW : 4 m. by B 3148 – Purse Caundle Manor★ NE : 5 m. by A 30.*
Exc. : *Cadbury Castle (≤★★) N : 8 m. by A 30 – Parish Church★, Crewkerne, W : 14 m. o 30.*
Higher Clatcombe ✆ (01935) 812475.
3 Tilton Court, Digby Rd ✆ (01935) 815341.
London 128 – Bournemouth 39 – Dorchester 19 – Salisbury 36 – Taunton 31.

Eastbury, Long St., DT9 3BY, ✆ (01935) 813131, *Fax (01935) 817296*, « Walled g den », – TV P – 60. AE VISA.
Meals 13.50/18.95 **t.** and dinner a la carte 8.75 – **14 rm** 49.50/89.00 **t.** – SB.

Pheasants with rm, 24 Greenhill, DT9 4EW, ✆ (01935) 815252, *andrew@pheasants.co. Fax (01935) 815252* – TV P. VISA.
closed 2 weeks January – **Meals** *(closed lunch Tuesday to Friday, Sunday dinner a Monday)* 16.50/30.00 **t.** 6.00 – **6 rm** 40.00/70.00 **t.** – SB.

at Oborne *Northeast : 2 m. by A 30 – ✉ Sherborne.*

The Grange, DT9 4LA, ✆ (01935) 813463, *karen@thegrangehotel-dorset.co. Fax (01935) 817464*, – TV P. AE VISA.
closed 12-20 August and 26 December-10 January – **Meals** *(closed Sunday dinner)* (dinn only and Sunday lunch)/dinner a la carte 25.50/30.50 **t.** 7.75 – **10 rm** 65.00/105.00 SB.

at Milborne Port *Northeast : 3 m. on A 30 – ✉ Sherborne.*

Old Vicarage, Sherborne Rd, DT9 5AT, ✆ (01963) 251117, *Fax (01963) 251515*, ≤, TV P. AE VISA JCB.
closed 10 January-10 February – **Meals** *(closed Sunday to Thursday)* (dinner only) 20.5 7.60 – **7 rm** 27.00/95.00 **st.** – SB.

at Hermitage *South : 7½ m. by A 352 – ✉ Sherborne.*

Almshouse Farm without rest., DT9 6HA, ✆ (01963) 210296, *almshousefarm@li ne.net, Fax (01963) 210296*, ≤, « Former monastery, working farm », – TV P.
closed December and January – **3 rm** 30.00/50.00.

at Yetminster *Southwest : 5½ m. by A 352 and Yetminster rd – ✉ Sherborne.*

Manor Farmhouse, DT9 6LF, ✆ (01935) 872247, *Fax (01935) 872247*, « 17C », – TV P. VISA.
closed 30 December-6 January – **Meals** (by arrangement) 15.00 – **3 rm** 35.00/70.00.

at Leigh *Southwest : 6¼ m. by A 352 – ✉ Sherborne.*

Huntsbridge Farm without rest., DT9 6JA, Southeast : ¼ m. on Batcombe ✆ (01935) 872150, *huntsbridge@lineone.net, Fax (01935) 872150*, ≤, « Working farm – TV P. VISA.
closed mid December-February – **3 rm** 50.00/55.00 **s.**

SHERBOURNE *Warks.* – *see Warwick.*

SHERE *Surrey* 404 S 30 – *see Guildford.*

HIFNAL *Shrops.* 402 403 404 M 25 – *pop. 5 893* – ✉ *Telford.*
London 150 – Birmingham 28 – Shrewsbury 16.

Park House, Park St., TF11 9BA, ✆ (01952) 460128, *info@parkhouse.macdonald-hotels.co.uk, Fax (01952) 461658,* – 180. **Meals** *(closed dinner 25 December and Saturday lunch)* 14.50 **t.** (lunch) and dinner a la carte 20.50/33.15 **t.** 9.50 – 10.50 – **52 rm** 105.00/120.00 **t.**, 2 suites – SB.

HIPHAM *Somerset* 403 L 30 *The West Country G.* – *pop. 1 094* – ✉ *Winscombe.*
Env. : *Cheddar Gorge*** (Gorge**, Caves*, Jacobs's Ladder ※*) – Axbridge** – King John's Hunting Lodge* – St. John the Baptist*, SW : 5 m. on A 38 – St. Andrew's Church*, S : 2½ m.*
Mendip Spring, Honeyhall Lane, Congresbury, Avon ✆ (01934) 853337.
London 135 – Bristol 14 – Taunton 20.

Daneswood House, Cuck Hill, BS25 1RD, ✆ (01934) 843145, *info@daneswoodhotel.co.uk, Fax (01934) 843824,* – 40. *closed 25 December-5 January* – **Meals** 13.95/29.95 **st.** 6.95 – **14 rm** 79.50/95.00 **st.**, 3 suites – SB.

HIPLEY *W. Yorks.* 402 O 22 – *pop. 28 165.*
Northcliffe, High Bank Lane ✆ (01274) 584085 – Beckfoot Lane, Cottingley Bridge, Bingley ✆ (01274) 563212.
London 216 – Bradford 4 – Leeds 12.

Marriott Hollins Hall H. and Country Club, Hollins Hill, Baildon, BD17 7QW, Northeast : 2 ½ m. on A 6038 ✆ (01274) 530053, *Fax (01274) 530187,* rm, – 200. **Meals** 16.00/25.00 **t.** and a la carte 7.45 – 12.50 – **121 rm** 99.00 **t.**, 1 suite – SB.

Ibis without rest., Salts Mill Rd, BD18 3TT, ✆ (01274) 589333, Reservations (Freephone) 0800 897121, *Fax (01274) 589444* – – 30. **78 rm** 49.50 **st.**

Aagrah, 27 Westgate, BD18 3QX, ✆ (01274) 530880 – . *closed 25 December* – **Meals** - Indian (Kashmiri) - (booking essential) (dinner only) a la carte 8.65/13.15 **t.**

HIPTON GORGE *Dorset – see Bridport.*

HIPTON-UNDER-WYCHWOOD *Oxon.* 403 404 P 28 – *pop. 1 154.*
London 81 – Birmingham 50 – Gloucester 37 – Oxford 25.

Lamb Inn, High St., OX7 6DQ, ✆ (01993) 830465, *Fax (01993) 832025* – . **Meals** (bar lunch Monday to Saturday and bar dinner Sunday and Monday)/dinner 15.00 **t.** and a la carte 9.00 – **5 rm** 55.00/70.00 **t.** – SB.

HIRLEY *W. Mids.* 403 404 O 26 – *see Solihull.*

HOBDON *Herefordshire* 403 L 27 – *pop. 741* – ✉ *Leominster.*
London 158 – Birmingham 55 – Hereford 18 – Shrewsbury 37 – Worcester 33.

The Paddock, HR6 9NQ, West : ¼ m. on B 4362 ✆ (01568) 708176, *thepaddock@talk21.com, Fax (01568) 708829* – . **Meals** (by arrangement) 15.00 **s.** – **5 rm** 35.00/48.00 **s.**

HOTTISHAM *Suffolk* 404 X 27 – *see Woodbridge.*

HOTTLE *Derbs. – see Belper.*

Bitte beachten Sie die Geschwindigkeitsbeschränkungen in Großbritannien
- 60 mph (= 96 km/h) außerhalb geschlossener Ortschaften
- 70 mph (= 112 km/h) auf Straßen mit getrennten Fahrbahnen und Autobahnen.

SHREWSBURY *Shrops.* 402 403 L 25 *Great Britain G. – pop. 64 219.*

See : *Abbey*★ **D**.

Exc. : *Ironbridge Gorge Museum*★★ *AC (The Iron Bridge*★★ *- Coalport China Museum*★★ *Blists Hill Open Air Museum*★★ *– Museum of the River and Visitor Centre*★ *) SE : 12 m. by A and B 4380.*

18 *Condover* ✆ *(01743) 872976 –* 9 *Meole Brace* ✆ *(01743) 364050.*

The Music Hall, The Square ✆ *(01743) 350761.*

London 164 – Birmingham 48 – Chester 43 – Derby 67 – Gloucester 93 – Manchester 68 Stoke-on-Trent 39 – Swansea 124.

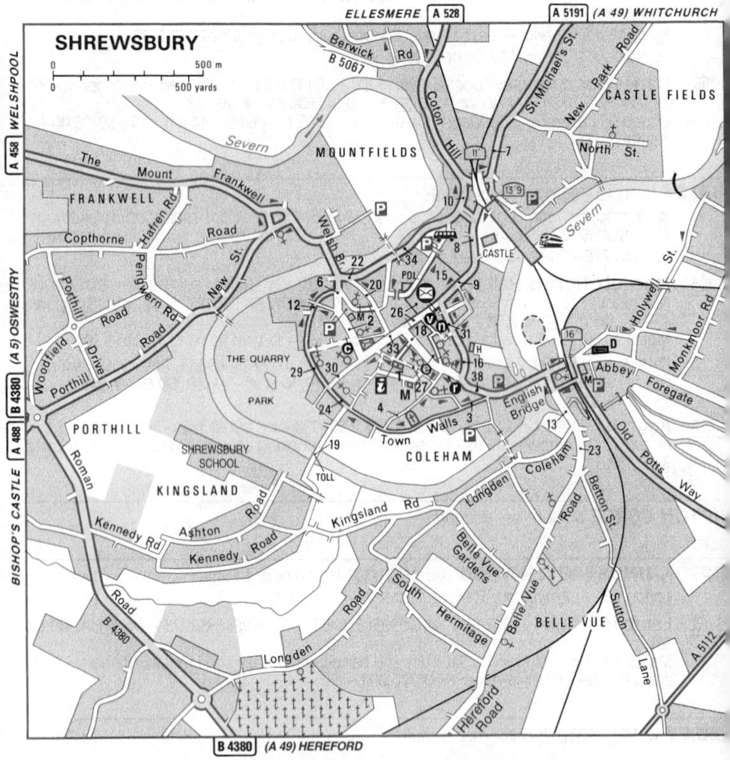

Barker Street	2	Coleham Head	13	Pride Hill	
Beeches Lane	3	Darwin Centre	15	Princess Street	
Belmont	4	Dogpole	16	St. Chad's Terrace	
Bridge Street	6	High Street	18	St. John's Hill	
Castle Foregate	7	Kingsland Bridge	19	St. Mary's Street	
Castle Gates	8	Mardol	20	Shoplatch	
Castle Street	9	Mardol Quay	22	Smithfield Road	
Chester Street	10	Moreton Crescent	23	Wyle Cop	
Claremont Bank	12	Murivance	24		

Lion, Wyle Cop, SY1 1UY, ✆ (01743) 353107, *Fax (01743) 352744* – TV P – 2
Meals 6.00/15.00 **st.** and dinner a la carte 7.95 – 9.75 – **59 rm** 70.00/105.00 **t.** – SB.

Prince Rupert, Butcher Row, SY1 1UQ, ✆ (01743) 499955, *post@prince-rupert-hotel uk, Fax (01743) 357306,* – , rest, TV P – 100. VISA JCB
Meals 14.00 **st.** (lunch) and a la carte 16.00/30.00 **st.** – 10.50 – **67 rm** 75.00/95.00 2 suites – SB.

Lord Hill, Abbey Foregate, SY2 6AX, East : 1 m. ✆ (01743) 232601, *reservations@lordhi net.com, Fax (01743) 369734* – rest, rest, TV P – 180. VISA JCB
Meals 12.50/18.75 **st.** and a la carte 7.00 – **35 rm** 63.50/82.00 **st.**, 1 suite – SB.

Travelodge, Bayston Hill Service Area, SY3 0DA, South : 2 ¾ m. by Belle Vue Rd (A 5191) and A 5112 at junction with A 5 ☎ (01743) 874256 – rm, TV, P. MC AE VISA JCB. Meals (grill rest.) – **40 rm** 49.95 **t.**

The Bellstone, Bellstone, SY1 1HU, ☎ (01743) 242100, *admin@bellstone-hotel.co.uk, Fax (01743) 242103* – rm, TV. MC VISA c
Brasserie : **Meals** a la carte 15.15/21.60 **st.** – 5.95 – **23 rm** 37.50 **st.** – SB.

Pinewood House without rest., Shelton Park, The Mount, SY3 8BL, Northwest : 1 ½ m. on A 458 ☎ (01743) 364200, – TV P
closed 2 weeks Spring and 1 week Christmas – **3 rm** 40.00/60.00 **s.**

Tudor House without rest., 2 Fish St., SY1 1UR, ☎ (01743) 351735, « 15C » – TV.
closed 24 to 26 December – **3 rm** 34.00/54.00 **st.** e

Fieldside without rest., 38 London Rd, SY2 6NX, East : 1 ¼ m. by Abbey Foregate on A 5064 (via Shirehall) ☎ (01743) 353143, *Fax (01743) 354687*, – TV P.
closed 2 weeks February and 1 week May – **5 rm** 35.00/48.00 **s.**

Sol, 82 Wyle Cop, SY1 1UT, ☎ (01743) 340560, *Fax (01743) 340552* – MC AE VISA JCB r
closed 10 days winter, Sunday and Monday – **Meals** 15.00/32.00 **t.** and lunch a la carte 7.50.

Royal Siam, Butcher Row, SY1 1VW, ☎ (01743) 353117, *Fax (01743) 353117* – MC AE VISA v
*closed 25 December and Sunday***Meals** - Thai - (dinner only and lunch Friday and Saturday) 6.50/18.50 **t.** and a la carte 5.90.

Albrighton *North : 3 m. on A 528 – ✉ Shrewsbury.*

Albrighton Hall, Ellesmere Rd, SY4 3AG, ☎ (01939) 291000, *info@albrighton.macdonald hotels.uk, Fax (01939) 291123*, , squash – rm, TV P – 400. MC AE VISA
Meals 18.50/22.50 **st.** and a la carte 6.95 – 10.50 – **71 rm** 72.00/112.00 **st.** – SB.

Albright Hussey, Ellesmere Rd, SY4 3AF, ☎ (01939) 290571, *abhhotel@aol.com, Fax (01939) 291143*, « 16C moated manor house », – TV P – 200. MC AE VISA JCB.
Meals 14.00/30.00 **t.** and a la carte 6.95 – **13 rm** 79.00/148.50 **t.**, 1 suite – SB.

Cross Houses *Southeast : 5 m. on A 458 – ✉ Shrewsbury.*

Upper Brompton Farm, SY5 6LE, East : ½ m. by Lower Cross ☎ (01743) 761629, *Fax (01743) 761679*, « Working farm », – TV P. MC AE VISA JCB.
closed 1 week Christmas – **Meals** (by arrangement) 25.00 **st.** – **5 rm** 49.50/90.00 **st.**

Dorrington *South : 7 m. on A 49 – ✉ Shrewsbury.*

Country Friends, SY5 7JD, ☎ (01743) 718707, *whittaker@countryfriends.demon.co.uk, Fax (01743) 718707*, – P. MC VISA JCB
closed 2 weeks mid July, Sunday and Monday – **Meals** 29.90 **t.** and lunch a la carte 6.50.

Hanwood *Southwest : 4 m. on A 488 – ✉ Shrewsbury.*

White House, SY5 8LP, ☎ (01743) 860414, *mgm@whitehousehanwood.freeserve.co.uk, Fax (01743) 860414*, « 16C farmhouse », – P.
Meals (by arrangement) 20.00 **s.** 9.00 – **6 rm** 30.00/60.00 – SB.

URDINGTON *Glos.* 403 404 N 28 – *see Cheltenham.*

SON *Leics. – see Nuneaton (Warks.).*

FORD *Devon* 403 K 31 – *see Sidmouth.*

MOUTH *Devon* 403 K 31 *The West Country G. – pop. 12 982.*

Env. : *Bicton★ (Gardens★) AC, SW : 5 m.*
Cotmaton Rd ☎ (01395) 513023.
Ham Lane ☎ (01395) 516441.
London 176 – Exeter 14 – Taunton 27 – Weymouth 45.

Victoria, The Esplanade, EX10 8RY, ☎ (01395) 512651, *info@victoriahotel.co.uk, Fax (01395) 579154*, heated, – rest, TV P. MC AE VISA.
Meals (dancing Saturday evening) 15.00/25.00 **t.** and a la carte 6.50 – **59 rm** 95.00/226.00 **t.**, 2 suites – SB.

Riviera, The Esplanade, EX10 8AY, ☎ (01395) 515201, *enquiries@hotelriviera.co.uk, Fax (01395) 577775*, – , rest, TV – 85. MC AE VISA
Meals 17.00/27.00 **t.** and a la carte 6.00 – **27 rm** (dinner included) 97.00/206.00 **t.** – SB.

ENGLAND

Belmont, The Esplanade, EX10 8RX, (01395) 512555, *info@belmont.hotel.co. Fax (01395) 579101,* ≤, – |‡|, ⇆ rest, TV P. MO AE VISA.
Meals (dancing Saturday evening) 14.00/24.00 **t.** and a la carte 5.25 – **53 rm** 85.(194.00 – SB.

Fortfield, Station Rd, EX10 8NU, (01395) 512403, *reservation@fortfield-hotel.d on.co.uk, Fax (01395) 512403,* – |‡| ⇆ TV P. MO AE VISA JCB.
Meals 10.00/26.00 **st.** 8.50 – 7.50 – **55 rm** 44.00/88.00 **st.** – SB.

Salcombe Hill House, Beatlands Rd, EX10 8JQ, (01395) 514697, *salcombehillh sehotel@eclipse.co.uk, Fax (01395) 578310,* heated, – |‡|, ⇆ rest, TV P. MO JCB
closed 12 January-28 February – **Meals** (bar lunch Monday to Saturday)/dinner 16.5(and a la carte 4.75 – **28 rm** (dinner included) 64.00/128.00 **t.** – SB.

Hunters Moon, Sid Rd, EX10 9AA, (01395) 513380, *huntersmoon.hotel@virgin.r Fax (01395) 514270,* – ⇆ TV P. MO VISA JCB
March-November – **Meals** (booking essential to non-residents) (dinner only) 17.95 7.95 – **18 rm** (dinner included) 50.00/100.00 **st.**

Brownlands, Brownlands Rd, EX10 9AG, by Sid Rd (01395) 513053, *brownlands tel@virgin.net, Fax (01395) 513053,* ≤, – ⇆ rest, TV P
closed November-mid March except Christmas – **Meals** (bar lunch)/dinner 21.50 **t.** 6.9 **14 rm** (dinner included) 68.00/136.00 **t.**

Mount Pleasant, Salcombe Rd, EX10 8JA, (01395) 514694, – ⇆ TV P
March-October – **Meals** (residents only) (dinner only) 12.95/14.95 **t.** 5.50 – **16 rm** (dinner included) 47.00/94.00 **st.** – SB.

Woodlands, Station Rd, Cotmaton Cross, EX10 8HG, (01395) 513120, *info@woodla _hotel.com, Fax (01395) 513348,* – ⇆ rest, TV P. MO VISA JCB
Meals (dinner only and Sunday lunch)/dinner 12.50/20.00 **t.** and a la carte 4.65 – **19** (dinner included) 33.50/80.00 **t.** – SB.

at Sidford *North : 2 m. – Sidmouth.*

Salty Monk, Church St., EX10 9QP, on A 3052 (01395) 513174, *saltymonk@tesco.r* « Part 16C », – ⇆ TV P. MO VISA JCB
closed 2 weeks January and November – **Meals** (light lunch)/dinner 17.50 **st.** and a la ca 4.50 – **5 rm** 35.00/70.00 **t.** – SB.

SILCHESTER *Hants.* 403 404 Q 29 – *pop. 1 428 – Reading (Berks.).*

London 62 – Basingstoke 8 – Reading 14 – Winchester 26.

Romans, Little London Rd, RG7 2PN, (01189) 700421, *romanhotel@hotmail.c Fax (01189) 700691,* heated, – ⇆ rest, TV P – 80. MO AE VISA JCB
closed 1-7 January – **Meals** 19.50 **st.** and a la carte 7.50 – **25 rm** 95.00/105.00 **st.** –

SIMONSBATH *Somerset* 403 I 30 *The West Country G. – Minehead.*

Env. : *Exmoor National Park★★ – Exford (Church★) E : 5½ m. by B 3223 and B 3224.*
London 200 – Exeter 40 – Minehead 19 – Taunton 38.

Simonsbath House, TA24 7SH, (01643) 831259, *simonsbath@talk21.c Fax (01643) 831557,* ≤, « 17C country house », – ⇆ rest, TV P. MO VISA
Meals (dinner only) 22.50 **st.** 5.95 – **7 rm** 40.00/80.00 **t.**

SINDLESHAM *Wokingham – see Reading.*

SINGLETON *Lancs.* 402 L 22 – *see Blackpool.*

SINNINGTON *N. Yorks.* 402 R 21 – *see Pickering.*

SISSINGHURST *Kent* 404 V 30 – *see Cranbrook.*

SITTINGBOURNE *Kent* 404 W 29.

London 44 – Canterbury 18 – Maidstone 15 – Sheerness 9.

Hempstead House, London Rd, Bapchild, ME9 9PP, East : 2 m. on (01795) 428020, *info@hempsteadhouse.co.uk, Fax (01795) 436362,* « Part Victo country house », heated, – ⇆ TV P. MO AE VISA JCB
Meals *(closed Sunday)* 27.50/30.50 **st.** and a la carte 8.50 – **14 rm** 65.00/75.00 **st.** -

Travel Inn, Bobbing Corner, Sheppey Way, Bobbing, ME9 8PD, Northwest : 2 ¼ m. by A 2 on Sheerness rd ✆ (01795) 431890, *Fax (01795) 436748* – rm, rest, TV, P. MC AE VISA.
Meals (grill rest.) – **40 rm** 40.95 **t.**

Beaumont without rest., 74 London Rd, ME10 1NS, West : ½ m. on A 2 ✆ (01795) 472536, *beaumont74@aol.com, Fax (01795) 425921* – TV P. MC AE VISA
9 rm 35.00/60.00 **st.**

X MILE BOTTOM *Cambs. – see Newmarket (Suffolk).*

KELTON *N. Yorks.* 402 Q 22 *– see York.*

KELWITH BRIDGE *Cumbria* 402 K 20 *– see Ambleside.*

IPTON *N. Yorks.* 402 N 22 *Great Britain G. – pop. 13 583.*

See : *Castle*★ *AC.*

off NW Bypass ✆ (01756) 793922.

The Old Town Hall, 9 Sheep St. ✆ (01756) 792809.

London 217 – Kendal 45 – Leeds 26 – Preston 36 – York 43.

Hanover International, Keighley Rd, BD23 2TA, South : 1 ¼ m. on A 629 ✆ (01756) 700100, *hihskipton@totalise.co.uk, Fax (01756) 700107,* ≤, squash – TV P – 420. MC AE VISA.
closed 25 and 26 December – **Meals** (bar lunch)/dinner 16.95/18.95 **st.** and a la carte 5.00 – 9.50 – **75 rm** 80.00/100.00 **t.** – SB.

The Unicorn, Devonshire Pl., Keighley Rd, BD23 2LP, ✆ (01756) 794146, *christine@unicornhotel.freeserve.co.uk, Fax (01756) 793376* – TV. MC AE VISA
closed 1 week Christmas – **Meals** (residents only) (dinner only) 7.95/10.00 **st.** and a la carte 7.00 – **9 rm** 46.00/55.00 **st.** – SB.

Travelodge, Gargrave Rd, BD23 1UD, Northwest : 1 ¼ m. by Water St. at A 65/A 59 roundabout ✆ (01756) 798091, *Fax (01756) 798091* – rm, TV P. MC AE VISA JCB.
Meals (grill rest.) – **32 rm** 39.95 **t.**

Aagrah, Unit 4, Unicorn House, Devonshire Pl., Keighley Rd, BD23 2LP, ✆ (01756) 790807 – MC AE VISA JCB
closed 25 December – **Meals** - Indian (Kashmiri) - (booking essential) (dinner only) a la carte 8.65/13.15 **t.**

Rylstone *North : 5 m. on B 6265 – Skipton.*

The Manor House without rest., BD23 6LH, ✆ (01756) 730226, ≤, « Working farm », – TV P.
3 rm 70.00 **t.**

Hetton *North : 5 ¾ m. by B 6265 – Skipton.*

Angel Inn, BD23 6LT, ✆ (01756) 730263, *info@angelhetton.co.uk, Fax (01756) 730363,* « Characterful 18C inn » – P. MC AE VISA
closed second week January, 25 December and Sunday dinner – ***The Restaurant :*** **Meals** (dinner only and Sunday lunch)/dinner a la carte 17.50/25.50 **t.** 5.90 – (see also below).

Angel Inn, BD23 6LT, ✆ (01756) 730263, *info@angelhetton.co.uk, Fax (01756) 730363,* « Characterful 18C inn » – P. MC AE VISA
Bar/Brasserie : **Meals** (bookings not accepted) a la carte 17.50/25.50 **t.** 5.90.

Elslack *West : 5 ¼ m. by A 59 off A 56 – Skipton.*

The Tempest Arms, BD23 3AY, ✆ (01282) 842450, *Fax (01282) 843331* – TV P – 50. MC AE VISA.
Meals a la carte 12.15/22.95 **t.** – **10 rm** 52.50/65.00 **t.**

Coniston Cold *Northwest : 6 ½ m. on A 65 – Skipton.*

Coniston Hall Lodge, BD23 4EB, on A 65 ✆ (01756) 748080, *conistonhall@clara.net, Fax (01756) 749487,* ≤, – TV P – 40. MC AE VISA JCB
Meals (lunch only) a la carte 10.00/25.50 **st.** 6.50 – ***Winston's Bistro :*** **Meals** (dinner only) 16.50 **st.** and a la carte 6.75 – 11.00 – **40 rm** 65.00 **st.** – SB.

ALEY *Northd.* 401 402 N 19 *– see Hexham.*

SLEAFORD *Lincs.* 402 404 S 25 – *pop. 10 388.*
Willoughby Rd, South Rauceby *(01529) 488273.*
The Mill, Money's Yard, Carre St. *(01529) 414294.*
London 119 – Leicester 45 – Lincoln 17 – Nottingham 39.

Lincolnshire Oak, East Rd, NG34 7EH, Northeast : ¾ m. on B 1517 (01529) 413807, *cs.oak@pipermedia.co.uk, Fax (01529) 413710,* – rm, P – 140. VISA.
Meals (booking essential) a la carte 15.95/21.25 **t.** – **17 rm** 49.00/84.00 **t.** – SB.

Travelodge, NG34 8NP, Northwest : 1 m. on A 15 at junction with A (01529) 414752, *Fax (01529) 414752* – rm, P. VISA JCB.
Meals (grill rest.) – **40 rm** 39.95 **t.**

Tally Ho Inn with rm, Aswarby, NG34 8SA, South : 4 ½ m. on A 15 (01529) 4552(*Fax (01529) 455205,* – P. VISA
closed 26 December – **Meals** (bar lunch Monday to Saturday) (in bar Sunday dinn a la carte 14.20/22.85 **t.** – **6 rm** 35.00/50.00 **t.**

SLEIGHTS *N. Yorks.* – *see Whitby.*

SLINFOLD *W. Sussex* – *see Horsham.*

SLOUGH *Slough* 404 S 29 – *pop. 110 708.*
London 29 – Oxford 39 – Reading 19.

Slough/Windsor Marriott, Ditton Rd, Langley, SL3 8PT, Southeast : 2 ½ m. on (01753) 544244, *Fax (01753) 540272,* – rm, P – 3 VISA.
Meals (bar lunch Saturday and Sunday) 16.50/19.50 **st.** and dinner a la carte – 12.5 **379 rm** 125.00/185.00 **st.**, 1 suite – SB.

Copthorne, Cippenham Lane, SL1 2YE, Southwest : 1 ¼ m. by A 4 on A 355 off junction 6 (01753) 516222, *copthorne@mill.cop.com, Fax (01753) 516237,* rm, P – 250. VISA.
***Veranda :* Meals** *(closed lunch Saturday and Sunday)* 21.50 **t.** and a la carte 8.50 – 12.50 – **217 rm** 160.00/185.00 **st.**, 2 suites – SB.

Courtyard by Marriott Slough/Windsor, Church St., Chalvey, SL1 2NH, Sou west : 1 ¼ m. by A 4 on A 355 off M 4 junction 6 (01753) 551551, *Fax (01753) 553333,* – P – 40. VISA.
Meals (bar lunch)/dinner a la carte 19.00/24.20 **st.** 7.45 – **149 rm** 125.00/135.00 **st.**

SMITE *Worcestershire* – *see Droitwich.*

SNAPE *Suffolk* 404 Y 27 – *pop. 1 509.*
London 113 – Ipswich 19 – Norwich 50.

Crown Inn with rm, Bridge Rd, IP17 1SL, (01728) 688324, « 15C inn », – rm VISA.
closed 25-26 December – **Meals** a la carte 17.20/23.65 **t.** 6.00 – **3 rm** 40.00/60.00 **t**

SNETTISHAM *Norfolk* 402 404 V 25 – *pop. 2 294.*
London 115 – Cambridge 58 – Norwich 45 – Peterborough 49.

Rose and Crown with rm, Old Church Rd, PE31 7LX, (01485) 541382, *roseandcrow btclick.com, Fax (01485) 543172,* « Part 14C inn », – P. VISA
Meals a la carte 13.70/21.20 **t.** 7.25 – **11 rm** 50.00/80.00 **t.** – SB.

SOAR MILL COVE *Devon* – *see Salcombe.*

SOLIHULL *W. Mids.* 403 404 O 26 – *pop. 94 531.*
Central Library, Homer Rd *(0121) 704 6130.*
London 109 – Birmingham 7 – Coventry 13 – Warwick 13.

Solihull Moat House, Homer Rd, B91 3QD, (0121) 623 9988, *revsol@queensmoat uk, Fax (0121) 711 2696,* – rm, rest, P – 200.
Meals (bar lunch Saturday and Bank Holidays) 18.00 **t.** (dinner) and a la carte 18.20/28.4 7.25 – 14.00 – **113 rm** 160.00/180.00 **t.**, 2 suites – SB.

Swallow St. John's (becoming a Renaissance by Marriott spring 2001), 651 Warwick Rd, B91 1AT, ☎ (0121) 711 3000, *info@swallowhotels.com, Fax (0121) 711 3963,* – rm, rest, – 700. VISA.
***Warwick :* Meals** a la carte 21.20/27.75 **st.** – **177 rm** 150.00/165.00 **st.**, 1 suite – SB.

Jarvis International, The Square, B91 3RF, ☎ (0121) 711 2121, *Fax (0121) 711 3374* – rm, – 200. VISA
Meals 12.50/14.50 **st.** (lunch) and dinner a la carte 18.00/21.25 **st.** – 10.95 – **135 rm** 145.00/165.00 **st.**, 10 suites – SB.

Shirley *West : 2½ m. by B 4102 on A 34 – ✉ Solihull.*

Regency, Stratford Rd, B90 4EB, Southeast : 1 m. on A 34 ☎ (0121) 745 6119, *regencyhotel.regalhotels@pop3.hiway.com, Fax (0121) 733 3801,* – rm, – 150. VISA
Meals (bar lunch Saturday) 11.50/18.95 **st.** and a la carte 5.75 – **110 rm** 150.00/160.00 **st.**, 2 suites – SB.

Travel Inn, Stratford Rd, B90 4EP, Southeast : 1 ½ m. on A 34 ☎ (0121) 744 2942, *Fax (0121) 733 7075* – rm, VISA.
Meals (grill rest.) – **51 rm** 40.95 **t.**

Chez Julien, 1036 Stratford Rd, Monkspath, B90 4EE, Southeast : 1 ½ m. on A 34 ☎ (0121) 744 7232, *chezjulien@yahoo.com, Fax (0121) 745 4775,* – VISA
closed Saturday lunch and Sunday – **Meals** - French - 9.90 **t.** (lunch) and a la carte 21.90/29.50 **t.** 5.80.

Olton *Northwest : 2½ m. on A 41 – ✉ Solihull.*

Rajnagar, 256 Lyndon Rd, B92 7QW, ☎ (0121) 742 8140, *info@rajnagar.com, Fax (0121) 743 3147* – VISA JCB
*closed 25-26 December***Meals** - Indian - (dinner only) 12.95/16.95 **st.** and a la carte.

*Le Guide change, changez de **guide Michelin** tous les ans.*

MERTON *Somerset* 403 L 30 *The West Country G. – pop. 4 489.*
See : *Town★ - Market Place★ (cross★) – St. Michael's Church★.*
Env. : *Long Sutton★ (Church★★) SW : 2½ m. by B 3165 – Huish Episcopi (St. Mary's Church Tower★★) SW : 4½ m. by B 3153 – Lytes Cary★, SE : 3½ m. by B 3151 – Street - The Shoe Museum★, N : 5 m. by B 3151.*
Exc. : *Muchelney★★ (Parish Church★★) SW : 6½ m. by B 3153 and A 372 – High Ham (≤★★, St. Andrew's Church★), NW : 9 m. by B 3153, A 372 and minor rd – Midelney Manor★ AC, SW : 9 m. by B 3153 and A 378.*
London 138 – Bristol 32 – Taunton 17.

Lynch Country House without rest., 4 Behind Berry, TA11 7PD, ☎ (01458) 272316, *the_lynch@talk21.com, Fax (01458) 272590,* ≤, « Regency house », – VISA.
closed 25 and 31 December – **5 rm** 45.00/75.00 **t.**

NNING-ON-THAMES *Wokingham* 404 R 29 – *pop. 1 354.*
London 48 – Reading 4.

French Horn with rm, RG4 6TN, ☎ (01189) 692204, *thefrenchhorn@compuserve.com, Fax (01189) 442210,* ≤ River Thames and gardens – VISA.
closed Good Friday, 25-31 December – **Meals** (booking essential) 22.50/35.00 **st.** and a la carte 10.50 – **16 rm** 110.00/185.00 **st.**, 4 suites.

UTHAMPTON *Southampton* 403 404 P 31 *Great Britain G. – pop. 210 138.*
See : *Old Southampton* **AZ** : *Bargate★* **B** - *Tudor House Museum★* **M1**.
18, 9 *Southampton Municipal, Golf Course Rd, Bassett ☎ (023) 8076 8407,* **AY** – 18 *Stoneham, Monks Wood Close, Bassett ☎ (023) 8076 8151,* **AY** – 18 *Chilworth Golf Centre, Main Rd, Chilworth ☎ (023) 8074 0544,* **AY**.
Itchen Bridge (toll) **AZ**.
Southampton/Eastleigh Airport : ☎ (023) 8062 0021, N : 4 m. **BY**.
to France (Cherbourg) (Stena Line) 1-2 daily (5 h) – to the Isle of Wight (East Cowes) (Red Funnel Ferries) frequent services daily (1 h).
to Hythe (White Horse Ferries Ltd) frequent services daily (12 mn) – to the Isle of Wight (Cowes) (Red Funnel Ferries) frequent services daily (approx. 22 mn).
9 Civic Centre Rd ☎ (023) 8022 1106.
London 87 – Bristol 79 – Plymouth 161.

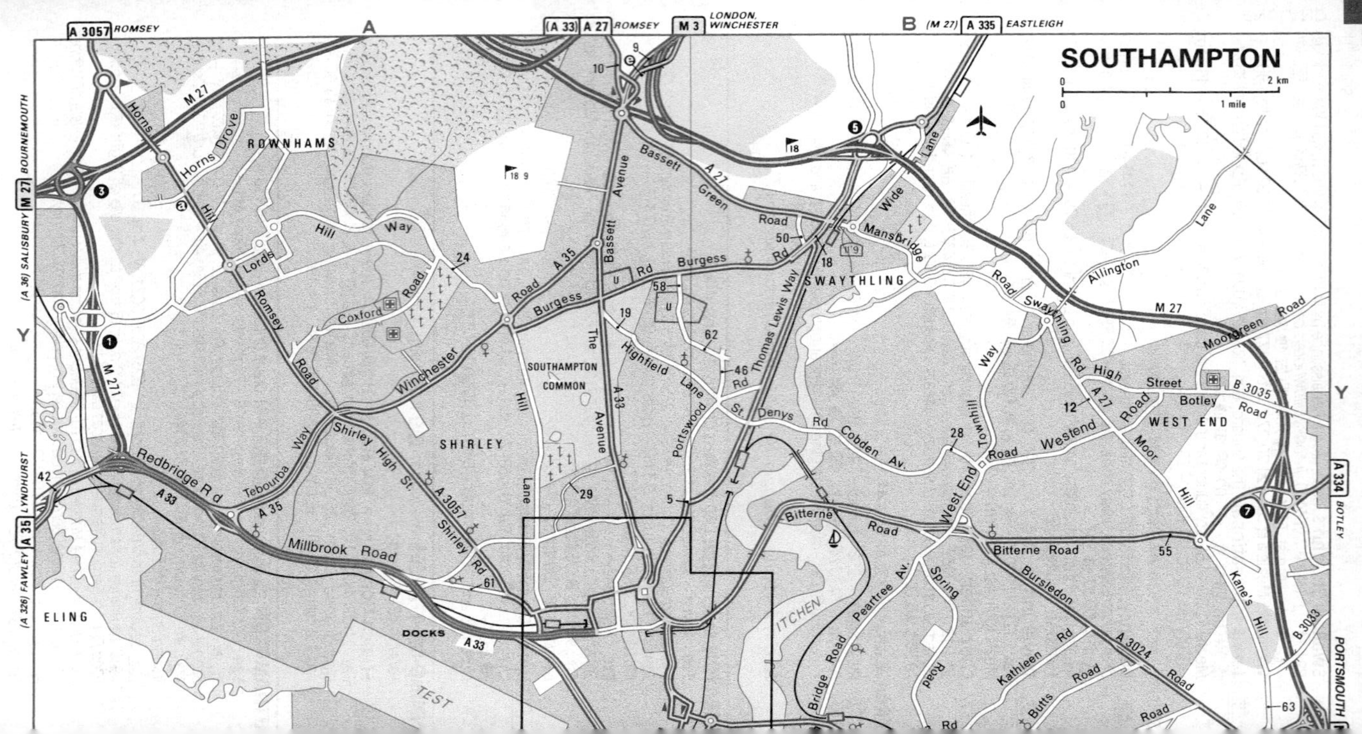
SOUTHAMPTON
0 2 km
0 1 mile
A 3057 ROMSEY
A
(A 33) A 27 ROMSEY
M 3 LONDON, WINCHESTER
B (M 27) A 335 EASTLEIGH
(A 36) SALISBURY M 27 BOURNEMOUTH
(A 326) FAWLEY A 35 LYNDHURST
A 334 BOTLEY
PORTSMOUTH
ROWNHAMS
SWAYTHLING
WEST END
SHIRLEY
SOUTHAMPTON COMMON
DOCKS
ELING
ITCHEN
TEST
M 27
M 271
A 27
A 33
A 35
A 3057
A 3024
B 3035
B 3033
Horns Hill
Horns Drove
Lords Hill Way
Romsey Road
Coxford Road
Winchester Road
Shirley High St.
Shirley Rd
Tebourba Way
Millbrook Road
Redbridge Rd
Hill Lane
The Avenue
Bassett Avenue
Burgess Rd
Bassett Green Road
Highfield Lane
Portswood Rd
St. Denys Rd
Thomas Lewis Way
Wide Lane
Mansbridge
Allington Lane
Swaythling Rd
Road
Way
Cobden Av.
Townhill Way
West End Road
Westend Road
High Street
Botley Road
Moorgreen Road
Moor Hill
Kane's Hill
Bitterne Road
Bursledon Road
Spring Road
Peartree Av.
Bridge Road
Kathleen Rd
Butts Road

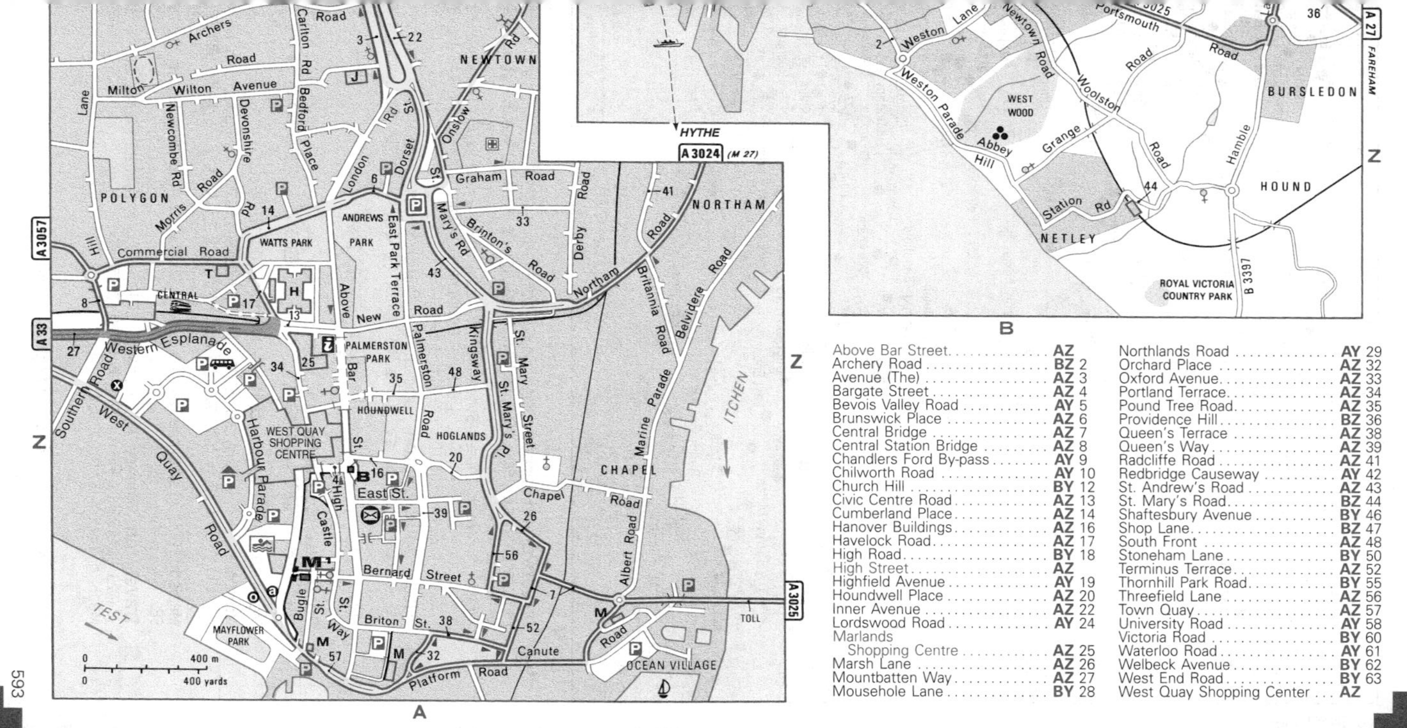

Street	Grid	No.
Above Bar Street	AZ	
Archery Road	BZ	2
Avenue (The)	AZ	3
Bargate Street	AZ	4
Bevois Valley Road	AY	5
Brunswick Place	AZ	6
Central Bridge	AZ	7
Central Station Bridge	AZ	8
Chandlers Ford By-pass	AY	9
Chilworth Road	AY	10
Church Hill	BY	12
Civic Centre Road	AZ	13
Cumberland Place	AZ	14
Hanover Buildings	AZ	16
Havelock Road	AZ	17
High Road	BY	18
High Street	AZ	
Highfield Avenue	AY	19
Houndwell Place	AZ	20
Inner Avenue	AZ	22
Lordswood Road	AY	24
Marlands Shopping Centre	AZ	25
Marsh Lane	AZ	26
Mountbatten Way	AZ	27
Mousehole Lane	BY	28
Northlands Road	AY	29
Orchard Place	AZ	32
Oxford Avenue	AZ	33
Portland Terrace	AZ	34
Pound Tree Road	AZ	35
Providence Hill	BZ	36
Queen's Terrace	AZ	38
Queen's Way	AZ	39
Radcliffe Road	AZ	41
Redbridge Causeway	AY	42
St. Andrew's Road	AZ	43
St. Mary's Road	BZ	44
Shaftesbury Avenue	BY	46
Shop Lane	BZ	47
South Front	AZ	48
Stoneham Lane	BY	50
Terminus Terrace	AZ	52
Thornhill Park Road	BY	55
Threefield Lane	AZ	56
Town Quay	AZ	57
University Road	AY	58
Victoria Road	BY	60
Waterloo Road	AY	61
Welbeck Avenue	BY	62
West End Road	BY	63
West Quay Shopping Center	AZ	

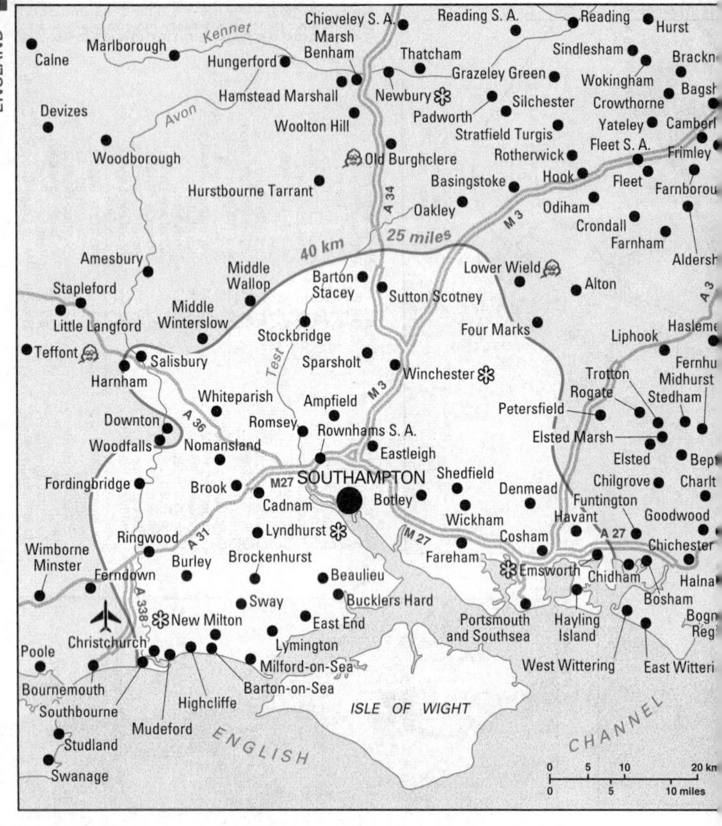

De Vere Grand Harbour, West Quay Rd, SO15 1AG, ✆ (023) 8063 3033, *grand.southampton@airtime.co.uk, Fax (023) 8063 3066,* – 500. AZ

Allerton's : **Meals** *(closed Sunday dinner)* (booking essential) 12.75 **t.** (lunch) and dinner a la carte 28.85/41.10 **t.** 12.00 – ***Brewster's :*** **Meals** (dinner only) 24.50/35.85 10.75 – **169 rm** 150.00/170.00 **t.**, 3 suites – SB.

Hilton Southampton, Bracken Pl., Chilworth, SO16 3RB, ✆ (023) 8070 27 *Fax (023) 8076 7233,* rest, – 200. AY

Meals *(closed Saturday lunch)* a la carte 15.15/29.15 **st.** – 11.50 – **133 rm** 160.00/180.00 **t.**, 2 suites.

Posthouse Southampton, Herbert Walker Av., SO15 1HJ, ✆ (0870) 400 90 *Fax (023) 8033 2510,* rm, – 200. AZ

Meals 6.00/24.95 **t.** 6.95 – 11.95 – **126 rm** 105.00/125.00 **st.**, 2 suites – SB.

Novotel, 1 West Quay Rd, SO15 1RA, ✆ (023) 8033 0550, *h1073@accor-hotel.co* *Fax (023) 8022 2158,* rm, – 450. AZ

Meals 16.50/17.50 **st.** (dinner) and a la carte 17.50/38.20 **st.** – 9.50 – **121 rm** 79.00 st. SB.

Travel Inn, Romsey Rd, Nursling, SO16 0XJ, Northwest : 4 m. on A 3 ✆ (023) 8073 2262 – rm, AY

Meals (grill rest.) – **32 rm** 40.95 **t.**

La guida cambia, cambiate la guida ogni anno.

OUTHBOURNE *Bournemouth* 403 404 O 31 – *see Bournemouth.*

OUTH BRENT *Devon* 403 I 32 *The West Country G.* – *pop. 2 087.*
Env. : *Dartmoor National Park*★★.
London 227 – Exeter 29 – Plymouth 17 – Torquay 16.

Brookdale House, North Huish, TQ10 9NR, Southeast : 4 ½ m. by B 3210 via Avonwick village ☎ (01548) 821661, *brookdalehouse@yahoo.com, Fax (01548) 821606,* – TV P. MC AE VISA.
Meals 15.00/30.00 **t.** 5.00 – **8 rm** 65.00/200.00 **t.** – SB.

OUTH CAVE *East Riding* 402 S 22 – *pop. 2 669.*
18 *Cave Castle Hotel* ☎ *(01430) 421286.*
London 176 – Kingston-upon-Hull 12 – Leeds 40 – York 30.

Travelodge, Beacon Service Area, HU15 1RZ, Southwest : 2 ½ m. on A 63 (eastbound carriageway) ☎ (01430) 424455, *Fax (01430) 424455* – rm, TV P. MC AE VISA JCB.
Meals (grill rest.) – **40 rm** 39.95 **t.**

OUTHEND-ON-SEA *Southend* 404 W 29 – *pop. 158 517.*
18 *Belfairs, Eastwood Road North, Leigh-on-Sea* ☎ *(01702) 525345* – 18 *Ballards Gore G & C.C., Gore Rd, Canewdon, Rochford* ☎ *(01702) 258917.*
Southend-on-Sea Airport : ☎ *(01702) 608100, N : 2 m.*
19 High St. ☎ *(01702) 215120.*
London 39 – Cambridge 69 – Croydon 46 – Dover 85.

Balmoral, 32-36 Valkyrie Rd, Westcliff-on-Sea, SS0 8BU, ☎ (01702) 342947, *balmoralhotel@netscapeonline.co.uk, Fax (01702) 337828* – TV P. MC AE VISA.
closed 27-30 December – **Meals** *(closed Sunday dinner)* (bar lunch)/dinner 9.95/12.95 **t.** and a la carte 4.95 – **28 rm** 59.00/70.00 **t.**, 1 suite.

Camelia, 178 Eastern Esplanade, Thorpe Bay, SS1 3AA, ☎ (01702) 587917, *cameliahotel@fsbdial.co.uk, Fax (01702) 585704* – rm, rest, TV. MC AE VISA JCB.
Meals *(room service only Sunday dinner)* (dinner only and Sunday lunch)/dinner 12.95 **st.** and a la carte 4.95 – **20 rm** 46.00/60.00 **st.** – SB.

Travel Inn, Thanet Grange, SS2 6GB, Northwest : 2 ½ m. by A 127 off B 1013 ☎ (01702) 338787, *Fax (01702) 337436* – rm, TV P. MC AE VISA.
Meals (grill rest.) – **60 rm** 40.95 **t.**

Pebbles, 190 Eastern Esplanade, Thorpe Bay, SS1 3AA, ☎ (01702) 582329, *Fax (01702) 582329,* – rest, TV. MC VISA.
Meals (by arrangement) 15.00 **st.** – **5 rm** 35.00/60.00 **st.**

Beaches without rest., 192 Eastern Esplanade, Thorpe Bay, SS1 3AA, ☎ (01702) 586124, *Fax (01702) 588377,* – TV. MC AE VISA JCB.
8 rm 25.00/50.00.

The Bay without rest., 187 Eastern Esplanade, Thorpe Bay, SS1 3AA, ☎ (01702) 588415, *thebayguesthouse@hotmail.com* – TV. MC AE VISA JCB.
4 rm 35.00/50.00 **s.**

Moorings without rest., 172 Eastern Esplanade, Thorpe Bay, SS1 3AA, ☎ (01702) 587575, *Fax (01702) 586791* – TV.
3 rm 30.00/45.00 **s.**

XX **Paris,** 719 London Rd, Westcliff-on-Sea, SS0 9ST, ☎ (01702) 344077, *Fax (01702) 344077* – MC AE VISA JCB
closed Saturday lunch, Sunday dinner, Monday and Bank Holidays – **Meals** 15.95/25.95 **st.** 7.00.

UTH LEIGH *Oxon.* 403 404 P 28 – *see Witney.*

UTH MIMMS SERVICE AREA *Herts.* 404 T 28 – ✉ *Potters Bar.*
London 21 – Luton 17.

Posthouse South Mimms, Bignells Corner, EN6 3NH, M 25 junction 23 at junction with A 1 (M) ☎ (0870) 400 9072, *Fax (01707) 646728,* – rm, TV P – 100. MC AE VISA JCB
Meals *(closed Saturday lunch)* a la carte 25.00/43.00 **t.** 8.00 – 11.95 – **144 rm** 99.00 **st.** – SB.

Days Inn, Bignells Corner, EN6 3QQ, M 25 junction 23 at junction with A 1((01707) 665440, Reservations (Freephone) 0800 0280400, *Fax (01707) 660189* – r
Meals (grill rest.) a la carte 9.65/13.90 **t.** – 7.45 – **74 rm** 65.00/70.00 **t.**

SOUTH MOLTON *Devon* 403 I 30 – *pop. 4 066.*

1 East St. (01769) 574122 (restricted opening in winter).

London 210 – Exeter 35 – Taunton 39.

Marsh Hall Country House, EX36 3HQ, Northeast : 1 ½ m. on North Molton (01769) 572666, *Fax (01769) 574230*, – rest, VISA JCB.
Meals (dinner only) 21.00 **st.** 6.00 – **7 rm** 55.00/85.00 **st.** – SB.

SOUTH NORMANTON *Derbs.* 402 403 404 Q 24 – *pop. 13 044 (inc. Pinxton).*

London 130 – Derby 17 – Nottingham 15 – Sheffield 31.

Swallow (becoming a Renaissance by Marriott spring 2001), Carter Lane East, DE55 2E on A 38 (01773) 812000, *info@swallowhotels.com, Fax (01773) 580032*, rm, rest, – 200. VISA
Meals 12.95/18.95 **st.** and dinner a la carte 7.00 – **157 rm** 95.00/115.00 **t.** – SB.

Travel Inn, Carter Lane East, DE55 2EH, on A 38 (01773) 862899, *Fax (01773) 86115* rm, VISA.
Meals (grill rest.) – **82 rm** 40.95 **t.**

To visit a town or region: use the ***Michelin Green Guides.***

SOUTHPORT *Mersey.* 402 K 23 – *pop. 90 959.*

Southport Municipal, Park Road West (01704) 535286.

112 Lord St. (01704) 533333.

London 221 – Liverpool 25 – Manchester 38 – Preston 19.

Scarisbrick, 239 Lord St., PR8 1NZ, (01704) 543000, *scarisbrickhotel@talk21.co Fax (01704) 533335*, – – 180. VISA
Meals (dancing Saturday evening) (carving lunch Sunday) (dinner only and Sunday lunc dinner 12.00 **t.** and a la carte 4.95 – (see also ***Cloisters*** below) – **88 rm** 77.00/99.00 1 suite – SB.

Prince of Wales, Lord St., PR8 1JS, (01704) 536688, *princeofwales@paramount-ho s.co.uk, Fax (01704) 543488* – rm, – 350. VISA JCB.
Meals 9.95/17.00 **t.** and dinner a la carte 7.45 – **98 rm** 99.00/115.00 **t.**, 3 suites – SB

Stutelea, Alexandra Rd, PR9 0NB, (01704) 544220, *info@stutelea.co. Fax (01704) 500232*, – VISA JCB.
closed 25-26 December – **Meals** (bar lunch)/dinner a la carte 18.00/21.00 **st.** 6.00 – **20** 65.00/120.00 **st.** – SB.

Cambridge House, 4 Cambridge Rd, PR9 9NG, Northeast : 1 m. on A 5 (01704) 538372, *Fax (01704) 547183*, – VISA.
Meals (dinner only and Saturday and Sunday lunch)/dinner 14.50 **t.** and a la carte 5.7 **16 rm** 33.00/60.00 **t.** – SB.

Ambassador, 13 Bath St., PR9 0DP, (01704) 543998, *ambassador.walton@virgin.r Fax (01704) 536269* – VISA.
closed Christmas and New Year – **Meals** 10.00 **st.** – **8 rm** 38.00/54.00 **st.**

Warehouse Brasserie, 30 West St., PR8 1QN, (01704) 544662, *info@warehousebr erie.co.uk, Fax (01704) 500074* – VISA
closed 25 December and Sunday – **Meals** (light lunch)/dinner and a la carte 19.40/25.50 7.95.

Ho'Lee Chow's, Rotton Row, Victoria Park, PR8 2BZ, (01704) 5511 *Fax (01704) 550519* – VISA JCB
Meals - Chinese - (dinner only) 14.50/35.00 **t.** and a la carte 6.00.

Cloisters (at Scarisbrick H.), Back Passage, Lord St., PR8 1NZ, (01704) 5351 *Fax (01704) 535153* – VISA
Meals a la carte 14.45/20.60 **t.** 4.95.

SOUTHSEA *Portsmouth* 403 404 Q 31 – *see Portsmouth and Southsea.*

SOUTH STOKE *Oxon.* 403 404 Q 29 – *see Goring.*

)UTHWAITE SERVICE AREA *Cumbria* 401 402 L 19 – ✉ *Carlisle.*

M 6 Service Area ✆ (016974) 73445.

London 300 – Carlisle 14 – Lancaster 58 – Workington 48.

Travelodge, CA4 0NT, M 6 between junctions 41 and 42 ✆ (016974) 73131, *Fax (016974) 73669* – rm, TV ♿ P. MC AE D VISA JCB. **Meals** (grill rest.) – **39 rm** 49.95 **t.**

)UTH WALSHAM *Norfolk* 404 Y 26 *Great Britain G. – pop. 1 612 –* ✉ *Norwich.*

Env. : *The Broads*★.

London 120 – Great Yarmouth 11 – Norwich 9.

South Walsham Hall, The Street, NR13 6DQ, ✆ (01603) 270378, *alexsuss@btinternet.com, Fax (01603) 270519,* ≤, heated, , , , – TV P – 25. MC AE D VISA JCB.

Meals 19.50 **t.** and a la carte 5.50 – **17 rm** 55.00/200.00 **st.** – SB.

)UTHWATER *W. Sussex* 404 T 30 – *see Horsham.*

)UTHWELL *Notts.* 402 404 R 24 *Great Britain G. – pop. 6 498.*

See : *Minster*★★ *AC.*

London 135 – Lincoln 24 – Nottingham 14 – Sheffield 34.

Old Forge without rest., 2 Burgage Lane, NG25 0ER, ✆ (01636) 812809, *Fax (01636) 816302,* – TV P. MC AE VISA

5 rm 45.00/66.00 **s.**

Les prix — Pour toutes précisions sur les prix indiqués dans ce guide, reportez-vous aux pages de l'introduction.

)UTHWOLD *Suffolk* 404 Z 27 – *pop. 3 905.*

The Common ✆ (01502) 723234.

69 High St. ✆ (01502) 523007.

London 108 – Great Yarmouth 24 – Ipswich 35 – Norwich 34.

Swan, Market Pl., IP18 6EG, ✆ (01502) 722186, *swan.hotel@adnams.co.uk, Fax (01502) 724800,* – , rest, TV P – 40. MC AE D VISA.

closed 7-25 January – **Meals** (bar lunch Monday to Friday January-May) 20.00/24.50 **t.** and dinner a la carte 10.00 – **41 rm** 60.00/135.00 **t.**, 2 suites – SB.

Crown, 90 High St., IP18 6DP, ✆ (01502) 722275, *crownhotelreception/adnams@adnams.co.uk, Fax (01502) 727263,* « Part 18C inn » – TV P – 40. MC AE D VISA.

Meals 18.50/25.50 **t.** and a la carte – 4.00 – **14 rm** 50.00/75.00 **st.** – SB.

Uggeshall *Northwest : 4 m. by A 1095 and B 1126 over A 12 at Wangford –* ✉ *Southwold.*

Uggeshall Manor Farm without rest., NR34 8BD, ✆ (01502) 578546, *Fax (01502) 578560,* ≤, « Working farm », , – TV P. MC VISA

closed January and 1 week Christmas – **3 rm** 34.00/65.00 **s.**

)WERBY BRIDGE *W. Yorks.* 402 O 22 – *pop. 9 901 –* ✉ *Halifax.*

London 211 – Bradford 10 – Burnley 35 – Manchester 32 – Sheffield 40.

The Millbank, Mill Bank, HX6 3DY, Southwest : 2 ¼ m. by A 58 ✆ (01422) 825588, *millbankph@ukonline.co.uk, Fax (01422) 822080,* – . MC VISA

closed Monday, Sunday dinner and Tuesday lunch – **Meals** (booking essential) a la carte 15.85/24.15 **t.**

'ALDING *Lincs.* 402 404 T 25 – *pop. 18 731.*

Ayscoughfee Hall Museum, Churchgate ✆ (01775) 725468.

London 111 – Lincoln 40 – Leicester 56 – Norwich 65.

Bedford Court without rest., 10 London Rd, PE11 2TA, ✆ (01775) 722377, *Fax (01775) 722377,* – TV P.

closed 30 Jan-1 March – **4 rm** 25.00/45.00.

'ARSHOLT *Hants.* 403 404 P 30 – *see Winchester.*

SPEEN *Bucks.* 404 R 28 – ✉ *Princes Risborough.*
London 41 – Aylesbury 15 – Oxford 33 – Reading 25.

Old Plow (Restaurant), Flowers Bottom, HP27 0PZ, West : ½ m. by Chapel Hill and Highwood Bottom ✆ (01494) 488300, *Fax (01494) 488702,* – P. MC AE VISA
closed 3 weeks August, 25 December, 1 January, Monday, Saturday lunch, Sunday dinner and Bank Holiday Mondays – **Meals** 23.95/28.95 **t.** and a la carte 10.95 – (see also ***Bistro*** below).

Bistro (at Old Plow), Flowers Bottom, HP27 0PZ, West : ½ m. by Chapel Hill and Highwood Bottom ✆ (01494) 488300, *Fax (01494) 488702,* , – P. MC AE VISA
closed 3 weeks August, 25 December, 1 January, Monday, Saturday lunch, Sunday dinner and Bank Holiday Mondays – **Meals** (booking essential) a la carte 23.85/31.85 **t.** 10.95.

SPRATTON *Northants.* 404 R 27 – *see Northampton.*

SPRIG'S ALLEY *Oxon.* – *see Chinnor.*

STADDLEBRIDGE *N. Yorks.* – *see Northallerton.*

STADHAMPTON *Oxon.* 403 404 Q 28 – *pop. 718.*
London 53 – Aylesbury 18 – Oxford 10.

Crazy Bear with rm, Bear Lane, OX44 7UR, off Wallingford rd ✆ (01865) 8907[illegible] *Fax (01865) 400481,* , – TV P. MC AE VISA.
closed 24 December-2 January **Meals** *(closed Sunday dinner and Monday)* 15.95 (lunch) and a la carte approx. 24.50/40.50 **t.** – ***Thai Thai* : Meals** - Thai - *(closed Sunday lunch)* 18.00/22.00 **t.** and a la carte – 8.50 – **11 rm** 80.00/190.00 **t.**, 1 suite.

STAFFORD *Staffs.* 402 403 404 N 25 – *pop. 61 885.*
Stafford Castle, Newport Rd ✆ (01785) 223821.
The Ancient High House, Greengate St. ✆ (01785) 619136.
London 142 – Birmingham 26 – Derby 32 – Shrewsbury 31 – Stoke-on-Trent 17.

Garth, Wolverhampton Rd, ST17 9JR, South : 2 m. on A 449 ✆ (01785) 25612[illegible] *Fax (01785) 255152,* – rm, rest, TV P – 175. MC AE VISA JCB
Meals (bar lunch Saturday) (carving rest.) 18.75/25.00 **t.** and a la carte 7.25 – 9.75 **60 rm** 77.00/87.00 **st.** – SB.

Express by Holiday Inn without rest., Acton Court, Acton Gate, ST18 9AR, South : 3 [illegible] on A 449 ✆ (01785) 212244, *express.stafford@ingramhotels.co.uk, Fax (01785) 212377* , rm, rest, TV P – 40. MC AE VISA.
closed 24 to 26 December – **103 rm** 52.50 **st.**

STAFFORD SERVICE AREA *Staffs.* 403 404 N 25 – ✉ *Stafford.*

Travelodge, Stone, ST15 0EU, M 6 between junctions 14 and 15 (northbound carriageway) ✆ (01785) 811188, *Fax (01785) 810500* – TV P. MC AE VISA JCB.
Meals (grill rest.) – **49 rm** 49.95 **t.**

Travel inn without rest., Stone, ST15 0EU, M 6 between junctions 15 and 14 (southbound carriageway) ✆ (01785) 826300, *Fax (01785) 826303* – TV P – 50. MC AE VISA.
42 rm 40.95 **t.**

STAINES *Middx.* 404 S 29 – *pop. 51 167.*
London 26 – Reading 25.

Thames Lodge, Thames St., TW18 4SF, ✆ (0870) 400 8121, *heritagehotels-staines.thames-lodge@forte-hotels.com, Fax (01784) 454858,* ≤, « Riverside setting » – , rest, P – 50. MC AE VISA JCB.
Meals a la carte 17.20/26.20 **t.** 8.75 – 12.75 – **78 rm** 135.00/155.00 **st.** – SB.

STAITHES *Redcar & Cleveland* 402 R 20 – ✉ *Saltburn (Cleveland).*
London 269 – Middlesbrough 22 – Scarborough 31.

Endeavour, 1 High St., TS13 5BH, ✆ (01947) 840825 –
closed January-March, November, 25-26 December, Sunday and Monday – **Meals** - Seafood - (lunch booking essential) a la carte 20.15/23.65 **t.** 5.95.

ALLINGBOROUGH *N.E. Lincs.* 402 404 T 23.

London 178 – Boston 53 – Doncaster 48 – Lincoln 36 – Scunthorpe 25.

Stallingborough Grange, Riby Rd, DN41 8BU, Southwest : 1 ¼ m. on A 1173 ✆ (01469) 561302, *grange.hot@virgin.net, Fax (01469) 561338,* – TV P – 80. MC AE VISA.
Meals (bar lunch Monday-Saturday) a la carte 11.95/21.15 **t.** 4.25 – **32 rm** 68.00/80.00 **t.**

AMFORD *Lincs.* 402 404 S 26 *Great Britain G. – pop. 17 492.*

See : *Town★★ - St. Martin's Church★ – Lord Burghley's Hospital★ – Browne's Hospital★ AC.*
Env. : *Burghley House★★ AC, SE : 1½ m. by B 1443.*
Stamford Arts Centre, 27 St. Mary's St. ✆ (01780) 755611.
London 92 – Leicester 31 – Lincoln 50 – Nottingham 45.

The George of Stamford, 71 St. Martin's, PE9 2LB, ✆ (01780) 750750, *reservations@georgehotelofstamford.com, Fax (01780) 750701,* « Part 16C coaching inn with walled monastic garden » – TV P – 50. MC AE VISA JCB
Meals 14.50/16.50 **st.** (lunch) and a la carte 29.10/40.35 **st.** 6.95 – **46 rm** 78.00/105.00 **st.**, 1 suite – SB.

Garden House, 42 High St., St. Martin's, PE9 2LP, ✆ (01780) 763359, *gardenhousehotel@stamford60.freeserve.co.uk, Fax (01780) 763339,* – rest, TV P. MC AE VISA JCB
Meals 15.00 **st.** and dinner a la carte 4.50 – **20 rm** 60.00/85.00 **st.** – SB.

Ram Jam Inn, Great North Rd, Stretton, LE15 7QX, Northwest : 8 m. by B 1081 on A 1 (northbound carriageway) ✆ (01780) 410776, *rji@rutnet.co.uk, Fax (01780) 410361,* – TV P – 30. MC AE VISA.
closed 25 December and 1 January – **Meals** a la carte 14.20/20.65 **t.** 6.95 – 5.25 – **7 rm** 45.00/55.00 **t.**

Lady Anne's, 37-38 High St., St. Martin's Without, PE9 2LJ, ✆ (01780) 481184, *Fax (01780) 765422,* – rest, TV P – 100. MC AE VISA
closed 27 to 30 December – **Meals** (booking essential Saturday lunch) 10.00/20.50 **t.** and a la carte – **28 rm** 52.00/90.00 **st.** – SB.

The Bombay Cottage, 52 Scotgate, PE9 2YQ, ✆ (01780) 480138 – . MC AE VISA JCB
Meals - Indian - a la carte 10.10/16.80 **t.** 4.50.

Tallington *East : 5 m. by A 6121 on A 16 – ✉ Stamford.*

The Mill without rest., Mill Lane, PE9 4RR, ✆ (01780) 740815, *Fax (01780) 740280,* « Converted 17C mill », – TV P. MC
6 rm 35.00/60.00 **st.**

Normanton Park *(Leics.) West : 6½ m. by A 606 on Edith Weston Rd – ✉ Oakham.*

Normanton Park , South Shore, LE15 8RP, ✆ (01780) 720315, *Fax (01780) 721086,* « Converted Georgian stables on shores of Rutland Water », – rm, rest, TV P – 30. MC AE VISA
Meals 14.95/17.95 **t.** and dinner a la carte – **23 rm** 65.00/85.00 **t.** – SB.

ANDISH *Gtr. Manchester* 402 404 M 23 – *pop. 12 196 – ✉ Wigan.*

London 210 – Liverpool 25 – Manchester 21 – Preston 15.

Kilhey Court, Chorley Rd, WN1 2XN, East : 1 ¾ m. by B 5239 on A 5106 ✆ (01257) 472100, *info@kilheycourt.macdonald-hotels.co.uk, Fax (01257) 422401,* – , rest, TV P – 180. MC AE VISA
Laureate : **Meals** *(closed Saturday lunch)* 14.95/26.00 **st.** and dinner a la carte 9.00 – **62 rm** 75.00/120.00 **t.**

Wigan/Standish Moat House, Almond Brook Rd, WN6 0SR, West : 1 m. on A 5209 ✆ (01257) 499988, *revwig@queensmoat.co.uk, Fax (01257) 427327,* – , rm, rest, TV P – 170. MC AE VISA JCB
Meals (carving rest.) 14.95 **t.** (dinner) and a la carte 10.90/15.70 **t.** 5.75 – 10.50 – **124 rm** 84.00/99.00 **t.** – SB.

Ashfield House, Ashfield Park Drive, WN6 0EQ, Southeast : ¾ m. by A 49 ✆ (01257) 473500, *arb355@compuserve.com, Fax (01257) 400311,* – rest, TV P. MC AE VISA JCB.
Barkers : **Meals** 8.95/17.95 **t.** and a la carte 5.95 – **15 rm** 65.00/85.00 **t.**

Premier Lodge, Almond Brook Rd, WN6 0SS, West : 1 m. on A 5209 ✆ (0870) 7001574, *Fax (0800) 7001575* – TV P – 30. MC AE VISA.
Meals (grill rest.) a la carte 11.25/16.35 **t.** – 6.00 – **36 rm** 42.00 **t.**

ENGLAND

at Wrightington Bar *Northwest : 3½ m. by A 5209 on B 5250 – ✉ Wigan.*

The Mulberry Tree, WN6 9SE, ✆ (01257) 451400, *Fax (01257) 451400* – ⚟ P. MC VISA
closed 1 January, 25 December and Monday except Bank Holidays – **Meals** a la ca
13.00/21.25 **t.**

STANLEY *Durham* 401 402 O 19 – *pop. 1 733.*
London 284 – Newcastle upon Tyne 11 – Carlisle 68 – Darlington 31 – Middlesbrough 39.

Beamish Park, Beamishburn Rd, Marley Hill, NE16 5EG, North : 2 ½ m. by A 6(
✆ (01207) 230666, *reception@beamish-park-hotel.co.uk, Fax (01207) 281260,* – ⚟
P. MC AE ◑ VISA
Meals a la carte 14.45/25.15 **st.** 6.50 – ☕ 8.95 – **47 rm** 44.50/65.50 **st.** – SB.

STANNERSBURN *Northd.* 401 402 M 18 – ✉ *Hexham.*
London 363 – Carlisle 56 – Newcastle upon Tyne 46.

Pheasant Inn with rm, Falstone, NE48 1DD, ✆ (01434) 240382, *thepheasantinn@*
derwater.demon.co.uk, Fax (01434) 240382 – ⚟ TV P. MC VISA JCB
closed Monday, January-February and 25-26 December – **Meals** a la carte 15.40/20.6
4.75 – **8 rm** ☕ 40.00/64.00 **t.** – SB.

STANSTEAD ABBOTTS *Herts.* 404 U 28 – *pop. 1 909* – ✉ *Ware.*
Briggens House Hotel, Briggens Park, Stanstead Rd ✆ (01279) 793742.
London 22 – Cambridge 37 – Luton 32 – Ipswich 66.

Briggens House, Stanstead Rd, SG12 8LD, East : 2 m. by A 414 ✆ (01279) 8299
Fax (01279) 793685, ≤, heated, , , , – , ⚟ rest, TV P – 100. MC AE ◑
closed 27-30 December – **Meals** 18.25/21.95 **st.** and a la carte 9.00 – ☕ 11.00 – **53**
110.00/128.00 **st.**, 1 suite – SB.

STANSTED AIRPORT *Essex* 404 U 28 – ✉ *Stansted Mountfitchet.*
London 37 – Cambridge 29 – Chelmsford 18 – Colchester 29.

Hilton London Stansted Airport, Round Coppice Rd, CM24 8SE, ✆ (01279) 6808
Fax (01279) 680890, , , – , ⚟ rm, ▤ rest, TV ✆ ♿ P – 300. MC AE ◑
JCB.
Meals (bar lunch Saturday) 13.95/19.95 **st.** and dinner a la carte – ☕ 12.95 – **235**
182.00 **st.**, 5 suites.

Days Inn without rest., Birchanger Green Service Area, Old Dunmow Rd, CN23 5QZ
junction 8 of M 11 ✆ (01279) 656477, Reservations (Freephone) 0800 02804
Fax (01279) 656590 – ⚟ TV ♿ P. MC AE ◑ VISA JCB
☕ 7.45 – **60 rm** 69.00/74.00 **t.**

at Broxted *Northeast : 3 ¾ m. by Broxted rd* – ✉ *Great Dunmow.*

Whitehall, Church End, CM6 2BZ, on B 1051 ✆ (01279) 850603, *sales@whitehallhotel*
uk, Fax (01279) 850385, ≤, « Part 12C and 15C manor house, walled garden » – TV
100. MC AE ◑ VISA.
closed 26 to 31 December – **Meals** *(closed Saturday lunch and Sunday dinner)* 23.50/35.0
and dinner a la carte 7.50 – ☕ 10.00 – **26 rm** 95.00/220.00 **t.**

STANTON *Suffolk* 404 W 27 – *pop. 2 490.*
London 88 – Cambridge 38 – Ipswich 40 – King's Lynn 38 – Norwich 39.

Leaping Hare, Wyken Vineyards, IP31 2DW, South : 1 ¼ m. by Wyken
✆ (01359) 250287, *Fax (01359) 252256,* , « Converted 17C barn, vineyard and work
farm », – ⚟ P. MC VISA
closed 25 December-9 January – **Meals** *(Wednesday to Sunday lunch and dinner Friday a*
Saturday) (booking essential) a la carte 18.00/24.50 **t.** 7.00.

STANTON FITZWARREN *Wilts.* – *see Swindon.*

STANTON SAINT QUINTIN *Wilts.* 403 404 N 29 – *see Chippenham.*

STANTON WICK *Bath & North East Somerset* 403 404 M 29 – *see Bristol.*

STAPLEFORD *Wilts.* 403 404 O 30 – *see Salisbury.*

TAVERTON *Devon* 403 I 32 – *pop. 682* – ✉ *Totnes.*
London 220 – Exeter 20 – Torquay 33.

Kingston House ⑤, TQ9 6AR, Northwest : 1 m. on Kingston rd ☎ (01803) 762235, *info@kingston-estate.net, Fax (01803) 762444,* ←, « Georgian mansion, antiques and marquetry staircase », ⛪, ♧ – ⇔ 🅿. MC AE ⓓ VISA JCB. ✂
closed 23 December-4 January – **Meals** (set menu only) (residents only) (dinner only) 32.50 **st.** – **3 rm** ⊒ 85.00/150.00 – SB.

Sea Trout Inn with rm, TQ9 6PA, ☎ (01803) 762274, *Fax (01803) 762506,* ⌂ – ⇔ rest, TV 🅿. MC AE VISA
Meals (bar lunch Monday to Saturday and bar meals Sunday dinner)/dinner 16.50/19.75 **st.** and a la carte – **11 rm** ⊒ 46.50/80.00 **st.** – SB.

TAVERTON *Glos.* – *see Cheltenham.*

TAVERTON *Northants.* 404 Q 27 – *see Daventry.*

TEDHAM *W. Sussex* 404 R 31 – *see Midhurst.*

TEEPLE ASTON *Oxon.* 403 404 Q 28 – *pop. 874* – ✉ *Bicester.*
London 69 – Coventry 38 – Oxford 10.

The Holt, OX25 5QQ, Southwest : 1 ¼ m. at junction of A 4260 with B 4030 ☎ (01869) 340259, *info@holthotel_oxford.co.uk, Fax (01869) 340865,* ⛪ – ⇔ TV 🅿 – 🏛 120. MC AE ⓓ VISA
Meals (bar lunch Saturday) 22.00/25.00 **t.** (dinner) and a la carte 25.45/33.65 **t.** 🍷 6.75 – **86 rm** ⊒ 85.00/149.00 **s.**

TEVENAGE *Herts.* 404 T 28 *Great Britain G.* – *pop. 76 064.*
Env. : *Knebworth House★ AC, S : 2 ½ m.*
⛳18, ⛳9 *Aston Lane ☎ (01438) 880424 – ⛳18, ⛳9 Chesfield Downs, Jack's Hill, Graveley ☎ (01462) 482929.*
London 36 – Bedford 25 – Cambridge 27.

Cromwell, High St., Old Town, SG1 3AZ, ☎ (01438) 779954, *Fax (01438) 742169,* ⛪ – ⇔ rm, ≡ rest, TV ☎ 🅿 – 🏛 150. MC AE ⓓ VISA. ✂
Meals *(closed Saturday lunch)* a la carte 14.50/20.65 **st.** 🍷 7.95 – ⊒ 10.50 – **76 rm** 96.00/120.00 **st.** – SB.

Novotel Stevenage, Knebworth Park, SG1 2AX, Southwest : 1 ½ m. by A 602 at junction with A 1 (M) ☎ (01438) 346100, *h0992@accor-hotels.com, Fax (01438) 723872,* ⛱ heated – |♦|, ⇔ rm, ≡ rest, TV ☎ ♿ 🅿 – 🏛 120. MC AE ⓓ VISA
Meals 16.75 **st.** and a la carte – ⊒ 10.00 – **100 rm** 89.00 **st.**

Travel Inn, Corey's Mill Lane, SG1 4AA, Northwest : 2 m. on A 602 ☎ (01438) 351318, *Fax (01438) 721609* – |♦|, ⇔ rm, ≡ rest, TV ♿ 🅿. MC AE ⓓ VISA. ✂
Meals (grill rest.) – **39 rm** 40.95 **t.**

TEYNING *W. Sussex* 404 T 31 – *pop. 8 692 (inc. Upper Beeding).*
London 52 – Brighton 12 – Worthing 10.

The Old Tollgate, The Street, Bramber, BN44 3WE, Southwest : 1 m. ☎ (01903) 879494, *otr@fastnet.co.uk, Fax (01903) 813399,* ⛪ – |♦| TV ♿ 🅿. MC AE ⓓ VISA JCB. ✂
Meals (carving rest.) 13.95/20.95 **t.** 🍷 5.80 – ⊒ 6.95 – **31 rm** 70.00/95.00 **t.** – SB.

Springwells without rest., 9 High St., BN44 3GG, ☎ (01903) 812446, *Fax (01903) 879823,* ⌂s, ⛱ heated, ⛪ – TV 🅿. MC AE ⓓ VISA
closed 2 weeks Christmas-New Year – **10 rm** ⊒ 44.00/88.00 **t.**

TILTON *Cambs.* 404 T 26 – *pop. 2 219* – ✉ *Peterborough.*
London 76 – Cambridge 30 – Northampton 43 – Peterborough 6.

Bell Inn, Great North Rd, PE7 3RA, ☎ (01733) 241066, *reception@thebellstilton.co.uk, Fax (01733) 245173,* « Part 16C », ⛪ – ⇔ rm, TV 🅿 – 🏛 100. MC AE ⓓ VISA. ✂
closed 25 December – **Meals** 21.50 **st.** 🍷 7.25 – (see also ***Village Bar*** below) – **19 rm** ⊒ 69.50/109.50 **st.**

Village Bar (at Bell Inn), Great North Rd, PE7 3RA, ☎ (01733) 241066, ⛱, « Part 16C » – 🅿. MC AE ⓓ VISA
*closed 25 December***Meals** a la carte 15.70/25.40 **st.** 🍷 7.25.

STOCKBRIDGE *Hants.* 403 404 P 30 – *pop. 570.*
London 75 – Salisbury 14 – Winchester 9.

Carbery, Salisbury Hill, SO20 6EZ, on A 30 ☎ (01264) 810771, *Fax (01264) 811022,* he ed, – rest, TV P.
closed 2 weeks Christmas – **Meals** (by arrangement) 14.50 **st.** – **11 rm** 35.00/54.00 st

Peat Spade Inn with rm, Longstock, SO20 6DR, North : 1 ½ m. on A 30 ☎ (01264) 810612, *peat.spade@virgin.net, Fax (01264) 810612,* « 18C inn », – TV P
closed 1 January, 25 December, Sunday dinner and Monday – **Meals** a la carte 15.2 20.40 **t.** – **2 rm** 50.00/58.75 **t.**

STOCKPORT *Gtr. Manchester* 402 403 404 N 23 – *pop. 132 813.*
Heaton Moor, Mauldeth Rd ☎ (0161) 432 2134 – Romiley, Goosehouse Green ☎ (01 430 2392 – Ladythorn Rd, Bramhall ☎ (0161) 439 4057 – Hazel Grove ☎ (0161) 4 3217.
Graylaw House, Chestergate ☎ (0161) 474 4444.
London 201 – Liverpool 42 – Manchester 6 – Sheffield 37 – Stoke-on-Trent 34.

Jarvis Alma Lodge, 149 Buxton Rd, SK2 6EL, South : 1 ¼ m. on A 6 ☎ (0161) 483 44 *Fax (0161) 483 1983* – rm, TV P – 200. MC AE VISA.
Meals (carving rest.) (bar lunch Saturday) a la carte 20.00/34.50 **t.** – 8.95 – **53** 75.00/110.50 **st.** – SB.

Premier Lodge, Churchgate, SK1 1YG, East : ¼ m. by Wellington St. ☎ (0870) 70014 *Fax (0870) 7001485* – , rest, TV P. MC AE VISA.
Meals 10.95 **t.** (dinner) and a la carte 9.35/18.15 **t.** – 6.00 – **46 rm** 46.00 **t.**

Saxon Holme, 230 Wellington Rd North, SK4 2QN, North : 1 m. on A ☎ (0161) 432 2335, *info@saxonholmehotel.co.uk, Fax (0161) 431 8076* – TV P. AE VISA.
closed 25 December-1 January – **Meals** 12.95 **t.** (dinner) and a la carte 12.95/20.45 **t.** 7 – **33 rm** 49.50/59.50 **st.** – SB.

Wycliffe, 74 Edgeley Rd, Edgeley, SK3 9NQ, West : 1 m. on B 5465 ☎ (0161) 477 5395, *liffe_hotel@yahoo.co.uk, Fax (0161) 476 3219* – rm, TV P – 30. MC AE VISA.
Meals - Italian -*(closed Saturday lunch and Bank Holiday Mondays)* 8.50/16.50 and a la carte 7.25 – **20 rm** 48.00/58.00 **st.**

Travel Inn, Buxton Rd, SK2 6NB, South : 1 m. on A 6 ☎ (0161) 480 29 *Fax (0161) 477 8320* – rm, rest, TV P. MC AE VISA.
Meals (grill rest.) – **40 rm** 40.95 **t.**

STOCKTON-ON-TEES *Stockton-on-Tees* 402 P 20 – *pop. 83 576.*
Eaglescliffe, Yarm Rd ☎ (01642) 780098 – Knotty Hill Golf Centre, Sedgefield ☎ (017 620320 – Norton, Junction Rd ☎ (01642) 676385.
Teesside Airport : ☎ (01325) 332811, SW : 6 m. by A 1027, A 135 and A 67.
Theatre Yard, off High St. ☎ (01642) 393936.
London 251 – Leeds 61 – Middlesbrough 4.

Swallow, 10 John Walker Sq., TS18 1AQ, ☎ (01642) 679721, *stockton@swallow-hotels. uk, Fax (01642) 601714,* – TV P – 300. MC AE VISA
Portcullis : **Meals** (dinner only) 21.50/23.50 **st.** and a la carte 7.50 – ***Matchmaker Br serie :*** **Meals** (lunch only) a la carte 10.45/17.45 **st.** 7.50 – **125 rm** 95.00/130.00 st SB.

Travel Inn, Yarm Rd, TS18 3RT, Southwest : 1 ¾ m. on A 135 at junction with A ☎ (01642) 633354, *Fax (01642) 633339* – rm, rest, TV P. MC AE VISA.
Meals (grill rest.) – **62 rm** 40.95 **t.**

at Eaglescliffe *South : 3½ m. on A 135 – ✉ Stockton-on-Tees.*

Parkmore, 636 Yarm Rd, TS16 0DH, ☎ (01642) 786815, *enquiries@parkmorehotel.co. Fax (01642) 790485,* – TV P – 120. MC AE VISA
Reeds at Six Three Six : **Meals** a la carte 14.50/23.50 **t.** – 7.95 – **54 rm** 59.00/82.00 1 suite – SB.

STOKE BRUERNE *Northants.* 404 R 27 – *pop. 347* – ✉ *Towcester.*
London 69 – Coventry 33 – Northampton 9 – Oxford 33.

Bruerne's Lock, 5 The Canalside, NN12 7SB, ☎ (01604) 863654, *bruernes_lock@msn m, Fax (01604) 863330,* « Canalside setting » – . MC AE VISA.
closed 26 December to 8 January, 1 week spring, 1 week October, Monday, Sunday din and Saturday lunch – **Meals** 17.00 **t.** and dinner a la carte 8.95.

TOKE BY NAYLAND *Suffolk* 404 W 28.

London 70 – Bury St. Edmunds 24 – Cambridge 54 – Colchester 11 – Ipswich 14.

Ryegate House without rest., CO6 4RA, ☎ (01206) 263679, *ryegate@lineone.net*, ≤, – ⇔ TV P
closed 1 week in spring, 1 week in autumn and 2-3 days at Christmas – **3 rm** ☐ 35.00/50.00 **st.**

Angel Inn with rm, Polstead St., CO6 4SA, ☎ (01206) 263245, *Fax (01206) 263373*, « Part timbered 17C inn » – TV P. MO AE ① VISA.
closed 25-26 December and 1 January – **Meals** a la carte 14.95/24.75 **t.** 5.40 – **6 rm** ☐ 48.00/65.00 **t.**

TOKE CANON *Devon* 403 J 31 – *see Exeter.*

TOKE D'ABERNON *Surrey* 404 ㊷ – *see Cobham.*

TOKE FLEMING *Devon* 403 J 33 – *see Dartmouth.*

TOKE HOLY CROSS *Norfolk* 404 X 26 – *see Norwich.*

When visiting Scotland,
*use the **Michelin Green Guide** **"Scotland".***
- *Detailed descriptions of places of interest*
- *Touring programmes*
- *Maps and street plans*
- *The history of the country*
- *Photographs and drawings of monuments, beauty spots, houses...*

TOKE-ON-TRENT *Stoke-on-Trent* 402 403 404 N 24 *Great Britain G. – pop. 266 543.*

See : *The Potteries Museum and Art Gallery*★ **Y M** – *Gladstone Pottery Museum*★ *AC* **V**.
Env. : *Wedgwood Visitor Centre*★ *AC, S : 7 m. on A 500, A 34 and minor rd* **V**.
Exc. : *Little Moreton Hall*★★ *AC, N : 10 m. by A 500 on A 34* **U**.

Greenway Hall, Stockton Brook ☎ (01782) 503158, **U** – *Parkhall, Hulme Rd, Weston Coyney ☎ (01782) 599584,* **V**.

Quadrant Rd, Hanley ☎ (01782) 236000.

London 162 – Birmingham 46 – Leicester 59 – Liverpool 58 – Manchester 41 – Sheffield 53.

Plans on following pages

Stoke-on-Trent Moat House, Etruria Hall, Festival Park, Etruria, ST1 5BQ, ☎ (01782) 609988, *Fax (01782) 284500*, – ⇔ TV P – 600. MO AE ① VISA JCB. U n
Meals (bar lunch Saturday and Bank Holidays) a la carte 13.95/27.95 **st.** 7.00 – ☐ 10.50 – **147 rm** 120.00/140.00 **st.** – SB.

North Stafford, Station Rd, ST4 2AE, ☎ (01782) 744477, *Fax (01782) 744580* – TV P – 450. MO AE ① VISA X a
Meals 9.95/17.95 **st.** and dinner a la carte 5.50 – ☐ 10.00 – **80 rm** 95.00/110.00 **st.** – SB.

Burslem *North : 3½ m. by A 500 and A 53 on A 50 – ✉ Stoke-on-Trent.*

The George, Swan Sq., ST6 2AE, ☎ (01782) 577544, *georgestoke@btinternet.com*, *Fax (01782) 837496* – TV P – 200. MO AE ① VISA JCB. U e
closed 24-26 December – **Meals** 10.95/16.95 **t.** and a la carte 5.10 – **39 rm** ☐ 65.00/90.00 **t.** – SB.

Talke *Northwest : 4 m. on A 500 at junction with A 34 – ✉ Stoke-on-Trent.*

Travelodge, Newcastle Rd, ST7 1UP, ☎ (01782) 777000, *Fax (01782) 777000* – ⇔ rm, TV P. MO AE ① VISA JCB. U s
Meals (grill rest.) – **62 rm** 49.95 **t.**

ENGLAND

STOKE-ON-TRENT
NEWCASTLE-UNDER-LYME
BUILT UP AREA

Alexandra Road . . . . **U** 3
Bedford Road . . . . **U** 4
Brownhills Road . . . . **U** 12
Church Lane . . . . **U** 19
Cobridge Road . . . . **U** 21
Davenport Street . . . . **U** 23
Elder Road . . . . **U** 24
Etruria Vale Road . . . . **U** 27
Grove Road . . . . **V** 30
Hanley Road . . . . **U** 31
Heron Street . . . . **V** 34
High Street . . . . **U** 35
Higherland . . . . **V** 37
Manor Street . . . . **V** 44
Mayne Street . . . . **V** 45
Moorland Road . . . . **U** 48
Porthill Road . . . . **U** 59
Snow Hill . . . . **U** 63
Stoke Road . . . . **U** 68
Strand (The) . . . . **V** 69
Victoria Park Road . . . . **U** 75
Victoria Place Link . . . . **V** 76
Watlands View . . . . **U** 77
Williamson Street . . . . **U** 78

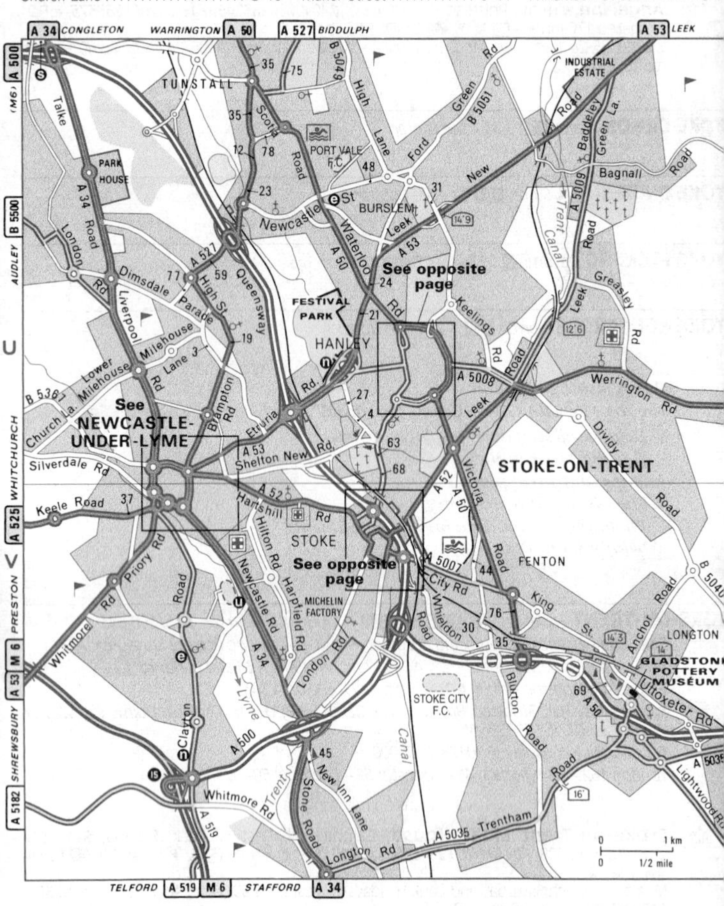

When visiting London use the Green Guide **"London"**

- Detailed descriptions of places of interest
- Useful local information
- A section on the historic square-mile of the City of London with a detailed fold-out plan
- The lesser known London boroughs
  - their people, places and sights
- Plans of selected areas and important buildings.

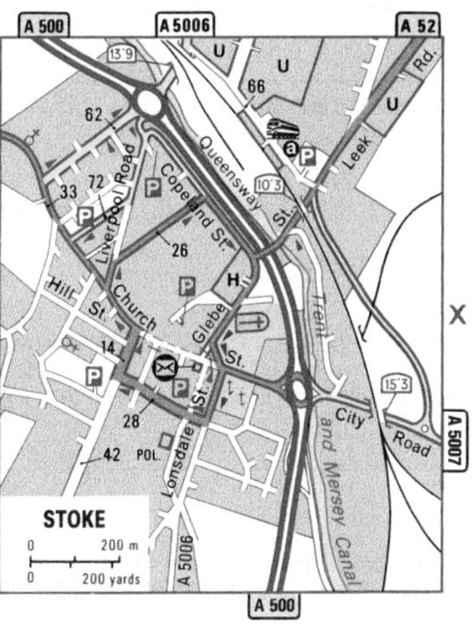

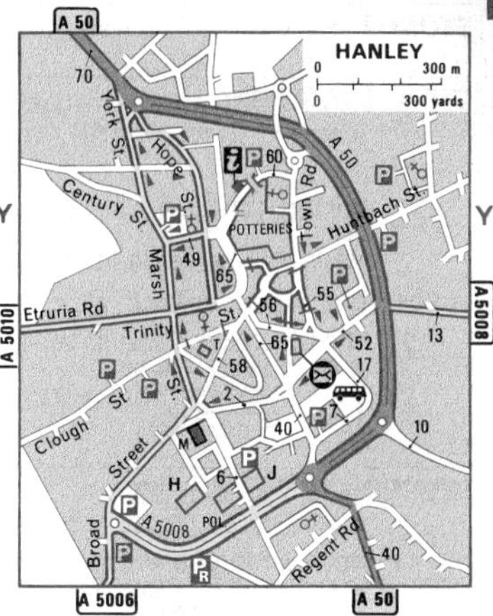

ɔion Street . . . . **Y** 2
thesda Street . . . . **Y** 6
ch Terrace . . . . **Y** 7
tteslow Street . . . . **Y** 10
cknall New Road . . . . **Y** 13
mpbell Place . . . . **X** 14
arles Street . . . . **Y** 17
urch Street . . . . **X**
ɔnora Street . . . . **X** 26
Fleming Road . . . . **X** 28
Hartshill Road . . . . **X** 33
Lichfield Street . . . . **Y** 40
London Road . . . . **X** 42
New Hall Street . . . . **Y** 49
Old Hall Street . . . . **Y** 52
Parliament Row . . . . **Y** 55
Percy Street . . . . **Y** 56
Piccadilly . . . . **Y** 58
Potteries
Shopping Centre . . . . **Y**
Quadrant Road . . . . **Y** 60
Shelton
Old Road . . . . **X** 62
Stafford Street . . . . **Y** 65
Station Road . . . . **X** 66
Vale Place . . . . **Y** 70
Vale Street . . . . **X** 72

TOKE POGES *Bucks.* 404 S 29 – *pop. 4 508.*

Park Rd ☎ (01753) 717171.

London 30 – Aylesbury 28 – Oxford 44.

Stoke Park , Park Rd, SL2 4PG, ☎ (01753) 717171, *info@stokepark.co.uk, Fax (01753) 717181,* « Palladian mansion in parkland by Capability Brown », – 100. MC AE VISA JCB.
Stoke's Brasserie : **Meals** *(closed Saturday lunch)* 17.00 **st.** and a la carte 12.75 – **19 rm** 245.00/275.00 **st.**, 1 suite.

TOKESLEY *N. Yorks.* 402 Q 20 *Great Britain G. – pop. 4 008 – ✉ Middlesbrough.*

Env. : *Great Ayton (Captain Cook Birthplace Museum★ AC), NE : 2½ m. on A 173.*

London 239 – Leeds 59 – Middlesbrough 8 – York 52.

Chapter's with rm, 27 High St., TS9 5AD, ☎ (01642) 711888, *Fax (01642) 713387,* – rm, . MC AE VISA
closed 25 December – **Meals** *(closed Sunday)* a la carte 17.95/28.95 **t.** 5.75 – **13 rm** 59.00/77.00 **t.**

TONE *Staffs.* 402 403 404 N 25 – *pop. 12 305.*

Barlaston, Meaford Rd ☎ (01782) 372867.

London 150 – Birmingham 36 – Stoke-on-Trent 9.

Stone House, ST15 0BQ, South : 1 ¼ m. by A 520 on A 34 ☎ (01785) 815531, *Fax (01785) 814764,* – 180. MC AE VISA JCB
Meals (bar lunch Saturday and Bank Holidays) 7.95/18.95 **st.** and a la carte – 9.50 – **50 rm** 89.00/119.00 **st.** – SB.

TON EASTON *Somerset* 403 404 M 30 – *pop. 579 – ✉ Bath (Bath & North East Somerset).*

London 131 – Bath 12 – Bristol 11 – Wells 7.

Ston Easton Park , BA3 4DF, ☎ (01761) 241631, *info@stoneaston.co.uk, Fax (01761) 241377,* « Palladian mansion », – 30. MC AE VISA
Meals 16.00/39.50 **st.** 14.00 – 5.00 – **19 rm** 155.00/405.00 **st.**, 2 suites – SB.

STONOR *Oxon.* 404 R 29 – *see Henley-on-Thames.*

STONY STRATFORD *Milton Keynes* 404 R 27 – *pop. 55 733 (inc. Wolverton).*
London 58 – Birmingham 68 – Northampton 14 – Oxford 32.

Plans : see Milton Keynes

XX **Peking,** 117 High St., MK11 1AT, ☎ (01908) 563120, *Fax (01908) 560084* – ▤. MC AE ① VISA JCB AV
Meals - Chinese (Peking, Szechuan) - 15.00 **t.** and a la carte.

at Cosgrove *(Northants.) North : 2½ m. by A 508 –* ✉ *Milton Keynes.*

The Old Bakery, Main St., MK19 7JL, ☎ (01908) 262255, *Fax (01908) 263620* – ⇔ rm, P. MC AE ① VISA JCB. ✻ AU
Meals *(closed Friday-Sunday)* (residents only) (dinner only) 12.50 **t.** and a la carte 4.50
6 rm ☐ 60.00/75.00 **t.**

STORRINGTON *W. Sussex* 404 S 31 – *pop. 7 429.*
London 54 – Brighton 20 – Portsmouth 36.

No. 1 Lime Chase without rest., RH20 4LX, by B 2139 (Thakeham Rd) off Fryern
☎ (01903) 740437, *fionawarton@limechase.co.uk, Fax (01903) 740437,* – ⇔ TV P. ✻
3 rm ☐ 45.00/80.00.

XXX **Fleur de Sel** (Perraud), Manleys Hill, RH20 4BT, East : ¼ m. on A 283 ☎ (01903) 74223
✿ *Fax (01903) 740649* – P. MC AE VISA
closed first 2 weeks September, Saturday lunch, Sunday dinner and Monday – **Meals** French - 16.50/20.50-31.00 **t.** 7.50
Spec. Cornish crab cake with hazelnuts and mixed peppers. Roast rack of lamb with he and mustard crust. White and dark chocolate mousses, coconut ice cream.

XX **Old Forge,** 6 Church St., RH20 4LA, ☎ (01903) 743402, *enquiries@oldforge.co.*
Fax (01903) 742540 – MC AE ① VISA JCB
closed 2 weeks in spring, 2 weeks in autumn, Christmas, New Year, Saturday lunch, Sunc dinner, Monday and Tuesday – **Meals** 14.50/25.00-30.00 **t.** 6.00.

STOURBRIDGE *W. Mids.* 403 404 N26 – *pop. 55 624.*
London 147 – Birmingham 14 – Wolverhampton 10 – Worcester 21.

Plan : see Birmingham p. 4

Travel Inn, Birmingham Rd, Hagley, DY9 9JS, Southeast : 3 ½ m. by A 491 on A 4 (eastbound carriageway) ☎ (01562) 883120, *Fax (01562) 884416* – ⇔ rm, TV ♿ P. MC ① VISA. ✻ AU
Meals (grill rest.) – **40 rm** 40.95 **t.**

STOURPORT-ON-SEVERN *Worcs.* 403 404 N 26 – *pop. 18 283.*
London 137 – Birmingham 21 – Worcester 12.

Stourport Manor, Hartlebury Rd, DY13 9JA, East : 1 ¼ m. on B 4193 ☎ (01299) 2899
stourport@menzies-hotels.co.uk, Fax (01299) 878520, Lб, ≘s, heated, , ,
squash – ⇔ TV ☎ P – 350. MC AE ① VISA JCB
Meals 10.95/15.95 **st.** and a la carte 6.95 – ☐ 10.50 – **66 rm** 95.00/105.00 **st.**, 2 suite SB.

STOWMARKET *Suffolk* 404 W/X 27 – *pop. 13 229.*
ℹ *Wilkes Way* ☎ *(01449) 676800.*
London 81 – Cambridge 42 – Ipswich 12 – Norwich 38.

Travelodge, IP14 3PY, Northwest : 2 m. by A 1038 on A 14 (westbour
☎ (01449) 615347 – ⇔ rm, TV ♿ P. MC AE ① VISA JCB. ✻
Meals (grill rest.) – **40 rm** 39.95 **t.**

Gipping Heights, Creeting Rd, IP14 5BT, East : 1 m. by Station Rd East (B 11
☎ (01449) 675264 – TV P. MC VISA. ✻
Meals 12.00 **s.** 6.00 – **3 rm** ☐ 38.00/48.00 **s.** – SB.

at Mendlesham Green *Northeast : 6 ¼ m. by B 1115, A 1120 and Mendlesham rd –* ✉ *Sto market.*

Cherry Tree Farm, Mendlesham Green, IP14 5RQ, ☎ (01449) 766376, « Part Elizabeth house », – ⇔ P. ✻
closed Christmas and January – **Meals** (by arrangement) (communal dining) 17.00 **s.** – **3**
☐ 35.00/52.00 **s.**

TOW-ON-THE-WOLD *Glos.* 403 404 O 28 *Great Britain G. – pop. 1 999.*

Exc. : *Chastleton House★★, NE : 6½ m. by A 436 and A 44.*

Hollis House, The Square ☎ (01451) 831082.

London 86 – Birmingham 44 – Gloucester 27 – Oxford 30.

Wyck Hill House, GL54 1HY, South : 2 ¼ m. by A 429 on A 424 ☎ (01451) 831936, *wyckhill@wrensgroup.com, Fax (01451) 832243*, « Part Victorian country house », – rest, rest, – 50. VISA.
Meals 14.00/36.50 **t.** 9.95 – **31 rm** 105.00/250.00 **t.**, 1 suite – SB.

Grapevine, Sheep St., GL54 1AU, ☎ (01451) 830344, *enquires@vines.co.uk, Fax (01451) 832278*, « Mature grapevine in restaurant » – rm, – 25. VISA.
Meals (light lunch)/dinner 26.00 **t.** 6.15 – **22 rm** 73.50/130.00 **t.**

Fosse Manor, Fosse Way, GL54 1JX, South : 1 ¼ m. on A 429 ☎ (01451) 830354, *Fax (01451) 832486*, – rest, – 40. VISA
closed 1 week Christmas – **Meals** 16.50/26.00 **st.** 6.95 – **23 rm** 55.00/118.00 **st.** – SB.

Unicorn, Sheep St., GL54 1HQ, ☎ (01451) 830257, *bookings@cotswold-inns-hotels.co.uk, Fax (01451) 831090* – – 40. VISA JCB.
Meals (bar lunch Monday to Saturday)/dinner 19.50/21.50 **st.** – **20 rm** 60.00/120.00 **st.** – SB.

The Royalist, Digbeth St., GL54 1BN, ☎ (01451) 830670, *info@theroyalisthotel.co.uk, Fax (01451) 870048*, « Part 10C inn » – . VISA JCB.
947 AD : **Meals** 16.00/29.00 **t.** 7.00 – (see also ***Eagle & Child*** below) – **12 rm** 45.00/120.00 **st.** – SB.

Stow Lodge, The Square, GL54 1AB, ☎ (01451) 830485, *enquiries@stowlodge.com, Fax (01451) 831671*, – . VISA JCB.
closed 17 December-late January – **Meals** (bar lunch)/dinner 18.00/20.00 **t.** 8.50 – **21 rm** 70.00/100.00 **t.**

Number Nine without rest., 9 Park St., GL54 1AQ, ☎ (01451) 870333, *numbernine@talk21.com, Fax (01451) 870445* – . VISA.
closed 3 weeks January – **3 rm** 40.00/54.00 **s.**

Wyck Hill Lodge without rest., Wyck Hill, GL54 1HT, South : 2 m. by A 429 on A 424 ☎ (01451) 830141, *gkhwyck@compuserve.com*, – .
March-November – **3 rm** 50.00 **s.**

Eagle & Child (at The Royalist H.), Digbeth St., GL54 1BN, ☎ (01451) 830670, *Fax (01451) 870048* – VISA JCB
Meals (bookings not accepted) a la carte 14.00/20.00 **t.** 7.00.

Lower Oddington *East : 3 m. by A 436 – ✉ Stow-on-the-Wold.*

Fox Inn with rm, GL56 0UR, ☎ (01451) 870555, *Fax (01451) 870669*, – rm, . VISA
closed 25 and 31 December and 1 January – **Meals** (bookings not accepted) a la carte 12.45/19.20 **t.** – **3 rm** 45.00/85.00 **st.**

Bledington *Southeast : 4 m. by A 436 on B 4450 – ✉ Kingham.*

Kings Head, OX7 6XQ, ☎ (01608) 658365, *kingshead@orr-ewing.com, Fax (01608) 658902*, « Part 15C inn » – rm, . VISA JCB.
Meals a la carte 12.85/24.85 **t.** 5.00 – **12 rm** 45.00/90.00 **t.**

RATFIELD TURGIS *Hants.* 403 404 Q 29 – *pop. 94 – ✉ Basingstoke.*

London 46 – Basingstoke 8 – Reading 11.

Wellington Arms, RG27 0AS, on A 33 ☎ (01256) 882214, *wellington.arms@virgin.net, Fax (01256) 882934*, – rm, – 200. VISA
Meals (in bar Saturday lunch and Sunday dinner) a la carte 18.65/28.45 **t.** 7.50 – **28 rm** 100.00/130.00 **st.**, 2 suites.

RATFORD-UPON-AVON *Warks.* 403 404 P 27 *Great Britain G. – pop. 22 231.*

See : *Town★ - Shakespeare's Birthplace★* **AC, AB.**

Env. : *Mary Arden's House★* **AC**, *NW : 4 m. by A 3400* **A.**

Exc. : *Ragley Hall★* **AC**, *W : 9 m. by A 422* **A.**

Tiddington Rd ☎ (01789) 297296, **B** – *Welcombe Hotel, Warwick Rd ☎ (01789) 299012*, **B** – *Stratford Oaks, Bearley Rd, Snitterfield ☎ (01789) 731982*, **B.**

Bridgefoot ☎ (01789) 293127.

London 96 – Birmingham 23 – Coventry 18 – Oxford 40.

ENGLAND

STRATFORD-UPON-AVON

For maximum information from town plans: consult the conventional signs key.

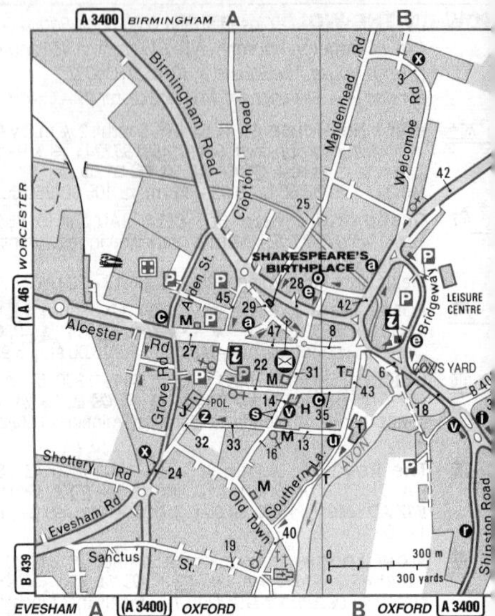

Welcombe H. & Golf Course, Warwick Rd, CV37 0NR, Northeast : 1 ½ m. on A 4
(01789) 295252, *sales@welcombe.co.uk, Fax (01789) 414666*, «19C Jacobean st mansion, formal garden », – rest, – 100.
closed 2 to 8 January – ***Trevelyan :*** Meals 21.50/32.50 **t.** and dinner a la carte – **59**
120.00/185.00 **t.**, 5 suites – SB.

Ettington Park, Alderminster, CV37 8BU, Southeast : 6 ¼ m. on A 34
(01789) 450123, *ettington@arcadianhotels.co.uk, Fax (01789) 450472*, « Victorian G thic mansion », – rest, – 60.
Meals 17.50/30.50 **t.** and dinner a la carte – **43 rm** 125.00/185.00 **t.**, 5 suites.

Alveston Manor, Clopton Bridge, CV37 7HP, (0870) 4008181, *Fax (01789) 4140*
« Part Elizabethan house », – – 120. B
Manor : Meals 18.00/25.00 **t.** 8.00 – 11.95 – **109 rm** 125.00/145.00 **st.**, 5 suites – SB

Stratford Moat House, Bridgefoot, CV37 6YR, (01789) 279988, *revsfd@queensm t.co.uk, Fax (01789) 298589*, – rm, – 600. B
The Terrace : Meals (dinner only) a la carte 15.35/24.40 **st.** 6.80 – ***The Riverside :*** Me (carving rest.) 11.95/17.00 **st.** 6.00 – 11.50 – **249 rm** 125.00/145.00 **st.**, 2 suites – SB

The Shakespeare, Chapel St., CV37 6ER, (0870) 4008182, *Fax (01789) 415411*, « 1 timbered inn » – – 100. A
David Garrick : Meals *(closed lunch in summer)* 28.00 **t.** and dinner a la carte – ***Othell***
Bistro : Meals *(closed Sunday-Wednesday dinner)* a la carte 12.00/17.00 **t.** – 11.95
73 rm 125.00/165.00 **st.**, 1 suite – SB.

Thistle Stratford-Upon-Avon, Waterside, CV37 6BA, (01789) 294949, *stratford-onavon@thistle.co.uk, Fax (01789) 415874*, – – 60. B
Bards : Meals a la carte 22.00/38.00 **st.** – 10.50 – **62 rm** 113.00/165.00 **st.** – SB.

Stratford Manor, Warwick Rd, CV37 0PY, Northeast : 3 m. on A 439 (01789) 73117 *tratfordmanor@marstonhotels.com, Fax (01789) 731131*, – rest, – 350.
Meals (bar lunch Saturday) 19.50/27.00 **st.** and dinner a la carte – 11.00 – **103** 99.00/120.00 **t.** – SB.

Stratford Victoria, Arden St., CV37 6QQ, (01789) 271000, *stratfordvictoria@mars hotels.co.uk, Fax (01789) 271001*, – rm, rest, – 140. A
Meals (carving lunch Sunday) 20.00/30.00 **t.** (dinner) and a la carte 20.00/30.00 **t.** – 11.00 – **99 rm** 89.50/129.50 **t.**, 1 suite – SB.

Grosvenor, 12-14 Warwick Rd, CV37 6YT, ☎ (01789) 269213, *sales@patenhotels.co.uk, Fax (01789) 266087,* – rm, TV – 100. MC AE VISA B a
Meals (bar lunch Saturday) 10.95/16.50 **st.** and a la carte 8.00 – 8.95 – **67 rm** 78.50/110.00 **st.** – SB.

Swans Nest, Bridgefoot, CV37 7LT, ☎ (0870) 4008183, *Fax (01789) 414547,* – rm, TV P – 150. MC AE VISA. B v
Meals a la carte 12.00/15.00 **t.** 6.50 – 11.95 – **68 rm** 95.00/115.00 **st.** – SB.

Dukes, Payton St., CV37 6UA, ☎ (01789) 269300, *Fax (01789) 414700,* – TV P. MC AE VISA JCB. AB o
closed 15 December-15 January – **Meals** *(closed Sunday)* (residents only) (dinner only) a la carte 19.50/24.95 **t.** 6.75 – **22 rm** 57.50/130.00 **t.** – SB.

Stratford Court, Avenue Rd, CV37 6UX, ☎ (01789) 297799, *stratfordcourt@easynet.co.uk, Fax (01789) 262449,* « Edwardian house », – TV P. MC VISA B x
Meals (booking essential) (residents only) (dinner only) 18.50 **st.** 6.50 – **13 rm** 65.00/160.00 **st.**

Caterham House without rest., 58-59 Rother St., CV37 6LT, ☎ (01789) 267309, *Fax (01789) 414836* – TV P. MC VISA. A z
10 rm 70.00/84.00 **st.**

Sequoia House without rest., 51-53 Shipston Rd, CV37 7LN, ☎ (01789) 268852, *info@sequoiahotel.co.uk, Fax (01789) 414559,* – TV P – 40. MC AE VISA JCB. B r
closed 25 December and 1 January – **23 rm** 55.00/89.00 **st.**

Stratheden without rest., 5 Chapel St., CV37 6EP, ☎ (01789) 297119, *richard@stratheden.fsnet.co.uk, Fax (01789) 297119* – TV. MC AE VISA. A s
closed Christmas-New Year – **9 rm** 42.00/72.00 **st.**

Twelfth Night without rest., Evesham Pl., CV37 6HT, ☎ (01789) 414595 – TV P. MC VISA JCB. A x
6 rm 62.00 **st.**

The Payton without rest., 6 John St., CV37 6UB, ☎ (01789) 266442, *payton@waverider.co.uk, Fax (01789) 294410* – TV. MC VISA JCB A e
closed 24 December-30 January – **5 rm** 68.00 **st.**

Victoria Spa Lodge without rest., Bishopton Lane, CV37 9QY, Northwest : 2 m. by A 3400 on Bishopton Lane turning left at roundabout with A 46 ☎ (01789) 267985, *ptozer@victoriaspalodge.demon.co.uk, Fax (01789) 204728,* – TV P. MC VISA.
7 rm 50.00/65.00 **st.**

Virginia Lodge without rest., 12 Evesham Pl., CV37 6HT, ☎ (01789) 292157, – TV P. A x
7 rm 22.00/48.00 **t.**

Desport's, 13-14 Meer St., CV37 6QB, ☎ (01789) 269304, *bookings@desports.co.uk, Fax (01789) 269304* – MC AE VISA JCB A a
closed 1 week Christmas, Sunday and Monday – **Meals** 10.50/27.95 **t.** and a la carte 9.95.

Hussain's, 6a Chapel St., CV37 6EP, ☎ (01789) 267506, *Fax (01789) 415341* – . MC AE A s
Meals - Indian - 5.95/12.50 **t.** and a la carte.

Lambs, 12 Sheep St., CV37 6EF, ☎ (01789) 292554, *lambs@ukgateway.net,* « 16C » – MC VISA B c
closed 25-26 December – **Meals** 12.95 **t.** (lunch) and a la carte 14.45/24.85 **t.** 7.95.

Charlecote *East : 4 ¾ m. by B 4086* – **B** – ✉ *Stratford-upon-Avon.*

The Charlecote Pheasant, CV35 9EW, ☎ (01789) 279954, *Fax (01789) 470222,* heated, , – TV P – 160. MC AE VISA
Meals (carving rest.) 8.95/17.95 **st.** and dinner a la carte 7.25 – 9.95 – **70 rm** 95.00/130.00 **st.** – SB.

Binton *Southwest : 4½ m. by B 439* – **A** – ✉ *Stratford-upon-Avon.*

Gravelside Barn without rest., CV37 9TU, Northwest : ¾ m. by Binton Hill ☎ (01789) 750502, *Fax (01789) 298056,* ≤, « Converted barn », , – TV P. MC VISA.
3 rm 40.00/70.00 **s.**

Billesley *West : 4½ m. by A 422* – **A** – *off A 46* – ✉ *Stratford-upon-Avon.*

Billesley Manor , B49 6NF, ☎ (01789) 279955, *Fax (01789) 764145,* ≤, « Part Elizabethan manor, topiary garden », , , – TV P – 120. MC AE VISA JCB
Meals 24.95 **st.** and a la carte 6.95 – 9.75 – **39 rm** 125.00/205.00 **st.**, 2 suites – SB.

ENGLAND

at Wilmcote *Northwest : 3½ m. by A 3400 – A – ✉ Stratford-upon-Avon.*

Pear Tree Cottage without rest., 7 Church Rd, CV37 9UX, ✆ (01789) 205889, *ma er@peartreecot.co.uk, Fax (01789) 262862,* « Part Elizabethan », – ⊠ TV P. *closed 25 December-20 January* – **5 rm** 40.00/54.00 **st.**

STRATTON *Glos.* 403 404 O 28 – *see Cirencester.*

STREATLEY *Newbury* 403 404 Q 29 *Great Britain G. – pop. 4 193 (inc. Goring) – ✉ Goring.*

Env. : *Basildon Park★ AC, SE : 2½ m. by A 329 – Mapledurham★ AC, E : 6 m. by A 329, B and B 4526.*

Exc. : *Ridgeway Path★★.*

Goring & Streatley, Rectory Rd ✆ (01491) 873229.

London 56 – Oxford 16 – Reading 11.

Swan Diplomat, High St., RG8 9HR, ✆ (01491) 878800, *sales@swan_diplomat.co. Fax (01491) 872554,* , « ≤ Thames-side setting », – TV P. – VISA

The Racing Swan : **Meals** 25.00/32.00 **st.** and a la carte 7.50 – 9.50 – **45 rm** 108. 138.00 **st.**, 1 suite – SB.

STRENSHAM SERVICE AREA *Worcs.* 403 N 27.

London 114 – Birmingham 37 – Gloucester 17.

Travel Inn without rest., WR8 0BZ, M 5 between junctions 7 and 8 (northbound carria way) ✆ (01684) 293004, *Fax (01684) 273606* – ⊠ TV P. VISA. *closed Christmas-New Year* – **40 rm** 40.95, 1 suite.

STRETTON *Ches.* 402 403 404 M 23 – *see Warrington.*

STRETTON *Staffs.* 402 403 404 P 25 – *see Burton-upon-Trent.*

STROUD *Glos.* 403 404 N 28 – *pop. 38 835.*

Minchinhampton ✆ (01453) 832642 (old course) (01453) 833840 (new course) - Painswick ✆ (01452) 812180.

Subscription Rooms, George St. ✆ (01453) 765768.

London 113 – Bristol 30 – Gloucester 9.

Stonehouse Court, Stonehouse, GL10 3RA, West : 4 m. on A 419 ✆ (01453) 825155, *nehouse.court@pageant.co.uk, Fax (01453) 824611,* « Part 16C manor house », ⊠ rest, TV P. – 150. VISA

Meals 9.95/24.95 **t.** and dinner a la carte 7.50 – **34 rm** 85.00/140.00 **st.**, 1 suite – S

Premier Lodge, Stratford Lodge, Stratford Rd, GL5 4AF, North : ½ m. by A ✆ (0870) 7001548, *Fax (0870) 7001549,* – ⊠ rm, TV P. VISA JCB.

Meals (grill rest.) a la carte 8.15/16.35 **st.** – 6.00 – **30 rm** 42.00 **st.**

at Brimscombe *Southeast : 2¼ m. on A 419 – ✉ Stroud.*

Burleigh Court, Burleigh Lane, GL5 2PF, South : ½ m. by Burleigh rd via Roundabouts ✆ (01453) 883804, *burleighcourthotel@talk21.com, Fax (01453) 886870,* heated, – ⊠ rest, TV P. VISA JCB

Meals 13.95/35.00 **t.** 6.50 – **18 rm** 70.00/170.00 **t.** – SB.

at North Woodchester *South : 2 m. by A 46 – ✉ Stroud.*

Royal Oak, Church Rd, GL5 5PQ, ✆ (01453) 872735, – P. VISA

Meals (booking essential) a la carte 12.00/23.70 **st.**

STUDLAND *Dorset* 403 404 O 32 – *pop. 471.*

London 135 – Bournemouth 25 – Southampton 53 – Weymouth 29.

Shell Bay, Ferry Rd, BH19 3BA, North : 3 m. or via car ferry from Sandba ✆ (01929) 450363, *Fax (01929) 450570,* ≤ Poole Harbour and Brownsea Island, – *April-September and restricted opening in winter* – **Meals** - Seafood - a la carte 19 32.20 **t.**

TUDLEY *Warks.* 403 404 O 27 – *pop. 5 883* – ✉ *Redditch.*
London 109 – Birmingham 15 – Coventry 33 – Gloucester 39.

XX **Peppers,** 45 High St., B80 7HN, ☎ (01527) 853183 – ▤. MC AE VISA
closed 25 December – **Meals** - Indian - (dinner only) a la carte 11.65/22.60 **t.**

TURMINSTER NEWTON *Dorset* 403 404 N 31 *The West Country G.* – *pop. 2 155.*
See : *Mill★ AC.*
London 123 – Bournemouth 30 – Bristol 49 – Salisbury 28 – Taunton 41.

Stourcastle Lodge, Gough's Close, DT10 1BU, (off the Market Place) ☎ (01258) 472320, *enquiries@stourcastle-lodge.co.uk, Fax (01258) 473381,* – TV P. MC VISA.
Meals 19.00 **st.** – **5 rm** 37.00/72.00 **st.**

XXX **Plumber Manor** with rm, DT10 2AF, Southwest : 1 ¾ m. by A 357 on Hazelbury Bryan rd ☎ (01258) 472507, *enquiries@plumbermanor.com, Fax (01258) 473370,* ←, « 18C manor house », – TV P – 25. MC AE ① VISA
closed February – **Meals** (dinner only and Sunday lunch)/dinner 22.50/30.00 **st.** 5.50 – **16 rm** 80.00/145.00 **st.**

UDBURY *Suffolk* 404 W 27 *Great Britain G.* – *pop. 19 512.*
See : *Gainsborough's House★ AC.*
Town Hall, Market Hill ☎ (01787) 881320.
London 59 – Cambridge 37 – Colchester 15 – Ipswich 21.

Mill, Walnut Tree Lane, CO10 6BD, ☎ (01787) 375544, *Fax (01787) 373027,* ←, « Converted 19C mill » – ▤ rest, TV P – 70. MC AE ① VISA JCB
Meals 13.50/15.25 **t.** (lunch) and a la carte 21.20/28.45 **t.** 7.45 – 8.95 – **56 rm** 59.00/99.00 **t.** – SB.

UMMERBRIDGE *N. Yorks.* 402 O 21 – *see Pateley Bridge.*

UNDERLAND *Tyne and Wear* 401 402 P 19 – *pop. 183 310.*
See : *National Glass Centre★.*
Whitburn, Lizard Lane, South Shields ☎ (0191) 529 2144.
50 Fawcett St. ☎ (0191) 553 2000.
London 272 – Leeds 92 – Middlesbrough 29 – Newcastle upon Tyne 12.

Plan on next page

Swallow (becoming a Marriott spring 2001), Queens Par., Seaburn, SR6 8DB, ☎ (0191) 529 2041, *sunderland@swallow-hotels.co.uk, Fax (0191) 529 3843,* ←, – , ▤ rest, TV P – 300. MC AE ① VISA A e
Meals 11.95/21.95 **st.** and dinner a la carte 7.50 – **98 rm** 99.00/175.00 **st.** – SB.

Roker, Roker Terrace, Roker, SR6 0PH, ☎ (0191) 567 1786, *Fax (0191) 510 0289* – TV P – 300. MC AE ① VISA A c
Meals (grill rest.) a la carte 10.35/15.45 **st.** – 6.95 – **44 rm** 47.50 **st.** – SB.

Premier Lodge, Timber Beach Rd, off Wessington Way, Castletown, SR5 3XG, Northwest : 4 m. by A 1231 ☎ (0870) 7001550, *Fax (0870) 7001551* – rm, TV P. MC AE ① VISA JCB.
Meals (grill rest.) a la carte 13.15/25.35 **st.** – 6.00 – **63 rm** 46.00 **t.**

Travel Inn, Wessington Way, SR5 3HR, Northwest : 3 ¾ m. by A 1231 ☎ (0191) 548 9384, *Fax (0191) 548 4148* – rm, TV P – 25. MC AE ① VISA.
Meals (grill rest.) – **41 rm** 40.95 **t.**

X **Brasserie 21,** Wylam Wharf, Low St., SR1 2AD, ☎ (0191) 567 6594, *Fax (0191) 510 3994,* « Converted 17C riverside warehouse » – P. MC AE ① VISA A a
closed Sunday, Monday and Bank Holidays – **Meals** (booking essential) 12.50/14.50 **t.** (lunch) and a la carte 17.50/25.50 **t.** 8.30.

Boldon *Northwest : 3 ¾ m. by A 1018 on A 184* – A – ✉ *Newcastle upon Tyne.*

Quality, Witney Way, Boldon Business Park, NE35 9PE, ☎ (0191) 519 1999, *admin@gb621.u_net.com, Fax (0191) 519 0655,* – rm, ▤ rest, TV P – 200. MC AE ① VISA JCB
closed Saturday lunch – **Meals** 8.25/14.50 **st.** and a la carte – 9.75 – **82 rm** 83.00/109.00 **st.** – SB.

XX **Forsters,** 2 St. Bedes, Station Rd, East Boldon, NE36 0LE, ☎ (0191) 519 0929, *info@forsters-restaurant.co.uk* – . MC AE ① VISA
closed 2 weeks in summer, 1 week in winter, 25 December, Sunday and Monday – **Meals** (dinner only) a la carte 17.50/31.50 **t.** 5.00.

SUNDERLAND

Street	Map	No.
Albion Place	B	2
Barnes Park Road	A	3
Bedford Street	B	4
Borough Road	B	5
Bridge Street	B	6
Charlton Road	A	8
Chester Road	B	10
Crowtree Road	B	11
Dame Dorothy Street	A	12
Derwent Street	B	13
Fawcett Street	B	
Harbour View	A	14
High Street West	B	15
Holmeside	B	
John Street	B	16
Kayll Road	A	17
Livingstone Road	B	18
New Durham Road	B	19
Ormonde Street	A	21
Pallion Road	A	22
Park Lane	B	23
Queens Road	A	24
Roker Terrace	A	25
St. Luke's Terrace	A	26
St. Mary's Way	B	27
Shields Road	A	29
Southwick Road	B	30
Station Road	A	32
The Bridges	B	
Trimdon Street	A	35
Vine Place	B	36
Wessington Way	A	38

***Town plans:** the names of main shopping streets are indicated in red at the beginning*

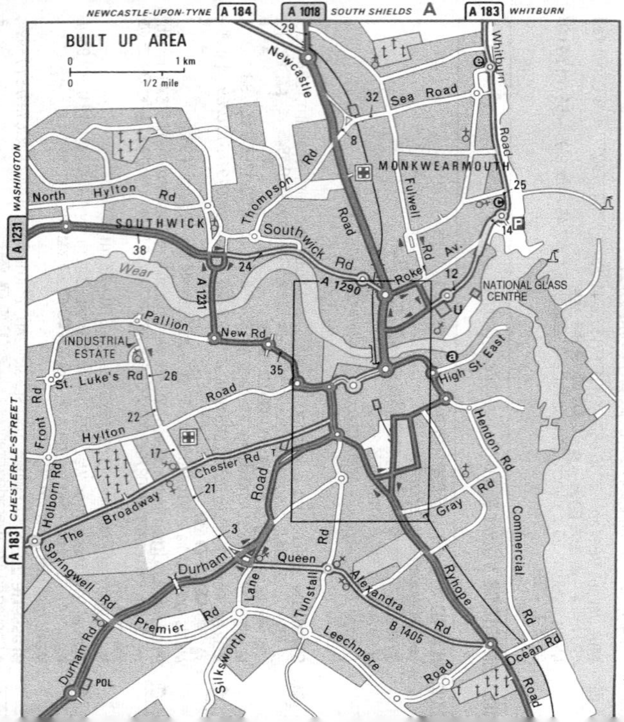

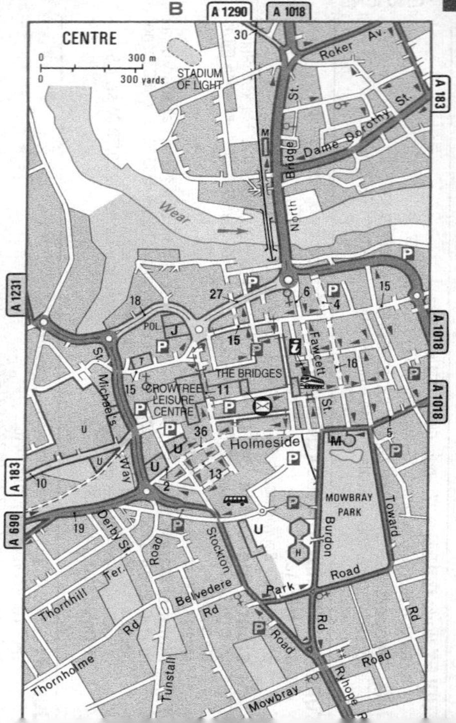

A — BUILT UP AREA

B — CENTRE

UNNINGHILL *Windsor & Maidenhead* 404 S 29 – *see Ascot.*

UTTON *W. Sussex – see Petworth.*

UTTON COLDFIELD *W. Mids.* 403 404 O 26 – *pop. 106 001.*

Pype Hayes, Eachelhurst Rd, Walmley ☎ (0121) 351 1014, **DT** – *Boldmere, Monmouth Dr. ☎ (0121) 354 3379,* **DT** – *110 Thornhill Rd ☎ (0121) 353 2014,* **DT** – *, The Belfry, Lichfield Rd, Wishaw ☎ (01675) 470301* **DT**.

London 124 – Birmingham 8 – Coventry 29 – Nottingham 47 – Stoke-on-Trent 40.

Plan : see Birmingham pp. 4 and 5

The Belfry, Wishaw, B76 9PR, East : 6 ½ m. by A 453 on A 446 ☎ (01675) 470301, *belfry@airtime.co.uk, Fax (01675) 470178,* squash – rm, rest, – 450. AE VISA.
Atrium : **Meals** 14.95/23.95 **st.** 9.50 – ***French Restaurant :*** **Meals** *(closed Saturday lunch and Sunday dinner)* 15.95/35.00 **st.** and a la carte 9.50 – **315 rm** 160.00/230.00 **st.**, 9 suites – SB.

New Hall, Walmley Rd, B76 1QX, Southeast : 1 ½ m. by Coleshill St., Coleshill Rd and Reddicap Hill on B 4148 ☎ (0121) 378 2442, *new.hall@thistle.co.uk, Fax (0121) 378 4637,* « Part 13C moated manor house, gardens », – – 50. AE VISA JCB. **DT i**
Meals 28.50/38.50 **st.** – 14.50 – **55 rm** 149.00/195.00 **st.**, 5 suites – SB.

Moor Hall, Moor Hall Drive, B75 6LN, Northeast : 2 m. by A 453 and Weeford Rd ☎ (0121) 308 3751, *mail@moorhallhotel.co.uk, Fax (0121) 308 8974,* – rm, – 250. AE VISA JCB. **DT r**
Meals (carving lunch) 10.95/21.00 **t.** and a la carte 6.50 – **74 rm** 105.00/190.00 **t.** – SB.

Penns Hall, Penns Lane, Walmley, B76 1LH, Southeast : 2 ¾ m. by A 5127 ☎ (0121) 351 3111, *Fax (0121) 313 1297,* squash – rm, – 400. AE VISA **DT v**
Meals *(closed Saturday lunch)* 10.95/18.95 **st.** and a la carte 8.60 – 9.95 – **166 rm** 130.00/155.00 **st.**, 3 suites – SB.

Royal, High St., B72 1UD, ☎ (0121) 355 8222, *Fax (0121) 355 1837* – – 40. AE VISA. **DT c**
Meals (grill rest.) a la carte 11.40/20.40 **st.** – **22 rm** 60.00/72.00 **st.**

Travelodge, Boldmere Rd, B72 5UP, Southwest : 1 ¼ m. by A 5127 and A 453 on B 4142 ☎ (0121) 355 0017 – rm, AE VISA JCB. **DT n**
Meals (grill rest.) – **32 rm** 49.95 **t.**

Curdworth *Southeast : 6 ½ m. by A 5127, A 452 and A 38 –* **DT** *– on A 4097 – ✉ Sutton Coldfield.*

Old School House, Kingsbury Rd, B76 7DR, on A 4097 ☎ (01675) 470177, *Fax (01675) 470884,* – VISA.
Meals (by arrangement) 7.50 4.50 – **8 rm** 39.50/48.00 **s.**

TTON COURTENAY *Oxon.* 403 404 Q 29 – ✉ *Abingdon.*

London 57 – Newbury 21 – Oxford 11 – Swindon 27.

The Fish with rm, 4 Appleford Rd, OX14 4NQ, ☎ (01235) 848242, *maccha@aol.com, Fax (01235) 848014,* – AE VISA.
closed 25-26 December – **Meals** 12.95/19.95 **t.** and a la carte 6.00 – **2 rm** 40.00/50.00 **st.** – SB.

TTON GAULT *Cambs.* 404 U 26 – *see Ely.*

TTON-ON-THE-FOREST *N. Yorks.* 402 P 21 – *pop. 281.*

London 230 – Kingston-upon-Hull 50 – Leeds 52 – Scarborough 40 – York 12.

Rose & Crown, Main St., YO61 1DP, ☎ (01347) 811333, *mail@rosecrown.co.uk, Fax (01374) 811444* – rest, VISA
closed 29 January-13 February, 25-26 December, Monday, Tuesday and Sunday dinner – **Meals** (booking essential) 16.50/19.50 **t.** and a la carte 16.50/29.00 **t.** 6.50.

Si vous cherchez un hôtel tranquille,
consultez d'abord les cartes de l'introduction
ou repérez dans le texte les établissements indiqués avec le signe ou .

ENGLAND

SUTTON SCOTNEY SERVICE AREA *Hants.* 403 404 P 30 – ✉ *Winchester.*
London 66 – Reading 32 – Salisbury 21 – Southampton 19.

Travelodge, SO21 3JY, on A 34 ☎ (01962) 761016 (northside), 7607779 (southside) rm, TV ♿ P. MC AE DI VISA JCB.
Meals (grill rest.) – **71 rm** 39.95 **t.**

SWAFFHAM *Norfolk* 404 W 26 *Great Britain G. – pop. 5 332.*
Exc.: *Oxburgh Hall★★ AC, SW : 7½ m.*
London 97 – Cambridge 46 – King's Lynn 16 – Norwich 27.

Strattons, Ash Close, PE37 7NH, off Market Sq. ☎ (01760) 72384
Fax (01760) 720458, « Part Queen Anne house with Victorian additions », – TV
MC AE VISA.
closed 24 to 26 December – **Meals** (booking essential to non-residents) (dinner or
33.00 **st.** 7.50 – **6 rm** 70.00/150.00 **st.**

SWANAGE *Dorset* 403 404 O 32 *The West Country G. – pop. 9 037.*
See: *Town★.*
Env.: *St. Aldhelm's Head★★ (≤★★★), SW : 4 m. by B 3069 – Durlston Country Park (≤★★), 1 m. – Studland (Old Harry Rocks★★, Studland Beach (≤★), St. Nicholas Church★), N : 3 m Worth Matravers (Anvil Point Lighthouse ≤★★), S : 2 m. – Great Globe★, S : 1¼m.*
Exc.: *Corfe Castle★ (≤★★) AC, NW : 6 m. by A 351 – Blue Pool★, NW : 9 m. by A 351 a minor roads – Lulworth Cove★, W : 18 m. by A 351 and B 3070.*
18, 9 *Isle of Purbeck, Studland ☎ (01929) 450361.*
The White House, Shore Rd ☎ (01929) 422885.
London 130 – Bournemouth 22 – Dorchester 26 – Southampton 52.

Cauldron Bistro, 5 High St., BH19 2LN, ☎ (01929) 422671 – MC AE DI VISA
closed 2 weeks November-December, 2 weeks January, Monday, Tuesday lunch, Wednes lunch in summer and Tuesday dinner in winter – **Meals** a la carte 19.40/26.70 **t.** 7.15.

The Galley, 9 High St., BH19 2LN, ☎ (01929) 427299 – MC AE DI VISA JCB
closed 31 December-19 February and 3 weeks November – **Meals** (dinner only) 21.50 **t.**

SWAVESEY SERVICE AREA *Cambs.* 404 U 27 – *see Cambridge.*

SWAY *Hants.* 403 404 P 31 – *see Brockenhurst.*

SWINDON *Swindon* 403 404 O 29 *The West Country G. – pop. 145 236.*
See: *Great Western Railway Museum★* **AC** – *Railway Village Museum★* **AC Y M.**
Env.: *Lydiard Park (St. Mary's★) W : 4 m.* **U.**
Exc.: *Ridgeway Path★★, S : 8½ m. by A 4361 – Whitehorse (≤★)E : 7½ m. by A 4312, A and B 400 off B 4057.*
18, 9 *Broome Manor, Pipers Way ☎ (01793) 532403 –* 18 *Shrivenham Park, Penny Ho Shrivenham ☎ (01793) 783853 –* 18 *The Wiltshire, Vastern, Wootton Bassett ☎ (01 849999 –* 18 *Wrag Barn G & C.C., Shrivenham Rd, Highworth ☎ (01793) 861327.*
37 Regent St. ☎ (01793) 530328.
London 83 – Bournemouth 69 – Bristol 40 – Coventry 66 – Oxford 29 – Reading 4 Southampton 65.

Plans on following pages

De Vere, Shaw Ridge Leisure Park, Whitehill Way, SN5 7DW, West : 2 ¾ m. by A 3102 c 4553 ☎ (01793) 878785, *devere.swindon@airtime.co.uk, Fax (01793) 877822,* , rest, TV ♿ P – 400. MC AE DI VISA U
Meals *(closed Saturday lunch)* 18.50 **t.** (dinner) and a la carte 24.15/29.65 **t.** 5.65 – 12.50 – **146 rm** 125.00/140.00 **st.**, 8 suites – SB.

Swindon Marriott, Pipers Way, SN3 1SH, South : 1 ½ m. by Marlborough Road c 4006 ☎ (01793) 512121, *Fax (01793) 513114,* – rm, TV ♿ 280. MC AE DI VISA V
Meals (bar lunch Saturday) 15.00/18.00 **st.** and dinner a la carte 7.45 – 12.50 – **153** 130.00/190.00 **st.** – SB.

Hilton Swindon, Lydiard Fields, Great Western Way, SN5 8UZ, West : 3 ½ m. by A 310 junction 16 of M 4 ☎ (01793) 881777, *Fax (01793) 881881,* – rm, P – 350. MC AE DI VISA V
Meals *(closed Saturday lunch)* 18.95 **st.** and a la carte – 12.95 – **171 rm** 139 221.00 **st.** – SB.

SWINDON

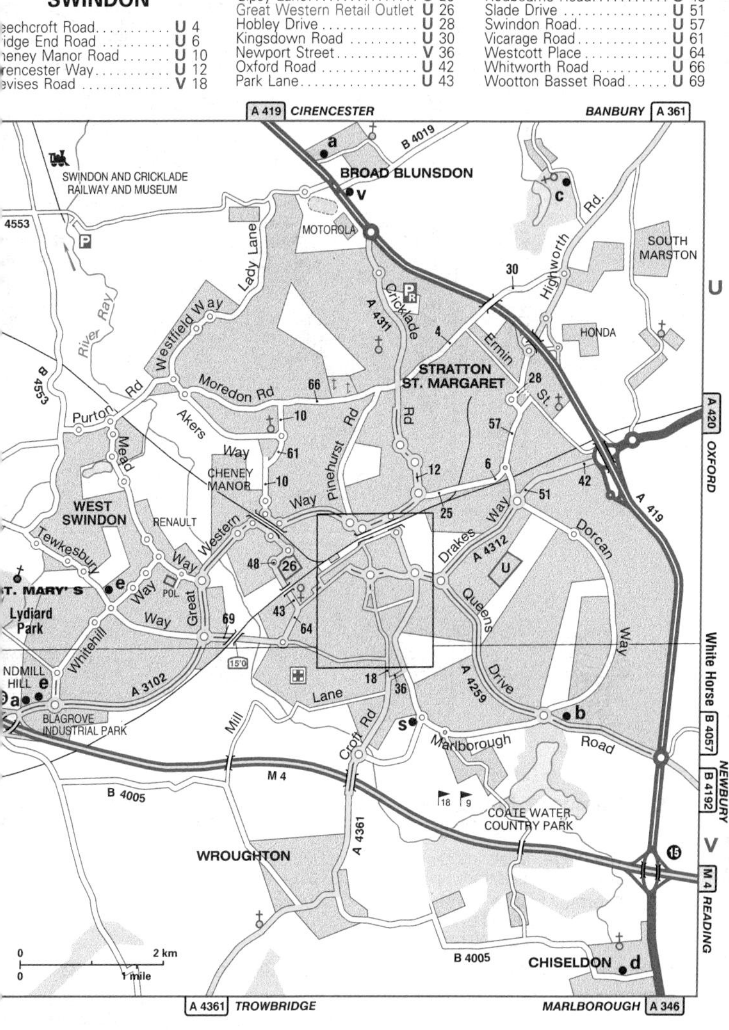

Posthouse Swindon, Marlborough Rd, SN3 6AQ, Southeast : 2 ½ m. on A 4259 (0870) 400 9079, *Fax (01793) 512887*, – rm, – 70. VISA V b
Meals *(closed Saturday lunch)* a la carte 16.85/28.35 **t.** – 11.95 – **100 rm** 99.00 **t.** – SB.

Thistle Swindon, Fleming Way, SN1 1TN, (01793) 528282, *swindon@thistle.co.uk, Fax (01793) 541283* – – 150. VISA JCB. Y c
Meals (bar lunch)/dinner a la carte 16.95/27.50 **st.** 6.50 – 10.25 – **94 rm** 119.00 **st.**

Goddard Arms, High St., Old Town, SN1 3EG, (01793) 692313, *customercare@zoffanyhotels.co.uk, Fax (01793) 512984*, – – 200. VISA. Z a
Meals (bar lunch Monday to Saturday)/dinner a la carte 15.00/22.50 **st.** 6.50 – **65 rm** 90.00/95.00 **st.**

Travel Inn, Lydiard Fields, Great Western Way, SN5 8UY, West : 3 ½ m. by A 3102 at junction 16 of M 4 (01793) 881490, *Fax (01793) 886890* – rm, VISA V e
Meals (grill rest.) – **63 rm** 40.95 **t.**

SWINDON

- Beckhampton Street . . . . . Y 3
- Bridge Street. . . . . Y 7
- Brunel Shopping Centre. YZ
- Canal Walk. . . . . Y 9
- Cricklade Street . . . . Z 13
- Cross Street . . . . Z 15
- Deacon Street. . . . . Z 16
- Dryden Street . . . . Z 19
- Edmund Street . . . . Z 21
- Faringdon Road. . . . . Y 22
- Farnsby Street . . . . YZ 24
- High Street . . . . Z 27
- Islington Street. . . . . Y 29
- London Street. . . . . Y 31
- Milton Road . . . . YZ 33
- North Star Avenue . . . . . . Y 37
- North Street. . . . . Z 39
- Ocotal Way . . . . Y 40
- Prospect Hill . . . . Z 45
- Regent Street. . . . . YZ 46
- Sheppard Street . . . . Y 49
- South Street . . . . Z 52
- Southampton Street . . . . Y 54
- Spring Gardens. . . . . Y 55
- The Parade . . . . Y 58
- Upham Road . . . . Z 60
- Warwick Road. . . . . Z 63
- Wood Street . . . . Z 67

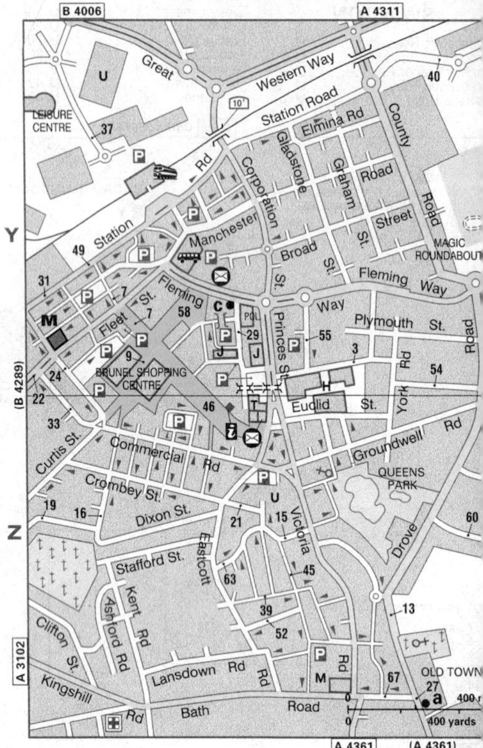

at Blunsdon *North : 4½ m. by A 4311 on A 419 – ✉ Swindon.*

Blunsdon House, SN2 4AD, ✆ (01793) 721701, *info@blunsdonhouse.co.* *Fax (01793) 721056,* squash – TV P – 300. MO VISA. U
The Ridge : **Meals** (dinner only and Sunday lunch)/dinner 21.50 **st.** and a la carte – ***Chri-stophers :*** **Meals** (carving rest.) 11.50/15.00 **t.** – **116 rm** 98.00/126.00 **t.**, 4 suites – S

Premier Lodge, Ermine St., SN2 4DJ, on A 419 ✆ (0870) 7001554, *Fax (0870) 700155* rm, TV P. MO AE VISA. U
Meals (grill rest.) – **40 rm** 42.00 **t.**

at Stanton Fitzwarren *Northeast : 5¼ m. by A 4312 and A 419 off A 361 – ✉ Swindon.*

Stanton House, The Avenue, SN6 7SD, ✆ (01793) 861777, *r.knight@stantonhous o.uk, Fax (01793) 861857,* – rest, TV P – 110. MO AE VISA U
Meals - Japanese - 15.00/22.00 **st.** (lunch) and a la carte 20.00/35.00 **st.** – **86 rm** 69. 99.00 **t.** – SB.

at Chiseldon *South : 6¼ m. by A 4259, A 419 and A 346 on B 4005 – ✉ Swindon.*

Chiseldon House, New Rd, SN4 0NE, ✆ (01793) 741010, *chiseldonhousehotel@uko e.co.uk, Fax (01793) 741059,* heated, – TV P – 50. MO AE VISA JCB V
Orangery : **Meals** 15.75 **st.** (lunch) and a la carte 20.45/28.20 **st.** 8.25 – **21 rm** 75. 115.00 **st.** – SB.

at Wootton Bassett *West : 6¼ m. on A 3102 –* **V** *– ✉ Swindon.*

Marsh Farm, SN4 8ER, North : 1 m. by A 3102 on Purton rd ✆ (01793) 848044, *marsh mhotel@btconnect.com, Fax (01793) 851528,* – rest, TV P – 120. MO AE
closed 24-30 December – **Meals** *(closed lunch Saturday and Bank Holidays)* 11.50/22.50 and a la carte – **38 rm** 100.00/140.00 **st.** – SB.

Hook *West : 6 ¼ m. by A 3102 – V – , B 4534 and Hook rd – ✉ Swindon.*

The School House, Hook St., SN4 8EF, ✆ (01793) 851198, *schoolhotel@email.msn.com, Fax (01793) 851025,* – rest, TV P. MC AE VISA.
Meals *(closed Saturday lunch, Sunday and Bank Holidays)* a la carte 18.00/27.00 **t.** 7.50 – **11 rm** 99.00 **t.**

VINTON *Gtr.Manchester* 402 403 404 N 23 – *see Manchester.*

'MONDS YAT WEST *Herefordshire* 403 404 M 28 *Great Britain G.* – ✉ *Ross-on-Wye.*

See : *Town★ – Yat Rock (≤★).*

Env. : *S : Wye Valley★.*

London 126 – Gloucester 23 – Hereford 17 – Newport 31.

Norton House, Whitchurch, HR9 6DJ, ✆ (01600) 890046, *norton@osconwhi.source.co.uk, Fax (01600) 890045,* « 18C farmhouse of 15C origins », – TV P
closed 25 December – **Meals** (by arrangement) (communal dining) 15.95 – **3 rm** 30.00/44.00.

DCASTER *N. Yorks.* 402 Q 22 – *pop. 6 915.*

London 206 – Harrogate 16 – Leeds 14 – York 11.

Hazlewood Castle ⑤, Paradise Lane, Hazlewood, LS24 9NJ, Southwest : 2 ¾ m. by A 659 off A 64 ✆ (01937) 535353, *info@hazelwood-castle.co.uk, Fax (01937) 530630,* ≤, « Part 13C fortified manor house in parkland », – rest, TV P – 120. MC AE VISA JCB.
1086 *(✆ (01937) 535354)* **: Meals** *(closed Sunday dinner)* (dinner only and Sunday lunch)/dinner 25.00/35.00 **st.** 11.00 – ***Prickly Pear Café*** *(✆ (01937) 535317)* **: Meals** *(closed Monday dinner)* 15.50 **st.** and lunch a la carte 11.00 – **12 rm** 125.00/250.00 **t.**, **9 suites** 195.00/300.00 **t.** – SB.

Aagrah, York Rd, Steeton, LS24 8EG, Northeast : 2 ½ m. on A 64 (westbound carriageway) ✆ (01937) 530888 – P. MC AE VISA JCB
closed 25 December – **Meals** - Indian - (booking essential) (dinner only) a la carte 8.65/13.15 **t.**

Saxton *South : 5 m. by A 162 – ✉ Tadcaster.*

The Plough Inn, Headwell Lane, LS24 9PX, ✆ (01937) 557242, *Fax (01937) 557655* – P. MC VISA JCB
closed first 2 weeks January, 24-25 December, Sunday dinner and Monday – **Meals** a la carte 17.75/22.70 **t.**

DWORTH *Surrey* 404 T 30 – *pop. 37 245 (inc. Banstead).*

London 23 – Brighton 36 – Guildford 22 – Maidstone 41.

Gemini, 28 Station Approach, KT20 5AH, ✆ (01737) 812179, *Fax (01737) 812179* – . MC AE VISA
closed 2 weeks Christmas, Saturday lunch, Sunday dinner and Monday – **Meals** 15.50 **t.** (lunch) and a la carte 24.55/28.65 **t.** 7.90.

LKE *Staffs.* 402 403 404 N 24 – *see Stoke-on-Trent.*

LLAND BAY *Cornwall* 403 G 32 – *see Looe.*

LLINGTON *Lincs. – see Stamford.*

MWORTH *Staffs.* 402 403 404 O 26 – *pop. 68 440.*

18 *Eagle Dr., Amington ✆ (01827) 53850.*

Town Hall, 29 Market St. ✆ (01827) 709581.

London 128 – Birmingham 12 – Coventry 29 – Leicester 31 – Stoke-on-Trent 37.

Travel Inn, Bitterscote, Bonehill Rd, B78 3HQ, on A 51 ✆ (01827) 54414, *Fax (01827) 310420* – , rest, TV P – 60. MC AE VISA.
Meals (grill rest.) – **40 rm** 40.95 **t.**

ENGLAND

at Bodymoor Heath *South : 6 ¾ m. by A 4091 – ✉ Sutton Coldfield.*

Marston Farm, B76 9JD, ☎ (01827) 872133, *marston.farm@lineone.n* *Fax (01827) 875043,* – 50.
Meals 9.00/21.95 **st.** and a la carte 6.25 – **37 rm** 99.00/125.00 **st.** – SB.

at Hopwas *Northwest : 2 m. on A 51 – ✉ Tamworth.*

Oak Tree Farm without rest., Hints Rd, B78 3AA, ☎ (01827) 56807, *Fax (01827) 568* – rm,
6 rm 52.00/66.00 **st.**

TAMWORTH SERVICE AREA *Staffs.* 402 403 404 P 26 – ✉ *Tamworth.*

Travelodge, Green Lane, B77 5PS, at junction 10 of M 42 ☎ (01827) 2601 *Fax (01827) 260145* – – 25.
Meals (grill rest.) – **62 rm** 49.95 **t.**

TAPLOW *Windsor & Maidenhead* 404 R 29.
London 33 – Maidenhead 2 – Reading 12.

Cliveden , SL6 0JF, North : 2 m. by Berry Hill ☎ (01628) 668561, *reservations@clivec house.co.uk, Fax (01628) 661837,* « Mid-Victorian stately home ← National Trust Garde parterre and River Thames », , heated, , , , indoor/outdoor, squash – – 40.
Terrace : **Meals** 26.00 **t.** (lunch) and a la carte 43.00/64.00 **t.** 10.00 – (see also ***Walo*** below) – 17.00 – **33 rm** 345.00/460.00 **st.**, 6 suites 560.00/875.00 **st.** – SB.

Taplow House, Berry Hill, SL6 0DA, ☎ (01628) 670056, *taplow@wrensgroup.cc Fax (01628) 773625,* « Part 16C mansion », – – 100.
Meals 20.00/35.00 **st.** and a la carte 8.00 – 12.50 – **31 rm** 152.00/180.00 **st.**, 1 suit SB.

Waldo's (at Cliveden H.), SL6 0JF, North : 2 m. by Berry Hill ☎ (01628) 6685 *Fax (01628) 661837* –
closed Sunday and Monday – **Meals** (booking essential) (dinner only) 58.00/84.00 **t.** 10
Spec. Vanilla-roasted monkfish with lobster risotto. Best end of lamb, tian of vegetab red pepper jus. Caramelised banana soufflé, rum and coconut ice cream.

TARPORLEY *Ches.* 402 403 404 M 24 – *pop. 2 308.*
Portal G & C.C., Cobblers Cross Lane ☎ (01829) 733933 – Portal Premier, Forest Rc (01829) 733884.
London 186 – Chester 11 – Liverpool 27 – Shrewsbury 36.

Swan, 50 High St., CW6 0AG, ☎ (01829) 733838, *swanhotel@pernickety.co Fax (01829) 732932* – – 100.
Meals *closed Monday and Sunday dinner* (dinner only and Sunday lunch) a la carte 13 21.00 **t.** – **17 rm** 45.00/72.50 **t.**

at Bunbury *South : 3 ¼ m. by A 49 – ✉ Tarporley.*

Dysart Arms, Bowes Gate Rd, CW6 9PH, by Bunbury Mill rd ☎ (01829) 260183, *dysa ms@brunningandprice.co.uk, Fax (01829) 261286,* –
Meals a la carte 13.40/21.45 **t.**

TATTENHALL *Ches.* 402 403 404 L 24 – *pop. 1 854.*
London 200 – Birmingham 71 – Chester 10 – Liverpool 29 – Manchester 38 – Stoke-on-T 30.

Higher Huxley Hall , CH3 9BZ, North : 2 ¼ m. on Huxley rd ☎ (01829) 781484, *ir huxleyhall.co.uk, Fax (01829) 781142,* ←, « Working farm », , –
booking essential – **Meals** (by arrangement) (communal dining) 22.50 **s.** 8.00 – 3 45.00/70.00 **s.**

Newton Hall without rest., CH3 9NE, North : 1 m. by Huxley rd on Gatesheat ☎ (01829) 770153, *newton.hall@farming.co.uk, Fax (01829) 770655,* « Working farm » –
3 rm 25.00/50.00 **s.**

Les prix — Pour toutes précisions sur les prix indiqués dans ce guide, reportez-vous aux pages de l'introduction.

UNTON *Somerset* 403 K 30 *The West Country G. – pop. 55 855.*

See : *Town★ – St. Mary Magdalene★* V – *Somerset County Museum★* AC U – *St. James'★* U – *Hammett St.★* V 25 – *The Crescent★* V – *Bath Place★* V 3.

Env. : *Trull (Church★), S : 2½ m. by A 38.*

Exc. : *Bishops Lydeard★ (Church★), NW : 6 m. – Wellington : Church★, Wellington Monument (≤★★), SW : 7½ m. by A 38 – Combe Florey★, NW : 8 m. – Gaulden Manor★* AC, *NW : 10 m. by A 358 and B 3227.*

Taunton Vale, Creech Heathfield ℘ (01823) 412220 – Vivary, Vivary Park ℘ (01823) 289274 – Taunton and Pickeridge, Corfe ℘ (01823) 421240.

Paul St. ℘ (01823) 336344.

London 168 – Bournemouth 69 – Bristol 50 – Exeter 37 – Plymouth 78 – Southampton 93 – Weymouth 50.

Plan on next page

The Castle, Castle Green, TA1 1NF, ℘ (01823) 272671, *reception@the-castle-hotel.com, Fax (01823) 336066,* « Part 12C castle with Norman garden » – rest, – 100. VISA — V a
Meals 24.00 **t.** and a la carte approx. 35.50 **t.** 11.00 – **44 rm** 95.00/230.00 **t.** – SB.

Posthouse Taunton, Deane Gate Av., TA1 2UA, East : 2 ½ m. by A 358 at junction with M 5 ℘ (0870) 400 9080, *gm1437@forte-hotels.com, Fax (01823) 332266,* – rm, rest, – 300. VISA JCB — BY h
Meals (bar lunch Saturday) 15.00/45.00 **t.** (dinner) and a la carte 18.80/33.00 **t.** 6.95 – 11.95 – **99 rm** 89.00 **st.** – SB.

Express by Holiday Inn without rest., Blackbrook Business Park, TA1 2RW, ℘ (01823) 624000, *james.coggan@basshotels.com, Fax (01823) 624024,* – rm, rest, – 30. VISA JCB. — BY a
92 rm 54.50 **st.**

Travel Inn, 81 Bridgwater Rd, TA1 2DU, East : 1 ¾ m. by A 358 ℘ (01823) 321112, *Fax (01823) 322054* – rm, VISA. — BY e
Meals (grill rest.) – **40 rm** 40.95 **t.**

Travelodge without rest., Riverside Retail Park, Hankridge Farm, TA1 2LR, East : 2 m. by A 358 ℘ (01823) 444702, *Fax (01823) 444702* – rm, VISA JCB. — BY x
48 rm 39.95 **t.**

Orchard House without rest., Fons George, Middleway, TA1 3JS, off Wilton St. ℘ (01823) 351783, *orch-hse@dircon.co.uk, Fax (01823) 351785,* « Georgian house », – VISA. — AZ d
closed 31 December and 1 January – **6 rm** 35.00/60.00.

Forde House without rest., 9 Upper High St., TA1 3PX, ℘ (01823) 279042, *Fax (01823) 279042,* – VISA. — V b
closed Christmas and New Year – **5 rm** 32.00/52.00 **s.**

Gatchells, Angersleigh, TA3 7SY, South : 3 ½ m. by Trull rd turning right on Dipford Rd ℘ (01823) 421580, *gatchells@somerweb.co.uk,* ≤, « 16C thatched cottage », heated, – VISA
Meals (by arrangement) 13.00 – **3 rm** 30.00/54.00 **s.**

Brazz, Castle Bow, TA1 1NF, ℘ (01823) 252000, *Fax (01823) 336066* – VISA
Meals a la carte 14.50/27.50 **t.** 6.50. — V e

West Monkton *Northeast : 3½ m. by A 361* – **AZ** – *off A 38 – ✉ Taunton.*

Springfield House without rest., Walford Cross, TA2 8QW, on A 38 ℘ (01823) 412116, *Fax (01823) 412844,* – .
closed 15 December-31 January – **5 rm** 30.00/45.00 **st.**

Henlade *East : 3½ m. on A 358* – **BZ** – *✉ Taunton.*

Mount Somerset, Lower Henlade, TA3 5NB, South : ½ m. by Stoke Rd and Ash Cross rd ℘ (01823) 442500, *Fax (01823) 442900,* ≤, « Regency country house », – rest, – 60. VISA JCB.
Meals 19.95/24.95 **t.** 6.00 – **11 rm** 95.00/170.00 **t.** – SB.

Hatch Beauchamp *Southeast : 6 m. by A358* – **BZ** – *✉ Taunton.*

Farthings, TA3 6SG, ℘ (01823) 480664, *farthings1@aol.com, Fax (01823) 481118,* « Georgian country house », – VISA.
Meals (dinner only and Sunday lunch)/dinner 22.50 **t.** 6.95 – **9 rm** 64.00/130.00 **t.** – SB.

Frog Street Farm, Beercrocombe, TA3 6AF, Southeast : 1 ¼ m. by Beercrocombe Rd ℘ (01823) 480430, *Fax (01823) 480430,* « 15C farmhouse, working farm », – .
Meals (by arrangement) 16.00 **st.** – **3 rm** 30.00/60.00 **st.** – SB.

TAUNTON

Bath Place . . . . V 3
Billet Street . . . . V 4
Billetfield . . . . V 6
Birch Grove . . . . U 7
Bishop's Hull Road . . . . . AZ 9
Bridge (The) . . . . U 10
Bridge Street . . . . U 12
Burton Place . . . . V 13
Cann Street . . . . V 15
Cleveland Street . . . . U 16
Comeytrowe Lane . . . . . . AZ 18
Corporation Street . . . . V 19
County Walk Shopping Centre V
Duke Street . . . . V 21
East Street V
Fore Street . . . . V 22
Hamilton Road . . . . BZ 24
Hammet Street . . . . V 25
High Street V
Hurdle Way . . . . V 27
Ilminster Road . . . . BZ 28
Magdalene Street . . . . V 30
Middleway . . . . AZ 31
North Street . . . . V 33
Obridge Viaduct . . . . BY 34
Old Market Shopping Centre V
Portland Street . . . . U 36
Priory Avenue . . . . U 37
Shoreditch Road . . . . BZ 39
Shuttern . . . . V 40
Silver Street South . . . . . VZ 42
Upper High Street . . . . V 43
Upper Wood Street . . . . U 44
Victoria Parkway . . . . . . BYZ 45
Wellington New Road . . AZ 46
Wilton Street . . . . V 48
Winchester Street . . . . U 49
Wood Street . . . . U 51

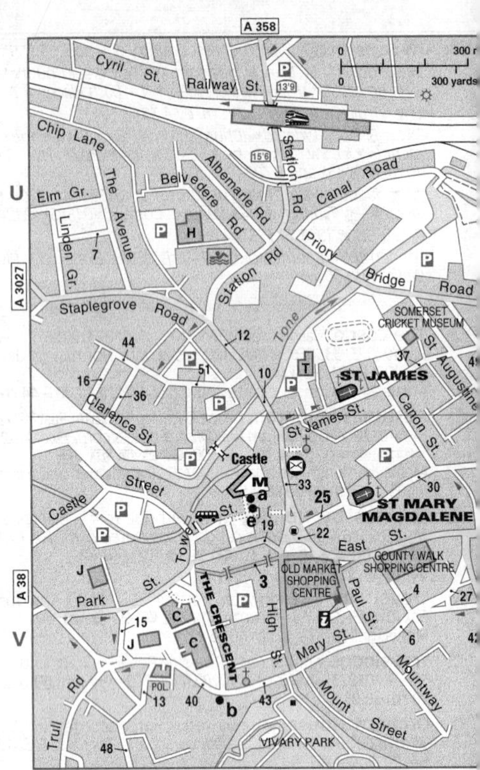

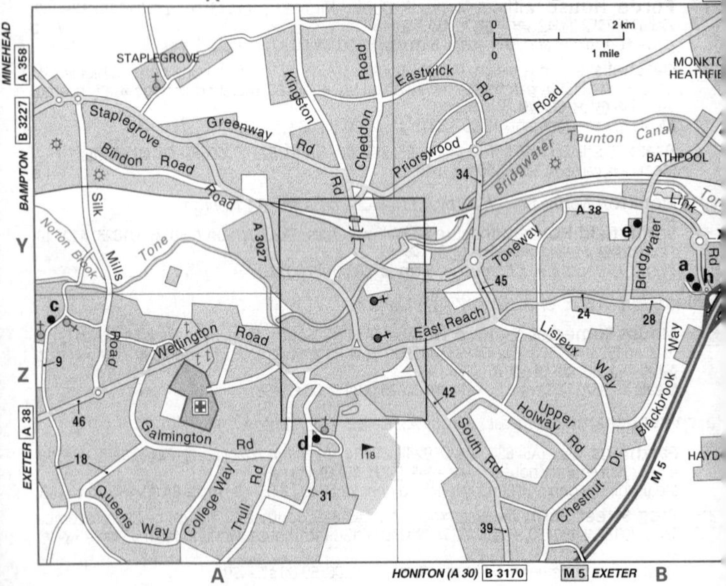

STAPLEGROVE
MINEHEAD A 358
BAMPTON B 3227
Staplegrove Road
Bindon Road
Greenway
Kingston Rd
Cheddon Road
Eastwick Rd
Priorswood Rd
Taunton Canal
Bridgwater Road
BATHPOOL
MONKTON HEATHFIELD
A 3027
A 38
Silk Mills Road
Norton Brook
Tone
Toneway
Link
Bridgwater Rd
East Reach
Wellington Road
Lisieux Way
Upper Holway Rd
South Rd
Blackbrook Way
Chestnut Dr.
M 5
Galmington Rd
Queens Way
College Way
Trull Rd
EXETER A 38
HONITON (A 30) B 3170
M 5 EXETER
HAYD
Y
Z
A
B
0 2 km
0 1 mile

Rumwell *Southwest : 2½ m. on A 38 –* **AZ** *– ✉ Taunton.*

Rumwell Manor, TA4 1EL, ☎ (01823) 461902, *rumhotel@aol.com, Fax (01823) 254861,* – rest, TV P – 40. MC AE VISA.
Meals (bar lunch)/dinner 18.50/19.50 **st.** and a la carte 6.50 – 8.00 – **20 rm** 59.00/95.00 **st.** – SB.

Bishop's Hull *West : 1¾ m. by A 38 – ✉ Taunton.*

Meryan House, Bishop's Hull Rd, TA1 5EG, ☎ (01823) 337445, *anglo@dircon.co.uk, Fax (01823) 322355,* – TV P. MC VISA JCB AZ c
Meals *(closed Sunday)* (dinner only) 12.00/18.00 **st.** 5.95 – **12 rm** 55.00/75.00 **st.** – SB.

West Bagborough *Northwest : 10½ m. by A 358 –* **AY** *– ✉ Taunton.*

Bashfords Farmhouse, TA4 3EF, ☎ (01823) 432015, *charlieritchie@netscapeonline.co.uk, Fax (0870) 1671587,* « 18C », – TV P.
Meals (by arrangement) (communal dining) 17.50 **st.** – **3 rm** 30.00/50.00 **st.**

Tilbury Farm, Cothelstone, TA4 3DY, East : ¾ m. ☎ (01823) 432391, ≤ Vale of Taunton, « 18C », – TV P.
Meals (by arrangement) (communal dinning) 25.00 **s.** 3.00 – **3 rm** 30.00/50.00 **s.**

UNTON DEANE SERVICE AREA *Somerset* 403 K 31 – ✉ *Taunton.*

Travel Inn without rest., TA3 7PF, M 5 between junctions 25 and 26 (southbound carriageway) ☎ (01823) 332228, *Fax (01823) 338131* – TV P. MC AE VISA.
closed Christmas and New Year – **40 rm** 40.95 **t.**

VISTOCK *Devon* 403 H 32 *The West Country G. – pop. 10 222.*

Env. : *Morwellham★ AC, SW : 4½ m.*

Exc. : *E : Dartmoor National Park★★ – Buckland Abbey★★ AC, S : 7 m. by A 386 – Lydford★★, N : 8½ m. by A 386.*

Down Rd ☎ (01822) 612344 – Hurdwick, Tavistock Hamlets ☎ (01822) 612746.

Town Hall, Bedford Sq. ☎ (01822) 612938.

London 239 – Exeter 38 – Plymouth 16.

Bedford, 1 Plymouth Rd, PL19 8BB, ☎ (01822) 613221, *Fax (01822) 618034* – TV P – 60. MC AE VISA
Meals 9.95/21.95 **st.** 6.00 – **29 rm** 37.50/75.00 **st.** – SB.

Quither Mill, PL19 0PZ, Northwest : 5 ¾ m. by Chillaton rd on Quither rd ☎ (01822) 860160, *quither.mill@virgin.net, Fax (01822) 860160,* ≤, « 18C converted water mill », – TV P. MC VISA JCB.
closed Christmas and New Year – **Meals** (communal dining) 19.00 7.50 – **2 rm** 40.00/70.00, 1 suite.

April Cottage without rest., Mount Tavy Rd, PL19 9JB, ☎ (01822) 613280 – TV P
3 rm 30.00/42.00 **s.**

Colcharton Farm, Gulworthy, PL19 8HU, West : 2 ½ m. by A 390 on Colcharton rd ☎ (01822) 616435, *Fax (01822) 616435,* – P.
Meals (by arrangement) (communal dining) 10.00 **st.** – **3 rm** 25.00/40.00 **st.**

Neils, 27 King St., PL19 0DT, ☎ (01822) 615550 – . MC AE VISA
closed Sunday and Monday – **Meals** (dinner only) 19.50 **t.** and a la carte 6.00.

Gulworthy Cross *West : 3 m. on A 390 – ✉ Tavistock.*

Horn of Plenty with rm, PL19 8JD, Northwest : 1 m. by Chipshop rd ☎ (01822) 832528, *enquiries@hornofplenty.co.uk, Fax (01822) 832528,* ≤ Tamar Valley and Bodmin Moor, – TV P. MC AE VISA.
closed 25-26 December – **Meals** *(closed Monday lunch)* 23.00/37.00 **t.** – **10 rm** 105.00/200.00 **t.** – SB
Spec. Pan-fried lamb sweetbreads with wild mushrooms and pancetta. Roast sea bass with black pepper, ginger and saffron sauce. Candied kumquat sponge pudding, coconut and nougatine ice cream.

Chillaton *Northwest : 6¼ m. by Chillaton rd – ✉ Tavistock.*

Tor Cottage without rest., PL16 0JE, Southwest : ¼ m. by Tavistock rd, turning right at bridle path sign, down unmarked track for ½ m. ☎ (01822) 860248, *info@torcottage.co.uk, Fax (01822) 860126,* ≤, heated, – TV P. MC VISA JCB.
closed 2 weeks Christmas-New Year – **3 rm** 76.00/98.00 **s.**, 1 suite.

FONT *Wilts. – see Salisbury.*

ENGLAND

TEIGNMOUTH *Devon* 403 J 32 – *pop. 13 403.*

The Den, Sea Front ✆ (01626) 779769.

London 216 – Exeter 16 – Torquay 8.

Thomas Luny House without rest., Teign St., TQ14 8EG, follow signs for the Quays, the A 381 ✆ (01626) 772976, *alisonandjohn@thomas-luny-house.co.uk*, « Georgian ho built by Thomas Luny », – TV P. MC VISA.
4 rm 40.00/75.00.

at Shaldon *South : 1 m. on B 3199 – ✉ Teignmouth.*

Ness House, Marine Drive, TQ14 0HP, ✆ (01626) 873480, *nesshouse@talk21.c* *Fax (01626) 873486*, – rest, TV P. MC AE VISA.
closed 24-25 December – **Meals** (carving lunch Sunday) 17.50/23.50 **t.** and a la carte – **12 rm** 45.00/115.00 **t.** – SB.

TELFORD *Wrekin* 402 403 404 M 25 *Great Britain G. – pop. 119 340.*

Env. : *Ironbridge Gorge Museum★★ AC (The Iron Bridge★★, Coalport China Museum Blists Hill Open Air Museum★★, Museum of the River and Visitor Centre★) S : 5 m. by B 4.*

Exc. : *Weston Park★★ AC, E : 7 m. by A 5.*

18, 9 *Telford, Great Hay, Sutton Heights ✆ (01952) 429977 – 18 Wrekin, Wellin ✆ (01952) 244032 – 9, 9, 9 The Shropshire, Muxton Grange, Muxton ✆ (01952) 6778*

The Telford Centre, Management Suite ✆ (01952) 238008.

London 152 – Birmingham 33 – Shrewsbury 12 – Stoke-on-Trent 29.

Clarion H. Madeley Court, Castlefields Way, Madeley, TF7 5DW, South : 4 ½ m. 442 and A 4169 on B 4373 ✆ (01952) 680068, *admin@gb068u-net.c* *Fax (01952) 684275*, « Part 16C manor house », – rest, TV P – 200. MC AE VISA JCB.
Priory : **Meals** (dinner only and Sunday lunch)/dinner 21.00 **st.** and a la carte 7.9
Cellar Vaults : **Meals** *(closed Sunday)* 6.50/17.50 **st.** and a la carte 6.50 – 10.5
47 rm 95.00/130.00 **st.** – SB.

Holiday Inn Telford/Ironbridge, Telford International Centre, St. Quentin Gate, 4EH, Southeast : ½ m. ✆ (01952) 527000, *holidayinn.telford@virgin.* *Fax (01952) 291949*, , squash – , rm, rest, TV P – 250. VISA JCB.
Meals (bar lunch Monday-Saturday)/dinner 12.95 **st.** and a la carte 6.50 – 9.9
146 rm 118.00/128.00 **st.**, 3 suites – SB.

Telford Moat House, Forgegate, Telford Centre, TF3 4NA, ✆ (01952) 429988, *revt ueensmoat.co.uk, Fax (01952) 292012*, – , rest, TV P – 400. VISA JCB
Casa Med : **Meals** (bar lunch Monday to Saturday)/dinner a la carte 15.45/23.95 **t.** 7. 10.50 – **151 rm** 103.00/119.00 **st.** – SB.

Travel Inn, Euston Way, TF3 4LY, North : ½ m. by Cannock rd at jucntion with A ✆ (01952) 201075, *Fax (01952) 290742* – , rm, rest, TV P – 30. MC AE
Meals (grill rest.) – **60 rm** 40.95 **t.**

Travelodge, Shawbirch Crossroads, Shawbirch, TF1 3QA, Northwest : 5 ½ m. by A 4 junction with B 5063 ✆ (01952) 251244, *Fax (01952) 246534* – rm, TV P. MC AE VISA JCB.
Meals (grill rest.) – **40 rm** 49.95 **t.**

White House, Wellington Rd, Muxton, TF2 8NG, North : 4 ½ m. by A 442 off A ✆ (01952) 604276, *james@whhotel.co.uk, Fax (01952) 670336*, – TV P. MC AE VISA
Meals *(closed Saturday lunch)* 9.50/13.50 **st.** and a la carte 5.25 – **32 rm** 62 75.00 **st.** – SB.

at Norton *South : 7 m. on A 442 – ✉ Shifnal.*

Hundred House with rm, Bridgnorth Rd, TF11 9EE, ✆ (01952) 730353, *hphundred e@messages.co.uk, Fax (01952) 730355*, « Characterful inn, gardens » – TV P. MC VISA.
Meals a la carte 16.40/29.85 **t.** – **10 rm** 69.00/120.00 **t.** – SB.

at Wellington *West : 6 m. by M 54 on B 5061 – ✉ Telford.*

Charlton Arms, Church St., TF1 1DG, ✆ (01952) 251351, Reservations (F phone) 0800 118833, *Fax (01952) 222077* – TV P – 150. MC AE VISA.
Meals *(closed Saturday lunch)* (grill rest.) (bar lunch)/dinner a la carte 10.15/17.45 **st.** 6.00 – **22 rm** 45.50 **st.**

TEMPLE SOWERBY *Cumbria* 402 M 20 – *see Penrith.*

ENBURY WELLS *Worcs.* 403 404 M 27 – *pop. 2 219.*
London 144 – Birmingham 36 – Hereford 20 – Shrewsbury 37 – Worcester 28.

Cadmore Lodge ⛰, St. Michaels, WR15 8TQ, Southwest : 2 ¾ m. by A 4112 ℘ (01584) 810044, *info@cadmorelodge.demon.co.uk, Fax (01584) 810044*, ≤, ⛆, 9, ⛐, ⛑, ✗ – ✗ TV ✆ P – 🏢 100. MC AE ① VISA JCB. ✗
closed 25 December – **Meals** 11.50/18.50 🍷 5.00 – **14 rm** ⊋ 35.00/115.00 **st.** – SB.

ENTERDEN *Kent* 404 W 30 – *pop. 6 803.*
Town Hall, High St. ℘ (01580) 763572 (summer only).
London 57 – Folkestone 26 – Hastings 21 – Maidstone 19.

White Lion, High St., TN30 6BD, ℘ (01580) 765077, *whitelion@lionheartinns.co.uk, Fax (01580) 764157* – TV P – 🏢 40. MC AE VISA
Meals a la carte 11.85/21.65 **t.** 🍷 5.50 – **15 rm** ⊋ 59.00/94.00 **t.** – SB.

Little Silver Country H., Ashford Rd, St. Michaels, TN30 6SP, North : 2 m. on A 28 ℘ (01233) 850321, *enquiries@little-silver.co.uk, Fax (01233) 850647*, ⛱ – ✗ rest, TV P – 🏢 120. MC AE VISA. ✗
Meals (booking essential) (lunch by arrangement) a la carte 16.25/26.00 **st.** 🍷 7.00 – **10 rm** ⊋ 60.00/110.00 **st.** – SB.

Collina House, 5 East Hill, TN30 6RL, ℘ (01580) 764852, *collina.house@dial.pipex.com, Fax (01580) 762224* – ✗ TV P. MC AE VISA. ✗
closed 24 December-2 January – **Meals** (lunch by arrangement) 16.50/25.00 **st.** and dinner a la carte 🍷 4.50 – **14 rm** ⊋ 45.00/75.00 **st.** – SB.

TBURY *Glos.* 403 404 N 29 *Great Britain G.* – *pop. 4 618.*
Env. : *Westonbirt Arboretum★ AC, SW : 2½ m. by A 433.*
9 Westonbirt ℘ (01666) 880242.
33 Church St. ℘ (01666) 503552.
London 113 – Bristol 27 – Gloucester 19 – Swindon 24.

The Close, 8 Long St., GL8 8AQ, ℘ (01666) 502272, *Fax (01666) 504401*, « 16C town house with walled garden » – ✗ rest, TV P – 🏢 70. MC AE VISA
Meals 14.50/29.50 **t.** and a la carte 29.50/34.70 **t.** 🍷 14.50 – ***The Brasserie :*** **Meals** a la carte approx. 10.85 **t.** – **15 rm** ⊋ 75.00/120.00 **t.** – SB.

Snooty Fox, Market Pl., GL8 8DD, ℘ (01666) 502436, *res@snooty-fox.co.uk, Fax (01666) 503479* – ✗ rest, TV. MC AE ① VISA. ✗
Meals (bar lunch)/dinner a la carte 22.40/25.45 **t.** 🍷 8.95 – **12 rm** ⊋ 67.50/90.00 **t.** – SB.

Willesley *Southwest : 4 m. on A 433 – ✉ Tetbury.*

Tavern House without rest., GL8 8QU, ℘ (01666) 880444, *Fax (01666) 880254*, « Part 17C former inn and staging post », ⛱ – ✗ TV P. MC VISA. ✗
4 rm ⊋ 49.50/72.00.

Calcot *West : 3½ m. on A 4135 – ✉ Tetbury.*

Calcot Manor ⛰, GL8 8YJ, ℘ (01666) 890391, *reception@calcotmanor.com, Fax (01666) 890394*, ⛱, « Converted Cotswold farm buildings », ⛆ heated, ⛱, ✗ – ✗ rest, TV ✆ P – 🏢 65. MC AE ① VISA. ✗
Conservatory : **Meals** (booking essential) a la carte 15.00/35.00 **t.** 🍷 10.00 – (see also ***The Gumstool Inn*** below) – **24 rm** ⊋ 115.00/175.00 **st.**, 4 suites – SB.

The Gumstool Inn (at Calcot Manor H.), GL8 8YJ, ℘ (01666) 890391, *reception@calcotmanor.com, Fax (01666) 890394*, ⛱, ⛱ – P. MC AE ① VISA JCB
Meals (booking essential) a la carte approx. 17.00 **t.**

WKESBURY *Glos.* 403 404 N 28 *Great Britain G.* – *pop. 9 488.*
See : *Town★ – Abbey★★ (Nave★★, vault★).*
Env. : *St. Mary's, Deerhurst★, SW : 4 m. by A 38 and B 4213.*
18 Tewkesbury Park Hotel, Lincoln Green Lane ℘ (01684) 295405.
64 Barton St. ℘ (01684) 295027.
London 108 – Birmingham 39 – Gloucester 11.

Jessop House, 65 Church St., GL20 5RZ, ℘ (01684) 292017, *lestms@aol.com, Fax (01684) 273076* – ✗ rest, TV P. MC VISA JCB. ✗
closed 10 days Christmas-New Year – **Meals** (booking essential) (dinner only) 15.00/20.00 **st.** 🍷 4.50 – **8 rm** ⊋ 55.00/75.00 **st.**

Evington Hill Farm without rest., Tewkesbury Rd, The Leigh, GL19 4AQ, South : 5 m. on A 38 ℘ (01242) 680255, ⛱ – ✗ TV P. ✗
closed January and February – **4 rm** ⊋ 40.00/70.00.

Bistrot André, 78 Church St., GL20 5RX, ℘ (01684) 290357 – MC VISA
closed Sunday and Monday – **Meals** - French - (dinner only) a la carte 15.80/24.70 **st.** 🍷 6.50.

ENGLAND

at Puckrup *North : 2½ m. on A 38 – ✉ Tewkesbury.*

Hilton Puckrup Hall, GL20 6EL, ☎ (01684) 296200, *Fax (01684) 850788,* – rest, TV P – 200. MC AE VISA
Meals a la carte 19.95/33.35 **t.** – 10.95 – **110 rm** 125.00/135.00 **t.**, 2 suites – SB.

at Kemerton *Northeast : 5¼ m. by A 46 – ✉ Tewkesbury.*

Upper Court, GL20 7HY, take right turn at stone cross in village ☎ (01386) 725351, *percourt@compuserve.com, Fax (01386) 725472,* « Georgian manor house, antique f nishings, gardens », – TV P. MC AE VISA.
Meals (by arrangement) 32.00 – **5 rm** 70.00/140.00 **t.**

at Corse Lawn *Southwest : 6 m. by A 38 and A 438 on B 4211 – ✉ Gloucester.*

Corse Lawn House, GL19 4LZ, ☎ (01452) 780771, *hotel@corselawnhouse.u_net m, Fax (01452) 780840,* « Queen Anne house », heated, – TV P – 40. MC VISA
closed 25 and 26 December – ***Bistro :*** **Meals** a la carte 18.40/25.45 **st.** 6.00 – (see also ***Restaurant*** below) – **17 rm** 70.00/120.00 **st.**, 2 suites – SB.

The Restaurant (at Corse Lawn House H.), GL19 4LZ, ☎ (01452) 780771, *hotel@corse nhouse.u_net.com, Fax (01452) 780840,* – P. MC AE VISA
closed 25-26 December – **Meals** 17.95/27.50 **st.** and a la carte 6.00.

THAME *Oxon.* 404 R 28 *The West Country G. – pop. 10 806.*

Exc. : *Ridgeway Path★★.*

Market House, North St. ☎ (01844) 212834.

London 48 – Aylesbury 9 – Oxford 13.

Spread Eagle, 16 Cornmarket, OX9 2BW, ☎ (01844) 213661, *enquiries@spreadeagleh l.fsnet.co.uk, Fax (01844) 261380* – TV P – 250. MC AE VISA.
closed 28-30 December – **Meals** *(closed Sunday dinner and Bank Holiday Mond* a la carte 20.50/26.00 **st.** 5.95 – 9.95 – **31 rm** 87.95/129.00 **st.**, 2 suites – SB.

Travelodge, OX9 3XA, Northwest : 1 m. by B 4445 on B 4011 at junction with A ☎ (01844) 218740, *Fax (01844) 218740* – rm, rest, TV P. MC AE VISA JCB.
Meals (grill rest.) – **31 rm** 49.95 **t.**

The Old Trout with rm, 29-30 Lower High St., OX9 2AA, ☎ (01844) 212146, *mj4trout@ com, Fax (01844) 212614,* « 15C thatched inn » – TV P. MC VISA.
closed 24 December-7 January – **Meals** *(closed Sunday)* 10.50/13.00 (lunch) and a la carte 19.00/26.50 **st.** 6.50 – **7 rm** 55.00/85.00 **st.**

THANET WAY SERVICE AREA *Kent* 404 W 30 – *see Whitstable.*

THATCHAM *Newbury* 403 404 Q 29 – *pop. 20 726 – ✉ Newbury.*

London 69 – Bristol 68 – Oxford 30 – Reading 15 – Southampton 40.

Premier Lodge, Bath Rd, Midgham, RG7 5UX, East : 2 m. on A 4 ☎ (0870) 7001 *Fax (0870) 7001499* – TV P. MC AE VISA.
Meals (grill rest.) – **29 rm** 49.50 **t.**

THAXTED *Essex* 404 V 28 – *pop. 1 899.*

London 44 – Cambridge 24 – Colchester 31 – Chelmsford 20.

Four Seasons, Walden Rd, CM6 2RE, Northwest : ½ m. on B 184 ☎ (01371) 830 *Fax (01371) 830835* – TV P. MC VISA JCB.
Meals *(closed dinner Sunday and Bank Holidays)* a la carte 14.75/23.75 **t.** 8.00 – 8.
9 rm 60.00/75.00 **t.** – SB.

Crossways without rest., 32 Town St., CM6 2LA, ☎ (01371) 830348, – TV.
restricted opening in winter – **3 rm** 35.00/52.00.

THIRSK *N. Yorks.* 402 P 21 – *pop. 6 860.*

Thornton-Le-Street ☎ (01845) 522170.

The World of James Herriot, 25 Kirkgate ☎ (01845) 522755.

London 227 – Leeds 37 – Middlesbrough 24 – York 24.

Golden Fleece, 42 Market Pl., YO7 1LL, ☎ (01845) 523108, *Fax (01845) 523996* – TV P – 80. MC AE VISA
Meals a la carte 14.15/24.45 **t.** 5.65 – **18 rm** 65.00/105.00 **t.** – SB.

Sheppard's, Front St., Sowerby, YO7 1JF, South : 1/2 m. ✆ (01845) 523655, *sheppards@thirskny.freeserve.co.uk, Fax (01845) 524720* – rm, TV P. MC VISA. closed first week January – ***Bistro :*** **Meals** a la carte 15.90/28.45 **st.** 5.85 – **8 rm** 62.00/84.00 **st.**

Spital Hill, York Rd, YO7 3AE, Southeast : 1 3/4 m. on A 19, entrance between 2 white posts ✆ (01845) 522273, *Fax (01845) 524970,* – P. MC AE VISA. **Meals** (by arrangement) (communal dining) 25.00 **st.** 6.00 – **3 rm** 46.00/75.00 **st.**

Thornborough House Farm, YO7 2NP, North : 1 3/4 m. following signs for A 19 Teesside, entrance off A 19 Teesside sliproad ✆ (01845) 522103, *williamson@thornboroughhousefarm.freeserve.co.uk, Fax (01845) 522103,* « Working farm », – TV P. MC VISA. *January-September* – **Meals** (by arrangement) (communal dining) 11.00 **st.** – **3 rm** 25.00/40.00 **st.**

Topcliffe *Southwest : 4 1/2 m. by A 168 – ✉ Thirsk.*

Angel Inn, Long St., YO7 3RW, ✆ (01845) 577237, *Fax (01845) 578000,* – TV P – 150. MC VISA JCB. **Meals** a la carte 15.75/20.50 **st.** 5.95 – **15 rm** 44.50/60.00 **t.**

Asenby *Southwest : 5 1/4 m. by A 168 – ✉ Thirsk.*

Crab Manor, Dishforth Rd, YO7 3QL, ✆ (01845) 577286, *info@crabandlobster.co.uk, Fax (01845) 577109,* « Part Georgian manor, memorabilia », – TV P. MC AE VISA **Meals** – (see ***Crab and Lobster*** below) – **12 rm** 80.00/120.00 **t.**

Crab and Lobster, Dishforth Rd, YO7 3QL, ✆ (01845) 577286, *Fax (01845) 577109,* « Thatched inn, memorabilia », – P. MC AE VISA ***The Restaurant :*** **Meals** - Seafood - (booking essential) 10.00/23.00 **t.** and a la carte.

Crab and Lobster, Dishforth Rd, YO7 3QL, ✆ (01845) 577286, *Fax (01845) 577109,* « Thatched inn, memorabilia », – P. MC AE VISA ***The Brasserie :*** **Meals** - Seafood - (bookings not accepted) 10.00/23.00 **t.** and a la carte.

ORNABY-ON-TEES *Stockton-on-Tees* 402 Q 20 – *pop. 12 108 – ✉ Middlesbrough.*

London 250 – Leeds 62 – Middlesbrough 3 – York 49.

Posthouse Teesside, Low Lane, Stainton Village, TS17 9LW, Southeast : 3 1/2 m. by A 1045 on A 1044 ✆ (0870) 4009081, *amizzi@forte-hotels.com, Fax (01642) 594989,* – rm, TV P – 120. MC AE VISA **Meals** a la carte 15.85/19.85 **t.** 6.95 – 10.95 – **136 rm** 69.00/89.00 **st.** – SB.

Travel Inn, Whitewater Way, TS17 6QB, Northeast : 1 1/2 m. by A 66 following signs to Teeside Park ✆ (01642) 671573, *Fax (01642) 671464* – rm, rest, TV P. MC AE VISA. **Meals** (grill rest.) – **42 rm** 40.95 **t.**

ORNBURY *South Gloucestershire* 403 404 M 29 – *pop. 12 108 – ✉ Bristol.*

London 128 – Bristol 12 – Gloucester 23 – Swindon 43.

Thornbury Castle, Castle St., BS35 1HH, ✆ (01454) 281182, *thornburycastle@compuserve.com, Fax (01454) 416188,* « 16C castle, antiques, gardens and vineyard », – rest, TV P. MC AE VISA. *closed 7-12 January* – **Meals** 19.50/39.50 **t.** 10.50 – 8.95 – **18 rm** 105.00/350.00 **t.**, 2 suites.

ORNHAM MAGNA *Suffolk – ✉ Eye.*

London 96 – Cambridge 47 – Ipswich 20 – Norwich 30.

Thornham Hall, IP23 8HA, ✆ (01379) 783314, *lhenniker@aol.com, Fax (01379) 788347,* « Within grounds of Thornham estate », – P. MC VISA JCB **Meals** (by arrangement) (communal dining) 18.00 – **3 rm** 40.00/60.00.

ORNTHWAITE *Cumbria* 402 K 20 – *see Keswick.*

ORNTON HOUGH *Mersey.* 402 403 K 24 – *✉ Wirral.*

London 215 – Birkenhead 12 – Chester 17 – Liverpool 12.

Thornton Hall, CH63 1JF, on B 5136 ✆ (0151) 336 3938, *thorntonhallhotel@btinternet.com, Fax (0151) 336 7864,* – TV P – 250. MC AE VISA JCB *closed 28-30 December* – ***The Italian Room :*** **Meals** (bar lunch Saturday) 11.50/24.00 **st.** and dinner a la carte 8.00 – 10.00 – **62 rm** 76.00/86.00, 1 suite – SB.

THORNTON-LE-DALE *N. Yorks.* 402 R 21 – *see Pickering.*

THORPE *Derbs.* 402 403 404 O 24 *Great Britain G.* – *pop. 201* – *Ashbourne.*
See : *Dovedale★★ (Ilam Rock★).*
London 151 – Derby 16 – Sheffield 33 – Stoke-on-Trent 26.

Peveril of the Peak, DE6 2AW, (01335) 350333, *Fax (01335) 350507*, ←, – 50. VISA JCB.
Meals 11.95/21.95 **t.** 9.50 – 10.95 – **46 rm** 105.00/95.00 **st.** – SB.

THORPE MARKET *Norfolk* 404 X 25 – *pop. 303* – *North Walsham.*
London 130 – Norwich 21.

Elderton Lodge, Gunton Park, NR11 8TZ, South : 1 m. on A 149 (01263) 833547
nquiries@eldertonlodge.co.uk, Fax (01263) 834673, ←, – rest, VISA JC
*closed 3 weeks in January***Meals** 8.50/28.00 **t.** and a la carte 8.00 – **11 rm** 67.5
110.00 **t.** – SB.

THRAPSTON SERVICE AREA *Northants.* 404 S 26 – *Kettering.*

Travelodge, NN14 4UR, at junction of A 14 with A 605 and A 45 (01832) 7351
Fax (01832) 735199 – rm, VISA JCB.
Meals (grill rest.) – **40 rm** 39.95 **t.**

THREE BRIDGES *W. Sussex* – *see Crawley.*

THRELKELD *Cumbria* 402 K 20 – *see Keswick.*

THRUSSINGTON *Leics.* 402 403 404 Q 25 – *pop. 512* – *Leicester.*
London 101 – Leicester 10 – Nottingham 22 – Lincoln 50.

Travelodge, Green Acres Filling Station, LE7 8TE, on A 46 (southbound carriagew
(01664) 424525, *Fax (01664) 424525* – rm, rest, VISA JCB.
Meals (grill rest.) – **32 rm** 39.95 **t.**

THURLESTONE *Devon* 403 I 33 – *see Kingsbridge.*

THURROCK SERVICE AREA *Thurrock* 404 V 29 – *West Thurrock.*
Belhus Park, South Ockendon (01708) 854260.
Granada Motorway Service Area (M 25) (01708) 863733.

Travelodge, RM16 3BG, (01708) 891111, *Fax (01708) 860971* –
VISA JCB.
Meals (grill rest.) – **44 rm** 59.95 **t.**

TIBSHELF SERVICE AREA *Derbs.* – *Derby.*

Travel Inn without rest., DE55 5TZ, M 1 between junctions 28 and 29 (northbo
carriageway) (01773) 876600, *Fax (01773) 876609* – – 30.
40 rm 40.95 **t.**

TICEHURST *E. Sussex* 404 V 30 – *pop. 3 118* – *Wadhurst.*
Dale Hill Hotel, Ticehurst (01580) 200112.
London 49 – Brighton 44 – Folkestone 38 – Hastings 15 – Maidstone 24.

Dale Hill, TN5 7DQ, Northeast : ½ m. on B 2087 (01580) 200112, *info@dalehill.cc*
Fax (01580) 201249, – – 30. VISA JCB
Meals (restricted lunch) a la carte 18.85/28.85 **t.** – **31 rm** 70.00/80.00 **t.**, 1 suite.

King John's Lodge, Sheepstreet Lane, Etchingham, TN19 7AZ, South : 2 m
Church St. (01580) 819232, *Fax (01580) 819562*, ←, « Part Tudor hunting lodge v
Jacobean additions, gardens », heated, – rm,
closed Christmas and New Year – **Meals** (by arrangement) (communal dining) 25.00 s
4 rm 50.00/70.00 **st.**

NTAGEL *Cornwall* 403 F 32 *The West Country G. – pop. 1 721.*
See : *Arthur's Castle (site★★★) AC – Church★ – Old Post Office★ AC.*
Env. : *Boscastle★, E : off B 3263 – W : Hell's Mouth★.*
Exc. : *Camelford★, SE : 6½ m. by B 3263 and B 3266.*
London 264 – Exeter 63 – Plymouth 49 – Truro 41.

Trebrea Lodge, Trenale, PL34 0HR, Southeast : 1 ¼ m. by Boscastle Rd (B 3263) and Trenale Lane on Trewarmett rd ☎ (01840) 770410, *Fax (01840) 770092*, ≤, « Part 18C manor house, 14C origins », – TV P. MC AE VISA
closed January – **Meals** (booking essential to non-residents) (dinner only) 24.00 **t.** 7.50 – **7 rm** 62.00/96.00 **t.** – SB.

Wootons Country H., Fore St., PL34 0DD, ☎ (01840) 770170, *Fax (01840) 770978* – TV P. MC AE VISA JCB.
Meals a la carte 9.20/17.40 **t.** 3.95 – **11 rm** 30.00/80.00 **t.**

Polkerr without rest., Molesworth St., PL34 0BY, ☎ (01840) 770382, – TV P.
closed 25-26 December – **7 rm** 25.00/50.00 **s.**

The Old Borough House, Bossiney, PL34 0AY, Northeast : ½ m. on B 3263 ☎ (01840) 770475, *borough@fsdial.co.uk, Fax (01840) 770475* – TV P. MC VISA JCB.
closed Christmas and New Year – **Meals** (by arrangement) 20.00 **st.** – **4 rm** 40.00/65.00 **st.**

CHWELL *Norfolk* 404 V 25 – *pop. 99 – ✉ Brancaster.*
London 130 – Cambridge 82 – Norwich 48.

Titchwell Manor, PE31 8BB, ☎ (01485) 210221, *margaret@titchwellmanor.co.uk, Fax (01485) 210104*, – rm, TV P. MC AE VISA
Meals (bar lunch)/dinner 23.00 **t.** 7.00 – **16 rm** 45.00/110.00 **t.** – SB.

LEY *Herefordshire* 403 L 27 – *see Kington.*

DDINGTON SERVICE AREA *Beds.* 404 S 28 – *pop. 4 500 – ✉ Luton.*
18 *Chalgrave Manor, Dunstable Rd, Toddington ☎ (01525) 876556.*

Travelodge, LU5 6HR, M 1 (southbound carriageway) ☎ (01525) 878424, *Fax (01525) 878452* – TV P. MC AE VISA JCB.
Meals (grill rest.) – **43 rm** 59.95 **t.**

DMORDEN *W. Yorks.* 402 N 22.
London 217 – Burnley 10 – Leeds 35 – Manchester 22.

Scaitcliffe Hall, Burnley Rd, OL14 7DQ, Northwest : 1 m. on A 646 ☎ (01706) 818888, *Fax (01706) 818825*, – TV P – 30. MC AE VISA
Meals a la carte 19.50/28.95 **t.** 6.00 – **28 rm** 35.00/84.00 **st.**

FT *Lincs. – see Bourne.*

LESHUNT KNIGHTS *Essex – see Maldon.*

PCLIFFE *N. Yorks.* 402 P 21 – *see Thirsk.*

RQUAY *Torbay* 403 J 32 *The West Country G. – pop. 59 587.*
See : *Torbay★ – Kent's Cavern★ AC* **CX A.**
Env. : *Paignton Zoo★★ AC, SE : 3 m. by A 3022 – Cockington★, W : 1 m.* **AX.**
18 *Petitor Rd, St. Marychurch ☎ (01803) 327471,* **B.**
Vaughan Par. ☎ (01803) 297428.
London 223 – Exeter 23 – Plymouth 32.

Plans on following pages

Imperial, Parkhill Rd, TQ1 2DG, ☎ (01803) 294301, *imperialtorquay@paramount-hotels.co.uk, Fax (01803) 298293*, ≤ Torbay, heated, squash – rest, TV P – 350. MC AE VISA. CZ a
Regatta : **Meals** (dinner only and Sunday lunch) 25.00 **t.** and a la carte 11.50 – ***TQ1 :*** **Meals** a la carte 21.00/39.00 **t.** – 9.50 – **137 rm** 95.00/200.00 **t.**, 17 suites – SB.

TORBAY
TORQUAY-PAIGNTON

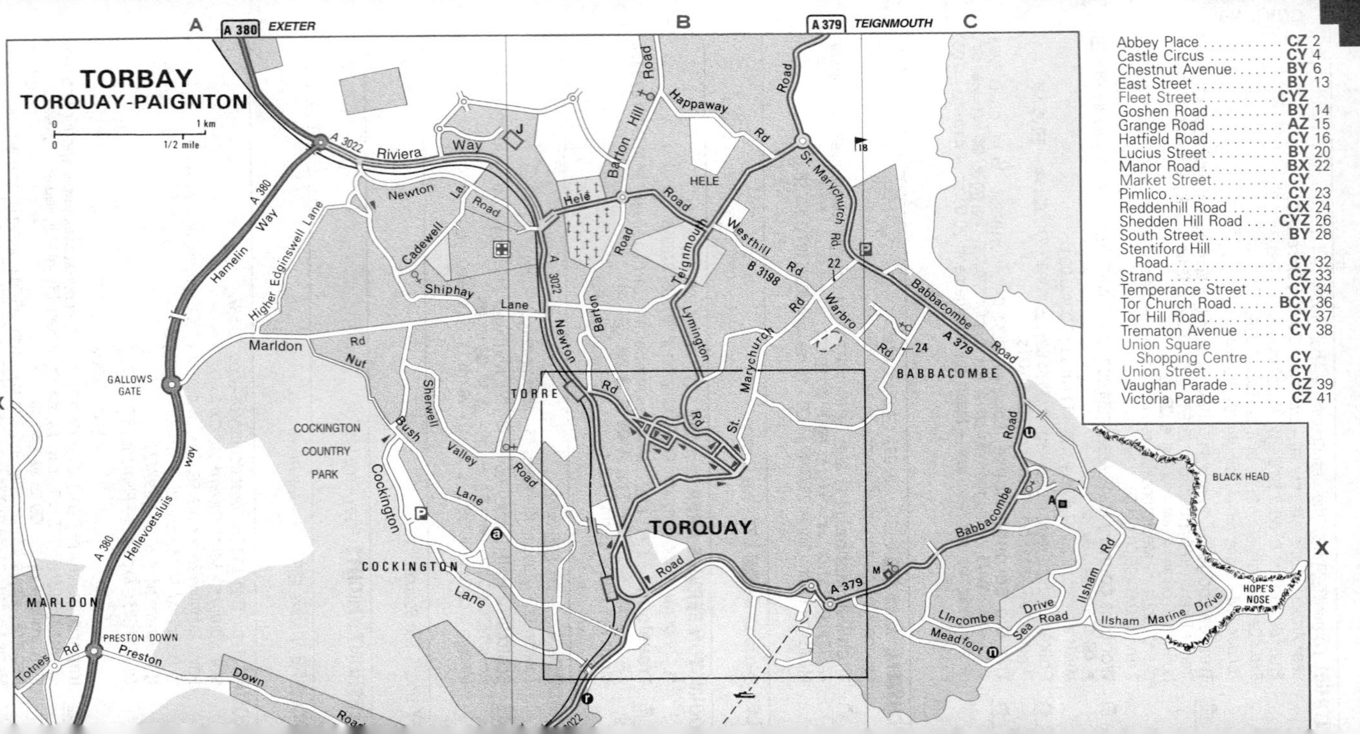

Street	Grid	No.
Abbey Place	CZ	2
Castle Circus	CY	4
Chestnut Avenue	BY	6
East Street	BY	13
Fleet Street	CYZ	
Goshen Road	BY	14
Grange Road	AZ	15
Hatfield Road	CY	16
Lucius Street	BY	20
Manor Road	BX	22
Market Street	CY	
Pimlico	CY	23
Reddenhill Road	CX	24
Shedden Hill Road	CYZ	26
South Street	BY	28
Stentiford Hill Road	CY	32
Strand	CZ	33
Temperance Street	CY	34
Tor Church Road	BCY	36
Tor Hill Road	CY	37
Trematon Avenue	CY	38
Union Square Shopping Centre	CY	
Union Street	CY	
Vaughan Parade	CZ	39
Victoria Parade	CZ	41

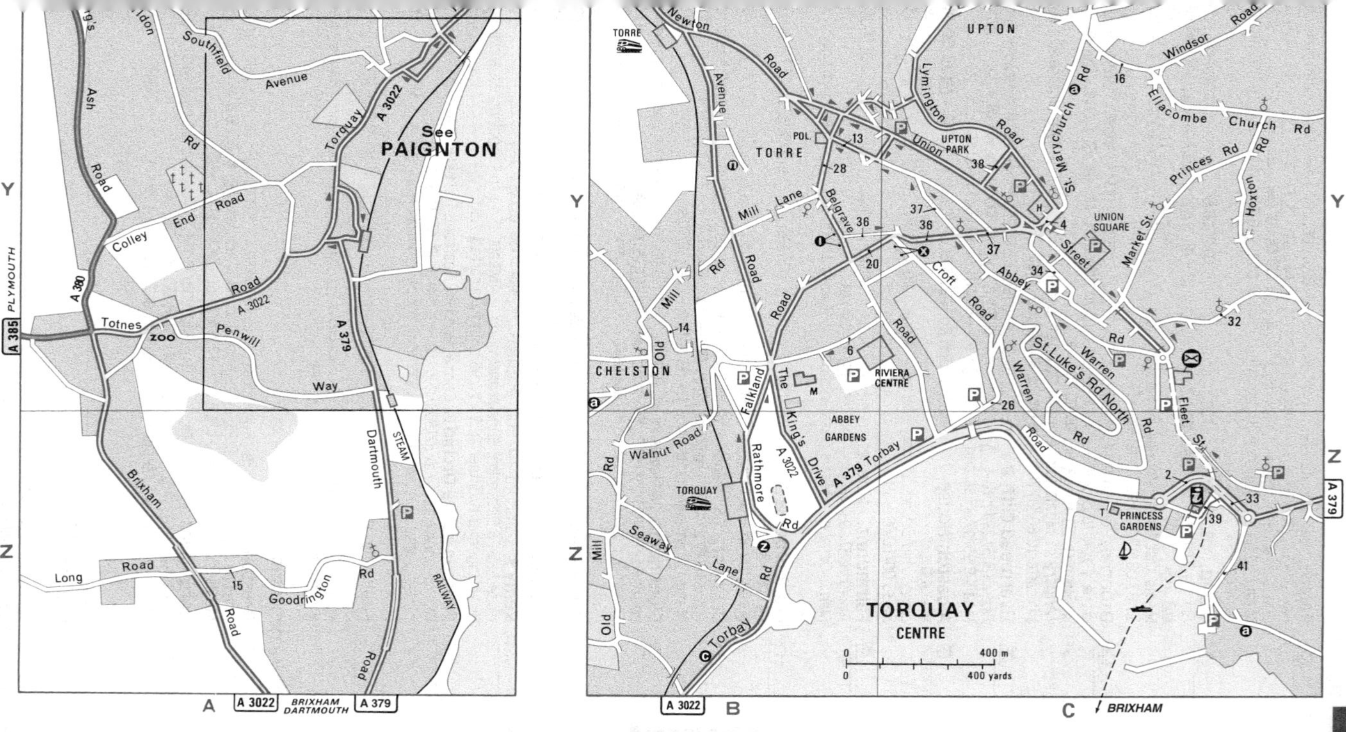

TORQUAY
CENTRE
See
PAIGNTON
UPTON
TORRE
CHELSTON
UNION SQUARE
UPTON PARK
RIVIERA CENTRE
ABBEY GARDENS
PRINCESS GARDENS
POL.
TORRE
TORQUAY
BRIXHAM
A 379
A 3022
A 385
PLYMOUTH
A 380
BRIXHAM DARTMOUTH
Newton Road
Avenue Road
Mill Lane
Belgrave Road
Lymington Road
Union Street
St. Marychurch Rd
Windsor Road
Ellacombe Church Rd
Princes Rd
Hoxton Rd
Market St.
Abbey Road
Croft Road
Warren Rd
St.Luke's Rd North
Fleet St
The King's Drive
A 379 Torbay Road
Rathmore Rd
Falkland Road
Walnut Road
Old Mill Rd
Seaway Lane
Torbay Rd
Ash Road
Colley End Road
Southfield Avenue
Torquay Road
Totnes Road
Penwill Way
Dartmouth Road
STEAM RAILWAY
Goodrington Rd
Brixham Road
Long Road
ZOO
400 m
400 yards
Y
Z
A
B
C

Palace, Babbacombe Rd, TQ1 3TG, ☎ (01803) 200200, *mail13@palacetorquay.co* *Fax (01803) 299899*, ←, « Extensive gardens », heated, indoor, outdoor, squash – 350. VISA JCB CX
Meals 22.50 **t.** (dinner) and a la carte 27.50/40.00 **t.** 6.50 – **135 rm** 61.00/196.00 6 suites – SB.

Grand, Sea Front, TQ2 6NT, ☎ (01803) 296677, *grandhotel@netsite.co* *Fax (01803) 213462*, ←, heated, – rest, – 300. VISA JCB BZ
Meals (bar lunch Monday to Saturday)/dinner a la carte 25.00/37.85 **st.** 7.80 – **99** 65.00/190.00 **st.**, 11 suites – SB.

Osborne, Hesketh Cres., Meadfoot, TQ1 2LL, ☎ (01803) 213311, *enq@osbourne-torq* *co.uk, Fax (01803) 296788*, ←, « Regency town houses », heated, rest, – 80. VISA. CX
Langtry's **: Meals** (dinner only) 20.00 **st.** and a la carte 7.00 – ***The Brasserie*** **: Me** a la carte 10.60/20.70 **t.** – **29 rm** 80.00/160.00 **st.** – SB.

Livermead Cliff, Seafront, TQ2 6RQ, ☎ (01803) 299666, *enquiries@livermeadcliff.co* *Fax (01803) 294496*, ←, heated, – – 70. VISA JCB. BX
Meals 9.95/17.95 **st.** and a la carte 5.75 – **64 rm** 52.00/119.00 **st.** – SB.

Albaston House, 27 St. Marychurch Rd, TQ1 3JF, ☎ (01803) 296758 – VISA JCB CY
closed mid December-mid January – **Meals** (dinner only) 12.00/15.00 **st.** 4.50 – **13** 35.00/80.00 – SB.

Fairmount House, Herbert Rd, Chelston, TQ2 6RW, ☎ (01803) 605 *Fax (01803) 605446*, – rest, VISA AX
March-October – **Meals** (residents only) (bar lunch)/dinner 14.95 – **6 rm** 33.50/67.0 SB.

Cranborne, 58 Belgrave Rd, TQ2 5HY, ☎ (01803) 298046, *Fax (01803) 215477* – VISA JCB. BY
Meals (by arrangement) 10.00 **st.** 3.00 – **10 rm** 30.00/60.00 – SB.

Belmont, 66 Belgrave Rd, TQ2 5HY, ☎ (01803) 295028, *belmont@fsbdial.co* *Fax (01803) 211668* – rest, VISA JCB BY
Meals (by arrangement) 10.00 **s.** – **13 rm** 17.00/50.00 **s.**

Glenorleigh, 26 Cleveland Rd, TQ2 5BE, ☎ (01803) 292135, *glenorleigh@netscapeon* *co.uk, Fax (01803) 292135*, heated, – VISA. BY
March-October and New Year – **Meals** (by arrangement) 9.75 **st.** – **16 rm** 30.00/60.00 – SB.

Cedar Court, 3 St. Matthews Rd, Chelston, TQ2 6JA, ☎ (01803) 607851 – BY
Meals (by arrangement) 10.00 – **9 rm** 25.00/50.00 **st.** – SB.

Remy's, 3 Croft Rd, TQ2 5UF, ☎ (01803) 292359 – VISA JCB CY
closed 25-26 December, Sunday and Monday – **Meals** - French - (booking essential) (lu by arrangement)/dinner 18.95/26.95 **t.** and a la carte 7.50.

Pearson at The Orchid (at Corbyn Head H.), Seafront, TQ2 6RH, ☎ (01803) 296366, *@corbynhead.com, Fax (01803) 296152*, ← – VISA BZ
closed 2 weeks in January, 2 weeks in October/November, Sunday and Monday – **M** 36.95 **t.** and a la carte 10.00.

Mulberry House with rm, 1 Scarborough Rd, TQ2 5UJ, ☎ (01803) 213639 – CY
Meals *(closed lunch Monday to Thursday)* (booking essential) a la carte 15.50/21.5 7.50 – **3 rm** 35.00/55.00 **st.** – SB.

at Maidencombe *North : 3½ m. by B 3199* – **BX** – ✉ *Torquay.*

Orestone Manor, Rockhouse Lane, TQ1 4SX, ☎ (01803) 328098, *reservations@c* *one.co.uk, Fax (01803) 328336*, ←, heated, – rest, VISA JCB
Meals (dinner only) 30.00 **t.** 6.20 – **12 rm** 50.00/160.00 **t.** – SB.

Barn Hayes, Brim Hill, TQ1 4TR, ☎ (01803) 327980, *barnhayes@barnhayes.jungle* *co.uk, Fax (01803) 327980*, ←, – VISA JCB.
March-November – **Meals** (light lunch)/dinner 15.00 **st.** 4.75 – **10 rm** 36.00/72.00 SB.

TORVER *Cumbria* 402 K 20 – *see Coniston.*

TOTLAND *I.O.W.* 403 404 P 31 – *see Wight (Isle of).*

ENGLAND

TNES *Devon* 403 I 32 *The West Country G. – pop. 7 018.*

See : *Town★ – Elizabethan Museum★ – St. Mary's★ – Butterwalk★ – Castle (≤★★★) AC.*

Env. : *Paignton Zoo★★ AC, E : 4½ m. by A 385 and A 3022 – British Photographic Museum, Bowden House★ AC, S : 1 m. by A 381 – Dartington Hall (High Cross House★), NW : 2 m. on A 385 and A 384.*

Exc. : *Dartmouth★★ (Castle ≤★★★) SE : 12 m. by A 381 and A 3122.*

18, 9 Dartmouth G & C.C., Blackawton ☎ (01803) 712686.

The Town Mill, Coronation Rd ☎ (01803) 863168.

London 224 – Exeter 24 – Plymouth 23 – Torquay 9.

Gabriel Court, Stoke Hill, Stoke Gabriel, TQ9 6SF, Southeast : 4 m. by A 385 ☎ (01803) 782206, *obeacom@aol.com, Fax (01803) 782333,* heated, – rest, TV P. MC AE VISA JCB
Meals (dinner only and Sunday lunch)/dinner 27.00 **st.** 6.00 – **19 rm** 55.00/80.00 **st.**

Bow Bridge *South : 3½ m. by A 381 – ✉ Totnes.*

Waterman's Arms, TQ9 7EG, ☎ (01803) 732214, *Fax (01803) 732314,* « Part 15C inn », – TV P. MC AE VISA
Meals a la carte 14.85/23.85 **t.** – **15 rm** 54.00/69.00 **st.** – SB.

Tuckenhay *South : 4¼ m. by A 381 – ✉ Totnes.*

Maltsters Arms with rm, Bow Creek, TQ9 7EQ, ☎ (01803) 732350, *pubtuckennay.demon.co.uk, Fax (01803) 732823,* ≤, , « Riverside setting » – TV P. MC VISA
closed 25 December – **Meals** a la carte 14.85/23.25 **t.** 5.50 – **4 rm** 65.00/105.00 **st.**

WCESTER *Northants.* 403 404 R 27 – *pop. 7 006.*

18, 18 Whittelbury Park G. & C.C., Whittlebury ☎ (01327) 858092 – 18 Farthingstone Hotel, Farthingstone ☎ (01327) 361291.

London 70 – Birmingham 50 – Northampton 9 – Oxford 36.

Saracens Head, 219 Watling St., NN12 7BX, ☎ (01327) 350414, *Fax (01327) 359879* – TV P. – 100. MC AE VISA JCB
Meals 6.95/10.95 **t.** and a la carte 6.50 – **21 rm** 60.00/85.00 **t.** – SB.

Travelodge, East Towcester bypass, NN12 6TQ, Southwest : ½ m. by Brackley rd on A 43 ☎ (01327) 359105, *Fax (01327) 359105* – rm, TV P. MC AE VISA JCB.
Meals (grill rest.) – **33 rm** 49.95 **t.**

Paulerspury *Southeast : 3¼ m. by A 5 – ✉ Towcester.*

Vine House with rm, 100 High St., NN12 7NA, ☎ (01327) 811267, *Fax (01327) 811309,* – rest, TV P. MC VISA.
closed 24-30 December – **Meals** *(closed Sunday)* (dinner only and lunch Thursday-Saturday) 24.95 **t.** 7.00 – **6 rm** 49.00/75.00 **t.**

AFFORD CENTRE *Gtr. Manchester – see Manchester.*

AFFORD PARK *Gtr. Manchester – see Manchester.*

EGONY *Cornwall* 403 F 33 *The West Country G. – pop. 729 – ✉ Truro.*

Env. : *Trewithen★★★ AC, N : 2½ m.*

London 291 – Newquay 18 – Plymouth 53 – Truro 10.

Tregony House, 15 Fore St., TR2 5RN, ☎ (01872) 530671, *Fax (01872) 530671,* – P. MC VISA.
March-October – **Meals** (by arrangement) 11.50 **st.** – **5 rm** 19.50/48.00 **st.**

EGREHAN *Cornwall* 403 F 32 – *see St. Austell.*

ESCO *Cornwall* 403 (30) – *see Scilly (Isles of).*

NG *Herts.* 404 S 28 – *pop. 11 455.*

London 38 – Aylesbury 7 – Luton 14.

Pendley Manor, Cow Lane, HP23 5QY, East : 1 ½ m. by B 4635 off B 4251 ☎ (01442) 891891, *sales@pendley-manor.co.uk, Fax (01442) 890687,* ≤, , , – rest, TV P. – 220. MC AE VISA JCB
Meals 28.00 **st.** and a la carte 6.50 – **68 rm** 110.00/160.00 **st.**, 2 suites – SB.

Rose and Crown, High St., HP23 5AH, ☎ (01442) 824071, *Fax (01442) 890735* – ⅍ TV P – 🎤 80. MC AE ⓓ VISA JCB
Meals (dinner only and Sunday lunch)/dinner 19.95 **t.** 🍷 8.00 – ☕ 9.75 – **27 rm** 85.
125.00 **t.** – SB.

Travel Inn, Tring Hill, HP23 4LD, West : 1 ½ m. on A 41 ☎ (01442) 8248
Fax (01442) 890787 – ⅍ rm, TV ♿ P. MC AE ⓓ VISA. ✗
Meals (grill rest.) – **30 rm** 40.95 **t.**

TRINITY *Jersey (Channel Islands)* 403 P 33 and 230 ⑪ – *see Channel Islands.*

TROTTON *W. Sussex* – *see Midhurst.*

TROUTBECK *Cumbria* 402 L 20 – *see Windermere.*

TROWBRIDGE *Wilts.* 403 404 N 30 *The West Country G.* – *pop. 25 279.*

Env. : *Westwood Manor*★, *NW : 3 m. by A 363 – Farleigh Hungerford*★ *(St. Leona Chapel*★*) AC, W : 4 m.*

Exc. : *Longleat House*★★★ *AC, SW : 12 m. by A 363, A 350 and A 362 - Bratton Castle (< SE : 7½ m. by A 363 and B 3098 – Steeple Ashton*★ *(The Green*★*) E : 6 m. – Edington Mary, St. Katherine and All Saints*★*) SE : 7½ m.*

ℹ *St. Stephen's Pl.* ☎ *(01225) 777054.*

London 115 – Bristol 27 – Southampton 55 – Swindon 32.

Old Manor, Trowle, BA14 9BL, Northwest : 1 m. on A 363 ☎ (01225) 777393, *romantic s@easynet.co.uk, Fax (01225) 765443,* « Queen Anne house of 15C origins », 🌳 – ⅍ TV
P. MC AE ⓓ VISA JCB. ✗
closed 4 days Christmas – **Meals** *(closed Sunday)* (residents only) (dinner only) 17.0 and a la carte 🍷 3.95 – **18 rm** ☕ 49.50/120.00.

Brookfield House 🐦 without rest., Vaggs Hill, Wingfield, BA14 9NA, Southwest : 4 by A 366 on B 3109 ☎ (01373) 830615, *Fax (01373) 830615,* « Working farm », 🌳, 🐄 –
TV P. ✗
closed 25 and 26 December – **3 rm** ☕ 35.00/50.00 **st.**

Welam House without rest., Bratton Rd, West Ashton, BA14 6AZ, Southeast : 2 m. 361 on West Ashton Rd ☎ (01225) 755908, 🌳 – ⅍ P. ✗
April-October – **3 rm** ☕ 36.00 **st.**

at Holt *North : 3¼ m. by B 3106 off B 3105* – ✉ *Trowbridge.*

Tollgate Inn, Ham Green, BA14 6PX, ☎ (01225) 782326, *Fax (01225) 782326* – ⅍ P
VISA
closed Sunday dinner and Monday – **Meals** (booking essential) 12.95 **t.** (lunch) and a la c
18.45/23.85 **t.**

at Semington *Northeast : 2½ m. by A 361* – ✉ *Trowbridge.*

Lamb on the Strand, 99 The Strand, BA14 6LL, East : 1 ½ m. on A
☎ (01380) 870263, *Fax (01380) 871203,* 🌳 – P. MC AE VISA
closed 25 December and Sunday dinner – **Meals** a la carte 15.25/19.50 **st.** 🍷 5.25.

TROWELL SERVICE AREA *Notts.* 404 Q 25 – ✉ *Ilkeston.*

Travelodge, NG9 3PL, at junction 25/6 on M 1 (northbound carriage
☎ (0115) 932 0291, *Fax (0115) 930 7261* – ⅍ TV ♿ P. MC AE ⓓ VISA JCB. ✗
Meals (grill rest.) – **35 rm** 49.95 **t.**

TRURO *Cornwall* 403 E 33 *The West Country G.* – *pop. 16 522.*

See : *Royal Cornwall Museum*★★ *AC.*

Env. : *Trelissick Garden*★★ *(<★★) AC, S : 4 m. by A 39 – Feock (Church*★*) S : 5 m. by A 39 B 3289.*

Exc. : *Trewithen*★★★, *NE : 7½ m. by A 39 and A 390 – Probus*★ *(tower*★ *- garden*★*) NE : by A 39 and A 390.*

⛳18 *Treliske* ☎ *(01872) 272640* – ⛳18 *Killiow Park, Killiow, Kea* ☎ *(01872) 270246.*

ℹ *Municipal Buildings, Boscawen St.* ☎ *(01872) 274555.*

London 295 – Exeter 87 – Penzance 26 – Plymouth 52.

Alverton Manor, Tregolls Rd, TR1 1ZQ, ✆ (01872) 276633, *alverton@connexions.co.uk, Fax (01872) 222989,* « Mid 19C manor house, former Bishop's residence and convent », – rest, – 200.
Meals 18.00/21.50 **st.** and dinner a la carte 6.00 – **30 rm** 67.00/139.00 **st.**, 4 suites – SB.

Royal, Lemon St., TR1 2QB, ✆ (01872) 270345, *reception@royalhotelcornwall.co.uk, Fax (01872) 242453* – rm,
closed 25 and 26 December – **Meals** *(closed Sunday lunch)* (grill rest.) 10.00/15.00 **t.** (dinner) and a la carte 15.00/24.50 **t.** – 5.50 – **35 rm** 57.00/95.00 **st.** – SB.

Carnon Downs *Southwest : 3 1/4 m. by A 39 – ✉ Truro.*

Travel Inn, Old Carnon Hill, TR3 6JT, ✆ (01872) 863370, *Fax (01872) 865620*, – rm, rest,
Meals (grill rest.) – **40 rm** 40.95 **t.**

Blackwater *West : 7 m. by A 390 – ✉ Truro.*

Rock Cottage without rest., TR4 8EU, ✆ (01872) 560252, *rockcottage@yahoo.com, Fax (01872) 560252* –
closed Christmas and New Year – **3 rm** 26.00/44.00 **s.**

CKENHAY *Devon – see Totnes.*

NBRIDGE WELLS *Kent* 404 U 30 – *see Royal Tunbridge Wells.*

RNERS HILL *W. Sussex* 404 T 30 – *pop. 1 534.*

London 33 – Brighton 24 – Crawley 7.

Alexander House, East St., RH10 4QD, East : 1 m. on B 2110 ✆ (01342) 714914, *info@alexanderhouse.co.uk, Fax (01342) 717328*, « Part 17C country house in extensive parkland », – rest, – 60.
Meals 21.50/36.00 **st.** and a la carte 9.50 – **9 rm** 135.00/235.00 **st.**, 6 suites – SB.

RVILLE *Bucks. – ✉ Henley-on-Thames.*

London 45 – Oxford 22 – Reading 17.

Bull & Butcher, RG9 6QU, ✆ (01491) 638283, –
closed Sunday dinner – **Meals** a la carte 18.85/24.85 **t.**

TBURY *Staffs.* 402 403 404 O 25 *Great Britain G. – pop. 5 646 (inc. Hatton) – ✉ Burton-upon-Trent.*

Env. : *Sudbury Hall★★ AC, NW : 5 1/2 m. by A 50.*

London 132 – Birmingham 33 – Derby 11 – Stoke-on-Trent 27.

Ye Olde Dog and Partridge, High St., DE13 9LS, ✆ (01283) 813030, *Fax (01283) 813178,* « Part 15C timbered inn », – rm, rest,
closed 25-26 December and 1 January – **Meals** (carving rest.) a la carte 13.25/18.85 **t.** 6.25 – (see also ***Brasserie at The Dog*** below) – **20 rm** 55.00/99.00 **t.** – SB.

Mill House without rest., Cornmill Lane, DE13 9HA, Southeast : 3/4 m. ✆ (01283) 813634, « Georgian house and watermill », –
closed 25 and 26 December – **3 rm** 40.00/55.00 **s.**

Brasserie at The Dog (at Ye Olde Dog and Partridge H.), High St., DE13 9LS, ✆ (01283) 813030, *Fax (01283) 813178* –
closed Monday, Saturday lunch and Sunday dinner – **Meals** a la carte 14.05/23.70 **t.** 7.50.

O BRIDGES *Devon* 403 I 32 *The West Country G. – ✉ Yelverton.*

Env. : *Dartmoor National Park★★.*

London 226 – Exeter 25 – Plymouth 17.

Prince Hall, PL20 6SA, East : 1 m. on B 3357 ✆ (01822) 890403, *bookings@princehall.co.uk, Fax (01822) 890676*, – rest,
closed mid December-12 February – **Meals** (booking essential to non-residents) (dinner only) 29.00 **st.** 5.90 – **8 rm** (dinner included) 90.00/145.00 **st.**

O MILLS *Ches. – see Chester.*

TYNEMOUTH *Tyne and Wear* 401 402 P 18 – *pop. 17 422.*
London 290 – Newcastle upon Tyne 8 – Sunderland 7.

Grand, Grand Par., NE30 4ER, ✆ (0191) 293 6666, *Fax (0191) 293 6665,* ≤, « Victor mansion » – |‡| TV P – 250. MC AE ⊕ VISA. ✂
Meals *(closed Sunday dinner)* 12.75/16.75 **t.** and a la carte 7.65 – **45 rm** ☕ 60.0 130.00 **t.**

Sidney's, 3-5 Percy Park Rd, NE30 4LZ, ✆ (0191) 257 8500, *bookings@sidneys.co.* *Fax (0191) 257 9800* – MC AE VISA
closed 25-26 December, 1 January and dinner Sunday and Bank Holidays – **Meals** 9.95 (lunch) and a la carte 15.45/20.40 **t.**

UCKFIELD *E. Sussex* 404 U 31 – *pop. 13 531.*
London 45 – Brighton 17 – Eastbourne 20 – Maidstone 34.

Horsted Place ⛰, Little Horsted, TN22 5TS, South : 2 ½ m. by B 2102 and A 22 on A ✆ (01825) 750581, *hotel@horstedplace.co.uk, Fax (01825) 750459,* ≤, « Victor Gothic country house and gardens », ⛰, 18, ✂ – |‡|, ✂ rest, TV P – 80. MC AE VISA. ✂
closed 30 December-2 January – **Meals** 14.95/33.00 **t.** and a la carte 9.50 – **15** ☕ 145.00 **t.**, 5 suites – SB.

Hooke Hall without rest., 250 High St., TN22 1EN, ✆ (01825) 761578, *Fax (01825) 7680* « Queen Anne town house », – TV P. MC VISA. ✂
closed 24 December-2 January – ☕ 7.50 – **10 rm** 50.00/120.00 **st.**

UFFINGTON *Oxon.* 403 404 P 29.
London 75 – Oxford 29 – Reading 32 – Swindon 17.

Craven ⛰, Fernham Rd, SN7 7RD, ✆ (01367) 820449, « 17C thatched house », – P. MC AE VISA. ✂
Meals (by arrangement) (communal dining) 19.50 4.25 – **5 rm** ☕ 30.00/75.00 – SB.

UGGESHALL *Suffolk* – *see Southwold.*

ULLINGSWICK *Herefordshire* 403 404 M 27 – *pop. 237* – ✉ *Hereford.*
London 134 – Hereford 12 – Shrewsbury 52 – Worcester 19.

Steppes Country House ⛰, HR1 3JG, ✆ (01432) 820424, *bookings@steppeshotel usiness.co.uk, Fax (01432) 820042,* « Converted farmhouse of 14C origins », – ✂ TV MC VISA JCB
closed December and January – **Meals** (dinner only) (residents only) 26.00 **st.** 5.50 – **6** ☕ (dinner included) 75.00/142.00 **st.** – SB.

ULLSWATER *Cumbria* 402 L 20 – *pop. 1 199* – ✉ *Penrith.*
Main Car Park, Glenridding ✆ (017684) 82414 (summer only).
London 296 – Carlisle 25 – Kendal 31 – Penrith 6.

at Pooley Bridge *on B 5320* – ✉ *Penrith.*

Sharrow Bay Country House ⛰, CA10 2LZ, South : 2 m. on Howtown ✆ (017684) 86301, *enquiries@sharrow-bay.com, Fax (017684) 86349,* ≤ Ullswater and f « Victorian country house on the shores of Lake Ullswater, gardens », – ✂, rest, P. MC VISA JCB. ✂
March-November – **Meals** (booking essential) 30.00/47.25 **st.** 9.50 – **23 rm** ☕ (dir included) 105.00/400.00 **st.**, 5 suites
Spec. Fillet steak with braised oxtail and Burgundy sauce. Pan-fried sea bass with vençale vegetables. Assiette of chocolate desserts.

at Watermillock *on A 592* – ✉ *Penrith.*

Leeming House ⛰, CA11 0JJ, on A 592 ✆ (017684) 86622, *Fax (017684) 86443,* ≤, « Lakeside country house and gardens », – ✂ TV P – 35. MC AE ⊕ VISA JCB
Meals 13.95/27.50 **t.** and lunch a la carte 9.45 – ☕ 14.50 – **40 rm** 90.00/160.00 **t.** – SB

Rampsbeck Country House ⛰, CA11 0LP, ✆ (017684) 86442, *enquiries@rampsb .fsnet.co.uk, Fax (017684) 86688,* ≤ Ullswater and fells, « Lakeside setting », – ✂ P. MC VISA JCB
closed early January-early February – **Meals** – (see ***The Restaurant*** below) – **19** ☕ 60.00/190.00 **t.**, 1 suite – SB.

Old Church , CA11 0JN, (017684) 86204, *info@oldchurch.co.uk, Fax (017684) 86368*, Ullswater and fells, « Georgian country house on the shores of Lake Ullswater », rest, . *March-November* – **Meals** *(closed Sunday)* (booking essential) (dinner only) a la carte 21.20/27.00 **st.** 9.25 – **10 rm** 65.00/145.00 **st.** – SB.

The Restaurant (at Rampsbeck Country House H.), CA11 0LP, (017684) 86442, *Fax (017684) 86688*, Ullswater and fells, « Lakeside setting », – *closed early January-early February* – **Meals** (booking essential) (lunch by arrangement Monday to Saturday)/dinner 29.00/39.50 **t.** 7.50.

Brackenrigg Inn with rm, CA11 0LP, (017684) 86206, *enquiries@brackenrigginn.co.uk, Fax (017684) 86945*, – rest, . **Meals** 9.95/16.95 **st.** and a la carte – **11 rm** 42.00/64.00 **st.** – SB.

VERSTON *Cumbria* 402 K 21 – *pop. 11 866.*

Coronation Hall, County Sq. (01229) 587120.
London 278 – Kendal 25 – Lancaster 36.

Trinity House without rest., 1 Princes St., LA12 7NB, off A 590 (01229) 587639, *trinityhousehotel@fitness.co.uk, Fax (01229) 588552* – **6 rm** 48.00/75.00 **st.**

Church Walk House without rest., Church Walk, LA12 7EW, (01229) 582211 – *closed 2 weeks Christmas-New Year* – **3 rm** 20.00/46.00 **st.**

Bay Horse with rm, Canal Foot, LA12 9EL, East : 2 ¼ m. by A 5087, turning left at Morecambe Tavern B&B and beyond Industrial area, on the coast (01229) 583972, *reservations@bayhorsehotel.co.uk, Fax (01229) 580502*, Morecambe bay – rest, *closed 2-6 January* – **Meals** (booking essential) (bar lunch Sunday and Monday) 17.75 **t.** (lunch) and a la carte 25.75/30.65 **t.** – **9 rm** (dinner included) 90.00/170.00 **t.**

IBERLEIGH *Devon* 403 I 31.

London 218 – Barnstaple 7 – Exeter 31 – Taunton 49.

Rising Sun Inn, EX37 9DU, on A 377 (01769) 560447, *risingsuninn@btinternet.com, Fax (01769) 560764* – rm, – 50. *closed 25 December* – **Meals** a la carte 13.40/21.40 **t.** – **9 rm** 40.00/77.00 **st.** – SB.

HOLLAND *Lancs.* 402 M 23 – *see Wigan.*

PER HARBLEDOWN SERVICE AREA *Kent – see Canterbury.*

PER QUINTON *Warks.* – *Stratford-upon-Avon.*

London 95 – Cheltenham 24 – Oxford 43 – Stratford-upon-Avon 6.

Winton House without rest., The Green, CV37 8SX, (01789) 720500, *gail@wintonhouse.com, Fax (0831) 485483*, « Victorian farmhouse », – **3 rm** 60.00 **t.**

PER SLAUGHTER *Glos.* 403 404 O 28 – *see Bourton-on-the-Water.*

PINGHAM *Rutland* 404 R 26 – *pop. 3 140.*

London 101 – Leicester 19 – Northampton 28 – Nottingham 35.

Rutland House without rest., 61 High St. East, LE15 9PY, (01572) 822497, *rutlandhouse@virgin.net, Fax (01572) 820065* – **5 rm** 34.00/44.00 **st.**

Lake Isle with rm, 16 High St. East, LE15 9PZ, (01572) 822951, *Fax (01572) 822951* – rest, **Meals** *(closed Monday lunch)* 19.50/26.50 **t.** (dinner) and lunch a la carte 11.70/17.20 **t.** 6.75 – **10 rm** 52.00/74.00 **t.**, 2 suites – SB.

Morcott Service Area *East : 4 ¼ m. by A 6003 on A 47 – Uppingham.*

Travelodge, Glaston Rd, LE15 8SA, (01572) 747719, *Fax (01572) 747719* – rm, **Meals** (grill rest.) – **40 rm** 39.95 **t.**

TON ST. LEONARDS *Glos. – see Gloucester.*

UPTON-UPON-SEVERN *Worcs.* 403 404 N 27 – *pop. 1 756.*
4 High St. (01684) 594200.
London 116 – Hereford 25 – Stratford-upon-Avon 29 – Worcester 11.

Welland Court without rest., WR8 0ST, West : 3 ¾ m. by A 4104 (01684) 5944 *wellandcourt@onetelnet.uk, Fax (01684) 594426,* ≤ The Malvern Hills, « Georgian ma house of 13C origins », – P.
closed 25 December – **3 rm** 47.50/75.00.

Tiltridge Farm without rest., Upper Hook Rd, WR8 0SA, West : 1 ½ m. by A 4104 Greenfields Rd off Hyde Lane (01684) 592906, *elgarwine@aol.com, Fax (01684) 594* « Part 17C farmhouse, working vineyard », – P
closed Christmas-New Year – **3 rm** 30.00/48.00 **s.**

at Welland Stone *Southwest : 3 ¼ m. by A 4104 – Upton-upon-Severn.*

Bridge House without rest., WR8 0RW, (01684) 593046, *Fax (01684) 593046* – P.
3 rm 35.00/60.00.

UTTOXETER *Staffs.* 402 403 404 O 25 *Great Britain G. – pop. 10 329.*
Env. : *Sudbury Hall★★ AC, E : 5 m. by A 518 and A 50.*
18 Wood Lane (01889) 566552 – 9 Manor (Kingstone), Leese Hill (01889) 563234.
London 145 – Birmingham 33 – Derby 19 – Stafford 13 – Stoke-on-Trent 16.

White Hart, Carter St., ST14 8EU, (01889) 562437, *white.hart.hotel@punchgroup.co.uk, Fax (01889) 565099* – rest, P – 50. VISA.
Meals (grill rest.) a la carte 11.35/21.35 **t.** – 7.00 – **21 rm** 49.00 **t.**

Travelodge, Ashbourne Rd, ST14 5AA, at junction of A 50 with B 5030 (01889) 562 *Fax (01889) 562043* – rm, rest, P. VISA JCB.
Meals (grill rest.) – **32 rm** 49.95 **t.**

at Doveridge *(Derbs.) Northeast : 2 ½ m. by Ashbourne rd (A 515) off A 50 – Ashbourne.*

Beeches with rm, Waldley, DE6 5LR, North : 2 m. by Waldley Rd (01889) 590288 *echesfa@aol.com, Fax (01889) 590559,* – P. VISA.
closed 23-26 December – **Meals** a la carte 18.45/32.45 **t.** 5.75 – **10 rm** 48.00/74.00

VALE *Guernsey (Channel Islands)* 403 O/P 33 – *see Channel Islands.*

VAZON BAY *Guernsey (Channel Islands)* 403 P 33 and 230 ⑨ – *see Channel Islands.*

VENTNOR *I.O.W.* 403 404 Q 32 – *see Wight (Isle of).*

VERYAN *Cornwall* 403 F 33 *The West Country G. – pop. 877 – Truro.*
See : *Village★.*
London 291 – St. Austell 13 – Truro 13.

Nare , Carne Beach, TR2 5PF, Southwest : 1 ¼ m. (01872) 501111, *office@narehotel.co.uk, Fax (01872) 501856,* ≤ Carne Bay, , , , heated, , , – P VISA
Meals 15.00/32.00 **t.** and a la carte 8.50 – **38 rm** (dinner included) 170.00/310.0 2 suites.

Crugsillick Manor , TR2 5LJ, West : 1 m. on St. Mawes rd (01872) 501214, *bars@adtel.co.uk, Fax (01872) 501228,* « Queen Anne manor house of Elizabethan origins » – rm, P. VISA
Meals (by arrangement) (communal dining) 25.00/32.00 **st.** 8.50 – **3 rm** 45 96.00 **st.**

at Ruan High Lanes *West : 1 ¼ m. on A 3078 – Truro.*

The Hundred House, TR2 5JR, (01872) 501336, *Fax (01872) 501151,* – VISA
March-October – **Meals** (dinner only) 25.00 **t.** – **10 rm** (dinner included) 72.00/142. – SB.

Wenn Sie ein ruhiges Hotel suchen,
benutzen Sie zuerst die Karte in der Einleitung
oder wählen Sie im Text ein Hotel mit dem Zeichen oder .

RGINSTOW *Devon* 403 H 31.

London 227 – Bideford 25 – Exeter 41 – Launceston 11 – Plymouth 33.

Percy's with rm, Coombeshead Estate, EX21 5EA, Southwest : 1 ¼ m. on Tower Hill rd ℘ (01409) 211236, *info@percys.co.uk, Fax (01409) 211275,* – P. MC AE VISA JCB
Meals (bar lunch) 22.50/28.50 **t.** 4.95 – **8 rm** 79.50/99.50 **t.** – SB.

ADDESDON *Bucks.* 404 R 28 *Great Britain G. – pop. 1 864 – ✉ Aylesbury.*

See : *Chiltern Hills★.*

Env. : *Waddesdon Manor★★, S : ½ m. by a 41 and minor rd – Claydon House★, N : by minor rd.*

London 51 – Aylesbury 5 – Northampton 32 – Oxford 31.

Five Arrows with rm, High St., HP18 0JE, ℘ (01296) 651727, *thefivearrows@netscapeonline.co.uk, Fax (01296) 658596,* – TV P. MC VISA.
Meals a la carte 18.05/27.10 **t.** 10.75 – **10 rm** 68.50/95.00 **t.**, 1 suite.

ADDINGTON *Lancs.* 402 M 22 – *see Clitheroe.*

AKEFIELD *W. Yorks.* 402 P 22 *Great Britain G. – pop. 73 955.*

Env. : *Nostell Priory★ AC, SE : 4½ m. by A 638.*

18 *City of Wakefield, Lupset Park, Horbury Rd ℘ (01924) 367442 – 18 28 Woodthorpe Lane, Sandal ℘ (01924) 255104 – 9 Painthorpe House, Painthorpe Lane, Crigglestone ℘ (01924) 255083.*

Town Hall, Wood St. ℘ (01924) 305000.

London 188 – Leeds 9 – Manchester 38 – Sheffield 23.

Cedar Court, Denby Dale Rd., Calder Grove, WF4 3QZ, Southwest : 3 m. on A 636 at junction 39 of M 1 ℘ (01924) 276310, *sales@cedarcourthotel.co.uk, Fax (01924) 280221,* – rm, rest, TV P – 400. MC AE VISA JCB
Meals (bar lunch Saturday) 12.50/18.50 **st.** – 9.95 – **146 rm** 95.00 **st.**, 5 suites – SB.

Posthouse Wakefield, Queen's Drive, Ossett, WF5 9BE, West : 2 ½ m. on A 638 ℘ (0870) 400 9082, *Fax (01924) 276437,* – rm, rest, TV P – 160. MC AE VISA JCB.
Meals 8.50/15.00 **st.** and a la carte 6.95 – 10.95 – **105 rm** 79.00 **st.** – SB.

Travel Inn, Denby Dale Rd, Thornes Park, WF2 8DY, West : ½ m. on A 636 ℘ (01924) 367901, *Fax (01924) 373620,* – rm, rest, TV P – 60. MC AE VISA.
Meals (grill rest.) – **42 rm** 40.95 **t.**

Aagrah, 108 Barnsley Rd, Sandal, WF1 5NX, South : 1 ¼ m. on A 61 ℘ (01924) 242222, *Fax (01924) 240562* – P. MC AE VISA JCB
closed 25 December – **Meals** - Indian - (booking essential) (dinner only) 13.00 **t.** and a la carte 8.95.

Newmillerdam *South : 3½ m. on A 61 – ✉ Wakefield.*

St. Pierre, Barnsley Rd, WF2 6QG, ℘ (01924) 255596, *enq@hotelstpierre.co.uk, Fax (01924) 252746,* – rest, TV P – 120. MC AE VISA.
Meals (bar lunch Saturday) 9.95/14.95 **st.** and a la carte 7.95 – 8.50 – **52 rm** 73.00/83.00 **st.**, 2 suites.

Midgley *Southwest : 6¼ m. by A 636 on A 637 – ✉ Wakefield.*

Midgley Lodge Motel without rest., Barr Lane, WF4 4JJ, ℘ (01924) 830069, *Fax (01924) 830087,* – TV P. MC AE VISA JCB.
closed 25 December – – 5.50 – **25 rm** 38.00/45.00 **t.**

ALBERTON *W. Sussex – see Arundel.*

ALKINGTON *East Riding* 402 S 22 – *see Beverley.*

ALLASEY *Mersey.* 402 403 K 23 – *pop. 15 642 – ✉ Wirral.*

18 *Wallasey, Bayswater Rd ℘ (0151) 639 3630.*

London 222 – Birkenhead 3 – Liverpool 4.

Grove House, Grove Rd, CH45 3HF, ℘ (0151) 639 3947, *Fax (0151) 639 0028* – TV P – 100. MC AE VISA.
Meals *(closed Bank Holidays)* 12.95/16.95 **t.** and a la carte – 5.95 – **14 rm** 49.50/90.00 **t.** – SB.

WALLINGFORD *Oxon.* 403 404 Q 29 *The West Country G. – pop. 9 315.*
Exc. : *Ridgeway Path★★.*
Town Hall, Market Pl. (01491) 826972.
London 54 – Oxford 12 – Reading 16.

at North Stoke *South : 2 ¾ m. by A 4130 and A 4074 on B 4009 – Wallingford.*

The Springs, Wallingford Rd, OX10 6BE, (01491) 836687, *info@thespringshotel.uk, Fax (01491) 836877,* ≤, « Lakeside setting », heated, 18, – 50. VISA JCB
Meals (carving lunch Sunday) 25.00 **t.** (dinner) and a la carte 15.00/18.50 **t.** 8.50 – **29** 95.00/170.00 **t.**, 2 suites – SB.

WALMERSLEY *Gtr. Manchester* 402 ㉒ 403 ③ 404 ⑨ *– see Bury.*

WALSALL *W. Mids.* 403 404 O 26 *– pop. 174 739.*
18 *Calderfields, Aldridge Rd (01922) 632243* **CT** – 18 *Broadway (01922) 613512.*
London 126 – Birmingham 9 – Coventry 29 – Shrewsbury 36.

Plan of enlarged area : see Birmingham pp. 4 and 5

Travel Inn, Bentley Green, Bentley Road North, WS2 0WB, West : 2 ¾ m. by A 454 a Bentley South rd (01922) 724485, *Fax (01922) 724098* – rm, rest, VISA **BT**
Meals (grill rest.) – **40 rm** 40.95 **t.**

WALTHAM *Kent* 404 X 30 *– pop. 397 – Canterbury.*
London 59 – Canterbury 12 – Folkestone 14 – Maidstone 24.

Beech Bank without rest., Duckpit Lane, CT4 5QA, East : 1 ¾ m. by Church L (01227) 700302, *Fax (01227) 700302,* « Converted 15C coach house », –
closed 23 December-2 January – **3 rm** 35.00/47.00 **s.**

WALTHAM ABBEY *Essex* 404 U 28 *– pop. 15 629.*
4 Highbridge St. (01992) 652295.
London 15 – Cambridge 44 – Ipswich 66 – Luton 30 – Southend-on-Sea 35.

Swallow (becoming a Marriott spring 2001), Old Shire Lane, EN9 3LX, Southeast : 1 ½ on A 121 (01992) 717170, *info@swallowhotels.com, Fax (01992) 711841,* rm, rest, – 220. VISA JCB
Meals 14.50/21.50 **st.** and a la carte 7.95 – **163 rm** 120.00/150.00 **st.** – SB.

WALTON LE DALE *Lancs.* 402 M 22 *– see Preston.*

WANSFORD *Peterborough* 404 S 26 *– see Peterborough.*

WANTAGE *Oxon.* 403 404 P 29 *– pop. 9 452.*
Vale and Downland Museum, 19 Church St. (01235) 760176.
London 71 – Oxford 16 – Reading 24 – Swindon 21.

Boar's Head, Church St., Ardington, OX12 8QA, East : 2 ½ m. by A 417 (01235) 8332 *Fax (01235) 833254,* – VISA JCB
closed 25 December and Sunday dinner – **Meals** a la carte 16.00/23.75 **t.** 4.75.

WARE *Herts.* 404 T 28 *– pop. 17 000.*
18 *Whitehill, Dane End (01920) 438495.*
London 24 – Cambridge 30 – Luton 22.

Marriott Hanbury Manor H. & Country Club, Thundridge, SG12 0SD, North : 1 ¾ by A 1170 on A 10 (01920) 487722, *Fax (01920) 487692,* ≤, « Jacobean style mans in extensive grounds, walled garden », 18, – rm, rest, 100. VISA JCB.
Vardon : **Meals** 20.00 **st.** and a la carte 19.50 – (see also ***Zodiac*** below) – 14.5 **125 rm** 130.00/260.00 **st.**, 9 suites – SB.

XXXX **Zodiac** (at Marriott Hanbury Manor H. & Country Club), Thundridge, SG12 0SD, North : m. by A 1170 on A 10 (01920) 487722, *Fax (01920) 487692* – VISA JCB
Meals 27.50/35.00 **st.** and a la carte 19.50.

REHAM *Dorset* 403 404 N 31 *The West Country G. – pop. 5 644.*

See : *Town★ – St. Martin's★★.*

Env. : *Blue Pool★ AC, S : 3 ½ m. by A 351 – Bovington Tank Museum★ AC, Woolbridge Manor★, W : 5 m. by A 352.*

Exc. : *Moreton Church★★, W : 9½ m. by A 352 – Corfe Castle★ (≤★★) AC, SE : 6 m. by A 351 – Lulworth Cove★, SW : 10 m. by A 352 and B 3070 – Bere Regis★ (St. John the Baptist Church★), NW : 6½ m. by minor rd.*

Trinity Church, South St. ☎ (01929) 552740.

London 123 – Bournemouth 13 – Weymouth 19.

Springfield Country H., Grange Rd, BH20 5AL, South : 1 ¼ m. by South St. and West Lane ☎ (01929) 552177, *enquiries@springfield-country-hotel.co.uk, Fax (01929) 551862,* heated, squash – rest, – 200. VISA JCB
Grange : **Meals** (bar lunch)/dinner 20.00/25.00 **t.** and a la carte 6.50 – ***Springers :*** **Meals** *(closed Sunday)* (dinner only) a la carte 11.95/17.00 **t.** 6.50 – **48 rm** 66.00/130.00 **t.** – SB.

Priory , Church Green, BH20 4ND, ☎ (01929) 551666, *reception@theprioryhotel.co.uk, Fax (01929) 554519,* ≤, « Part 16C priory, riverside gardens », – rest, VISA.
Meals a la carte 26.95/46.25 **t.** – **17 rm** 80.00/250.00 **t.**, 2 suites – SB.

Gold Court House, St. John's Hill, BH20 4LZ, ☎ (01929) 553320, *Fax (01929) 553320,* « Georgian house », –
closed 25 to 31 December – **Meals** (by arrangement winter only) (communal dining) 12.00 – **3 rm** 30.00/50.00.

REN MILL *Northd.* 401 402 O 17 – *see Bamburgh.*

RMINSTER *Wilts.* 403 404 N 30 *The West Country G. – pop. 16 379.*

Env. : *Longleat House★★★ AC, SW : 3 m.*

Exc. : *Stonehenge★★★ AC, E : 18 m. by A 36 and A 303 – Bratton Castle (≤★★) NE : 6 m. by A 350 and B 3098.*

Central Car Park ☎ (01985) 218548.

London 111 – Bristol 29 – Exeter 74 – Southampton 47.

Bishopstrow House, BA12 9HH, Southeast : 1 ½ m. on B 3414 ☎ (01985) 212312, *enquiries@bishopstrow.co.uk, Fax (01985) 216769,* ≤, « Georgian country house », heated, indoor/outdoor – rest, – 60. VISA JCB.
Meals 35.00 **t.** (dinner) and a la carte 15.50/28.50 **t.** 6.75 – 7.00 – **29 rm** 99.00/235.00 **t.**, 3 suites – SB.

Travelodge, BA12 7RU, Northwest : 1 ¼ m. by B 3414 at junction of A 36 and A 350 ☎ (01985) 21953, *Fax (01985) 214380* – rm, VISA JCB.
Meals (grill rest.) – **30 rm** 49.95 **t.**

Heytesbury *Southeast : 3 ¾ m. by B 3414 – ✉ Warminster.*

Angel Inn with rm, High St., BA12 0ED, ☎ (01985) 840330, *Fax (01985) 840931,* « 17C » – VISA
Meals a la carte 13.95/23.40 **t.** 7.95 – **8 rm** 30.00/65.00 **t.**

Crockerton *South : 1 ¾ m. by A 350 – ✉ Warminster.*

Springfield House, BA12 8AU, on Potters Hill rd ☎ (01985) 213696, *Fax (01985) 213696,* « Part 16C cottage », –
closed 25-26 December – **Meals** (by arrangement) (communal dining) 17.00 – **3 rm** 40.00/60.00.

RRINGTON *Warrington* 402 403 404 M 23 – *pop. 82 812.*

Hill Warren, Appleton ☎ (01925) 261620 – Walton Hall, Warrington Rd, Higher Walton ☎ (01925) 266775 – Birchwood, Kelvin Close ☎ (01925) 818819 – Leigh, Kenyon Hall, Culcheth ☎ (01925) 763130 – Alder Root, Alder Root Lane, Winwick ☎ (01925) 291919.

21 Rylands St. ☎ (01925) 442180.

London 195 – Chester 20 – Liverpool 18 – Manchester 21 – Preston 28.

Village H. and Leisure Club, Centre Park, WA1 1QA, ☎ (01925) 240000, *Fax (01925) 445240,* squash – rest, – 250. VISA.
Meals 12.95 **st.** (lunch) and a la carte 11.95/22.65 **st.** **89 rm** 89.00/116.00 **st.**

ENGLAND

Holiday Inn Garden Court, Woolston Grange Av., Woolston, WA1 4PX, East : 3 ¼ m A 57 on B 5210 at junction 21 of M 6 ☎ (01925) 838779, *Fax (01925) 838859* – |‡|, ⇔ rest, TV ☎ ♿ P. MC AE O VISA JCB
Meals 14.95 **st.** (dinner) and a la carte 17.15/25.85 **st.** ₰ 7.50 – ☐ 10.95 – **98 rm** 87.00 SB.

Travel Inn, 1430 Centre Park, Park Boulevard, WA1 1QA, ☎ (01925) 242 *Fax (01925) 244259* – |‡|, ⇔ rm, ▤ rest, TV ♿. MC AE O VISA. ⚘
Meals (grill rest.) – **42 rm** 40.95 **t.**

Travel Inn, Woburn Rd, WA2 8RN, North : 2 ¼ m. on A 49 ☎ (01925) 414 *Fax (01925) 414544* – ⇔ rm, ▤ rest, TV ♿ P. MC AE O VISA. ⚘
Meals (grill rest.) – **40 rm** 40.95 **t.**

at Stretton *South : 3½ m. by A 49 on B 5356 – ✉ Warrington.*

Park Royal International, Stretton Rd, WA4 4NS, ☎ (01925) 730706, *hotel@park-int.co.uk, Fax (01925) 730740,* ⚲, ⌂s, ⊡, ✂ – |‡|, ⇔ rm, ▤ rest, TV ☎ P – 🏔 400. MC O VISA JCB. ⚘
The Harlequin : **Meals** 10.45/19.95 **t.** and a la carte ₰ 6.85 – ☐ 9.50 – **137 rm** 101 111.50 **t.**, 3 suites – SB.

Premier Lodge, Tarporley Rd, WA4 4NB, ☎ (01925) 730451, *Fax (01925) 730709* – ⇔ ☎ ♿ P. MC AE O VISA. ⚘
Meals a la carte 8.95/16.35 **st.** – ☐ 6.00 – **29 rm** 42.00 **t.**

WARTLING *E. Sussex* 404 V 31 – *see Herstmonceux.*

WARWICK *Warks.* 403 404 P 27 *Great Britain G. – pop. 22 476.*

See : *Town★ – Castle★★ AC* Y – *Leycester Hospital★ AC* Y B – *Collegiate Church o Mary★ (Tomb★)* Y A.
Warwick Racecourse ☎ (01926) 494316 Y.
The Court House, Jury St. ☎ (01926) 492212.
London 96 – Birmingham 20 – Coventry 11 – Oxford 43.

Plan opposite

Old Fourpenny Shop, 27-29 Crompton St., CV34 6HJ, ☎ (01926) 491 *Fax (01926) 411892* – ⇔ TV ☎ P. MC AE O VISA JCB. ⚘ Y
Meals *(closed Sunday and dinner Monday to non-residents)* a la carte 14.45/26.45 **t.** ₰ – **11 rm** ☐ 39.50/69.50 **t.**

Charter House without rest., 87 West St., CV34 6AH, ☎ (01926) 496965, *penon@cha house8.freeserve.co.uk, Fax (01926) 411910,* « Part 15C », ⛆ – ⇔ TV P. MC O VISA ⚘ Y
closed 25-26 December – **3 rm** ☐ 49.50/80.00.

Park Cottage without rest., 113 West St., CV34 6AH, ☎ (01926) 410319, *parkcott@a m, Fax (01926) 410319,* « Part 16C » – ⇔ TV P. MC VISA. ⚘ Y
closed Christmas – **4 rm** ☐ 45.00/60.00 **s.**

Saffron, Unit 1, Westgate House, Market St., CV34 4DE, ☎ (01926) 402061 – ▤. MC A VISA Y
closed 25 December – **Meals** - Indian - (dinner only) a la carte 8.60/12.75 **t.**

at Barford *South : 3½ m. on A 429 – Z – ✉ Warwick.*

Glebe, Church St., CV35 8BS, on B 4462 ☎ (01926) 624218, *Fax (01926) 624625,* ⚲, ⊡, ⛆ – |‡|, ▤ rest, TV P – 🏔 120. MC AE O VISA
Meals 19.95 **t.** (dinner) and a la carte 20.40/29.40 **t.** – **38 rm** ☐ 95.00/115.00 **t.**, 1 su SB.

at Longbridge *Southwest : 2 m. on A 429 – Z – ✉ Warwick.*

Hilton Warwick, Stratford Rd, CV34 6RE, on A 429 at junction 15 of M ☎ (01926) 499555, *Fax (01926) 410020,* ⚲, ⌂s, ⊡ – |‡|, ⇔ rm, ▤ rest, TV ☎ ♿ 🏔 250. MC AE O VISA JCB. ⚘
Meals *(closed Saturday lunch)* 12.75 **st.** (lunch) and a la carte 17.70/34.95 **st.** – ☐ 11. **181 rm** 150.00/170.00 **st.** – SB.

Express by Holiday Inn without rest., Stratford Rd, CV34 6TW, on A 429 at junctio of M 40 ☎ (01926) 483000, *Fax (01926) 483033* – |‡| ⇔ ▤ TV ☎ ♿ P – 🏔 25. MC AE O JCB
117 rm 60.00 **st.**

at Sherbourne *Southwest : 2 ¾ m. by A 429 – Z – ✉ Warwick.*

Old Rectory, Vicarage Lane, CV35 8AB, at junction with A 46 ☎ (01926) 624 *Fax (01926) 624995,* ⛆ – ⇔ rest, TV P. MC O VISA JCB
Meals (dinner only) a la carte approx. 18.00 **st.** ₰ 5.00 – **14 rm** ☐ 35.00/75.00 **st.** – SB.

WARWICK ROYAL LEAMINGTON SPA

latton *Northwest : 3½ m. by A 425 on A 4177 –* **Z** *– ✉ Warwick.*

Northleigh House without rest., Five Ways Rd, CV35 7HZ, Northwest : 2½ m. by A 4177, turning left at roundabout with A 4141 ✆ (01926) 484203, *Fax (01926) 484006,* – TV P. MC VISA.
closed December and January – **7 rm** ☐ 35.00/60.00 **st.**

loniley *Northwest : 6¾ by A 425 on A 4177 –* **Z** *– ✉ Warwick.*

Honiley Court, CV8 1NP, on A 4177 ✆ (01926) 484234, *Fax (01926) 484474* – TV P – 200. MC AE VISA
Meals a la carte 18.10/27.90 **st.** – **62 rm** ☐ 90.00/100.00 **st.** – SB.

*Pour visiter une ville ou une région : utilisez les Guides Verts **Michelin**.*

WARWICK SERVICE AREA *Warks.* 404 P 27.
The Court House, Jury St. (01926) 492212.

Days Inn, Banbury Rd, Ashorn, CV35 0AA, M 40 (northbound) between junctions 12 13 (01926) 651681, Reservations (Freephone) 0800 0280400, *Fax (01926) 65163*
rm, TV P. MC AE VISA JCB
Meals (grill rest.) a la carte 8.60/13.90 **st.** – 7.45 – **54 rm** 49.00/54.00 **t.**

Days Inn, Banbury Rd, Ashorn, CV35 0AA, M 40 (southbound) between junctions 12 13 (01926) 651699, Reservations (Freephone) 0800 0280400, *Fax (01926) 6516C*
rm, TV P. MC AE VISA JCB
Meals (grill rest.) a la carte 8.60/13.90 **t.** – 7.45 – **40 rm** 49.00/54.00 **t.**

WASDALE HEAD *Cumbria* 402 K 20 – *Gosforth.*
London 324 – Kendal 72 – Workington 30.

Wasdale Head Inn, CA20 1EX, (019467) 26229, *wasdaleheadinn@msn.c*
Fax (019467) 26334, Wasdale Head, – rest, P. MC AE VISA JCB
Meals (bar lunch)/dinner 22.00 **st.** 7.50 – **13 rm** 45.00/90.00 **st.**

WASHINGBOROUGH *Lincs.* 402 404 S 24 – *see Lincoln.*

WASHINGTON *Tyne and Wear* 401 402 P 19 – *pop. 56 848.*
Washington Moat House, Stone Cellar Rd, Usworth (0191) 402 9988.
London 278 – Durham 13 – Middlesbrough 32 – Newcastle upon Tyne 7.

George Washington, Stone Cellar Rd, District 12, NE37 1PH, (0191) 402 9
Fax (0191) 415 1166, squash – TV P – 200. MC AE VISA
Meals 15.00/22.00 **st.** and a la carte 6.50 – 12.00 – **102 rm** 95.00/110.00 **st.**, 1 su
SB.

Posthouse Washington, Emerson, District 5, NE37 1LB, at junction of A 1(M) wi
195 (0870) 400 9084, *Fax (0191) 415 3371* – rm, TV P – 100. MC AE VISA
Meals 15.00 **t.** (dinner) and a la carte 19.35/28.85 **t.** 6.95 – 11.95 – **138 rm** 69
89.00 **st.** – SB.

WASHINGTON SERVICE AREA *Tyne and Wear* 401 402 P 19 – *Washington.*

Travelodge, DH3 2SJ, on A 1(M) (southbound carriageway) (0191) 410 3
Fax (0191) 410 0057 – TV P. MC AE VISA JCB.
Meals (grill rest.) – **36 rm** 49.95 **t.**

Travelodge, DH3 2SJ, on A 1(M) northbound carriageway (0191) 410 3
Fax (0191) 410 9258 – rm, TV P. MC AE VISA JCB.
Meals (grill rest.) – **31 rm** 49.95 **t.**

WASS *N. Yorks. – see Helmsley.*

WATERHEAD *Cumbria* 402 L 20 – *see Ambleside.*

WATERHOUSES *Staffs.* 402 403 404 O 24 *Great Britain G. – pop. 1 182 – Stoke-on-Trent.*
Env. : *Dovedale★★ (Ilam Rock★) E : 6 m. by A 523.*
London 115 – Birmingham 63 – Derby 23 – Manchester 39 – Stoke-on-Trent 17.

Old Beams (Wallis) with rm, Leek Rd, ST10 3HW, on A 523 (01538) 308
Fax (01538) 308157, – TV P. MC AE VISA.
closed January and 1 week September – **Meals** *(closed Sunday dinner and Monday)* (booking essential) (dinner only and Sunday lunch)/dinner a la carte 27.25/41.95 **t.** 9.50 – 6.50 – **5 rm** 65.00/120.00 **t.**
Spec. Tartare of tuna and prawns with oriental sauce. Seared sea bass and scallops, lentils and red wine sauce. Aberdeen Angus with wild mushrooms and rosemary rösti.

WATERINGBURY *Kent* 404 V 30 – *see Maidstone.*

WATERMILLOCK *Cumbria* 402 L 20 – *see Ullswater.*

WATER YEAT *Cumbria – see Coniston.*

TFORD Herts. 404 S 29 – pop. 113 080.

18 West Herts., Cassiobury Park ✆ (01923) 224264 – 9 Oxhey Park, Prestwick Rd, South Oxhey ✆ (01923) 248312, AT.

London 21 – Aylesbury 23.

Plan : see Greater London (North-West) p. 8

Hilton Watford, Elton Way, WD2 8HA, Watford Bypass, East : 3 ½ m. on A 41 at junction with B 462 ✆ (01923) 235881, *rm_watford@hilton.com, Fax (01923) 220836,* – rm, rest, – 375. AE VISA JCB BT e
Patio rest. : Meals *(closed dinner 25 December, lunch Saturday and Bank Holidays)* (carving rest.) (live music and dancing Saturday) a la carte 15.95/19.95 **st.** 6.95 – ***Patio Brasserie :*** Meals *(closed dinner 25 December, lunch Saturday and Bank Holidays)* 15.50/19.95 **st.** and a la carte 6.95 – 12.75 – **200 rm** 89.00/99.00 **st.**, 1 suite – SB.

TFORD GAP SERVICE AREA Northants. 403 404 Q 27 – ✉ Northampton.

Travel Inn without rest., NN6 7UZ, M 1 between junctions 16 and 17 ✆ (01327) 879001, *Fax (01327) 871333* – . AE VISA
closed Christmas and New Year – **36 rm** 40.95.

TH-IN-NIDDERDALE N. Yorks. – see Pateley Bridge.

AVERHAM Ches. 402 403 404 M 24 – pop. 6 604.

London 191 – Chester 15 – Liverpool 28 – Manchester 28.

Oaklands, Millington Lane, Gorstage, CW8 2SU, Southwest : 2 m. by A 49 ✆ (01606) 853249, *Fax (01606) 852419,* – – – 150. AE VISA.
Meals a la carte 16.00/20.00 **t.** – **11 rm** 55.00/75.00 **t.**

Tall Trees Lodge without rest., Tarporley Rd, Lower Whitley, WA4 4EZ, North : 2 ¾ m. on A 49 at junction with A 533 ✆ (01928) 790824, *bookings@talltreeslodge.co.uk, Fax (01928) 791330* – – 40. AE VISA
20 rm 43.00 **st.**

LLAND Worcs. 403 404 N 27 – see Great Malvern.

LLAND STONE Worcs. 403 404 N 27 – see Upton-upon-Severn.

LLINGBOROUGH Northants. 404 R 27 – pop. 41 602.

Library, Pebble Lane ✆ (01933) 276412.

London 73 – Cambridge 43 – Leicester 34 – Northampton 10.

Ibis without rest., Enstone Court, NN9 2DR, Southwest : 2 ½ m. by A 5128 (Northampton rd) on A 509 at junction with A 45 ✆ (01933) 228333, *Fax (01933) 228444* – – 25. AE VISA
78 rm 49.50 **st.**

Travel Inn, London Rd, NN8 2DP, Southeast : ¾ m. on A 5193 ✆ (01933) 278606, *Fax (01933) 275947* – rm, rest, . AE VISA
Meals (grill rest.) – **40 rm** 40.95 **t.**

inedon Northeast : 3½ m. by A 510 – ✉ Wellingborough.

Tudor Gate, High St., NN9 5JN, ✆ (01933) 680408, *info@tudorgate-hotel.co.uk, Fax (01933) 680745* – rest, – 45. AE VISA JCB
Meals 14.95/33.00 **t.** and a la carte 4.95 – **27 rm** 49.00/110.00 **t.** – SB.

LLINGTON Wrekin 402 403 404 M 25 – see Telford.

LLINGTON Somerset 403 K 31 – pop. 11 302.

London 176 – Barnstaple 42 – Exeter 32 – Taunton 10.

Bindon Country House, Langford Budville, TA21 0RU, Northwest : 4 ½ m. by B 3187 via Langford Budville village following signs for Wiveliscombe ✆ (01823) 400070, *bindonhouse@msn.com, Fax (01823) 400071,* « Part 17C country house with distinctive Flemish gables », heated, – – 45. AE VISA JCB.
The Wellesley : Meals 16.95/29.50 **t.** and a la carte 29.50/42.60 **t.** 10.00 – **12 rm** 85.00/185.00 **t.** – SB.

ENGLAND

ENGLAND

WELLS *Somerset* 403 404 M 30 *The West Country G.* – *pop. 9 763.*

See : *City*★★ – *Cathedral*★★★ – *Vicars' Close*★ – *Bishop's Palace*★ (<★★) *AC* – *St. Cuthbe*
Env. : *Glastonbury*★★ – *Abbey*★★ *(Abbot's Kitchen*★) *AC, St. John the Baptist*★★, *Some Rural Life Museum*★ *AC, Glastonbury Tor*★ (<★★★), *SW : 5 ½ m. by A 39 – Wookey Hc (Caves*★ *AC, Papermill*★), *NW : 2 m.*
Exc. : *Cheddar Gorge*★★ *(Gorge*★★, *Caves*★, *Jacob's Ladder* ✻★) – *St. Andrew's Churc NW : 7 m. by A 371 – Axbridge*★★ *(King John's Hunting Lodge*★, *St. John the Bap Church*★), *NW : 8½ m. by A 371.*
East Horrington Rd ℘ *(01749) 675005.*
Town Hall, Market Pl. ℘ *(01749) 672552.*
London 132 – Bristol 20 – Southampton 68 – Taunton 28.

The Market Place, BA5 2RW, ℘ (01749) 672616, *marketplace@bhere.co Fax (01749) 679670,* – TV P – 80. MC AE VISA
Meals *(closed Sunday lunch)* (booking essential) a la carte 13.00/23.70 **t.** 7.00 – **34** 84.50/99.50 **t.** – SB.

Swan, 11 Sadler St., BA5 2RX, ℘ (01749) 678877, *swan@bhere.co.uk, Fax (01749) 6776* rest, TV P – 150. MC AE VISA
Meals 13.95/24.00 **t.** and lunch a la carte 6.50 – **35 rm** 75.00/99.50 – SB.

Beryl , BA5 3JP, East : 1 ¼ m. by B 3139 off Hawkers Lane ℘ (01749) 678738, *stay@l l-wells.co.uk, Fax (01749) 670508,* <, « Victorian Gothic country house, antique furr ings », heated, , – TV P. MC VISA
closed 3 days Christmas – **Meals** *(closed Sunday)* (booking essential) (residents only) (c munal dining) (dinner only) 22.50 **st.** 6.00 – **7 rm** 50.00/95.00 **st.**

White Hart, Sadler St., BA5 2RR, ℘ (01749) 672056, *whitehart@wells.demon.co Fax (01749) 672056* – TV P – 60. MC AE VISA
Meals *(closed Sunday dinner)* (bar lunch Monday-Saturday)/dinner a la carte 12.45/18.9 – **13 rm** 57.50/80.00 **t.** – SB.

Infield House, 36 Portway, BA5 2BN, ℘ (01749) 670989, *infield@talk21.c Fax (01749) 679093,* – TV P. MC VISA
closed 1 week January and 1 week December – **Meals** (by arrangement) 12.70 **s.** – **3** 34.50/49.00.

Littlewell Farm, Coxley, BA5 1QP, Southwest : 1 ½ m. on A 39 ℘ (01749) 677914, TV P.
Meals (by arrangement) (communal dining) 21.00 **st.** 6.50 – **5 rm** 26.00/48.00 **st.**

Ritchers, 5A Sadler St., BA5 2RR, ℘ (01749) 679085, *ritcher@btinternet.co Fax (01749) 673866,* – MC VISA
closed 26 December and 1 January – **Meals** (booking essential) 8.50/18.50 **t.** 5.95.

at Wookey Hole *Northwest : 1 ¾ m. by A 371* – ✉ *Wells.*

Glencot House , Glencot Lane, BA5 1BH, ℘ (01749) 677160, *glencot@ukonline.cc Fax (01749) 670210,* « Victorian mansion built in Jacobean style », , , , – P – 40. MC AE VISA JCB
closed first week January – **Meals** (dinner only) 25.50/28.50 **t.** 9.95 – **13 rm** 64 104.00 **t.** – SB.

at Easton *Northwest : 3 m. on A 371* – ✉ *Wells.*

Beaconsfield Farm without rest., BA5 1DU, on A 371 ℘ (01749) 870308, *beaconsfi dial.pipex.com, Fax (01749) 870166,* – TV P.
Easter-mid November – **3 rm** 40.00/46.00 **st.**

at Priddy *Northwest : 6 ¼ m. by A 39* – ✉ *Wells.*

Highcroft without rest., Wells Rd, BA5 3AU, Southeast : 1 ¼ m. ℘ (01749) 673446, <, – P.
March-October – **4 rm** 25.00/40.00.

WELWYN *Herts.* 404 T 28 – *pop. 10 512 (inc. Codicote).*
London 31 – Bedford 31 – Cambridge 31.

Tewin Bury Farm, AL6 0JB, Southeast : 3 ½ m. by A 1000 on B 1000 ℘ (01438) 717 *hotel@tewinbury.co.uk, Fax (01438) 840440,* « Converted farm buildings », , rest, TV P – 70. MC AE VISA.
closed 24-26 December – **Meals** *(closed 24 December-1 January)* 17.95/19.50 **t.** ner) and a la carte 11.40/15.20 **t.** 6.50 – **25 rm** 84.00/99.00 **st.**

Die Preise — Einzelheiten über die in diesem Reiseführer angegebenen Preise finden Sie in der Einleitung.

ELWYN GARDEN CITY *Herts.* 404 T 28.

18, 9 *Panshanger Golf Complex, Old Herns Lane* ☎ *(01707) 333312.*
London 22 – Luton 21.

XXX **Auberge du Lac,** Brocket Hall, AL8 7XG, West : 3 m. by A 6129 on B 653 ☎ (01707) 368888, *aubergedulac@brocket-hall.co.uk, Fax (01707) 368898,* ≤, « Part 18C former hunting lodge in the grounds of Brocket Hall estate, lakeside setting », – P. MC AE VISA
closed Sunday dinner and Monday – **Meals** 25.00 **t.** (lunch) and a la carte 38.00/45.00 **t.** 14.00.

EM *Shrops.* 402 403 L 25 – *pop. 4 882* – ✉ *Shrewsbury.*
London 167 – Birmingham 50 – Chester 32 – Stoke-on-Trent 36 – Shrewsbury 8.

Soulton Hall, SY4 5RS, East : 2 m. on B 5065 ☎ (01939) 232786, *j.ashton@soultonhall.fsbusiness.co.uk, Fax (01939) 234097,* « Part 15C manor house », – TV P. MC AE VISA JCB.
Meals (booking essential) (dinner only) 22.50/28.50 **st.** and a la carte 6.00 – **5 rm** 34.50/95.00 **st.**, 1 suite – SB.

ENDLING *Norfolk* 404 W 25 – *see East Dereham.*

ENTBRIDGE *W. Yorks.* 402 404 Q 23 – ✉ *Pontefract.*
London 183 – Leeds 19 – Nottingham 55 – Sheffield 28.

Wentbridge House, Old Great North Rd, WF8 3JJ, ☎ (01977) 620444, *info@wentbridgehouse.co.uk, Fax (01977) 620148,* – TV P – 120. MC AE VISA JCB.
closed 25 December – **Meals** 12.50/23.00 **t.** and a la carte 8.75 – **18 rm** 72.50/110.00 **t.**

Per visitare una città o una regione : utilizzate le guide verdi ***Michelin.***

EOBLEY *Herefordshire* 403 L 27 – *pop. 1 076* – ✉ *Hereford.*
London 145 – Brecon 30 – Hereford 12 – Leominster 9.

Red Lion, HR4 8SE, ☎ (01544) 318220, *Fax (01544) 319075,* « 14C former inn » – TV P. MC VISA.
March-November – **Meals** (residents only) (dinner only) 19.50/25.00 **s.** – **5 rm** 42.50/65.00 **t.** – SB.

XX **The Salutation Inn** with rm, Market Pitch, HR4 8SJ, ☎ (01544) 318443, *info@salutationinn.com, Fax (01544) 318216,* « Part 13C former cider house » – TV P. MC AE VISA JCB.
Meals *(closed Sunday dinner and Monday lunch)* a la carte 16.05/27.85 **t.** 5.00 – **4 rm** 44.00/74.00 **t.** – SB.

EST BAGBOROUGH *Somerset* 403 K 30 – *see Taunton.*

EST BEXINGTON *Dorset* 403 404 M 31 – ✉ *Dorchester.*
London 150 – Bournemouth 43 – Bridport 6 – Weymouth 13.

Manor, Beach Rd, DT2 9DF, ☎ (01308) 897616, *themanorhotel@btconnect.com, Fax (01308) 897035,* ≤, – TV P. MC AE VISA.
Meals 15.95/20.95 **t.** 6.95 – **13 rm** 60.00/150.00 **t.** – SB.

EST BRIDGFORD *Nottingham* 403 404 Q 25 – *see Nottingham.*

EST BROMWICH *W. Mids.* 403 404 O 26 – *see Birmingham.*

EST BURTON *N. Yorks.* 402 O 21 – ✉ *Leyburn.*
London 260 – Carlisle 81 – Darlington 34 – Kendal 40 – Leeds 62 – York 58.

The Grange, DL8 4JR, ☎ (01969) 663348, – rm, TV P.
Meals (by arrangement) (communal dining) 15.00 **st.** 5.00 – **3 rm** 35.00/60.00 **st.** – SB.

STDEAN *E. Sussex* – *see Seaford.*

WEST DOWN *Devon* 403 H 30.

Env. : *Exmoor National Park★★ – Ilfracombe : Hillsborough (≤★★) AC, Capstone Hill★ (≤ St. Nicholas' Chapel (≤★) AC, N : 3 m. by A 361 and minor rd.*

London 221 – Exeter 52 – Taunton 59.

Long House, The Square, EX34 8NF, ☎ (01271) 863242, – .
March-October – **Meals** (by arrangement) 14.00 **st.** 4.00 – **3 rm** 30.00/52.00 **st.** – SB

WESTFIELD *E. Sussex* 404 V 31 – *pop. 2 461.*

London 66 – Brighton 38 – Folkestone 45 – Maidstone 30.

XX **The Wild Mushroom,** Woodgate House, Westfield Lane, TN35 4SB, Southwest : ½ on A 28 ☎ (01424) 751137, – P. VISA JCB
closed 3 weeks January, 1 week November, Monday, Sunday dinner and Bank Holiday
Meals (booking essential) 15.95/17.95 **st.** (lunch) and dinner a la carte 17.50/29.45 7.95.

WEST ILSLEY *Newbury* 403 404 Q 29 – *pop. 334* – ✉ *Newbury.*

London 56 – Oxford 21 – Reading 20 – Swindon 31 – Southampton 50.

Harrow Inn, RG20 7AR, ☎ (01635) 281260, *Fax (01635) 281139,* – VISA
closed dinner Sunday and Monday – **Meals** (booking essential) a la carte 21.40/27.2 10.95.

***Groß-London** (GREATER LONDON) besteht aus der City und 32 Verwaltungsbezirken (Borough). Diese sind wiederum in kleinere Bezirke (Area) unterteilt, deren Mittelpunkt ehemalige Dörfer oder Stadtviertel sind, die oft ihren eigenen Charakter bewahrt haben.*

WESTLETON *Suffolk* 404 Y 27 – *pop. 1 317* – ✉ *Saxmundham.*

London 97 – Cambridge 72 – Ipswich 28 – Norwich 31.

Crown, IP17 3AD, ☎ (01728) 648777, *reception@westletoncrown.co*
Fax (01728) 648239, – P. VISA JCB.
closed 25-26 December – **Meals** (bar lunch)/dinner 19.50 **t.** and a la carte 6.85 – **19** 69.50/157.00 **t.** – SB.

Pond House without rest., The Hill, IP17 3AN, ☎ (01728) 648773, – P.
closed 1 week Christmas – **3 rm** 46.00.

WEST LULWORTH *Dorset* 403 404 N 32 *The West Country G.* – *pop. 838* – ✉ *Wareham.*

See : *Lulworth Cove★.*

London 129 – Bournemouth 21 – Dorchester 17 – Weymouth 19.

Cromwell House, Main Rd, BH20 5RJ, ☎ (01929) 400253, *catriona@lulworthcove.co*
Fax (01929) 400566, ≤, heated, – rest, P. VISA JCB
closed 21 December-4 January – **Meals** (dinner only) 13.00 **t.** and a la carte 5.00 – **17** 29.50/71.00 **t.** – SB.

Gatton House without rest., Main Rd, BH20 5RU, ☎ (01929) 400252, *avril.mike@gatt ouse.co.uk, Fax (01929) 400252,* – P. VISA JCB
March-October – **8 rm** 40.00/65.00 **st.**

WEST MALLING *Kent* 404 V 30 – *pop. 2 479.*

18, 18 *Addington, Maidstone ☎ (01732) 844785.*

London 35 – Maidstone 7 – Royal Tunbridge Wells 14.

Travel Inn, Leybourne, ME19 5TR, Northeast : 1 m. on A 228 ☎ (01732) 521
Fax (01732) 521609 – rm, rest, P. VISA.
Meals (grill rest.) – **40 rm** 40.95 **t.**

Scott House without rest., 37 High St., ME19 6QH, ☎ (01732) 841380, *mail@scott-ho co.uk, Fax (01732) 522367,* « Part Georgian town house » – . VISA JCB.
closed Christmas-New Year – **3 rm** 49.00/69.00 **st.**

X **The Swan,** 35 Swan St., ME19 6JU, ☎ (01732) 521910, *Fax (01732) 522898,* , – VISA
Meals a la carte 13.20/27.50 **t.** 5.00.

WEST MONKTON *Somerset* 403 K 30 – *see Taunton.*

ESTON-SUPER-MARE *North Somerset* 403 K 29 *The West Country G. – pop. 69 372.*

See : *Seafront (≤★★)* **BZ**.

Exc. : *Axbridge★★ (King John's Hunting Lodge★, St. John the Baptist Church★) SE : 9 m. by A 371 –* **BY** *– and A 38 – Cheddar Gorge★★ (Gorge★★, Caves★, Jacob's Ladder ✲★) – Clevedon★ (≤★★, Clevedon Court★), NE : 10 m. by A 370 and M 5 – St. Andrew's Church★, SE : 10½ m. by A 371.*

Worlebury, Monks Hill ☎ (01934) 623214 **BY**.

Beach Lawns ☎ (01934) 888800.

London 147 – Bristol 24 – Taunton 32.

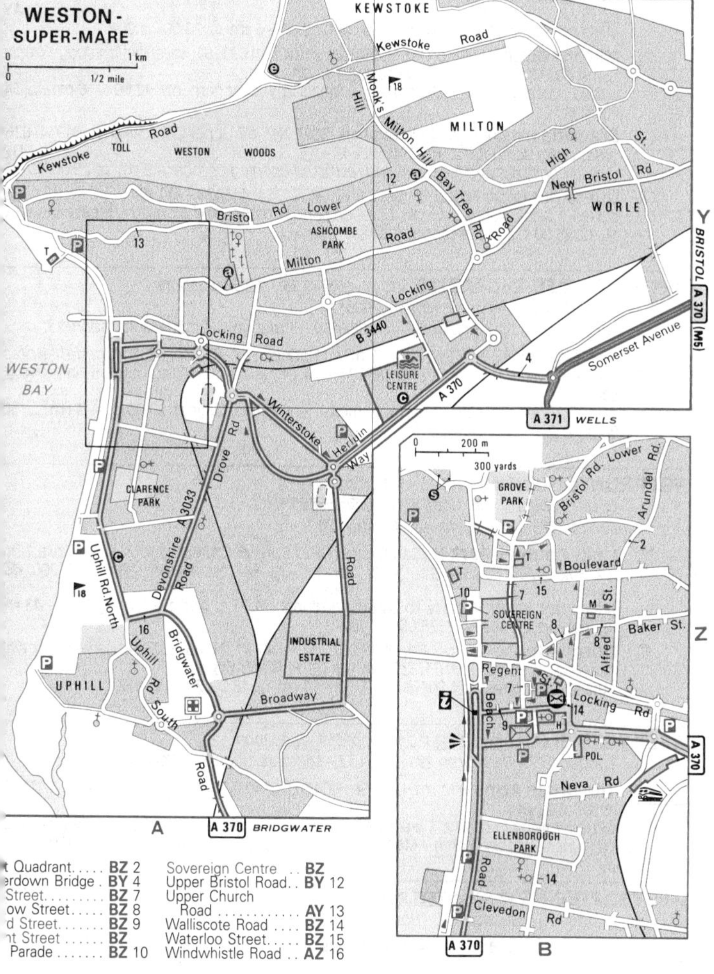

t Quadrant . . . . . **BZ** 2
erdown Bridge . **BY** 4
Street. . . . . **BZ** 7
ow Street. . . . . **BZ** 8
d Street. . . . . . . **BZ** 9
nt Street . . . . . . **BZ**
Parade . . . . **BZ** 10

Sovereign Centre . . **BZ**
Upper Bristol Road. . **BY** 12
Upper Church Road . . . . **AY** 13
Walliscote Road . . . . **BZ** 14
Waterloo Street. . . . . **BZ** 15
Windwhistle Road . . **AZ** 16

Beachlands, 17 Uphill Road North, BS23 4NG, ☎ (01934) 621401, *info@beachlandshotel.com, Fax (01934) 621966,* ≋, ⛶, ⛱ – ⚟ rest, TV P – 🏋 60. MC AE VISA JCB. ✂
closed 24 December-5 January – **Meals** (bar lunch Monday to Saturday)/dinner 17.50/19.50 **t.** 🍷 7.25 – **24 rm** ☕ 49.50/85.00 **t.** – SB. **AZ** **c**

ENGLAND

Commodore, Beach Rd, Sand Bay, Kewstoke, BS22 9UZ, by Kewstoke rd (01934) 415778, *Fax (01934) 636483* – 120. AY
Meals (bar lunch Monday to Saturday)/dinner a la carte 16.00/21.00 **t.** 5.95 – 19 60.00/95.00 **t.** – SB.

Queenswood, Victoria Park, BS23 2HZ, off Upper Church Rd (01934) 416141, *queenswood.hotel@btinternet.com, Fax (01934) 621759* – rest, *closed 13 December-8 January* – **Meals** (bar lunch)/dinner 16.50 – **17 rm** 48.00/80.00 BZ

Travel Inn, Hutton Moor Rd, BS22 8LY, East : 1 ½ m. by A 370 (01934) 622 *Fax (01934) 627401*, – rm, BY
Meals (grill rest.) – **60 rm** 40.95 **t.**

Ashcombe Court, 17 Milton Rd, BS23 2SH, (01934) 625104, *Fax (01934) 625104* – AY
March-October – **Meals** (by arrangement) 10.00 – **6 rm** 28.00/44.00.

Milton Lodge, 15 Milton Rd, BS23 2SH, (01934) 623161, *valler@miltonlodge.freeserve.co.uk, Fax (01934) 623210* – rest, AY
closed November and December – **Meals** (by arrangement) 12.00 – **6 rm** 34 48.00 **st.**

Braeside without rest., 2 Victoria Park, BS23 2HZ, off Upper Church Rd (01934) 626 *braeside@tesco.net, Fax (01934) 626642* – BZ
closed Christmas and New Year and restricted opening October – **9 rm** 25.00/50.00

Duets, 103 Upper Bristol Rd, BS22 8ND, (01934) 413428 – BY
closed 1 week March, 2 weeks October, Sunday dinner and Monday – **Meals** (dinner c 16.95/25.00 **t.** and a la carte 8.50.

WESTON-UNDER-REDCASTLE *Shrops.* 402 M 25 – *Shrewsbury.*
18, 18 *Hawkstone Park (01939) 200611.*
London 178 – Birmingham 58 – Chester 30 – Stoke-on-Trent 30 – Shrewsbury 13.

The Citadel, SY4 5JY, East : ½ m. on Hodnet rd (01630) 685204, *griffiths@citac 00.freeserve.co.uk, Fax (01630) 685204*, « Castellated Georgian house », –
April-October – **Meals** (by arrangement) (communal dining) 20.00 **s.** – **3 rm** 50 80.00 **s.**

WEST RUNTON *Norfolk* 404 X 25 – *Cromer.*
9 *Links Country Park Hotel (01263) 838383.*
London 135 – King's Lynn 42 – Norwich 24.

Links Country Park H., Sandy Lane, NR27 9QH, (01263) 838383, *sales@links_hot .uk, Fax (01263) 838264*, 9, – rest, rest, – 200.
Meals (bar lunch Monday to Saturday)/dinner 21.75 **t.** and a la carte 6.25 – **43 rm** (dinner included) 80.00/175.00 **t.** – SB.

Dormy House, Cromer Rd, NR27 9QA, on A 149 (01263) 837537, *jjjarvis@dormyhotel.co.uk, Fax (01263) 837537*, –
Meals (carving rest.) 11.90/13.75 5.50 – **14 rm** 48.00/76.00 **t.** – SB.

WEST TANFIELD *N. Yorks.* 402 P 21 – *pop. 551* – *Ripon.*
London 237 – Darlington 29 – Leeds 32 – Middlesbrough 39 – York 36.

The Bruce Arms with rm, Main St., HG4 5JJ, (01677) 470325, *Fax (01677) 470796*
closed 1 week in spring, 1 week in autumn, Sunday dinner, Monday and Tuesday-Wednesday lunch October-March – **Meals** a la carte 15.70/23.25 **t.** – **3 rm** 35.00/50.00 **t.**

WEST WITTERING *W. Sussex* 404 R 31 – *pop. 2 750.*
London 76 – Brighton 37 – Portsmouth 24 – Southampton 37.

Home Farm House without rest., Elms Lane, PO20 8LW, (01243) 514252,
3 rm 33.00/65.00 **s.**

Halten Sie beim Betreten des Hotels oder des Restaurants den Führer in der Hand.
Sie zeigen damit, daß Sie aufgrund dieser Empfehlung gekommen sind

EST WITTON *N. Yorks.* 402 O 21 – *pop. 325* – ✉ *Leyburn.*
London 241 – Kendal 39 – Leeds 60 – York 53.

Wensleydale Heifer Inn, Main St., DL8 4LS, ☎ (01969) 622322, *heifer@daelnet.co.uk, Fax (01969) 624183,* « Part 17C », – TV P. MC AE ① VISA JCB
Meals (bar lunch)/dinner 24.50 **t.** – **14 rm** 60.00/98.00 **t.** – SB.

Ivy Dene, DL8 4LP, ☎ (01969) 622785, *Fax (01969) 622785,* – TV P.
closed 24-26 December – **Meals** (by arrangement) 16.00 – **5 rm** 35.00/52.00 – SB.

ETHERAL *Cumbria* 401 402 L 19 – *see Carlisle.*

ETHERBY *W. Yorks.* 402 P 22 *Great Britain G.* – *pop. 8 154.*
Env. : *Harewood House★★ (The Gallery★) AC, SW : 5½ m. by A 58 and A 659.*
18 *Linton Lane, Linton ☎ (01937) 580089.*
Council Offices, 17 Westgate ☎ (01937) 582151.
London 208 – Harrogate 8 – Leeds 13 – York 14.

Wood Hall , Trip Lane, Linton, LS22 4JA, Southwest : 3 m. by A 661 and Linton Rd ☎ (01937) 587271, *woodhall@arcadianhotels.co.uk, Fax (01937) 584353,* ≤, « Part Jacobean and Georgian country house in park », , , , – , rest, TV P – 140. MC AE ① VISA
Meals *(closed Saturday lunch)* 15.95/24.95 **t.** and dinner a la carte 9.95 – 12.50 – **42 rm** 90.00/125.00 **t.** – SB.

Linton Springs , Sicklinghall Rd, LS22 4AF, West : 1 ¾ m. by A 661 ☎ (01937) 585353, *info@lintonsprings.co.uk, Fax (01937) 587579,* , , – TV P – 70. MC AE ① VISA.
The Gun Room : **Meals** *(closed Sunday dinner)* (dinner only and Sunday lunch)/dinner a la carte 17.30/24.10 **t.** 5.65 – **11 rm** 75.00/95.00 **st.**, 1 suite.

ETHERSFIELD *Essex* 404 V 28 – *pop. 1 204* – ✉ *Braintree.*
London 52 – Cambridge 31 – Chelmsford 19 – Colchester 22.

Dicken's, The Green, CM7 4BS, ☎ (01371) 850723, *Fax (01371) 850723,* « Part 17C house » – P. MC VISA
closed 24-26 December, 1 January, Sunday dinner, Monday, Tuesday and Bank Holidays – **Meals** a la carte 19.45/27.75 **t.**

YBRIDGE *Surrey* 404 S 29 – *pop. 52 802 (inc. Walton).*
London 23 – Crawley 27 – Guildford 17 – Reading 33.

Oatlands Park, Oatlands Drive, KT13 9HB, Northeast : ¾ m. by A 317 on A 3050 ☎ (01932) 847242, *oatlandspark@btinternet.com, Fax (01932) 842252,* , 9, , , – , rm, TV P – 300. MC AE ① VISA
Meals 21.00/26.00 **st.** and a la carte 7.50 – 13.50 – **134 rm** 120.00/185.00 **st.**, 3 suites.

The Ship, Monument Green, High St., KT13 8BQ, off A 317 ☎ (01932) 848364, *info@ship-hotel.weybridge.com, Fax (01932) 857153* – rest, rest, TV P – 150. MC AE ① VISA JCB.
Meals 13.75/19.75 **t.** and a la carte 6.50 – 11.50 – **39 rm** 121.00/150.00 **st.** – SB.

Casa Romana, 2 Temple Hall, Monument Hill, KT13 8RH, on A 317 ☎ (01932) 843470, *Fax (01932) 854221* – P. MC AE ① VISA JCB
closed 25-26 December, Saturday lunch and Bank Holidays – **Meals** - Italian - 14.95/18.95 **t.** and a la carte 10.95.

YMOUTH *Dorset* 403 404 M 32 *The West Country G.* – *pop. 46 065.*
See : *Town★ – Timewalk★ AC – Nothe Fort (≤★) AC – Boat Trip★ (Weymouth Bay and Portland Harbour) AC.*
Env. : *Chesil Beach★★ – Portland★ - Portland Bill (★★) S : 2½ m. by A 354.*
Exc. : *Maiden Castle★★ (≤★) N : 6 ½ m. by A 354 – Abbotsbury★★ (Swannery★ AC, Sub-Tropical Gardens★ AC, St. Catherine's Chapel★) NW : 9 m. by B 3157.*
18 *Links Rd ☎ (01305) 773981.*
to Guernsey (St. Peter Port) and Jersey (St. Helier) (Condor Ferries Ltd).
The King's Statue, The Esplanade ☎ (01305) 785747.
London 142 – Bournemouth 35 – Bristol 68 – Exeter 59 – Swindon 94.

Moonfleet Manor , DT3 4ED, Northwest : 4 ½ m. by B 3157 ☎ (01305) 786948, *info@moonfleetmanor.com, Fax (01305) 774395,* ≤, « Special facilities for children », , , , , squash – rest, TV P – 60. MC AE ① VISA
Meals (bar lunch Monday to Saturday)/dinner 22.50 **st.** and a la carte – **37 rm** 90.00/150.00 **st.**, 2 suites – SB.

Rex, 29 The Esplanade, DT4 8DN, ☎ (01305) 760400, *Fax (01305) 760500,* ≤ – |♦| TV
MC AE ① VISA
closed Christmas – **Meals** (bar lunch)/dinner 12.25 **t.** and a la carte – **31 rm** ⊐ 55.
98.00 **t.** – SB.

Bay Lodge, 27 Greenhill, DT4 7SW, ☎ (01305) 782419, *barbara@baylodge.co*
Fax (01305) 782828 – ⇎ rest, TV P. MC AE ① VISA JCB
Meals (booking essential) (dinner only) a la carte 12.45/16.45 **st.** 3.75 – **12 rm** ⊐ 49.
68.00 **st.** – SB.

Travel Inn, Greenhill, DT4 7SX, East : ½ m. on A 353 ☎ (01303) 767
Fax (01303) 768113 – ⇎ rm, TV ♿ P. MC AE ① VISA. ✻
Meals (grill rest.) – **40 rm** 40.95 **t.**

Chatsworth, 14 The Esplanade, DT4 8EB, ☎ (01305) 785012, *dave@chatsworth.frees*
.co.uk, Fax (01305) 766342, ≤, – TV. MC VISA. ✻
Meals 15.00 **st.** 4.00 – **8 rm** ⊐ 35.00/70.00 **st.** – SB.

Bay View without rest., 35 The Esplanade, DT4 8DH, ☎ (01305) 782
Fax (01305) 782083, ≤ – TV P. MC ① VISA. ✻
February-early November – **8 rm** ⊐ 40.00/60.00 **s.**

Perry's, The Old Harbour, 4 Trinity Rd, DT4 8TJ, ☎ (01305) 785799, *Fax (01305) 7857*
MC AE VISA
closed 25-26 December, 1 January, lunch Monday and Saturday and Sunday dinner in wi
– **Meals** a la carte 16.45/24.25 **t.** 6.65.

WHALLEY *Lancs.* 402 M 22 – *pop. 5 364* – ✉ *Blackburn.*

Long Leese Barn, Clerkhill ☎ (01254) 822236.

London 233 – Blackpool 32 – Burnley 12 – Manchester 28 – Preston 15.

Clarion H. Foxfields, Whalley Rd, Billington, BB7 9HY, Southwest : 1 ¼
☎ (01254) 822556, *admin@gbo65.u-net.com, Fax (01254) 824613,* Fø, ≘s, ⊠, –
rest, TV ♿ P – 180. MC AE ① VISA JCB
***Expressions :* Meals** (bar lunch Saturday and Bank Holidays) (dancing Saturday even
11.40/19.50 **t.** and a la carte 7.50 – **18 rm** ⊐ 97.00/104.00 **t., 26 suites** 117.00 **t.** – SB

WHASHTON *N. Yorks. – see Richmond.*

WHEATLEY *Oxon.* 403 404 Q 28 – *see Oxford.*

WHEELOCK *Ches. – see Sandbach.*

WHIMPLE *Devon* 403 J 31 – *see Exeter.*

WHITBY *N. Yorks.* 402 S 20 *Great Britain G.* – *pop. 13 640.*

See : *Abbey*★.

18 Sandsend Rd, Low Straggleton ☎ (01947) 602768.

Langborne Rd ☎ (01947) 602674.

London 257 – Middlesbrough 31 – Scarborough 21 – York 45.

Bagdale Hall, 1 Bagdale, YO21 1QL, ☎ (01947) 602958, *Fax (01947) 820714,* « Part 1
– ⇎ rest, TV P. MC AE ① VISA. ✻
Meals (dinner only and Sunday lunch)/dinner a la carte 15.70/25.70 **t.** 6.50 – 1
⊐ 45.50/98.00 **st.**

Crescent House, 6 East Cres., YO21 3HD, ☎ (01947) 600091, *Fax (01947) 600091,*
⇎ TV. ✻
mid March-mid November – **Meals** (by arrangement) 9.50 **s.** – **6 rm** ⊐ 40.00/44.00 **s.**

at Sleights *Southwest : 3 m. by A 171 and A 169 –* ✉ *Whitby.*

The Lawns, 73 Carr Hill Lane, Briggswath, YO21 1RS, North : ½ m. by B
☎ (01947) 810310, *thelortons@tesco.net, Fax (01947) 810310,* ≤, – ⇎ TV P. ✻
restricted opening in winter – **Meals** (by arrangement) – **3 rm** ⊐ 25.00/50.00 **t.**

at Dunsley *West : 3 ¼ m. by A 171 –* ✉ *Whitby.*

Dunsley Hall ⛰, YO21 3TL, ☎ (01947) 893437, *reception@dunsleyhall.c*
Fax (01947) 893505, ≤, ≘s, ⊠, , ✂ – ⇎ TV P. MC AE VISA
Meals 15.95/25.95 **st.** and a la carte 9.95 – **18 rm** ⊐ 69.85/129.70 **t.** – SB.

WHITEPARISH *Wilts.* 403 404 P 30 – *see Salisbury.*

HITEWELL *Lancs.* 402 M 22 – *pop. 5 617* – ✉ *Clitheroe.*
London 281 – Lancaster 31 – Leeds 55 – Manchester 41 – Preston 13.

Inn at Whitewell, Forest of Bowland, BB7 3AT, ☎ (01200) 448222, *Fax (01200) 448298,* ≤, « Memorabilia », 🐟, 🌳 – TV P. MC AE ⓓ VISA. ✂
Meals (bar lunch)/dinner a la carte 15.50/24.55 **st.** 🍷 8.00 – **14 rm** ☕ 60.00/94.00 **st.**, 1 suite.

HITLEY *W. Yorks.* 402 P 23 – *see Dewsbury.*

HITLEY *Wilts.* – *see Melksham.*

HITLEY BAY *Tyne and Wear* 401 402 P 18 – *pop. 33 335.*
ℹ *Park Rd* ☎ *(0191) 200 8535.*
London 295 – Newcastle upon Tyne 10 – Sunderland 10.

Windsor, South Parade, NE26 2RF, ☎ (0191) 251 8888, *info@windsor-hotel.demon.co.uk, Fax (0191) 297 0272* – |♦|, ▤ rest, TV P. MC AE ⓓ VISA. ✂
Meals *(closed Sunday)* (bar lunch)/dinner 14.75 **t.** and a la carte – **63 rm** ☕ 70.00/75.00 **t.**

Bay's Bistro, 183 Park View, NE26 3RE, ☎ (0191) 251 3567, *Fax (0191) 251 8688* – ▤. MC VISA
closed 25-26 December, Saturday lunch, Sunday dinner and Monday – **Meals** 11.95 **t.** (lunch) and a la carte 15.15/26.40 **t.** 🍷 6.20.

HITNEY-ON-WYE *Herefordshire* 403 K 27 – *pop. 133* – ✉ *Hereford.*
London 150 – Birmingham 56 – Cardiff 73 – Hereford 17.

Rhydspence Inn, HR3 6EU, West : 1 ½ m. on A 438 ☎ (01497) 831262, *Fax (01497) 831751,* « Part 14C », 🌳 – TV P. MC AE VISA. ✂
closed 2 weeks January and 25 December – **Meals** a la carte 21.25/36.95 **t.** 🍷 5.75 – **7 rm** ☕ 37.50/75.00 **t.** – SB.

HITSTABLE *Kent* 404 X 29 – *pop. 28 907* – ✉ *Whitstable.*
ℹ *7 Oxford St.* ☎ *(01227) 275482.*
London 68 – Dover 24 – Maidstone 37 – Margate 12.

Continental, 29 Beach Walk, CT5 2BP, East : ½ m. by Sea St. and Harbour St. ☎ (01227) 280280, *Fax (01227) 280257,* ≤, 🍴 – ⊁ rm, TV P. MC AE ⓓ VISA. ✂
Meals (bar lunch Monday to Friday)/dinner a la carte 15.20/23.90 **t.** 🍷 6.50 – **23 rm** ☕ 45.00/125.00 **t.**

Travel Inn, Thanet Way, CT5 3BD, Southwest : 2 m. by A 290 ☎ (01227) 272459, *Fax (01227) 263151* – ⊁ rm, TV ♿ P. MC AE ⓓ VISA. ✂
Meals (grill rest.) – **40 rm** 40.95 **t.**

Windyridge 🐦, Wraik Hill, CT5 3BY, Southwest : 2 m. off A 290 ☎ (01227) 263506, *Fax (01227) 771191,* ≤, 🌳 – ⊁ rest, TV P. MC VISA
closed 23 December-1 February – **Meals** (by arrangement) 15.00 – **10 rm** ☕ 30.00/50.00.

Whitstable Oyster Fishery Co., Royal Native Oyster Stores, The Horsebridge, CT5 1BU, ☎ (01227) 276856, *Fax (01227) 770666,* ≤, « Converted warehouse on beach » – MC AE ⓓ VISA JCB
closed 25-26 December, Sunday dinner September-May and Monday – **Meals** - Seafood - a la carte 26.95/38.95 **t.** 🍷 7.00.

Thanet Way Service Area *Southwest : 3 ¼ m. by A 290 on A 299* – ✉ *Faversham.*

Travelodge, ME13 9EL, (eastbound carriageway) ☎ (01227) 770980, *Fax (01227) 281135* – ⊁ rm, TV ♿ P. MC AE ⓓ VISA JCB. ✂
Meals (grill rest.) – **40 rm** 39.95 **t.**

HITTLE-LE-WOODS *Lancs.* 402 M 23 – *see Chorley.*

HITWELL-ON-THE-HILL *N. Yorks.* 402 R 21 – *pop. 136* – ✉ *York.*
London 240 – Kingston-upon-Hull 47 – Scarborough 29 – York 13.

The Stone Trough Inn, Kirkham Abbey, YO60 7JS, East : 1 m. ☎ (01653) 618713, *info@stonetroughinn.co.uk, Fax (01653) 618819,* 🍴 – P. MC VISA
closed 25 December and Monday – **Meals** a la carte 17.50/24.20 **t.**

CK *South Gloucestershire* 403 404 M 29 – *see Bristol.*

WICKFORD *Essex* 404 V 29 – *see Basildon.*

WICKHAM *Hants.* 403 404 Q 31 – *pop. 2 941.*
London 74 – Portsmouth 12 – Southampton 11 – Winchester 16.

The Old House, The Square, PO17 5JG, ✆ (01329) 833049, *enq@theoldhotel.co* *Fax (01329) 833672,* « Queen Anne house », – rest, TV P. MC AE VISA JCB. *closed 26 December-3 January* – **Meals** *(closed Monday lunch and Sunday)* 18 and a la carte 9.25 – 5.00 – **9 rm** 65.00/100.00 **t.** – SB.

WIDNES *Halton* 402 403 404 L 23 – *pop. 57 162.*
Highfield Rd ✆ (0151) 424 2440.
London 205 – Liverpool 15 – Manchester 27 – Stoke-on-Trent 42.

Everglades Park, Derby Rd, WA8 3UJ, Northeast : 3 m. by A 568 on A 5 ✆ (0151) 495 2040, *reserv@evergladesparkhotel.co.uk, Fax (0151) 424 6536* – rest, TV P – 200. MC AE VISA.
Meals (bar lunch)/dinner a la carte 14.00/25.50 **t.** 5.50 – **65 rm** 65.00/90.00 **st.** – SB

at Cronton *Northwest : 2 m. by A 568 on A 5080 – ✉ Widnes.*

Hillcrest, Cronton Lane, WA8 9AR, ✆ (0151) 424 1616, *Fax (0151) 495 1348* – , TV P – 120. MC AE VISA
Meals (bar lunch)/dinner 14.95 **t.** and a la carte 8.25 – **50 rm** 67.00/125.00 **st.** – SB

***Le Grand Londres** (GREATER LONDON) est composé de la City et de 32 arrondissements administratifs (Borough) eux-mêmes divisés en quartiers ou en villages ayant conservé leur caractère propre (Area).*

WIGAN *Gtr. Manchester* 402 M 23 – *pop. 85 819.*
Trencherfield Mill, Wallgate ✆ (01942) 825677.
London 203 – Liverpool 22 – Manchester 24 – Preston 18.

The Bellingham, 149 Wigan Lane, WN1 2NB, North : 1 ¼ m. on A 49 ✆ (01942) 243 *Fax (01942) 821027* – TV P – 100. MC AE VISA.
Meals *(closed Sunday dinner)* (bar lunch)/dinner a la carte 10.00/17.00 **t.** – **32 rm** 59 89.50 **t.** – SB.

Quality H. Wigan, Riverway, WN1 3SS, access by Orchard St. ✆ (01942) 826888, *adm gb058.u-net.com, Fax (01942) 825800* – , rm, TV P – 200. MC AE VISA JCB.
Meals 16.95 **st.** (dinner) and a la carte 11.50/19.50 **st.** 5.00 – **88 rm** 87.00/97.00 s SB.

Travel Inn, Warrington Rd, Marus Bridge, WN3 6XB, South : 2 ¾ m. on A ✆ (01942) 493469, *Fax (01942) 498679* – rm, TV P. MC AE VISA
Meals (grill rest.) – **41 rm** 40.95 **t.**

Travel Inn, Orrell Rd, Orrell, WN5 8HQ, West : 3 ½ m. on A 577 ✆ (01942) 211 *Fax (01942) 215002* – TV P – 80. MC AE VISA.
Meals (grill rest.) – **40 rm** 40.95 **t.**

at Up Holland *West : 4 ¾ m. on A 577 – ✉ Wigan.*

Quality H. Skelmersdale, Prescott Rd, WN8 9PU, Southwest : 2 ¾ m. by A 577 Stannanought Rd ✆ (01695) 720401, *admin@gb656.u_net.com, Fax (01695) 509* rm, rest, TV P – 200. MC AE VISA
Meals 9.50/16.75 **st.** and a la carte 8.95 – 9.95 – **55 rm** 75.00/120.00 **st.** – SB.

WIGHT (Isle of) 403 404 PQ 31 32 *Great Britain G.* – *pop. 124 577.*
See : *Island*★★.
Env. : *Osborne House, East Cowes*★★ *AC* – *Carisbrooke Castle, Newport*★★ *AC (Keep* *Brading*★ *(Roman Villa*★ *AC, St. Mary's Church*★, *Nunwell House*★ *AC)* – *Shorwell Peter's Church*★ *(wall paintings*★*).*
from East Cowes to Southampton (Red Funnel Ferries) frequent services daily (1 from Yarmouth to Lymington (Wightlink Ltd) frequent services daily (30 mn) – from bourne to Portsmouth (Wightlink Ltd) frequent services daily (35 mn).
from Ryde to Portsmouth (Hovertravel Ltd) frequent services daily (10 mn) – from to Portsmouth (Wightlink Ltd) frequent services daily (15 mn) – from West Cowe Southampton (Red Funnel Ferries) frequent services daily (22 mn).

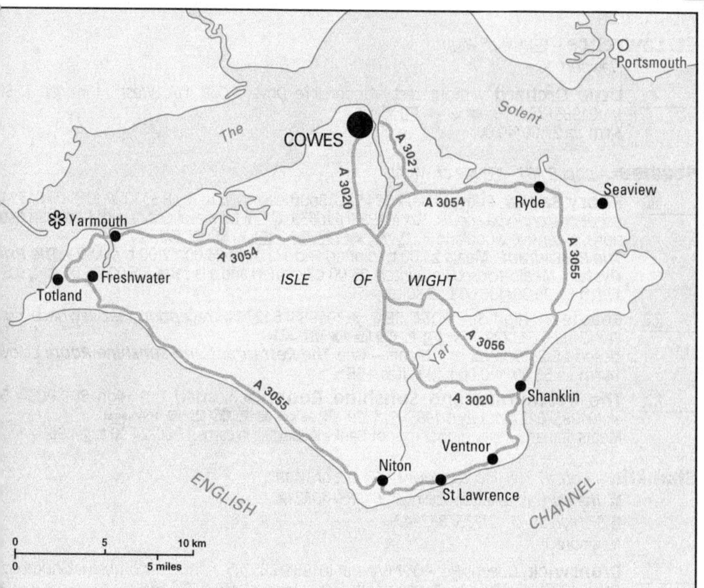

eshwater – *pop. 7 317 (inc. Totland)* – ✉ *Isle of Wight.*
Newport 13.

Sandpipers, Coastguard Lane, Freshwater Bay, PO40 9QX, South : 1 ½ m. by A 3055 ✆ (01983) 753634, *sandpipers@fatcattrading.demon.co.uk, Fax (01983) 755966,* – TV P. MC VISA
Meals (bar lunch Monday-Saturday)/dinner 17.95 **t.** and a la carte – **14 rm** 28.95/65.00 – SB.

Rockstone Cottage, Colwell Chine Rd, PO40 9NR, Northwest : ¾ m. by A 3055 off A 3054 ✆ (01983) 753723, *enquiries@rockstonecottage.co.uk, Fax (01983) 753721,* – TV P.
Meals (by arrangement) 14.00 **st.** – **5 rm** 37.00/54.00 **s.**

Red Lion, Church Pl., PO40 9BP, via Hooke Hill ✆ (01983) 754925, *Fax (01983) 754925,* , « Part 14C » – P. MC VISA JCB
closed 25 December – **Meals** a la carte 12.95/24.90 **t.**

ton – ✉ *Isle of Wight.*

Windcliffe Manor, Sandrock Rd, Undercliffe, PO38 2NG, ✆ (01983) 730215, *enquiries@windcliffe.co.uk, Fax (01983) 730215,* heated, – rest, TV P. MC AE VISA JCB
Meals (light lunch Monday to Saturday)/dinner a la carte approx. 20.00 **t.** 5.85 – **14 rm** (dinner included) 67.50/130.00 **t.** – SB.

de – ✉ *Isle of Wight.*
Binstead Rd ✆ (01983) 614809.
81-83 Union St. ✆ (01983) 562905.
Newport 7.

Biskra Beach, 17 St. Thomas's St., PO33 2DL, ✆ (01983) 567913, *info@biskrahotel.com, Fax (01983) 616976,* ←, – TV P. MC AE VISA
Meals a la carte 18.50/23.00 **t.** 6.50 – **14 rm** 57.50/140.00 **t.**

Little Upton Farm without rest., Gatehouse Rd, Ashey, PO33 4BS, Southwest : 2 m. by West St. ✆ (01983) 563236, *Fax (01983) 563236,* ←, « 17C farmhouse, working farm », – TV P.
3 rm 25.00/50.00.

St. Lawrence – ✉ *Isle of Wight.*
Newport 16.

Little Orchard without rest., Undercliffe Drive, PO38 1YA, West : 1 m. on A 30
(01983) 731106, – TV P.
3 rm 27.00/40.00.

Seaview – *pop. 2 181* – ✉ *Isle of Wight.*

Priory Bay, Priory Drive, PO34 5BU, Southeast : 1 1/2 m. by B 3330 (01983) 61314
eception@priorybay.co.uk, Fax (01983) 616539, « Medieval priory with Georgian exte-
sions, extensive woodland », , 9, , , – TV P. MC AE VISA.
The Restaurant : **Meals** 23.00 **t.** (dinner) and a la carte 23.00/32.00 **t.** 9.50 – ***The Prio***
Oyster : **Meals** *(closed in winter)* 25.00 **t.** (dinner) and a la carte 25.00/35.00 **t.** 9.50
17 rm 99.00/196.00 **t.**, 2 suites – SB.

Seaview, High St., PO34 5EX, (01983) 612711, *reception@seaviewhotel.co*
Fax (01983) 613729 – TV P. MC AE VISA JCB
closed 25-26 December – **Meals** – (see ***The Restaurant and Sunshine Room*** below
14 rm 55.00/120.00 **t.**, 2 suites – SB.

The Restaurant and Sunshine Room (at Seaview H.), High St., PO34 5
(01983) 612711, *Fax (01983) 613729*, – P. MC AE VISA JCB
Meals (in bar Sunday dinner except Bank Holidays) a la carte 17.00/24.50 **t.** 4.95.

Shanklin – *pop. 17 305 (inc. Sandown)* – ✉ *Isle of Wight.*
18 *The Fairway, Lake Sandown (01983) 403217.*
67 High St. (01983) 862942.
Newport 9.

Brunswick, Queens Rd, PO37 6AN, (01983) 863245, *enquiries@brunswick-hotel.co*
Fax (01983) 868398, , heated, , – rest, TV P. MC VISA
February-October – **Meals** (residents only) (dinner only) a la carte approx. 14.00 **st.** 5.0
35 rm 35.00/88.00 **st.** – SB.

Bourne Hall, Luccombe Rd, PO37 6RR, (01983) 862820, *bhch@dialstark.*
Fax (01983) 865138, , heated, , , – rest, TV P. MC AE.
mid February-mid November – **Meals** (bar lunch)/dinner a la carte 16.50/24.00 **t.** 5.5
30 rm 50.00/82.40 – SB.

Foxhills, 30 Victoria Av., PO37 6LS, (01983) 862329, *info@foxhillshotel.co*
Fax (01983) 866666, , – TV P. MC VISA.
Meals (residents only Monday) 10.50/18.00 **st.** 4.25 – **8 rm** 44.00/68.00 **st.** – SB.

Rylstone Manor, Rylstone Gdns., PO37 6RG, (01983) 862806, *rylstone@dialsta*
et, « Part Victorian », – TV P. MC AE VISA.
Meals (dinner only) 17.50 **t.** 6.50 – **8 rm** 39.00/78.00 **t.**

Grange Bank, Grange Rd, PO37 6NN, (01983) 862337, *grangebank@netguides.co*
Fax (01983) 862737 – TV P.
Easter-October – **Meals** (booking essential) (residents only) (dinner only) (unlicensed) 7.5
– **9 rm** 26.00/52.00 – SB.

Totland – *pop. 7 317 (inc. Freshwater)* – ✉ *Isle of Wight.*
Newport 13.

Sentry Mead, Madeira Rd, PO39 0BJ, (01983) 753212, *sentrymead.co*
Fax (01983) 753212, – TV P. MC VISA JCB
closed 22 December-2 January – **Meals** (bar lunch)/dinner 17.00 **t.** 6.00 – **14 rm** 40
80.00 **t.**

Ventnor – *pop. 5 978* – ✉ *Isle of Wight.*
9 *Steephill Down Rd (01983) 853326.*
34 High St. (01983) 853625 (summer only).
Newport 10.

Royal, Belgrave Rd, PO38 1JJ, (01983) 852186, *royalhotel@zetnet.co*
Fax (01983) 855395, , – TV P – 40. MC AE VISA
closed 5-22 January – **Meals** (light lunch Monday to Saturday)/dinner 27.50/37.50 **t.**
– **54 rm** 90.00/180.00 **t.**, 1 suite – SB.

Winterbourne, Bonchurch, PO38 1RQ, via Bonchurch Shute (01983) 852
Fax (01983) 853056, « Country house ≤ gardens and sea », heated – rest, TV P
AE VISA
April-October – **Meals** (dinner only) 17.95 **t.** 7.95 – **14 rm** (dinner included) 59
155.00 **t.**

Lake ⛭, Shore Rd, Bonchurch, PO38 1RF, ✆ (01983) 852613, *mich@lakehouse.co.uk*, – ⊭ TV P.
March-October – **Meals** (dinner only) 10.00 **st.** 4.50 – **20 rm** 28.00/60.00 **st.** – SB.

armouth – ✉ *Isle of Wight.*
Newport 10.

The George, Quay St., PO41 0PE, ✆ (01983) 760331, *res@thegeorge.co.uk, Fax (01983) 760425*, ≤, « 17C former governor's residence », – ⊭ rm, ▤ rest, TV ✆. MC AE VISA JCB
The Restaurant*: Meals** *(closed Sunday and Monday)* (booking essential) (dinner only) 45.00 **t.** 6.95 – (see also ***The Brasserie below) – **16 rm** 105.00/205.00 **t.**, 1 suite – SB
Spec. Trio of duck tastings. Millefeuille of red mullet and braised pork skin, artichoke and wild mushrooms. Trio of chocolate desserts on a raspberry sauce.

The Brasserie (at The George H.), Quay St., PO41 0PE, ✆ (01983) 760331, *Fax (01983) 760425*, – MC AE VISA JCB
Meals 18.95/24.50 **t.** (lunch) and a la carte 27.25/30.85 **t.** 6.95.

IGSTON *Leics.* 402 403 404 Q 26 – *see Leicester.*

ILLERBY *East Riding* 402 S 22 – *see Kingston-upon-Hull.*

ILLERSEY HILL *Glos.* 403 404 O 27 – *see Broadway (Worcestershire).*

ILLESLEY *Glos.* 403 404 N 29 – *see Tetbury.*

ILLITON *Somerset* 403 K 30 *The West Country G.* – *pop. 2 025* – ✉ *Taunton.*
Env. : *Exmoor National Park*★★ – *Cleeve Abbey*★★ *AC, W : 2 m. by A 39.*
London 177 – Minehead 8 – Taunton 16.

White House, 11 Long St., TA4 4QW, ✆ (01984) 632306 – ⊭ rest, TV P. ✻
24 May-4 November – **Meals** (dinner only) 32.00 **t.** 8.50 – **10 rm** 49.00/132.00 **t.** – SB.

Curdon Mill ⛭, Lower Vellow, TA4 4LS, Southeast : 2 ½ m. by A 358 on Stogumber rd ✆ (01984) 656522, *curdonmill@compuserve.com, Fax (01984) 656197*, ≤, « Converted water mill on working farm », heated, – ⊭ TV P. MC AE VISA. ✻
closed Christmas and New Year – **Meals** *(closed Monday lunch and Sunday dinner)* (booking essential to non-residents) 24.00 **st.** (dinner) and lunch a la carte 12.00/21.50 **st.** 4.45 – **6 rm** 40.00/70.00 **st.** – SB.

ILMCOTE *Warks.* 403 404 O 27 – *see Stratford-upon-Avon.*

ILMINGTON *Devon* 403 K 31 – *see Honiton.*

ILMINGTON *East Sussex* 404 U 31 – *see Eastbourne.*

ILMSLOW *Ches.* 402 403 404 N 24 – *pop. 28 604.*
18 *Great Warford, Mobberley* ✆ *(01565) 872148.*
London 189 – Liverpool 38 – Manchester 12 – Stoke-on-Trent 27.

Stanneylands, Stanneylands Rd, SK9 4EY, North : 1 m. by A 34 ✆ (01625) 525225, *enquiries@stanneylandshotel.co.uk, Fax (01625) 537282*, « Gardens » – ⊭ rm, TV ♿ P – 100. MC AE VISA. ✻
Meals – (see ***The Restaurant*** below) – 10.50 – **31 rm** 88.00/118.00 **st.** – SB.

Manchester Airport Moat House, Oversley Ford, Altrincham Rd, SK9 4LR, Northwest : 2 ¾ m. on A 538 ✆ (01625) 889988, *Fax (01625) 531876*, , , , squash – , ⊭ rm, TV ♿ P – 300. MC AE VISA. ✻
Meals a la carte 18.00/24.00 **st.** – 11.50 – **126 rm** 99.00 **st.** – SB.

Premier Lodge, Racecourse Rd, SK9 5LR, West : 1 m. by A 538 ✆ (01625) 525849, *Fax (01625) 548382* – ⊭, ▤ rest, TV ✆ ♿ P. MC AE VISA. ✻
Meals (grill rest.) 10.95 **st.** and a la carte – 5.95 – **37 rm** 46.00 **st.**

The Restaurant (at Stanneylands H.), Stanneylands Rd, SK9 4EY, North : 1 m. by A 34 ✆ (01625) 525225, *Fax (01625) 537282*, « Gardens » – ▤ P. MC AE VISA
Meals *(closed Sunday dinner)* 13.50/32.00 **st.** and a la carte 8.50.

Bank Square, 4-6 Bank Sq., SK9 1AN, ✆ (01625) 539754 – ▤. MC AE VISA
closed Sunday – **Meals** (booking essential) 10.00/15.00 **st.** and a la carte 6.00.

at Handforth *North : 3 m. on A 34 – ✉ Wilmslow.*

Belfry House, Stanley Rd, SK9 3LD, ✆ (0161) 437 0511, *office@belfryhousehot* *Fax (0161) 499 0597* – |♦|, ⇹ rm, TV ✆ P – 180. MC AE D VISA. ✻
Meals (dancing Friday and Saturday evening) 17.95/19.95 **st.** and a la carte 9.50 – **74 r** 79.00/89.00 **st.**, 2 suites – SB.

WIMBORNE MINSTER *Dorset* 403 404 O 31 *The West Country G. – pop. 15 274.*
See : *Town★ – Minster★ – Priest's House Museum★ AC.*
Env. : *Kingston Lacy★★ AC, NW : 3 m. by B 3082.*
29 High St. ✆ (01202) 886116.
London 112 – Bournemouth 10 – Dorchester 23 – Salisbury 27 – Southampton 30.

Beechleas, 17 Poole Rd, BH21 1QA, ✆ (01202) 841684, *beechleas@hotmail.co.* *Fax (01202) 849344,* « Georgian town house » – ⇹ rest, TV P. MC AE D VISA JCB
closed 24 December-15 January – **Meals** (lunch by arrangement) 15.75/22.75 **t.** 5.95 **9 rm** 69.00/109.00 **t.** – SB.

Les Bouviers, Oakley Hill, Merley, BH21 1RJ, South : 1 ¼ m. on A 349 ✆ (01202) 88955 *nfo@lesbouviers.co.uk, Fax (01202) 889555* – P. MC AE D VISA JCB
closed first week January, Saturday lunch and Sunday dinner – **Meals** 9.95/24.95 and a la carte 8.95.

Groß-London (GREATER LONDON) besteht aus der City und 32 Verwaltungsbezirken (Borough). Diese sind wiederum in kleinere Bezirke (Area) unterteilt, deren Mittelpunkt ehemalige Dörfer oder Stadtviertel sind, die oft ihren eigenen Charakter bewahrt haben.

WINCHCOMBE *Glos.* 403 404 O 28 – *pop. 4 243.*
Town Hall, High St. ✆ (01242) 602925.
London 100 – Birmingham 43 – Gloucester 26 – Oxford 43.

Isbourne Manor House without rest., Castle St., GL54 5JA, ✆ (01242) 6022 *Fax (01242) 602281,* « Part Georgian and Elizabethan manor house », – ⇹ TV P. ✻
closed Easter and Christmas – **3 rm** 40.00/75.00 **st.**

Sudeley Hill Farm without rest., GL54 5JB, East : 1 m. by Castle ✆ (01242) 602344, *scudamore4@aol.com, Fax (01242) 602344,* ←, « Part 15C house, wo ing farm », – ⇹ TV P. ✻
closed Christmas – **3 rm** 30.00/50.00 **st.**

Westward , Sudeley Lodge, GL54 5JB, East : 1 ½ m. by Castle St. on Sudeley Lod Parks/Farm rd ✆ (01242) 604372, *jimw@haldon.co.uk, Fax (01242) 602206,* ←, ⇹ rm, TV P. MC VISA
closed December-early January – **Meals** (by arrangement) (communal dining) 22.50 4.00 – **3 rm** 45.00/85.00 **s.**

Wesley House with rm, High St., GL54 5LJ, ✆ (01242) 602366, *enquiries@wesleyhous o.uk, Fax (01242) 602405,* « Part 15C » – ⇹ TV. MC AE VISA. ✻
closed 14 January-12 February and Sunday dinner – **Meals** 8.95/28.50 **st.** 8.50 – **6** 35.00/80.00 **st.** – SB.

WINCHELSEA *E. Sussex* 404 W 31 *Great Britain G.*
See : *Town★ – St. Thomas Church (effigies★).*
London 64 – Brighton 46 – Folkestone 30.

The Strand House without rest., Tanyard's Lane, TN36 4JT, East : ¼ m. on A ✆ (01797) 226276, *strandhouse@winchelsea.freeserve.co.uk, Fax (01797) 224806,* « P 14C and 15C », – ⇹ TV P. MC VISA JCB. ✻
closed Christmas and New Year – **10 rm** 34.00/68.00 **st.**

WINCHESTER *Hants.* 403 404 P 30 *Great Britain G. – pop. 36 121.*
See : *City★★ - Cathedral★★★ AC* B – *Winchester College★ AC* B B – *Castle Great Hall★* B *God Begot House★* B A.
Env. : *St. Cross Hospital★★ AC* A.
Guildhall, The Broadway ✆ (01962) 840500.
London 72 – Bristol 76 – Oxford 52 – Southampton 12.

WINCHESTER

esford Road . . . . **A** 2
dover Road . . . . **B** 3
reweeke Road . . . . **A** 5
idge Street . . . . **B** 6
oadway (The) . . . . **B** 7
ooks Shopping Centre . . . . . **B** 8
ilbolton Avenue . . . . **A** 9
City Road . . . . **B** 10
Clifton Terrace . . . . **B** 12
East Hill . . . . **B** 15
Eastgate Street . . . . **B** 16
Easton Lane . . . . **A** 18
Friarsgate . . . . **B** 19
High Street . . . . **B**
Kingsgate Road . . . . **A** 22
Magdalen Hill . . . . **B** 23
Middle Brook Street . . . . **B** 24
Park Road . . . . **A** 26
St. George's Street . . . . **B** 32
St. Paul's Hill . . . . **B** 33
St. Peter's Street . . . . **B** 34
Southgate Street . . . . **B** 35
Stoney Lane . . . . **A** 36
Stockbridge Road . . . . **B** 37
Sussex Street . . . . **B** 38
Union Street . . . . **B** 39
Upper High Street . . . . **B** 40

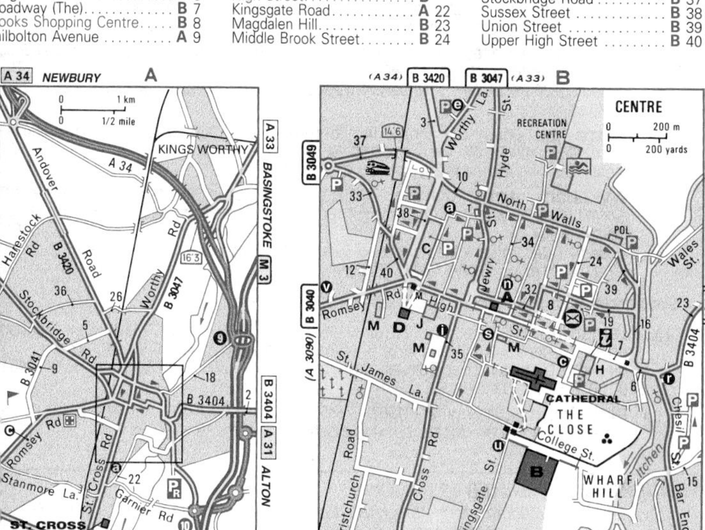

Wessex, Paternoster Row, SO23 9LQ, (0870) 400 8126, *wessex@wessexhotel.co.uk, Fax (01962) 841503,* – rest, – 100. VISA — B c
William Walker **:** Meals 10.95/23.00 **t.** and a la carte – 13.95 – **93 rm** 125.00/145.00 **st.**, 1 suite – SB.

Hotel du Vin, 14 Southgate St., SO23 9EF, (01962) 841414, *admin@winchester.hoteld uvin.co.uk, Fax (01962) 842458,* « Georgian town house, wine themed interior », – – 30. VISA. — B i
Meals – (see ***Bistro*** below) – 11.50 – **22 rm** 89.00/125.00 **t.**, 1 suite.

Royal, St. Peter St., SO23 8BS, (01962) 840840, *info@the.royal.com, Fax (01962) 841582,* – rest, – 100. VISA JCB — B n
Meals 7.50/16.50 **t.** (lunch) and a la carte 21.50/27.50 **t.** 6.00 – 11.75 – **75 rm** 87.50/120.00 **st.** – SB.

Winchester Moat House, Worthy Lane, SO23 7AB, (01962) 709988, *Fax (01962) 840862,* – rest, – 200. VISA JCB. — B e
Meals *(closed lunch Saturday and Sunday)* a la carte 16.25/22.75 **st.** – 10.50 – **71 rm** 106.00/123.00 **st.**

Dawn Cottage without rest., Romsey Rd, SO22 5PQ, (01962) 869956, *Fax (01962) 869956,* – VISA JCB. — A c
3 rm 47.00/60.00 **s.**

East View without rest., 16 Clifton Hill, SO22 5BL, (01962) 862986, – VISA. — B v
closed Christmas and New Year – **3 rm** 40.00/50.00 **st.**

Portland House without rest., 63 Tower St., SO23 8TA, (01962) 865195, *tony@knight world.com, Fax (01962) 865195* – . — B a
closed 25 December – **4 rm** 48.00/55.00 **s.**

Florum House, 47 St. Cross Rd, SO23 9PS, (01962) 840427, *florum.house@barclays.ne t, Fax (01962) 862287,* – VISA — A a
closed 24-27 December – **Meals** (by arrangement) 14.80 **st.** – **9 rm** 48.00/63.00 **st.** – SB.

Chesil Rectory (Storey), Chesil St., SO23 8HU, ✆ (01962) 851555, *Fax (01962) 86970* B
« 15C » – MC AE VISA JCB
closed 1 week in summer, 24 December-4 January, Sunday and Monday – **Meals** 20.0
34.00 **t.** 8.95
Spec. Jerusalem artichoke soup with seared scallops wrapped in pancetta. Fillet of po with black pudding and spinach. Lemon curd soufflé, raspberry sorbet.

Nine The Square, 9 Great Minster St., The Square, SO23 9HA, ✆ (01962) 8640 B
Fax (01962) 879586 – MC AE VISA
closed 25-26 December, 1 January, 1 week January and Sunday – **Meals** a la carte 20.7
28.70 **st.**

Bistro (at Hotel du Vin), 14 Southgate St., SO23 9EF, ✆ (01962) 84141 B
Fax (01962) 842458, – P. MC AE VISA
Meals (booking essential) a la carte 26.40/31.65 **t.** 9.95.

Wykeham Arms with rm, 75 Kingsgate St., SO23 9PE, ✆ (01962) 85383 B
Fax (01962) 854411, « Characterful 18C inn, memorabilia », – rm, TV
MC AE VISA.
closed 25 December – **Meals** *(closed Sunday)* (booking essential) a la carte 20.95/22.50
7.95 – **13 rm** 45.00/97.50 **t.**, 1 suite.

at Sparsholt *Northwest : 3½ m. by B 3049* – **A** – ✉ *Winchester.*

Lainston House, SO21 2LT, ✆ (01962) 863588, *Fax (01962) 776672*, ≤, « 17C man house, gardens and parkland », – rest, TV P – 80. MC AE VISA JCB
Meals 17.00 **t.** (lunch) and dinner a la carte approx. 45.00 **t.** 12.50 – 13.00 – **40 r**
95.00/265.00 **t.**, 1 suite – SB.

Plough Inn, SO21 2NW, ✆ (01962) 776353, *Fax (01962) 776400*, – P. MC VISA
closed 25 December – **Meals** (booking essential) a la carte 15.20/25.85 **t.**

WINDERMERE *Cumbria* 402 L 20 *Great Britain G.* – *pop. 6 847.*

Env. : *Lake Windermere*★★ – *Brockhole National Park Centre*★ *AC, NW : 2 m. by A 591.*
Victoria St. ✆ *(015394) 46499.*
London 274 – Blackpool 55 – Carlisle 46 – Kendal 10.

Plan opposite

Langdale Chase, LA23 1LW, Northwest : 3 m. on A 591 ✆ (015394) 322
Fax (015394) 32604, ≤ Lake Windermere and mountains, « Victorian country house lakeside setting, carvings and artefacts », – rest, rest, TV P. MC AE
VISA JCB.
Meals 14.95/28.00 **t.** and a la carte 7.00 – **27 rm** (dinner included) 65.00/180.00
1 suite – SB.

Holbeck Ghyll, Holbeck Lane, LA23 1LU, Northwest : 3 ¼ m. by A 5
✆ (015394) 32375, *accommodation@holbeck_ghyll.co.uk*, *Fax (015394) 34743*, ≤ Lake W dermere and mountains, « Victorian former hunting lodge, gardens », –
P. MC AE VISA JCB
Meals 19.50/42.50 **t.** 10.95 – **19 rm** (dinner included) 125.00/300.00 **t.**, 1 suite – SB
Spec. Roast quail with onion compote, truffle jus. Roast sea bass with sweet pepper a fennel bouillon. Biscuit glacé with exotic fruit.

Cedar Manor, Ambleside Rd, LA23 1AX, ✆ (015394) 43192, *cedarmanor@fsbdial.co.*
Fax (015394) 45970, – rest, TV P. MC VISA Y
Meals (dinner only) 13.00/18.50 **st.** and a la carte 7.00 – **12 rm** (dinner includ
42.00/84.00 **t.**

Glenburn, New Rd, LA23 2EE, ✆ (015394) 42649, *Fax (015394) 88998* – TV P. MC
JCB. Y
Meals (dinner only) 16.50 5.75 – **16 rm** 35.00/65.00 **st.** – SB.

Woodlands without rest., New Rd, LA23 2EE, ✆ (015394) 43915, *Fax (015394) 4391*
TV P. MC VISA. Y
closed 5 days at Christmas – **14 rm** 29.00/80.00 **st.** – SB.

Beaumont without rest., Holly Rd, LA23 2AF, ✆ (015394) 47075, *thebeaumonthotel@ nternet.com*, *Fax (015394) 47075* – TV P. MC VISA JCB. Y
10 rm 35.00/90.00 **t.**

Glencree without rest., Lake Rd, LA23 2EQ, ✆ (015394) 45822, *h.butterworth@btinter .com*, *Fax (015394) 45822* – TV P. MC VISA Z
closed January-February – **6 rm** 30.00/60.00 **st.**

Fir Trees without rest., Lake Rd, LA23 2EQ, ✆ (015394) 42272, *firtreeshotel@email.ms om*, *Fax (015394) 42272* – TV P. MC AE VISA JCB. Z
7 rm 35.00/60.00 **st.**

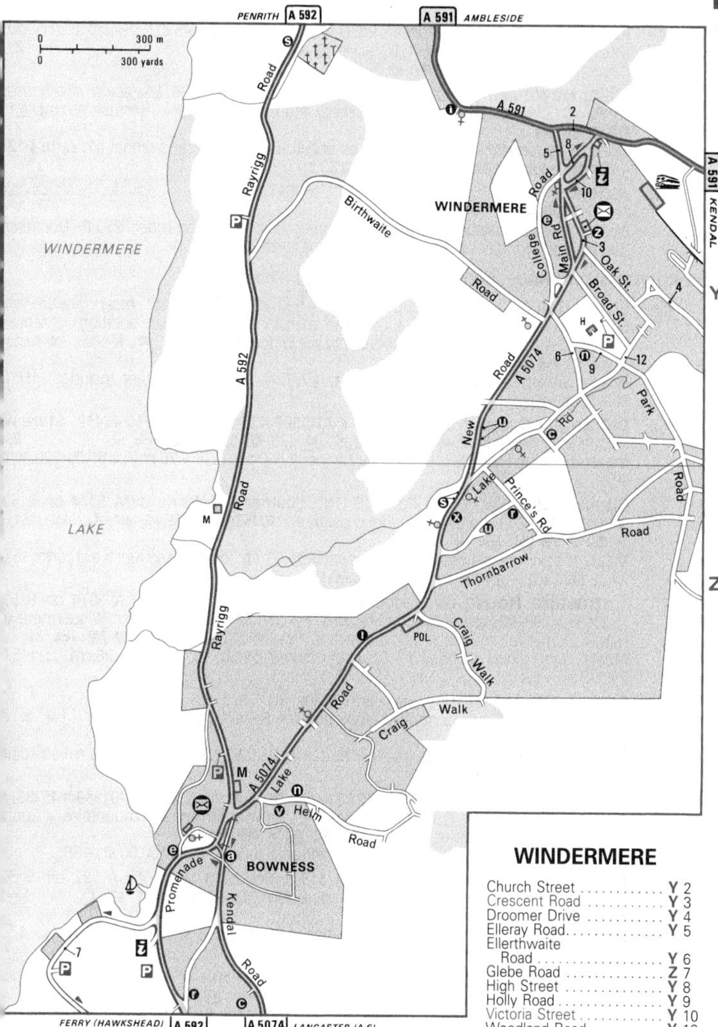

Oldfield House without rest., Oldfield Rd, LA23 2BY, ☎ (015394) 88445, *oldfield.house@virgin.net, Fax (015394) 43250* – ⇔ TV P. MC AE ◑ VISA JCB. ✗ Y c
8 rm ⊒ 25.00/55.00 s.

Braemount House without rest., Sunny Bank Rd, LA23 2EN, by Queens Drive ☎ (015394) 45967, *braemount.house@virgin.net, Fax (015394) 45967* – ⇔ TV P. MC VISA JCB Z u
closed 3 days Christmas – **6 rm** ⊒ 30.00/58.00.

Hawksmoor without rest., Lake Rd, LA23 2EQ, ☎ (015394) 42110, *tyson@hawksmoor.net1.co.uk, Fax (015394) 42110*, – ⇔ TV P. MC VISA. ✗ Z s
10 rm ⊒ 43.00/64.00 **st.**

Archway, 13 College Rd, LA23 1BU, ☎ (015394) 45613, *archway@btinternet.com, Fax (015394) 45328* – ⇔ TV. MC AE VISA JCB. ✗ Y e
Meals (by arrangement) 13.50 **st.** – **4 rm** ⊒ 48.00/60.00 **st.**

ENGLAND

Kirkwood without rest., Prince's Rd, LA23 2DD, ☎ (015394) 43907, *neil.cox@kirkwood5 freeserve.co.uk, Fax (015394) 43907* – ⇔ TV. MC VISA JCB. ✻ Z
closed 24-25 December – **7 rm** ☐ 30.00/60.00 **st.**

Miller Howe with rm, Rayrigg Rd, LA23 1EY, ☎ (015394) 42536, *lakeview@millerhouse. m, Fax (015394) 45664*, ≤ Lake Windermere and mountains, – ⇔ rest, ▤ rest, TV MC AE VISA Y
closed 3-19 January – **Meals** (booking essential) 15.00/35.00 **t.** and dinner a la carte 12. – **12 rm** ☐ (dinner included) 200.00/250.00 **t.**

Jerichos, Birch St., LA23 1EG, ☎ (015394) 42522, *enquiries@jerichos.co. Fax (015394) 42522* – ⇔. MC VISA JCB Y
closed 1 week February, last week November, first week December, 25-26 December, January and Monday – **Meals** (dinner only) a la carte 22.00/26.50.

at Bowness-on-Windermere *South : 1 m.* – **Z** – ✉ *Windermere.*

Storrs Hall ⛰, LA23 3LG, South : 2 m. on A 592 ☎ (015394) 47111, *reception@storrsh. co.uk, Fax (015394) 47555*, ≤, « Georgian mansion with Victorian additions extensive furnished with antiques, on the shores of Lake Windermere », – ⇔ rest, P. MC AE VISA JCB. ✻
closed January – **Meals** 15.00/32.00 **st.** 7.95 – **18 rm** ☐ (dinner included) 160.0 365.00 **st.** – SB.

Old England, Church St., LA23 3DF, ☎ (015394) 42444, *Fax (015394) 43432*, ≤ Lake W dermere, heated, – ⇔ TV P – 120. MC AE VISA JCB. ✻ Z
Meals (bar lunch Monday to Saturday)/dinner 22.50 **t.** 6.95 – **76 rm** ☐ 85.00/220.00 **t** SB.

Gilpin Lodge ⛰, Crook Rd, LA23 3NE, Southeast : 2 ½ m. by A 5074 on B 52 ☎ (015394) 88818, *hotel@gilpin-lodge.co.uk, Fax (015394) 88058*, ≤, – ⇔ rest, P. MC AE VISA JCB. ✻
Meals (booking essential to non-residents) 35.00 **st.** (dinner) and lunch a la carte 15. 24.25 **st.** 6.25 – **14 rm** ☐ 100.00/250.00 **st.** – SB.

Linthwaite House ⛰, Crook Rd, LA23 3JA, South : ¾ m. by A 5074 on B 52 ☎ (015394) 88600, *admin@linthwaite.com, Fax (015394) 88601*, ≤ Lake Windermere a fells, « Extensive grounds and private lake », – ⇔ TV P. MC AE VISA JCB. ✻
Meals (light lunch Monday to Saturday)/dinner 39.00 **st.** 8.90 – **26 rm** ☐ 115. 235.00 **st.** – SB.

Fayrer Garden House ⛰, Lyth Valley Rd, LA23 3JP, South : 1 m. on A 50 ☎ (015394) 88195, *lakescene@fayrergarden.com, Fax (015394) 45986*, ≤, – ⇔, ▤ re TV P. MC AE VISA
closed 7-18 January – **Meals** (bar lunch)/dinner 25.00/29.50 **t.** 6.95 – **18 rm** ☐ (din included) 77.50/198.00 **t.** – SB.

Lindeth Fell ⛰, Lyth Valley Rd, LA23 3JP, South : 1 m. on A 5074 ☎ (015394) 43286, *k nedy@lindethfell.co.uk, Fax (015394) 47455*, ≤ Lake Windermere and mountains, « Cour house atmosphere, gardens », – ⇔ rest, TV P. MC VISA. ✻
Meals 14.00/23.00 **st.** 6.00 – **14 rm** ☐ (dinner included) 72.50/180.00 **st.** – SB.

Lindeth Howe ⛰, Storrs Park, LA23 3JF, South : 1 ¼ m. by A 592 off B 52 ☎ (015394) 45759, *hotel@lindeth-howe.co.uk, Fax (015394) 46368*, ≤, ≘s, – ⇔ P. MC VISA JCB. ✻
Meals (dinner only and Sunday lunch)/dinner 22.50/27.50 **st.** 7.95 – **36 rm** ☐ 47. 155.00 **st.** – SB.

Burn How Garden House, Back Belsfield Rd, LA23 3HH, ☎ (015394) 46226, *burnho otel@btinternet.com, Fax (015394) 47000*, – ⇔ rest, TV P. MC AE VISA JCB. ✻
closed first 2 weeks January – **Meals** (light lunch)/dinner 18.50 **t.** 8.50 – **26 rm** ☐ 75. 94.00 **st.** – SB. Z

Burnside, Kendal Rd, LA23 3EP, ☎ (015394) 42211, *stay@burnsidehotel.c Fax (015394) 43824*, ≘s, , squash – ⇔ TV P – 100. MC AE JCB Z
Meals (bar lunch Monday to Saturday) (carving lunch Sunday and dinner Monday-Tuesd dinner 20.00/25.00 **st.** and a la carte 6.50 – **57 rm** ☐ 80.00/140.00 **t.** – SB.

Craig Manor, Lake Rd, LA23 2JF, ☎ (015394) 88877, *craigmanor@btinternet.c Fax (015394) 88878*, ≤ – ⇔ rest, TV P. MC AE VISA JCB Z
Meals (dinner only and Sunday lunch) (carving lunch Sunday) 18.00/25.00 **st.** and a la c 6.60 – **25 rm** ☐ 60.00/90.00 **st.** – SB.

Wild Boar, Crook Rd, LA23 3NF, Southeast : 4 m. by A 5074 on B 5284 ☎ (015394) 45 *wildboar@elh.co.uk, Fax (015394) 42498*, – ⇔ TV P – 40. MC AE VISA JCB. ✻
Meals a la carte 16.80/25.65 **st.** 5.75 – **36 rm** ☐ 65.00/170.00 **st.** – SB.

Crag Brow Cottage, Helm Rd, LA23 3BU, ☎ (015394) 44080, *cragbrow@aol.c Fax (015394) 46003*, – ⇔ TV P. MC VISA JCB. ✻ Z
Meals (light lunch)/dinner 18.75 **st.** and a la carte 6.50 – **11 rm** ☐ 65.00/80.00 **st.** – S

Oakbank House without rest., Helm Rd, LA23 3BU, ☎ (015394) 43386, *enquiries@oakbankhousehotel.co.uk, Fax (015394) 47965,* ≤ – ⅍ TV P. MC VISA JCB Z n
closed 24-26 December – **12 rm** 45.00/80.00 **st.**

Laurel Cottage without rest., St. Martins Sq., Kendal Rd, LA23 3EF, ☎ (015394) 45594, *Fax (015394) 45594* – ⅍ TV P. MC AE D VISA JCB. ⅍ Z a
14 rm 25.00/62.00 **st.**

White Foss without rest., Longtail Hill, LA23 3JD, South : ¾ m. by A 592 on B 5284 ☎ (015394) 46593, *nicholson@whitefoss.co.uk,* ≤, – P. ⅍
April-October – **3 rm** 60.00 **s.**

Troutbeck *North : 4 m. by A 592* – **Y** – ✉ *Windermere.*

Broadoaks, Bridge Lane, LA23 1LA, South : 1 m. ☎ (015394) 45566, *trev@broadoaksf9.co.uk, Fax (015394) 88766,* ≤, – ⅍ TV P. MC VISA. ⅍
Meals (lunch by arrangement)/dinner 20.00/35.00 **st.** and a la carte 5.95 – **14 rm** 65.00/195.00 **st.** – SB.

Queens Head with rm, LA23 1PW, East : ¼ m. on A 592 ☎ (015394) 32174, *enquiries@queensheadhotel.com, Fax (015394) 31938,* ≤, « 17C inn » – ⅍ rm, TV P. MC VISA
closed 25 December – **Meals** 15.50 **t.** and a la carte – **9 rm** 45.00/75.00 **t.** – SB.

NDLESHAM *Surrey* 404 **S 29** – *pop. 4 525.*
London 40 – Reading 18 – Southampton 53.

The Brickmakers, Chertsey Rd, GU20 5HC, East : 1 m. on B 386 ☎ (01276) 472267, *Fax (01276) 451014,* – P. MC AE D VISA
Meals a la carte 23.85/27.85 **t.** 7.75.

Se cercate un albergo tranquillo,
oltre a consultare le carte dell'introduzione,
rintracciate nell'elenco degli esercizi quelli con il simbolo o .

NDSOR *Windsor & Maidenhead* 404 **S 29** *Great Britain G.* – *pop. 30 136 (inc. Eton).*
See : *Town★ – Castle★★★ : St. George's Chapel★★★ AC (stalls★★★), State Apartments★★ AC, North Terrace (≤★★)* **Z** – *Eton College★★ AC (College Chapel★★, Wall paintings★)* **Z**.
Env. : *Windsor Park★ AC* **Y**.
to Marlow, Maidenhead and Cookham (Salter Bros. Ltd) (summer only).
24 High St. ☎ *(01753) 743900.*
London 28 – Reading 19 – Southampton 59.

Plan on next page

Oakley Court, Windsor Rd, Water Oakley, SL4 5UR, West : 3 m. on A 308 ☎ (01753) 609988, *Fax (01628) 637011,* ≤, « Part Gothic mansion on banks of River Thames », , , , , , , – , ⅍ rm, TV ♿ P – 160. MC AE D VISA. ⅍
The Oakleaf **:** **Meals** 24.50/29.50 **st.** and a la carte 14.95 – 14.95 – **114 rm** 195.00/250.00 **st.**, 1 suite – SB.

Castle, High St., SL4 1LJ, ☎ (01753) 851011, *heritagehotels-windsor.castle@fortehotels.com, Fax (01753) 830244,* « Former inn built by monks » – ⅍ TV P – 400. MC AE D VISA JCB. ⅍ Z c
Castle restaurant **:** **Meals** 13.95/22.95 **t.** and a la carte 7.50 – ***Freshfields*** **:** **Meals** a la carte 15.85/25.80 **t.** 7.50 – 12.50 – **108 rm** 155.00/220.00 **st.**, 3 suites – SB.

Sir Christopher Wren's House, Thames St., SL4 1PX, ☎ (01753) 861354, *Fax (01753) 860172,* – ⅍ TV P – 90. MC AE D VISA. ⅍ Z e
Meals 21.50/35.00 **st.** and a la carte 10.50 – **79 rm** 155.00/205.00 **st.**, 5 suites – SB.

Royal Adelaide, 46 Kings Rd, SL4 2AG, ☎ (01753) 863916, *royaladelaide@meridianleisure.com, Fax (01753) 830682* – TV P – 80. MC AE D VISA. ⅍ Z v
Meals (dinner only) 12.50/17.50 **st.** and a la carte 6.95 – **42 rm** 90.00/100.00 **st.** – SB.

The Dorset without rest., 4 Dorset Rd, SL4 3BA, ☎ (01753) 852669, *Fax (01753) 852669* – ⅍ TV P. MC AE VISA JCB. ⅍ Z x
closed 18 December-5 January – **4 rm** 62.00/78.00 **s.**

Al Fassia, 27 St. Leonards Rd, SL4 3BP, ☎ (01753) 855370, *Fax (01753) 855370* – MC AE D VISA JCB Z n
closed Sunday and Bank Holidays – **Meals** - Moroccan - (booking essential) 15.95/24.95 **t.** and a la carte 16.85/20.40 **t.**

Bel and the Dragon, Thames St., SL4 1PQ, ☎ (01753) 866056, *Fax (01753) 865707,* – MC AE VISA Z a
Meals a la carte 20.40/32.40 **t.**

WINDSOR

Bexley Street. . . . . Z 2
Bolton Road. . . . . Y 3
Castle Hill. . . . . Z 4
Claremont Road . . . . Z 6
Clarence Crescent . . . . Z 7
Clewer Crescent Road . . . Z 8
Datchet Rd. . . . . Z 9
Goswell Road . . . . Z 10
Grove Road . . . . Z 12
High Street . . . . Z 13
High Street
(DATCHET). . . . . Y 14
Horton Road . . . . Y 16
Keats Lane. . . . . Z 17
King Edward
Court Centre . . . . Z
King Edward VIII Avenue . Z 18
Peascod Street . . . . Z 19
Peascod Street . . . . Z
Ragstone Road. . . . . Y 20
River Street . . . . Z 22
Stovell Road . . . . Z 23
Thames Avenue . . . . Z 24
Thames Street . . . . Z 25
Trinity Place . . . . Z 27
Windsor Bridge. . . . . Z 28
Windsor Road. . . . . Y 29

North is at the top on all town plans.

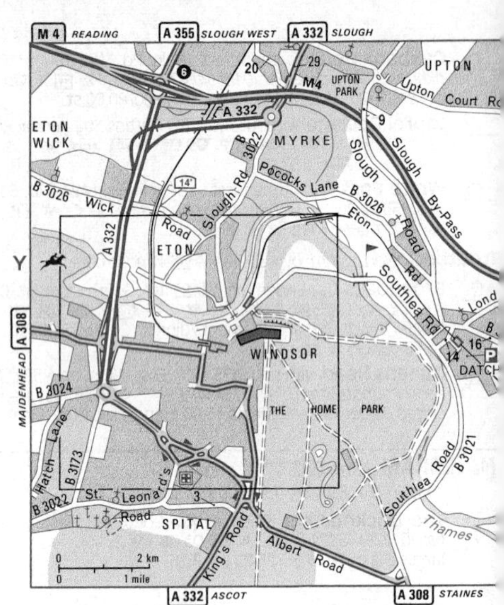

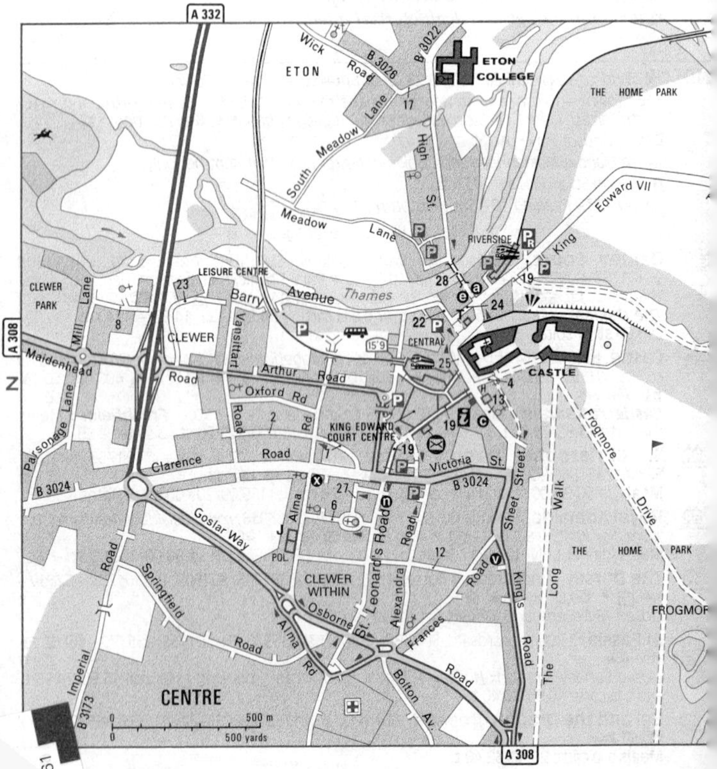

A 332
Wick Road
B 3026
B 3022
ETON
ETON COLLEGE
THE HOME PARK
South Meadow Lane
High St.
Meadow Lane
King Edward VII
RIVERSIDE
LEISURE CENTRE
CLEWER PARK
Mill Lane
Barry Avenue
Thames
CLEWER
Vansittart Road
CENTRAL
CASTLE
A 308
Maidenhead Road
Arthur Road
Oxford Rd
KING EDWARD COURT CENTRE
Victoria St.
Frogmore Drive
Parsonage Lane
Clarence Road
B 3024
Sheet Street
Long Walk
Goslar Way
Alma Rd
St. Leonard's Road
POL
CLEWER WITHIN
Alexandra Road
Osborne Rd
Frances Road
Kings Road
THE HOME PARK
FROGMORE
Springfield Road
Imperial Road
B 3173
Bolton Av.
CENTRE
The Long Walk
0 500 m
0 500 yards
A 308
Z

NEHAM *W. Sussex* 404 T 31 – *see Henfield.*

NFORTON *Herefordshire* 403 K 27 – ✉ *Hereford.*

London 155 – Birmingham 71 – Cardiff 66 – Hereford 15.

Winforton Court without rest., HR3 6EA, ☏ (01544) 328498, *winfortoncourt@talk21.com, Fax (01544) 328498,* « 16C », – P
closed 20-28 December – **3 rm** 40.00/68.00.

Sun Inn with rm, HR3 6EA, ☏ (01544) 327677, *Fax (01544) 327677,* « Part 17C », – rm, TV P
closed Tuesday – **Meals** a la carte 12.85/22.80 **t.** 5.95 – **3 rm** 32.00/60.00 **st.** – SB.

NGFIELD *Suffolk – see Diss.*

NKLEIGH *Devon* 403 I 31 – *pop. 1 063.*

London 218 – Barnstaple 25 – Exeter 23 – Plymouth 43 – Truro 76.

Pophams, Castle St., EX19 8HU, ☏ (01837) 83767 – . MC VISA
closed February and Saturday-Tuesday – **Meals** (booking essential) (lunch only) (unlicensed) a la carte approx. 23.75.

NSCOMBE *Somerset* 403 L 30 *The West Country G. – pop. 4 192.*

Env. : *Axbridge★★ (King John's Hunting Lodge★, St. John the Baptist Church★), S : 1¾m. by A 38 and A 371.*

London 137 – Bristol 16 – Taunton 22.

Premier Lodge, Bridgwater Rd, BS25 1NN, on A 38 ☏ (0870) 7001340, *Fax (0870) 7001341,* – rm, TV P. MC AE VISA.
Meals (grill rest.) – **31 rm** 46.00 **t.**

NSFORD *Somerset* 403 J 30 *The West Country G. – pop. 270 –* ✉ *Minehead.*

See : *Village★.*

Env. : *Exmoor National Park★★.*

London 194 – Exeter 31 – Minehead 10 – Taunton 32.

Royal Oak Inn, Exmoor National Park, TA24 7JE, ☏ (01643) 851455, *enquiries@royaloak-somerset, Fax (01643) 851009,* « Attractive part 12C thatched inn », – TV P. MC AE VISA
Meals (bar lunch Monday to Saturday)/dinner a la carte 20.40/24.20 **t.** 10.95 – **14 rm** 75.00/135.00 **t.** – SB.

Karslake House with rm, Halse Lane, Exmoor National Park, TA24 7JE, ☏ (01643) 851242, *karslakehouse@aol.com, Fax (01643) 851242,* – TV P. MC VISA
closed February-mid March – **Meals** (dinner only) (residents only Sunday and Monday) 27.50 **t.** 6.95 – **6 rm** (dinner included) 72.50/150.00 **t.**

WINSLEY *Wilts.* 403 404 N 29 – *see Bradford-on-Avon.*

WINTERBOURNE *South Gloucestershire* 403 404 M 29 – *see Bristol.*

WINTERBOURNE STEEPLETON *Dorset* 403 404 M 31 – *see Dorchester.*

WINTERINGHAM *North Lincolnshire* 402 S 22 – *pop. 4 714* – ✉ *Scunthorpe.*
London 176 – Kingston-upon-Hull 16 – Sheffield 67.

Winteringham Fields (Schwab) with rm, Silver St., DN15 9PF, ✆ (01724) 733096, *wi elds@aol.com, Fax (01724) 733898,* « Part 16C manor house » – ⅔ TV P. MC AE VISA
closed last week March, first week August and 2 weeks Christmas – **Meals** *(closed Sun and Monday)* (booking essential to non-residents) 25.00/32.00 **st.** and a la carte 51. 61.75 **st.** 9.00 – 10.00 – **8 rm** 80.00/150.00 **st.**, 2 suites
Spec. Paupiette of wood pigeon, beetroot tortellini, parsnip purée. Baked sea bass salted crust, Choron sauce. Apricot and chocolate tiramisu cone with poached apricot.

WITCOMBE *Glos.* – *see Gloucester.*

WITHERSLACK *Cumbria* 402 L 21 – *see Grange-over-Sands.*

WITNEY *Oxon.* 403 404 P 28 – *pop. 20 377.*
51A Market Sq. ✆ (01993) 775802.
London 69 – Gloucester 39 – Oxford 13.

Witney Four Pillars, Ducklington Lane, OX8 7TJ, South : 1 ½ m. on A ✆ (01993) 779777, *enquiries@fourpillars.co.uk, Fax (01993) 703467,* – TV P – 160. MC AE VISA
Meals 7.95/18.95 **st.** and dinner a la carte 5.25 – 8.75 – **83 rm** 89.00/99.00 **st.** – SB

at Hailey *North : 1 ¼ m. on B 4022* – ✉ *Witney.*

Bird in Hand, White Oak Green, OX8 5XP, North : 1 m. on B 4022 ✆ (01993) 868 *Fax (01993) 868702,* – TV P. MC AE VISA.
Meals a la carte 14.40/30.40 **t.** – **16 rm** 57.50/65.50 **st.**

at Barnard Gate *East : 3 ¼ m. by B 4022 off A 40* – ✉ *Eynsham.*

The Boot Inn, OX8 6XE, ✆ (01865) 881231, *bootinn@barnardgate.fsnet.co Fax (01865) 882119,* , « Collection of celebrities boots » – P. MC AE VISA
Meals (booking essential) a la carte 17.50/24.50 **t.** 7.50.

at South Leigh *Southeast : 3 m. by B 4022* – ✉ *Witney.*

Mason Arms with rm, OX8 6XN, ✆ (01993) 702485, « 15C thatched inn », – TV P.
closed 1 week Christmas, 2 weeks August, Sunday dinner, Monday and Bank Holida
Meals a la carte 23.95/37.45 **t.** 6.00 – **2 rm** 35.00/60.00 **t.**

WITTERSHAM *Kent* 404 W 30 – *pop. 1 431* – ✉ *Tenterden.*
London 59 – Brighton 54 – Folkestone 22 – Maidstone 28.

Wittersham Court , The Street, TN30 7EA, ✆ (01797) 270425, *watsoni5@aol.c Fax (01797) 270425,* « Part 17C », – P. MC VISA.
closed Christmas and New Year – **Meals** (by arrangement) (communal dining) 22.00
3 rm 50.00/75.00 **s.**

WIVELISCOMBE *Somerset* 403 K 30 *The West Country G.* – *pop. 1 753* – ✉ *Taunton.*
Env. : *Gaulden Manor★ AC, NE : 3 m. by B 3188.*
London 185 – Barnstaple 38 – Exeter 37 – Taunton 14.

Langley House, Langley Marsh, TA4 2UF, North : ¾ m. ✆ (01984) 623318, *user@lang n2home.co.uk, Fax (01984) 624573,* – rest, TV P. MC AE VISA
Meals (booking essential to non-residents) (dinner only) (set menu only) 27.50 **st.** 6.
8 rm 85.00/127.50 **st.** – SB.

IX *Essex* 404 X 28 – ✉ *Manningtree.*
London 70 – Colchester 10 – Harwich 7 – Ipswich 16.

Dairy House Farm without rest., Bradfield Rd, CO11 2SR, Northwest : 1 m. ℘ (01255) 870322, *Fax (01255) 870186*, ←, « Working farm », – TV P.
3 rm 26.00/40.00.

OBURN *Beds.* 404 S 28 *Great Britain G. – pop. 1 534 –* ✉ *Milton Keynes.*
See : *Woburn Abbey*★★.
London 49 – Bedford 13 – Luton 13 – Northampton 24.

Bedford Arms, 1 George St., MK17 9PX, ℘ (01525) 290441, *Fax (01525) 290432* – rm, rest, TV P – 60. MC AE VISA.
Meals 10.50/18.50 **t.** 6.50 – 11.00 – **51 rm** 105.00/148.00 **st.**, 2 suites.

Paris House, Woburn Park, MK17 9QP, Southeast : 2 ¼ m. on A 4012 ℘ (01525) 290692, *gailbaker@parishouse.co.uk, Fax (01525) 290471,* « Reconstructed timbered house in park », – P. MC AE VISA
closed February, Sunday dinner and Monday – **Meals** 25.00/50.00 **t.** 7.50.

The Birch, 20 Newport Rd, MK17 9HX, North : ½ m. on A 5130 ℘ (01525) 290295, *Fax (01525) 290899*, – rest, P. MC AE VISA
closed Sunday dinner and 25 December – **Meals** a la carte 20.45/26.45 **t.**

OKINGHAM *Wokingham* 404 R 29 – *pop. 38 063.*
18 *Sand Martins, Finchampstead Rd* ℘ *(0118) 979 2711* – 9 *Hurst, Sandford Lane* ℘ *(01734) 344355.*
London 43 – Reading 7 – Southampton 52.

Hilton St. Anne's Manor, London Rd, RG40 1ST, East : 1 ½ m. on A 329 ℘ (01189) 772550, *reservations@stannes.stakis.co.uk, Fax (01189) 772526*, , , , , , – , rm, rest, TV P – 200. MC AE VISA.
closed 26-30 December – **Meals** *(closed Saturday lunch)* (carving lunch)/dinner 25.00 **st.** and a la carte – 13.45 – **167 rm** 210.00/245.00 **st.**, 3 suites – SB.

Rose Street, 6 Rose St., RG40 1XU, ℘ (01189) 788025, *Fax (0118) 989 1314* – MC AE VISA
closed 25-26 – **Meals** 13.95/18.95 **t.** (lunch) and a la carte 22.20/25.95 **t.** 7.50.

WOLVERHAMPTON *W. Mids.* 402 403 404 N 26 – *pop. 257 943.*

18 Queen Sq. ☎ (01902) 556110.

London 132 – Birmingham 15 – Liverpool 89 – Shrewsbury 30.

Plan of Enlarged Area : see Birmingham pp. 4 and 5

Quality, 126 Penn Rd, WV3 0ER, ☎ (01902) 429216, *Fax (01902) 710419,* – – 120. – B
Meals (bar lunch Saturday) 10.50/18.50 **st.** and a la carte 6.70 – 9.95 – **92 rm** 81.(107.00 **st.** – SB.

Novotel, Union St., WV1 3JN, ☎ (01902) 871100, *Fax (01902) 870054,* heated – rm, rest, – 200. B
Meals 15.00/17.00 **st.** (dinner) and a la carte 17.00/24.00 **st.** 4.00 – 9.00 – **132** 72.00 **st.**

Holiday Inn Garden Court, Dunstall Park, WV6 0PE, North : 1 ¾ m. by A 4 ☎ (01902) 713313, *dunstallparkuk.freeserve.co.uk, Fax (01902) 714364,* – rm, A
Meals (bar lunch Sunday) 12.95 **st.** (dinner) and lunch a la carte 13.00/21.95 **st.** 9.00 – 9.50 – **54 rm** 62.00 **st.** – SB.

WOLVERHAMPTON

Street	Grid	No.
Birmingham New Road	A	3
Bridgnorth Road	A	6
Cleveland Street	B	7
Darlington Street	B	
Garrick Street	B	8
High Street	A	9
Lichfield Road	A	10
Lichfield Street	B	12
Mander Centre	B	
Market Street	B	14
Princess Street	B	15
Queen Square	B	
Railway Drive	B	
Salop Street	B	
School Street	B	
Thompson Avenue	A	
Victoria Street	B	
Wulfrun Centre	B	

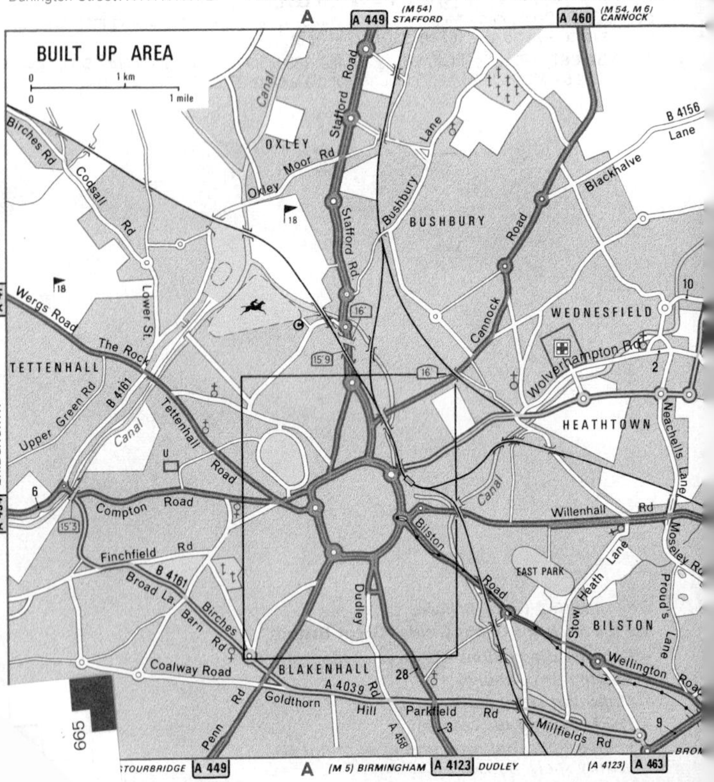

A
A 449 (M 54) STAFFORD
A 460 (M 54, M 6) CANNOCK
BUILT UP AREA
0 1 km
0 1 mile
A 41 WHITCHURCH
A 454 BRIDGNORTH
Birches Rd
Codsall Rd
Canal
OXLEY
Oxley Moor Rd
Stafford Road
Stafford Rd
Bushbury Lane
BUSHBURY
Cannock Road
B 4156 Lane
Blackhalve
WEDNESFIELD
Wolverhampton Rd
HEATHTOWN
Neachells Lane
Wergs Road
The Rock
TETTENHALL
Lower St.
Upper Green Rd
B 4161
Tettenhall Road
Compton Road
Finchfield Rd
B 4161
Broad La.
Barn Rd
Birches
Coalway Road
BLAKENHALL
A 4039 Rd
Goldthorn Hill
Penn Rd
Dudley
Parkfield Rd
A 458
Willenhall Rd
Bilston Road
EAST PARK
Stow Heath Lane
Moseley Rd
Proud's Lane
BILSTON
Wellington Road
Millfields Rd
STOURBRIDGE A 449
A
(M 5) BIRMINGHAM A 4123 DUDLEY
(A 4123) A 463

Ely House, 53 Tettenhall Rd, WV3 9NB, ☎ (01902) 311311, *Fax (01902) 421098* – TV P. MC AE ⓓ VISA. ✈ B u
closed 25 to 29 December
Meals *(closed Sunday dinner)* (lunch by arrangement)/dinner 18.50 **st.** and a la carte 5.95
19 rm ☕ 54.00/74.00 **st.**

Travel Inn, Wolverhampton Business Park, Greedfield Lane, Stafford Rd, WV10 6NZ, North : 3 ½ m. by A 449 at junction with M 54 ☎ (01902) 397755, *Fax (01902) 785260* – lift, ⇔ rm, ▤ rest, TV & P – 50. MC AE ⓓ VISA. ✈
Meals (grill rest.) – **54 rm** 40.95 **t.**

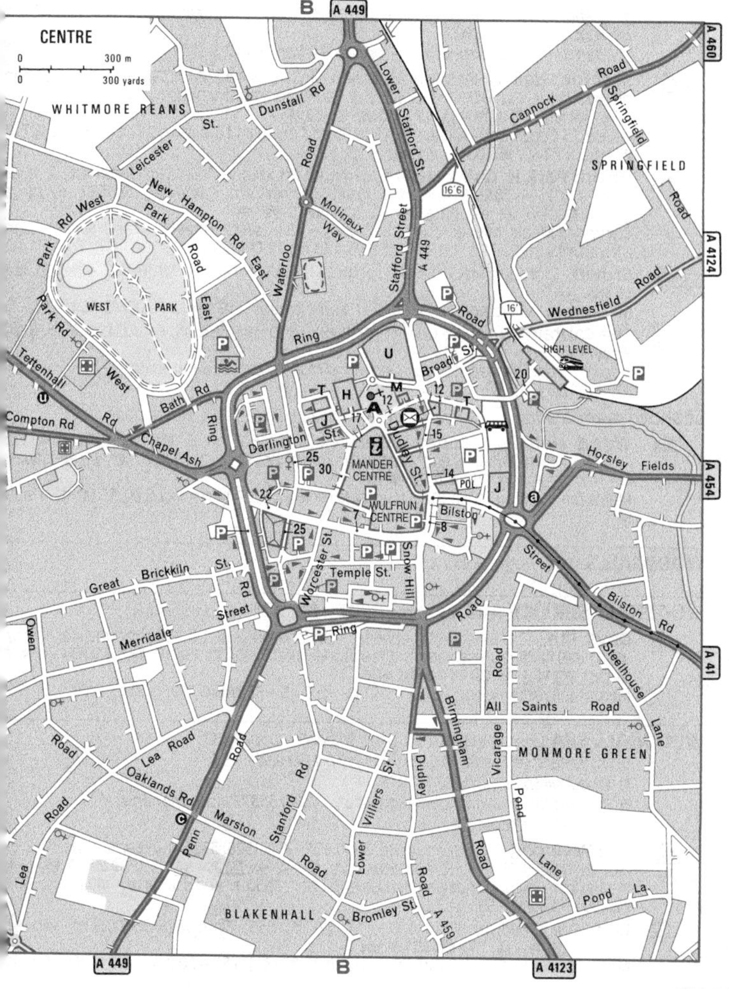

WOLVISTON *Cleveland* 402 Q 20 – *pop. 2 482* – ✉ *Stockton-on-Tees.*
London 280 – Carlisle 93 – Middlesbrough 8 – Newcastle upon Tyne 37 – Sunderland 23.

Express by Holiday Inn, Wynyard Park Services, Coal Lane, TS22 5PZ, on A 689 junction with A 19 ✆ (01740) 644000, *Fax (01740) 644111* – ⇔ rm, TV ✆ ♿ P – 🏛 30. AE ⓓ VISA JCB. ✂
Meals (grill rest.) a la carte 8.35/17.85 **st.** – **49 rm** 49.95 **st.**

WOOBURN COMMON *Bucks. – see Beaconsfield.*

WOODBOROUGH *Wilts.* 403 404 O 29 – *pop. 1 495* – ✉ *Pewsey.*
London 89 – Bristol 53 – Salisbury 21 – Southampton 45 – Swindon 19.

Seven Stars, Bottlesford, SN9 6LU, Southeast : ¾ m. on Bottlesford ✆ (01672) 851325, *sevenstars@dialin.net, Fax (01672) 851583,* « Part 16C thatched inn – P. MC VISA JCB. ✂
closed Sunday dinner and Monday – **Meals** - French - a la carte 16.45/25.45 **t.** 5.75.

WOODBRIDGE *Suffolk* 404 X 27 – *pop. 10 950.*
Cretingham, Grove Farm ✆ (01728) 685275 – Seckford, Seckford Hall Rd, Gre Bealings ✆ (01394) 388000.
London 81 – Great Yarmouth 45 – Ipswich 8 – Norwich 47.

Seckford Hall ⛰, IP13 6NU, Southwest : 1 ¼ m. by A 12 ✆ (01394) 385678, *reception eckford.co.uk, Fax (01394) 380610,* ←, « Part Tudor country house », Fā, 🏊, 18, ⛰, – ⇔, ▤ rest, TV ♿ P – 🏛 120. MC AE ⓓ VISA JCB
closed 25 December – **Meals** 13.50/16.95 **st.** (lunch) and a la carte 24.45/39.00 **st.** 7.25
25 rm ☕ 79.00/165.00 **st.**, 7 suites – SB.

Ufford Park H. Golf & Leisure, Yarmouth Rd, Ufford, IP12 1QW, Northeast : 2 m. or 1438 ✆ (01394) 383555, *uffordparkltd@btinternet.com, Fax (01394) 383582,* ←, Fā, 🏊, 18, 🎾 – ⇔, ▤ rest, TV ♿ P – 🏛 200. MC AE VISA. ✂
Carvery : **Meals** (dinner only) 16.95 **st.** 6.70 – ***Vista :*** **Meals** *(closed Sunday dinn* a la carte 19.20/22.70 **t.** 6.70 – ☕ 8.95 – **44 rm** 79.00/129.00 **t.** – SB.

Crown, Thoroughfare, IP12 1AD, ✆ (01394) 384242, *Fax (01394) 387192* – ⇔ TV P. AE VISA JCB
Meals (bar lunch)/dinner 11.95/15.95 **t.** and a la carte – **19 rm** ☕ 70.00/85.00 **t.** – SB.

The Captain's Table, 3 Quay St., IP12 1BX, ✆ (01394) 383145, *Fax (01394) 388508,* P. MC VISA
closed 2 weeks January, Sunday dinner and Monday except Bank Holidays – **Meals** a la ca 12.40/21.00 **t.** 6.50.

at Shottisham *Southeast : 5 ¾ m. by B 1438, A 1152 on B 1083* – ✉ *Woodbridge.*

Wood Hall H. & Country Club ⛰, IP12 3EG, on B 1083 ✆ (01394) 41128 *Fax (01394) 410007,* ←, « Part Elizabethan manor house », 🏊 heated, 🎾, ✂, squash ⇔ rest, TV P – 🏛 150. MC AE ⓓ VISA
Meals (bar lunch)/dinner 18.95 **t.** and a la carte 4.95 – **14 rm** ☕ 65.00/85.00 **st.**, 1 suite SB.

WOODFALLS *Wilts. – see Salisbury.*

WOODHALL SERVICE AREA *S. Yorks.* 402 403 404 Q 24 – ✉ *Sheffield.*

Days Inn, S31 8XR, M 1 between junctions 30 and 31 (southbound carriagew ✆ (01142) 487992, Reservations (Freephone) 0800 0280400, *Fax (01142) 485634* – ⇔ r ▤ rest, TV ✆ ♿ P. MC AE ⓓ VISA JCB
Meals (grill rest.) a la carte 8.60/13.90 **t.** – ☕ 7.45 – **38 rm** 45.00/50.00 **t.**

WOODHALL SPA *Lincs.* 402 404 T 24 *Great Britain G.* – *pop. 3 337.*
Env. : *Tattershall Castle★ AC, SE : 4 m. by B 1192 and A 153.*
Woodhall Spa ✆ (01526) 351835.
The Cottage Museum, Iddesleigh Rd ✆ (01526) 353775 (summer only).
London 138 – Lincoln 18.

The Petwood ⛰, Stixwould Rd, LN10 6QF, ✆ (01526) 352411, *reception@petwood. uk, Fax (01526) 353473,* ←, « Gardens », 18, 🎾 – ⇔ TV P – 🏛 150. MC AE ⓓ VISA JCB
Meals (bar lunch Monday to Saturday)/dinner 18.50 **t.** and a la carte – **49 rm** ☕ 60.0 120.00 **t.**, 1 suite – SB.

Golf, The Broadway, LN10 6SG, ✆ (01526) 353535, *Fax (01526) 353096,* 18, ✂, ⇔ rest, TV P – 🏛 150. MC AE ⓓ VISA
Meals (bar lunch Monday-Saturday)/dinner 15.95 **st.** 6.50 – **50 rm** ☕ 70.00/90.00 **t.** –

WOODSTOCK *Oxon.* 403 404 P 28 *Great Britain G. – pop. 2 898.*

See : *Blenheim Palace*★★★ *(The Grounds*★★★*) AC.*

Oxfordshire Museum, Park St. ☎ (01993) 813276.

London 65 – Gloucester 47 – Oxford 8.

Bear, Park St., OX20 1SZ, ☎ (0870) 4008202, *heritagehotelswoodstock.bear@fortehotels.com, Fax (01993) 813380,* « Part 16C inn » – 30. VISA JCB
Meals 11.95/19.95 **t.** (lunch) and dinner a la carte 16.85/37.75 **t.** 7.95 – 13.50 – **51 rm** 125.00/180.00 **t.**, 3 suites.

Feathers, Market St., OX20 1SX, ☎ (01993) 812291, *enquiries@feathers.co.uk, Fax (01993) 813158,* « Restored 17C houses » – rest, rest, . VISA
closed 1 week January – **Meals** (booking essential) 20.50/22.00 **t.** (lunch) and dinner a la carte 31.50/46.50 **t.** 12.10 – **18 rm** 115.00/185.00 **t.**, 4 suites – SB
Spec. Roast foie gras with split peas, Madeira and salsify. Risotto of dorade with crab and pak choi. Poached figs with honeycomb ice cream.

Shipton Glebe, OX20 1QQ, East : 2 ½ m. by A 44 and A 4095 turning left onto unmarked rd after Shipton Rd ☎ (01993) 812688, *stay@shipton-glebe.com, Fax (01993) 813142,* , – . VISA
Meals (by arrangement) 25.00 6.0 – **3 rm** 65.00/85.00 **st.** – SB.

The Laurels without rest., Hensington Rd, OX20 1JL, ☎ (01993) 812583, *malnikk@aol.com, Fax (01993) 812583* – . VISA JCB.
closed 15 December-3 January – **3 rm** 40.00/55.00 **s.**

at Wootton *North : 2½ m. by A 44 – ✉ Woodstock.*

Kings Head with rm, Chapel Hill, OX20 1DX, ☎ (01993) 811340, *tfay@kingshead.co.uk, Fax (01993) 811340* – . VISA
closed Sunday dinner – **Meals** a la carte 15.85/32.85 **t.** – **3 rm** 65.00/95.00 **t.** – SB.

WOOFFERTON *Shrops. – see Ludlow.*

WOOKEY HOLE *Somerset* 403 L 30 – *see Wells.*

WOOLACOMBE *Devon* 403 H 30 *The West Country G.*

Env. : *Exmoor National Park*★★ – *Mortehoe*★★ *(St. Mary's Church*★*, Morte Point – vantage point*★*) N : ½ m. – Ilfracombe : Hillsborough (*≤★★*) AC, Capstone Hill*★ *(*≤★*), St. Nicholas' Chapel (*≤★*) AC, NE : 5½ m. by B 3343 and A 361.*

Exc. : *Braunton*★ *(St. Braunton's Church*★*, Braunton Burrows*★*), S : 8 m. by B 3343 and A 361.*

The Esplanade ☎ (01271) 870553.

London 237 – Barnstaple 15 – Exeter 55.

Woolacombe Bay, South St., EX34 7BN, ☎ (01271) 870388, *woolacombebayhotel@btinternet.com, Fax (01271) 870613,* ≤, , , heated, , , , squash – , rest, rest, – 200. VISA JCB.
closed 3 January-mid February – **Meals** (dancing Thursday evening) (dinner only and Sunday lunch)/dinner 24.00 **st.** 7.50 – **64 rm** 84.00/218.00 **st.** – SB.

Little Beach, The Esplanade, EX34 7DJ, ☎ (01271) 870398, ≤ – . VISA
March-October – **Meals** (residents only) (dinner only) 15.00 **s.** 3.95 – **8 rm** 48.00/76.00 **s.**

at Mortehoe *North : ½ m. – ✉ Woolacombe.*

Watersmeet, The Esplanade, EX34 7EB, ☎ (01271) 870333, *watersmeethotel@compuserve, Fax (01271) 870890,* ≤ Morte Bay, heated, , , – rest, . VISA.
Meals (bar lunch Monday to Saturday)/dinner 22.00 **t.** and a la carte 6.50 – **22 rm** (dinner included) 110.00/210.00 **t.**

Cleeve House, EX34 7ED, ☎ (01271) 870719, *cleevehouse@mcmail.com, Fax (01271) 870719,* – . VISA JCB.
April-October – **Meals** (dinner only) 15.00/16.00 **s.** 6.00 – **7 rm** 42.00/60.00 **s.** – SB.

Sunnycliffe, Chapel Hill, EX34 7EB, ☎ (01271) 870597, *Fax (01271) 870597,* ≤ Morte Bay – . VISA.
2 February-October – **Meals** (dinner only) (residents only) 15.00 **st.** 4.30 – **8 rm** 39.00/68.00 **st.**

WOOLAVINGTON *Somerset* 403 L 30 – *see Bridgwater.*

WOOLLEY EDGE SERVICE AREA *W. Yorks.* 402 404 P 23 – ✉ *Wakefield.*

Travelodge without rest., WF4 4LQ, M 1 between junctions 38 and 39 (northbour carriageway) ℘ (01924) 830371, *Fax (01924) 830609* – ⇔ TV ♿ P. MC AE ◑ VISA JCB. ℅ 32 rm 59.95 t.

WOOLSTONE *Glos. – see Cheltenham.*

WOOLTON *Mersey.* 402 403 L 23 – *see Liverpool.*

WOOLVERSTONE *Suffolk* 404 X 27 – *see Ipswich.*

WOOTTON *Oxon.* 403 404 P 28 – *see Woodstock.*

WOOTTON BASSETT *Wilts.* 403 404 O 29 – *see Swindon.*

WORCESTER *Worcs.* 403 404 N 27 *Great Britain G. – pop. 82 661.*

See : *City★ – Cathedral★★ – Royal Worcester Porcelain Works★ (Dyson Perrins Museum* M.

Exc. : *The Elgar Trail★.*

⛳ *Perdiswell Park, Bilford Rd ℘ (01905) 754668.*

ℹ *The Guildhall, High St. ℘ (01905) 726311.*

London 124 – Birmingham 26 – Bristol 61 – Cardiff 74.

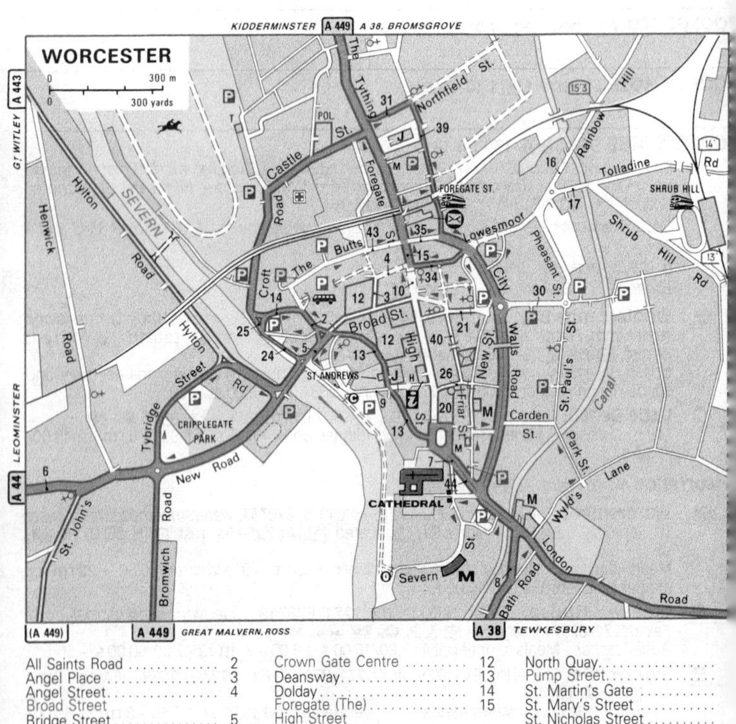

All Saints Road 2
Angel Place 3
Angel Street 4
Broad Street
Bridge Street 5
Bromyard Road 6
College Street 7
Commandery Road 8
Copenhagen Street 9
Cross (The) 10

Crown Gate Centre 12
Deansway 13
Dolday 14
Foregate (The) 15
High Street
Lowesmoor Place 16
Lowesmoor Terrace 17
Lychgate Shopping Centre . . . 20
Mealcheapen Street 21
North Parade 24

North Quay . . . .
Pump Street . . . .
St. Martin's Gate . . . .
St. Mary's Street . . . .
St. Nicholas Street . . . .
Sansome Street . . . .
Sansome Walk . . . .
Shambles (The) . . . .
Shaw Street . . . .
Sidbury . . . .

Diglis House, Severn St., WR1 2NF, ☎ (01905) 353518, *diglis@england.com, Fax (01905) 767772,* ←, ☗, « Georgian house on banks of River Severn », – rest, TV P. MC AE ① VISA. o
Meals (bar lunch)/dinner 19.50 **st.** 7.20 – **24 rm** 80.00/125.00, 1 suite – SB.

Travel Inn, Wainwright Way, Warndon, WR4 9FA, Northeast : 5 ½ m. by A 449 (at junction 6 of M 5) ☎ (01905) 451240, *Fax (01905) 756601* – rm, TV ♿. MC AE ① VISA.
Meals (grill rest.) – **60 rm** 40.95 **t.**

Brown's, 24 Quay St., WR1 2JJ, ☎ (01905) 26263, *Fax (01905) 25768,* « Converted riverside corn mill » – MC AE VISA JCB c
closed 1 week Christmas, Monday, Sunday dinner and Saturday lunch – **Meals** 18.50/35.50 **st.** 6.00.

ORFIELD *Shrops. – see Bridgnorth.*

ORKSOP *Notts.* 402 403 404 Q 24 *Great Britain G. – pop. 37 247.*
See : *Mr. Straw's House★.*
Kilton Forest, Blyth Rd ☎ (01909) 472488.
Worksop Library, Memorial Av. ☎ (01909) 501148.
London 163 – Derby 47 – Lincoln 28 – Nottingham 30 – Sheffield 19.

Clumber Park, Clumber Park, S80 3PA, Southeast : 6 ½ m. by B 6040 and A 57 on A 614 ☎ (01623) 835333, *Fax (01623) 835525,* – TV ♿ P – 180. MC AE ① VISA.
Meals 11.95/20.00 **st.** and a la carte 9.00 – 9.50 – **48 rm** 75.00/115.00 **st.** – SB.

Travelodge, Dukeries Mill, St. Anne's Drive, S80 3QD, West : ½ m. off A 57 ☎ (01909) 501528, *Fax (01909) 501528* – rm, TV ♿ P. MC AE ① VISA JCB.
Meals (grill rest.) – **40 rm** 39.95 **t.**

ORMALD GREEN *N. Yorks.* 402 P 21 – *see Ripon.*

ORMINGTON *Glos.* 403 404 O 27 – *see Broadway (Worcestershire).*

ORSLEY *Gtr. Manchester* 402 403 404 MN 23 – *see Manchester.*

ORTHING *W. Sussex* 404 S 31 – *pop. 95 732.*
Hill Barn, Hill Barn Lane ☎ (01903) 237301 **BY** – , *Links Rd ☎ (01903) 260801* **AY**.
Shoreham Airport : ☎ (01273) 296900, E : 4 m. by A 27 **BY**.
Chapel Rd ☎ (01903) 210022 – Marine Par. ☎ (01903) 210022.
London 59 – Brighton 11 – Southampton 50.

Plan on next page

Beach, Marine Par., BN11 3QJ, ☎ (01903) 234001, *thebeachhotel@btinternet.com, Fax (01903) 234567,* ← – TV ♿ P – 250. MC AE ① VISA. AZ e
closed 30 December-4 January – **Meals** (bar lunch Monday to Saturday)/dinner 18.95 **t.** and a la carte 6.25 – **75 rm** 58.00/97.50 **st.**, 4 suites – SB.

Chatsworth, Steyne, BN11 3DU, ☎ (01903) 236103, *chatsworth@wakefordhotels.co.uk, Fax (01903) 823726* – , rest, TV – 150. MC AE ① VISA BZ x
Meals (dinner only) 14.95 **st.** 4.75 – **107 rm** 50.00/80.00 **st.** – SB.

Berkeley, 86-95 Marine Par., BN11 3QD, ☎ (01903) 820000, *berkeley@wakefordhotels.co.uk, Fax (01903) 821333,* ← – TV ♿ P – 150. MC AE ① VISA. BZ a
Meals (bar lunch Monday to Saturday)/dinner 14.95 **st.** 5.50 – **84 rm** 60.00/99.00 **st.** – SB.

The Windsor, 14-20 Windsor Rd, BN11 2LX, ☎ (01903) 239655, Reservations (Freephone) 0800 9804242, *thewindsorhotel@compuserve.com, Fax (01903) 210763,* – rest, rest, TV P – 120. MC AE ① VISA JCB. BY i
closed 24-31 December – **Meals** (buffet lunch)/dinner 15.95 **t.** and a la carte 6.50 – **30 rm** 65.00/110.00 **t.** – SB.

Beacons without rest., 18 Shelley Rd, BN11 1TU, ☎ (01903) 230948, *beaconshotel@zoom.co.uk, Fax (01903) 230948* – TV P. MC VISA BZ e
8 rm 31.00/54.00 **st.**

Bonchurch House without rest., 1 Winchester Rd, BN11 4DJ, ☎ (01903) 202492, *bonchurch@enta.net, Fax (01903) 202492* – TV P. MC VISA JCB. AZ v
closed January and February – **7 rm** 24.00/50.00.

WORTHING

Street	Grid	No.
Broadwater Road	BZ	3
Broadwater Street West	BY	5
Broadway (The)	BZ	6
Brougham Road	BY	7
Brunswick Road	AZ	8
Chapel Road	BZ	
Church Road	AY	12
Cowper Road	AZ	13
Crockhurst Hill	AY	14
Durrington Hill	AY	15
Eriswell Road	ABZ	16
Goring Street	AY	17
Goring Way	AY	18
Grafton Road	BZ	20
Guildbourne Centre	BZ	
High Street	BZ	21
Liverpool Road	BZ	22
Montague Street	BZ	
Montague Centre Shopping Centre	BZ	
Mulberry Lane	AY	24
Portland Road	BZ	25
Rectory Road	AY	26
Reigate Road	AY	27
Sompting Avenue	BY	28
Sompting Road	BY	29
South Street (WEST TARRING)	AY, AZ	
South Street (WORTHING)	BZ	
Southfarm Road	ABZ	
Steyne (The)	BZ	
Steyne Garden	BZ	
Stoke Abbot Road	BZ	
Tennyson Road	AZ	
Thorn Road	AZ	
Union Place	BZ	
Warwick Road	BZ	
Warwick Street	BZ	
West Street	BZ	
Western Place	BZ	
Wykeham Road	AZ	

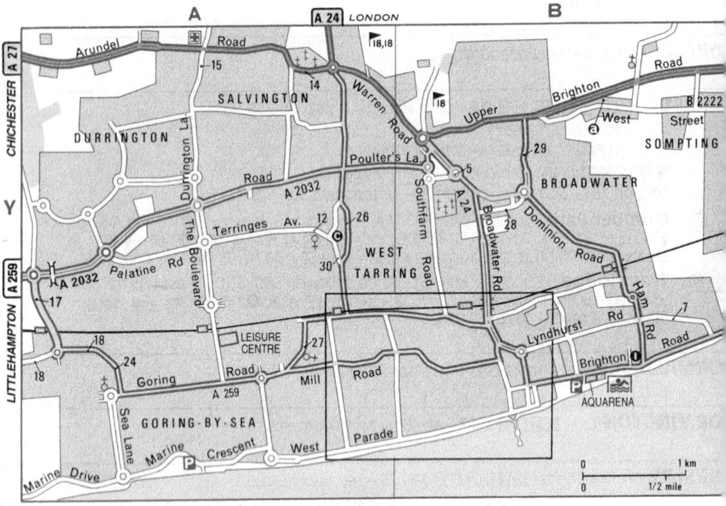

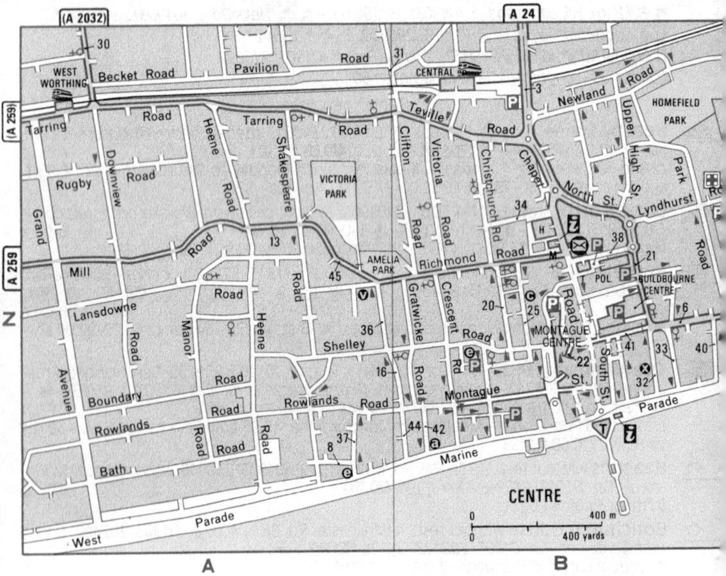

Upton Farm House without rest., Upper Brighton Rd, Sompting Village, BN14 9JU, (01903) 233706, – TV P BY a
3 rm 25.00/55.00 st.

Trenchers, 118-120 Portland Rd, BN11 1QA, (01903) 820287, *Fax (01903) 820305* – MC VISA BZ c
closed Sunday dinner and Monday – **Meals** 25.00/30.00 **t.** and a la carte 39.00/52.00 **t.** 7.00.

Parsonage, 6-10 High St., Tarring, BN14 7NN, (01903) 820140, *Fax (01903) 523233,* « 15C cottages » – MC AE VISA JCB. AY c
closed Sunday and Bank Holidays – **Meals** 11.95/22.25 **st.** and a la carte 7.50.

The Brasserie (at Trenchers), 118-120 Portland Rd, BN11 1QA, (01903) 820287, *Fax (01903) 820305* – BZ c
closed Sunday dinner and Monday – **Meals** a la carte 16.40/25.95 **t.**

WREA GREEN *Lancs.* 402 L 22 – *see Kirkham.*

WRESSLE *East Riding* 402 R 22 *Great Britain G.* – *Selby (N. Yorks.).*
Env. : *Selby (Abbey Church★), W : 5 m. by minor road and A 63.*
London 208 – Kingston-upon-Hull 31 – Leeds 31 – York 19.

Loftsome Bridge Coaching House, YO8 6EN, South : ½ m. (01757) 630070, *reception@loftsomebridge-hotel.co.uk, Fax (01757) 630070,* – , rest, TV P. MC AE VISA.
Meals *(closed Sunday dinner)* (dinner only and Sunday lunch)/dinner 17.95/18.95 **st.** 4.70 – **16 rm** 45.00/55.00 **st.**, 1 suite.

WRIGHTINGTON BAR *Gtr. Manchester* 402 404 L 23 – *see Standish.*

WROTHAM HEATH *Kent* 404 U 30 – *pop. 1 767* – *Sevenoaks.*
London 35 – Maidstone 10.

Posthouse Maidstone/Sevenoaks, London Rd, TN15 7RS, on A 20 (0870) 400 9054, *Fax (01732) 885850,* , , , – rm, TV P – 60. MC AE VISA JCB
Meals 15.00 **t.** (dinner) and a la carte 20.30/29.15 **t.** 6.95 – 11.95 – **108 rm** 79.00/99.00 **st.** – SB.

Travel Inn, London Rd, TN15 7RX, on A 20 (01732) 884214, *Fax (01732) 780368* – rm, TV P. MC AE VISA.
Meals (grill rest.) – **40 rm** 40.95 **t.**

WROXHAM *Norfolk* 404 Y 25 *Great Britain G.* – *pop. 3 247 (inc. Hoveton).*
Env. : *The Broads★.*
London 118 – Great Yarmouth 21 – Norwich 7.

Garden Cottage, 96 Norwich Rd, NR12 8RY, (01603) 784376, *Fax (01603) 783734* – TV P. MC VISA
closed 1-8 January – **Meals** (by arrangement) 18.00 **s.** – **3 rm** 35.00/60.00 **s.** – SB.

WROXTON *Oxon.* 403 404 P 27 – *see Banbury.*

WYCH CROSS *E. Sussex* 404 U 30 – *see Forest Row.*

WYE *Kent* 404 W 30 – *pop. 1 608* – *Ashford.*
London 60 – Canterbury 10 – Dover 28 – Hastings 34.

Wife of Bath with rm, 4 Upper Bridge St., TN25 5AF, (01233) 812540, *reservations@wifeofbath.com, Fax (01233) 813630,* – rm, TV P. MC AE VISA JCB.
closed 26 December-1 January – **Meals** *(closed Sunday and Monday)* 15.25/23.75 **t.** and lunch a la carte 7.50 – 5.00 – **5 rm** 45.00/90.00 **st.**

WYMONDHAM *Norfolk* 404 X 26 – *pop. 10 869.*
London 102 – Cambridge 55 – King's Lynn 49 – Norwich 12.

Wymondham Consort, 28 Market St., NR18 0BB, (01953) 606721, *wymondham@bestwestern.co.uk, Fax (01953) 601361,* – TV P. MC AE VISA JCB
Meals 10.95/16.95 **st.** and a la carte 6.75 – 8.50 – **20 rm** 57.00/63.00 **t.** – SB.

YARCOMBE *Devon* 403 K 31 – *see Honiton.*

YARM *Stockton-on-Tees* 402 P 20 – *pop. 8 929.*
London 242 – Middlesbrough 8.

Crathorne Hall, Crathorne, TS15 0AR, South : 3 ½ m. by A 67 ☎ (01642) 700398, *re crathorne@arcadianhotels.co.uk, Fax (01642) 700814*, ≤, « Converted Edwardian man sion », – rest, TV P – 140. MC AE VISA JCB
Leven : **Meals** a la carte 27.45/33.90 **t.** 7.90 – **37 rm** 93.00/148.00 **t.** – SB.

Judges at Kirklevington Hall, Kirklevington, TS15 9LW, South : 1 ½ m. on A ☎ (01642) 789000, *Fax (01642) 782878*, ≤, « Former Victorian judges residence », rest, TV P – 180. MC AE VISA.
Meals *(closed Saturday lunch)* 9.95/27.50 **t.** and a la carte 7.95 – **21 rm** 132.0 167.00 **st.** – SB.

YARMOUTH *I.O.W.* 403 404 P 31 – *see Wight (Isle of).*

YATELEY *Hants.* 404 R 29 – *pop. 15 663* – ✉ *Camberley.*
London 37 – Reading 12 – Southampton 58.

Casa Dei Cesari, Handford Lane, Cricket Hill, GU46 6BT, ☎ (01252) 87327 *Fax (01252) 870614*, – TV P. MC AE VISA.
closed 26 December and 1 January – **Meals** - Italian - 16.95 **t.** and a la carte 6.25 – **41 r** 82.50/97.50 **t.**, 2 suites.

YATTENDON *Newbury* 403 404 Q 29 – *pop. 288* – ✉ *Newbury.*
London 61 – Oxford 23 – Reading 12.

Royal Oak with rm, The Square, RG18 0UG, ☎ (01635) 201325, *Fax (01635) 201926*, « Pa 17C coaching inn », – rest, TV P. MC AE VISA
Meals (booking essential) (in bar Monday to Saturday lunch and Sunday dinner)/dinn a la carte 22.20/26.70 **st.** – 9.50 – **5 rm** 95.00/125.00 – SB.

YEADON *W. Yorks.* 402 O 22 – *see Leeds.*

YELVERTON *Devon* 403 H 32 *The West Country G.* – *pop. 3 609 (inc. Horrabridge).*
See : *Yelverton Paperweight Centre★.*
Env. : *Buckland Abbey★★ **AC**, SW : 2 m.*
Exc. : *E : Dartmoor National Park★★.*
Golf Links Rd ☎ (01822) 852824.
London 234 – Exeter 33 – Plymouth 10.

Moorland Links, PL20 6DA, South : 2 m. on A 386 ☎ (01822) 85224 *Fax (01822) 855004*, ≤, – TV P – 200. MC AE VISA
Meals (bar lunch Saturday and Bank Holidays) 19.00/21.00 **t.** 5.75 – **44 rm** 85.0 105.00 **t.**, 1 suite – SB.

Harrabeer Country House, Harrowbeer Lane, PL20 6EA, ☎ (01822) 853302, *recepti @harrabeer.co.uk, Fax (01822) 853302*, – rm, TV P. MC VISA JCB
closed 23 December-2 January – **Meals** (by arrangement) 13.50 **s.** – **6 rm** 25.00/57.00 – SB.

YEOVIL *Somerset* 403 404 M 31 *The West Country G.* – *pop. 28 317.*
See : *St. John the Baptist★.*
Env. : *Monacute House★★ **AC**, W : 4 m. on A 3088 – Fleet Air Arm Museum, Yeovilton **AC**, NW : 5 m. by A 37 – Tintinhull House Garden★ **AC**, NW: 5½ m. – Ham Hill (≤★★) W : 5 m. by A 3088 – Stoke sub-Hamdon (parish church★) W : 5¼ m. by A 3088.*
Exc. : *Muchelney★★ (Parish Church★★) NW : 14 m. by A 3088, A 303 and B 3165 – Ly Cary★, N : 7½ m. by A 37, B 3151 and A 372 – Sandford Orcas Manor House★, NW : 8 m. A 359 – Cadbury Castle (≤★★) NE : 10½ m. by A 359 – East Lambrook Manor★ **AC**, W : 12 by A 3088 and A 303.*
Sherborne Rd ☎ (01935) 475949.
Petter's House, Petter's Way ☎ (01935) 471279 – at Podimore : South Somerset Visi Centre, Service Area (A 303) ☎ (01935) 841302 (summer only).
London 136 – Exeter 48 – Southampton 72 – Taunton 26.

Yeovil Court, West Coker Rd, BA20 2HE, Southwest : 2 m. on A 30 (01935) 863746, *venue@yeovilcourt.freeserve.co.uk, Fax (01935) 863990* – 60.
Meals *(closed Saturday lunch and Sunday dinner)* 9.50 **t.** (lunch) and a la carte 15.65/23.60 **t.** 9.50 – **29 rm** 66.50/75.00 **t.**, 1 suite – SB.

Holywell House without rest., Holywell, East Coker, BA22 9NQ, Southwest : 2 ¾ m. by A 30 on Hardington rd (01935) 862612, *b+b@holywellhouse.freeserve.co.uk, Fax (01935) 863035,* « Georgian manor house », , – .
closed 2 weeks Christmas and New Year – **2 rm** 45.00/70.00 **s.**, 1 suite.

t Podimore *North : 9½ m. by A 37 off A 303 –* *Yeovil.*

Travelodge, BA22 8JG, West : ½ m. (01935) 840074 – rm, .
Meals (grill rest.) – **31 rm** 49.95 **t.**

t Barwick *South : 2 m. by A 30 off A 37 –* *Yeovil.*

Little Barwick House with rm, BA22 9TD, (01935) 423902, *Fax (01935) 420908,* « Georgian dower house », – .
Meals *(closed Sunday and Monday to non-residents)* 12.95/25.95 **t.** and lunch a la carte 6.60 – **6 rm** (dinner included) 63.50/103.00 **t.** – SB.

ETMINSTER *Dorset* 403 404 M 31 – *see Sherborne.*

The Guide is updated annually so renew your Guide every year.

ORK *N. Yorks.* 402 Q 22 *Great Britain G. – pop. 124 609.*

See : *City★★★ – Minster★★★ (Stained Glass★★★, Chapter House★★, Choir Screen★★)* **CDY** – *National Railway Museum★★★* **CY** – *The Walls★★* **CDXYZ** – *Castle Museum★* **AC DZ M2** – *Jorvik Viking Centre★* **AC DY M1** – *Fairfax House★* **AC DY A** – *The Shambles★* **DY 54.**

Lords Moor Lane, Strensall (01904) 491840 **BY** – *Heworth, Muncaster House, Muncastergate (01904) 424618* **BY**.

The De Grey Rooms, Exhibition Sq. (01904) 621756 – York Railway Station, Outer Concourse (01904) 621756.

London 203 – Kingston-upon-Hull 38 – Leeds 26 – Middlesbrough 51 – Nottingham 88 – Sheffield 62.

Plan on next page

Middlethorpe Hall, Bishopthorpe Rd, YO23 2GB, South : 1 ¾ m. (01904) 641241, *info@middlethorpe.com, Fax (01904) 620176,* , « William and Mary house, gardens », , , – , rest, – 50. .
Meals *(closed to non-residents on 25 December)* (booking essential to non-residents) 15.50/34.00 **st.** – 14.50 – **23 rm** 105.00/175.00 **st.**, 7 suites – SB.

The Grange, Clifton, YO30 6AA, (01904) 644744, *info@grangehotel.co.uk, Fax (01904) 612453,* « Regency town house » – – 45. . CX u
***The Ivy* :** **Meals** *(closed Sunday)* (dinner only) 25.00 **t.** and a la carte 9.25 – ***The Brasserie* :** **Meals** a la carte 17.90/21.90 **t.** 7.00 – **29 rm** 99.00/185.00 **st.**, 1 suite – SB.

Swallow (becoming a Marriott spring 2001), Tadcaster Rd, YO24 1QQ, (01904) 701000, *york@swallow.hotels.co.uk, Fax (01904) 702308,* , , , , – , , rest, – 170. AZ a
***Ridings* :** **Meals** 14.50/21.50 **st.** and a la carte 7.00 – **111 rm** 115.00/160.00 **st.**, 1 suite – SB.

York Moat House, North St., YO1 6JF, (01904) 459988, *cbyrk@queensmoat.co.uk, Fax (01904) 641793,* , , – – 390. CY n
Meals (bar lunch)/dinner 16.95 **st.** and a la carte 6.25 – 11.50 – **199 rm** 120.00/165.00 **st.**, 1 suite – SB.

Dean Court, Duncombe Pl., YO1 7EF, (01904) 625082, *info@deancourt-york.co.uk, Fax (01904) 620305* – – 50. . CY c
Meals 14.50/25.00 **t.** and dinner a la carte 7.95 – **38 rm** 80.00/170.00 **t.**, 1 suite – SB.

Monkbar, St. Maurice's Rd, YO31 7JA, (01904) 638086, *sales@monkbar.hotel.co.uk, Fax (01904) 629195* – – 200. DX a
Meals 7.50/21.50 **st.** and a la carte 6.50 – **99 rm** 90.00/135.00 **st.** – SB.

Ambassador, 123-125 The Mount, YO24 1DU, (01904) 641316, *stay@ambassadorhotel.co.uk, Fax (01904) 640259,* – , rest, – 50. . AZ c
closed 24-27 December – ***Gray's* :** **Meals** (dinner only) 19.95 **t.** and a la carte 9.00 – **25 rm** 98.00/120.00 **t.** – SB.

YORK

Bishopgate Street . . . . CZ 3
Bishophill Senior . . . . CZ 4
Blake Street . . . . CY 5
Campleshon Road . . . . . . AZ 7
Church Street . . . . DY 8
Clifford Street . . . . DY 10
Colliergate . . . . DY 12
Coney Street . . . . CY 13
Cromwell Road . . . . CZ 15
Davygate . . . . CY 16
Deangate . . . . DY 18
Duncombe Place . . . . CY 20
Fawcett Street . . . . DZ 21
Fetter Lane . . . . CY 22
Goodramgate . . . . DY 25
High Ousegate . . . . DY 26
High Petergate . . . . CY 28
Knavesmire Road . . . . AZ 29
Leeman Road . . . . AY, CY 30
Lendal . . . . CY 32
Lord Mayor's Walk . . . . . . DX 33
Low Petergate . . . . DY 35
Melrosegate . . . . BY 36
Museum Street . . . . CY 39
Parliament Street . . . . DY 42
Pavement . . . . DY 43
Peasholme Green . . . . DY 45
Penley's Grove Street . . . . DX 46
Queen Street . . . . CZ 49
St. Helen's Road . . . . AZ 50
St. Leonard's Place . . . . . . CY 52
St. Maurice's Road . . . . DXY 53
Shambles (The) . . . . DY 54
Station Road . . . . CY 55
Stonebow (The) . . . . DY 56
Stonegate . . . . CY 58
Tower Street . . . . DZ 59
University Road . . . . BZ 60

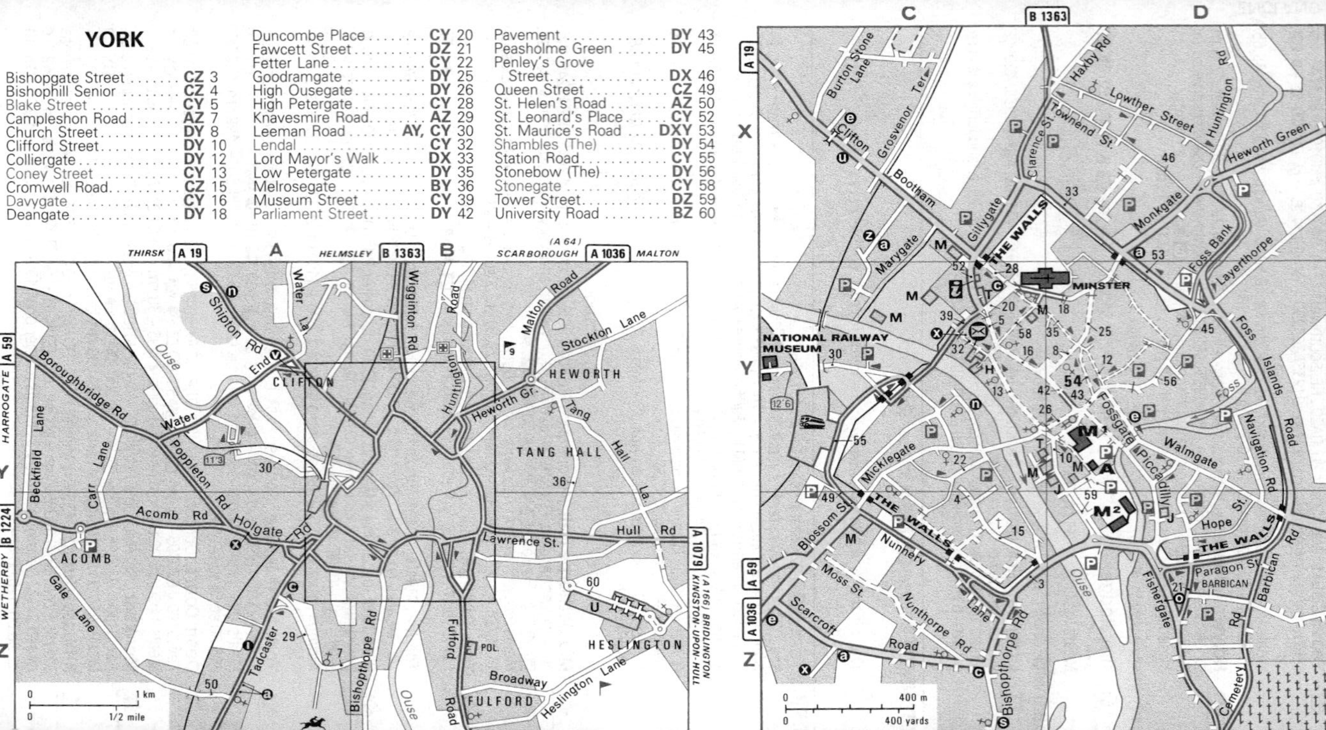

York Pavilion, 45 Main St., Fulford, YO10 4PJ, South : 1 m. on A 19 ☎ (01904) 622099, *reservations@yorkpavilionhotel.co.uk, Fax (01904) 626939* – TV P – 200. MC AE VISA.
Langtons Brasserie : **Meals** 14.95 **t.** (lunch) and dinner a la carte 17.95/27.95 **t.** – **57 rm** 97.00/150.00 **t.** – SB.

Judges' Lodging, 9 Lendal, YO1 8AQ, ☎ (01904) 638733, *judgeshotel@aol.com, Fax (01904) 679947,* « 18C former judges' residence » – TV P. MC AE VISA JCB CY x
Meals 9.95/11.95 **t.** (dinner) and lunch a la carte 7.45/12.50 **t.** 6.25 – **12 rm** 50.00/150.00 **t.**, 3 suites – SB.

Novotel, Fishergate, YO10 4FB, ☎ (01904) 611660, *h0949@accor-hotels.com, Fax (01904) 610925,* – rest, TV P – 210. MC AE VISA JCB DZ o
Meals 16.00 **st.** and a la carte – 9.95 – **124 rm** 79.00 **st.** – SB.

Savages, St. Peter's Grove, Clifton, YO30 6AQ, ☎ (01904) 610818, *Fax (01904) 627729* – rest, TV P. MC AE VISA. CX e
closed Christmas – **Meals** (dinner only) 11.50 **st.** 4.95 – **21 rm** 29.50/59.00 **st.**

Cottage, 3 Clifton Green, YO30 6LH, ☎ (01904) 643711, *Fax (01904) 611230* – rest, TV P. MC AE VISA. AY v
closed 25-26 December and 2 weeks January – **Meals** (residents only) (dinner only) a la carte 14.70/21.00 **t.** 6.95 – **21 rm** 35.00/75.00 – SB.

Arndale without rest., 290 Tadcaster Rd, YO24 1ET, ☎ (01904) 702424, *Fax (01904) 709800,* – TV P. MC VISA JCB. AZ i
12 rm 50.00/80.00 **st.**

Holmwood House without rest., 114 Holgate Rd, YO24 4BB, ☎ (01904) 626183, *holmwood.house@dial.pipex.com, Fax (01904) 670899,* – TV P. MC AE VISA. AZ x
14 rm 55.00/90.00 **t.**

Express by Holiday Inn without rest., Malton Rd, YO32 9TE, Northeast : 2 ¾ m. on A 1036 ☎ (01904) 438660, *Fax (01904) 438560* – TV P – 30. MC AE VISA.
49 rm 49.95 **t.**

Express by Holiday Inn without rest., Shipton Rd, Clifton Park, YO30 5PA, Northwest : 1 ½ m. on A 19 ☎ (01904) 659992, *Fax (01904) 659994,* – TV P – 25. MC AE VISA. AY s
49 rm 44.95 **st.**

Grasmead House without rest., 1 Scarcroft Hill, YO24 1DF, ☎ (01904) 629996, *stansue@grasmeadhouse.freeserve.co.uk, Fax (01904) 629996* – TV. MC AE VISA JCB.
6 rm 60.00/75.00 **st.** CZ a

23 St. Mary's without rest., 23 St. Mary's, Bootham, YO30 7DD, ☎ (01904) 622738, *Fax (01904) 628802* – TV. CX a
closed 22 December-4 January – **9 rm** 34.00/76.00 **t.**

Curzon Lodge and Stable Cottages without rest., 23 Tadcaster Rd, YO24 1QG, ☎ (01904) 703157, *Fax (01904) 703157* – TV P. MC VISA JCB. AZ a
closed Christmas and New Year – **10 rm** 52.00/80.00 **st.**

Eastons's without rest., 90 Bishopthorpe Rd, YO23 1JS, ☎ (01904) 626646, *eastonsbbyork@aol.com, Fax (01904) 626165* – TV P. CZ s
closed 3 days Christmas – **10 rm** 40.00/71.00.

Crook Lodge without rest., 26 St. Mary's, Bootham, YO30 7DD, ☎ (01904) 655614, *Fax (01904) 655614* – TV P. CX z
closed 25 December-1 February – **7 rm** 30.00/58.00 **st.**

Acer without rest., 52 Scarcroft Hill, YO24 1DE, ☎ (01904) 653839, *info@acerhotel.co.uk, Fax (01904) 677017* – TV. MC VISA CZ x
3 rm 35.00/60.00 **s.**

Ashbury without rest., 103 The Mount, YO24 1AX, ☎ (01904) 647339, *ashbury@talk21.com, Fax (01904) 647339,* – TV. MC VISA. CZ e
closed 17-28 December – **5 rm** 45.00/60.00 **t.**

The Heathers without rest., 54 Shipton Rd, Clifton-Without, YO30 5RQ, Northwest : 1 ½ m. on A 19 ☎ (01904) 640989, *thghyork@globalnet.co.uk, Fax (01904) 640989,* – TV P. MC AE VISA. AY n
closed 24-26 December – **8 rm** 42.00/104.00 **st.**

Melton's, 7 Scarcroft Rd, YO23 1ND, ☎ (01904) 634341, *great-food@meltons-restaurant.co.uk, Fax (01904) 635115* – . MC VISA CZ c
closed 3 weeks Christmas, 1 week August, Sunday dinner and Monday lunch – **Meals** (booking essential) 16.00 **st.** (lunch) and a la carte 21.10/26.70 **st.** 7.00.

Blue Bicycle, 34 Fossgate, YO1 9TA, ☎ (01904) 673990, *Fax (01904) 780366* – . MC AE VISA DY e
Meals (booking essential) a la carte 20.50/29.90 **t.** 7.50.

ENGLAND

at Acaster Malbis *South : 4 ¾ m. by Bishopthorpe Rd* – **BZ** – ⊠ *York.*

The Manor Country House without rest., Mill Lane, YO23 2UL, (01904) 70672 *manorhouse@sekom.co.uk, Fax (01904) 706723,* – rm P. MC VISA JCB. *closed 20 December-5 January* – **10 rm** 39.00/70.00 **st.**

at Escrick *South : 5 ¾ m. on A 19* – **BZ** – ⊠ *York.*

Parsonage Country House, Main St., YO19 6LF, (01904) 728111, *sales@parsonage otel.co.uk, Fax (01904) 728151,* – P – 160. MC AE VISA. **Meals** 7.00/43.00 **st.** 7.50 – **21 rm** 95.00/130.00 **st.** – SB.

at Bilbrough *Southwest : 5½ m. by A 1036* – **AZ** – *off A 64* – ⊠ *York.*

Travel Inn, Bilbrough Top, Colton, YO23 3PP, South : ½ m. on A 64 (westbound carriag way) (01937) 835067, *Fax (01937) 835934* – , rm, rest, P – 30. MC AE VISA. **Meals** (grill rest.) (dinner only) – **60 rm** 40.95 **t.**

Travelodge, Steeton, LS24 8EG, Southwest : ¾ m. on A 64 (eastbound carriagewa (01937) 531823, *Fax (01937) 531823* – rm, P. MC AE VISA JCB. **Meals** (grill rest.) – **62 rm** 49.95 **t.**

at Skelton *Northwest : 3 m. on A 19* – **AY** – ⊠ *York.*

Jarvis International, Shipton Rd, YO30 1XW, (01904) 670222, *Fax (01904) 67031* – , rest, P – 200. MC AE VISA **Meals** *(closed Saturday lunch)* 16.75 **st.** (lunch) and a la carte 10.10/28.15 **st.** 6.85 – 8.95 – **83 rm** 105.00/125.00 **st.**, 6 suites – SB.

at York Business Park *Northwest : 3 ¾ m. by A 59* – **AY** – *on A 1237* – ⊠ *York.*

Travel Inn, White Rose Close, YO2 7NY, (01904) 787630, *Fax (01904) 787663* – rm, rest, P. MC AE VISA. **Meals** (grill rest.) – **44 rm** 40.95 **t.**

Maxi's, Ings Lane, Nether Poppleton, YO26 6RA, (01904) 783898, *info@maxi_s.co.u Fax (01904) 783818,* « Pagoda, ornate decor » – P. MC AE VISA *closed 25-27 December* – **Meals** - Chinese (Canton and Peking) - 17.50/24.00 and a la carte.

Scotland

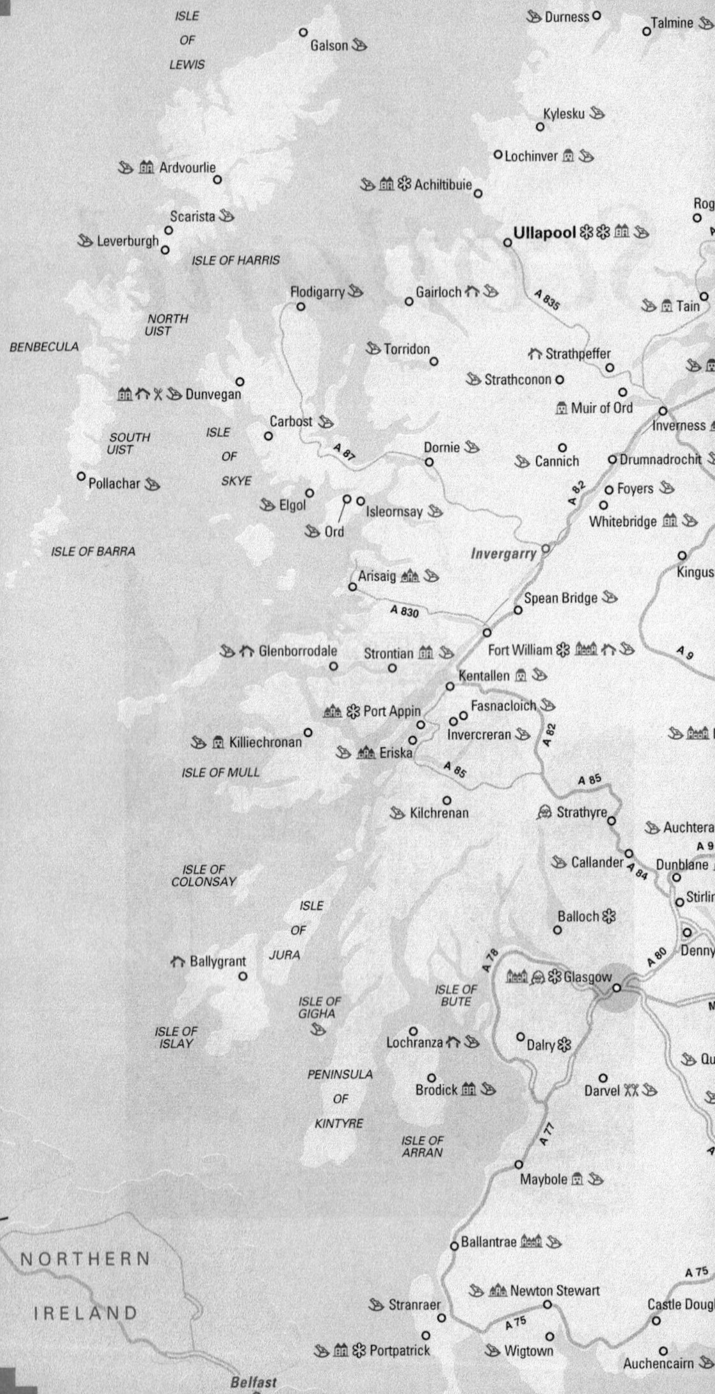
ISLE OF LEWIS
Galson
Durness
Talmine
Kylesku
Lochinver
Ardvourlie
Achiltibuie
Scarista
Leverburgh
Ullapool
ISLE OF HARRIS
Flodigarry
Gairloch
A 835
Tain
NORTH UIST
BENBECULA
Torridon
Strathpeffer
Strathconon
Dunvegan
Muir of Ord
Carbost
Inverness
SOUTH UIST
ISLE OF SKYE
A 87
Dornie
Cannich
Drumnadrochit
Pollachar
A 82
Foyers
Elgol
Isleornsay
Whitebridge
Ord
ISLE OF BARRA
Invergarry
Kinguss
Arisaig
Spean Bridge
A 830
Fort William
A 9
Glenborrodale
Strontian
Kentallen
Port Appin
Fasnacloich
Killiechronan
Invercreran
A 82
Eriska
A 85
ISLE OF MULL
A 85
Kilchrenan
Strathyre
Auchterar
A 9
Callander
A 84
Dunblane
ISLE OF COLONSAY
Stirlin
ISLE OF JURA
Balloch
Denny
Ballygrant
A 78
A 80
Glasgow
ISLE OF BUTE
ISLE OF GIGHA
ISLE OF ISLAY
Lochranza
Dalry
PENINSULA OF KINTYRE
Brodick
Darvel
ISLE OF ARRAN
A 77
Maybole
Ballantrae
NORTHERN IRELAND
A 75
Newton Stewart
Stranraer
Castle Dougl
A 75
Portpatrick
Wigtown
Auchencairn
Belfast

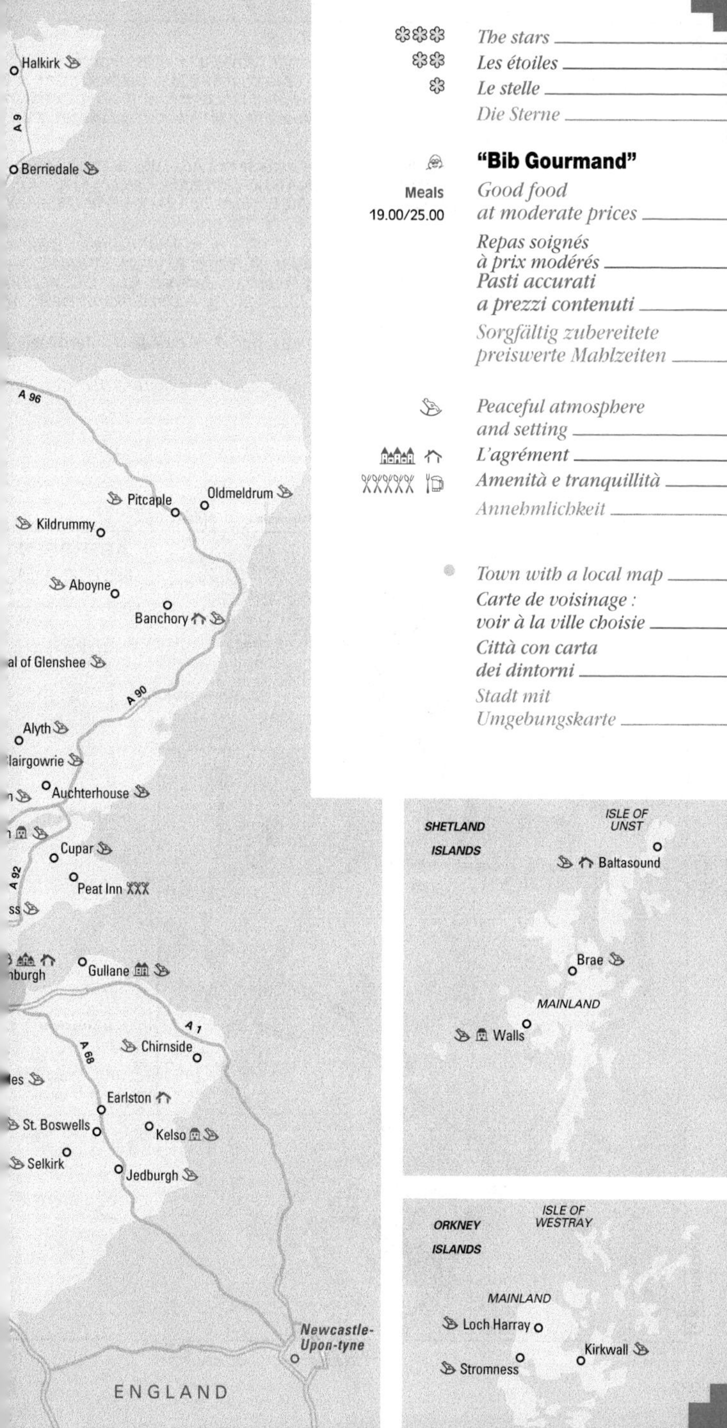

The stars
Les étoiles
Le stelle
Die Sterne
"Bib Gourmand"
Meals
19.00/25.00
Good food at moderate prices
Repas soignés à prix modérés
Pasti accurati a prezzi contenuti
Sorgfältig zubereitete preiswerte Mahlzeiten
Peaceful atmosphere and setting
L'agrément
Amenità e tranquillità
Annehmlichkeit
Town with a local map
Carte de voisinage : voir à la ville choisie
Città con carta dei dintorni
Stadt mit Umgebungskarte
Halkirk
A 9
Berriedale
A 96
Pitcaple
Oldmeldrum
Kildrummy
Aboyne
Banchory
A 90
Alyth
Auchterhouse
Cupar
A 92
Peat Inn
Gullane
A 1
A 68
Chirnside
Earlston
St. Boswells
Kelso
Selkirk
Jedburgh
Newcastle-Upon-tyne
ENGLAND
SHETLAND ISLANDS
ISLE OF UNST
Baltasound
Brae
MAINLAND
Walls
ORKNEY ISLANDS
ISLE OF WESTRAY
MAINLAND
Loch Harray
Kirkwall
Stromness

ABERDEEN *Aberdeen* **401** N 12 *Scotland G. – pop. 204 885.*

See : *City★★ – Old Aberdeen★★* **X** *– St. Machar's Cathedral★★ (West Front★★★, Hera Ceiling★★★)* **X A** *– Art Gallery★★ (Macdonald Collection★★)* **Y M** *– Mercat Cross★★* **Y E** *King's College Chapel★ (Crown Spire★★★, medieval fittings★★★)* **X D** *– Provost Sken House★ (painted ceilings★★)* **Y E** *– Maritime Museum★* **Z M1** *– Marischal College★* **Y U.**

Env. : *Brig o' Balgownie★, by Don St.* **X.**

Exc. : *SW : Deeside★★ – Crathes Castle★★ (Gardens★★★)* **AC**, *SW : 16 m. by A 93* **X** *Dunnottar Castle★★* **AC** *(site★★★), S : 18 m. by A 90* **X** *– Pitmedden Garden★★, N : 14 m. A 90 on B 999* **X** *– Castle Fraser★ (exterior★★)* **AC**, *W : 16 m. by A 944* **X** *– Fyvie Castle★, N 26½ m. on A 947.*

18, 18, 9 Hazelhead, Hazelhead Park ☎ (01224) 321830 – 18, 18 Royal Aberdeen, Balgowr Bridge of Don ☎ (01224) 702571, **X** *– 18 Balnagask, St. Fitticks Rd ☎ (01224) 876407,* **X** *– King's Links, Golf Rd ☎ (01224) 632269,* **X** *– 18 Portlethen, Badentoy Rd ☎ (01224) 7810* **X** *– 18, 9 Murcar, Bridge of Don ☎ (01224) 704354,* **X** *– 18 Auchmill, Bomyview Rd, W Heatheryfold ☎ (01224) 715214,* **X.**

✈ *Aberdeen Airport, Dyce : ☎ (01224) 722331, NW : 7 m. by A 96* **X** – **Terminal** : *Station, Guild St. (adjacent to Railway Station).*

⛴ *to Shetland Islands (Lerwick) and via Orkney Islands (Stromness) (P & O Scottish Ferr 1-2 weekly.*

i *St. Nicholas House, Broad St. ☎ (01224) 632727.*

Edinburgh 130 – Dundee 67.

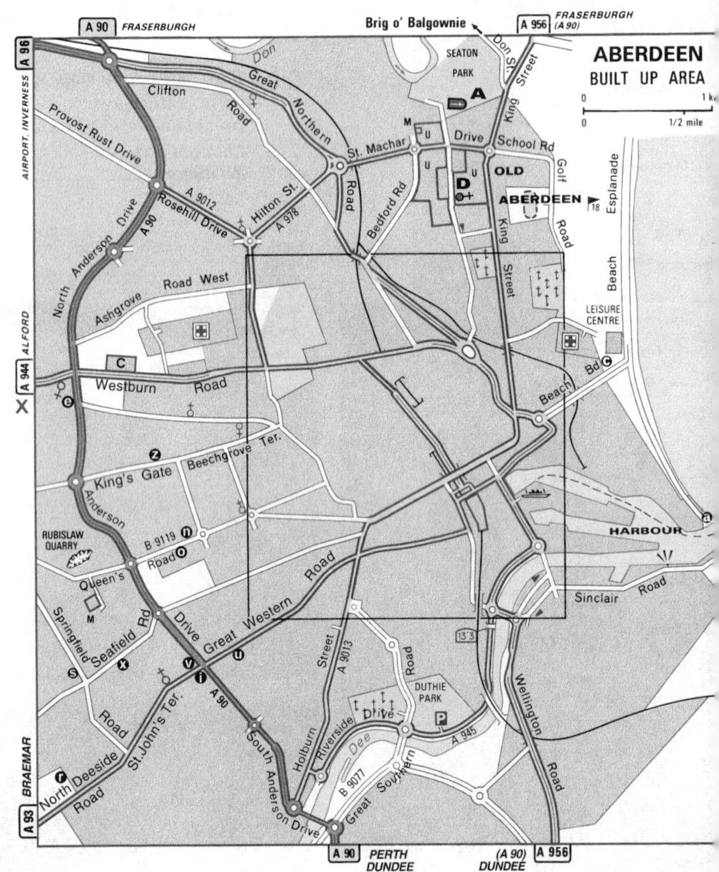

ABERDEEN

n Accord Centre . . . . Y
ad Street . . . . Y 6
stle Street . . . . Y 7
lege Street . . . . Z 9
igie Loanings . . . . Y 12
nburn Road . . . . YZ 14
st North Street . . . . Y 16
orge Street . . . . Y
eat Southern Road . . . . Z 18

Guild Street . . . . Z 19
Justice Street . . . . Y 21
Millburn Street . . . . Z 23
Rosemount Terrace . . . . Y 25
Rosemount Viaduct . . . . Y 26
St. Andrew Street . . . . Y 28
St. Nicholas Centre . . . . Y 29
St. Nicholas Street . . . . YZ 30
School Hill . . . . YZ 32
South Esplanade
West . . . . Z 33
South Mount Street . . . . Y 34

Springbank Terrace . . . . Z 35
Spring Garden . . . . Y 36
Trinity Centre . . . . Z
Trinity Quay . . . . Z 37
Union Street . . . . Z
Union Terrace . . . . Z 39
Upperkirkgate . . . . Y 40
Victoria Street . . . . Z 42
Waverley Place . . . . Z 43
Wellington Place . . . . Z 45
Wellington Road . . . . Z 47
Woolmanhill . . . . Y 48

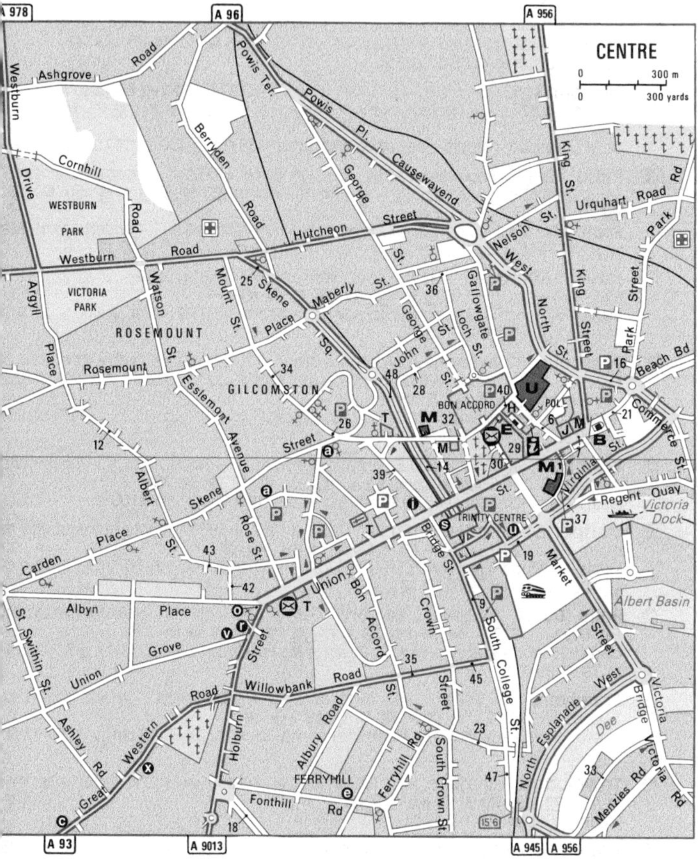

The Marcliffe at Pitfodels, North Deeside Rd, AB15 9YA, ✆ (01224) 861000, *enquiries@marcliffe.com, Fax (01224) 868860,* ⁂, ⁂ – |‡| ⁂, ▤ rest, TV ✆ ♿ P – 400. MC AE ① VISA JCB. ⁂ X r

Invery Room : Meals (dinner only) a la carte 27.00/38.00 **st.** 🍷 10.50 – ***Conservatory :*** Meals a la carte 21.00/32.00 **st.** 🍷 8.50 – **42 rm** ☕ 145.00/275.00 **st.** – SB.

Ardoe House ⁂, South Deeside Rd, Blairs, AB12 5YP, Southwest : 5 m. on B 9077 ✆ (01224) 860600, *info@ardoe.macdonaldhotels.co.uk, Fax (01224) 861283,* ≤, « Part 19C baronial mansion », ⁂, ⁂, ⁂, ⁂, ⁂, ⁂ – |‡| ⁂ TV ✆ ♿ P – 500. MC AE ① VISA

Meals 27.50/29.50 **t.** (dinner) and a la carte 25.20/37.45 **t.** 🍷 8.00 – ☕ 10.50 – **110 rm** 95.00/110.00 **st.**, 2 suites – SB.

Thistle Aberdeen Caledonian, 10-14 Union Terr., AB10 1WE, ✆ (01224) 640233, *aberdeencaledonian@thistle.co.uk, Fax (01224) 641627* – |‡| ⁂ TV ✆ P – 45. MC AE ① VISA JCB Z i

Meals (bar lunch)/dinner 17.95 **t.** and a la carte 🍷 8.00 – ☕ 12.30 – **75 rm** 136.00/157.00 **st.**, 2 suites – SB.

Hilton Aberdeen Tree Tops, 161 Springfield Rd, AB15 7AQ, (01224) 313377, *sale berdeen@hilton.com, Fax (01224) 312028,* – rm, 900. VISA JCB. X
Bar Bacoa : **Meals** a la carte approx. 18.45 **t.** – 6.95 – **119 rm** 95.00/125.00, 1 suite –

Copthorne, 122 Huntly St., AB10 1SU, (01224) 630404, *Fax (01224) 640573* – rm, rest, – 220. VISA JCB Z
Meals (bar lunch Saturday and Sunday) 7.95/18.50 **t.** and a la carte 8.95 – 12.50
89 rm 150.00 **st.**

Skene House Holburn without rest., 6 Union Grove, AB10 6SY, (01224) 580000, *h urn@skene-house.co.uk, Fax (01224) 585193* – VISA JCB. Z
8.50, **39 suites** 75.00/119.00 **st.**

Simpson's, 59 Queen's Rd, AB15 4YP, (01224) 327777, *address@simpsonhotel.co. Fax (01224) 327700,* « Contemporary interior » – – 25. JCB. X
closed 1 January – **Meals** – (see ***Brasserie*** below) – **35 rm** 120.00/140.00 **t.**, 2 suites.

Patio, Beach Boulevard, AB24 5EF, (01224) 633339, *patioab@globalnet.co. Fax (01224) 638833,* – rm, rest, – 150. VISA X
Footdee's : **Meals** (dinner only) a la carte 15.65/29.20 **st.** 6.50 – ***Conservatory :*** **Me** 10.50/15.50 **st.** and a la carte 6.50 – 11.95 – **124 rm** 117.00/137.00 **st.** – SB.

Jarvis Aberdeen, 448 Great Western Rd, AB10 6NP, (01224) 3187 *Fax (01224) 312716* – – 400. VISA JCB X
Meals (bar lunch Monday-Saturday)/dinner a la carte 15.00/21.50 **st.** 6.00 – 9.50
53 rm 92.00/102.00 **st.** – SB.

Posthouse Aberdeen, Aberdeen Exhibition and Conference Centre, Bridge of D AB23 8BL, North : 3 m. by A 956 at junction with A 90 (0870) 4009046, *Fax (01224) 823* – rm, VISA
Meals (bar lunch)/dinner 12.50 **st.** and a la carte 7.50 – 11.95 – **123 rm** 69. 119.00 **st.** – SB.

Grampian, Stirling St., AB11 6JU, (01224) 589101, *info@grampian.macdonald-hote o.uk, Fax (01224) 574288* – – 150. VISA. Z
Meals (bar lunch)/dinner 15.00 **st.** and a la carte – **49 rm** 82.50/98.00 **st.**

Mariner, 349 Great Western Rd, AB10 6NW, (01224) 588901, *enquires@vagabond-h s.com, Fax (01224) 571621* – VISA JCB. X
Meals - Seafood - (bar lunch Saturday) (carvery lunch Sunday) 12.50/14.50 and a la ca 10.00 – **22 rm** 70.00/95.00 **t.** – SB.

Palm Court, 81 Seafield Rd, AB15 7YU, (01224) 310351, *info@palmcourt.co. Fax (01224) 312707* – , rest, – 100. VISA. X
closed 25-26 December and 1-2 January – **Meals** a la carte 9.90/22.40 **t.** 8.50 – **24** 79.00/99.00 **t.** – SB.

Craiglynn, 36 Fonthill Rd, AB11 6UJ, (01224) 584050, *info@craiglynn.co Fax (01224) 212225* – VISA JCB. Z
closed 25 and 26 December – **Meals** (dinner only) 15.95 **st.** 4.95 – **9 rm** 49.50/78.00 – SB.

Travelodge, 9 Bridge St., AB11 6JL, (01224) 584555, *Fax (01224) 584587* – , rest, VISA JCB. Z
Meals (cafe bar) – **97 rm** 49.95 **t.**

Premier Lodge, North Anderson Drive, AB15 6DW, (0870) 70013 *Fax (0870) 7001301* – rm, rest, VISA. X
Meals (grill rest.) a la carte 8.75/16.35 **st.** – 6.00 – **60 rm** 42.00 **st.** – SB.

Mannofield, 447 Great Western Rd, AB10 6NL, (01224) 315888, *info@mannofield.c k, Fax (01224) 208971* – rest, VISA X
Meals (by arrangement) 20.00 **st.** 9.95 – **9 rm** 49.00/69.00 **st.**

Ewood House without rest., 12 King's Gate, AB15 4EJ, (01224) 648408, *ewood@ifb .uk, Fax (01224) 648408,* – VISA JCB. X
5 rm 45.00/65.00 **st.**

Penny Meadow without rest., 189 Great Western Rd., AB10 6PS, (01224) 588 *Fax (01224) 573639,* – VISA JCB. Z
3 rm 40.00//50.00 **s.**

Manorville without rest., 252 Great Western Rd, AB10 6PJ, (01224) 594 *Fax (01224) 594190,* – VISA. Z
3 rm 25.00/42.00.

XX **Silver Darling,** Pocra Quay, North Pier, AB11 5DQ, ℘ (01224) 576229, ≤, « Quayside setting » – MC AE ⓓ VISA X a
closed 2 weeks Christmas-New Year, Saturday lunch and Sunday September-May – **Meals** - Seafood - 23.00 **t.** (lunch) and dinner a la carte 28.45/34.75 **t.**

XX **Brasserie** (at Simpson's H.), 59 Queens Rd, AB15 4YP, ℘ (01224) 327799, – ▤ P. MC AE ⓓ VISA JCB X o
closed 1 January – **Meals** a la carte 13.55/25.70 **t.** 7.95.

XX **Olive Tree,** 32 Queens Rd, AB15 4YF, ℘ (01224) 208877, *info@olive-tree.co.uk, Fax (01224) 314255* – ▤ P. MC AE ⓓ VISA X n
closed Saturday lunch, Sunday and 1-3 January – **Meals** 14.75 **t.** (lunch) and a la carte 14.75/26.60 **t.**

XX **Babylon,** 9 Alford Pl., AB10 1YD, ℘ (01224) 595001, *Fax (01224) 582245* – ▤. MC AE ⓓ VISA JCB Z o
closed Sunday and Monday – **Meals** (dinner only and Friday lunch)/dinner a la carte 18.85/28.85 **t.**

XX **Nargile,** 77-79 Skene St., AB10 1QD, ℘ (01224) 636093, *Fax (01224) 636202* – ▤. MC AE ⓓ VISA Y a
closed 25-26 December, 1 January and Sunday – **Meals** - Turkish - (dinner only) 16.95/20.75 **t.** and a la carte 6.95.

X **Courtyard,** 1 Alford Lane, AB1 1YD, ℘ (01224) 213795, *courtyardcitycafe@hotmail.com, Fax (01224) 212961* – MC AE VISA JCB Z r
closed 25-26 December, 1-2 January, Sunday and Bank Holidays – **Meals** (light lunch) a la carte 19.00/25.50 **t.** 8.75.

Murcar *North : 4½ m. by A 90* – **X** – ✉ *Aberdeen.*

Travel Inn, AB23 8BP, on B 999 ℘ (01224) 821217, *Fax (01224) 706869* – TV ♿ P. MC AE ⓓ VISA.
Meals (grill rest.) – **40 rm** 40.95 **t.**

Altens *(Aberdeenshire) South : 3 m. on A 956* – **X** – ✉ *Aberdeen.*

Thistle Aberdeen Alterns, Souter Head Rd, AB12 3LF, ℘ (01224) 877000, *aberdeen@thistle.co.uk, Fax (01224) 896964*, – , ▤ rest, TV ♿ P – 400. MC AE ⓓ VISA JCB.
Cairngorm : **Meals** (dinner only) 18.50 **st.** 7.50 – ***Brasserie :*** **Meals** (lunch only) a la carte 13.05/30.45 **st.** 7.50 – 10.95 – **208 rm** 123.00 **st.**, 1 suite – SB.

Portlethen *(Aberdeenshire) South : 6 m. on A 90* – **X** – ✉ *Aberdeen.*

Travel Inn, Mains of Balquuarn, AB12 4QS, ℘ (01224) 783856, *Fax (01224) 783836* – rm, TV ♿ P. MC AE ⓓ VISA
Meals (grill rest.) – **40 rm** 40.95 **t.**

Kirkton of Maryculter *(Aberdeenshire) Southwest : 8 m. by B 9077* – **X** – ✉ *Aberdeen.*

Maryculter House , South Deeside Rd, AB12 5GB, Southwest : 1 ½ m. on B 9077 ℘ (01224) 732124, *info@maryculterhousehotel.co.uk, Fax (01224) 733510*, , « Part 13C house on River Dee », – TV P – 200. MC AE ⓓ VISA.
Priory : **Meals** *(closed Sunday)* (dinner only) a la carte 21.40/28.20 **t.** 7.50 – ***Poachers Pocket :*** **Meals** 9.95 **t.** (lunch) and a la carte 9.25/17.00 **t.** 7.50 – **23 rm** 95.00/120.00 **t.** – SB.

Bankhead *(Aberdeenshire) Northwest : 4½ m. by A 96* – **X** – ✉ *Aberdeen.*

Craighaar, Waterton Rd, AB21 9HS, ℘ (01224) 712275, *info@craighaar.co.uk, Fax (01224) 716362* – TV P – 90. MC AE ⓓ VISA
Meals 11.00/36.00 **st.** and a la carte 7.50 – **49 rm** 79.00/89.00 **st.**, 6 suites – SB.

Dyce *(Aberdeenshire) Northwest : 5½ m. by A 96* – **X** – *on A 947* – ✉ *Aberdeen.*

Aberdeen Marriott, Overton Circle, AB21 7AZ, ℘ (01224) 770011, *Fax (01224) 722347*, , , – rm, ▤ TV ♿ P – 400. MC AE ⓓ VISA.
Meals (bar lunch Saturday) 15.95/40.00 **t.** and a la carte – 12.95 – **154 rm** 130.00/160.00 **st.**, 1 suite – SB.

Travel Inn, Burnside Drive, AB21 7HW, off Wellheads Rd ℘ (01224) 772787, *Fax (01224) 772968*, – rm, ▤ rest, TV ♿ P. MC AE ⓓ VISA.
Meals (grill rest.) – **40 rm** 40.95 **t.**

Aberdeen Airport *(Aberdeenshire) Northwest : 6 m. by A 96* – **X** – ✉ *Aberdeen.*

Thistle Aberdeen Airport, Argyll Rd, AB21 7DU, ℘ (01224) 725252, *aberdeenairport@thistle.co.uk, Fax (01224) 723745*, , heated, – rm, TV ♿ P – 600. MC AE VISA
Meals (bar lunch Saturday and Sunday) 12.95/20.50 **t.** and dinner a la carte 6.40 – 11.00 – **146 rm** 138.00/158.00 **st.**, 1 suite – SB.

SCOTLAND

SCOTLAND

Speedbird Inn, Argyll Rd, AB21 0AF, ☎ (01224) 772884, *reservation@speedbirdinns.co.uk, Fax (01224) 772560* – ⇔, ▤ rest, TV ♿ P – 🏟 35. MC AE D VISA
Meals (bar lunch Monday-Saturday)/dinner a la carte approx. 10.15 **st.** 4.00 – ☕ 4.95 – **100 rm** 45.50 **st.** – SB.

ABERDEEN AIRPORT *Aberdeenshire* 401 N 12 – *see Aberdeen.*

ABERFELDY *Perthshire and Kinross* 401 I 14 *Scotland G. – pop. 4 083.*
See : *Town*★.
Env. : *St. Mary's Church (painted ceiling*★*) NE : 2 m. by A 827.*
Exc. : *Loch Tay*★★*, SW : 6 m. by A 827 – Ben Lawers*★★*, SW : 16 m. by A 827 – Blair Castle*★ *AC, N : 20½ m. by A 827 and A 9.*
Taybridge Rd ☎ (01887) 820535.
The Square ☎ (01887) 820276.
Edinburgh 76 – Glasgow 73 – Oban 77 – Perth 32.

Farleyer House ⛰, PH15 2JE, West : 2 m. on B 846 ☎ (01887) 820332, *reservations@farleyer.com, Fax (01887) 829430*, ≤, « Part 16C former dower house », ⛳, 🌳, ⚓ – ⇔ P. MC AE D VISA JCB. ✂
Glen Lyon : **Meals** a la carte 18.15/26.45 **t.** 8.95 – **19 rm** ☕ 65.00/120.00 **t.**

Guinach House ⛰, Urlar Rd, PH15 2ET, off Crieff Rd ☎ (01887) 82025 *Fax (01887) 829607*, ≤, 🌳 – ⇔ TV P. MC VISA
closed 4 days Christmas – **Meals** (dinner only) 25.00 **st.** 8.45 – **7 rm** ☕ 45.50/91.00 **st.**

Fernbank House without rest., Kenmore St., PH15 2BL, on A 827 (Killin ☎ (01887) 820345, ≘, 🌳 – ⇔ TV P. ✂
closed 14 December-14 January – **7 rm** ☕ 30.00/62.00 **st.**

Le Grand Londres (GREATER LONDON) est composé de la City et de 32 arrondissements administratifs (Borough) eux-mêmes divisés en quartiers ou en villages ayant conservé leur caractère propre (Area).

ABERFOYLE *Stirling* 401 G 15.
Trossachs Discovery Centre, Main St. ☎ (01877) 382352.
Edinburgh 57 – Glasgow 30 – Perth 49.

Forest Hills ⛰, Kinlochard, FK8 3TL, West : 4 ¼ m. on B 829 ☎ (01877) 3872 *Fax (01877) 387307*, ≤ Loch Ard, 🏋, ≘, ⛲, ⛳, 🌳, ⚓, ✂ – 🛗 ⚓ ⇔ TV ☎ P – 🏟 120. AE D VISA
Garden : **Meals** (dinner only) 24.95/35.00 9.50 – *Rafters :* **Meals** a la carte appr 15.00 **t.** 8.50 – **53 rm** ☕ (dinner included) 75.00/150.00 **t.**, 2 suites – SB.

ABERLOUR *Aberdeenshire* 401 K 11 *Scotland G. – pop. 1 780.*
Env. : *Dufftown (Glenfiddich Distillery*★*), SE : 6 m. by A 95 and A 941.*
Rothes, Blackhall ☎ (01340) 831443.
Edinburgh 192 – Aberdeen 60 – Elgin 15 – Inverness 55.

Dowans, AB38 9LS, Southwest : ¾ m. by A 95 ☎ (01340) 871488, *penny@thedowans.freeserve.co.uk, Fax (01340) 871038*, ⛳, 🌳 – ⇔ rest, TV P. MC AE VISA
closed 23 December-10 March – **Meals** 24.50 **st.** 5.75 – **19 rm** ☕ 44.00/94.00 **st.**

ABINGTON SERVICE AREA *South Lanarkshire* 401 I 17 – ✉ *Biggar.*
Welcome Break Service Area, junction 13, M 74 ☎ (01864) 502436.
Edinburgh 43 – Dumfries 37 – Glasgow 38.

Days Inn, ML12 6RG, at junction 13 of M 74 ☎ (01864) 502782, Reservations (Freephone) 0800 0280400, *Fax (01864) 502759* – ⇔ rm, TV ☎ ♿ P. MC AE D VISA JCB
Meals (grill rest.) a la carte 8.70/13.90 **t.** – ☕ 7.45 – **56 rm** 45.00/50.00 **t.**

ABOYNE *Aberdeenshire* 401 L 12 *Scotland G. – pop. 3 793 (inc. Cromar).*
Exc. : *Craigievar Castle*★ *AC, NE : 12 m. by B 9094, B 9119 and A 980.*
Formanston Park ☎ (013398) 86328.
Edinburgh 131 – Aberdeen 30 – Dundee 68.

Struan Hall without rest., Ballater Rd, AB34 5HY, ☎ (013398) 87241, *struanhall@zetnet.co.uk, Fax (013398) 87241*, – ⊬ TV P. MC VISA JCB. ⚡
March-October – **4 rm** 28.50/57.00 **st.**

Arbor Lodge without rest., Ballater Rd, AB34 5HY, ☎ (013398) 86951, *arborlodge@aol.com, Fax (013398) 86951*, – ⊬ TV P. MC VISA
March-November – **3 rm** 30.00/52.00 **st.**

Birse Lodge without rest., Charleston Rd, AB34 5EL, on B 968 ☎ (013398) 86253, *birse_lodge@compuserve.com, Fax (013398) 87796*, – ⊬ TV P. MC VISA
closed Christmas and New Year – **3 rm** 32.00/55.00 **st.**

Birkwood Lodge without rest., Gordon Cres., AB34 5HJ, off A 93 ☎ (013398) 86347, *Fax (013398) 86347*, – ⊬ TV P. ⚡
April-October – **3 rm** 35.00/55.00 **s.**

Migvie *Northwest : 10 m. by A 93 off A 97 – ✉ Aboyne.*

Migvie House ⚡, by Logie Coldstone, AB34 4XL, ☎ (013398) 81313, *bluffman.cv@aberdeenshire.gov.uk, Fax (013398) 81635*, ≤, – ⊬ P. ⚡
March-October – **Meals** (by arrangement) (communal dining) 17.00 **s.** – **3 rm** 35.00/50.00 **s.**

CHILTIBUIE *Highland* 401 D 9.

Edinburgh 243 – Inverness 84 – Ullapool 25.

Summer Isles ⚡, IV26 2YG, ☎ (01854) 622282, *summerisleshotel@aol.com, Fax (01854) 622251*, « Picturesque setting ≤ Summer Isles », – ⊬ P. MC VISA
7 April-mid October – **Meals** (booking essential) (set menu at dinner) (light seafood lunch)/dinner 39.00 **st.** 9.00 – (see also ***Summer Isles Bar*** below) – **9 rm** 67.00/124.00 **st.**, 3 suites
Spec. Ravioli verdi stuffed with crab. Fillet of halibut with langoustine tails and steamed mussels. Roast rib of beef with garlic and roast red onions.

Summer Isles Bar (at Summer Isles H.), IV26 2YG, ☎ (01854) 622282, *Fax (01854) 622251*, – P. MC VISA
7 April-October – **Meals** - Seafood - (bookings not accepted) a la carte 13.05/24.25 **st.** 9.00.

IRDRIE *North Lanarkshire* 401 I 16.

Edinburgh 34 – Glasgow 14 – Perth 54 – Stirling 22.

Bouzy Rouge, 1 Rochsolloch Rd, Coatdyke, ML6 9BB, Southwest : 1 m. off A 89 ☎ (01236) 763853, *reservations@bouzyrouge.com, Fax (01236) 770340* – P. MC AE ⓓ VISA JCB
closed 1 January – **Meals** 7.95/11.95 **t.** (lunch) and a la carte 16.00/27.50 **t.** 8.95.

IRTH *Falkirk* 401 I 15 – *pop. 1 519* – ✉ *Falkirk.*

Edinburgh 30 – Dunfermline 14 – Falkirk 7 – Stirling 8.

Radisson SAS Airth Castle, FK2 8JF, South : ¼ m. on A 905 ☎ (01324) 831411, *Fax (01324) 831419*, , , , , – | ⊬ TV P – 380. MC AE ⓓ VISA
The Castle : **Meals** *(closed Sunday)* (dinner only) 18.00/30.00 **t.** and a la carte 8.50 – ***The Conservatory :*** **Meals** 9.95/25.00 **t.** and a la carte 8.50 – 11.95 – **122 rm** 105.00/195.00 **st.** – SB.

Travel Inn, Bowtrees Roundabout, FK2 8PG, South : 1 m. by A 905 at junction with M 876/A 876 ☎ (01324) 831125, *Fax (01324) 831934* – |, ⊬ rm, TV P. MC AE ⓓ VISA. ⚡
Meals (grill rest.) – **40 rm** 40.95 **t.**

LLOWAY *South Ayrshire* 401 402 G 17 – *see Ayr.*

LTENS *Aberdeenshire – see Aberdeen.*

LTNAHARRA *Highland* 401 G 9 *Scotland G.* – ✉ *Lairg.*

Exc. : *Ben Loyal★★, N : 10 m. by A 836 – Ben Hope★ (≤★★★) NW : 14 m.*
Edinburgh 239 – Inverness 83 – Thurso 61.

Altnaharra ⚡, IV27 4UE, ☎ (01549) 411222, *altnaharra@btinternet.com, Fax (01549) 411222*, ≤, – ⊬ rest, P. MC VISA
March-October – **Meals** (bar lunch)/dinner 22.00/36.00 **st.** 8.55 – **15 rm** (dinner included) 69.00/158.00 **st.** – SB.

ALYTH *Perthshire and Kinross* 401 J 14 – *pop. 4 650.*

Pitcrocknie ☎ *(01828) 632268.*

Edinburgh 63 – Aberdeen 69 – Dundee 16 – Perth 21.

Lands of Loyal, Loyal Rd, PH11 8JQ, North : ½ m. by B 952 ☎ (01828) 633151, *enc andsofloyal.co.uk, Fax (01828) 633313*, ≤, – TV P. VISA
Meals a la carte 16.95/27.95 **t.** 7.50 – **14 rm** 55.00/89.00 **t.** – SB.

Drumnacree House, St. Ninians Rd, PH11 8AP, ☎ (01828) 6321 *Fax (01828) 632194*, – TV P. AE VISA
closed 31 December and 1 January – **Meals** *(closed Monday)* (booking essential) (resider only) 20.00 **t.** 5.00 – ***The Oven Bistro*** *(☎ (01828) 633355)* **: Meals** *(closed Mond* a la carte 15.00/19.50 **t.** 5.00 – **6 rm** 48.00/90.00 **st.** – SB.

ANNANDALE WATER SERVICE AREA *Dumfries and Galloway* 401 J 18 – ✉ *Lockerbie.*

Travel Inn without rest., Johnstonebridge, DG11 1HD, junction 16 A 74 ☎ (01576) 470870, *Fax (01576) 470644*, ≤, – rm, TV & P. AE VISA.
closed Christmas and New Year – **40 rm** 40.95.

ANSTRUTHER *Fife* 401 L 15 *Scotland G.* – *pop. 1 307.*

See : *Scottish Fisheries Museum★★ AC.*

Env. : *The East Neuk★★ – Crail★★ (Old Centre★★, Upper Crail★) NE : 4 m. by A 917.*

Exc. : *Kellie Castle★ AC, NW : 7 m. by B 9171, B 942 and A 917.*

Marsfield Shore Rd ☎ *(01333) 310956.*

Scottish Fisheries Museum ☎ *(01333) 311073 (summer only).*

Edinburgh 46 – Dundee 23 – Dunfermline 34.

The Spindrift, Pittenweem Rd, KY10 3DT, ☎ (01333) 310573, *thespindrift@btinternet .uk, Fax (01333) 310573* – TV P. VISA.
closed Christmas – **Meals** (by arrangement) 20.00 **st.** 5.50 – **8 rm** 45.00/64.00 **st.** –

Cellar, 24 East Green, KY10 3AA, ☎ (01333) 310378, *Fax (01333) 312544* – . AE VISA
closed 24-26 December, Monday and Tuesday lunch and Sunday November-April – **Mea** Seafood - (booking essential) 16.50/28.50 **t.** 9.95.

ARCHIESTOWN *Moray* 401 K 11 – ✉ *Aberlour (Aberdeenshire).*

Edinburgh 194 – Aberdeen 62 – Inverness 49.

Archiestown, AB38 7QL, ☎ (01340) 810218, *judith.bulger@btconnect.co Fax (01340) 810239*, – P. VISA
9 February-September – ***Bistro :*** **Meals** a la carte 17.75/31.00 **t.** 10.50 – **8 rm** 45. 90.00 **t.**

ARDEONAIG *Perthshire and Kinross* 401 H 14 – *see Killin (Stirling).*

ARDRISHAIG *Argyll and Bute* 401 D 15 – *pop. 1 315* – ✉ *Lochgilphead.*

Edinburgh 132 – Glasgow 86 – Oban 40.

Allt-na-Craig, Tarbert Rd, PA30 8EP, on A 83 ☎ (01546) 603245, ≤, – P.
closed December-mid January – **Meals** (by arrangement) 16.50 **s.** 5.00 – **6 rm** 30. 60.00 **s.**

ARDUAINE *Argyll and Bute* 401 D 15 *Scotland G.* – ✉ *Oban.*

Exc. : *Loch Awe★★, E : 12 m. by A 816 and B 840.*

Edinburgh 142 – Oban 20.

Loch Melfort, PA34 4XG, ☎ (01852) 200233, *lmhotel@aol.com, Fax (01852) 2002* ≤ Sound of Jura, – rest, TV P – 45. AE VISA
closed January and February – **Meals** - Seafood specialities - (bar lunch)/dinner 30.0 8.00 – **26 rm** 75.00/110.00 **t.** – SB.

ARDVASAR *Highland* 401 C 12 – *see Skye (Isle of).*

ARDVOURLIE *Western Isles (Outer Hebrides)* 401 Z 10 – *see Lewis and Harris (Isle of).*

RISAIG *Highland* **401** C 13 *Scotland G.*

See : *Village*★.

Env. : *Silver Sands of Morar*★, *N : 5½ m. by A 830.*

Traigh ℘ *(01687) 450337.*

Edinburgh 172 – Inverness 102 – Oban 88.

Arisaig House , Beasdale, PH39 4NR, Southeast : 3 ¼ m. on A 830 ℘ (01687) 450622, *arisaighse@aol.com, Fax (01687) 450626*, ← Loch nan Uamh and Roshven, « Gardens », – TV P. MC VISA.
March-November – **Meals** (dinner booking essential to non-residents) 25.00/39.50-55.00 **t.** and lunch a la carte 13.20/22.00 **t.** 4.50 – **10 rm** 125.00/290.00 **t.**, 2 suites – SB.

Arisaig, PH39 4NH, ℘ (01687) 450210, *arisaighotel@dial.pipex.com, Fax (01687) 450310*, ← – rest, TV P. MC VISA
closed 24 to 26 December – **Meals** (bar lunch)/dinner a la carte 12.20/20.60 **t.** 5.50 – **13 rm** 34.00/76.00 **t.**

Old Library Lodge with rm, High St., PH39 4NH, ℘ (01687) 450651, *Fax (01687) 450219*, ← Loch nan Ceall and Inner Hebridean Isles, – TV. MC AE VISA JCB.
March-October – **Meals** *(closed Tuesday lunch)* a la carte 12.00/24.50 **t.** – **6 rm** 48.00/76.00 **t.**

When looking for a quiet hotel
use the maps found in the introduction
or look for establishments with the sign or .

RRAN (Isle of) *North Ayrshire* **401 402** DE 16 17 *Scotland G. – pop. 4 474.*

See : *Island*★★ - *Brodick Castle*★★ *AC.*

from Brodick to Ardrossan (Caledonian MacBrayne Ltd) 4-6 daily (55 mn) – from Lochranza to Kintyre Peninsula (Claonaig) (Caledonian MacBrayne Ltd) frequent services daily (30 mn) – from Brodick to Isle of Bute (Rothesay) (Caledonian MacBrayne Ltd) 3 weekly (2 h 5 mn).

odick – *pop. 822.*

Brodick ℘ *(01770) 302349 – Machrie Bay* ℘ *(01770) 850232.*

The Pier ℘ *(01770) 302140.*

Auchrannie Country House, KA27 8BZ, ℘ (01770) 302234, *info@auchrannie.co.uk, Fax (01770) 302812*, , , , – rest, TV P. MC AE VISA.
Meals a la carte 11.45/16.55 **st.** – ***The Garden :*** **Meals** (dinner only) 17.50/24.00 **st.** 10.00 – **26 rm** 71.00/122.00 **st.**, 2 suites – SB.

Kilmichael Country House , Glen Cloy, KA27 8BY, West : 1 m. by Shore Rd, taking left turn opposite Golf Club ℘ (01770) 302219, *geoffreybotterill@hotmail.com, Fax (01770) 302068*, – TV P. MC VISA JCB
March-October – **Meals** (booking essential) (dinner only) 25.50 **t.** – **5 rm** 75.00/130.00 **t.**, 3 suites.

Dunvegan House, Shore Rd, KA27 8AJ, ℘ (01770) 302811, *Fax (01770) 302811*, ←, – TV P.
Meals (residents only) 16.00 **st.** – **9 rm** 35.00/58.00 **s.**

mlash – *pop. 900 – Brodick.*

Lamlash ℘ *(01770) 600296.*

Lilybank without rest., Shore Rd, KA27 8LS, ℘ (01770) 600230, *carol.berry@virgin.net, Fax (01770) 600230*, ←, – TV P. MC VISA
closed January-February – **8 rm** 25.00/55.00 **st.**

chranza.

Lochranza ℘ *(0177083) 0273.*

Apple Lodge, KA27 8HJ, South : ½ m. on Brodick rd ℘ (01770) 830229, *applelodge@easicom.com, Fax (01770) 830229*, ←, – TV P.
closed Christmas and New Year (minimum stay 2 nights) – **Meals** 18.00 **t.** – **3 rm** 45.00/60.00 **t.**, 1 suite.

Butt Lodge Country House , KA27 8JF, Southeast : ¾ m. by Brodick Rd ℘ (01770) 830240, *butt.lodge@virgin.net, Fax (01770) 830211*, ←, – TV P. MC VISA.
March-October – **Meals** (booking essential to non-residents) (dinner only) 16.00/20.00 9.00 – **5 rm** 48.00/80.00.

Whiting Bay – ✉.

Whiting Bay, Golf Course Rd ✆ (01770) 700775.

Argentine House, Shore Rd, KA27 8PZ, ✆ (01770) 700662, *info@argentinearran.co.* *Fax (01770) 700693*, ≤, 🛋 – ⅹ rest, TV P. MC VISA JCB
closed 10 January-February – **Meals** (by arrangement) 18.00 **st.** 7.00 – **5 rm** 34.(68.00 **st.** – SB.

Royal, Shore Rd, KA27 8PZ, ✆ (01770) 700286, *b.wilson@which.net, Fax (01770) 7002* ≤, 🛋 – ⅹ rest, TV P
March-October – **Meals** (by arrangement) 15.00 **st.** – **5 rm** 25.00/50.00 **st.**

AUCHENCAIRN *Dumfries and Galloway* 401 402 I 19 – ✉ *Castle Douglas.*
Edinburgh 94 – Dumfries 21 – Stranraer 60.

Balcary Bay 🔇, DG7 1QZ, Southeast : 2 m. on Balcary rd ✆ (01556) 640217, *reservati @balcary-bay-hotel.co.uk, Fax (01556) 640272*, ≤ Auchencairn Bay and Solway Firth, TV P. MC AE VISA JCB
4 March-24 November – **Meals** (bar lunch Monday to Saturday)/dinner 25.75 and a la carte 6.25 – **17 rm** 61.00/122.00 **st.** – SB.

AUCHTERARDER *Perthshire and Kinross* 401 I 15 *Scotland G. – pop. 3 910.*
Env. : *Tullibardine Chapel★, NW : 2 m.*
Ochil Rd ✆ (01764) 662804 – Dunning, Rollo Park ✆ (01764) 684747.
90 High St. ✆ (01764) 663450.
Edinburgh 55 – Glasgow 45 – Perth 14.

Gleneagles, PH3 1NF, Southwest : 2 m. by A 824 on A 823 ✆ (01764) 662231, *resort.s @gleneagles.com, Fax (01764) 662134*, ≤, « Championship golf courses and extens leisure facilities », squash – ⅹ rm, rest, TV – 360. MC AE VISA JCB
Strathearn : **Meals** (dinner only and Sunday lunch)/dinner 42.50 **t.** and a la carte 25.0
The Club : **Meals** a la carte 20.15/25.15 **t.** – **206 rm** 200.00/410.00 **t.**, 14 suites – SB.

Auchterarder House 🔇, PH3 1DZ, North : 1 ½ m. on B 8062 ✆ (01764) 663646, *au erarder@wrensgroup.com, Fax (01764) 662939*, ≤, « Victorian mansion in Jacobean style – TV P – 65. MC AE VISA
Meals – (see ***The Dining Room*** below) – **14 rm** 125.00/160.00 **t.**, 1 suite – SB.

Cairn Lodge, Orchil Rd, PH3 1LX, ✆ (01764) 662634, *email@cairnlodge.co.* *Fax (01764) 664866*, – ⅹ TV P. MC AE VISA JCB.
Meals (bar lunch)/dinner 29.50 **t.** and a la carte 8.50 – **11 rm** 80.00/160.00 **t.** – SB.

Coll Earn House, PH3 1DF, ✆ (01764) 663553, *Fax (01764) 662376*, – ⅹ rm, TV 60. MC AE VISA
closed 24 December-4 January – **Meals** a la carte 15.20/19.95 **t.** 5.95 – **8 rm** 55. 95.00 **t.**

The Dining Room (at Auchterarder House H.), PH3 1DZ, North : 1 ½ m. on B 8(✆ (01764) 663646, *Fax (01764) 662939*, – ⅹ P. MC AE VISA
closed Saturday lunch – **Meals** (dinner booking essential to non-residents) 12.95/38.0 9.50.

AUCHTERHOUSE *Angus* 401 K 14 – *pop. 794* – ✉ *Dundee.*
Edinburgh 69 – Dundee 7 – Perth 24.

Old Mansion House 🔇 with rm, DD3 0QN, ✆ (01382) 320366, *oldmansionhouse@r capeonline.co.uk, Fax (01382) 320400*, ≤, « Part 15C and 17C country house », heat , squash – ⅹ TV P. MC AE VISA.
Meals 18.50/33.50 **t.** and a la carte 6.75 – **6 rm** 85.00/110.00 **st.**, 1 suite – SB.

AVIEMORE *Highland* 401 I 12 *Scotland G. – pop. 2 214 – Winter sports.*
See : *Town★.*
Exc. : *The Cairngorms★★ (≤★★★) – ★★★ from Cairn Gorm, SE : 11 m. by B 970 – Landr Visitor Centre (The Highlander★)* **AC**, *N : 7 m. by A 9 – Highland Wildlife Park★* **AC**, *SW : 7 by A 9.*
Grampian Rd ✆ (01479) 810363.
Edinburgh 129 – Inverness 29 – Perth 85.

Hilton Aviemore, PH22 1PF, ✆ (01479) 810681, *Fax (01479) 810534*, ≤ Cairngorms, – ⅹ, rest, TV P – 110. MC AE VISA
Meals (dancing Saturday evening) (bar lunch)/dinner 19.95 **st.** and a la carte – 10.0 **88 rm** 105.00/170.00 **t.** – SB.

Corrour House ⚘, Inverdruie, PH22 1QH, Southeast : 1 m. on B 970 ☎ (01479) 810220, *Fax (01479) 811500*, ≤, ⚘, 🌳 – ⅌ rest, TV P. MC VISA
closed 1 November-26 December – **Meals** (dinner only) 20.00/25.00 **t.** 7.00 – **8 rm** 40.00/80.00 **t.** – SB.

Aviemore Inn, PH22 1PH, ☎ (01479) 810261, *Fax (01479) 814671* – |‡| ⅌, ▤ rest, TV P – 🎤 40. MC AE ① VISA JCB
Meals (dinner only) 14.50 **st.** – 9.50 – **62 rm** 80.00/90.00 **st.**

Lynwilg House, Lynwilg, PH22 1PZ, South : 2 m. by B 9152 on A 9 ☎ (01479) 811685, *Fax (01479) 811685*, ≤, ⚘, 🌳 – ⅌ TV P. MC VISA
closed November-28 December – **Meals** (by arrangement) 25.00 **st.** – **3 rm** 30.00/70.00 **st.** – SB.

R *South Ayrshire* **401** **402** G 17 *Scotland G.* – *pop. 47 872.*

Env. : *Alloway★ (Burns Cottage and Museum★ AC) S : 3 m. by B 7024* **BZ**.

Exc. : *Culzean Castle★ AC (setting★★★, Oval Staircase★★) SW : 13 m. by A 719* **BZ**.

18 Belleisle, Bellisle Park, Doonfoot Rd ☎ (01292) 441258, **BZ** *– 18 Dalmilling, Westwood Av. ☎ (01292) 263893,* **BZ** *– 9 Doon Valley, Hillside, Patna ☎ (01292) 531607,* **BZ**.

22 Sandgate ☎ (01292) 288688.

Edinburgh 81 – Glasgow 35.

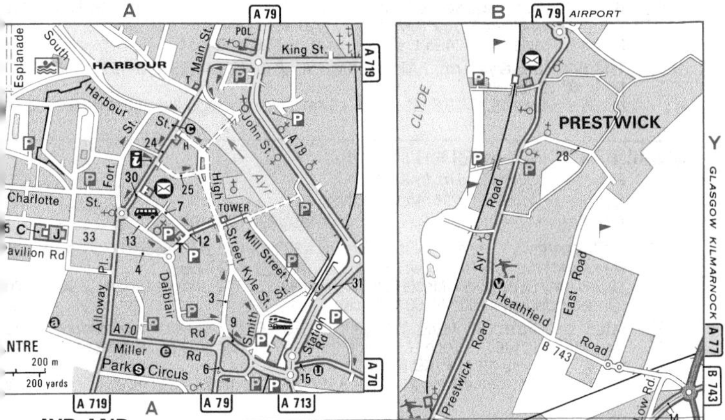

AYR AND PRESTWICK

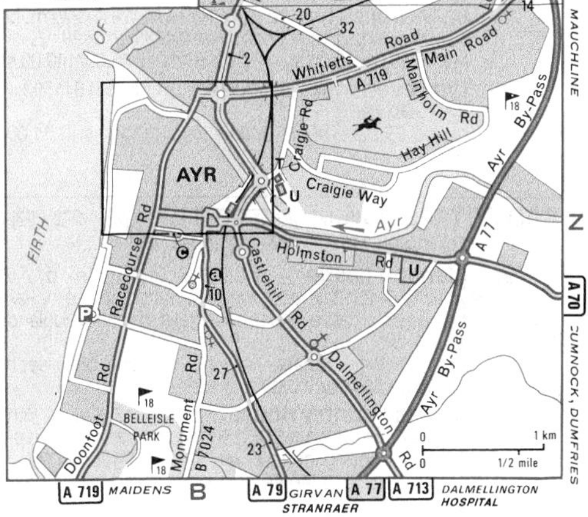

SCOTLAND

Fairfield House, 12 Fairfield Rd, KA7 2AR, ☎ (01292) 267461, *reservations@fairfieldh .co.uk, Fax (01292) 261456*, – TV P – 120. MC AE VISA JCB.
Meals a la carte 14.25/27.95 **st.** 9.00 – **44 rm** 85.00/130.00 **st.** – SB. AY

Kylestrome, 11 Miller Rd, KA7 2AX, ☎ (01292) 262474, *info@kylestrome.c Fax (01292) 260863* – TV P – 35. MC AE VISA JCB. AY
closed 26 December and 1 January – **Meals** (bar lunch) 17.95/25.00 **t.** and a la carte – **12** 55.00/70.00 **t.**

No. 26 The Crescent without rest., 26 Bellevue Cres., KA7 2DR, ☎ (01292) 287329, *e@26crescent.freeserve.co.uk, Fax (01292) 286779* – TV P. MC VISA. BZ
closed mid November-mid January – **5 rm** 32.00/52.00.

Coila without rest., 10 Holmston Rd, KA7 3BB, ☎ (01292) 262642, *hazel@coila.cc Fax (01292) 285439* – TV P. MC VISA AY
4 rm 25.00/44.00 **st.**

Langley Bank without rest., 39 Carrick Rd, KA7 2RD, ☎ (01292) 264 *Fax (01292) 282628*, – TV P. MC AE VISA. BZ
4 rm 45.00/60.00 **s.**

Chaz-Ann without rest., 17 Park Circus, KA7 2DJ, ☎ (01292) 611215, *chazannayr@ac m, Fax (01292) 285491* – TV. AY
3 rm 25.00/40.00 **s.**

Fouters Bistro, 2a Academy St., KA7 1HS, ☎ (01292) 261391, *laurie-fran@fouters.de n.co.uk, Fax (01292) 619323* – MC AE VISA AY
closed 1-3 January, 25-26 December and Sunday – **Meals** a la carte 15.85/23.40 **t.** 5.25

at Alloway *South : 3 m. on B 7024* – **BZ** – ✉ *Ayr.*

Brig O'Doon House, KA7 4PQ, ☎ (01292) 442466, *brigodoon@costleyhotels.cc Fax (01292) 441999*, – TV – 220. MC AE VISA.
Meals a la carte 14.50/24.95 **t.** 8.00 – **5 rm** 75.00/120.00 **t.**

The Ivy House with rm, 2 Alloway, KA7 4NL, ☎ (01292) 442336, *Fax (01292) 445572* – TV P. MC AE VISA.
Meals a la carte 15.25/29.65 **st.** 8.75 – **5 rm** (dinner included) 110.00/190.00 **st.** – S

BALLACHULISH *Highland* 401 E 13 *Scotland G.*

Exc. : *Glen Coe★★, E : 6 m. by A 82.*
Argyll ☎ (01855) 811296 (April-October).
Edinburgh 117 – Inverness 80 – Kyle of Lochalsh 90 – Oban 38.

Ballachulish, PH49 4JY, West : 2 ¼ m. by A 82 on A 828 ☎ (01855) 811606, *reservatio freedomglen.co.uk, Fax (01855) 821463*, – TV P. MC VISA
closed early December – **Meals** (bar lunch)/dinner 25.50 **t.** and a la carte 12.00 – **54 rm** (dinner included) 79.50/159.00 **t.**, 1 suite.

Isles of Glencoe, PH49 4HL, ☎ (01855) 811602, *reservations@freedomglen.cc Fax (01855) 821463*, Loch Leven and the Pap of Glencoe, « Lochside setting », – rest, TV P. MC VISA
Meals 21.00 **t.** (dinner) and a la carte 8.90/12.65 **t.** 10.00 – **59 rm** (dinner incluc 82.50/165.00 **t.**

Ballachulish House, PH49 4JX, West : 2 ½ m. by A 82 on A 828 ☎ (01855) 81126 *claughlins@btconnect.com, Fax (01855) 811498*, – P. MC VISA JCB
Meals 30.00/35.00 **st.** 8.50 – **6 rm** 45.00/140.00 **st.**

Lyn Leven, White St., PA39 4JP, ☎ (01855) 811392, *Fax (01855) 811600*, – TV P. MC VISA
closed 25 December – **Meals** (by arrangement) 11.00 **t.** 4.20 – **8 rm** 30.00/48.00 SB.

BALLANTRAE *South Ayrshire* 401 402 E 18 – *pop. 672* – ✉ *Girvan.*

Edinburgh 115 – Ayr 33 – Stranraer 18.

Glenapp Castle, KA26 0NZ, South : 1 m. by A 77 taking first right turn after br ☎ (01465) 831212, *enquiries@glenappcastle.com, Fax (01465) 831000*, « Victorian S tish Baronial castle in extensive gardens and woodland », – rest, TV P. AE VISA.
April-October – **Meals** - French - (residents only) (set menu only) (light lunch) – **14 rm** (inclusive) 300.00/500.00 **t.**, 3 suites.

Cosses Country House, KA26 0LR, East : 2 ¼ m. by A 77 (south) taking first turn after bridge ☎ (01465) 831363, *cosses@compuserve.com, Fax (01465) 831598*, « Part former shooting lodge », – TV P. MC VISA
March-October – **Meals** (by arrangement) (communal dining) 25.00 – **1 rm** 42.00/76 **2 suites** 76.00.

LLATER *Aberdeenshire* 401 K 12 – *pop. 1 362.*

Victoria Rd ☎ (013397) 55567.
Station Sq. ☎ (013397) 55306 (summer only).
Edinburgh 111 – Aberdeen 41 – Inverness 70 – Perth 67.

Hilton Craigendarroch, Braemar Rd, AB35 5XA, on A 93 ☎ (013397) 55858, *Fax (013397) 55447,* ← Dee Valley and Grampians, squash – rest, TV P – 110. MC AE VISA
Meals (bar lunch Monday-Saturday) a la carte 14.25/25.15 **st.** 7.00 – ***Oaks :*** **Meals** (dinner only) 28.00 **st.** and a la carte 7.00 – 10.95 – **40 rm** 130.00/150.00 **st.**, 5 suites – SB.

Darroch Learg, Braemar Rd, AB35 5UX, ☎ (013397) 55443, *nigel@darroch-learg.demon.co.uk, Fax (013397) 55252,* ← Dee Valley and Grampians, – TV P. MC AE VISA JCB
closed 3 weeks January and 5 days Christmas – **Meals** – (see ***Conservatory*** below) – **18 rm** (dinner included) 90.00/210.00 **st.**

Glen Lui, Invercauld Rd, AB35 5RP, ☎ (013397) 55402, *infos@glen-lui-hotel.co.uk, Fax (013397) 55545,* ←, – TV P. MC AE VISA.
Meals 6.50/21.00 **st.** and a la carte 7.50 – **17 rm** 27.00/80.00 **st.**, 2 suites – SB.

Balgonie Country House, Braemar Pl., AB35 5NQ, ☎ (013397) 55482, *balgonie@lineone.net, Fax (013397) 55482,* ←, – rest, TV P. MC AE VISA JCB
closed January and February – **Meals** (booking essential) (lunch by arrangement)/dinner 30.00/31.50 **t.** 9.50 – **9 rm** 70.00/130.00 **t.** – SB.

Auld Kirk, Braemar Rd, AB35 5RQ, ☎ (013397) 55762, *Fax (013397) 55707,* « Former 19C church » – rest, TV P. MC VISA
Meals a la carte 15.20/23.80 **t.** 5.50 – **7 rm** 48.00/56.00 **t.**

Moorside House without rest., 26 Braemar Rd, AB35 5RL, ☎ (013397) 55492, *moorsidehouse@virgin.net, Fax (013397) 55492,* – TV P. MC VISA.
April-October – **9 rm** 40.00.

Oaklands House without rest., 30 Braemar Rd, AB35 5RL, ☎ (013397) 55013, – TV P
May-September – **3 rm** 30.00/48.00.

Conservatory (at Darroch Learg H.), Braemar Rd, AB35 5UX, ☎ (013397) 55443, *Fax (013397) 55252,* ←, – P. MC AE VISA
closed 3 weeks January and 5 days Christmas – **Meals** 19.50/39.00 **st.** and lunch a la carte 9.60.

Green Inn with rm, 9 Victoria Rd, AB35 5QQ, ☎ (013397) 55701, *greeninn@nest.org.uk, Fax (013397) 55701,* – TV. MC AE VISA JCB
closed 2 weeks October, 23-27 December and Sunday and Monday October-March – **Meals** (dinner only) 29.50 **st.** 9.55 – **3 rm** (dinner included) 65.00/115.00 **st.** – SB.

LLOCH *West Dunbartonshire* 401 G 15 *Scotland G.* – ✉ *Alexandria.*

Env. : *N : Loch Lomond*★★.
Balloch Rd ☎ (01389) 753533 (April-October).
Edinburgh 72 – Glasgow 20 – Stirling 30.

Cameron House, Loch Lomond, G83 8QZ, Northwest : 1 ½ m. by A 811 on A 82 ☎ (01389) 755565, *devere.cameron@airtime.co.uk, Fax (01389) 759522,* ← Loch Lomond, « Lochside setting », squash – rest, TV P – 300. MC AE VISA.
Smolletts : **Meals** *(closed lunch Saturday, Sunday and Bank Holiday Monday)* 14.50/35.00 **st.** and dinner a la carte 8.00 – ***Breakers :*** **Meals** a la carte 14.00/22.00 **st.** – (see also ***Georgian Room*** below) – **89 rm** 170.00/225.00 **st.**, 7 suites – SB.

Georgian Room (at Cameron House H.), Loch Lomond, G83 8QZ, Northwest : 1 ½ m. by A 811 on A 82 ☎ (01389) 755565, *Fax (01389) 759522,* ← Loch Lomond, « Lochside setting », – P. MC AE VISA
closed 26 December, Monday, lunch Saturday and Sunday and Bank Holidays – **Meals** (booking essential) 21.00/41.50 **t.** and a la carte 46.50/62.85 **t.** 13.50
Spec. Roulade of monkfish with watercress cream. Roast squab pigeon with foie gras, apple and chestnut compote. Lavender crème brûlée.

LLYGRANT *Argyll and Bute* 401 B 16 – *see Islay (Isle of).*

LTASOUND *Shetland Islands* 401 R 1 – *see Shetland Islands (Island of Unst).*

NAVIE *Highland* 401 E 13 – *see Fort William.*

BANCHORY *Aberdeenshire* 401 M 12 *Scotland G. – pop. 6 230.*

Env. : *Crathes Castle★★ (Gardens★★★)* **AC**, *E : 3 m. by A 93 – Cairn o'Mount Road★ (≤★★ by B 974.*

Exc. : *Dunnottar Castle★★ (site★★★)* **AC**, *SW : 15 ½ m. by A 93 and A 957 – Aberdeer NE : 17 m. by A 93.*

Kinneskie ☎ (01330) 822365 – Torphins ☎ (013398) 82115.

Bridge St. ☎ (01330) 822000.

Edinburgh 118 – Aberdeen 17 – Dundee 55 – Inverness 94.

Raemoir House, AB31 4ED, North : 2 ½ m. on A 980 ☎ (01330) 824884, *enquiries@raemoir.com, Fax (01330) 822171*, ≤, « 18C mansion with 16C Ha-Hoose », – rest, TV P – 50. MC AE VISA
Meals 16.50/28.50 **t.** 10.50 – **21 rm** 60.00/110.00 **t.** – SB.

Banchory Lodge, Dee St., AB31 5HS, ☎ (01330) 822625, *banchorylodgeht@btconnect.com, Fax (01330) 825019*, ≤, « Part 16C former coaching inn on River Dee », – rm, TV P – 30. MC AE VISA
Meals 18.50/27.50 **st.** (dinner) and lunch a la carte 12.50/25.50 **t.** 5.50 – **22 rm** 65 175.00 **t.** – SB.

Tor-na-Coille, Inchmarlo Rd, AB31 4AB, ☎ (01330) 822242, *tornacoille@btinternet.c Fax (01330) 824012*, – TV P – 90. MC AE VISA
closed 25 to 28 December – **Meals** (bar lunch Monday to Saturday)/dinner 22.50/26. 9.00 – **22 rm** 75.00/130.00 **t.** – SB.

Old West Manse, 71 Station Rd, AB31 5UD, ☎ (01330) 822202, *Fax (01330) 822202*, TV P. MC VISA JCB.
Meals (by arrangement) 18.50 **s.** 4.50 – **3 rm** 35.00/55.00 **s.**

Milton, Milton of Crathes, North Deeside Rd, Crathes, AB31 5QH, East : 3 m. on ☎ (01330) 844566, *info@themilton.co.uk, Fax (01330) 844666* – P. MC AE VISA
closed 25 December, 1 January and Sunday dinner – **Meals** a la carte 16.20/28.40 **st.**

BANFF *Aberdeenshire* 401 M 10 *Scotland G. – pop. 4 402.*

See : *Town★ – Duff House★★ (baroque exterior★)* **AC** *– Mercat Cross★.*

Royal Tarlair, Buchan St., Macduff ☎ (01261) 832897 – Duff House Royal, The Barny ☎ (01261) 812062.

Collie Lodge ☎ (01261) 812419 (summer only).

Edinburgh 177 – Aberdeen 47 – Fraserburgh 26 – Inverness 74.

The Orchard without rest., Duff House, AB45 3TA, by Duff House rd and Wrack W rd ☎ (01261) 812146, *jma6914291@aol.com, Fax (01261) 812146*, – TV P.
February-November – **4 rm** 23.00/46.00.

Links Cottage without rest., Inverboyndie, AB45 2JJ, West : 1 ½ m. by ☎ (01261) 812223, *Fax (01261) 812223*, – P.
March-November – **3 rm** 35.00/52.00 **s.**

Milo's, 2 Crook 'o' Ness St., Macduff, AB44 1TR, East : 1 ½ m. on A 98 ☎ (01261) 8312. MC VISA
closed Monday, 25, 26 December and 1 January – **Meals** (dinner booking essential) a la c 12.25/21.60 **st.**

BANKHEAD *Aberdeenshire* 401 N 12 – *see Aberdeen.*

BARRA (Isle of) *Western Isles* 401 X 12/13 *– pop. 1 316 –* ✉ *Castlebay.*

from Castlebay to Oban, South Uist (Lochboisdale) and Mallaig (Caledonian MacBr Ltd) (summer only).

Castlebay.

Castlebay, HS9 5XD, ☎ (01871) 810223, *Fax (01871) 810455*, ≤ Kisimul Castle and Is of Vatersay – rest, TV P. MC VISA
closed 18 December-15 January **Meals** a la carte 11.90/25.00 **st.** 6.50 – **12 rm** 40 65.00 **st.**

Grianamul without rest., HS9 5XD, ☎ (01871) 810416, *ronnie.macneil@virgin Fax (01871) 810319*, – TV P
April-September – **3 rm** 25.00/50.00.

Tigh na Mara without rest., HS9 5XD, ☎ (01871) 810304, *Fax (01871) 810858*, ≤ – P.
April-October – **5 rm** 24.00/48.00 **s.**

THGATE *West Lothian* 401 J 16 – *pop. 23 368.*
Edinburgh 24 – Dundee 62 – Glasgow 29 – Perth 50.

Express by Holiday Inn without rest., Starlaw Rd, EH48 1LQ, ☎ (01506) 650650, *Fax (01506) 650651* – 🛗 ⊭ TV ☎ ♿ P – 🏢 40. MC AE ◎ VISA JCB. ✻
74 rm 49.95 **st.**

AULY *Highland* 401 G 11 – *pop. 1 154.*
Edinburgh 169 – Inverness 13 – Wick 125.

Lovat Arms, High St., IV4 7BS, ☎ (01463) 782313, *lovatarms@cali.co.uk, Fax (01463) 782862* – ⊭ rest, TV P – 🏢 60. MC VISA JCB
Meals a la carte 9.75/25.70 **t.** 🍷 5.00 – **22 rm** ☐ 35.00/110.00 **t.** – SB.

Priory, The Square, IV4 7BX, ☎ (01463) 782309, *reservations@priory-hotel.com, Fax (01463) 782531* – 🛗 TV. MC AE ◎ VISA JCB
Meals 16.95 **t.** (dinner) and a la carte 7.70/16.25 **t.** 🍷 5.95 – **36 rm** ☐ 39.50/79.00 **t.** – SB.

NBECULA *Western Isles* 401 X/Y 11 – *see Uist (Isles of).*

RRIEDALE *Highland* 401 J 9.
Edinburgh 251 – Inverness 94 – Thurso 28 – Wick 14.

The Factor's House 🐦, Langwell, KW7 6HD, take private road to Langwell House - 2.9 m. ☎ (01593) 751280, *robert@welbeck2.freeserve.co.uk, Fax (01593) 751251,* ≤, 🌳, ♞ – ⊭ rm, P
closed Christmas and New Year – **Meals** (communal dining) 20.00 **t.** 🍷 5.00 – **3 rm** ☐ 35.00/70.00 **t.**

GAR *South Lanarkshire* 401 J 17 – *pop. 2 238.*
⛳18 *The Park, Broughton Rd* ☎ *(01899) 220319.*
ℹ *155 High St.* ☎ *(01899) 221066.*
Edinburgh 31 – Dumfries 49 – Glasgow 40.

Lindsaylands 🐦, Lindsaylands Rd, ML12 6NR, Southwest : ¾ m. via Park Place and The Wynd ☎ (01899) 220033, *elspeth@lindsaylands.co.uk, Fax (01899) 221009,* ≤, 🌳, ♞, 🎾 – ⊭ P. ✻
March-November – **Meals** (by arrangement) 15.00 **st.** – **3 rm** ☐ 30.00/50.00 **st.**

AIR ATHOLL *Perthshire and Kinross* 401 I 13 – *pop. 906.*
⛳9 *Blair Atholl, Invertilt Rd* ☎ *(01796) 481407.*
Edinburgh 79 – Inverness 83 – Perth 35.

The Loft, Golf Course Rd, PH18 5TE, ☎ (01796) 481377, *Fax (01796) 481511,* « Converted hayloft » – ⊭ P. MC AE ◎ VISA JCB
closed Monday-Wednesday January-March – **Meals** (lunch booking essential) a la carte 11.70/22.45 **st.** 🍷 6.50.

AIRGOWRIE *Perthshire and Kinross* 401 J 14 *Scotland G.* – *pop. 5 208.*
Exc. : *Scone Palace★★ AC, S : 12 m. by A 93.*
ℹ *26 Wellmeadow* ☎ *(01250) 872960.*
Edinburgh 60 – Dundee 19 – Perth 16.

Kinloch House 🐦, PH10 6SG, West : 3 m. on A 923 ☎ (01250) 884237, *info@kinlochhouse.com, Fax (01250) 884333,* ≤, « Victorian country house », 🏋, ≘s, 🏊, 🌳, ♞ – ⊭ rest, TV ☎ P. MC AE ◎ VISA JCB. ✻
closed 18 to 29 December – **Meals** (bar lunch Monday to Saturday)/dinner 34.00 **st.** 🍷 7.95 – **20 rm** ☐ (dinner included) 105.00/265.00 **st.** – SB.

Laurels, PH10 6LH, Southwest : 1 ¼ m. on A 93 ☎ (01250) 874920, *Fax (01250) 874920,* 🌳 – ⊭ TV P. MC VISA. ✻
closed 20 November-20 January – **Meals** 10.50 **st.** 🍷 4.00 – **6 rm** ☐ 20.00/40.00.

Altamount House 🐦 with rm, Coupar Angus Rd, PH10 6JN, on A 923 ☎ (01250) 873512, *althotel@netcomuk.co.uk, Fax (01250) 876200,* 🌳 – ⊭ rest, TV P – 🏢 150. MC AE ◎ VISA. ✻
closed first 2 weeks January – **Meals** (booking essential to non-residents) (light lunch)/dinner 22.50 **t.** and a la carte – **7 rm** ☐ 57.50/115.00 **t.** – SB.

Cargills, Lower Mill St., PH10 6AQ, ☎ (01250) 876735, *exceed@btconnect.com, Fax (01250) 876735,* « Former grain store » – P. MC VISA
closed last 2 weeks January and Tuesday – **Meals** a la carte 12.45/19.25 **t.** 🍷 8.50.

BOAT OF GARTEN *Highland* 401 I 12.
Boat of Garten (01479) 831282.
Edinburgh 133 – Inverness 28 – Perth 89.

The Boat, PH24 3BH, (01479) 831258, *holidays@boathotel.co.uk, Fax (01479) 831*
– TV P – 60. VISA.
Meals (bar lunch)/dinner 27.50/34.00 **st.** 9.50 – **32 rm** (dinner included) 65
130.00 **st.** – SB.

BONNYRIGG *Midlothian* 401 K 16 – *see Edinburgh.*

BORGIE *Highland* 401 H 8.
Edinburgh 262 – Inverness 93 – Thurso 31.

Borgie Lodge, KW14 7TH, (01641) 521332, *info@borgielodgehotel.co*
Fax (01641) 521332, – rest, P. VISA
booking essential November-February – **Meals** (bar lunch)/dinner 26.00 **t.** 6.00 – 7
50.00/80.00 **t.** – SB.

BOWMORE *Argyll and Bute* 401 B 16 – *see Islay (Isle of).*

BRAE *Shetland Islands* 401 P 2 – *see Shetland Islands (Mainland).*

BRAEMAR *Aberdeenshire* 401 J 12 *Scotland G.*
Env. : *Lin O'Dee*★, *W : 5 m.*
Cluniebank Rd (013397) 41618.
The Mews, Mar Rd (013397) 41600.
Edinburgh 85 – Aberdeen 58 – Dundee 51 – Perth 51.

Braemar Lodge, Glenshee Rd, AB35 5YQ, (013397) 41627, *Fax (013397) 41627,*
TV P. VISA JCB
Meals (dinner only) a la carte 14.50/24.50 **t.** 7.95 – **7 rm** 40.00/80.00 **t.** – SB.

BREAKISH *Highland* 401 C 12 – *see Skye (Isle of).*

BREASCLETE *Western Isles (Outer Hebrides)* 401 Z 9 – *see Lewis and Harris (Isle of).*

BRIDGEND *Argyll and Bute* 401 B 16 – *see Islay (Isle of).*

BROADFORD *Highland* 401 C 12 – *see Skye (Isle of).*

BRODICK *North Ayrshire* 401 402 E 17 – *see Arran (Isle of).*

BRORA *Highland* 401 I 9 – *pop. 1 687.*
Golf Rd (01408) 621417.
Edinburgh 234 – Inverness 78 – Wick 49.

Royal Marine, Golf Rd, KW9 6QS, (01408) 621252, *highlandescape@btinternet.c*
Fax (01408) 621181, , , , , – rest, TV P – 90. AE VISA
Meals a la carte 17.00/24.00 **t.** 6.00 – **22 rm** 65.00/138.00 **t.** – SB.

Links, Golf Rd, KW9 6QS, (01408) 621225, *highlandescape@btinternet.c*
Fax (01408) 621383, , , – rest, TV P. AE VISA
April-October – **Meals** (bar lunch)/dinner 25.00/30.00 **t.** 6.00 – **20 rm** 65.00/98.0
2 suites – SB.

Glenaveron without rest., Golf Rd, KW9 6QS, (01408) 621601, *glenaveron@hotma*
m, Fax (01408) 621601, – TV P. VISA.
closed Christmas – **3 rm** 35.00/50.00 **st.**

Tigh Fada without rest., 18 Golf Rd, KW9 6QS, (01408) 621332, *clarkson@tighfada.*
t.co.uk, Fax (01408) 621332, , – P.
closed Christmas and New Year – **3 rm** 25.00/50.00.

BROUGHTY FERRY *Dundee City* 401 L 14 – *see Dundee.*

CKIE *Moray* 401 L 10 – *pop. 8 324.*

Buckpool, Barhill Rd (01542) 832236 – Strathlene, Portessie (01542) 831798 – Cullen, The Links (01542) 840685.

Edinburgh 195 – Aberdeen 66 – Inverness 56.

Rosemount without rest., 62 East Church St., AB56 1ER, (01542) 833434, *rosemount-bck@btinternet.com, Fax (01542) 833434,* – TV P.
closed 23 December-3 January – **3 rm** 27.50/45.00.

Old Monastery, Drybridge, AB56 5JB, Southeast : 3 ½ m. by A 942 on Deskford rd (01542) 832660, *buchanan@oldmonasteryrestaurant.freeserve.co.uk, Fax (01542) 839437,* « Former chapel overlooking Spey Bay » – P. MC AE VISA
closed 3 weeks January, Sunday dinner and Monday – **Meals** a la carte 24.45/30.95 **t.** 7.50.

NCHREW *Highland – see Inverness.*

NESSAN *Argyll and Bute* 401 B 15 – *see Mull (Isle of).*

RNTISLAND *Fife* 401 K 15 *Scotland G.* – *pop. 5 951.*

Env. : *Aberdour★ – Aberdour Castle★* AC, *W : 3 m. by A 921.*

Burntisland Golf House Club, Dodhead (01592) 874093 – Kinghorn Municipal, McDuff Cres., Kingham (01592) 890345.

Edinburgh 20 – Dunfermline 10 – Kirkcaldy 6.

The Kingswood, Kinghorn Rd, KY3 9LL, East : 1 m. on A 921 (01592) 872329, *rankin@kingswoodhotel.co.uk, Fax (01592) 873123,* – TV P – 100. MC AE VISA
closed 26 December – **Meals** (bar lunch)/dinner a la carte 12.85/17.40 **t.** 5.95 – **10 rm** 52.00/75.00 **t.** – SB.

RRAY *Orkney Islands* 401 L 7 – *see Orkney Islands.*

TE (Isle of) *Argyll and Bute* 401 402 E 16 – *pop. 7 354.*

from Rothesay to Wemyss Bay (Mainland) (Caledonian MacBrayne Ltd) frequent services daily (35 mn) – from Rhubodach to Colintraive (Mainland) (Caledonian MacBrayne Ltd) frequent services daily (5 mn).

thesay.

Canada Hill (01700) 502244 – Sithean, Academy Rd (01700) 504369 – Port Bannatyne, Bannatyne Mains Rd (01700) 504544.

15 Victoria St. (01700) 502151.

Cannon House, 5 Battery Pl., PA20 9DP, (01700) 502819, *Fax (01700) 505725,* ≤ – rest, TV. MC VISA.
Meals (booking essential) (dinner only) 15.00 **st.** 7.00 – **8 rm** 45.00/80.00 **st.**

Ardmory House, Ardmory Rd, Ardbeg, PA20 0PG, North : 1 ¾ m. by A 866 (01700) 502346, *ardmory.house.hotel@dial.pipex.com, Fax (01700) 505596,* ≤, – TV P. MC AE VISA.
Meals (bar lunch Monday to Saturday)/dinner 18.50 **t.** and a la carte 4.00 – **5 rm** 47.50/75.00 **t.** – SB.

DBOLL *Highland – see Tain.*

RNBAAN *Argyll and Bute* 401 D 15 – *see Lochgilphead.*

LLANDER *Stirling* 401 H 15 *Scotland G.* – *pop. 3 268.*

See : *Town★.*

Exc. : *The Trossachs★★★ (Loch Katrine★★) – Hilltop Viewpoint★★★ (★★★) W : 10 m. by A 821.*

Aveland Rd (01877) 330090.

Rob Roy & Trossachs Visitor Centre, Ancaster Sq. (01877) 330342.

Edinburgh 52 – Glasgow 43 – Oban 71 – Perth 41.

Roman Camp, Main St., FK17 8BG, (01877) 330003, *mail@roman-camp-hotel.co.uk, Fax (01877) 331533,* ≤, « Part 17C hunting lodge in extensive gardens », – TV P. MC AE VISA JCB
Meals – (see ***The Restaurant*** below) – **10 rm** 85.00/165.00 **t.**, 4 suites – SB.

Invertrossachs Country House ⑤, Invertrossachs Rd, FK17 8HG, Southwest : 5 m. by A 81 and Invertrossachs rd taking no through road after 1 ¾ m. ☎ (01877) 331126, *reservations@invertrossachs.freeserve.co.uk, Fax (01877) 331229,* ≤, « Edwardian hunting lodge in extensive grounds », ↖, ⚘ – ⅙ rest, TV P. MC AE Ⓓ VISA
Meals (by arrangement) (dinner only) (unlicensed) 22.50 **st.** – **3 rm** ⊒ 65.00/130.00 **st.** – SB.

Lubnaig, Leny Feus, FK17 8AS, ☎ (01877) 330376, *reception@lubnaighotel.co.uk, Fax (01877) 330376,* ⚘ – ⅙ TV P. MC VISA JCB. ⅗
April-October – **Meals** (residents only) (dinner only) a la carte 11.25/19.75 **t.** 🍷 8.15 – **10 rm** ⊒ 40.00/76.00 **t.**

Priory ⑤ without rest., Bracklinn Rd, FK17 8EH, ☎ (01877) 330001, *judith@bracklinnroad.fsnet.co.uk, Fax (01877) 339200,* ⚘ – ⅙ TV P. MC VISA JCB. ⅗
April-October – **6 rm** ⊒ 40.00/60.00 **s.**

Brook Linn ⑤ without rest., Leny Feus, FK17 8AU, ☎ (01877) 330103, *derek@blinn.freeserve.co.uk, Fax (01877) 330103,* ≤, ⚘ – ⅙ TV P. MC VISA. ⅗
mid March-October – **7 rm** ⊒ 27.00/54.00 **s.**

East Mains House without rest., Bridgend, FK17 8AG, ☎ (01877) 3305[illegible], *Fax (01877) 330535,* ⚘ – ⅙ TV P. MC VISA
6 rm ⊒ 29.00/48.00 **st.**

Dunmor without rest., Leny Rd, FK17 8AL, ☎ (01877) 330756 – ⅙ TV P. MC VISA JCB
April-October – **4 rm** ⊒ 30.00/52.00 **st.**

XXX **The Restaurant** (at Roman Camp H.), Main St., FK19 8BG, ☎ (01877) 330003, *mail@roman-camp-hotel-co.uk, Fax (01877) 331533* – ⅙ P. MC AE Ⓓ VISA JCB
Meals 19.50/35.00 **t.** 🍷 9.10.

CAMPBELTOWN *Argyll and Bute* 401 D 17 – *see Kintyre (Peninsula).*

CANNICH *Highland* 401 F 11 – ✉ *Beauly.*
Edinburgh 184 – Inverness 28 – Kyle of Lochalsh 54.

Mullardoch House ⑤, IV4 7LX, West : 8 ½ m. ☎ (01456) 415460, *andy@mullhouse.demon.co.uk, Fax (01456) 415460,* ≤ Loch Sealbanach and Affric Hills, « Former hunting lodge », ↖, ⚘ – ⅙ TV P. MC AE VISA
Meals (booking essential to non-residents) (set menu only) (bar lunch)/dinner 27.0[illegible] 🍷 6.75 – **6 rm** ⊒ 62.00/108.00 **t.**

CANONBIE *Dumfries and Galloway* 401 402 L 18 – *pop. 1 144.*
Edinburgh 80 – Carlisle 15 – Dumfries 34.

Riverside Inn with rm, DG14 0UX, ☎ (013873) 71295 – ⅙ rest, TV P. MC VISA JCB
closed 25-26 December – **Meals** 19.50 **t.** (dinner) and a la carte 15.25/21.40 **t.** 🍷 6.95 – **7 rm** ⊒ 55.00/70.00 **t.** – SB.

CARBOST *Highland* 401 A 12 – *see Skye (Isle of).*

CARDROSS *Argyll and Bute* 401 G 16 *Scotland G.*
Env. : *The Clyde Estuary*★.
Edinburgh 63 – Glasgow 17 – Helensburgh 5.

Kirkton House ⑤, Darleith Rd, G82 5EZ, ☎ (01389) 841951, *kirktonhouse@cs.com, Fax (01389) 841868,* ≤, ⚘ – TV P. MC AE Ⓓ VISA JCB
closed December and January – **Meals** (by arrangement) 19.75 **st.** – **6 rm** ⊒ 45[illegible]/70.00 **st.** – SB.

CARNOUSTIE *Angus* 401 L 14 – *pop. 12 337.*
18, 18 Monifieth Golf Links, Medal Starter's Box, Princes St., Monifieth ☎ (01382) 532767 – Burnside, Links Par. ☎ (01241) 853789 – 18 Panmure, Barry ☎ (01241) 853120 – 18 Buddon Links, Links Par. ☎ (01241) 853789.
1b High St. ☎ (01241) 852258 (summer only).
Edinburgh 68 – Aberdeen 59 – Dundee 12.

The Carnoustie Golf Course H., The Links, DD7 7JE, ☎ (01241) 411999, *sales@carnoustie-hotel.com, Fax (01241) 411998,* ≤, Ⓕ, ≘s, ⊠, 18, ↖ – ⇅ ⅙, ▤ rest, TV ☎ ♿ 🎪 280. MC AE Ⓓ VISA
Dalhousie : **Meals** (light lunch)/dinner 29.50 **t.** and a la carte 🍷 8.75 – **81 rm** ⊒ 155[illegible]/200.00 **t.**, 4 suites.

XX **11 Park Avenue,** 11 Park Av., DD7 7JA, ☎ (01241) 853336, *11parkavenue@compuserve.com, Fax (01241) 853336* – ⇔. MC AE ① VISA JCB
closed first 2 weeks January, Sunday and Monday – **Meals** (dinner only and lunch by arrangement April-September) a la carte 19.40/28.65 **t.** 🍷 7.50.

RRBRIDGE *Highland* 401 I 12.
Carrbridge ☎ (01479) 841623.
Edinburgh 135 – Aberdeen 92 – Inverness 23.

Fairwinds, PH23 3AA, ☎ (01479) 841240, *fairwindsinfo@tesco.net, Fax (01479) 841240,* ⇔ TV P. MC VISA JCB.
closed 25-26 December – **Meals** *(closed Monday to non-residents)* (booking essential) (dinner only) a la carte 15.00/21.75 **t.** 🍷 5.70 – **5 rm** ☐ 34.00/68.00 **t.** – SB.

Feith Mho'r Country House without rest., Station Rd, PH23 3AP, West : 1 ¼ m. ☎ (01479) 841621, *feith.mhor@btinternet.com,* ←, – TV P
closed 25 December – **6 rm** ☐ 25.00/50.00.

STLEBAY *Western Isles* 401 X 12/13 – *see Barra (Isle of).*

STLE DOUGLAS *Dumfries and Galloway* 401 402 I 19 *Scotland G. – pop. 4 187.*
Env. : *Threave Garden★★ AC, SW : 2½ m. by A 75 – Threave Castle★ AC, W : 1 m.*
Abercromby Rd ☎ (01556) 502801.
Markethill Car Park ☎ (01556) 502611 (summer only).
Edinburgh 98 – Ayr 49 – Dumfries 18 – Stranraer 57.

Longacre Manor, Ernespie Rd, DG7 1LE, Northeast : ¾ m. on Dumfries rd (A 75) ☎ (01556) 503576, *ball.longacre@btinternet.com, Fax (01556) 503886,* ←, – ⇔ rest, TV P. MC VISA JCB
Meals (by arrangement) (communal dining) 17.50 **st.** 🍷 4.50 – **4 rm** ☐ 35.00/90.00 **st.** – SB.

rossmichael *Northwest : 3 ¾ m. on A 713 – ✉ Castle Douglas.*

XX ✿ **Plumed Horse** (Borthwick), Main St., DG7 3AU, ☎ (01556) 670333, *plumed.horse@virgin.net, Fax (01556) 670302* – ⇔ P. MC VISA JCB
closed 10 days September, 1 week January, Monday, Sunday dinner September-Easter and Saturday lunch – **Meals** (booking essential) 11.95/14.50 **st.** (lunch) and a la carte 21.50/28.95 **st.**
Spec. Asparagus, pea and herb risotto. Crisp fillet of sea bass, sauté of scallops. Prune and Armagnac parfait.

WDOR *Highland* 401 I 11 – *pop. 812 – ✉ Inverness.*
Edinburgh 170 – Aberdeen 100 – Inverness 14.

Cawdor Tavern, The Lane, IV12 5XP, ☎ (01667) 404777, *Fax (01667) 404777,* – P. MC AE ① VISA JCB
closed 1 week January and 25 December – **Meals** (booking essential Saturday and Sunday) 22.95 **t.** (dinner) and a la carte 13.90/21.85 **t.** 🍷 6.95.

RNSIDE *Borders* 401 N 16 – *pop. 1 680 – ✉ Duns.*
Edinburgh 52 – Berwick-upon-Tweed 8 – Glasgow 95 – Newcastle-upon-Tyne 70.

Chirnside Hall, TD11 3LD, East : 1 ¼ m. on A 6105 ☎ (01890) 818219, *chirnsidehall@globalnet.co.uk, Fax (01890) 818231,* ←, , , , – ⇔ rest, TV P. MC VISA
Meals (booking essential to non-residents) (dinner only) 21.50 **t.** 🍷 10.50 – **10 rm** ☐ 70.00/120.00 **st.** – SB.

CHAN SEIL *Argyll and Bute* 401 D 15 – *see Seil (Isle of).*

ISH *Perthshire and Kinross* 401 J 15 – *see Kinross.*

ANIE INN *Highland – ✉ Glenmoriston.*
Edinburgh 176 – Inverness 39 – Kyle of Lochalsh 32 – Oban 135.

Cluanie Inn, IV3 6YW, ☎ (01320) 340238, *cluanie@ecosse.net, Fax (01320) 340293,* ← – P. MC AE VISA
Meals (bar lunch)/dinner 14.50/18.50 **st.** – **14 rm** ☐ 35.50/79.00 **st.**

CLYDEBANK *West Dunbartonshire* 401 G 16 – *pop. 45 717.*

Clydebank Municipal, Overtoun Rd, Dalmuir (0141) 952 8698.
Edinburgh 52 – Glasgow 6.

The Beardmore, Beardmore St., G81 4SA, off A 814 (0141) 951 6000, *beardmore.el@hei.co.uk, Fax (0141) 951 6018,* – 170. VISA JCB.
Citrus : **Meals** (closed Sunday) (dinner only) 20.50 **st.** and a la carte – ***B bar cafe :*** **M** a la carte 12.60/20.00 **st.** 8.50 – 12.95 – **162 rm** 93.00 **st.**, 6 suites.

COLONSAY (Isle of) *Argyll and Bute* 401 B 15 – *pop. 106 (inc. Oronsay).*

Isle of Colonsay (019512) 316.
– from Scalasaig to Oban (Caledonian MacBrayne Ltd) 3 weekly (2 h) – from Scala to Kintyre Peninsula (Kennacraig) via Isle of Islay (Port Askaig) (Caledonian MacBrayne weekly.

Scalasaig – *Colonsay.*

Isle of Colonsay, PA61 7YP, (01951) 200316, *colonsay.hotel@pipemedia.cc Fax (01951) 200353,* – rest, VISA JCB
Meals (booking essential) (bar lunch)/dinner 25.00 **t.** 5.50 – **11 rm** (dinner incluc 80.00/160.00 **t.** – SB.

COMRIE *Perthshire* 401 I 14 – *pop. 1 926.*

Comrie, Laggan Braes (01764) 70055.
Edinburgh 66 – Glasgow 56 – Oban 70 – Perth 24.

The Royal, Melville Sq., PH6 2DN, (01764) 679200, *reception@royalhotel.cc Fax (01764) 679219,* « Attractively furnished », – AE VISA JCB
Meals 9.95 **t.** and a la carte 6.00 – **11 rm** 85.00/130.00 **t.**

CONNEL *Argyll and Bute* 401 D 14 – *Oban.*

Edinburgh 118 – Glasgow 88 – Inverness 113 – Oban 5.

Ards House, PA37 1PT, on A 85 (01631) 710255, *jh@ardshouse.demon.co.uk,* VISA JCB.
closed December and January – **Meals** 28.00 **t.** – **7 rm** (dinner included) 62.00/124. – SB.

Ronebhal without rest., PA37 1PJ, on A 85 (01631) 710310, *ronebhal@btinternet.k, Fax (01631) 710310,* – VISA.
closed January and December – **6 rm** 23.00/57.00.

CONON BRIDGE *Highland* 401 G 11.

Edinburgh 168 – Inverness 12.

Kinkell House, Easter Kinkell, IV7 8HY, Southeast : 3 m. by B 9163 and A 835 9169 (01349) 861270, *kinkell@aol.com, Fax (01349) 865902,* – VISA
Meals (booking essential) (residents only Saturday lunch and Sunday dinner) a la c 17.95/23.45 **t.** 7.00 – **9 rm** 57.50/120.00 **t.** – SB.

CONTIN *Highland* 401 G 11 – *pop. 1 194 – Strathpeffer.*

Edinburgh 175 – Inverness 19.

Coul House, IV14 9EY, (01997) 421487, *Fax (01997) 421945,* – rest, AE VISA JCB
Mackenzie's : **Meals** 24.95 **t.** (dinner) and a la carte 21.50/31.50 **t.** 8.00 – ***Tartan Bis*** **Meals** (dinner only) a la carte 12.00/21.50 **t.** 6.00 – **19 rm** 70.00/122.00 **t.**, 1 suite -

Achilty, IV14 9EG, Northwest : 3/4 m. on A 835 (01997) 421355, *Fax (01997) 421923* – VISA
Meals a la carte 12.50/27.95 **t.** – **13 rm** 56.00/76.00 **t.** – SB.

COUPAR ANGUS *Perthshire and Kinross* 401 K 14 – *pop. 3 844 – Blairgowrie.*

Edinburgh 63 – Dundee 14 – Perth 13.

Moorfield House, Myreiggs Rd, PH13 9HS, Northwest : 2 1/2 m. by A (01828) 627303, *Fax (01828) 627339,* – rm, – 120. AE VISA
Meals (lunch booking essential) 13.50/25.50 **st.** 6.95 – **11 rm** 50.00/120.00 **st.** – S

AIGELLACHIE *Moray* 401 K 11 *Scotland G.*

Env. : *Dufftown (Glenfiddich Distillery★), SE : 5 m. by A 941.*

Edinburgh 190 – Aberdeen 58 – Inverness 53.

Craigellachie, Victoria St., AB38 9SR, ☎ (01340) 881204, *info@craigellachie.com, Fax (01340) 881253,* ←, Fø – ⇔ rest, TV P – 🏛 60. MC AE ① VISA JCB
Meals 28.00 **st.** and lunch a la carte 18.20/29.70 **st.** – **26 rm** ☐ 95.00/115.00 **st.** – SB.

AIGHOUSE *Argyll and Bute* 401 C 16 – *see Jura (Isle of).*

IEFF *Perthshire and Kinross* 401 I 14 *Scotland G. – pop. 6 096.*

See : *Town★.*

Env. : *Drummond Castle Gardens★ AC, S : 2 m. by A 822 – Comrie (Scottish Tartans Museum★) W : 6 m. by A 85.*

Exc. : *Scone Palace★★ AC, E : 16 m. by A 85 and A 93.*

18, 9 *Perth Rd ☎ (01764) 652909 – 9 Muthill, Peat Rd ☎ (01764) 681523.*

Town Hall, High St. ☎ (01764) 652578.

Edinburgh 60 – Glasgow 50 – Oban 76 – Perth 18.

Murraypark, Connaught Terr., PH7 3DJ, ☎ (01764) 653731, *welcome@murraypark.com, Fax (01764) 655311,* – ⇔ rest, TV & P – 🏛 25. MC AE VISA
Meals (bar lunch)/dinner a la carte 9.95/22.55 **st.** 6.50 – **19 rm** ☐ 50.00/125.00 **st.**, 1 suite – SB.

Gwydyr House, Comrie Rd, PH7 4BP, West : ½ m. on A 85 ☎ (01764) 653277, *george.blackie@iclweb.com, Fax (01764) 653277,* ←, – ⇔ rest, TV P. MC VISA.
closed 2 weeks October/November Christmas and New Year – **Meals** (by arrangement) a la carte 14.85/23.45 **t.** – **8 rm** ☐ 40.00/70.00 **t.** – SB.

When looking for a quiet hotel
use the maps found in the introduction
or look for establishments with the sign or .

INAN *Argyll and Bute* 401 D 15 *Scotland G.* – ✉ *Lochgilphead.*

See : *Hamlet★.*

Exc. : *Kilmory Knap (Macmillan's Cross★) SW : 14 m.*

Edinburgh 137 – Glasgow 91 – Oban 36.

Crinan, PA31 8SR, ☎ (01546) 830261, *nryan@crinanhotel.com, Fax (01546) 830292,* « Commanding setting, ← Loch Crinan and Sound of Jura », – |$|, ⇔ rest, TV P. MC AE VISA
closed 25 December – **Meals** (bar lunch)/dinner 32.50 **t.** 10.00 – (see also ***Lock 16*** below) – **20 rm** ☐ (dinner included) 95.00/140.00 **t.** – SB.

Lock 16 (at Crinan H.), PA31 8SR, ☎ (01546) 830261, *nryan@crinanhotel.com, Fax (01546) 830292,* « Commanding setting, ← Loch Crinan and Sound of Jura » – ⇔ P. MC AE VISA
May-September – **Meals** - Seafood - *(closed 25 December and Monday)* (booking essential) (dinner only) 42.50 **t** 10.00.

OSSFORD *Fife* 401 J 15 – *see Dunfermline.*

OSSMICHAEL *Dumfries and Galloway* 401 402 I 19 – *see Castle Douglas.*

LLODEN *Highland* 401 H 11 – *see Inverness.*

LNAKNOCK *Highland* 401 B 11 – *see Skye (Isle of).*

MBERNAULD *North Lanarkshire* 401 I 16 – *pop. 62 412.*

Edinburgh 40 – Glasgow 11 – Stirling 13.

Travel Inn, 4 South Muirhead Rd, G67 1AX, off A 8011 ☎ (01236) 725339, *Fax (01236) 736380* – ⇔ rm, ▤ rest, TV & P. MC AE ① VISA.
Meals (grill rest.) – **37 rm** 40.95 **t.**

CUPAR *Fife* 401 K 15 – *pop. 8 174.*
Edinburgh 45 – Dundee 15 – Perth 23.

Todhall House ⛰, Dairsie, KY15 4RQ, East : 2 m. by A 91 ☎ (01334) 656344, *todhallh e@ukgateway.net, Fax (01334) 650791*, ←, « Part Georgian, part Victorian country hous – TV P. VISA. ✻
March-October – **Meals** (by arrangement) (communal dining) 25.00 **s.** – **3 rm** 33. 68.00 **st.**

Ostler's Close, 25 Bonnygate, KY15 4BU, ☎ (01334) 655574, *Fax (01334) 654036* – VISA JCB. ✻
closed 2 weeks summer, 25-26 December, 1 January, Sunday, Monday and lunch Wedn day and Thursday – **Meals** a la carte 16.95/33.50 **t.** 6.95.

DALBEATTIE *Dumfries and Galloway* 401 402 I 19 *Scotland G.* – *pop. 4 421.*
Env. : *Kippford★, S : 5 m. by A 710.*
Dalbeattie ☎ (01556) 611421.
Edinburgh 94 – Ayr 56 – Dumfries 14 – Stranraer 62.

Auchenskeoch Lodge ⛰, DG5 4PG, Southeast : 6 ¼ m. by A 711 on B ☎ (01387) 780277, *Fax (01387) 780277*, – rest, TV P. VISA JCB
Easter-October – **Meals** (by arrangement) (communal dining) 18.00 **st.** 6.00 – 2 39.00/64.00 **st.**, 1 suite – SB.

The Guide is updated annually so renew your Guide every year.

DALRY *North Ayrshire* 401 402 F 16.
Edinburgh 70 – Ayr 21 – Glasgow 25.

Braidwoods, Drumastle Mill Cottage, KA24 4LN, Southwest : 1 ½ m. by A 737 Saltcoats rd ☎ (01294) 833544, *Fax (01294) 833553* – P. AE VISA
closed first 3 weeks January, 2 weeks September, Monday, Sunday dinner and Tuesday lu – **Meals** (booking essential) 17.00/30.00 **t.** 11.00
Spec. Confit of duck, stir-fry vegetables, oriental sauce. Baked turbot, lobster risotto shellfish jus. Millefeuille of Scottish raspberries.

DARVEL *East Ayrshire* 401 402 H 17.
Edinburgh 60 – Ayr 22 – Glasgow 21.

Scoretulloch House ⛰ with rm, KA17 0LR, Southeast : 2 m. by A 71 ☎ (01560) 323 *mail@scoretulloch.com, Fax (01560) 323441*, ←, – TV P. AE VISA JCB
closed 25-26 December and 1 January – ***Loudoun Room :*** **Meals** *(closed Sunday dir Monday and Tuesday)* 29.50 **t.** (dinner) and lunch a la carte 15.00/25.00 **t.** 7.50 – ***Osc Brasserie :*** **Meals** *(closed Sunday dinner, Monday and Tuesday)* a la carte 15.00/25.0 7.50 – **2 rm** 75.00/110.00 **t.**

DENNY *Falkirk* 401 I 15 *Scotland G.* – *pop. 11 061.*
Exc. : *Stirling★★, N : 8 m. by A 872.*
Edinburgh 34 – Glasgow 25 – Stirling 7.

Topps Farm ⛰, Fintry Rd, FK6 5JF, West : 4 m. on B 818 ☎ (01324) 822471, *jennifer etopps.f9.co.uk, Fax (01324) 823099*, ← – TV P. VISA. ✻
closed 24-27 December – **Meals** 12.00 **st.** – **8 rm** 32.00/50.00 **st.** – SB.

DERVAIG *Argyll and Bute* 401 B 14 – *see Mull (Isle of).*

DINGWALL *Highland* 401 G 11 – *pop. 5 572.*
Edinburgh 172 – Inverness 14.

Cafe India Brasserie, Lockhart House, Tulloch St., IV15 9JZ, ☎ (01349) 862552 – VISA
Meals - Indian - 6.95 **t.** (lunch) and a la carte 12.10/23.55 **t.** 5.50.

DORNIE *Highland* 401 D 12 *Scotland G.* – ✉ *Kyle of Lochalsh.*
See : *Eilean Donan Castle★ AC (site★★).*
Env. : *Glen Shiel★, SE : 4 m. on A 87.*
Edinburgh 212 – Inverness 74 – Kyle of Lochalsh 8.

Conchra House 🙈, Ardelve, IV40 8DZ, North : 1 ¾ m. by A 87 on Conchra rd ✆ (01599) 555233, *email@conchra.co.uk, Fax (01599) 555433,* ≤ Loch Long, « Part Georgian country house », 🌳 – ⚡ P – 🏃 40. MC AE VISA. ✂
booking essential in winter – **Meals** (booking essential to non-residents) (dinner only) 18.50 🍷 4.50 – **6 rm** ☐ 40.00/70.00 **s.**

RNOCH *Highland* 401 H 10 *Scotland G. – pop. 2 042.*

See : *Town*★.

18, 18 *Royal Dornoch, Golf Rd ✆ (01862) 810219.*

The Square ✆ (01862) 810400.

Edinburgh 219 – Inverness 63 – Wick 65.

Highfield House without rest., Evelix Rd, IV25 3HR, ✆ (01862) 810909, *enquiries@highfieldhouse.co.uk, Fax (01862) 811605,* ≤, 🌳 – ⚡ TV P
3 rm ☐ 40.00/56.00.

2 Quail with rm, Castle St., IV25 3SN, ✆ (01862) 811811, *bookings@2quail.com* – ⚡ rm, TV. MC AE VISA. ✂
restricted opening in winter – **Meals** *(closed Sunday and Monday)* (dinner only) 29.50 **t.** 🍷 7.95 – **2 rm** ☐ 55.00/75.00.

UNBY *Orkney Islands* 401 K 6 – *see Orkney Islands (Mainland).*

UMBEG *Highland* 401 E 9 – ✉ *Lairg.*

Edinburgh 262 – Inverness 105 – Ullapool 48.

Drumbeg, Assynt, IV27 4NW, ✆ (01571) 833236, *Fax (01571) 833333,* ≤ – ⚡ rest, TV P. MC VISA. ✂
April-October – **Meals** (booking essential to non-residents) (bar lunch) a la carte 11.00/17.25 **st.** 🍷 4.00 – **6 rm** ☐ 40.00/52.00 **st.**

UMNADROCHIT *Highland* 401 G 11 *Scotland G. – pop. 852 –* ✉ *Milton.*

Env. : *Loch Ness*★★ – *Loch Ness Monster Exhibition*★ *AC* – *The Great Glen*★.

Edinburgh 172 – Inverness 16 – Kyle of Lochalsh 66.

Polmaily House 🙈, IV63 6XT, West : 2 m. on A 831 ✆ (01456) 450343, *polmaily@btinternet.com, Fax (01456) 450813,* « Special facilities for young children », 🏊, 🌳, 🐎, 🎾 – ⚡ TV P. MC VISA
April-October and New Year – **Meals** (bar lunch)/dinner 25.00 **t.** and a la carte 🍷 9.00 – **11 rm** ☐ 58.00/156.00 **st.** – SB.

Drumbuie Farm without rest., Drumbuie, IV3 6XP, East : ¾ m. by A 82 ✆ (01456) 450634, *drumbuie@amserve.net, Fax (01456) 450595,* ≤, « Working farm », 🐎 – ⚡ TV P. MC VISA. ✂
closed 25 December – **3 rm** ☐ 48.00.

YMEN *Stirling* 401 G 15 *Scotland G. – pop. 1 565.*

Env. : *Loch Lomond*★★, *W : 3 m.*

Drymen Library, The Square ✆ (01360) 660068 (summer only).

Edinburgh 64 – Glasgow 18 – Stirling 22.

Buchanan Arms, Main St., G63 0BQ, ✆ (01360) 660588, *Fax (01360) 660943,* 🏋, ≘s, 🏊, 🌳 – ⚡ TV P – 🏃 150. MC AE ⦿ VISA JCB
Meals 11.50/25.00 **st.** and a la carte 🍷 8.50 – **52 rm** ☐ (dinner included) ☐ 75.00/150.00 **st.** – SB.

LNAIN BRIDGE *Highland* 401 J 12 – *see Grantown-on-Spey.*

MBARTON *West Dunbartonshire* 401 G 16 *Scotland G. – pop. 77 173.*

See : *Dumbarton Castle (site*★*) AC.*

Env. : *Loch Lomond*★★, *N : 5½ m. by A 82.*

18 *Vale of Leven, Northfield Rd, Bonhill, Alexandria ✆ (01389) 752351 –* 18 *Broadmeadow ✆ (01389) 732830.*

Milton, by Dumbarton A 82 (northbound) ✆ (01389) 742306.

Edinburgh 64 – Glasgow 12 – Greenock 17.

Travelodge, Milton, G82 2TY, East : 3 m. by A 814 on A 82 ✆ (01389) 65202, *Fax (01389) 65202* – ⚡ rm, TV ♿ P. MC AE ⦿ VISA JCB. ✂
Meals (grill rest.) – **32 rm** 39.95 **t.**

DUMFRIES *Dumfries and Galloway* **401** **402** J 18 *Scotland G. – pop. 21 164.*

See : *Town★ – Midsteeple★* **A A.**

Env. : *Lincluden College (Tomb★) AC, N : 1½ m. by College St.* **A.**

Exc. : *Drumlanrig Castle★★ (cabinets★) AC, NW : 16 ½ m. by A 76* **A** *– Shambellie Ho Museum of Costume (Costume Collection★) S : 7¼m. by A 710* **A** *– Sweetheart Abbey★ S : 8 m. by A 710* **A** *– Caerlaverock Castle★ (Renaissance façade★★) AC, SE : 9 m. by B 72 – Glenkiln (Sculptures★) W : 9 m. by A 780 –* **A** *– and A 75 – Ruthwell Cross★, SE : 12 m. b 780 –* **B** *– A 75 and B 724.*

18 Dumfries & Galloway, 2 Laurieston Av., Maxwelltown ☎ (01387) 253582 **A** *– 18 Dumfrie County, Nuffield, Edinburgh Rd ☎ (01387) 253585 – 9 Crichton, Bankend Rd ☎ (013 247894,* **B.**

Whitesands ☎ (01387) 253862, **A.**

Edinburgh 80 – Ayr 59 – Carlisle 34 – Glasgow 79 – Manchester 155 – Newcastle upon T 91.

DUMFRIES

Aldermanhill Road	B	2
Bank Street	A	3
Buccleuch Street	A	4
Cardoness Street	B	5
Cassalands	A	6
Castle Street	A	7
Castle Douglas Road	A	8
Catherine Street	B	9
Corberry Avenue	A	10
Cornwall Mount Rd	B	12
Friars Vennel	A	13
Galloway Street	A	14
Glebe Street	B	15
Great King Street	A	16
Hermitage Drive	A	17
High Street	A	18
Loreburn Centre	A	20
Loreburn Street	A	21
Nith Street	AB	22
Queen Street	B	23
Queensberry Street	A	24
Rae Street	B	26
St. Mary's Street	B	27
St. Michael Street	B	28
St. Michael's Bridge Road	A	
Shakespeare Street	B	
Union Street	A	
Whitesands	A	

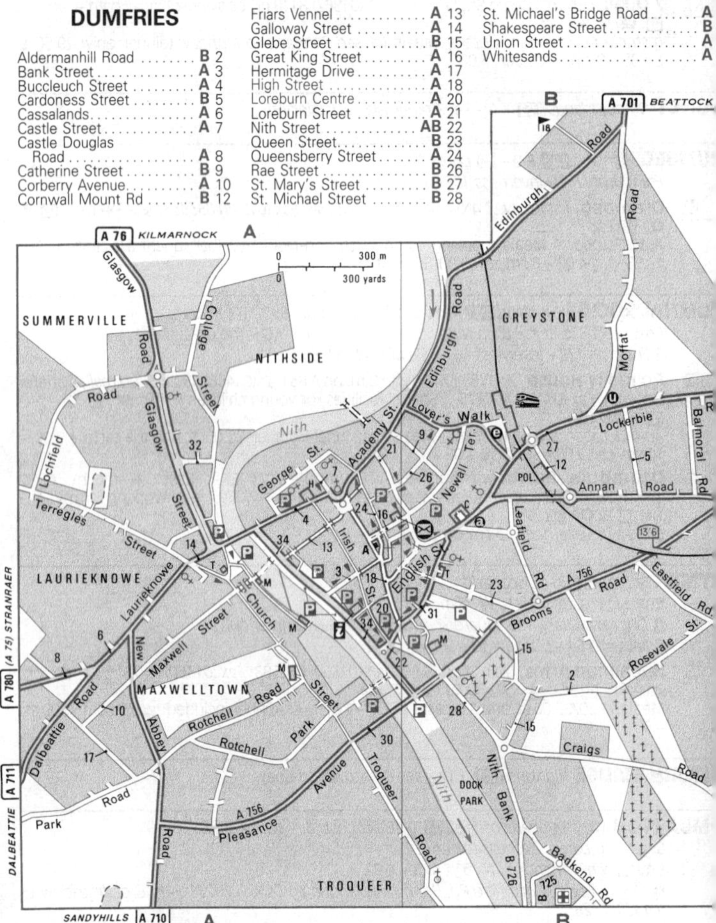

Cairndale, English St., DG1 2DF, ☎ (01387) 254111, *Fax (01387) 250555,* – rm, – 300. *VISA.*
Meals 8.95/22.50 **st.** and a la carte 8.50 – **91 rm** 85.00/145.00 **st.** – SB.

Station, 49 Lovers Walk, DG1 1LT, (01387) 254316, *info@stationhotel.co.uk, Fax (01387) 250388* – rm, – 70. VISA B e
closed 25-26 December and 1-3 January – **Meals** (bar lunch Sunday-Wednesday)/dinner 9.95/12.95 **t.** and a la carte 6.00 – **32 rm** 66.00/110.00 **t.** – SB.

Travel Inn, Annan Rd, Collin, DG1 3JX, East : 2 m. on A 780 (Carlisle rd) at junction with A 75 (01387) 249785, *Fax (01387) 249287* – rm, rest, VISA.
Meals (grill rest.) – **40 rm** 40.95 **t.**

Travelodge, Annan Rd, Collin, DG1 3SE, East : 2 ¼ m. by A 780 (Carlisle rd) on A 75 (01387) 750658, *Fax (01387) 750658* – rm, VISA JCB.
Meals (grill rest.) – **40 rm** 39.95 **t.**

Redbank House, New Abbey Rd, DG2 8EW, South : 1 ½ m. by A 711 (Stranraer rd) on A 710 (01387) 247034, *Fax (01387) 266220*, – VISA JCB.
Meals (by arrangement) 10.00 **s.** – **6 rm** 30.00/50.00 **s.**

Hazeldean without rest., 4 Moffat Rd, DG1 1NJ, (01387) 266178, *Fax (01387) 266178*, – VISA. B u
closed 25-26 December – **7 rm** 30.00/44.00 **st.**

DUNAIN PARK *Highland – see Inverness.*

DUNBLANE *Stirling* 401 I 15 *Scotland G. – pop. 8 007 (inc. Lecropt).*
See : *Town★ – Cathedral★ (west front★★).*
Env. : *Doune★ (castle★ AC) W : 4½ m. by A 820 – Doune Motor Museum★ AC, W : 5½ m. by A 820 and A 84.*
Stirling Rd (01786) 824428 (summer only).
Edinburgh 42 – Glasgow 33 – Perth 29.

Cromlix House, Kinbuck, FK15 9JT, North : 3 ½ m. on B 8033 (01786) 822125, *reservations@cromlixhouse.com, Fax (01786) 825450*, « Antique furnishings, 19C chapel », – rest, VISA.
closed 2-20 January **Meals** (booking essential) (lunch by arrangement)/dinner 26.00/40.00 **t.** 11.00 – **6 rm** 150.00/235.00 **t.**, **8 suites** 260.00/325.00 **t.** – SB.

Rokeby House, Doune Rd, FK15 9AT, (01786) 824447, *rokeby.house@btconnect.com, Fax (01786) 821399*, – VISA JCB.
Meals (booking essential) (residents only) (dinner only) 15.00/25.00 **st.** – **4 rm** 65.00/110.00 **st.** – SB.

DUNDEE *Dundee* 401 L 14 *Scotland G. – pop. 165 873.*
See : *Town★ – The Frigate Unicorn★ AC* Y A – *Discovery Point★ AC* Y B – *Verdant Works★ – McManus Galleries★.*
18, 9, 9 *Caird Park, Mains Loan (01382) 453606 –* 18 *Camperdown, Camperdown Park (01382) 623398 –* 18 *Downfield, Turnberry Av. (01382) 825595.*
Tay Road Bridge (toll) **Y.**
Dundee Airport : (01382) 643242, SW : 1½ m. **Z.**
7-21 Castle St. (01382) 527527.
Edinburgh 63 – Aberdeen 67 – Glasgow 83.

Plan on next page

Hilton Dundee, Earl Grey Pl., DD1 4DE, (01382) 229271, *reservations@dundee-stakis.co.uk, Fax (01382) 200072*, – rest, – 400. VISA
Meals (bar lunch Saturday) 9.95/19.50 **t.** and dinner a la carte – 10.50 – **128 rm** 120.00/140.00 **st.**, 1 suite – SB. Y a

Swallow, Kingsway West (Dundee Ring Rd), DD2 5JT, West : 4 ¾ m. at junction of A 85 with A 90 (01382) 641122, *Fax (01382) 568340*, – rest, – 100. VISA
Meals 20.50 **st.** (dinner) and a la carte 19.95/33.50 **st.** – **105 rm** 95.00/115.00 **st.**, 1 suite – SB.

Premier Lodge, Dayton Drive, Camperdown Retail Park, Kingsway, DD2 3SQ, Northwest : 3 ¼ m. by A 923 at junction with A 90 (01382) 880170, *Fax (01382) 880172* – rm, rest, VISA. Z e
Meals (grill rest.) a la carte 10.45/21.95 **st.** – 6.00 – **78 rm** 42.00 **st.**

Premier Lodge, Panmurefield, DD5 3TS, East : 4 ¾ m. on A 92 (01382) 738112, *Fax (01382) 736042* – rm, rest, VISA.
Meals (grill rest.) a la carte 11.30/22.55 **7.** – 10.00 – **60 rm** 42.00.

Travel Inn, Discovery Quay, Riverside Drive, DD1 4XA, (01382) 203240, *Fax (01382) 203237*, – rm, rest, VISA. Z a
Meals (grill rest.) – **40 rm** 40.95 **t.**

Travel Inn, Ethiebeaton Park, Monifieth, DD5 4HB, East : 5 ¾ m. on A 92 (01382) 530565, *Fax (01382) 530468* – rm, rest, VISA.
Meals (grill rest.) – **40 rm** 40.95 **t.**

DUNDEE

Albert Street	Z
Ancrum Road	Z
Bell Street	Y
City Square	Y
Commercial Street	Y
Coupar Angus Road	Z
Douglas Road	Z
Drumgeith Road	Z
Dudhope Terrace	Z
East Dock Street	Z
East Marketgait	Y
Greendykes Road	Z
High Street	Y
Logie Street	Z
Longtown Road	Z
Mains Road	Z
Meadowside	Y
Moncur Crescent	Z
Murraygate	Y
Nethergate	Y
Old Glamis Road	Z
Overgate Centre	Y
Provost Road	Z
Reform Street	Y
St. Andrews Street	Y
South Union Street	Y
Strathmartine Road	Z
Trades Lane	Y
Ward Road	Y
Wellgate Centre	Y
West Bell Street	Y
West Marketgait	Y

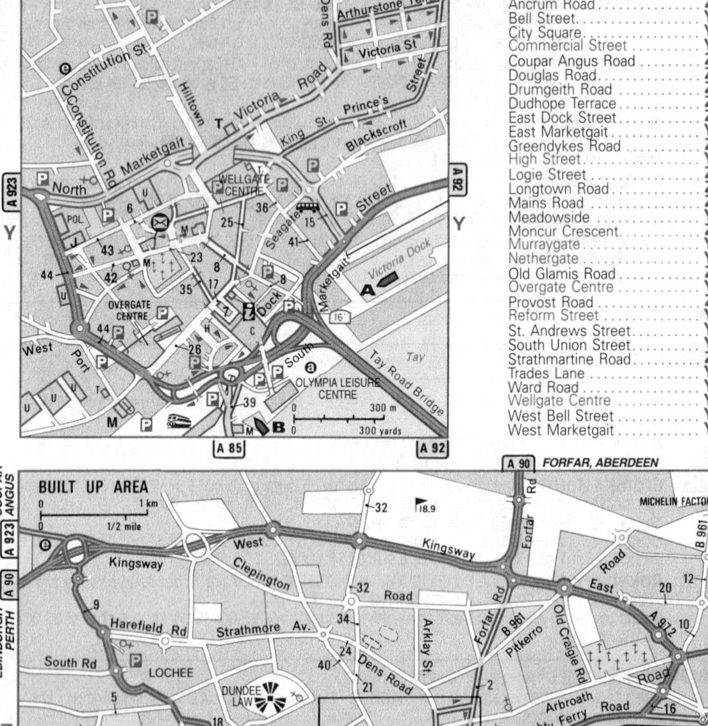

Travel Inn, Kingsway West, Invergowrie, DD2 5JU, West : 5 m. by A 85 on A ... ✆ (01382) 561115, *Fax (01382) 568431* – ⇷ rm, ▤ rest, TV ♿ P. MC AE ① VISA. ✗
Meals (grill rest.) – **64 rm** 40.95 **t.**

Travelodge, Kingsway West, Invergowrie, DD2 4TD, Northwest : 3 ¾ m. by A 923 on A ... ✆ (01382) 610488, *Fax (01382) 610488* – ⇷ rm, TV ♿ P. MC AE ① VISA. ✗
Meals (grill rest.) – **32 rm** 39.95 **t.**

Hillside without rest., 43 Constitution St., DD3 6JH, ✆ (01382) 223443, *info@tildab.co...* Y
Fax (01382) 800222, – ⇷ TV P. MC VISA. ✗
closed 25 December **3 rm** ☕ 24.00/42.00.

at Broughty Ferry *East : 4½ m. by A 930 –* **Z** *– (Dundee Rd) – ✉ Dundee.*

Broughty Ferry, 16 West Queen St., DD5 1AR, ✆ (01382) 480027, *jghm@hotelbroug... ferry.co.uk, Fax (01382) 477660,* – ⇷ TV P. MC AE VISA. ✗
Meals – (see ***Bombay Brasserie*** below) – **15 rm** ☕ 59.00/74.00 **t.** – SB.

Beach House, 22 Esplanade, DD5 2EN, ✆ (01382) 776614, *Fax (01382) 480241* – ⇷ r...
TV. MC VISA JCB. ✗
Meals 12.50 **st.** – **5 rm** ☕ 38.00/48.00 **st.**

Invermark House without rest., 23 Monifieth Rd, DD5 2RN, ☎ (01382) 739430, *Fax (01382) 739430*, – TV P. MC VISA. closed Christmas and New Year – **4 rm** 30.00/45.00 **s.**

Bombay Brasserie (at Broughty Ferry H.), 16 West Queen St., DD5 1AR, ☎ (01382) 480490, *Fax (01382) 477660* – P. MC AE VISA *closed lunch Sunday and Monday* – **Meals** - Indian - (lunch by arrangement) a la carte 10.40/23.90 **t.** 6.60.

Cafe Montmartre, 289 Brook St., DD5 2DS, ☎ (01382) 739313, *Fax (01382) 739636* – MC AE VISA JCB *closed Monday lunch* – **Meals** - French - 9.95/19.95 **t.** and a la carte 4.90.

DUNDONNELL *Highland* 401 E 10 *Scotland G.* – ✉ *Garve.*

Env. : *Wester Ross*★★★ – *Loch Broom*★★, *N : 4½ m. via Allt na h–Airbhe.*

Exc. : *Falls of Measach*★★, *SE : 10 m. by A 832* – *Corrieshalloch Gorge*★, *SE : 11½ m. by A 832 and A 835.*

Edinburgh 215 – *Inverness 59.*

Dundonnell, Little Loch Broom, IV23 2QR, ☎ (01854) 633204, *selbie@dundonnellhotel.co.uk, Fax (01854) 633366*, ≤ Dundonnell Valley – TV P – 60. MC AE VISA *closed January-mid February* – **Meals** (booking essential in winter) (bar lunch)/dinner a la carte 22.85/26.00 **t.** 6.00 – **28 rm** 57.50/115.00 **t.** – SB.

DUNFERMLINE *Fife* 401 J 15 *Scotland G.* – *pop. 29 436.*

See : *Town*★ – *Abbey*★ *(Abbey Church*★★*)* **AC**.

Env. : *Forth Bridges*★★, *S : 5 m. by A 823 and B 980.*

Exc. : *Culross*★★ *(Village*★★★, *Palace*★★ **AC**, *Study*★ **AC**), *W : 7 m. by A 994 and B 9037.*

18 Canmore, Venturefair Av. ☎ *(01383) 724969* – *18 Pitreavie, Queensferry Rd* ☎ *(01383) 722591* – *18 Pitfirrane, Crossford* ☎ *(01383) 723534* – *9 Saline, Kinneddar Hill* ☎ *(01383) 852591.*

13-15 Maygate ☎ *(01383) 720999.*

Edinburgh 16 – *Dundee 48* – *Motherwell 39.*

Garvock House, St. John's Drive, Transy, KY12 7TU, East : ¾ m. by A 907 off Garvock hill ☎ (01383) 621067, *sales@garvock.co.uk, Fax (01383) 621168*, – TV P – 40. MC AE VISA **Meals** (light dinner Sunday) 15.50 **t.** (lunch) and dinner a la carte 18.95/27.50 **t.** 8.50 – **11 rm** 70.00/110.00 **t.** – SB.

King Malcolm, Queensferry Rd, KY11 8DS, South : 1 m. on A 823 ☎ (01383) 722611, *info@kingmalcolm-hotel.dunfermline.com, Fax (01383) 730865* – rm, rest, TV P – 150. MC AE D VISA JCB. **Meals** a la carte 10.70/18.50 **t.** 4.10 – 10.25 – **48 rm** 80.00/120.00 **st.** – SB.

Crossford *Southwest : 1¾ m. on A 994* – ✉ *Dunfermline.*

Keavil House, Main St., KY12 8QW, ☎ (01383) 736258, *Fax (01383) 621600*, – TV P – 350. MC AE D VISA. **Meals** (buffet lunch) 10.00/22.50 **st.** and a la carte 9.50 – 9.75 – **47 rm** 75.00/125.00 **st.** – SB.

DUNKELD *Perthshire and Kinross* 401 J 14 *Scotland G.* – *pop. 4 069.*

See : *Village*★ – *Cathedral Street*★.

9 Dunkeld & Birnam, Fungarth ☎ *(01350) 727524.*

The Cross ☎ *(01350) 727688.*

Edinburgh 58 – *Aberdeen 88* – *Inverness 98* – *Perth 14.*

Kinnaird , Dalguise, PH8 0LB, Northwest : 6¾ m. by A 9 on B 898 ☎ (01796) 482440, *enquiry@kinnairdestate.com, Fax (01796) 482289*, ≤ Tay valley and hills, « Sporting estate, antique furnishings », – rest, TV P. MC AE VISA. *closed Monday to Wednesday January-February* – **Meals** 30.00/45.00 **st.** 15.00 – **8 rm** (dinner included) 300.00/440.00 **t.**, 3 suites.

Hilton Dunkeld House , PH8 0HX, ☎ (01350) 727771, *gm-dunkeld@hilton.com, Fax (01350) 728924*, ≤, « Tayside setting », – TV P – 80. MC AE D VISA. **Meals** (bar lunch)/dinner 26.00 **st.** and a la carte – 10.75 – **89 rm** 115.00/130.00 **st.**, 7 suites – SB.

DUNOON *Argyll and Bute* 401 F 16 *Scotland G. – pop. 13 781 (inc. Kilmun).*
Env. : *The Clyde Estuary*★.
18 Cowal, Ardenslate Rd ☎ (01369) 702216 – 9 Innellan, Knockamillie Rd ☎ (01369) 8302
from Dunoon Pier to Gourock Railway Pier (Caledonian MacBrayne Ltd) frequ services daily (20 mn) – from Hunters Quay to McInroy's Point, Gourock (Western Fer (Clyde) Ltd) frequent services daily (20 mn).
7 Alexandra Par. ☎ (01369) 703785 (closed weekends in winter).
Edinburgh 73 – Glasgow 27 – Oban 77.

Enmore, Marine Par., Kirn, PA23 8HH, North : 1 ¼ m. on A 815 ☎ (01369) 702230, *enm hotel@btinternet.com, Fax (01369) 702148,* ≤ Firth of Clyde, squash – rest, TV. MC AE VISA
closed 20 December-20 January – **Meals** (booking essential in winter) 15.00/25.00 and a la carte 8.00 – **8 rm** 35.00/150.00 **st.**, 1 suite – SB.

Anchorage, Shore Rd, Ardanadam, PA23 8QG, North : 3 m. on A 815 ☎ (01369) 70510 *nfo@anchorage.co.uk,* ≤, – TV P. MC VISA.
closed November and 25 December – **Meals** *(closed Monday-Thursday October-Mar* a la carte 15.00/30.00 **st.** 7.25 – **5 rm** 45.00/80.00 **st.** – SB.

DUNVEGAN *Highland* 401 A 11 – *see Skye (Isle of).*

DURNESS *Highland* 401 F 8 – ✉ *Lairg.*
9 Durness, Balnakeil ☎ (01971) 511364.
Sango ☎ (01971) 511259 (April-October).
Edinburgh 266 – Thurso 78 – Ullapool 71.

Port-na-Con House, Loch Eribol, IV27 4UN, Southeast : 6 m. on A 8 ☎ (01971) 511367, *portnacon70@hotmail.com, Fax (01971) 511367,* ≤ Loch Eribol, « Lo side setting » – P. MC VISA JCB
restricted opening in winter – **Meals** (by arrangement) 12.50 **st.** – **3 rm** 28.00/40.00

DYCE *Aberdeenshire* 401 N 12 – *see Aberdeen.*

EARLSTON *Borders* 401 402 L 17 – *pop. 1 968.*
Edinburgh 34 – Hawick 22 – Newcastle upon Tyne 71.

Birkhill, TD4 6AR, North : 3 ¼ m. by A 68 and Birkenside rd on Lauder ☎ (01896) 849307, *birkhill@btinternet.com, Fax (01896) 848206,* ≤, « Georgian cour house », – P. MC VISA.
closed Christmas and New Year – **Meals** (by arrangement) (communal dining) 22.00 **3 rm** 43.00/66.00 **s.**

EASDALE *Argyll and Bute* 401 D 15 – *see Seil (Isle of).*

EAST KILBRIDE *South Lanarkshire* 401 402 H 16 – *pop. 73 378.*
18 Torrance House, Strathaven Rd ☎ (01355) 248638.
Edinburgh 46 – Ayr 35 – Glasgow 10.

Crutherland House, Strathaven Rd, G75 0QZ, Southeast : 2 m. on A ☎ (01355) 237633, *info@crutherland.macdonald-hotels.co.uk, Fax (01355) 220855,* – TV P. – 500. MC AE VISA JCB.
Meals (bar lunch Saturday) 25.00 **t.** (dinner) and a la carte 27.45/33.70 **t.** 9.50 – **74** 75.00/105.00 **t.**, 2 suites.

Hilton East Kilbride, Stewartfield Way, G74 5LA, Northwest : 2 ¼ m. on A ☎ (01355) 236300, *reservations@stakis.co.uk, Fax (01355) 233552,* – rest, TV P. – 400. MC AE VISA JCB.
Meals a la carte 15.95/24.95 **t.** – **99 rm** 135.00/155.00 **st.**, 2 suites.

Bruce, 35 Cornwall St., G74 1AF, ☎ (01355) 229771, *enquiries@maksu-group.co Fax (01355) 242216* – rm, TV – 400. MC AE VISA.
Meals (bar lunch)/dinner 16.50/17.50 **t.** and a la carte – **65 rm** 65.00/95.00 **t.**

Premier Lodge, Eaglesham Rd, G75 8LW, Northwest : 1 ½ m. off A 7 ☎ (0870) 7001398, *Fax (0870) 7001399* – rm, TV P. MC AE VISA.
Meals (grill rest.) a la carte 9.00/19.00 **st.** – 6.00 – **40 rm** 42.00 **st.**

Travel Inn, Brunel Way, The Murray, G75 0JY, ☎ (01355) 222809, *Fax (01355) 23051* rm, rest, TV P. MC AE VISA.
Meals (grill rest.) – **40 rm** 40.95 **t.**

EDINBURGH

401 K 16 *Scotland G. – pop. 418 914.*

Glasgow 46 – Newcastle upon Tyne 105.

TOURIST INFORMATION

Edinburgh & Scotland Information Centre, 3 Princes St. ☎ (0131) 473 3800.
Edinburgh Airport, Tourist Information Desk ☎ (0131) 473 3800.

PRACTICAL INFORMATION

18, 18 *Braid Hills, Braid Hills Rd ☎ (0131) 447 6666,* **BX**.
18 *Craigmillar Park, 1 Observatory Rd ☎ (0131) 667 2837,* **BX**.
18 *Carrick Knowe, Glendevon Park ☎ (0131) 337 1096,* **AX**.
18 *Duddingston, Duddingston Road West ☎ (0131) 661 1005,* **BV**.
18 *Silverknowes, Parkway ☎ (0131) 336 3843,* **AV**.
18 *Liberton, 297 Gilmerton Rd ☎ (0131) 664 3009,* **BX**.
18, 18 *Marriott Dalmahoy Hotel C.C., Kirknewton ☎ (0131) 333 4105,* **AX**.
9 *Portobello, Stanley St. ☎ (0131) 669 4361,* **BV**.
Edinburgh Airport : ☎ (0131) 333 1000, W : 6 m. by A 8 **AV** – **Terminal :** *Waverley Bridge.*

SIGHTS

See : *City★★★ – Edinburgh International Festival★★★ (August) – National Gallery of Scotland★★* **DY M4** *– Royal Botanic Garden★★★* **AV** *– The Castle★★ AC* **DYZ** *: Site★★★ – Palace Block (Honours of Scotland★★★) – St. Margaret's Chapel (※★★★) – Great Hall (Hammerbeam Roof★★) – ≤★★ from Argyle and Mill's Mount* **DZ** *– Abbey and Palace of Holyroodhouse★★ AC (Plasterwork Ceilings★★★, ※★★ from Arthur's Seat)* **BV** *– Royal Mile★★ : St. Giles' Cathedral★★ (Crown Spire★★★)* **EYZ** *– Gladstone's Land★ AC* **EYZ A** *– Canongate Talbooth★* **EY B** *– New Town★★ (Charlotte Square★★★* **CY 14** *– Royal Museum of Scotland★★* **EZ M2** *– The Georgian House★ AC* **CY D** *– Scottish National Portrait Gallery★* **EY M3** *– Dundas House★* **EY E** *) – Scottish National Gallery of Modern Art★* **AV M1** *– Victoria Street★* **EZ 84** *– Scott Monument★ (≤★) AC* **EY F** *– Craigmillar Castle★ AC* **BX** *– Calton Hill (※★★★ AC from Nelson's Monument)* **EY**.

Env. : *Edinburgh Zoo★★ AC* **AV** *– Hill End Ski Centre (※★★) AC, S : 5½ m. by A 702* **BX** *– The Royal Observatory (West Tower ≤★) AC* **BX** *– Ingleston, Scottish Agricultural Museum★, W : 6½ m. by A 8* **AV**.

Exc. : *Rosslyn Chapel★★ AC (Apprentice Pillar★★★) S : 7½ m. by A 701 –* **BX** *– and B 7006 – Forth Bridges★★, NW : 9½ m. by A 90* **AV** *– Hopetoun House★★ AC, NW : 11½ m. by A 90 –* **AV** *– and A 904 – Dalmeny★ – Dalmeny House★ AC, St. Cuthbert's Church★ (Norman South Doorway★★) NW : 7 m. by A 90* **AV** *– Crichton Castle (Italianate courtyard range★) AC, SE : 10 m. by A 7 –* **X** *– and B 6372.*

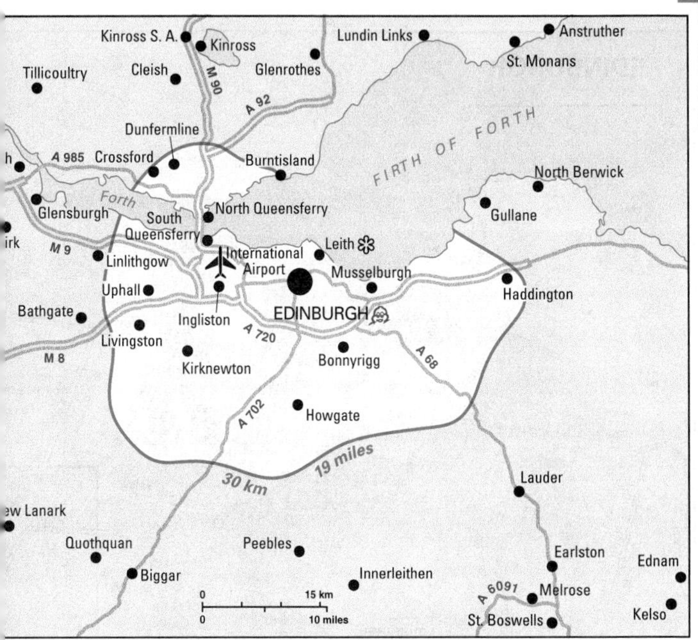

Balmoral, 1 Princes St., EH2 2EQ, (0131) 556 2414, *reservations@thebalmoralhotel.com, Fax (0131) 557 3747,* – – 400. VISA JCB EY n
Meals – (see ***Number One*** and ***Hadrian's*** below) – 16.75 – **164 rm** 210.00/300.00 **st.**, 20 suites – SB.

Caledonian Hilton, Princes St., EH1 2AB, (0131) 459 9988, *caley.edinburgh@wcom.net, Fax (0131) 225 6632,* – rm, rest, – 250. VISA. CY n
La Pompadour : Meals *(closed Saturday lunch, Sunday and Monday)* 18.00/25.00 **t.** and a la carte 9.00 – ***Chisholms :*** Meals (bar lunch Sunday) a la carte 13.00/30.00 **t.** 7.00 – 15.00 – **236 rm** 165.00/295.00 **t.**, 13 suites – SB.

Sheraton Grand, 1 Festival Sq., EH3 9SR, (0131) 229 9131, *carla.well@sheraton.com, Fax (0131) 229 6254,* – rm, – 500. VISA JCB. CDZ v
Terrace : Meals (buffet only) 19.95 **t.** and a la carte – (see also ***Grill Room*** below) – 15.50 – **243 rm** 156.00/280.00 **t.**, 17 suites – SB.

George Inter-Continental, 19-21 George St., EH2 2PB, (0131) 225 1251, *edinburgh@interconti.com, Fax (0131) 226 5644* – rm, – 200. VISA. DY z
Le Chambertin *((0131) 240 7178)* **: Meals** *(closed Saturday lunch, Sunday and Monday)* a la carte 26.00/37.50 – ***Carvers*** *((0131) 459 2305)* **: Meals** 15.50/18.50 **st.** and a la carte 8.50 – 15.50 – **192 rm** 180.00/230.00 **st.**, 3 suites.

The Howard, 34 Great King St., EH3 6QH, (0131) 557 3500, *reserve@thehoward.com, Fax (0131) 557 6515,* « Georgian town houses » – – 30. VISA. *closed 22-27 December* – **Meals** – (see ***36*** below) – **15 rm** 140.00/325.00 **t.** – SB. DY s

The Edinburgh Residence, 7 Rothesay Terr., EH3 7RY, (0131) 226 3380, *Fax (0131) 226 3381,* « Georgian town houses » – VISA. CY x
Meals (room service only) – 9.65 – **21 rm** 175.00/525.00 **t.**, 8 suites.

Channings, 12-16 South Learmonth Gdns., EH4 1EZ, (0131) 315 2226, *reserve@channings.co.uk, Fax (0131) 332 9631,* « Edwardian town houses » – – 35. VISA. CY e
closed 22-27 December – **Meals** – (see ***Channings*** below) – **43 rm** 130.00/195.00 **t.**, 3 suites – SB.

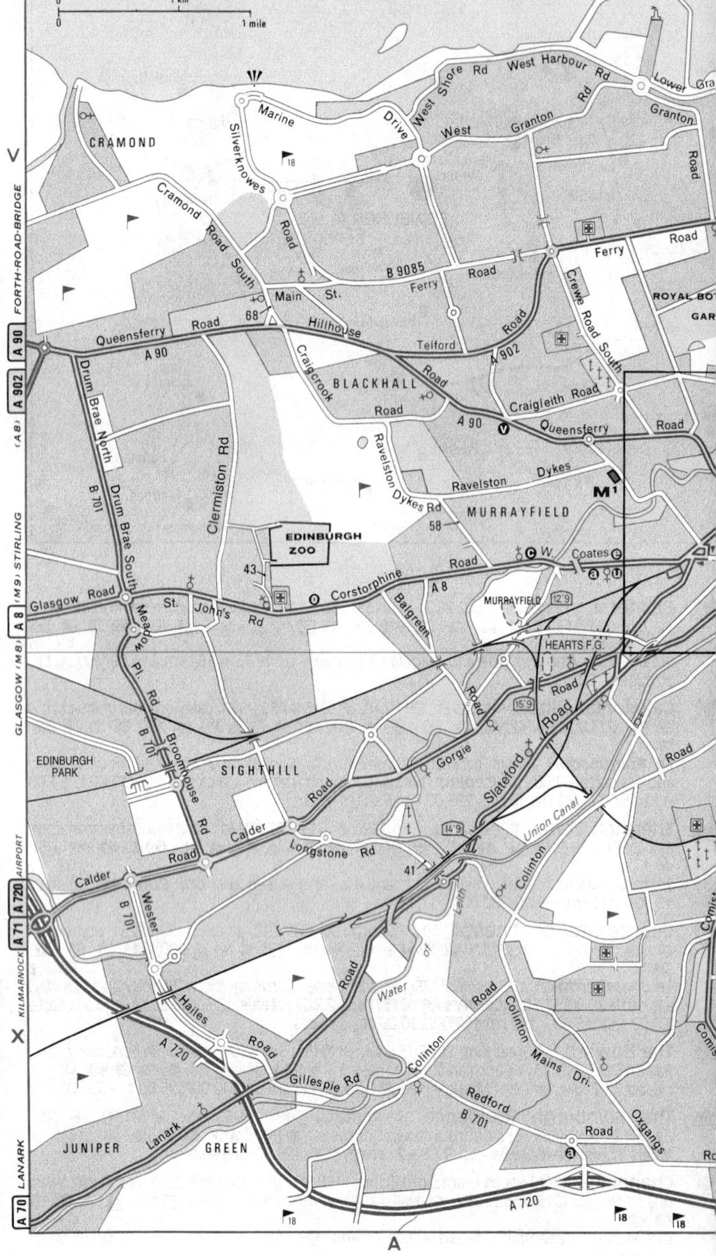

EDINBURGH
0 1 km
0 1 mile
FIRTH
CRAMOND
Marine Drive
Silverknowes Road
West Shore Rd
West Harbour Rd
West Granton Rd
Granton Road
Lower Gra
Cramond Road South
Ferry Road
B 9085
Main St.
Hillhouse Road
Queensferry Road
A 90
Telford Road
A 902
Crewe Road South
ROYAL BO
GAR
Craigcrook Road
BLACKHALL
Craigleith Road
Drum Brae North
Drum Brae South
B 701
Clermiston Rd
Ravelston Dykes Rd
Ravelston Dykes
M1
MURRAYFIELD
EDINBURGH ZOO
Glasgow Road
St. John's Rd
Corstorphine Road
A 8
Balgreen Road
Coates
MURRAYFIELD
HEARTS F.G.
Meadow Pl. Rd
Broomhouse Rd
SIGHTHILL
EDINBURGH PARK
Gorgie Road
Slateford Road
Union Canal
Calder Road
Longstone Rd
Wester Hailes Road
Water of Leith
Colinton Road
Colinton Mains Dri.
Redford Road
Oxgangs Road
Gillespie Rd
Lanark Road
A 720
JUNIPER GREEN
FORTH-ROAD-BRIDGE
A 90
A 902
(A8) STIRLING (M9)
A 8
GLASGOW (M8)
AIRPORT
A 720
A 71
KILMARNOCK
A 70
LANARK
A
V
X

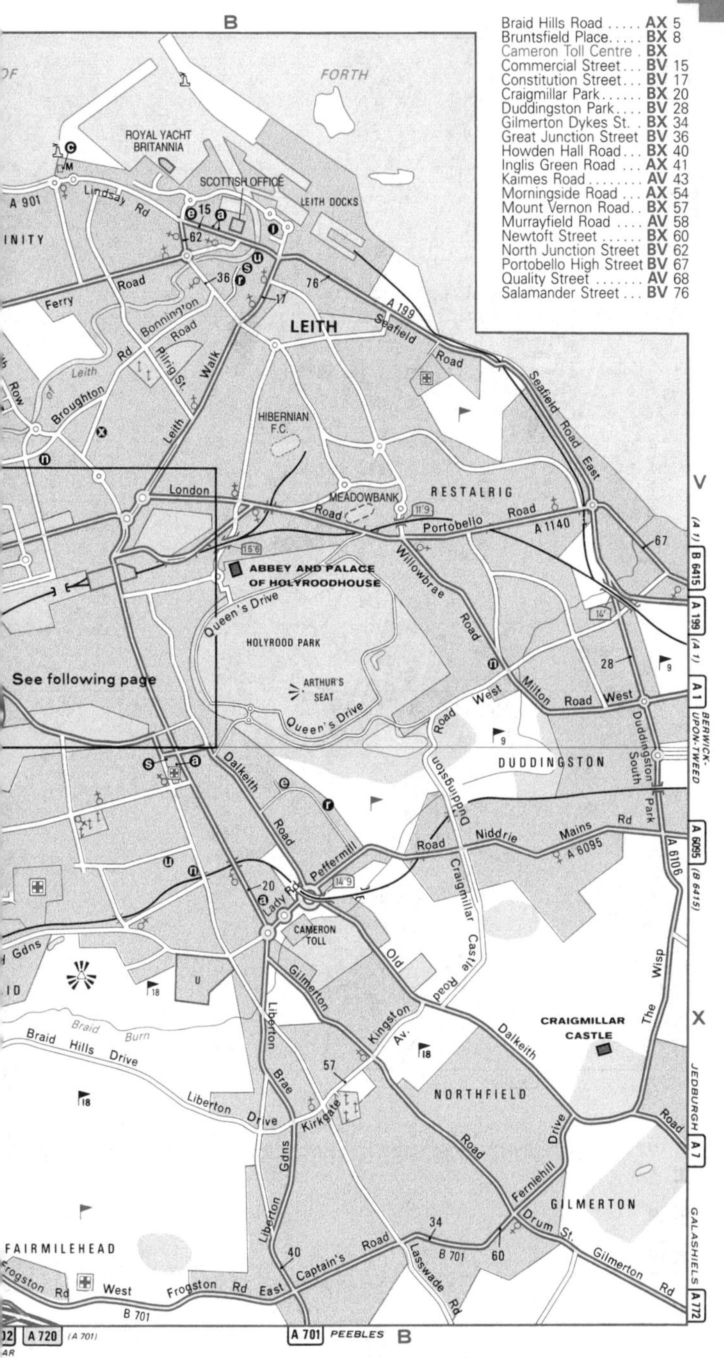
Braid Hills Road ..... AX 5
Bruntsfield Place..... BX 8
Cameron Toll Centre . BX
Commercial Street ... BV 15
Constitution Street ... BV 17
Craigmillar Park ...... BX 20
Duddingston Park .... BV 28
Gilmerton Dykes St. . BX 34
Great Junction Street BV 36
Howden Hall Road ... BX 40
Inglis Green Road ... AX 41
Kaimes Road .... AV 43
Morningside Road ... AX 54
Mount Vernon Road .. BX 57
Murrayfield Road .... AV 58
Newtoft Street ...... BX 60
North Junction Street BV 62
Portobello High Street BV 67
Quality Street .... AV 68
Salamander Street ... BV 76
B
FORTH
ROYAL YACHT
BRITANNIA
SCOTTISH OFFICE
LEITH DOCKS
A 901
Lindsay Rd
Ferry
Road
Bonnington
Road
Pilrig St.
Leith Walk
LEITH
A 199
Seafield
Road
Seafield Road East
Broughton
Leith
HIBERNIAN
F.C.
London
Road
MEADOWBANK
RESTALRIG
Portobello
Road
A 1140
ABBEY AND PALACE
OF HOLYROODHOUSE
Queen's Drive
HOLYROOD PARK
ARTHUR'S
SEAT
See following page
Willowbrae
Road
Milton
Road
West
DUDDINGSTON
Duddingston
South
Dalkeith
Road
Peffermill
Road
Niddrie
Mains
Rd
A 6095
A 6106
Craigmillar
Castle
Road
Lady Rd
CAMERON
TOLL
Old
Dalkeith
Road
Gilmerton
Liberton
Brae
Kingston
Av.
The Wisp
CRAIGMILLAR
CASTLE
Braid
Burn
Braid Hills Drive
Liberton Drive
Kirkgate
NORTHFIELD
Ferniehill
Drive
GILMERTON
Drum St.
Gilmerton
Rd
Liberton
Gdns
Captain's
Road
Lasswade
Rd
B 701
FAIRMILEHEAD
Frogston
Rd
West
Frogston
Rd
East
B 701
V
X
(A 1)
B 6415
A 199
(A 1)
A 1
BERWICK-
UPON-TWEED
A 6095
(B 6415)
JEDBURGH
A 7
GALASHIELS
A 772
A 720
(A 701)
A 701
PEEBLES
B

EDINBURGH
CENTRE

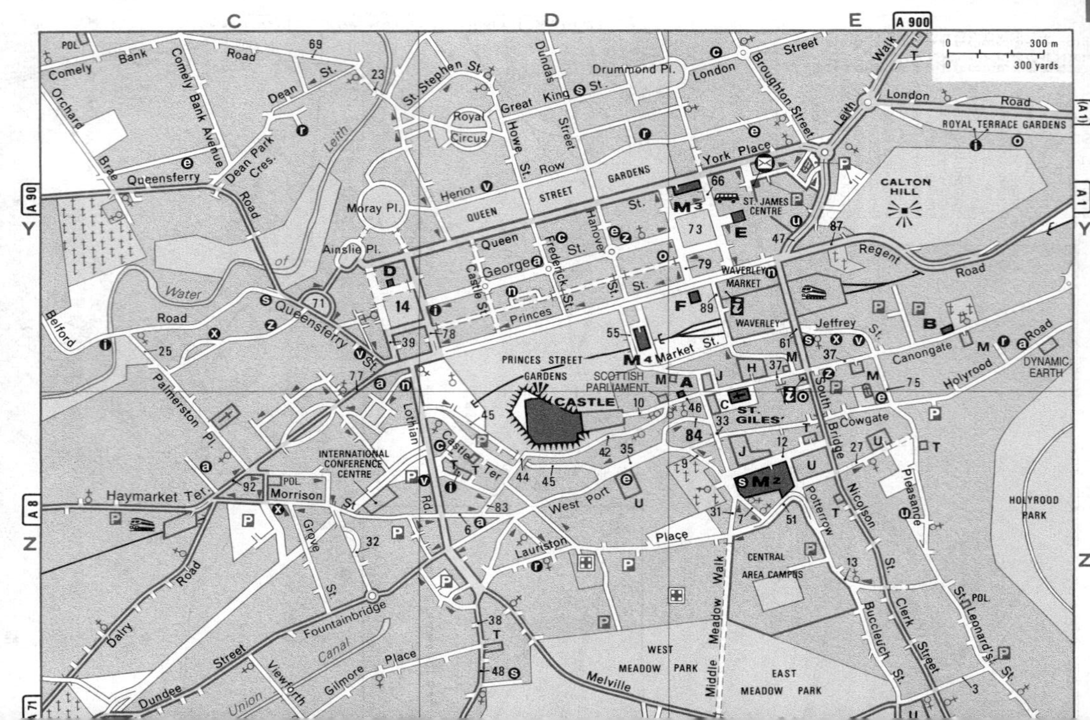

The Bonham, 35 Drumsheugh Gdns., EH3 7RN, (0131) 226 6050, *reserve@thebonham.com, Fax (0131) 226 6080,* « Contemporary interior design » – – 50. CY z
closed 3-7 January – **Meals** 11.75/15.00 **t.** (lunch) and a la carte 25.00/29.75 **t.** 12.00 – 7.50 – **46 rm** 135.00/235.00 **t.**, 2 suites – SB.

The Roxburghe, 38 Charlotte Sq., EH2 4HG, (0131) 240 5500, *info@roxburghe.macdonald-hotels.co.uk, Fax (0131) 240 5555,* – rest, – 400. DY i
closed 25-26 December – ***The Melrose :*** **Meals** 15.00 **st.** (lunch) and a la carte 17.35/23.95 **st.** – **196 rm** 125.00/180.00 **st.**, 1 suite – SB.

The Holyrood, 81 Holyrood Rd, EH8 6AE, (0131) 550 4500, *info@holyrood.macdonald-hotels.co.uk, Fax (0131) 550 4545,* – – 180. EY a
Flints : **Meals** 7.00/18.00 **t.** and a la carte 9.00 – 12.50 – **157 rm** 160.00/350.00 **st.** – SB.

Posthouse Edinburgh, Corstorphine Rd, EH12 6UA, West : 3 m. on A 8 (0870) 400 9026, *Fax (0131) 334 9237* – rm, rest, – 120. AV o
Sampans : **Meals** - Asian - *(closed Sunday dinner)* (dinner only) a la carte 15.95/22.40 **t.** 8.95 – ***Rotisserie :*** **Meals** *(closed Saturday lunch)* (carvery rest.) 12.95 **t.** – 11.95 – **303 rm** 109.00 **t.** – SB.

Crowne Plaza, 80 High St., EH1 1TH, (0131) 557 9797, *res.cpedinburgh@alliance.uk.com, Fax (0131) 557 9789,* – rm, – 250. EY z
closed 24 to 27 December – **Meals** 14.95/18.95 **t.** and a la carte 11.00 – 13.50 – **229 rm** 155.00/250.00 **st.**, 9 suites – SB.

Prestonfield House, Priestfield Rd, EH16 5UT, (0131) 668 3346, *prestonfield_house@compuserve.com, Fax (0131) 668 3976,* « Part 17C country house, collection of paintings », – rm, – 500. BX r
The Old Dining Room : **Meals** 10.00/19.00 **t.** (lunch) and dinner a la carte 22.15/25.45 **t.** 9.00 – **31 rm** 185.00/375.00 **t.** – SB.

Point, 34 Bread St., EH3 9AF, (0131) 221 5555, *info@point-hotel.co.uk, Fax (0131) 221 9929,* « Contemporary interior » – rm, – 100. DZ a
closed 24 to 26 December – **Meals** *(closed lunch Saturday and Sunday)* 10.90/12.90 **st.** – 10.00 – **136 rm** 80.00/110.00 **st.**, 4 suites.

Royal Terrace, 18 Royal Terr., EH7 5AQ, (0131) 557 3222, *Fax (0131) 557 5334,* « Georgian town houses », – rest, – 80. EY i
Meals (light lunch)/dinner 18.95/25.00 **t.** and a la carte – 10.50 – **104 rm** 130.00/170.00, 3 suites – SB.

Thistle Edinburgh, 107 Leith St., EH1 3SW, (0131) 556 0111, *edinburgh@thistle.co.uk, Fax (0131) 557 5333* – – 250. EY u
Craig's : **Meals** (dinner only) 16.95 **st.** and a la carte – 12.50 – **139 rm** 131.00/155.00 **st.**, 4 suites – SB.

Hilton Edinburgh Belford, 69 Belford Rd, EH4 3DG, (0131) 332 2545, *Fax (0131) 332 3805* – rm, – 130. CY i
Meals 17.95 **st.** (lunch) and dinner a la carte 16.85/25.85 **st.** 7.95 – 10.95 – **144 rm** 180.00/220.00 **st.** – SB.

Swallow Royal Scot (becoming a Marriott spring 2001), 111 Glasgow Rd, EH12 8NF, West : 4 ½ m. on A 8 (0131) 334 9191, *info@swallowhotels.com, Fax (0131) 316 4507,* – rm, rest, – 200.
Meals *(closed Saturday lunch)* 14.00/22.50 **st.** and a la carte 7.95 – **255 rm** 125.00/145.00 **st.**, 4 suites – SB.

The Carlton, North Bridge St., EH1 1SD, (0131) 472 3000, *carlton@paramount-hotels.co.uk, Fax (0131) 556 2691,* squash – rm, rest, – 250. EY s
Meals 10.95/26.95 **t.** and dinner a la carte 5.95 – 12.95 – **179 rm** 155.00/220.00 **st.**, 4 suites – SB.

Hilton Edinburgh Grosvenor, Grosvenor St., EH12 5EF, (0131) 226 6001, *reservations@edinburgh.stakis.co.uk, Fax (0131) 220 2387* – rm, – 300. CZ a
Meals a la carte 14.00/21.00 **t.** – 10.95 – **187 rm** 140.00/160.00 **t.**, 2 suites – SB.

Holyrood Aparthotel without rest., 1 Nether Bakehouse (via Gentles entry), EH8 8PE, (0131) 524 3200, *reservations@holyroodaparthotel.com, Fax (0131) 524 3210,* – EY r
41 suites 200.00 **st.**

SCOTLAND

Simpsons without rest., 79 Lauriston Pl., EH3 9HZ, ℘ (0131) 622 7979, *rez@simpsons-el.com, Fax (0131) 622 7900* – |‡| ⇔ TV ☎ ♿. MC AE ◑ VISA JCB DZ
closed 24-28 December – – ☕ 6.50 **57 rm** 80.00/100.00 **st.**, 1 suite.

Frederick House without rest., 42 Frederick St., EH2 1EX, ℘ (0131) 226 1999, *frede house@ednet.co.uk, Fax (0131) 624 7064* – |‡| TV ☎. MC AE ◑ VISA JCB. ✗ DY
☕ 5.00 **44 rm** 65.00/95.00 **t.**, 1 suite.

Apex International, 31-35 Grassmarket, EH1 2HS, ℘ (0131) 300 3456, *mail@apexhc .co.uk, Fax (0131) 220 5345* – |‡|, ⇔ rm, ▤ rest, TV ☎ P – 🎤 225. MC AE ◑ ✗ DZ
Meals (bar lunch)/dinner 8.00/25.00 **st.** and a la carte 🍷 6.00 – ☕ 8.50 – **175 rm** 140.00

Jurys Inn Edinburgh, 43 Jeffrey St., EH1 1DG, ℘ (0131) 200 3300, *edinburgh-inn@j doyle.com, Fax (0131) 200 0400* – |‡|, ⇔ rm, TV ☎ ♿ P – 🎤 50. MC AE ◑ VISA. ✗
closed 24 to 27 December – **Meals** (bar lunch)/dinner a la carte 15.50/20.00 **st.** 🍷 7.C
186 rm 87.00 **t.** EY

Holiday Inn Garden Court, 107 Queensferry Rd, EH4 3HL, ℘ (0131) 332 24 *Fax (0131) 332 3408*, ≤, Ⅎ – |‡|, ⇔ rm, ▤ rest, TV ☎ ♿ P – 🎤 200. MC AE ◑ JCB AV
Meals (bar lunch)/dinner 13.50/16.50 **t.** and a la carte – ☕ 10.50 – **102 rm** 130.00 **t.**

Maitland without rest., 23-33 Shandwick Pl., EH2 4RG, ℘ (0131) 229 1467, *maitland@e se.ie.co.uk, Fax (0131) 229 7549* – |‡| ⇔ TV ☎. MC AE VISA. ✗ CY
☕ 9.25 **65 rm** 80.00/110.00 **t.**

The Lodge, 6 Hampton Terr., West Coates, EH12 5JD, ℘ (0131) 337 3682, *thelodgehot btconnect.com, Fax (0131) 313 1700* – ⇔ TV P. MC AE VISA JCB. ✗ AV
Meals *(closed Sunday)* (booking essential) (residents only) (dinner only) 18.50/22.50 🍷 5.95 – **10 rm** ☕ 48.00/120.00 **st.**

Kildonan Lodge without rest., 27 Craigmillar Park, EH16 5PE, ℘ (0131) 667 2793, *kil anlodge@compuserve.com, Fax (0131) 667 9777* – ⇔ TV P. MC AE ◑ VISA JCB. ✗
closed 25 December – **12 rm** ☕ 55.00/98.00 **st.** BX

Albany, 39 Albany St., EH1 3QY, ℘ (0131) 556 0397, *info@albanyhoteledinburgh.co Fax (0131) 557 6633*, « Georgian town houses » – TV ☎. MC AE VISA JCB EY
closed 24-26 December – **Meals** – (see ***Haldanes*** below) – ☕ 12.30 – **21 rm** 95. 185.00 **st.**

Ailsa Craig, 24 Royal Terr., EH7 5AH, ℘ (0131) 556 1022, *ailsacraighotel@ednet.co Fax (0131) 556 6055*, « Georgian town house », 🌳 – TV. MC AE ◑ VISA. ✗ EY
Meals (booking essential) (residents only) (dinner only) 9.50/12.50 **st.** – **18 rm** ☕ 55. 90.00 **st.**

Greenside, 9 Royal Terr., EH7 5AB, ℘ (0131) 557 0022, *greensidehotel@ednet.co Fax (0131) 557 0022*, « Georgian town house », 🌳 – TV. MC AE ◑ VISA JCB. ✗ EY
Meals (booking essential) (residents only) (dinner only) 9.50/13.50 **st.** 🍷 6.00 – **16** ☕ 45.00/80.00 **st.**

Travel Inn Metro, 1 Morrison Link, EH3 8DN, ℘ (0131) 228 9819, *Fax (0131) 228 98* |‡| ⇔, ▤ rest, TV ☎ ♿ P. MC AE ◑ VISA. ✗ CZ
Meals (grill rest.) (dinner only) – **281 rm** 46.95 **t.**

Travelodge, 33 St. Mary's St., EH1 1TA, ℘ (0131) 557 6281, *Fax (0131) 557 3681* – ⇔ rm, ▤ rest, TV ☎ ♿. MC AE ◑ VISA JCB. ✗ EZ
Meals (cafe bar) – **193 rm** 49.95 **t.**

Ibis without rest., 6 Hunter Sq., EH1 1QW, ℘ (0131) 240 7000, *h2039@accor.hotels.c Fax (0131) 240 7007* – |‡| ⇔ TV ☎ ♿. MC AE ◑ VISA EZ
99 rm 52.00 **st.**

Travel Inn, 228 Willowbrae Rd, EH8 7NG, ℘ (0131) 661 3396, *Fax (0131) 652 278* ⇔ rm, ▤ rest, TV ♿ P. MC AE ◑ VISA. ✗ BV
Meals (grill rest.) – **39 rm** 40.95 **t.**

Travelodge, 48 Dreghorn Link, City Bypass, EH13 9QR, ℘ (0131) 441 4 *Fax (0131) 441 4296* – ⇔ rm, TV ♿ P. MC AE ◑ VISA JCB. ✗ AX
Meals (grill rest.) – **72 rm** 49.95 **t.**

27 Heriot Row without rest., 27 Heriot Row, EH3 6EN, ℘ (0131) 225 9474, *t.a@bluey er.co.uk, Fax (0131) 220 1699*, « Georgian town house », 🌳 – ⇔ TV. MC VISA. ✗ DY
3 rm ☕ 60.00/100.00 **st.**

17 Abercromby Place without rest., 17 Abercromby Pl., EH3 6LB, ℘ (0131) 557 803 *irlys.lloyd@virgin.net, Fax (0131) 558 3453*, « Georgian town house » – ⇔ TV ☎ P. MC ✗ DY
10 rm ☕ 60.00/120.00 **st.**

Saxe Coburg House without rest., 24 Saxe Coburg Pl., EH3 5BP, ℘ (0131) 332 2717 *rell@zetnet.co.uk, Fax (0131) 315 3375*, « Georgian town house », 🌳 – ⇔ TV. MC AE ✗ BV
closed 24-26 December – **5 rm** ☕ 40.00/95.00 **st.**

Number Two Saxe Coburg Place without rest., 2 Saxe Coburg Pl., EH3 5BR, (0131) 315 4752, *ogilvy@dial.pipex.com, Fax (0131) 332 4934,* « Georgian town house », – . VISA. BV v
3 rm 50.00/100.00 st.

Seven Danube Street without rest., 7 Danube St., EH4 1NN, (0131) 332 2755, *seven.danubestreet@virgin.net, Fax (0131) 343 3648,* « Georgian town house », – . VISA CY r
closed Christmas – **3 rm** 55.00/110.00 **st.**

16 Lynedoch Place without rest., EH3 7PY, (0131) 225 5507, *susie.lynedoch@btinternet.com, Fax (0131) 226 4185,* « Georgian town house », – . VISA CY s
3 rm 40.00/90.00 st.

22 Murrayfield Gardens without rest., EH12 6DF, (0131) 337 3569, *macnetic@dial.pipex.com, Fax (0131) 337 3803,* « Victorian house », – . VISA JCB AV c
3 rm 45.00/80.00 st.

The Stuarts without rest., 17 Glengyle Terr., EH3 9LN, (0131) 229 9559, *gloria@the-stuarts.com, Fax (0131) 229 2226* – . AE VISA JCB. DZ s
closed 1 week Christmas – **3 rm** 70.00/90.00.

Kew House without rest., 1 Kew Terr., Murrayfield, EH12 5JE, (0131) 313 0700, *kewhouse@worldsites.net, Fax (0131) 313 0747* – . AE VISA JCB. AV a
6 rm 46.00/84.00 st.

Teviotdale without rest., 53 Grange Loan, EH9 2ER, (0131) 667 4376, *teviotdale.house@btinternet.com, Fax (0131) 667 4376* – . AE VISA JCB. BX u
closed 20-28 December – **8 rm** 28.00/78.00.

Stuart House without rest., 12 East Claremont St., EH7 4JP, (0131) 557 9030, *stuartho@globalnet.co.uk, Fax (0131) 557 0563* – . AE VISA JCB. BV x
closed 1 week Christmas – **7 rm** 45.00/90.00 **t.**

Dorstan, 7 Priestfield Rd, EH16 5HJ, (0131) 667 6721, *reservations@dorstan_hotel.demon.co.uk, Fax (0131) 668 4644* – . AE VISA. BX e
Meals (by arrangement) 17.00 **t.** – **14 rm** 30.00/82.00 **t.**

Twenty London Street without rest., 20 London St., EH7 4PQ, (0131) 332 2717, *birrell@zetnet.co.uk, Fax (0131) 315 3375,* « Georgian town house », – . AE VISA
5 rm 45.00/85.00 st. EY c

Classic House without rest., 50 Mayfield Rd, EH9 2NH, (0131) 667 5847, *info@classichouse.demon.co.uk, Fax (0131) 662 1016* – . VISA. BX n
7 rm 30.00/80.00 st.

Number One (at Balmoral H.), 1 Princes St., EH2 2EQ, (0131) 622 8831, *Fax (0131) 557 8740* – . AE VISA JCB EY n
closed lunch Saturday and Sunday – **Meals** 18.00/70.00 **t.** and a la carte.

Grill Room (at Sheraton Grand H.), 1 Festival Sq., EH3 9SR, (0131) 221 6422, *Fax (0131) 229 6254* – . AE VISA JCB CDZ v
closed Saturday lunch and Sunday – **Meals** 27.50/29.00 **st.** and a la carte.

Atrium, 10 Cambridge St., EH1 2ED, (0131) 228 8882, *Fax (0131) 228 8808* – . AE VISA DZ c
closed 24 December-2 January, Sunday and Saturday lunch – **Meals** 18.00/25.00 **t.** and a la carte 25.00/34.00 **t.** 10.00.

Duck's at Le Marche Noir, 2-4 Eyre Pl., EH3 5EP, (0131) 558 1608, *malcolm@ducks.co.uk, Fax (0131) 556 0798* – . AE VISA JCB BV n
closed 25-26 December, lunch Saturday and Sunday – **Meals** a la carte 24.90/32.30 **t.** 7.50.

The Marque, 19-21 Causewayside, EH9 1QF, (0131) 466 6660, *themarque@daramail.com, Fax (0131) 466 6661* – . AE VISA BX s
closed 25-26 December, 1-3 January and Monday – **Meals** 10.00/12.50 **t.** (lunch) and dinner a la carte 17.50/27.70 **t.** 9.50.

Channings (at Channings H.), 12-16 South Learmonth Gdns., EH4 1EZ, (0131) 315 2225, *Fax (0131) 332 9631,* – . AE VISA CY e
closed Sunday lunch – **Meals** 12.00/24.50 **t.** 6.70.

Martins, 70 Rose St., North Lane, EH2 3DX, (0131) 225 3106, *Fax (0131) 220 3403* – . AE VISA JCB DY n
closed 1-22 January, 1 week May-June, 1 week September-October, Sunday and Monday except during Edinburgh Festival and Saturday lunch – **Meals** (booking essential) 25.00 **t.** (dinner) and a la carte 17.00/34.00 **t.** 9.85.

36 (at The Howard H.), 36 Great King St., EH3 6QH, (0131) 556 3636, *Fax (0131) 556 3663,* « Contemporary decor » – . AE VISA DY s
Meals (dinner only and Sunday lunch)/dinner a la carte 21.45/31.95 **t.** 14.50.

Kelly's, 46 West Richmond St., EH8 9DZ, (0131) 668 3847, *Fax (0131) 668 3847* – VISA
closed January, 25-26 December and Sunday – **Meals** 10.00 **t.** (lunch) and a la carte 22.70/26.40 **t.** 6.00. EZ u

XX **Hadrian's** (at Balmoral H.), 2 North Bridge, EH1 1TR, ☎ (0131) 557 50 *Fax (0131) 557 3747* – ▤. MC AE ⓓ VISA JCB EY
Meals 20.00/25.00 **t.** and a la carte.

XX **Rhodes & Co.,** 3-15 Rose St. (first floor), EH2 2YJ, ☎ (0131) 220 9190, *Fax (0131) 220 9* – ▤. MC AE ⓓ VISA DY
closed Sunday dinner – **Meals** a la carte 14.00/23.25 **t.** 8.50.

XX **Banks,** 10 Newington Rd (first floor), EH9 1QS, ☎ (0131) 667 0707, *Fax (0131) 667 070* MC AE VISA BX
closed Monday – **Meals** 9.95/35.00 **t.** and a la carte 10.00.

XX **Yumi,** 2 West Coates, EH12 5JQ, ☎ (0131) 337 2173, *Fax (0131) 337 2818* – ⅍ P. MC VISA JCB AV
closed 2 weeks Christmas-New Year and Sunday – **Meals** - Japanese - (dinner only) 24. 50.00 **t.** 5.50.

XX **The Tower,** Museum of Scotland (fifth floor), EH1 1JF, ☎ (0131) 225 3003, *mail@towe staurant.com, Fax (0131) 247 4220,* – ⅍ ▤. MC AE ⓓ VISA JCB EZ
closed 25 December – **Meals** a la carte 18.15/33.40 **t.** 6.75.

XX **Iggs,** 15 Jeffrey St., EH1 1DR, ☎ (0131) 557 8184, *Fax (0131) 441 7111* – MC AE ⓓ VISA J
closed 2-4 January and Sunday – **Meals** 9.50/15.00 **t.** (lunch) and a la carte approx. 26.5 6.00. EY

XX **Haldanes** (at Albany H.), 39A Albany St., EH1 3QY, ☎ (0131) 556 8407, *info@haldanesre urant.com, Fax (0131) 556 2662,* – ⅍. MC AE ⓓ VISA JCB EY
closed lunch Saturday and Sunday – **Meals** 18.95/24.50 **t.** and a la carte 7.95.

X **Tuscan Square,** 30b Grindley St. (first floor), EH3 9AX, ☎ (0131) 229 98 *Fax (0131) 221 9515* – MC AE VISA DZ
closed 24-25 December, 1-2 January, Sunday and Monday – **Meals** 9.50/12.95 and a la carte.

X **Bouzy Rouge,** 1 Alva St., EH2 4PH, ☎ (0131) 225 9594, *res@bouzy-rouge.c Fax (0131) 225 9593* – ▤. MC AE ⓓ VISA CY
closed 1 January – **Meals** 12.00 **t.** (lunch) and a la carte 16.40/27.40 **t. 9.95**

X **Nargile,** 73 Hanover St., EH2 1EE, ☎ (0131) 225 5755. MC AE ⓓ VISA DY
closed 25-26 December, 1-2 January and Sunday lunch – **Meals** - Turkish - 15.95/18.9 (dinner) and a la carte 12.65/21.70 **t.**

X **Le Café Saint-Honoré,** 34 North West Thistle Street Lane, EH2 1EA, ☎ (0131) 226 2 – ⅍. MC AE ⓓ VISA JCB DY
closed 2 days Christmas, 2 days New Year, Saturday lunch and Sunday except du Edinburgh Festival – **Meals** (booking essential) a la carte 17.40/28.70 **t.** 8.75.

X **Blue,** 10 Cambridge St., EH1 2ED, ☎ (0131) 221 1222, *Fax (0131) 228 8808* – ▤. MC VISA DZ
closed 1 week Christmas and Sunday – **Meals** 9.00/12.00 **st.** (lunch) a la carte 18. 23.50 **st.**

Leith.

Malmaison, 1 Tower Pl., EH6 7DB, ☎ (0131) 468 5000, *edinburgh@malmaison.c Fax (0131) 468 5002,* « Contemporary interior », – |‡| TV P – 55. MC AE ⓓ VISA. **Meals** - Brasserie - 11.95/12.95 **t.** and a la carte – 10.75 – **55 rm** 105.00/165.0 5 suites. BV

Express by Holiday Inn without rest., Britannia Way, Ocean Drive, EH6 6 ☎ (0131) 555 4422, *info@hiex-edinburgh.com, Fax (0131) 555 4646* – |‡|, ⅍ rm, TV – 30. MC AE ⓓ VISA BV
102 rm 57.50 **st.**

Travel Inn, 51-53 Newhaven Pl., EH6 4TX, ☎ (0131) 555 1570, *Fax (0131) 554 5994* – ⅍ rm, ▤ rest, TV P – 30. MC AE ⓓ VISA. BV
Meals (grill rest.) – **60 rm** 40.95 **t.**

XX **Martin Wishart,** 54 The Shore, Leith, EH6 6RA, ☎ (0131) 553 3557, *Fax (0131) 467 70* ⅍. MC VISA BV
closed 2 weeks January, 2 weeks October, 25-26 December, 1 January, Sunday and Mon – **Meals** (booking essential) 12.50/14.50 **t.** (lunch) and dinner a la carte 28.00/32.0 11.50
Spec. Terrine of Bayonne ham, foie gras, chicken and wild mushrooms. Gressingham d with cauliflower cream, sarladaise potato.

XX **(fitz)Henry,** 19 Shore Pl., EH6 6SW, ☎ (0131) 555 6625, *rpmckni@ibm. Fax (0131) 228 2998,* « Part 17C warehouse » – MC AE VISA BV
closed 25-26 December, 1-2 January and Sunday – **Meals** 14.00/17.00 (lunch) and a la carte 21.90/32.90 **t.** 9.95.

XX **The Rock,** 78 Commercial St., EH6 6LX, ☎ (0131) 555 2225, *Fax (0131) 337 2153* – P. AE VISA BV
closed lunch Sunday-Wednesday – **Meals** a la carte 17.40/34.85 **t.** 6.95.

XX **Vintners Room,** The Vaults, 87 Giles St., EH6 6BZ, ☎ (0131) 554 6767, *thevintners@thevintnersrooms-demon.co.uk, Fax (0131) 467 7130* – ⇔. MC AE VISA BV r
closed 2 weeks Christmas and Sunday – **Meals** 15.00 **t.** (lunch) and dinner a la carte 23.75/32.75 **t.** 6.00.

X **Daniels Bistro,** 88 Commercial St., EH6 6LX, ☎ (0131) 553 5933, *Fax (0131) 553 3966,* – ⇔. MC AE VISA JCB BV a
closed 25-26 December and 1-2 January – **Meals** - French - 5.95/6.95 **t.** (lunch) and a la carte 11.55/20.45 **t.** 5.95.

Bonnyrigg *(Midlothian) Southeast : 8 m. by A 7 on A 6094* – **BX** – ✉ *Edinburgh.*

Dalhousie Castle, EH19 3JB, Southeast : 1 ¼ m. on B 704 ☎ (01875) 820153, *res@dalhousiecastle.co.uk, Fax (01875) 821936,* ≤, « Part 13C and 15C castle with Victorian additions », – ⇔ TV & P – 120. MC AE VISA JCB
closed 7-19 January – ***Dungeon :*** **Meals** (booking essential to non-residents) (dinner only) 27.00 **t.** and a la carte – ***The Orangery :*** **Meals** 5.50/15.00 **t.** and a la carte – **33 rm** 80.00/235.00 **t.**, 1 suite.

Kirknewton *Southwest : 7 m. on A 71* – **AX** – ✉ *Edinburgh.*

Marriott Dalmahoy H. & Country Club, EH27 8EB, ☎ (0131) 333 1845, *Fax (0131) 333 1433,* ≤, « Part Georgian mansion », 18, – ⇔, rest, TV & P – 350. MC AE VISA JCB.
Pentland : **Meals** *(closed Sunday lunch)* 15.00/25.00 **st.** 7.75 – ***Long Weekend :*** **Meals** (grill rest.) a la carte 10.00/21.25 **st.** 7.75 – 12.00 – **212 rm** 149.00/179.00 **t.**, 3 suites – SB.

Edinburgh International Airport *West : 7½ m. by A 8* – **AV** – ✉ *Edinburgh.*

Hilton Edinburgh Airport, EH28 8LL, ☎ (0131) 519 4400, *Fax (0131) 519 4422,* – ⇔ rm, rest, TV & P – 240. MC AE VISA.
Meals (grill rest.) 10.00/16.75 **t.** and a la carte – 12.50 – **150 rm** 150.00/170.00 **st.** – SB.

Ingliston *West : 7¾ m. on A 8* – **AV** – ✉ *Edinburgh.*

Norton House, EH28 8LX, on A 8 ☎ (0131) 333 1275, *Fax (0131) 333 5305,* – ⇔ rm, TV P – 200. MC AE VISA.
Meals *(closed Saturday lunch)* 28.50 **st.** (dinner) and a la carte 14.50/28.00 **st.** 7.95 – **46 rm** 130.00/150.00 **t.**, 1 suite.

INBURGH INTERNATIONAL AIRPORT *Edinburgh City* 401 J 16 – *see Edinburgh.*

NAM *Borders* 401 402 M 17 – *see Kelso.*

ZELL *Angus* 401 M 13 *Scotland G.* – *pop. 830.*
Env. : *Castle★ AC (The Pleasance★★★) W : 2 m.*
Exc. : *Glen Esk★, NW : 7 m.*
Edinburgh 94 – Aberdeen 36 – Dundee 31.

Glenesk, High St., DD9 7TF, ☎ (01356) 648319, *Fax (01356) 647333,* – ⇔ rest, TV P – 150. MC AE VISA
Meals 15.00/20.00 **t.** and a la carte 5.00 – **24 rm** 55.00/95.00 **t.** – SB.

GIN *Moray* 401 K 11 *Scotland G.* – *pop. 11 855.*
See : *Town★ – Cathedral★ (Chapter house★★) AC.*
Exc. : *Glenfiddich Distillery★, SE : 10 m. by A 941.*
18, 18 *Moray, Stotfield Rd, Lossiemouth ☎ (01343) 812018 – 18 Hardhillock, Birnie Rd ☎ (01343) 542338 – 18 Hopeman, Moray ☎ (01343) 830578.*
17 High St. ☎ (01343) 542666.
Edinburgh 198 – Aberdeen 68 – Fraserburgh 61 – Inverness 39.

Mansion House, The Haugh, IV30 1AW, via Haugh Rd and Murdocks Wynd ☎ (01343) 548811, *Fax (01343) 547916,* – ⇔ rest, TV P – 200. MC AE VISA JCB.
Meals 15.50/23.50 **t.** and a la carte – **23 rm** 80.00/150.00 **t.** – SB.

Mansefield House, Mayne Rd, IV30 1NY, ☎ (01343) 540883, *Fax (01343) 552491* – ⇔ TV P. MC AE VISA.
Meals 27.50 **t.** (dinner) and a la carte 13.65/28.00 **t.** 7.00 – **21 rm** 68.00/110.00 **t.** – SB.

Travel Inn, Linkwood Industrial Estate, East Rd, IV30 1XB, East : 1 ¼ m. on A 96 ☎ (01343) 550747, *Fax (01343) 540635* – ⇔ rm, rest, TV & P. MC AE VISA
Meals (grill rest.) – **40 rm** 40.95 **t.**

Pines, East Rd, IV30 1XG, East : ½ m. on A 96 ☎ (01343) 542766, *thepines@talk21.c*
Fax (01343) 542766, – rest, TV P. MC VISA JCB
Meals (by arrangement) a la carte 9.50/12.50 **st.** – **6 rm** 30.00/48.00 **st.** – SB.

The Croft without rest., 10 Institution Rd, IV30 1QX, via Duff Av. ☎ (01343) 546C
Fax (01343) 546004, – TV P.
3 rm 25.00/50.00.

Lodge without rest., 20 Duff Av., IV30 1QS, ☎ (01343) 549981, *marilynspence5@hotm*
om, Fax (01343) 540527, – TV P. MC VISA JCB
8 rm 25.00/50.00 **st.**

ELGOL *Highland* 401 B 12 – *see Skye (Isle of).*

ERBUSAIG *Highland* 401 C 12 *Scotland G.* – ✉ *Kyle of Lochalsh.*

Env. : *Wester Ross*★★★.

Skye Bridge (toll).

Edinburgh 206 – Dundee 184 – Inverness 84 – Oban 127.

Old Schoolhouse with rm, IV40 8BB, ☎ (01599) 534369, *cuminecandj@lineone.*
Fax (01599) 534369, – rest, TV P. MC AE VISA JCB
April-November – **Meals** (booking essential) (dinner only) a la carte 17.00/25.50 **t.** 4.9
3 rm 45.00/60.00 **t.**

ERISKA (Isle of) *Argyll and Bute* 401 D 14 – ✉ *Oban.*

Isle of Eriska, Ledaig, PA37 1SD, ☎ (01631) 720371, *office@eriska-hotel.co*
Fax (01631) 720531, ≤ Lismore and mountains, « 19C Scottish Baronial mansion, priv
island setting », – rest, TV P. MC AE VISA
closed January – **Meals** (booking essential) (bar lunch residents only)/dinner 37.50
17 rm 180.00/270.00 **t.**

ETTRICKBRIDGE *Borders* 401 402 L 17 – *see Selkirk.*

FAIRLIE *North Ayrshire* 401 402 F 16.

Edinburgh 75 – Ayr 50 – Glasgow 36.

Fins, Fencebay Fisheries, Fencefoot Farm, KA29 0EG, South : 1 ½ m. on A
☎ (01475) 568989, *fencebay@aol.com, Fax (01475) 568921* – P. MC AE VISA
closed 25 December, 1 January and Monday – **Meals** - Seafood - (booking essen
a la carte 17.85/27.85 **t.** 7.20.

FALKIRK *Falkirk* 401 I 16 – *pop. 42 353.*

18 *Grangemouth, Polmonthill ☎ (01324) 711500* – 9 *Polmont, Manuel Rigg, Maddis*
☎ (01324) 711277 – 18 *Stirling Rd, Camelon ☎ (01324) 611061* – 18 *Falkirk Tryst,*
Burnhead Rd, Larbet ☎ (01324) 562415.

2-4 Glebe St. ☎ (01324) 620244.

Edinburgh 26 – Dunfermline 18 – Glasgow 25 – Motherwell 27 – Perth 43.

Inchyra Grange, Grange Rd, Polmont, FK2 0YB, Southeast : 3 m. by A 803 and Kirk E
Bo'ness Rd ☎ (01324) 711911, *info@inchyra.macdonald-hotels.co.uk, Fax (01324) 716*
, rest, TV P – 700. MC AE VISA JCB
Priory : **Meals** 13.95/28.50 **st.** and dinner a la carte 7.95 – ***Peligrino's :*** **Meals** a la c
10.00/15.00 **st.** 8.95 – **108 rm** 85.00/125.00 **st.**, 1 suite – SB.

Premier Lodge, Glenbervie Business Park, Bellsdyke Rd, Larbert, FK5 4EG, Northwes
¾ m. by A 803 and A 9 on A 88 ☎ (0870) 7001386, *Fax (0870) 7001387* – , rest,
P. MC AE VISA
Meals (grill rest.) a la carte 9.00/12.00 **st.** 4.50 – 6.00 – **60 rm** 42.00 **t.** – SB.

Travel Inn, Beancross Rd, Polmont, FK2 0YS, East : 3 m. by A 904 on
☎ (01324) 720726, *Fax (01324) 716801* – , rest, TV P. MC AE VISA.
Meals (grill rest.) – **40 rm** 40.95 **t.**

at Glensburgh *Northeast : 2 m. by A 904 on A 905* – ✉ *Falkirk.*

Grange Manor, Glensburgh Rd, FK3 8XJ, ☎ (01324) 474836, *info@grangemanor.cc*
Fax (01324) 665851 – TV P – 160. MC AE VISA JCB.
Le Chardon : **Meals** 12.75/23.95 **t.** and a la carte 6.50 – ***Wallace's :*** **Meals** a la c
22.10/31.70 **t.** 6.50 – **37 rm** 70.00/120.00 **t.** – SB.

THE CALL OF THE NEW

As the 21st century beckons with its promise of major advances in technology, the Michelin Group is well positioned to take on the challenge of innovation. With a business presence in more than 170 countries, Michelin is world leader in tyre technology, as evidenced by the new Pax System, probably the most radical development since Michelin launched the radial during the late 1940's. Today 80 manufacturing plants in 19 countries produce over 830,000 tyres a day across a broad product range for all types of vehicles from mountain bikes to the NASA Space Shuttle. Michelin's route to the future is based on "the capacity to listen, the audacity to innovate and the passion for demonstration" where "dialogue is the very essence of progress applied to an activity that constitutes a technological, financial and, above all, a human challenge."

Michelin has thrown down the gauntlet. After many years of speculation and rumour in the press, the company has announced that it will bring its formidable tyre technology to Formula 1 racing in 2001.

It was in 1977 that Michelin first made its impact with the kind of innovation that alters the nature of a sport forever and for the better. That great leap forward was witnessed at the Silverstone British Grand Prix when Renault took to the starting grid in mid-season. The bright yellow 1.5 litre V6 turbocharged car was equipped with what was to become the most radical development since the invention of the pneumatic tyre - the radial! Not only did the radial design quickly come to dominate racing, it also became the norm for all cars and trucks on the road.

Between 1978 and 1984, Michelin equipped teams won no fewer than 59 Grand Prix races - eleven more than the company's nearest rival. The victory tally included three drivers' and two manufacturers' World Championship titles.

The teams partnered with Michelin this year are Williams-BMW and Jaguar Racing. In 2002, Toyota will enter the fray on Michelin. Much of the year 2000 was spent track testing and developing new compounds, reflecting Michelin's philosophy of developing technology in the heat of competition as well as in the cool of the laboratory. To quote Edouard Michelin: "This sport has evolved considerably in the past 15 years. That's why we say we are entering, not re-entering. Automotive technology has changed and the tyres have changed too. It's going to be a challenge and at Michelin we love challenges."

Everything will change

Pax System - the future now

Thanks to a revolutionary new design concept from Michelin, there is now a tyre that tells you when it needs more air and can continue to be driven for a long period after a puncture. The Michelin PAX System is an integrated tyre-and-wheel assembly that, at the very least, offers noticeable improvements in cornering, braking, fuel consumption and ride comfort. More significantly, an indicator on the dash board linked to a pressure loss detector in the wheel tells the driver of any sudden change. In the event of a puncture, PAX will continue to run safely for up to 200km at 80km/h.

The difference is in the design

Modern radial tyres offer extremely high levels of performance and safety. Because of their design, however, there is a limit to the extent of product improvement that can be achieved. The PAX System offers all the benefits of the radial and much more. It has a tyre that cannot come off the rim, a flexible inner support ring and, of course, the all-important pressure loss detector.

RADIAL TYRE

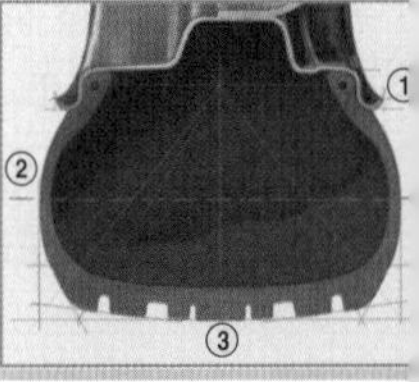

① The bead, which is extremely rigid, anchors the tyre to the rim by means of air pressure and provides the link between the highly flexible tyre sidewall and the tyre rim.

② The sidewall permits the flexibility needed for comfort and roadholding.

③ The crown area provides grip and braking power.

PAX SYSTEM

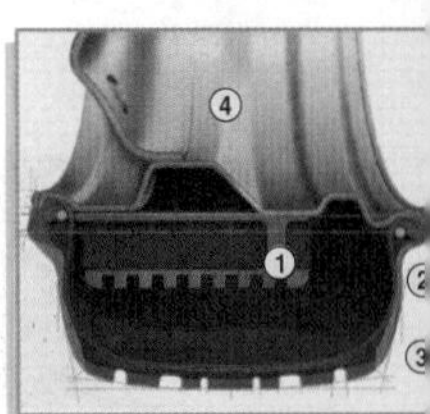

① A flexible injected-elastomer run-flat support ring incorporates a pressure loss detector.

② The tyre is locked to the rim by the use of clips, giving better security.

③ The sidewalls are short and rigid, offering a lower profile and improved handling.

④ There is a choice of a one-piece steel or alloy wheel.

Travelling with space comes of age

As an innovation, the PAX System opens up new horizons for car designers, enabling them to develop cars that are more spacious, comfortable, manoeuvrable and arguably more stylish.

Metrocubo is the first vehicle to be designed specifically around Michelin's radical PAX System. Pininfarina, the legendary Italian design house that created the metrocubo concept, describes PAX as "a genuine technological revolution with immense innovative potential that inspired us to create a city car that is as revolutionary in its architecture as it is in the way that it is used." The result is a car with front wheels that are smaller in diameter than those at the rear, minimising the size of the front of the vehicle bodywork, which makes driving in town easier by reducing the turning circle. Moreover, both cabin and luggage space are increased because there is no need to carry a spare tyre and, despite its compactness, the car can accommodate five passengers.

PAX SYSTEM

Pax momentum

In daring to re-invent the tyre, Michelin has remained faithful to its reputation as a leader in technology. As in the case of the radial, PAX will evolve and create its own impetus for the development and improvement of automotive design and technology.

A NEW RANGE OF GUIDES FOR INDEPENDENT TRAVELLERS

Roughing it in exotic places is not everyone's cup of tea, which is why Michelin Travel Publications have launched a new series of guides called NEOS with the discerning independent traveller in mind. The ever-expanding range of titles covers Cuba, Guatemala, Belize, Réunion, Mauritius, Seychelles, Syria, Jordan, Tunisia and Turkey. Carrying the Michelin hallmark of reliability, depth of information and accuracy, each NEOS guide takes a personal approach to the region concerned and is written by authors who have travelled in the country over a period of time. This detailed research enables NEOS to provide a wide selection of where to stay, what to see and where to eat while catering for all budgets and tastes. The guides are illustrated with unique watercolour paintings and stunning colour photography and there are fully comprehensive colour maps, town and site plans.

New – In the NEOS guides emphasis is placed on the discovery and enjoyment of a new destination through meeting the people, tasting the food and absorbing the exotic atmosphere. In addition to recommendations on which sights to see, we give details on the most suitable places to stay and eat, on what to look out for in traditional markets and where to go in search of the hidden character of the region, its crafts and its dancing rhythms. For those keen to explore places on foot, we provide guidelines and useful addresses in order to help organise walks to suit all tastes.

Expert – The NEOS guides are written by people who have travelled in the country and researched the sites before recommending them by the allocation of stars. Accommodation and restaurants are similarly recommended by a on the grounds of quality and value for money. Cartographers have drawn easy-to-use maps with clearly marked itineraries, as well as detailed plans of towns, archeological sites and large museums.

Open to all cultures, the NEOS guides provide an insight into the daily lives of the local people. In a world that is becoming ever more accessible, it is vital that religious practices, regional etiquette, traditional customs and languages be understood and respected by all travellers. Equipped with this knowledge, visitors can seek to share and enjoy with confidence the best of the local cuisine, musical harmonies and the skills involved in the production of arts and crafts.

Sensitive to the atmosphere and heritage of a foreign land, the NEOS guides encourage travellers to see, hear, smell and feel a country, through words and images. Take inspiration from the enthusiasm of our experienced travel writers and make this a journey full of discovery and enchantment.

Capital coverage for tourists and drivers

Michelin now has a map covering central London to complement its range of European city plans. Probably one of the best maps available for tourists visiting the city centre on foot as well as for drivers, the 1:8000 scale map offers an extremely high level of detail, including bridge heights and weight restrictions. There is essential information on the likes of one-way streets, car parks, railway stations, taxi ranks, shopping centres, landmarks and police stations. The Plan also lists telephone numbers for emergency services, doctors, chemists, credit card providers, 23 embassies, airports, coach and train stations. With its colourful, easy-to-read mapping, the Plan covers from Regent's Park to Denmark Hill and from Shepherd's Bush to Tower Bridge. It is available from bookshops in three formats: a standard folded map, a folded map with street index and a small spiral bound edition. To help when looking up street names or places in the index, the map reference is printed in each grid square.

SNACLOICH *Argyll and Bute* – ✉ *Appin.*
Edinburgh 133 – Fort William 34 – Oban 19.

Lochside Cottage ⑤, PA38 4BJ, ☎ (01631) 730216, *broadbent@lochsidecottage.fsnet.co.uk, Fax (01631) 730216,* ≤ Loch Baile Mhic Chailen and mountains, « Lochside setting », – TV P
Meals (by arrangement) (communal dining) 17.50 – **3 rm** ☐ 23.00/60.00 **s.**

ONNPHORT *Argyll and Bute* 401 A 15 – *Shipping Services : see Mull (Isle of).*

ODIGARRY *Highland* 401 B 11 – *see Skye (Isle of).*

RFAR *Angus* 401 L 14 *Scotland G.* – *pop. 14 159.*
Env. : *Aberlemno Stones*★, *NE : 5 m. by B 9134.*
Exc. : *Brechin (Round Tower*★*), NE : 9½ m. by B 9134.*
18 *Cunninghill, Arbroath Rd* ☎ *(01307) 462120.*
40 East High St. ☎ *(01307) 467876 (summer only).*
Edinburgh 75 – Aberdeen 55 – Dundee 12 – Perth 31.

Chapelbank House, 69 East High St., DD8 2EP, ☎ (01307) 463151, *ewenallardyce@btconnect.com, Fax (01307) 461922* – TV P. MO AE VISA.
closed 26 December – **Meals** *(closed 1-14 January, Monday and Sunday dinner)* 22.00 **t.** and a la carte 10.65/26.50 **t.** 7.00 – **4 rm** ☐ 55.00/82.00 **t.** – SB.

Finavon Farmhouse, Finavon, DD8 3PX, Northeast : 5 ½ m. by B 9128 and A 90 on Milton of Finavon rd ☎ (01307) 850269, *jlr@finfarm.freeserve.co.uk, Fax (01307) 850380,* – TV P
March-October – **Meals** (by arrangement) 10.00 **s.** – **3 rm** ☐ 21.00/44.00 – SB.

RRES *Moray* 401 J 11 *Scotland G.* – *pop. 5 559.*
Env. : *Sueno's Stone*★★, *N : ½ m. by A 940 on A 96* – *Brodie Castle*★ *AC, W : 3 m. by A 96.*
Exc. : *Elgin*★ *(Cathedral*★, *chapter house*★★ *AC), E : 10¼ m. by A 96.*
18 *Muiryshade* ☎ *(01309) 672949.*
116 High St. ☎ *(01309) 672938 (summer only).*
Edinburgh 165 – Aberdeen 80 – Inverness 27.

Knockomie ⑤, Grantown Rd, IV36 2SG, South : 1 ½ m. on A 940 ☎ (01309) 673146, *stay@knockomie.co.uk, Fax (01309) 673290,* – TV & P – 40. MO AE VISA JCB
closed 25-26 December – ***Restaurant :*** **Meals** (dinner only) 28.50/29.50 **t.** 10.00 – ***Bistro :*** **Meals** a la carte 14.00/21.40 **t.** 10.00 – **14 rm** ☐ 87.00/150.00 **t.**, 1 suite – SB.

Ramnee, Victoria Rd, IV36 3BN, ☎ (01309) 672410, *ramneehotel@btconnect.com, Fax (01309) 673392,* – rest, TV P – 100. MO AE VISA JCB
closed 25-26 December and 1-3 January – **Meals** 11.00/27.00 **st.** 5.00 – **19 rm** ☐ 62.50/95.00 **st.**, 1 suite – SB.

RT WILLIAM *Highland* 401 E 13 *Scotland G.* – *pop. 10 391.*
See : *Town*★.
Exc. : *The Road to the Isles*★★ *(Neptune's Staircase (≤★★), Glenfinnan*★ *≤*★, *Arisaig*★, *Silver Sands of Morar*★, *Mallaig*★*), NW : 46 m. by A 830* – *Ardnamurchan Peninsula*★★ – *Ardnamurchan Point (≤★★), NW : 65 m. by A 830, A 861 and B 8007* – *SE : Ben Nevis*★★ *(≤★★) - Glen Nevis*★.
18 *North Rd* ☎ *(01397) 704464.*
Cameron Sq., Inverness-shire ☎ *(01397) 703781.*
Edinburgh 133 – Glasgow 104 – Inverness 68 – Oban 50.

Inverlochy Castle ⑤, Torlundy, PH33 6SN, Northeast : 3 m. on A 82 ☎ (01397) 702177, *info@inverlochy.co.uk, Fax (01397) 702953,* ≤ loch and mountains, « Victorian castle in extensive parkland », – rest, TV P. MO AE VISA.
closed 4 January-1 March – **Meals** (dinner booking essential to non-residents) 18.00/50.00 **st.** 8.50 – **16 rm** ☐ 180.00/380.00 **st.**, 1 suite – SB
Spec. Salad of roasted scallops, lemon oil dressing. Pot-roasted pheasant with wild mushroom risotto. Poached peach with vanilla ice cream.

Travel Inn, An Aird, PH33 6AN, Northwest : ½ m. by A 82 ☎ (01397) 703707, *Fax (01397) 703618* – , rm, rest, TV & P. MO AE VISA
Meals (grill rest.) – **40 rm** 40.95 **t.**

Distillery House without rest., Nevis Bridge, North Rd, PH33 6LR, ☎ (01397) 700103, *disthouse@aol.com, Fax (01397) 702980* – TV P. MO AE VISA
closed 25 December – **7 rm** ☐ 35.00/70.00 **st.**

The Grange without rest., Grange Rd, PH33 6JF, South : 3/4 m. by A 82 and Ashb Lane (01397) 705516, *jcampbell@grangefortwilliam.com, Fax (01397) 701595*, ≤,
April-October – **4 rm** 70.00/92.00 **st.**

Crolinnhe without rest., Grange Rd, PH33 6JF, South : 3/4 m. by A 82 and Ashburn L (01397) 702709, *crolinnhe@yahoo.com, Fax (01397) 700506*, ≤,
Easter-October – **3 rm** 76.00/110.00.

Ashburn House without rest., 18 Achintore Rd, PH33 6RM, South : 1/2 m. on A (01397) 706000, *ashburn.house@tinyworld.co.uk, Fax (01397) 702024*,
closed December and January – **7 rm** 45.00/90.00.

Cabana House without rest., Union Rd, PH33 6RB, (01397) 7059 *Fax (01397) 705991*,
closed 17 December-January – **3 rm** 40.00/54.00 **s.**

Factors House with rm, Torlundy, PH33 6SN, Northeast : 3 m. on A (01397) 702177, *info@inverlochy.co.uk, Fax (01397) 702953*,
Meals a la carte 20.50/25.50 **st.** 6.50 – 10.00 – **10 rm** 60.00/95.00 **st.**

at Banavie *North : 3 m. by A 82 and A 830 on B 8004 – Fort William.*

Moorings, PH33 7LY, (01397) 772797, *reservations@moorings-fortwilliam.co Fax (01397) 772441*, ≤, – rest,
closed 1 week Christmas – **Meals** (bar lunch)/dinner 21.00/26.00 **t.** 7.50 – **21 rm** 70. 130.00 **t.** – SB.

Your recommendation is self-evident if you always walk into a hotel Guide in hand.

FOYERS *Highland* 401 G 12 *Scotland G.* – *Loch Ness.*

Env. : *Loch Ness*★★ – *The Great Glen*★.

Edinburgh 175 – Inverness 19 – Kyle of Lochalsh 63 – Oban 96.

Craigdarroch House , IV2 6XU, North : 1/4 m. on B 852 (01456) 486400, *davem o@hotel_loch_ness.co.uk, Fax (01456) 486444*, ≤ Loch Ness and mountains, –
closed 5 January-12 February – **Meals** 12.50/29.50 **st.** and dinner a la carte 8.50 – **14** 87.50/150.00 **st.** – SB.

Foyers Bay House, Lower Foyers, IV2 6YB, West : 1 1/4 m. by B 852 on Lower Foyers (01456) 486624, *panciroli@foyersbay.freeserve.co.uk, Fax (01456) 486337*, ≤, rm,
Meals (dinner only) 9.95/15.95 **t.** and a la carte – **5 rm** 39.00/58.00 **t.** – SB.

GAIRLOCH *Highland* 401 C 10 *Scotland G.* – *pop. 2 194.*

Env. : *Wester Ross*★★★ – *Loch Maree*★★★, *E : 5 1/2 m. by A 832.*

Exc. : *Inverewe Gardens*★★★ **AC**, *NE : 8 m. by A 832 – Victoria Falls*★, *SE : 8 m. by A 832.*

Gairloch (01445) 712407.

Auchtercairn, Ross-shire (01445) 712130.

Edinburgh 228 – Inverness 72 – Kyle of Lochalsh 68.

Creag Mor, Charleston, IV21 2AH, South : 1 3/4 m. on A 832 (01445) 712068, *enquirie creagmor-hotel.co.uk, Fax (01445) 712044*, ≤, – rest,
March-October – **Meals** a la carte 15.00/26.25 **st.** 6.00 – **16 rm** 57.50/120.00 1 suite – SB.

Little Lodge , North Erradale, IV21 2DS, Northwest : 6 m. on B 80 (01445) 771237, ≤ Torridon Mountains and Skye, –
May-October (minimum stay 2 nights) – **Meals** - Organic produce - (by arrangeme 21.00/25.00 – **3 rm** (dinner included) 110.00.

GALSON *Western Isles (Outer Hebrides)* 401 A 8 – *see Lewis and Harris (Isle of).*

GATEHEAD *East Ayrshire* 401 402 G 17 – *Kilmarnock.*

Edinburgh 72 – Ayr 10 – Glasgow 25 – Kilmarnock 5.

Cochrane Inn, 45 Main Rd, KA2 0AP, (01563) 570122 –
Meals (booking essential) a la carte 10.00/16.00 **st.** 5.75.

TEHOUSE OF FLEET *Dumfries and Galloway* 401 402 H 19 – *pop. 919.*

Gatehouse, Innisfree, Lauriestown, Castle Douglas ℰ (01557) 814766.

Car Park ℰ (01557) 814212 (Easter-October).

Edinburgh 113 – Dumfries 33 – Stranraer 42.

Cally Palace, DG7 2DL, East : 1/2 m. on B 727 ℰ (01557) 814341, *info@callypalace.co.uk, Fax (01557) 814522*, ≤, « Part 18C country mansion », rest, – 80. VISA.
closed January and restricted opening February – **Meals** 26.00 **st.** (dinner) and lunch a la carte 20.00/24.00 **st.** 7.90 – **50 rm** (dinner included) 90.00/184.00 **st.**, 5 suites – SB.

FFNOCK *East Renfrewshire* 401 (41) – *see Glasgow.*

GHA (Isle of) *Argyll and Bute* 401 C 16.

to Tayinloan (Caledonian MacBrayne Ltd) 8-10 daily (20 mn).

Edinburgh 168.

Gigha, PA41 7AA, ℰ (01583) 505254, *william@isle-of-gigha.co.uk, Fax (01583) 505244*, ≤ Sound of Gigha and Kintyre Peninsula, – rest, VISA JCB
restricted opening in winter – **Meals** (bar lunch)/dinner 23.00 **t.** 5.50 – **13 rm** (dinner included) 66.00/120.00 **t.** – SB.

RVAN *South Ayrshire* 401 402 F 18 – *pop. 7 719.*

Brunston Castle, Dailly ℰ (01465) 811471 – Golf Course Rd ℰ (01465) 714272.

Edinburgh 100 – Ayr 20 – Glasgow 56 – Stranraer 31.

Glendrissaig, Newton Stewart Rd., KA26 0HJ, South : 1 3/4 m. by A 77 on A 714 ℰ (01465) 714631, *Fax (01465) 714631*, ≤, –
April-October – **Meals** (by arrangement) 15.00 – **3 rm** 34.00/58.00 – SB.

Wildings, 56 Montgomerie St., KA26 9HE, ℰ (01465) 713481, *info@wildingsrestaurant.co.uk, Fax (01465) 715971* –
closed October, 24 December-mid January, Monday, Tuesday and Sunday dinner – **Meals** (booking essential) 10.50/21.00 **t.**

GLASGOW

401 402 H 16 *Scotland G.* – *pop. 662 853.*

Edinburgh 46 – Manchester 221.

TOURIST INFORMATION

11 George Square ☎ (0141) 204 4400.
Glasgow Airport, Tourist Information Desk, Paisley ☎ (0141) 848 4440.

PRACTICAL INFORMATION

18 *Littlehill, Auchinairn Rd ☎ (0141) 772 1916.*
18 *Rouken Glen, Stewarton Rd, Thornliebank ☎ (0141) 638 7044* **AX**.
18 *Linn Park, Simshill Rd ☎ (0141) 637 5871,* **BX**.
18 *Lethamhill, Cumbernauld Rd ☎ (0141) 770 6220,* **BV**.
9 *Alexandra Park, Dennistown ☎ (0141) 556 1294* **BV**.
9 *King's Park, 150a Croftpark Av., Croftfoot ☎ (0141) 630 1597,* **BX**.
9 *Knightswood, Lincoln Av. ☎ (0141) 959 6358* **AV**.
9 *Ruchill, Ruchill Park Brassey St. ☎ (0141) 946 7676.*
Access to Oban by helicopter.
Erskine Bridge (toll) **AV**.
✈ *Glasgow Airport : ☎ (0141) 887 1111, W : 8 m. by M 8* **AV** – **Terminal :** *Coach service from Glasgow Central and Queen Street main line Railway Stations and from Anderston Cross and Buchanan Bus Stations.*
✈ *see also Prestwick.*

SIGHTS

See : *City★★★ – Cathedral★★★ (≤★)* **DZ** – *The Burrell Collection★★★* **AX M1** – *Hunterian Art Gallery★★ (Whistler Collection★★★ – Mackintosh Wing★★★) AC* **CY M4** – *Museum of Transport★★ (Scottish Built Cars★★★, The Clyde Room of Ship Models★★★)* **AV M3** – *Art Gallery and Museum Kelvingrove★★* **CY** – *Pollok House★ (The Paintings★★)* **AX D** – *Tolbooth Steeple★* **DZ A** – *Hunterian Museum (Coin and Medal Collection★)* **CY M1** – *City Chambers★* **DZ C** – *Glasgow School of Art★ AC,* **CY B** – *Necropolis (≤★ of Cathedral)* **DYZ** – *Gallery of Modern Art★.*

Env. : *Paisley Museum and Art Gallery (Paisley Shawl Section★), W : 4 m. by M 8* **AV**.

Exc. : *The Trossachs★★★, N : 31 m. by A 879 –* **BV** *–, A 81 and A 821 – Loch Lomond★★, NW : 19 m. by A 82* **AV** – *New Lanark★★, SE : 20 m. by M 74 and A 72* **BX**.

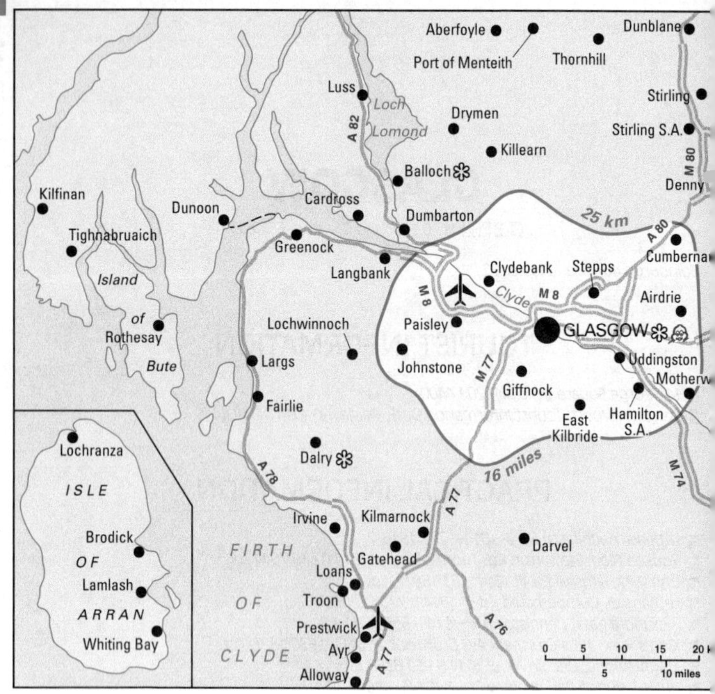

Hilton Glasgow, 1 William St., G3 8HT, ℘ (0141) 204 5555, *glahitwgm@hilton.co* *Fax (0141) 204 5004,* ≤, Ⅎ, ≘, ▨ – |‡|, ⇸ rm, ▤ TV ✆ ♿ ⇌ P – 🏛 1000. MC AE ① JCB. ✗ CZ
Minsky's : Meals 16.00/20.50 **t.** and a la carte – (see also ***Camerons*** and ***Shimla Pi*** below) – ☕ 13.95 – **315 rm** 150.00/190.00 **st.**, 4 suites – SB.

One Devonshire Gardens, 1 Devonshire Gdns., G12 0UX, ℘ (0141) 339 2001, *onede nshire@btconnect.com, Fax (0141) 337 1663,* « Victorian town houses » – ⇸ rest, TV ✆ 🏛 40. MC AE ① VISA. ✗ AV
Meals *(closed Saturday lunch)* 27.00 **st.** (lunch) and dinner a la carte 31.00/44.75 **st.** 🍷 18 – ☕ 14.50 – **25 rm** 175.00/275.00 **st.**, 2 suites
Spec. Roast scallops, mousseline of carrots, scallop and foie gras velouté. Stuffed fillet veal, wild mushrooms and truffle sauce. Chocolate fondant with vanilla ice cream.

Glasgow Moat House, Congress Rd, G3 8QT, ℘ (0141) 306 9988, *Fax (0141) 221 20* ≤, Ⅎ, ≘, ▨ – |‡|, ⇸ rm, ▤ TV ✆ ♿ P – 🏛 3000. MC AE ① VISA CZ
The Mariner : Meals *(closed Sunday)* (dinner only) a la carte 19.75/29.85 **t.** 🍷 7.50 – ***No*** ***Dockside :*** Meals (buffet) 9.50/19.00 **t.** and a la carte 🍷 7.00 – ☕ 11.25 – **267 rm** 146.(172.00 **st.**, 16 suites – SB.

Glasgow Marriott, 500 Argyle St., Anderston, G3 8RR, ℘ (0141) 226 55 *Fax (0141) 221 7676,* ≤, Ⅎ, ≘, ▨ – |‡|, ⇸ rm, ▤ TV ✆ ♿ P – 🏛 700. MC AE ① V ✗ CZ
Mediterrano : Meals (dinner only) 18.00 and a la carte 🍷 7.50 – ☕ 12.50 – **300 rm** 115.(250.00 **st.**

Thistle Glasgow, 36 Cambridge St., G2 3HN, ℘ (0141) 332 3311, *thistleglasgow@cix. uk, Fax (0141) 332 4050* – |‡|, ⇸ rm, ▤ rest, TV ✆ P – 🏛 1500. MC AE ① VISA J ✗ DY
Gengis : Meals 18.50 **st.** (dinner) and a la carte 15.00/28.60 **st.** – ☕ 12.95 – **297 rm** 165.(175.00 **st.**, 3 suites – SB.

The Devonshire, 5 Devonshire Gdns., G12 0UX, ℘ (0141) 339 7878, *devonshir5@ao m, Fax (0141) 339 3980,* « Victorian town house » – TV ✆ – 🏛 50. MC AE ① V ✗ AV
Meals *(closed lunch Saturday and Sunday)* (booking essential) (lunch by arrangeme 21.50/28.00 **t.** (dinner) and a la carte 25.00/37.50 **t.** 🍷 6.95 – ☕ 10.75 – **14 rm** 115.(175.00 **t.** – SB.

Malmaison, 278 West George St., G2 4LL, (0141) 572 1000, *glasgow@malmaison.com, Fax (0141) 572 1002,* « Contemporary interior », – rm, – 30. VISA. CY c
Café Mal *((0141) 572 1003)* **: Meals** 11.95/12.95 **t.** and a la carte – ***The Brasserie*** *((0141) 572 1001)* **: Meals** *(closed Saturday lunch)* 9.95/12.95 **st.** and a la carte – 10.75 – **68 rm** 105.00 **st.**, 8 suites.

Millennium Glasgow, 40 George Sq., G2 1DS, (0141) 332 6711, *sales.glasgow@mill-cop.com, Fax (0141) 332 4264,* – rm, – 40. VISA JCB.
closed 24-26 December – ***Brasserie on George Square*** **: Meals** 9.95 **st.** and a la carte 7.95 – 12.95 – **112 rm** 195.00/215.00 **st.**, 5 suites – SB. DZ v

ArtHouse, 129 Bath St., G2 2SY, (0141) 221 6789, *info@arthousehotel.com, Fax (0141) 221 6777,* « Contemporary interior » – rm, rest, – 30. VISA DY v
Grill **: Meals** 9.95/12.50 **t.** (lunch) and a la carte 19.20/30.00 **t.** – 9.25 – **65 rm** 90.00/140.00 **st.**

Carlton George, 44 West George St., G2 1DH, (0141) 353 6373, *george@carltonhotels.co.uk, Fax (0141) 353 6263* – – 35. VISA JCB. DZ a
Windows **: Meals** 13.95/19.95 **st.** – 11.00 – **65 rm** 150.00 **st.** – SB.

Hilton Glasgow Grosvenor, Grosvenor Terr., Great Western Rd, G12 0TA, (0141) 339 8811, *res@glasgrosvenor.hilton.co.uk, Fax (0141) 334 0710,* « Victorian terraced town houses » – rm, – 450. VISA JCB. CY s
Meals *(closed Saturday lunch)* 12.95/15.95 **st.** and a la carte – **94 rm** 118.00/158.00 **st.**, 2 suites.

Posthouse Glasgow City, Bothwell St., G2 7EN, (0870) 400 9032, *gm1786@forte-hotels.com, Fax (0141) 221 8986,* – rm, rest, – 1000. VISA CZ z
The Original Carvery **: Meals** (dinner only and Sunday lunch)/dinner 14.95 **st.** and a la carte 6.95 – ***Jules*** **: Meals** (piano at dinner) 9.00/16.00 **t.** and a la carte 8.50 – 11.95 – **246 rm** 59.00/99.00 **t.**, 1 suite – SB.

Sherbrooke Castle, 11 Sherbrooke Av., Pollokshields, G41 4PG, (0141) 427 4227, *mail@sherbrooke.co.uk, Fax (0141) 427 5685,* – , rest, – 120. VISA AX r
Morrisons **: Meals** 16.00/23.75 **t.** and dinner a la carte 9.75 – **24 rm** 65.00/85.00 **t.**, 1 suite – SB.

Ewington, Balmoral Terr., 132 Queen's Drive, G42 8QW, (0141) 423 1152, *ewington@aol.com, Fax (0141) 422 2030* – – 80. VISA JCB BX a
Meals 6.95/15.95 **t.** and a la carte 7.00 – 10.50 – **42 rm** 79.00/119.00 **t.**, 1 suite – SB.

City Inn, Finnieston Quay, G3 8HN, (0141) 240 1002, *glasgowreservations@cityinn.com, Fax (0141) 248 2754,* , , – rm, – 50. VISA JCB CZ u
City Café **: Meals** 13.95 **t.** (dinner) and a la carte 13.65/24.95 **t.** – 8.50 – **164 rm** 57.50 **st.**

Bewley's, 110 Bath St., G2 2EN, (0141) 353 0800, *res@bewleyshotels.com, Fax (0141) 353 0900* – rm, rest, . VISA. DY i
closed 25-26 December – ***Loop*** **: Meals** a la carte 15.00/25.00 **st.** 10.25 – 6.50 – **98 rm** 59.00 **st.**, 5 suites.

Holiday Inn, Theatreland, 161 West Nile St., G1 2RL, (0141) 352 8300, *info@higlasgow.com, Fax (0141) 332 7447,* – , rest, – 130. VISA.
La Bonne Auberge Brasserie **: Meals** 9.95/12.95 **st.** and a la carte – 10.95 – **110 rm** 105.00/122.50 **st.**, 3 suites – SB. DY a

Swallow Glasgow, 517 Paisley Road West, G51 1RW, (0141) 427 3146, *glasgow@swallowhotels.co.uk, Fax (0141) 427 4059,* , , – , rest, – 300. VISA AX a
Meals *(closed Saturday lunch)* (carving lunch) 9.50/18.50 **st.** and dinner a la carte 6.50 – **117 rm** 95.00/115.00 **st.** – SB.

Theatre without rest., 25-27 Elmbank St., G2 4PB, (0141) 227 2772, *theatrehotel@clara.net, Fax (0141) 227 2774* – . VISA JCB. CY a
58 rm 40.00/90.00 **st.**

Terrace House, 14 Belhaven Terr., G12 0TG, (off Great Western Rd) (0141) 337 3377, *admin@the-terrace.fsnet.co.uk, Fax (0141) 400 3378* – . VISA. AV x
Meals (booking essential) (dinner only) (residents only) 13.95 **st.** – **13 rm** 45.00/78.00 **st.** – SB.

Express by Holiday Inn without rest., Theatreland, 165 West Nile St., G1 2RL, (0141) 331 6800, *hi@holidayinn.demon.co.uk, Fax (0141) 331 6828* – . VISA JCB. DY o
88 rm 58.00.

Express by Holiday Inn without rest., Stockwell St., G1 4LT, (0141) 548 5000, *Fax (0141) 548 5048* – – 35. VISA JCB DZ x
128 rm 60.00 **st.**

GLASGOW
BUILT UP AREA

Aikenhead Road . . . . **BX** 3
Alexandra Parade . . . . **BV** 4
Balgrayhill Road . . . . **BV** 5
Ballater Street . . . . **BX** 6
Balornock Road . . . . **BV** 8
Balshagray Avenue . . . . **AV** 9
Battlefield Road . . . . **BX** 12
Berryknowes Road . . . . **AX** 15
Bilsland Drive . . . . **BV** 16
Blairbeth Road . . . . **BX** 18
Braidcraft Road . . . . **AX** 20
Broomloan Road . . . . **AV** 26
Burnhill Chapel Street . . . . . **BX** 28
Byres Road . . . . **AV** 29
Caledonia Road . . . . **BX** 30
Carmunnock Road . . . . **BX**
Cook Street . . . . **BV**
Cumbernauld Road . . . . **BV**
Edmiston Drive . . . . **AV**
Farmeloan Road . . . . **BX**
Fenwick Road . . . . **AX**
Glasgow Road (PAISLEY) . . . . **AX**
Gorbals Street . . . . **BX**
Grange Road . . . . **BX**

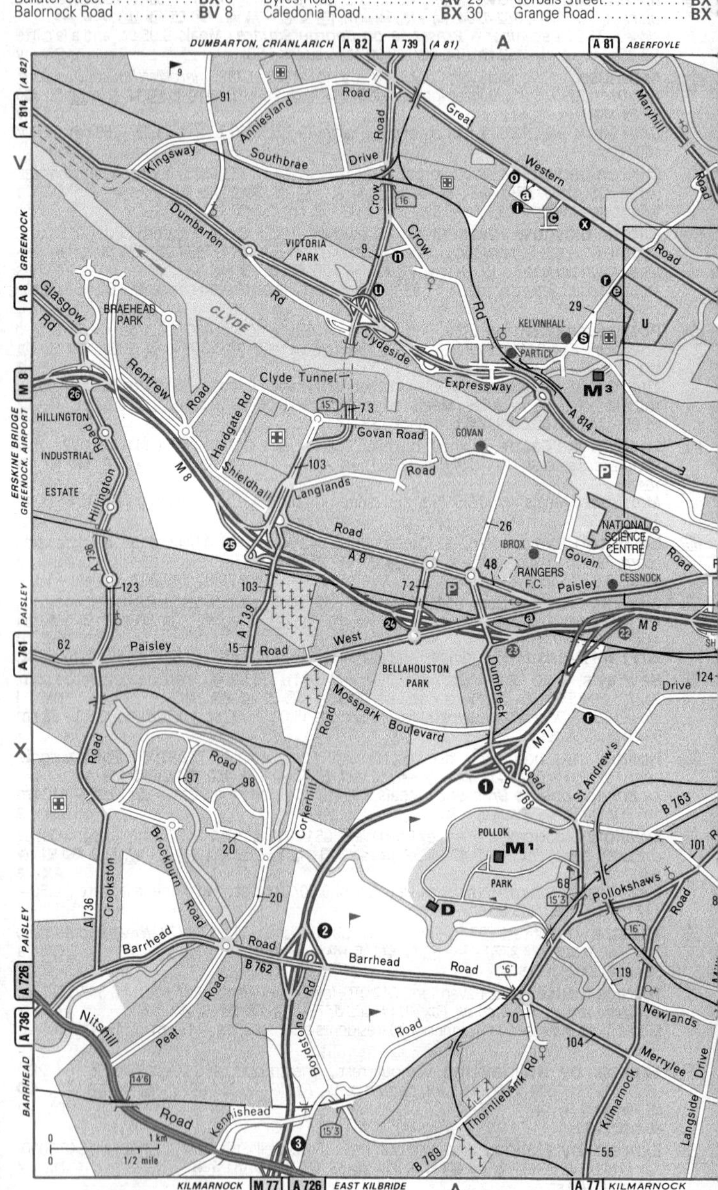

For Street Index see Glasgow p. 8

A 803 KIRKINTILLOCH B

(A 80) M 80 STIRLING A 80

V

EDINBURGH M 8

A 8 (M 74, M 8)

CARLISLE A 74 M 74

X

A 724 HAMILTON

B EAST-KILBRIDE A 749

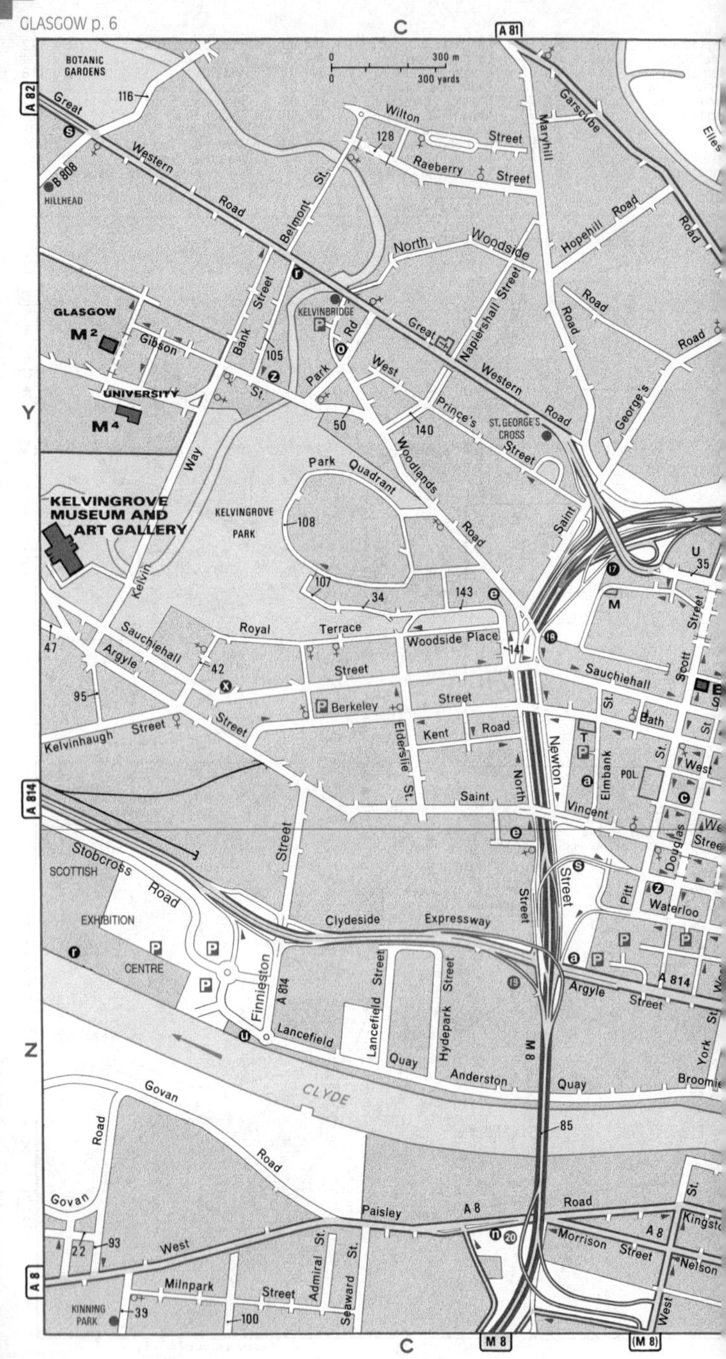
C
A 81
BOTANIC GARDENS
0 300 m
0 300 yards
A 82
Great Western Road
116
B 808
HILLHEAD
Wilton Street
128
Raeberry Street
Belmont St.
Maryhill Road
Garscube Road
Hopehill Road
North Woodside Road
Napiershall Street
GLASGOW UNIVERSITY
M²
M⁴
Gibson St.
Bank Street
105
KELVINBRIDGE
Park Rd
West Prince's Street
ST. GEORGE'S CROSS
George's Road
Y
50
140
Kelvin Way
Park Quadrant
Woodlands Road
Saint
KELVINGROVE MUSEUM AND ART GALLERY
KELVINGROVE PARK
108
107
34
143
U
35
M
Royal Terrace
Woodside Place
141
Sauchiehall Street
Argyle Street
47
42
95
Berkeley Street
Kent Road
Elderslie St.
Scott Street
Bath St.
West
Kelvinhaugh Street
Newton
Elmbank St.
POL
A 814
Saint Vincent Street
North Street
Douglas St.
Stobcross Road
SCOTTISH EXHIBITION CENTRE
Pitt St.
Waterloo
Clydeside Expressway
Finnieston
Lancefield Street
Hydepark Street
Argyle Street
A 814
Lancefield Quay
M 8
Anderston Quay
York St.
Broomie
Z
Govan Road
CLYDE
85
Paisley Road
A 8
Morrison Street
Kingston
Nelson
22
93
West
Milnpark Street
Admiral St.
Seaward St.
KINNING PARK
39
100
M 8
(M 8)
C

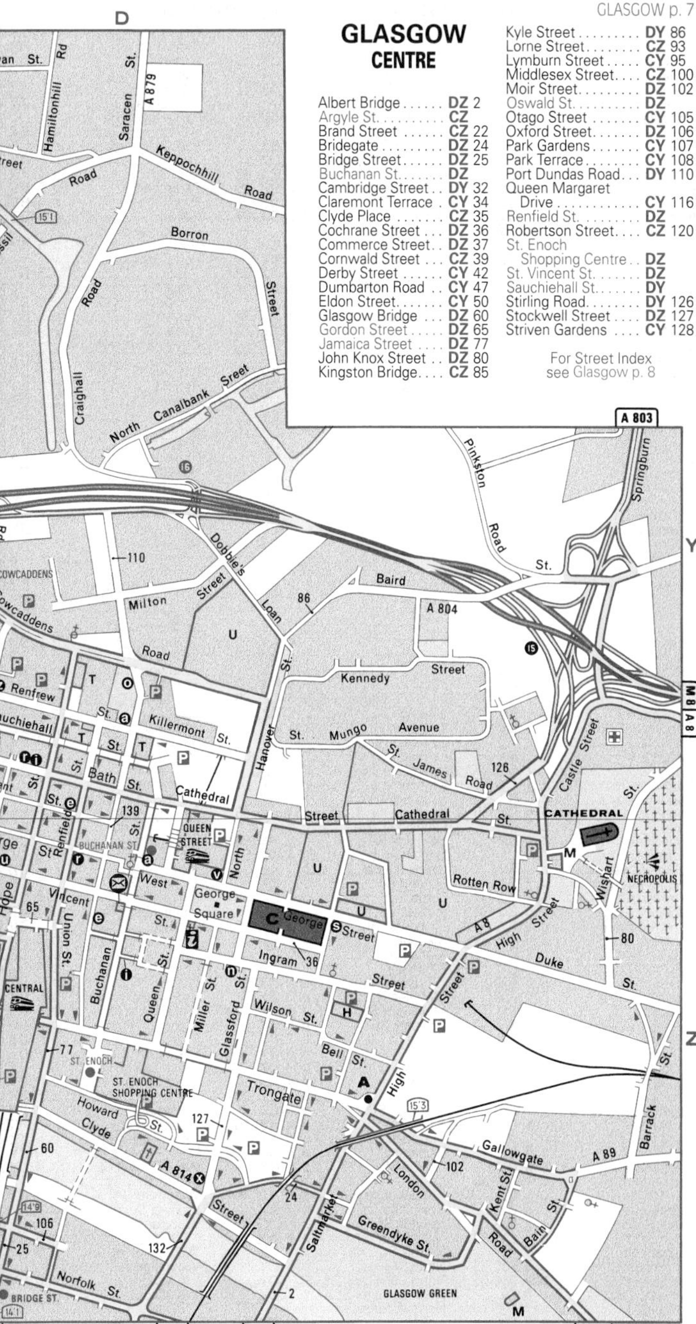
GLASGOW
CENTRE
Albert Bridge . . . . . . DZ 2
Argyle St. . . . . CZ
Brand Street . . . . . . CZ 22
Bridegate . . . . DZ 24
Bridge Street . . . . . . DZ 25
Buchanan St. . . . . . . DZ
Cambridge Street . . DY 32
Claremont Terrace . CY 34
Clyde Place . . . . CZ 35
Cochrane Street . . . DZ 36
Commerce Street . . DZ 37
Cornwald Street . . . CZ 39
Derby Street . . . . . . CY 42
Dumbarton Road . . CY 47
Eldon Street. . . . . . . CY 50
Glasgow Bridge . . . DZ 60
Gordon Street . . . . . DZ 65
Jamaica Street . . . . DZ 77
John Knox Street . . DZ 80
Kingston Bridge. . . . CZ 85
Kyle Street . . . . DY 86
Lorne Street. . . . . CZ 93
Lymburn Street . . . . . CY 95
Middlesex Street. . . . CZ 100
Moir Street. . . . . DZ 102
Oswald St. . . . . DZ
Otago Street . . . . CY 105
Oxford Street. . . . . . . DZ 106
Park Gardens . . . . CY 107
Park Terrace . . . . CY 108
Port Dundas Road . . . DY 110
Queen Margaret Drive . . . . CY 116
Renfield St. . . . . DZ
Robertson Street. . . . CZ 120
St. Enoch Shopping Centre . . DZ
St. Vincent St. . . . . . . DZ
Sauchiehall St. . . . . . . DY
Stirling Road. . . . . DY 126
Stockwell Street . . . . DZ 127
Striven Gardens . . . . CY 128
For Street Index see Glasgow p. 8
D
Y
Z
A 803
A 804
A 8
A 814
A 89
A 749
M 8
Keppochhill Road
Borron Street
Craighall Road
North Canalbank Street
Pinkston Road
Springburn
Baird St.
Dobbie's Loan
Milton Street
Cowcaddens Road
COWCADDENS
Kennedy Street
St. Mungo Avenue
St. James Road
Castle Street
Cathedral Street
CATHEDRAL
NECROPOLIS
Killermont St.
Renfrew St.
Sauchiehall
Bath St.
Hanover St.
North
QUEEN STREET
BUCHANAN ST
West George St.
George Square
George Street
Vincent
Rotten Row
High Street
Duke St.
Wishart
Hope
Union St.
Buchanan
Queen St.
Ingram
Miller St.
Glassford St.
Wilson St.
Bell St.
CENTRAL
ST. ENOCH
ST. ENOCH SHOPPING CENTRE
Trongate
Howard St.
Clyde
Gallowgate
London Road
Greendyke St.
Saltmarket
Kent St.
Bain St.
Barrack St.
Norfolk St.
BRIDGE ST.
GLASGOW GREEN

SCOTLAND

STREET INDEX TO GLASGOW TOWN PLAN

Street	Page	Grid	No.
Albert Bridge	p. 7	**DZ**	2
Admiral St.	p. 6	**CZ**	
Aikenhead Rd	p. 5	**BX**	3
Alexandra Par.	p. 5	**BV**	4
Allison St.	p. 5	**BX**	
Anderston Quay	p. 6	**CZ**	
Anniesland Rd	p. 4	**AV**	
Argyle St.	p. 4	**CZ**	
Bain St.	p. 7	**DZ**	
Baird St.	p. 7	**DY**	
Balgrayhill	p. 5	**BV**	5
Ballater St.	p. 5	**BX**	6
Balmore Rd	p. 5	**BV**	
Balornock Rd	p. 5	**BV**	8
Balshagray Av.	p. 4	**AV**	9
Bank St.	p. 6	**CY**	
Barrack St.	p. 7	**DZ**	
Barrhead Rd	p. 4	**AX**	
Bath St.	p. 6	**CY**	
Battlefield Rd	p. 5	**BX**	12
Bell St.	p. 7	**DZ**	
Belmont St.	p. 6	**CY**	
Berkeley St.	p. 6	**CY**	
Berryknowes Rd	p. 4	**AX**	15
Bilsland Drive	p. 5	**BV**	16
Blairbeth Rd	p. 5	**BX**	18
Borron St.	p. 7	**DY**	
Boydstone Rd	p. 4	**AX**	
Braidcraft Rd	p. 4	**AX**	20
Brand St.	p. 6	**CZ**	22
Bridegate	p. 7	**DZ**	24
Bridge St.	p. 7	**DZ**	25
Brockburn Rd	p. 4	**AX**	
Broomfield Rd	p. 5	**BV**	
Broomielaw	p. 6	**CZ**	
Broomloan Rd	p. 4	**AV**	26
Brownside Rd	p. 5	**BX**	
Buchanan St.	p. 5	**DZ**	
Burnhill Chapel St.	p. 5	**BX**	28
Byres Rd	p. 4	**AV**	29
Caldarvan St.	p. 7	**DY**	
Calder St.	p. 5	**BX**	
Caledonia Rd	p. 5	**BX**	30
Cambridge St.	p. 7	**DY**	32
Cambuslang Rd	p. 5	**BX**	
Cardowan Rd	p. 5	**BV**	
Carmunnock Rd	p. 5	**BX**	33
Carntyne Rd	p. 5	**BV**	
Carntynehall Rd	p. 5	**BV**	
Castle St.	p. 7	**DY**	
Cathcart Rd	p. 5	**BX**	
Cathedral St.	p. 7	**DY**	
Claremont Ter	p. 6	**CY**	34
Clarkston Rd	p. 5	**BX**	
Clyde Place	p. 6	**CZ**	35
Clyde St.	p. 7	**DZ**	
Clyde Tunnel	p. 4	**AV**	
Clydeside Expressway	p. 4	**AV**	
Cochrane St.	p. 7	**DZ**	36
Commerce St.	p. 7	**DZ**	37
Cook St.	p. 5	**BV**	38
Corkerhill Rd	p. 4	**AX**	
Cornwald St.	p. 6	**CZ**	39
Cowcaddens St.	p. 7	**DY**	
Craighall Rd	p. 7	**DY**	
Croftfoot Rd	p. 5	**BX**	
Crookston Rd	p. 4	**AX**	
Crow Rd	p. 4	**AV**	
Cumbernauld Rd	p. 5	**BV**	40
Dalmarnock Rd	p. 5	**BX**	
Derby St.	p. 6	**CY**	42
Dobbie's Loan	p. 7	**DY**	
Douglas St.	p. 6	**CZ**	
Duke's Rd	p. 5	**BX**	
Duke St.	p. 7	**DZ**	
Dumbarton Rd	p. 6	**CY**	47
Dumbreck Rd	p. 4	**AX**	
East Kilbride Rd	p. 5	**BX**	
Edinburgh Rd	p. 5	**BV**	
Edmiston Drive	p. 4	**AV**	48
Eglinton Rd	p. 5	**BX**	
Eglinton St.	p. 5	**BX**	
Elderslie St.	p. 6	**CY**	
Eldon St.	p. 6	**CY**	50
Elmbank St.	p. 6	**CY**	
Farmeloan Rd	p. 5	**BX**	53
Fenwick Rd	p. 4	**AX**	55
Finnieston St.	p. 6	**CZ**	
Gallowgate	p. 7	**DZ**	
Garscube Rd	p. 7	**DY**	
George Square	p. 7	**DZ**	
George St.	p. 7	**DZ**	
Gibson St.	p. 6	**CY**	
Glasgow Bridge	p. 7	**DZ**	60
Glasgow Rd (PAISLEY)	p. 4	**AX**	62
Glasgow Rd (RENFREW)	p. 4	**AV**	
Glasgow Rd (RUTHERGLEN)	p. 5	**BX**	
Glassford St.	p. 7	**DZ**	
Gorbals St.	p. 5	**BX**	63
Gordon St.	p. 5	**DZ**	65
Govan Rd	p. 6	**CZ**	
Grange Rd	p. 5	**BX**	67
Great Western Rd	p. 6	**CY**	
Greendyke St.	p. 7	**DZ**	
Haggs Rd	p. 4	**AX**	68
Hamiltonhill Rd	p. 7	**DY**	
Hardgate Rd	p. 4	**AV**	
Harriet St.	p. 4	**AX**	70
Helen St.	p. 4	**AV**	72
High St.	p. 7	**DZ**	
Hillington Rd	p. 4	**AV**	
Holmfauld Rd	p. 4	**AV**	73
Holmlea Rd	p. 5	**BX**	74
Hope St.	p. 7	**DZ**	
Hopehill Rd	p. 6	**CY**	
Hospital St.	p. 5	**BX**	75
Howard St.	p. 7	**DZ**	
Hydepark St.	p. 6	**CZ**	
Ingram St.	p. 7	**DZ**	
Jamaica St.	p. 5	**DZ**	77
James St.	p. 5	**BX**	79
John Knox St.	p. 7	**DZ**	80
Kelvin Way	p. 6	**CY**	
Kelvinhaugh St.	p. 6	**CY**	
Kennedy St.	p. 7	**DY**	
Kennishead Rd	p. 4	**AX**	
Kent Rd	p. 6	**CY**	
Kent St.	p. 7	**DZ**	
Keppoch Hill Rd	p. 7	**DY**	
Killermont St.	p. 7	**DY**	
Kilmarnock Rd	p. 4	**AX**	
King's Drive	p. 5	**BX**	83
King's Park Av.	p. 5	**BX**	
Kings Park Rd	p. 5	**BX**	84
Kingston Bridge	p. 6	**CZ**	85
Kingston St.	p. 6	**CZ**	
Kingsway	p. 4	**AV**	
Kyle St.	p. 7	**DY**	86
Lamont Rd	p. 5	**BV**	88
Lancefield Quay	p. 6	**CZ**	
Lancefield St.	p. 6	**CZ**	
Langlands Rd	p. 4	**AV**	
Langside Av.	p. 4	**AX**	89
Langside Drive	p. 4	**AX**	
Langside Rd	p. 5	**BX**	90
Lincoln Av.	p. 4	**AV**	91
Linthaugh Rd	p. 4	**AX**	
London Rd	p. 5	**BX**	
Lorne St.	p. 6	**CZ**	93
Lymburn St.	p. 6	**CY**	95
Lyoncross Rd	p. 4	**AX**	97
Main St.	p. 5	**BX**	
Maryhill Rd	p. 6	**CY**	
Meiklerig Crescent	p. 4	**AX**	98
Merrylee Rd	p. 4	**AX**	
Middlesex St.	p. 6	**CZ**	100
Milnpark St.	p. 6	**CZ**	
Milton St.	p. 7	**DY**	
Mill St.	p. 5	**BX**	
Miller St.	p. 7	**DZ**	
Minard Rd	p. 4	**AX**	101
Moir St.	p. 7	**DZ**	102
Morrison St.	p. 6	**CZ**	
Moss Rd	p. 4	**AV**	103
Mosspark Blvd.	p. 4	**AX**	
Napiershall St.	p. 6	**CY**	
Nelson St.	p. 6	**CZ**	
Nether Auldhouse Rd	p. 4	**AX**	104
Newlands Rd	p. 4	**AX**	
Newton St.	p. 6	**CYZ**	
Nitshill Rd	p. 4	**AX**	
Norfolk St.	p. 7	**DZ**	
North St.	p. 6	**CY**	
North Canalbank St.	p. 7	**DY**	
North Hanover St.	p. 7	**DY**	
North Woodside Rd	p. 6	**CY**	
Oswald St.	p. 5	**DZ**	
Otago St.	p. 6	**CY**	1
Oxford St.	p. 7	**DZ**	1
Paisley Rd	p. 4	**AV**	
Paisley Rd West	p. 4	**AX**	
Park Gdns	p. 6	**CY**	1
Parkhead Forge Shopping Centre	p. 3	**BX**	
Park Quadrant	p. 6	**CY**	
Park Ter	p. 6	**CY**	1
Peat Rd	p. 4	**AX**	
Petershill Rd	p. 5	**BV**	
Pinkston Rd	p. 5	**BV**	
Pitt St.	p. 6	**CZ**	
Pollokshaws Rd	p. 4	**AX**	
Port Dundas Rd	p. 7	**DY**	1
Possil Rd	p. 7	**DY**	
Prospecthill Rd	p. 5	**BX**	1
Provan Rd	p. 5	**BV**	1
Queen St.	p. 7	**DZ**	
Queen Margaret Drive	p. 6	**CY**	1
Raeberry St.	p. 6	**CY**	
Red Rd	p. 5	**BV**	1
Renfield St.	p. 5	**DZ**	
Renfrew Rd	p. 4	**AV**	
Renfrew St.	p. 7	**DY**	
Ring Rd	p. 5	**BV**	
Riverford Road	p. 4	**AX**	1
Robertson St.	p. 6	**CZ**	
Rotten Row	p. 7	**DZ**	
Royal Ter	p. 6	**CY**	
Royston Rd	p. 5	**BV**	
Rutherglen Rd	p. 5	**BX**	
St. Andrew's Drive	p. 4	**AX**	
St. Enoch Shopping Centre	p. 5	**DZ**	
St. George's Rd	p. 6	**CY**	
St. James Rd	p. 7	**DY**	
St. Mungo Av.	p. 7	**DY**	
St. Vincent St.	p. 5	**DZ**	
Saltmarket	p. 7	**DZ**	
Sandwood Rd	p. 4	**AV**	1
Saracen St.	p. 7	**DY**	
Sauchiehall St.	p. 5	**DY**	
Scott St.	p. 6	**CY**	
Seaward St.	p. 6	**CZ**	
Shettleston Rd	p. 5	**BX**	
Shieldhall Rd	p. 4	**AV**	
Shields Rd	p. 4	**AX**	
Southbrae Drive	p. 4	**AV**	
Springburn Rd	p. 5	**BV**	
Springfield Rd	p. 5	**BX**	
Stirling Rd	p. 7	**DY**	1
Stobcross Road	p. 6	**CZ**	
Stockwell St.	p. 7	**DZ**	
Stonelaw Rd	p. 5	**BX**	
Striven Gdns	p. 6	**CY**	
Thornliebank Rd	p. 4	**AX**	
Todd St.	p. 5	**BV**	
Tollcross Rd	p. 5	**BX**	
Trongate	p. 5	**DZ**	
Union St.	p. 5	**DZ**	
Victoria Bridge	p. 7	**DZ**	1
Victoria Rd	p. 5	**BX**	
Wallacewell Rd	p. 5	**BV**	
Waterloo St.	p. 6	**CZ**	
West St.	p. 6	**CZ**	
West Campbell St.	p. 6	**CZ**	
West George St.	p. 7	**DZ**	
West Graham St.	p. 6	**CY**	
Westmuir Place	p. 5	**BX**	
Westmuir St.	p. 5	**BX**	
West Nile St.	p. 7	**DYZ**	
West Paisley Rd	p. 6	**CZ**	
West Prince's St.	p. 6	**CY**	
West Regent St.	p. 7	**DY**	
Wilson St.	p. 7	**DZ**	
Wilton St.	p. 6	**CY**	
Wishart St.	p. 7	**DZ**	
Woodlands Drive	p. 6	**CY**	
Woodlands Rd	p. 6	**CY**	
Woodside Crescent	p. 6	**CY**	1
Woodside Place	p. 6	**CY**	
Woodside Ter	p. 6	**CY**	
York St.	p. 6	**CZ**	

SCOTLAND

Travel Inn Metro, Montrose House, 187 George St., G1 1YU, ☎ (0141) 553 2700, *Fax (0141) 553 2719* – |♦|, ⇔, ▤ rest, TV ☎ ♿ P – 🚗 40. MC AE ⓓ VISA. ✄ DZ s
Meals (dinner only) – **254 rm** 46.95 **t.**

Travel Inn, Cambuslang Investment Park, Drumhead Pl., G32 8EY, Southeast : 5 m. by A 749 off A 74 ☎ (0141) 764 2655, *Fax (0141) 778 1703* – ⇔ rm, ▤ rest, TV ♿ P. MC AE ⓓ VISA. ✄
Meals (grill rest.) – **40 rm** 40.95 **t.**

Travelodge, Hill St., G3 6PR, ☎ (0141) 333 1515, *Fax (0141) 333 1221* – |♦| ⇔, ▤ rest, TV ♿ – 🚗 30. MC AE ⓓ VISA. ✄ DY c
Meals (cafe bar) (dinner only) – **95 rm** 49.95 **t.**

Travelodge, 251 Paisley Rd, G5 8RA, ☎ (0141) 420 3882, *Fax (0141) 420 3884* – ⇔ rm, ▤ rest, TV ☎ ♿ P. MC AE ⓓ VISA JCB. ✄ CZ n
Meals (grill rest.) – **75 rm** 49.95 **t.**

Park House, 13 Victoria Park Gardens South, G11 7BX, ☎ (0141) 339 1559, *richardanddi.parkhouse.glasgow@dial.pipex.com, Fax (0141) 576 0915* – ⇔ TV P. MC VISA. ✄
closed 2 weeks Easter – **Meals** (by arrangement) 22.00 **st.** – **3 rm** ☕ 50.00/80.00 **st.** AV n

Manor Park, 28 Balshagray Drive, G11 7DD, ☎ (0141) 339 2143, *manorparkhotel@aol.com, Fax (0141) 339 5842* – TV. MC AE ⓓ VISA JCB AV u
Meals (by arrangement) 16.50 **st.** – **10 rm** ☕ 40.00/70.00 **st.** – SB.

The Town House without rest., 4 Hughenden Terr., G12 9XR, ☎ (0141) 357 0862, *hospitality@thetownhouseglasgow.com, Fax (0141) 339 9605* – TV. MC VISA. ✄ AV i
booking essential December and January – **10 rm** ☕ 60.00/75.00 **st.**

Kirklee without rest., 11 Kensington Gate, G12 9LG, ☎ (0141) 334 5555, *kirklee@clara.net, Fax (0141) 339 3828* – ⇔ TV. MC VISA. ✄ AV c
closed 25-26 December – **9 rm** ☕ 52.00/68.00 **t.**

Camerons (at Hilton Glasgow H.), 1 William St., G3 8HT, ☎ (0141) 204 5511, *Fax (0141) 204 5004* – ▤ P. MC AE ⓓ VISA JCB CZ s
closed Saturday lunch and Sunday – **Meals** 19.90/24.90 **t.** (lunch) and dinner a la carte 33.00/45.00 **t.** 🍷 10.50.

Lux, 1051 Great Western Rd, G12 0XP, ☎ (0141) 576 7576, *info@luxstazione.com* – ⇔ ▤ P. MC VISA AV o
closed 1-2 January, 25-26 December, Sunday and Monday – **Meals** (dinner only) 11.95/25.00 **t.**.

Eurasia, 150 St. Vincent St., G2 5NE, ☎ (0141) 204 1150, *reservations@eurasia-restaurant.co.uk, Fax (0141) 204 1140* – ▤. MC AE ⓓ VISA DZ u
closed 2 days Christmas, 2 days New Year, Saturday lunch and Sunday – **Meals** 13.95/16.95 **t.** (lunch) and dinner a la carte 16.95/30.50 **t.**

Rogano, 11 Exchange Pl., G1 3AN, ☎ (0141) 248 4055, *Fax (0141) 248 2608,* « Art Deco » – ▤. MC AE ⓓ VISA DZ i
closed 25 December and 1 January – **Meals** - Seafood - 16.50 **t.** (lunch) and a la carte 27.90/37.95 **t.** 🍷 9.00.

Buttery, 652 Argyle St., G3 8UF, ☎ (0141) 221 8188, *Fax (0141) 204 4639* – ⇔ P. MC AE ⓓ VISA CZ e
closed 25 December, 1 January, Sunday and Saturday lunch – **Meals** 17.50/19.50 **t.** (lunch) and a la carte 27.25/42.60 **t.** 🍷 6.50.

Yes, 22 West Nile St., G1 2PW, ☎ (0141) 221 8044, *Fax (0141) 248 9159* – ▤. MC AE ⓓ VISA
closed 25-26 December, 1-2 January, Sunday and Bank Holidays – **Meals** 14.95/29.50 **t** 🍷 8.00. DZ e

Nairns with rm, 13 Woodside Cres., G3 7UL, ☎ (0141) 353 0707, *info@nairns.co.uk, Fax (0141) 331 1684,* « Contemporary interior » – ⇔ rest, TV ☎. MC AE ⓓ VISA. ✄
closed Christmas, Sunday and Monday lunch – **Meals** 13.50/27.50 **t.** – **4 rm** 110.00/140.00 **t.** CY e

Rococo, 202 West George St., G2 2NR, ☎ (0141) 221 5004, *Fax (0141) 221 5006* – ▤. MC AE ⓓ VISA DYZ z
closed Sunday and 1 January – **Meals** 16.00/27.00 **t.** (lunch) and dinner a la carte 28.50/41.50 **t.** 🍷 8.00.

Puppet Theatre, 11 Ruthven Lane, G12 9BG, off Byres Rd ☎ (0141) 339 8444, *puppet@bigbeat.co.uk, Fax (0141) 339 7666* – ⇔. MC AE ⓓ VISA AV r
closed Monday and Saturday lunch – **Meals** a la carte 27.00/41.00 **t.** 🍷 7.50.

The Restaurant at Corinthian, 191 Ingram St., G1 1DA, ☎ (0141) 552 1101, *smcintosh@corinthian.uk.com, Fax (0141) 559 6826,* « Former Glasgow Ship Bank, fine Victorian architecture » – MC AE VISA DZ n
closed lunch Saturday and Sunday – **Meals** 12.00 **t.** (lunch) and dinner a la carte 18.75/27.75 **t.**

SCOTLAND

XX **Papingo,** 104 Bath St., G2 2EN, ✆ (0141) 332 6678, *info@papingo.co.* *Fax (0141) 332 6549* – MC AE D VISA DY
closed 25-26 December, 1-2 January, Sunday lunch and Bank Holiday Mondays – **Me** 9.95/12.95 **t.** (lunch) and a la carte 19.95/30.40 **t.** 🍷 7.00.

XX **Ho Wong,** 82 York St., G2 8LE, ✆ (0141) 221 3550, *Fax (0141) 248 5330* – ▤. MC AE D
closed Sunday dinner – **Meals** - Chinese (Peking) - 8.50 **t.** (lunch) and dinner a la ca 19.10/45.50 **t.** 🍷 6.95. CZ

XX **Amber Regent,** 50 West Regent St., G2 2QZ, ✆ (0141) 331 1655, *Fax (0141) 353 339* ▤. MC AE D VISA JCB DY
closed 3 days Chinese New Year and Sunday – **Meals** - Chinese - 7.95/35.95 **t.** and a la car

XX **Shish Mahal,** 66-68 Park Rd, G4 9JF, ✆ (0141) 334 7899, *mail@shishmahal.co.* *Fax (0141) 572 0800* – ⋟. MC AE VISA CY
closed Sunday lunch – **Meals** - Indian - 5.25/6.50 **t.** (lunch) and a la carte 9.35/18.4 🍷 4.50.

XX **Shimla Pinks** (at Hilton Glasgow H.), 1 William St., G3 8HT, ✆ (0141) 248 19 *Fax (0141) 248 2913* – ▤ P. MC AE D VISA CZ
closed 1 January, lunch Saturday and Sunday – **Meals** - Indian - 6.95/7.95 (lunch) and a la carte 9.70/23.40 **t.**

X **Stravaigin,** 28 Gibson St., (basement), G12 8NX, ✆ (0141) 334 2665, *stravaigin@btinte t.com, Fax (0141) 334 4099* – ⋟ ▤. MC AE D VISA CY
closed 25-26 December and 1-2 January – **Meals** (dinner only and lunch Friday a Saturday) 24.95 **t.** 🍷 11.45.

X **Groucho Saint Jude's** with rm, 190 Bath St., G2 4HG, ✆ (0141) 352 8800, *info@grou osaintjudes.com, Fax (0141) 352 8801,* « Contemporary interior » – ▤ TV ✆ – 🎤 35. MC D VISA CY
Meals *(closed Saturday, Sunday and Bank Holidays)* 14.50 **t.** (lunch) and a la carte 18. 29.00 **t.** 🍷 7.50 – **5 rm** 95.00/105.00 **t.**, 1 suite.

X **Gamba,** 225a West George St., G2 2ND, ✆ (0141) 572 0899, *info@gamba.co.* *Fax (0141) 572 0896* – MC AE VISA DY
closed 25-26 December, 1-2 January, Sunday and Bank Holiday Mondays – **Meals** - Seafoo 11.95/19.95 **t.** (lunch) and a la carte 22.20/30.65 **t.** 🍷 7.50.

X **Gran Caffe',** 42 Renfield St., G2 1NE, ✆ (0141) 572 7000, *grancaffeglasgow@netscape ine.com, Fax (0141) 572 1125* – MC AE VISA DZ
closed 25 December and Sunday lunch – **Meals** - Italian - (bookings not accepted at lun 22.90 **t.** (dinner) and a la carte 18.10/34.75 🍷 5.90.

X **Air Organic,** 36 Kelvingrove St., G3 7SA, ✆ (0141) 564 5200, *airorganic@email.msn.cc* *Fax (0141) 564 1396* – MC AE VISA CY
closed 25 December – **Meals** 20.00/25.00 **t.** and a la carte.

X **The Ubiquitous Chip,** 12 Ashton Lane, G12 8SJ, off Byres Rd ✆ (0141) 334 50 *Fax (0141) 337 1302* – MC AE D VISA AV
closed 25 and 31 December and 1 January – **Meals** 23.95/32.95 **t.**.

X **La Parmigiana,** 447 Great Western Rd, Kelvinbridge, G12 8HH, ✆ (0141) 334 06 *Fax (0141) 332 3533* – ▤. MC AE D VISA JCB CY
closed 25-26 December, 1-2 January, Sunday and Bank Holidays – **Meals** - Italian - 9. 11.50 **st.** and a la carte 🍷 7.90.

X **No Sixteen,** 16 Byres Rd, G11 5JY, ✆ (0141) 339 2544 – MC VISA AV
closed first 2 weeks January, 25 December and Sunday – **Meals** (dinner only and Satur lunch) a la carte 17.10/23.00 **t.**

X **Bouzy Rouge,** 111 West Regent St., G2 2RU, ✆ (0141) 221 8804, *Fax (0141) 221 694* ▤. MC AE D VISA DY
closed 1 January – **Meals** 9.95/12.20 **t.** (lunch) and a la carte 19.95/29.40 **t.** 🍷 6.50.

X **Shimla Pinks,** 777 Pollokshaws Rd, G41 2AX, ✆ (0141) 423 4488, *Fax (0141) 423 243* ▤. MC AE D VISA AX
closed 1 January and lunch Saturday and Sunday – **Meals** - Indian - 6 (lunch) and a la carte 11.10/21.85 **t.**

at Stepps *(North Lanarkshire) Northeast : 5½ m. by M 8 on A 80* – **BV** – ✉ *Glasgow.*

Garfield House, Cumbernauld Rd, G33 6HW, ✆ (0141) 779 2111, *rooms@garfieldhot o.uk, Fax (0141) 779 9799* – ⋟ TV P – 🎤 100. MC AE D VISA
closed 1-2 January – **Meals** a la carte 9.95/21.50 **t.** 🍷 7.00 – **46 rm** ☕ 73.50/102.00 **t.**

at Giffnock *(East Renfrewshire) South : 5¼ m. by A 77* – **AX** – ✉ *Glasgow.*

X **Turban Tandoori,** 2 Station Rd, G46 6JF, ✆ (0141) 638 0069 – MC AE VISA JCB
closed 1 January – **Meals** - Indian - (dinner only) a la carte 9.30/14.15 **st.** 🍷 7.25.

X **The Cook's Room,** 205 Fenwick Rd, G46 6JD, ✆ (0141) 621 1903, *Fax (0141) 621 190* MC VISA
closed 25 December and 1 January – **Meals** (dinner only and Sunday lunch) a la ca 15.00/25.00 **t.** 🍷 6.00.

Glasgow Airport *(Renfrewshire) West : 8 m. by M 8 –* **AV** *– ✉ Paisley.*

Posthouse Glasgow Airport, Abbotsinch, PA3 2TR, ✆ (0870) 400 9031, *gm1791@forte_hotels.com, Fax (0141) 887 3738* – rm, – 250.
The Junction : **Meals** (closed Saturday lunch and Bank Holidays) (carving rest. Friday-Sunday) 12.95/14.95 **t.** and a la carte – 11.95 – **296 rm** 89.00/109.00 **st.**, 2 suites – SB.

Express by Holiday Inn, St. Andrews Drive, PA3 2TJ, ✆ (0141) 842 1100, *info@hiex-glasgow.com, Fax (0141) 842 1122* – rest, – 80.
Meals (dinner only) a la carte 9.80/19.45 **st.** – **143 rm** 57.50 **st.** – SB.

Travel Inn Metro, Whitecart Rd, PA3 2TH, ✆ (0141) 842 1563, *Fax (0141) 842 1570* – rest, – 30.
Meals (grill rest.) (dinner only) – **104 rm** 46.95 **t.**

.ASGOW AIRPORT *Renfrewshire* 401 402 G 16 – *see Glasgow.*

.ENBORROD ALE *Highland* 401 C 13 – ✉ *Acharacle.*
Edinburgh 190 – Inverness 116 – Oban 106.

Feorag House, PH36 4JP, ✆ (01972) 500248, *admin@feorag.demon.co.uk, Fax (01972) 500285,* ≤ Loch Sunart, « Lochside setting », –
Meals 20.00/25.00 **st.** – **3 rm** (dinner included) 77.00/130.00 **st.**

.ENSBURGH *Falkirk – see Falkirk.*

.ENELG *Highland* 401 D 12.
Edinburgh 229 – Inverness 75 – Kyle of Lochalsh 25.

Glenelg Inn, IV40 8JR, ✆ (01599) 522273, *Fax (01599) 522283,* ≤ Glenelg Bay, –
Meals 24.00 **st.** (dinner) and lunch a la carte approx. 17.00 **st.** 5.00 – **6 rm** (dinner included) 134.00 **st.** – SB.

.ENFINNAN *Highland* 401 D 13 – ✉ *Fort William.*
Edinburgh 150 – Inverness 85 – Oban 66.

The Prince's House, PH37 4LT, West : ¾ m. on A 830 ✆ (01397) 722246, *princeshouse@glenfinnan.co.uk, Fax (01397) 722307,* ≤ –
Easter-Christmas – **Meals** (bar lunch Monday to Saturday)/dinner 26.95 **t.** 10.25 – **9 rm** 45.00/90.00 – SB.

.ENLIVET *Moray* 401 J 11 – *pop. 3 559* – ✉ *Ballindalloch.*
Edinburgh 180 – Aberdeen 59 – Elgin 27 – Inverness 49.

Minmore House, AB37 9DB, South : ¾ m. on Glenlivet Distillery rd ✆ (01807) 590378, *minmorehouse@ukonline.co.uk, Fax (01807) 590472,* ≤, –
restricted opening in winter – **Meals** (booking essential to non-residents) 25.00/35.00 **t.** (dinner) and lunch a la carte 14.70/25.95 **t.** 8.75 – **9 rm** 50.00/100.00 **t.** – SB.

.ENROTHES *Fife* 401 K 15 *Scotland G. – pop. 38 650.*
Env. : *Falkland★ (Village★, Palace of Falkland★* **AC**, *Gardens★* **AC***) N : 5½ m. by A 92 and A 912.*
18 Thornton, Station Rd ✆ (01592) 771173 – 18 Golf Course Rd ✆ (01592) 754561 – 18 Balbirnie Park, Markinch ✆ (01592) 612095 – 9 Auchterderran, Woodend Rd, Cardenden ✆ (01592) 721579 – 9 Leslie, Balsillie Laws ✆ (01592) 620040.
Edinburgh 33 – Dundee 25 – Stirling 36.

Balbirnie House, Markinch, KY7 6NE, Northeast : 1 ¾ m. by A 911 and A 92 on B 9130 ✆ (01592) 610066, *balbirnie@breathnet.com, Fax (01592) 610529,* « Part Georgian mansion in country park », 18, – rest, – 200.
Orangery : **Meals** 13.75/29.50 **st.** and lunch a la carte – **28 rm** 125.00/245.00 **st.**, 2 suites – SB.

Express by Holiday Inn without rest., Leslie Roundabout, Leslie Rd, KY7 6XX, West : 2 m. on A 911 ✆ (01592) 745509, *Fax (01592) 743377* – – 25.
49 rm 49.95 **st.**

Travel Inn, Beaufort Drive, Bankhead Roundabout, KY7 4UJ, Southeast : 1 ¾ m. by A 9 and A 92 at junction with B 921 ☏ (01592) 773473, *Fax (01592) 773453* – ⇝, ▤ rest, TV P. MC AE ⓘ VISA. ✻
Meals (grill rest.) – **41 rm** 40.95 **t.**

GRANTOWN-ON-SPEY *Highland* 401 J 12 – *pop. 2 391.*

Golf Course Rd ☏ (01479) 872079 – Abernethy, Nethy Bridge ☏ (01479) 821305.
High St. ☏ (01479) 872773 (April-October).
Edinburgh 143 – Inverness 34 – Perth 99.

Culdearn House, Woodlands Terr., PH26 3JU, ☏ (01479) 872106, *culdearn@globalnet.uk, Fax (01479) 873641,* – ⇝ TV P. MC AE ⓘ VISA JCB. ✻
mid March-October – **Meals** (booking essential to non-residents) (dinner only) 21.0 25.00 **st.** 7.50 – **9 rm** (dinner included) 75.00/150.00 **st.** – SB.

Ravenscourt House, Seafield Av., PH26 3JG, ☏ (01479) 872286, *Fax (01479) 873260,* – ⇝ TV P.
closed January – **Meals** (residents only) (dinner only) 15.00/17.50 **st.** 4.50 – **8 r** 35.00/80.00 **st.**

at Dulnain Bridge *Southwest : 3 m. by A 95 on A 938 – ✉ Grantown-on-Spey.*

Muckrach Lodge ♨, PH26 3LY, West : ½ m. on A 938 ☏ (01479) 851257, *stay@muck.h.sol.co.uk, Fax (01479) 851325,* ≤, – ⇝ TV ♿ P. – 35. MC AE ⓘ VISA JCB
Meals (lunch by arrangement)/dinner 27.50 **st.** 6.75 – **11 rm** 55.00/125.00 **st.**, 2 sui – SB.

Auchendean Lodge, PH26 3LU, South : 1 m. on A 95 ☏ (01479) 851347, *hotel@auchdean.com, Fax (01479) 851347,* ≤ Spey Valley and Cairngorms, – ⇝ rest, TV P. MC ⓘ VISA
closed August – **Meals** (dinner only) 26.00 **st.** 4.50 – **7 rm** 43.00/94.00 **st.** – SB.

GREENOCK *Inverclyde* 401 F 16 – *pop. 35 272.*

Forsyth St. ☏ (01475) 720793.
Edinburgh 70 – Ayr 48 – Glasgow 24.

Howard Johnson, Cartsburn, PA15 4RT, East : ¾ m. off A 8 ☏ (01475) 786666, *greenc@howardjohnson.co.uk, Fax (01475) 786777* – ⇝ TV ♿ P. – 35. MC AE ⓘ VISA.
closed 25 December – **Meals** a la carte 6.90/11.85 **st.** 3.95 – 6.00 **72 rm** 55.00 **st.**

Travel Inn, James Watt Dock, PA15 2AD, East : 1 m. by A 8 ☏ (01475) 7309 *Fax (01475) 730890* – ⇝, ▤ rest, TV ♿ P. MC AE ⓘ VISA. ✻
Meals (grill rest.) – **40 rm** 40.95 **t.**

GRETNA GREEN SERVICE AREA *Dumfries and Galloway* 401 402 K 18 – ✉ *Gretna.*

Days Inn, DG16 5HQ, on A 74 (M) ☏ (01461) 337566, Reservations (Freephone) 0800 0280400, *Fax (01461) 337823* – ⇝ rm, TV ♿ P. MC AE ⓘ VISA JCB
Meals (grill rest.) a la carte 9.65/13.90 **st.** – 5.95 – **64 rm** 45.00 **t.**

GRIMSAY *Western Isles (Outer Hebrides)* 401 Y 11 – *see Uist (Isles of).*

GUILDTOWN *Perthshire and Kinross* 401 J 14 – *see Perth.*

GULLANE *East Lothian* 401 L 15 *Scotland G.* – *pop. 2 229.*

Env. : *Dirleton★ (Castle★) NE : 2 m. by A 198.*
Edinburgh 19 – North Berwick 5.

Greywalls ♨, Duncur Rd, Muirfield, EH31 2EG, ☏ (01620) 842144, *hotel@greywalls.co.uk, Fax (01620) 842241,* ≤ Gardens and Muirfield golf course, « Edwardian country hou designed by Sir Edwin Lutyens, gardens by Gertrude Jekyll », – ⇝ rest, TV P. – MC AE ⓘ VISA
April-October – **Meals** (booking essential to non-residents) 18.00-22.00/35.00 **t.** 6.5 **23 rm** 110.00/220.00 **t.** – SB.

Faussetthill House without rest., Main St., EH31 2DR, ☏ (01620) 8423 *Fax (01620) 842396,* – ⇝ P. MC VISA. ✻
closed January-February – **3 rm** 45.00/60.00.

Hopefield House without rest., Main St., EH31 2DP, ☏ (01620) 842191, *10rad@inigh.business.co.uk, Fax (01620) 842191,* – ⇝ P. ✻
April-September – **3 rm** 30.00/50.00 **s.**

ADDINGTON *East Lothian* 401 L 16 *Scotland G. – pop. 7 342.*

See : *Town★ - High Street★.*

Env. : *Lennoxlove★ AC, S : 1 m – Gifford★, SE : 5 m. by B 6369.*

Exc. : *Tantallon Castle★★ (clifftop site★★★) AC, NE : 12 m. by A 1 and A 198 – Northern foothills of the Lammermuir Hills★★, S : 14 m. by A 6137 and B 6368 – Stenton★, E : 7 m.*

18 Amisfield Park (01620) 823627.

Edinburgh 17 – Hawick 53 – Newcastle upon Tyne 101.

Maitlandfield Country House, 24 Sidegate, EH41 4BZ, (01620) 826513, *info@maitlandfieldhotels.fsnet.co.uk, Fax (01620) 826713,* – TV P – 200. MC AE VISA
Meals 9.95/28.50 **st.** and dinner a la carte – **22 rm** 60.00/150.00 **st.** – SB.

Brown's with rm, 1 West Rd, EH41 3RD, (01620) 822254, *info@browns-hotel.com, Fax (01620) 822254,* – rest, TV P. MC AE VISA JCB.
closed 1 week in spring and 2 weeks November – **Meals** (booking essential) (dinner only and Sunday lunch)/dinner 29.50 **t.** – **5 rm** 70.00/120.00 **t.**

ALKIRK *Highland* 401 J 8 *– pop. 1 913.*

Edinburgh 285 – Thurso 8 – Wick 17.

Bannochmore Farm, Harpsdale, KW12 6UN, South : 3 ¼ m. (01847) 841216, – P.
April-October – **Meals** (by arrangement) 12.00 – **3 rm** 21.00/38.00.

AMILTON SERVICE AREA *South Lanarkshire* 401 H 16.

9 Larkhall, Burnhead Rd (01698) 881113 – 9 Strathclyde Park, Mote Hill (01698) 429350.

Road Chef Services, M 74 northbound (01698) 285590.

Edinburgh 38 – Glasgow 12.

Travel Inn without rest., ML3 6JW, M 74 between junctions 6 and 5 (northbound carriageway) (01698) 891904, *Fax (01698) 891682* – TV P – 25. MC AE VISA.
closed Christmas and New Year – **36 rm** 40.95.

ARRIS (Isle of) *Western Isles (Outer Hebrides)* 401 Z 10 *– see Lewis and Harris (Isle of).*

ELMSDALE *Highland* 401 J 9.

Coupar Park, Sutherland (01431) 821640 (April-September).

Edinburgh 227 – Inverness 71 – Thurso 45 – Wick 37.

Navidale House, KW8 6JS, North : ½ m. on A 9 (01431) 821258, *Fax (01431) 821531,* – TV P. MC VISA
mid February-October – **Meals** (bar lunch)/dinner 25.00 **t.** 6.50 – **15 rm** (dinner included) 60.00/160.00 **t.** – SB.

OWGATE *Midlothian* 401 402 K 16 *– Penicuik.*

Edinburgh 12 – Glasgow 54.

The Howgate, EH26 8PY, Southwest : ¾ m. on A 6094 (01968) 670000, *Fax (01968) 670000,* – P. MC AE VISA JCB.
closed 25-26 December and 1-2 January – **Meals** a la carte 13.50/28.70 **t.**

GLISTON *Edinburgh City* 401 K 16 *– see Edinburgh.*

NERLEITHEN *Borders* 401 402 K 17 *– pop. 2 663 – Peebles.*

Edinburgh 31 – Dumfries 57 – Glasgow 60.

Caddon View, 14 Pirn Rd, EH44 6HH, (01896) 830208, *caddonview@aol.com, Fax (01896) 830104,* – TV P. MC VISA.
closed 25 December and January – **Meals** 17.00/22.00 **st.** 7.00 – **6 rm** 40.00/60.00 **t.** – SB.

VERARAY *Argyll and Bute* 401 E 15.

9 Inveraray, North Cromalt (01499) 302508.

Front St. (01499) 302063.

Edinburgh 102 – Glasgow 58 – Oban 38.

Loch Fyne, PA32 8XT, Southwest : ½ m. on A 83 ℘ (01499) 302148, *lochfyne@british-t-hotels.com, Fax (01499) 302348,* – 50.
Meals (bar lunch)/dinner 18.00 **st.** and a la carte 6.95 – **80 rm** 55.00/95.00 **st.** – SB.

INVERCRERAN *Argyll and Bute* 401 E 14 – ✉ *Appin.*
Edinburgh 142 – Fort William 29 – Oban 19.

Invercreran Country House, Glen Creran, PA38 4BJ, ℘ (01631) 730414, *inveran@dial.pipex.com, Fax (01631) 730532,* ≤ Glen Creran and mountains, – rest,
16 March-14 November – **Meals** 30.00 **t.** (dinner) and lunch a la carte 20.00/31.00 **t.** 9 – **9 rm** 55.00/200.00 **t.** – SB.

INVERGARRY *Highland* 401 F 12 *Scotland G.* – ✉ *Inverness.*
Env. : *The Great Glen★.*
Edinburgh 159 – Fort William 25 – Inverness 43 – Kyle of Lochalsh 50.

Glengarry Castle, PH35 4HW, on A 82 ℘ (01809) 501254, *castle@glengarry.n Fax (01809) 501207,* ≤, –
April-5 November – **Meals** (light lunch Monday to Saturday)/dinner 25.00/28.00 **st.** 6.0 **26 rm** 55.00/140.00 **st.** – SB.

Invergarry, PH35 4HJ, ℘ (01809) 501206, *hotel@invergarry.net, Fax (01809) 501400,* – rest,
closed 1 week Christmas – **Meals** (bar lunch)/dinner 18.00/22.00 **st.** 5.50 – **10** 40.00/70.00 **st.** – SB.

INVERKEILOR *Angus* 401 M 14 – *pop. 902* – ✉ *Arbroath.*
Edinburgh 85 – Aberdeen 32 – Dundee 22.

Gordon's with rm, Homewood House, Main St., DD11 5RN, ℘ (01241) 8303 *Fax (01241) 830364* –
closed last 3 weeks January, last week October and first week November – **Meals** *(clos Monday, lunch Tuesday and Saturday and dinner Sunday)* (booking essential) a la ca 18.45/26.90 **t.** 6.95 – **2 rm** 45.00/70.00 **t.**

INVERNESS *Highland* 401 H 11 *Scotland G.* – *pop. 62 186.*
See : *Town★ – Museum and Art Gallery★* **Y M.**
Exc. : *Loch Ness★★, SW : by A 82* **Z** *– Clava Cairns★, E : 9 m. by Culcabock Rd, B 9006 an 851* **Z** *– Cawdor Castle★ AC, NE : 14 m. by A 96 and B 9090* **Y**.
Culcabock Rd ℘ (01463) 239882 **Z** *– Torvean, Glenurquhart Rd ℘ (01463) 711434.*
Inverness Airport, Dalcross : ℘ (01667) 464000, NE : 8 m. by A 96 **Y**.
Castle Wynd ℘ (01463) 234353 **Y**.
Edinburgh 156 – Aberdeen 107 – Dundee 134.

Plan opposite

Inverness Marriott, Culcabock Rd, IV2 3LP, ℘ (01463) 237166, *Fax (01463) 225208,* – rest, – 60. Z
Meals 15.00/25.00 **st.** and dinner a la carte 6.50 – 12.50 – **75 rm** 120.00 **st.**, 7 suite SB.

Thistle Inverness, Millburn Rd, IV2 3TR, East : 1 m. on B 865 ℘ (01463) 239666, *inverns@thistle.co.uk, Fax (01463) 711145,* – – 230.
Meals 7.95/10.95 **st.** 7.95 – 11.95 – **117 rm** 127.00/147.00 **st.**, 1 suite – SB.

Jarvis Caledonian, 33 Church St., IV1 1DX, ℘ (01463) 235181, *caledonianinverness@is.co.uk, Fax (01463) 711206,* ≤, – rm, rest, – 300. Y
Waterside : **Meals** (dinner only) a la carte 12.15/28.10 **st.** 7.95 – ***Arts :*** **Meals** *(clos dinner in winter)* a la carte approx. 10.95 **st.** 7.95 – 8.95 – **103 rm** 109.00/159.00 3 suites – SB.

Craigmonie, 9 Annfield Rd, IV2 3HX, ℘ (01463) 231649, *info@craigmonie.cc Fax (01463) 233720,* – – 180. Z
closed 1-2 January, 24-26 and 31 December – ***Chardonnay :*** **Meals** - Seafood - (dinner o and Sunday lunch) 24.50/26.50 **t.** a la carte 9.00 – ***Conservatory :*** **Meals** (dinner only a Sunday lunch) a la carte 11.70/21.50 7.50 – **32 rm** 80.00/118.00 **t.**, 3 suites – SB.

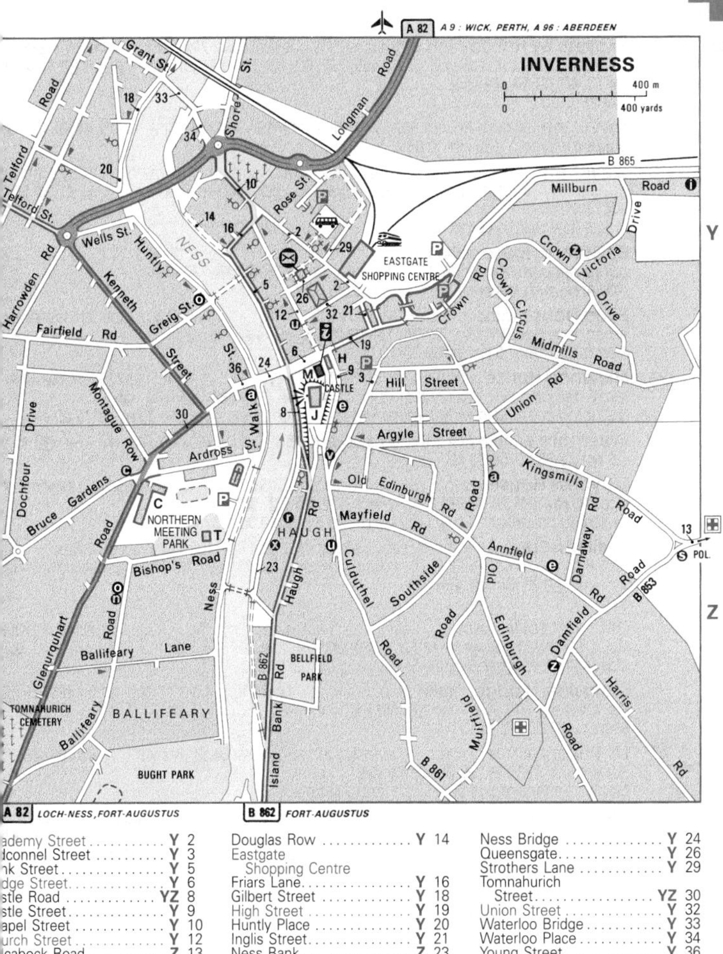

ademy Street .... Y 2
lconnel Street .... Y 3
nk Street .... Y 5
dge Street .... Y 6
stle Road .... YZ 8
stle Street .... Y 9
apel Street .... Y 10
urch Street .... Y 12
cabock Road .... Z 13
Douglas Row .... Y 14
Eastgate Shopping Centre
Friars Lane .... Y 16
Gilbert Street .... Y 18
High Street .... Y 19
Huntly Place .... Y 20
Inglis Street .... Y 21
Ness Bank .... Z 23
Ness Bridge .... Y 24
Queensgate .... Y 26
Strothers Lane .... Y 29
Tomnahurich Street ...... YZ 30
Union Street .... Y 32
Waterloo Bridge .... Y 33
Waterloo Place .... Y 34
Young Street .... Y 36

Glenmoriston Town House, 20 Ness Bank, IV2 4SF, ☎ (01463) 223777, *glenmoriston@cali.co.uk, Fax (01463) 712378* – TV ☏ P – 30. MC AE DC VISA. Z x
closed 26 December and 1-2 January – ***La Terrazza :*** **Meals** (lunch only) a la carte 15.15/21.40 **t.** 6.95 – (see also ***La Riviera*** below) – **15 rm** ☐ 85.00/135.00 **t.**

Glen Mhor, 9-12 Ness Bank, IV2 4SG, ☎ (01463) 234308, *user@glenmhor.co.uk, Fax (01463) 713170* – rm, TV ☏ & P. MC AE DC VISA. Z r
closed 1-2 January – ***Riverview :*** **Meals** *(closed in winter)* (dinner only) a la carte 13.40/30.40 **t.** 6.50 – ***Nico's :*** **Meals** a la carte approx. 25.30 **t.** 6.50 – **42 rm** ☐ 59.00/120.00 **t.**, 3 suites – SB.

Culduthel Lodge, 14 Culduthel Rd, IV2 4AG, ☎ (01463) 240089, *culduth@globalnet.co.uk, Fax (01463) 240089* – TV P. MC VISA Z u
closed 3 weeks spring, Christmas and New Year – **Meals** (booking essential) (residents only) (dinner only) 19.50/21.00 **t.** 5.00 – **11 rm** ☐ 45.00/110.00 **t.**, 1 suite.

Glendruidh House, Old Edinburgh Rd South, IV2 6AR, Southeast : 2 m. ☎ (01463) 226499, *michael@cozzee-nessie-bed.co.uk, Fax (01463) 710745*, – TV P. MC AE DC VISA JCB.
closed Christmas and New Year – **Meals** (residents only) (dinner only) 29.50 **t.** 8.50 – **5 rm** ☐ 79.00/135.00 **t.** – SB.

Express by Holiday Inn without rest., Stoneyfield, IV2 7PA, East : 1 ½ m. by A 865 on 96 (eastbound carriageway) ☎ (01463) 732700, *Fax (01463) 732732* – 30. MC AE VISA JCB
94 rm 52.50 **t.**

Travel Inn, Milburn Rd, IV2 3QX, ☎ (01463) 712010 – rm, MC AE VISA. Y
Meals (grill rest.) – **39 rm** 40.95 **t.**

Travel Inn, Beechwood Retail Park, IV2 3BW, Southeast : 2 m. on A 9 (northbound carriageway) ☎ (01463) 232727, *Fax (01463) 231553* – rm, rest, MC AE VISA
Meals (grill rest.) – **60 rm** 40.95 **t.**

Ballifeary House without rest., 10 Ballifeary Rd, IV3 5PJ, ☎ (01463) 235572, *ballifhotel@btinternet.com, Fax (01463) 717583*, – MC VISA JCB. Z
mid April-mid October – **5 rm** 58.00/76.00 **s.**

Eden House without rest., 8 Ballifeary Rd, IV3 5PJ, ☎ (01463) 230278, *edenhouse@btinternet.com, Fax (01463) 230278* – MC VISA. Z
March-October – **5 rm** 60.00/70.00.

Millwood House without rest., 36 Old Mill Rd, IV2 3HR, ☎ (01463) 237254, *millwood@ma96.demon.co.uk, Fax (01463) 719400*, – MC VISA JCB. Z
restricted opening in winter, minimum stay 2 nights July-August – **3 rm** 75.00 **s.**

Braemore without rest., 1 Victoria Drive, IV2 3QB, ☎ (01463) 243318, – – **3 rm** 35.00/60.00 **st.** Y

Moyness House without rest., 6 Bruce Gdns., IV3 5EN, ☎ (01463) 233836, *stay@moyness.co.uk, Fax (01463) 233836*, – MC VISA. Z
closed 20 December-11 January – **7 rm** 31.00/70.00 **st.**

Sealladh Sona without rest., 3 Whinpark, Canal Rd, Muirtown, IV3 8NQ, West : 1 ¼ m. by A 862 ☎ (01463) 239209, *cooksona@aol.com, Fax (01463) 239209*, « Canalside setting », – MC VISA JCB.
3 rm 32.00/60.00 **s.**

Old Rectory without rest., 9 Southside Rd, IV2 3BG, ☎ (01463) 22096... *Fax (01463) 220969*, – MC VISA JCB. Z
closed 20 December-5 January – **4 rm** 28.00/44.00.

Craigside Lodge without rest., 4 Gordon Terr., IV2 3HD, ☎ (01463) 23157... *Fax (01463) 713409*, ← – MC VISA. Z
6 rm 22.00/40.00.

La Riviera (at Glenmoriston Town House), 20 Ness Bank, IV2 4SF, ☎ (01463) 2237... *Fax (01463) 712378* – MC AE VISA Z
Meals (dinner only) 18.95/23.00 **t.** and a la carte 6.95.

Riverhouse, 1 Greig St., IV5 3PT, ☎ (01463) 222033, *Fax (01463) 220890* – MC AE VI... Y
closed 25 December-1 February – **Meals** *(closed Sunday and Monday)* (booking essential) (dinner only and lunch Thursday-Saturday) 25.95 **t.** 7.50.

Café 1, Castle St., IV2 3EA, ☎ (01463) 226200, *Fax (01463) 716363* – MC VISA JCB Y
closed last week November, 25 December, 1 January and Sunday – **Meals** a la carte 12.0... 24.25 **t.**

Riva, 4-6 Ness Walk, IV3 5NE, ☎ (01463) 237377, *Fax (01463) 224605* – MC VISA Y
closed 25 December, 1 January and Sunday lunch – **Meals** a la carte 12.35/25.90 **st.** 5.9...

at Culloden *East : 3 m. by A 96* – Y – ✉ *Inverness.*

Culloden House , IV2 7BZ, ☎ (01463) 790461, *reserv@cullodenhouse.co.uk, Fax (01463) 792181*, ←, « Georgian mansion », , , , – MC AE VISA JCB.
closed 25 December **Meals** 35.00 **st.** (dinner) and lunch a la carte 19.25/26.75 **st.** 15.00 – **22 rm** 145.00/270.00 **st.**, 6 suites – SB.

at Dunain Park *Southwest : 2½ m. on A 82* – Z – ✉ *Inverness.*

Dunain Park , IV3 8JN, ☎ (01463) 230512, *dunainparkhotel@btinternet.com, Fax (01463) 224532*, ←, « Country house, gardens », , – MC AE VISA.
Meals (lunch by arrangement)/dinner a la carte 27.85/29.85 **t.** 9.50 – **5 rm** 138.00/198.00 **t.**, **8 suites** 158.00/198.00 **t.** – SB.

at Bunchrew *West : 3 m. on A 862* – Y – ✉ *Inverness.*

Bunchrew House , IV3 8TA, ☎ (01463) 234917, *welcome@bunchrew-inverness.co.uk, Fax (01463) 710620*, ←, « Part 17C Scottish mansion on the shores of Beauly Firth », , – rest, MC AE VISA JCB
Meals a la carte 20.25/28.95 **t.** 9.00 – **11 rm** 135.00/190.00 **t.** – SB.

VERURIE *Aberdeenshire* 401 M 12 *Scotland G. – pop. 8 647.*

Exc. : *Castle Fraser★ (exterior★★) AC, SW : 6 m. by B 993 – Pitmedden Gardens★★, NE : 10 m. by B 9170 and A 920 – Haddo House★, N : 14 m. by B 9170 and B 9005 – Fyvie Castle★, N : 13 m. by B 9170 and A 947.*

Blackhall Rd ☎ (01467) 620207 – Kintore, Balbithan Rd ☎ (01467) 632631 – Kemnay, Monymusk Rd ☎ (01467) 642060.

18 High St. ☎ (01467) 625800.

Edinburgh 147 – Aberdeen 17 – Inverness 90.

Thainstone House H. & Country Club, AB51 5NT, South : 2 m. by B 993 off A 96 ☎ (01467) 621643, *info@thainstonehouse.macdonald.hotels.co.uk, Fax (01467) 625084,* – 300.
Simpson's : **Meals** 16.50/28.50 **st.** 8.00 – **47 rm** 50.00/100.00 **st.**, 1 suite – SB.

Strathburn, Burghmuir Drive, AB51 4GY, Northwest : 1 ¼ m. by Inverness rd (A 96) ☎ (01467) 624422, *strathburn@btconnect.com, Fax (01467) 625133,* – , rest, – 30.
closed 25-26 December and 1-2 January – **Meals** (bar dinner Sunday) a la carte 11.95/27.25 **st.** 5.25 – **25 rm** 70.00/100.00 **t.** – SB.

VINE *North Ayrshire* 401 F/G 17.

New St. ☎ (01294) 313886.

Edinburgh 76 – Ayr 15 – Glasgow 30 – Kilmarnock 8.

Thistle, 46 Annick Rd, KA11 4LD, Southeast : 1 m. on B 7081 ☎ (01294) 274272, *irvine@thistle.co.uk, Fax (01294) 277287,* – rm, – 250.
Mirage : **Meals** (dinner only) a la carte 12.00/21.00 **st.** 12.00 – ***Lagoon :*** **Meals** 12.00/25.00 **st.** 12.00 – 10.95 – **128 rm** 128.00/178.00 **st.** – SB.

LAY (Isle of) *Argyll and Bute* 401 B 16 – *pop. 3 840.*

Western Cottage, Port Ellen ☎ (01496) 302409.

Port Ellen Airport : ☎ (01496) 302022.

from Port Askaig to Isle of Jura (Feolin) (Serco Denholm Ltd) frequent services daily (approx. 4 mn) – from Port Ellen or Port Askaig to Kintyre Peninsula (Kennacraig) (Caledonian MacBrayne Ltd) 1-2 daily – from Port Askaig to Oban via Isle of Colonsay (Scalasaig) (Caledonian MacBrayne Ltd) weekly – from Port Askaig to Isle of Colonsay (Scalasaig) and Kintyre Peninsula (Kennacraig) (Caledonian MacBrayne Ltd) weekly.

at Bowmore, The Square ☎ (01496) 810254.

allygrant.

Kilmeny Country Guest House, PA45 7QW, Southwest : ½ m. on A 846 ☎ (01496) 840668, *Fax (01496) 840668,* « Working farm », –
closed Christmas and New Year – **Meals** (by arrangement) (communal dining) – **3 rm** (dinner included) 70.00/120.00 **s.**

owmore.

Harbour Inn with rm, The Square, PA43 7JR, ☎ (01496) 810330, *harbour@harbour_inn.com, Fax (01496) 810990* –
Meals *(closed Sunday lunch and Sunday dinner October-March)* a la carte 16.00/24.25 **st.** 6.25 – **8 rm** 42.00/85.00 **st.**

idgend – *Bowmore.*

Bridgend, PA44 7PQ, ☎ (01496) 810212, *Fax (01496) 810960,* –
Meals (bar lunch)/dinner 17.50/22.50 **t.** – **10 rm** 43.50/87.00 **t.**

ort Charlotte.

Port Charlotte, Main St., PA48 7TU, ☎ (01496) 850360, *carl@portcharlottehot.demon.co.uk, Fax (01496) 850361,* –
closed 25 December – **Meals** (light lunch)/dinner a la carte 15.55/36.00 **st.** 7.95 – **10 rm** 55.00/85.00 **st.**

ort Ellen.

Glenmachrie Farmhouse, PA42 7AW, Northwest : 4 ½ m. on A 846 ☎ (01496) 302560, *glenmachrie@isle-of-islay.com, Fax (01496) 302560,* « Working farm », –
Meals (by arrangement) 20.00 **s.** – **5 rm** 40.00/60.00 **s.**

ISLEORNSAY *Highland* 401 C 12 – *see Skye (Isle of).*

JEDBURGH *Borders* 401 402 M 17 *Scotland G. – pop. 4 768.*

See : *Town★ - Abbey★★* **AC** *– Mary Queen of Scots House Visitor Centre★* **AC** *– T Canongate Bridge★.*

Env. : *Waterloo Monument (★★) N : 4 m. by A 68 and B 6400.*

Jedburgh, Dunion Rd ☎ (01835) 863587.

Murray's Green ☎ (01835) 863435.

Edinburgh 48 – Carlisle 54 – Newcastle upon Tyne 57.

Jedforest, Camptown, TD8 6PJ, South : 4 m. on A 68 ☎ (01835) 840222, *mail@jedfores otel.freeserve.co.uk, Fax (01835) 840226,* – P. VISA JCB
Bardoulets : Meals a la carte 13.20/28.45 **st.** 8.95 – **8 rm** 70.00/115.00 **st.** – SB.

Glenfriars Country House, The Friars, TD8 6BN, ☎ (01835) 8620(*Fax (01835) 862000,* – P. VISA
closed 23-30 December – **Meals** (booking essential) (dinner only) 17.50 **t.** 6.00 – **6** 37.00/80.00 **t.** – SB.

Hundalee House without rest., TD8 6PA, South : 1 ½ m. by A 68 ☎ (01835) 86301 *heila.whittaker@btinternet.com, Fax (01835) 863011,* – P.
15 March-October – **5 rm** 25.00/46.00 **s.**

The Spinney without rest., Langlee, TD8 6PB, South : 2 m. on A 68 ☎ (01835) 863525, *espinney@btinternet.com, Fax (01835) 864883,* – P. VISA.
mid March-mid November – **3 rm** 44.00/50.00 **st.**

JOHN O'GROATS *Highland* 401 K 8 – *Shipping Services : see Orkney Islands.*

JOHNSTONE *Renfrewshire* 401 G 16 – *pop. 18 635.*

Cochrane Castle, Scott Av., Craigstone ☎ (01505) 320146.

Edinburgh 58 – Ayr 35 – Glasgow 13 – Greenock 18.

Shimla Pinks, 4 William St., PA5 8DS, ☎ (01505) 322588 – VISA
closed 1 January – **Meals** - Indian - (dinner only) a la carte 11.10/19.85 **t.**

JURA (Isle of) *Argyll and Bute* 401 C 15 – *pop. 196.*

from Feolin to Isle of Islay (Port Askaig) (Serco Denholm Ltd) frequent services d (approx. 4 mn).

Craighouse – ✉ *Jura.*

Jura, PA60 7XU, ☎ (01496) 820243, *jurahotel@aol.com, Fax (01496) 820249,* Small Is Bay, – P. VISA
closed 2 weeks Christmas and New Year – **Meals** (bar lunch)/dinner a la carte 14.9 19.75 **st.** – **17 rm** 32.00/76.00.

KELSO *Borders* 401 402 M 17 *Scotland G. – pop. 6 167.*

See : *Town★ – The Square★★ – ★ from Kelso Bridge.*

Env. : *Tweed Valley★★ – Floors Castle★* **AC**, *NW : 1½ m. by A 6089.*

Exc. : *Mellerstain★★ (Ceilings★★★, Library★★★)* **AC**, *NW : 6 m. by A 6089 – Waterloo Mor ment (★★), SW : 7 m. by A 698 and B 6400 – Jedburgh Abbey★★* **AC**, *SW : 8½ m. by A 6 – Dryburgh Abbey★★* **AC** *(setting★★★), SW : 10½ m. by A 6089, B 6397 and B 6404 – Scot View★★, W : 11 m. by A 6089, B 6397, B 6404 and B 6356 – Smailholm Tower★ (★★), NW m. by A 6089 and B 6397 – Lady Kirk (Kirk o'Steil★), NE : 16 m. by A 698, A 697, A 6112 an 6437.*

Berrymoss Racecourse Rd ☎ (01573) 23009.

Town House, The Square ☎ (01573) 223464 (summer only).

Edinburgh 44 – Hawick 21 – Newcastle upon Tyne 68.

The Roxburghe, Heiton, TD5 8JZ, Southwest : 3 ½ m. by A 698 ☎ (01573) 450331 *otel@roxburghe.net, Fax (01573) 450611,* « Jacobean style country house », – P. – 60. VISA
closed 24-29 December **Meals** closed lunch Monday 14.50/25.00 **t.** and a la carte 10.5(**21 rm** 120.00/165.00 **t.**, 1 suite.

Ednam House, Bridge St., TD5 7HT, ☎ (01573) 224168, *ednamhouse@excite.co. Fax (01573) 226319,* « Part Georgian mansion on the banks of the River Tweed », – rm, P. – 200. VISA
closed Christmas-8 January **Meals** 11.50/20.00 **st.** (dinner) and lunch a la carte 9.2 16.80 **st.** – **32 rm** 62.00/115.00 **st.** – SB.

Ednam *North : 2¼ m. on B 6461 – ✉ Kelso.*

Edenwater House ⑤, TD5 7QL, off Stichill rd ☎ (01573) 224070, *Fax (01573) 224070,* ≤, – ⅍ TV P. MC VISA JCB. ⅌
closed first 2 weeks January and last 2 weeks May – **Meals** *(closed Sunday-Thursday to non-residents)* (booking essential) (dinner only) 30.00 **st.** 6.00 – **3 rm** 55.00/75.00 **st.** – SB.

KENMORE *Perthshire and Kinross* 401 I 14 *Scotland G. – pop. 596.*
See : *Village*★.
Env. : *Loch Tay*★★.
Exc. : *Ben Lawers*★★, *SW : 8 m. by A 827.*
18 *Taymouth Castle, Aberfeldy ☎ (01887) 830228* – 18, 9 *Mains of Taymouth ☎ (01887) 830226.*
Edinburgh 82 – Dundee 60 – Oban 71 – Perth 38.

Kenmore, PH15 2NU, ☎ (01887) 830205, *reservations@kenmorehotel.com, Fax (01887) 830262,* ≤, 18, – ⅍ rest, TV P – 35. MC AE VISA
Meals a la carte 11.75/27.15 **st.** – **39 rm** 70.00/125.00 **st.** – SB.

KENTALLEN *Highland* 401 E 14 – ✉ *Appin (Argyll and Bute).*
Edinburgh 123 – Fort William 17 – Oban 33.

Ardsheal House ⑤, PA38 4BX, Southwest : ¾ m. by A 828 ☎ (01631) 740227, *info@ardsheal.co.uk, Fax (01631) 740342,* ≤, « Part 18C country house », – ⅍ rest, P. MC AE VISA JCB
closed January and December – **Meals** (residents only) (dinner only) (set menu only) 25.00 **st.** 10.00 – **8 rm** 45.00/90.00 **st.**

KILBERRY *Argyll and Bute* 401 D 16 – *see Kintyre (Peninsula).*

KILCHOAN *Highland* 401 B 13 – ✉ *Acharacle.*
Argyll ☎ (01972) 510222.
Edinburgh 163 – Inverness 120 – Oban 84.

Far View Cottage ⑤, Mingary Pier Rd, PH36 4LH, ☎ (01972) 510357, *Fax (01972) 510357,* ≤ Sound of Mull, – ⅍ TV P. ⅌
*closed 1 week January***Meals** – **3 rm** (dinner included) 60.00/100.00 **st.**

KILCHRENAN *Argyll and Bute* 401 E 14 *Scotland G.* – ✉ *Taynuilt.*
Env. : *Loch Awe*★★, *E : 1¼m.*
Edinburgh 117 – Glasgow 87 – Oban 18.

Ardanaiseig ⑤, PA35 1HE, Northeast : 4 m. ☎ (01866) 833333, *ardanaiseig@clara.net, Fax (01866) 833222,* ≤ gardens and Loch Awe, « Country house in extensive informal gardens beside Loch Awe », – ⅍ rest, TV P. MC AE VISA
closed 2 January-8 Febuary – **Meals** (dinner only and Sunday lunch)/dinner 38.50 **t.** 9.50 – **16 rm** 124.00/230.00 **t.** – SB.

Taychreggan ⑤, PA35 1HQ, Southeast : 1 ¼ m. ☎ (01866) 833211, *taychreggan@btinternet.com, Fax (01866) 833244,* ≤ Loch Awe and mountains, « Lochside setting », – ⅍ P. MC AE VISA
Meals 35.00 **t.** 9.00 – **18 rm** 120.00/126.00 **t.**, 1 suite – SB.

KILDRUMMY *Aberdeenshire* 401 L 12 *Scotland G.* – ✉ *Alford.*
See : *Castle*★ *AC.*
Exc. : *Huntly Castle (Heraldic carvings*★★★*) N : 15 m. by A 97 – Craigievar Castle*★, *SE : 13 m. by A 97, A 944 and A 980.*
Edinburgh 137 – Aberdeen 35.

Kildrummy Castle ⑤, AB33 8RA, South : 1 ¼ m. on A 97 ☎ (019755) 71288, *bookings@kildrummycastlehotel.co.uk, Fax (019755) 71345,* ≤ gardens and Kildrummy Castle, « 19C mansion in extensive park », – ⅍ rest, TV P. MC AE VISA JCB
closed January – **Meals** 17.50/32.00 **st.** and a la carte 6.50 – **16 rm** 90.00/170.00 **st.** – SB.

KILLEARN *Stirling* 401 G 15 – ✉ *Glasgow.*
Edinburgh 60 – Glasgow 19 – Perth 55 – Stirling 22.

Black Bull, 2 The Square, G63 9NG, ✆ (01360) 550215, *Fax (01360) 550143,* rm, TV P. MC AE VISA.
Meals *(closed Sunday dinner)* a la carte 11.85/20.85 **st.** – **11 rm** 50.00/70.00 **st.** – SB.

KILLIECHRONAN *Argyll and Bute* 401 C 14 – *see Mull (Isle of).*

KILLIECRANKIE *Perthshire and Kinross* 401 I 13 – *see Pitlochry.*

KILLIN *Stirling* 401 H 14 *Scotland G.* – *pop. 1 108.*
Exc. : *Loch Tay★★, Ben Lawers★★, NE : 8 m. by A 827 – Loch Earn★★, SE : 7 m. by A 827 a A 85.*
Killin ✆ (01567) 820312.
Breadalbane Folklore Centre, Falls of Dochart, Main St. ✆ (01567) 820254 (March-Oc ber).
Edinburgh 72 – Dundee 65 – Perth 43 – Oban 54.

Dall Lodge Country House, Main St., FK21 8TN, ✆ (01567) 820217, *wilson@dalllodg otel.co.uk, Fax (01567) 820726,* – , rest, TV P. MC VISA JCB
March-October – **Meals** (dinner only) 18.50/24.50 **t.** 6.90 – **10 rm** 45.50/105.00 **st** SB.

Breadalbane House without rest., Main St., FK21 8UT, ✆ (01567) 820134, *stay@brea bane48.freeserve.co.uk, Fax (01567) 820798* – TV P. MC VISA JCB.
closed 15 December-February – **5 rm** 33.00/45.00.

at Ardeonaig *(Perthshire and Kinross) Northeast : 6 ¾ m.* – ✉ *Killin (Stirling).*

Ardeonaig, South Lochtayside, FK21 8SU, ✆ (01567) 820400, *ardeonaighotel@btir rnet.com, Fax (01567) 820282,* – rest, P. MC VISA JCB
restricted opening November-March – **Meals** (dinner only) 34.50 **t.** 7.35 – **12 rm** (dinner included) 83.00/151.00 **t.** – SB.

KILMARNOCK *East Ayrshire* 401 402 G 17 *Scotland G.*
See : *Dean Castle (arms and armour★, musical instruments★).*
62 Bank St. ✆ (01563) 539090.
Edinburgh 64 – Ayr 13 – Glasgow 25.

Travel Inn, Moorfield, KA1 2RS, Southwest : 2 m. by A 759 at junction with A ✆ (01563) 570534, *Fax (01563) 570536* – , rest, TV P. MC AE VISA.
Meals (grill rest.) – **40 rm** 40.95 **t.**

Travelodge, Kilmarnock bypass, Bellfield Interchange, KA1 5LQ, Southeast : 1 ½ m. b 735 at junction of A 71 with A 76 and A 77 ✆ (01563) 573810, *Fax (01563) 573810* – r TV P. MC AE VISA JCB.
Meals (grill rest.) – **40 rm** 39.95 **t.**

KILMORE *Argyll and Bute* 401 D 14 – *see Oban.*

KILNINVER *Argyll and Bute* 401 D 14 – *see Oban.*

KINCLAVEN *Perthshire and Kinross* 401 J 14 – *pop. 394* – ✉ *Stanley.*
Edinburgh 56 – Perth 12.

Ballathie House, Stanley, PH1 4QN, ✆ (01250) 883268, *email@ballathiehousehote om, Fax (01250) 883396,* « Country house in extensive grounds on banks of River Tay – rest, TV P – 60. MC AE VISA
Meals 18.50/35.00 **t.** and a la carte – **39 rm** (dinner included) 105.00/210.00 4 suites – SB.

KINCRAIG *Highland* 401 I 12 *Scotland G.* – ✉ *Kingussie.*
See : *Highland Wildlife Park★ AC.*
Exc. : *The Cairngorms★★ (★★★) – ★★★ from Cairn Gorm, E : 14 m. by A 9 and B 970.*
Edinburgh 119 – Inverness 37 – Perth 75.

Ossian, The Brae, PH21 1QD, ☎ (01540) 651242, *Fax (01540) 651633*, ≤, ⛵, 🌳 – ⇹ rest, TV P. MC VISA JCB
closed January and November – **Meals** (bar lunch)/dinner a la carte 18.45/26.75 **t.** 5.95 – **9 rm** 31.00/62.00 **st.**

INGUSSIE *Highland* 401 H 12 *Scotland G. – pop. 1 298.*
Env. : *Highland Wildlife Park★ AC, NE : 4 m. by A 9.*
Exc. : *Aviemore★, NE : 11 m. by A 9 – The Cairngorms★★ (≤★★★) – ✳★★★ from Cairn Gorm, NE : 18 m. by B 970.*
18 Gynack Rd ☎ (01540) 661374.
King St. ☎ (01540) 661297 (May-September).
Edinburgh 117 – Inverness 41 – Perth 73.

Scot House, Newtonmore Rd, PH21 1HE, ☎ (01540) 661351, *shh@sirocco.globalnet.co.uk, Fax (01540) 661111* – ⇹ TV P. MC VISA JCB
closed January and 25 December – **Meals** (bar lunch)/dinner a la carte 20.80/30.30 **t.** 6.55 – **9 rm** (dinner included) 59.50/110.00 **t.** – SB.

Columba House, Manse Rd, PH21 1JF, ☎ (01540) 661402, *reservations@columba-hotel.co.uk, Fax (01540) 661652*, 🌳 – ⇹ TV P. MC AE ⓓ VISA JCB
Meals 18.00 **t.** (dinner) and lunch a la carte 10.95/17.15 **t.** 5.65 – **8 rm** 48.00/75.00 **t.** – SB.

Hermitage, Spey St., PH21 1HN, ☎ (01540) 662137, *thehermitage@clara.net, Fax (01540) 662177*, 🌳 – ⇹ rest, TV P. MC VISA. ⊘
closed first 2 weeks November and Christmas – **Meals** (by arrangement) 15.00 4.75 – **5 rm** 26.00/46.00 – SB.

Avondale, Newtonmore Rd, PH21 1HF, ☎ (01540) 661731, *walsh.lorraine@talk21.com, Fax (01540) 661731*, 🌳 – ⇹ TV P
Meals (by arrangement) 10.00 – **6 rm** 18.00/42.00 – SB.

Homewood Lodge ⛰, Newtonmore Rd, PH21 1HD, ☎ (01540) 661507, *homewood-lodge@bigfoot.com, Fax (01540) 661507*, ≤, 🌳 – ⇹ TV P
Meals (by arrangement) 10.00 **st.** – **4 rm** 20.00/40.00 **st.** – SB.

The Cross ⛰ with rm, Tweed Mill Brae, Ardbroilach Rd, PH21 1TC, ☎ (01540) 661166, *relax@thecross.co.uk, Fax (01540) 661080*, « Converted tweed mill » – ⇹ P. MC VISA. ⊘
March-November – **Meals** *(closed Tuesday)* (booking essential) (dinner only) 37.50 **st.** 4.95 – **9 rm** (dinner included) 115.00/230.00 **st.**

INROSS *Perthshire and Kinross* 401 J 15 – *pop. 5 047.*
18, 18 Green Hotel, 2 The Muirs ☎ (01577) 863407 – 9 Milnathort, South St. ☎ (01577) 864069 – 9 Bishopshire, Kinnesswood ☎ (01592) 780203.
Kinross Service Area, junction 6, M 90 ☎ (01577) 863680.
Edinburgh 28 – Dunfermline 13 – Perth 18 – Stirling 25.

The Green, 2 The Muirs, KY13 8AS, ☎ (01577) 863467, *reservations@green-hotel.com, Fax (01577) 863180*, ≘s, 🏊, 18, ⛵, 🌳, 🎾, squash – ⇹ rm, TV ☎ P – 🏔 140. MC AE ⓓ VISA JCB
accommodation closed 21-29 December – **Meals** (bar lunch)/dinner 25.00/27.50 **t.** 5.50 – **46 rm** 78.00/155.00 **t.** – SB.

Windlestrae, The Muirs, KY13 8AS, ☎ (01577) 863217, *Fax (01577) 864733*, Fø, ≘s, 🏊, 🌳 – ⇹ rm, TV ♿ P – 🏔 200. MC AE ⓓ VISA JCB
Meals (bar lunch Monday-Saturday)/dinner 21.30/30.00 6.00 – **43 rm** 94.50/114.50 **t.**, 2 suites – SB.

Cleish *Southwest : 4½ m. by B 996 off B 9097 – ✉ Kinross.*

Nivingston House ⛰, KY13 0LS, ☎ (01577) 850216, *info@nivingstonhousehotel.co.uk, Fax (01577) 850238*, ≤, 🌳, ⛳ – ⇹ rest, TV P – 🏔 60. MC AE VISA
Blues : **Meals** 16.50/27.50 **t.** 11.00 – **17 rm** 85.00/140.00 **st.** – SB.

NTORE *Aberdeenshire* 401 M 12.
Edinburgh 136 – Aberdeen 14 – Inverness 91.

Torryburn, School Rd, AB51 0XP, ☎ (01467) 632269, *Fax (01467) 632271*, 🌳, 🎾 – ⇹ TV P – 🏔 100. MC AE VISA JCB. ⊘
closed 1 January – **Meals** (bar lunch Monday to Friday) a la carte 11.65/24.40 **st.** – **8 rm** 39.50/62.50 **st.**

Your recommendation is self-evident if you always walk into a hotel Guide in hand.

KINTYRE (Peninsula) *Argyll and Bute* 401 D 16 *Scotland G.*

See : *Carradale★ – Saddell (Collection of grave slabs★).*

18, 9 *Machrihanish, Campbeltown ✆ (01586) 810213 –* 18 *Dunaverty, Southend, Cam beltown ✆ (01586) 830677 –* 9 *Gigha, Isle of Gigha ✆ (01583) 505287.*

Campbeltown Airport : ✆ (01586) 553797.

from Claonaig to Isle of Arran (Lochranza) (Caledonian MacBrayne Ltd) freque services daily (30 mn) – from Kennacraig to Isle of Islay (Port Ellen or Port Askaig) (Calec nian MacBrayne Ltd) 1-3 daily – from Kennacraig to Oban via Isle of Colonsay (Scalasaig) a Isle of Islay (Port Askaig) weekly.

Campbeltown.

MacKinnon House, The Pier ✆ (01586) 552056.
Edinburgh 176.

Seafield, Kilkerran Rd, PA28 6JL, ✆ (01586) 554385, *Fax (01586) 552741* – TV P. MC AE
Meals a la carte 13.10/27.20 **t.** 5.95 – **9 rm** 45.00/70.00 **t.** – SB.

Rosemount without rest., Low Askomil, PA28 6EN, ✆ (01586) 553552, ←, – TV P
5 rm 25.00/42.00 **s.**

Kilberry.

Edinburgh 165 – Glasgow 121 – Oban 75.

Kilberry Inn with rm, PA29 6YD, ✆ (01880) 770223, *Fax (01880) 770223* – TV
MC VISA
mid March-mid October – **Meals** *(closed Sunday)* a la carte 13.45/24.15 **t.** 6.25 – **3 r** 42.50/73.00 **st.**

Machrihanish – *pop. 5 722 – ✉ Campbeltown.*

Edinburgh 182 – Oban 95.

Ardell House without rest., PA28 6PT, ✆ (01586) 810235, *Fax (01586) 810235*, ←,
TV P. MC VISA JCB.
March-October – **9 rm** 30.00/62.00 **s.**

Tarbert.

9 *Kilberry Rd, Tarbert ✆ (01880) 820565.*
Harbour St. ✆ (01880) 820429 (April-October).

Columba, East Pier Rd, PA29 6UF, East : ¾ m. ✆ (01880) 820808, *Fax (01880) 820808*, – rest, TV P. MC AE VISA
closed 24-26 December – **Meals** (bar lunch)/dinner 21.50 **t.** 6.50 – **9 rm** 35.95/71.90 1 suite – SB.

Anchorage, Harbour St., PA29 6UD, ✆ (01880) 820881, *Fax (01880) 820881* – MC VISA
closed January, Sunday and Monday October-May – **Meals** (dinner only) a la carte 17.8 25.15 **t.**

KIRKCOLM *Dumfries and Galloway* 401 402 E 19 – *see Stranraer.*

KIRKCUDBRIGHT *Dumfries and Galloway* 401 402 H 19 *Scotland G. – pop. 4 188.*

See : *Town★.*
Env. : *Dundrennan Abbey★ AC, SE : 5 m. by A 711.*
18 *Stirling Cres. ✆ (01557) 330314.*
Harbour Sq. ✆ (01557) 330494 (summer only).
Edinburgh 108 – Dumfries 28 – Stranraer 50.

Selkirk Arms, High St., DG6 4JG, ✆ (01557) 330402, *reception@selkirkarmshotel.co. Fax (01557) 331639*, – TV P. MC AE VISA JCB
Meals (bar lunch)/dinner 22.95 **st.** 5.25 – **16 rm** 62.00/90.00 **st.** – SB.

Baytree House, 110 High St., DG6 4JQ, ✆ (01557) 330824, *baytree@currantbun.cc Fax (01557) 330824*, « Georgian town house », – TV P.
Meals 16.50 **s.** – **3 rm** 37.00/60.00 **s.**

Gladstone House without rest., 48 High St., DG6 4JX, ✆ (01557) 3317 *Fax (01557) 331734*, – TV. MC VISA.
closed Christmas and New Year – **3 rm** 39.00/60.00.

Les prix — Pour toutes précisions sur les prix indiqués dans ce guide, reportez-vous aux pages de l'introduction.

IRKMICHAEL *Perthshire and Kinross* 401 J 13.
Edinburgh 73 – Aberdeen 85 – Inverness 102 – Perth 29.

Cruachan Country Cottage, PH10 7NZ, on A 924 ☎ (01250) 881226, *michael@kirkmichael.net, Fax (01250) 881226,* – TV P. MC VISA
Meals (by arrangement) a la carte 12.05/17.75 **t.** – **3 rm** 28.50/47.00 **t.**

IRKNEWTON *Edinburgh* 401 J 16 – *see Edinburgh.*

IRKTON OF MARYCULTER *Aberdeenshire* 401 N 12 – *see Aberdeen.*

IRKWALL *Orkney Islands* 401 L 7 – *see Orkney Islands (Mainland).*

IRRIEMUIR *Angus* 401 K 13 – *pop. 6 347.*
Cumberland Close ☎ (01575) 574097.
Edinburgh 65 – Aberdeen 50 – Dundee 16 – Perth 30.

Purgavie Farm, Lintrathen, DD8 5HZ, West : 6 ¾ m. on B 951 ☎ (01575) 560213, *purgavie@aol.com, Fax (01575) 560213,* ≤ – TV P
Meals (communal dining) 15.00 **st.** – **3 rm** 30.00/50.00 **st.**

YLE OF LOCHALSH *Highland* 401 C 12 – *pop. 1 019.*
Car park, Inverness-shire ☎ (01599) 534276.
Edinburgh 207 – Dundee 177 – Inverness 81 – Oban 123.

The Seafood, Railway Station, IV40 8AE, ☎ (01599) 534813, *theseafoodrestaurant@fs.business.co.uk, Fax (01599) 577230,* – rest. MC VISA
Easter-October – **Meals** - Seafood - a la carte 15.50/22.25 **t.**

YLESKU *Highland* 401 E 9 *Scotland G.*
Env. : *Loch Assynt★★, S : 6 m. by A 894.*
Edinburgh 256 – Inverness 100 – Ullapool 34.

Newton Lodge, IV27 4HW, South : 2 m. on A 894 ☎ (01971) 502070, *newtonlge@aol.com, Fax (01971) 502070,* ≤ Loch Glencoul and mountains – TV P. MC VISA.
mid March-September – **Meals** (residents only) (dinner only) 15.00 **t.** 5.60 – **7 rm** 60.00 **t.**

ADYBANK *Fife* 401 K 15 *Scotland G.* – *pop. 1 373.*
Env. : *Falkland★ – Palace of Falkland★ – Gardens★ – Village★, S : ½ m. by A 914 on A 912.*
Ladybank, Annsmuir ☎ (01337) 830320.
Edinburgh 38 – Dundee 20 – Stirling 40.

Redlands Country Lodge, Pitlessie Rd, KY15 7SH, East : ¾ m. by Kingskettle rd taking first left after railway bridge on unmarked road ☎ (01337) 831091, *Fax (01337) 831091,* – TV P. MC VISA
closed December and January – **Meals** (by arrangement) 12.00 – **4 rm** 40.00/50.00 – SB.

AIDE *Highland* 401 D 10 – ✉ *Gairloch.*
Edinburgh 233 – Inverness 75 – Kyle of Lochalsh 85.

The Old Smiddy, IV22 2NB, on A 832 ☎ (01445) 731425, *oldsmiddy@aol.com, Fax (01445) 731425,* – P. MC VISA
closed December and January – **Meals** (by arrangement) 25.00 **t.** – **3 rm** (dinner included) 40.00/80.00 **t.**

AIRG *Highland* 401 G9 – *pop. 857.*
Sutherland ☎ (01549) 402160.
Edinburgh 218 – Inverness 61 – Wick 72.

Park House, IV27 4AU, ☎ (01549) 402208, *dwalkerparkhouse@tinyworld.co.uk, Fax (01549) 402693,* ≤, – rest, TV P. MC VISA JCB
closed Christmas and New Year – **Meals** 16.00 8.75 – **3 rm** (dinner included) 54.00/96.00 – SB.

AMLASH *North Ayrshire* 401 E 17 – *see Arran (Isle of).*

LANGBANK *Renfrewshire* 401 G 16 *Scotland G.*
Env. : *Greenock (≤★★), W : 6 m. by A 8.*
Edinburgh 63 – Glasgow 17 – Greenock 7.

Gleddoch House, PA14 6YE, Southeast : 1 m. by B 789 ☎ (01475) 54071 *Fax (01475) 540201,* ≤ Clyde and countryside, 18, – TV P – 40. MC AE VISA
Meals 20.00/35.00 **t.** and a la carte 6.75 – ***La Gioconda*** *(☎ (01475) 540304)* **: Meals** Italian - *(closed Sunday and Monday)* 8.95 **st.** (lunch) and dinner a la carte 22.95/27.95 5.50 – **38 rm** 99.00/180.00 **st.** – SB.

LARGS *North Ayrshire* 401 402 F 16 *Scotland G. – pop. 11 297.*
See : *Largs Old Kirk★ AC.*
18 *Irvine Rd ☎ (01475) 674681.*
to Great Cumbrae Island (Cumbrae Slip) (Caledonian MacBrayne Ltd) frequent servic daily (10 mn).
Promenade ☎ (01475) 673765.
Edinburgh 76 – Ayr 32 – Glasgow 30.

Priory House, Broomfield Pl., KA30 8DH, South : ½ m. by A 78 and Charles ☎ (01475) 686460, *enquiries@maksu-group.co.uk, Fax (01475) 689070,* ≤, – TV P 60. MC AE VISA
Meals 7.00/25.00 **st.** and a la carte 6.95 – **21 rm** 75.00/95.00 **st.** – SB.

Brisbane House, 14 Greenock Rd, Esplanade, KA30 8NF, ☎ (01475) 687200, *enquirie maksu_group.co.uk, Fax (01475) 676295,* ≤ – TV P. MC AE VISA.
Meals (bar lunch)/dinner 15.75/19.75 **t.** and a la carte 6.95 – **23 rm** 70.00/120.00 **t** SB.

LAUDER *Berwickshire* 401 L 16 *– pop. 2 199.*
9 *Galashiels Rd ☎ (01578) 722526.*
Edinburgh 27 – Berwick-upon-Tweed 34 – Carlisle 74 – Newcastle-upon-Tyne 77.

The Lodge, Carfraemill, TD2 6RA, Northwest : 4 m. by A 68 on A 697 ☎ (01578) 75075C *nquiries@carfraemill.co.uk, Fax (01578) 750751* – TV P – 150. MC AE VISA JCB.
Meals (grill rest.) a la carte 14.50/22.00 4.95 – **10 rm** 48.00/70.00 **t.** – SB.

LEITH *Edinburgh* 401 K 16 *– see Edinburgh.*

LERWICK *Shetland Islands* 401 Q 3 *– see Shetland Islands (Mainland).*

LESLIE *Fife* 401 K 15 *– pop. 3 269.*
Edinburgh 35 – Dundee 26 – Perth 25 – Stirling 33.

Rescobie House, 6 Valley Drive, KY6 3BQ, ☎ (01592) 749555, *rescobiehotel@compus e.com, Fax (01592) 620231,* – TV P. MC AE VISA JCB
closed Christmas and New Year – **Meals** (booking essential) (Sunday and Monday reside only) (dinner only) 17.95 **st.** 7.50 – **10 rm** 45.00/85.00 **st.** – SB.

LEUCHARS *Fife* 401 L 14 *– pop. 5 207.*
Edinburgh 54 – Dundee 7 – Perth 29 – Stirling 52.

Drumoig, KY16 0BE, Northwest : 3 m. by A 919 off A 914 ☎ (01382) 541800, *drumoig@ .co.uk, Fax (01382) 541122,* ≤, , , 18 – TV P. MC AE VISA.
Meals 10.95/17.50 **st.** and a la carte 7.55 – **29 rm** (dinner included) 65.00/175.00 **st** SB.

LEVERBURGH *Western Isles (Outer Hebrides)* 401 Y 10 *– see Lewis and Harris (Isle of).*

Cet ouvrage n'est pas un répertoire de tous les hôtels et restaurants,
ni même de tous les bons hôtels et restaurants de Grande-Bretagne et d'Irlande.
Comme nous cherchons à rendre service à tous les touristes
nous sommes amenés à indiquer des établissements
de toutes les classes et à n'en citer que quelques-uns de chaque sorte.

EWIS and HARRIS (Isle of) *Western Isles (Outer Hebrides)* 401 A 9 *Scotland G.*

See : *Callanish Standing Stones★★ – Carloway Broch★ – St. Clement's Church, Rodel (tomb★).*

from Stornoway to Ullapool (Mainland) (Caledonian MacBrayne Ltd) 2 daily (2 h 40 mn) – from Kyles Scalpay to the Isle of Scalpay (Caledonian MacBrayne Ltd) (10 mn) – from Tarbert to Isle of Skye (Uig) (Caledonian MacBrayne Ltd) 1-2 daily (1 h 45 mn) – from Tarbert to Portavadie (Caledonian MacBrayne Ltd) (summer only) frequent services daily (25 mn) – from Leverburgh to North Uist (Otternish) (Caledonian MacBrayne Ltd) (1 h 10 mn).

SCOTLAND

LEWIS.

reasclete.

Eshcol, 21 Breasclete, HS2 9ED, (01851) 621357, *Fax (01851) 621357*, – TV P.
closed 2 weeks Christmas and New Year – **Meals** (by arrangement) 18.00 – **3 rm** 39.00/62.00 **st.**

Loch Roag, 22A Breasclete, HS2 9EF, (01851) 621357, *Fax (01851) 621357*, – TV P.
closed 2 weeks Christmas and New Year – **Meals** (by arrangement) 18.00 – **4 rm** 27.00/54.00 **st.**

alson.

Galson Farm, South Galson, HS2 0SH, (01851) 850492, *galsonfarm@yahoo.com*, *Fax (01851) 850492*, « Working farm », – P. MC VISA
Meals (by arrangement) (communal dining) 19.95 **s.** – **3 rm** 35.00/58.00 **s.** – SB.

tornoway.

Lady Lever Park (01851) 702240.
26 Cromwell St. (01851) 703088.

Cabarfeidh, Manor Park, HS1 2EU, North : ½ m. on A 859 (01851) 702604, *cabarfeidh@calahotels.com*, *Fax (01851) 705572* – , rest, TV P – 300. MC AE DC VISA
closed 1-14 January – **Meals** 21.50 **st.** (dinner) and a la carte 23.50/29.95 **st.** 7.50 – **46 rm** 72.00/96.00 **st.** – SB.

Ravenswood without rest., 12 Matheson Rd, HS1 2LR, (01851) 702673, *Fax (01851) 702673*, – TV P.
closed 2 weeks November and 2 weeks Christmas-New Year – **3 rm** 22.50/45.00.

HARRIS.

rdvourlie.

Ardvourlie Castle, HS3 3AB, (01859) 502307, *Fax (01859) 502348*, Loch Seaforth and mountains, « Restored Victorian hunting lodge on shores of Loch Seaforth », – rest, P.
April-September – **Meals** (residents only) (dinner only) (set menu only) 25.00 **st.** 7.00 – **4 rm** (dinner included) 115.00/190.00 **st.**

everburgh.

Carminish, 1a Strond, HS5 3UD, South : 1 m. on Srandda rd (01859) 520400, *Fax (01859) 520307*, Carminish Islands and Sound of Harris, – P. MC VISA JCB.
April-September – **Meals** (by arrangement) (communal dining) 15.00 – **3 rm** 45.00/60.00 **st.**

carista.

9 (01859) 520236.

Scarista House, HS3 3HX, (01859) 550238, *tnpmartin@ukgateway.net*, *Fax (01859) 550277*, Scarista Bay, « Part 18C former manse », – P. MC VISA
restricted opening in winter – **Meals** (booking essential to non-residents) (dinner only) (set menu only) 29.50 **t.** 6.30 – **5 rm** 75.00/126.00 **t.**

arbert – *pop. 795* – *Harris.*

Leachin House, HS3 3AH, Northwest : 1 ¼ m. on A 859 (01859) 502157, *leachin.house@virgin.net*, *Fax (01859) 502157*, Loch Tarbert, – TV P. MC VISA.
closed 18 December-18 January – **Meals** (communal dining) 30.00 **st.** – **3 rm** 45.00/90.00 **st.**

Allan Cottage, HS3 3DJ, (01859) 502146, *Fax (01859) 502146* – TV
April-September – **Meals** (communal dining) 25.00 **s.** – **3 rm** 35.00/70.00 **s.**

Hillcrest, PA85 3BG, Northwest : 1 ¾ m. on A 859 (01859) 502119, – P.
Meals (by arrangement) (communal dining) 13.00 **s.** – **3 rm** 28.00/38.00 **s.**

LEWISTON *Highland* 401 G 12 *Scotland G.*

Env. : *Loch Ness*★★ – *The Great Glen*★.

Edinburgh 173 – Inverness 17.

Woodlands without rest., East Lewiston, IV63 6UJ, (01456) 45035 *Fax (01456) 450199,* – TV P. MC VISA.
closed 25 and 26 December – **3 rm** 40.00.

Glen Rowan without rest., West Lewiston, IV3 6UW, (01456) 450235, *glenrowan@loc ness.demon.co.uk, Fax (01456) 450817,* – TV P. MC VISA.
March-October – **3 rm** 40.00/46.00 **st.**

LINICLATE *Western Isles (Outer Hebrides)* 401 X/Y 11 – *see Uist (Isles of).*

LINLITHGOW *West Lothian* 401 J 16 *Scotland G.* – *pop. 13 689.*

See : *Town*★★ – *Palace*★★ *AC* : *Courtyard (fountain*★★*), Great Hall (Hooded Fireplace*★★ *Gateway*★ – *Old Town*★ – *St. Michaels*★.

Env. : *Cairnpapple Hill*★ *AC, SW : 5 m. by A 706* – *House of the Binns (plasterwork ceilings AC, NE : 4½ m. by A 803 and A 904.*

Exc. : *Hopetoun House*★★ *AC, E : 7 m. by A 706 and A 904* – *Abercorn Parish Churc (Hopetoun Loft*★★*) NE : 7 m. by A 803 and A 904.*

18 *Braehead* *(01506) 842585* – 18 *West Lothian, Airngath Hill* *(01506) 826030.*

Burgh Halls, The Cross *(01506) 844600.*

Edinburgh 19 – Falkirk 9 – Glasgow 35.

Champany Inn, Champany, EH49 7LU, Northeast : 2 m. on A 803 at junction with A 9 (01506) 834532, *info@champany.com, Fax (01506) 834302,* – TV P. MC AE VI JCB.
closed 25 December and 1-2 January – ***The Chop and Ale house :*** **Meals** (grill res a la carte 14.25/25.40 **st.** 6.50 – (see also ***The Restaurant*** below) – **16 rm** 95.0 135.00 **st.**

The Restaurant (at Champany Inn H.), Champany, EH49 7LU, Northeast : 2 m. on A 8 at junction with A 904 (01506) 834532, *Fax (01506) 834302,* « Converted horse mill », – P. MC AE VISA JCB
closed 25 December, 1-2 January, Saturday lunch and Sunday – **Meals** - Beef specialities and a la carte 29.50/55.50 **t.** 15.00.

Livingston's, 52 High St., EH49 7AE, (01506) 846565, , – . MC VISA.
closed 1 week June, 1 week October, first 2 weeks January, Sunday and Monday – **Mea** (light lunch)/dinner 23.50/27.50 **t.** 7.00.

LIVINGSTON *West Lothian* 401 J 16 – *pop. 22 357.*

18 *Bathgate, Edinburgh Rd* *(01506) 652232* – 18 *Deer Park C.C., Knightsridge* *(015 431037.*

Edinburgh 16 – Falkirk 23 – Glasgow 32.

Jarvis International, Almondview, EH54 6QB, (01506) 431222, *Fax (01506) 4346* , – rm, rest, TV P – 120. MC AE VISA JCB
Meals *(closed Sunday lunch)* 17.95 **t.** (dinner) and a la carte 17.40/31.45 **t.** – 10.25 **120 rm** 140.00 **st.** – SB.

Travel Inn, Deer Park Av., Knightsridge, EH54 8AD, Northwest : 2 ¾ m. by A 899 junction 3 of M 8 (01506) 439202, *Fax (01506) 438912* – , rm, rest, TV P. AE VISA.
Meals (grill rest.) – **83 rm** 40.95 **t.**

LOANS *South Ayrshire* 401 402 G 17 – *see Troon.*

LOCHBOISDALE *Western Isles (Outer Hebrides)* 401 Y 12 – *see Uist (Isles of).*

LOCHCARRON *Highland* 401 D 11 *Scotland G.* – *pop. 870.*

Env. : *Wester Ross*★★★ – *Loch Earn*★★.

Main St. *(01520) 722357 (summer only).*

Edinburgh 221 – Inverness 65 – Kyle of Lochalsh 23.

Rockvilla, Main St., IV54 8YB, (01520) 722379, *rockvillahotel@btinternet.co Fax (01520) 722844,* Loch Carron – rest, TV. MC AE VISA JCB.
closed 25 December and 1 January – **Meals** (booking essential in winter) (bar lunch)/dinn a la carte 15.50/23.75 **st.** 5.50 – **4 rm** 37.00/60.00 **st.**

OCHEARNHEAD *Stirling* 401 H 14 *Scotland G.*

Env. : *Loch Earn*★★.

Edinburgh 65 – Glasgow 56 – Oban 57 – Perth 36.

Mansewood Country House, FK19 8NS, South : ½ m. on A 84 ℘ (01567) 830213, – rest, TV P. MC VISA.
Meals (residents only) (dinner only) 20.00 **t.** 6.50 – **6 rm** 34.00/48.00 **t.**

OCHGILPHEAD *Argyll and Bute* 401 D 15 *Scotland G. – pop. 2 421.*

Env. : *Loch Fyne*★★, *E : 3½ m. by A 83.*

Blarbuie Rd ℘ (01546) 602340.

Lochnell St. ℘ (01546) 602344 (summer only).

Edinburgh 130 – Glasgow 84 – Oban 38.

Empire Travel Lodge without rest., Union St., PA31 8JS, ℘ (01546) 602381, *Fax (01546) 606606* – TV P. MC VISA JCB.
closed 24 December-2 January – **9 rm** 23.00/46.00 **st.**

at Cairnbaan *Northwest : 2¼ m. by A 816 on B 841 – Lochgilphead.*

Cairnbaan, PA31 8SJ, ℘ (01546) 603668, *cairnbaan.hotel@virgin.net, Fax (01546) 606045* – TV P – 170. MC VISA
Meals (bar lunch)/dinner a la carte 15.00/28.25 **t.** 6.00 – **11 rm** 65.50/110.00 **t.** – SB.

When looking for a quiet hotel
use the maps found in the introduction
or look for establishments with the sign or .

OCH HARRAY *Orkney Islands* 401 K 6 – *see Orkney Islands (Mainland).*

OCHINVER *Highland* 401 E 9 *Scotland G. – Lairg.*

See : *Village*★.

Env. : *Loch Assynt*★★, *E : 6 m. by A 837.*

Main St. ℘ (01571) 844330 (summer only).

Edinburgh 251 – Inverness 95 – Wick 105.

Inver Lodge, IV27 4LU, ℘ (01571) 844496, *stay@inverlodge.com, Fax (01571) 844395,* ≤ Loch Inver Bay, Suilven and Canisp mountains, – rest, TV P. MC AE VISA JCB
April-October – **Meals** (bar lunch)/dinner 25.00/35.00 **st.** 5.75 – **20 rm** 80.00/130.00 **st.** – SB.

The Albannach, Baddidarroch, IV27 4LP, West : 1 m. by Baddidarroch rd ℘ (01571) 844407, *Fax (01571) 844285,* ≤ Loch Inver Bay, Suilven and Canisp mountains, – P. MC VISA JCB.
March-November – **Meals** (booking essential) (dinner only) (set menu only) 30.00 **t.** 7.25 – **5 rm** (dinner included) 105.00/170.00 **t.**

Veyatie without rest., 66 Baddidarroch, IV27 4LP, West : 1 ¼ m. by Baddidarroch rd ℘ (01571) 844424, *veyatie@baddid.freeserve.co.uk,* ≤ Loch Inver Bay, Suilven and Canisp mountains, – P. MC VISA.
restricted opening December-February – **3 rm** 40.00/50.00 **st.**

Davar without rest., Baddidarroch Rd, IV27 4LJ, West : ½ m. on Baddidarroch rd ℘ (01571) 844501, ≤ Loch Inver Bay and Suilven – TV P.
March-November – **3 rm** 44.00 **s.**

OCHMADDY *Western Isles (Outer Hebrides)* 401 Y 11 – *see Uist (Isles of).*

OCHRANZA *North Ayrshire* 401 402 E 16 – *see Arran (Isle of).*

OCHWINNOCH *Renfrewshire* 401 402 G 16 – *pop. 4 228 – Paisley.*

Edinburgh 61 – Glasgow 15 – Ayr 37 – Greenock 20.

East Lochhead Country House, PA12 4DX, Southwest : 1 ¼ m. on A 760 ℘ (01505) 842610, *winnoch@aol.com, Fax (01505) 842610,* – TV P. MC AE VISA.
Meals (by arrangement) 18.00 **st.** – **3 rm** 40.00/70.00 **st.** – SB.

SCOTLAND

LOCKERBIE Dumfries and Galloway 401 402 J 18 – pop. 2 301.

Corrie Rd ☎ (01576) 203363 – Lochmaben, Castlehill Gate ☎ (01387) 810552.
Edinburgh 74 – Carlisle 27 – Dumfries 13 – Glasgow 73.

Dryfesdale, DG11 2SF, Northwest : 1 m. by Glasgow rd off B 7076 ☎ (01576) 202427, r eption@dryfesdalehotel.co.uk, Fax (01576) 204187, ←, – rest, TV P. MC AE VISA JCB
Meals 10.25/22.50 **st.** and a la carte 6.50 – **15 rm** 55.00/120.00 **st.** – SB.

LOSSIEMOUTH Moray 401 K 10.

Edinburgh 181 – Aberdeen 70 – Fraserburgh 66 – Inverness 44.

Stotfield, Stotfield Rd, IV31 6QS, ☎ (01343) 812011, Fax (01343) 814820, ←, – P – 150. MC AE VISA.
closed 23-27 December – **Meals** (bar lunch Monday to Saturday)/dinner 8.95/15.50 and a la carte 5.00 – **45 rm** 45.00/80.00 **t.**

LUNDIN LINKS Fife 401 L 15.

Edinburgh 38 – Dundee 29 – Perth 31 – Stirling 46.

Old Manor, Leven Rd, KY8 6AJ, ☎ (01333) 320368, enquiries@oldmanorhotel.co. Fax (01333) 320911, ←, – rest, TV P – 120. MC AE VISA JCB
closed 25-26 December – ***Aithernie :*** **Meals** (dinner only) 26.50/32.75 **t.** and a la car 6.50 – ***Coachman's :*** **Meals** a la carte 10.25/21.95 **t.** 5.75 – **24 rm** 80.00/180.00 t SB.

at Upper Largo Northeast : 1¼ m. by A 915 on A 917 – ✉ Lundin Links.

Scotland's Larder, KY8 6EA, ☎ (01333) 360414, scotlandslarder@connectfree.co. Fax (01333) 360427 – P. MC VISA
Meals (light lunch only November-March) 8.95/21.50 **st.** and a la carte 6.50.

LUSS Argyll and Bute 401 G 15 Scotland G. – pop. 402.

See : Village★.
Env. : E : Loch Lomond★★.
Edinburgh 89 – Glasgow 26 – Oban 65.

Lodge on Loch Lomond, G83 8PA, ☎ (01436) 860201, lusslomond@aol.co Fax (01436) 860203, ← Loch Lomond, « Lochside setting », – rest, TV P 40. MC AE VISA
Meals a la carte 17.65/23.45 **t.** 6.95 – **28 rm** 105.00/129.00 **t.**, 1 suite – SB.

Inverbeg Inn, Loch Lomond, G83 8PD, North : 3 m. on A 82 ☎ (01436) 860678, inver @onyxnet.co.uk, Fax (01436) 860686, ←, , – , rest, TV P. MC AE VISA.
closed 25 December – **Meals** (bar lunch)/dinner a la carte 13.85/20.15 **t.** 7.25 – 20 75.00/140.00 **t.**

LYBSTER Highland 401 K 9 Scotland G.

Env. : The Hill o'Many Stanes★, NE : 3½ m. by A 9 – Grey Cairns of Camster★, N : 6 m. by and minor rd.
Edinburgh 251 – Inverness 94 – Thurso 28 – Wick 14.

Portland Arms, Main St., KW3 6BS, on A 9 ☎ (01593) 721721, portlandarms@btconne com, Fax (01593) 721722 – rest, TV P – 200. MC AE VISA.
Meals (bar lunch Monday to Saturday)/dinner a la carte 13.00/18.50 **t.** 5.00 – 22 50.00/75.00 **t.** – SB.

MACHRIHANISH Argyll and Bute 401 C 17 – see Kintyre (Peninsula).

MAYBOLE South Ayrshire 401 402 F 17 Scotland G. – pop. 8 749.

Env. : Culzean Castle★ AC (setting★★★, Oval Staircase★★) W : 5 m. by B 7023 and A 719.
Memorial Park.

Ladyburn , KA19 7SG, South : 5½ m. by B 7023 off B 741 (Girvan rd) ☎ (01655) 7405 Fax (01655) 740580, ←, , – TV P. MC AE VISA.
restricted opening in winter – **Meals** (booking essential to non-residents) (dinner or 30.00/40.00 **t.** 7.50 – **5 rm** 110.00/145.00 **st.** – SB.

MELROSE *Borders* 401 402 L 17 *Scotland G.* – *pop. 2 414.*

See : Town★ - Abbey★★ (decorative sculpture★★★) AC.

Env. : *Eildon Hills (※★★★) – Scott's View★★ – Abbotsford★★ AC, W : 4½ m. by A 6091 and B 6360 – Dryburgh Abbey★★ AC (setting★★★), SE : 4 m. by A 6091 – Tweed Valley★★.*

Exc. : *Bowhill★★ AC, SW : 11½ m. by A 6091, A 7 and A 708 – Thirlestane Castle (plasterwork ceilings★★) AC, NE : 21 m. by A 6091 and A 68.*

Melrose, Dingleton ☎ (01896) 822855.

Abbey House, Abbey St. ☎ (01896) 822555 (Easter-October).

Edinburgh 38 – Hawick 19 – Newcastle upon Tyne 70.

Burts, Market Sq., TD6 9PN, ☎ (01896) 822285, *burtshotel@aol.com, Fax (01896) 822870,* – 30. VISA JCB
Meals – (see ***The Restaurant*** below) – **20 rm** 50.00/88.00 **t.** – SB.

Dunfermline House without rest., Buccleuch St., TD6 9LB, ☎ (01896) 822148, *bestacco m@dunmel.freeserve.co.uk, Fax (01896) 822148* –
5 rm 25.00/50.00 **st.**

The Restaurant (at Burts H.), Market Sq., TD6 9PN, ☎ (01896) 822285, *Fax (01896) 822870* – VISA JCB
Meals 20.75/27.75 **t.** 8.25.

MELVICH *Highland* 401 I 8 *Scotland G.* – ✉ *Thurso.*

Env. : *Strathy Point★ (≤★★★, Ben Loyal★★), NW : 5 m. by A 836 and minor rd.*

Edinburgh 267 – Inverness 110 – Thurso 18 – Wick 40.

The Sheiling without rest., KW14 7YJ, on A 836 ☎ (01641) 531256, *thesheiling@btintern et.com, Fax (01641) 531256,* ≤,
April-October – **3 rm** 40.00/50.00.

MEY *Highland* 401 K 8.

Edinburgh 302 – Inverness 144 – Thurso 13 – Wick 21.

Castle Arms, KW14 8XH, ☎ (01847) 851244, *info@castlearms.co.uk, Fax (01847) 851244* – VISA JCB
Meals (bar lunch Monday to Saturday)/dinner a la carte 10.50/22.00 **st.** 4.65 – **8 rm** 39.00/58.00 **st.** – SB.

MIGVIE *Aberdeenshire* 401 L 12 – *see Aboyne.*

MOFFAT *Dumfries and Galloway* 401 402 J 17 *Scotland G.* – *pop. 2 647.*

Exc. : *Grey Mare's Tail★★, NE : 9 m. by A 708.*

Coatshill ☎ (01683) 220020.

Churchgate ☎ (01683) 220620 (Easter-October).

Edinburgh 61 – Dumfries 22 – Carlisle 43 – Glasgow 60.

Auchen Castle, DG10 9SH, Southwest : 3 m. by A 701 off B 7076 (Abington rd) ☎ (01683) 300407, *reservations@auchen-castle-hotel.co.uk, Fax (01683) 300667,* ≤, – 50. VISA
closed 2 weeks Christmas and New Year – **Meals** (bar lunch Monday to Saturday)/dinner 17.45/21.20 **t.** – **14 rm** 55.00/110.00 **t.** – SB.

Moffat House, High St., DG10 9HL, ☎ (01683) 220039, *Fax (01683) 221288,* – rest, VISA JCB
Meals (bar lunch)/dinner 17.50/22.00 **t.** and a la carte 6.50 – **21 rm** 50.00/140.00 **t.** – SB.

Beechwood Country House, Harthope Pl., DG10 9RS, North : ½ m. by A 701 ☎ (01683) 220210, *info@beechwoodhousehotel.co.uk, Fax (01683) 220889,* ≤, – rest, VISA JCB
closed 2 January-17 February – **Meals** *(closed lunch Monday to Thursday)* 15.50/25.50 **t.** 7.50 – **7 rm** 55.00/78.50 **t.** – SB.

Burnside without rest., Well Rd, DG10 9BW, East : ½ m. by Selkirk rd (A 708) taking first left turning before bridge ☎ (01683) 221900, *Fax (01683) 221900,* –
closed December and January – **3 rm** 30.00/50.00 **st.**

Hartfell House, Hartfell Cres., DG10 9AL, Northeast : ½ m. by Well St. and Old Well Rd ☎ (01683) 220153, *robert.white@virgin.net,* – rest,
closed Christmas and New Year – **Meals** (by arrangement) 12.50 **t.** 4.50 – **7 rm** 25.00/46.00 **t.**

Well View with rm, Ballplay Rd, DG10 9JU, East : 3/4 m. by Selkirk rd (A 70
(01683) 220184, *Fax (01683) 220088*, – rest. TV P. MC AE VISA
Meals *(closed Saturday lunch)* (booking essential) 14.00/30.00 **t.** 9.00 – **5 rm** 63.0
100.00 **t.**, 1 suite – SB.

MONTROSE *Angus* 401 M 13 *Scotland G. – pop. 8 473.*

Exc. : *Edzell Castle★ (The Pleasance★★★)* **AC**, *NW : 17 m. by A 935 and B 966 – Ca O'Mount Road★ (≤★★) N : 17 m. by B 966 and B 974 – Brechin (Round Tower★) W : 7 m. by 935 – Aberlemno (Aberlemno Stones★, Pictish sculptured stones★) W : 13 m. by A 935 a B 9134.*

18, 18 *Traill Drive (01674) 672932.*

Bridge St. (01674) 672000 (April-September).

Edinburgh 92 – Aberdeen 39 – Dundee 29.

Oaklands without rest., 10 Rossie Island Rd, DD10 9NN, on A 92 (01674) 672018, *oa nds@altavista.net, Fax (01674) 672018* – TV P. MC VISA
7 rm 22.00/40.00 **st.**

MOTHERWELL *North Lanarkshire* 401 I 16.

Edinburgh 38 – Glasgow 12.

Hilton Strathclyde, Phoenix Cres., Bellshill, ML4 3JQ, Northwest : 4 m. by A 721 on 725 (01698) 395500, *reservations@strathclyde.stakis.co.uk, Fax (01698) 395511*, – rest, TV – 400. MC AE VISA JCB.
Meals *(closed Saturday lunch)* a la carte 13.85/26.50 **st.** – 10.50 – **107 rm** 125.0
195.00 **st.** – SB.

Express by Holiday Inn without rest., Strathclyde Country Park, Hamilton Rd, M 3RB, Northwest : 4 1/4 m. by A 721 and B 7070 off A 725 (01698) 8585 *Fax (01698) 852375* – TV P – 30. MC AE VISA.
120 rm 59.00 **t.**

Travel Inn, Edinburgh Rd, Newhouse, ML1 5SY, Northeast : 4 1/4 m. by A 723 on A 7
(01698) 860277, *Fax (01698) 861353* – rm, rest, TV P – 80. MC AE VISA.
Meals (grill rest.) – **40 rm** 40.95 **t.**

Travel Inn, Bellziehill Farm, Bellshill, ML4 3HH, Northwest : 3 1/2 m. on A 721 at juncti with A 725 (01698) 740180, *Fax (01698) 845969* – , rm, rest, TV P. MC AE
VISA.
Meals (grill rest.) – **40 rm** 40.95 **t.**

MUIR OF ORD *Highland* 401 G 11 – *pop. 2 033.*

18 *Great North Rd (01463) 870825.*

Edinburgh 173 – Inverness 10 – Wick 121.

Dower House , Highfield, IV6 7XN, North : 1 m. on A 862 (01463) 870090, *info@t dowerhouse.co.uk, Fax (01463) 870090*, « Part 17C », – TV P. MC VISA.
closed 25 December – **Meals** (set menu only) (booking essential to non-residents) (lunch arrangement)/dinner 30.00 **st.** 8.50 – **5 rm** 110.00/130.00 **st.**, 1 suite.

MULL (Isle of) *Argyll and Bute* 401 BC 14/15 *Scotland G. – pop. 2 838.*

See : *Island★ - Calgary Bay★★ – Torosay Castle* **AC** *(Gardens★ ≤★).*

Env. : *Isle of Iona★ (Maclean's Cross★, St. Oran's Chapel★, St. Martin's High Cross★, firmary Museum★* **AC** *(Cross of St. John★)).*

9 *Craignure, Scallastle (01680) 812487.*

from Craignure to Oban (Caledonian MacBrayne Ltd) frequent services daily (45 mn from Fishnish to Lochaline (Mainland) (Caledonian MacBrayne Ltd) frequent services d (15 mn) – from Tobermory to Isle of Tiree (Scarinish) via Isle of Coll (Arinagour) (Caledon MacBrayne Ltd) 3 weekly (2 h 30 mn) – from Tobermory to Kilchoan (Caledonian MacBray Ltd) 4 daily (summer only) (35 mn).

from Fionnphort to Isle of Iona (Caledonian MacBrayne Ltd) frequent services daily mn) – from Pierowall to Papa Westray (Orkney Ferries Ltd) (summer only) (25 mn).

The Pier, Tobermory (01688) 302182 (April-October).

Bunessan – ✉ *Fionnphort.*

Assapol House , PA67 6DW, Southeast : 1 1/2 m. by A 849 (01681) 700258, *alex@ apolhouse.com, Fax (01681) 700445*, ≤, « Lochside setting », – TV P. MC VISA.
Easter-October – **Meals** (residents only) (dinner only) 27.00 **st.** 6.50 – **5 rm** (dinr included) 58.00/146.00 **st.**

ervaig – ✉ *Tobermory.*

Druimard Country House ⛔, PA75 6QW, on Salen rd ✆ (01688) 400345, *druimard@talk21.com, Fax (01688) 400345*, ≤, ⚘ – ⊁ rest, TV P. MC VISA
April-October – **Meals** (dinner only) (set menu only) 29.50 **t.** 8.95 – **7 rm** ⊐ (dinner included) 76.00/152.00 **t.**

Balmacara, PA75 6QN, East : ¼ m. on B 8073 ✆ (01688) 400363, *balmacara@mull.com, Fax (01688) 400363*, ≤, ⚘ – ⊁ rm, TV P. ✻
closed 22 December-5 January – **Meals** (by arrangement) 14.50 **st.** – **3 rm** ⊐ 35.00/58.00 – SB.

illiechronan.

Killiechronan House ⛔, PA72 6JU, on B 8073 ✆ (01680) 300403, *me@managedestates.co.uk, Fax (01680) 300463*, ≤, ⚲, ⚘, ⚘ – ⊁ P. MC AE VISA
March-October – **Meals** (booking essential to non-residents) (dinner only) 25.90 **t.** 6.85 – **6 rm** ⊐ (dinner included) 87.00/156.00 **t.** – SB.

obermory – *pop. 2 708.*

Erray Rd ✆ (01688) 302140.

Western Isles, PA75 6PR, ✆ (01688) 302012, *wihotel@aol.com, Fax (01688) 302297*, ≤ Tobermory harbour and Calve Island – ⊁ rest, TV P. MC AE VISA
closed 18 to 28 December – **Meals** (bar lunch)/dinner 25.00/26.50 **t.** – **24 rm** ⊐ 46.00/113.00 **t.**, 1 suite – SB.

Tobermory, 53 Main St., PA75 6NT, ✆ (01688) 302091, *tobhotel@tinyworld.co.uk, Fax (01688) 302254*, ≤ – ⊁ rest, TV. MC VISA. ✻
closed 1 week Christmas – ***Waters Edge :*** **Meals** *(closed Monday)* (booking essential to non-residents) (dinner only) 19.95 **t.** 5.85 – **16 rm** ⊐ 40.00/92.00 **t.** – SB.

Fairways Lodge ⛔ without rest., Golf Course, PA75 6PS, Northeast : ½ m. by B 882 ✆ (01688) 302238, *derek_mcadam@msn.com, Fax (01688) 302238*, ≤ Calve Island and Sound of Mull, 9, ⚘ – ⊁ TV P
5 rm ⊐ 36.00/72.00 **st.**

URCAR *Aberdeenshire* 401 N 12 – *see Murcar.*

USSELBURGH *East Lothian* 401 K 16 – *pop. 18 425.*

18 Monktonhall ✆ (0131) 665 2005 – 18 Royal Musselburgh, Prestongrange House, Prestonpans ✆ (01875) 810276 – 9 Musselburgh Old Course, Balcarres Rd ✆ (0131) 665 6981.

Granada Service Area (A 1), Old Craighall ✆ (0131) 653 6172.

Edinburgh 6 – Berwick 54 – Glasgow 53.

Travel Inn, Carberry Rd, Inveresk, EH21 8PT, Southeast : 1 ½ m. on A 6124 ✆ (0131) 665 3005, *Fax (0131) 653 2270*, ⚘ – ⊁ rm, ▤ rest, TV ♿ P – 🏛 70. MC AE ⓓ VISA
Meals (grill rest.) – **40 rm** 40.95 **t.**

AIRN *Highland* 401 I 11 *Scotland G.* – *pop. 10 623.*

Env. : Forres (Sueno's Stone★★) E : 11 m. by A 96 and B 9011 – Cawdor Castle★ AC, S : 5½ m. by B 9090 – Brodie Castle★ AC, E : 6 m. by A 96.

Exc. : Fort George★, W : 8 m. by A 96, B 9092 and B 9006.

18, 9 Seabank Rd ✆ (01667) 452103 – 18 Nairn Dunbar, Lochloy Rd ✆ (01667) 452741.

62 King St. ✆ (01667) 452753 (April-October).

Edinburgh 172 – Aberdeen 91 – Inverness 16.

Golf View, 63 Seabank Rd, IV12 4HD, ✆ (01667) 452301, *rooms@morton-hotels.com, Fax (01667) 455267*, ≤, Ƒ₆, ≘s, ⛱, ⚘, ✂ – |♀| ⊁, ▤ rest, TV P – 🏛 120. MC AE ⓓ VISA JCB
Restaurant : **Meals** 26.00 **t.** (dinner) and lunch a la carte 11.15/21.40 **t.** 6.95 – ***Conservatory :*** **Meals** *(closed 24-27 and 30 December and 1-2 January)* 26.00 **t.** (dinner) and lunch a la carte 11.15/21.40 **t.** 6.95 – **47 rm** ⊐ 98.00/165.00 **t.**, 1 suite – SB.

Newton ⛔, IV12 4RX, ✆ (01667) 453144, *info@morton-hotels.com, Fax (01667) 454026*, ⚘, ⚘ – |♀| ⊁ TV ♿ P – 🏛 400. MC AE ⓓ VISA JCB
Meals (bar lunch)/dinner 26.00 **t.** 6.95 – **53 rm** ⊐ 98.00/165.00 **t.**, 4 suites – SB.

Clifton House ⛔, Viewfield St., IV12 4HW, ✆ (01667) 453119, *macintyre@clara.net, Fax (01667) 452836*, ≤, « Antiques, memorabilia and objets d'art », ⚘ – P. MC AE ⓓ VISA
closed mid December-mid January – **Meals** (booking essential) a la carte 23.50/30.00 **t.** 5.00 – **12 rm** ⊐ 60.00/107.00 – SB.

Claymore House, 45 Seabank Rd, IV12 4EY, ☎ (01667) 453731, *claymorenairnscotland@compuserve.com, Fax (01667) 455290,* – TV P. MC AE VISA.
Meals (bar lunch) a la carte 11.95/20.65 **st.** 4.95 – **13 rm** 42.50/85.00 **st.**, 1 suite – SB.

Boath House, Auldearn, IV12 5TE, East : 2 m. on A 96 ☎ (01667) 454896, *wendy@boathhouse.demon.co.uk, Fax (01667) 454896,* ←, « Georgian mansion », – TV P. MC AE VISA.
closed 25-26 December and last 3 weeks January – **Meals** *(closed Monday-Wednesday lunch)* (booking essential) 18.95/29.50 **t.** 8.80 – **7 rm** 55.00/175.00 **t.** – SB.

Sunny Brae, Marine Rd, IV12 4EA, ☎ (01667) 452309, *sunnybrae@easynet.co.uk, Fax (01667) 454860,* ←, – TV P. MC VISA JCB
mid March-November – **Meals** (booking essential to non-residents) (lunch for residents only)/dinner 22.50 **st.** and a la carte 6.30 – **9 rm** 49.00/90.00 **st.** – SB.

Links, 1 Seafield St., IV12 4HN, ☎ (01667) 453321, *linkcoop@aol.com, Fax (01667) 4560*
←, – rest, TV P. MC AE VISA JCB
closed January-February – **Meals** (dinner only) 17.50/22.50 **st.** and a la carte – **10 rm** 35.00/80.00 **st.** – SB.

Inveran Lodge without rest., Seabank Rd, IV12 4HG, ☎ (01667) 455666, *claymorenairnscotland@compuserve.com, Fax (01667) 455666,* – TV P. MC AE VISA.
3 rm 60.00 **st.**

NETHERLEY *Aberdeenshire* 401 N 12 *Scotland G.* – ✉ *Stonehaven.*
Env. : *Muchalls Castle (plasterwork ceilings★★) AC, SE : 5 m. by B 979 – Deeside★★, N : 2 by B 979 – Aberdeen★★, NE : 3 m. by B 979 and B 9077.*
Exc. : *Aberdeen★★, NE : 12 m. by – Dunnottar Castle★★ (site★★★) AC, S : 7 m. by B 979 Crathes Castle★★ (Gardens★★★) AC, NW : 13 m. by B 979, B 9077 and A 93.*
Edinburgh 117 – Aberdeen 12 – Dundee 54.

Lairhillock Inn, AB39 3QS, Northeast : 1 ½ m. by B 979 on Portlethen ☎ (01569) 730001, *lairhillock@breathemail.net, Fax (01569) 731175* – P. MC AE VISA JCB
closed 25-26 December and 1 January – **Meals** a la carte 16.50/28.00 **t.** 6.25.

The Guide is updated annually so renew your Guide every year.

NEWBURGH *Aberdeenshire* 401 N 12 *Scotland G.*
Exc. : *Pitmedden Gardens★★ AC, W : 6½ m. by B 9000 – Haddo House★ AC, NW : 14 m. B 900, A 92 and B 9005.*
18 *McDonald, Hospital Rd, Ellon ☎ (01358) 720576 –* 18 *Newburgh-on-Ythan, Ellon ☎ (01358) 789058.*
Edinburgh 144 – Aberdeen 14 – Fraserburgh 33.

Udny Arms, Main St., AB41 6BL, ☎ (01358) 789444, *enquiry@udny.demon.co.uk, Fax (01358) 789012,* – TV P – 45. MC AE VISA
Meals – (see ***The Bistro*** below) – **26 rm** 66.00/82.00 **t.** – SB.

The Bistro (at Udny Arms H.), Main St., AB41 6BL, ☎ (01358) 789444, *Fax (01358) 78901*
P. MC AE VISA
Meals (booking essential) a la carte 13.85/34.85 **t.** 8.85.

NEW LANARK *Lanarkshire* 401 I 17.
Edinburgh 44 – Dumfries 55 – Glasgow 31.

New Lanark Mill, Mill One, New Lanark Mills, MK11 9DB, ☎ (01555) 667200, *hotel@newlanark.org, Fax (01555) 667222,* ←, « Converted riverside cotton mill in restored Georgian village » – TV P – 150. MC AE VISA
Meals 16.50/19.50 **t.** (dinner) and lunch a la carte 10.00/17.00 **t.** – **38 rm** 57.50/75.00 – SB.

NEW SCONE *Perthshire and Kinross* 401 J 14 – *see Perth.*

NEWTON STEWART *Dumfries and Galloway* 401 402 G 19 *Scotland G.* – *pop. 2 543.*
Env. : *Galloway Forest Park★, Queen's Way★ (Newton Stewart to New Galloway) N : 19 m. A 712.*
18, *Kirroughtree Av., Minnigaff ☎ (01671) 402172 –* 18 *Wigtownshire County, Mains of Park, Glenluce ☎ (01581) 300420.*
Dashwood Sq. ☎ (01671) 402431 (Easter-October).
Edinburgh 131 – Dumfries 51 – Glasgow 87 – Stranraer 24.

Kirroughtree House ⑤, DG8 6AN, Northeast : 1 ½ m. by A 75 on A 712 ℘ (01671) 402141, *info@kirroughtreehouse.co.uk, Fax (01671) 402425,* ← woodland and Wigtown Bay, « 18C mansion in landscaped gardens », – rest, TV P. VISA.
closed January and restricted opening February-March – **Meals** (booking essential to non-residents) 35.00 **st.** (dinner) and lunch a la carte 16.50/22.00 **st.** 9.50 – **15 rm** 105.00/200.00 **st.**, 2 suites – SB.

Creebridge House, Minnigaff, DG8 6NP, ℘ (01671) 402121, *info@creebridge.co.uk, Fax (01671) 403258,* – rest, TV P. AE VISA JCB
closed 24 and 26 December – **Meals** (carving lunch Sunday) 19.95 **t.** (dinner) and a la carte 13.25/26.10 **t.** – **19 rm** 69.00/118.00 **t.**

Oakbank, Corsbie Rd, via Jubilee Rd off Dashwood Sq., DG8 6JB, ℘ (01671) 402822, *Fax (01671) 403050,* – TV P
closed December and January – **Meals** (by arrangement) (communal dining) 12.00 **st.** – **3 rm** 22.00/44.00 **s.**

ORTH BERWICK *East Lothian* 401 L 15 *Scotland G. – pop. 5 871.*

Env. : *North Berwick Law (★★★) S : 1 m. - Tantallon Castle★★ (clifftop site★★★) AC, E : 3½ m. by A 198 – Dirleton★ (Castle★ AC) SW : 2½ m. by A 198.*

Exc. : *Museum of Flight★, S : 6 m. by B 1347 – Preston Mill★, S : 8½ m. by A 198 and B 1047 – Tyninghame★, S : 7 m. by A 198 – Coastal road from North Berwick to Portseton★, SW : 13 m. by A 198 and B 1348.*

18 North Berwick, West Links, Beach Rd ℘ (01620) 895040 – 18 The Glen, East Links ℘ (01620) 892726.

Quality St. ℘ (01620) 892197.

Edinburgh 24 – Newcastle upon Tyne 102.

The Marine, 18 Cromwell Rd, EH39 4LZ, ℘ (01620) 892406, *heritagehotels_northberwick .marine@forte_hotels.com, Fax (01620) 894480,* ← golf course and Firth of Forth, heated, – TV P – 250. AE VISA JCB
Meals (bar lunch Saturday) 6.50/22.50 **t.** 9.15 – 15.00 – **79 rm** 140.00 **t.**, 4 suites – SB.

Glebe House ⑤ without rest., Law Rd, EH39 4PL, ℘ (01620) 892608, *jascott@tesco.net, Fax (01620) 892608,* « Georgian manse », – TV P.
closed Christmas – **3 rm** 40.00/70.00 **st.**

Craigview without rest., 5 Beach Rd, EH39 4AB, ℘ (01620) 892257 – TV.
3 rm 50.00 **st.**

ORTH QUEENSFERRY *Fife* 401 J 15 *Scotland G.* – ✉ *Inverkeithing.*

Env. : *Forth Bridges★★ (toll).*

Edinburgh 13 – Dunfermline 7 – Glasgow 42 – Kirkcaldy 16 – Perth 33.

Queensferry Lodge, St. Margarets Head, KY11 1HP, North : ½ m. on B 981 ℘ (01383) 410000, *Fax (01383) 419708,* ← – TV P – 150. AE VISA
Meals a la carte 13.95/19.85 **st.** 4.50 – 9.50 – **77 rm** 89.00/109.00 **st.** – SB.

ORTH UIST *Western Isles (Outer Hebrides)* 401 XY 10/11 – *see Uist (Isles of).*

BAN *Argyll and Bute* 401 D 14 *Scotland G. – pop. 8 203.*

Exc. : *Loch Awe★★, SE : 17 m. by A 85 – Bonawe Furnace★, E : 12 m. by A 85 – Cruachan Power Station★ AC, E : 16 m. by A 85 – Sea Life Centre★ AC, N : 14 m. by A 828.*

18 Glencruitten, Glencruitten Rd ℘ (01631) 562868.

Access to Glasgow by helicopter.

to Isle of Mull (Craignure) (Caledonian MacBrayne Ltd) (45 mn) – to South Uist (Lochboisdale) via Isle of Barra (Castlebay) (Caledonian MacBrayne Ltd) (summer only) – to Isle of Tiree (Scarinish) via Isle of Mull (Tobermory) and Isle of Coll (Arinagour) (Caledonian MacBrayne Ltd) – to Isle of Islay (Port Askaig) and Kintyre Peninsula (Kennacraig) via Isle of Colonsay (Scalasaig) (Caledonian MacBrayne Ltd) (summer only) – to Isle of Lismore (Achnacroish) (Caledonian MacBrayne Ltd) 2-3 daily (except Sunday) (50 mn) – to Isle of Colonsay (Scalasaig) (Caledonian MacBrayne Ltd) 3 weekly (2 h).

Argyll Sq. ℘ (01631) 563122.

Edinburgh 123 – Dundee 116 – Glasgow 93 – Inverness 118.

Manor House, Gallanach Rd, PA34 4LS, ℘ (01631) 562087, *Fax (01631) 563053,* ←, – TV P. AE VISA.
closed Sunday and Monday November-February – **Meals** (lunch by arrangement)/dinner 24.95 **t.** and a la carte 6.00 – **11 rm** (dinner included) 110.00/160.00 **t.** – SB.

Dungallan House, Gallanach Rd, PA34 4PD, ✆ (01631) 563799, *welcome@dungallanhotel-oban.co.uk, Fax (01631) 566711,* ←, – rest, TV P. VISA
March-October – **Meals** (lunch booking essential) 25.00 **t.** (dinner) and lunch a la carte 10.10/21.95 **st.** 8.50 – **13 rm** 40.00/96.00 **st.** – SB.

Barriemore without rest., Corran Esplanade, PA34 5AQ, ✆ (01631) 566356, *barriemorehotel@dnet.co.uk, Fax (01631) 566356,* ← – TV P. VISA
March-November – **13 rm** 30.00/60.00 **t.**

Glenburnie without rest., Corran Esplanade, PA34 5AQ, ✆ (01631) 562089, *graeme.strachan@btinternet.com, Fax (01631) 562089,* ← – TV P. VISA.
March-November – **13 rm** 32.00/70.00 **st.**, 1 suite.

Kilchrenan House without rest., Corran Esplanade, PA34 5AQ, ✆ (01631) 562663, *kilchrenanhouse@netline.uk, Fax (01631) 562663,* ← – TV P. VISA.
Easter-October – **10 rm** 30.00/64.00 **t.**

The Waterfront, No. 1, The Pier, PA34 4LW, ✆ (01631) 563110, *Fax (01631) 563110* – AE VISA
closed December-January except 25 December – **Meals** - Seafood - a la carte 13.?/26.00 **t.** 5.95.

at Kilmore *South : 4 m. on A 816 – ✉ Oban.*

Invercairn without rest., Musdale Rd, PA34 4XX, ✆ (01631) 770301, *invercairnkilmore@virgin.net, Fax (01631) 770301,* ←, – P.
May-October – **3 rm** 30.00/50.00.

at Kilninver *Southwest : 8 m. by A 816 on B 844 – ✉ Oban.*

Knipoch, PA34 4QT, Northeast : 1 ½ m. on A 816 ✆ (01852) 316251, *reception@knipochhotel.co.uk, Fax (01852) 316249,* ←, – rest, TV P. AE VISA
mid February-mid December – **Meals** (lunch by arrangement)/dinner 29.50/39.50 **t.** 7 – **15 rm** 69.00/138.00 **t.**, 1 suite – SB.

Groß-London (GREATER LONDON) besteht aus der City und 32 Verwaltungsbezirken (Borough). Diese sind wiederum in kleinere Bezirke (Area) unterteilt, deren Mittelpunkt ehemalige Dörfer oder Stadtviertel sind, die oft ihren eigenen Charakter bewahrt haben.

OLDMELDRUM *Aberdeenshire* 401 N 11 *Scotland G.*

Exc. : *Haddo House★, NE : 9 m. by B 9170 on B 9005.*
Oldmeldrum, Kirkbrae ✆ (01651) 872648.
Edinburgh 140 – Aberdeen 17 – Inverness 87.

Meldrum House, AB51 0AE, North : 1 ½ m. on A 947 ✆ (01651) 872294, *dpmeldrum@aol.com, Fax (01651) 872464,* ←, « Part 13C baronial house », 18, – rest, TV 50. VISA.
Meals (dinner only and Sunday lunch)/dinner 26.50 **st.** and a la carte 7.00 – **9** 85.00/120.00 **st.** – SB.

Cromlet Hill without rest., South Rd, AB51 0AB, ✆ (01651) 872315, *Fax (01651) 8721* – TV P.
2 rm 35.00/65.00 **st.**, 1 suite.

ONICH *Highland* 401 E 13 – ✉ *Fort William.*

Edinburgh 123 – Glasgow 93 – Inverness 79 – Oban 39.

The Lodge on the Loch, Creag Dhu, PH33 6RY, on A 82 ✆ (01855) 821237, *reservations@freedomglen.co.uk, Fax (01855) 821463,* ← Loch Linnhe and mountains, – rest, TV P. VISA
Easter-October and Christmas-New Year – **Meals** (bar lunch)/dinner 29.50 **t.** 11.00 – **19 rm** (dinner included) 70.00/200.00 **t.**, 1 suite – SB.

Allt-nan-Ros, PH33 6RY, on A 82 ✆ (01855) 821210, *allt_nan_ros@zetnet.co.uk, Fax (01855) 821462,* ← Loch Linnhe and mountains, – rest, TV P. AE VISA
Meals (bar lunch)/dinner 12.85/29.95 **st.** 7.00 – **20 rm** 50.00/110.00 **st.**

Onich, PH33 6RY, on A 82 ✆ (01855) 821214, *reservations@onich-fortwilliam.co.uk, Fax (01855) 821484,* ← Loch Linnhe and mountains, « Lochside setting », – rest, P. AE VISA JCB
Meals (bar lunch)/dinner 21.00/26.00 **t.** 7.50 – **28 rm** 70.00/130.00 **t.** – SB.

ORD *Highland* 401 C 12 – *see Skye (Isle of).*

RKNEY ISLANDS *Orkney Islands* 401 KL 6/7 *Scotland G. – pop. 19 612.*

See : *Old Man of Hoy*★★★ *– Islands*★★ *– Maes Howe*★★ *AC – Skara Brae*★★ *AC – Corrigal Farm Museum*★ *AC – Brough of Birsay*★ *AC – Birsay (≤★) – Ring of Brodgar*★ *– Unstan Cairn*★.

see Kirkwall.

service between Isle of Hoy (Longhope), Isle of Hoy (Lyness), Isle of Flotta and Houton (Orkney Ferries Ltd) – from Stromness to Scrabster (P & O Scottish Ferries) (2 h) – from Stromness to Shetland Islands (Lerwick) and Aberdeen (P & O Scottish Ferries) 2 weekly – from Kirkwall to Westray, Stronsay via Eday and Sanday (Orkney Ferries Ltd) – from Tingwall to Wyre via Egilsay and Rousay (Orkney Ferries Ltd) – from Kirkwall to Shapinsay (Orkney Ferries Ltd) (25 mn) – from Stromness to Isle of Hoy (Moness) and Graemsay (Orkney Ferries Ltd) – from Kirkwall to North Ronaldsay (Orkney Ferries Ltd) weekly (2 h 40 mn) – from Kirkwall to Invergordon (Orcargo Ltd) daily (8 h 30 mn) – from Houton to Isle of Hoy (Lyness), Flotta and Longhope (Orkney Ferries Ltd) – from Stromness to Graemsay via Isle of Hoy (Orkney Ferries Ltd).

from Burwick (South Ronaldsay) to John O'Groats (John O'Groats Ferries) 4-5 daily (45 mn).

SCOTLAND

rray.

Ankersted, KW17 2SS, East : ½ m. on A 961 ☎ (01856) 731217, *Fax (01856) 731217*, ≤, – rm, TV P.
Meals (by arrangement) 12.00 **st.** – **4 rm** 19.00/36.00.

unby.

Smithfield, KW17 2HT, ☎ (01856) 771215, *Fax (01856) 771494* – TV P. MC VISA.
April-October – **Meals** 18.00 **st.** (dinner) and a la carte 7.60/19.80 **st.** – **6 rm** 30.00/60.00 **st.**

rkwall *Scotland G. – pop. 5 952.*

See : *Kirkwall*★★ *– St. Magnus Cathedral*★★ *– Western Mainland*★★*, Eastern Mainland (Italian Chapel*★*) – Earl's Palace*★ *AC – Tankerness House Museum*★ *AC – Orkney Farm and Folk Museum*★.

18 *Grainbank ☎ (01856) 872457.*

Kirkwall Airport : ☎ (01856) 872421, S : 3½ m.

6 Broad St. ☎ (01856) 872856.

Ayre, Ayre Rd, KW15 1QX, ☎ (01856) 873001, *ayre.hotel@orkney.com, Fax (01856) 876289* – rm, TV P – 200. MC AE VISA
closed 25 December and 1 January – **Meals** 7.95/19.00 **t.** and a la carte – **33 rm** 64.00/98.00 **t.**

Foveran, St. Ola, KW15 1SF, Southwest : 3 m. on A 964 ☎ (01856) 872389, *foveranhotel@aol.com, Fax (01856) 876430*, « Overlooking Scapa Flow », – rest, TV P. MC VISA JCB.
Meals (lunch by arrangement)/dinner a la carte 15.15/27.35 **t.** 4.50 – **8 rm** 45.00/70.00 **t.**

Queens, Shore St., KW15 1LG, ☎ (01856) 872200, *Fax (01856) 873871* – rest, TV. MC VISA.
closed 25-26 December – **Meals** (in bar) a la carte 11.75/19.75 **t.** – **9 rm** 35.00/50.00 **t.**

West End, Main St., KW15 1BU, ☎ (01856) 872368, *westendhotel@orkney.com, Fax (01856) 876181* – TV P. MC AE VISA JCB.
Meals *(closed Sunday lunch)* (in bar) 12.00/20.00 **st.** and a la carte 4.50 – **16 rm** 43.00/58.00 **st.**

St. Ola without rest., Harbour St., KW15 1LE, ☎ (01856) 875090, *Fax (01856) 875090* – TV. MC VISA JCB.
closed 22 December-3 January – **6 rm** 32.00/46.00 **st.**

Lav'rockha, Inganess Rd, KW15 1SP, Southeast : 1 ¼ m. by A 960 ☎ (01856) 876103, *lavrockha@orkney.com, Fax (01856) 876103*, – TV P. MC VISA JCB.
Meals (by arrangement) 12.50 **st.** 5.00 – **5 rm** 30.00/48.00 **st.**

Polrudden, Peerie Sea Loan, KW15 1UH, West : 1 m. by Pickaquoy Rd ☎ (01856) 874761, *linda@scapaflow.com, Fax (01856) 870950* – rest, TV P. MC VISA JCB.
closed Christmas – **Meals** (by arrangement) 13.50 **s.** – **7 rm** 30.00/44.00 **st.**

Brekk-Ness without rest., Muddisdale Rd, KW15 1RS, West : ¾ m. by Pickaquoy Rd ☎ (01856) 874317, *Fax (01856) 874317* – TV P. MC VISA JCB.
closed 25 December – **11 rm** 30.00/48.00.

SCOTLAND

Loch Harray.

Merkister ⛵, KW17 2LF, off A 986 ✆ (01856) 771366, *merkister-hotel@hotmail.co*
Fax (01856) 771515, ⩽ Loch Harray, « Lochside setting », – rest, TV P. MC AE JCB
closed 26 December and 1 January – **Meals** (bar lunch Monday to Saturday)/dinner 18.
20.00 **t.** and a la carte 6.00 – **14 rm** 45.00/105.00 **t.** – SB.

St. Margaret's Hope.

Creel with rm, Front Rd, KW17 2SL, ✆ (01856) 831311, *alan@thecreel.freeserve.co.uk*,
TV P. MC VISA.
mid March-December – **Meals** (dinner only) 27.50/30.50 **t.** 7.60 – **3 rm** 45.00/70.00

Stenness.

Standing Stones, KW16 3JX, on A 965 ✆ (01856) 850449, *standingstones@sol.co*
Fax (01856) 851262, – rm, TV P. MC AE VISA JCB
closed 22 December-7 January – **Meals** *(closed October-April)* (booking essential) (
lunch)/dinner 18.50 **t.** and a la carte – **17 rm** 40.00/76.00 **st.**

Mill of Eyrland, KW16 3HA, Southwest : 2 ¾ m. by A 965 on A 964 ✆ (01856) 850136,
andmorag@millofeyrland.demon.co.uk, *Fax (01856) 851633*, « Victorian windmill »,
TV P
Meals (by arrangement) (communal dining) 25.00 **st.** 5.00 – **5 rm** 35.00/80.00 **st.** –

Stromness *Scotland G.*

See : *Town★ - Pier Gallery (collection of abstract art★).*

Stenigar without rest., Ness Rd, KW16 3DW, South : ½ m. by Main St. ✆ (01856) 8504
⩽, – TV P.
April-November – **3 rm** 30.00/50.00 **st.**

Thira ⛵, Innertown, KW16 3JP, Northwest : 1 ½ m. by Back Rd, turning right at r
roundabout, taking first right onto unmarked road and then left at two juncti
✆ (01856) 851181, *Fax (01856) 851182*, ⩽ Hoy Island and Sound, – TV P.
May-December – **Meals** (by arrangement) (communal dining) 10.00 – **4 rm** 24.
48.00 **st.**

PAISLEY *Renfrewshire* 401 G 16 – *pop. 43 602.*

Braehead ✆ (0141) 884 2292.
Edinburgh 56 – Ayr 36 – Glasgow 11 – Greenock 16 – Kilmarnock 22.

Travel Inn, Phoenix Retail Park, Linwood, PA1 2BH, West : 2 ¼ m. by A
✆ (0141) 887 4865, *Fax (0141) 887 2799* – , rm, rest, TV P – 30. MC AE
VISA.
Meals (grill rest.) – **40 rm** 40.95 **t.**

Myfarrclan, 146 Corsebar Rd, PA2 9NA, Southwest : 1 ¾ m. on B 775 ✆ (0141) 884 82
myfarrclan-guest@compuserve.com, *Fax (0141) 581 1566*, – TV. MC VISA.
Meals (by arrangement) (communal dining) 18.00 **st.** – **3 rm** 60.00/70.00 **st.** – SB.

PEAT INN *Fife* 401 L 15 *Scotland G.* – ✉ *Cupar.*

Exc. : *Kellie Castle★, SE : 7½ m. by B 940 and minor roads.*
Edinburgh 45 – Dundee 21 – Perth 28.

The Peat Inn ⛵ with rm, KY15 5LH, ✆ (01334) 840206, *reception@thepeatinn.co*
Fax (01334) 840530, – rest, TV P. MC AE VISA.
closed 25 December, 1 January, Sunday and Monday – **Meals** (booking essential) 19.
29.50 **st.** and dinner a la carte 28.50/32.50 **st.** 10.00 – **1 rm** 95.00 **st.**, **7 suites** 145.
155.00 **st.** – SB.

PEEBLES *Borders* 401 402 K 17 *Scotland G.* – *pop. 7 065.*

Env. : *Tweed Valley★★.*
Exc. : *Traquair House★★ AC, SE : 7 m. by B 7062 – Rosslyn Chapel★★ AC, N : 16½ m. b*
703, A 6094, B 7026 and B 7003.
Kirkland St. ✆ (01721) 720197.
High St. ✆ (01721) 720138.
Edinburgh 24 – Hawick 31 – Glasgow 53.

Cringletie House 🛇, EH45 8PL, North : 3 m. on A 703 ☎ (01721) 730233, *enquiries@cringletie.com, Fax (01721) 730244*, ≤, « Victorian country house built in Scottish Baronial style in extensive grounds », ... – rest, TV P – 30. MC AE VISA JCB
Meals 14.95/35.00 **st.** 10.00 – **14 rm** (dinner included) 85.00/200.00 **st.** – SB.

Peebles Hydro, Innerleithen Rd, EH45 8LX, ☎ (01721) 720602, *reservations@peebleshotelhydro.co.uk, Fax (01721) 722999*, ≤, ... – TV P – 250. MC AE VISA.
Meals 17.50/26.00 **st.** – **131 rm** (dinner included) 97.50/181.00 **st.**, 2 suites – SB.

Castle Venlaw 🛇, EH45 8QG, North : 1 ¼ m. by A 703 ☎ (01721) 720384, *stay@venlaw.co.uk, Fax (01721) 724066*, ≤, ... – TV P – 25. MC VISA
Meals (booking essential to non-residents) (bar lunch)/dinner 23.00/28.00 **t.** 6.50 – **12 rm** 75.00/140.00 **t.**, 1 suite – SB.

Park, Innerleithen Rd, EH45 8BA, ☎ (01721) 720451, *reserve@parkpeebles.co.uk, Fax (01721) 723510*, ... – TV P. MC AE VISA
Meals 20.75 **st.** (dinner) and a la carte 9.50/18.55 **st.** 7.15 – **24 rm** (dinner included) 69.00/150.00 **st.** – SB.

Dilkusha House without rest., Chambers Terr., EH45 9DZ, South : ½ m. by B 7062 taking first right after bridge onto Caledonian Rd then first left onto Frankscroft ☎ (01721) 722888, *forbes_dilkusha@excite.com, Fax (01721) 722888*, ... – TV P. MC VISA.
March-October – **3 rm** 35.00/54.00 **st.**

Rowanbrae without rest., 103 Northgate, EH45 8BU, ☎ (01721) 721630, *john@rowanbrae.freeserve.co.uk, Fax (01721) 723324* – TV.
closed mid December-mid January – **3 rm** 25.00/40.00.

PERTH

Perthshire and Kinross 401 J 14 *Scotland G. – pop. 14 432.*

See : *City★ – Black Watch Regimental Museum★* Y **M1** – *Georgian Terraces★* Y – *Museum and Art Gallery★* Y **M2**.

Env. : *Scone Palace★★ AC, N : 2 m. by A 93* Y – *Branklyn Garden★ AC, SE : 1 m. by A 85* Z – *Kinnoull Hill (≤★) SE : 1¼m. by A 85* Z – *Huntingtower Castle★ AC, NW : 3 m. by A 85* Y – *Elcho Castle★ AC, SE : 4 m. by A 912 –* Z *– and Rhynd rd.*

Exc. : *Abernethy (11C Round Tower★), SE : 8 m. by A 912 –* Z *– and A 913.*

Craigie Hill, Cherrybank ☎ (01738) 624377 Z – *King James VI, Moncreiffe Island ☎ (01738) 625170* Z – *Murrayshall, New Scone ☎ (01738) 551171* Y – *North Inch, c/o Perth & Kinross Council, 5 High St. ☎ (01738) 636481* Y.

Lower City Mills, West Mill St. ☎ (01738) 450600.

Edinburgh 44 – Aberdeen 86 – Dundee 22 – Dunfermline 29 – Glasgow 64 – Inverness 112 – Oban 94.

Plan on next page

Kinfauns Castle, PH2 7JZ, East : 3 m. by A 90 ☎ (01738) 620777, *email@kinfaunscastle.co.uk, Fax (01738) 620778*, ≤, « Restored 19C castle, oriental furnishings », ... – rest, TV P – 60. MC AE VISA JCB.
closed 3 weeks January – **Meals** 18.50/35.00 **t.** 9.50 – **14 rm** 120.00/300.00 **t.**, 2 suites – SB.

Hunting Tower 🛇, Crieff Rd, PH1 3JT, West : 3 ½ m. by A 85 ☎ (01738) 583771, *reception.huntingtower@talk21.com, Fax (01738) 583777*, ... – TV P – 180. MC AE VISA.
Meals a la carte 12.85/28.85 **t.** 6.95 – **31 rm** 89.50/110.00 **t.** – SB.

Parklands, St. Leonard's Bank, PH2 8EB, ☎ (01738) 622451, *parklands.perth@virgin.net, Fax (01738) 622046*, ... – rest, TV P – 25. MC AE VISA Z n
closed 1-2 January – **Meals** a la carte 17.90/25.90 **t.** 8.50 – ***Ancanthus :*** **Meals** a la carte 15.70/26.70 **t.** 8.50 – – **14 rm** 79.00/115.00 **st.** – SB.

Dupplin Castle 🛇, PH2 0PY, Southwest : 6 ¼ m. off A 9 ☎ (01738) 623224, *dupplin@netcomuk.co.uk, Fax (01738) 444140*, ≤, « Scottish mansion house, gardens », ... – P. MC AE VISA JCB.
Meals (booking essential) (residents only) (communal dining) (dinner only) 30.00 **t.** – **7 rm** 70.00/130.00 **t.**

Sunbank House, 50 Dundee Rd, PH2 7BA, ☎ (01738) 624882, *Fax (01738) 442515*, ... – TV P. MC VISA Z a
closed January – **Meals** (dinner only) 13.95/18.95 **t.** and a la carte 6.75 – **10 rm** 59.00/72.00 **t.** – SB.

Express by Holiday Inn without rest., 200 Dunkeld Rd, Inveralmond, PH1 3AQ, Northwest : 2 m. on A 912 ☎ (01738) 636666, *Fax (01738) 633363* – TV P – 40. MC AE VISA JCB.
81 rm 55.00 **st.**

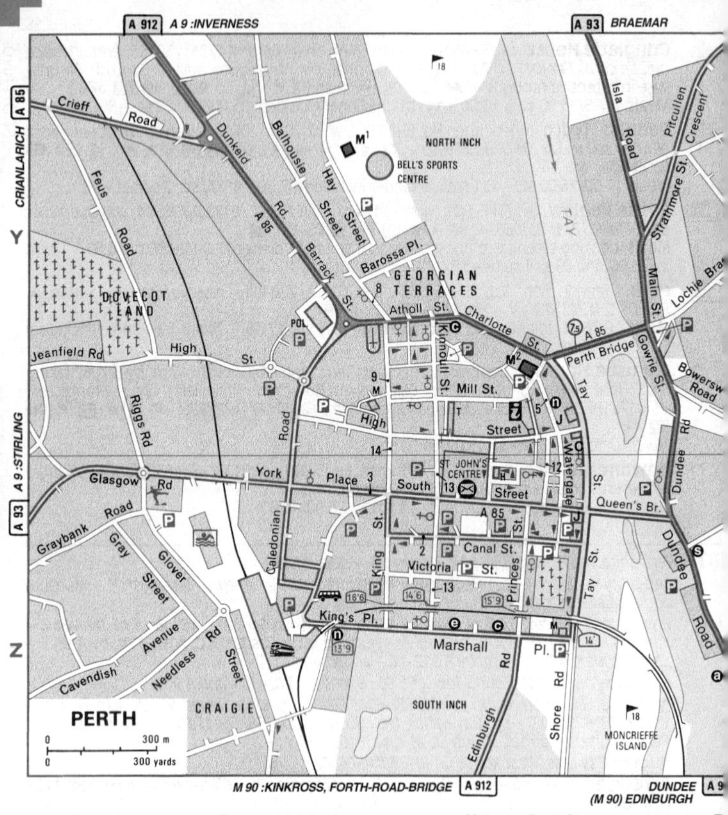

Charterhouse Lane . . . . Z 2
County Place . . . . Z 3
George Street . . . . Y 5
High Street . . . . Y
Melville Street . . . . Y 8
North Methven Street . . . . . . Y 9
St. John's Centre . . . . Z
St. John Street . . . . Z 12
Scott Street . . . . Z
South Street . . . . Z
South Methven Street . . . . Y

Beechgrove without rest., Dundee Rd, PH2 7AQ, ✆ (01738) 636147, *beechgrove.h@ co.uk, Fax (01738) 636147,* « Victorian manse », – TV P. MC VISA. Z
8 rm 35.00/65.00 **st.**

Kinnaird without rest., 5 Marshall Pl., PH2 8AH, ✆ (01738) 628021, *tricia@kinnaird-gh mon.co.uk, Fax (01738) 444056,* – TV P. MC VISA. Z
7 rm 28.00/48.00 **st.**

Park Lane without rest., 17 Marshall Pl., PH2 8AG, ✆ (01738) 637218, *stay@parklane-u om, Fax (01738) 643519,* – TV P. MC AE VISA JCB. Z
closed December-22 January – **6 rm** 24.00/50.00.

Let's Eat, 77-79 Kinnoull St., PH1 5EZ, ✆ (01738) 643377, *enquiries@letseatperth.co Fax (01738) 621464* – . MC AE VISA JCB Y
closed 2 weeks July, 2 weeks January, Sunday and Monday – **Meals** a la carte 16.15/24.7 5.50.

Let's Eat Again, 33 George St., PH1 5LA, ✆ (01738) 633771, *Fax (01738) 621464* – MC AE VISA JCB Y
closed 2 weeks July, 2 weeks January, Sunday and Monday – **Meals** a la carte 15.20/23.9 5.25.

at Guildtown *North : 5 m. on A 93* – Y – ✉ *Perth.*

Newmiln, PH2 6AE, South : 1 m. on A 93 ✆ (01738) 552364, *newmiln.estate@virg et, Fax (01738) 553505,* ←, « Victorian mansion, sporting estate », – rest, P. MC AE VISA
Meals 19.50/32.50 **t.** – **7 rm** 70.00/200.00 **t.** – SB.

New Scone *Northeast : 2½ m. on A 94 – Y – ✉ Perth.*

 **Murrayshall Country House**, PH2 7PH, East : 1 ¼ m. by Murraysall Rd ☎ (01738) 551171, *Fax (01738) 552595*, ←, – rest, – 180. MC AE VISA JCB
Old Masters : **Meals** (dinner only and lunch Saturday and Sunday) 23.00/31.00 **st.** and a la carte 6.00 – **24 rm** 80.00/130.00 **st.**, 17 suites 140.00/160.00 **st** – SB.

SCOTLAND

TERHEAD *Aberdeenshire* 401 O 11 – *pop. 20 789.*

Cruden Bay ☎ (01779) 812285 – Craigewan Links ☎ (01779) 472149 – Longside, West End ☎ (01779) 821558.
Edinburgh 165 – Aberdeen 35 – Fraserburgh 18.

Waterside Inn, Fraserburgh Rd, AB42 3BN, Northwest : 2 m. on A 90 ☎ (01779) 471121, *waterside@macdonald-hotels.co.uk, Fax (01779) 470670*, – – 200. MC AE VISA
Meals 10.00/21.00 **st.** and a la carte 13.50 – **69 rm** 79.50/90.00 – SB.

CAPLE *Aberdeenshire* 401 M 12.

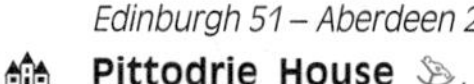
Edinburgh 51 – Aberdeen 21.

Pittodrie House, AB51 5HS, Southwest : 1 ¾ m. by Chapel of Garioch rd ☎ (01467) 681444, *info@pittodrie.macdonald.hotels.co.uk, Fax (01467) 681648*, ←, « Part 15C country house in extensive grounds », squash – rest, – 120. MC AE VISA
Meals 17.50/31.00 **st.** 7.50 – **27 rm** 85.00/125.00 **st.** – SB.

LOCHRY *Perthshire and Kinross* 401 I 13 *Scotland G. – pop. 3 126.*

See : *Town★.*
Exc. : *Blair Castle★★ AC, NW : 7 m. by A 9 A – Queen's View★★, W : 7 m. by B 8019 A – Falls of Bruar★, NW : 11 m. by A 9 A.*
Golf Course Rd ☎ (01796) 472792.
22 Atholl Rd ☎ (01796) 472215.
Edinburgh 71 – Inverness 85 – Perth 27.

Plan on next page

Pine Trees, Strathview Terr., PH16 5QR, ☎ (01796) 472121, *info@pinetrees-hotel.demon.co.uk, Fax (01796) 472460*, ←, – MC AE VISA JCB A b
Meals 23.50 **st.** (dinner) and a la carte 17.25/38.00 **st.** 7.75 – **20 rm** (dinner included) 72.00/196.00 **st.** – SB.

Green Park, Clunie Bridge Rd, PH16 5JY, ☎ (01796) 473248, *bookings@thegreenpark.co.uk, Fax (01796) 473520*, ←, « Lochside setting », – MC VISA A a
Meals (booking essential to non-residents) (dinner only) 23.00 **t.** 4.95 – **39 rm** (dinner included) 67.00/134.00 **t.** – SB.

Dunfallandy House, Logierait Rd, Dunfallandy, PH16 5NA, South : 1 ¼ m. by Bridge Rd ☎ (01796) 472648, *dunfalhse@aol.com, Fax (01796) 472017*, ←, « Georgian mansion house », – MC VISA JCB.
February-October – **Meals** (dinner only) 16.00/18.00 5.50 – **8 rm** 60.00/80.00 **st.**

Knockendarroch House, 2 Higher Oakfield, PH16 5HT, ☎ (01796) 473473, *info@knockendarroch.co.uk, Fax (01796) 474068*, ←, – MC AE VISA. B m
March-October – **Meals** (dinner only) 21.00 **t.** 6.50 – **12 rm** (dinner included) 77.00/120.00 **t.**

Birchwood, 2 East Moulin Rd, PH16 5DW, ☎ (01796) 472477, *jandv@birchwoodhotel.co.uk, Fax (01796) 473951*, – MC VISA. B p
15 March-14 November – **Meals** (dinner only) 22.00 **t.** 6.00 – **12 rm** 39.00/78.00 **t.** – SB.

Balrobin, Higher Oakfield, PH16 5HT, ☎ (01796) 472901, *balrobin@globalnet.co.uk, Fax (01796) 474200*, ←, – rest, MC VISA B n
April-October – **Meals** (residents only) (dinner only) 16.50/19.50 **t.** 8.00 – **15 rm** 42.00/79.00 **st.** – SB.

Westlands of Pitlochry, 160 Atholl Rd, PH16 5AR, ☎ (01796) 472266, *info@westlandshotel.co.uk, Fax (01796) 473994*, – rest, – 50. MC VISA A f
closed 25-26 December – **Meals** (bar lunch)/dinner a la carte 11.70/20.00 **st.** 5.50 – **15 rm** 44.00/88.00 **st.** – SB.

Kinnaird House without rest., Kirkmichael Rd, Kinnaird, PH16 5JL, Northeast : 1 ½ m. on A 924 ☎ (01796) 472843, *kinnaird@hotmail.com, Fax (01796) 472843*, ←, – MC VISA.
closed 1 week Christmas – **6 rm** 30.00/60.00 **st.**

PITLOCHRY

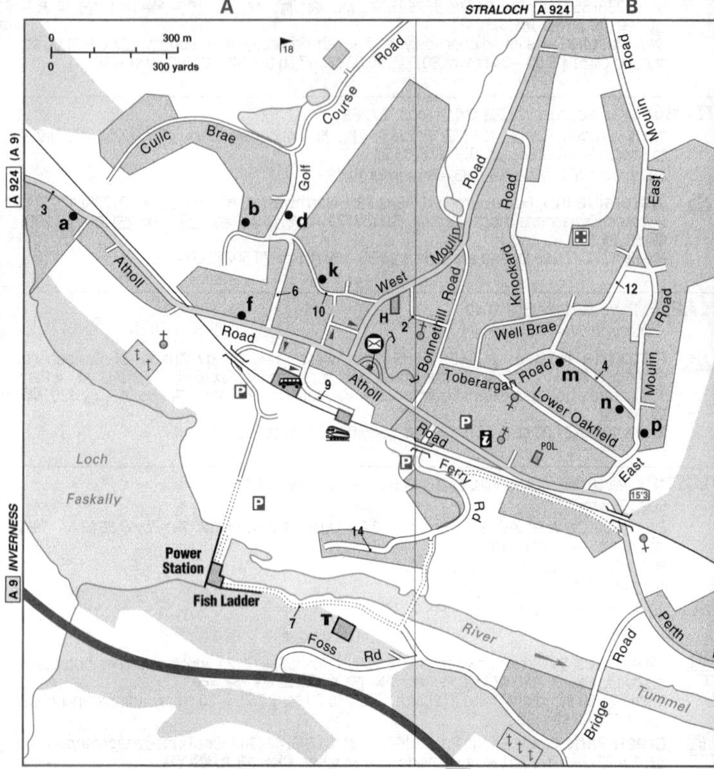

Torrdarach, Golf Course Rd, PH16 5AU, ℘ (01796) 472136, *torrdarach@email.msn.c* *Fax (01796) 473733,* « Gardens » – TV P. MC VISA. A
closed January and February – **Meals** (by arrangement) 15.00 **st.** 5.50 – **7 rm** 26 52.00 **st.** – SB.

Dundarave, Strathview Terr., PH16 5AT, ℘ (01796) 473109, *dundarave.guesthouse@ n.net, Fax (01796) 473109,* ≤, – TV P. MC VISA. A
Meals (by arrangement) 14.00 **s.** – **7 rm** 24.00/52.00 **s.**

at Killiecrankie *Northwest : 4 m. by A 924* – A – *and B 8019 on B 8079* – ✉ *Pitlochry.*

Killiecrankie , PH16 5LG, ℘ (01796) 473220, *enquiries@killiecrankiehotel.cc Fax (01796) 472451,* ≤, – TV P. MC VISA
closed 3 January-2 February, December except Christmas, Monday-Tuesday in Febr and early March – **Meals** (bar lunch)/dinner a la carte 13.85/20.95 **t.** 8.00 – **9 rm** (dinner included) 92.00/184.00 **st.**, 1 suite.

PLOCKTON *Highland* 401 D 11 *Scotland G.*

See : *Village*★.
Env. : *Wester Ross*★★★.
Edinburgh 210 – Inverness 88.

Plockton, Harbour St., IV52 8TN, ℘ (01599) 544274, *sales@plocktonhotel.co Fax (01599) 544475,* ≤ Loch Carron and mountains, – rest, TV. MC AE VISA JCB
***Courtyard* :** **Meals** a la carte 9.85/21.20 **t.** 4.95 – **14 rm** 35.00/70.00 **t.**

The Haven, 3 Innes St., IV52 8TW, ☎ (01599) 544223, *Fax (01599) 544467*, – rest, TV P. MC VISA JCB
closed 20 December-1 February – **Meals** (lunch by arrangement)/dinner 27.00 **t.** 5.75 – **13 rm** 39.00/78.00 **t.**, 2 suites – SB.

Plockton Inn with rm, Innes St., IV52 8TW, ☎ (01599) 544222, *Fax (01599) 544487*, – rest, TV P. MC VISA JCB
Meals - Seafood - a la carte 13.05/19.95 **st.** – **6 rm** 32.00/58.00 **st.** – SB.

LLACHAR *Western Isles (Outer Hebrides)* 401 X 12 – *see Uist (Isles of).*

OLEWE *Highland* 401 D 10 *Scotland G.*

Env. : *Wester Ross*★★★ – *Inverewe Gardens*★★★, *N : 1 m. on B 8057* – *Loch Maree*★★★.
Edinburgh 234 – Inverness 78 – Kyle of Lochalsh 74.

Pool House, IV22 2LD, ☎ (01445) 781272, *poolhouse@inverewe.co.uk*, *Fax (01445) 781403*, ≤ Loch Ewe – TV P. MC AE VISA JCB.
April-December – **Meals** (bar lunch)/dinner 28.00/35.50 **t.** and a la carte 8.50 – **8 rm** 50.00/200.00 **t.**, 1 suite – SB.

RT APPIN *Argyll and Bute* 401 D 14 – ✉ *Appin.*

Edinburgh 136 – Ballachulish 20 – Oban 24.

Airds (Allen) , PA38 4DF, ☎ (01631) 730236, *airds@airds-hotel.com, Fax (01631) 730535*, ≤ Loch Linnhe and mountains of Kingairloch, « Former ferry inn », , – rest, TV P. MC VISA.
closed 16-26 December and 6-26 January – **Meals** (booking essential) (light lunch)/dinner 40.00 **t.** 16.50 – **12 rm** (dinner included) 280.00/310.00 **t.** – SB
Spec. Ravioli of lobster and langoustine with basil and tomato. Saddle of rabbit with caramelised onion tart and foie gras. Fillet of halibut with baby squid, lemon butter sauce.

RT CHARLOTTE *Argyll and Bute* 401 A 16 – *see Islay (Isle of).*

RT ELLEN *Argyll and Bute* 401 B 17 – *see Islay (Isle of).*

RTLETHEN *Aberdeenshire* 401 N 12 – *see Aberdeen.*

RT OF MENTEITH *Perthshire and Kinross* 401 H 15 – ✉ *Stirling.*

Edinburgh 52 – Glasgow 43 – Perth 44.

The Lake , FK8 3RA, ☎ (01877) 385258, *enquiries@lake-of-menteith-hotel.com*, *Fax (01877) 385671*, ≤, « Lakeside setting », – , rest, TV P. MC AE VISA
closed first 2 weeks January and 25 December – **Meals** *(closed Monday and Tuesday November-March)* 16.50/32.50 **t.** and lunch a la carte 8.50 – **16 rm** (dinner included) 90.00/192.00 **t.** – SB.

RTPATRICK *Dumfries and Galloway* 401 402 E 19 – *pop. 842* – ✉ *Stranraer.*

18, 9 *Golf Course Rd* ☎ *(01776) 810273.*
Edinburgh 141 – Ayr 60 – Dumfries 80 – Stranraer 9.

Knockinaam Lodge , DG9 9AD, Southeast : 5 m. by A 77 off B 7042 ☎ (01776) 810471, *Fax (01776) 810435*, ≤, « Victorian former shooting lodge in picturesque coastal setting », , , – rest, TV P. MC AE VISA
Meals (booking essential to non-residents) (set menu only) 29.00/38.00 **t.** – **10 rm** (dinner included) 140.00/330.00 **t.** – SB
Spec. Seared scallops with pasta and caviar. Breast of duck with steamed foie gras. Plum soufflé, vanilla bean ice cream.

Fernhill, Heugh Rd, DG9 8TD, ☎ (01776) 810220, *info@fernhillhotel.co.uk*, *Fax (01776) 810596*, ≤, – rest, TV P. MC VISA
Meals 24.00 **st.** (dinner) and a la carte 15.70/45.95 **st.** 9.00 – **23 rm** (dinner included) 80.00/155.00 **st.** – SB.

SCOTLAND

Blinkbonnie without rest., School Brae, DG9 8LG, ☎ (01776) 810282, *Fax (01776) 810*
<, – rest, TV P.
5 rm 25.00/40.00 **st.**

Crown with rm, North Cres., DG9 8SX, ☎ (01776) 810261, *Fax (01776) 810551,*
rest, TV. MC AE VISA
closed 25 December – **Meals** 14.50 **t.** and a la carte 6.50 – **12 rm** 38.00/72.00 **t.** – S

PORTREE *Highland* 401 B 11 – *see Skye (Isle of).*

PRESTWICK *South Ayrshire* 401 402 G 17 – *pop. 13 705.*

Prestwick, 2 Links Rd ☎ (01292) 477404 – Prestwick St. Nicholas, Grangemuir Rd (01292) 477608.

Prestwick International Airport : ☎ (01292) 479822 – **BY** – **Terminal** : *Buchanan Station.*

see also Glasgow.

Edinburgh 78 – Ayr 2 – Glasgow 32.

Plan of Built up Area : see Ayr

Travel Inn, Kilmarnock Rd, Monkton, KA9 2RJ, Northeast : 3 m. by A 79 and A 78 junction with A 77 ☎ (01292) 678262, *Fax (01292) 678248* – rm, TV P – 70. MC VISA.
Meals (grill rest.) – **40 rm** 40.95 **t.**

QUOTHQUAN *South Lanarkshire* 401 J 27 *Scotland G.* – *Biggar.*

Env. : *Biggar★ (Gladstone Court Museum★ AC – Greenhill Covenanting Museum★ AC) 4½ m. by B 7016.*

Edinburgh 32 – Dumfries 50 – Glasgow 36.

Shieldhill Castle, ML12 6NA, Northeast : ¾ m. ☎ (01899) 220035, *enquiries@shieldhill.co.uk, Fax (01899) 221092,* <, « Part 12C fortified manor house with 16C additions »,
– TV P – 25. MC VISA
Meals 12.50/17.50 **t.** and a la carte – **16 rm** 90.00/297.00 **t.** – SB.

RHICONICH *Highland* 401 F 8 *Scotland G.* – *Lairg.*

Exc. : *Cape Wrath★★★ (<★★) AC, N : 21 m. (including ferry crossing) by A 838 and minor*

Edinburgh 249 – Thurso 87 – Ullapool 57.

Rhiconich, IV27 4RN, ☎ (01971) 521224, *rhiconichhotel@cs.com, Fax (01971) 52173*
Loch Inchard, – rest, TV P. MC VISA JCB
Meals (bar lunch)/dinner 14.95/17.95 **st.** and a la carte 5.50 – **11 rm** 36.00/74.00
SB.

ROGART *Highland* 401 H 9 – *pop. 419.*

Edinburgh 229 – Inverness 73 – Wick 63.

Sciberscross Lodge, Strath Brora, IV28 3YQ, North : 7 m. by Balnacoil
☎ (01408) 641246, *Fax (01408) 641465,* < Brora valley and hills, – P. MC VISA
restricted opening December and January – **Meals** (booking essential) (communal din (dinner only) (set menu only) 25.00/40.00 **st.** – **4 rm** 40.00/80.00 **st.**

ROTHESAY *Argyll and Bute* 401 402 E 16 – *see Bute (Isle of).*

ROYBRIDGE *Highland* 401 F 13 – *see Spean Bridge.*

ST. ANDREWS *Fife* 401 L 14 *Scotland G.* – *pop. 11 136.*

See : *City★★ – Cathedral★ (★★) AC* **B** – *West Port★* **A**.

Env. : *Leuchars (parish church★), NW : 6 m. by A 91 and A 919.*

Exc. : *The East Neuk★★, SE : 9 m. by A 917 and B 9131* **B** – *Crail★★ (Old Centre★★, Up Crail★) SE : 9 m. by A 917* **B** – *Kellie Castle★ AC, S : 9 m. by B 9131 and B 9171* **B** – *Cere SW : 9 m. by B 939 - E : Inland Fife★* **A**.

(x4), Eden, Jubilee, New, Strathtyrum and Balgove Course ☎ (01334) 466666 - Duke's, Craigtoun Park ☎ (01334) 474371.

70 Market St. ☎ (01334) 472021.

Edinburgh 51 – Dundee 14 – Stirling 51.

ST ANDREWS

…ey Street . . . B 2
…ey Walk . . . B 3
…xandra Place . . . A 5
…ed Place . . . A 6
…ge Street . . . A 7
…ts Wynd . . . B 9
Castle Street . . . B 10
Church Street . . . AB 13
Ellice Place . . . A 15
Gibson Place . . . A 17
Gillespie Terrace . . . A 18
Greenside Place . . . B 20
Gregory Lane . . . B 21
Gregory Place . . . B 22
Greyfriars Garden . . . A 24
Hepburn Gardens . . . A 25
Link Crescent . . . A 27
Murray Park . . . A 28
Murray Place . . . A 29
Pilmour Links . . . A 31
Pilmour Place . . . A 32
Playfair Terrace . . . A 34
St. Mary's Place . . . A 35
Union Street . . . B 36

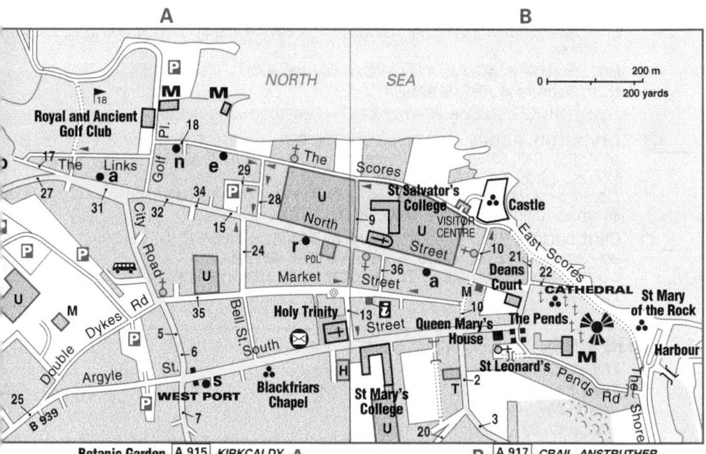

The Old Course H. Golf Resort and Spa, Old Station Rd, KY16 9SP, ✆ (01334) 474371, *oldcoursehotel@standrews.co.uk, Fax (01334) 477668,* ≤ Championship golf course and St. Andrews Bay, rm, 300. VISA JCB. A b
closed 1 week Christmas – ***Road Hole Grill :*** Meals (dinner only) 38.50 **t.** and a la carte 9.00 – ***Sands :*** Meals *(May-October and lunch November-April)* a la carte 16.00/26.95 **t.** 8.00 – **118 rm** 259.00/364.00 **t.**, 28 suites 385.00/520.00 **t** – SB.

Rusacks, Pilmour Links, KY16 9JQ, ✆ (01334) 474321, *heritagehotel_standrews.rusacks@forte-hotels.com, Fax (01334) 477896,* ≤, – rest, – 80. VISA JCB A a
Meals (light lunch Monday to Saturday)/dinner a la carte 14.65/32.50 **st.** – 15.00 – **61 rm** 130.00/210.00 **st.**, 7 suites – SB.

Rufflets Country House , Strathkinness Low Rd, KY16 9TX, West : 1 ½ m. on B 939 ✆ (01334) 472594, *reservations@rufflets.co.uk, Fax (01334) 478703,* ≤, « Country house, gardens » – VISA.
closed 3-9 January – **Meals** (bar lunch Monday to Saturday)/dinner 32.00/36.00 **st.** – **22 rm** 95.00/220.00 **st.** – SB.

St. Andrews Golf, 40 The Scores, KY16 9AS, ✆ (01334) 472611, *thegolfhotel@standrews.co.uk, Fax (01334) 472188,* ≤ – rest, – 200. VISA JCB A e
closed 25 December – **Meals** 9.50 **t.** (dinner) and lunch a la carte 19.25/27.50 **t.** 6.00 – **22 rm** 96.00/160.00 **st.** – SB.

The Scores, 76 The Scores, KY16 9BB, ✆ (01334) 472451, *Fax (01334) 473947,* ≤, – rest, – 160. VISA JCB. A n
closed 25-26 December – **Meals** (bar lunch)/dinner 16.95 **t.** and a la carte – **29 rm** 88.00/169.00 **t.**, 1 suite – SB.

Albany without rest., 56-58 North St., KY16 9AH, ✆ (01334) 477737, *enq@standrewsalbany.co.uk, Fax (01334) 477742,* – . VISA. B a
21 rm 75.00/155.00 **st.**

Aslar House without rest., 120 North St., KY16 9AF, ✆ (01334) 473460, *enquiries@aslar.com, Fax (01334) 477540,* – . VISA. A r
5 rm 28.00/62.00 **st.**

Westport, 170-172 South St., KY16 9EG, ✆ (01334) 473186, *Fax (01334) 479732* – . VISA JCB A s
closed Monday – **Meals** a la carte 19.50/29.45 **t.**

SCOTLAND

at Strathkinness *West : 3 ¾ m. on B 939* – **A** – ✉ *St. Andrews.*

Fossil House and Cottage without rest., 12-14 Main St., KY16 9RU, ☎ (01334) 8506 *the.fossil@virgin.net, Fax (01334) 850639,* – TV P. MC AE VISA JCB.
4 rm 25.00/56.00 **st.**

ST. BOSWELLS *Borders* 401 402 L 17 *Scotland G. – pop. 2 092.*

Env. : *Dryburgh Abbey★★ AC (setting★★★), NW : 4 m. by B 6404 and B 6356 – Tw Valley★★.*

Exc. : *Bowhill★★ AC, SW : 11½ m. by A 699 and A 708.*

St. Boswells ☎ (01835) 823527.

Edinburgh 39 – Glasgow 79 – Hawick 17 – Newcastle upon Tyne 66.

Dryburgh Abbey, Dryburgh, TD6 0RQ, North : 3 ½ m. by B 6404 on B 6 ☎ (01835) 822261, *enquiries@dryburgh.co.uk, Fax (01835) 823945,* ≤, – rest, TV P – 150. MC AE VISA JCB
closed 3-12 January – **Meals** (bar lunch Monday to Saturday)/dinner 24.00/28.00 **s**
36 rm (dinner included) 75.00/170.00, 2 suites.

Clint Lodge, TD6 0DZ, North : 2 ¼ m. by B 6404 on B 6356 ☎ (01835) 822027, *clintlod aol.com, Fax (01835) 822656,* ≤, – TV P. MC VISA
closed 3 weeks February, 25-26 December and 1 January – **Meals** 20.00 **t.** – **3 rm** 30. 70.00.

ST. CATHERINES *Argyll and Bute* 401 E 15 *Scotland G.* – ✉ *Cairndow.*

Env. : *Loch Fyne★★.*

Exc. : *Inveraray★★ : Castle★★ (interior★★★) AC, NW : 12 m. by A 815 and A 83 – Auc drain★, NW : 18 m. by A 815 and A 83.*

Edinburgh 99 – Glasgow 53 – Oban 53.

Arnish Cottage without rest., Poll Bay, PA25 8BA, Southwest : 2 m. on A ☎ (01499) 302405, *Fax (01499) 302405,* ≤ Loch Fyne, « Lochside setting », – P.
closed Christmas and New Year – **3 rm** 25.00/50.00.

Thistle House without rest., PA25 8AZ, on A 815 ☎ (01499) 302209, *Fax (01499) 302* ≤, – TV P. MC VISA.
April-October – **4 rm** 50.00 **s.**

ST. FILLANS *Perthshire and Kinross* 401 H 14 *Scotland G.*

Env. : *Loch Earn★★.*

Edinburgh 67 – Glasgow 57 – Oban 64 – Perth 30.

Achray House, PH6 2NF, ☎ (01764) 685231, *achrayhotelsltd@btinternet.c Fax (01764) 685320,* ≤ Loch Earn and mountains, – rest, TV P. MC AE VISA.
Meals (bar lunch Monday to Saturday)/dinner 19.50 **st.** and a la carte 4.95 – 9
46.50/69.00 **st.**

ST. MARGARET'S HOPE *Orkney Islands* 401 K 6 – *see Orkney Islands.*

ST. MONANS *Fife* 401 L 15 – *pop. 3 965 (inc. Elie and Pinttenweem).*

Edinburgh 47 – Dundee 26 – Perth 40 – Stirling 56.

The Seafood, 16 West End, KY10 2BX, ☎ (01333) 730327, *theseafood.restaurant@vi net.co.uk, Fax (01333) 730327,* ≤, – . MC AE VISA JCB
closed January, December, Sunday dinner except July-August and Monday – **Mea** Seafood - (booking essential) 18.00/22.50 **t.** and dinner a la carte 10.00.

SANDYHILLS *Dumfries and Galloway* 401 402 I 19 – ✉ *Dalbeattie.*

Edinburgh 99 – Ayr 62 – Dumfries 19 – Stranraer 68.

Cairngill House without rest., DG5 4NZ, ☎ (01387) 780681, *tricksharmony@virgi t,* ≤, – TV P. MC VISA JCB
closed November-5 January – **6 rm** 25.00/58.00 **t.**

SCALASAIG *Argyll and Bute* 401 B 15 – *see Colonsay (Isle of).*

SCALLOWAY *Shetland Islands* 401 Q 3 – *see Shetland Islands (Mainland).*

:ARISTA *Western Isles (Outer Hebrides)* 401 Y 10 – *see Lewis and Harris (Isle of).*

:OURIE *Highland* 401 E 8 *Scotland G.* – ✉ *Lairg.*

Exc. : *Cape Wrath*★★★ (≤★★) *AC, N : 31 m. (including ferry crossing) by A 894 and A 838 – Loch Assynt*★★, *S : 17 m. by A 894.*

Edinburgh 263 – Inverness 107.

Eddrachilles ⛰, Badcall Bay, IV27 4TH, South : 2 ½ m. on A 894 ✆ (01971) 502080, *eddrachilles@compuserve.com, Fax (01971) 502477,* ≤ Badcall Bay and islands, ⛵, 🌳, ♿ – TV P. MC VISA JCB. ✗
15 March-19 October – **Meals** (bar lunch)/dinner 12.75 **st.** and a la carte 🍷 5.30 – **11 rm** ☕ 59.00/88.00 **st.** – SB.

:IL (Isle of) *Argyll and Bute* 401 D 15 – ✉ *Oban.*

achan Seil – ✉ *Oban.*

Willowburn ⛰, PA34 4TJ, ✆ (01852) 300276, *willowburn.hotel@virgin.net, Fax (01852) 300597,* ≤, 🌳 – ⚟ TV P. MC VISA JCB
closed January and February – **Meals** (dinner only) 25.00 **st.** 🍷 6.75 – **7 rm** ☕ (dinner included) 59.00/118.00 **st.** – SB.

sdale – ✉ *Oban.*

Inshaig Park ⛰, PA34 4RF, ✆ (01852) 300256, *reception@inshaigparkhotel.demon.co.uk, Fax (01852) 300256,* ≤ Inner Hebridean Islands, 🌳 – ⚟ rest, TV P
April-October – **Meals** (bar lunch)/dinner 16.50 **t.** and a la carte – **6 rm** ☕ 41.00/78.00.

LKIRK *Borders* 401 402 L 17 *Scotland G.* – *pop. 6 469.*

Env. : *Bowhill*★★ *AC, W : 3½ m. by A 708 – Abbotsford*★★ *AC, NE : 5½ m. by A 7 and B 6360 – Tweed Valley*★★.

Exc. : *Melrose Abbey*★★ *(decorative sculpture*★★★*) AC, NE : 8 ½ m. by A 7 and A 6091 – Eildon Hills (*✳★★★*) NE : 7½ m. by A 699 and B 6359.*

⛳9 *The Hill* ✆ *(01750) 20621.*

ℹ *Halliwell's House* ✆ *(01750) 20054 (Easter-October).*

Edinburgh 48 – Hawick 11 – Newcastle upon Tyne 77.

Philipburn Country House, TD7 5LS, West : 1 m. at junction of A 707 with A 708 ✆ (01750) 20747, *info@philipburnhousehotel.co.uk, Fax (01750) 21690,* 🏊 heated, 🌳 – ⚟ rest, ▤ rest, TV P – 🎪 30. MC AE VISA
closed 2 weeks early January – ***Restaurant 1745 :*** **Meals** (lunch by arrangement Monday to Saturday)/dinner 26.50 **t.** 🍷 8.50 – ***Charlies Bar and Bistro :*** **Meals** a la carte 13.50/24.50 **t.** 🍷 8.50 – **12 rm** ☕ 79.50/99.50 **t.**, 3 suites – SB.

Ettrickbridge *Southwest : 7 m. by A 707 on B 7009* – ✉ *Selkirk.*

Ettrickshaws Country House ⛰, TD7 5HW, Southwest : 1 m. on B 7009 ✆ (01750) 52229, *jenny@ettrickshaws.co.uk, Fax (01750) 52229,* ≤, ⛵, 🌳, ♿ – ⚟ TV P. MC VISA. ✗
Meals (booking essential to non-residents) (dinner only) 22.50 **st.** – **5 rm** ☕ (dinner included) 72.50/155.00 **st.** – SB.

ETLAND ISLANDS *Shetland Islands* 401 PQ 3 *Scotland G.* – *pop. 22 522.*

See : *Islands*★ *- Up Helly Aa*★★ *(last Tuesday in January) – Mousa Broch*★★★ *AC (Mousa Island) – Jarlshof*★★ *- Lerwick to Jarlshof*★ *(≤★) – Shetland Croft House Museum*★ *AC.*

✈ *Tingwall Airport :* ✆ *(01595) 840306, NW : 6½ m. of Lerwick by A 971.*

⛴ *from Lerwick (Mainland) to Aberdeen and via Orkney Islands (Stromness) (P & O Scottish Ferries) – from Vidlin to Skerries (Shetland Islands Council) booking essential 2-3 weekly (1 h 30 mn) – from Lerwick (Mainland) to Skerries (Shetland Islands Council) 2 weekly (booking essential) (2 h 30 mn) – from Lerwick (Mainland) to Bressay (Shetland Islands Council) frequent services daily (5 mn) – from Laxo (Mainland) to Isle of Whalsay (Symbister) (Shetland Islands Council) frequent services daily (30 mn) – from Toft (Mainland) to Isle of Yell (Ulsta) (Shetland Islands Council) frequent services daily (20 mn) – from Isle of Yell (Cutcher) to Isle of Fetlar (Oddsta) and via Isle of Unst (Belmont) (Shetland Islands Council) – from Fair Isle to Sumburgh (Mainland) (Shetland Islands Council) weekly (2 h 40 mn).*

⛴ *from Foula to Walls (Shetland Islands Council) 2 weekly (2 h 30 mn) – from Fair Isle to Sumburgh (Shetland Islands Council) weekly (2 h 40 mn).*

MAINLAND.

Brae.

Busta House ⛺, ZE2 9QN, Southwest : 1 ½ m. by A 970 ☎ (01806) 522506, *busta@m co.uk, Fax (01806) 522588*, ≤, « Part 16C and 18C country house », – , ⛔ rest, TV
MC AE VISA
Meals (bar lunch Monday to Saturday)/dinner 24.50 **t.** 6.00 – **20 rm** 70.00/91.00 t
SB.

Lerwick *Scotland G. – pop. 7 590.*

See : *Clickhimin Broch★.*
Env. : *Gulber Wick (≤★), S : 2 m. by A 970.*
18 *Shetland, Dale, Gott ☎ (01595) 840369.*
The Market Cross, Lerwick ☎ (01595) 693434.

Kveldsro House, Greenfield Pl., ZE1 0AQ, ☎ (01595) 692195, *info@kgqhotels.co. Fax (01595) 696595* – TV P. MC AE VISA.
closed 24 December-6 January – **Meals** (carving lunch Sunday) (bar lunch Monday Saturday)/dinner 17.50 **t.** and a la carte 10.50 – **17 rm** 70.00/94.00 **t.** – SB.

Grand, 149 Commercial St., ZE1 0EX, ☎ (01595) 692826, *info@kgqhotels.co. Fax (01595) 694048* – TV. MC AE VISA.
Meals 12.75/15.75 **t.** and dinner a la carte 10.50 – **24 rm** 65.00/90.00 **t.** – SB.

Shetland, Holmsgarth Rd, ZE1 0PW, ☎ (01595) 695515, *shetland_hotels@mes.co. Fax (01595) 695828*, ≤ – ⛔ TV & P – 250. MC AE VISA.
closed 25-26 December – **Meals** (bar lunch)/dinner 12.95/24.95 **st.** and a la carte 4.9
64 rm 76.00/92.00 **t.**, 1 suite – SB.

Glen Orchy House, 20 Knab Rd, ZE1 0AX, ☎ (01595) 692031, *glenorchyhouse@virgin t, Fax (01595) 692031* – ⛔ TV & P. MC VISA JCB
Meals (residents only) (dinner only) 15.00 – **21 rm** 38.50/66.00 **st.**

Scalloway.

Scalloway, Main St., ZE1 0TR, ☎ (01595) 880444, *Fax (01595) 880445*, ≤ – ⛔ TV P.
AE VISA.
Meals 7.00/25.00 **t.** and a la carte 9.90 – **24 rm** 50.00/70.00 **t.** – SB.

Veensgarth.

Herrislea House, ZE2 9SB, ☎ (01595) 840208, *herrislea.house@zetnet.co. Fax (01595) 840630*, – ⛔ TV P. MC VISA JCB
closed 25 December-5 January – **Meals** *(closed Sunday)* (booking essential to non-re dents) (bar lunch)/dinner 12.50/18.50 **st.** and a la carte – **13 rm** 50.00/80.00 **st.**

Walls.

Burrastow House ⛺, ZE2 9PD, Southwest : 2 ½ m. ☎ (01595) 809307, *burr.hs.hote etnet.co.uk, Fax (01595) 809213*, « Part 18C house overlooking Vaila Sound », –
& P. MC AE VISA JCB.
closed 24-December to early March – **Meals** *(closed Sunday and Monday to non-reside* (booking essential) a la carte 19.95/24.00 **t.** 6.55 – **5 rm** (dinner included) 85.
170.00 **t.**

White Ness.

The Westings, ZE2 9LJ, on A 971 ☎ (01595) 840242, *kergord@aol.cc Fax (01595) 840500*, ≤ Whiteness Voe – ⛔ rest, TV P. MC VISA
Meals *(closed Sunday dinner and Monday September-March)* a la carte 10.70/20.05 t
6 rm 40.00/75.00 **st.**

ISLAND OF UNST.

Baltasound.

Buness House ⛺, ZE2 9DS, East : ½ m. by A 968 ☎ (01957) 711315, *bunesshouse@z et.co.uk, Fax (01957) 711815*, ≤ Balta Sound, – ⛔ P. MC VISA.
closed January – **Meals** (by arrangement) (communal dining) 23.00 **st.** 6.50 – 3
30.00/60.00 **st.**

When looking for a quiet hotel
use the maps found in the introduction
or look for establishments with the sign ⛺ or ⛺.

IELDAIG *Highland* 401 D 11 *Scotland G.* – ✉ *Strathcarron.*
Env. : *Wester Ross*★★★.
Edinburgh 226 – Inverness 70 – Kyle of Lochalsh 36.

Tigh An Eilean, IV54 8XN, ✆ (01520) 755251, *tighaneileanhotel@shieldaig.fsnet.co.uk, Fax (01520) 755321,* ← Shieldaig Islands and Loch, « Attractively furnished inn » – ⇔ rest. MC VISA
April-mid October – **Meals** (booking essential to non-residents) (bar lunch)/dinner 26.25 **t.** 5.00 – **11 rm** 48.55/107.60 **t.**

YE (Isle of) *Highland* 401 B 11 /12 *Scotland G.* – *pop. 8 868.*
See : *Island*★★ – *The Cuillins*★★★ – *Skye Museum of Island Life*★ *AC.*
Env. : *N : Trotternish Peninsula*★★ – *W : Duirinish Peninsula*★ – *Portree*★.
Skye Bridge (toll).
– *from Mallaig to Armadale (Caledonian MacBrayne Ltd) 1-2 weekly (30 mn) – from Uig to North Uist (Lochmaddy) or Isle of Harris (Tarbert) (Caledonian MacBrayne Ltd) 1-3 daily (1 h 50 mn) – from Sconser to Isle of Raasay (Caledonian MacBrayne Ltd) 9-10 daily (except Sunday) (15 mn).*
from Mallaig to Isles of Eigg, Muck, Rhum and Canna (Caledonian MacBrayne Ltd) – from Mallaig to Armadale (Caledonian MacBrayne Ltd) (summer only) 1-2 weekly (30 mn).
Bayfield House, Bayfield Rd, Portree ✆ (01478) 612137.

dvasar.

Ardvasar, IV45 8RS, ✆ (01471) 844223, *christine@ardvasar-hotel.demon.co.uk, Fax (01471) 844495,* ←, – TV P. MC VISA
Meals (bar lunch)/dinner 28.50 **st.** and a la carte 7.95 – **9 rm** 50.00/100.00 – SB.

eakish.

Rendezvous, Old School House, IV42 8PY, ✆ (01471) 822001, *Fax (01471) 822986* – P. MC VISA JCB
closed January, February and Tuesday – **Meals** - Seafood - (booking essential) (dinner only and Sunday lunch) a la carte 16.50/24.50 **st.**

oadford.

Corry Lodge ⛺, Liveras, IV49 9AA, North : 1 m. by An Acarsaid rd ✆ (01471) 822235, *Fax (01471) 822318,* ←, « Part 18C house », – ⇔ TV P. MC VISA.
April-October – **Meals** (by arrangement) (communal dining) 17.00 – **4 rm** 35.00/ 60.00 **st.**

Ptarmigan without rest., Harrapool, IV49 9AQ, East : ¾ m. on A 87 ✆ (01471) 822744, *info@ptarmigan-cottage.com, Fax (01471) 822745,* ← Broadford Bay and islands, « Waterside setting », – ⇔ TV P. MC AE VISA
closed 2 weeks winter – **3 rm** 52.00.

Earsary without rest., 7-8 Harrapool, IV49 9AQ, East : ¾ m. on A 87 ✆ (01471) 822697, *earsary@isleofskye.net, Fax (01471) 822781,* ←, , – ⇔ TV P.
3 rm 30.00/50.00 **st.**

Westside without rest., Elgol Rd, IV49 9AB, on B 8083 ✆ (01471) 822320, *dolly.skye@talk21.com, Fax (01471) 822320,* – TV P.
closed January and December **3 rm** 22.00/44.00.

rbost.

Talisker House ⛺, Talisker Bay, IV47 8SF, West : 4 ¼ m. on Talisker rd ✆ (01478) 640245, *jon_and_ros.wathen@virgin.net, Fax (01478) 640214,* ←, « Part 18C country house », , , – ⇔ & P. MC VISA JCB.
15 March-26 October – **Meals** (by arrangement) 25.00 **st.** – **4 rm** 58.00/86.00 **st.**

lnaknock – ✉ *Portree*

Glenview Inn, IV51 9JH, ✆ (01470) 562248, *valtos@lineone.net, Fax (01470) 562211,* ← – ⇔ P. MC VISA
mid March-mid October – **Meals** a la carte 13.45/22.55 **t.** 6.50 – **5 rm** 40.00/70.00 **t.**

nvegan.

The House Over-By, Colbost, IV55 8ZT, Northwest : 5 ¾ m. by A 863 on B 884 ✆ (01470) 511258, *eatandstay@threechimneys.co.uk, Fax (01470) 511358,* ← Loch Dunvegan – ⇔ TV & P. MC AE VISA.
closed last 2 weeks January – **Meals** – (see ***Three Chimneys*** below) – **6 rm** 135.00/ 160.00 **st.** – SB.

Dunorin House , Herebost, IV55 8GZ, Southeast : 2 ½ m. by A 863 on Roag (01470) 521488, *stay@dunorin.freeserve.co.uk, Fax (01470) 521488*, ←, – .
April-mid October – **Meals** (booking essential) (dinner only) 23.00/24.00 **st.** 5.00 – **10** 40.00/86.00 **st.** – SB.

Kinlochfollart , IV55 8WQ, South : ¾ m. on Glendale rd (01470) 5214 *Fax (01470) 521740*, ←, – .
closed Christmas and New Year – **Meals** (by arrangement) (communal dining) 20.00 s **3 rm** 42.00/70.00 **s.**

Roskhill, Roskhill, IV55 8ZD, Southeast : 2 ½ m. by A 863 (01470) 521317, *stay@rosk demon.co.uk, Fax (01470) 521761* –
Meals 14.50 **s.** 6.00 – **4 rm** 40.00/70.00 **s.** – SB.

Three Chimneys (at The House Over-By), Colbost, IV55 8ZT, Northwest : 5 ¾ m. by A 8 on B 884 (01470) 511258, *eatandstay@threechimneys.co.uk, Fax (01470) 511358*,
closed last 2 weeks January, Sunday lunch and lunch in winter – **Meals** - Seafood speciali - (booking essential) 17.95/35.00 **st.** and a la carte 29.00/42.00 **st.**

Elgol.

Rowan Cottage , 9 Glasnakille, IV49 4BQ, Southeast : 2 m. (01471) 866287, *rov @rowancott.demon.co.uk, Fax (01471) 866287*, ← Loch Slapin and Sleat peninsula, – .
21 March-20 November – **Meals** (by arrangement) 21.00 **st.** – **3 rm** 35.00/48.00 **st.** –

Flodigarry – *Staffin.*

Flodigarry Country House , IV51 9HZ, (01470) 552203, *info@flodigarry.co. Fax (01470) 552301*, ← Staffin Island and coastline, –
Meals (bar lunch Monday to Saturday)/dinner 32.00 **t.** and a la carte 8.95 – **19** 55.00/160.00 **t.**

Isleornsay – *Sleat*

Kinloch Lodge , IV43 8QY, North : 3 ½ m. by A 851 (01471) 833214, *kinloch@dia pex.com, Fax (01471) 833277*, ← Loch Na Dal, « 17C former shooting lodge », , ,
closed 23-28 December – **Meals** (booking essential to non-residents) (dinner only) 28. 37.00 **t.** 5.00 – **14 rm** 55.00/190.00 **t.** – SB.

Duisdale Country House , IV43 8QW, North : 1 ¼ m. on A 851 (01471) 833202 *arie@duisdalehotel.demon.co.uk, Fax (01471) 833404*, ← Sound of Sleat and mounta « Gardens », – rest, .
Easter-October – **Meals** (booking essential to non-residents) (dinner only) 30.00 **t.** 6.5 **17 rm** 65.00/120.00 **t.** – SB.

Eilean Iarmain , IV43 8QR, (01471) 833332, *Fax (01471) 833275*, ←, « 19C inn , , –
Meals (lunch by arrangement)/dinner 27.00 **t.** 11.75 – **12 rm** 90.00/150.00 **t.**, 4 su – SB.

Ord – *Sleat.*

Fiordhem , IV44 8RN, (01471) 855226, *sales@fiordhem.co.uk*, ← Loch Eishort The Cuillins, « Idyllic setting on shores of Loch Eishort », – .
Easter-October – **Meals** (by arrangement) (communal dining) – **3 rm** (dinner includ 90.00 **st.**

Portree – *pop. 2 126.*

Bayfield House, Bayfield Rd (01478) 612137.

Cuillin Hills , IV51 9QU, Northeast : ¾ m. by A 855 (01478) 612003, *office@cuillin .demon.co.uk, Fax (01478) 613092*, ←, , – rest, – 140. .
Meals (bar lunch Monday to Saturday) (buffet lunch Sunday)/dinner 19.00/26.00 **st.** 6.5 **30 rm** 60.00/120.00 **st.** – SB.

Bosville, Bosville Terr., IV51 9DG, (01478) 612846, *bosville@macleodhotels.co Fax (01478) 613434*, ← –
***Chandlery* :** **Meals** - Seafood - (dinner only) 18.00/22.50 **st.** 8.00 – **15 rm** 60. 110.00 **st.** – SB.

Rosedale, Beaumont Cres., IV51 9DB, (01478) 613131, *rosedale@achnacraig.freese co.uk, Fax (01478) 612531*, ← harbour, – rest,
mid March-mid November – **Meals** (dinner only) 21.00 **t.** 7.30 – 5.00 – **23 rm** 43. 98.00 **st.**

Almondbank without rest., Viewfield Rd, IV51 9EU, Southwest : ¾ m. on A 87 ☎ (01478) 612696, *jansvans@aol.com, Fax (01478) 613114,* ≤ Portree Bay, – TV P. MC VISA JCB
4 rm ☐ 35.50/55.00.

Kings Haven without rest., 11 Bosville Terr., IV51 9DG, ☎ (01478) 612290, *Fax (01478) 612290,* – TV. MC VISA.
closed February and Christmas – **6 rm** ☐ 70.00 **t.**

easlane – ✉ *Skeabost Bridge.*

Auchendinny , IV51 9NX, South : 1 m. on A 850 ☎ (01470) 532470, *Fax (01470) 532470,* ≤ Loch Snizort Beag, – P. MC VISA.
Easter-September – **Meals** (by arrangement) 14.00 **st.** – **7 rm** ☐ 37.00/58.00 **st.**

UTH QUEENSFERRY *West Lothian* 401 J 16 – ✉ *Edinburgh.*
Edinburgh 10 – Glasgow 42 – Perth 35.

Travel Inn, Queen's Crossing, Builyeon Rd, EH30 3YJ, ☎ (0131) 331 5056, *Fax (0131) 331 4746* – , rm, rest, TV P. MC AE VISA.
Meals (grill rest.) – **46 rm** 40.95 **t.**

UTH UIST *Western Isles (Outer Hebrides)* 401 XY 11/12 – *see Uist (Isles of).*

EAN BRIDGE *Highland* 401 F 13.
☎ *(01397) 704954.*
Inverness-shire ☎ (01397) 712576 (Easter-October).
Edinburgh 143 – Fort William 10 – Glasgow 94 – Inverness 58 – Oban 60.

Corriegour Lodge, Loch Lochy, PH34 4EB, North : 8 ¾ m. on A 82 ☎ (01397) 712685, *info@corriegour-lodge-hotel.com, Fax (01397) 712696,* ≤, , – TV P. MC AE VISA JCB.
closed December and January except New Year and weekends only February, March and November – **Meals** (dinner only) 29.50 **t.** 6.75 – **9 rm** ☐ (dinner included) ☐ 69.50/139.00 **t.** – SB.

Corriechoille Lodge , PH34 4EY, Southeast : 2 ½ m. by Corriechoille rd ☎ (01397) 712002, *enquiry@corriechoille.com, Fax (01397) 712002,* – TV P. MC VISA JCB.
March-October – **Meals** (by arrangement) 16.00 **s.** – **5 rm** ☐ 34.00/59.00 **s.** – SB.

Springburn Farmhouse without rest., Stronaba, PH34 4DX, North : 2 ½ m. on A 82 ☎ (01397) 712707, *info@springburn.freewine.co.uk, Fax (01397) 712702,* ≤, – TV P.
4 rm ☐ 25.00/45.00.

Coinachan, Gairlochy Rd, PH34 4EG, Northwest : 1 ¼ m. by A 82 on B 8004 ☎ (01397) 712417, *Fax (01397) 712417,* ≤, – P.
Meals 15.00 **st.** – **3 rm** ☐ 30.00/50.00 **st.** – SB.

Old Station, Station Rd, PH34 4EP, ☎ (01397) 712535, « Former Victorian railway station » – P. MC VISA JCB
Easter-October – **Meals** *(closed Monday and dinner Tuesday-Thursday and Sunday)* (booking essential) a la carte 13.70/22.95 7.50.

Old Pines with rm, PH34 4EG, Northwest : 1 ½ m. by A 82 on B 8004 ☎ (01397) 712324, *goodfood@oldpines.co.uk, Fax (01397) 712433,* ≤, – P. MC VISA JCB.
closed 2 weeks in winter – **Meals** (light lunch and Sunday dinner) (set menu only)/dinner 24.50/30.00 **t.** 7.50 – **8 rm** ☐ (dinner included) 70.00/140.00 **t.** – SB.

Roybridge *East : 3 m. on A 86.*

Glenspean Lodge , PH31 4AW, East : 2 m. on A 86 ☎ (01397) 712223, *wdgsl@aol.com, Fax (01397) 712660,* ≤, – TV P. MC AE VISA.
March-October – **Meals** a la carte 18.40/29.95 **st.** 6.00 – **15 rm** ☐ 53.00/150.00 **st.** – SB.

TTAL OF GLENSHEE *Perthshire and Kinross* 401 J 13 *Scotland G.* – ✉ *Blairgowrie.*
Env. : *Glenshee (★★) (chairlift AC).*
Edinburgh 69 – Aberdeen 74 – Dundee 35.

Dalmunzie House , PH10 7QG, ☎ (01250) 885224, *dalmunzie@aol.com, Fax (01250) 885225,* ≤, , , , , – , rest, TV P. MC VISA JCB
closed December – **Meals** (bar lunch)/dinner 23.00/25.00 **t.** and a la carte 5.50 – **16 rm** ☐ 54.00/112.00 **t.** – SB.

STENNESS *Orkney Islands* 401 K 7 – *see Orkney Islands.*

STEPPS *North Lanarkshire* 401 H 16 – *see Glasgow.*

STIRLING *Stirling* 401 I 15 *Scotland G.* – *pop. 30 515.*

See : *Town★★* – *Castle★★* **AC** *(Site★★★, external elevations★★★, Stirling Heads★★, Argyll and Sutherland Highlanders Regimental Museum★)* **B** – *Argyll's Lodging★ (Renaissance decoration★)* **B A** – *Church of the Holy Rude★* **B B.**

Env. : *Wallace Monument (✻★★) NE : 2½ m. by A 9* – **A** – *and B 998.*

Exc. : *Dunblane★ (Cathedral★★, West Front★★), N : 6½ m. by A 9* **A.**

ℹ *41 Dumbarton Rd ☏ (01786) 475019 – Royal Burgh Stirling Visitor Centre ☏ (01786) 479901 – Motorway Service Area, M 9/M 80, junction 9 ☏ (01786) 814111 (April-October)*

Edinburgh 37 – Dunfermline 23 – Falkirk 14 – Glasgow 28 – Greenock 52 – Motherwell 3 Oban 87 – Perth 35.

STIRLING

Barnton Street . . . . **B** 2
Borestone Crescent . . . . **A** 3
Causewayhead Road . . . . **A, B** 4
Corn Exchange Road . . . . **B** 5
Cornton Road . . . . **A** 7
Coxithill Road . . . . **A** 8
Drummond Place . . . . **B** 9
Dumbarton Road . . . . **B** 10
Goosecroft Road . . . . **B** 12
King Street . . . . **B** 13
Leisure Centre . . . . **B**
Murray Place . . . . **B** 15
Newhouse . . . . **A** 16
Park Place . . . . **A** 18
Port Street . . . . **B**
Queen Street . . . . **B** 20
Randolph Terrace . . . . A
St. John Street . . . . B
St. Mary's Wynd . . . . B
Seaforth Place . . . . B
Shirra's Brae Road . . . . A
Spittal Street . . . . B
Thistle Centre . . . . B
Union Street . . . . B
Upper Craigs . . . . B
Weaver Row . . . . A

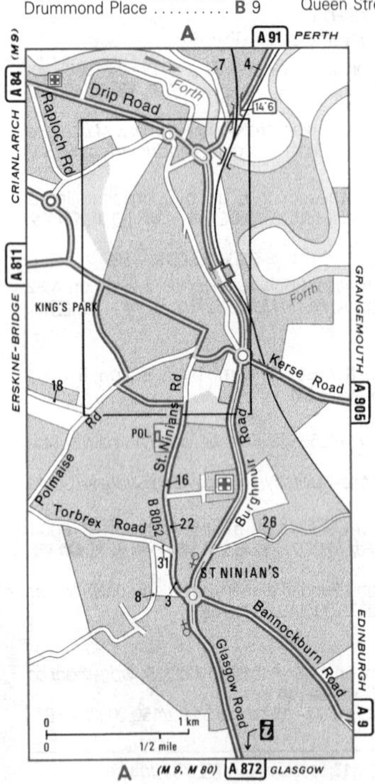

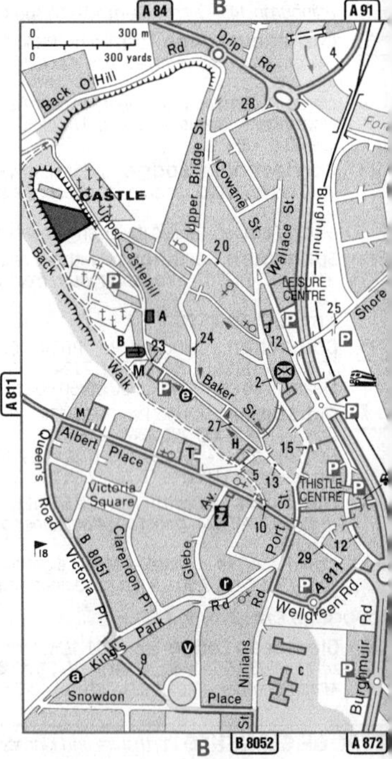

Stirling Highland, Spittal St., FK8 1DU, ☏ (01786) 272727, *stirling@paramount-hotels.co.uk, Fax (01786) 272829,* « Converted Victorian high school », Lб, ≘s, 🏊, squash – |‡| rest, TV ☏ ♿ P – 🏛 120. MC AE ① VISA JCB B
Scholars : Meals *(closed Saturday lunch)* 10.50/22.50 **st.** and a la carte – ***Rizzios :*** Meals Italian - a la carte 15.40/24.65 **t.** – ☕ 12.50 – **94 rm** 107.00/144.00 **t.**, 2 suites – SB.

Park Lodge, 32 Park Terr., FK8 2JS, ☎ (01786) 474862, *parklodge@stirlinghotel.fsnet.co.uk, Fax (01786) 449748,* « Part Georgian, part Victorian house, antiques », – TV P – 100. VISA. B a
closed Christmas and New Year – **Meals** 12.00/18.00 **st.** and a la carte 7.50 – **10 rm** 60.00/85.00 **st.**

Express by Holiday Inn without rest., Springkerse Business Park, FK7 7XH, East : 2 m. by A 905 off A 91 ☎ (01786) 449922, *infohiex-stirling.com, Fax (01786) 449932* – TV P – 30. AE VISA JCB
80 rm 55.00 **st.**

Travel Inn, Whins of Milton, Glasgow Rd, FK7 8EX, South : 3 m. by A 9 on A 872 ☎ (01786) 811256, *Fax (01786) 816415* – rm, TV P. AE VISA.
Meals (grill rest.) – **40 rm** 40.95 **t.**

Ashgrove House without rest., 2 Park Av., FK8 2LX, ☎ (01786) 472640, *Fax (01786) 472640,* – TV P. B r
Arpil-October – **3 rm** 35.00/55.00.

Number 10 without rest., Gladstone Pl., FK8 2NN, ☎ (01786) 472681, *cameron-10@tinyonline.co.uk, Fax (01786) 472681,* – TV. B v
3 rm 30.00/45.00 **st.**

West Plean House without rest., FK7 8HA, South : 3 ½ m. on A 872 (Denny rd) ☎ (01786) 812208, *west.plean@virgin.net, Fax (01786) 480550,* « Working farm », – TV P.
closed January and December – **3 rm** 30.00/50.00.

There is no paid advertising in this Guide.

IRLING SERVICE AREA *Stirling* 401 I 15 – *Stirling.*

Travelodge without rest., Pirnhall roundabout, Snabhead, FK7 8EU, at junction 9 of M 9 ☎ (01786) 813614, *Fax (01786) 815900* – TV P. AE VISA JCB.
37 rm 49.95 **t.**

ONEHAVEN *Aberdeenshire* 401 N 13 *Scotland G.*

Env. : *Dunnottar Castle★★ (site★★★), SE : 1 m.*

Exc. : *Crathes Castle★★ (Gardens★★★), NW : 14½ m. by A 957 and A 93.*

66 Allardice St. ☎ (01569) 762806.

Edinburgh 114 – Aberdeen 16 – Dundee 51.

The Tolbooth, Old Pier Rd, AB39 2JU, ☎ (01569) 762287, *Fax (01569) 762287* – VISA
closed 3 weeks after Christmas, 1 week October, Sunday and Monday – **Meals** - Seafood - (dinner only) a la carte 18.00/27.00 **t.** 6.50.

ORNOWAY *Western Isles (Outer Hebrides)* 401 A 9 – *see Lewis and Harris (Isle of).*

RANRAER *Dumfries and Galloway* 401 402 E 19 *Scotland G. – pop. 11 348.*

Exc. : *Logan Botanic Garden★ AC, S : 11 m. by A 77, A 716 and B 7065.*

Creachmore, Leswalt ☎ (01776) 870245.

to Northern Ireland (Belfast) (Stena Line) (1 h 45 mn) – to Northern Ireland (Belfast) (Stena Line) 4-5 daily (1 h 45 mn/3 h 15 mn).

Burns House, 28 Harbour St. ☎ (01776) 702595.

Edinburgh 132 – Ayr 51 – Dumfries 75.

North West Castle, Port Rodie, DG9 8EH, ☎ (01776) 704413, *info@northwestcastle.co.uk, Fax (01776) 702646,* , – , rest, TV P – 180. VISA.
Meals 24.00 **st.** (dinner) and (lunch) a la carte 11.35/19.75 **st.** 8.50 – **73 rm** (dinner included) 75.00/150.00 **st.** – SB.

Kildrochet House, DG9 9BB, South : 3 ¼ m. by A 77 on A 716 at junction with B 7077 (Newton Stewart rd) ☎ (01776) 820216, *kildrochet@compuserve.com, Fax (01776) 820216,* « 18C former dower house », – P. VISA JCB.
Meals (by arrangement) 19.00 – **3 rm** 33.00/54.00.

Glenotter without rest., Leswalt Rd, DG9 0EP, Northwest : 1 m. on A 718 ☎ (01776) 703199, *glenotter.bb@talk20.com,* – TV P. VISA.
closed November, Christmas and 1 January – **3 rm** 25.00/40.00.

Windyridge Villa without rest., 5 Royal Cresent, DG9 8HB, off Port Rodie (A77 Ayr rd) ☎ (01776) 889900, *windyridge-villa@hotmail.com, Fax (01776) 889900* – TV
closed 2 weeks November and 25 December – **3 rm** 25.00/46.00 **st.**

SCOTLAND

SCOTLAND

at Kirkcolm *Northwest : 6 m. by A 718 – ✉ Stranraer.*

Corsewall Lighthouse ⑤, Corsewall Point, DG9 0QG, Northwest : 4 ¼ m. by B
✆ (01776) 853220, *jim-neilson@masn.com, Fax (01776) 854231*, ≤, – rest, TV, P. MC VISA JCB
Meals a la carte 15.75/27.00 **t.** 11.00 – **6 rm** (dinner included) 90.00/220.00 **t.**, 2 su
– SB.

STRATHCONON *Highland* 401 F 11 *Scotland G.* – ✉ *Muir of Ord.*
Exc. : *Wester Ross*★★★.
Edinburgh 184 – Inverness 28.

East Lodge ⑤, IV6 7QQ, West : 11 m. from Marybank off A 832 ✆ (01997) 477222, *ea dgehotel@globewide.com, Fax (01997) 477243*, ≤, – rest, TV P. MC VISA
Meals *(closed Monday and Tuesday to non-residents)* (bar lunch)/dinner 15.00 **st.** 4.9
10 rm 35.00/70.00 **st.** – SB.

STRATHKINNESS *Fife* 401 L 14 – *see St. Andrews.*

STRATHPEFFER *Highland* 401 G 11 – *pop. 966.*
18 *Strathpeffer Spa* ✆ *(01997) 421219.*
The Square ✆ *(01997) 421415 (April-November).*
Edinburgh 174 – Inverness 18.

Craigvar without rest., The Square, IV14 9DL, ✆ (01997) 421622, *ms@gilsmith.demon uk, Fax (01997) 421796*, – TV P. MC VISA.
closed Christmas and New Year – **3 rm** 27.00/54.00 **st.**

STRATHYRE *Stirling* 401 H 15 *Scotland G.* – ✉ *Callander.*
Exc. : *The Trossachs*★★★ *(Loch Katherine*★★*) SW : 14 m. by A 84 and A 821 – Hil viewpoint*★★★ *(*★★★*) SW : 16½ m. by A 84 and A 821.*
Edinburgh 62 – Glasgow 53 – Perth 42.

Ardoch Lodge ⑤, FK18 8NF, West : ¼ m. ✆ (01877) 384666, *ardoch@btinternet.co Fax (01877) 384666*, ≤, – rest, P. MC VISA JCB
mid March-November – **Meals** (by arrangement) 21.00 **t.** – **3 rm** 33.50/62.00 **t.** – SB.

Creagan House with rm, FK18 8ND, on A 84 ✆ (01877) 384638, *mail@creaganhouse et.co.uk, Fax (01877) 384319*, ≤ – P. MC AE VISA
closed February and 1 week October – **Meals** (booking essential) (dinner only) 19.50/23.5
8.00 – **5 rm** 52.50/85.00 **t.** – SB.

STROMNESS *Orkney Islands* 401 K 7 – *see Orkney Islands.*

STRONTIAN *Highland* 401 D 13.
Argyll ✆ *(01967) 402131 (April-October).*
Edinburgh 139 – Fort William 23 – Oban 66.

Kilcamb Lodge ⑤, PH36 4HY, ✆ (01967) 402257, *kilcamblodge@aol.co Fax (01967) 402041*, ≤, « Lochside setting », – TV P. MC VISA JCB.
closed January, February and Christmas – **Meals** (light lunch) (dinner booking essentia non-residents) 20.50/29.50 **t.** 9.50 – **11 rm** 60.00/130.00 **st.**

STRUY *Highland* 401 F 11.
Edinburgh 180 – Inverness 19 – Kyle of Lochalsh 82.

The Glass at the Struy Inn, IV4 7JS, ✆ (01463) 761219, *glassrest@supanet.co*
rest, P. MC VISA JCB
March-25 December – **Meals** (booking essential) a la carte 14.50/23.50 **t.** 4.50.

SWINTON *Borders* 401 402 N 16 – *pop. 472* – ✉ *Duns.*
Edinburgh 49 – Berwick-upon-Tweed 13 – Glasgow 93 – Newcastle upon Tyne 66.

The Wheatsheaf with rm, TD11 3JJ, ✆ (01890) 860257, *Fax (01890) 860688*,
TV P. MC VISA JCB
closed 2 weeks January, 25 December and 1 January – **Meals** *(closed Monday to n residents)* a la carte 20.00/26.20 **t.** 6.00 – **7 rm** 52.00/98.00 **t.**

SCOTLAND

IN *Highland* 401 H 10 – *pop. 4 540.*

Tain, Chapel Rd (01862) 892314 – Tarbat, Portmahomack (01862) 871512.
Edinburgh 191 – Inverness 35 – Wick 91.

Mansfield House, Scotsburn Rd, IV19 1PR, (01862) 892052, *mansfield@cali.co.uk, Fax (01862) 892260,* – – 35. MC AE VISA
Fowler's : **Meals** (bar lunch)/dinner 25.00 **t.** and a la carte 7.50 – **19 rm** 65.00/170.00 **t.**

Morangie House, Morangie Rd, IV19 1PY, (01862) 892281, *wynne@morangiehotel.com, Fax (01862) 892872,* – rm, MC AE VISA
Meals a la carte 15.00/23.00 **t.** 5.50 – **26 rm** 65.00/95.00 **t.**

Aldie House, IV19 1LZ, Southeast : 1 ½ m. by B 9174 off A 9 (01862) 893787, *Fax (01862) 893787,* – MC VISA.
Meals (by arrangement) 13.00 – **3 rm** 32.00/52.00 **s.**

Golf View House without rest., 13 Knockbreck Rd, IV19 1BN, (01862) 892856, *golfview@btinternet.com, Fax (01862) 892172,* – MC VISA.
closed January and December – **5 rm** 30.00/50.00.

Cadboll *Southeast : 8½ m. by A 9 and B 9165 (Portmahomack rd) off Hilton rd – Tain.*

Glenmorangie House, Fearn, IV20 1XP, (01862) 871671, *relax@glenmorangieplc.co.uk, Fax (01862) 871625,* « Distillery owned, restored part 17C house », – MC AE VISA
Meals (booking essential to non-residents) (lunch by arrangement) (communal dining) 15.00/38.50 **t.** – **9 rm** (dinner included) 120.00/260.00 **t.** – SB.

LLADALE *Highland* 401 D 10 *Scotland G.* – *Achnasheen.*

Env. : *Wester Ross*★★★ – *Loch Maree*★★★ – *Victoria Falls*★, *N : 2 m. by A 832.*
Edinburgh 218 – Inverness 62 – Kyle of Lochalsh 58.

Old Mill Highland Lodge, Loch Maree, IV22 2HL, (01445) 760271, –
closed 15 October-15 December – **Meals** 25.00 **st.** 7.00 – **6 rm** (dinner included) 130.00 **st.** – SB.

LMINE *Highland* 401 G 8 – *Lairg.*

Edinburgh 245 – Inverness 86 – Thurso 48.

Cloisters without rest., Church Holme, IV27 4YP, (01847) 601286, *Fax (01847) 601286,* Rabbit Islands and Tongue Bay, –
3 rm 25.00/40.00 **t.**

RBERT *Argyll and Bute* 401 D 16 – *see Kintyre (Peninsula).*

RBERT *Western Isles (Outer Hebrides)* 401 Z 10 – *see Lewis and Harris (Isle of).*

ORNHILL *Dumfries and Galloway* 401 402 I 18 *Scotland G.* – *pop. 1 633.*

Env. : *Drumlanrig Castle*★★ *(cabinets*★*) AC, NW : 4 m. by A 76.*
Edinburgh 64 – Ayr 44 – Dumfries 15 – Glasgow 63.

Trigony House, Closeburn, DG3 5EZ, South : 1 ½ m. on A 76 (01848) 331211, *info@trigonyhotel.co.uk, Fax (01848) 331303,* – rest, MC
Meals a la carte 12.10/19.80 **t.** 5.00 – **8 rm** 37.50/80.00 **t.** – SB.

ORNHILL *Stirling* 401 H 15 – *pop. 550* – *Stirling.*

Thornhill, Blacknest (01848) 330546.
Edinburgh 46 – Glasgow 36.

Corshill Cottage, FK8 3QD, East : 1 m. on A 873 (01786) 850270, *corshillbandb@talk21.com, Fax (01786) 850270,* –
Meals (by arrangement) 15.00/17.00 **st.** – **3 rm** 28.00/48.00.

URSO *Highland* 401 J 8 *Scotland G.* – *pop. 9 110.*

Exc. : *Strathy Point*★ *(★★★) W : 22 m. by A 836.*
Newlands of Geise (01847) 893807.
from Scrabster to Stromness (Orkney Islands) (P & O Scottish Ferries) (2 h).
Riverside (01847) 892371 (April-October).
Edinburgh 289 – Inverness 133 – Wick 21.

SCOTLAND

Forss House ⛓, Bridge of Forss, KW14 7XY, West : 5 1/2 m. on A 836 ✆ (01847) 86120 amie@forsshouse.freeserve.co.uk, Fax (01847) 861301, ≤, ⛩, ⛸ – ⛔ rest, TV ♿ P. AE VISA
closed 23 December-6 January – **Meals** (bar lunch)/dinner 22.50 **t.** 6.80 – **9 rm** ☐ 57. 110.00 **t.**, 1 suite.

Murray House without rest., 1 Campbell St., KW14 7HD, ✆ (01847) 895759 – ⛔ TV
closed 24 December-5 January – **4 rm** ☐ 20.00/40.00 **s.**

TIGHNABRUAICH *Argyll and Bute* 401 E 16.
Edinburgh 113 – Glasgow 63 – Oban 66.

Royal, PA21 2BE, ✆ (01700) 811239, *royalhotel@btinternet.com, Fax (01700) 811300,* ⛔ TV P. MC AE VISA
closed 25 December – **Meals** (bar lunch)/dinner 24.95/26.50 7.45 – **11 rm** ☐ 77. 94.00 **st.** – SB.

TILLICOULTRY *Clackmannanshire* 401 I 15 – *pop. 4 586.*
Alva Rd ✆ (01259) 50124.
Edinburgh 35 – Dundee 43 – Glasgow 38.

Harviestoun Country Inn, Dollar Rd, FK13 6PQ, East : 1/4 m. by A 91 ✆ (01259) 7525 *Fax (01259) 752523,* – ⛔ TV P – 70. MC VISA JCB
closed 24 December-2 January – **Meals** a la carte 10.00/21.00 **t.** 4.95 – **10 rm** ☐ 50. 80.00 **st.** – SB.

TOBERMORY *Argyll and Bute* 401 B 14 – *see Mull (Isle of).*

TONGUE *Highland* 401 G 8 *Scotland G.* – *pop. 552* – ✉ *Lairg.*
Exc. : *Cape Wrath★★★ (≤★★) W : 44 m. (including ferry crossing) by A 838 – Ben Loyal★★ 8 m. by A 836 – Ben Hope★ (≤★★★) SW : 15 m. by A 838 – Strathy Point★ (≤★★★) E : 22 by A 836 – Torrisdale Bay★ (≤★★) NE : 8 m. by A 836.*
Edinburgh 257 – Inverness 101 – Thurso 43.

Ben Loyal, Main St., IV27 4XE, ✆ (01847) 611216, *thebenloyalhotel@btinternet.c Fax (01847) 611212,* ≤ Ben Loyal and Kyle of Tongue – ⛔ rest, TV P. MC VISA
Meals (bar lunch)/dinner 22.50 **st.** and a la carte – **11 rm** ☐ 35.00/80.00 **st.**

TORRIDON *Highland* 401 D 11 *Scotland G.* – ✉ *Achnasheen.*
Env. : *Wester Ross★★★.*
Edinburgh 234 – Inverness 62 – Kyle of Lochalsh 44.

Loch Torridon ⛓, IV22 2EY, South : 1 1/2 m. on A 896 ✆ (01445) 791242, *enquiries@ torridonhotel.com, Fax (01445) 791296,* ≤ Upper Loch Torridon and mountains, « former shooting lodge », ≤, ⛩, ⛸ – ⛔ TV ♿ P – 25. MC AE VISA.
Meals (booking essential) (bar lunch)/dinner 38.00 **t.** 11.25 – **18 rm** ☐ 90.00/260.0 2 suites.

Ben Damph Lodges ⛓, IV22 2EY, South : 1 1/2 m. on A 896 ✆ (01445) 791242, *benc ph@lochtorridonhotel.com, Fax (01445) 791296* – TV P. MC AE VISA.
restricted opening in winter – **Meals** (grill rest.) a la carte 12.50/17.50 **t.** – **12 rm** ☐ 46 64.00 **t.**

TREASLANE *Highland* – *see Skye (Isle of).*

TROON *South Ayrshire* 401 402 G 17 – *pop. 15 116.*
18, 18, 18 Troon Municipal, Harling Drive ✆ (01292) 312464.
to Northern Ireland (Belfast) (Sea Containers Ferries Scotland Ltd) 2 daily (2 h 30 m
Municipal Buildings, South Beach ✆ (01292) 317696 (Easter-October).
Edinburgh 77 – Ayr 7 – Glasgow 31.

Lochgreen House ⛓, Monktonhill Rd, Southwood, KA10 7EN, Southeast : 2 m. c 749 ✆ (01292) 313343, *lochgreen@costley-hotels.co.uk, Fax (01292) 318661,* « Edwar house, antiques », ⛩, ⛸, – ⛔, rest, TV P – 30. MC AE VISA JCB.
Meals 32.50 **t.** (dinner) and lunch a la carte 18.85/27.40 **t.** – **14 rm** ☐ 99.00/160.0 1 suite.

The Marine, 8 Crosbie Rd, KA10 6HE, ✆ (01292) 314444, *marine@paramount-hotels.co.uk, Fax (01292) 316922,* ≤, Fб, ≘s, ⊠, squash – |‡|, ⇔, ▤ rest, TV ✆ P – 🔺 220. MC AE ⓓ VISA JCB. ✈
Rizzio's : **Meals** a la carte 14.95/18.70 **t.** 7.95 – ***Fairways :*** **Meals** (restricted opening in winter) a la carte 15.85/24.45 **t.** 9.75 – ☐ 13.00 – **69 rm** 98.00/160.00 **t.**, 5 suites – SB.

Piersland House, Craigend Rd, KA10 6HD, ✆ (01292) 314747, *reception.piersland@talk21.com, Fax (01292) 315613,* ⇔ – ⇔ rest, TV ♿ P – 🔺 70. MC AE ⓓ VISA. ✈
Meals 12.95 **st.** and dinner a la carte 17.85/26.85 **st.** 8.00 – **13 rm** ☐ 62.50/165.00 **t.**, **15 suites** – SB.

Loans *East : 2 m. on A 759 – ✉ Troon.*

Highgrove House with rm, Old Loans Rd, KA10 7HL, East : ¼ m. on Dundonald rd ✆ (01292) 312511, *highgrove@costley-hotels.co.uk, Fax (01292) 318228,* ≤, ⇔ – TV ✆ P. MC AE VISA. ✈
Meals 12.00/25.95 **t.** and a la carte 7.95 – **9 rm** ☐ 69.00/89.00 **st.**

RNBERRY *South Ayrshire* 401 402 F 18 *Scotland G.* – ✉ *Girvan.*
Env. : *Culzean Castle★ AC (setting★★★, Oval Staircase★★) NE : 5 m. by A 719.*
Edinburgh 97 – Ayr 15 – Glasgow 51 – Stranraer 36.

Turnberry ♨, KA26 9LT, on A 719 ✆ (01655) 331000, *Fax (01655) 331706,* ⇔, « Part Edwardian, ≤ golf courses, bay, Ailsa Craig and Mull of Kintyre », Fб, ≘s, ⊠, 18, ⇔, ✂, squash – |‡|, ⇔ rest, ▤ rest, TV ✆ P – 🔺 150. MC AE ⓓ VISA JCB. ✈
Turnberry : **Meals** (dinner only and Sunday lunch)/dinner 49.00 **t.** and a la carte – ***Terrace Brasserie :*** **Meals** a la carte 24.40/42.30 **t.** – ***Tappie Toonie Grill :*** **Meals** (lunch only) a la carte 13.80/25.20 **t.** – **202 rm** ☐ 245.00/285.00 **t.**, 19 suites – SB.

YNHOLM *Dumfries and Galloway* 402 H 19 – *pop. 1 068.*
Edinburgh 107 – Ayr 54 – Dumfries 27 – Stranraer 48.

Fresh Fields ♨, Arden Rd, DG6 4PB, Southwest : ¾ m. by Burn Brae ✆ (01557) 860221, *Fax (01557) 860221,* ⇔ – ⇔ P
March-October – **Meals** (by arrangement) 15.00 4.75 – **5 rm** ☐ 28.00/56.00.

DINGSTON *South Lanarkshire* 401 402 H 16 – *pop. 5 367* – ✉ *Glasgow.*
18 *Coatbridge, Townhead Rd* ✆ *(01236) 28975.*
Edinburgh 41 – Glasgow 10.

Redstones, 8-10 Glasgow Rd, G71 7AS, ✆ (01698) 813774, *redstones@morris-inns.com, Fax (01698) 815319* – ⇔ rm, TV P – 🔺 30. MC AE ⓓ VISA. ✈
closed 1 January – ***Le Papillon :*** **Meals** (dinner only) 20.00/22.50 **st.** and a la carte – ***Brooklands :*** **Meals** a la carte 13.85/27.65 **st.** – **15 rm** ☐ 52.00/100.00 **st.**

Travel Inn, 601 Hamilton Rd, G71 7SA, Northwest : 2 m. by B 7071 and A 74 following signs for Glasgow Zoo park ✆ (0141) 773 1133, *Fax (0141) 771 8354,* ⇔ – |‡|, ⇔ rm, ▤ rest, TV ♿ P. MC AE ⓓ VISA. ✈
Meals (grill rest.) – **66 rm** 40.95 **t.**

ST (Isles of) *Western Isles (Outer Hebrides)* 401 XY 10 /11/12 – *pop. 3 510.*
✈ *see Liniclate.*
⛴ *from Lochboisdale to Oban via Isle of Barra (Castlebay) and Mallaig (Mainland) (Caledonian MacBrayne Ltd) (summer only) – from Lochmaddy to Isle of Skye (Uig) (Caledonian MacBrayne Ltd) 1-3 daily (1 h 50 mn) – from Otternish to Isle of Harris (Leverburgh) (Caledonian MacBrayne Ltd) (1 h 10 mn).*

NORTH UIST.

imsay.

Glendale ♨, 7 Kallin, HS6 5HY, ✆ (01870) 602029, *glendale@ecosse.net,* ≤ – ⇔ P. ✈
closed Christmas and New Year – **Meals** (by arrangement) (communal dining) 12.00 **st.** – **3 rm** ☐ 25.00/38.00 **st.**

chmaddy.

Lochmaddy, HS6 5AA, ✆ (01876) 500331, *Fax (01876) 500210,* ≤, ⚲ – ⇔ rest, TV P. MC AE VISA
Meals (bar lunch)/dinner 18.00 **st.** and a la carte 6.00 – **15 rm** ☐ 42.50/80.00 **st.** – SB.

SCOTLAND

BENBECULA.

Liniclate.

Benbecula Airport : (01870) 602051.

Dark Island, HS7 5PJ, (01870) 603030, *Fax (01870) 602347* – TV P – 100. MC VISA
closed 26 December and 1 January – **Meals** 11.00/19.00 **t.** and a la carte – **42 rm** 65.
93.00 **st.** – SB.

SOUTH UIST.

Lochboisdale.

Brae Lea, Lasgair, HS8 5TH, Northwest : 1 m. by A 865 (01878) 7004
Fax (01878) 700497, – rm, P
Meals (by arrangement) 15.00 **t.** – **6 rm** 30.00/60.00 **st.** – SB.

Pollachar.

Polochar Inn, HS8 5TT, (01878) 700215, *Fax (01878) 700768*, ≤ Sound of Barr
, rm, TV P. MC VISA.
Meals a la carte 13.40/25.85 **t.** – **11 rm** 35.00/60.00 **t.** – SB.

ULLAPOOL *Highland* 401 E 10 *Scotland G. – pop. 1 231.*
See : *Town*★.
Env. : *Wester Ross*★★★ – *Loch Broom*★★.
Exc. : *Falls of Measach*★★, *S : 11 m. by A 835 and A 832 - Corrieshalloch Gorge*★, *SE : 10*
by A 835 – Northwards to Lochinver★★, *Morefield (≤★★ of Ullapool), ≤★ Loch Broom.*
to Isle of Lewis (Stornoway) (Caledonian MacBrayne Ltd) (2 h 40 mn).
Argyle St. (01854) 612135 (April-November).
Edinburgh 215 – Inverness 59.

Altnaharrie Inn (Gunn Eriksen), IV26 2SS, Southwest : ½ m. by private fe
(01854) 633230, « Former drovers' inn on shores of Loch Broom, ≤ Ullapool », –
MC AE VISA.
Easter-early November – **Meals** (booking essential) (residents only) (dinner only) (set me
only) 75.00 **st.** 7.50 – **8 rm** (dinner included) 195.00/410.00 **st.**
Spec. Scallops and truffles on roasted kohlrabi with three sauces. Warm salad of lobs
and caviar, Champagne sauce. Squab and foie gras with cake of chicken livers.

Ardvreck without rest., Morefield Brae, IV26 2TH, Northwest : 2 m. by A
(01854) 612028, *ardvreck.guesthouse@btinternet.com*, *Fax (01854) 613000*, ≤ Lo
Broom and mountains, – TV P. MC VISA.
March-November – **10 rm** 27.00/54.00 **st.**

The Sheiling without rest., Garve Rd, IV26 2SX, (01854) 612947, *Fax (01854) 612947*
Loch Broom, , , – P.
closed Christmas and New Year – **6 rm** 50.00/52.00 **st.**

Point Cottage without rest., West Shore St., IV26 2UR, (01854) 612494, *stay@poin*
ttage.co.uk, *Fax (01854) 613464*, ≤ Loch Broom, – TV P.
10 February-October – **3 rm** 45.00/52.50 **s.**

Dromnan without rest., Garve Rd, IV26 2SX, (01854) 612333, *dromnan@msn.co*
Fax (01854) 613364, ≤, – TV P. MC VISA.
7 rm 40.00/50.00 **t.**

UNST (Island of) *Shetland Islands* 401 R 1 – *see Shetland Islands.*

UPHALL *West Lothian* 401 J 16 – *pop. 14 600.*
18 *Uphall, Houston Mains (01506) 856404.*
Edinburgh 13 – Glasgow 32.

Houstoun House, EH52 6JS, (01506) 853831, *info@houstoun.macdonald-hotels.c*
k, *Fax (01506) 854220*, « Gardens », , , , , – TV P – 400. MC AE
VISA.
The Great Dining rooms : **Meals** 18.50 **st.** (lunch) and dinner a la carte 24.40/33.40
8.50 – ***Peligrinas :*** **Meals** *(closed Sunday)* (dinner only) a la carte 15.00/28.50 **st.** 8.5
10.50 – **72 rm** 89.00/200.00 **st.** – SB.

UPPER LARGO *Fife – see Lundin Links.*

VEENSGARTH *Shetland Islands – see Shetland Islands (Mainland).*

ALLS *Shetland Islands* 401 PQ 3 – *see Shetland Islands (Mainland).*

HITEBRIDGE *Highland* 401 G 12 *Scotland G.*

Env. : *Loch Ness*★★ – *The Great Glen*★.

Edinburgh 171 – Inverness 23 – Kyle of Lochalsh 67 – Oban 92.

Knockie Lodge ⛰, IV2 6UP, Southwest : 3 ½ m. by B 862 ☎ (01456) 486276, *info@knockielodge.co.uk, Fax (01456) 486389,* ← Loch Nan Lann and mountains, « 18C former shooting lodge », ... – ... P. MC AE D VISA

April-October – **Meals** (booking essential) (set menu only) (light lunch residents only)/ dinner 37.50 **st.** 6.00 – **10 rm** 75.00/190.00 **st.** – SB.

HITE NESS *Shetland Islands* 401 Q 3 – *see Shetland Islands (Mainland).*

HITING BAY *North Ayrshire* 401 402 E 17 – *see Arran (Isle of).*

CK *Highland* 401 K 8 *Scotland G.* – *pop. 9 713.*

Exc. : *Duncansby Head*★ *(Stacks of Duncansby*★★*) N : 14 m. by A 9 – Grey Cairns of Camster*★ *(Long Cairn*★★*) S : 17 m. by A 9 – The Hill O'Many Stanes*★*, S : 10 m. by A 9.*

18 *Reiss* ☎ *(01955) 602726.*

Wick Airport : ☎ *(01955) 602215, N : 1 m.*

Whitechapel Rd ☎ *(01955) 602596.*

Edinburgh 282 – Inverness 126.

The Clachan without rest., South Rd, KW1 5NJ, South : ¾ m. on A 99 ☎ (01955) 605384, *enquiry@clachan.co.uk,* ... – ... TV. ...

3 rm 25.00/44.00 **st.**

Meadowbank House without rest., Thurso Rd, KW1 5LE, West : 1 m. on A 882 ☎ (01955) 603760 – ... TV P. ...

April-September – **3 rm** 20.00/40.00.

GTOWN *Dumfries and Galloway* 401 G 19 *Scotland G.* – *pop. 1 344* – ✉ *Newton Stewart.*

Exc. : *Whithorn Museum (early Christian crosses*★★*) S : 10 m. by A 746.*

9 *Wigtown & Bladnoch, Lightlands Terr.* ☎ *(01988) 403354.*

Edinburgh 137 – Ayr 61 – Dumfries 61 – Stranraer 26.

Corsemalzie House ⛰, DG8 9RL, Southwest : 6 ½ m. by A 714 on B 7005 ☎ (01988) 860254, *corsemalzie@ndirect.co.uk, Fax (01988) 860213,* ..., ..., ... – ... TV P. MC AE VISA

closed 16 January-1 March and 4 days Christmas – **Meals** 23.50 **t.** (dinner) and a la carte 10.75/20.35 **t.** 5.50 – **14 rm** 49.50/99.00 **t.** – SB.

RMIT *Fife* 401 L 14 – ✉ *Newport-on-Tay.*

18 *Scotscraig, Golf Rd, Tayport* ☎ *(01382) 552515.*

Edinburgh 53 – Dundee 6 – St. Andrews 12.

Sandford Country House ⛰, DD6 8RG, South : 2 m. on B 946 ☎ (01382) 541802, *sandford.hotel@btinternet.com, Fax (01382) 542136,* ←, ... – ... rest, TV P – 45. MC D VISA

Meals (dinner only) 30.00/40.00 **t.** and a la carte 8.00 – **16 rm** 85.00/130.00 **t.** – SB.

"The West Country of England"

Wales

The stars
Les étoiles
Le stelle
Die Sterne

Town with a local map
Carte de voisinage : voir à la ville choisie
Città con carta dei dintorni
Stadt mit Umgebungskarte

"Bib Gourmand"

Meals 19.00/25.00
Good food at moderate prices
Repas soignés à prix modérés
Pasti accurati a prezzi contenuti
Sorgfältig zubereitete preiswerte Mahlzeiten

Peaceful atmosphere and setting
L'agrément
Amenità e tranquillità
Annehmlichkeit

ERDARE (**Aberdâr**) *Rhondda Cynon Taff* 403 J 28 – *pop. 29 040.*
London 178 – Cardiff 23 – Swansea 27.

Ty Newydd Country, Penderyn Rd, Hirwaun, CF44 9SX, Northwest : 5 m. on A 4059 ☎ (01685) 813433, *Fax (01685) 813139,* – rm, TV P – 300. MC AE VISA JCB.
Meals 8.55/15.00 **st.** and a la carte 4.50 – **27 rm** 46.00/70.00 **st.** – SB.

ERDOVEY (**Aberdyfi**) *Gwynedd* 403 H 26 *Wales G. – pop. 869.*
Env. : *Snowdonia National Park★★★.*
London 230 – Dolgellau 25 – Shrewsbury 66.

Plas Penhelig Country House, LL35 0NA, East : 1 m. by A 493 ☎ (01654) 767676, *plaspen@netcomuk.co.uk, Fax (01654) 767783,* ≤, , « Edwardian house with terraced gardens », – TV P – 35. MC AE VISA JCB
mid March-mid December – **Meals** (bar lunch Monday to Saturday)/dinner 20.00 **t.** – **11 rm** (dinner included) 66.00/132.00 **t.** – SB.

Trefeddian, Tywyn Rd, LL35 0SB, West : 1 m. on A 493 ☎ (01654) 767213, *tref@soqnet.co.uk, Fax (01654) 767777,* ≤ Cardigan Bay and golf course, , , , – TV P. MC VISA
closed 3 January-5 March – **Meals** 12.00/20.75 **t.** 7.20 – **48 rm** (dinner included) 67.00/134.00 **t.** – SB.

Penhelig Arms, LL35 0LT, ☎ (01654) 767215, *penheligarms@sagnet.co.uk, Fax (01654) 767690,* ≤, « Part 18C inn » – TV P. MC VISA
closed 25 and 26 December – **Meals** (bar lunch Monday to Saturday)/dinner 22.00 **st.** – **10 rm** 39.50/79.00 **st.** – SB.

Preswylfa, Garth Rd, LL35 0LE, North : ¼ m. turning into Copperfield St. (by Dovey Inn), Church St. then first left up steep hill, first left again into Garth Rd ☎ (01654) 767239, *preswylfa@cwcom.net, Fax (01654) 767983,* ≤ Dovey estuary and Cardigan Bay, – TV P.
Meals (by arrangement) 17.50 – **3 rm** 50.00/55.00 **s.** – SB.

Brodawel without rest., Tywyn Rd, LL35 0SA, West : 1 ¼ m. on A 493 ☎ (01654) 767347, ≤, – TV P
late March-October – **5 rm** 30.00/54.00 **st.**

ERGAVENNY (**Y-Fenni**) *Monmouthshire* 403 L 28 *Wales G. – pop. 9 593.*
See : *Town★ – St. Mary's Church★ (Monuments★★).*
Env. : *Brecon Beacons National Park★★ – Blaenavon Ironworks★, SW : 5 m. by A 465 and B 4246.*
Exc. : *Raglan Castle★ AC, SE : 9 m. by A 40.*
18 Monmouthshire, Llanfoist ☎ (01873) 852606.
Swan Meadow, Monmouth Rd ☎ (01873) 857588.
London 163 – Gloucester 43 – Newport 19 – Swansea 49.

Llansantffraed Court, Llanvihangel Gobion, NP7 9BA, Southeast : 6 ½ m. by A 40 and B 4598 off old Raglan rd ☎ (01873) 840678, *reception@llch.co.uk, Fax (01873) 840674,* ≤, « Country house in William and Mary style », , – TV P. MC AE VISA JCB
Meals 10.00/40.00 **t.** and a la carte 6.00 – **21 rm** 70.00/98.00 **t.** – SB.

lanfihangel Crucorney *North : 6½ m. by A 40 on A 465 – ✉ Abergavenny.*

Penyclawdd Court without rest., NP7 7LB, South : 1 ¼ m. by Pantygelli rd and following signs to Penyclawdd Farm ☎ (01873) 890719, *Fax (01873) 890848,* ≤, « Tudor manor house with medieval origins », – TV P. MC VISA.
3 rm 60.00/100.00 **st.**

ovilon *West : 5 ¼ m. by A 465 on B 4246 – ✉ Abergavenny.*

Llanwenarth House, NP7 9SF, North : 1 m. on B 4246 ☎ (01873) 830289, *Fax (01873) 832199,* ≤, « 16C manor house », – TV P
closed Christmas and February – **Meals** (by arrangement) (communal dining) 24.50 **s.** 9.50 – **5 rm** 62.00/82.00.

lanwenarth *Northwest : 3 m. on A 40 – ✉ Abergavenny.*

Llanwenarth Arms, Brecon Rd, NP8 1EP, ☎ (01873) 810550, *mcgregor@netmatters.co.uk, Fax (01873) 811880,* ≤, – TV P. MC AE VISA JCB.
Meals a la carte 15.95/26.15 **t.** – **18 rm** 63.00/73.00 **t.**

s prix — Pour toutes précisions sur les prix indiqués dans ce guide, reportez-vous aux pages de l'introduction.

ABERSOCH *Gwynedd* 402 403 G 25 *Wales G.* – *pop. 805* – ✉ *Pwllheli.*

Env. : *Lleyn Peninsula★★* – *Plas-yn-Rhiw★* **AC**, *W : 6 m. by minor roads.*

Exc. : *Bardsey Island★, SW : 15 m. by A 499 and B 4413* – *Mynydd Mawr★, SW : 17 m. 499, B 4413 and minor roads.*

Golf Rd ☎ (01758) 712622.

London 265 – *Caernarfon 28* – *Shrewsbury 101.*

White House, LL53 7AG, ☎ (01758) 713427, *whitehousehotel@btinternet.c Fax (01758) 713512*, ≤, – TV P. MC VISA JCB

Meals 15.00/25.00 **t.** (dinner) and lunch a la carte 18.40/40.00 **t.** 12.00 – **13 rm** 42 110.00 **t.** – SB.

Neigwl, Lon Sarn Bach, LL53 7DY, ☎ (01758) 712363, *neigwl.hotel@which. Fax (01758) 712544*, ≤ Cardigan Bay – TV P. MC VISA JCB.

closed 4-26 January – **Meals** (dinner only) 20.50/25.50 **t.** 7.50 – **9 rm** 53.00/115.0C SB.

at Bwlchtocyn *South : 2 m.* – ✉ *Pwllheli.*

Porth Tocyn , LL53 7BU, ☎ (01758) 713303, *porthtocyn.hotel@virgin. Fax (01758) 713538*, ≤ Cardigan Bay and mountains, heated, , – TV P. MC

Easter-mid November – **Meals** (bar lunch Monday to Saturday)/dinner 24.50/31.00 **t.** – 5.50 – **17 rm** 66.00/123.00 **st.**

ABERYSTWYTH *Ceredigion* 403 H 26 *Wales G.* – *pop. 8 359.*

See : *Town★★* – *The Seafront★* – *National Library of Wales★ (Permanent Exhibition★).*

Env. : *Vale of Rheidol★ (Railway★★* **AC***)* – *St. Padarn's Church★, SE : 1 m. by A 44.*

Exc. : *Devil's Bridge (Pontarfynach)★, E : 12 m. by A 4120* – *Strata Florida Abbey★* **AC** *(Door★), SE : 15 m. by B 4340 and minor rd.*

Bryn-y-Mor ☎ (01970) 615104.

Terrace Rd ☎ (01970) 612125.

London 238 – *Chester 98* – *Fishguard 58* – *Shrewsbury 74.*

Belle Vue Royal, 23 Marine Terrace, The Promenade, SY23 2BA, ☎ (01970) 617558, *ption@bellevueroyalhotel.fsnet.co.uk, Fax (01970) 612190*, ≤ – rm, rest, TV – MC AE VISA.

closed 24-26 December – **Meals** 16.50 **t.** (lunch) and dinner a la carte 16.95/21.95 **t.** – **34 rm** 60.00/90.00 **t.** – SB.

Four Seasons, 50-54 Portland St., SY23 2DX, ☎ (01970) 612120, *info@fourseasonsh demon.co.uk, Fax (01970) 627458* – TV P. MC VISA.

closed 1 week Christmas – **Meals** (bar lunch)/dinner 18.00 **st.** – **14 rm** 55.00/82.00 SB.

Sinclair without rest., 43 Portland St., SY23 2DX, ☎ (01970) 615158, *Fax (01970) 615* TV.

closed 2 weeks Christmas-New Year – **3 rm** 35.00/50.00 **st.**

at Chancery (Rhydgaled) *South : 4 m. on A 487* – ✉ *Aberystwyth.*

Conrah Country House , SY23 4DF, ☎ (01970) 617941, *hotel@conrah.freeserv uk, Fax (01970) 624546*, ≤, « Part 18C mansion house », , , , – , rest, – 50. MC AE VISA JCB.

closed 1 week Christmas – **Meals** 16.75/30.00 **t.** 7.00 – **17 rm** 90.00/140.00 **t.** – SE

BALA *Gwynedd* 402 403 J 25 *Wales G.* – *pop. 1 922.*

Env. : *Snowdonia National Park★★★* – *Bala Lake★.*

Exc. : *Bwlch y Groes★★, SE : 11 m. by A 494, B 4403 and minor rd.*

Bala Lake Hotel ☎ (01678) 520344 – *Penlan ☎ (01678) 520359.*

Penllyn, Pensarn Rd ☎ (01678) 521021 (Easter-October).

London 216 – *Chester 46* – *Dolgellau 18* – *Shrewsbury 52.*

Fron Feuno Hall , LL23 7YF, Southwest : 1 m. on A 494 ☎ (01678) 521115, *fronf @moneypenny.uk.com, Fax (01678) 521151*, ≤ Bala Lake, , , – , rest, P

March-October – **Meals** (by arrangement) (communal dining) 16.00/25.00 **st.** – 40.00/80.00 **st.**

Melin Meloch without rest., LL23 7DP, East : 1 ¾ m. by A 494 on B ☎ (01678) 520101, *theoldmill@mac.com*, « Part 13C converted water mill, gardens » TV P

5 rm 25.00/48.00 **st.**

NGOR Gwynedd 402 403 H 24 Wales G. – pop. 11 173.

Env. : Snowdonia National Park★★★ – Penrhyn Castle★★ AC, E : 3 m. by A 5122 – Menai Bridge★, SW : 1½ m. by A 5122.

Exc. : Anglesey★★ – Plas Newydd★★ AC, SW : 7½ m. by A 5122 and A 4080 – Anglesey Sea Zoo★ AC, SW : 10 m. by A 5122, A 4080 and B 4419 – Llangefni (Oriel Ynys Mon★ AC), NW : 7 m. by A 5122 and B 5420.

18 St. Deiniol, Penybryn ☎ (01248) 353098.

London 247 – Birkenhead 68 – Holyhead 23 – Shrewsbury 83.

Travel Inn, Menai Business Park, LL57 4FA, Southwest : 2 ½ m. by A 5122 and A 487 at junction with A 5 ☎ (01248) 679070, *Fax (01248) 679099* – rm, rest, TV P. MC AE D VISA.
Meals (grill rest.) – **40 rm** 40.95 **t.**

Travelodge, One Stop Services, Llandegai, LL57 4BG, Southeast : 2 ½ m. by A 5122, at junction of A 5 with A 55 ☎ (01248) 370345, *Fax (01248) 370345* – rm, rest, TV P. MC AE D VISA JCB.
Meals (grill rest.) – **62 rm** 39.95 **t.**

Country Bumpkin without rest., Cefn-y-Coed, Llandegai, LL57 4BG, South : 2 m. on A 5122 ☎ (01248) 370477, *Fax (01248) 354166*, – TV P. MC AE VISA
closed December-mid January – **3 rm** 30.00/40.00.

Caerhun *South : 7 m. by A 5122, A 5 and B 4366 on Caerhun rd* – Bangor.

Penhower Uchaf, LL57 4DT, ☎ (01248) 362427, – TV P
closed 25-26 December – **Meals** (by arrangement) 12.50 **st.** – **3 rm** 23.00/40.00 **st.**

RMOUTH (Abermaw) Gwynedd 402 403 H 25 Wales G. – pop. 2 306.

See : Town★ – Bridge★ AC.

Env. : Snowdonia National Park★★★.

The Old Library, Station Rd ☎ (01341) 280787 (Easter-October).

London 231 – Chester 74 – Dolgellau 10 – Shrewsbury 67.

Llwyndû Farmhouse, LL42 1RR, Northwest : 2 ¼ m. on A 496 ☎ (01341) 280144, *intouch@llwyndu-farmhouse.co.uk, Fax (01341) 281236*, « Part 17C farmhouse and 18C barn conversion », – TV P. MC VISA JCB
closed 1 week November and 25-26 December – **Meals** (by arrangement) 17.95 **t.** 5.60 – **7 rm** 60.00/68.00 **t.** – SB.

RRY (Barri) Vale of Glamorgan 403 K 29 – pop. 46 368.

9 RAF St. Athan ☎ (01446) 751043.

The Triangle, Paget Rd, Barry Island ☎ (01446) 747171 (Easter-October).

London 167 – Cardiff 10 – Swansea 39.

Egerton Grey Country House, CF62 3BZ, Southwest : 4 ½ m. by B 4226 and A 4226 and Porthkerry rd via Cardiff Airport ☎ (01446) 711666, *info@egertongrey.co.uk, Fax (01446) 711690*, « Part Victorian rectory », – rest, TV P. MC AE D VISA JCB.
Meals 14.50 **st.** (lunch) and dinner a la carte 20.40/25.40 **st.** 7.50 – **10 rm** 70.00/130.00 **st.** – SB.

Mount Sorrel, Porthkerry Rd, CF62 7XY, ☎ (01446) 740069, *reservations@mountsorrel.co.uk, Fax (01446) 746600*, – rest, TV P – 150. MC AE D VISA JCB
Meals 11.50 **st.** (lunch) and a la carte 14.75/19.00 **st.** 6.50 – **41 rm** 55.00/95.00 **st.** – SB.

Aberthaw House, 28 Porthkerry Rd, CF62 7AX, ☎ (01446) 737314, *derek@aberthawhouse.freeserve.co.uk, Fax (01446) 732376* – rest, TV. MC AE VISA.
closed 24 December-8 January – **Meals** *(closed Sunday and Monday)* (dinner only) 8.95 **t.** and a la carte 4.75 – 7.50 – **9 rm** 39.50/59.50 **t.**

AUMARIS Anglesey 402 403 H 24 Wales G. – pop. 2 050.

See : Town★ – Castle★★ AC.

Env. : Anglesey★★ – Penmon Priory★, NE : 4 m. by B 5109 and minor roads.

Exc. : Plas Newydd★ AC, SW : 7 m. by A 545 and A 4080.

9 Baron Hill ☎ (01248) 810231.

London 253 – Birkenhead 74 – Holyhead 25.

Ye Olde Bull's Head Inn, Castle St., LL58 8AP, ☎ (01248) 810329, *info@bullheadinn.co.uk, Fax (01248) 811294* – rm, TV. MC AE VISA JCB.
closed 25-26 December and 1 January – ***The brasserie :*** **Meals** a la carte 12.00/17.40 **t.** – (see also ***The Restaurant*** below) – **15 rm** 55.00/97.00 **t.** – SB.

Bishopsgate House, 54 Castle St., LL58 8BB, ✆ (01248) 810302, *hazel@johnson-ollie eeserve.co.uk, Fax (01248) 810166* – TV P. MC AE VISA
closed 1-10 January – **Meals** (booking essential to non-residents) 12.95/15.95 and a la carte 4.90 – **9 rm** 40.00/75.00 **t.** – SB.

Plas Cichle without rest., LL58 8PS, Northwest : 2 ¾ m. by B 5109 and Llanfaes ✆ (01248) 810488, ≤, « Working farm », – TV P. MC VISA.
February-October – **3 rm** 35.00/50.00 **s.**

The Restaurant (at Ye Olde Bull's Head Inn H.), Castle St., LL58 8AP, ✆ (01248) 810 *Fax (01248) 811294* – . MC AE VISA JCB
closed Sunday – **Meals** (dinner only) 28.50 **t.** 7.00.

BEDDGELERT *Gwynedd* 402 403 H 24 *Wales G. – pop. 535.*
Env. : *Snowdonia National Park★★★ – Aberglaslyn Pass★, S : 1½ m. on A 498.*
London 249 – Caernarfon 13 – Chester 73.

Sygun Fawr Country House, LL55 4NE, Northeast : ¾ m. by A ✆ (01766) 890258, *sygunfawr@aol.com, Fax (01766) 890258,* ≤ Snowdon and Gwynant ley, « Part 16C stone built house », – P. MC VISA JCB
closed January – **Meals** (booking essential to non-residents) (dinner only) 18.00 **st.** 5.
9 rm 46.00/72.00 **st.** – SB.

BENLLECH *Anglesey* 402 403 H 24.
London 277 – Caernarfon 17 – Chester 76 – Holyhead 29.

Hafod without rest., Amlwch Rd, LL74 8SR, ✆ (01248) 853092, – TV P.
4 rm 30.00/50.00 **t.**

BETWS-Y-COED *Conwy* 402 403 I 24 *Wales G. – pop. 848.*
See : *Town★.*
Env. : *Snowdonia National Park★★★.*
Exc. : *Blaenau Ffestiniog★ (Llechwedd Slate Caverns★ AC), SW : 10½ m. by A 470 – Glyders and Nant Ffrancon (Cwm Idwal★), W : 14 m. by A 5.*
Clubhouse ✆ (01690) 710556.
Royal Oak Stables ✆ (01690) 710426.
London 226 – Holyhead 44 – Shrewsbury 62.

Tan-y-Foel Country House, LL26 ORE, East : 4 m. by A 5 and A 470 on Neb ✆ (01690) 710507, *tanyfoel@wiss.co.uk, Fax (01690) 710681,* ≤ Vale of Conwy and Sn donia, « Stylishly decorated part 16C country house », – TV P. MC AE VISA
closed Christmas and restricted opening January – **Meals** *(closed Saturday and Sun lunch)* (booking essential) (light lunch)/dinner 29.00 **t.** 9.65 – **7 rm** 70.00/150.00 SB.

Henllys The Old Courthouse without rest., Old Church Rd, LL24 ✆ (01690) 710534, *henllys@betws-y-coed.co.uk, Fax (01690) 710534,* « Former Victo magistrates court and police station », – TV P. MC VISA JCB.
February-October except Christmas and New Year – **8 rm** 30.00/60.00.

Pengwern Country House, Allt Dinas, LL24 0HF, Southeast : 1 ½ m. on ✆ (01690) 710480, *marilyn@pengwern49.freeserve.co.uk, Fax (01690) 710480,* ≤ Val Conwy, – P. MC VISA JCB.
Meals (by arrangement) (communal dining) 17.95 5.50 – **3 rm** 35.00/60.00 – SB.

Glyntwrog House, LL24 0SG, Southeast : ¾ m. on A 5 ✆ (01690) 710930, *ken@glyn g.freeserve.co.uk, Fax (01690) 710512,* – TV P.
Meals (by arrangement) 12.50 **st.** 4.00 – **4 rm** 32.00/54.00 **st.**

Bryn Bella without rest., Lôn Muriau, Llanrwst Rd, LL24 0HD, Northeast : 1 m. by A 5 470 ✆ (01690) 710627, *brynbella@clara.net,* ≤ Vale of Conwy – TV P.
5 rm 22.00/45.00 **s.**

BLAENAU FFESTINIOG *Gwynedd* 402 403 I 25.
Unit 3, High St. ✆ (01766) 830360 (Easter-October).
London 237 – Bangor 32 – Caernarfon 32 – Dolgellau 23 – Chester 70.

Queen's, 1 High St., LL41 3ES, ✆ (01766) 830055, *cathy@queensffestiniog.freeserve. k, Fax (01766) 830046* – rest, TV P – 100. MC VISA.
closed 25 December – **Meals** a la carte 9.65/16.35 **st.** 4.95 – **12 rm** 40.00/80.00 **st**

BODUAN *Gwynedd* 402 403 G 25 – *see Pwllheli.*

NTDDU *Gwynedd* 402 403 I 25 – *see Dolgellau.*

NVILSTON (Tresimwn) *Vale of Glamorgan* 403 J 29.
London 164 – Cardiff 9 – Swansea 25.

The Great Barn without rest., Lillypot, CF5 6TR, Northwest : 1 m. by A 48 off Tre-Dodridge rd ✆ (01446) 781010, *Fax (01446) 781185,* ≤, « Converted corn barn », – TV P
5 rm 35.00/52.00 **st.**

ECON (Aberhonddu) *Powys* 403 J 28 *Wales G. – pop. 7 523.*
See : *Town★ – Cathedral★ AC – Penyclawdd Court★.*
Env. : *Brecon Beacons National Park★★.*
Exc. : *Llanthony Priory★★, S : 8 m. of Hay-on-Wye by B 4423 – Dan-yr-Ogof Showcaves★ AC, SW : 20 m. by A 40 and A 4067 – Pen-y-Fan★★, SW : by A 470.*
18 *Cradoc, Penoyre Park ✆ (01874) 623658 –* 9 *Newton Park, Llanfaes ✆ (01874) 622004.*
Cattle Market Car Park ✆ (01874) 622485/625692.
London 171 – Cardiff 40 – Carmarthen 31 – Gloucester 65.

Peterstone Court, Llanhamlach, LD3 7YB, Southeast : 3 ¼ m. on A 40 ✆ (01874) 665387, *peterstone-court@virgin.net, Fax (01874) 665376,* ≤, « Georgian manor house », heated, – rm, rest, TV P – 150. VISA
Meals 24.95 **t.** (dinner) and lunch a la carte 16.95/25.20 **t.** 7.00 – **12 rm** 85.00/95.00 **t.** – SB.

Cantre Selyf, 5 Lion St., LD3 7AU, ✆ (01874) 622904, *cantreselyf@imaginet.co.uk, Fax (01874) 622315,* « 17C town house », – P.
closed January and December – **Meals** (by arrangement) 15.00 – **3 rm** 30.00/50.00.

DGEND (Pen-y-Bont) *Bridgend* 403 J 29 – *pop. 35 841.*
McArthur Glen Design Outlet, The Derwen ✆ (01656) 654906.
London 177 – Cardiff 20 – Swansea 23.

Heronston, Ewenny Rd, CF35 5AW, South : 2 m. on B 4265 ✆ (01656) 668811, *reservations@heronston-hotel.demon.co.uk, Fax (01656) 767391,* heated, – TV P – 200. AE VISA
Meals *(closed Sunday dinner and Bank Holidays)* (bar lunch Monday to Saturday)/dinner 12.95/18.95 **st.** – 8.95 – **75 rm** 85.00/95.00 **t.** – SB.

encoed *Northeast : 4½ m. by A 473.*

Travel Inn, Pantruthyn Farm, CF35 5HY, East : 1 m. by A 473 at junction 35 on M 4 ✆ (01656) 860133, *Fax (01656) 864792* – rm, TV P. AE VISA.
Meals (grill rest.) – **40 rm** 40.95 **t.**

Travelodge without rest., CF3 5HU, East : 1 ¼ m. by Felindre rd ✆ (01656) 864404, *Fax (01656) 864404* – rm, TV P. AE VISA JCB.
40 rm 39.95 **t.**

oychurch (Llangrallo) *East : 2¼ m. by A 473 – ✉ Bridgend.*

Coed-y-Mwstwr , CF35 6AF, North : 1 m. by Bryn Rd ✆ (01656) 860621, *enquiries@coed-y-mwstwr.com, Fax (01656) 863122,* ≤, heated, – TV P – 150. AE VISA JCB.
Meals 9.95/22.95 **st.** and a la carte – **23 rm** 95.00/150.00 **st.**

outherndown *Southwest : 5½ m. by A 4265 – ✉ Bridgend.*

Frolics, Beach Rd, CF32 0RP, ✆ (01656) 880127 – AE VISA
closed Sunday dinner and Monday – **Meals** (dinner only and Sunday lunch except July-August) 15.95 **t.** and a la carte.

aleston *West : 2 m. on A 473 – ✉ Bridgend.*

Great House, High St., CF32 0HP, on A 473 ✆ (01656) 657644, *greathse@aol.com, Fax (01656) 668892,* – TV P. AE VISA JCB.
closed 25-29 December – **Meals** – (see ***Leicester's*** below) – **16 rm** 90.00/135.00 **t.** – SB.

Leicester's (at Great House H.), High St., CF32 0HP, on A 473 ✆ (01656) 657644, *Fax (01656) 668892,* – P. AE VISA.
closed 25-29 December – **Meals** (Sunday dinner booking essential) a la carte 12.45/24.95 **t.** 6.95.

.CHTOCYN *Gwynedd* 402 403 G 25 – *see Abersoch.*

CAERHUN *Gwynedd – see Bangor.*

CAERNARFON *Gwynedd* 402 403 H 24 *Wales G. – pop. 9 695.*

See : *Town*★★★ – *Castle*★★★ *AC – Town Walls*★.
Env. : *Snowdonia National Park*★★★.
Aberforeshore, Llanfaglan ☎ *(01286) 673783.*
Oriel Pendeitsh, Castle St. ☎ *(01286) 672232.*
London 249 – Birkenhead 76 – Chester 68 – Holyhead 30 – Shrewsbury 85.

Seiont Manor, Llanrug, LL55 2AQ, East : 3 m. on A 4086 ☎ (01286) 673
Fax (01286) 672840, – 100.
Meals 12.00/35.00 **t.** and a la carte 5.50 – **28 rm** 75.00/140.00 **t.** – SB.

Celtic Royal, Bangor St., LL55 1AY, ☎ (01286) 674477, *enquiries@celticroyal.wales.c*
Fax (01286) 674139, – 500.
Meals (bar lunch)/dinner 14.95 – **110 rm** 65.00/90.00 **s.** – SB.

Isfryn without rest., 11 Church St., LL55 1SW, ☎ (01286) 675628, *Fax (01286) 6756*
rest, .
mid March-October – **6 rm** 20.00/46.00 **s.**

at Seion *Northeast : 5½ m. by A 4086 and B 4366 on Seion rd – Caernarfon.*

Ty'n Rhos Country H., Llanddeiniolen, LL55 3AE, Southwest : ¼
☎ (01248) 670489, *enquiries@tynrhos.co.uk, Fax (01248) 670079*, ≤, –
.
closed 1 week January and Christmas – **Meals** (booking essential to non-residents) (
dinner Sunday) 12.95/19.50 **st.** and a la carte 8.40 – **14 rm** 55.00/150.00 **st.** – SB.

at Saron *Southwest : 3¼ m. by A 487 on Saron rd – Caernarfon.*

Pengwern, LL54 5UH, Southwest : ¼ m. ☎ (01286) 831500, *jhjgr@enterprise*
Fax (01286) 830741, « Working farm », – .
closed December and January – **Meals** (by arrangement) 15.00 **st.** – **3 rm** 35.00/56.
– SB.

CAERSWS *Powys* 402 403 J 26.

London 194 – Aberystwyth 39 – Chester 63 – Shrewsbury 42.

Maesmawr Hall, SY17 5SF, East : 1 m. on A 489 ☎ (01686) 688255, *reception@r*
mawr.co.uk, Fax (01686) 688410, « Part 16C hunting lodge », – rest, –
.
closed 27-30 December – **Meals** (bar lunch Monday to Saturday)/dinner 25.00 **st.** 6.
17 rm 56.00/80.00 **st.** – SB.

Lower Ffrydd, SY17 5QS, West : 2 m. by B 4569 ☎ (01686) 688
Fax (01686) 688269, ≤, « 16C farmhouse, working farm », – .
closed 2 weeks Christmas – **Meals** (by arrangement) (communal dining) 14.00 **st.** –
25.00/44.00 **st.** – SB.

Upper Ffrydd Farm without rest., SY17 5QS, West : 2 m. by B
☎ (01686) 688963, « 17C farmhouse, working farm », – .
April-October – **3 rm** 27.00/46.00 **s.**

Cefn-Gwyn Farm without rest., Trefeglwys, SY17 5RF, West : 2 ½ m. on B
☎ (01686) 430648, *cefngwyn@talk21.com*, ≤, « Working farm », – .
closed 25 December – **3 rm** 25.00/46.00 **st.**

at Pontdolgoch *Northwest : 1½ m. on A 470 – Newtown.*

The Talkhouse with rm, SY17 5JE, ☎ (01686) 688919, *Fax (01686) 689134*,
.
closed 1 week March, 1 week September and 25-26 December – **Meals** *(closed Mo*
lunch and Sunday) a la carte 16.70/21.25 **t.** 7.00 – **3 rm** 65.00/95.00 **t.**

RDIFF **(Caerdydd)** *Cardiff* 403 K 29 *Wales G.* – *pop. 279 055.*

See : *City*★★★ – *National Museum and Gallery*★★★ **AC** *(Evolution of Wales*★★, *Picture galleries*★★ *(Galleries 12 and 13*★★*), Pottery and Porcelain*★*)* **BY** – *Castle*★★ **AC BZ** – *Civic Centre*★ **BY** – *Llandaff Cathedral*★ **AV B** – *Cardiff Bay*★ *(Techniquest*★ **AC**) **AX**.

Env. : *Museum of Welsh Life*★★★ **AC**, *St. Fagan's, W : 5 m. by A 4161* **AV** – *Castell Coch*★★ **AC**, *NW : 5 m. by A 470* **AV**.

Exc. : *Caerphilly Castle*★★ **AC**, *N : 7 m. by A 469* **AV** – *Dyffryn Gardens*★ **AC**, *W : 8 m. by A 48* **AX**.

Dinas Powis, Old Highwalls ☎ *(029) 2051 2727*, **AX**.

Cardiff (Wales) Airport : ☎ *(01446) 711111, SW : 8 m. by A 48* **AX** – **Terminal** : *Central Bus Station.*

16 Wood St. ☎ *(029) 2022 7281.*

London 155 – Birmingham 110 – Bristol 46 – Coventry 124.

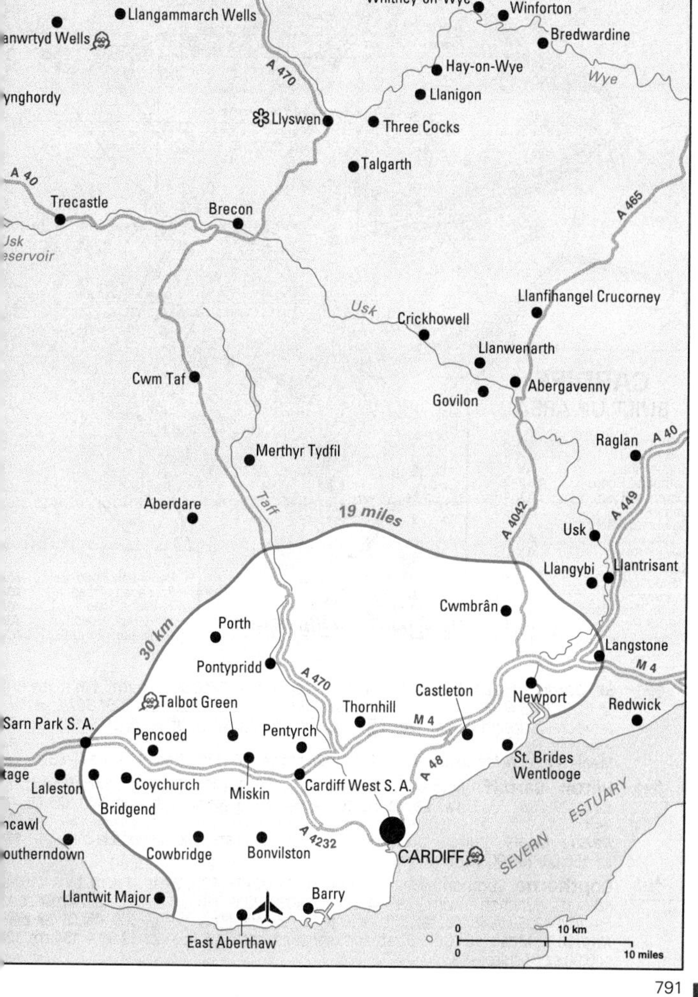

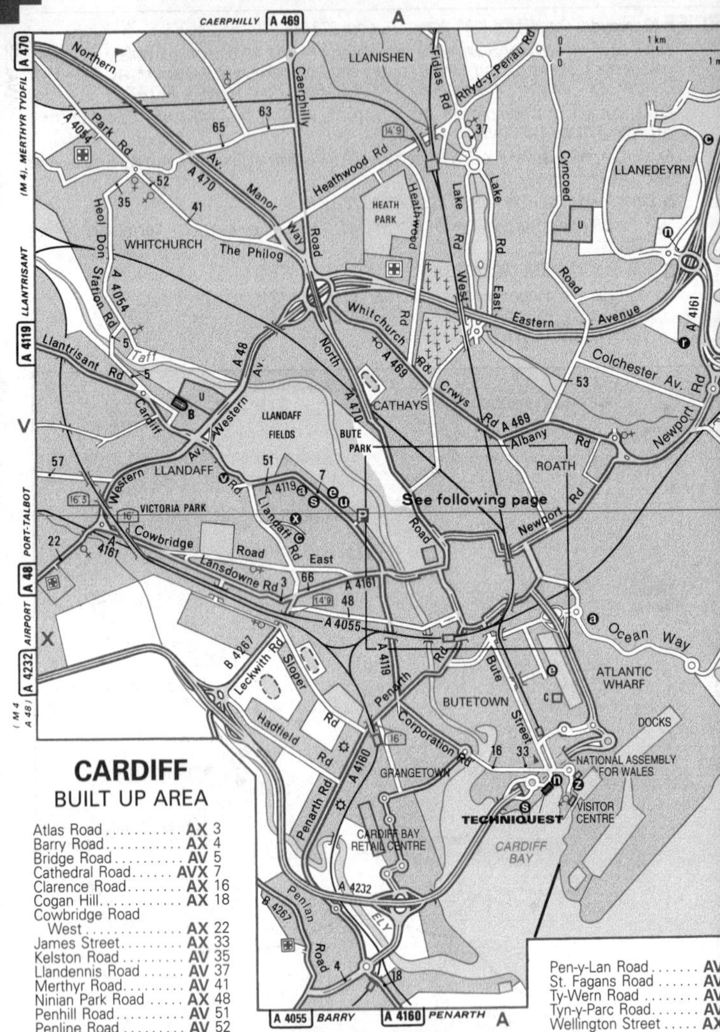

St. David's Hotel & Spa, Havannah St., Cardiff Bay, CF10 5SD, South : 1 ¾ m. by But (029) 2045 4045, *reservations@thestdavidshotel.com, Fax (029) 2031 3075,* ≤, « temporary design », Lб, ≘s, – – rm, ▤ TV ✆ ♿ P – 300. MC AE ⓓ JCB A
Meals – (see ***Tides*** below) – ☕ 13.50 – **124 rm** 140.00/170.00 **st.**, 12 suites – SB.

Hilton Cardiff, Kingsway, CF10 3HH, (029) 2064 6300, *gm-cardiff@hilton. Fax (029) 2064 6333,* Lб, ≘s, heated – rm, ▤ TV ✆ ♿ P – 340. MC AE ⓓ JCB B
Razzi : **Meals** (buffet lunch)/dinner 17.50/23.50 **st.** and dinner a la carte – 17
☕ 150.00/290.00 **st.**, 27 suites – SB.

Copthorne, Copthorne Way, Culverhouse Cross, CF5 6DH, West : 4 ¾ m. by A 4161 a 48 at junction with A 4232 (029) 2059 9100, *sales.cardiff@mill-cop. Fax (029) 2059 9648,* Lб, ≘s, , – – , ▤ rest, TV ♿ P – 300. MC AE ⓓ VISA
Raglan's : **Meals** 16.00/19.00 **st.** and dinner a la carte 6.95 – ☕ 12.50 – **134 rm** 12
140.00 **st.**, 1 suite – SB.

CARDIFF

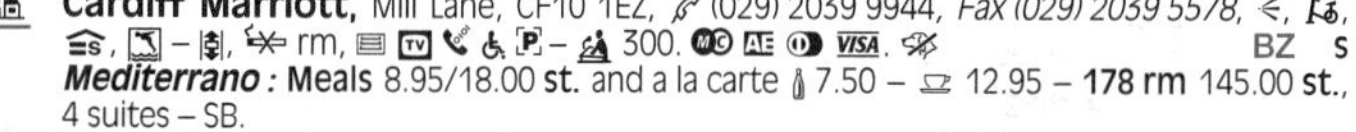

Cardiff Marriott, Mill Lane, CF10 1EZ, ☎ (029) 2039 9944, *Fax (029) 2039 5578*, ≤, ⅠⅠ, ≘s, ⌧ – |‡|, ⇔ rm, ▤ TV ☏ & P – ⚰ 300. MC AE ⓓ VISA. ✂ BZ s
Mediterrano : Meals 8.95/18.00 **st.** and a la carte ₰ 7.50 – ☐ 12.95 – **178 rm** 145.00 **st.**, 4 suites – SB.

Thistle Cardiff, Park Pl., CF10 3UD, ☎ (029) 2038 3471, *cardiff@thistle.co.uk*, *Fax (029) 2039 9309* – |‡|, ⇔ rm, ▤ rest, TV & P – ⚰ 300. MC AE ⓓ VISA JCB. ✂ BZ c
Oval Brasserie : Meals 11.00/18.95 **t.** and dinner a la carte ₰ 8.00 – ☐ 12.50 – **132 rm** 112.00/146.00 **st.**, 4 suites – SB.

Cardiff Bay, Schooner Way, Atlantic Wharf, CF10 4RT, ☎ (029) 2047 5000, *reservations@cardiff-bay-hotel.co.uk*, *Fax (029) 2048 1491*, « Part Victorian warehouse », ⅠⅠ, ≘s, ⌧ – |‡|, ⇔ rm, ▤ rest, TV ☏ & P – ⚰ 250. MC AE ⓓ VISA BZ r
Halyards : Meals *(closed Saturday lunch)* a la carte 14.95/27.45 **st.** ₰ 7.50 – ☐ 9.50 – **153 rm** 100.00/140.00 **st.**, 3 suites.

Angel, Castle St., CF10 1SZ, ✆ (029) 2064 9200, *angel@paramount-hotels.co. Fax (029) 2039 6212* – 300. VISA JCB BZ
Meals 12.50/17.50 **st.** and dinner a la carte – 10.50 – **100 rm** 105.00/120.00 **st.**, 2 sui – SB.

Village H. and Leisure Club, 29 Pendwyallt Rd, Coryton, CF14 7EF, Northwest : 5 by A 470 on A 4054 at southern side of junction 32 of M 4 ✆ (029) 2052 4300, *village.car base.co.uk, Fax (029) 2052 4313,* – 250.
Meals (grill rest.) 10.95/12.95 **st.** and a la carte – **98 rm** 88.00/98.00 **st.**

Jurys Cardiff, Mary Ann St., CF10 2JH, ✆ (029) 2034 1441, *cardiff_hotel@jurysdo com, Fax (029) 2022 3742* – rm, rest, – 300. VISA. BZ
Meals *(closed 24-27 December)* (bar lunch Monday to Saturday)/dinner a la carte 15. 25.00 **st.** 9.00 – 10.50 – **146 rm** 125.00/140.00 **t.**, 3 suites.

Forte Posthouse Cardiff, Pentwyn Rd, CF2 7XA, Northeast : 4 m. by A ✆ (0870) 400 8141, *Fax (029) 2054 9147,* rest, – 120. VISA JCB
Meals a la carte 17.85/28.35 **st.** – 11.95 – **142 rm** 69.00 **st.** – SB.

Posthouse Cardiff City, Castle St., CF10 1XD, ✆ (0870) 4008140, *Fax (029) 2037 14* rm, rest, – 150. VISA JCB BZ
Meals a la carte 22.40/31.90 **t.** 7.95 – 11.95 – **155 rm** 79.00 **st.** – SB.

Cardiff Moat House, Circle Way East, Llanedeyrn, CF23 7XF, Northeast : 3 m. by A ✆ (029) 2058 9988, *Fax (029) 2054 9092,* rest, – 3 VISA. AV
Meals (bar lunch Monday to Saturday)/dinner 16.95 and a la carte 5.85 – 11.5 **130 rm** 95.00/110.00 **st.**, 2 suites.

Churchills, Cardiff Rd, CF5 2AD, ✆ (029) 2040 1300, *reservations@churchillshotel.co Fax (029) 2056 8347* – – 110. VISA AV
Meals *(closed Saturday lunch)* 9.50/16.50 **t.** and a la carte 4.25 – **28 rm** 75. 90.00 **st.**, 7 suites – SB.

Lincoln House without rest., 118 Cathedral Rd, CF11 9LQ, ✆ (029) 2039 5558, *reserv ns@lincolnhotel.co.uk, Fax (029) 2023 0537* – VISA JCB. AV
23 rm 48.00/68.00 **st.**

Express by Holiday Inn without rest., Schooner Way, Atlantic Wharf, CF10 ✆ (029) 2044 9000, *holidayinn-cardiff@.msn.com, Fax (029) 2048 8922* – 30. VISA JCB. AX
87 rm 59.50 **st.**

Ibis without rest., Malthouse Av., Cardiff Gate Business Park, Pontprennau, CF23 Northeast : 5 ¾ m. by A 48 and A 4232 at junction 30 of M 4 ✆ (029) 2073 3 *Fax (029) 2073 4222* – – 30. VISA
78 rm 49.50 **st.**

Ibis, Churchill Way, CF10 2HJ, ✆ (029) 2064 9250, *h2936@accor-hotels.c Fax (029) 2064 9260* – rm, . VISA BZ
Meals (grill rest.) (dinner only) a la carte approx. 12.00 **st.** – **102 rm** 45.00 **st.**

Travel Inn without rest., The David Lloyd Leisure Club, Ipswich Rd, Roath, CF23 Northeast : 2 ½ m. by A 4161 ✆ (029) 2046 2481, *Fax (029) 2046 2482* – . VISA. AV
70 rm 40.95 **t.**

Travel Inn, Keen Rd, CF24 5JT, ✆ (029) 2048 9675, *Fax (029) 2048 9757* – rm, – 30. VISA. AX
Meals (grill rest.) – **73 rm** 40.95 **t.**

Travel Inn, Port Rd, Nant Isaf, Wenvoe, CF5 6DD, Southwest : 5 ¾ m. by A 4161 and on A 4050 ✆ (029) 2059 3896, *Fax (029) 2059 1436* – rm, rest, – 100. VISA.
Meals (grill rest.) – **39 rm** 40.95 **t.**

Travelodge without rest., 65-67 St.Marys St., Imperial Gate, CF10 ✆ (029) 2039 8697, *Fax (029) 2039 8737* – . VISA JCB. BZ
100 rm 49.95 **t.**

Travelodge without rest., Circle Way East, Llanedeyrn, CF23 9PD, Northeast : 3 ½ m. 48 on Coed-y-Gores rd ✆ (029) 2054 9564, *Fax (029) 2054 9564* – . JCB. AV
32 rm 39.95 **t.**

Townhouse without rest., 70 Cathedral Rd, CF11 9LL, ✆ (029) 2023 9399, *thetownh @msn.com, Fax (029) 2022 3214* – . VISA JCB AV
9 rm 39.50/59.50 **t.**

Georgian without rest., 179 Cathedral Rd, CF11 9PL, (029) 2023 2594, *gmenin@georgianhotelcardiff.co.uk, Fax (029) 2023 2594* – TV. AV a
8 rm 27.00/44.00 **st.**

Annedd Lon without rest., 157 Cathedral Rd, CF11 9PL, (029) 2022 3349, *annedd.lon@virgin.net, Fax (029) 2064 0885* – TV P. MC VISA. AV s
closed 25-31 December – **6 rm** 30.00/50.00 **s.**

XXX **Tides** (at St. David's H. & Spa), Havannah St., Cardiff Bay, CF10 5SD, South : 1 3/4 m. by Bute St. (029) 2045 4045, *Fax (029) 2031 3075*, ← – P. MC AE D VISA AX s
Meals 19.50/25.00 **t.** and a la carte 7.50.

XX **Woods Brasserie,** The Pilotage Building, Stuart St., Cardiff Bay, CF10 5BW, South : 1 1/2 m. by Bute St. (029) 2049 2400, *Fax (029) 2048 1998*, – . MC AE D VISA JCB
closed 1 week in spring, 1 week in autumn, 25-26 and 31 December, 1 January and Sunday dinner – **Meals** a la carte 18.40/28.95 **t.** 5.90. AX n

XX **Gilby's,** Old Port Rd, Culverhouse Cross, CF5 6DN, West : 5 m. by A 4161 and A 48 off A 4050 (029) 2067 0800, *info@gilbysrestaurant.co.uk, Fax (029) 2059 4437*, – P. MC AE VISA
closed Christmas, New Year, Sunday dinner and Monday – **Meals** a la carte 19.35/26.10 **t.**

X **Le Gallois,** 6-10 Romilly Cres., CF11 9NR, (029) 2034 1264, *le-gallois@virgin.net, Fax (029) 2023 7911* – . MC AE VISA JCB AX x
closed 3 weeks August, 1 week Christmas, Sunday and Monday – **Meals** 13.95/32.00 **t.** and a la carte 6.95.

X **Le Cassoulet,** 5 Romilly Cres., Canton, CF11 9NP, (029) 2022 1905, *lecassoulet@ukonline.co.uk, Fax (029) 2022 1905* – MC AE D VISA JCB AX c
closed August, 1 week Christmas, Sunday and Monday – **Meals** - French - 15.00 **t.** (lunch) and a la carte 23.50/31.50 **t.** 7.50.

X **Cutting Edge,** Discovery House, Scott Harbour, CF10 4PJ, (029) 2047 0780, *Fax (029) 2044 0876* – . MC VISA AX z
closed 25-26 December, 1 January and Sunday – **Meals** (lunch booking essential) a la carte 18.95/22.95 **t.** 6.50.

Thornhill *North : 5 1/4 m. by A 470 on A 469* – **AV** – *Cardiff.*

New House Country, Thornhill Rd, CF14 9UA, on A 469 (029) 2052 0280, *Fax (029) 2052 0324*, ←, , – rest, TV P – 200. MC AE D VISA JCB.
closed 1 January – **Meals** 12.50/18.50 **t.** and a la carte – **33 rm** 89.50/107.50 **st.**, 3 suites – SB.

Manor Parc, Thornhill Rd, CF14 5UA, on A 469 (029) 2022 1905, *Fax (029) 2061 4624*, , – TV P – 120. MC AE VISA.
closed 24-27 December and 1 January – **Meals** *(closed Sunday dinner)* 15.00/17.00 **t.** (lunch) and a la carte 25.00/33.50 **t.** 6.50 – **12 rm** 65.00/130.00 **t.** – SB.

Castleton (Cas-Bach) *(Newport) Northeast : 7 m. on A 48* – **AV** – *Cardiff.*

St. Mellons, CF3 2XR, (01633) 680355, *stmellons@bestwestern.co.uk, Fax (01633) 680399*, , , , , , squash – rest, TV P – 200. MC AE VISA
Meals *(closed Saturday lunch)* 16.00 **t.** and dinner a la carte 4.95 – **41 rm** 95.00/135.00 **st.**

Travel Inn, Newport Rd, CF3 2UQ, (01633) 680070, *Fax (01633) 681143* – rm, rest, TV P. MC AE D VISA.
Meals (grill rest.) – **49 rm** 40.95 **t.**

Pentyrch *Northwest : 7 m. by A 4119* – **AV** – *Cardiff.*

XX **De Courcey's,** Tyla Morris Av., CF15 9QN, South : 1 m. (029) 2089 2232, *Fax (029) 2089 1949*, – P – 100. MC AE D VISA JCB
closed 1 week Christmas, Sunday dinner and Monday – **Meals** 15.95/24.75 **st.** and a la carte 8.95.

RDIFF WEST SERVICE AREA *Cardiff* 403 K 29 – *Pontycwn (Rhondda Cynon Taff).*

Travelodge, CF72 8SA, M 4 junction 33 (029) 2089 1141, *Fax (029) 2089 2497* – TV P – 30. MC AE D VISA JCB.
Meals (grill rest.) – **50 rm** 39.95 **t.**

Don't confuse:

Comfort of hotels : ... ,
Comfort of restaurants : XXXXX ..... X,
Quality of the cuisine : , , , **Meals**

CARDIGAN (Aberteifi) *Ceredigion* 403 G 27 *Wales G. – pop. 3 758.*
Env. : *Pembrokeshire Coast National Park★★.*
Gwbert-on-Sea ☎ (01239) 612035.
Theatr Mwldan, Bath House Rd ☎ (01239) 613230.
London 250 – Carmarthen 30 – Fishguard 19.

Penbontbren Farm ⌘, Glynarthen, SA44 6PE, Northeast : 9 ½ m. by A 4
☎ (01239) 810248, *Fax (01239) 811129*, – rest, TV P – 50. MC AE VISA JCB
closed Christmas – **Meals** (dinner only) a la carte 15.00/23.00 **st.** 4.95 – **10 rm** 51.
90.50 – SB.

at St. Dogmaels *West : 1½ m. by A 487 on B 4546 – ✉ Cardigan.*

Berwyn ⌘ without rest., Cardigan Rd, SA43 3HS, ☎ (01239) 613555, ←, – TV
closed December – **3 rm** 25.00/50.00 **st.**

at Gwbert on Sea *Northwest : 3 m. on B 4548 – ✉ Cardigan.*

Gwbert, SA43 1PP, on B 4548 ☎ (01239) 612638, *gwbert@enterprise.r*
Fax (01239) 621474, ← Cardigan Bay – , rest, TV P. MC AE VISA.
Meals *(closed Sunday in winter)* (bar lunch Monday to Saturday)/dinner 14.95
and a la carte 6.85 – **16 rm** 51.50/127.00 **t.** – SB.

CARMARTHEN (Caerfyrddin) *Carmarthenshire* 403 H 28 – *pop. 12 247.*
See : *Kidwelly Castle★ – National Botanic Garden★.*
Lammas St. ☎ (01267) 231557.
London 219 – Fishguard 47 – Haverfordwest 32 – Swansea 27.

at Nantgaredig *East : 5 m. on A 40 – ✉ Carmarthen.*

Four Seasons with rm, SA32 7NY, North : ½ m. on B 4310 ☎ (01267) 290238, *jen4sea*
ol.com, Fax (01267) 290808, , , – rm, TV P. MC VISA JCB
closed 1 week in summer and 25 December – **Meals** *(closed Sunday and Monday)* (din
only) 25.00/28.00 **t.** 5.00 – **6 rm** 40.00/80.00 **t.**

CASTLETON (Cas-Bach) *Newport* 403 K 29 – *see Cardiff.*

CEMAES (Cemais) *Anglesey* 402 403 G 23 *Wales G.*
Env. : *Anglesey★★.*
London 272 – Bangor 25 – Caernarfon 32 – Holyhead 16.

Hafod Country House ⌘ without rest., LL67 0DS, South : ½ m. on Llanfechel
☎ (01407) 710500, *hirst.hafod@tesco.net, Fax (01407) 710055*, ←, – TV P. MC AE
VISA JCB.
Easter-September – **3 rm** 40.00/48.00.

CHANCERY (Rhydgaled) *Ceredigion* 403 H 26 – *see Aberystwyth.*

CHEPSTOW (Cas-gwent) *Monmouthshire* 403 404 M 29 *Wales G. – pop. 9 461.*
See : *Town★ – Castle★★ AC (Great Tower★★).*
Env. : *Wynd Cliff★, N : 2½ m. by A 466 – Caerwent★ (Roman Walls★), SW : 4 m. by A 48.*
Castle Car Park, Bridge St. ☎ (01291) 623772.
London 131 – Bristol 17 – Cardiff 28 – Gloucester 34.

Marriott St. Pierre H. & Country Club, St. Pierre Park, NP16 6YA, Southwest : 3 ½
on A 48 ☎ (01291) 625261, *Fax (01291) 629975*, , , , , , – TV
250. MC AE VISA JCB.
Orangery : **Meals** (booking essential) (dinner only and Sunday lunch)/dinner 25.00
Long Weekend : **Meals** a la carte 13.70/21.35 **st.** – 12.50 – **132 rm** 104.00 **st.**, 16 sui

George, Moor St., NP16 5DB, ☎ (01291) 625363, *Fax (01291) 627418* – TV P –
MC AE VISA.
Meals a la carte 8.95/16.95 **st.** 9.50 – 8.95 – **14 rm** 70.00/100.00 **st.** – SB.

Castle View, 16 Bridge St., NP6 5EZ, ☎ (01291) 620349, *mart@castview.demon.co*
Fax (01291) 627397, – rest, TV. MC AE VISA
Meals (bar lunch Monday to Saturday) (Sunday dinner residents only)/dinner a la c
16.00/21.00 **t.** 6.95 – 5.95 – **13 rm** 42.00/70.00 **t.** – SB.

OLWYN BAY (Bae Colwyn) *Conwy* 402 403 I 24 *Wales G. – pop. 29 883.*

See : *Welsh Mountain Zoo★ AC (≤★).*

Env. : *Bodnant Garden★★ AC, SW : 6 m. by A 55 and A 470.*

18 Abergele, Tan-y-Goppa Rd ☎ (01745) 824034 – 9 Old Colwyn, Woodland Av. ☎ (01492) 515581.

Imperial Buildings, Station Sq., Princes Dr. ☎ (01492) 530478 – The Promenade, Rhos-on-Sea ☎ (01492) 548778 (summer only).

London 237 – Birkenhead 50 – Chester 42 – Holyhead 41.

Norfolk House, 39 Princes Drive, LL29 8PF, ☎ (01492) 531757, *booking@norfolkhousehotel.fsnet.co.uk, Fax (01492) 533781,* – TV P – 35. MC AE VISA JCB
closed 22 December-14 January – **Meals** 9.95/17.00 **st.** and a la carte – **21 rm** 45.00/59.00 **st.** – SB.

Café Niçoise, 124 Abergele Rd, LL29 7PS, ☎ (01492) 531555 – MC AE VISA JCB
closed 1 week in spring, 1 week in autumn, 25-26 December, Sunday and lunch Monday and Tuesday – **Meals** 14.95 **t.** and a la carte 13.75/24.85 **t.** 4.75.

ONWY *Conwy* 402 403 I 24 *Wales G. – pop. 3 627.*

See : *Town★★ – Castle★★★ AC – Town Walls★★ – Plas Mawr★★.*

Env. : *Snowdonia National Park★★★ – Bodnant Garden★★ AC, S : 8 m. by A 55 and A 470 – Conwy Crossing (suspension bridge★).*

9 Penmaenmawr, Conway Old Rd ☎ (01492) 623330.

Conwy Castle Visitor Centre, Castle St. ☎ (01492) 592248.

London 241 – Caernarfon 22 – Chester 46 – Holyhead 37.

Sychnant Pass House, Sychnant Pass Rd, LL32 8BJ, Southwest : 2 m. by A 547 and Sychnant rd, turning right at T junction ☎ (01492) 596868, *bresykes@sychnant-pass-house.co.uk, Fax (01492) 596868,* ≤, – TV P. MC VISA
Meals *(closed Monday)* (booking essential to non-residents) (dinner only and Sunday lunch)/dinner a la carte 13.85/21.85 **t.** 5.00 – **9 rm** 45.00/60.00 **t.**, 1 suite – SB.

Berthlwyd Hall, Llechwedd, LL32 8DQ, Southwest : 2 ¾ m. by A 547 and Sychnant rd, turn right at T junction then left at National Park sign ☎ (01492) 592409, *griffen-properties@virgin.net, Fax (01492) 572290,* ≤, « Victorian manor house », heated, – TV P. MC AE VISA JCB
closed January and February – **Meals** (booking essential to non-residents) (dinner only) (set menu only) 20.00 **st.** – **5 rm** 40.00/100.00 **st.**

Tyn-y-Groes *(Gwynedd) South : 4 m. on B 5106 – ✉ Conwy.*

Groes Inn with rm, LL32 8TN, North : 1 ½ m. on B 5106 ☎ (01492) 650545, *Fax (01492) 650855,* ≤, , « Part 16C », – TV P. MC AE VISA
Meals 12.50/25.00 **t.** and lunch a la carte 8.50 – **14 rm** 64.00/125.00 **t.** – SB.

WBRIDGE (Y Bont Faen) *Vale of Glamorgan* 403 J 29 *– pop. 6 167.*

London 170 – Cardiff 15 – Swansea 30.

Huddarts, 69 High St., CF71 7AF, ☎ (01446) 774645 – . MC AE VISA
closed first 2 weeks in January, Sunday dinner and Monday – **Meals** 16.95 **t.** (dinner) and a la carte 14.65/27.40 **t.** 9.75.

YCHURCH (Llangrallo) *Bridgend* 403 J 29 *– see Bridgend.*

ICCIETH *Gwynedd* 402 403 H 25 *Wales G. – pop. 1 720.*

Env. : *Lleyn Peninsula★★ – Ffestiniog Railway★★.*

18 Ednyfed Hill ☎ (01766) 522154.

London 249 – Caernarfon 17 – Shrewsbury 85.

Mynydd Ednyfed Country House, Caernarfon Rd, LL52 0PH, Northwest : ¾ m. on B 4411 ☎ (01766) 523269, *mynedd-ednyfed@criccieth.net, Fax (01766) 522929,* ≤, , , – rest, TV P. MC VISA.
closed 23 December-2 January – **Meals** (dinner only and Sunday lunch)/dinner a la carte 15.25/20.95 **t.** 6.95 – **9 rm** 30.00/75.00 **t.** – SB.

Tir-a-Môr, 1-3 Mona Terr., LL52 0HG, ☎ (01766) 523084, *Fax (01766) 523049* – MC VISA JCB
closed Sunday and restricted opening in winter – **Meals** (dinner only) a la carte 19.30/25.20 **t.** 6.55.

The Guide is updated annually so renew your Guide every year.

CRICKHOWELL (Crucywel) *Powys* 403 K 28 *Wales G. – pop. 2 166.*

Env. : Brecon Beacons National Park★★.

Exc. : Llanthony Priory★★, NE : 10 m. by minor roads.

Beaufort Chambers, Beaufort St. ℘ (01873) 812105 (Easter-October).

London 169 – Abergavenny 6 – Brecon 14 – Newport 25.

Bear, High St., NP8 1BW, ℘ (01873) 810408, *bearhotel@aol.com, Fax (01873) 8116* « Part 15C former coaching inn », – TV P – 50. MO AE VISA JCB
Meals *(closed Sunday dinner)* (lunch booking essential) a la carte 21.95/30.95 **t.** 4.95
33 rm 49.50/120.00 **t.**, 1 suite.

Gliffaes Country House, NP8 1RH, West : 3 ¾ m. by A 40 ℘ (01874) 730371, *cal gliffaeshotel.com, Fax (01874) 730463,* <, « Victorian country house and gardens on t banks of the River Usk », – rest, TV P – 50. MO AE VISA
Meals (light lunch Monday to Saturday)/dinner 24.50 **st.** 7.50 – **22 rm** 52.50/134.50

Ty Croeso, The Dardy, NP8 1PU, West : 1 ½ m. by A 4077 off Llangynidr ℘ (01873) 810573, *tycroeso@ty-croeso-hotel.freeserve.co.uk, Fax (01873) 810573,* <, TV P. MO AE VISA
closed 1 week January and 24-25 December – **Meals** (lunch booking essential) 9.95/16.95 and a la carte 5.50 – **8 rm** 35.00/70.00 **t.** – SB.

Glangrwyney Court, NP8 1ES, South : 2 m. on A 40 ℘ (01873) 810288, *glangrwyne@ l.com, Fax (01873) 810317,* « Georgian house », – TV P
Meals (by arrangement) (communal dining) 20.00 **s.** – **5 rm** 35.00/55.00 **s.** – SB.

Nantyffin Cider Mill Inn, Brecon Rd, NP8 1SG, West : 1 ½ m. on A ℘ (01873) 810775, *nantyffin@aol.com, Fax (01873) 810775,* « Converted 16C cider mil – P. MO AE VISA
closed 1 week January, 1 week November and Monday – **Meals** a la carte 15.85/18.40 7.95.

CROSSGATES *Powys* 403 J 27 – *see Llandrindod Wells.*

CROSS HANDS *Carmarthenshire* 403 H 28 – *pop. 9 520.*

London 208 – Fishguard 63 – Swansea 19.

Travelodge, SA14 6NW, on A 48 ℘ (01269) 845700, *Fax (01269) 845700* – rm, TV P. MO AE VISA JCB.
Meals (grill rest.) – **32 rm** 39.95 **t.**

CRUGYBAR *Carmarthenshire* 403 I 27 – ✉ *Llanwrda.*

London 213 – Carmarthen 26 – Swansea 36.

Glanrannell Park, SA19 8SA, Southwest : ½ m. by B 4302 ℘ (01558) 685230, *glan khotel@btinternet.com, Fax (01558) 685784,* <, – rest, TV P. MO AE VISA
closed 23-27 December – **Meals** (booking essential to non-residents) (dinner only) 17.00 – **8 rm** 38.00/76.00 **st.** – SB.

CWMBRAN (Cwmbrân) *Torfaen* 403 K 29 – *pop. 46 021.*

London 149 – Bristol 35 – Cardiff 17 – Newport 5.

Parkway, Cwmbran Drive, NP44 3UW, South : 1 m. by A 4051 ℘ (01633) 8711 *Fax (01633) 869160,* – rm, rest, TV P – 500. MO AE VISA
Meals *(closed Saturday lunch)* (light lunch Monday to Friday)/dinner 17.95 **t.** and a la ca 7.80 – **69 rm** 103.00/124.65 **st.**, 1 suite – SB.

CWM GWAUN *Pembrokeshire* 403 F 28 – *see Fishguard.*

CWM TAF *Merthyr Tydfil* 403 J 28 – *see Merthyr Tydfil.*

CYNGHORDY *Carmarthenshire* 403 I 27 – ✉ *Llandovery.*

London 210 – Carmarthen 31 – Swansea 41.

Llanerchindda Farm, SA20 0NB, North : 2 ½ m. by Station rd, turning right T-junction and under viaduct ℘ (01550) 750274, *nick@cambrianway.co Fax (01550) 750300,* < Black Mountains, « Working farm », – TV P
Meals (by arrangement) (communal dining) 12.00 **st.** 4.00 – **9 rm** 24.00/48.00 **st.** –

DEGANWY *Conwy* 402 403 I 24 – *see Llandudno.*

NBIGH **(Dinbych)** *Denbighshire* 402 403 J 24.
London 218 – Chester 30 – Shrewsbury 53.

Berllan Bach, Ffordd Las, LL16 4LR, Southeast : 5 ¾ m. by A 543 and Llandyrnog rd on Llangynhafel rd (01824) 790725, – TV P
closed 2 weeks Christmas – **Meals** (by arrangement) (communal dining) 22.50 **st.** – **3 rm** 25.00/45.00 **st.**

LGELLAU *Gwynedd* 402 403 I 25 *Wales G. – pop. 2 396.*
See : *Town*★.
Env. : *Snowdonia National Park*★★★ – *Cadair Idris*★★★ – *Precipice Walk*★, *NE : 3 m. on minor roads.*
Hengwrt Estate, Pencefn Rd (01341) 422603.
Ty Meirion, Eldon Sq. (01341) 422888.
London 221 – Birkenhead 72 – Chester 64 – Shrewsbury 57.

Penmaenuchaf Hall, Penmaenpool, LL40 1YB, West : 1 ¾ m. on A 493 (Tywyn Rd) (01341) 422129, *relax@penhall.co.uk, Fax (01341) 422787,* Rhinog mountains and Mawddach estuary, « Victorian mansion in extensive gardens », – TV P. MO AE VISA JCB
closed 7-18 January – **Meals** 15.75/27.50 **t.** and a la carte 10.50 – **14 rm** 70.00/170.00 **t.** – SB.

Dolserau Hall, LL40 2AG, Northeast : 2 ¾ m. by A 494 (01341) 422522, *pk@dhh.co.uk, Fax (01341) 422400,* – rest, TV P. MO VISA
closed 2 January-15 February and 4 November-23 December – **Meals** (residents only) (dinner only) 21.95 **t.** – **15 rm** (dinner included) 56.00/125.00 **t.** – SB.

George III, Penmaenpool, LL40 1YD, West : 2 m. by A 493 (01341) 422525, *reception@george-3rd.co.uk, Fax (01341) 423565,* Mawddach estuary and mountains, « Part 17C inn on banks of Mawddach estuary », – rest, TV P. MO VISA JCB
Meals (bar lunch Monday to Saturday)/dinner a la carte 18.85/30.45 **t.** 8.80 – **11 rm** 57.50/94.00 **t.** – SB.

Abergwynant Hall, Penmaenpool, LL40 1YF, West : 3 ½ m. on A 493 (01341) 422160, *relax@abergwynant.co.uk, Fax (01341) 422046,* « Victorian mansion in extensive parkland », – TV P. MO VISA.
closed January and February – **Meals** (by arrangement) 22.00 **st.** 8.00 – **4 rm** 75.00/140.00 **st.**

Ganllwyd *North : 5½ m. on A 470 – Dolgellau.*

Plas Dolmelynllyn, LL40 2HP, (01341) 440273, *info@dolly-hotel.co.uk, Fax (01341) 440640,* « Part 17C manor house », – TV P. MO AE VISA
March-October – **Meals** (booking essential to non-residents) 26.50 **st.** 7.50 – **8 rm** 55.00/100.00 **st.**, 2 suites – SB.

Llanfachreth *Northeast : 3 ¾ m. – Dolgellau.*

Ty Isaf Farmhouse, LL40 2EA, (01341) 423261, *raygear@tyisaf78.freeserve.co.uk, Fax (01341) 423261,* « 17C longhouse », – P.
March-October – **Meals** (by arrangement) (communal dining) 17.50 – **3 rm** 37.00/54.00 **s.** – SB.

Bontddu *West : 5 m. on A 496 (Barmouth Rd) – Dolgellau.*

Bontddu Hall Country House, LL40 2UF, (01341) 430661, *reservations@bontdduhall.co.uk, Fax (01341) 430284,* Mawddach estuary and mountains, « Victorian mansion in extensive gardens » – rest, TV P. MO AE VISA JCB
March-October – ***Garden :*** **Meals** (carving lunch Sunday) (dinner only and Sunday lunch) a la carte 17.20/23.95 **t.** 6.95 – ***Brasserie :*** **Meals** 15.00/25.00 **t.** and a la carte 6.95 – **17 rm** 86.00/98.50 **t.**, 3 suites – SB.

Borthwnog Hall, LL40 2TT, East : 1 m. on A 496 (01341) 430271, *borthwnoghall@enterprise.net, Fax (01341) 430682,* Mawddach estuary and mountains, « Part Regency country house on the banks of Mawddach estuary, art gallery », – rest, TV P. MO AE VISA
closed 23 to 27 December – **Meals** 20.00 **t.** 8.50 – **3 rm** 106.00 **t.** – SB.

ENEWYDD YN NOTAIS **(Nottage)** *Bridgend* 403 I 29 – *see Porthcawl.*

Si vous cherchez un hôtel tranquille,
consultez d'abord les cartes de l'introduction
ou repérez dans le texte les établissements indiqués avec le signe ou .

DYFFRYN ARDUDWY *Gwynedd* 402 403 H 25 *Wales G. – pop. 1 452 (inc. Tal-y-Bont).*
Env. : *Snowdonia National Park*★★★.
London 237 – Dolgellau 16 – Caernarfon 44.

Ystumgwern Hall Farm without rest., LL44 2DD, Northwest : 1 m. by A 4 (01341) 247249, *ystumgwern@aol.com, Fax (01341) 247171,* « Working farm », TV P.
minimum stay 2 nights – , **5 suites** 52.00 **s.**

EAST ABERTHAW (Aberddawan) *Vale of Glamorgan* 403 J 29 – ✉ *Barry.*
London 180 – Cardiff 20 – Swansea 33.

Blue Anchor Inn, CF62 3DD, (01446) 750329, *Fax (01446) 750077,* « Characterful p 14C thatched inn » – P. MC VISA
closed Sunday dinner – **Meals** 12.95 **t.** and a la carte 5.00.

ERBISTOCK *Wrexham* 402 403 L 25 – *see Wrexham.*

EWLOE *Flintshire* 402 403 K 24 – *pop. 3 263.*
London 200 – Chester 8.5 – Liverpool 18 – Shrewsbury 48.

St David's Park, St. David's Park, CH5 3YB, on B 5125 at junction with A (01244) 520800, *reservations@stdavids-park.hotel.co.uk, Fax (01244) 520930,* 18, – rest, TV P – 250. MC AE VISA.
Fountains : **Meals** *(closed Sunday lunch)* 19.50/25.00 **st.** and a la carte 6.50 – 10.9
145 rm 114.00/124.00 **st.** – SB.

FISHGUARD (Abergwaun) *Pembrokeshire* 403 F 28 *Wales G. – pop. 3 128.*
Env. : *Pembrokeshire Coast National Park*★★.
to Republic of Ireland (Rosslare) (Stena Line) 2-4 daily (1 h 40 mn/3 h 30 mn).
Town Hall, The Square (01348) 873484 – Ocean Lab, The Parrog, Goodwick (013 872037.
London 265 – Cardiff 114 – Gloucester 176 – Holyhead 169 – Shrewsbury 136 – Swansea

Manor House, 11 Main St., SA65 9HG, (01348) 873260, *Fax (01348) 873260,* TV. MC VISA
closed Christmas and restricted opening in winter – **Meals** *(closed Sunday to non-r dents)* (booking essential to non-residents) (dinner only) 18.00/20.00 **st.** and a la ca 6.00 – **6 rm** 30.00/60.00 **st.**

Three Main Street with rm, 3 Main St., SA65 9HG, (01348) 8742 *Fax (01348) 874017* – TV.
closed February – **Meals** *(closed Tuesday in winter, Sunday and Monday)* (light lur 28.00 **t.** 7.50 – **3 rm** 40.00/80.00 **t.**

at Cwm Gwaun *Southeast : 5½ m. by B 4313 – ✉ Fishguard.*

Tregynon Country Farmhouse, SA65 9TU, East : 6 ¼ m. (01239) 820531, *tr non@online-holidays.net, Fax (01239) 820808,* – P. MC VISA JCB.
closed Sunday, Wednesday in winter and Thursday – **Meals** (booking essential) (dinner o 22.50 **t.** 9.30.

at Letterston *South : 5 m. on A 40.*

Heathfield Mansion, SA62 5EG, Northwest : 1 ½ m. by B 4331 (01348) 84026 *ngelica.rees@virgin.net, Fax (01348) 840263,* – TV P
April-October – **Meals** (by arrangement) 15.00 **st.** 3.75 – **3 rm** 26.00/50.00 **st.**

at Welsh Hook *Southwest : 7½ m. by A 40 – ✉ Haverfordwest.*

Stone Hall with rm, SA62 5NS, (01348) 840212, *Fax (01348) 840815,* « Part manor house with 17C additions », – TV P. MC AE VISA.
Meals (dinner only) a la carte 16.00/25.00 **t.** 5.75 – **5 rm** 49.00/75.00 **t.** – SB.

GANLLWYD *Gwynedd* 402 403 I 25 – *see Dolgellau.*

GARTHMYL *Powys – see Montgomery.*

GELLILYDAN *Gwynedd – see Llan Ffestiniog.*

GLANWYDDEN *Conwy – see Llandudno.*

OVILON (Gofilon) *Monmouthshire – see Abergavenny.*

RESFORD (Groes-ffordd) *Wrexham* 402 403 L 24 – *see Wrexham.*

UILSFIELD (Cegidfa) *Powys* 402 403 K 26 – *see Welshpool.*

WBERT ON SEA *Ceredigion* 403 F 27 – *see Cardigan.*

ALKYN (Helygain) *Flintshire* 402 403 K 24 – ✉ *Holywell.*
London 208 – Chester 22 – Liverpool 31 – Shrewsbury 48.

Travelodge, CH8 8RF, on A 55 (westbound carriageway) ☎ (01352) 780952, *Fax (01352) 780952* – ⇆ rm, ▤ rest, TV ♿ P. MC AE Ⓓ VISA JCB. ✻
Meals (grill rest.) – **31 rm** 39.95 **t.**

ANMER *Wrexham* 402 403 L 25 – *pop. 565* – ✉ *Whitchurch (Shrops.).*
London 178 – Chester 26 – Shrewsbury 27 – Stoke-on-Trent 28.

Hanmer Arms, SY13 3DE, ☎ (01948) 830532, *enquiry@thehanmerarms.co.uk, Fax (01948) 830740,* ⌂, ⌂ – ⇆ rest, TV P – 🏃 80. MC AE Ⓓ VISA JCB
Meals a la carte 10.50/23.00 **t.** 🍷 5.60 – **21 rm** ☕ 44.50/65.00, 6 suites.

ARLECH *Gwynedd* 402 403 H 25 *Wales G.* – *pop. 1 233.*
See : *Castle★★ AC.*
Env. : *Snowdonia National Park★★★.*
⛳18 *Royal St. David's ☎ (01766) 780203.*
ℹ *Gwyddfor House, High St. ☎ (01766) 780658.*
London 241 – Chester 72 – Dolgellau 21.

Hafod Wen, LL46 2RA, South : ¾ m. on A 496 ☎ (01766) 780356, *hafodwen@enterprise.net, Fax (01766) 780356,* ≤ Tremadoc bay and Snowdonia, ⌂ – ⇆ TV P. MC VISA
closed 2 weeks November and 25-26 December – **Meals** 17.00 **t.** – **7 rm** ☕ 24.00/59.00 **t.**

Gwrach Ynys without rest., LL47 6TS, North : 2 ¼ m. on A 496 ☎ (01766) 780742, *gwynfor@talk21.com, Fax (01766) 781199,* ⌂ – ⇆ TV P. ✻
March-October – **7 rm** ☕ 22.00/50.00.

XX **Castle Cottage** with rm, Pen Llech, LL46 2YL, off B 4573 ☎ (01766) 780479, *gh.roberts@talk21.com, Fax (01766) 780479* – ⇆. MC VISA. ✻
closed 2 weeks February – **Meals** (booking essential) (dinner only) 24.00 **t.** 🍷 6.00 – **6 rm** ☕ 29.00/60.00 **t.** – SB.

AVERFORDWEST (Hwlffordd) *Pembrokeshire* 403 F 28 *Wales G.* – *pop. 11 099.*
See : *Scolton Museum and Country Park★.*
Env. : *Pembrokeshire Coast National Park★★.*
Exc. : *Skomer Island and Skokholm Island★, SW : 14 m. by B 4327 and minor roads.*
⛳18 *Arnolds Down ☎ (01437) 763565.*
ℹ *Old Bridge ☎ (01437) 763110.*
London 250 – Fishguard 15 – Swansea 57.

Wilton House, 6 Quay St., SA61 1BG, ☎ (01437) 760033, *phil@wiltonhousehotel.freeserve.co.uk, Fax (01437) 760297,* ⛱ heated – TV P. MC AE VISA. ✻
closed 23 December-2 January – **Meals** *(closed Sunday lunch)* a la carte 11.35/19.95 **st.** 🍷 4.00 – **10 rm** ☕ 39.50/59.50 **st.**

Lower Haythog Farm ⛰, Spittal, SA62 5QL, Northeast : 5 m. on B 4329 ☎ (01437) 731279, *Fax (01437) 731279,* « Working farm », ⌂, ⌂ – ⇆ TV P
closed 25 December – **Meals** (by arrangement) 15.00 **s.** – **4 rm** ☕ 45.00/60.00 **s.** – SB.

AWARDEN (Penarlâg) *Flintshire* 402 K 24.
London 205 – Chester 9 – Liverpool 17 – Shrewsbury 45.

X **The Brasserie,** 68 The Highway, CH5 3DH, ☎ (01244) 536353, *Fax (01244) 520888* – ▤. MC VISA
closed Saturday lunch – **Meals** 12.50 **t.** (lunch) and dinner a la carte 18.95/22.70 **t.**

HAY-ON-WYE (Y Gelli) *Powys* 403 K 27 *Wales G. – pop. 1 407.*

See : *Town*★.
Env. : *Brecon Beacons National Park*★★.
Exc. : *Llanthony Priory*★★, *SE : 12 m. by minor roads.*
Rhosgoch, Builth Wells ☎ *(01497) 851251.*
London 154 – Brecon 16 – Hereford 21 – Newport 62.

The Swan at Hay, Church St., HR3 5DQ, ☎ (01497) 821188, *Fax (01497) 821424*, – rest, – 160.
Meals (bar lunch Monday-Saturday)/dinner a la carte 12.45/23.00 **t.** 5.85 – **19 r** 50.00/90.00 **t.** – SB.

York House, Hardwick Rd, Cusop, HR3 5QX, East : ½ m. on B 4348 ☎ (01497) 8207 *Fax (01497) 820705*, –
Meals (by arrangement) 15.00 **t.** – **4 rm** 27.00/54.00 **t.** – SB.

Old Black Lion with rm, Lion St., HR3 5AD, ☎ (01497) 820841, « Part 13C and 17C inn
closed 25 December and 1 week January – **Meals** a la carte 16.40/25.45 **t.** 8.00 – **10** 30.00/65.00 **t.** – SB.

at Llanigon *Southwest : 2½ m. by B 4350 – ✉ Hay-on-Wye.*

Old Post Office without rest., HR3 5QA, ☎ (01497) 820008, « 17C house » –
3 rm 30.00/60.00 **s.**

HOLYHEAD (Caergybi) *Anglesey* 402 403 G 24 *Wales G. – pop. 11 796.*

Env. : *South Stack Cliffs*★, *W : 3 m. by minor roads.*
to Republic of Ireland (Dun Laoghaire) (Stena Line) 4-5 daily (1 h 40 mn) – to Repu of Ireland (Dublin) (Irish Ferries) 2 daily (3 h 15 mn) – to Republic of Ireland (Dublin) (Ste Line) 1-2 daily (3 h 45 mn).
Penrhos Beach Rd ☎ *(01407) 762622.*
London 269 – Birkenhead 94 – Cardiff 215 – Chester 88 – Shrewsbury 105 – Swansea 19

Yr Hendre, Porth-y-Felin Rd, LL65 1AH, Northwest : ¾ m. by Prince of Wales Rd Walthew Av. ☎ (01407) 762929, *rita@yrhendre.freeserve.co.uk, Fax (01407) 762929*,
Meals (by arrangement) 12.00 – **3 rm** 30.00/45.00.

HOLYWELL (Treffynnon) *Flintshire* 402 403 K 24 *Wales G. – pop. 8 770.*

See : *Town*★.
Holywell, Brynford ☎ *(01352) 710040.*
London 217 – Chester 19 – Liverpool 29.

Kinsale Hall, Llanerchymor, CH8 9DX, North : 3 ½ m. by B 5121 off A 5 ☎ (01745) 560001, *Fax (01745) 561298*, rest, – 400.
closed 26-27 December and 1 January – **Meals** *(closed Sunday)* (lunch by arrangeme dinner 18.95 **st.** and a la carte 7.95 – **34 rm** 69.00/85.00 **st.**, 1 suite.

HOWEY *Powys – see Llandrindod Wells.*

KNIGHTON (Trefyclawdd) *Powys* 403 K 26 *Wales G. – pop. 2 851.*

See : *Town*★.
Exc. : *Offa's Dyke*★, *NW : 9½ m.*
Little Ffrydd Wood ☎ *(01547) 528646.*
The Offas Dyke Centre, West St. ☎ *(01547) 529424.*
London 162 – Birmingham 59 – Hereford 31 – Shrewsbury 35.

Milebrook House, Ludlow Rd, Milebrook, LD7 1LT, East : 2 m. on A 4 ☎ (01547) 528632, *hotel@milebrook.kc3ltd.co.uk, Fax (01547) 520509*, « Gardens »,
Meals *(closed Monday lunch)* 9.75/25.50 **t.** and dinner a la carte 5.60 – **10 rm** 51. 110.00 **t.** – SB.

at Llanfair Waterdine *Northwest : 4 m. by B 4355 – ✉ Knighton.*

The Waterdine with rm, LD7 1TD, ☎ (01547) 528214, *Fax (01547) 529992*, –
closed 1 week in spring, 1 week in late autumn-early winter and Monday – **Meals** a la ca 19.50/30.00 **t.** 7.40 – **3 rm** 40.00/75.00 **t.**

KE VYRNWY *Powys* 402 403 J 25 *Wales G.* – ✉ *Llanwddyn.*
See : *Lake*★.
Unit 2, Vyrnwy Craft Workshops ☎ *(01691) 870346.*
London 204 – Chester 52 – Llanfyllin 10 – Shrewsbury 40.

Lake Vyrnwy ⛰, SY10 0LY, ☎ (01691) 870692, *res@lakevyrnwy.com, Fax (01691) 870259,* ≤ Lake Vyrnwy, « Victorian sporting estate », 🎣, 🌳, 🎾 – ⛔ rest, TV P – 🏛 120. MC AE VISA
Meals 15.95/27.50 **st.** – **34 rm** ☕ (dinner included) 80.00/237.00 **st.**, 1 suite – SB.

LESTON *Bridgend* 403 J 29 – *see Bridgend.*

MPHEY (Llandyfai) *Pembrokeshire* 403 F 28 – *see Pembroke.*

NGSTONE *Newport* 403 L 29 – *see Newport.*

TTERSTON (Treletert) *Pembrokeshire* 403 F 28 – *see Fishguard.*

ANARMON DYFFRYN CEIRIOG *Wrexham* 402 403 K 25 – ✉ *Llangollen (Denbighshire).*
London 196 – Chester 33 – Shrewsbury 32.

West Arms, LL20 7LD, ☎ (01691) 600665, *Fax (01691) 600622,* « Part 16C », 🎣, 🌳 – ⛔ rest, TV P – 🏛 30. MC VISA
Meals (bar lunch Monday to Saturday)/dinner 21.80/24.90 **t.** and a la carte 🍷 7.95 – **15 rm** ☕ 46.50/103.00 **t.**, 1 suite – SB.

es prix — Pour toutes précisions sur les prix indiqués dans ce guide, reportez-vous aux pages de l'introduction.

ANBERIS *Gwynedd* 403 H 24 *Wales G.* – *pop. 1 986.*
See : *Town*★ – *Welsh Slate Museum*★ *AC* – *Power of Wales*★.
Env. : *Snowdonia National Park*★★★ *(Snowdon*★★★, *Snowdon Mountain Railway*★★ *AC* – *panorama*★★★*).*
416 High St. ☎ *(01286) 870765.*
London 243 – Caernarfon 7 – Chester 65 – Shrewsbury 78.

Y Bistro, 43-45 High St., LL55 4EU, ☎ (01286) 871278, *ybistro@fsbdial.co.uk, Fax (01286) 871278* – ⛔. MC VISA JCB
closed Monday in winter and Sunday – **Meals** (booking essential) (dinner only) 14.50/15.50 **t.** and a la carte 🍷 7.10.

ANDEGLA *Denbighshire* 402 403 K 24 – ✉ *Wrexham.*
London 201 – Birkenhead 31 – Caernarfon 66 – Chester 22 – Liverpool 34 – Llandudno 43 – Shrewsbury 40.

Bodidris Hall ⛰, LL11 3AL, Northeast : 1 ½ m. on A 5104 ☎ (01978) 790434, *bodidrishall@micro-plus-web.net, Fax (01978) 790335,* « 15C manor of 12C origins », 🎣, 🌳, 🎾 – ⛔ TV P – 🏛 30. MC AE ⓓ VISA JCB. ✂
Meals 17.50/35.00 **t.** 🍷 7.50 – **9 rm** ☕ 65.00/155.00 **t.** – SB.

ANDEGLEY *Powys* 403 K 27 – *see Llandrindod Wells.*

ANDEILO *Carmarthenshire* 403 I 28 *Wales G.* – *pop. 850.*
See : *Town*★ – *Dinefwr Park*★ *AC.*
Env. : *Brecon Beacons National Park*★★ – *Black Mountain*★, *SE : by minor roads* – *Carreg Cennen Castle*★ *AC, SE : 4 m. by A 483 and minor roads.*
London 218 – Brecon 34 – Carmarthen 15 – Swansea 25.

Plough Inn, Rhosmaen, SA19 6NP, North : 1 m. on A 40 ☎ (01558) 823431, *enquiries@ploughrhosemaen.co.uk, Fax (01558) 823969,* ≤, 🏋, ≘s – ⛔ rm, TV ♿ P – 🏛 45. MC AE VISA JCB. ✂
closed 24-26 December – **Meals** (bar meals Sunday dinner) a la carte 17.90/26.95 **t.** 🍷 8.00 – ☕ 5.50 – **12 rm** 50.00/70.00 **t.**

LLANDRILLO *Denbighshire* 402 403 J 25 – *pop. 1 048* – ✉ *Corwen.*
London 210 – Chester 40 – Dolgellau 26 – Shrewsbury 46.

Tyddyn Llan Country House 🐁, LL21 0ST, ✆ (01490) 440264, *tyddynllanhotel@c puserve.com, Fax (01490) 440414,* « Part Georgian country house, gardens », – r TV P. MC AE VISA JCB
closed 2 weeks January **Meals** *(closed Monday lunch)* 25.00 **t.** dinner and a la carte 11. 33.50 **t.** 10.00 – **10 rm** 67.50/140.00 **t.** – SB.

LLANDRINDOD WELLS *Powys* 403 J 27 *Wales G.* – *pop. 4 943.*
Exc. : *Elan Valley★★ (Dol-y-Mynach and Claerwen Dam and Reservoir★★, Caban Coch D and Reservoir★, Garreg-ddu Viaduct★, Pen-y-Garreg Reservoir and Dam★, Craig Goch D and Reservoir★), NW : 12 m. by A 4081, A 470 and B 4518.*
18 *Llandrindod Wells* ✆ *(01597) 822010.*
Old Town Hall, Memorial Gardens ✆ *(01597) 822600.*
London 204 – Brecon 29 – Carmarthen 60 – Shrewsbury 58.

Metropole, Temple St., LD1 5DY, ✆ (01597) 823700, *info@metropole.co. Fax (01597) 824828,* , , – , rest, TV P – 300. MC AE VISA
Meals 7.95/17.95 **t.** 5.95 – **120 rm** 69.00/92.00 **t.**, 2 suites – SB.

Charis without rest., Pentrosfa, LD1 5AL, South : ¾ m. by A 483 ✆ (01597) 824732, *ifor gimson@care4free.net, Fax (01597) 824732,* – TV P
closed December and January – **3 rm** 30.00/38.00 **t.**

at Crossgates *Northeast : 3½ m. on A 483* – ✉ *Llandrindod Wells.*

Guidfa House, LD1 6RF, ✆ (01597) 851241, *guidfa@globalnet.co.uk, Fax (01597) 8518* – TV P. MC VISA.
Meals (by arrangement) 17.50 **t.** 6.25 – **6 rm** 31.50/53.00 **s.** – SB.

at Llandegley *East : 7 m. by A 483 on A 44* – ✉ *Llandrindod Wells.*

Ffaldau Country House, LD1 5UD, ✆ (01597) 851421, *langstaff@ffaldau.co.uk,* « origins », – P. MC VISA.
closed 1 week February and 25-26 December **Meals** (by arrangement) 15.00 – **3** 36.00/52.00 – SB.

at Howey *South : 1½ m. by A 483* – ✉ *Llandrindod Wells.*

Acorn Court Country House 🐁 without rest., Chapel Rd, LD1 5PB, Northeast : ½ ✆ (01597) 823543, *acorncourt@wiredwales.com, Fax (01597) 823543,* , – TV
4 rm 50.00/56.00 **st.**

Holly Farm 🐁, Holly Lane, LD1 5PP, off A 483 ✆ (01597) 822402, *Fax (01597) 822* « Working farm », , – rest, TV P. MC VISA.
closed Christmas **Meals** (by arrangement) 12.00 **s.** – **5 rm** 22.00/50.00.

LLANDUDNO *Conwy* 402 403 I 24 *Wales G.* – *pop. 18 647.*
See : *Town★ – Seafront★ (Pier★)* **B** – *The Great Orme★ (panorama★★, Tramway★, Anc Copper Mines★ AC)* **AB**.
Exc. : *Bodnant Garden★★ AC, S : 7 m. by A 470* **B**.
18 *Rhos-on-Sea, Penrhyn Bay* ✆ *(01492) 549641* **A** – 18 *72 Bryniau Rd, West Sh* ✆ *(01492) 875325* **A** – 18 *Hospital Rd* ✆ *(01492) 876450* **B**.
1-2 Chapel St. ✆ *(01492) 876413.*
London 243 – Birkenhead 55 – Chester 47 – Holyhead 43.

Plan opposite

Bodysgallen Hall 🐁, LL30 1RS, Southeast : 2 m. on A 470 ✆ (01492) 584466, *info@ ysgallen.com, Fax (01492) 582519,* ≤ gardens and mountains, « Part 17C and 18C hall w terraced gardens », , , , , – TV P – 40. MC VISA JCB.
Meals (booking essential) 14.50/33.90 **st.** 16.50 – 13.50 – **19 rm** 109.00/240.00 16 suites 180.00/240.00 **st.** – SB.

Imperial, The Promenade, LL30 1AP, ✆ (01492) 877466, *imphotel@btinternet.c Fax (01492) 878043,* ≤, , , – TV P – 180. MC AE VISA JCB B
Chantrey's : **Meals** 12.00/20.00 **st.** 8.00 – **96 rm** 65.00/115.00, 4 suites – SB.

The Empire, 73 Church Walks, LL30 2HE, (see also ***The Empire (No. 72)*** be ✆ (01492) 860555, *emphotel@aol.com, Fax (01492) 860791,* « Collection of Russell prints », , heated, – , rest, TV P – 40. MC AE VISA JCB. A
closed 16 to 30 December – – ***Watkins and Co. :*** **Meals** (dinner only and Sunday lun dinner 24.50/35.00 **st.** 7.90 – **43 rm** 55.00/110.00 **st.**, 7 suites – SB.

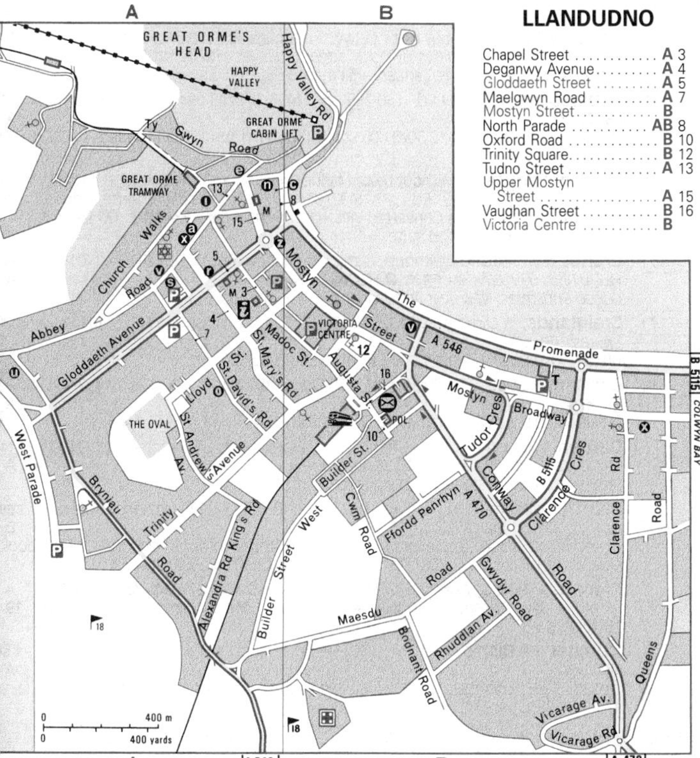

The Empire (No. 72) (at The Empire H.), 72 Church Walks, LL30 2HE, ✆ (01492) 860555, *empire@empirehotel@aol.com*...

St. Tudno, North Par., LL30 2LP, ✆ (01492) 874411, *sttudnohotel@btinternet.com, Fax (01492) 860407*, ≤, 🏊 – |‡| TV 🚗. MC AE ① VISA JCB. 🚫 A c
Meals – (see ***Garden Room*** below) – **18 rm** ☐ 78.00/195.00 **st.**, 1 suite – SB.

Dunoon, Gloddaeth St., LL30 2DW, ✆ (01492) 860787, *reservations@dunoonhotel.demon.co.uk, Fax (01492) 860031* – |‡| TV P. MC AE VISA A r
mid March-mid November – **Meals** 9.00/15.50 **st.** 🍷 6.00 – **55 rm** ☐ 45.00/90.00 **st.** – SB.

Bryn Derwen, 34 Abbey Rd, LL30 2EE, ✆ (01492) 876804, *brynderwen@msn.com, Fax (01492) 876804* – ⇔ TV P. MC VISA. 🚫 A v
March-October – **Meals** *(closed Sunday)* (booking essential to non-residents) (dinner only) 18.00 **t.** 🍷 6.50 – **10 rm** 45.00/84.00 **t.**

The Wilton, 14 South Par., LL30 2LN, ✆ (01492) 876086, *info@wiltonhotel.com, Fax (01492) 876086* – TV P. MC VISA JCB AB z
March-November – **Meals** (dinner only) (residents only) 11.00 **st.** 🍷 3.95 – **14 rm** ☐ 23.00/52.00 **st.** – SB.

Tan Lan, 14 Great Orme's Rd, West Shore, LL30 2AR, ✆ (01492) 860221, *info@tanlanhotel.co.uk, Fax (01492) 870219* – ⇔ TV P. MC VISA JCB A u
restricted opening in winter – **Meals** (bar lunch)/dinner 12.00/15.00 **st.** 🍷 4.95 – **17 rm** ☐ 32.00/54.00 **st.** – SB.

Abbey Lodge, 14 Abbey Rd, LL30 2EA, ✆ (01492) 878042, *Fax (01492) 878042*, 🌳 – ⇔ TV P. 🚫 A x
closed 25-26 December – **Meals** (by arrangement) (communal dining) 17.50 **s.** 🍷 3.95 – **4 rm** ☐ 30.00/55.00 **s.** – SB.

Lympley Lodge without rest., Colwyn Rd, Craigside, LL30 3AL, East : 1 ½ m. on B 51
(01492) 549304, *enquiries@lympleylodge.co.uk*, – P.
closed mid December-mid January – **3 rm** 32.50/55.00 **s.**

Epperstone, 15 Abbey Rd, LL30 2EE, (01492) 878746, *Fax (01492) 871223* –
MC AE VISA A
Meals (by arrangement) 12.50/21.00 **st.** 5.00 – **8 rm** (dinner included) 40.00/75.00
SB.

The Lighthouse without rest., Marine Drive, Great Orme's Head, LL30 2XD, North ½ m. by Happy Valley Rd (01492) 876819, *enquiries@lighthouse-llandudno.co.* *Fax (01492) 876668*, ≤, « Converted Victorian lighthouse » – TV P. MC VISA.
2 rm 70.00/110.00 **st.**, 1 suite.

Cranberry House without rest., 12 Abbey Rd, LL30 2EA, (01492) 8797
Fax (01492) 879760 – TV P. MC AE VISA JCB. A
closed Christmas, New Year and January – **5 rm** 27.50/50.00 **s.**

Craiglands, 7 Carmen Sylva Rd, LL30 1LZ, East : 1 m. by B 5115 (01492) 87509
rest, TV.
March-November – **Meals** 12.50 – **6 rm** 28.00/56.00.

Banham House, 2 St. David's Rd, LL30 2UL, (01492) 875680, *Fax (01492) 875680* –
TV P. A
Meals 11.50 **s.** 4.30 – **6 rm** 30.00/50.00 **s.** – SB.

Garden Room (at St. Tudno H.), North Par., LL30 2LP, (01492) 8744
Fax (01492) 860407 – . MC AE VISA JCB A
Meals 15.00/36.50 **st.** and dinner a la carte 8.00.

Martin's with rm, 11 Mostyn Av., LL30 1YS, (01492) 870070, *martins@walesuk4.frees e.co.uk, Fax (01492) 876661* – TV. MC AE VISA. B
closed first 2 weeks January and Sunday and Monday to non-residents – **Meals** (book essential) a la carte 16.00/38.00 **st.** 7.50 – **4 rm** 40.00/56.00 **st.** – SB.

Richard's Bistro, 7 Church Walks, LL30 2HD, (01492) 877924 – MC AE VISA A
closed 4 days Christmas, Sunday and Monday – **Meals** (dinner only) a la carte 19.
25.40 **st.** 5.50.

Number 1's Bistro, 1 Old Rd, LL30 2HA, (01492) 875424, *Fax (01492) 875424* – MC
VISA JCB A
closed 25-26 December, Monday lunch and Sunday – **Meals** 18.50 **t.** (dinner) and a la ca
17.15/24.45 **t.** 6.95.

at Glanwydden *Southeast : 3 m. by A 470* – **B** – *off Penthyn Bay rd* – *Llandudno.*

Queens Head, LL31 9JP, (01492) 546570, *Fax (01492) 546487* – P. MC VISA
closed 25 December – **Meals** a la carte 12.40/23.30 **t.** 5.95.

at Llandudno Junction *Southeast : 4 m. by A 470 on A 547 at junction with A 55* –**B** – *Ll dudno.*

Travel Inn, LL28 5LB, (01492) 583320, *Fax (01492) 583514* – rm, rest, TV
MC AE VISA.
Meals (grill rest.) – **40 rm** 40.95 **t.**

at Deganwy *South : 2 ¾ m. on A 546* – **A** – *Llandudno.*

Nikki Ip's, 57 Station Rd, LL31 9DF, (01492) 596611, *Fax (01492) 596600* – MC AE
JCB
closed Monday – **Meals** - Chinese - (booking essential) (dinner only) 17.50 **t.** and a la ca
16.50/34.00 **t.**

Paysanne, Station Rd, LL31 9EJ, (01492) 582079, *Fax (01492) 583848* – . MC VISA
closed 25-26 December, 1 January, Sunday and Monday – **Meals** (booking essential) (din only) 15.00/17.50 **t.** 7.00.

LLANDUDNO JUNCTION (Cyffordd Llandudno) Conwy 402 403 I 24 – *see Llandudno.*

ANERCHYMEDD *Anglesey* 402 403 G 24 *Wales G.*

Env. : *Anglesey*★★.

London 262 – Bangor 18 – Caernarfon 23 – Holyhead 15.

Llwydiarth Fawr ⓢ, LL71 8DF, North : 1 m. on B 5111 ✆ (01248) 470321, ⩽, « Georgian farmhouse », ⓢ, ⓢ, ⓢ – ⓢ TV P. MC VISA. ⓢ
closed Christmas – **Meals** (by arrangement) 15.00 **st.** – **3 rm** ⓢ 25.00/50.00 **st.**

Tre-wyn ⓢ without rest., Maenaddwyn, LL71 8AE, East : 2 ¼ m. by B 5111 on Benllech rd ✆ (01248) 470875, *nia@trewyn.fsnet.co.uk*, ⩽, « Working farm », ⓢ, ⓢ – ⓢ TV P. ⓢ
closed 1 week Christmas **3 rm** ⓢ 25.00/45.00 **t.**

Drws-Y-Coed ⓢ without rest., LL71 8AD, East : 1 ½ m. by B 5111 on Benllech rd ✆ (01248) 470473, *Fax (01248) 470473*, ⩽, « Working farm », ⓢ, ⓢ – ⓢ TV P. MC AE. ⓢ
closed 25 December – **3 rm** ⓢ 29.50/49.00 **s.**

ANFACHRETH *Gwynedd* 402 403 I 25 – *see Dolgellau.*

ANFAIR WATERDINE *Shrops.* – *see Knighton.*

AN FFESTINIOG *Gwynedd.*

Cae'r Blaidd Country House ⓢ, LL41 4PH, North : ¾ m. by A 470 on Blaenau Rd ✆ (01766) 762765, *Fax (01766) 762765*, ⩽ Vale of Ffestiniog and Moelwyn mountains, ⓢ – ⓢ TV P. ⓢ
closed January – **Meals** (communal dining) 14.50 **st.** ⓢ 4.00 – **3 rm** ⓢ 28.00/56.00 **st.**

Gellilydan *Southwest : 2 ¾ m. by A 470 off A 487* – ✉ *Ffestiniog.*

Tyddyn du Farm, LL41 4RB, East : ½ m. by A 487 on A 470 ✆ (01766) 590281, *paula@snowdonia-farm.com, Fax (01766) 590281*, ⩽, « Working farm », ⓢ, ⓢ – ⓢ TV P
closed 25 December – **Meals** (by arrangement) 15.00 **st.** – **4 rm** ⓢ 46.00/70.00 **st.**, 1 suite.

ANFIHANGEL *Powys* 402 403 J 25 – *see Llanfyllin.*

ANFIHANGEL CRUCORNEY *Monmouthshire* 403 L 28 – *see Abergavenny.*

ANFYLLIN *Powys* 402 403 K 25 *Wales G.* – *pop. 1 267.*

Exc. : *Pistyll Rhaeadr*★, *NW : 8 m. by A 490, B 4391, B 4580 and minor roads.*

London 188 – Chester 42 – Shrewsbury 24 – Welshpool 11.

Seeds, 5 Penybryn Cottages, High St., SY22 5AP, ✆ (01691) 648604, « 16C cottages » – ⓢ. MC VISA
closed 3 weeks January, 25 December and Monday – **Meals** 19.75 **t.** (dinner) and lunch a la carte 12.70/21.00 **t.** ⓢ 6.85.

Llanfihangel *Southwest : 5 m. by A 490 and B 4393 on B 4382* – ✉ *Llanfyllin.*

Cyfie Farm ⓢ, SY22 5JE, South : 1 ½ m. by B 4382 ✆ (01691) 648451, *Fax (01691) 649015*, ⩽ Meifod valley, « Restored 17C longhouse, working farm », ⓢ, ⓢ – ⓢ TV P. ⓢ
Meals (by arrangement) (communal dining) 15.00 **st.** – **1 rm** ⓢ 28.00/52.00 **st.**, **3 suites** 56.00/60.00 **st.** – SB.

ANGAMMARCH WELLS *Powys* 403 J 27.

London 200 – Brecon 17 – Builth Wells 8.

Lake Country House ⓢ, LD4 4BS, East : ¾ m. ✆ (01591) 620202, *reception@lakecountryhouse.co.uk, Fax (01591) 620457*, ⩽, « Victorian country house in extensive grounds », ⓢ, ⓢ, ⓢ, ⓢ – ⓢ TV P – ⓢ 30. MC AE ⓢ VISA JCB
Meals 17.00/30.00 **st.** ⓢ 6.45 – **8 rm** ⓢ 90.00/205.00 **st.**, **10 suites** 175.00/205.00 **st.** – SB.

ANGEFNI *Anglesey* 402 403 H 24.

London 277 – Caernarfon 17 – Chester 75 – Holyhead 17.

Cefn Cwmwd without rest., Rhostrehwfa, LL77 7YL, Southwest : 2 m. by B 5109 on B 4422 ✆ (01248) 722106, *geriant@cefncwmwd.decom.co.uk, Fax (01248) 722106*, ⓢ – ⓢ TV P. MC AE VISA. ⓢ
9 rm 49.00/99.00.

LLANGOLLEN *Denbighshire* 402 403 K 25 *Wales G. – pop. 3 267.*
See : *Town★ – Railway★ AC – Plas Newydd★ AC.*
Env. : *Pontcysyllte Aqueduct★★, E : 4 m. by A 539 – Castell Dinas Bran★, N : by footpat Valle Crucis Abbey★ AC, N : 2 m. by A 542.*
Exc. : *Chirk Castle★★ AC (wrought iron gates★), SE : 7½ m. by A 5 – Rug Chapel★ AC, 11 m. by A 5 and A 494.*
Vale of Llangollen, Holyhead Rd (01978) 860613.
Town Hall, Castle St. (01978) 860828.
London 194 – Chester 23 – Holyhead 76 – Shrewsbury 30.

Bryn Howel, LL20 7UW, East : 2 ¾ m. by A 539 (01978) 860331, *hotel@brynhowel.d on.co.uk, Fax (01978) 860119,* ←, ≘s, – rest, P – 300. MC AE JCB.
Cedar Tree : Meals a la carte 13.00/29.50 **t.** 7.20 – 9.00 – **35 rm** 75.00/95.00 **t.**, 1 su – SB.

Gales, 18 Bridge St., LL20 8PF, (01978) 860089, *rgales@galesofllangollen.co. Fax (01978) 861313,* « Part 17C and 18C » – rm, P. MC AE VISA JCB.
closed 25 December-2 January – **Meals** *(closed Sunday)* (in bar) a la carte 7.95/16.8 5.95 – **13 rm** 45.00/58.00 **t.**, 2 suites.

Hillcrest, Hill St., LL20 8EU, (01978) 860208, *colin@hillcrest-llangollen.freeserve.co. Fax (01978) 860208,* – P.
Meals 12.00 **s.** 5.00 – **7 rm** 30.00/45.00 **s.**

Oakmere without rest., Regent St., LL20 8HS, on A 5 (01978) 861126, *oakmeregh@. com,* – P.
closed 1 week Christmas – **6 rm** 25.00/45.00 **st.**

The Corn Mill, Dee Lane, LL20 8PN, (01978) 869555, *Fax (01978) 869930,* « Forr corn mill on banks of River Dee » – rest. MC AE VISA
closed 25-26 December – **Meals** a la carte 14.00/21.15 **t.**

LLANGYBI *Monmouthshire* 403 L 28/29 – *see Usk.*

LLANIGON *Powys* 403 K 27 – *see Hay-on-Wye.*

LLANRHIDIAN *Swansea* 403 H 29 – *see Swansea.*

LLANSANFFRAID GLAN CONWY *Conwy* 402 403 I24 *Wales G. – pop. 2 194 – ✉ Abercon*
Env. : *Snowdonia National Park★★★ – Bodnant Garden★★ AC, S : 2½ m. by A 470.*
London 241 – Colwyn Bay 4 – Holyhead 42.

Old Rectory Country House (Wendy Vaughan), Llanrwst Rd, LL28 5LF, on A (01492) 580611, *info@oldrectorycountryhouse.co.uk, Fax (01492) 584555,* ← Conwy tuary, « Part Georgian country house with antique furnishings », – P. MC JCB
closed December-January – **Meals** (booking essential to non-residents) (dinner only) (menu only) 29.90 **t.** 7.90 – **6 rm** 129.00/149.00 **st.** – SB
Spec. Welsh lamb with spinach parcels. Spiced monkfish with vanilla risotto, red wine sa and basil oil. Passion fruit tart with mango sorbet.

LLANTRISANT *Monmouthshire* 403 L 28 – *pop. 9 136 (inc. Pontyclun) – ✉ Usk.*
London 148 – Bristol 34 – Gloucester 43 – Newport 8.

Greyhound Inn, NP5 1LE, Northeast : ½ m. on Usk rd (01291) 672505, *enquiry@gr ound-inn.com, Fax (01291) 673255,* – P. MC VISA.
closed 25 December – **Meals** *(closed Sunday dinner)* a la carte 12.80/18.70 **t.** 4.50 – **10** 48.00/68.00 **t.**

LLANTWIT MAJOR **(Llanilltud Fawr)** *Vale of Glamorgan* 403 J 29 – *pop. 12 909.*
London 175 – Cardiff 18 – Swansea 33.

West House Country, West St., CF61 1SP, (01446) 792406, *nhoward@westhouse net.com, Fax (01446) 796147,* – rest, P. MC AE VISA JCB.
Meals (lunch booking essential) 7.50/15.50 **t.** and a la carte 4.50 – **21 rm** 50. 69.50 **st.** – SB.

LLANWENARTH *Monmouthshire – see Abergavenny.*

ANWRTYD WELLS *Powys* 403 J 27 *Wales G. – pop. 649.*

Exc. : *Abergwesyn-Tregaron Mountain Road*★, *NW : 19 m. on minor roads.*

Ty Barcud, The Square ☎ (01591) 610666.

London 214 – Brecon 32 – Carmarthen 39.

Lasswade Country House, Station Rd, LD5 4RW, ☎ (01591) 610515, *lasswade.kencarol@virgin.net, Fax (01591) 610611,* ≤, – TV P. MC VISA.
Meals (dinner only) 24.95 **st.** and a la carte 6.50 – **8 rm** (dinner included) 54.95/109.90 **st.** – SB.

Carlton House with rm, Dolycoed Rd, LD5 4RA, ☎ (01591) 610248, *info@carltonrestaurant.co.uk, Fax (01591) 610242* – rest, TV. MC VISA JCB
closed 10-28 December – **Meals** *(closed Sunday to non-residents)* (booking essential to non-residents) (dinner only) 24.00/29.50 **t.** 7.50 – **6 rm** 30.00/75.00 **t.** – SB.

WYNGWRIL *Gwynedd* 402 403 H 25 *Wales G. – ✉ Dolgellau.*

Env. : *Snowdonia National Park*★★★.

London 226 – Aberystwyth 44 – Birkenhead 80 – Chester 72 – Shrewsbury 67.

Pentre Bach, LL37 2JU, ☎ (01341) 250294, *mick@pentrebach.com, Fax (01341) 250885,* ≤, – TV P. MC VISA JCB.
February-October – **Meals** (by arrangement) 18.95 – **3 rm** 31.00/60.00.

YSWEN *Powys* 403 K 27 *Wales G. – ✉ Brecon.*

Env. : *Brecon Beacons National Park*★★.

London 188 – Brecon 8 – Cardiff 48 – Worcester 53.

Llangoed Hall, LD3 0YP, Northwest : 1 ¼ m. on A 470 ☎ (01874) 754525, *llangoed_hall_co_wales_uk@compuserve.com, Fax (01874) 754545,* ≤, « Edwardian mansion by Sir Clough Williams-Ellis of 17C origins », – rest, TV P. MC AE VISA JCB.
Meals *closed 24-26 December* (booking essential to non-residents) 16.50/42.50 **t.** 14.00 – **20 rm** 110.00/270.00 **t.**, 3 suites – SB
Spec. Ragoût of lobster and red mullet with poached oyster. Breast of duck with plum "Tarte Tatin", redcurrant jus. Mignons of Welsh black beef with balsamic jus.

Griffin Inn with rm, LD3 0UR, on A 470 ☎ (01874) 754241, *info@griffin-inn.freeserve.co.uk, Fax (01874) 754592,* « Part 15C », – rest, TV P. MC AE VISA JCB
closed 25 and 26 December – **Meals** (Sunday dinner residents only) (bar lunch Monday to Saturday)/dinner a la carte 16.15/27.70 **t.** 9.95 – **7 rm** 45.00/80.00 **st.** – SB.

ACHYNLLETH *Powys* 402 403 I 26 *Wales G. – pop. 2 033.*

See : *Town*★ – *Celtica*★ *AC.*

Env. : *Snowdonia National Park*★★★ – *Centre for Alternative Technology*★★ *AC, N : 3 m. by A 487.*

Ffordd Drenewydd ☎ (01654) 702000.

Canolfan Owain Glyndwr ☎ (01654) 702401.

London 220 – Shrewsbury 56 – Welshpool 37.

Ynyshir Hall, Eglwysfach, SY20 8TA, Southwest : 6 m. on A 487 ☎ (01654) 781209, *info@ynyshir-hall.co.uk, Fax (01654) 781366,* ≤, « Part Georgian country house, gardens », – TV P. MC AE VISA JCB.
closed 5 to 25 January – **Meals** (booking essential) 23.00/39.00 **st.** 10.00 – **8 rm** 110.00/190.00 **st.**, 2 suites – SB.

ENAI BRIDGE (Porthaethwy) *Anglesey* 402 403 H 24.

London 270 – Caernarfon 10 – Chester 69 – Holyhead 22.

Wern Farm without rest., Pentraeth, LL59 5RR, North : 2 ¼ m. by B 5420 off A 5025 ☎ (01248) 712421, *brayshaw_wernfarm@compuserve.com, Fax (01248) 712421,* ≤, – TV P.
closed 15 December-15 January – **3 rm** 46.00/54.00 **st.**

ERTHYR TYDFIL *Merthyr Tydfil* 403 J 28 *Wales G. – pop. 59 317.*

Env. : *Brecon Beacons National Park*★★.

Exc. : *Ystradfellte*★, *NW : 13 m. by A 4102, A 465, A 4059 and minor roads.*

18 *Morlais Castle, Pant, Dowlais ☎ (01685) 722822* – 9 *Cilsanws Mountain, Cefn Coed ☎ (01685) 723308.*

14a Glebeland St. ☎ (01685) 379884.

London 179 – Cardiff 25 – Gloucester 59 – Swansea 33.

Tregenna, Park Terr., CF47 8RF, (01685) 723627, *reception@tregenna.co.* *Fax (01685) 721951* – rm, TV P. MC AE VISA JCB
Meals 6.95/15.95 **t.** and a la carte 5.50 – **21 rm** 48.00/60.00 **st.** – SB.

Travel Inn, Pentrebach, CF48 4BD, South : 2 ½ m. by A 470 (01443) 6936 *Fax (01443) 690188* – rm, TV P – 75. MC AE VISA.
Meals (grill rest.) – **40 rm** 40.95 **t.**

at Cwm Taf *Northwest : 6 m. on A 470 – Merthyr Tydfil.*

Nant Ddu Lodge, CF48 2HY, on A 470 (01685) 379111, *enquiries@nant_ddu_lodg o.uk, Fax (01685) 377088,* – rest, TV P. MC AE VISA
Meals (in bar Monday to Saturday lunch) a la carte 17.30/23.40 **t.** 4.95 – **22 rm** 55.0 89.50 **t.**

MISKIN (Meisgyn) *Rhondda Cynon Taff* 403 J 29 – *Cardiff.*
London 169 – Cardiff 22 – Swansea 31.

Miskin Manor, Pendoylan Rd, Groes Faen, CF72 8ND, East : 1 ¾ m. by A 4119 (Groesfa rd) (01443) 224204, *info@miskin-manor.co.uk, Fax (01443) 237606,* « Part 17C mar house », squash – rest, TV P – 170. MC AE VISA.
Meals a la carte 20.85/28.65 **t.** 6.50 – **42 rm** 90.00/120.00 **st.**, 1 suite – SB.

MOLD (Yr Wyddgrug) *Flintshire* 402 403 K 24 *Wales G. – pop. 9 168.*
See : *St. Mary's Church★.*
18 Clicain Rd, Pantmywyn (01352) 740318 – 18, 9 Clicain Rd, Old Padeswood, Station (01244) 547701 – 18 Padeswood & Buckley, The Caia, Station Lane, Padeswood (012 550537 – 9 Caerwys (01352) 720692.
Library, Museum and Art Gallery, Earl Rd (01352) 759331.
London 211 – Chester 12 – Liverpool 22 – Shrewsbury 45.

Soughton Hall, CH7 6AB, North : 2 ½ m. by A 5119 and Alltami rd (01352) 8408 *Fax (01352) 840382,* « Early 18C Italianate mansion, antiques », – TV P – MC AE VISA.
Meals – (see ***The Stables*** below) – **14 rm** 80.00/170.00 **st.**

Tower without rest., Nercwys, CH7 4EW, South : 1 m. by B 5444 and Nercwys (01352) 700220, *wynne.eyton@virgin.net,* « 15C fortified house », – TV P. AE VISA.
3 rm 40.00/60.00 **s.**

The Stables (at Soughton Hall H.), CH7 6AB, North : 2 ½ m. by A 5119 and Alltami (01352) 840577, *Fax (01352) 840382,* « Converted 17C stables » – P. MC AE VI
Meals (booking essential) a la carte 16.15/23.70 **st.** 6.25.

Glas Fryn, Raikes Lane, Sychdyn, CH7 6LR, North : 1 m. by A 5119 on Civic Centre (Theatr Clwyd) (01352) 750500, *glasfryn@brunningandprice.co.uk, Fax (01352) 7519* – P. MC AE VISA.
closed 25 December **Meals** a la carte 12.85/20.85 **t.**

MONTGOMERY (Trefaldwyn) *Powys* 403 K 26 *Wales G. – pop. 1 059.*
See : *Town★.*
London 194 – Birmingham 71 – Chester 53 – Shrewsbury 30.

Dragon, Town Square, SY15 6PA, (01686) 668359, *reception@dragonhotel.co Fax (01686) 668287,* – rm, TV P – 60. MC AE VISA JCB
Meals (bar lunch Monday-Saturday)/dinner 18.50 **t.** and a la carte 5.25 – **20 rm** 45.0 75.00 **t.** – SB.

Little Brompton Farm without rest., SY15 6HY, Southeast : 2 m. on B 43 (01686) 668371, *gaynor.brompton@virgin.net, Fax (01686) 668371,* « Working farm – TV P.
3 rm 25.00/50.00.

at Garthmyl *Northwest : 3 m. by A 4385 on A 483 – Montgomery.*

Garthmyl Hall, SY15 6RS, on A 483 (01686) 640550, *Fax (01686) 640609,* « P 18C manor house, gardens », – P. MC VISA JCB.
Meals *(closed Sunday)* (residents only) (dinner only) 20.00 **st.** 5.00 – **9 rm** 45.0 100.00 **t.**

MOYLGROVE (Trewyddel) *Pembrokeshire* 403 F 27 – *see Newport.*

MUMBLES (The) *Swansea* 403 I 29 – *see Swansea.*

ANNERCH *Flintshire* 402 403 K 24 – *pop. 513* – ✉ *Mold.*
London 218 – Chester 19 – Liverpool 29 – Shrewsbury 52.

Old Mill, Melin-y-Wern, Denbigh Rd, CH7 5RH, Northwest : 3/4 m. on A 541 ☎ (01352) 741542, *welcome@old-mill.co.uk, Fax (01352) 740254,* « Converted 19C corn mill and stables », – TV P. MC AE VISA JCB
closed January – **Meals** *(closed Monday to Thursday)* (residents only) (dinner only) 16.75 **st.** 4.95 – **6 rm** 44.00/65.00 **st.** – SB.

ANTGAREDIG *Carmarthenshire* 403 H 28 – *see Carmarthen.*

NEATH **(Castell-Ned)** *Neath Port Talbot* 403 I 29 *Wales G.* – *pop. 45 965.*
Env. : *Aberdulais Falls★ AC, NE : 2½ m. by B 4434 and A 4109.*
18 *Swansea Bay, Jersey Marine ☎ (01792) 812198* – 18 *Cadoxton ☎ (01639) 643615.*
London 188 – Cardiff 40 – Swansea 8.

Cwmbach Cottages without rest., Cwmbach Rd, Cadoxton, SA10 8AH, Northwest : 1 3/4 m. by A 474 ☎ (01639) 639825, *cwmbachcottages@guesthouse25.fsnet.co.uk, Fax (01639) 639825,* ←, – TV P.
5 rm 28.00/48.00 **st.**

NEFYN *Gwynedd* 402 403 G 25 *Wales G.* – *pop. 1 987.*
Env. : *Lleyn Peninsula★★ – Tre'r Ceiri★, NE : 5½ m. by B 4417 – Porth Dinllaen★, W : 1½ m. by B 4417.*
18, 9 *Nefyn & District, Morfa Nefyn ☎ (01758) 720218.*
London 265 – Caernarfon 20.

Caeau Capel , Rhodfar Mor, LL53 6EB, ☎ (01758) 720240, *caeau.capel.hotel@tinyworld.co.uk, Fax (01758) 720750,* – rest, TV P. MC VISA JCB
April-October – **Meals** (booking essential to non-residents) (bar lunch)/dinner 13.50/14.50 **t.** 5.95 – **18 rm** 30.00/75.00 **t.** – SB.

Les prix — Pour toutes précisions sur les prix indiqués dans ce guide, reportez-vous aux pages de l'introduction.

NEWPORT **(Casnewydd-Ar-Wysg)** *Newport* 403 L 29 *Wales G.* – *pop. 115 522.*
See : *Museum and Art Gallery★* **AX** – *Transporter Bridge★ AC* **AY** – *Civic Centre (murals★)* **AX**.
Env. : *Caerleon Roman Fortress★★ AC (Fortress Baths★ – Legionary Museum★ – Amphitheatre★), NE : 2½ m. by B 4596* **AX** – *Tredegar House★★ (Grounds★ – Stables★), SW : 2½ m. by A 48* **AY**.
Exc. : *Penhow Castle★, E : 8 m. by A 48* **AX**.
18 *Tredegar Park, Bassaleg Rd ☎ (01633) 895219* – 9 *Caerleon, Broadway ☎ (01633) 420342* – 18 *Parc, Church Lane, Coedkernew ☎ (01633) 680933.*
Museum and Art Gallery, John Frost Sq. ☎ (01633) 842962.
London 145 – Bristol 31 – Cardiff 12 – Gloucester 48.

Plan on next page

The Celtic Manor, Coldra Woods, NP18 1HQ, East : 3 m. on A 48 ☎ (01633) 413000, *postbox@celtic-manor.com, Fax (01633) 412910,* , , , 18, – , rm, TV P – 1500. MC AE VISA JCB.
Owens : **Meals** *(closed Sunday)* (dinner only) 30.00/35.00 **t.** and a la carte 11.00 – ***The Olive Tree :*** **Meals** (buffet lunch) 16.50/19.50 **t.** and a la carte 9.00 – 13.00 – **358 rm** 140.00/162.00, 32 suites – SB.

Holiday Inn, The Coldra, NP18 2YG, East : 3 m. on A 48 ☎ (01633) 412777, *newport@holidayinns.co.uk, Fax (01633) 413087,* , , – , rest, TV P – 500. MC AE VISA.
Meals (bar lunch Monday to Saturday)/dinner a la carte 15.45/23.15 **st.** 6.50 – 10.50 – **119 rm** 98.00/108.00 **st.** – SB.

Newport Lodge, Brynglas Rd, NP20 5QN, North : 3/4 m. by A 4042 off A 4051 ☎ (01633) 821818, *infor@newportlodgehotel.co.uk, Fax (01633) 856360* – rm, TV P. MC AE VISA JCB
Meals (dinner only) a la carte 17.00/24.00 **st.** 4.95 – **27 rm** 60.00/85.00 **st.**

Kepe Lodge, 46a Caerau Rd, NP9 4HH, ☎ (01633) 262351, *Fax (01633) 262351,* – TV P. AY s
Meals (by arrangement) 9.00 **st.** – **8 rm** 25.00/50.00 **st.**

NEWPORT

Street	Grid	No.
Allt-yr-yn Avenue	AY	2
Bellevue Lane	BX	5
Blewitt Street	AX	7
Caerau Crescent	AXY	9
Cambrian Centre	AX	
Capel Street	AY	10
Clarence Place	AX	12
Clyffard Crescent	AX	13
Clytha Park Road	AX	14
Commercial Street	AXY	15
Dewsland Park Road	AY	17
Dock Street	AX	19
Godfrey Road	AX	21
Hereford Street	AX	24
High Street	AX	26
John Frost Square	AX	27
Kensington Place	AX	
Keynsham Avenue	AY	
Kingsway Centre	AX	
Lower Dock Street	AXY	
Malpas Road	AX	
Newport Bridge	AX	
Oakfield Road	AX	
Queensway	AX	
Summerhill Avenue	AX	
Waterloo Road	AY	

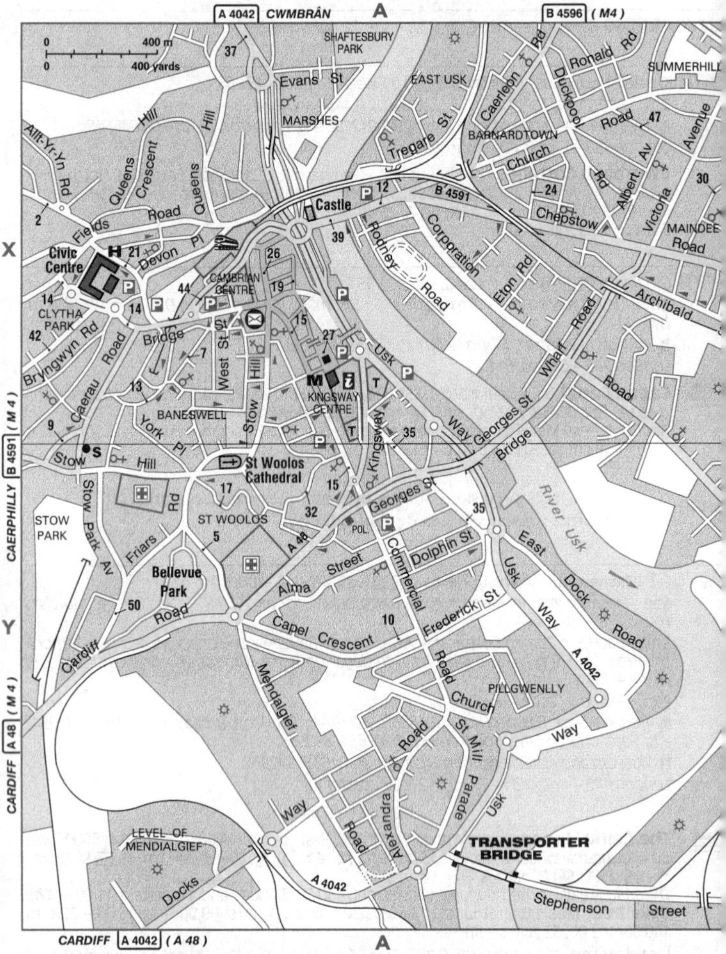

A 4042 CWMBRÂN — A — B 4596 (M 4)

CAERPHILLY B 4591 (M 4)

CARDIFF A 48 (M 4)

CARDIFF A 4042 (A 48) — A

at Langstone *East : 4½ m. on A 48* – **AX** – ✉ *Newport.*

Hilton Newport, Chepstow Rd, NP18 2LX, ☎ (01633) 413737, *reservations@stakis.co* *Fax (01633) 413713,* ⛶, ⛶, ⛶ – ⛶ rm, ⛶ rest, ⛶ ☎ ♿ P – ⛶ 300. ⛶ ⛶ ⛶ VISA ⛶ ⛶
Meals (bar lunch Monday to Saturday)/dinner 17.25 **st.** and a la carte – ⛶ 9.95 – **146** 109.00/119.00 **st.**, 2 suites – SB.

Travel Inn, Coldra Junction, Chepstow Rd, NP18 2NX, on A 48 (westbound carriagew ☎ (01633) 411390, *Fax (01633) 411376* – ⛶, ⛶ rm, ⛶ rest, ⛶ ♿ P. ⛶ ⛶ ⛶ VISA. ⛶
Meals (grill rest.) – **63 rm** 40.95 **t.**

Redwick *Southeast : 9½ m. by M 4 –* **AY** *– off B 4245 – ✉ Magor.*

Brick House Country Guesthouse ⚲, NP26 3DX, ☎ (01633) 880230, *brickhouse@compuserve.com, Fax (01633) 882441,* – ⚲ TV P. ⚲
Meals (by arrangement) 14.00 – **7 rm** ⚲ 35.00/50.00.

St. Brides Wentlooge *Southwest : 4½ m. by A 48 –* **AY** *– on B 4239 – ✉ Newport.*

The Inn at The Elm Tree, NP10 8SQ, ☎ (01633) 680225, *inn@the-elm-tree.co.uk, Fax (01633) 681035,* – ⚲ rm, TV ☎ ♿ P. MC AE VISA
Meals 13.00/15.00 **t.** (lunch) and a la carte 20.15/31.85 **t.** 🍾 8.50 – **10 rm** ⚲ 75.00/95.00 **st.** – SB.

EWPORT **(Trefdraeth)** *Pembrokeshire* 403 F 27 *Wales G. – pop. 1 162.*

Env. : *Pembrokeshire Coast National Park★★.*

⛳9 *Newport ☎ (01239) 820244.*

ℹ *2 Bank Cottages, Long St. ☎ (01239) 820912.*

London 258 – Fishguard 7.

Cnapan, East St., SA42 0SY, on A 487 ☎ (01239) 820575, *cnapan@online-holidays.net, Fax (01239) 820878,* – ⚲ TV P. MC VISA. ⚲
closed January-February and 25-26 December – **Meals** *(closed Tuesday)* (booking essential) (light lunch) a la carte 11.00/22.50 **t.** 🍾 6.50 – **5 rm** ⚲ 36.00/66.00 **t.**

Moylgrove *Northeast : 6 m. – ✉ Cardigan (Cardiganshire).*

The Old Vicarage ⚲, SA43 3BN, South : ¼ m. on Glanrhyd rd ☎ (01239) 881231, *stay@old-vic.co.uk, Fax (01239) 881341,* ←, – ⚲ P. ⚲
restricted opening December-February – **Meals** (by arrangement) 18.00 **st.** 🍾 6.00 – **3 rm** ⚲ 38.00/56.00 **st.** – SB.

Wenn Sie ein ruhiges Hotel suchen,
benutzen Sie zuerst die Karte in der Einleitung
oder wählen Sie im Text ein Hotel mit dem Zeichen ⚲ oder ⚲.

ORTHOP HALL **(Pentre-moch)** *Flintshire* 402 403 K 24 *– pop. 4 155 (Northop).*

London 220 – Chester 9 – Liverpool 21 – Shrewsbury 52.

Holiday Inn, Gateway Services, A 55 (westbound carriageway), CH7 6HB, ☎ (01244) 550011, *info@holidayinn.a55chesterwest.i12.com, Fax (01244) 550763* – ⚲ rm, TV ☎ ♿ P – 🎤 200. MC AE ⓓ VISA JCB. ⚲
closed 24 and 25 December – **Meals** (bar lunch Monday to Saturday)/dinner 10.95/18.95 **t.** – ⚲ 7.95 – **55 rm** 59.50/90.00 **st.**

Travelodge, CH7 6HB, A 55 (eastbound carriageway) ☎ (01244) 816473 – ⚲, ▤ rest, TV ♿ P. MC AE ⓓ VISA JCB. ⚲
Meals (grill rest.) – **40 rm** 39.95 **t.**

OTTAGE **(Drenewydd Yn Notais)** *Bridgend* 403 I 29 *– see Porthcawl.*

EMBROKE **(Penfro)** *Pembrokeshire* 403 F 28 *Wales G. – pop. 7 230.*

See : *Town★★ – Castle★★ AC.*

Env. : *Pembrokeshire Coast National Park★★ – Carew★ (Castle★ AC), NE : 4 m. by A 4075.*

Exc. : *Bosherston (St. Govan's Chapel★), S : 7 m. by B 4319 and minor roads – Stack Rocks★, SW : 9 m. by B 4319 and minor roads.*

⛳18 *Military Rd, Pembroke Dock ☎ (01646) 621453.*

Cleddau Bridge (toll).

⛴ *to Republic of Ireland (Rosslare) (Irish Ferries) 2 daily (3 h 45 mn) – to Republic of Ireland (Cork) (Swansea Cork Ferries) 2 weekly (8 h 30 mn).*

ℹ *Pembroke Visitor Centre, Commons Rd ☎ (01646) 622388.*

London 252 – Carmarthen 32 – Fishguard 26.

Coach House, 116 Main St., SA71 4HN, ☎ (01646) 684602, *Fax (01646) 687456* – TV P. MC AE VISA
Meals (bar lunch)/dinner 10.95/15.95 **st.** and a la carte – **14 rm** ⚲ 45.00/70.00 **st.** – SB.

Left Bank, 63 Main St., SA71 4DA, ☎ (01646) 622333, *emmagriffith@leftbankrestaurant.co.uk* – ⚲. MC AE VISA
closed 25-26 December, 3 weeks January, Sunday and Monday – **Meals** (light lunch)/dinner 24.50 **t.** 🍾 6.95.

at Lamphey *East : 1 ¾ m. on A 4139 – ✉ Pembroke.*

Court ⛰, SA71 5NT, ☎ (01646) 672273, *info@lampheycourt.co.uk, Fax (01646) 6724…* – rest, 80. MC AE VISA
Meals 6.95/9.50 and a la carte 17.50/24.95 **st.** 6.25 – **35 rm** 75.00/130.00 **st.** – SB.

Lamphey Hall, SA71 5NR, ☎ (01646) 672394, *lamphey@globalnet.co.…*
Fax (01646) 672369, – rest, MC AE VISA JCB.
Meals 14.00/25.00 **t.** (dinner) and a la carte 12.40/24.95 **t.** 4.75 – **10 rm** 35.…
65.00 **st.**

at Stackpole *South : 5 m. by B 4319 – ✉ Pembroke.*

Armstrong Arms, SA71 5DF, ☎ (01646) 672324, – P. MC VISA JCB
closed Sunday dinner and Monday in January and February – **Meals** a la carte 13.70/22.4…
4.95.

PENALLY (Penalun) *Pembrokeshire* 403 F 29 – *see Tenby.*

PENCOED *Bridgend* 403 J 29 – *see Bridgend.*

PENTYRCH *Cardiff* 403 K 29 – *see Cardiff.*

PONTARDDULAIS *Swansea* 403 H 28 – *pop. 1 634 – ✉ Swansea.*
London 203 – Fishguard 69 – Swansea 15.

The Fountain Inn with rm, 11 Bolgoed Rd, SA4 1JP, ☎ (01792) 882501, *joannefounta…
nn.com, Fax (01792) 885340* – rm, P – 30. MC AE VISA JCB.
*closed 25 December***Meals** a la carte 12.15/22.15 **st.** 3.95 – **10 rm** 14.95/37.50 **st.** – …

PONTDOLGOCH *Powys – see Caersws.*

PONTYPRIDD *Rhondda Cynon Taff* 403 K 29 *Wales G. – pop. 28 487.*
Exc. : *Caerphilly Castle★★ AC, SE : 7 m. by A 470 and A 468 – Llancaiach Fawr Manor★ A…
NE : 6½ m. by A 4054, A 472, B 4255 and B 4254.*
Historical Centre, The Old Bridge ☎ (01443) 409512.
London 164 – Cardiff 9 – Swansea 40.

Llechwen Hall ⛰, Llanfabon, CF37 4HP, Northeast : 4 ¼ m. by A 4223 off A 40…
☎ (01443) 742050, *llechwen@aol.com, Fax (01443) 742189,* – rm, P – 80. …
AE VISA
Meals 10.95/18.95 **st.** and a la carte 5.50 – 5.95 – **20 rm** 48.50/95.00 **t.** – SB.

PORTH *Rhondda Cynon Taff* 403 J 29 *Wales G. – pop. 6 225 – ✉ Pontypridd.*
Env. : *Trehafod (Rhondda Heritage Park★), E : 1½ m. by A 4058.*
London 168 – Cardiff 13 – Swansea 45.

Heritage Park, Coed Cae Rd, Trehafod, CF37 2NP, on A 4058 ☎ (01443) 6870…
Fax (01443) 687060, – rest, P – 200. MC AE VISA JCB
Meals 11.50 **st.** and a la carte – **44 rm** 58.00/80.00 **st.** – SB.

PORTHCAWL *Bridgend* 403 I 29 *Wales G. – pop. 16 099.*
Env. : *Glamorgan Heritage Coast★.*
The Old Police Station, John St. ☎ (01656) 786639.
London 183 – Cardiff 28 – Swansea 18.

Atlantic, West Drive, CF36 3LT, ☎ (01656) 785011, *enquiries@atlantichotelporthcawl.c…
k, Fax (01656) 771877,* – P. MC AE VISA.
Meals *(closed Sunday dinner)* 9.20/13.50 **t.** and a la carte 5.50 – **18 rm** 59.00/100.0…
– SB.

at Nottage *North : 1 m. by A 4229 – ✉ Porthcawl.*

Rose and Crown, Heol-y-Capel, CF36 3ST, ☎ (01656) 784850, *Fax (01656) 77234…*
rest, P. MC AE VISA.
Meals (carving rest.) a la carte 7.45/16.85 **t.** – **8 rm** 35.00/45.00 **t.**

PORTHGAIN *Pembrokeshire* 403 E 28 – *see St. Davids.*

RTMEIRION *Gwynedd* 402 403 H 25 *Wales G.*
See : *Village*★★★ *AC*.
Env. : *Snowdonia National Park*★★★ – *Lleyn Peninsula*★★ – *Ffestiniog Railway*★★ *AC*.
London 245 – Caernarfon 23 – Colwyn Bay 40 – Dolgellau 24.

Portmeirion, LL48 6ET, ☎ (01766) 770000, *hotel@portmeirion-village.com, Fax (01766) 771331*, ≤ village and estuary, « Private Italianate village in extensive gardens and woodland designed by Sir Clough Williams-Ellis, antiques », heated, – rest, TV P – 120. MC AE VISA JCB.
closed 7 January-2 February – **Meals** *(closed Monday lunch)* (booking essential to non-residents) 12.50/34.00 **t.** and a la carte 9.50 – 11.00 – **28 rm** 100.00/165.00 **st.**, 12 suites – SB.

RT TALBOT *Neath Port Talbot* 403 I 29 *Wales G. – pop. 37 647.*
Env. : *Margam Park*★ *AC (Orangery*★*), SE : 4 m. by A 48.*
London 193 – Cardiff 35 – Swansea 11.

Travel Inn, Baglan Rd, SA12 8ES, M 4 junction 41 (westbound) or junction 42 (eastbound) ☎ (01639) 813017, *Fax (01639) 823096* – rm, rest, TV P. MC AE VISA.
Meals (grill rest.) – **42 rm** 40.95 **t.**

ESTATYN *Denbighshire* 402 403 J 23 – *pop. 15 020.*
Offa's Dyke Centre, Central Beach ☎ (01745) 889092.
London 230 – Bangor 35 – Birkenhead 43 – Chester 35 – Holyhead 56.

Traeth Ganol, 41 Beach Rd West, LL19 7LL, ☎ (01745) 853594, *hotel@dnetw.co.uk, Fax (01745) 886687* – TV P. MC AE VISA JCB.
Meals (booking essential) (dinner only) 12.50 **t.** 9.50 – **9 rm** 39.00/62.00 **t.** – SB.

VLLHELI *Gwynedd* 402 403 G 25 *Wales G. – pop. 3 974.*
Env. : *Lleyn Peninsula*★★.
18 *Golf Rd ☎ (01758) 701644.*
Min-y-Don, Station Sq. ☎ (01758) 613000.
London 261 – Aberystwyth 73 – Caernarfon 21.

Plas Bodegroes with rm, LL53 5TH, Northwest : 1 ¾ m. on A 497 ☎ (01758) 612363, *gunna@bodegroes.co.uk, Fax (01758) 701247*, « Georgian country house », – TV P. MC VISA
closed 1 January-15 March, December and Monday except Bank Holidays – **Meals** *(closed Monday)* (booking essential) (dinner only and Sunday lunch)/dinner a la carte 24.50/29.00 **t.** 7.00 – **11 rm** 40.00/110.00 **t.** – SB.

Boduan *Northwest : 3 ¾ m. on A 497 – ✉ Pwllheli.*

The Old Rectory, LL53 6DT, ☎ (01758) 721519, *Fax (01758) 721519*, « Part Georgian house », – TV P
closed Christmas – **Meals** (by arrangement) 15.00/25.00 8.95 – **4 rm** 40.00/60.00 – SB.

GLAN *Monmouthshire* 403 L 28 *Wales G. – pop. 1 857 – ✉ Abergavenny.*
See : *Castle*★ *AC*.
London 154 – Gloucester 34 – Newport 18 – Swansea 58.

Travelodge without rest., NP5 4BG, Northeast : 2 m. on A 40 (eastbound carriageway) ☎ (01600) 740455, *Fax (01600) 740329* – TV P. MC AE VISA JCB.
42 rm 39.95 **t.**

Clytha Arms, NP7 9BW, West : 3 m. on Clytha rd (old Abergavenny Rd) ☎ (01873) 840206, *one.bev@lineone.net, Fax (01873) 840206* – rest, P. MC AE VISA
*closed 25 December***Meals** *(closed Sunday dinner and Monday)* 11.95/14.95 **t.** and a la carte 6.25.

DWICK *Newport* 403 L 29 – *see Newport (Newport).*

AYADER **(Rhaeadr)** *Powys* 403 J 27 – *pop. 1 626.*
The Leisure Centre ☎ (01597) 810591.
London 195 – Aberystwth 39 – Carmarthen 67 – Shrewsbury 60.

Beili Neuadd without rest., LD6 5NS, Northeast : 2 m. by A 44 off Abbey-cwm-hir rd ☎ (01597) 810211, *ann-carl@thebeili.freeserve.co.uk, Fax (01597) 810211*, ≤, – P
closed Christmas and New Year **3 rm** 25.00/46.00 **st.**

RHYDLEWIS *Ceredigion* 403 G 27 *Wales G.* – ✉ *Llandysul.*
Exc. : *Aberaeron★, NE : 11½ m. by B 4334 and A 487.*
London 235 – Carmarthen 26 – Fishguard 38.

Broniwan ⛰, SA44 5PF, Northeast : ¼ m. by Pentregat rd, taking first turn right o unmarked road ☎ (01239) 851261, *broniwan@compuserve.com, Fax (01239) 8512* « Working farm », ⛩, ⛩ – ⛩ P
Meals (by arrangement) 14.00 **st.** – **3 rm** ☐ 25.00/50.00 **s.** – SB.

ROSSETT (Yr Orsedd) *Wrexham* 402 403 L 24 – *pop. 1 986.*
London 203 – Chester 8 – Liverpool 29 – Shrewsbury 39.

Llyndir Hall, Llyndir Lane, LL12 0AY, North : ¾ m. by B 5445 ☎ (01244) 571648, *llyndir. @pageant.co.uk, Fax (01244) 571258,* ⛩, ⛩, ⛩ – ⛩ rm, TV ☎ P – ⛩ 120. MC AE VISA
Meals a la carte 20.05/34.00 **st.** 8.25 – **37 rm** ☐ 70.00/95.00 **st.**, 1 suite – SB.

Rossett Hall, Chester Rd, LL12 0DE, ☎ (01244) 571000, *reservations@rossetthallhotel uk, Fax (01244) 571505,* ⛩ – ⛩, ⛩ rest, TV P – ⛩ 120. MC AE ⛩ VISA. ⛩
***Oscars :* Meals** a la carte 15.95/24.40 **st.** 5.95 – ☐ 8.95 – **29 rm** 70.00/90.00 **st.**, 1 suit SB.

RUTHIN (Rhuthun) *Denbighshire* 402 403 K 24 *Wales G.* – *pop. 5 029.*
Env. : *Llandyrnog (St. Dyfnog's Church★), Llanrhaeder-yng-Nghinmeirch (Jesse W dow★★), N : 5½ m. by A 494 and B 5429.*
Exc. : *Denbigh★ (Castle★), NW : 7 m. on A 525.*
Ruthin-Pwllglas ☎ (01824) 702296.
Ruthin Craft Centre, Park Rd ☎ (01824) 703992.
London 210 – Birkenhead 31 – Chester 23 – Liverpool 34 – Shrewsbury 46.

Ye Olde Anchor Inn, Rhos St., LL15 1DY, ☎ (01824) 702813, *hotel@anchorinn.co Fax (01824) 703050* – ⛩ rest, TV P. MC AE VISA JCB
Meals 18.00/20.00 **st.** and a la carte – **26 rm** ☐ 37.50/53.00 **st.** – SB.

Firgrove, Llanfwrog, LL15 2LL, West : 1 ¼ m. by A 494 on B 5105 ☎ (01824) 702677, *a @firgrove.fsnet.co.uk, Fax (01824) 702677,* ⛩ – ⛩ TV P. MC VISA JCB. ⛩
March-November – **Meals** (by arrangement) (communal dinning) 19.50 **st.** – **3** ☐ 35.00/60.00 **st.**

Eyarth Station ⛰, Llanfair Dyffryn Clwyd, LL15 2EE, South : 1 ¾ m. by A ☎ (01824) 703643, *eyarthstation@amserve.net, Fax (01824) 707464,* ⛩, ⛩ heated, ⛩ ⛩ P. MC VISA
mid March-mid November and Christmas – **Meals** 15.00 **st.** 4.50 – **6 rm** ☐ 32. 50.00 **st.**

ST. ASAPH (Llanelwy) *Denbighshire* 402 403 J 24 *Wales G.* – *pop. 3 399.*
See : *Cathedral★.*
Env. : *Rhuddlan Castle★★ AC, N : 2½ m. by A 525 and A 547 – Bodelwyddan★★ AC, W : m. by A 55 – Denbigh★ (Castle★), S : 6 m. by A 525 and A 543.*
London 225 – Chester 29 – Shrewsbury 59.

Plough Inn, The Roe, LL17 0LU, North : ½ m. on A 525 ☎ (01745) 5850 *Fax (01745) 585363,* ⛩ – ⛩ P. MC VISA
Meals (booking essential) a la carte 14.65/19.85 **st.** 4.95.

ST. BRIDES WENTLOOGE *Newport* 403 K 29 – *see Newport.*

ST. CLEARS (Sancler) *Carmarthenshire* 403 G 28 *Wales G.* – *pop. 3 014.*
Env. : *Laugharne★ (Castle★, The Boat House★), S : 4 m. on A 4066.*
London 229 – Carmarthen 9 – Fishguard 37.

Forge Lodge, SA33 4NA, East : 1 m. on A 40 ☎ (01994) 230300, *theforge@supanet.co Fax (01994) 231577,* ⛩, ⛩, ⛩ – TV P – ⛩ 100. MC AE VISA
closed 25 and 26 December – **Meals** (grill rest.) a la carte 8.95/20.00 **t.** 4.95 – **18** ☐ 44.00/60.00 **t.**

Travelodge, Tenby Rd, SA33 4JN, on A 40 ☎ (01994) 231227, *Fax (01994) 23122* ⛩ rm, TV ⛩ P. MC AE ⛩ VISA JCB. ⛩
Meals (grill rest.) – **32 rm** 39.95 **t.**

*Le Guide change, changez de **guide Michelin** tous les ans.*

. DAVIDS **(Tyddewi)** *Pembrokeshire* 403 E 28 *Wales G. – pop. 1 959 – ✉ Haverfordwest.*
See : *Town★★ – Cathedral★★ – Bishop's Palace★ AC.*
Env. : *Pembrokeshire Coast National Park★★.*
St. Davids City, Whitesands Bay ☎ (01437) 721751.
The Grove ☎ (01437) 720392.
London 266 – Carmarthen 46 – Fishguard 16.

Warpool Court, SA62 6BN, Southwest : ½ m. by Porth Clais rd ☎ (01437) 720300, *warpool@enterprise.net, Fax (01437) 720676*, ←, – rest, TV P. MC AE VISA
closed January – **Meals** 19.95/37.00 **st.** 10.50 – **25 rm** 69.00/138.00 **st.** – SB.

St. Nons, Catherine St., SA62 6RJ, Southwest : ¼ m. on Porth Clais rd ☎ (01437) 720239, *stnons@enterprise.net, Fax (01437) 721839* – rest, TV P. MC VISA
closed November and December – **Meals** a la carte 16.70/24.40 **st.** – **19 rm** 55.00/90.00 **st.** – SB.

Old Cross, Cross Sq., SA62 6SP, ☎ (01437) 720387, *enquiries@oldcrosshotel.co.uk, Fax (01437) 720394*, – rest, TV P. MC VISA JCB
closed 22 December-1 March – **Meals** (bar lunch)/dinner a la carte 17.00/20.50 **st.** 4.75 – **16 rm** 49.00/84.00 **st.** – SB.

The Waterings without rest., Anchor Drive, SA62 6QH, East : ¼ m. on A 487 ☎ (01437) 720876, *waterings@supanet.com, Fax (01437) 720876*, – TV P.
5 rm 55.00/60.00 **s.**

Y-Gorlan, 77 Nun St., SA62 6NU, ☎ (01437) 720837, *Fax (01437) 721148* – TV. MC VISA
Meals (by arrangement) 15.50 **st.** 4.50 – **5 rm** 26.50/49.00 **st.**

Morgan's Brasserie, 20 Nun St., SA62 6NT, ☎ (01437) 720508, *morgans@stdavids.co.uk, Fax (01437) 720508* – . MC AE VISA
closed January-February and Sunday-Tuesday, restricted opening November and December – **Meals** (booking essential) (dinner only) a la carte 19.25/26.50 **st.** 7.50.

Porthgain *Northeast : 7 ¾ m. by A 487 and Llanrian rd – ✉ Haverfordwest.*

Harbour Lights, SA62 5BW, ☎ (01348) 831549, *info@wales-pembs-art.com, Fax (01348) 831193* – MC VISA JCB
closed Monday-Wednesday and Thursday and Sunday in winter – **Meals** - Seafood - (booking essential) (dinner only) 25.00 **st.** 9.50.

There is no paid advertising in this Guide.

. DOGMAELS **(Llandudoch)** *Ceredigion* 403 G 27 – *see Cardigan.*

. GEORGE *Conwy – ✉ Abergele.*
London 230 – Chester 30 – Shrewsbury 65.

Kinmel Arms, LL22 9BP, ☎ (01745) 832207, *gary@gourmetevent.freeserve.co.uk, Fax (01745) 832207* – P. MC VISA
closed 25 December **Meals** a la carte 10.50/22.00 **st.** 5.75.

RN PARK SERVICE AREA *Bridgend* 403 J 29 – *✉ Bridgend.*
junction 36, M 4 ☎ (01656) 654906.
London 174 – Cardiff 17 – Swansea 20.

Days Inn, CF32 9RW, M 4 junction 36 ☎ (01656) 655332, Reservations (Freephone) 0800 0280400, *Fax (01656) 645004* – rm, TV P. MC AE VISA JCB
Meals (grill rest.) (bar lunch)/dinner a la carte 9.65/13.90 **st.** – 7.45 – **40 rm** 45.00/50.00 **t.**

RON *Gwynedd – see Caernarfon.*

UNDERSFOOT *Pembrokeshire* 403 F 28 *Wales G. – pop. 3 221.*
Env. : *Pembrokeshire Coast National Park★★.*
The Barbecue, Harbour Car Park ☎ (01834) 813672.
London 245 – Carmarthen 25 – Fishguard 34 – Tenby 3.

Vine Farm, The Ridgeway, SA69 9LA, ☎ (01834) 813543, *vinefarm@amserve.net*, – TV P.
April-October – **Meals** (by arrangement) 13.00 **st.** – **5 rm** 23.00/50.00 **st.**

SEION *Gwynedd* 402 403 H 24 – *see Caernarfon.*

SOUTHERNDOWN *Bridgend* 403 J 29 – *see Bridgend.*

STACKPOLE *Pembrokeshire* 403 F 29 – *see Pembroke.*

SWANSEA **(Abertawe)** *Swansea* 403 I 29 *Wales G. – pop. 181 906.*

See : *Town★ – Maritime Quarter★* **B** *– Maritime and Industrial Museum★* **B M** *– Glynn Viv Art Gallery★ – Guildhall (British Empire Panels★).*

Env. : *Gower Peninsula★★ (Rhossili★★), W : by A 4067* **A**.

Exc. : *The Wildfowl and Wetlands Trust★, Llanelli, NW : 6½ m. by A 483 and A 484* **A**.

18 Morriston, 160 Clasemont Rd ☎ (01792) 771079, **A** *– 18 Clyne, 120 Owls Lodge La Mayals ☎ (01792) 401989,* **A** *– 18 Langland Bay ☎ (01792) 366023,* **A** *– 18 Fairwood P Blackhills Lane, Upper Killay ☎ (01792) 203648,* **A** *– 9 Inco, Clydach ☎ (01792) 844216, 9 Allt-y-Graban, Allt-y-Graban Rd, Pontllin ☎ (01792) 885757 – 9 Palleg, Lower Cwmtwr Swansea Valley ☎ (01639) 842193.*

to Republic of Ireland (Cork) (Swansea Cork Ferries) (10 h).

Plymouth St. ☎ (01792) 468321.

London 191 – Birmingham 136 – Bristol 82 – Cardiff 40 – Liverpool 187 – Stoke-on-Tr 175.

SWANSEA
BUILT UP AREA

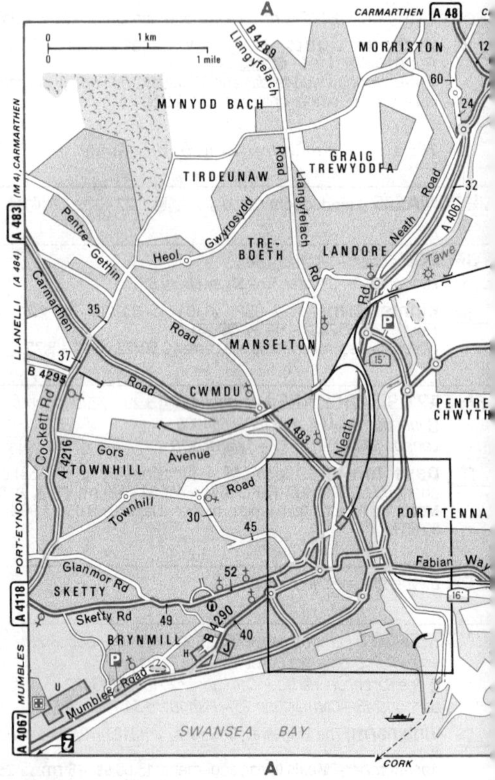

This Guide is not a comprehensive list of all hotels and restaurants, nor even of all good hotels and restaurants in Great Britain and Ireland.

Since our aim is to be of service to all motorists, we must show establishments in all categories and so we have made a selection of some in each.

SWANSEA

exandra Road . . . . B 2
lle Vue Way. . . . . B 4
rmarthen Road . . . . B 7
stle Street . . . . B 8
ristina Street . . . . B 9
arence Terrace . . . . B 10
llege Street . . . . B 13
De la Beche Street. . . . . B 15
Dillwyn Street . . . . B 17
East Bank Way . . . . C 18
Grove Place . . . . B 22
Kingsway (The) . . . . B
Nearth Road. . . . . B 25
Nelson Street . . . . B 26
New Cut Bridge . . . . C 27
Oxford Street. . . . . B
Parc Tawe Shopping Centre . B
Princess Way. . . . . B
Quadrant Centre . . . . B
St. David's Square . . . . B
St. Mary's Square. . . . . B 42
Tawe Bridge. . . . . C 43
Union Street . . . . B 47
Wellington Street . . . . B 54
West Way . . . . B 55

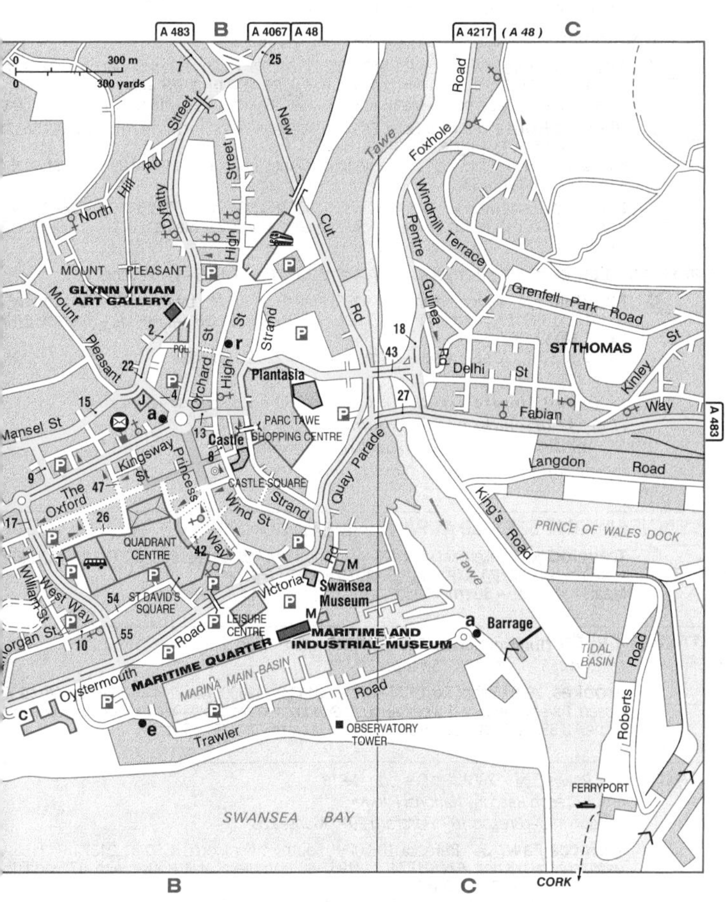

Swansea Marriott, Maritime Quarter, SA1 3SS, ✆ (01792) 642020, *Fax (01792) 650345*, 300. B e
Meals a la carte 20.00/24.60 **st.** 7.75 – 12.50 – **117 rm** 93.00 **st.**

Posthouse Swansea, 39 The Kingsway, SA1 5LS, ✆ (0870) 400 9078, *gm212@fortehotels.com.web, Fax (01792) 456044*, rm, 350. B a
Meals (bar lunch Monday to Saturday)/dinner 15.00 **t.** and a la carte 6.95 – 10.95 – **100 rm** 79.00 **t.**, 6 suites – SB.

Beaumont, 72-73 Walter Rd, SA1 4QA, ✆ (01792) 643956, *info@beaumonthotel.co.uk, Fax (01792) 643044* – A n
Meals (dinner only) 9.50/12.50 **t.** and a la carte – **16 rm** 59.50/89.50 **t.** – SB.

Dermott's, 219 High St., SA1 1NN, ☏ (01792) 459050, *Fax (01792) 459050* – VISA B
closed 2 weeks August, 25 December-9 January, Sunday and Monday – **Meals** (dinner on 23.50 **t.** 6.75.

Hanson's, Pilot House Wharf, Trawler Rd, Swansea Marina, SA1 1UN, ☏ (01792) 4662 *Fax (01792) 201774* – P. MC VISA JCB C
closed 1 week November, 25-26 December and Sunday dinner – **Meals** (booking essent 9.95/12.95 **t.** (lunch) and a la carte 17.40/24.85 **t.** 6.95.

at The Mumbles *Southwest : 7 ¾ m. by A 4067 – A – ✉ Swansea.*

Norton House, 17 Norton Rd, SA3 5TQ, ☏ (01792) 404891, *nortonhouse@btconnect.m, Fax (01792) 403210,* – rest, TV P – 25. MC AE VISA JCB.
closed 23 to 27 December – **Meals** (dinner only) 28.50 **t.** 4.95 – **15 rm** 65.00/90.00 t

Hillcrest House, 1 Higher Lane, SA3 4NS, West : ¾ m. on Langland rd ☏ (01792) 3637 *Fax (01792) 363768* – TV P. MC AE VISA.
Meals *(closed Sunday)* (booking essential) (dinner only) a la carte 14.90/20.20 **st.** – **6 r** 55.00/75.00 **st.** – SB.

L'Amuse, 93 Newton Rd, SA3 4BN, ☏ (01792) 366006, *Fax (01792) 368090* – MC AE VISA
closed 3 weeks December-January, Sunday and Monday – **Meals** - Bistro - 7.95/22.50 4.75.

at Llanrhidian *West : 10½ m. by A 4118 – A – and B 4271 on B 4295 – ✉ Reynoldston.*

Fairyhill, Reynoldston, SA3 1BS, West : 2 ½ m. by B 4295 (Llangennith ☏ (01792) 390139, *postbox@fairyhill.net, Fax (01792) 391358,* – rest, TV 35. MC AE VISA JCB.
Meals 17.50/32.00 **st.** 10.00 – **8 rm** 110.00/225.00 **st.** – SB.

Le Grand Londres (GREATER LONDON) est composé de la City et de 32 arrondissements administratifs (Borough) eux-mêmes divisés en quartiers ou en villages ayant conservé leur caractère propre (Area).

SWANSEA WEST SERVICE AREA *Swansea* 403 I 28.

Travelodge, Penllergaer, SA4 1GT, M 4 junction 47 ☏ (01792) 896222, *Fax (01792) 898* – rm, rest, TV P – 25. MC AE VISA JCB.
Meals (grill rest.) – **50 rm** 49.95 **t.**

TALBOT GREEN (Tonysguborian) *Rhondda Cynon Taff – pop. 2 405.*

London 165 – Cardiff 17 – Swansea 60.

Brookes, 79-81 Talbot Rd, CF72 8AE, ☏ (01443) 239600, *Fax (01443) 239600* – MC AE VI
closed 1 week January, 1 week August, Sunday and Monday – **Meals** (booking essential dinner) 8.95/11.95 **st.** (lunch) and dinner a la carte 21.15/31.35 **st.**

TALGARTH *Powys* 403 K 28 *Wales G. – pop. 1 818.*

Env. : *Brecon Beacons National Park*★★.

London 182 – Brecon 10 – Hereford 29 – Swansea 53.

Trefecca Fawr, Trefecca, LD3 0PW, South : 1 ¼ m. on B 4560 ☏ (01874) 712195, *ge@trefecca.zx3.net, Fax (01874) 712196,* ≤, « Medieval Hall House with 17C additio gardens » – TV P. MC VISA.
March-November – **Meals** (by arrangement) 24.00 – **3 rm** 60.00/98.00.

Upper Trewalkin, Pengenffordd, LD3 0HA, South : 2 m. by A 479 ☏ (01874) 7113 *Fax (01874) 711349,* ≤, « Part Georgian farmhouse, working farm », – P.
April-November – **Meals** (by arrangement) (communal dining) 14.00 **st.** – **3 rm** 23. 46.00 **st.** – SB.

TALSARNAU *Gwynedd* 402 403 H 25 *Wales G. – pop. 647 – ✉ Harlech.*

Env. : *Snowdonia National Park*★★★.

London 236 – Caernafon 33 – Chester 67 – Dolgellau 25.

Maes-y-Neuadd, LL47 6YA, South : 1 ½ m. by A 496 off B 4573 ☏ (01766) 780200, *aes@neuadd.com, Fax (01766) 780211,* ≤, « Part 14C country house, gardens » – TV – 25. MC AE VISA
Meals 27.00/34.00 **t.** (dinner) and lunch a la carte 11.20/18.95 **t.** 8.50 – **15 rm** (din included) 94.00/230.00 **t.**, 1 suite – SB.

AL-Y-LLYN *Gwynedd* 402 403 I 25 *Wales G.* – ✉ *Tywyn.*

Env. : *Snowdonia National Park*★★★ – *Cadair Idris*★★★.

London 224 – Dolgellau 9 – Shrewsbury 60.

Tynycornel, LL36 9AJ, on B 4405 ☎ (01654) 782282, *tynycornel@sagnet.co.uk, Fax (01654) 782679,* ≤ Tal-y-Llyn Lake and Cadair Idris, ♨, 🐟, 🌳 – ⚡ TV P. MC AE VISA
Meals (bar lunch Monday to Saturday)/dinner 21.50 **t.** 7.95 – 7.50 – **15 rm** 41.00/82.00 **t.**, 2 suites – SB.

Minffordd, LL36 9AJ, Northeast : 2 ¼ m. by B 4405 on A 487 ☎ (01654) 761665, *hotel@minffordd.com, Fax (01654) 761517,* ≤, 🌳 – ⚡ P. MC VISA
restricted opening November-February – **Meals** (booking essential to non-residents) (dinner only) 22.50 **st.** 6.95 – **7 rm** 39.50/79.00 **st.** – SB.

ENBY (Dinbych-Y-Pysgod) *Pembrokeshire* 403 F 28 *Wales G.* – *pop. 4 809.*

See : *Town*★★ – *Harbour and seafront*★★.

Env. : *Pembrokeshire Coast National Park*★★ – *Caldey Island*★, *S : by boat.*

18 *The Burrows* ☎ *(01834) 842787.*

The Croft ☎ *(01834) 842402.*

London 247 – Carmarthen 27 – Fishguard 36.

Waterwynch House 🐦, Narberth Rd, Waterwynch Bay, SA70 8TJ, North : 1 ¾ m. by A 478 ☎ (01834) 842464, *enquiries@waterwynchhousehotel.co.uk, Fax (01834) 845076,* ≤, 🌳, – ⚡ TV P. MC VISA
10 March-October – **Meals** *(closed Sunday dinner)* (dinner only and Sunday lunch)/dinner 18.00 **t.** – **14 rm** 50.00/100.00 **t.**, 2 suites.

Atlantic without rest., Esplanade, SA70 7DU, ☎ (01834) 842881, *enquiries@atlantic-hotel.co.uk, Fax (01834) 842881 (ext. 256),* , 🌳 – ⚡ TV ♿ P. MC AE VISA JCB
closed 20 December-11 January – **42 rm** 60.00/130.00 **t.**

Broadmead, Heywood Lane, SA70 8DA, Northwest : ¾ m. ☎ (01834) 842641, *Fax (01834) 845757,* 🌳 – ⚡ rest, TV P. MC AE VISA JCB.
March-23 December – **Meals** (dinner only) 14.00/17.00 **st.** 4.25 – **20 rm** 31.00/62.00 **st.** – SB.

Fourcroft, North Beach, SA70 8AP, ☎ (01834) 842886, *hospitality@fourcroft-hotel.co.uk, Fax (01834) 842888,* ≤, ♨, heated – ⚡ TV – 80. MC AE VISA JCB
Meals (bar lunch)/dinner 15.00/20.00 **st.** and a la carte 5.00 – **45 rm** 31.00/102.00 **st.** – SB.

Myrtle House, St. Marys St., SA70 7HW, ☎ (01834) 842508, *kg2508@aol.com, Fax (01834) 842508* – ⚡ TV . MC VISA
March-October – **Meals** (by arrangement) 10.00 **s.** – **8 rm** 26.00/52.00 **s.**

Penally (Penalun) *Southwest : 2 m. by A 4139* – ✉ *Tenby.*

Penally Abbey 🐦, SA70 7PY, ☎ (01834) 843033, *penallyabbey@btinternet.com, Fax (01834) 844714,* ≤, 🌳 – ⚡ rest, TV P. MC AE VISA JCB.
Meals (lunch by arrangement)/dinner 16.00/34.00 **st.** 6.50 – **12 rm** 98.00/136.00 **st.** – SB.

ORNHILL *Cardiff* 403 K 29 – *see Cardiff.*

REE COCKS (Aberllynfi) *Powys* 403 K 27 *Wales G.* – ✉ *Brecon.*

Env. : *Brecon Beacons National Park*★★.

London 184 – Brecon 11 – Hereford 25 – Swansea 55.

Three Cocks with rm, LD3 0SL, on A 438 ☎ (01497) 847215, *Fax (01497) 847339,* « Part 15C inn », 🌳 – P. MC VISA.
closed December and January – **Meals** *(closed Tuesday)* (lunch by arrangement)/dinner 28.00 **st.** and a la carte 9.25 – **7 rm** 45.00/67.00 **st.** – SB.

NTERN (Tyndyrn) *Monmouthshire* 403 404 L 28 *Wales G.* – *pop. 749* – ✉ *Chepstow.*

See : *Abbey*★★ *AC.*

London 137 – Bristol 23 – Gloucester 40 – Newport 22.

The Royal George, NP16 6SF, on A 466 ☎ (01291) 689205, *royalgeorge@bestwestern.co.uk, Fax (01291) 689448,* 🌳 – ⚡ TV P – 100. MC AE VISA
Meals (bar lunch Monday to Saturday)/dinner 22.00/24.50 **st.** and a la carte 4.75 – **16 rm** 62.00/88.00 **st.** – SB.

Parva Farmhouse with rm, NP16 6SQ, on A 466 ☎ (01291) 689411, *Fax (01291) 689557* – ⚡ rest, TV P. MC AE VISA JCB
Meals (dinner only) 19.50/21.75 **st.** 7.00 – **9 rm** 50.00/76.00 **st.** – SB.

TREARDDUR BAY *Anglesey* 402 403 G 24 *Wales G.* – ✉ *Holyhead.*

Env. : *Anglesey*★★.

Exc. : *Barclodiad y Gawres Burial Chamber*★, *SE : 10 m. by B 4545, A 5 and A 4080.*

London 269 – Bangor 25 – Caernarfon 29 – Holyhead 3.

Trearddur Bay, LL65 2UN, ☎ (01407) 860301, *markdgul@trearddurbayhotel.co.* *Fax (01407) 861181,* 🏊, 🌳 – ⊭ rest, 📺 🅿 – 🏛 65. ⓜⓒ AE
Meals (bar lunch)/dinner 22.50 **st.** – **42 rm** ☕ 75.50/113.00 **st.**

TRECASTLE **(Tregastell)** *Powys* 403 J 28.

London 192 – Aberystwyth 60 – Cardiff 47 – Carmarthen 37 – Gloucester 81.

Castle Coaching Inn, LD3 8UH, ☎ (01874) 636354, *hotel.reservation@btinternet.cc* *Fax (01874) 636457* – ⊭ rest, 📺 🅿. ⓜⓒ VISA JCB
Meals (bar lunch)/dinner 21.45/24.95 **st.** and a la carte 🍷 6.00 – **9 rm** ☕ 50.00/55.00
1 suite – SB.

TREMEIRCHION *Denbighshire* 402 403 J 24 – ✉ *St. Asaph.*

London 225 – Chester 29 – Shrewsbury 59.

Bach-Y-Graig 🐄 without rest., LL17 0UH, Southwest : 2 m. by B 5429 off Denbigh ☎ (01745) 730627, *anwenroberts@bachygraig.fsnet.co.uk, Fax (01745) 730971,* « 16C b built house, working farm », 🌳, 🎣 – ⊭ 📺 🅿. ✗
closed Christmas and New Year – **3 rm** ☕ 28.00/48.00 **s.**

TYN-Y-GROES *Gwynedd – see Conwy (Aberconwy and Colwyn).*

USK **(Brynbuga)** *Monmouthshire* 403 L 28 *Wales G.* – *pop. 2 187.*

Exc. : *Raglan Castle*★ *AC, NE : 7 m. by A 472, A 449 and A 40.*

⛳18, ⛳18 *Alice Springs, Bettws Newydd* ☎ *(01873) 880772.*

London 144 – Bristol 30 – Gloucester 39 – Newport 10.

Glen-yr-Afon House, Pontypool Rd, NP15 1SY, ☎ (01291) 672302, *enquiries@glen-y fon.co.uk, Fax (01291) 672597,* 🌳 – |♦| ⊭ 📺 ♿ 🅿 – 🏛 200. ⓜⓒ AE ⓓ VISA
Meals (Sunday dinner residents only) a la carte 20.20/25.50 **t.** 🍷 7.60 – **28 rm** ☕ 60. 75.00 – SB.

Three Salmons, Bridge St., NP15 IRY, ☎ (01291) 672133, *reservations@threesalmons m, Fax (01291) 673979* – 📺 🅿 – 🏛 100. ⓜⓒ AE ⓓ VISA
Meals *(closed Sunday dinner)* 16.00 **st.** and a la carte 🍷 6.95 – **24 rm** ☕ 75.00/120.00 **st.**

at Llangybi *South : 2½ m. on Llangybi rd* – ✉ *Usk.*

Cwrt Bleddyn, NP5 1PG, South : 1 m. ☎ (01633) 450521, *gm.cbh@arcadianhotels.co. Fax (01633) 450220,* 🏋, 🏊, 🏊, 🌳, 🎣, 🎾, squash – ⊭ 📺 🅿 – 🏛 200. ⓜⓒ AE ⓓ VISA
– ***Jesters :*** **Meals** *(closed Saturday lunch)* 14.50/28.50 **st.** and a la carte 🍷 6.50 – **33** ☕ 80.00/100.00 **st.** – SB.

WELSH HOOK *Pembrokeshire* 403 F 28 – *see Fishguard.*

WELSHPOOL **(Trallwng)** *Powys* 402 403 K 26 *Wales G.* – *pop. 5 900.*

See : *Town*★.

Env. : *Powis Castle*★★★ *AC, SW : 1½ m. by A 483.*

⛳18 *Golfa Hill* ☎ *(01938) 83249.*

ℹ *Vicarage Gdn, Church St.* ☎ *(01938) 552043.*

London 182 – Birmingham 64 – Chester 45 – Shrewsbury 19.

Royal Oak, The Cross, SY21 7DG, ☎ (01938) 552217, *oakwpool@aol.cc Fax (01938) 556652* – ⊭ 📺 🅿 – 🏛 150. ⓜⓒ AE VISA
Meals a la carte 16.40/19.50 **t.** 🍷 5.00 – **24 rm** ☕ 58.50/90.00 **t.** – SB.

Buttington Country House, Buttington, SY21 8HD, Northeast : 2 m. by A 483 an 458 on B 4388 ☎ (01938) 553351, *Fax (01938) 640604,* « Georgian house », 🌳 – ⊭ 🅿.
closed Christmas and New Year – **Meals** (by arrangement) 25.00 – **3 rm** ☕ 60.00/75.0 SB.

Moat Farm 🐄, SY21 8SE, South : 2 ¼ m. on A 483 ☎ (01938) 5531 *Fax (01938) 553179,* « Working farm », 🌳, 🎣 – ⊭ 📺 🅿. ✗
closed December and January – **Meals** (by arrangement) (communal dining) 14.00 🍷 3.50 – **3 rm** ☕ 25.00/44.00 **st.**

: Guilsfield *North : 3 m. by A 490 on B 4392 – ✉ Welshpool.*

Lower Trelydan ⛶, SY21 9PH, South : ¾ m. by B 4392 on unmarked road ℘ (01938) 553105, *stay@lowertrelydan.com, Fax (01938) 553105,* « 16C farmhouse, working farm », ⛶, ⛶ – ⛶ TV P. ⛶
closed Christmas and New Year – **Meals** (by arrangement) (communal dining) 13.00 **st.** 🍷 4.25 – **3 rm** ⛶ 28.00/50.00 **st.** – SB.

WOLF'S CASTLE (Cas-Blaidd) *Pembrokeshire* 403 F 28 *Wales G.* – *pop. 616* – ✉ *Haverfordwest.*
Env. : *Pembrokeshire Coast National Park*★★.
London 258 – Fishguard 7 – Haverfordwest 8.

Wolfscastle Country H., SA62 5LZ, ℘ (01437) 741225, *andy741225@aol.com, Fax (01437) 741383,* ⛶ – ⛶ TV P – ⛶ 150. MC AE VISA JCB
closed 24 to 26 December – **Meals** (lunch by arrangement Monday-Saturday)/dinner a la carte 13.50/28.20 **t.** 🍷 4.75 – **20 rm** ⛶ 43.00/77.00 **t.** – SB.

WREXHAM (Wrecsam) *Wrexham* 402 403 L 24 *Wales G.* – *pop. 40 614.*
See : *St. Giles Church*★.
Env. : *Erddig*★★ *AC (Gardens*★★*), SW : 2 m – Gresford (All Saints Church*★*), N : 4 m. by A 5152 and B 5445.*
18, 9 *Chirk* ℘ *(01691) 774407 –* 18 *Clays Farm, Bryn Estyn Rd* ℘ *(01978) 661406 –* 9 *Moss Valley, Moss Rd* ℘ *(01978) 720518 –* 9 *Pen-y-Cae, Ruabon Rd* ℘ *(01978) 810108 –* 9 *The Plassey, Eyton* ℘ *(01978) 780020.*
ℹ *Lambpit St.* ℘ *(01978) 292015.*
London 192 – Chester 12 – Liverpool 35 – Shrewsbury 28.

Llwyn Onn Hall ⛶, Cefn Rd, LL13 0NY, Northeast : 2 ½ m. by A 534 off Cefn Rd ℘ (01978) 261225, *Fax (01978) 363233,* ⛶, ⛶, ⛶ – ⛶ TV P. MC AE ⛶ VISA JCB. ⛶
closed Christmas-New Year – **Meals** *(closed Sunday dinner to non-residents)* 11.90/17.50 **t.** and dinner a la carte 🍷 4.95 – **13 rm** ⛶ 64.00/84.00 **t.** – SB.

Travel Inn, Chester Rd, LL12 8PW, Northeast : 2 ½ m. by A 483 on B 5445 ℘ (01978) 853214, *Fax (01978) 856838* – ⛶ rm, TV ♿ P. MC AE ⛶ VISA. ⛶
Meals (grill rest.) – **38 rm** 40.95 **t.**

Travelodge, Croes-Foel roundabout, Rhostyllen, LL14 4EJ, Southwest : 2 m. by A 5152 at junction with A 483 ℘ (01978) 365705, *Fax (01978) 765705* – ⛶ rm, ⛶ rest, TV ♿ P. MC AE ⛶ VISA JCB. ⛶
Meals (grill rest.) – **32 rm** 39.95 **t.**

: Gresford *Northeast : 3 m. by A 483 on B 5445.*

Pant-yr-Ochain, Old Wrexham Rd, LL12 8TY, South : 1 m. ℘ (01978) 853525, *pant.yr.ochain@brunningandprice.co.uk, Fax (01978) 853505,* ⛶, « Part 16C inn », ⛶ – ⛶ P. MC AE VISA
closed 25-26 December and 1 January – **Meals** (booking essential) a la carte 17.60/22.40 **t.**

: Erbistock *South : 5 ¼ m. by A 525 off A 528 – ✉ Wrexham.*

The Cross Foxes, LL13 0DR, on A 528 ℘ (01978) 780380, *cross.foxes@brunningandprice.co.uk, Fax (01978) 780879,* ⛶, « Riverside setting », ⛶ – P. MC AE VISA
Meals (booking essential) and a la carte 15.85/22.85 **t.** 🍷 4.95.

Pour vos déplacements en ***Grande-Bretagne*** *et en* ***Irlande*** *:*
- cinq cartes détaillées n°s 401, 402, 403, 404, 923 à 1/400 000
- utilisez-les conjointement avec ce guide,
  un **souligné rouge** signale toutes les localités dans ce guide.

Ireland

The stars ______
Les étoiles ______
Le stelle ______
Die Sterne ______

"Bib Gourmand"
Meals 19.00/25.00

Good food at moderate prices ______
Repas soignés à prix modérés ______
Pasti accurati a prezzi contenuti ______
Sorgfältig zubereitete preiswerte Mahlzeiten ______

Peaceful atmosphere and setting ______
L'agrément ______
Amenità e tranquillità ______
Annehmlichkeit ______

Town with a local map ______
Carte de voisinage : voir à la ville choisie ______
Città con carta dei dintorni ______
Stadt mit Umgebungskarte ______

ATLANTIC
Ballina
Crossmolina
Letterfrack
Leenane
Clifden
Cong
Recess
Ballyconneely
Caherlistran
Ballynahinch
Cashel
Oughterard
Moycullen
Inishmore
Galw
ARAN ISLANDS
Ballyvaug
Lahinch
Glin
Ada
Ballinga
N 21
Dingle
Caragh Lake
Kanturk
Valencia Island
Killarney
N 22
Tahilla
Kenmare
Caherdaniel
Ahakista
Kilbrittain
Schull
Baltimore

C E A N
Portrush
Rathmullan
Bushmills
Londonderry
Letterkenny
N 13
A 6
N 15
Donegal
M 2
Bangor
Belfast
Holywood
Dungannon
M 1
Sligo
A 4
Monaghan
A 1
Riverstown
Castlebaldwin
Belturbet
N 4
Dundalk
Castlerea
Ardee
IRISH
SEA
N 1
Athboy
Mullingar
Athlone
N 4
Maynooth
N 6
Dublin
Straffan
N 7
Dun Laoghaire
Birr
Borrisokane
Dunlavin
Laragh
Wicklow
Castledermot
N 7
N 8
Aughrim
Avoca
Bagenalstown
Ballon
N 11
Kilkenny
N 24
Tipperary
Gorey
Thomastown
Inistioge
Enniscorthy
N 24
N 25
Wexford
Waterford
Arthurstown
Castlelyons
Dunmore East
Dungarvan
N 25
Shanagarry

Northern Ireland

NNAHILT *Down* 923 N/O 4 – *see Hillsborough.*

NNALONG (Áth na Long) *Down* 923 O 5 *Ireland G. – pop. 1 937.*

Exc. : *W : Mourne Mountains★★ :– Bryansford, Tollymore Forest Park★ AC – Silent Valley Reservoir★ (<★) – Spelga Pass and Dam★ – Drumena Cashel and Souterrain★ – Kilbroney Forest Park (viewpoint★).*

Belfast 37 – Dundalk 36.

Glassdrumman Lodge ⑤, 85 Mill Rd, BT34 4RH, ℰ (028) 4376 8451, *Fax (028) 4376 7041,* < Irish Sea and Mourne mountains, ⑤, 🌲, 🏃 – ⅙ rest, TV P. MC AE ① VISA. ⅙
Meals (booking essential) (dinner only) 25.00/35.00 **t.** 6.00 – **8 rm** ⊒ 90.00/125.00 **t.**, 2 suites – SB.

ALLYCASTLE (Baile an Chaistil) *Antrim* 923 N 2.

18 Cushendall Rd ℰ (028) 2076 2536.

to Rathlin Island (Caledonian MacBrayne Ltd) 4 daily (40 mn).

7 Mary St. ℰ (028) 2076 2024 (July-December).

Belfast 55 – Ballymena 27 – Coleraine 22.

Marine, North St., BT54 6BN, ℰ (028) 2076 2222, *Fax (028) 2076 9507,* < Fair Head and Rathlin Island, Fa, ≘s, ⊠ – |‡|, ⅙ rm, TV P – 🎪 300. MC AE ① VISA. ⅙
Meals 8.95/14.00 **st.** and dinner a la carte – **32 rm** ⊒ 50.00/75.00 **st.** – SB.

Le Grand Londres (GREATER LONDON) est composé de la City et de 32 arrondissements administratifs (Borough) eux-mêmes divisés en quartiers ou en villages ayant conservé leur caractère propre (Area).

ALLYCLARE (Bealach Cláir) *Antrim* 923 N/O 3.

18 25 Springvale Rd ℰ (028) 9334 2352.

Belfast 17 – Ballymena 14 – Larne 10.

Ginger Tree, 29 Ballyrobert Rd, BT39 9RY, South : 3 ¼ m. by A 57 on B 56 ℰ (028) 9084 8176, *Fax (028) 9084 0777* – P. MC AE ① VISA
closed 11-13 July, 24-26 December, Saturday lunch and Sunday – **Meals** - Japanese - 13.95/30.00 **t.** and dinner a la carte 5.50.

ALLYDUGAN *Down.*

Belfast 24 – Bangor 27.

The Mill ⑤, BT30 8HZ, ℰ (028) 4461 3654, *nkillen@btinternet.com, Fax (028) 4461 7608,* « 18C » – |‡| TV P. MC AE VISA. ⅙
Meals *(closed Monday)* 12.95/15.95 **t.** – **11 rm** ⊒ 55.00/60.00 **st.**

ALLYMENA (An Baile Meánach) *Antrim* 923 N 3 *Ireland G. – pop. 28 717.*

Exc. : *Antrim Glens★★★ – Murlough Bay★★ (Fair Head <★★), Glengariff Forest Park★★ AC (Waterfall★★), Glengariff★, Glendun★ – Antrim (Round Tower★) S : 9½ m. by A 26.*

18 128 Raceview Rd ℰ (028) 2586 1207.

Council Offices, 80 Galgorm Rd ℰ (028) 2566 0300 – 76 Church St. (028) 2563 8494 (May-December).

Belfast 27 – Dundalk 78 – Larne 21 – Londonderry 51 – Omagh 53.

Galgorm Manor ⑤, 136 Fenhaghy Rd, BT42 1EA, West : 3 ¾ m. by A 42 on Cullybackey rd ℰ (028) 2588 1001, *mail@galgorm.com, Fax (028) 2588 0080,* <, « Part 19C country house on banks of River Main », 18, ⑤, 🌲, 🏃 – TV P – 🎪 500. MC AE ① VISA. ⅙
Meals 12.95/29.50 **t.** 10.00 – **24 rm** ⊒ 99.00/119.00 **t.**, 3 suites – SB.

Rosspark ⑤, 20 Doagh Rd, BT42 3LZ, Southeast : 6 m. by A 36 on B 59 ℰ (028) 2589 1663, *info@rosspark.com, Fax (028) 2589 1477,* Fa, ≘s, 🌲 – TV ♿ P – 🎪 300. ⅙
closed 25 December – **Meals** 18.95 **st.** (dinner) and a la carte 20.50/29.80 **st.** 5.25 – **40 rm** ⊒ 75.00/85.00 **st.** – SB.

Adair Arms, Ballymoney Rd, BT43 5BS, ℰ (028) 2565 3674, *reservations@adairarms.com, Fax (028) 2564 0436* – TV P – 🎪 250. MC AE ① VISA. ⅙
closed 25 December – **Meals** 5.95/16.95 and a la carte – **44 rm** ⊒ 59.50/85.00 **st.** – SB.

BANGOR **(Beannchar)** *Down* 923 O/P 4 *Ireland G.*

See : *North Down Heritage Centre★.*

Exc. : *Priory (Cross Slabs★) – Mount Stewart★★★* ***AC****, SE : 10 m. by A 2, A 21 and A 20 – Scrabo Tower (<★★) S : 6½ m. by A 21 – Ballycopeland Windmill★, SE : 10 m. by B 21 and A 2, turning right at Millisle – Strangford Lough★ (Castle Espie Centre★* ***AC*** *- Nendrum Monastery★) – Grey Abbey★* ***AC****, SE : 20 m. by A 2, A 21 and A 20.*

34 Quay St. (028) 9127 0069 (June-December).

Belfast *15 – Newtownards 5.*

Marine Court, The Marina, BT20 5ED, (028) 9145 1100, *marine.court@dial.pipex.com, Fax (028) 9145 1200,* – rm, – 350. MC AE VISA.
closed 25 December – **Meals** a la carte 13.15/20.70 **t.** – **52 rm** 80.00/100.00 **t.** – SB.

Clandeboye Lodge, 10 Estate Rd, Clandeboye, BT19 1UR, Southwest : 3 m. by A 2 and B 170 following signs for Blackwood Golf Centre (028) 9185 2500, *info@clandeboyelodge.com, Fax (028) 9185 2772,* – rm, – 350. MC AE VISA.
closed 23-26 December – **Meals** 19.50 **st.** (dinner) and a la carte 11.95/24.00 **st.** 6.75 – 8.75 – **43 rm** 75.00/95.00 **st.**

Royal, 26 Quay St., BT20 5ED, (028) 9127 1866, *theroyalhotel@compuserve.com, Fax (028) 9146 7810,* < – rest, – 60. MC AE VISA.
closed 25 December – **Meals** 14.50 **t.** (dinner) and a la carte 10.20/23.00 **t.** 5.25 – **50 rm** 72.50/105.00 **t.** – SB.

Cairn Bay Lodge, 278 Seacliffe Rd, BT20 5HS, East : 1 ¼ m. by Quay St. (028) 9146 7636, *info@cairnbaylodge.com, Fax (028) 9145 7728,* <, – VISA.
closed 1 week Christmas – **Meals** (by arrangement) (communal dining) 15.00 **st.** – **3 rm** 35.00/55.00 **st.** – SB.

Shelleven House, 59-61 Princetown Rd, BT20 3TA, (028) 9127 1777, *Fax (028) 9127 1777* – rest, MC VISA.
Meals (by arrangement) 14.00 **t.** 4.00 – **11 rm** 30.00/50.00 **t.**

Shanks (Millar), The Blackwood, Crawfordsburn Rd, Clandeboye, BT19 1GB, Southwest : 3 ¼ m. by A 2 and B 170 following signs for Blackwood Golf Centre (028) 9185 3313, *Fax (028) 9185 2493,* – MC AE VISA
closed Easter Tuesday, 25-26 December, 1 January, Saturday lunch, Sunday and Monday – **Meals** 18.95/32.50 **t.** 8.25
Spec. Seared foie gras with duck confit spring roll, mango and basil salsa. Steamed fillet of halibut, morels and asparagus. Fig and pistachio tart, honey ice cream.

BELFAST - (Béal Feirste)

Antrim 923 O 4 Ireland G. – pop. 279 237.

Dublin 103 – Londonderry 70.

TOURIST INFORMATION

St. Anne's Court, 59 North St. ☎ (028) 9024 6609.
Belfast International Airport, Information Desk ☎ (028) 9442 2888.
Belfast City Airport, Sydenham Bypass ☎ (028) 9045 7745.

PRACTICAL INFORMATION

Balmoral, 518 Lisburn Rd ☎ (028) 9038 1514, **AZ**.
Belvoir Park, Church Rd, Newtonbreda ☎ (028) 9049 1693 **AZ**.
Fortwilliam, Downview Av. ☎ (028) 9037 0770, **AY**.
The Knock Club, Summerfield, Dundonald ☎ (028) 9048 2249.
Shandon Park, 73 Shandon Park ☎ (028) 9079 3730.
Cliftonville, Westland Rd ☎ (028) 9074 4158, **AY**.
Ormeau, 50 Park Rd ☎ (028) 9064 1069, **AZ**.
Belfast International Airport, Aldergrove : ☎ (028) 9442 2888, W : 15 ½ m. by A 52 **AY** – *Belfast City Airport : ☎ (028) 9045 7745 –* **Terminal :** *Coach service (Ulsterbus Ltd.) from Great Victoria Street Station (40 mn).*
to Isle of Man (Douglas) (Isle of Man Steam Packet Co. Ltd) (summer only) (2 h 45 mn) – to Stranraer (Stena Line) (3 h 15 mn), (Sea Containers Ferries Scotland Ltd and Stena Line) 4-5 daily (1 h 30 mn) – to Liverpool (Norse Irish Ferries Ltd) daily (11 h).

SIGHTS

See : *City★ - Ulster Museum★★ (Spanish Armada Treasure★★, Shrine of St. Patrick's Hand★)* **AZ M1** – *City Hall★* **BY** – *Donegall Square★* **BY 20** – *Botanic Gardens (Palm House★)* **AZ** – *St Anne's Cathedral★* **BX** – *Crown Liquor Saloon★* **BY** – *Sinclair Seamen's Church★* **BX** – *St Malachy's Church★* **BY**.

Env. : *Belfast Zoological Gardens★★ AC, N : 5 m. by A 6* **AY**.

Exc. : *Carrickfergus (Castle★★ AC, St. Nicholas' Church★) NE : 9 ½ m. by A 2 – Talnotry Cottage Bird Garden, Crumlin★ AC, W : 13 ½ m. by A 52.*

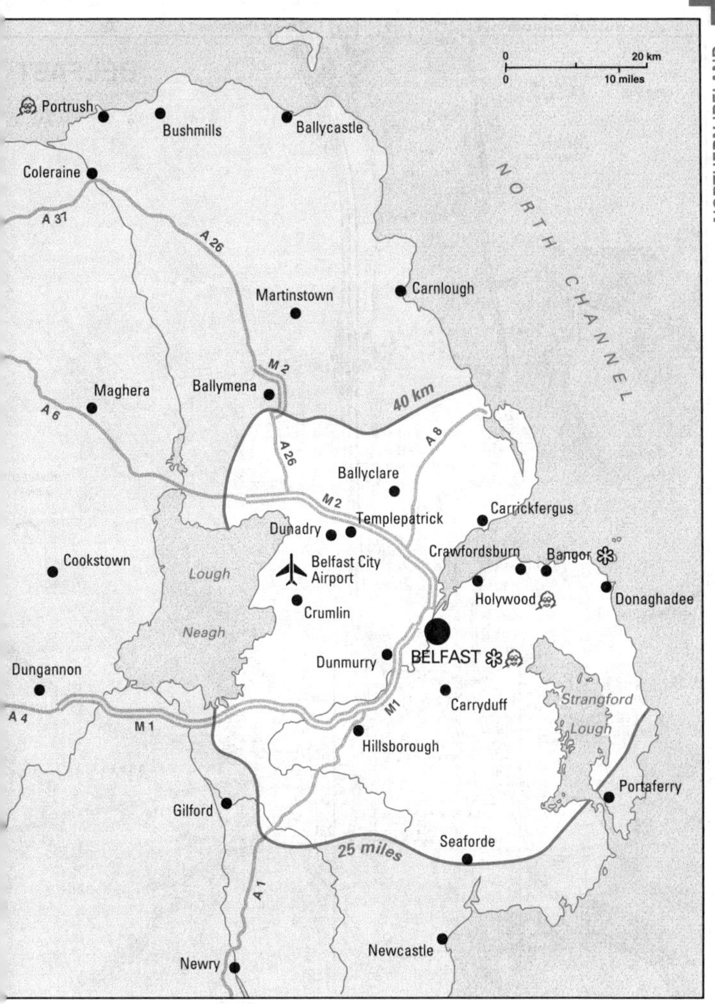

Particularly pleasant hotels and restaurants are shown in the Guide by a **red symbol**.

Please send us the names of anywhere you have enjoyed your stay.

Your **Michelin Guide** will be even better.

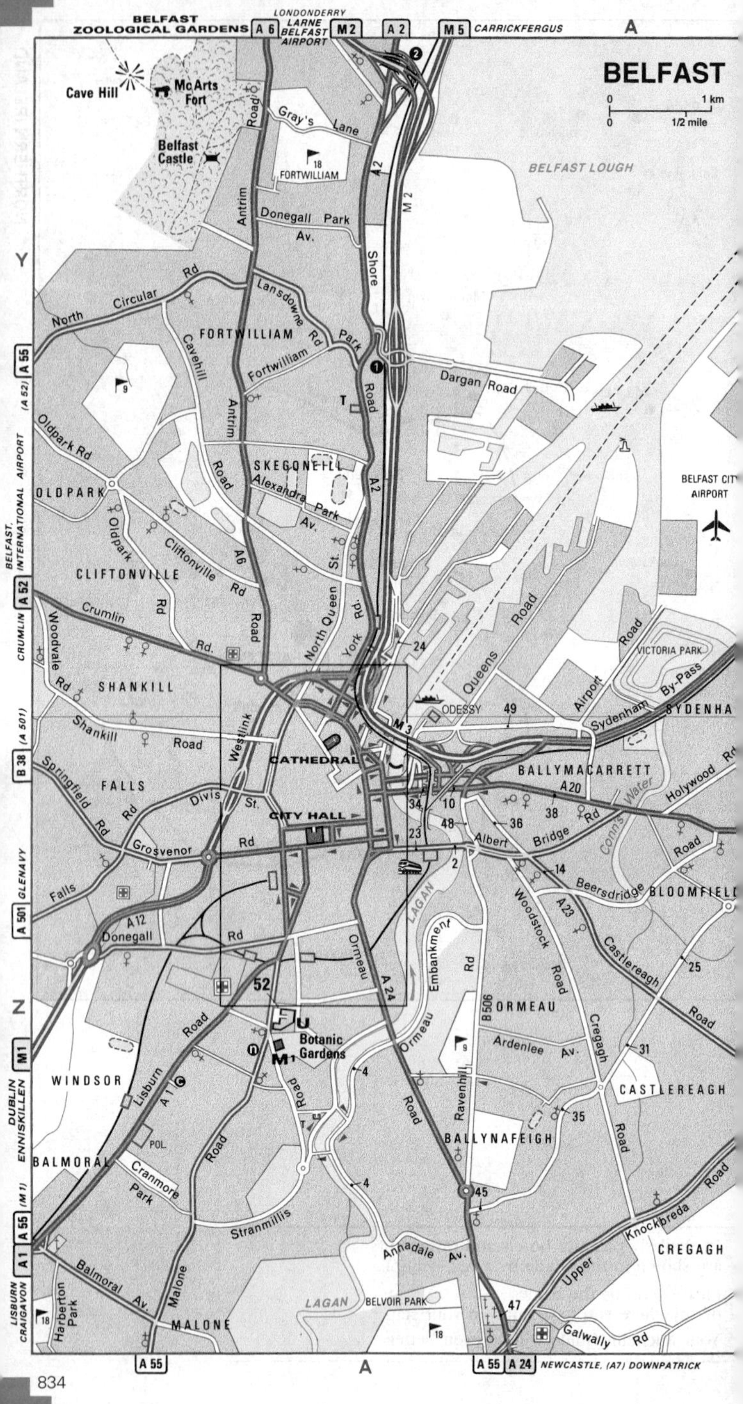
BELFAST
BELFAST ZOOLOGICAL GARDENS
LONDONDERRY LARNE BELFAST AIRPORT
CARRICKFERGUS
Cave Hill
McArts Fort
Belfast Castle
FORTWILLIAM
BELFAST LOUGH
Donegall Park Av.
Gray's Lane
North Circular Rd
Lansdowne Rd
Fortwilliam Park
Antrim Road
Shore Road
Dargan Road
Oldpark Rd
OLDPARK
SKEGONEILL
Alexandra Park Av.
Cavehill Road
Cliftonville Rd
CLIFTONVILLE
Crumlin Rd.
North Queen St.
York Rd.
Queens Road
Airport Road
VICTORIA PARK
Sydenham By-Pass
SYDENHAM
ODESSY
BELFAST CITY AIRPORT
Woodvale Rd
SHANKILL
Shankill Road
Westlink
CATHEDRAL
Springfield Rd
FALLS
Divis St.
CITY HALL
BALLYMACARRETT
Holywood Rd
Connswater
Grosvenor Rd
Albert Bridge Rd
Falls
Donegall Rd
LAGAN
Beersbridge Road
BLOOMFIELD
Woodstock Road
Castlereagh Road
Ormeau Road
Embankment
ORMEAU
Botanic Gardens
Lisburn Road
WINDSOR
Ardenlee Av.
Cregagh Road
CASTLEREAGH
Ravenhill Rd
BALLYNAFEIGH
BALMORAL
Cranmore Park
Stranmillis Road
Annadale Av.
Knockbreda Road
Upper
CREGAGH
Balmoral Av.
Malone Road
MALONE
Harberton Park
LAGAN
BELVOIR PARK
Galwally Rd
NEWCASTLE, (A7) DOWNPATRICK
LISBURN CRAIGAVON
DUBLIN ENNISKILLEN
GLENAVY
CRUMLIN
BELFAST, INTERNATIONAL AIRPORT

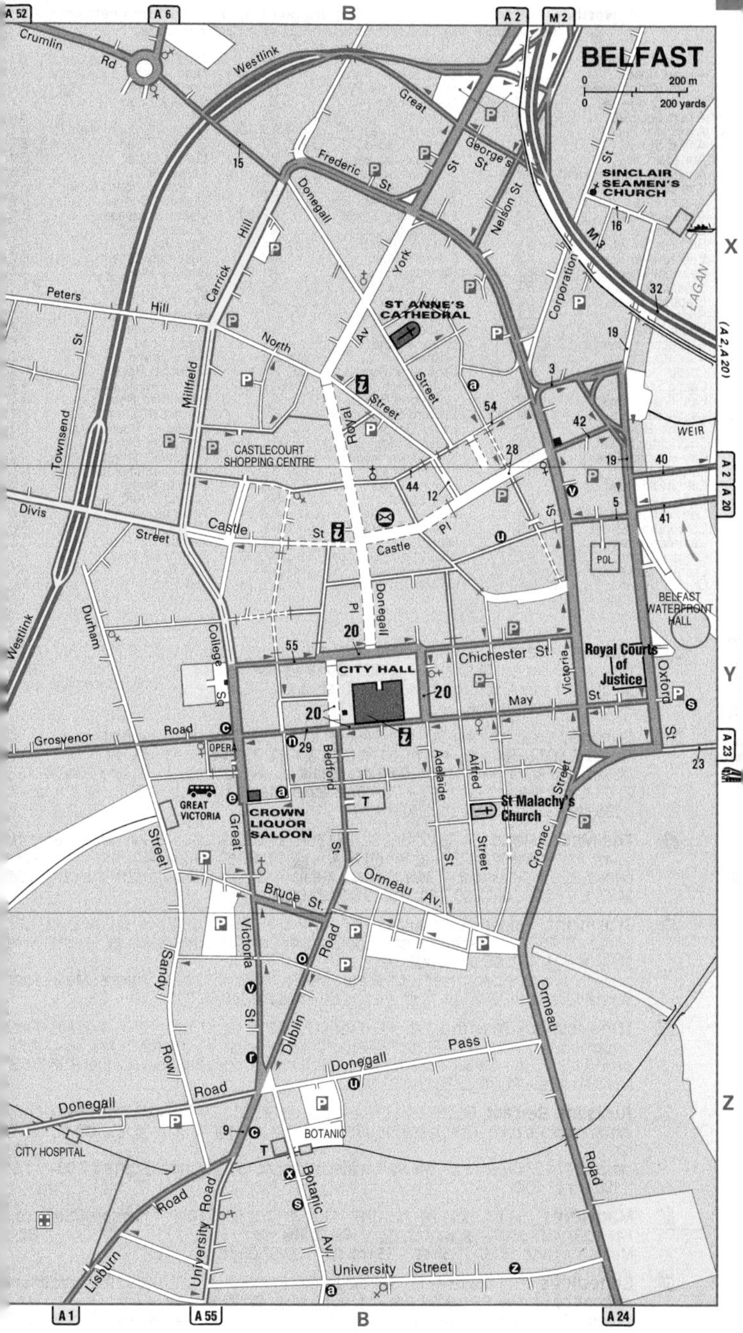

BELFAST
0 200 m
0 200 yards
A 52
A 6
B
A 2
M 2
Crumlin Rd
Westlink
Great George's St
Frederic St
Donegall
York St
Nelson St
SINCLAIR SEAMEN'S CHURCH
Corporation St
LAGAN
ST ANNE'S CATHEDRAL
Peters Hill
Carrick Hill
North Street
Royal Av
Millfield
Townsend St
CASTLECOURT SHOPPING CENTRE
WEIR
Divis Street
Castle St
Castle Pl
Donegall Pl
POL.
BELFAST WATERFRONT HALL
Durham
College Sq
CITY HALL
Chichester St.
Royal Courts of Justice
Victoria
May St
Oxford St
Grosvenor Road
OPERA
Bedford St
Adelaide St
Alfred Street
St Malachy's Church
Cromac Street
GREAT VICTORIA
CROWN LIQUOR SALOON
Great Victoria St.
Street
Bruce St.
Ormeau Av.
Sandy Row
Dublin Road
Ormeau Road
Donegall Pass
Donegall Road
BOTANIC
CITY HOSPITAL
Lisburn Road
University Road
Botanic Av
University Street
A 1
A 55
A 24
X
Y
Z
(A 2, A 20)
A 2
A 20
A 23

In Northern Ireland traffic and parking are controlled in the town centres. No vehicle may be left unattended in a Control Zone.

Hilton Belfast, 4 Lanyon Pl., BT1 3LP, ☎ (028) 9027 7000, *Fax (028) 9027 7277,* – |‡|, ⇎ rm, ▤ TV ☏ ♿ P – 🎙 400. MC AE ⓓ VISA JCB. ✗ BY
Meals (bar lunch Saturday) 14.50/17.50 **st.** and a la carte – ☐ 14.50 – **189 rm** 160.0 210.00 **st.**, 6 suites – SB.

Europa, Great Victoria St., BT2 7AP, ☎ (028) 9032 7000, *res@eur.hastingshotels.co Fax (028) 9032 7800* – |‡|, ⇎ rm, ▤ rest, TV ♿ – 🎙 750. MC AE ⓓ VISA. ✗ BY
closed 24 and 25 December – ***Gallery :*** **Meals** *(closed Saturday lunch and Sunday)* 13.5 21.95 **t.** and dinner a la carte 🍷 7.00 – ***Brasserie :*** **Meals** a la carte 12.20/16.85 **t.** – ☐ 12. – **235 rm** 125.00/166.00 **st.**, 5 suites.

The McCausland, 34-38 Victoria St., BT1 3GH, ☎ (028) 9022 0200, *info@mccauslandhc l.com, Fax (028) 9022 0220* – |‡| ⇎ TV ☏ ♿ – 🎙 60. MC AE ⓓ VISA JCB. ✗ BY
closed 25-27 December – ***Merchants :*** **Meals** *(closed Saturday lunch)* a la carte 16.9 24.65 **t.** 🍷 6.50 – ☐ 12.00 – **60 rm** 120.00/190.00 **st.** – SB.

Stormont, Upper Newtownards Rd, BT4 3LP, East : 4 ½ m. by A 2 on A ☎ (028) 9065 8621, *res@stor.hastingshotels.com, Fax (028) 9048 0240* – |‡|, ⇎ rm, ▤ re TV ♿ P – 🎙 400. MC AE ⓓ VISA. ✗
closed 24 and 25 December – ***La Scala :*** **Meals** 10.95/16.95 **st.** – ***Shiraz :*** **Meals** *(clos Sunday)* a la carte 15.45/24.15 **st.** – ☐ 12.00 – **109 rm** 110.00/215.00 **st.** – SB.

The Crescent Townhouse, 13 Lower Cres., BT7 1NR, ☎ (028) 9032 3349, *info@cres nttownhouse.com, Fax (028) 9032 0646,* « Regency house » – TV. MC AE VISA. ✗ BZ
closed 11-13 July – **Meals** *(closed Sunday)* (bar lunch Monday-Saturday)/dinner 9.95/12.5C and a la carte – **11 rm** ☐ 80.00/125.00 **t.**

Jurys Inn Belfast, Fisherwick Pl., Great Victoria St., BT2 7AP, ☎ (028) 9053 3500, *belfa inn@jurysdoyle.com, Fax (028) 9053 3511* – |‡|, ⇎ rm, TV ☏ ♿ – 🎙 35. MC AE ⓓ V ✗ BY
closed 24 to 27 December – **Meals** (bar lunch)/dinner 15.95 **t.** and a la carte 🍷 7.00 – ☐ 8. – **190 rm** 67.00 **t.**

Madison's, 59-63 Botanic Av., BT7 1JL, ☎ (028) 9033 0040, *madisons@unite.co. Fax (028) 9032 8007* – |‡|, ▤ rest, TV ♿. MC AE VISA. ✗ BZ
Meals a la carte 13.00/19.50 **st.** – **35 rm** ☐ 70.00/87.00 **st.**

Benedict's, 7-21 Bradbury Pl., Shaftsbury Sq., BT7 1RQ, ☎ (028) 9059 1999, *info@bene ctshotel.co.uk, Fax (028) 9059 1990* – |‡| ▤ TV ☏ ♿. MC AE VISA. ✗ BZ
closed 12 July and 25 December – **Meals** 20.00/25.00 **t.** (dinner) and a la carte 16.4 24.00 **t.** 🍷 9.50 – **32 rm** ☐ 65.00/75.00 **st.**

Dukes, 65 University St., BT7 1HL, ☎ (028) 9023 6666, *info@dukes-hotel-belfast.co.uk, Fax (028) 9023 7177,* – rm, rest, – 130. BZ a
Meals (bar lunch Monday-Saturday and Sunday dinner)/dinner 15.00/18.00 **st.** and a la carte 4.95 – **21 rm** 95.00/110.00 **st.** – SB.

Express by Holiday Inn, 106A University St., BT7 1HP, ☎ (028) 9031 1909, *express@holidayinn_ireland.com, Fax (028) 9031 1910* – , rm, rest, – 200. BZ z
Meals a la carte 12.15/14.95 **st.** – 5.95 – **114 rm** 64.95 **st.** – SB.

Travelodge, 15 Brunswick St., BT2 7GE, ☎ (028) 9033 3555, *Fax (028) 9023 2999* – , rm, rest, – 70. BY a
Meals (grill rest.) – **76 rm** 59.95 **t.** – SB.

Ash Rowan, 12 Windsor Av., BT9 6EE, ☎ (028) 9066 1758, *Fax (028) 9066 3227,* – . AZ c
closed23 December-6 January – **Meals** (by arrangement) 29.00 **st.** – **5 rm** 48.00/84.00 **st.**

Malone without rest., 79 Malone Rd, BT9 6SH, ☎ (028) 9066 9565, *Fax (028) 9022 3020* – . AZ n
8 rm 35.00/55.00.

Roseleigh House, 19 Rosetta Park, BT6 0DL, South : 1 ½ m. by A 24 Ormeau Rd ☎ (028) 9064 4414, *roseleighhouse@ukonline.co.uk, Fax (028) 9064 2983* – .
closed 25 December – **Meals** (by arrangement) 15.00 – **9 rm** 38.50/54.00 **st.**

Restaurant Michael Deane, 38-40 Howard St., BT1 6PD, ☎ (028) 9033 1134, *Fax (028) 9056 0001* – . BY n
closed 2 days Easter, 1 week July, Christmas, New Year, Sunday and Monday – **Meals** (dinner only) 39.50 **t.** 9.50 – (see also ***Deanes Brasserie*** below).
Spec. Terrine of squab pigeon and foie gras en gelée. Fillet of turbot with fricassee of lobster. Crème caramel with roast and dried pears.

Cayenne, 7 Lesley House, Shaftesbury Sq., BT2 7DB, ☎ (028) 9033 1532, *Fax (028) 9026 1575* – . BZ r
closed 25-26 December, 1 January, Easter Monday, 12-13 July, Sunday and lunch Saturday – **Meals** a la carte 16.50/22.50 **t.** 8.75.

Aldens, 229 Upper Newtownards Rd, BT4 3JF, East : 1 ½ m. on A 20 ☎ (028) 9065 0079, *Fax (028) 9065 0032* –
closed 2 weeks July, 25 December, 1 January, Saturday lunch and Sunday dinner – **Meals** 13.00 **t.** (lunch) and a la carte 16.10/25.90 **t.** 7.35.

Deanes Brasserie, 38-40 Howard St., BT1 6PD, ☎ (028) 9056 0000, *Fax (028) 9056 0001* – . BY n
closed Easter, 12-13 July, 25-26 December, 1 January and Sunday – **Meals** a la carte 18.50/24.00 **t.** 10.00.

Nick's Warehouse, 35-39 Hill St., BT1 2LB, ☎ (028) 9043 9690, *nicks@warehouse.dnet.co.uk, Fax (028) 9023 0514* – . BX a
closed 2 days Easter, 1 May, 12 July, 25-26 December, 1 January, Saturday lunch, Monday dinner and Sunday – **Meals** a la carte 17.95/24.40 **t.** 5.10.

Keating, 103 Great Victoria St., BT2 7AG, ☎ (028) 9059 4949, *Fax (028) 9059 4359* – . BZ v
closed 11-18 July, 25-28 December, Sunday and Saturday lunch – **Meals** 8.50/11.50 **t.** (dinner) and a la carte 19.45/28.00 **t.** 6.25.

La Belle Epoque, 61-63 Dublin Rd, BT2 7HE, ☎ (028) 9032 3244, *Fax (028) 9020 3111* – BZ o
closed 12-13 July, 25-26 December, 1 January, Saturday lunch and Sunday – **Meals** 8.75/15.00 **t.** and a la carte 5.00.

Manor House, 43-47 Donegall Pass, BT7 1DQ, ☎ (028) 9023 8755, *Fax (028) 9023 8755* – . BZ u
closed 24-25 December and lunch Saturday and Sunday – **Meals** - Chinese (Canton) - 5.95/17.00 **t.** and a la carte 4.75.

Morning Star, (first floor), 17-19 Pottinger's Entry, off High St., BT1 4DT, ☎ (028) 9023 5986, *morning-star@pottingers-entry.freeserve.co.uk, Fax (028) 9032 9311* – BY u
closed 12 July, 25 December and Sunday – **Meals** a la carte 9.55/22.85 **st.**

Carryduff *South : 6 m. by A 24* – **AZ** – ✉ *Belfast.*

Ivanhoe, 556 Saintfield Rd, BT8 8EU, North : 1 m. on A 24 ☎ (028) 9081 2240, *info@ivanhoehotel.freeserve.co.uk, Fax (028) 9081 5516* – – 150. .
closed 25 December – **Meals** 12.95/18.95 **t.** – **21 rm** 69.00/89.00 **t.** – SB.

NORTHERN IRELAND

at Dunmurry *Southwest : 5½ m. on A 1* – **AZ** – ✉ *Belfast.*

🏨 **Beechlawn House,** 4 Dunmurry Lane, BT17 9RR, ☎ (028) 9060 2010, *info@beechlawnhotel.co.uk, Fax (028) 9060 2080* – 📺 📞 🅿 – 🏛 300. 🅜🅒 AE ⓪ VISA. ✂
closed 12 July and 25 December – **Meals** 10.95/19.95 **st.** and a la carte 🍷 5.95 – **42 rm** ☕ 69.00/79.00 **st.** – SB.

BELFAST INTERNATIONAL AIRPORT (Aerphort Béal Feirste) *Antrim* 923 N 4 – ✉ *Aldergrove.*

✈ *Belfast International Airport, Aldergrove : ☎ (028) 9442 2888.*

Belfast 6 – Ballymena 20 – Larne 23.

🏨 **Aldergrove,** Aldergrove, BT29 4ZY, ☎ (028) 9442 2033, *Fax (028) 9442 3500,* Lã, ≘s, – |‡|, ⇔ rm, ▤ 📺 ♿ 🅿 – 🏛 230. 🅜🅒 AE ⓪ VISA. ✂
Meals (buffet lunch)/dinner a la carte 19.00/25.00 **st.** 🍷 5.40 – ☕ 8.50 – **108 rm** 75.00 **st.**

BELLEEK (Béal Leice) *Fermanagh* 923 H 4 – *pop. 550.*

Belfast 117 – Londonderry 56.

🏨 **Carlton,** Main St., BT93 3FX, ☎ (028) 6865 8282, *reception@hotel-carlton.co.uk, Fax (028) 6865 9005* – ⇔ rm, 📺 🅿 – 🏛 200. 🅜🅒 AE VISA. ✂
closed 24-25 December – **Meals** (bar lunch)/dinner 7.00/15.00 **t.** and a la carte 🍷 5.25 – **19 rm** ☕ 52.50/75.00 **t.** – SB.

BUSHMILLS (Muileann na Buaise) *Antrim* 923 M 2 *Ireland G.* – *pop. 1 348* – ✉ *Bushmills.*

Exc. : *Causeway Coast*★★ : *Giant's Causeway*★★★ *(Hamilton's Seat* ≤★★*), Carrick-a-rede Rope Bridge*★★*, Dunluce Castle*★★ *AC, Gortmore Viewpoint*★ – *Dunseverick Castle (*≤★*), Magilligan Strand*★*, Downhill*★ *(Mussenden Temple*★*).*

⛳9 *Bushfoot, 50 Bushfoot Rd, Portballintrae ☎ (028) 2073 1317.*

Belfast 57 – Ballycastle 12 – Coleraine 10.

🏨 **Bushmills Inn,** 9 Dunluce Rd, BT57 8QG, ☎ (028) 2073 2339, *mail@bushmillsinn.com, Fax (028) 2073 2048,* « Part 18C » – 📺 ♿ 🅿 – 🏛 50. 🅜🅒 AE VISA. ✂
Meals (carving lunch Sunday)/dinner 24.00/28.00 **st.** 🍷 7.00 – **32 rm** ☕ 78.00/128.00 **t.** – SB.

⌂ **Craig Park** 🐎 without rest., 24 Carnbore Rd, BT57 8YF, Southeast : 2 ½ m. by B 66 and Ballycastle rd (B 17), off How Rd ☎ (028) 2073 2496, *jan@craigpark.co.uk, Fax (028) 2073 2479,* ≤, 🌳 – ⇔ 📺 🅿. 🅜🅒 VISA. ✂
closed Christmas and New Year – **3 rm** ☕ 35.00/55.00 **st.**

CARNLOUGH (Carnlach) *Antrim* 923 O 3 – *pop. 1 493.*

Belfast 36 – Ballymena 16 – Larne 14.

🏨 **Londonderry Arms,** 20 Harbour Rd, BT44 0EU, ☎ (028) 2888 5255, *ida@glensofantrim.com, Fax (028) 2888 5263* – |‡| 📺 ♿ 🅿 – 🏛 120. 🅜🅒 AE ⓪ VISA. ✂
Meals a la carte 20.45/26.60 **t.** 🍷 6.25 – **35 rm** ☕ 55.00/90.00 **t.** – SB.

CARRICKFERGUS (Carraig Fhearghais) *Antrim* 923 O 3.

⛳18 *35 North Rd ☎ (028) 9336 3713.*

ℹ *Heritage Plaza ☎ (028) 9336 6455 (April-September).*

Belfast 11 – Ballymena 25.

🏨 **Quality,** 75 Belfast Rd, BT38 8PH, on A 2 ☎ (028) 9336 4556, *info@qualitycarrick.co.uk, Fax (028) 9335 1620* – |‡| 📺 📞 ♿ 🅿 – 🏛 600. 🅜🅒 AE ⓪ VISA. ✂
closed 25 December – **Meals** (carving lunch Sunday) a la carte 11.95/20.00 **st.** 🍷 3.75 – **68 rm** ☕ 85.00/100.00 **st.** – SB.

CARRY BRIDGE *Fermanagh* 923 J 5 – ✉ *Lisbellaw.*

Belfast 80 – Dundalk 62 – Londonderry 60.

⌂ **Aghnacarra House,** BT94 5HX, ☎ (028) 6638 7077, *ensor-aghnacarra@gofornet.co.uk, Fax (028) 6638 5811,* 🎣, 🌳 – 🅿. ✂
mid March-mid October – **Meals** (by arrangement) 9.00 **st.** – **7 rm** ☕ 24.00/38.00.

CARRYDUFF (Ceathrú Aodha Dhuibh) *Antrim* – *see Belfast.*

NORTHERN IRELAND

OLERAINE (Cúil Raithin) *Londonderry* 923 L 2 *Ireland G. – pop. 20 721.*

Exc. : *Antrim Glens★★★ – Murlough Bay★★ (Fair Head ≤★★), Glenariff Forest Park★★ AC (Waterfall★★), Glenariff★, Glendun★ – Causeway Coast★★ : Giant's Causeway★★★ (Hamilton's Seat ≤★★) – Carrick-a-rede Rope Bridge★★ – Dunluce Castle★★ AC – Dunseverick Castle (≤★★) – Gortmore Viewpoint★ – Magilligan Strand★ – Downhill★ (Mussenden Temple★).*

18, 9 *Castlerock, Circular Rd ☎ (028) 7084 8314 – 9 Brown Trout, 209 Agivey Rd ☎ (028) 7086 8209.*

Railway Rd ☎ (028) 7034 4723.

Belfast 53 – Ballymena 25 – Londonderry 31 – Omagh 65.

Bushtown House, 283 Drumcroone Rd, BT51 3QT, South : 2 ½ m. on A 29 ☎ (028) 7035 8367, *bushtownhousehotel@talk21.com, Fax (028) 7032 0909,* – TV P – 300. MO AE VISA.
closed 24-26 December – **Meals** 10.00/20.00 **t.** and dinner a la carte – **39 rm** 55.00/120.00 **t.** – SB.

Brown Trout Golf and Country Inn, 209 Agivey Rd, Aghadowey, BT51 4AD, South-east : 9 m. on A 54 ☎ (028) 7086 8209, *bill@browntroutinn.com, Fax (028) 7086 8878,* 9, – rest, TV P – 40. MO AE VISA
Meals a la carte 14.00/20.00 **st.** – **15 rm** 60.00/85.00 **t.** – SB.

Greenhill House, 24 Greenhill Rd, Aghadowey, BT51 4EU, South : 9 m. by A 29 on B 66 ☎ (028) 7086 8241, *greenhill.house@btinternet.com, Fax (028) 7086 8365,* – rest, TV P. MO VISA.
March-October – **Meals** (by arrangement) 17.50 – **6 rm** 30.00/50.00 – SB.

In alta stagione, e soprattutto nelle stazioni turistiche, è prudente prenotare con un certo anticipo. Avvertite immediatamente l'albergatore se non potete più occupare la camera prenotata.

Se scrivete ad un albergo all'estero, allegate alla vostra lettera un tagliando-risposta internazionale (disponibile presso gli uffici postali).

OOKSTOWN (An Chorr Chráochach) *Tyrone* 923 L 4 *Ireland G.*

Env. : *Ardboe Cross★, E : 4 m. by B 73.*

18 *Killymoon, 200 Killymoon Rd ☎ (028) 8676 3762.*

The Burnavch, Burn Rd ☎ (028) 8676 6727 (July-October).

Belfast 45 – Ballymena 27 – Londonderry 49.

Tullylagan Country House, 40B Tullylagan Rd, Sandholes, BT80 8UP, South : 4 m. by A 29 ☎ (028) 8676 5100, *Fax (028) 8676 1715,* – TV P – 180. MO AE VISA
closed24-26 December – **Meals** *(closed Sunday dinner)* a la carte 15.60/21.15 **st.** 6.00 – **15 rm** 52.50/95.00 **st.** – SB.

RAWFORDSBURN (Sruth Chráfard) *Down* 923 O 4 *Ireland G. – pop. 572.*

Env. : *North Down Heritage Centre, Bangor★, E : 3 m. by B 20.*

Exc. : *Priory (Cross Slabs★) – Mount Stewart★★★ AC, SE : 12 m. by A 2, A 21 and A 20 – Scrabo Tower (≤★★), SW : 8 m. – Ballycopeland Windmill★ AC, E : 13 m. by A 2, A 21 and B 172 – Strangford Lough★ (Castle Espie Centre★ AC - Nendrum Monastery★) – Grey Abbey★ AC, SE : 14 m. by A 2, A 21 and A 20.*

Belfast 12 – Bangor 3.

Old Inn, 15 Main St., BT19 1JH, ☎ (028) 9185 3255, *info@theoldinn.com, Fax (028) 9185 2775,* – TV P – 120. MO AE VISA.
Meals 15.00/24.00 **t.** 6.95 – **32 rm** 65.00/150.00 **t.** – SB.

RUMLIN (Cromghlinn) *Antrim* 923 N 4 *– pop. 2 697.*

Belfast 14 – Ballymena 20.

Caldhame Country Guest Lodge, 102 Moira Rd, Nutts Corner, BT29 4HG, Southeast : 1 ¼ m. on A 26 ☎ (028) 9442 3099, *info@caldhamelodge.co.uk, Fax (028) 9442 3099,* – TV P. MO AE VISA.
Meals (by arrangement) 15.00 **st.** – **6 rm** 30.00/46.00 **s.**

Keef Halla, 20 Tully Rd, BT29 4SW, Northeast : 3 ¾ m. by A 52 on A 26 ☎ (028) 9082 5491, *info@keefhalla.com, Fax (028) 9082 5940,* – TV P. MO AE VISA.
Meals (by arrangement) 15.00 **st.** – **7 rm** 25.00/50.00 **st.**

DONAGHADEE **(Domhnach Daoi)** *Down* 923 P 4.
Warren Rd (028) 9188 3624.
Belfast 18 – *Ballymena* 44.

Grace Neill's, 33 High St., BT21 0AH, (028) 9188 4595, *Fax (028) 9188 2553* – P. VISA
closed 12-13 July, 25-26 December, 1 January, Sunday dinner and Monday – **Meals** a la car 15.75/23.65 **t.** 6.95.

Pier 36, 36 The Parade, BT21 0HE, (028) 9188 4466, *info@pier36.co.u Fax (028) 9188 4636* – VISA
closed 25 December – **Meals** - Seafood specialities - a la carte 10.00/29.45 **t.**

DUNADRY **(Dún Eadradh)** *Antrim* 923 N 3 *Ireland G.*
Env. : *Antrim (Round tower★) NW : 4 m. by A 6.*
Exc. : *Crumlin : Talnotry Cottage Bird Garden★ AC, SW : 10½ m. by A 5, A 26 and A 52.*
Belfast 16 – *Larne* 18 – *Londonderry* 56.

Dunadry, 2 Islandreagh Drive, BT41 2HA, (028) 9443 2474, *mooneyhotelgroup@talk com, Fax (028) 9443 3389,* – rm, P – 300. AE VISA.
closed 24-26 December – **Meals** (buffet lunch) 9.95 **st.** (lunch) and dinner a la carte appro 24.75 **st.** 8.00 – 8.95 – **82 rm** 99.00/145.00 **st.**, 1 suite – SB.

DUNGANNON **(Dún Geanainn)** *Tyrone* 923 L 4 *Ireland G.*
Env. : *The Argory★, S : 5 m. by A 29 and east by minor rd.*
Exc. : *Armagh★★ (St. Patrick's Cathedral★ (Anglican), St. Patrick's Cathedral★ (Roman Cat olic), The Mall★, Armagh County Museum★ – Regimental Museum of the Royal Ir Fusiliers★, Navan Fort★), S : 12 m. by A 29.*
Belfast 42 – *Ballymena* 37 – *Dundalk* 47 – *Londonderry* 60.

Oaklin House, Parkmount, Moy Rd, BT71 6BS, South : ¾ m. on A 29 (028) 8772 5151 *aklin@aol.com, Fax (028) 8772 4953,* – P – 120. AE VISA.
closed 25 December – **Meals** 6.00/30.00 **st.** 5.00 – **19 rm** 50.00/90.00 **st.** – SB.

Cohannon Inn & Auto Lodge, 212 Ballynakelly Rd, BT71 6HJ, East : 6 ¼ m. by A 29 and 1 on A 45 (028) 8772 4488, *enquiries@cohannon-inn.com, Fax (028) 8775 2217* – r P – 150. AE VISA.
closed 25 December – **Meals** (carving lunch)/dinner 11.95 **t.** and a la carte 4.95 – 4.6 **46 rm** 34.95 **t.** – SB.

Grange Lodge , 7 Grange Rd, BT71 7EJ, Southeast : 3 ½ m. by A (028) 8778 4212, *grangelodge@nireland.com, Fax (028) 8778 4313,* – P. VISA.
closed 20 December-1 February – **Meals** (by arrangement) 25.00 **t.** 5.00 – **5 rm** 49.0 69.00 **st.**

DUNMURRY **(Dún Muiríghe)** *Antrim* 923 N 4 – *see Belfast.*

ENNISKILLEN **(Inis Ceithleann)** *Fermanagh* 923 J 4 *Ireland G. – pop. 11 436.*
Env. : *Castle Coole★★★ AC, SE : 1 m.*
Exc. : *NW : Lough Erne★★ : Cliffs of Magho Viewpoint★★★ AC – Devenish Island★ AC White Island★ – Janus Figure★ – Tully Castle★ AC – Florence Court★★ AC, SW : 8 m. by and A 32 – Marble Arch Caves and Forest Nature Reserve★ AC, SW : 10 m. by A 4 and A 3*
Castlecoole (028) 6632 5250.
Wellington Rd (028) 6632 3110 (April-December).
Belfast 87 – *Londonderry* 59.

Killyhevlin, Killyhevlin, BT74 6RW, Southeast : 1 ¾ m. on A 4 (028) 6632 3481, *info@ yhevlin.com, Fax (028) 6632 4726,* – rest, P – 500. AE VISA
closed 24 and 25 December – **Meals** 13.50/25.00 **st.** and a la carte 9.00 – **42 rm** 72.5 105.00 **st.**, 1 suite – SB.

Manor House Country , Killadeas, BT94 1NY, North : 7 ½ m. by A 32 on B (028) 6862 2200, *manorhousehotel@lakelands.net, Fax (028) 6862 1545,* – P – 300. AE VISA.
Meals 12.75/23.00 **t.** and a la carte 5.65 – **46 rm** 85.00/110.00 **t.** – SB.

Si vous cherchez un hôtel tranquille,
consultez d'abord les cartes de l'introduction
ou repérez dans le texte les établissements indiqués avec le signe ou

ILFORD (Áth Mhic Giolla) *Down* 923 M 4 – *pop. 1 639.*
Belfast 30 – Dundalk 32.

XX **The Oriel,** Whinney Hill, BT63 6HF, ☎ (028) 3883 1543, *Fax (028) 3883 1180* – ⇔. MC AE VISA JCB
closed 2 weeks July, 25-26 December, Saturday lunch, Sunday dinner and Monday – **Meals** 11.95/15.95 **t.** (lunch) and dinner a la carte 23.40/26.70 **t.** 8.00.

ILLSBOROUGH (Cromghlinn) *Down* 923 N 4 *Ireland G.*
See : *Town★ – Fort★.*
Exc. : *The Argory★, W : 25 m. by A 1 and M 1.*
The Courthouse, The Square ☎ (028) 9268 9717 (July-December).
Belfast 12.

White Gables, 14 Dromore Rd, BT26 6HS, Southwest : ½ m. ☎ (028) 9268 2755, *Fax (028) 9268 9532* – ⇔ rm, rest, TV P – 120. MC AE VISA.
closed25 December – **Meals** (dinner only) a la carte 22.25/29.25 **t.** – **31 rm** 80.00/125.00 **t.**

Fortwilliam without rest., 210 Ballynahinch Rd, BT26 6BH, Southeast : 3 ½ m. on B 177 ☎ (028) 9268 2255, *fortwilliam.countryhouse@ukgateway.net, Fax (028) 9268 9608*, « Working farm », – ⇔ TV P. MC VISA.
3 rm 35.00/55.00.

XX **Hillside,** 21 Main St., BT26 6AE, ☎ (028) 9268 2765, *Fax (028) 9268 9888* – MC AE VISA
closed 25 December – **Meals** (dinner only) a la carte 17.95/23.40 **t.** 6.95.

The Plough Inn, The Square, BT26 6AG, ☎ (028) 9268 2985, *Fax (028) 9268 2472* – P. MC AE VISA
closed 12-13 July and 25-26 December – **Meals** a la carte 19.55/24.80 **t.**

Annahilt *Southeast : 4 m. by B 177 – ✉ Hillsborough.*

The Pheasant, 410 Upper Ballynahinch Rd, BT26 6NR, North : 1 m. by Lisburn rd ☎ (028) 9268 3056, *Fax (028) 9268 3056* – ⇔ P. MC AE VISA
closed 25-26 December and Monday except Bank Holiday Monday – **Meals** a la carte 14.45/26.10 **t.** 5.75.

In alta stagione, e soprattutto nelle stazioni turistiche, è prudente prenotare con un certo anticipo.
Avvertite immediatamente l'albergatore se non potete più occupare la camera prenotata.

Se scrivete ad un albergo all'estero, allegate alla vostra lettera un tagliando-risposta internazionale (disponibile presso gli uffici postali).

OLYWOOD (Ard Mhic Nasca) *Down* 923 O 4 *Ireland G. – pop. 9 252.*
Env. : *Cultra : Ulster Folk and Transport Museum★★ AC, NE : 1 m. by A 2.*
Holywood, Nuns Walk, Demesne Rd ☎ (028) 9042 2138.
Belfast 7 – Bangor 6.

Culloden, Bangor Rd, BT18 0EX, East : 1 ½ m. on A 2 ☎ (028) 9042 5223, *res@cull.hastings hotel.com, Fax (028) 9042 6777*, ≤, « Part Victorian Gothic manor », squash – rest, TV P – 500. MC AE VISA.
closed 25 December – ***Mitre :*** **Meals** (dinner only and Sunday lunch)/dinner 29.50 **st.** 13.00 – ***Cultra Inn :*** **Meals** (grill rest.) a la carte 13.15/19.25 **st.** 6.50 – 11.50 – **76 rm** 150.00/180.00 **st.**, 1 suite – SB.

Rayanne House, 60 Demesne Rd, BT18 9EX, by High St. and Downshire Rd ☎ (028) 9042 5859, *Fax (028) 9042 3364*, ≤, – ⇔ TV P. MC AE VISA.
Meals *(closed Sunday)* (residents only) (dinner only) 30.00 **t.** 7.50 – **8 rm** 67.50/90.00 **st.** – SB.

Beech Hill without rest., 23 Ballymoney Rd, Craigantlet, BT23 4TG, Southeast : 4 ½ m. by A 2 on Craigantlet rd ☎ (028) 9042 5892, *beech.hill@btinternet.com, Fax (028) 9042 5892*, – ⇔ TV P. MC VISA
3rm 40.00/60.00 **st.**

X **Sullivans,** Unit 5, 2 Sullivan Pl., BT18 9JF, ☎ (028) 9042 1000, *Fax (028) 9042 6664* – MC AE VISA
closed 12-13 July and 25-26 December – **Meals** a la carte 13.00/21.50 **t.** 6.95.

X **Fontana,** 61A High St., BT18 9AE, ☎ (028) 9080 9908, *Fax (028) 9080 9912* – MC VISA
closed 1 week July, Christmas, Monday, Saturday lunch and Sunday dinner – **Meals** 10.50 **t.** (lunch) and a la carte 16.35/32.35 **t.** 8.50.

LARNE (Latharna) *Antrim* 923 O 3 *Ireland G. – pop. 17 575.*

Env. : *SE : Island Magee (Ballylumford Dolmen★).*

Exc. : *NW : Antrim Glens★★★ – Murlough Bay★★ (Fair Head ⩽★★), Glenariff Forest Park★ AC (Waterfall★★), Glenariff★, Glendun★ – Carrickfergus (Castle★★ – St. Nicholas' Church★ SW : 15 m. by A 2.*

18 Cairndhu, 192 Coast Rd, Ballygally ☎ (028) 2858 3248.

to Fleetwood (P & O Irish Sea) daily (8 h) – to Cairnryan (P & O Irish Sea) 3-5 daily (1 h. h 15 mn).

Narrow Gauge Rd ☎ (028) 2826 0088 (April-December).

Belfast 23 – Ballymena 20.

Derrin House without rest., 2 Prince's Gdns., BT40 1RQ, off Glenarm Rd (A ☎ (028) 2827 3762, *info@derrinhouse.co.uk, Fax (028) 2827 3269* – TV P. MC AE VISA
closed 25 and 26 December – **6 rm** 20.00/38.00 **s.**

LIMAVADY (Léim an Mhadaidh) *Londonderry* 923 L 2.

9 Benone Par Three, 53 Benone Av., Benone ☎ (028) 7775 0555.

7 Connell St. ☎ (028) 7776 0307 (April-December).

Belfast 62 – Ballymena 39 – Coleraine 13 – Londonderry 17 – Omagh 50.

Radisson Roe Park H. & Golf Resort, Roe Park, BT49 9LB, West : ½ m. on A ☎ (028) 7772 2222, *reservations@radissonroepark.com, Fax (028) 7772 2313*, 18 – TV P – 440. MC AE VISA.
The Courtyard : **Meals** *(closed Sunday and Monday)* (dinner only and Sunday lunc a la carte 20.40/31.50 **st.** 7.95 – ***The Coach House :*** **Meals** a la carte 13.00/19.00 s 7.95 – **63 rm** 90.00/130.00 **t.**, 1 suite – SB.

Lime Tree, 60 Catherine St., BT49 9DB, ☎ (028) 7776 4300 – MC AE VISA
closed 1 week February, March, 1 week July, 1 week November, Monday and Tuesday exce December – **Meals** a la carte 16.50/25.20 **t.** 5.50.

The Guide is updated annually so renew your Guide every year.

LONDONDERRY (Doire) *Londonderry* 923 K 2/3 *Ireland G. – pop. 72 334.*

See : *Town★ – City Walls and Gates★★ – Long Tower Church★ – Tower Museum★.*

Env. : *Grianan of Aileach★★ (⩽★★) (Republic of Ireland) NW : 5 m. by A 2 and N 13.*

Exc. : *SE : by A 6 – Sperrin Mountains★ : Ulster-American Folk Park★★ – Glenshane Pass (★★) – Sawel Mountain Drive★ (⩽★★) – Roe Valley Country Park★ – Beaghmore Stor Circles★ – Ulster History Park★ – Oak Lough Scenic Road★.*

18, 9 City of Derry, 49 Victoria Rd ☎ (028) 7131 1610.

Eglinton Airport : ☎ (028) 7181 0784, E : 6 m. by A 2.

44 Foyle St. ☎ (028) 7126 7284 (April-December).

Belfast 70 – Dublin 146.

Everglades, Prehen Rd, BT47 2NH, South : 1 ½ m. on A 5 ☎ (028) 7134 6722, *res.egh@stingshotels.com, Fax (028) 7134 9200* – rest, TV P – 400. MC AE VISA.
closed 25 December – ***The Satchmo :*** **Meals** (bar lunch)/dinner 15.95 **t.** – **64 rm** 95.0 200.00 **st.**

Waterfoot H. & Country Club, 14 Clooney Rd, Caw Roundabout, BT47 6TB, Northeas 3 ¾ m. at junction of A 39 with A 5 and A 2 ☎ (028) 7134 5500, *Fax (028) 7131 1006*, – TV P – 100. MC AE VISA.
closed 25 and 26 December – **Meals** a la carte 15.65/21.35 **st.** 4.95 – 6.00 – **48 r** 65.00/75.00 **st.**

Trinity, 22-24 Strand Rd, BT48 7AB, ☎ (028) 7127 1271, *info@thetrinityhotel.co Fax (028) 7127 1277* – rest, TV P – 150. MC AE VISA.
closed 24-25 December – **Meals** (dinner only) 15.50 **st.** and a la carte 6.50 – **37 r** 75.00/90.00 **st.**, 3 suites – SB.

Beech Hill House, 32 Ardmore Rd, BT47 3QP, Southeast : 3 ½ m. by A ☎ (028) 7134 9279, *info@beech-hill.com, Fax (028) 7134 5366*, « 18C merchant's house – rest, TV P – 100. MC AE VISA.
closed 24-25 December – **Meals** 17.95/27.95 **t.** and a la carte 6.95 – **23 rm** 75.0 115.00 **t.**, 4 suites – SB.

White Horse, 68 Clooney Rd, BT47 3PA, Northeast : 6 ½ m. on A 2 (Coleraine r ☎ (028) 7186 0606, *info@white_horse.demon.co.uk, Fax (028) 7186 0371* – TV P – 50 MC AE VISA.
closed 25 December – **Meals** (grill rest.) (dinner only) 7.95/15.00 **t.** and a la carte – **43 r** 75.00/110.00 **t.** – SB.

AGHERA (Machaire Rátha) *Londonderry* 923 L 3.

Belfast 40 – Ballymena 19 – Coleraine 21 – Londonderry 32.

Ardtara Country House , 8 Gorteade Rd, Upperlands, BT46 5SA, North : 3 ¼ m. by A 29 off B 75 ℘ (028) 7964 4490, *Fax (028) 7964 5080*, ≤, « 19C », , – rest, TV P. MC AE VISA.
closed 25 and 26 December – **Meals** (booking essential) 14.50/23.50 **t.** and dinner a la carte 5.50 – **8 rm** 80.00/150.00 **st.** – SB.

ARTINSTOWN (Baile Uí Mháirtán) *Antrim* 923 N 3 – ✉ *Ballymena.*

Belfast 36 – Dundalk 86 – Larne 28 – Londonderry 58 – Omagh 61.

Caireal Manor without rest., 90 Glenravel Rd, Glen's of Antrim, BT43 6QQ, ℘ (028) 2175 8465, *info@cairealmanor.co.uk, Fax (028) 2175 8465* – TV P. MC VISA.
4 rm 25.00/50.00 **st.**

EWCASTLE (An Caisleán Nua) *Down* 923 O 5 *Ireland G.* – *pop. 7 214.*

Env. : *Castlewellan Forest Park★★ AC, NW : 4 m. by A 50 – Dundrum Castle★ AC, NE : 4 m. by A 2 – Downpatrick (Down Cathedral★ – Down County Museum★), NE : by A 2.*

Exc. : *SW : Mourne Mountains★★ : Bryansford, Tollymore Forest Park★ AC – Silent Valley Reservoir★ (≤★) – Spelga Pass and Dam★ – Kilbroney Forest Park (viewpoint★) – Struell Wells★, NE : 12 m. by A 2 – Ardglass★, NE : 18 m. by A 2.*

The Newcastle Centre, 10-14 Promenade ℘ (028) 4372 2222.

Belfast 32 – Londonderry 101.

Burrendale H. & Country Club, 51 Castlewellan Rd, BT33 0JY, North : 1 m. on A 50 ℘ (028) 4372 2599, *reservations@burrendale.com, Fax (028) 4372 2328*, , , , – , rest, TV P. – 150. MC AE VISA.
Meals 10.00/25.00 **st.** and a la carte 6.50 – **67 rm** 65.00/99.00 **st.**, 1 suite – SB.

Briers , 39 Middle Tollymore Rd, BT33 0JJ, North : 1 ½ m. by Bryansford Rd (B 180) and Tollymore Rd ℘ (028) 4372 4347, *michelle-bowater@thebriers.fsnet.co.uk, Fax (028) 4372 6633*, ≤, – TV P. MC AE VISA.
Meals ala carte 12.00/22.00 **st.** 5.00 – **9 rm** 40.00/60.00 **st.** – SB.

EWRY (An Iúr) *Down* 923 M 5 *Ireland G.* – *pop. 21 633.*

See : *Bernish Rock Viewpoint★★.*

Town Hall, Bank Par. ℘ (028) 3026 8877.

Belfast 37 – Dundalk 16.

Mourne Country, 52 Belfast Rd, BT34 1TR, North : 1 ¼ m. ℘ (028) 3026 7922, *Fax (028) 3026 0896* – TV P. – 400. MC AE VISA.
closed 25 December – **Meals** *(closed Saturday lunch and Sunday)* (bar lunch Monday to Saturday)/dinner 14.95 **t.** 5.00 – **41 rm** 49.50/70.00 **t.**, 2 suites – SB.

ORTAFERRY (Port an Pheire) *Down* 923 P 4 *Ireland G.* – *pop. 2 324.*

See : *Aquarium★.*

Env. : *Castle Ward★★ AC, SW : 4 m. by boat and A 25.*

Exc. : *SE : Lecale Peninsula★★ – Struell Wells★, Quoile Pondage★, Ardglass★, Strangford★, Audley's Castle★.*

Castle St. ℘ (028) 4272 9882 (Easter-September).

Belfast 29 – Bangor 24.

Portaferry, 10 The Strand, BT22 1PE, ℘ (028) 4272 8231, *info@portaferryhotel.com, Fax (028) 4272 8999*, ≤, « Part 18C, loughside setting » – TV. MC AE VISA.
closed 24-25 December – **Meals** (bar lunch Monday to Saturday)/dinner a la carte 20.00/26.45 **t.** 7.50 – **11 rm** 60.00/95.00 **t.** – SB.

The Narrows, 8 Shore Rd, BT22 1JY, ℘ (028) 4272 8148, *reservations@narrows.co.uk, Fax (028) 4272 8105*, ≤, « Loughside setting », , – TV P. – 50. MC AE VISA.
Meals – (see ***The Restaurant*** below) – **13 rm** 42.50/85.00 **t.** – SB.

The Restaurant (at The Narrows H.), 8 Shore Rd, BT22 1JY, ℘ (028) 4272 8148, *Fax (028) 4272 8105* – P. MC AE VISA
Meals - Seafood specialities - a la carte 18.85/32.85 **t.** 6.50.

Les prix — Pour toutes précisions sur les prix indiqués dans ce guide, reportez-vous aux pages de l'introduction.

PORTRUSH (Port Rois) *Antrim* 923 L 2 *Ireland G. – pop. 5 703.*

Exc. : *Causeway Coast*★★ : *Giant's Causeway*★★★ *(Hamilton's Seat ≤★★) – Carrick-a-re Rope Bridge*★★ *– Dunluce Castle*★★ *AC – Dunseverick Castle (≤★★) – Gortmore Viewpoi – Magilligan Strand*★ *– Downhill*★ *(Mussenden Temple*★*).*

18, 18, 9 *Royal Portrush, Dunluce Rd ℘ (028) 7082 2311.*

Sandhill Dr. ℘ (028) 7082 3333 (April-October).

Belfast 58 – Coleraine 4 – Londonderry 35.

Magherabuoy House, 41 Magheraboy Rd, BT56 8NX, Southwest : 1 m. by A ℘ (028) 7082 3507, *admin@magherabuoy.co.uk, Fax (028) 7082 4687,* ≤, – rest, P – 60. VISA JCB.
closed Christmas – **Meals** (bar lunch)/dinner 12.00/15.00 **st.** and a la carte – **40** 60.00/100.00 **st.** – SB.

Ramore, The Harbour, BT56 8BN, ℘ (028) 7082 4313, *Fax (028) 7082 3194* – P.
closed 1 January, 24-26 December, Sunday and Monday – **Meals** (booking essential) (din only) a la carte 7.85/26.80 **t.** 5.50 – (see also ***Ramore Wine Bar*** and ***The Harbour*** below).

Ramore Wine Bar, The Harbour, BT56 8BN, ℘ (028) 7082 4313, *Fax (028) 7082 319* VISA
closed 25 December and January – **Meals** a la carte 8.95/19.40 **t.** 5.50.

The Harbour Bar, The Harbour, BT56 8BN, ℘ (028) 7082 2430 – P
closed Monday – **Meals** a la carte 9.40/19.40 **t.** 5.50.

SEAFORDE (Baile Forda) *Down* 923 O 5 *– pop. 186 – ✉ Downpatrick.*

Belfast 25 – Dundalk 45 – Dungannon 53.

Drumgooland House without rest., 29 Dunnanew Rd, BT30 8PJ, North : 2 m. b 24 ℘ (028) 4481 1956, *frank.mc_leigh@virgin.net, Fax (028) 4481 1265,* ≤, –
P. VISA
3 rm 29.50/49.00 **st.**

STRABANE (An Srath Bán) *Tyrone* 923 J 3 *Ireland G. – pop. 11 981.*

Exc. : *Sperrin Mountains*★ : *Ulster-American Folk Park*★★ *– Glenshane Pass*★ *(★★) – Sa Mountain Drive*★ *(≤★★) – Roe Valley Country Park*★ *– E : Beaghmore Stone Circles*★ *– Uls History Park*★ *– Oak Lough Scenic Road*★.

18 *Ballycolman ℘ (028) 7138 2271.*

Abercorn Sq. ℘ (028) 7188 3735 (April-October).

Belfast 87 – Donegal 34 – Dundalk 98 – Londonderry 14.

Fir Trees, Melmount Rd, BT82 9JT, South : 1 ¼ m. on A 5 ℘ (028) 7138 23 *Fax (028) 7138 3116* – TV P – 150. VISA.
Meals 9.95/12.95 **t.** and a la carte 6.95 – **24 rm** 39.00/60.00 **st.** – SB.

TEMPLEPATRICK (Teampall Phádraig) *Antrim* 923 N 3 *– pop. 1 414 – ✉ Ballyclare.*

Belfast 13 – Ballymena 16 – Dundalk 65 – Larne 16.

Hilton Templepatrick, Castle Upton Estate, BT39 0DD, North : 1 m. on B 95 (Parkg rd) ℘ (028) 9443 5500, *Fax (028) 9443 5511,* 18, – rm, rest, P – 500. VISA
Meals *(closed Saturday lunch)* 11.50/20.50 **st.** and dinner a la carte – 11.50 – **130** 140.00/200.00 **st.** – SB.

Templeton, 882 Antrim Rd, BT39 0AH, ℘ (028) 9443 2984, *Fax (028) 9443 3406,* – P – 300. VISA.
closed 25 and 26 December – ***Templeton :*** **Meals** *(closed Monday and Tuesday)* (din only and Sunday lunch)/dinner 21.50 **t.** 6.95 – ***Upton Grill :*** **Meals** (grill rest.) a la carte prox. 18.20 **st.** – **24 rm** 90.00/130.00 **t.** – SB.

Republic of Ireland

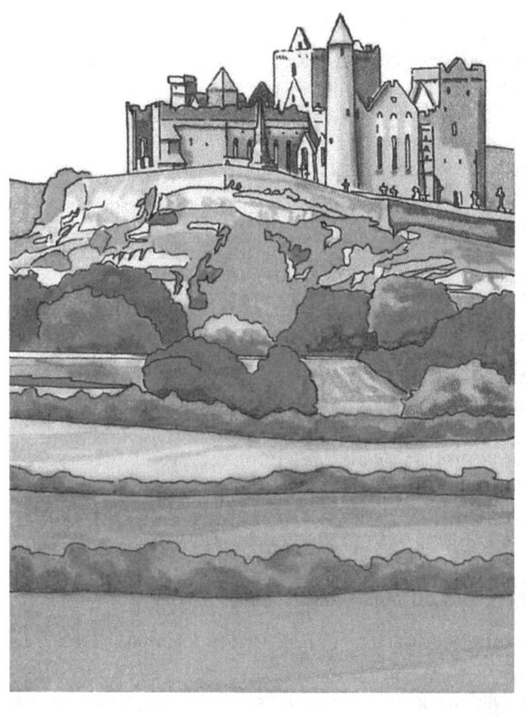

- *Prices quoted in this section of the guide are in Irish pounds (punt)*
- *Dans cette partie du guide, les prix sont indiqués en monnaie irlandai «Punt»*
- *In questa parte della guida, i prezzi sono indicati in livres irlandesi «Pun*
- *In diesem Teil des Führers sind die Preise in irländischer Währung «Pun angegeben*

ABBEYLEIX **(Mainistir Laoise)** *Laois* 923 J 9 – *pop. 1 299.*

Abbeyleix, Rathmoyle ☎ (0502) 31450.

Dublin 60 – Kilkenny 22 – Limerick 67.

Abbeyleix Manor,, Southwest : ½ m. on N 8 ☎ (0502) 30111, *info@abbeyleixmanorh el.com, Fax (0502) 30220* – 450.
*closed 25 December***Meals** (carving lunch Monday-Friday) (bar lunch Saturday) a la car 13.15/25.25 **st.** 5.00 – **23 rm** 55.00/75.00 **st.** – SB.

Preston House, Main St., ☎ (0502) 31432, *Fax (0502) 31662,* « Georgian former scho house »,
closed 10 days Christmas – ***Preston House Café :*** **Meals** (by arrangement) a la car 15.00/23.50 **t.** 6.00 – **4 rm** 30.00/52.00 **t.**

ACHILL ISLAND **(Acaill)** *Mayo* 923 B 5/6 *Ireland G.*

See : *Island*★.

Achill Island, Keel ☎ (098) 43456.

Achill ☎ (098) 45384 (June-August).

Doogort **(Dumha Goirt)** – ✉ *Achill Island.*

Gray's, ☎ (098) 43244, – rest,
closed December – **Meals** (by arrangement) 17.50 **t.** – **15 rm** 30.00/60.00 **st.**

Keel **(An Caol)** – ✉ *Achill Island.*

Achill Cliff House, ☎ (098) 43400, *achillcliffe@anu.ie, Fax (098) 43007,* – r
closed 23-26 December – **Meals** 8.95/21.00 **t.** and a la carte 8.00 – **10 rm** 50.C 100.00 **t.** – SB.

ADARE **(Áth Dara)** *Limerick* 923 F 10 *Ireland G.* – *pop. 1 042.*

See : *Town*★ – *Adare Friary*★ – *Adare Parish Church*★.

Exc. : *Rathkeale (Castle Matrix*★ *AC – Irish Palatine Heritage Centre*★*) W : 7½ m. by N 2 Newcastle West*★, *W : 16 m. by N 21 – Glin Castle*★ *AC, W : 29 m. by N 21, R 518 and N 6*

Heritage Centre ☎ (061) 396255 (May-December).

Dublin 131 – Killarney 59 – Limerick 10.

Adare Manor, ☎ (061) 396566, *reservations@adaremanor.com, Fax (061) 396124,* « 19C Gothic mansion on banks of River Maigue in extensive parkland », – rest, – 180.
Meals 18.00/34.50 **t.** and a la carte – **138 rm** 250.00/500.00 **st.** – SB.

Dunraven Arms, Main St., ☎ (061) 396633, *dunraven@iol.ie, Fax (061) 396541,* – 180.
The Inn Between : **Meals** *(closed October-April, Tuesday and Wednesday)* (dinner or a la carte 15.00/30.00 **st.** 5.50 – (see also ***Maigue*** below) – 12.20 – **74 rm** 110.C 200.00 **t.** – SB.

Carrabawn Guesthouse without rest., Killarney Rd, Southwest : ½ m. on N ☎ (061) 396067, *carrabawn@indigo.ie, Fax (061) 396925,* –
closed 23 December-30 January – **8 rm** 45.00/60.00.

Berkeley Lodge without rest., Station Rd, ☎ (061) 396857, *berlodge@iol. Fax (061) 396857* –
6 rm 40.00/50.00 **st.**

The Wild Geese, Rose Cottage, ☎ (061) 396451, *wildgeese@indigo.ie, Fax (061) 3964* –
closed 3 weeks January, Sunday and Monday – **Meals** (light lunch April-October) 24.50 (dinner) and a la carte 30.90/36.95 **t.** 7.50.

Maigue (at Dunraven Arms H.), Main St., ☎ (061) 396633, *Fax (061) 396541,* –
Meals (dinner only) 26.00/35.00 **t.** 11.50.

LISH (An Eaglais) *Tipperary* 923 H 8 – ✉ *Borrisokane.*
Dublin 114 – Galway 53 – Limerick 43.

Ballycormac House ⛰, ✆ (067) 21129, *ballyc@indigo.ie, Fax (067) 21200,* – P. VISA.
Meals (by arrangement) (communal dining) 25.00 **t.** 5.00 – **5 rm** 25.00/70.00 **t.**, 1 suite.

AKISTA (Áth an Chiste) *Cork* 923 D 13 – ✉ *Bantry.*
Dublin 217 – Cork 63 – Killarney 59.

Shiro (Kei Pilz), ✆ (027) 67030, *pilzw@gofree.indigo.ie, Fax (027) 67206,* ≤ Dunmanus Bay, – P. AE VISA JCB
closed 25 December and New Year – **Meals** - Japanese - (booking essential) (dinner only) 46.00 **t.**
Spec. Sashimi. Tempura. Sushi.

ERLOW (Eatharlach) *Tipperary* 923 H 10 – *see Glen of Aherlow.*

AN ISLANDS (Oileáin Árann) *Galway* 923 CD 8 *Ireland G.*
See : *Islands★ – Inishmore (Dun Aenghus★★★).*
Access by boat or aeroplane from Galway city or by boat from Kilkieran, Rossaveel or Fisherstreet (Clare) and by aeroplane from Inverin.
Aran Kilranan ✆ (099) 61263.

ishmore – ✉ *Aran Islands.*

Pier House ⛰ without rest., Kilronan, ✆ (099) 61417, *pier@iol.ie, Fax (099) 61122,* ≤, – TV P. VISA
March-October – **12 rm** 40.00/60.00.

Ard Einne ⛰, Killeany, ✆ (099) 61126, *ardeinne@tinet.ie, Fax (099) 61388,* ≤ Killeany Bay – P. VISA.
February-10 December – **Meals** (by arrangement) 14.00 **t.** 6.00 – **15 rm** 38.00/46.00 **t.** – SB.

Kilmurvey House ⛰, Kilmurvey, ✆ (099) 61218, *kilmurveyhouse@eircom.net, Fax (099) 61397,* ≤, – rest. VISA.
March-October – **Meals** (by arrangement) 16.00 **st.** 12.00 – **12 rm** 32.00/50.00 **st.**

DEE (Baile Átha Fhirdhia) *Louth* 923 M 6 *Ireland G.* – *pop. 3 440.*
Exc. : *Dún a' Rá Forest Park★, SW : by N 52 and northwest by R 165.*
Ardee ✆ (041) 685 3227.
Dublin 44 – Drogheda 15 – Dundalk 13.

Red House ⛰,, Northeast : ¾ m. on N 52 ✆ (041) 6853523, *redhouse@eircom.net, Fax (041) 6853523,* ≤, « Georgian house », – rm, P. AE VISA.
closed mid December-mid January – **Meals** (by arrangement) (communal dining) 25.00 **st.** 10.00 – **3 rm** 55.00/90.00 **st.**

THURSTOWN (Colmán) *Wexford* 923 L 11.
Dublin 103 – Cork 99 – Limerick 101 – Waterford 26.

Dunbrody Country House ⛰, ✆ (051) 389600, *dunbrody@indigo.ie, Fax (051) 389601,* ≤, « Part Georgian former hunting lodge », – TV P.
AE VISA JCB
closed 23 December-January – **Meals** (booking essential to non-residents) (Sunday dinner residents only) (bar lunch Monday to Saturday)/dinner 30.00 **t.** and a la carte 27.00/38.50 **t.** 6.80 – **16 rm** 95.00/164.00 **t.**, 4 suites – SB.

HTOWN *Dublin* 923 ㊱ – *see Dublin.*

HBOY *Meath* 923 L 7 – *pop. 1 172.*
Dublin 42 – Drogheda 28 – Tullamore 44.

Woodtown House ⛰,, Southwest : 5 ½ m. by N 51, following obvious signage ✆ (046) 35022, *woodtown@iol.ie, Fax (046) 35022,* ≤, « Georgian country house », – P. VISA.
April-September – **Meals** (by arrangement) 12.50 **st.** – **3 rm** 25.00/30.00 **st.**

ATHLONE (Baile Átha Luain) *Westmeath* 923 I 7 *Ireland G. – pop. 7 691.*

Exc. : *Clonmacnois*** (Grave Slabs*, Cross of the Scriptures*) S : 13 m. by N 6 and N 6 N : Lough Ree (Ballykeeran Viewpoint*, Glassan*).*

Hodson Bay ☎ (0902) 92073.

Athlone ☎ (0902) 94630 (June-December).

Dublin 75 – Galway 57 – Limerick 75 – Roscommon 20 – Tullamore 24.

Hodson Bay,, Northwest : 4 ¾ m. by N 61 ☎ (0902) 92444, *info@hodsonbayhotel.cc Fax (0902) 80520*, ≤, « Loughside setting », – 750. MC AE VISA.
L'Escale : **Meals** 12.00/25.00 **st.** and dinner a la carte 7.00 – 13.00 – **95 rm** 98.(122.00 **st.**, 2 suites – SB.

Creggan Court, N6 Centre, Dublin Rd, Southeast : 2 ½ m. by R 446 at junction with ☎ (0902) 77777, *info@creggancourt.com, Fax (0902) 77111* – rm, 30. MC AE VISA.
closed 25 December – **Meals** (bar lunch) 12.00/20.00 **st.** and a la carte 6.95 – **73** 45.00/100.00 **st.** – SB.

Castledaly Manor, Castledaly, Southeast : 7 m. by N 6 ☎ (0902) 81221, *castledaly ircom.net, Fax (0902) 81600*, ≤, « Part 17C country mansion », – rest, MC AE VISA.
closed 25 December – **Meals** *(closed Monday-Wednesday and Sunday lunch)* a la carte prox. 18.95 **t.** – **10 rm** 69.50/89.50 **t.**

Riverview House without rest., Summerhill, Galway Rd, West : 3 m. on ☎ (0902) 94532, *riverviewhouse@hotmail.com, Fax (0902) 94532*, – rest, AE VISA.
closed 15 December-1 March – **5 rm** 25.00/40.00.

Shelmalier House without rest., Retreat Rd, Cartrontroy, East : 1 ½ m. by Dublin rd 6) ☎ (0902) 72245, *shelmal@iol.ie, Fax (0902) 73190*, – MC VISA.
closed 20 December-1 February – **7 rm** 25.00/38.00 **st.**

The Mill without rest., Tuam Rd, Northwest : 3 ½ m. on R 362 ☎ (0902) 92927, *osheam ol.ie* – MC VISA.
closed 23 December-8 January – **7 rm** 25.00/40.00 **st.** – SB.

at Glassan *Northeast : 5 m. on N 55 – ✉ Athlone.*

Wineport,, Southwest : 1 m. ☎ (0902) 85466, *restaurant@wineport.ie, Fax (0902) 854* « Loughside setting ≤ Lough Ree » – MC AE VISA JCB
closed 24-26 December, 1 January, Good Friday and Monday-Tuesday November-Easte **Meals** (dinner only and Sunday lunch November-Easter)/dinner a la carte 20.00/33.50 10.00.

Glasson Village, ☎ (0902) 85001 – MC AE VISA
closed 3 weeks mid October-November, 24-26 December, Sunday and Monday – **Me** (dinner only and Sunday lunch)/dinner 22.00 **t.** and a la carte 7.00.

ATHY (Baile Átha Á) *Kildare* 923 L 9 *Ireland G. – pop. 5 306.*

Exc. : *Emo Court**, N : 20 m. by R 417 (L 18), west by N 7 (T 5) and north by R 42 Stradbally*, NW : 9 m. by R 428 (L 109) – Castledermot High Crosses*, SE : 9½ m. by R 41 Moone High Cross*, E : 12 m. by Ballitore minor rd and south by N 9 – Rock of Dunamas (≤*), NW : 12 m. by R 428 (L 109) and N 80 (T 16) – Timahoe Round Tower*, W : 10 m. b 428 (L 109) and N 80 (T 16).*

Athy, Geraldine ☎ (0507) 31729.

Dublin 40 – Kilkenny 29 – Wexford 59.

Tonlegee House with rm,, Southwest : 1 ½ m. by N 78 ☎ (0507) 31473, *tonlegee use@tinet.ie, Fax (0507) 31473*, ≤, – MC AE VISA.
closed first 2 weeks November and 2 weeks Christmas – **Meals** *(closed Sunday and Mon to non-residents)* (dinner only) a la carte 23.50/28.00 **st.** 7.00 – **12 rm** 55.00/95.00 **s** SB.

JGHRIM (Eachroim) *Wicklow* 923 N 9 – *pop. 745.*

The Battle of Aughrim Visitors Centre, Ballinasloe ☎ (0905) 73939 (10 April-September).
Dublin 46 – Waterford 77 – Wexford 60.

Brook Lodge ⑤, Macreddin Village, North : 2 m. ☎ (0402) 36444, *brooklodge@macreddin.ie, Fax (0402) 36580,* ⑤, ⑤, ⑤ – |⑤| ⑤ ⑤ ⑤ – ⑤ 220. ⑤ ⑤ ⑤ ⑤. ⑤
Meals – (see ***Strawberry Tree*** below) – **39 rm** ⑤ 100.00/170.00 **t.**, 1 suite – SB.

Lawless's, ☎ (0402) 36146, *lawhotel@iol.ie, Fax (0402) 36384,* ⑤ – ⑤ rm, ⑤ ⑤ – ⑤ 150. ⑤ ⑤ ⑤. ⑤
closed 24-25 December – **Meals** (bar lunch Monday to Saturday)/dinner a la carte 11.40/27.20 **st.** ⑤ 6.25 – **14 rm** ⑤ 65.00/94.00 **st.** – SB.

Strawberry Tree (at Brook Lodge), Macreddin Village, North : 2 m. ☎ (0402) 36444, *Fax (0402) 36580,* ⑤ – ⑤ rest, ⑤. ⑤ ⑤ ⑤ ⑤
Meals - Organic - (dinner only and Sunday lunch)/dinner 33.00 **t.** ⑤ 10.50.

'OCA (Abhóca) *Wicklow* 923 N 9 *Ireland G.* – *pop. 490.*

Exc. : *Meeting of the Waters*★, *N : by R 752 – Avondale*★, *N : by R 752.*
Dublin 47 – Waterford 72 – Wexford 55.

Keppel's Farmhouse ⑤ without rest., Ballanagh, South : 2 m. by unmarked rd ☎ (0402) 35168, *Fax (0402) 35168,* ⑤, « Working farm », ⑤, ⑤ – ⑤ ⑤. ⑤ ⑤. ⑤
April-October – **5 rm** ⑤ 35.00/50.00 **st.**

AGENALSTOWN (Muine Bheag) *Carlow* 923 L 9 – *pop. 2 553.*

Dublin 63 – Carlow 10 – Kilkenny 13 – Wexford 37.

Kilgraney Country House ⑤,, South : 4 m. by R 705 (Borris Rd) ☎ (0503) 75283, *kilgraney@indigo.ie, Fax (0503) 75595,* ⑤, « Late Georgian house with collection of Far Eastern furnishings and artefacts », ⑤ – ⑤ rm, ⑤. ⑤ ⑤ ⑤. ⑤
closed November-March and Sunday-Thursday except July-August – **Meals** (booking essential) (residents only) (communal dining) (dinner only) 28.00 **st.** ⑤ 7.50 – **6 rm** ⑤ 50.00/110.00 **st.** – SB.

ALLINA (Béal an Átha) *Mayo* 923 E 5 *Ireland G.* – *pop. 6 852.*

Env. : *Mayo*★ – *Rosserk Abbey*★, *N : 4 m. by R 314.*
Exc. : *Moyne Abbey*★, *N : 7 m. by R 314 – Pontoon Bridge View* (⑤★), *S : 12 m. by N 26 and R 310 – Downpatrick Head*★, *N : 20 m. by R 314.*
⑤ *Mossgrove, Shanaghy ☎ (096) 21050.*
⑤ *Cathedral Rd ☎ (096) 70848 (April-September).*
Dublin 150 – Galway 73 – Roscommon 64 – Sligo 37.

Ridgepool, Barratt St., ☎ (096) 24600, *ridgepool@eircom.net, Fax (096) 24602,* « Riverside setting », ⑤, ⑤, ⑤ – |⑤|, ⑤ rm, ⑤ rest, ⑤ ⑤ ⑤ ⑤ ⑤ – ⑤ 300. ⑤ ⑤ ⑤ ⑤. ⑤
Meals 20.00/25.50 **st.** (dinner) and a la carte 11.80/22.00 **st.** ⑤ 8.25 – **71 rm** ⑤ 95.00/125.00 **st.**, 4 suites – SB.

Downhill Inn, Sligo Rd, East : 1 m. off N 59 ☎ (096) 73444, *thedownhillinn@eircom.net, Fax (096) 73411* – ⑤ ⑤ ⑤. ⑤ ⑤ ⑤. ⑤
closed 21 December-1 January – **Meals** a la carte 9.95/21.50 **st.** ⑤ 6.50 – ⑤ 6.00 – **45 rm** 45.00/60.00 **st.** – SB.

ALLINADEE (Baile na Daidhche) *Cork* 923 G 12 – *see Kinsale.*

ALLINASCARTY (Béal na Scairte) *Cork* 923 F 12 – *see Clonakilty.*

ALLINASLOE (Béal Átha na Sluaighe) *Galway* 923 H 8 *Ireland G.* – *pop. 5 634.*

Env. : *Clonfert Cathedral*★ *(west doorway*★★*), SW : by R 355 and minor roads.*
Exc. : *Turoe Stone, Bullaun*★, *SW : 18 m. by R 348 and R 350 – Loughrea (St. Brendan's Cathedral*★*), SW : 18 m. by N 6.*
⑤ *Rossgloss ☎ (0905) 42126* – ⑤ *Mountbellew ☎ (0905) 79259.*
⑤ *Kellar Travel ☎ (0905) 42131 (July-August).*
Dublin 91 – Galway 41 – Limerick 66 – Roscommon 36 – Tullamore 34.

Hayden's Gateway, Dunlo St., ☎ (065) 682300, *cro@lynchotels.com, Fax (065) 6823759,* ⑤ – |⑤|, ⑤ rest, ⑤ ⑤ – ⑤ 250. ⑤ ⑤ ⑤ ⑤. ⑤
Meals (bar lunch in winter) 8.00/18.00 **st.** and a la carte ⑤ 5.00 – ⑤ 4.70 – **48 rm** 50.00/155.00 **st.** – SB.

REPUBLIC OF IRELAND

BALLINGARRY (Baile an GharraÁ) *Limerick* 923 F 10 *Ireland G. – pop. 389.*

Exc. : *Kilmallock★ (Kilmallock Abbey★, Collegiate Church★), SE : 15 m. by R 518 – Monasteranenagh Abbey★, NE : 15 m. – Lough Gur Interpretive Centre★, NE : 24 m.*

Dublin 141 – Killarney 56 – Limerick 18.

Mustard Seed at Echo Lodge, ℘ (069) 68508, *Fax (069) 68511*, – – 25. *closed 24-26 December and February* – **Meals** *(closed Sunday and Monday in low season)* (booking essential to non-residents) (dinner only) 33.00 **t.** 8.00 – **11 rm** 80.00/200.00 **t.**, 1 suite – SB.

BALLON (Balana) *Carlow* 923 L 9.

Dublin 65 – Kilkenny 36 – Wexford 35.

Ballykealey House, Northwest : ½ m. on N 80 ℘ (0503) 59288, *bh@iol.ie*, *Fax (0503) 59297*, – *April-16 December* – **Meals** *(closed Sunday and Monday)* (booking essential to non-residents) (dinner only) 25.00/32.50 **t.** and a la carte 6.00 – **12 rm** 55.00/145.00 **t.** – SB.

BALLSBRIDGE (Droichead na Dothra) *Dublin* 923 ⑩ – *see Dublin.*

BALLYBOFEY (Bealach Féich) *Donegal* 923 I 3 – *pop. 3 047 (inc. Stranorlar).*

Ballybofey & Stranorlar, The Glebe ℘ (074) 31093.

Dublin 148 – Londonderry 30 – Sligo 58.

Kee's, Main St., Stranorlar, Northeast : ½ m. on N 15 ℘ (074) 31018, *info@keeshotel...*, *Fax (074) 31917*, – *Looking Glass :* **Meals** (dinner only and Sunday lunch)/dinner 25.00/27.00 **t.** and a la carte 8.50 – *Old Gallery :* **Meals** *(closed 25 December)* a la carte 12.00/20.35 **t.** 8.50 – **53 rm** 53.00/120.00 **t.** – SB.

Jackson's, ℘ (074) 31021, *bjackson@iol.ie, Fax (074) 31096*, – rest, **Meals** (carvery lunch)/dinner 20.00 and a la carte 6.50 – **88 rm** 60.00/94.00 – SB.

BALLYBUNNION (Baile an Bhuinneánaigh) *Kerry* 923 D 10 *Ireland G. – pop. 1 470.*

Exc. : *Carrigafoyle Castle★, NE : 13 m. by R 551 – Glin Castle★* AC, *E : 19 m. by R 551 and N 69.*

Ballybunnion, Sandhill Rd ℘ (068) 27146.

Dublin 176 – Limerick 56 – Tralee 26.

Harty Costello Townhouse, Main St., ℘ (068) 27129, *hartycostello@eircom.net*, *Fax (068) 27489* – rm, *6 April-October* – **Meals** *(closed Sunday)* (dinner only) 15.95/25.00 **s.** and a la carte 7.00 – **8 rm** 40.00/90.00 **st.** – SB.

The Southern, Sandhill Rd, ℘ (068) 27022, *southotel@eircom.net, Fax (068) 27085*, *March-October* – **Meals** 9.95/25.00 and dinner a la carte – **16 rm** 45.00/70.00 **s.** – SB.

Teach de Broc Country House without rest., Link Rd, South : 1 ½ m. by Golf Club ℘ (068) 27581, *teachdebroc@tinet.ie, Fax (068) 27919* – **10 rm** 60.00/90.00 **t.**

BALLYCONNEELY (Baile Conaola) *Galway* 923 B 7 *Ireland G. – ✉ Clifden.*

Exc. : *Connemara★★★ – Sky Road★★ (≤★★), N : by R 341.*

Dublin 189 – Galway 54.

Erriseask House (Matz) (may move during 2001) with rm, ℘ (095) 23553, *erriseask@connemara_ireland.com, Fax (095) 23639*, ≤ Mannin Bay and Twelve Bens, – rest, *Easter-September* – **Meals** *(closed Wednesday to non-residents except July-August)* (booking essential) (dinner only) 27.50 **t.** and a la carte 25.30/36.30 **t.** 7.50 – **12 rm** 55.00/100.00 **t.** – SB

Spec. Broth of tomato and prawn. Suprême of Connemara lamb, rosemary jus. Lemon and ginger soufflé, vanilla ice cream.

Les prix — Pour toutes précisions sur les prix indiqués dans ce guide, reportez-vous aux pages de l'introduction.

ALLYCONNELL (Béal Atha Conaill) *Cavan* 923 J 5 – *pop. 433.*

Slieve Russell ℘ (049) 952 6444.

Dublin 89 – Drogheda 76 – Enniskillen 23.

Slieve Russell,, Southeast : 1 ¾ m. on R 200 ℘ (049) 952 6444, *slieverussell@quinn-hotels.com, Fax (049) 922 6474,* ≤, squash – rest, – 800. VISA.
Conall Cearnach : Meals (dinner only) 28.00 **st.** 6.00 – ***Brackley :*** Meals (carving lunch) 12.50 **st.** and dinner a la carte 14.40/23.95 **st.** 6.00 – **151 rm** 95.00/220.00 **st.** – SB.

ALLYCOTTON (Baile Choitán) *Cork* 923 H 12 *Ireland G.* – *pop. 477.*

Exc. : *Cloyne Cathedral★, NW : by R 629.*

Dublin 165 – Cork 27 – Waterford 66.

Bayview, ℘ (021) 4646746, *bayhotel@iol.ie, Fax (021) 4646075,* ≤ Ballycotton Bay, harbour and island, – – 25. VISA.
13 April-27 October – **Meals** (bar lunch Monday to Saturday)/dinner 30.00 **st.** 11.00 – **33 rm** 89.00/138.00 **st.**, 2 suites – SB.

Spanish Point with rm, ℘ (021) 4646177, *spanishp@indigo.ie, Fax (021) 4646179,* ≤ Ballycotton Bay and Island – rest, VISA
closed January-14 February – **Meals** - Seafood - *(closed Monday-Tuesday April and Sunday dinner-Friday November-March)* 14.95/26.50 **t.** and a la carte 7.50 – **5 rm** 35.00/60.00 **t.** – SB.

Si vous cherchez un hôtel tranquille,
consultez d'abord les cartes de l'introduction
ou repérez dans le texte les établissements indiqués avec le signe ou .

ALLYFERRITER (Baile an Fheirtéaraigh) *Kerry* 923 A 11 – ✉ *Dingle.*

Ceann Sibeal ℘ (066) 56255.

Dublin 226 – Killarney 53 – Limerick 104.

Smerwick Harbour, Gallarus Cross, East : 2 ¾ m. on R 559 ℘ (066) 9156470, *Fax (066) 9156473,* ≤ – VISA.
18 March-October – **Meals** (bar lunch)/dinner 14.00/20.00 **st.** and a la carte 6.00 – **32 rm** 50.00/100.00 **st.** – SB.

ALLYHEIGE (Baile Uí Thaidhg) *Kerry* 923 C 10 – *pop. 679.*

Dublin 186 – Limerick 73 – Tralee 11.

White Sands, Main St., ℘ (066) 7133102, *whitesands@eircom.net, Fax (066) 7133357* – VISA
5 April-9 October – **Meals** (bar lunch Monday to Saturday)/dinner a la carte 14.30/23.95 **st.** 5.90 – **81 rm** 50.00/90.00 **st.** – SB.

ALLYLICKEY (Béal Átha Leice) *Cork* 923 D 12 *Ireland G.* – ✉ *Bantry.*

Env. : *Bantry Bay★ – Bantry House★ AC, S : 3 m. by R 584.*

Exc. : *Glengarriff★ (Garinish Island★★, access by boat) NW : 8 m. by N 71 – Healy Pass★★ (≤★★) W : 23 m. by N 71, R 572 and R 574 – Slieve Miskish Mountains (≤★★) W : 29 m. by N 71 and R 572 – Lauragh (Derreen Gardens★ AC) NW : 27 ½ m. by N 71, R 572 and R 574 – Allihies (copper mines★) W : 41 ½ m. by N 71, R 572 and R 575 – Garnish Island (≤★) W : 44 m. by N 71 and R 572.*

Bantry Bay, Donemark ℘ (027) 50579.

Dublin 216 – Cork 55 – Killarney 45.

Ballylickey Manor House, ℘ (027) 50071, *ballymh@eircom.net, Fax (027) 50124,* « Extensive gardens », heated, – VISA.
April-mid October – ***Le Rendez-vous :*** **Meals** *(closed Wednesday)* (light lunch)/dinner 30.00/35.00 **t.** and a la carte 12.00 – **4 rm** 150.00 **t.**, **7 suites** 160.00/220.00 **t.** – SB.

Sea View House, ℘ (027) 50462, *seaviewhousehotel@eircom.net, Fax (027) 51555,* – VISA JCB
mid March-mid November – **Meals** (bar lunch Monday-Saturday)/dinner 25.00 **t.** – **17 rm** 65.00/110.00 **st.** – SB.

Larchwood House with rm, Pearsons Bridge, Northeast : 1 ¾ m. by R 584 ℘ (027) 66181, ≤, « Riverside gardens », – VISA.
restricted opening in winter – **Meals** *(closed Sunday)* (dinner only) 25.00/27.00 **t.** 8.00 – **4 rm** 28.00/56.00 **t.**

BALLYMACARBRY **(Baile Mhac Cairbre)** *Waterford* 923 I 11 *Ireland G.* – *pop. 381* – ✉ *Clonm*
Exc. : *W : Nier Valley Scenic Route*★★.
Dublin 118 – *Cork 49* – *Waterford 39.*

Hanora's Cottage ⑤, Nire Valley, East : 4 m. by Nire Drive rd and Nire Valley Lakes
☎ (052) 36134, *Fax (052) 36540,* – TV P. MC VISA.
Meals (by arrangement) 28.00 **t.** 10.00 – **11 rm** 45.00/130.00 **t.** – SB.

Glasha Farmhouse ⑤ without rest.,, Northwest : 2 ½ m. by R 671 ☎ (052) 36108, *g*
ha@eircom.net, Fax (052) 36108, « Working farm », – TV P. VISA.
February-October – **8 rm** 30.00/60.00 **st.**

Cnoc-na-Ri ⑤, Nire Valley, East : 3 ¾ m. on Nire Drive rd ☎ (052) 36239, *nharte@irela*
com, ←, – TV P.
closed 14 to 25 December – **Meals** (by arrangement) 20.00 **t.** – **4 rm** 26.50/42.00 **t.** –

BALLYMOTE **(Baile an Mhóta)** *Sligo* 923 G 5 – *pop. 994* – ✉ *Sligo.*
Ballymote, Ballinascarrow ☎ *(071) 83158.*
Dublin 124 – *Longford 48* – *Sligo 15.*

Mill House without rest., Keenaghan, ☎ (071) 83449, – TV P.
closed 20 December-10 January – **5 rm** 25.00/38.00.

BALLYNABOLA *Wexford* 923 L 10 – *see New Ross.*

BALLYNAHINCH **(Baile na hInse)** *Galway* 923 C 7 – ✉ *Recess.*
Exc. : *Connemara*★★★ – *Roundstone*★, *S : by R 341* – *Cashel*★, *SE : by R 341 and R 340.*
Dublin 140 – *Galway 41* – *Westport 49.*

Ballynahinch Castle ⑤, ☎ (095) 31006, *bhinch@iol.ie, Fax (095) 31085,* ← Owenm
River and woods, – TV P. MC AE ⓓ VISA.
closed February and 1 week Christmas – **Meals** (bar lunch)/dinner 27.50/30.00
and a la carte 8.50 – **37 rm** 90.00/200.00 **t.**, 3 suites – SB.

BALLYVAUGHAN **(Baile Uí Bheacháin)** *Clare* 923 E 8 *Ireland G.* – *pop. 257.*
Env. : *The Burren*★★ *(Cliffs of Moher*★★★, *Scenic Routes*★★, *Poulnabrone Dolmen*★, *Aillv*
Cave★ *AC (Waterfall*★★*), Corcomroe Abbey*★, *Kilfenora Crosses*★*).*
Dublin 149 – *Ennis 34* – *Galway 29.*

Gregans Castle ⑤,, Southwest : 3 ¾ m. on N 67 ☎ (065) 707 7005, *res@gregans*
Fax (065) 707 7111, ← countryside and Galway Bay, – P. MC AE VISA.
5 April-late October – **Meals** (bar lunch)/dinner 17.50/36.00 **st.** 9.50 – **18 rm** 126.
146.00 **st.**, 4 suites.

Hyland's, ☎ (065) 7077037, *hylands@tinet.ie, Fax (065) 7077131* – rm, TV P. MC
ⓓ VISA.
closed 25 December-early February – **Meals** (bar lunch)/dinner 20.00/25.00
and a la carte 7.00 – **30 rm** 65.00/93.00 **st.** – SB.

Rusheen Lodge without rest.,, Southwest : ¾ m. on N 67 ☎ (065) 7077092, *rusheen*
ol.ie, Fax (065) 7077152, – TV P. MC AE VISA.
March-October – **8 rm** 50.00/120.00 **st.**

Cappabhaile House without rest.,, Southwest : 1 m. on N 67 ☎ (065) 7077260, *capp*
haile@tinet.ie, Fax (065) 7077300, ←, – TV P. MC AE VISA.
10 March-October – **8 rm** 40.00/50.00 **st.**

BALTIMORE **(Dún na Séad)** *Cork* 923 D 13 *Ireland G.* – *pop. 232.*
Exc. : *Sherkin Island*★ *(by ferry).*
Dublin 214 – *Cork 59* – *Killarney 77.*

Baltimore Harbour, Lifeboat Rd, ☎ (028) 20361, *info@bhrhotel.ie, Fax (028) 204*
– TV – 130. MC AE ⓓ VISA.
closed January and February – **Meals** (bar lunch)/dinner a la carte 18.00/23.50 **t.** 9.6
58 rm 75.00/110.00 **st.**, 6 suites – SB.

Casey's of Baltimore,, East : ½ m. on R 595 ☎ (028) 20197, *caseys@eircom.r*
Fax (028) 20509, ← – rest, TV P. MC AE ⓓ VISA.
closed 19-26 February, 5-19 November and 21-27 December – **Meals** 24.00/30.00 **t.** (c
ner) and a la carte 13.50/29.00 **t.** 9.00 – **14 rm** 65.00/93.00 **t.** – SB.

Customs House, ☎ (028) 20200 –
closed November-Easter, Sunday and Monday – **Meals** - Seafood - (dinner only) 16.
23.00 **st.** 8.00.

ANDON (Droichead na Bandan) *Cork* 923 F 12 – *pop. 1 697.*

Bandon, Castlebernard ℘ (023) 41111.
Dublin 174 – Cork 19.

St. Anne's without rest., Clonakilty Rd, ℘ (023) 44239, *stannesbandon@eircom.net, Fax (023) 44239,* – TV P. MC VISA.
closed 25 December – **6 rm** 25.50/42.00 **st.**

ANSHA (An Bháinseach) *Tipperary* 923 H 10 – *pop. 288.*

Dublin 103 – Cork 55 – Limerick 30 – Waterford 48.

Bansha House, ℘ (062) 54194, *banshahouse@eircom.net, Fax (062) 54215,* , – P. MC VISA.
closed 20-28 December – **Meals** 16.50 **t.** – **8 rm** 29.00/54.00 **st.** – SB.

ANTRY (Beanntraá) *Cork* 923 D 12 *Ireland G.* – *pop. 2 936.*

See : *Bantry House★ AC (Bantry Bay★).*
Exc. : *Gougane Barra Forest Park★, NE : 15 m. by R 584.*
Old Courthouse ℘ (027) 50229 (April-October).
Dublin 210 – Cork 56 – Killarney 53.

Bantry House without rest., ℘ (027) 50047, *Fax (027) 50795,* ←, « Georgian country house, antiques, formal gardens and extensive parkland », , – P. MC AE VISA.
March-October – **8 rm** 95.00/170.00 **st.**

There is no paid advertising in this Guide.

ARNA (Bearna) *Galway* 923 E 8.

Dublin 141 – Galway 6.

Twelve Pins,, on R 336 ℘ (091) 592368, *the12pinshotel@eircom.net, Fax (091) 592485,* – rest, TV P. MC AE VISA.
closed 23-25 December – **Meals** (bar lunch Monday to Saturday)/dinner a la carte 15.20/30.80 **t.** 5.50 – **18 rm** 80.00/110.00.

ARRELLS CROSS *Cork – see Kinsale.*

EAUFORT (Lios an Phúca) *Kerry* 923 D 11 – *see Killarney.*

ELTURBET (Béal Tairbirt) *Cavan* 923 J 5 – *pop. 1 248.*

Belturbet, Erne Hill ℘ (049) 22287.
Dublin 89 – Drogheda 76 – Enniskillen 23.

International Fishing Centre,, North : 1 ½ m. ℘ (049) 9522616, *info@peche-irlande.com, Fax (049) 9522616,* « Riverside setting », , , – P. MC VISA.
March-15 November – **Meals** (dinner only) 12.00/25.00 **st.** and a la carte 8.00 – **16 rm** 30.00/50.00 **st.** – SB.

ERE ISLAND (An tOileán Mór) *Cork* 923 C 13.

errin (Raerainn) – *Bere Island.*

Lawrence Cove House, ℘ (027) 75063, *cove@indigo.ie, Fax (027) 75063,* – . MC VISA
May-September – **Meals** - Seafood - (booking essential) (dinner only) a la carte 19.90/29.00 **t.**

ETTYSTOWN (Baile an Bhiataigh) *Meath* 923 N 6.

Laytown & Bettystown ℘ (041) 982 7170.
Dublin 43 – Drogheda 6 – Dundalk 28.

Bacchus at the Coastguard, Bayview, ℘ (041) 9828251, *Fax (041) 9828236,* ← Bettystown Bay, – P. MC AE VISA
closed 2 weeks January, 1 week October, Christmas, Sunday dinner and Monday – **Meals** (dinner only and Sunday lunch)/dinner a la carte 23.50/29.50 **t.** 6.00.

BIRR (Biorra) *Offaly* 923 I 8 *Ireland G. – pop. 3 355.*

See : *Town★ – Birr Castle Demesne★★ AC (Telescope★★).*

Exc. : *Roscrea★ (Damer House★ AC) S : 12 m. by N 62 – Slieve Bloom Mountains★, E : 13 by R 440 – Clonfert Cathedral★ (West doorway★★), NW : 15 m. by R 439, R 356 and min roads.*

The Glenns ☎ (0509) 20082.

Castle St. ☎ (0509) 20110 (11 May-6 September).

Athlone 28 – Dublin 87 – Kilkenny 49 – Limerick 49.

County Arms, Railway Rd, South : ½ m. on N 62 ☎ (0509) 20791, *countyarmshotel@ti t.ie, Fax (0509) 21234,* squash – 300. VISA.
closed 25 December – **Meals** 11.00/20.00 **st.** and a la carte 8.00 – **24 rm** 45.0 96.00 **st.** – SB.

Dooly's, Emmet Sq., ☎ (0509) 20032, *doolyshotel@esatclear.ie, Fax (0509) 21332* – 300. VISA.
closed 25 December – **Meals** (bar lunch Monday to Saturday)/dinner a la carte appro 19.00 **t.** 6.00 – **18 rm** 37.00/70.00 **t.** – SB.

The Maltings, Castle St., ☎ (0509) 21345, *Fax (0509) 22073,* – VISA JC
Meals a la carte 9.20/14.95 **st.** 5.95 – **13 rm** 30.00/50.00 **st.** – SB.

Spinners Town House, Castle St., ☎ (0509) 21673, *spinners@indigo. Fax (0509) 21673,* « Minimalist interior » – VISA.
closed Monday – **Meals** (dinner only and Sunday lunch)/dinner a la carte 13.70/20.95 5.00 – **13 rm** 25.00/70.00 **st.** – SB.

Emmet Guest House without rest., Emmet Sq., ☎ (0509) 20395, *Fax (0509) 21436* –
closed 4 December-10 January – **6 rm** 25.00/40.00.

The Thatch, Crinkle, Southeast : 1 ¼ m. by N 62 ☎ (0509) 20682, *Fax (0509) 21847* – VISA
Meals 13.50/22.00 **t.** and a la carte 8.00.

at Kinnitty *East : 8¼ m. on R 440 – ✉ Birr.*

Kinnitty Castle ,, East : 1 m. on R 440 ☎ (0509) 37318, *kinnittycastle@eircom.n Fax (0509) 37284,* « 12C origins », – – 200. VISA
Meals (bar lunch Monday to Saturday)/dinner 35.00 **t.** and a la carte 12.00 – **37 r** 85.00/250.00 – SB.

BLACKLION (An Blaic) *Cavan* 923 I 5 – *pop. 153.*

Blacklion, Toam ☎ (072) 53024.

Dublin 121 – Drogheda 106 – Enniskillen 12.

Mac Nean House & Bistro with rm, ☎ (072) 53022, *Fax (072) 53404* – rest, VISA.
closed 1 week Christmas – **Meals** *(closed Tuesday and Wednesday October-May and Mo day)* (dinner only and Sunday lunch)/dinner 32.00/45.00 **t.** and a la carte 5.00 – **5 r** 26.00/46.00 **st.** – SB.

BLACKROCK (An Charraig Dhubh) *Dublin* 923 N 8 – *see Dublin.*

BLACKWATER *Wexford* 923 M 10.

Dublin 73 – Kilkenny 57 – Waterfotd 47 – Wexford 13.

Blackwater Lodge, The Square, ☎ (053) 27222, *blackwaterlodge@eircom.ne Fax (053) 27496* – rm, VISA JCB.
closed 25 December – **Meals** (bar lunch) a la carte 9.60/22.50 **t.** 7.95 – **12 rm** 40.0 70.00 **t.** – SB.

BLARNEY (An Bhlarna) *Cork* 923 G 12 *Ireland G. – pop. 1 963 – ✉ Cork.*

See : *Blarney Castle★★ AC – Blarney House★ AC.*

☎ (021) 4381624.

Dublin 167 – Cork 6.

Blarney Park, ☎ (021) 4385281, *info@blarneypark.com, Fax (021) 4381506,* – rm, rest, – 280. VISA.
Meals 25.00 **st.** 8.00 – **91 rm** 90.00/140.00 **st.** – SB.

Killarney House without rest., Station Rd, Northeast : 1 m. ☎ (021) 438184 *Fax (021) 4381841,* –
6 rm 26.00/46.00 **t.**

Tower *West : 2 m. on R 617 – ✉ Cork.*

Ashlee Lodge without rest., ☎ (021) 4385346, *info@ashleelodge.com, Fax (021) 4385726,* – TV P. MC AE VISA.
closed 20 December-4 January – **6 rm** 30.00/50.00 **st.**

ESSINGTON **(Baile Coimán)** *Wicklow* 923 M 8 *Ireland G. – pop. 1 860.*

Env. : *Russborough House★★★, SW : 2½ m. by N 81.*

Dublin 19 – Kilkenny 56 – Wexford 70.

Tulfarris House H. and Country Club, South : 6 m. by N 81 ☎ (045) 867555, *Fax (045) 867561*, ≤, « Part 17C », rm, rest, TV P – 150. MC AE VISA.
– **Meals** 30.00 **st.** 8.00 – **49 rm** 110.00/150.00 **st.**, 30 suites 290.00 **st.** – SB.

RRISOKANE *Tipperary* 923 H 8/9 – *pop. 850.*

Dublin 101 – Galway 53 – Limerick 37.

Dancer Cottage, Curraghmore, West : 2 m. by Ballinderry rd ☎ (067) 27414, *dcr@eircom.net, Fax (067) 27414,* – P. MC AE VISA.
February-November – **Meals** (by arrangement) (communal dining) 17.00 **st.** – **4 rm** 22.00/42.00 **st.** – SB.

AY **(Bré)** *Wicklow* 923 N 8 *Ireland G. – pop. 25 252.*

Env. : *Powerscourt★★ (Waterfall★★ AC) W : 4 m. – Killruddery House and Gardens★ AC, S : 2 m. by R 761.*

Exc. : *Wicklow Mountains★★.*

18 Woodbrook, Dublin Rd ☎ (01) 282 4799 – 18 Old Conna, Ferndale Rd ☎ (01) 282 6055 – 9 Ravenswell Rd ☎ (01) 286 2484.

Dublin 13 – Wicklow 20.

Woodland Court, Southern Cross, South : 2 ½ m. by R 761 on Greystones rd ☎ (01) 276 0258, *info@woodlandscourthotel.com, Fax (01) 276 0298* – rest, rest, TV P – 35. MC AE VISA.
closed 24 to 26 December – **Meals** (dinner only) 17.50 **st.** and a la carte – 7.50 – **65 rm** 65.00/110.00 **st.** – SB.

Tree of Idleness, Seafront, ☎ (01) 286 3498, *Fax (01) 282 8183* – MC AE VISA
closed 2 weeks September, 1 week Christmas and Monday – **Meals** - Greek-Cypriot - (dinner only) a la carte 22.70/28.70 **t.** 9.00.

NBEG **(An Bun Beag)** *Donegal* 923 H 2 *Ireland G. – pop. 1 400 (inc. Derrybeg).*

Exc. : *The Rosses★, S : by R 257.*

Dublin 195 – Donegal 66 – Londonderry 55.

Ostan Gweedore, ☎ (075) 31177, *boylec@iol.ie, Fax (075) 31726,* ≤ Gweedore Bay, – TV P – 200. MC AE VISA
restricted opening in winter – **Meals** (bar lunch)/dinner 24.00/29.00 **t.** 8.00 – **36 rm** 65.00/110.00 **t.**, 3 suites – SB.

NCRANA **(Bun Crannacha)** *Donegal* 923 J 2 *Ireland G. – pop. 3 312.*

Exc. : *Malin Head★★ (≤★★), NE : 31½ m. by R 238 and R 242 – Inishowen Peninsula★★ – Dunree Fort★, NW : 6 m. by coast rd – Carndonagh High Cross★, NE : 18½ m. by R 238 – Gap of Mamore★, NW : 8 m. – Lag Sand Dunes★, NE : 24½ m. by R 238 and R 242 – Inishowen Head★, E : 30 m. by R 238, R 244 and R 242.*

9 Buncrana ☎ (077) 62279.

Shore front ☎ (074) 21160 (June-August).

Dublin 160 – Londonderry 15 – Sligo 99.

Inishowen Gateway, Railway Rd, ☎ (077) 61144, *inigatho@iol.ie, Fax (077) 62278,* ≤, rm, rest, TV P – 150. MC AE VISA.
Meals (bar lunch Monday to Saturday)/dinner 18.95 **t.** and a la carte – **63 rm** 55.00/90.00 **st.** – SB.

Lake of Shadows, Grianan Park, ☎ (077) 61005, *Fax (077) 62131* – TV P. MC AE VISA.
closed 25 December – **Meals** (bar lunch Monday to Saturday)/dinner a la carte 14.00/18.00 **t.** 6.50 – **23 rm** 30.00/58.00 **t.** – SB.

BUNDORAN **(Bun Dobhráin)** *Donegal* 923 H 4 – *pop. 1 707.*
Main St. (072) 41350 (June-September).
Dublin 161 – Donegal 17 – Sligo 23.

Great Northern,, North : ¼ m. (072) 41204, *reservations@greatnorthernhote m, Fax (072) 41114*, – rest, – 500.
Meals (bar lunch Monday to Saturday)/dinner a la carte 15.50/23.70 **st.** 8.50 – **112**
75.00/130.00 **st.**

Grand Central, (072) 42722, *Fax (072) 42656* – rm, – 200.
VISA.
Meals 9.95/13.95 **st.** and dinner a la carte 4.95 – **62 rm** 50.00/90.00 **st.** – SB.

Holyrood, Main St., (072) 41232, *hrood@indigo.ie, Fax (072) 41100* – rest,
– 550. VISA.
closed 24-25 December – **Meals** (bar lunch)/dinner 15.00/18.00 **st.** and a la carte – **99**
50.00/90.00 **st.** – SB.

Allingham Arms, (072) 41075, *Fax (072) 41171* – – 400.
VISA.
closed 1 week Christmas – **Meals** 8.00/18.00 **st.** and dinner a la carte 5.50 – **118**
50.00/75.00 **st.** – SB.

Fitzgerald's, (072) 41336, *info@fitzgeraldshotel.com, Fax (072) 42121*, –
closed January and December – **Meals** *(closed Monday and Tuesday)* (dinner only) a la ca
17.50/22.50 **st.** 8.00 – **16 rm** 50.00/88.00 **st.** – SB.

Bay View without rest., Main St., (072) 41296, *Fax (072) 41147*, –
closed 1 week in spring and Christmas – **18 rm** 22.00/48.00 **t.**

Leitrim House without rest., Kinlough Rd, (072) 41904, *Fax (072) 41452*, –
VISA.
April-September – **8 rm** 25.00/40.00.

Le Chateaubrianne, Sligo Rd, West : 1 m. on N 5 (072) 42160, *Fax (072) 42160* –
VISA.
closed January, 25-26 December, Sunday dinner and Monday – **Meals** (dinner only a
Sunday lunch)/dinner 22.50/26.50 **t.** 10.50.

BUNRATTY **(Bun Raite)** *Clare* 923 F 9 *Ireland G.*
See : *Town★★ – Bunratty Castle★★.*
Dublin 129 – Ennis 15 – Limerick 8.

Bunratty Castle, (061) 707034, *info@bunrattycastlehotel.iol.ie, Fax (061) 364891* –
rm, VISA.
closed 15 December-2 January – ***Kathleen's*** **:** **Meals** (bar lunch Monday to Saturda
dinner a la carte 10.95/23.90 **t.** 7.50 – **60 rm** 75.00/120.00 **t.**

Fitzpatrick Bunratty, (061) 361177, *info@fitzpatricks.com, Fax (061) 471252*,
– rm, – 1200. VISA.
closed 24 to 26 December – **Meals** *(closed Saturday lunch)* 10.95/12.50 **t.** (lunch) and c
ner a la carte 7.50 – 10.00 – **115 rm** 115.00/160.00 **t.** – SB.

Bunratty Manor, (061) 707984, *bunrattymanor@eircom.net, Fax (061) 360588*,
– VISA.
closed 25 December and January – **Meals** *(closed Tuesday)* (dinner only) a la carte 14.
19.15 **t.** 7.50 – **14 rm** 54.50/79.00 **t.** – SB.

Bunratty Grove without rest., Castle Rd, North : 1 ½ m. (061) 369579, *bunratt ove@eircom.net, Fax (061) 369561*, – VISA.
April-October – **9 rm** 35.00/60.00 **st.**

Bunratty Lodge without rest.,, North : 1 ½ m. (061) 369402, *reservations@bunra odge.com, Fax (061) 369363*, – VISA.
March-November – **6 rm** 45.00/50.00 **st.**

Shannon View without rest.,, Northwest : 1 m. on N 18 (south-eastbound carriagew
completing U-turn at junction with R 471 (061) 364056, *Fax (061) 364056*, –
VISA.
April-October – **4 rm** 25.50/40.00 **s.**

Muses, Bunratty House Mews, (061) 364082, *muses@oceanfree.net, Fax (061) 3643*
VISA
closed Christmas, Sunday, Monday and Bank Holidays – **Meals** (dinner only) a la ca
21.50/27.00 **t.** 10.00.

TLERSTOWN (Baile an Bhuitléaraigh) *Cork* 923 F 13 *Ireland G.* – ✉ *Bandon.*
Env. : *Courtmacsherry★, N : 3 m.*
Exc. : *Carbery Coast★.*
Dublin 193 – Cork 32.

Butlerstown House without rest.,, North : ½ m. ☎ (023) 40137, *mail@butlerstownhouse.com, Fax (023) 40137*, ≤, « 18C », – P. MC VISA
March-November – **5 rm** 55.00/90.00 **t.**

TLERSTOWN (Baile an Bhuitléaraigh) *Waterford – see Waterford.*

HER (An Chathair) *Tipperary* 923 I 10 – *see Cahir.*

HERDANIEL (Cathair Dónall) *Kerry* 923 B 12 *Ireland G.* – ✉ *Killarney.*
Exc. : *Iveragh Peninsula★★ (Ring of Kerry★★) – Derrynane National Historic Park★★ – Staigue Fort★, E : 5 m. by N 70 and minor rd – Sneem★, E : 12 m. by N 70.*
Dublin 238 – Killarney 48.

Iskeroon without rest.,, West : 5 m. by N 70 turning right at Scarrif Inn, following signs to Bunavallla Pier taking left turn at junction then turning left onto track immediately before pier ☎ (066) 9475119, *info@iskeroon.com, Fax (066) 9475488*, ≤, – P. MC VISA
May-September – **3 rm** 45.00/76.00 **st.**

Derrynane Bay House,, West : ½ m. on N 70 ☎ (066) 9475404, *derrynanebayhouse@eircom.net, Fax (066) 9475436*, ≤, – TV P. MC AE VISA.
15 March-23 December – **Meals** 16.00 **s.** – **6 rm** 25.50/44.00 **s.**

HERLISTRANE (Cathair Loistreáin) *Galway* 923 E 7.
Dublin 159 – Ballina 46 – Galway 26.

Lisdonagh House,, Northwest : 1½ m. by Shrule rd ☎ (093) 31163, *cooke@lisdonagh.com, Fax (093) 31528*, ≤, « Early Georgian country house », – TV P. MC AE VISA
mid March-November – **Meals** (booking essential to non-residents) (dinner only) 30.00 **st.** 9.00 – **10 rm** 90.00/140.00 **st.**, 2 suites – SB.

HERSIVEEN (Cathair Saidhbhán) *Kerry* 923 B 12.
Dublin 221 – Killarney 40.

The Point, Renard Point, Southwest : 1 ¾ m. by N 70 ☎ (066) 9472165, *Fax (066) 9472165*, ≤ Valencia Harbour and Island, – P
closed late October-April, first Monday in August and Sunday lunch – **Meals** - Seafood - (bookings not accepted) a la carte 6.95/13.95 **st.**

HIR/CAHER (An Chathair) *Tipperary* 923 I 10 *Ireland G.* – *pop. 2 236.*
See : *Caher Castle★★ AC.*
Env. : *Swiss Cottage★ AC, S : 1 m. by R 670.*
Exc. : *Clonmel★ (County Museum★, St. Mary's Church★) E : 10 m. by N 24.*
Cahir Park, Kilcommon ☎ (052) 41474.
Castle St. ☎ (052) 41453.
Dublin 114 – Limerick 39 – Cork 47 – Waterford 39.

Cahir House, The Square, ☎ (052) 42727, *cahirhousehotel@eircom.ie, Fax (052) 42727* – rest, TV P – 500. MC AE VISA.
closed 25 December and Good Friday – **Meals** (bar lunch Monday to Saturday)/dinner 19.00 **st.** a la carte 5.50 – **41 rm** 69.00/90.00 **st.** – SB.

Kilcoran Lodge,, Southwest : 5 m. on N 8 ☎ (052) 41288, *Fax (052) 41994*, – TV P – 150. MC AE VISA.
Meals (carving lunch) 7.95/18.95 **st.** and a la carte 9.00 – **23 rm** 35.00/100.00 **st.** – SB.

MP (An Com) *Kerry* 923 C 11 – ✉ *Tralee.*
Dublin 195 – Killarney 44 – Limerick 76 – Tralee 10.

Barnagh Bridge without rest., Cappaclough, West : 2 m. on R 560 ☎ (066) 7130145, *bbguest@eircom.net, Fax (066) 7130299*, ≤, – TV P. MC AE VISA.
March-October – **5 rm** 35.00/50.00 **st.**

CAPPOQUIN (Ceapach Choinn) *Waterford* 923 I 11 *Ireland G. – pop. 780.*

Env. : *Lismore★ (Lismore Castle Gardens★ AC, St. Carthage's Cathedral★), W : 4 m. by N 7. Mount Melleray Abbey★, N : 4 m. by R 669.*

Exc. : *The Gap★ (≤★) NW : 9 m. by R 669.*

Dublin 136 – Cork 31 – Waterford 40.

XX **Richmond House** with rm,, Southeast : ½ m. on N 72 ✆ (058) 54278, *Fax (058) 549* « Georgian house », – rest, P. VISA. *closed 23 December-20 January* – **Meals** *(closed Sunday and Monday to non-resider* (dinner only) 32.00 **st.** 10.00 – **9 rm** 60.00/140.00 **t.** – SB.

CARAGH LAKE (Loch Cárthaí) *Kerry* 923 C 11 *Ireland G.*

See : *Lough Caragh★.*

Exc. : *Iveragh Peninsula★★ (Ring of Kerry★★).*

18 *Dooks, Glenbeigh ✆ (066) 976 8205.*

Dublin 212 – Killarney 22 – Tralee 25.

Caragh Lodge ✆ (066) 9769115, *caraghl@iol.ie, Fax (066) 9769316*, ≤, « Victor country house in extensive gardens on shores of Lough Caragh », – rest, P. VISA. *13 April-14 October* – **Meals** (booking essential to non-residents) (dinner only) 33.00 10.00 – **14 rm** 85.00/160.00 **st.**, 1 suite.

Ard-Na-Sidhe ✆ (066) 9769105, *khl@iol.ie, Fax (066) 9769282*, « Elizabethan st country house on shores of Lough Caragh », – rest, P. VISA. *May-September* – **Meals** (booking essential to non-residents) (dinner only) 26.00 **st** **19 rm** 80.00/176.00 **st.**

Carrig House ✆ (066) 9769100, *Fax (066) 9769166*, « Lough-side setting », rest, P. VISA. *April-December* – **Meals** (booking essential to non-residents) (dinner only) 25.00/30.0 9.00 – **6 rm** 75.00/130.00 **t.** – SB.

CARLINGFORD (Cairlinn) *Louth* 923 N 5 *Ireland G. – pop. 647.*

See : *Town★.*

Exc. : *Windy Gap★, NW : 8 m. by R 173 – Proleek Dolmen★, SW : 9 m. by R 173.*

Dublin 66 – Dundalk 13.

McKevitt's Village, Market Sq., ✆ (042) 9373116, *Fax (042) 9373144*, – VISA. *closed 25 December* – **Meals** (bar lunch)/dinner 25.00 **t.** and a la carte 5.95 – **13** 35.00/90.00 **st.** – SB.

CARLOW (Ceatharlach) *Carlow* 923 L 9 *– pop. 11 721.*

18 *Carlow, Deer Park, Dublin Rd ✆ (0503) 31695.*

Kennedy Ave. ✆ (0503) 31554 (April-December).

Dublin 50 – Kilkenny 23 – Wexford 47.

Dolmen, Kilkenny Rd, Southwest : 1 ¾ m. on N 9 ✆ (0503) 42002, *reservations@dolme otel.ie, Fax (0503) 42375*, – rest, P – 800. VISA. *closed 25 December* – **Meals** (carving lunch Monday to Saturday)/dinner 17.50 8.0 **40 rm** 65.00/130.00 **st.** – SB.

Seven Oaks, Athy Rd, ✆ (0503) 31308, *sevenoak@eircom.net, Fax (0503) 32155*, – P – 300. VISA JCB. *closed 25 December* – **Meals** (carving lunch Saturday) 12.95/18.50 **st.** and a la carte – **39** 50.00/100.00 **st.** – SB.

Barrowville Town House without rest., Kilkenny Rd, South : ½ m. on N ✆ (0503) 43324, *Fax (0503) 41953*, – P. VISA. **7 rm** 30.00/55.00 **t.**

CARNA *Galway* 923 C 8 *Ireland G.*

Exc. : *Connemara★★★ – Cashel★, N : by R 340.*

Dublin 186 – Cork 169 – Galway 48 – Limerick 112.

Carna Bay ✆ (095) 32255, *carnabay.iol.ie, Fax (095) 32530*, ≤, – rest, P. VISA *closed 23-27 December* – **Meals** (bar lunch Monday to Saturday)/dinner 20.00/22.0 and a la carte 6.95 – **26 rm** 50.00/80.00 **st.** – SB.

RNE *Wexford* 923 M 11.
Dublin 105 – Waterford 51 – Wexford 13.

Lobster Pot, ✆ (053) 31110, *Fax (053) 31401* – P. MC AE VISA
closed January, 25 December, Monday October-May except Bank Holidays and Good Friday – **Meals** - Seafood - (light lunch)/dinner a la carte 14.90/27.90 **t.** 5.95.

RRICKCARNON *Louth – see Dundalk.*

RRICKMACROSS **(Carraig Mhachaire Rois)** *Monaghan* 923 L 6 *Ireland G. – pop. 1 926.*
Env. : *Dún a' Rá Forest Park★, SW : 5 m. by R 179.*
18 *Nuremore* ✆ *(042) 64016.*
Dublin 57 – Dundalk 14.

Nuremore ,, South : 1 m. on N 2 ✆ (042) 9661438, *nuremore@tinet.ie, Fax (042) 9661853*, ≤, , , , 18, , , , squash – TV P – 600. MC AE VISA.
Meals – (see ***The Restaurant*** below) – **72 rm** 100.00/200.00 **t.** – SB.

The Restaurant (at Nuremore H.),, South : 1 m. on N 2 ✆ (042) 9661438, *Fax (042) 9661853* – P. MC AE VISA
closed Saturday lunch – **Meals** 16.50 **t.** (lunch) and dinner a la carte 27.50/35.00 **t.** 9.00.

RRICK-ON-SHANNON **(Cora Droma Rúisc)** *Leitrim* 923 H 6 *Ireland G. – pop. 1 868.*
See : *Town★.*
Exc. : *Lough Rynn Demesne★.*
9 *Carrick-on-Shannon, Woodbrook* ✆ *(079) 67015.*
Old Barnel Store ✆ *(078) 20170 (April-September).*
Dublin 97 – Ballina 50 – Galway 74 – Roscommon 26 – Sligo 34.

The Landmark,, on N 4 ✆ (078) 22222, *landmarkhotel@eircom.net, Fax (078) 22233*, ≤, , , – TV P – 500. MC AE VISA.
closed 25 December – **Meals** (bar lunch)/dinner a la carte approx. 29.00 **t.** 8.00 – **51 rm** 70.00/160.00 **st.** – SB.

Hollywell without rest., Liberty Hill, ✆ (078) 21124, *holywell@esatbiz.com, Fax (078) 21124*, ≤, « Part 18C country house », – P. MC AE VISA.
closed Christmas and New Year – **4 rm** 45.00/79.00.

RRICK-ON-SUIR **(Carraig na Siûire)** *Tipperary* 923 J 10 *Ireland G. – pop. 5 172.*
Env. : *Ormond Castle★ – Ahenny High Crosses★, N : by R 697.*
9 *Carravone* ✆ *(051) 640047.*
Dublin 95 – Cork 68 – Limerick 62 – Waterford 16.

Carraig, Main St., ✆ (051) 641455, *thecarraighotel@tinet.ie, Fax (051) 641604* – rest, TV P – 300. MC AE VISA.
Meals 6.95/18.95 **t.** and dinner a la carte – **14 rm** 45.00/90.00 **t.** – SB.

Bell and Salmon Arms, 95-97 Main St., ✆ (051) 645555, *bellsalmon@eircom.net, Fax (051) 641293* – TV P. MC AE VISA
closed Good Friday and 25 December – **Meals** (bar lunch Monday to Saturday)/dinner a la carte 8.95/15.00 **st.** 6.75 – **13 rm** 33.00/55.00 – SB.

RRIGALINE **(Carraig Uí Leighin)** *Cork* 923 G 12 *– pop. 7 827.*
18 *Fernhill* ✆ *(021) 372226.*
Dublin 163 – Cork 9.

Carrigaline Court, Cork Rd, ✆ (021) 4852100, *carrigcourt@eircom.net, Fax (021) 4371103*, , , – , rest, TV P – 300. MC AE VISA.
closed 25 December – ***The Kingfisher :*** **Meals** (bar lunch Monday to Saturday)/dinner a la carte 25.00/35.00 **st.** 7.50 – **50 rm** 65.00/100.00 **st.**, 2 suites – SB.

Glenwood House without rest., Ballinrea Rd, North : ¾ m. by R 611 (Cork rd) ✆ (021) 373878, *glenwoodhouse@eircom.net, Fax (021) 373878*, – TV P. MC VISA
closed 22 December-2 January – **14 rm** 45.00/70.00 **st.**

Raffeen Lodge without rest., Ringaskiddy Rd, Monkstown, Northeast : 2 ½ m. by R 611 and N 28 off R 610 ✆ (021) 371632, *Fax (021) 371632*, – TV P. MC VISA.
closed 22 December-4 January – **6 rm** 28.00/40.00 **t.**

CASHEL (An Caiseal) *Galway* 923 C 7 *Ireland G.*

See : *Town*★.

Exc. : *Connemara*★★★.

Dublin 173 – Galway 41.

Cashel House ⑤, ☎ (095) 31001, *info@cashel-house.com, Fax (095) 31077*, ≤, « Co
try house and gardens », ⑤, 🎾, 🍴 – ⇔ rm, TV 📞 P. MC AE ① VISA. ⚹
closed 10 January-5 February – **Meals** (booking essential to non-residents) (bar lunc
dinner 33.00/35.00 **t.** 🍷 8.50 – **32 rm** ☕ 85.00/210.00 **t.**

Zetland Country House ⑤, ☎ (095) 31111, *zetland@iol.ie, Fax (095) 31117*, ≤ Cas
Bay, « Gardens », ⑤, 🍴 – ⇔ rest, TV P. MC AE ① VISA
April-December – **Meals** (bar lunch)/dinner 31.50 **t.** 🍷 8.00 – **19 rm** ☕ 79.00/130.00 **t.** –

Glynsk House ⑤,, Southwest : 5 ¾ m. on R 340 ☎ (095) 32279, *glynsk@io*
Fax (095) 32342, ≤ – ▤ rest, TV P. MC AE VISA
May-September – **Meals** (dinner only) 18.00 **st.** 🍷 7.00 – **12 rm** ☕ 40.00/60.00 **st.** – SB.

CASHEL (Caiseal) *Tipperary* 923 I 10 *Ireland G. – pop. 2 346.*

See : *Town*★★★ – *Rock of Cashel*★★★ *AC* – *Cormac's Chapel*★★ – *Round Tower*★ –
seum★ – *Cashel Palace Gardens*★ – *GPA Bolton Library*★ *AC.*

Env. : *Holy Cross Abbey*★★, *N : 9 m. by R 660* – *Athassel Abbey*★, *W : 5 m. by N 74.*

ℹ *Town Hall* ☎ *(062) 61333 (April-September).*

Dublin 101 – Cork 60 – Kilkenny 34 – Limerick 36 – Waterford 44.

Cashel Palace, Main St., ☎ (062) 62707, *reception@cashel_palace.ie, Fax (062) 61*
« Former Archbishop's palace, extensive gardens », 🎾 – 🛗 TV P – 🏛 75. MC AE ① VISA.
closed 24 to 26 December – **Meals** a la carte 22.50/31.00 **t.** 🍷 8.50 – **23 rm** ☕ 90.
225.00 **t.** – SB.

Ros Guill House without rest.,, Northeast : ¾ m. by R 688 on R 691 ☎ (062) 62
Fax (062) 61507, 🌳 – ⇔ P. MC VISA. ⚹
May-late October – **5 rm** ☕ 32.50/50.00 **st.**

Chez Hans, Rockside, ☎ (062) 61177, « Converted synod hall » – P. MC VISA
closed 3 weeks January, 1 week September, 24 and 26 December, Sunday and Mond
Meals (dinner only) a la carte 25.75/36.25 **t.** 🍷 9.00.

CASTLEBALDWIN (Béal Átha na gCarraigíní) *Sligo* 923 G 5 *Ireland G.* – ✉ *Boyle (Roscomm*

Env. : *Carrowkeel Megalithic Cemetery (≤★★), S : 3 m.*

Exc. : *Arigna Scenic Drive*★, *N : 2 m. by N 4* – *Lough Key Forest Park*★ *AC, SE : 10 m. by N*
View of Lough Allen★, *N : 9 m. by N 4 on R 280* – *Mountain Drive*★, *N : 6 m. on N 4* – *B*
Abbey★ *AC, SE : 8 m. by N 4* – *King House*★, *SE : 8 m. by N 4.*

Dublin 118 – Longford 42 – Sligo 15.

Cromleach Lodge ⑤, Ballindoon, Southeast : 3 ½ m. ☎ (071) 65155, *info@cromle*
com, Fax (071) 65455, ≤ Lough Arrow and Carrowkeel Cairns, ⑤, 🌳, 🎾 – ⇔ TV P. MC
VISA
February-October – **Meals** (dinner only) a la carte 30.25/37.25 **t.** 🍷 9.50 – **10 rm** ☕ 119
218.00 **t.** – SB.

Hillcrest ⑤, Ballindoon, Southeast : 4 ½ m. ☎ (071) 65559, ≤ Lough Arrow and Carr
keel Cairns – ⇔ P. VISA
April-November – **Meals** (by arrangement) 13.00 – **4 rm** ☕ 22.50/38.00.

CASTLEBAR (Caisléan an Bharraigh) *Mayo* 923 E 6 *Ireland G. – pop. 6 585.*

Env. : *Ballintubber Abbey*★★, *S : 8 m. by N 84.*

Exc. : *Errew Abbey*★, *N : 22 m. by R 310, R 315 and minor rd.*

⛳18 *Castlebar, Hawthorn Av., Rocklands* ☎ *(094) 21649.*

ℹ *Linenhall* ☎ *(094) 21207 (April-August).*

Dublin 161 – Galway 49 – Sligo 47.

Breaffy House ⑤,, Southeast : 3 m. on N 60 ☎ (094) 22033, *breaffyhotel@an*
Fax (094) 22276, 🏋, 🌳, 🎾 – 🛗 TV ♿ P – 🏛 300. MC AE ① VISA
closed 24 to 27 December – **Meals** 10.00/28.00 **st.** – **59 rm** ☕ 90.00/140.00 **t.** – SB.

CASTLEBELLINGHAM (Baile an Ghearlánaigh) *Louth* 923 M 6 – *pop. 792 (inc. Kilsaran).*

Dublin 43 – Dundalk 8 – Drogheda 14.

Bellingham Castle ⑤, ☎ (042) 9372176, *bellinghamcastle@eircom.*
Fax (042) 9372766, ⑤, 🎾 – TV P – 🏛 650. MC AE VISA
closed 24 and 25 December – **Meals** 12.00/18.00 **st.** and dinner a la carte 🍷 7.50 – **21**
☕ 50.00/95.00 **st.** – SB.

STLECONNELL (Caisleán Uí Chonaill) *Limerick* 923 G 9 *Ireland G.* – *pop. 1 414* – ✉ *Limerick.*
See : *Town*★.
Env. : *Clare Glens*★, *SE : 5 m. by N 7 and R 503.*
Dublin 111 – Limerick 9.

Castle Oaks House ⛱, ☎ (061) 377666, *info@castle_oaks.com, Fax (061) 377717,* ≤, 🏋, 🏊, 🏊, 🎣, 🌳, 🌿, ✂ – TV P – 🪑 200. MC AE ⓓ VISA. ✂
closed 24 to 26 December – **Meals** (bar lunch Monday to Saturday)/dinner a la carte 16.50/25.75 **t.** 🍷 5.75 – **20 rm** ☕ 71.50/133.10 **t.** – SB.

STLEDERMOT (Díseart Diarmada) *Kildare* 923 L 9 *Ireland G.* – *pop. 733.*
Env. : *Castledermot High Crosses*★ – *Moone High Cross*★, *N : by N 9.*
Exc. : *Carlow Cathedral (Marble Monument*★) *NE : 7 m. by N 9.*
Dublin 44 – Kilkenny 30 – Wexford 54.

Kilkea Castle ⛱, Kilkea, Northwest : 3 m. by R 418 ☎ (0503) 45156, *kilkea@iol.ie, Fax (0503) 45187,* ≤, « Part 12C castle, gardens », 🏋, 🏊, 🏊, 18, 🎣, 🌿, ✂ – 🛗 TV P – 🪑 200. MC AE ⓓ VISA. ✂
closed 23-27 December – **Meals** 17.50/32.00 **t.** 🍷 7.25 – **29 rm** ☕ 135.00/190.00 **t.**, 7 suites – SB.

STLEKNOCK (Caisleán Cnucha) *Dublin* 923 ㊱ – *see Dublin.*

STLELYONS (Caisleán Ó Liatháin) *Cork* 923 H 11 – *pop. 164.*
Dublin 136 – Cork 19 – Killarney 65 – Limerick 40.

Ballyvolane House ⛱,, Southeast : 3 ½ m. by Midleton rd on Britway rd ☎ (025) 36349, *ballyvol@iol.ie, Fax (025) 36781,* ≤, « 18C Italianate mansion, extensive parklands », 🎣, 🌳 – ⇎ TV P. MC AE VISA. ✂
closed 23 to 31 December – **Meals** (by arrangement) (communal dining) 25.00 **st.** 🍷 6.50 – **6 rm** ☕ 57.00/100.00 **st.**

STLEREA (An Caisleán Riabhach) *Roscommon* 923 G 6 *Ireland G.* – *pop. 1 790.*
Env. : *Clonalis House*★, *W : ½ m. by N 60.*
9 *Castlerea, Clonalis* ☎ *(0907) 20068.*
Dublin 108 – Galway 62 – Limerick 105.

Clonalis House ⛱,, West : ½ m. on N 60 ☎ (0907) 20014, *Fax (0907) 20014,* ≤, « Victorian Italianate mansion in extensive grounds », 🎣, 🌳, ✂ – ⇎ P. MC AE VISA. ✂
booking essential, 15 April-September – **Meals** (by arrangement) (communal dining) 24.00 – **4 rm** ☕ 60.00/104.00.

STLETOWNBERE (Baile Chaisleáin Bhéarra) *Cork* 923 C 13 *Ireland G.* – *pop. 926.*
Env. : *Beara Peninsula*★, *W : by R 572 (Allihies, mines*★ *- Garnish Bay* ≤★) – *Slieve Miskish Mountains* (≤★).
9 *Berehaven, Millcove* ☎ *(027) 70700.*
Dublin 224 – Cork 81 – Killarney 58.

The Old Presbytery without rest., Brandy Hall House, East : ¼ m. on R 572 ☎ (027) 70424, *marywrigley@midnet.net, Fax (027) 70420,* ≤, 🌳 – ⇎ TV P. MC VISA. ✂
April-November – **5 rm** ☕ 30.00/50.00.

Rodeen ⛱,, East : 2 m. by R 572 ☎ (027) 70158, *taracentre@eircom.net, Fax (027) 70987,* ≤, 🌳 – ⇎ P. MC AE ⓓ VISA JCB. ✂
March-October – **Meals** (by arrangement) 20.00 **st.** – **6 rm** ☕ 25.00/44.00 **st.**

STLETOWNSHEND (Baile an Chaisleáin) *Cork* 923 E 13.
Dublin 215 – Cork 59 – Killarney 72.

Mary Ann's, ☎ (028) 36146, *golfer@indigo.ie, Fax (028) 36377,* 🍽 – MC VISA
closed last 3 weeks January, 24-26 December and dinner Monday and Tuesday in winter – **Meals** (bookings not accepted) 23.95 **t.** (dinner) and lunch a la carte 12.40/27.40 **t.** 🍷 7.50.

VAN (An Cabhán) *Cavan* 923 J 6 *Ireland G.* – *pop. 3 509.*
Env. : *Killykeen Forest Park*★, *W : 6 m. by R 198.*
ℹ *Farnham St.* ☎ *(049) 4331942.*
Dublin 71 – Drogheda 58 – Enniskillen 40.

Kilmore, Dublin Rd, East : 2 m. on N 3 ☎ (049) 4332288, *kilmore@quinn-hotels.cc* *Fax (049) 4332458* – TV ♿ P – 🎤 550. MC AE D VISA. ✂
Meals 10.00/25.00 **st.** and dinner a la carte 🍷 6.50 – **39 rm** ☕ 52.00/82.00 **st.** – SB.

CHEEKPOINT (Pointe na Ságe) *Waterford* 923 K/L 11 – *see Waterford.*

CLARINBRIDGE (Droichead an Chláirán) *Galway* 923 F 8.
Dublin 145 – Galway 11.

Oyster Manor, ☎ (091) 796777, *info@oystermanorhotel.com, Fax (091) 796770* – TV – 🎤 80. MC AE D VISA. ✂
closed 24-25 December and Good Friday – **Meals** (bar lunch Monday to Saturday)/dinr 23.50 **st.** and a la carte 🍷 7.00 – **26 rm** ☕ 70.00/120.00 **st.** – SB.

The Old Schoolhouse, ☎ (091) 796898, *Fax (091) 796117* – P. MC AE VISA
closed 3 weeks January and Monday – **Meals** (booking essential) (dinner only and Sunc lunch)/dinner a la carte 22.00/35.00 **t.** 🍷 7.00.

CLIFDEN (An Clochán) *Galway* 923 B 7 *Ireland G. – pop. 920.*
Exc. : *Connemara★★★, NE : by N 59 – Sky Road★★ (≤★★), NE : by N 59 – Connem National Park★, NE : 1 m by N 59.*
ℹ *Galway Rd ☎ (095) 21163 (March-25 October).*
Dublin 181 – Ballina 77 – Galway 49.

Station House, ☎ (095) 21699, *station@eircom.net, Fax (095) 21667,* Ls, ≘s, 🏊 – ⇔, ▤ rest, TV 📞 ♿ P – 🎤 200. MC AE D VISA. ✂
closed 25 December – **Meals** (bar lunch)/dinner 21.00/25.00 **st.** and a la carte 🍷 11.75 – ***F & Ice :*** **Meals** *(closed Monday)* (dinner only) a la carte 19.15/26.80 **t.** – **78 rm** ☕ 70.(110.00 **st.** – SB.

Rock Glen Country House ⛰,, South : 1 ¼ m. by R 341 ☎ (095) 21035, *rockglen@ e, Fax (095) 21737,* ≤, « Early 19C former shooting lodge », 🌳, 🎾, ⛳ – ⇔ rest, TV P. AE D VISA. ✂
16 March-November – **Meals** (bar lunch)/dinner 33.00 and a la carte 🍷 10.00 – **25** ☕ 91.00/171.00 **st.** – SB.

Ardagh ⛰, Ballyconneely rd, South : 1 ¾ m. on R 341 ☎ (095) 21384, *ardaghhotel@e m.net, Fax (095) 21314,* ≤ Ardbear Bay – TV P. MC AE D VISA
April-October – **Meals** (bar lunch)/dinner 26.00/32.00 **t.** and a la carte 🍷 8.50 – **14** ☕ 75.00/115.00 **t.**, 3 suites – SB.

Alcock & Brown, ☎ (095) 21206, *alcockandbrown@eircom.net, Fax (095) 21842* – ▤ r TV. MC AE D VISA. ✂
closed 22 to 26 December – **Meals** (bar lunch)/dinner a la carte 15.75/26.85 **st.** 🍷 6.0 **19 rm** ☕ 49.00/88.00 **st.** – SB.

Quay House without rest., Beach Rd, ☎ (095) 21369, *thequay@iol.ie, Fax (095) 2160* – TV. MC VISA. ✂
April-5 November – **14 rm** ☕ 60.00/100.00 **t.**

Sunnybank House ⛰, Church Hill, ☎ (095) 21437, *sunnybank@anu Fax (095) 21976,* ≘s, 🏊 heated, 🌳, ⛳ – TV P. MC VISA. ✂
March-November – **Meals** – (see ***O'Grady's*** below) – **8 rm** ☕ 50.00/80.00 **st.** – SB.

Buttermilk Lodge without rest., Westport Rd, ☎ (095) 21951, *buttermilk@anu Fax (095) 21953* – ⇔ TV P. MC VISA. ✂
closed 7-31 January – **11 rm** ☕ 40.00/60.00 **st.**

Mal Dua House without rest., Galway Rd, East : ½ m. on N 59 ☎ (095) 21171, *maldua .ie, Fax (095) 21739,* 🌳 – ⇔ TV P. MC AE D VISA. ✂
14 rm ☕ 40.00/80.00 **st.**

Dún Rí without rest., Hulk St., ☎ (095) 21625, *dunri@anu.ie, Fax (095) 21635* – TV. MC ✂
March-2 November – **13 rm** ☕ 35.00/50.00 **st.**

O'Grady's, Market St., ☎ (095) 21450, *Fax (095) 21976* – MC AE VISA
March-November – **Meals** *(closed Sunday)* a la carte 25.00/28.50 **st.** 🍷 8.00.

High Moors, Dooneen, Southeast : ¾ m. off Ballyconneely rd ☎ (095) 21342, ≤ – P. AE VISA
April-October – **Meals** *(closed Monday-Tuesday)* (dinner only) a la carte 17.75/24.1 🍷 5.95.

Jährlich eine neue Ausgabe
Aktuellste Informationen, jährlich für Sie!

ONAKILTY (Cloich na Coillte) *Cork* 923 F 13 *Ireland G. – pop. 2 724.*

See : *West Cork Regional Museum★ AC – West Cork Model Railway Village★.*

Env. : *Timoleague★ (Franciscan Friary★, gardens★) E : 5 m. by R 600.*

Exc. : *Carbery Coast★.*

Dunmore, Dunmore House, Muckross ☎ (023) 33352.

Ashe St. ☎ (023) 33226 (May-October).

Dublin 193 – Cork 32.

The Lodge and Spa at Inchydoney Island,, South : 3 ¼ m. by N 71 following signs for Inchydoney Beach ☎ (023) 33143, *reservations@inchydoneyisland.com, Fax (023) 35229,* – rm, rest, – 350. VISA. ***The Gulfstream :*** **Meals** (dinner only and Sunday lunch) 30.00 **t.** 8.50 – ***The Contented Plaice :*** **Meals** a la carte approx. 13.95 **t.** – 11.05 – **63 rm** 118.10/204.40 **t.**, 4 suites.

Dunmore House, Muckross, South : 3 ¾ m. by N 71 off Ardfield rd ☎ (023) 33352, *dunmorehousehotel@eircom.net, Fax (023) 34686,* – rest, – 200. VISA.
closed 23-28 December and 14 January-8 March – **Meals** (bar lunch Monday to Saturday)/dinner 23.00/28.00 **t.** and a la carte 7.50 – **23 rm** 60.00/110.00 **t.** – SB.

Emmet, Emmet Sq., ☎ (023) 33394, *emmethotel@titen.ie, Fax (023) 35058* – rest, . VISA.
closed 25 December – **Meals** (bar lunch Monday to Saturday)/dinner a la carte 11.95/21.90 **st.** – **20 rm** 35.00/90.00 **st.** – SB.

Quality, Clogheen, West : ½ m. by N 71 (Skibbereen rd) ☎ (023) 35400, *qualityhotel@eircom.net, Fax (023) 35404,* – rest, – 160. VISA.
closed 25 and 26 December – **Meals** (bar lunch)/dinner 15.00/18.00 **st.** and a la carte 7.65 – **58 rm** 60.00/90.00 **st.** – SB.

An Sugán, 41 Strand Rd, ☎ (023) 33498, *Fax (023) 33825* – VISA
closed 25 December and Good Friday – **Meals** a la carte 17.45/28.70 **t.** 6.00 **6 rms** 25.00/45.00 **t.**

Ballinascarty *Northeast : 4 ¼ m. on N 71 – ✉ Clonakilty.*

Árd na Gréine Farm House,, Northwest : 1 ¾ m. by N 71 ☎ (023) 39104, *normawalshi@eircom.net, Fax (023) 39397,* « Working farm », – . VISA
Meals 20.00 **st.** – **5 rm** 25.00/50.00.

ONBUR (An Fhairche) *Galway* 923 D 7.

Dublin 162 – Ballina 49 – Galway 29.

John J. Burke, ☎ (092) 46175, *tibhurca@eircom.net, Fax (092) 46290,* – VISA
restricted opening in winter – **Meals** *(closed Sunday dinner)* (live music Friday to Sunday) a la carte 14.70/26.45 **t.** 5.95.

ONMEL (Cluain Meala) *Tipperary* 923 I 10 *Ireland G. – pop. 15 215.*

See : *Town★ – County Museum★, St. Mary's Church★.*

Env. : *Fethard★, N : 8 m. by R 689.*

Exc. : *Nier Valley Scenic Route★★ – Ahenny High Crosses★, E : 19 m. by N 24 and R 697 – Ormond Castle★, E : 21 m. by N 24.*

Lyreanearla, Mountain Rd ☎ (052) 21138.

Community Office, Town Centre ☎ (052) 22960.

Dublin 108 – Cork 59 – Kilkenny 31 – Limerick 48 – Waterford 29.

Minella, Coleville Rd, ☎ (052) 22388, *hotelminella@eircom.net, Fax (052) 24381,* – rm, – 550. VISA.
closed 23-28 December – **Meals** 16.00/30.00 **t.** and a la carte 7.00 – **68 rm** 75.00/140.00 **st.**, 2 suites – SB.

ONTARF (Cluain Tarbh) *Dublin* 923 N 7 – *see Dublin.*

OYNE (Cluain) *Cork* 923 H 12 – ✉ *Midleton.*

Dublin 160 – Cork 20 – Waterford 60.

Barnabrow House,, East : 1 ¼ m. on R 629 ☎ (021) 4652534, *barnabrow@eircom.net, Fax (021) 4652534,* « Part 17C », – . VISA
closed 23-27 December – ***Trinity Rooms :*** **Meals** *(closed Sunday dinner)* (dinner only and Sunday lunch)/dinner a la carte 18.00/26.00 **t.** – **19 rm** 43.00/95.00 **st.** – SB.

COBH (An Cóbh) *Cork* 923 H 12 *Ireland G. – pop. 6 468.*

See : *Town★ – St Colman's Cathedral★ – Lusitania Memorial★.*

Exc. : *Fota Island★ (Fota Wildlife Park★), N : 4 m. by R 624 – Cloyne Cathedral★, SE : 15 m R 624/5, N 25, R 630 and R 629.*

Ballywilliam ☎ (021) 812399.

Dublin 164 – Cork 15 – Waterford 65.

WatersEdge,, (next to Cobh Heritage Centre) ☎ (021) 481 5566, *watersedge@eircom.net, Fax (021) 481 2011,* ≤ Cork harbour, – rest, TV P. MC AE VISA.
Jacob's Ladder : **Meals** (light lunch) a la carte 21.20/25.00 **t.** – **18 rm** 45.00/160.00 1 suite – SB.

Bella Vista Manor House, Bishop's Rd, ☎ (021) 812450, *bellavis@indigo Fax (021) 812215,* ≤ – TV P. MC AE VISA.
closed 25 December – **Meals** a la carte 16.85/24.00 **t.** 6.50 – **16 rm** 45.00/110.00 s SB.

Robin Hill House with rm, Rushbrooke, Northeast : 1 m. by R 624 ☎ (021) 4811395, *r nhillhouse@eircom.net, Fax (021) 4814680,* ≤, « Mid Victorian converted rectory, conte porary interior », – TV P. MC VISA.
closed 25-27 December and January and Bank Holidays – **Meals** *(closed Sunday dinner Monday)* (dinner only and Sunday lunch) 25.00 **st.** 6.00 – **6 rm** 45.00/80.00 **st.** – SB.

COLLOONEY (Cúil Mhuine) *Sligo* 923 G 5.

Dublin 129 – Sligo 9 – Galway 82.

Glebe House with rm,, West : ¾ m. off Coolaney rd ☎ (071) 67787, *glebehse@esa.com, Fax (071) 30438,* « Georgian house », – P. MC AE VISA
restricted opening in winter – **Meals** (dinner only) 22.50 **t.** and a la carte 6.00 – 6 35.00/80.00 **t.** – SB.

The Guide is updated annually so renew your Guide every year.

CONG (Conga) *Mayo* 923 E 7 *Ireland G. – pop. 197.*

See : *Town★.*

Env. : *Lough Corrib★★.*

Exc. : *Ross Abbey★ (Tower ≤★) – Joyce Country★★ (Lough Nafooey★) W : by R 345.*

☎ *(092) 46542 (March-September).*

Dublin 160 – Ballina 49 – Galway 28.

Ashford Castle, ☎ (092) 46003, *ashford@ashford.ie, Fax (092) 46260,* ≤, « Part and 18C castle in extensive formal gardens on shores of Lough Corrib », – , rest, TV P – 110. MC AE VISA.
George V Room : **Meals** (residents only) 26.00/42.00 **t.** and dinner a la carte 10.00 – 14.50 – **79 rm** 264.00/350.00 **st.**, 4 suites – SB.

Ballywarren House,, East : 2 ¼ m. on R 346 ☎ (092) 46989, *Fax (092) 46989,* ≤, TV P. AE VISA
closed 1 week in spring and 1 week in autumn – **Meals** (by arrangement) 25.00 **st.** 7.5 **3 rm** 55.00/98.00 **st.**

CORK (Corcaigh) *Cork* 923 G 12 *Ireland G. – pop. 127 187.*

See : *City★★ – Shandon Bells★★* **EY**, *St. Fin Bar's Cathedral★★ AC* **Z**, *Cork Public Museu* **X M** – *Grand Parade★* **Z** , *South Mall★* **Z** , *St. Patrick Street★* **Z** , *Crawford Art Gallery★ Christ the King Church★* **X D** , *Elizabethan Fort★* **Z** .

Env. : *Dunkathel House★ AC, E : 5¾m. by N 8 and N 25* **X**.

Exc. : *Fota Island★ (Fota Wildlife Park★), E : 8 m. by N 8 and N 25* **X** – *Cobh★ (St. Colm Cathedral★, Lusitania Memorial★) SE : 15 m. by N 8, N 25 and R 624* **X**.

Douglas ☎ (021) 891086, **X** – *Mahon, Cloverhill, Blackrock ☎ (021) 294280* **X** – *Monkstown, Parkgarriffe ☎ (021) 841376,* **X** – *Harbour Point, Clash, Little Island ☎ (0 353094,* **X**.

Cork Airport : ☎ (021) 313131, S : 4 m. by L 42 **X** – **Terminal :** *Bus Station, Parnell P*

to France (Roscoff) (Brittany Ferries and Irish Ferries) weekly (14 h/15 h) – to P broke (Swansea Cork Ferries) 2 weekly (8 h 30 mn) – to Swansea (Swansea Cork Ferries) h).

Cork City, Grand Par. ☎ (021) 4273251 – Cork Airport, Freephone facility at Arr Terminal.

Dublin 154.

CORK
BUILT UP AREA

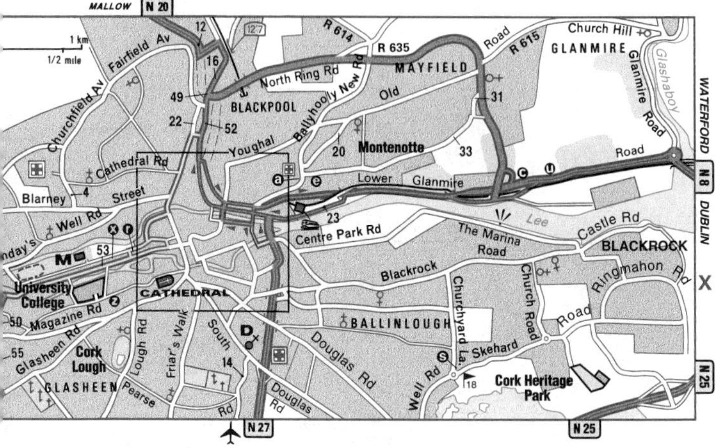

Hayfield Manor, Perrott Av., College Rd., ✆ (021) 4315600, *enquiries@hayfieldmanor.ie*, *Fax (021) 4316839*, [gym], [pool], – [lift] [air conditioning] [TV] [disabled] [P] – [conference] 100. [MC] [AE] [Diners] [VISA]. X z
Meals *(closed Saturday lunch)* 17.50/35.00 **st.** and dinner a la carte 12.00 – ***The Manor Room :*** Meals *(closed Saturday lunch)* 17.50/35.00 **t.** and dinner a la carte 12.00 – **82 rm** 160.00/260.00 **t.**, 5 suites – SB.

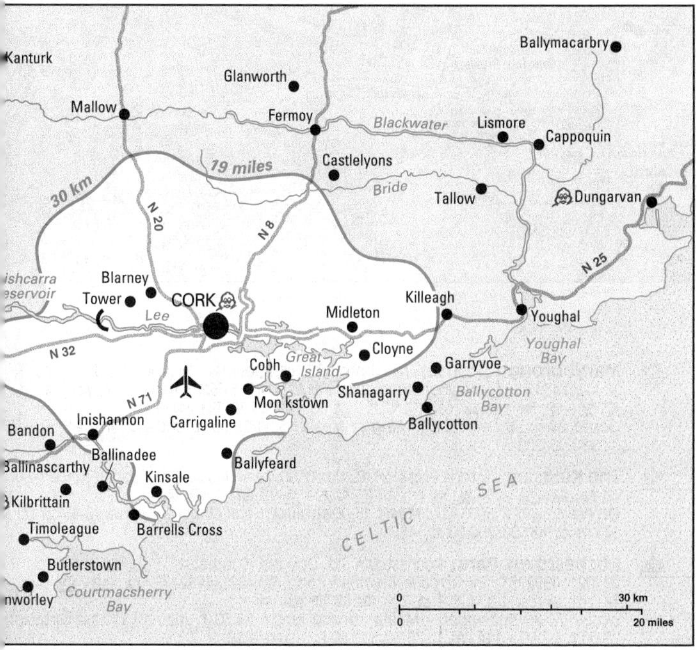

CORK

Camden Place . . . . Y 5
Coburg Street . . . . Y 10
Corn Market Street . . . . Y 13
Dominick Street . . . . Y 15
Eason's Hill . . . . Y 17
Emmet Place . . . . Y 18
Gerald Griffin St. . . . . Y 21
Infirmary Road . . . . Z 24
John Redmond Street . . . . . . Y 26

Lancaster Quay . . . . Z 28
Langford Row . . . . Z 29
Lower Glanmire Road . . . . Y 30
Merchant's Quay . . . . Y 32
Merchant's Quay Shopping Centre . . . . Y
Newsom's Quay . . . . Y 34
North Mall . . . . Y 35
O'Connell's Square. . . . . Y 36
Oliver Plunkett Street . . . . Z

Parnell Place. . . . .
Pembroke Street. . . . .
Proby's Quay . . . .
Roman Street . . . .
St Patrick's Quay . . . .
St. Patrick's Street . . . .
Southern Road. . . . .
South Link . . . .
South Main Street . . . .
Summer Hill. . . . .
Wolfe Tone Street . . . .

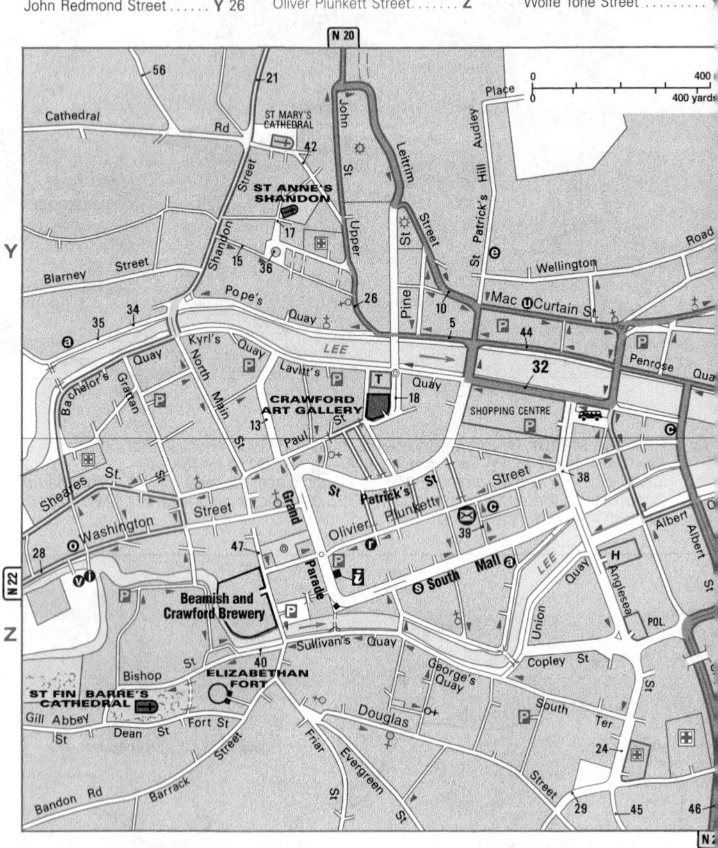

Maryborough House, Maryborough Hill, Douglas, Southeast : 3 m. by R
(021) 4365 555, *maryboro@indigo.ie, Fax (021) 4365 662,* « Part 18C », ...
– rm, rest, – 500. VISA.
closed 24 to 26 December – ***Zing's :*** **Meals** 15.00/25.00 **st.** and a la carte 8.50 – 75
180.00/200.00, 4 suites – SB.

The Kingsley, Victoria Cross, (021) 800500, *res@kingsleyhotel.com, Fax (021) 800.*
... – rm, – 90. VISA
Otters *((021) 800595) :* **Meals** 15.00 **st.** (lunch) and dinner a la carte 18.45/27.00 s
57 rm 120.00/200.00 **st.** – SB.

Rochestown Park, Rochestown Rd, Douglas, Southeast : 3 m. by R 609 on R
(021) 4892233, *info@rochestownpark.com, Fax (021) 4892178,* ... –
rm, rest, – 700. VISA.
closed 24-26 December – **Meals** (carving lunch) 22.50 **t.** (dinner) and a la carte app
25.00 **t.** 7.50 – **114 rm** 75.00/130.00 **t.**, 1 suite – SB.

Silversprings Moran H., Tivoli, East : 2 ½ m. by N 8 ☎ (021) 4507533, *Fax (021) 4507641*, squash – rm, rest, – 900. MC AE VISA. X c
closed 24 and 25 December – **Meals** 14.00/22.00 **st.** and a la carte 6.00 – 8.95 – **107 rm** 100.00/120.00 **st.**, 2 suites – SB.

Jurys Cork, Western Rd, by Washington St., ☎ (021) 4276622, *cork-hotel@jurysdoyle.com, Fax (021) 4274477*, heated, squash – rm, rest, – 700. MC AE VISA. Z v
Meals 12.00/18.00 **t.** and a la carte 7.00 – 9.95 – **184 rm** 130.00/180.00 **t.**, 1 suite.

Arbutus Lodge, Middle Glanmire Rd, Montenotte, ☎ (021) 4501237, *info@arbutuslodge.net, Fax (021) 4502893*, – rest, – 100. MC AE VISA. X e
closed 24 to 26 December – **Meals** (light lunch) a la carte 22.00/32.00 **t.** – **16 rm** 60.00/130.00 **t.** – SB.

Clarion H. and Suites Morrisons Island, Morrisons Quay, ☎ (021) 4275858, *morisons@iol.ie, Fax (021) 4275833* – . MC AE VISA. Z a
closed 24-27 December – **Meals** *(closed lunch Saturday and Sunday)* 12.00/25.00 **st.** and a la carte 6.50 – 8.00 – **32 rm** 90.00/150.00 **st.**, **24 suites** 140.00/220.00 **st.** – SB.

The Ambassador, Military Hill, ☎ (021) 4551996, *info@ambassadorhotel.ie, Fax (021) 4551997*, – rm, – 80. MC AE VISA JCB. X a
closed 25-26 December – **Meals** 9.00/15.00 **st.** (lunch) and dinner a la carte 24.50/30.50 **st.** 6.70 – **59 rm** 80.00/100.00 **st.**, 1 suite – SB.

Lancaster Lodge without rest., Lancaster Quay, Western Rd, ☎ (021) 4251125, *info@lancasterlodge.com, Fax (021) 4251126* – . MC AE VISA. Z i
closed 24-25 December – **39 rm** 60.00/90.00 **st.**

Jurys Inn Cork, Anderson's Quay, ☎ (021) 276444, *cork-inn@jurysdoyle.com, Fax (021) 276144* – rm, – 30. MC AE VISA. Y c
Meals (carving lunch)/dinner a la carte 11.90/20.70 **st.** 6.00 – 7.00 – **133 rm** 62.00 **t.**

The Commons Inn, Commons Rd, North : 2 ½ m. on N 20 ☎ (021) 4210300, *info@commonsinn.com, Fax (021) 4210333* – rest, – 500. MC AE VISA.
closed 23 December-3 January – **Meals** (dinner only and Sunday lunch)/dinner 20.00/22.00 **st.** and a la carte 6.50 – 6.00 – **40 rm** 50.00/60.00 **st.**

Victoria Lodge without rest., Victoria Cross, ☎ (021) 542233, *Fax (021) 542572*, – . MC AE VISA X v
closed 23 to 29 December – **30 rm** 39.00/60.00 **st.**

Ibis Cork, Lee Tunnel roundabout, Dunkettle, East : 4 ¾ m. by N 8, following signs for Glounthaune off N 25 slip rd ☎ (021) 354354, *h0580@accor_hotels.com, Fax (021) 354202* – rm, – 65. MC AE VISA
Meals (grill rest.) (dinner only) a la carte approx. 12.00 **st.** – **100 rm** 45.00 **st.**

Travelodge, Blackash, South : 2 ¼ m. by N 27 (south link) ☎ (021) 310722, *Fax (021) 310723* – rm, . MC AE VISA JCB.
Meals (grill rest.) – **40 rm** 44.95 **t.**

Seven North Mall without rest., 7 North Mall, ☎ (021) 397191, *sevennorthmall@eircom.ie, Fax (021) 300811* – . MC VISA. Y a
closed 17 December-8 January – **7 rm** 45.00/90.00.

Garnish House without rest., Western Rd, ☎ (021) 275111, *garnish@iol.ie, Fax (021) 273872* – . MC AE VISA. X r
14 rm 65.00/90.00.

Killarney House without rest., Western Rd, ☎ (021) 4270290, *killarneyhouse@iol.ie, Fax (021) 4271010* – . MC AE VISA. X x
19 rm 45.00/70.00 **st.**

Acorn House without rest., 14 St. Patrick's Hill, ☎ (021) 4502474, *jackie@acornhouse-cork.com, Fax (021) 4502474* – . MC VISA. Y e
closed 22 December-10 January – **9 rm** 30.00/60.00 **st.**

Flemings with rm, Silver Grange House, Tivoli, East : 2 ¾ m. on N 8 ☎ (021) 821621, *Fax (021) 821800*, – . MC AE VISA. X u
closed 24-27 December – **Meals** 18.50 **t.** (lunch) and a la carte 28.25/35.50 **t.** 8.50 – **4 rm** 49.00/70.00 **t.** – SB.

Jacobs on the Mall, 30A South Mall, ☎ (021) 4251530, *kingsley@eircom.net, Fax (021) 4251531*, « Contemporary Irish art collection » – . MC AE VISA Z s
closed 25-26 December, Good Friday, Sunday and lunch Bank Holidays – **Meals** (booking essential) 14.90 **t.** (lunch) and a la carte 18.90/29.00 **t.** 7.50.

Lovetts (Restaurant), Churchyard Lane, off Well Rd, Douglas, ☎ (021) 4294909, *lovetts@indigo.ie, Fax (021) 4294024* – . MC AE VISA X s
closed 2 weeks August-September, 1 week Christmas-New Year, Sunday, Monday and Bank Holidays – **Meals** (dinner only) a la carte 20.85/34.15 **t.** 6.95.

The Ivory Tower, The Exchange Buildings, 35 Princess St., (021) 274665 – MC AE VISA Z
closed 25 December, 1 January, Monday and Tuesday – **Meals** (dinner only) 30.0[…] and a la carte.

Jacques, Phoenix St., (021) 277387, *Fax (021) 270634* – . MC AE VISA Z
closed 25-27 December, Sunday and Bank Holidays – **Meals** 11.90/22.90 **t.** and a la ca[…] 8.90.

Isaacs, 48 MacCurtain St., (021) 503805, *Fax (021) 551348* – MC AE VISA Y
closed 1 week Christmas and Sunday lunch – **Meals** (booking essential) a la carte 13.[…] 21.45 **st.** 7.75.

Cafe Paradiso, 16 Lancaster Quay, Western Rd, (021) 277939, *Fax (021) 307469* – VISA Z
closed 2 weeks late August, 1 week Christmas, Sunday and Monday – **Meals** - Vegetari[…] (booking essential) a la carte 15.00/26.50 **t.** 7.50.

CRATLOE **(An Chreatalach)** *Clare* 923 F 9 – *pop. 557* – *Bunratty.*
Dublin 127 – Ennis 17 – Limerick 7.

Bunratty View without rest., (061) 357352, *bunrattyview@eircom.n[…]*
Fax (061) 357491, ←, – TV P. MC VISA.
closed 1 week Christmas – **6 rm** 30.00/46.00 **st.**

Cratloe Lodge without rest., Setrights Cross, (061) 357168, *Fax (061) 357168* – TV MC VISA
7 rm 25.00/40.00.

CRAUGHWELL **(Creachmhaoil)** *Galway* 923 F 8.
Dublin 121 – Galway 15 – Limerick 55.

St. Clerans ,, Northeast : 3 ½ m. off N 6 taking second turning left after 1 m. th[…] veering left after a further 2 m. (091) 846555, *stclerans@iol.ie, Fax (091) 846600,* « Part 18C country house », , , – TV P. MC AE VISA.
Meals (dinner only) 45.00 **st.** 12.00 – **12 rm** 320.00/380.00 **st.** – SB.

CROOKEDWOOD **(Tigh Munna)** *Westmeath* 923 K 7 – *see Mullingar.*

CROSSMOLINA **(Crois Mhaoilíona)** *Mayo* 923 E 5 *Ireland G.* – *pop. 1 103.*
Env. : *Errew Abbey★, SE : 6 m. by R 315.*
Exc. : *Broad Haven★, NW : 27 m. by N 59 and R 313.*
Dublin 157 – Ballina 6.5.

Enniscoe House , Castlehill, South : 2 m. on R 315 (096) 31112, *mail@enniscoe[…] m, Fax (096) 31773,* ←, « Georgian country house, antiques », , , – P. MC AE
April-mid October – **Meals** (booking essential to non-residents) (dinner only) 28.00 10.00 – **6 rm** 76.00/132.00 **st.** – SB.

DALKEY **(Deilginis)** *Dublin* 923 N 8.
Dublin 8 – Bray 6.

Tudor House without rest., off Castle St. (01) 285 1528, *Fax (01) 284 8133,* « Victo[…] manor house », – TV P. MC VISA.
6 rm 55.00/90.00.

Munkberrys, 22 Castle St., (01) 284 7185 – MC AE VISA
closed 25-26 December, Good Friday, lunch Saturday and dinner Sunday – **Meals** 14.[…] 21.95 **t.** (dinner) and a la carte 19.95/32.15 **t.**

DELGANY **(Deilgne)** *Wicklow* 923 N 8 – *pop. 6 682 (inc. Greystones)* – *Bray.*
18 *(01) 287 4536.*
Dublin 19.

Glenview, Glen of the Downs, Northwest : 2 m. on N 11 (01) 287 3399, *glenview@io[…] Fax (01) 287 7511,* ←, , , , , – , rest, TV – 250. MC AE JCB
Woodlands : **Meals** 17.00/30.00 **st.** and dinner a la carte 7.50 – **73 rm** 115.[…] 190.00 **st.**, 1 suite – SB.

NGLE (An Daingean) *Kerry* 923 B 11 *Ireland G. – pop. 1 536.*

See : *Town★ – St. Mary's Church★ (Presentation Convent Chapel★).*

Env. : *Gallarus Oratory★★, NW : 5 m. by R 559 – NE : Connor Pass★★ – Kilmalkedar★, NW : 5½ m. by R 559.*

Exc. : *Dingle Peninsula★★★ – Stradbally Strand★★, NE : 10½ m. via Connor Pass – Mount Eagle (Beehive Huts★), W : 9 m. by R 559 – Corca Dhuibhne Regional Museum★* **AC**, *NW : 8 m. by R 559 – Blasket Islands★, W : 13 m. by R 559 and ferry from Dunquin.*

The Quay ✆ (066) 9151188 (March-November).

Dublin 216 – Killarney 51 – Limerick 95.

Dingle Skellig,, Southeast : ½ m. by N 86 ✆ (066) 9150200, *dsk@iol.ie, Fax (066) 9151501*, ≤, Ⅰ₆, ▣, 🌳 – ▮ TV P – 🔔 300. MC AE ① VISA. ✗
closed 4 January-9 February and 25 December – **Meals** (bar lunch)/dinner 20.50/29.50 **st.** 10.00 – **113 rm** ☐ 119.00/228.00 **t.**, 3 suites – SB.

Benners, Main St., ✆ (066) 9151638, *benners@eircom.net, Fax (066) 9151412* – ▮ TV P. MC AE ① VISA. ✗
closed 25 December – **Meals** (bar lunch) (dinner in bar Monday to Thursday and Sunday in winter)/dinner 9.50/20.00 **t.** and a la carte – **52 rm** ☐ 90.00/140.00 **t.** – SB.

Milltown House without rest.,, West : ¾ m. by R 559 (Slea Head Drive) ✆ (066) 9151372, *milltown@indigo.ie, Fax (066) 9151095*, ≤, 🌳 – ✗ TV ♿ P. MC AE VISA. ✗
closed 23-29 December – **10 rm** ☐ 75.00/85.00 **st.**

Greenmount House without rest., Gortonora, by John St. ✆ (066) 9151414, *mary@greenmounthouse.com, Fax (066) 9151974*, ≤, 🌳 – ✗ TV P. MC VISA. ✗
closed 10 to 31 December – **12 rm** ☐ 60.00/90.00 **t.**

Heatons without rest., The Wood, West : ½ m. on R 559 ✆ (066) 9152288, *heatons@iol.ie, Fax (066) 9152324*, ≤ – ✗ TV P. MC VISA. ✗
– **12 rm** ☐ 65.00/120.00 **st.**

Doyle's Townhouse, 5 John St., ✆ (066) 9151174, *cdoyles@iol.ie, Fax (066) 9151816* – TV. MC ① VISA. ✗
closed mid December-10 February – **Meals** – (see ***Doyle's Seafood Bar*** below) – **8 rm** ☐ 78.00/84.00 **st.**

Captains House without rest., The Mall, ✆ (066) 9151531, *captigh@eircom.net, Fax (066) 9151079*, 🌳 – ✗ TV. MC AE VISA. ✗
16 March-November – **8 rm** ☐ 35.00/80.00 **st.**

Pax House without rest., Upper John St., Northeast : ¾ m. on John St. ✆ (066) 9151518, *paxhouse@iol.ie, Fax (066) 9152461*, ≤, 🌳 – ✗ TV P. MC VISA
closed December and January – **12 rm** ☐ 40.00/90.00 **st.**

Cleevaun without rest., Lady's Cross, Milltown, West : 1¼ m. on R 559 following signs for Slea Head Drive ✆ (066) 9151108, *cleevaun@iol.ie, Fax (066) 9152228*, ≤, 🌳 – ✗ TV P. MC VISA. ✗
mid March-mid November – **9 rm** ☐ 55.00/64.00.

Bambury's without rest., Mail Rd, East : on N 86 ✆ (066) 9151244, *berniebb@tinet.ie, Fax (066) 9151786*, ≤ – ✗ TV P. MC VISA. ✗
12 rm ☐ 40.00/60.00.

Beginish, Green St., ✆ (066) 9151321, *Fax (066) 9151321*, 🌳 – ✗ ▤. MC VISA
closed Monday and mid November-mid March except Christmas – **Meals** - Seafood - (dinner only) 18.50/25.00 **t.** and a la carte.

The Chart House, The Mall, ✆ (066) 9152255, *charthse@iol.ie, Fax (066) 9152255* – ▤. MC VISA
closed 7 January-14 February, Tuesday, and 25-26 December – **Meals** *(restricted opening in winter)* (dinner only) a la carte 20.25/28.00 **t.** 7.75.

Doyle's Seafood Bar, 4 John St., ✆ (066) 9151174, *cdoyles@iol.ie, Fax (066) 9151816* – ✗ ▤. MC ① VISA
closed mid December-10 February – **Meals** *(closed Sunday)* (dinner only) a la carte 19.40/28.50 **t.** 7.00.

The Half Door, 3 John St., ✆ (066) 9151600, *Fax (066) 9151883* – ✗ ▤ TV. MC VISA
closed mid January-mid February and Sunday – **Meals** - Seafood - a la carte 24.50/35.50 **t.** 8.50 – **7 rm** ☐ 50.00/100.00 **t.**

Remember the speed limits that apply in the United Kingdom, unless otherwise signposted.
- 60 mph on single carriageway roads
- 70 mph on dual carriageway roads and motorways

DONEGAL **(Dún na nGall)** *Donegal* 923 H 4 *Ireland G. – pop. 2 296.*

See : *Donegal Castle★ AC.*

Exc. : *Donegal Coast★★ – Cliffs of Bunglass★★, W : 30 m. by N 56 and R 263 – Glencolmc Folk Village★★ AC, W : 33 m. by N 56 and R 263 – Rossnowlagh Strand★★, S : 22 m. by N and R 231 – Trabane Strand★, W : 36 m. by N 56 and R 263.*

Donegal Airport ℘ (075) 48284.

The Quay ℘ (073) 21148 (April-October).

Dublin 164 – Londonderry 48 – Sligo 40.

St. Ernan's House, St. Ernan's Island, Southwest : 2 ¼ m. by N 15 ℘ (073) 21065, *o@sainternans.com, Fax (073) 22098,* « Wooded island setting ≤ Donegal Bay », rest, TV P. MC VISA.
Easter-late October – **Meals** (dinner only) 30.00 **t.** 9.00 – **10 rm** 125.00/280.00 1 suite.

Harvey's Point Country H., Lough Eske, Northeast : 4 ½ m. by T 27 (Killibegs ℘ (073) 22208, *reservations@harveyspoint.com, Fax (073) 22352,* ≤, « Loughside setting », – TV P. – 50. MC AE VISA
closed Monday and Tuesday November-Easter – **Meals** – (see ***The Restaurant*** below) **20 rm** 70.00/150.00 **st.** – SB.

Island View House without rest., Ballyshannon rd, Southwest : ¾ m. on N ℘ (073) 22411, *islandview@eirbyte.com,* ≤, – TV P.
closed 24-26 December **4 rm** 30.00/42.00 **t.**

The Restaurant (at Harvey's Point Country H.), Lough Eske, Northeast : 4 ½ m. by N (Killibegs rd) ℘ (073) 22208, *Fax (073) 22352,* ≤, « Loughside setting », – P. MC AE VISA
closed Monday and Tuesday November-Easter – **Meals** 13.75/30.00 **st.** and a la carte.

DONNYBROOK **(Domhnach Broc)** *Dublin* 923 ⑩ *– see Dublin.*

DOOGORT **(Dumha Goirt)** *Mayo* 923 B 5/6 *– see Achill Island.*

DOOLIN **(Dúlainm)** *Clare* 923 D 8 *Ireland G.*

Env. : *The Burren★★ (Cliffs of Moher★★★, Scenic Routes★★, Aillwee Cave★ AC (Wat fall★★), Corcomrow Abbey★, Kilfenora Crosses★).*

Dublin 171 – Galway 43 – Limerick 50.

Aran View House, Coast Rd, Northeast : ½ m. ℘ (065) 7074061, *bookings@aranview m, Fax (065) 7074540,* ≤, « Working farm », – TV P. MC AE VISA
April-October – **Meals** (dinner only and Sunday lunch)/dinner 18.00/22.00 **t.** and a la ca 5.95 – **19 rm** 50.00/100.00 **t.** – SB.

Doonmacfelim House without rest., ℘ (065) 7074503, *Fax (065) 7074129,* – P. VISA.
closed 23 to 28 December – **6 rm** 32.00/47.00 **t.**

DROGHEDA **(Droichead Átha)** *Louth* 923 M 6 *Ireland G. – pop. 24 460.*

See : *Town★ – Drogheda Museum★ – St. Laurence Gate★.*

Env. : *Monasterboice★★, N : 6 ½ m. by N 1 – Boyne Valley★★, on N 51 – Termonfecki NE : 5 m. by R 166.*

Exc. : *Newgrange★★★, W : 3 m. by N 51 on N 2 – Old Mellifont★ – Knowth★.*

Seapoint, Termonfeckin ℘ (041) 982 2333 – Towneley Hall, Tullyallen ℘ (041) 42229

Bus Eireann Depot, Donore Rd ℘ (041) 37070.

Dublin 29 – Dundalk 22.

Boyne Valley H. and Country Club,, Southeast : 1 ¼ m. by N 1 ℘ (041) 9837737, *ervations@boyne-valley-hotel.ie, Fax (041) 9839188,* – rm, TV P. – 350. MC AE VISA
Meals 12.50/26.00 **st.** and dinner a la carte 7.50 – **37 rm** 55.00/110.00 **st.** – SB.

Westcourt, West St., ℘ (041) 9830965, *Fax (041) 9830970* – TV P. – 350. MC VISA.
closed 25 December – **Meals** (carving lunch) 16.95 **t.** dinner and a la carte 9.75/18.50 **t.** – 5.00 – **27 rm** 45.00/90.00 – SB.

Tullyesker Country House without rest., Dundalk Rd, North : 3 ½ m. by N ℘ (041) 9830430, *mcdonnellfamily@ireland.com, Fax (041) 9832624,* ≤, – TV P.
closed December and January – **5 rm** 40.00/60.00 **st.**

Boyne Haven House without rest., Dublin Rd, Southeast : 2 ½ m. on N ℘ (041) 9836700, *Fax (041) 9836700,* – TV P. MC VISA.
4 rm 35.00/60.00 **st.**

DRUMCONDRA **(Droim Conrach)** *Dublin* 923 ㊱ *– see Dublin.*

DUBLIN - (Baile Átha Cliath)

Dublin 923 N 7 *Ireland G. – pop. 481 854.*

Belfast 103 – Cork 154 – Londonderry 146.

TOURIST INFORMATION

Bord Failte Offices Baggot Street Bridge, ℘ (01) 602 4000 – Suffolk St. – Arrivals Hall, Dublin Airport – The Square, Tallaght.

PRACTICAL INFORMATION

Elm Park, Nutley House, Donnybrook ℘ (01) 269 3438, **GV**.
Milltown, Lower Churchtown Rd ℘ (01) 467 6090.
Royal Dublin, North Bull Island, Dollymount ℘ (01) 833 6346.
Forrest Little, Cloghran ℘ (01) 840 1183.
Lucan, Celbridge Rd, Lucan ℘ (01) 628 0246.
Edmondstown, Rathfarnham ℘ (01) 493 2461.
Coldwinters, Newtown House, St. Margaret's ℘ (01) 864 0324.
Dublin Airport : ℘ (01) 814 1111, N : 5½ m. by N 1 **BS** – **Terminal** : *Busaras (Central Bus Station) Store St.*
to Holyhead (Irish Ferries) 2 daily (3 h 15 mn) – to Holyhead (Stena Line) daily (4 h) – to the Isle of Man (Douglas) (Isle of Man Steam Packet Co. Ltd) (2 h 45 mn/4 h 30 mn) – to Liverpool (steam Packet Co. Ltd) 2-3 daily (4 h).

SIGHTS

See : *City★★★ Trinity College★★* **JY** – *Old Library★★★ (Treasury★★★, Long Room★★) – Dublin Castle★★ (Chester Beatty Library★★★)* **HY** – *Christ Church Cathedral★★* **HY** – *St. Patrick's Cathedral★★* **HZ** – *Marsh's Library★★* **HZ** – *National Museum★★ (The Treasury★★)* **KZ** – *National Gallery★★* **KZ** – *Newman House★★* **JZ** – *Bank of Ireland★★* **JY** – *Custom House★★* **KX** – *Four Courts★★* **HY** – *Kilmainham Gaol Museum★★* **AT M6** – *Kilmainham Hospital★★* **AT** – *Phoenix Park★★ – National Botanic Gardens★★* **BS** – *Marino Casino★★* **CS** – *Tailors Hall★* **HY** – *City Hall★* **HY** – *Temple Bar★* **HJY** – *Liffey Bridge★* **JY** – *Merrion Square★* **KZ** – *Number Twenty-Nine★* **KZ D** – *Grafton Street★* **JYZ** – *Powerscourt Centre★* **JY** – *Rotunda Hospital Chapel★* **JX** – *O'Connell Street★ (GPO Building★)* **JX** – *Hugh Lane Municipal Gallery of Modern Art★* **JX M4** – *Pro-Cathedral★* **JX** – *Bluecoat School★* **BS F** – *Guinness Museum★* **BT M7** – *Rathfarnham Castle★ – Zoological Gardens★* **AS**.

Env. : *Howth★ (The Summit★, ≤★).*

Exc. : *Powerscourt★★ (Waterfall★★* **AC**), *S : 14 m. by N 11 and R 117* **EV** – *Russborough House★★★, SW : 22 m. by N 81* **BT**.

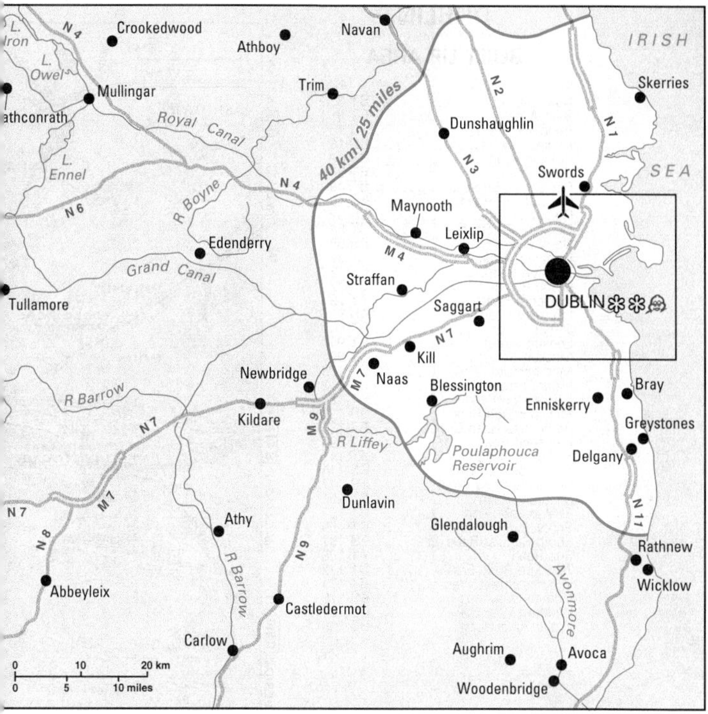

L. Iron
N 4
Crookedwood
Athboy
Navan
IRISH
L. Owel
Mullingar
Trim
N 2
Skerries
athconrath
Royal Canal
40 km / 25 miles
Dunshaughlin
N 1
L. Ennel
N 3
Swords
SEA
N 6
R Boyne
N 4
Maynooth
Leixlip
Edenderry
M 4
Grand Canal
Straffan
DUBLIN
Tullamore
Saggart
N 7
Kill
Newbridge
M 7
Naas
Blessington
Bray
R Barrow
Enniskerry
Kildare
M 9
Greystones
N 7
R Liffey
Poulaphouca Reservoir
Delgany
M 7
Dunlavin
N 7
N 11
N 8
Athy
Glendalough
Rathnew
N 9
R Barrow
Avonmore
Wicklow
Abbeyleix
Castledermot
Carlow
Aughrim
Avoca
Woodenbridge
0 10 20 km
0 5 10 miles

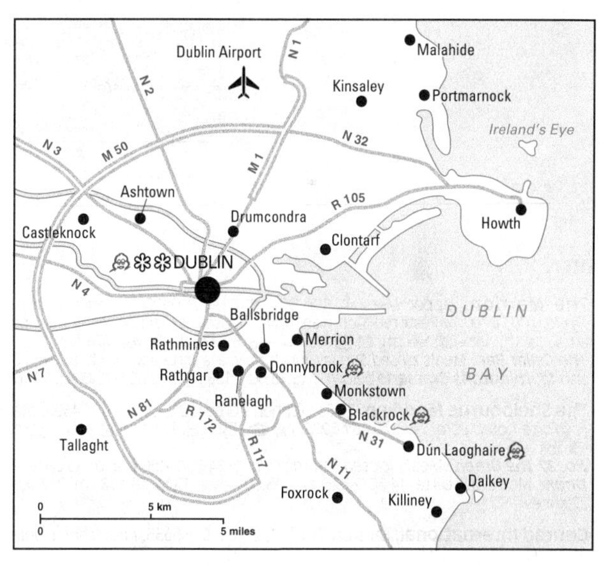

DUBLIN

BUILT UP AREA

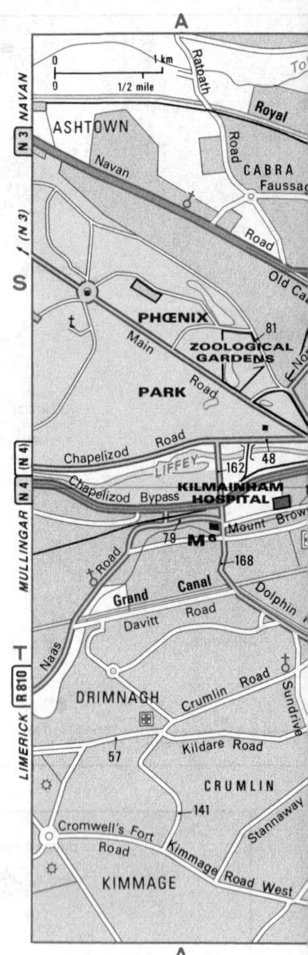

City Centre.

The Merrion, Upper Merrion St., D2, ✆ (01) 603 0600, *info@merrionhotel.co...* *Fax (01) 603 0700,* « Restored Georgian town houses, collection of contemporary Iri... art », 🏋, 🏊, – 🛗, ⌧ rm, ▤ 📺 ✆ 🚗 – 🎪 60. 🅜🅒 AE ⓓ VISA JCB. ✂ KZ
The Cellar Bar : Meals *closed Sunday* (lunch only) a la carte approx. 16.85 **st.** 🍷 8.00 – (s... also ***Morningtons Brasserie*** below) – ☕ 18.00 – **135 rm** 210.00/275.00 **t.**, 10 suites – S...

The Shelbourne Meridien, 27 St. Stephen's Green, D2, ✆ (01) 663 4500, *shelbourne... fo@forte-hotels.com, Fax (01) 661 6006,* 🏋, ≘s, 🏊 – 🛗, ⌧ rm, 📺 🚗 – 🎪 400. 🅜🅒 ⓓ VISA JCB JZ
No. 27 The Green : Meals *(closed Saturday lunch)* 24.50/27.50 **t.** and a la carte – ***The Si... Door :*** Meals a la carte 14.50/24.25 **t.** 🍷 13.00 – ☕ 15.50 – **168 rm** 237.00/308.00 22 suites – SB.

Conrad International, Earlsfort Terr., D2, ✆ (01) 676 5555, *info@conrad_internatior... ie, Fax (01) 676 5424,* 🏋 – 🛗, ⌧ rm, ▤ 📺 ✆ ♿ 🅿 – 🎪 370. 🅜🅒 AE ⓓ VISA. ✂ JZ
Alexandra : Meals 18.50 **st.** (lunch) and a la carte 28.25/33.45 **st.** 🍷 6.50 – ***Plurabe... Brasserie :*** Meals 17.00/23.00 **st.** and a la carte 🍷 6.50 – ☕ 14.50 – **182 rm** 240.0... 280.00 **st.**, 9 suites.

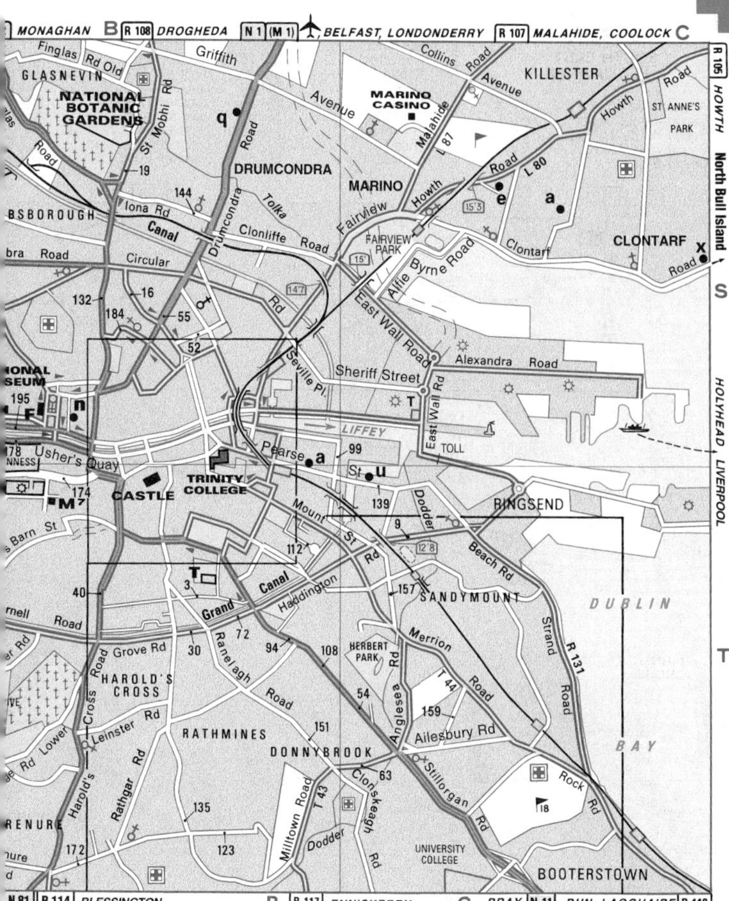

The Westbury, Grafton St., D2, ✆ (01) 679 1122, *westbury_hotel@jurysdoyle.com, Fax (01) 679 7078,* – rm, rest, – 200. JY b
Russell Room : Meals 17.00/30.00 **t.** and a la carte 7.00 – ***The Sandbank :*** Meals *(closed 25-27 and 31 December and 1 January)* 17.00/26.25 **t.** and a la carte 7.00 – 12.95 – **196 rm** 230.00/250.00 **t.**, 8 suites.

The Clarence, 6-8 Wellington Quay, D2, ✆ (01) 407 0800, *reservations@theclarence.ie, Fax (01) 407 0820,* « Contemporary interior design » – – 60. HY a
closed 25 and 26 December – **Meals** – (see ***The Tea Room*** below) – 15.00 – **45 rm** 210.00/225.00 **st.**, 4 suites.

The Fitzwilliam, St. Stephen's Green, D2, ✆ (01) 478 7000, *enq@fitzwilliam-hotel.com, Fax (01) 478 7878,* « Contemporary interior », – – 70. JZ d
Mango Toast : Meals - Asian - 16.95 **st.** (lunch) and a la carte 23.45/34.95 **st.** 7.00 – (see also ***Peacock Alley*** below) – 14.50 – **128 rm** 205.00/270.00 **st.**, 2 suites.

Morrison, Ormond Quay, D1, ✆ (01) 887 2400, *info@morrisonhotel.ie, Fax (01) 878 3185,* « Contemporary interior » – rm, HY r
Meals – (see ***Halo*** below) – 13.50 – **91 rm** 175.00 **t.**, 4 suites.

DUBLIN
SOUTH EAST BUILT UP AREA

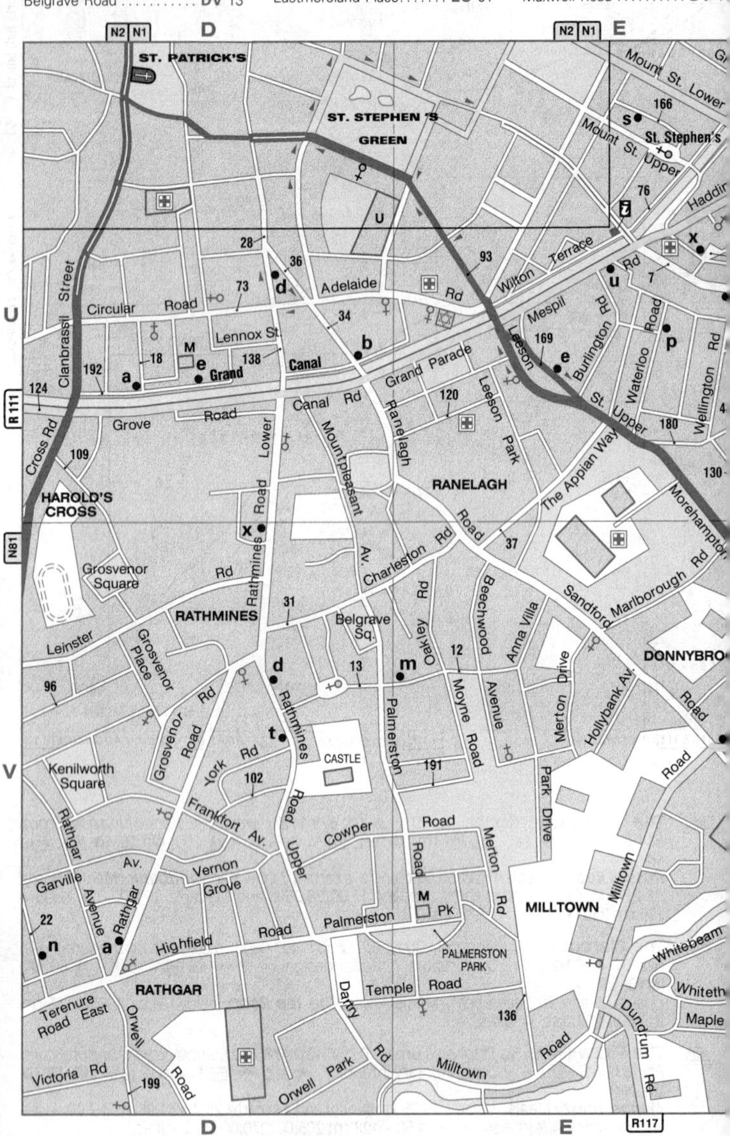

If you find you cannot take up a hotel booking you have made, please let the hotel know immediately.

rlyn Park . . . . GV 105
unt Drummond
Avenue . . . . DU 109
wbridge Avenue . . . . . . FU 115
wgrove Avenue . . . . . . GU 117
rthbrook Road . . . . EU 120
tgrove Park . . . . FV 121
nell Road . . . . DU 124
mbroke Park. . . . . EU 130
glan Road . . . . FU 133

Richmond Avenue
South . . . . EV 136
Richmond Street South . . DU 138
St Alban's Park . . . . GV 142
St John's Road East. . . . . GV 145
Seafort Avenue . . . . GU 153
Sean Moore Road. . . . . GU 154
Serpentine Avenue . . . . . . FU 156
Simmonscourt Road . . . . . FU 160
South Lotts Road. . . . . FU 163

Stephen's Lane . . . . EU 166
Sussex Road . . . . EU 169
Trimbleston
Avenue . . . . GV 175
Victoria Avenue . . . . FV 177
Wellington Place . . . . EU 180
Windsor Road. . . . . EV 191
Windsor Terrace . . . . DU 192
Wynnsward Drive . . . . FV 198
Zion Road . . . . DV 199

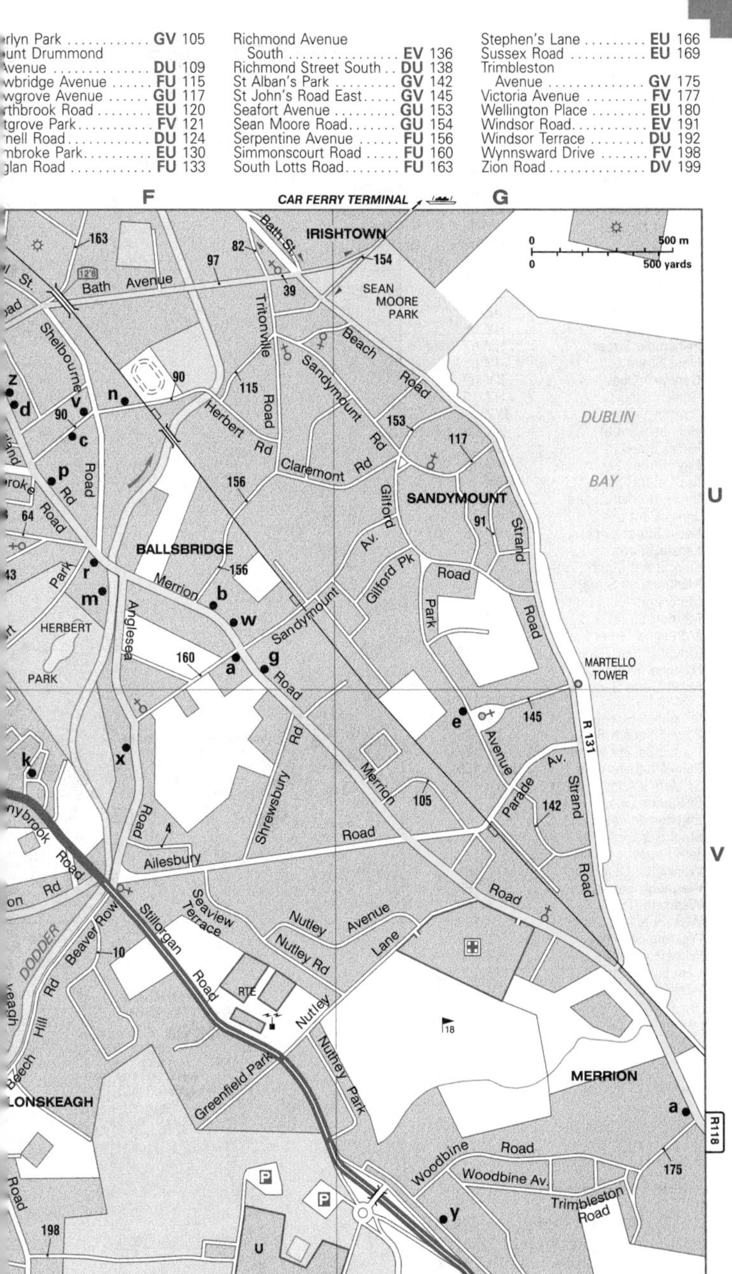

Prévenez immédiatement l'hôtelier si vous ne pouvez pas occuper la chambre que vous avez retenue.

DUBLIN
CENTRE

Anne Street South . . . . **JYZ** 6
Brunswick Street North . . . . . **HX** 24
Buckingham Street. . . . . **KX** 25
Bull Alley. . . . . **HZ** 27
Chancery Street . . . . **HY** 33
Clanbrassil Street . . . . **HZ** 40
College Green . . . . **JY** 45
College Street . . . . **JY** 46
Cornmarket . . . . **HY** 49
Dawson Street . . . . **JYZ**
D'Olier Street. . . . . **JY** 51
Duke Street . . . . **JY** 58
Earlsfort Terrace. . . . . **JZ** 60
Essex Quay . . . . **HY** 66
Fishamble Street. . . . . **HY** 67
Fleet Street. . . . . **JY** 68
George's Quay . . . . **KY** 69
Golden Lane. . . . . **HZ** 70
Grafton Street . . . . **JYZ**
Henrietta Street . . . . **HX** 75
Henry Street. . . . . **JX**
High Street. . . . . **HY** 78
Ilac Centre. . . . . **HJX**
Irish Life Mall Centre. . . . . . . **JKX**
Jervis Centre. . . . . **HJX**
Kevin Street Upper. . . . . **HZ** 85
Kildare Street. . . . . **JKZ** 87
King Street South . . . . **JZ** 88
Marlborough Street. . . . . **JX** 100
Merchants Quay . . . . **HY** 103
Merrion Street . . . . **KZ** 104
Montague Street . . . . **JZ** 106
Mount Street Upper. . . . . **KZ** 112
Nicholas Street . . . . **HY** 118
North Great Georges's Street. . . . . **JX** 119
O'Connell Street . . . . **JX**
Parnell Square East. . . . . **JX** 126
Parnell Square North . . . . **JX** 127
Parnell Square West . . . . **HJX** 129
St Mary's Abbey Street. . . . . . **HY** 148
St Patrick Close. . . . . **HZ** 150
Stephen Street . . . . **HJY** 165
Stephens Green. . . . . **JZ**
Tara Street . . . . **KY** 171
Wellington Quay. . . . . **HJY** 181
Werburgh Street. . . . . **HY** 183
Westland Row. . . . . **KY** 186
Westmoreland Street . . . . **JY** 187
Wexford Street . . . . **HZ** 189
Whitefriar Street . . . . **HZ** 190
Winetavern Street . . . . **HY** 193
Wood Quay . . . . **HY** 196

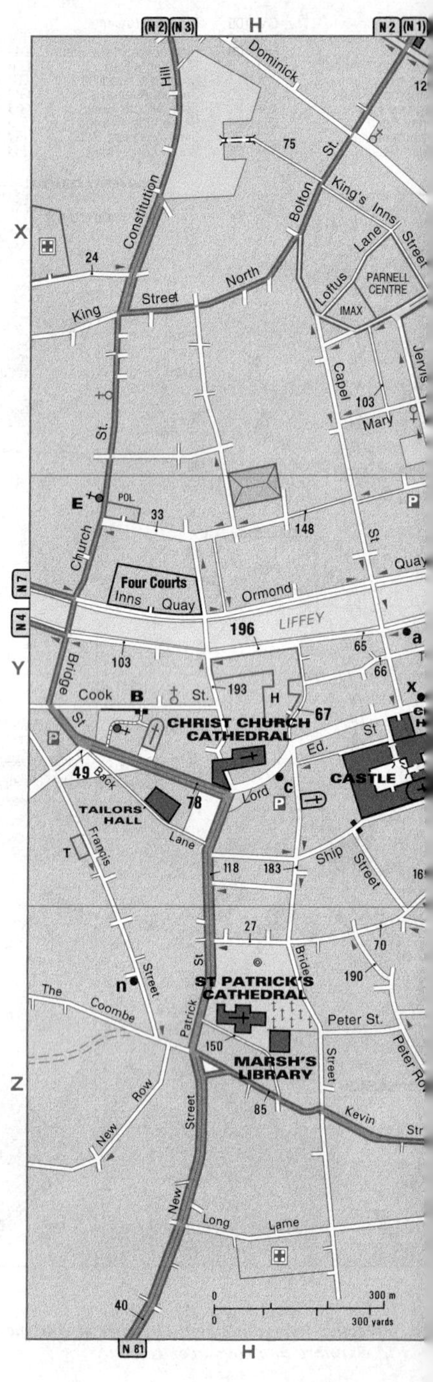

When looking
for a quiet hotel
use the maps found
in the introduction
or look
for establishments
with the sign or .

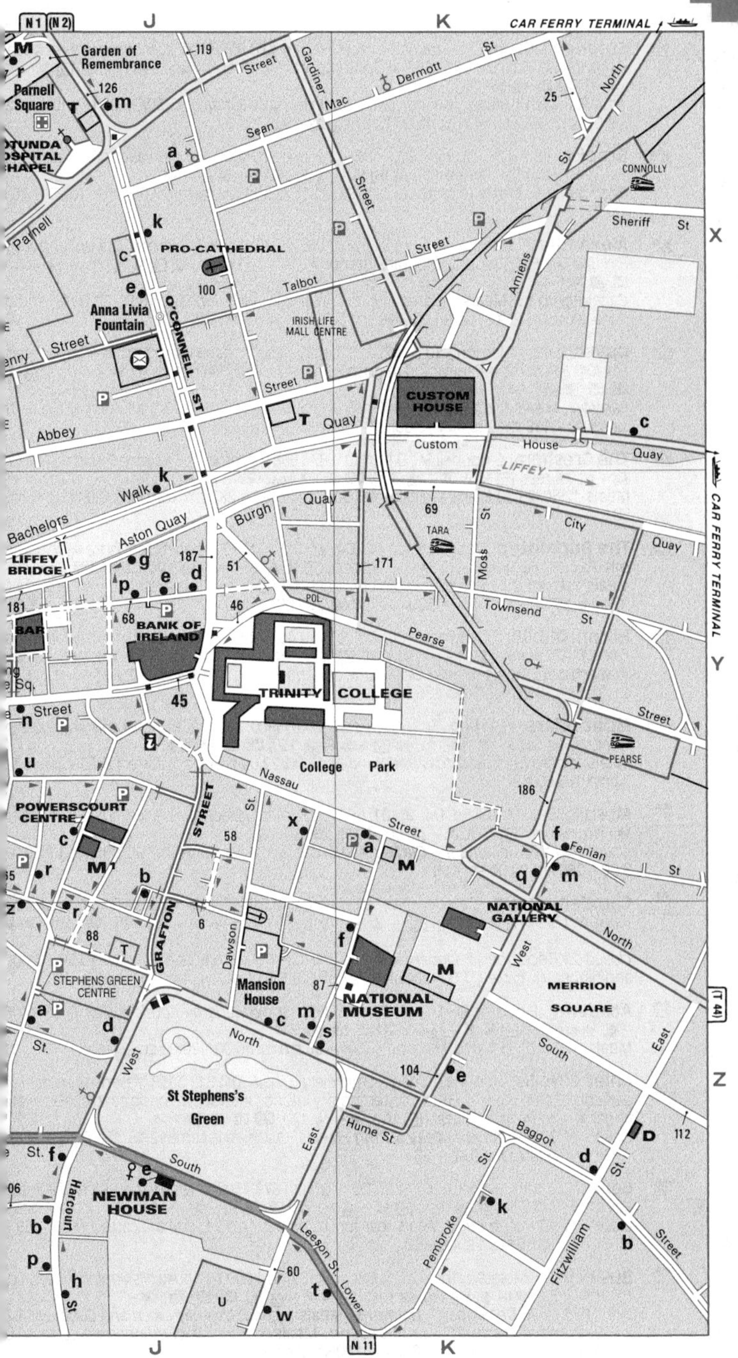
J
K
CAR FERRY TERMINAL
Garden of Remembrance
Parnell Square
ROTUNDA HOSPITAL CHAPEL
Sean Mac Dermott St
Gardiner Street
North St
CONNOLLY
Sheriff St
X
PRO-CATHEDRAL
Talbot Street
Amiens
Anna Livia Fountain
O'CONNELL ST
IRISH LIFE MALL CENTRE
Henry Street
CUSTOM HOUSE
Abbey Street
Eden Quay
Custom House Quay
LIFFEY
Bachelors Walk
Aston Quay
Burgh Quay
City Quay
TARA
Moss St
LIFFEY BRIDGE
Townsend St
Pearse Street
BANK OF IRELAND
TRINITY COLLEGE
Y
PEARSE
College Park
Nassau Street
POWERSCOURT CENTRE
GRAFTON STREET
Fenian St
NATIONAL GALLERY
Dawson St
Mansion House
NATIONAL MUSEUM
MERRION SQUARE
STEPHENS GREEN CENTRE
St Stephens's Green
Z
Hume St.
Baggot St.
NEWMAN HOUSE
Harcourt St
Leeson St. Lower
Pembroke St.
Fitzwilliam Street
N 11
N 1
N 2
T 44

Stephen's Green, St. Stephen's Green, D2, ℘ (01) 607 3600, *stephensgreenres@ocalhanhotels.ie, Fax (01) 661 5663,* « Contemporary interior », – rm, TV – 30. MC AE DC VISA. JZ
The Pie Dish : Meals *(closed lunch Saturday and Sunday)* 13.50/25.00 **t.** and a la ca 9.00 – 15.00 – **64 rm** 240.00 **t.**, 11 suites – SB.

Brooks, 59-62 Drury St., D2, ℘ (01) 670 4000, *reservations@brookshotel Fax (01) 670 4455* – |‡|, rm, TV – 70. MC AE DC VISA. JY
Francesca's : Meals (dinner only) 17.95/21.95 **t.** and a la carte 7.95 – 10.95 – **75** 135.00/230.00 **st.**

Alexander, Merrion Sq., D2, ℘ (01) 607 3700, *alexanderres@ocallaghanhotels Fax (01) 661 5663,* « Contemporary interior », – |‡|, rm, TV – 400. AE DC VISA. KY
Caravaggio's : Meals *(closed lunch Saturday and Sunday)* 18.50/30.00 **t.** and d ner a la carte 9.00 – 14.50 – **98 rm** 225.00 **t.**, 4 suites – SB.

Davenport, Merrion Sq., D2, ℘ (01) 607 3500, *davenportres@ocallaghanhotels Fax (01) 661 5663,* « Part Victorian gospel hall », – |‡|, rm, TV – 4(MC AE DC VISA. KY
Lanyon : Meals *(closed Saturday lunch and Sunday)* 18.50/30.00 **t.** and dinner a la carte 15.00 – **118 rm** 225.00 **t.**, 2 suites – SB.

The Gresham, O'Connell St., D1, ℘ (01) 874 6881, *gresham@indigo.ie, Fax (01) 878 71.* – |‡|, rest, TV P – 350. MC AE DC VISA. JX
Meals 12.50/25.50 **t.** and a la carte 8.50 – 15.95 – **282 rm** 180.00/200.00 **t.**, 6 suite SB.

The Burlington, Upper Leeson St., D4, ℘ (01) 660 5222, *burlington_hotel@jurysdoyl om, Fax (01) 660 8496* – |‡|, rm, rest, TV P – 1500. MC AE DC VISA JCB.
Meals *(closed 25 December)* (carvery lunch Monday to Friday)/dinner a la carte 24.(32.00 **t.** 7.00 – 14.00 – **500 rm** 160.00/205.00 **t.**, 4 suites. EU

Hilton Dublin, Charlemont Pl., D2, ℘ (01) 402 9988, *reservations_dublin@hilton.co Fax (01) 402 9966* – |‡|, rm, rest, TV – 390. MC AE DC VISA. DU
Waterfront : Meals *(closed lunch Saturday and Sunday)* a la carte 14.25/26.45 **st.** 6.5(11.50 – **189 rm** 175.00/195.00 **st.** – SB.

Mont Clare, Merrion Sq., D2, ℘ (01) 607 3800, *montclareres@ocallaghanhotels. Fax (01) 661 5663* – |‡|, rm, TV – 150. MC AE DC VISA. KY
Meals *(closed lunch Saturday and Sunday)* 16.00/22.00 **t.** and a la carte 8.00 – 13.5(**74 rm** 155.00 **t.** – SB.

Mespil, 50-60 Mespil Rd, D4, ℘ (01) 667 1222, *mespil@leehotels.ie, Fax (01) 667 1244* – rm, rest, TV P – 50. MC AE DC VISA. EU
closed 24 to 27 December – ***Glaze :*** Meals (bar lunch) a la carte 11.75/22.95 **st.** 9.50 – 9.00 – **250 rm** 90.00 **st.** – SB.

Camden Court, Camden St., D2, ℘ (01) 475 9666, *sales@camdencourthotel.co Fax (01) 475 9677,* , , – |‡|, rest, TV – 125. MC AE DC V DU
closed 23 December-3 January – **Meals** (bar lunch Saturday and Sunday) 10.50/22.00 and dinner a la carte 7.00 – **246 rm** 150.00/180.00 **st.**

Academy, Findlater Pl., D1, ℘ (01) 878 0666, *stay@academy-hotels.ie, Fax (01) 878 06* – |‡|, rm, TV P – 50. MC AE DC VISA. JX
Meals 14.95/20.95 **t.** and a la carte 7.00 – **96 rm** 80.00/120.00 **st.**, 2 suites – SB.

Chief O'Neills, Smithfield Village, Smithfield, D7, ℘ (01) 817 3838, *reservations@chief eills.com, Fax (01) 817 3839,* « Contemporary interior, interactive music centre, observati tower » – |‡|, rm, rest, TV P – 120. MC AE DC VISA. BS
closed 23-28 December – ***Kelly & Ping :*** Meals - Asian - a la carte 12.45/15.70 **st.** – 9. – **73 rm** 130.00/295.00 **st.** – SB.

Central, 1-5 Exchequer St., D2, ℘ (01) 679 7302, *reservations@centralhotel Fax (01) 679 7303* – |‡|, rest, TV – 80. MC AE DC VISA. JY
closed 24-28 December – **Meals** (bar lunch)/dinner 14.95 **t.** and a la carte 9.20 – **69 r** 84.00/150.00 **st.**, 1 suite – SB.

Buswells, Molesworth St., D2, ℘ (01) 614 6500, *buswells@quinn-hotels.co Fax (01) 676 2090* – |‡|, rm, rest, TV P – 80. MC AE VISA. KZ
closed 24 to 26 December – ***Trumans :*** Meals *(closed Saturday lunch and Sunday)* 14.7 26.00 **st.** and a la carte 8.50 – ***Brasserie :*** Meals (carving lunch)/dinner a la carte 16.(25.00 **st.** 8.50 – **67 rm** 126.00/170.00 **st.**, 2 suites – SB.

The Morgan, 10 Fleet St., D2, ☎ (01) 679 3939, *morganht@iol.ie, Fax (01) 679 3946,* « Contemporary interior design », – ▮, ⇔ rm, ▤ rest, TV – 25. MO AE ◑ VISA. JY p
closed 23-28 December – ***All Sports Cafe :*** Meals (grill rest.) a la carte 14.15/24.15 **t.** – ☕ 10.00 – **59 rm** 105.00/130.00 **st.**, 2 suites.

The Schoolhouse, 2-8 Northumberland Rd, D4, ☎ (01) 667 5014, *school@schoolhouse hotel.iol.ie, Fax (01) 667 5015,* « Converted Victorian schoolhouse », – ▮, ⇔ rm, ▤ TV P. MO AE ◑ VISA JCB. EU a
closed 24-28 December – ***Satchels :*** Meals (bar lunch Saturday) 14.50/28.50 **st.** and dinner a la carte 6.50 – **31 rm** ☕ 119.00/149.00 **st.**

The Mercer, Mercer Street Lower, D2, ☎ (01) 478 2179, *stay@mercerhotel.ie, Fax (01) 478 0328* – ▮, ⇔ rm, ▤ TV – 120. MO ◑ VISA. JZ a
Cusack's : Meals *(closed Saturday lunch and Sunday)* 12.00/35.00 **st.** and a la carte 6.50 – ☕ 3.50 – **21 rm** ☕ 115.00/145.00 – SB.

brownes townhouse, 22 St. Stephen's Green, D2, ☎ (01) 638 3939, *info@brownesdub lin.com, Fax (01) 638 9000,* « Georgian town house » – ▮ ⇔ ▤ TV P. MO AE ◑ VISA. JZ c
Meals – (see ***brownes brasserie*** below) – **12 rm** ☕ 110.00/295.00 **t.**

Temple Bar, Fleet St., D2, ☎ (01) 677 3333, *templeb@iol.ie, Fax (01) 677 3088* – ▮, ⇔ rm, TV P – 75. MO AE ◑ VISA. JY e
closed 23-27 December – **Meals** *(closed lunch Saturday and Sunday)* 9.75/21.00 **st.** and a la carte 11.50 – **129 rm** ☕ 105.00/140.00 **st.** – SB.

Cassidys, 7-8 Cavendish Row, Upper O'Connell St., D1, ☎ (01) 878 0555, *martin@cassidys.i ol.ie, Fax (01) 878 0687* – ▮, ⇔ rm, TV – 80. MO AE ◑ VISA. JX m
closed 24-26 December – **Meals** (lunch by arrangement)/dinner 13.95/27.00 **st.** and a la carte 7.95 – **73 rm** ☕ 78.00/120.00 **st.**, 1 suite.

Stephen's Hall, Earlsfort Centre, 14-17 Lower Leeson St., D2, ☎ (01) 638 1111, *stephens @premgroup.ie, Fax (01) 638 1122* – ▮ ⇔ TV P. MO AE ◑ VISA. JZ t
Meals – (see ***Morels at Stephen's Hall*** below) – ☕ 10.00 – **3 rm** 145.00/175.00 **t.**, **34 suites** 175.00/275.00 **t.**

Jurys Inn Custom House, Custom House Quay, D1, ☎ (01) 607 5000, *customhouse_in n@jurysdoyle.com, Fax (01) 829 0400* – ▮, ⇔ rm, TV – 100. MO AE ◑ VISA. KX c
closed 24 to 26 December – **Meals** *(closed lunch Saturday, Sunday and Bank Holidays)* (carving lunch Monday to Friday)/dinner 15.95 **t.** and a la carte – ☕ 7.00 – **239 rm** 67.00 **st.**

Jurys Inn Christchurch, Christchurch Pl., D8, ☎ (01) 454 0000, *christchurch_inn@jurys doyle.com, Fax (01) 454 0012* – ▮, ⇔ rm, ▤ rest, TV. MO AE ◑ VISA. HY c
closed 24-26 December – **Meals** *(closed lunch Saturday and Sunday)* (carving lunch Monday to Friday)/dinner a la carte 11.90/20.70 **st.** 5.50 – ☕ 7.00 – **182 rm** 67.00 **st.**

Holiday Inn Dublin, 99-107 Pearse St., D2, ☎ (01) 670 3666, *info@holidayinndublin.ie, Fax (01) 670 3636,* – ▮, ⇔ rm, ▤ rest, TV – 40. MO AE ◑ VISA JCB. BST a
Meals *(closed lunch Saturday and Sunday)* (carvery lunch)/dinner 18.95 **st.** and a la carte 6.00 – ☕ 9.95 – **88 rm** 129.00/149.00 – SB.

Bewley's, 19-20 Fleet St., D2, ☎ (01) 670 8122, *bewleyshotel@eircom.net, Fax (01) 670 8103* – ▮, ⇔ rm, TV. MO AE ◑ VISA. JY d
closed 24 to 27 December – ***Bewley's Café :*** **Meals** 16.00/18.00 **st.** (dinner) and a la carte 12.00 **st.** 8.50 – ☕ 8.50 – **70 rm** 86.00/110.00 **st.**

Arlington, 23-25 Bachelors Walk, D1, ☎ (01) 804 9100, *arlington@tinet.ie, Fax (01) 804 9112* – ▮, ⇔ rm, TV P – 35. MO AE VISA. JY k
closed 24-26 December – **Meals** (carving lunch)/dinner 14.95/17.95 **st.** and a la carte 6.00 – **115 rm** ☕ 110.00/180.00 **st.**

Russell Court, 21-25 Harcourt St., D2, ☎ (01) 478 4066, *Fax (01) 478 1576* – ▮ TV P – 150. MO AE ◑ VISA. JZ p
closed 24 to 26 December – **Meals** *(closed lunch Saturday and Sunday)* 13.95/35.00 and dinner a la carte – ☕ 7.50 – **40 rm** 80.00/110.00 **st.**, 6 suites – SB.

Adams Trinity, 28 Dame St., D2, ☎ (01) 670 7100, *adamshtl@indigo.ie, Fax (01) 670 7101* – ▮ TV. MO AE ◑ VISA. JY n
closed 24 to 27 December – **Meals** (carving lunch)/dinner 14.00 **st.** and a la carte – **28 rm** ☕ 75.00/120.00 **st.** – SB.

Longfield's, 10 Lower Fitzwilliam St., D2, ☎ (01) 676 1367, *lfields@indigo.ie, Fax (01) 676 1542,* « Georgian town house » – ▮ TV. MO AE ◑ VISA. KZ d
Meals – (see ***Number Ten*** below) – **26 rm** ☕ 105.00/150.00 **st.** – SB.

Lynam's, 63-64 O'Connell St., D1, (01) 888 0886, *lynamhtl@indigo.ie, Fax (01) 888 08* – rest, . JX
closed 24-30 December – ***West Coast Café :*** **Meals** a la carte 12.45/17.00 **st.** 7.50 **42 rm** 75.00/130.00 **st.**

Harrington Hall without rest., 70 Harcourt St., D2, (01) 475 3497, *harringtonhall@e om.net, Fax (01) 475 4544,* « Georgian town houses » – . JZ
28 rm 85.00/200.00 **st.**

Trinity Lodge without rest., 12 South Frederick St., D2, (01) 679 5044, *trinitylodge net.ie, Fax (01) 679 5223,* « Georgian town houses » – . JY
closed Chritmas and New Year – **10 rm** 65.00/180.00 **st.**, 3 suites.

Aston without rest., 7-9 Aston Quay, D2, (01) 677 9300, *stay@aston-hotel.co Fax (01) 677 9007,* . JY
closed 24 to 27 December – **27 rm** 70.00/120.00.

Drury Court, 28-30 Lower Stephens St., D2, (01) 475 1988, *druryct@indigo. Fax (01) 478 5730* – rm, . JYZ
closed 24 to 27 December – **Meals** (bar lunch)/dinner 14.70 **t.** and a la carte – **32 r** 93.00/139.00 **st.**

Patrick Guilbaud, 21 Upper Merrion St., D2, (01) 676 4192, *Fax (01) 661 0052,* « G orgian town house, contemporary Irish Art collection » – . KZ
closed first week in December, Sunday and Monday – **Meals** 22.00/34.00 (lunch) and a la carte 52.00/87.00 **st.** 12.00
Spec. Lobster ravioli with coconut cream and almonds. Roast squab pigeon with fenr marmalade and spiced Madeira sauce. Five chocolate desserts, with Banyuls sauce.

The Commons, Newman House, 85-86 St. Stephen's Green, D2, (01) 478 0530, *sale thecommonsrestaurant.ie, Fax (01) 478 0551,* « Contemporary collection of James Joy inspired Irish Art » – JZ
closed 2 weeks Christmas, Saturday, Sunday and Bank Holidays – **Meals** 22.00 (lunch) and a la carte 41.00/53.00 **t.** 9.00.

Peacock Alley (Gallagher) (at The Fitzwilliam H.), St. Stephen's Green, D (01) 478 7015, *conradgallagher@tinet.ie, Fax (01) 478 7043* – . JZ
closed Saturday lunch and Sunday – **Meals** 22.00/55.00 **st.** and a la carte 44.00/62.00 10.00
Spec. Ravioli of smoked chicken and truffle. Pan-fried John Dory with pea and bac galette. Caramel and chocolate mousse, caramel ice cream.

Thornton's, 1 Portobello Rd, D8, (01) 454 9067, *Fax (01) 453 2947* – . DU
closed 1 week August, 1 week Christmas, Sunday and Monday – **Meals** (booking essent (dinner only and Friday lunch) a la carte 46.50/53.50 **t.** 10.00
Spec. Sautéed foie gras with scallops and cep jus. Roast suckling pig with stuffed trott poitin sauce. Plum tartlet with Valhrona ice cream, lemon grass sauce.

Chapter One, The Dublin Writers Museum, 18-19 Parnell Sq., D1, (01) 873 2266, *cha erone@oceanfree.net, Fax (01) 873 2330,* « Contemporary Irish art collection » – . JX
closed 24 December-9 January, Sunday, Monday, Saturday lunch and Bank Holidays – **Mea** 16.50 **t.** (lunch) and dinner a la carte 26.75/30.45 **t.** 7.00.

L'Ecrivain, 109 Lower Baggot St., D2, (01) 661 1919, *enquiries@lecrivain.co Fax (01) 661 0617,* – . KZ
closed Saturday lunch, Sunday and Bank Holidays – **Meals** (booking essential) 18.00/35.00 and dinner a la carte 8.00.

The Tea Room (at The Clarence H.), 6-8 Wellington Quay, D2, (01) 670 776 *Fax (01) 670 7833* – HY
closed 25-26 December and Saturday lunch – **Meals** (booking essential) 13.50/17.00 (lunch) and a la carte 30.75/36.25 **st.** 11.00.

Halo (at Morrison H.), Ormond Quay, D1, (01) 887 2421, *Fax (01) 887 2499* – . HY
Meals 25.00/30.00 **st.** (lunch) and a la carte 21.95/28.50 **st.** 14.00.

Morningtons Brasserie (at The Merrion H.), Upper Merrion St., D2, (01) 603 063 *Fax (01) 603 0700* – . KZ
closed Saturday lunch – **Meals** 17.00 **t.** (lunch) and dinner a la carte 17.95/28.00 **st.** 8.0

brownes brasserie (at brownes townhouse H.), 22 St. Stephen's Green, D (01) 638 3939, *info@brownesdublin.ie, Fax (01) 638 3900* – . JZ
closed Saturday lunch – **Meals** (booking essential) a la carte 17.95/31.40 **t.** 14.95.

XX **Les Frères Jacques,** 74 Dame St., D2, ☎ (01) 679 4555, *Fax (01) 679 4725* – MC AE DC VISA HY x
closed 24 December-2 January, Saturday lunch, Sunday and Bank Holidays – **Meals** - French - 13.50/22.00 **t.** and a la carte 5.50.

XX **Morels at Stephen's Hall,** 14-17 Lower Leeson St., D2, ☎ (01) 662 2480, *Fax (01) 662 8595* – ▤. MC AE DC VISA JZ t
closed Sunday and Bank Holidays – **Meals** (booking essential) 14.00/30.00 **t.** and a la carte 24.00/33.00 **t.** 10.00.

XX **Number Ten** (at Longfield's H.), 10 Lower Fitzwilliam St., D2, ☎ (01) 676 1060, *Fax (01) 676 1542* – MC AE DC VISA KZ d
closed lunch Saturday, Sunday and Bank Holidays – **Meals** (booking essential) 11.95/26.95 **t.** and dinner a la carte 9.50.

XX **Diep Le Shaker,** 55 Penbroke Lane, D2, ☎ (01) 661 1829, *Fax (01) 661 5905* – ▤. MC AE DC VISA JCB KZ k
closed Good Friday, 25 December, Saturday lunch and Sunday – **Meals** - Thai - 12.50/50.00 **t.** and dinner a la carte 12.50.

XX **Saagar,** 16 Harcourt St., D2, ☎ (01) 475 5060, *saagar@iol.ie, Fax (01) 475 5741* – MC AE DC VISA JZ b
closed 25-26 December, Saturday lunch and Sunday dinner – **Meals** - Indian - a la carte 8.70/16.45 **t.** 6.00.

XX **Locks,** 1 Windsor Terr., Portobello, D8, ☎ (01) 4543391, *Fax (01) 4538352* – MC AE DC VISA DU a
closed 25 December-5 January, Saturday lunch, Sunday and Bank Holidays – **Meals** 17.95/28.95 **t.** and a la carte 9.50.

XX **Old Dublin,** 90-91 Francis St., D8, ☎ (01) 4542028, *Fax (01) 4541406* – MC AE DC VISA HZ n
closed Christmas, Saturday lunch, Sunday and Bank Holidays – **Meals** 13.50/22.50 **t.** and dinner a la carte 8.50.

X **bruno's,** 30 East Essex St., Temple Bar, D2, ☎ (01) 670 6767, *Fax (01) 670 8278* – ▤. MC AE DC VISA JY r
closed 25 December, Good Friday, Saturday lunch and Sunday – **Meals** (booking essential) a la carte 18.95/27.70 **t.**

X **Bruno's,** 21 Kildare St., D2, ☎ (01) 662 4724, *Fax (01) 662 3857* – ▤. MC AE DC VISA JZ m
closed 25 December, Good Friday and Sunday – **Meals** a la carte 18.95/26.40 **t.**

X **Dobbin's,** 15 Stephen's Lane, off Lower Mount St., D2, ☎ (01) 676 4679, *Fax (01) 661 3331*, – ▤ P. MC AE DC VISA EU s
closed 25 December, Good Friday, Sunday and Bank Holidays – **Meals** - Bistro - (booking essential) 14.50/16.50 **st.** (lunch) and a la carte 22.50/31.45 **st.** 6.75.

X **Jacobs Ladder,** 4-5 Nassau St., D2, ☎ (01) 670 3865, *Fax (01) 670 3868* – MC AE DC VISA KY a
closed 3 weeks Christmas-New Year, 1 week August, Sunday and Monday – **Meals** (booking essential) 25.00 **t.** (dinner) and a la carte 28.00/34.45 **t.** 12.50.

X **Eden,** Meeting House Sq., Temple Bar, D2, ☎ (01) 670 5372, *Fax (01) 670 3330*, – ▤. MC AE DC VISA HY e
closed 25 December-2 January and Bank Holidays – **Meals** 14.00/16.00 **t.** (lunch) and dinner a la carte 19.20/29.20 **t.** 7.00.

X **Cooke's Café,** 14 South William St., D2, ☎ (01) 679 0536, *cookes1@iol.ie, Fax (01) 679 0546*, – ▤. MC AE DC VISA JY c
closed Bank Holidays – **Meals** 16.95 **t.** (lunch) and a la carte 23.00/37.00 **st.** 10.50.

X **Rhino Room,** 14a South William St., D2, ☎ (01) 670 5260, *Fax (01) 679 0546* – ▤. MC AE DC VISA JY c
closed Monday-Wednesday and Bank Holidays – **Meals** a la carte 18.50/27.00 **st.** 10.50.

X **Mermaid Café,** 69-70 Dame St., D2, ☎ (01) 670 8236, *Fax (01) 670 8205* – ▤. MC VISA HY d
closed 24, 25 and 31 December, 1 January and Good Friday – **Meals** a la carte 14.95/28.65 **t.** 11.50.

X **Mao,** 2-3 Chatham Row, D2, ☎ (01) 670 4899, *Fax (01) 670 4999* – ▤. MC VISA
closed 25 and 26 December – **Meals** - South East Asian - (bookings not accepted) a la carte 12.95/21.15 **t.** JZ r

X **Ocean,** Charlotte Quay Dock, D4, ☎ (01) 668 8862, *Fax (01) 667 7435*, – ▤. MC AE VISA CT u
closed 25 December, Good Friday and Sunday dinner – **Meals** - Seafood - (light lunch) a la carte 24.40/32.85 **t.** 12.00.

Ballsbridge.

Dublin 4.

Berkeley Court, Lansdowne Rd, D4, ☎ (01) 660 1711, *berkeley_court@jurysdoyle.com*, *Fax (01) 661 7238*, – rm, rest, – 500. AE VISA JCB FU
Berkeley Room : **Meals** 24.75/32.95 **t.** and a la carte – ***Palm Court Café :*** **Meals** 13.95/15.95 **t.** (lunch) and a la carte 22.35/33.50 **t.** 7.50 – **183 rm** 200.00/245.00 **t.**, 5 suites.

Jurys, Pembroke Rd, D4, ☎ (01) 660 5000, *ballsbridge_hotel@jurysdoyle.com*, *Fax (01) 660 5540*, heated – , rest, – 850. AE VISA JCB. FU
Raglans : **Meals** a la carte 14.00/26.00 **t.** 8.00 – 13.50 – **303 rm** 175.00/199.00 **t.**, 3 suites.

Herbert Park, D4, ☎ (01) 667 2200, *info@herbertparkhotel.ie*, *Fax (01) 667 2595*, – rm, – 100. AE VISA. FU
The Pavilion : **Meals** *(closed dinner Sunday and Bank Holidays)* 19.50 **st.** (lunch) and dinner a la carte 24.00/30.00 **st.** 15.50 – 13.50 – **150 rm** 170.00/205.00 **st.**, 3 suites – SB.

The Hibernian, Eastmoreland Pl., D4, ☎ (01) 668 7666, *info@hibernianhotel.com*, *Fax (01) 660 2655* – rm, AE VISA JCB. EU
closed 24-27 December – ***Patrick Kavanagh Room :*** **Meals** *(closed Saturday and Sunday lunch and Sunday dinner to non-residents)* 15.95 **t.** (lunch) and dinner a la carte 26.95/34.75 **t.** 10.80 – 12.00 – **40 rm** 150.00/190.00 **st.** – SB.

Bewley's, Merrion Rd, D4, ☎ (01) 668 1111, *res@bewleyshotels.com*, *Fax (01) 668 1999*, « Victorian facade » – rm, rest, AE VISA. FU
closed 24-26 December – ***O'Connells*** *(☎ (01) 647 3400)* **: Meals** 12.75/14.75 (lunch) and dinner a la carte 22.70/31.40 **t.** 9.75 – 7.00 – **220 rm** 69.00/138.00 **st.**

Ariel House without rest., 52 Lansdowne Rd, D4, ☎ (01) 668 5512, *reservations@ariel-house.com*, *Fax (01) 668 5845* – VISA. FU
closed 20 December-7 January – 8.50 – **37 rm** 75.00/169.00 **t.**

Butlers Town House, 44 Lansdowne Rd, D4, ☎ (01) 667 4022, *info@butlers-hotel.com*, *Fax (01) 667 3960* – AE VISA. FU
closed 1 to 7 January – **Meals** (room service only) (dinner only) (residents only) a la carte 11.75/18.50 **st.** 9.40 – 5.00 – **19 rm** 110.00/170.00 **t.**

Aberdeen Lodge, 53-55 Park Av., D4, ☎ (01) 283 8155, *aberdeen@iol.ie*, *Fax (01) 283 7877*, – AE VISA JCB. GV
Meals (residents only) (dinner only) a la carte 15.50/23.50 **t.** 9.50 – **17 rm** 70.00/180.00 **t.** – SB.

Waterloo House without rest., 8-10 Waterloo Rd, D4, ☎ (01) 660 1888, *waterloohouse@tinet.ie*, *Fax (01) 667 1955*, « Georgian town house », – VISA. EU
closed 23 to 28 December – **17 rm** 65.00/110.00 **st.**

Merrion Hall, 54-56 Merrion Rd, D4, ☎ (01) 668 1426, *merrionhall@iol.ie*, *Fax (01) 668 4280*, – AE VISA JCB. FU
Meals a la carte 15.50/23.50 **t.** 9.50 – **17 rm** 70.00/180.00 **t.** – SB.

Glenogra House without rest., 64 Merrion Rd, D4, ☎ (01) 668 3661, *glenogra@indigo.ie*, *Fax (01) 668 3698* – AE VISA. FU
closed Christmas and 2 weeks Spring – **12 rm** 49.00/75.00.

Cedar Lodge Guesthouse without rest., 98 Merrion Rd, D4, ☎ (01) 668 4410, *info@cedarlodge.ie*, *Fax (01) 668 4533*, – AE VISA. FU
closed 24 to 28 December – **15 rm** 45.00/100.00 **st.**

Anglesea Town House without rest., 63 Anglesea Rd, D4, ☎ (01) 668 3877, *Fax (01) 668 3461* – AE VISA. FV
7 rm 60.00/98.00 **t.**

66 Townhouse without rest., 66 Northumberland Rd, D4, ☎ (01) 660 0333, *Fax (01) 660 1051* – VISA. FU
closed 25 December – **9 rm** 50.00/75.00 **t.**

Northumberland Lodge without rest., 68 Northumberland Rd, D4, ☎ (01) 660 5270, *info@northumberlandlodge.com*, *Fax (01) 668 8679*, – VISA. FU
9 rm 55.00/90.00 **st.**

Le Coq Hardi, 35 Pembroke Rd, D4, ☎ (01) 668 9070, *Fax (01) 668 9887* – AE VISA JCB EU
closed 2 weeks August, 2 weeks late December-early January, Sunday, Saturday lunch and Bank Holidays – **Meals** 24.00 **t.** (lunch) and a la carte 32.00/50.00 **t.** 12.00.

Roly's Bistro, 7 Ballsbridge Terr., D4, ☎ (01) 668 2611, *Fax (01) 660 8535* – AE VISA FU
– **Meals** (booking essential) 12.95 **t.** (lunch) and dinner a la carte 21.46/24.45 **t.** 6.00.

t Dublin Airport *North : 6½ m. by N 1 – BS – and M 1 – ✉ Dublin.*

Posthouse Dublin Airport, ℘ (01) 808 0500, *Fax (01) 844 6002* – ⇔ rm, ▤ rest, TV ☏ ♿ P – 🏫 130. MC AE ⓓ VISA. ✂
closed 24 and 25 December – ***Bistro :*** **Meals** *(closed Saturday lunch)* 11.95/20.95 **t.** and dinner a la carte ♁ 6.95 – ***Sampan's :*** **Meals** - South East Asian - *(closed Bank Holidays)* (dinner only) 18.95/22.95 **t.** ♁ 6.95 – ☕ 11.95 – **249 rm** 119.00/139.00 **t.** – SB.

Great Southern, ℘ (01) 844 6000, *res@dubairport.gsh.ie, Fax (01) 844 6001* – |♦|, ⇔ rm, TV ☏ ♿ P – 🏫 350. MC AE ⓓ VISA. ✂
closed 24 to 26 December – ***Potters Bistro :*** **Meals** (bar lunch Monday to Saturday)/dinner 25.00 **st.** and a la carte ♁ 11.00 – ☕ 13.00 – **147 rm** 140.00 **st.**

t Clontarf *Northeast : 3½ m. by R 105 – ✉ Dublin.*

Clontarf Castle, Castle Av., D3, ℘ (01) 833 2321, *info@clontarfcastle.ie, Fax (01) 833 0418,* « Part 18C », ℻ – |♦|, ⇔ rm, TV ☏ ♿ P – 🏫 600. MC AE ⓓ VISA. ✂ CS a
closed 24 and 25 December – ***Templars Bistro :*** **Meals** a la carte 25.00/35.00 **st.** ♁ 8.00 – ☕ 10.95 – **108 rm** 155.00/180.00 **st.**, 3 suites – SB.

Hedigan's without rest., Tullyallan House, 14 Hollybrook Park, D3, ℘ (01) 853 1663, *Fax (01) 833 3337,* ⛲ – ⇔ TV P. MC VISA. ✂ CS e
closed Christmas-New Year **9 rm** ☕ 45.00/70.00 **st.**

Liaison, 318 Clontarf Rd, D3, ℘ (01) 833 6759, *Fax (01) 833 6651,* ≤ – ▤. MC AE VISA CS x
closed first week January, last week August, first week September, Sunday and Monday – **Meals** 15.95 **t.** (lunch) and a la carte 23.70/32.75 **t.**

onnybrook.
Dublin 4.

Morehampton Lodge without rest., 113 Morehampton Rd, D4, ℘ (01) 283 7499, *Fax (01) 283 7595* – ⇔ TV P. MC AE VISA. ✂ EV b
closed 24-26 December – **17 rm** ☕ 65.00/95.00 **st.**

Eglinton Manor without rest., 83 Eglinton Rd, D4, ℘ (01) 269 3273, *Fax (01) 269 7527,* ⛲ – TV P. MC AE VISA. ✂ EV c
8 rm ☕ 50.00/80.00 **s.**

Ernie's, Mulberry Gdns., off Morehampton Rd, D4, ℘ (01) 269 3300, *Fax (01) 269 3260,* « Contemporary Irish Art collection » – ▤. MC AE ⓓ VISA FV k
closed 22 December-3 January, Sunday, Monday and Saturday lunch – **Meals** 10.00/28.00 **st.** and a la carte ♁ 9.60.

rumcondra.
Dublin 5.

Jurys Skylon, Upper Drumcondra Rd, D9, North : 2½ m. on N 1 ℘ (01) 837 9121, *skylon_hotel@jurysdoyle.com, Fax (01) 837 2778* – |♦|, ▤ rest, TV ☏ ♿ P. MC AE ⓓ VISA. ✂ BS q
closed 24-27 December – **Meals** 12.50/18.00 **t.** and a la carte – ☕ 7.25 – **88 rm** 99.00 **t.**

Merrion.
Dublin 6.

Jurys Tara, Merrion Rd, D4, Southeast : 4 m. on R 118 ℘ (01) 269 4666, *tara_hotel@jurysdoyle.com, Fax (01) 269 1027* – |♦| TV ☏ ♿ P – 🏫 300. MC AE ⓓ VISA. ✂ GV a
closed 24-25 December – **Meals** a la carte 17.65/24.95 **t.** ♁ 7.00 – ☕ 8.00 – **113 rm** 99.00/109.00 **t.**

Ranelagh.
Dublin 5.

Dunville Place, 23 Dunville Av., D6, ℘ (01) 496 8181, *dunvillepl@aol.com, Fax (01) 496 5710* – ▤. MC AE VISA EV m
closed Monday – **Meals** (dinner only and lunch Saturday and Sunday)/dinner a la carte 20.50/31.50 **t.** ♁ 9.95.

Rathgar.
Dublin 6.

St. Aiden's without rest., 32 Brighton Rd, D6, ℘ (01) 490 2011, *staidens@eircom.ie, Fax (01) 492 0234* – TV P. MC VISA. ✂ DV n
8 rm ☕ 37.50/70.00 **st.**

Poppadom, 91A Rathgar Rd, D6, ℘ (01) 490 2383, *Fax (01) 492 3900* – ▤. MC AE ⓓ VISA JCB DV a
closed 25-26 December – **Meals** - Indian - (dinner only) a la carte 20.00/28.50 **t.**

Rathmines. *Dublin 6.*

Charleville, Lower Rathmines Rd, D6, ✆ (01) 406 6100, *charleville@charleville.premgro .ie, Fax (01) 406 6200* – |‡|, ▤ rest, TV ✆ ♿ 🚗. MC AE ⓓ VISA. ✻ DV
closed 24-28 December – **Meals** *(closed 24 to 27 December)* (bar lunch Monday to Frida a la carte 12.40/22.40 **st.** – ☕ 9.50 – **9 rm** 125.00/150.00 **st.**, **43 suites** 180.00 **st.**

Uppercross House, 26-30 Upper Rathmines Rd, D6, ✆ (01) 4975486, *mahond@indig e, Fax (01) 4975361* – TV P. MC AE ⓓ VISA DV
closed 24-27 December – **Meals** (dinner only and lunch Saturday and Sunday) a la car 10.25/23.20 **st.** 🍷 595 – **50 rm** ☕ 59.50/89.00 **st.**

Zen, 89 Upper Rathmines Rd, D6, ✆ (01) 4979428 – ▤. MC AE ⓓ VISA DV
Meals - Chinese (Szechuan) - (dinner only and lunch Thursday, Friday and Sunday) a la car 15.00/29.00 **t.** 🍷 7.50.

at Blackrock *Southeast : 5½ m. by R 118* – **CT** – ✉ *Dublin.*

Dali's, 63-65 Main St., ✆ (01) 278 0660, *Fax (01) 278 0661* – ▤. MC AE ⓓ VISA
closed 25-26 and 31 December, 1 January, Monday and Sunday dinner – **Meals** 12.95 (lunch) and a la carte 20.00/24.00 **t.** 🍷 8.50.

Blueberry's, 1st floor (above Jack O'Rourkes pub), 15 Main St., ✆ (01) 278 8900, *bluebe ys@clubi.ie, Fax (01) 278 8903* – MC AE ⓓ VISA
closed 25-26 December, 1 January, Good Friday, Saturday lunch and Sunday – **Mea** (booking essential) 13.95 **t.** (lunch) and dinner a la carte 18.40/26.20 **t.** 🍷 11.00.

Ayumi-Ya, Newpark Centre, Newtownpark Av., Southeast : 1 ¼ m. on R 1 ✆ (01) 283 1767, *info@ayumiya.ie, Fax (01) 288 0478* – ▤. MC AE ⓓ VISA
closed 24 to 26 December, 1 January, Good Friday and Monday – **Meals** - Japanese - (dinn only) 20.95/25.95 **t.** and a la carte 🍷 6.95.

at Monkstown *Southeast : 6½ m. by R 118* – **CT** – *on R 119* – ✉ *Dublin.*

Siam, 8a The Crescent, ✆ (01) 284 3309, *siames@eircom.ie* – MC AE ⓓ VISA
closed Good Friday and 25-26 December – **Meals** - Thai - (dinner only) 18.50/25.50 **s** and a la carte 🍷 8.95.

at Foxrock *Southeast : 7½ m. by N 11* – **CT** – ✉ *Dublin.*

Bistro One, 3 Brighton Rd, D18, ✆ (01) 289 7711, *Fax (01) 2899 858* – MC VISA
closed 24 to 26 and 31 December, 1 January, Sunday and Monday – **Meals** (bookir essential) (dinner only) a la carte 19.00/30.00 **t.** 🍷 7.00.

at Tallaght *Southwest : 7½ m. by N 81* – **BT** – ✉ *Dublin.*

The Plaza, Belgard Rd, D24, at junction of N 81 and R 113 ✆ (01) 462 4200, *info@plazah tel.ie, Fax (01) 462 4600* – |‡|, ⊁ rm, ▤ rest, TV ✆ ♿ P – 🎤 300. MC AE ⓓ VISA. ✻
closed 24 to 30 December – ***The Olive Tree :*** **Meals** 12.95/32.00 **t.** and dinner a la car 🍷 9.00 – ☕ 10.00 – **120 rm** 115.00 **st.**, 2 suites.

Abberley Court, Belgard Rd, D24, on R 113 ✆ (01) 459 6000, *abberley@iol.i Fax (01) 462 1000* – |‡|, ⊁ rm, TV ♿ 🚗 – 🎤 150. MC AE ⓓ VISA. ✻
closed 23-30 December – **Meals** (bar lunch)/dinner a la carte approx. 15.50 **t.** 🍷 6.00 **38 rm** ☕ 79.00/98.00 **st.** – SB.

at Saggart *Southwest : 9¼ m. off N 7* – **AT** – ✉ *Dublin.*

Citywest, ✆ (01) 401 0500, *info@citywest_hotel.iol.ie, Fax (01) 458 8565*, Ⓕ, ≘s, 18, ... , – |‡|, ▤ rest, TV ✆ ♿ P – 🎤 600. MC AE ⓓ VISA. ✻
Meals 14.95/26.95 **st.** 🍷 7.50 – **197 rm** ☕ 115.00/130.00, 2 suites – SB.

Westpark, Naas Rd, ✆ (01) 458 7000, *info@qualitycitywest.com, Fax (01) 458 7019*, – |‡|, ⊁ rm, ▤ rest, TV ✆ ♿ P – 🎤 30. MC AE ⓓ VISA. ✻
closed 24-28 December – **Meals** 12.95/22.50 and a la carte – ☕ 6.50 – **74 rm** 89.00 99.00 **t.**, **78 suites** 99.00/150.00 **t.** – SB.

at Ashtown *Northwest : 4¾ m. by N 3* – **AS** – ✉ *Dublin.*

Ashbrook House without rest., River Rd, D15, ✆ (01) 838 5660, *Fax (01) 838 5660*, « Georgian country house », , – ⊁ TV P. MC VISA. ✻
closed 20 December-2 January – **4 rm** ☕ 40.00/70.00.

t Castleknock *Northwest : 5½ m. by N 3* – **AS** – ✉ *Dublin.*

Travelodge, Auburn Av. roundabout, D15, on N 3 ☎ (01) 820 2626, *Fax (01) 820 2151* – ⇔ rm, ▤ rest, TV & P. MC AE ◑ VISA JCB. ✖
Meals (grill rest.) – **60 rm** 59.95 **t.**

to the Southeast :

Radisson SAS St. Helen's, Stillorgan Rd, Southeast : 4 ½ m. on N 11 ☎ (01) 218 6000, *info@dubzh.rdsas.com, Fax (01) 218 6010,* « Part 18C », ⅃, – |‡|, ⇔ rm, ▤ TV ✆ & P – 🏃 350. MC AE ◑ VISA. ✖
Le Panto : **Meals** *(closed Monday and Sunday)* (dinner only) a la carte 32.00/60.00 **st.** 14.00 – ***Tolavera :*** **Meals** - Italian - (dinner only) 18.00/35.00 **st.** and a la carte 12.50 – 12.50 – **130 rm** 165.00/185.00 **t.**, 21 suites – SB.

Stillorgan Park, Stillorgan Rd, Southeast : 5 m. on N 11 ☎ (01) 288 1621, *sales@stillorganpark.com, Fax (01) 283 1610* – |‡|, ⇔ rm, ▤ TV & P – 🏃 180. MC AE ◑ VISA. ✖
Meals 12.95/22.95 **st.** and dinner a la carte 7.50 – **100 rm** 110.00/160.00 **st.** – SB.

Jurys Montrose, Stillorgan Rd, D4, Southeast : 4 m. by N 11 ☎ (01) 269 3311, *montrose_hotel@jurysdoyle.com, Fax (01) 269 1164* – |‡|, ⇔ rm, TV ✆ P – 🏃 70. MC AE ◑ VISA. ✖ GV y
closed 24-25 December – **Meals** a la carte 17.65/24.95 **t.** 7.00 – 8.50 – **179 rm** 99.00/109.00 **t.**

to the Southwest :

Red Cow Moran, Naas Rd, D22, Southwest : 5 m. on N 7 ☎ (01) 459 3650, *info@morangroup.ie, Fax (01) 459 1588* – |‡|, ⇔ rm, ▤ TV ✆ & P – 🏃 700. MC AE ◑ VISA. ✖
closed 25 and 26 December – **Meals** 14.50/23.00 **t.** and dinner a la carte 9.95 – **120 rm** 95.00/145.00 **t.**, 3 suites – SB.

Bewley's H. Newlands Cross, D22, Southwest : 7 m. by N 7 on R 113 ☎ (01) 464 0140, *res@bewleyshotels.com, Fax (01) 464 0900* – |‡|, ⇔ rm, ▤ rest, TV ✆ & P – 🏃 30. MC AE ◑ VISA. ✖
closed 24 to 26 December – **Meals** (carving lunch) a la carte 18.35/23.15 **t.** – 7.50 – **260 rm** 55.00 **st.**

Jurys Green Isle, Naas Rd, D22, Southwest : 7 ¾ m. off N7 (eastbound carriageway) ☎ (01) 459 3406, *green_isle@jurysdoyle.com, Fax (01) 459 2178* – |‡|, ⇔ rm, TV & P – 🏃 350. MC AE ◑ VISA. ✖
Meals 12.95/18.95 **t.** and dinner a la carte 5.60 – 8.50 – **90 rm** 99.00/109.00 **t.** – SB.

Sheldon Park, Kylemore Rd, D12, Southwest : 4 ¾ m. by N 7 on R 112 ☎ (01) 460 1055, *info@sheldonpark.ie, Fax (01) 460 1880,* ⅃, ≘s, ⊠ – |‡|, ⇔ rm, TV P – 🏃 550. MC AE ◑ VISA. ✖
closed 25 December – **Meals** *(closed lunch Saturday and Sunday)* (carving lunch)/dinner 19.95 **st.** and a la carte 6.95 – **72 rm** 69.00/92.00 **st.** – SB.

Ibis Dublin, Monastery Rd, Clondalkin, D22, Southwest : 5 ¼ m. off N 7 ☎ (01) 464 1480, *595@accor.hotels.com, Fax (01) 464 1484* – |‡|, ⇔ rm, TV ✆ & P – 🏃 30. MC AE ◑ VISA
Meals (dinner only) a la carte approx. 12.00 **st.** – **150 rm** 45.00/49.50 **st.**

DUBLIN AIRPORT *Dublin* 923 N 7 – *see Dublin.*

DUNDALK **(Dun Dealgan)** *Louth* 923 M 5/6 *Ireland G.* – *pop. 25 762.*

Exc. : *Dún a' Rá Forest Park★, W : 21 m. by R 178 and R 179.*

Killinbeg, Killin Park, Bridge a Chrin ☎ (042) 9339303.

Jocelyn St. ☎ (042) 9335484 (June-December).

Dublin 51 – Drogheda 22.

Ballymascanlon,, North : 3 ½ m. by N 1 on R 173 ☎ (042) 9371124, *info@ballymascanlon.com, Fax (042) 9371598,* ⅃, ≘s, ⊠, 18, ⚘ – |‡| TV & P – 🏃 100. MC AE ◑ VISA
closed 24 to 26 December – **Meals** 15.00/26.00 **t.** and dinner a la carte 10.00 – **74 rm** 74.00/150.00 **st.** – SB.

Fairways,, South : 3 m. on N 1 ☎ (042) 9321500, *info@fairways.ie, Fax (042) 9321511,* ≘s, – TV P – 🏃 400. MC AE ◑ VISA. ✖
closed 25 December – ***Modis :*** **Meals** (dinner only and Sunday lunch)/dinner a la carte 21.00/29.50 **t.** 8.00 – ***Fairways Grill :*** **Meals** a la carte 16.50/22.25 **t.** 8.00 – **40 rm** 60.00/90.00 **t.** – SB.

t Carrickcarnon *North : 8 m. on N 1* – ✉ *Dundalk.*

Carrickdale, ☎ (042) 9371397, *Fax (042) 9371740,* ⅃, ≘s, ⊠, – TV P – 🏃 150. MC AE ◑ VISA. ✖
closed 25 December – **Meals** (carving lunch) 14.00/23.00 dinner and a la carte 13.75/23.75 – **116 rm** 55.00/130.00 **st.** – SB.

DUNFANAGHY **(Dún Fionnachaidh)** *Donegal* 923 I 2 *Ireland G. – pop. 290 – ✉ Letterkenny.*

Env. : *Horn Head Scenic Route★, N : 2½ m.*

Exc. : *Doe Castle★, SE : 7 m. by N 56 – The Rosses★, SW : 25 m. by N 56 and R 259.*

Dunfanaghy, Letterkenny ℘ (074) 36335.

Dublin 172 – Donegal 54 – Londonderry 43.

Arnold's, Main St., ℘ (074) 36208, *arnoldshotel@teircom.net, Fax (074) 36352,* ⋖, – TV P. MC AE O VISA.
mid March-November – ***Tramore rest.*** *:* **Meals** (dinner only) 25.00/30.00 **t.** 6.50 – ***Garden bistro*** *:* **Meals** a la carte 16.45/22.20 **t.** 6.50 – **30 rm** 52.50/105.00 **t.** – SB.

Carrig Rua, Main St., ℘ (074) 36133, *carrigrua@eircom.net, Fax (074) 36277,* ⋖ – TV MC VISA.
closed 25 December – ***Sheephaven Room*** *:* **Meals** (dinner only) a la carte 19.00/24.40 **t.** ***The Thursday Club*** *:* **Meals** a la carte 9.95/13.85 **t.** – **22 rm** 40.00/100.00 **t.** – SB.

DUNGARVAN **(Dún Garbháin)** *Waterford* 923 J 11 *Ireland G. – pop. 7 175.*

See : *East Bank (Augustinian priory, ⋖★).*

Exc. : *Ringville (⋖★), S : 8 m. by N 25 and R 674 – Helvick Head★ (⋖★), SE : 8 m. by N 25 and R 674.*

Knocknagrannagh ℘ (058) 41605 – Gold Coast, Ballinacourty ℘ (058) 42249.

Town Centre ℘ (058) 41741.

Dublin 118 – Cork 44 – Waterford 30.

Lawlors, Meagher St., ℘ (058) 41122, *Fax (058) 41000* – |‡|, rest, TV – 300. MC AE O VISA
closed 25 December – **Meals** 10.95/25.00 **t.** and dinner a la carte 7.50 – **89 rm** 45.00/80.00 **t.** – SB.

The Tannery, 10 Quay St., via Parnell St. ℘ (058) 45420, *tannery@cablesurf.com, Fax (058) 45518,* « 19C former tannery » – MC AE O VISA
closed 3 weeks late January-early February, 25-26 December, 1 January and Monday –
Meals a la carte 13.55/25.40 **t.** 7.50.

DUNGLOW **(An Clochán Liath)** *Donegal* 923 G 3 *Ireland G. – pop. 1 042.*

Env. : *The Rosses★.*

Exc. : *Gweebarra Estuary★, S : by N 56.*

Cruit Island, Kincasslagh ℘ (075) 43296.

Lower Main St. ℘ (075) 21297 (May-September).

Dublin 173 – Londonderry 51 – Sligo 76.

Ostan na Rosann, Mill Rd, ℘ (075) 22444, *ostannarosann@iol.ie, Fax (075) 22400,* ⋖, – rest, TV P. MC AE O VISA
– **Meals** 21.95/25.00 **t.** (dinner) and lunch a la carte 13.40/25.85 **t.** – **48 rm** 60.00/90.00 SB.

Atlantic House without rest., Main St., ℘ (075) 21061, *jcannon@iol.ie, Fax (075) 21061* TV. MC VISA.
closed 20 to 30 December – **10 rm** 25.00/40.00.

DUNKINEELY **(Dún Cionnaola)** *Donegal* 923 G 4 *Ireland G. – pop. 395.*

Exc. : *Donegal Coast★★ – Cliffs of Bunglass★★ – Glengesh Pass★★ – Glencolmcille Folk Village★★.*

Dublin 157 – Londonderry 56 – Sligo 50.

Castle Murray House with rm, St. Johns Point, Southwest : 1 ¼ m. by N 56 and St. Johns Point rd turning left at T junction ℘ (073) 37022, *castlemurray@eircom.net, Fax (073) 37330,* ⋖ McSweeney Bay – TV P. MC VISA.
closed 15 January-9 February – **Meals** - French - (dinner only and Sunday lunch)/dinner 18.50/32.00 **t.** 7.00 – **10 rm** 40.00/64.00 **t.**

Don't confuse:

Comfort of hotels	:	...
Comfort of restaurants	:	XXXXX ..... X,
Quality of the cuisine	:	✿✿✿, ✿✿, ✿, Meals

UN LAOGHAIRE (Dún Laoghaire) *Dublin* 923 N 8 *Ireland G. – pop. 55 540.*

Env. : ≤★★ *of Killiney Bay from coast road south of Sorrento Point.*

Dun Laoghaire, Eglinton Park ℘ (01) 458 2622.

to Holyhead (Stena Line) 4-5 daily (1 h 40 mn).

Ferry Terminal.

Dublin 9.

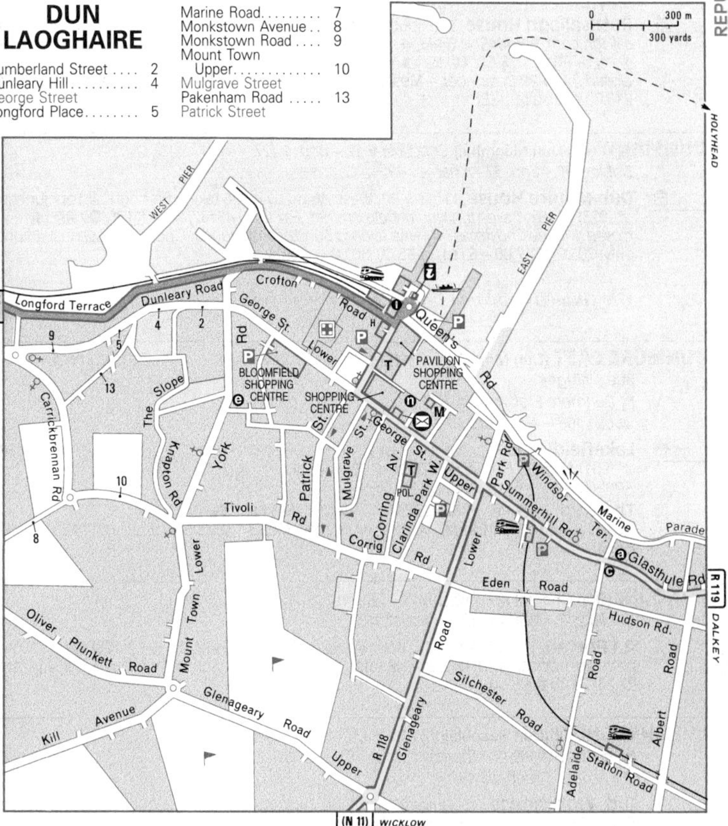

Royal Marine, Marine Rd, ℘ (01) 280 1911, *ryan@indigo.ie, Fax (01) 280 1089,* ≤, – rest, – 500. *VISA.* n
Meals 12.50/17.00 **t.** and a la carte 10.00 – 12.50 – **103 rm** 180.00 – SB.

Cumberland Lodge without rest., 54 York Rd, ℘ (01) 280 9665, *cumberlandlodge@tinet.ie, Fax (01) 284 3227,* « Regency town house », – *VISA.* e
4 rm 35.50/60.00 **st.**

Brasserie Na Mara, 1 Harbour Rd, ℘ (01) 280 6767, *Fax (01) 284 4649* – *VISA* i
closed Saturday lunch, Sunday and Bank Holidays – **Meals** 12.95/20.95 **t.** and dinner a la carte 6.50.

Duzy's Café, 1st floor (above Eagle House pub), 18 Glasthule Rd, ℘ (01) 230 0210, *duzyscafe@clubi.ie, Fax (01) 230 0466* – *VISA* c
closed 25-26 December, 1 January, Good Friday, Saturday lunch and Bank Holidays – **Meals** (light lunch)/dinner 15.50 **t.** and a la carte 16.85/25.50 **t.** 12.50.

REPUBLIC OF IRELAND

Cavistons, 59 Glasthule Rd, ☎ (01) 280 9245, *caviston@indigo.ie, Fax (01) 284 4054* – MC AE VISA
closedSunday, Monday and Bank Holidays – **Meals** - Seafood - (booking essential) (lunc only) a la carte 17.75/24.70 **t.**

DUNLAVIN (Dún Luáin) *Wicklow* 923 L 8 – *pop. 693.*
Rathsallagh ☎ (045) 403316.
Dublin 31 – Kilkenny 44 – Wexford 61.

Rathsallagh House,, Southwest : 2 m. on Grangecon Rd ☎ (045) 403112, *info@rat sallagh.com, Fax (045) 403343,* ≤, « 18C converted stables, walled garden », – TV P – 50. MC AE VISA
closed 23 to 28 December – **Meals** (dinner only) 35.00/45.00 **t.** 9.00 – **28 rm** 110.0C 210.00 **t.**, 1 suite – SB.

DUNMANWAY (Dún Mánmhaí) *Cork* 923 E 12 – *pop. 1 427.*
Dublin 191 – Cork 37 – Killarney 49.

Dún Mhuire House, Kilbarry Rd, West : ½ m. by R 586 taking first right at fork junctio ☎ (023) 45162, *hayesdunmhuire@eircom.net, Fax (023) 45162,* – TV P. MC VISA.
closed 1 week Christmas – **Meals** *(closed Sunday and Monday)* (booking essential) (dinne only) 20.00 **t.** 7.00 – **6 rm** 35.00/50.00 **t.** – SB.

The Guide is updated annually so renew your Guide every year.

DUNMORE EAST (Dún Mór) *Waterford* 923 L 11 *Ireland G.* – *pop. 1 430* – ✉ *Waterford.*
See : *Village*★.
Dunmore East ☎ (051) 383151.
Dublin 108 – Waterford 12.

LakefieldHouse without rest., Dunmore East Rd, Rosduff, Northwest : 5 m. by R 68 ☎ (051) 382582, *Fax (051) 382582,* ≤, – rest, TV P. MC VISA
April-October – **6 rm** 35.00/45.00.

The Ship, Dock Rd, ☎ (051) 383141, *Fax (051) 383144* – MC AE VISA
closed Sunday and Monday November-March – **Meals** - Seafood - a la carte 13.20/22.65 6.50.

DUNQUIN (Dún Chaoin) *Kerry* 923 A 11 – ✉ *Dingle.*
Dublin 226 – Killarney 52 – Limerick 103.

An Portan, ☎ (066) 9156212, *donn@tinet.ie, Fax (066) 9156222,* ≤ – P. MC VISA
restricted opening in winter – **Meals** (dinner only and Sunday lunch)/dinner a la cart 17.25/28.00 **t.** 8.00.

DUNSHAUGHLIN (Dún Seachlainn) *Meath* 923 M 7 – *pop. 2 139.*
The Black Bush, Thomastown ☎ (01) 825 0021.
Dublin 17 – Drogheda 19.

Old Workhouse,, South : 1 ½ m. on N 3 ☎ (01) 8259251, *comfort@a_vip.com Fax (01) 825 9251,* – rm, P. MC VISA
Meals (by arrangement) (communal dining) 35.00 **st.** – **5 rm** 45.00/90.00 **st.**

DURRUS (Dúras) *Cork* 923 D 13 – *pop. 204.*
Dublin 210 – Cork 56 – Killarney 53.

Blairs Cove with rm,, Southwest : 1 m. on R 591 ☎ (027) 61127, *blairscove@eircom. et, Fax (027) 61487,* ≤, « Converted 17C barn », – TV P. MC VISA.
April-October – **Meals** *(closed Sunday in July-August and Monday)* (booking essentia (dinner only) 24.00/32.00 **st.** –, **3 suites** 80.00/140.00 **st.**.

EDENDERRY *Offaly* 923 K 7 – *pop. 3 591.*
Dublin 39 – Kilkenny 63 – Tullamore 23.

Tyrells, Ballindoolin House, North : ½ m. ☎ (0405) 32400, *Fax (0405) 32377,* « Renovate 19C coach house, gardens » – P. MC VISA
closed 2 weeks January, Sunday dinner, Monday and Tuesday – **Meals** (booking essentia 13.95 **t.** (lunch) and dinner a la carte 19.00/25.00 **t.**

NNIS (Inis) *Clare* 923 F 9 *Ireland G. – pop. 15 333.*

See : *Ennis Friary★ AC.*

Exc. : *Dysert O'Dea★, N : 6 m. by N 85 and R 476, turning left after 4 m. and right after 1m. – Quin Franciscan Friary★, SE : 6½ m. by R 469 – Knappogue Castle★ AC, SE : 8 m. by R 469 – Corrofin (Clare Heritage Centre★ AC), N : 8½ m. by N 85 and R 476 – Craggaunowen Centre★ AC, SE : 11 m. by R 469 – Kilmacduagh Churches and Round Tower★, NE : 11 m. by N 18 – Kilrush★ (Scattery Island★ by boat) SW : 27 m. by N 68 – Bridge of Ross, Kilkee★, SW : 35½ m. by N 68 and N 67.*

Drumbiggle Rd ☎ (065) 682 4074.

Arthurs Row ☎ (065) 682 8308 (April-December).

Dublin 142 – Galway 42 – Limerick 22 – Roscommon 92 – Tullamore 93.

Woodstock, Shanaway Rd, Northwest : 2 ¾ m. by N 85, turning left at One Mile Inn ☎ (065) 6846600, *info@woodstockhotel.com, Fax (065) 6846611,* ←, – rm, rest, – 200. VISA JCB.
Spikes Brasserie : **Meals** (dinner only and Sunday lunch)/dinner 24.95 **t.** 8.50 – **67 rm** 145.00/215.00 **st.** – SB.

Temple Gate, The Square, ☎ (065) 6823300, *templegh@iol.ie, Fax (065) 6823322* – rm, – 220. VISA.
closed 25 December – **Meals** (carving lunch Monday to Saturday)/dinner 21.50/23.50 **t.** and a la carte 6.95 – **70 rm** 75.00/100.00 **st.**, 2 suites – SB.

West County, Clare Rd, Southeast : ¾ m. on N 18 ☎ (065) 6823000, Central reservations (065) 6823000, *cro@lynchotels.com, Fax (065) 6823759,* – rest, – 1650. VISA.
Meals 14.00/19.00 **st.** (dinner)and a la carte 13.60/14.80 **st.** 5.50 – 7.50 – **152 rm** 57.00/200.00 **st.** – SB.

Old Ground, O'Connell St., ☎ (065) 6828127, *oghotel@iol.ie, Fax (065) 6828112,* – rm, – 70. VISA.
closed 25 December – **Meals** 14.00/21.00 **st.** and dinner a la carte 9.00 – **83 rm** 80.00/140.00 **st.** – SB.

Cill Eoin House without rest., Killadysert Cross, Clare Rd, Southeast : 1 ½ m. at junction of N 18 with R 473 ☎ (065) 6841668, *cilleoin@iol.ie, Fax (065) 6841669,* – VISA
closed 20-30 December **14 rm** 30.00/50.00 **t.**

t Inch *Southwest : 4 m. on R 474 (Kilmaley rd) – ✉ Ennis.*

Magowna House, West : 1 m. by R 474 ☎ (065) 6839009, *info@magowna.com, Fax (065) 6839258,* ←, – – 350. VISA
closed 24 to 26 December – **Meals** 10.50/21.95 **st.** and a la carte 6.00 – **10 rm** 40.00/72.00 **st.** – SB.

NNISCORTHY (Inis Córthaidh) *Wexford* 923 M 10 *Ireland G. – pop. 3 788.*

See : *Enniscorthy Castle★ (County Museum★).*

Exc. : *Ferns★, NE : 8 m. by N 11 – Mount Leinster★, N : 17 m. by N 11.*

Knockmarshal ☎ (054) 33191.

The Castle ☎ (054) 34699 (mid June-August).

Dublin 76 – Kilkenny 46 – Waterford 34 – Wexford 15.

Riverside Park, The Promenade, ☎ (054) 37800, *riversideparkhotel@tinet.ie, Fax (054) 37900* – rm, rest, – 800. VISA.
closed 24-26 December – ***The Moorings :*** **Meals** (carving lunch Monday to Saturday)/dinner a la carte 17.00/29.00 **st.** 12.00 – **59 rm** 65.00/105.00 **st.**, 1 suite – SB.

Treacy's, ☎ (054) 37798, *sales@treacyshotel.com, Fax (054) 37733,* – rest, – 350. VISA.
closed 24-25 December – **Meals** (bar lunch Monday to Saturday)/dinner 19.95/23.95 **st.** and a la carte 6.95 – **48 rm** 45.00/90.00 – SB.

Ballinkeele House, Ballymurn, Southeast : 6 ½ m. by unmarked road on Curracloe rd ☎ (053) 38105, *info@ballinkeele.com, Fax (053) 38468,* ←, « 19C country house », – VISA JCB.
March-13 November – **Meals** (by arrangement) (communal dining) 26.00 **t.** – **5 rm** 67.00/120.00 **st.**

Bitte beachten Sie die Geschwindigkeitsbeschränkungen in Großbritannien
- 60 mph (= 96 km/h) außerhalb geschlossener Ortschaften
- 70 mph (= 112 km/h) auf Straßen mit getrennten Fahrbahnen und Autobahnen.

ENNISKERRY (Áth an Sceire) *Wicklow* 923 N 8 – *pop. 1 275.*
Powerscourt, Powerscourt Estate (01) 204 6033.
Dublin 16 – Wicklow 20.

Summerhill House, Cookstown Rd, South : ½ m. (01) 286 7928, *res@summerhillh el.iol.ie, Fax (01) 286 7929,* ≤, – rest, rest, – 220. VISA.
closed 24 to 27 December – **Meals** 15.00 **st.** dinner and a la carte 11.95/21.00 **st.** 10.50
57 rm 65.00/100.00 **st.** – SB.

ENNISTIMON (Inis Dáomáin) *Clare* 923 E 9 – *pop. 920.*
Dublin 158 – Galway 52 – Limerick 39.

Grovemount House without rest., Lahinch Rd, West : ½ m. on N 67 (065) 707143
Fax (065) 7071823, – . VISA.
May-October – **8 rm** 33.00/50.00 **st.**

FAHAN (Fathain) *Donegal* 923 J 2 *Ireland G.* – *pop. 284* – *Inishowen.*
Exc. : *Inishowen Peninsula*★★ – *Grianán of Aileach*★★ (≤★★), *SE : 7 m. by R 238 and west b N 13 – Dunree Fort*★ *AC, N : 11 m. by R 238 and coast rd – Gap of Mamore*★, *N : by R 23 and coast rd.*
North West, Lisfannon (077) 61027.
Dublin 156 – Londonderry 11 – Sligo 95.

St. John's Country House with rm, (077) 60289, *stjohnsrestaurant@eircom.ne Fax (077) 60612,* ≤, « Loughside setting », – , rest, . VISA JCB.
closed 15 February-2 March, Sunday and Monday – **Meals** (dinner only) 24.00/28.00 **s** and a la carte – **5 rm** 45.00/75.00 **st.**

Jährlich eine neue Ausgabe
Aktuellste Informationen, jährlich für Sie!

FERMOY (Mainistir Fhear Maá) *Cork* 923 H 11 – *pop. 2 310.*
Corrin (025) 32694.
Dublin 134 – Cork 24 – Killarney 59 – Limerick 42.

CastleHyde, West : 2 m. on N 72 (025) 31865, *cashyde@iol.ie, Fax (025) 3148*
« Restored 18C courtyard buildings », , – rest, – 30. VISA.
Meals (booking essential to non-residents) a la carte 13.50/26.20 **st.** 10.75 – **14 rr** 85.00/150.00 **st.** – SB.

FERNS (Fearna) *Wexford* 923 M 10 *Ireland G.* – *pop. 915* – *Enniscorthy.*
See : *Town*★.
Exc. : *Mount Leinster*★, *NW : 17 m. – Enniscorthy Castle*★ *(County Museum*★ *AC), S : 8 m by N 11.*
Dublin 69 – Kilkenny 53 – Waterford 41 – Wexford 22.

Clone House, South : 2 m. by Boolavogue rd off Monageer rd (054) 6611
Fax (054) 66225, « Working farm », , , – .
April-October – **Meals** (by arrangement) (communal dining) 12.50/14.00 **st.** – **5 rr** 35.00/50.00 **st.**

FOXROCK (Carraig an tSionnaigh) *Dublin* 923 N 7 – *see Dublin.*

FURBO (Na Forbacha) *Galway* 923 E 8 – *see Furbogh.*

FURBOGH/FURBO (Na Forbacha) *Galway* 923 E 8.
Dublin 142 – Galway 7.

Connemara Coast, (091) 592108, *sinnott@iol.ie, Fax (091) 592065,* ≤ Galway Bay,
, , , – – 500. VISA.
closed 24-26 December – **Meals** (bar lunch Monday to Saturday)/dinner 21.00 **st** and a la carte 5.95 – **111 rm** 100.00/190.00, 1 suite – SB.

Suan na Mara, Stripe, Northwest : ½ m. off R 336 (091) 591512, *Fax (091) 59163*
≤, – . VISA.
closed 31 December and January – **Meals** (by arrangement) 14.50 6.00 – **4 rm** 32.50 50.00 **st.** – SB.

ALWAY **(Gaillimh)** *Galway* 923 E 8 *Ireland G. – pop. 57 241.*

See : *City★★ – Lynch's Castle★* **BY** *– St. Nicholas' Church★* **BY** *– Roman Catholic Cathedral★* **AY** *– Eyre Square : Bank of Ireland Building (sword and mace★)* **BY D.**

Env. : *NW : Lough Corrib★★.*

Exc. : *W : by boat, Aran Islands (Inishmore – Dun Aenghus★★★)* **BZ** *– Thoor Ballylee★, SE : 21 m. by N 6 and N 18* **D** *– Athenry★, E : 14 m. by N 6 and R 348* **D** *– Dunguaire Castle, Kinvarra★* **AC**, *S : 16 m. by N 6, N 18 and N 67* **D** *– Aughnanure Castle★, NW : 16 m. by N 59 – Oughterard★ (≤★★), NW : 18 m. by N 59 – Knockmoy Abbey★, NE : 19 m. by N 17 and N 63* **D** *– Coole Park (Autograph Tree★), SE : 21 m. by N 6 and N 18* **D** *– St. Mary's Cathedral, Tuam★, NE : 21 m. by N 17* **D** *– Loughrea (St. Brendan's Cathedral★), SE : 22 m. by N 6* **D** *– Turoe Stone★, SE : 22 m. by N 6 and north by R 350.*

Galway, Blackrock, Salthill ☎ (091) 522033.

Carnmore Airport : ☎ (091) 752874, NE : 4 m.

Galway City Avas Failte, Victoria Pl., Eyre Sq. ☎ (091) 563081 – Railway Station ☎ (091) 561444 (June-August) – Salthill Promenade ☎ (091) 563081 (May-September).

Dublin 135 – Limerick 64 – Sligo 90.

GALWAY

shop O'Donnel Road	C 2
oneenageisha Road	D 4
Newcastle Road Lower	C 6
Rahoon Road	C 8
Salthill Road Lower	C 10
Sean Mulvoy Road	D 12
Shantalla Road	C 22
Threadneedle Road	C 24

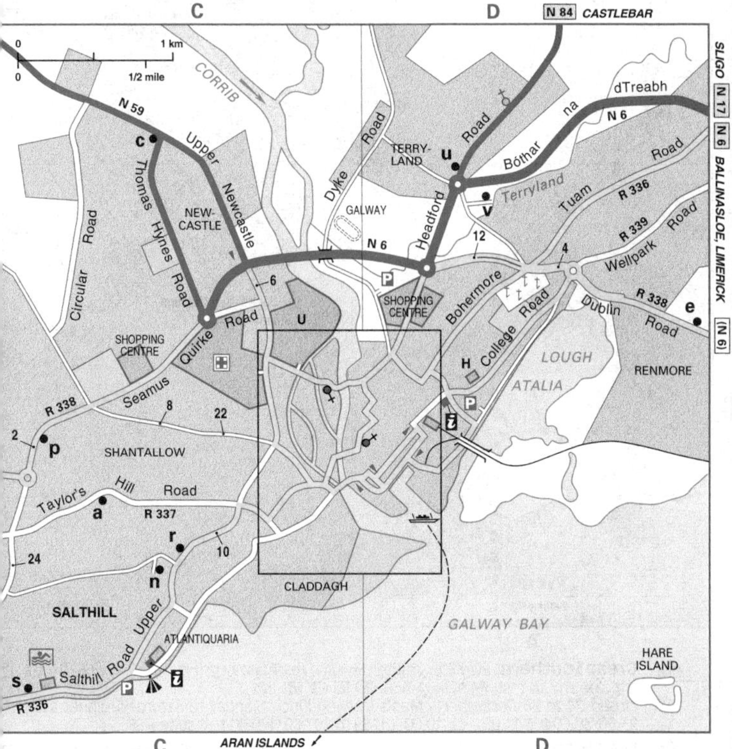

Glenlo Abbey , Bushypark, Northwest : 3 ¼ m. on N 59 ☎ (091) 526666, *glenlo@iol.ie*, *Fax (091) 527800*, ≤, « Restored part 18C house and church », 9, – , rest, TV ☎ , P – 200. MC AE VISA.
River Room : **Meals** (dinner only and Sunday lunch)/dinner a la carte 28.00/41.00 **t.** 16.00 – ***Pullman :*** **Meals** *(closed Monday and Tuesday)* (dinner only) 21.00/31.00 **t.** 13.50 – 12.00 – **41 rm** 160.00/235.00 **t.**, 5 suites.

GALWAY

Street	Ref
Bóthar Uí Eithir	BY 2
Claddagh Bridge	AZ 3
Corrib Shopping Centre	BY
Courthouse Street	BZ 4
Dominick Street	AZ 5
Father Griffin Avenue	AZ 6
Forster Street	BY 7
High Street	BY 8
Main Guard St.	BY 9
Market Street	BY 10
Mary Street	BY 11
New Dock Street	BZ 13
Newton Smith	BY 14
O'Brien Bridge	AY 1
Presentation Street	AY 1
Quay Street	BZ 1
St. Francis Street	BY 2
St. Vincent's Avenue	BY 2
Shantalla Road	AY 2
Shop Street	BY 2
William Street	BY 2

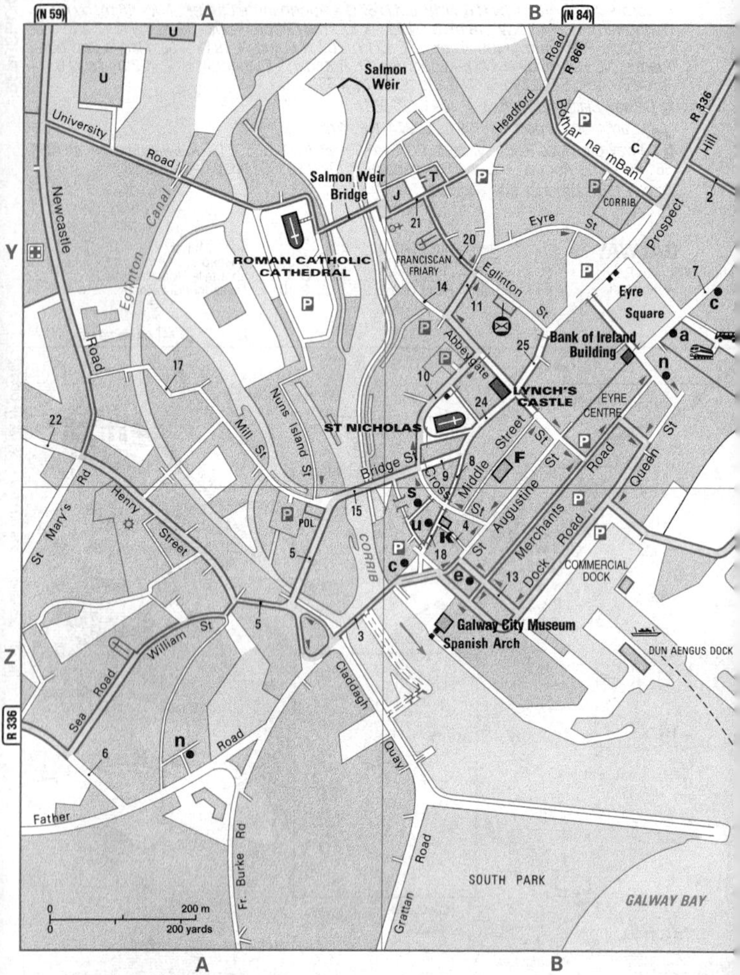

Great Southern, Eyre Sq., ✆ (091) 564041, *res@galway.gsh.ie, Fax (091) 566704,* ≘, – |☰|, ⇔ rm, ▤ rest, TV ✆ – 🏛 450. MC AE ⦿ VISA. ✱ BY
closed 24 to 26 December – **Meals** (carving lunch Monday to Saturday)/dinner a la carte 23.00/30.00 **t.** 🌡 11.00 – ☐ 10.00 – **115 rm** 107.00/170.00 **t.**, 1 suite – SB.

Westwood House, Dangan, Upper Newcastle, ✆ (091) 521442, *westwoodhotel@eircom.net, Fax (091) 521400* – |☰|, ⇔ rm, ▤ TV ✆ ♿ P – 🏛 350. MC AE ⦿ VISA. ✱ C
closed 24 and 25 December – ***Meridian :*** **Meals** (dinner only and Sunday lunch) a la carte 19.15/26.70 **st.** 🌡 8.00 – **58 rm** ☐ 99.00/189.00 **st.**

Corrib Great Southern, Renmore, East : 1 ¾ m. on R 338 ✆ (091) 755281, *res@corribgsh.ie, Fax (091) 751390,* ☐ – |☰|, ⇔ rm, ▤ rest, TV ✆ ♿ P – 🏛 750. MC AE ⦿ VISA. ✱
closed 24 to 26 December – **Meals** (carving lunch Monday to Saturday)/dinner a la carte 25.00/30.00 **st.** 🌡 11.00 – ☐ 9.00 – **176 rm** 100.00/156.00 **t.**, 4 suites – SB.

Ardilaun House, Taylor's Hill, West : 1 ½ m. on R 337 ☎ (091) 521433, *ardilaun@iol.ie, Fax (091) 521546,* – rm, – 450. C a
closed 23 to 28 December – **Meals** (bar lunch Saturday) 13.00/30.00 **t.** and dinner a la carte 8.50 – **88 rm** 110.00/170.00 **t.**, 1 suite – SB.

Park House, Forster St., Eyre Sq., ☎ (091) 564924, *parkhousehotel@eircom.net, Fax (091) 569219* – rest, – 35. BY c
closed 24 to 27 December – **Meals** (carving lunch)/dinner a la carte 20.95/26.00 **t.** 8.00 – **57 rm** 125.00/190.00 **t.**

Jurys Inn Galway, Quay St., ☎ (091) 566444, *galway-inn@jurysdoyle.com, Fax (091) 568415,* – rm, rest, – 35. BZ c
closed 24 to 27 December – **Meals** (carving lunch) (bar lunch Saturday and Sunday)/dinner 15.50 **t.** and a la carte 6.00 – 7.00 – **128 rm** 69.00 **st.**

Brennan's Yard, Lower Merchants Rd, ☎ (091) 568166, *brennansyard@eircom.net, Fax (091) 568262* – . BZ e
closed 21 to 28 December – **Meals** (booking essential) (bar lunch Monday-Saturday)/dinner 17.95 **t.** and a la carte 8.00 – **45 rm** 65.00/105.00 **t.** – SB.

Menlo Park, Terryland, Northeast : 1 ¼ m. by N 6 (Castlebar rd) ☎ (091) 761122, *menlopkh@iol.ie, Fax (091) 761222* – rest, – 160. D v
closed 25 and 26 December – **Meals** 14.00/22.00 **t.** and dinner a la carte 6.50 – **66 rm** 79.00/105.00 **st.** – SB.

Galway Ryan, Dublin Rd, East : 1 ¼ m. on R 338 ☎ (091) 753181, *ryan@indigo.ie, Fax (091) 753187,* – rm, rest, – 40. D e
Meals (bar lunch)/dinner 18.00 **st.** and a la carte 10.00 – **96 rm** 150.00 **st.** – SB.

Spanish Arch, Quay St., ☎ (091) 569600, *emcdgall@iol.ie, Fax (091) 569191,* « Part 18C Carmelite convent » – . BZ u
closed 25 December **Meals** (bar lunch)/dinner a la carte 25.00/33.00 **st.** 8.00 – 7.50 – **20 rm** 75.00/170.00 **st.** – SB.

Glen Oaks, Bishop O'Donnell Rd, West : 1 ½ m. ☎ (091) 589680, *info@glenoakshotel.com, Fax (091) 589509* – . C p
closed 24-25 December – **Meals** 8.00/20.00 **t.** and a la carte 5.00 – **20 rm** 40.00/90.00 **st.** – SB.

Ibis, Headford Rd, Northeast : 1 ¼ m. by N 84 (Castlebar rd) ☎ (091) 771166, *Fax (091) 771646* – rm, . D u
Meals (bar lunch) a la carte approx. 14.20 **st.** – 6.00 – **100 rm** 45.00/50.00 **st.**

Killeen House without rest., Killeen Bushypark, Northwest : 4 m. on N 59 ☎ (091) 524179, *killeenhouse@ireland.com, Fax (091) 528065,* – .
closed 23 to 27 December – **5 rm** 75.00/110.00 **t.**

Adare Guest House without rest., 9 Father Griffin Pl., ☎ (091) 582638, *adare@iol.ie, Fax (091) 583963* – . AZ n
closed 1 week Christmas – **12 rm** 45.00/70.00 **st.**

Archway, Victoria Pl., ☎ (091) 563693, *archway@indigo.ie, Fax (091) 563074* – . BY n
closed 25 December-10 January, Sunday, Monday and Tuesday after Bank Holidays – **Meals** (booking essential) 14.50/26.50 **st.** and dinner a la carte 28.85/40.65 **st.** 10.50.

Kirwan's Lane, Kirwan's Lane, ☎ (091) 568266, *Fax (091) 568266* – .
closed 25 to 30 December and Sunday – **Meals** a la carte 26.95/30.40 **t.** BZ s

at Salthill *Southwest : 2 m.*

Galway Bay, The Promenade, ☎ (091) 520520, *info@galwaybayhotel.net, Fax (091) 520530,* ≤ Galway Bay, – rm, rest, – 500. C s
***Lobster Pot :* Meals** (bar lunch)/dinner 23.50 **t.** and a la carte 7.50 – **149 rm** 115.00/160.00 **t.**, 4 suites – SB.

Norman Villa without rest., 86 Lower Salthill, ☎ (091) 521131, *normanvilla@oceanfree.net, Fax (091) 521131,* « Contemporary Irish art collection », – . C r
closed December and January – **5 rm** 40.00/75.00 **st.**

Devondell without rest., 47 Devon Park, Lower Salthill, off Lower Salthill Rd ☎ (091) 528306, *devondell@iol.ie* – . C n
February-October – **4 rm** 25.00/50.00.

GARRYVOE **(Garraí Uí Bhuaigh)** *Cork* 923 H 12 – ✉ *Castlemartyr.*
Dublin 161 – Cork 23 – Waterford 62.

Garryvoe, ✆ (021) 646718, *garryvoehotel@eircom.net, Fax (021) 646824,* ←, – rest, TV P – 300. MC AE VISA.
closed 25 December – **Meals** 12.50/22.00 **st.** and dinner a la carte 7.50 – **19 rm** 55.0 120.00 **st.** – SB.

GLANWORTH **(Gleannúir)** *Cork* 923 G 11 – *pop. 400.*
Dublin 136 – Cork 22 – Killarney 57 – Limerick 40.

Glanworth Mill Country Inn with rm, ✆ (025) 38555, *glanworth@iol.*
Fax (025) 38560, « Restored watermill on the banks of River Funcheon », – P.
VISA.
closed Christmas – **Meals** 14.50 **t.** (dinner) and a la carte 15.50/24.00 **t.** 6.50 – **10 r** 55.00/100.00 **st.**

GLASLOUGH **(Glasloch)** *Monaghan* 923 L 5 – *see Monaghan.*

GLASSAN **(Glasán)** *Westmeath* 923 I 7 – *see Athlone.*

GLENBEIGH **(Gleann Beithe)** *Kerry* 923 C 11 *Ireland G.* – *pop. 251.*
Exc. : *Iveragh Peninsula*★★ – *Ring of Kerry*★★ – *Lough Caragh*★.
Dooks ✆ *(066) 976 8205.*
Dublin 197 – Killarney 21 – Tralee 24.

Foxtrot without rest., Mountain Stage, Southwest : 3 m. on N 70 ✆ (066) 9768417, *fox ot@indigo.ie, Fax (066) 9768552,* ← Coomasaharn lake and mountains – P. AE.
Mid March-October – **4 rm** 25.00/40.00 **st.**

Les prix — Pour toutes précisions sur les prix indiqués dans ce guide, reportez-vous aux pages de l'introduction.

GLENDALOUGH **(Gleann dá Loch)** *Wicklow* 923 M 8 *Ireland G.*
See : *Monastic ruins*★★★ – *Lower Lake*★★★ – *Cathedral*★★ – *Upper Lake*★★ – *Round Tower* – *St. Kevin's Church*★ – *St. Saviour's Priory*★.
Exc. : *Wicklow Mountains*★★ – *Wicklow Gap*★★.
✆ *(0404) 45688 (June-September).*
Dublin 28 – Kilkenny 68 – Wexford 63.

Glendalough, ✆ (0404) 45135, *info@glendaloughhotel.ie, Fax (0404) 45142,* –
rm, TV P – 200. MC AE VISA.
closed 4 December-1 February – **Meals** 15.00/23.95 **t.** and a la carte – **40 rm** 60.0 120.00 **st.** – SB.

GLENGARRIFF **(An Gleann Garbh)** *Cork* 923 D 12 *Ireland G.*
See : *Town*★ – *Garinish Island*★★.
Env. : *Healy Pass*★★ (←★★), *W : by R 572 – Derreen Gardens*★, *W : by R 572 and north by 574 (Healy Pass).*
✆ *(027) 63084 (July-August).*
Dublin 213 – Cork 60 – Killarney 37.

Cois Coille without rest., ✆ (027) 63202, – P.
Easter-October – **6 rm** 30.00/42.00 **s.**

GLEN OF AHERLOW **(Gleann Eatharlaí)** *Tipperary* 923 H 10 *Ireland G.* – ✉ *Tipperary.*
See : *Glen of Aherlow*★.
Exc. : *Caher Castle*★★ *AC* – *Swiss Cottage*★ *AC, SE : 7 m. by N 24 and R 670 – Clonme (County Museum*★*, St. Mary's Church*★*), NE : 16 m. by N 24 – Kilmallock*★ *(Abbey Collegiate Church*★*), W : 27½ m. by R 664 and R 515.*
Dublin 118 – Cahir 6 – Tipperary 9.

Aherlow House , ✆ (062) 56153, *aherlow@iol.ie, Fax (062) 56212,* ← Galty Mountain – rest, TV P – 200. MC AE VISA.
Meals (bar lunch Monday to Saturday)/dinner 25.00 **st.** – **29 rm** 67.00/114.00 **st.** – SB.

.IN (An Gleann) *Limerick* 923 E 10 – *pop. 554.*
Dublin 152 – Limerick 32 – Tralee 32.

Glin Castle ⛰, ☎ (068) 34112, *knight@iol.ie, Fax (068) 34364*, ≤, « Crenellated Georgian country house, collection of antique furnishings, paintings and porcelain », ⛲, ♞, 🎾 – ⛔ rest, TV P. MC AE ⓓ VISA
April-December – **Meals** (booking essential to non-residents) (dinner only) 31.00 **t.** 🍷 12.00 – **15 rm** ☐ 190.00/300.00 **t.**

)REY (Guaire) *Wexford* 923 N 9 *Ireland G.* – *pop. 2 150.*
Exc. : *Ferns★, SW : 11 m. by N 11.*
⛳18 *Courtown, Kiltennel ☎ (055) 25166.*
ℹ *Main St. ☎ (055) 21248.*
Dublin 58 – Waterford 55 – Wexford 38.

Marlfield House ⛰, Courtown Rd, Southeast : 1 m. on R 742 ☎ (055) 21124, *info@marlfieldhouse.ie, Fax (055) 21572*, ≤, « Regency mansion, extensive gardens and woodland », ≘s, 🎾 – ⛔ TV P. MC AE ⓓ VISA
closed 1 to 30 January – **Meals** (booking essential to non-residents) (dinner only and Sunday lunch)/dinner 39.00/43.00 **t.** 🍷 10.00 – **19 rm** ☐ 105.00/180.00 **t.**, 1 suite – SB.

)RT (An Gort) *Galway* 923 F 8.
⛳18 *Castlequarter ☎ (091) 632244.*
Dublin 129 – Galway 24 – Limerick 40.

The Lady Gregory, Ennis Rd, on N 18 ☎ (091) 632333, *ladygregoryhotel@tinet.ie, Fax (091) 632332*, Fō – |‡|, ⛔ rm, ▤ rest, TV ☎ ♿ P – 🏛 400. MC AE ⓓ VISA. ✂
closed 24-28 December – **Meals** (carving lunch Monday to Saturday) 14.00/27.00 **st.** dinner and a la carte – **48 rm** ☐ 57.00/160.00 **st.** – SB.

RAIGUENAMANAGH (Gráig na Manach) *Kilkenny* 923 L 10.
Dublin 78 – Kilkenny 21 – Waterford 26 – Wexford 16.

Waterside, The Quay, ☎ (0503) 24246, *info@waterside.iol.ie, Fax (0503) 24733*, ≤, « Converted Victorian cornstore on banks of River Barrow » – TV. MC VISA. ✂
*closed 25 December*Meals (by arrangement) 15.45/24.20 **st.** 🍷 7.50 – **9 rm** ☐ 35.00/70.00 **st.** – SB.

REYSTONES (Na Clocha Liatha) *Wicklow* 923 N 8 – *pop. 9 995.*
⛳18 *Greystones ☎ (01) 287 6624.*
Dublin 22.

Hungry Monk, Southview Church Rd, ☎ (01) 287 5759, *Fax (01) 287 7183* – ▤. MC AE VISA
closed 24 to 26 December, Good Friday, Monday and Tuesday – **Meals** (dinner only and Sunday lunch)/dinner a la carte 21.45/29.45 **t.** 🍷 8.00.

OWTH (Binn Èadair) *Dublin* 923 N 7 *Ireland G.* – ✉ *Dublin.*
See : *Town★ – The Summit★ (≤★).*
⛳18, ⛳18, ⛳9 *Deer Park Hotel, Howth Castle ☎ (01) 822 2624.*
Dublin 10.

Marine, Sutton Cross, D13, West : 1 ½ m. ☎ (01) 839 0000, *info@marinehotel.ie, Fax (01) 839 0442*, Fō, ≘s, 🏊, ⛲ – TV P – 🏛 175. MC AE ⓓ VISA. ✂
closed 25 to 27 December – ***The Meridian :*** **Meals** a la carte 22.40/28.70 **t.** 🍷 6.50 – **50 rm** ☐ 110.00/165.00 **t.** – SB.

Inisradharc without rest., Balkhill Rd, D13, North : ½ m. ☎ (01) 8322306, *Fax (01) 8322306*, ≤, ⛲ – ⛔ TV P. MC AE VISA
closed Christmas and New Year – **3 rm** ☐ 38.00/52.00.

King Sitric with rm, East Pier, ☎ (01) 832 5235, *info@kingsitric.ie, Fax (01) 839 2442*, ≤ – ⛔ rm, TV ☎. MC AE ⓓ VISA. ✂
closed Christmas, 2 weeks January and Bank Holidays – **Meals** - Seafood - *(closed Saturday lunch and Sunday)* 18.50/32.00 **t.** and a la carte 🍷 7.00 – **8 rm** ☐ 65.00/150.00 **t.** – SB.

ICH (An Inis) *Clare* – *see Ennis.*

INISHCRONE (Inis Crabhann) *Sligo* 923 E 5 – *pop. 692.*
Dublin 160 – Ballina 8 – Galway 79 – Sligo 34.

Ceol na Mara without rest., Main St., ☎ (096) 36351, *Fax (096) 36642*, ≤ – TV P. MC VI
closed 20 December-30 January **9 rm** 28.00/42.00 **st.**

INISHMORE (Inis Mór) *Galway* 923 CD 8 – *see Aran Islands.*

INISTIOGE (Inis Tíog) *Kilkenny* 923 K 10.
Dublin 82 – Kilkenny 16 – Waterford 19 – Wexford 33.

Berryhill, Southeast : ¾ m. by R 700 ☎ (056) 58434, *info@berryhillhouse.co*
Fax (056) 58434, ≤, « Working farm », – rm, P. MC VISA.
May-October – **Meals** (by arrangement) (communal dining) 25.00 **s.** – **3 rm** 55.0
90.00 **s.**

Rathsnagadan House, Southeast : 4 ¾ m. by R 700 ☎ (051) 423641, *rathsnagad*
house@eircom.net, Fax (051) 423641, ≤, – P. MC VISA
February-November – **Meals** (by arrangement) 22.00 **st.** – **3 rm** 30.00/50.00 **st.**

The Motte, Plass Newid, Northwest : ¼ m. on R 700 ☎ (056) 58655, *atmotte@gofree.i*
go.ie – P. MC VISA
closed 1 week Christmas, Sunday except Bank Holidays and Monday – **Meals** (booki
essential) (dinner only) 23.50 **t.** 9.50.

INVERIN (Indreabhán) *Galway* 923 D8.
Dublin 149 – Galway 17.

Tig Cualain without rest., Kilroe East, on R 336 ☎ (091) 553609, *Fax (091) 553049* –
TV P.
March-October – **9 rm** 25.00/40.00.

KANTURK (Ceann Toirc) *Cork* 923 F 11 *Ireland G.* – *pop. 1 666.*
See : *Town★ - Castle★.*
Fairy Hill ☎ (029) 50534.
Dublin 161 – Cork 33 – Killarney 31 – Limerick 44.

Assolas Country House, East : 3 ¼ m. by R 576 and R 580 on Cecilstown
☎ (029) 50015, *assolas@eircom.net, Fax (029) 50795*, ≤, « Part 17C and 18C country hous
gardens, riverside setting », – P. MC VISA.
March-October – **Meals** (booking essential) (residents only) (dinner only) 30.00 **st.** 8.00
9 rm 75.00/170.00 **st.**

Glenlohane, East : 2 ½ m. by R 576 and R 580 on Cecilstown rd ☎ (029) 50014, *msk*
iol.ie, Fax (029) 51100, ≤, « Georgian country house, extensive parkland, working farm
– P. MC AE VISA.
Meals (by arrangement) (communal dining) 25.00 **st.** 10.00 – **4 rm** 65.00/130.00 **st.**

The Vintage, O'Brien St., ☎ (029) 50549, *Fax (029) 51209* – MC VISA
closed 25 December and Sunday lunch – **Meals** a la carte 9.45/21.90 **t.** 5.95.

KEEL (An Caol) *Mayo* 923 B 5/6 – *see Achill Island.*

KENMARE (Neidín) *Kerry* 923 D 12 *Ireland G.* – *pop. 1 420.*
See : *Town★.*
Exc. : *Ring of Kerry★★ – Healy Pass★★ (≤★★), SW : 19 m. by R 571 and R 574* **AY** *– Mounta*
Road to Glengarriff (≤★★) S : by N 71 **AY** *– Slieve Miskish Mountains (≤★★), SW : 30 m. by*
571 **AY** *– Cougane Barra Forest Park★★, SE : 10 m.* **AY** *– Lauragh (Derreen Gardens★* **A**
SW : 14½ m. by R 571 **AY** *– Allihies (Copper Mines★), SW : 35½ m. by R 571 and R 575* **AY**
Garnish Island (≤★), SW : 42½ m. by R 571, R 575 and R 572 **AY**.
Kenmare ☎ (064) 41291.
Heritage Centre ☎ (064) 41233 (April-October) **AY**.
Dublin 210 – Cork 58 – Killarney 20.

Plan opposite

Park, ☎ (064) 41200, *info@parkkenmare.com, Fax (064) 41402*, ≤ Kenmare Bay ar
hills, « Antiques and paintings », – TV – 35. MC AE
VISA. **BY**
13 April-5 November and 23 December-2 January – **Meals** (dinner only) a la carte 42.0
56.95 **st.** 10.50 – **49 rm** 168.00/524.00 **st.**

KENMARE

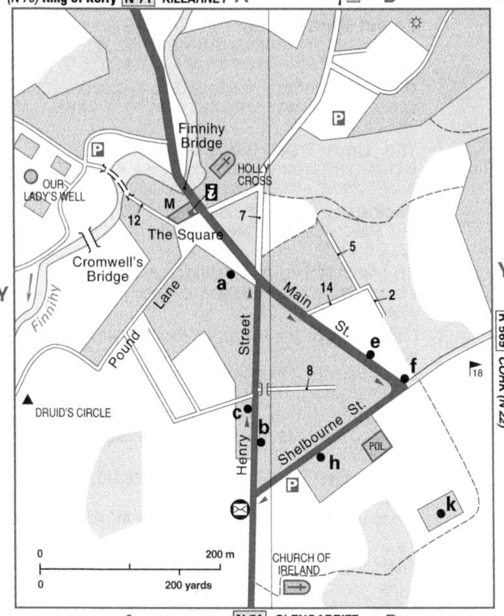

Sheen Falls Lodge,, Southeast : 1 ¼ m. by N 71 (064) 41600, *info@sheenfallslodge.ie, Fax (064) 41386*, « Wooded setting on banks of Sheen River and Kenmare Bay < Sheen Falls », – rm, – 120. MC AE VISA.
2 February-2 December and 23 December-2 January – ***La Cascade :*** **Meals** (dinner only) 32.50/40.00 **t.** 12.00 – ***Oscar's :*** **Meals** *(closed Monday and Tuesday, Wednesday February-April* (dinner only) a la carte 17.20/25.95 **t.** 7.95 – 17.00 – **53 rm** 180.00/285.00 **st.**, 8 suites – SB.

Dromquinna Manor, Blackwater Bridge P.O., West : 3 m. by N 71 on N 70 (Sneem rd) (064) 41657, *info@dromquinna.com, Fax (064) 41791*, <, « Situated on the shores of Kenmare Bay », – – 30. MC AE VISA
April-October – **Meals** (dinner only) 21.50 **t.** and a la carte 8.50 – ***Boathouse Bistro*** *((064) 42255)* **: Meals** *(closed dinner Sunday and Monday October-May)* a la carte 10.50/15.00 **t.** 7.50 – **46 rm** 45.00/180.00 **t.** – SB.

Shelburne Lodge,, East : ½ m. on R 569 (Cork Rd) (064) 41013, *Fax (064) 42135*, « Stylishly decorated 18C house », – MC VISA.
March-November – **Meals** – (see ***Packies*** below) – **9 rm** 60.00/90.00.

Dunkerron,, West : 2 ½ m. by N 71 on N 70 (Sneem rd) (064) 41102, *info@rentacottage.ie, Fax (064) 41102*, « Ruined 12C castle in grounds », – MC AE VISA.
April-March – **Meals** (booking essential) (residents only) (dinner only) 23.00 **st.** 8.50 – **10 rm** 45.00/90.00 **st.**

The Rosegarden,, West : ¾ m. by N 71 on N 70 (Sneem rd) (064) 42288, *rosegard@iol.ie, Fax (064) 42305*, – MC AE VISA.
April-October – **Meals** (dinner only) 14.95 **t.** and a la carte 6.50 – **8 rm** 37.50/55.00 **t.** – SB.

The Lodge without rest., Killowen Rd, East : ¼ m. on R 569 (Cork rd) (064) 41512, *thelodgekenmare@eircom.net, Fax (064) 47724* – MC VISA.
March-October **11 rm** 60.00/70.00 **st.**

Sallyport House without rest.,, South : ¼ m. on N 71 (064) 42066, *pot@iol.ie, Fax (064) 42067*, <, « Antique furnishings », –
April-October – **5rm** 70.00/100.00.

Mylestone House without rest., Killowen Rd, East : ¼ m. on R 569 (Cork rd) (064) 41753, *mylestonehouse@tinet.ie*, – MC VISA.
closed 10 November-15 February – **5 rm** 30.00/44.00 **st.**

Ceann Mara,, East : 1 m. on R 569 (Cork rd) (064) 41220, *ceann.mara@eircom.n* *Fax (064) 41220*, Kenmare Bay and hills, – P
June-September – **Meals** (by arrangement) 16.00 **st.** – **4 rm** 31.00/48.00 **s.**

d'Arcys, Main St., (064) 41589, *patgathe@iol.ie, Fax (064) 41589* – . MC VISA BY
closed Tuesday and restricted opening in winter – **Meals** (dinner only) a la carte 21.9 28.50 **t.** 7.50.

The Lime Tree, Shelburne St., (064) 41225, *benchmark@iol.ie, Fax (064) 418*
« Characterful former schoolhouse » – P. MC VISA BY
April-October – **Meals** (dinner only) a la carte 22.35/26.95 **st.** 8.50.

Packies, Henry St., (064) 41508 – MC VISA AY
Mid March-October – **Meals** *(closed Sunday and Monday)* (dinner only) a la carte 20.3 32.00 **t.** 6.00.

An Leath Phingin, 35 Main St., (064) 41559 – . MC VISA BY
closed 15 November-15 December and Wednesday – **Meals** - Italian - (dinner only) a la car 13.40/20.50 **st.** 5.50.

Café Indigo, The Square, (064) 42356, *cmacd@iol.ie, Fax (064) 42358* – . MC AE VISA AY
closed 3 weeks January and November, 25 December, Monday and Tuesday – **Meals** (dinr only) a la carte 23.00/28.40 **t.** 9.00.

Mulcahys, 16 Henry St., (064) 42383 – MC VISA AY
closed January-March and Wednesday except July-August – **Meals** (dinner only) a la car 15.95/35.40 **t.** 7.50.

The Square Pint, The Square, (064) 42357, *cmacd@iol.ie, Fax (064) 42358*, – MC AE VISA AY
closed Good Friday and 25 December – **Meals** (lunch only) a la carte 13.10/17.40 **t.** 9.00

KILBRITTAIN (Cill Briotáin) *Cork* 923 F 12.

Dublin 180 – Cork 24 – Killarney 60.

Casino House, Coolmain Bay, Southeast : 2 ¼ m. by unmarked rd on R 6 (023) 49944, *Fax (023) 49945*, , – P. MC VISA
closed January-mid March – **Meals** *(closed Wednesday except July and August)* (dinr only) a la carte 13.60/30.20 **t.** 6.25.

KILCOLGAN (Cill Cholgáin) *Galway* 923 F 8 – *Oranmore.*

Dublin 137 – Galway 11.

Moran's Oyster Cottage, The Weir, Northwest : 1 ¼ m. by N 18 (091) 7961 *Fax (091) 796503*, , « Part 18C thatched cottage » – MC AE VISA
closed 24-25 December and Good Friday – **Meals** a la carte 14.00/35.70 **t.**

KILCUMMIN (Cill Chuimán) *Kerry* 923 B 11 *Ireland G.*

Exc. : *Dingle Peninsula*★★★ – *Connor Pass*★★ – *Dingle*★, *SW : by Connor Pass.*
Dublin 203 – Killarney 34 – Limerick 85 – Tralee 21.

The Shores Country House,, East : ½ m. on R 560 (066) 7139196, *theshores@eir m.net, Fax (066) 7139196*, , – P. MC VISA.
*closed December and January***Meals** (by arrangement) 18.00 **st.** – **6 rm** 25.50/46.00 **st**

Strand View House without rest., Conor Pass Rd, (066) 7138131, *strandview@eir m.net, Fax (066) 7138386*, – P. VISA.
4 rm 28.00/44.00 **s.**

KILKEE (Cill Chaoi) *Clare* 923 D 9 *Ireland G.* – *pop. 1 331.*

Exc. : *Kilrush*★ *(Scattery Island*★ *by boat), SE : 10 m. by N 67 – SW : Loop Head Peninsu (Bridge of Ross*★*).*
Kilkee, East End (065) 9056048.
O'Connell Sq. (065) 9056112 (June-early September).
Dublin 177 – Galway 77 – Limerick 58.

Ocean Cove, Kilkee Bay, (065) 9083111, *cro@lynchhotels.com, Fax (065) 9083123*, – , rm, P. MC AE VISA.
restricted opening in winter – ***Pan Asian's :*** **Meals** (bar lunch Monday-Saturday)/dinn 10.50/21.00 **st.** and a la carte 7.00 – **50 rm** 69.50/109.00 **st.** – SB.

Kilkee Bay, (065) 9060060, *info@kilkee-bay.com, Fax (065) 9060062* – rest, – 150. MC AE VISA.
– **Meals** (bar lunch Monday to Saturday)/dinner 17.00/25.00 **st.** 6.50 – **40 rm** 52.5 75.00 **st.**, 1 suite – SB.

Halpin's, Erin St., ✆ (065) 9056032, *halpins@iol.ie, Fax (065) 9056317* – ⇔ rest, TV P. MC AE D VISA JCB. ✻
15 March-10 November – **Meals** (bar lunch Monday to Saturday)/dinner 20.00/24.00 **t.** and a la carte 8.50 – **12 rm** ☐ 45.00/110.00 **t.** – SB.

ILKENNY (Cill Chainnigh) *Kilkenny* 923 K 10 *Ireland G. – pop. 8 507.*

See : *Town★★ – St. Canice's Cathedral★★ – Kilkenny Castle and Grounds★★* AC *– Cityscope★* AC *– Black Abbey★ – Rothe House★.*

Exc. : *Jerpoint Abbey★★* AC, *S : 12 m. by R 700 and N 9 – Dunmore Cave★* AC, *N : 7 m. by N 77 and N 78 – Kells Priory★, S : 8 m. by R 697.*

Glendine ✆ (056) 65400 – Callan, Geraldine ✆ (056) 25136 – Castlecomer, Drumgoole ✆ (056) 41139.

Shee Alms House ✆ (056) 51500.

Dublin 71 – Cork 86 – Killarney 115 – Limerick 69 – Tullamore 52 – Waterford 29.

Kilkenny Ormonde, Ormonde St., ✆ (056) 23900, *info@kilkennyormonde.com, Fax (056) 23977,* ⇔, ⇔, ☐ – |♦|, ⇔ rest, TV ✆ & P – 400. MC AE D VISA. ✻
***Fredricks :* Meals** (dinner only) a la carte approx. 25.95 **t.** 8.60 – ***Earls Brasserie :* Meals** (carving rest.) a la carte approx. 20.00 **t.** 8.60 – **112 rm** 105.00/150.00 **t.**, 6 suites – SB.

The Hibernean, 1 Ormonde St., ✆ (056) 71888, *info@hibernean.com, Fax (056) 71877* – |♦|, ⇔ rest, TV & – 60. MC AE D VISA. ✻
Meals (bar lunch Monday-Saturday) a la carte 15.40/28.95 **st.** – **39 rm** ☐ 70.00 **st.**, 3 suites.

Kilkenny, College Rd, Southwest : ¾ m. at junction with N 76 ✆ (056) 62000, *kilkenny@griffingroup.ie, Fax (056) 65984,* ⇔, ⇔, ☐, ⇔ – ⇔ rest, TV P – 400. MC AE D VISA. ✻
***Brooms Bistro :* Meals** 11.95/27.00 **st.** and a la carte 8.00 – **103 rm** ☐ 75.00/140.00 **st.** – SB.

Newpark, Castlecomer Rd, North : 1 m. on N 77 ✆ (056) 22122, *info@newparkhotel.com, Fax (056) 61111,* ⇔, ⇔, ☐, ⇔, ⇔ – |♦|, ⇔ rm, TV & P – 600. MC AE D VISA. ✻
Meals (carvery lunch Monday to Saturday)/dinner 26.00 **st.** and a la carte – ☐ 9.50 – **111 rm** 75.00/119.00 **st.** – SB.

Langton's House, 69 John St., ✆ (056) 65133, *langtons@oceanfree.net, Fax (056) 63693,* ⇔ – ⇔ rest, TV P. MC AE D VISA. ✻
closed 25 December and Good Friday – **Meals** 10.00/18.50 **st.** and a la carte 6.50 – **26 rm** ☐ 45.00/160.00 **st.** – SB.

Springhill Court, Waterford Rd, South : 1 ¼ m. on N 10 ✆ (056) 21122, *springhillcourt@eircom.net, Fax (056) 61600* – |♦| TV P – 400. MC AE D VISA JCB. ✻
Meals 11.50/21.50 **st.** and a la carte 7.50 – **86 rm** ☐ 49.00/90.00 **st.** – SB.

Kilkenny River Court, The Bridge, John St., ✆ (056) 23388, *krch@iol.ie, Fax (056) 23389,* ⇔, ☐ – |♦|, ⇔ rest, TV ✆ P – 210. MC AE VISA. ✻
closed 25 December – **Meals** (bar lunch Monday to Saturday)/dinner 27.95 **st.** and a la carte 7.85 – **90 rm** ☐ 115.00/280.00 **st.** – SB.

Butler House, 15-16 Patrick St., ✆ (056) 65707, *res@butler.ie, Fax (056) 65626,* ⇔ – TV P – 100. MC AE D VISA JCB. ✻
closed 24 to 30 December – **Meals** 10.00/30.00 **st.** and a la carte – **12 rm** ☐ 89.00/149.00 **st.**, 1 suite.

Blanchville House ⇔, Dunbell, Maddoxtown, Southeast : 6 ½ m. by N 10 turning right ½ m. after the Pike Inn ✆ (056) 27197, *info@blanchville.ie, Fax (056) 27636,* ≤, « Georgian country house », ⇔, ⇔ – ⇔ P. MC AE VISA. ✻
March-October – **Meals** (by arrangement) (communal dining) 25.00 **s.** – **6 rm** ☐ 40.00/75.00 **st.** – SB.

Berkeley House without rest., 5 Patrick St., ✆ (056) 64848, *berkleyhouse@eircom.net, Fax (056) 64829* – TV P. MC VISA. ✻
closed 25 December – **10 rm** ☐ 45.00/70.00.

Newlands Country House ⇔, Sevenhouses, South : 5 ¾ m. by N 10 on Callan rd ✆ (056) 29111, *newlands@indigo.ie, Fax (056) 29171,* ⇔ – ⇔ TV P. MC VISA. ✻
closed 23 to 29 December – **Meals** (by arrangement) 25.00 **st.** – **6 rm** ☐ 35.00/70.00 **st.** – SB.

Shillogher House without rest., Callan Rd, Southwest : 1 m. on N 76 ✆ (056) 63249, *shillogherhouse@tinet.ie, Fax (056) 64865,* ⇔ – ⇔ TV P. MC VISA. ✻
6 rm ☐ 35.00/50.00.

Zuni with rm, 26 Patrick St., ✆ (056) 23999, *info@zuni.ie, Fax (056) 56400,* « Contemporary interior » – |♦|, ⇔ rm, ⇔ rest, TV ✆ & P. MC AE VISA. ✻
closed 23-27 December – **Meals** *(closed Monday)* a la carte 20.40/28.40 **t.** 7.95 – **13 rm** ☐ 60.00/90.00 **t.** – SB.

Ristorante Rinuccini with rm, 1 The Parade, ☎ (056) 61575, *Fax (056) 51288* – ▤ ▣ MC AE ⓓ VISA. ✗
closed 25 to 27 December – **Meals** - Italian - a la carte 13.85/22.85 **t.** 6.95 – **7 rm** 60.00/125.00 **st.** – SB.

KILL (An Chill) *Kildare* 923 M 8 – *pop. 1 711.*
Killeen, Killeenbeg ☎ (045) 866003.
Dublin 15 – Carlow 36.

Ambassador,, on N 7 ☎ (045) 877064, *ambassador-sales@quinn-direct.com* *Fax (045) 877515* – TV P – 280. MC ⓓ VISA. ✗
Meals (carving lunch Monday to Saturday)/dinner a la carte 18.00/28.00 **st.** 5.50 – **36 rm** 58.00/90.00 **st.**

KILLALOE (Cill Dalua) *Clare* 923 G 9 *Ireland G. – pop. 972.*
See : *Town★ – St. Flannan's Cathedral★.*
Env. : *Graves of the Leinstermen (≤★), N : 4½ m. by R 494.*
Exc. : *Nenagh★ (Heritage Centre★ AC, Castle★), NE : 12 m. by R 496 and N 7 – Holy Island AC, N : 16 m. by R 463 and boat from Tuamgraney.*
The Bridge ☎ (061) 376866 (May-September).
Dublin 109 – Ennis 32 – Limerick 13 – Tullamore 58.

Kincora Hall,, North : ¾ m. on R 463 ☎ (061) 376000, *kincora@iol.ie*, *Fax (061) 37666* – ▤ rest, TV P. MC AE ⓓ VISA JCB. ✗
closed 24-26 December – **Meals** (bar lunch Monday to Saturday)/dinner 14.95/25.0 and a la carte 6.95 – **31 rm** 75.00/120.00 **t.** – SB.

Waterman's Lodge, Ballina (Tipperary), ☎ (061) 376333, *info@watermanslodge.i* *Fax (061) 375445*, – rm, P. MC AE VISA. ✗
closed 20 December-15 January – **Meals** *(closed Sunday and Monday)* (booking essential non-residents) (dinner only) a la carte 21.40/33.45 **st.** 8.00 – **11 rm** 40.00/140.00 **st.** – SB.

Cherry Tree, Lakeside, Ballina, following signs for Lakeside H. ☎ (061) 37568 *Fax (061) 375689*, ≤, « Contemporary interior » – P. MC AE VISA
closed 25-26 December, last week January, first week November, Sunday and Monday **Meals** (dinner only) a la carte 22.40/39.45 **t.** 12.00.

at Ogonnelloe *North : 6¼ m. on R 463.*

Lantern House , ☎ (061) 923034, *Fax (061) 923139*, ≤, – rm, TV P. MC AE VIS ✗
15 March-October – **Meals** (by arrangement) 17.50 **st.** 5.50 – **6 rm** 26.00/50.00 **st.**

KILLARNEY (Cill Airne) *Kerry* 923 D 11 *Ireland G. – pop. 8 809.*
See : *Town★★ – St. Mary's Cathedral★* **CX**.
Env. : *Killarney National Park★★★ (Muckross Abbey★, Muckross House and Farms★)* **AZ** *Gap of Dunloe★★, SW : 6 m. by R 562* **AZ** *– Ross Castle★* **AC**, *S : 1 m. by N 71 and minor ro Torc Waterfall★, S : 5 m. by N 71* **BZ**.
Exc. : *Iveragh Peninsula★★ (Ring of Kerry★★) – Ladies View★★, SW : 12 m. by N 71* **BZ** *Moll's Gap★, SW : 15½ m. by N 71* **BZ**.
Mahoney's Point ☎ (064) 31034 **AZ**.
Kerry (Farranfore) Airport : ☎ (066) 976 4644, N : 9½ m. by N 22.
Beech Rd ☎ (064) 31633.
Dublin 189 – Cork 54 – Limerick 69 – Waterford 112.

Plans on following pages

Killarney Park, Kenmare Pl., ☎ (064) 35555, *info@killarneyparkhotel.ie*, *Fax (064) 3526* – rm, ▤ TV P – 150. MC AE ⓓ VISA. ✗ DX
closed 24 to 26 December – ***Park*** **: Meals** (dinner only) 30.00/42.00 **t.** and a la carte 9.50 **73 rm** 250.00 **t.**, 3 suites – SB.

Europe , Fossa, West : 3 by R 562 on N 72 ☎ (064) 31900, *khl@iol.ie*, *Fax (064) 32118*, Lough Leane and Macgillycuddy's Reeks, « Loughside setting », indoor – TV P – 500. MC AE ⓓ VISA
mid March-October – **Meals** (light lunch)/dinner 25.00 **st.** and a la carte – **202 r** 108.00/170.00 **st.**, 3 suites.

Killarney Royal, College St., ☎ (064) 31853, *royalhot@iol.ie*, *Fax (064) 34001* – rm, ▤ rest, TV MC AE ⓓ VISA DX
*closed 22-28 December***Meals** (bar lunch Monday to Saturday)/dinner 25.00/30.00 and a la carte 7.00 – **29 rm** 120.00/210.00 **t.** – SB.

Aghadoe Heights ,, Northwest : 2 ¾ m. by N 22 ☎ (064) 31766, *aghadoeheights@eircom.net, Fax (064) 31345,* ≤ Lough Leane, Macgillycuddy's Reeks and countryside, ,, , , – , rm, rest, – 100. *Fredrick's :* Meals (bar lunch Monday-Saturday)/dinner a la carte approx. 37.50 **t.** 14.00 – **74 rm** 160.00/220.00 **t.**, 2 suites – SB.

Great Southern, ☎ (064) 31262, *res@killarney.gsh.ie, Fax (064) 31642,* , , , , , – – 900. DX j
Dining Room : Meals (dinner only) 25.00/30.00 **t.** 11.00 – 10.00 – **177 rm** 104.00/164.00 **t.**, 3 suites – SB.

Muckross Park,, South : 2 ½ m. on N 71 ☎ (064) 31938, *muckrossparkhotel@tinet.ie, Fax (064) 31965,* – – – 200.
closed 20 November-mid February – **Meals** (bar lunch)/dinner a la carte 22.25/31.00 **t.** 7.00 – **25 rm** 92.00/140.00 **t.**, 2 suites – SB.

Randles Court, Muckross Rd, ☎ (064) 35333, *randles@iol.ie, Fax (064) 35206* – DY p
closed 20 to 30 December – ***Cleaver's :*** Meals (bar lunch)/dinner 20.00/28.00 **st.** and a la carte 8.00 – **49 rm** 140.00/180.00 **st.** – SB.

Dromhall, Muckross Rd, ☎ (064) 31431, *randles@iol.ie-info@dromhall.com, Fax (064) 34262,* , , – , rm, rest, – 300. DY p
closed January and 21-29 December – ***Abbey :*** Meals (dinner only) 17.50 **t.** 7.00 – ***Kayne's :*** Meals (dinner only) a la carte 18.95/27.95 **t.** 7.00 – **72 rm** 120.00 **st.** – SB.

Holiday Inn, Muckross Rd, ☎ (064) 33000, *holidayinn@eurcom.net, Fax (064) 33001,* , , – , rm, rest, . AZ n
Meals (bar lunch)/dinner 18.00 **st.** 7.00 – 8.50 – **86 rm** 120.00 **st.**, 14 suites – SB.

Killarney Heights, Cork Rd, East : 1 ¼ m. by R 876 on N 22 ☎ (064) 31158, *khh@iol.ie, Fax (064) 35198* – – 300. BZ r
Meals (carving lunch)/dinner a la carte 14.20/23.95 **t.** 6.95 – **71 rm** 65.00/110.00 **st.** – SB.

Killeen House , Aghadoe, Northwest : 3 ½ m. by N 22 ☎ (064) 31711, *charming@indigo.ie, Fax (064) 31811,* – rest,
April-October – **Meals** (dinner only) 29.50 **t.** 8.00 – **23 rm** 50.00/100.00 **t.**

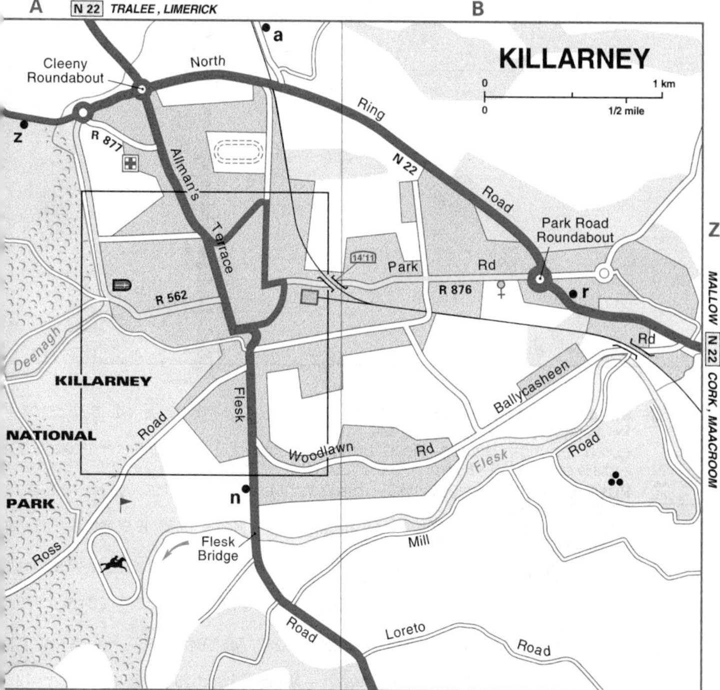

KILLARNEY

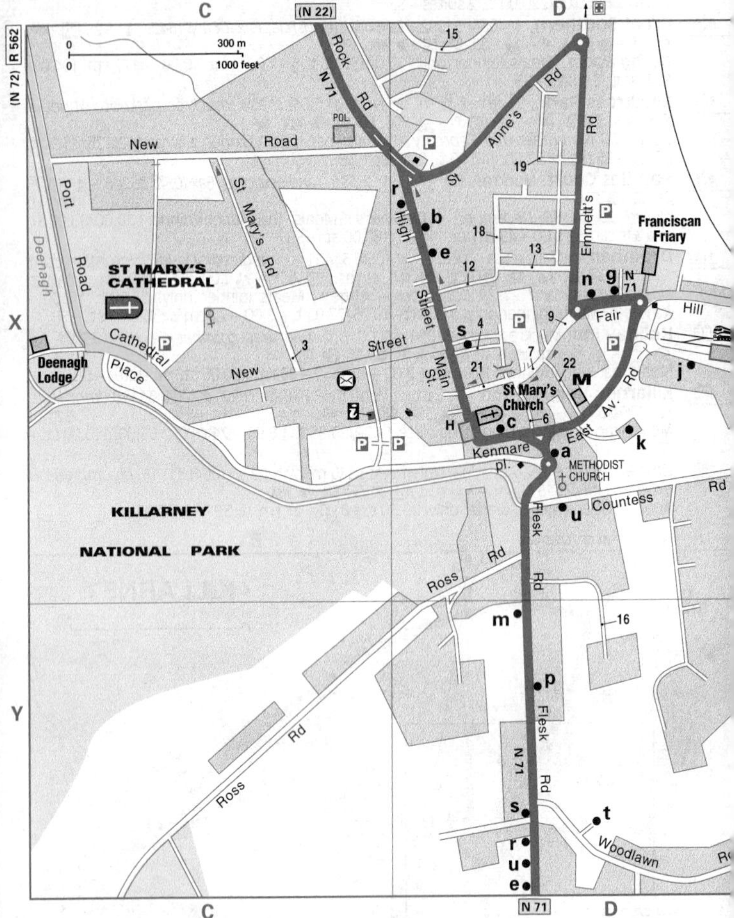

Killarney Avenue, Kenmare Pl., ☎ (064) 32522, *towersky@iol.ie, Fax (064) 33707* – ✻, rest, TV, ♿, 🚗. MC AE D VISA. ✻ DX

closed December-January – **Meals** (bar lunch Monday to Saturday)/dinner 15.00/25.00 and a la carte 9.50 – **66 rm** 100.00/200.00 **st.** – SB.

Ross, Kenmare Pl., ☎ (064) 31855, *ross@kph.iol.ie, Fax (064) 31139* – |‡|, ✻ rest, rest, TV. MC AE VISA. ✻ DX

closed January, February and 4 days at Christmas – **Meals** 13.50/19.95 **st.** and a la carte 8.50 – **32 rm** 68.00/96.00 **st.** – SB.

McSweeney Arms, College St., ☎ (064) 31211, *mcsweeney@eircom.n Fax (065) 34553* – |‡| ✻, rest, TV. MC AE VISA. ✻ DX

closed 4 January-5 February – **Meals** a la carte 17.50/27.50 **st.** 7.00 – **28 rm** 75.0 120.00 **st.** – SB.

Foley's Townhouse, 23 High St., ☎ (064) 31217, *Fax (064) 34683* – ✻, rest, TV MC AE VISA. ✻ DX

Accommodation closed November-March – **Meals** *(closed 23 to 26 December)* 12.5 35.00 **st.** and a la carte 8.50 – **28 rm** 49.50/82.50 **t.**

Fuchsia House without rest., Muckross Rd, ✆ (064) 33743, *fuchiahouse@eircom.net, Fax (064) 36588*, – TV P. MC VISA. DY u
March-November – **10 rm** 65.00/84.00.

Earls Court House without rest., Woodlawn Junction, Muckross Rd, ✆ (064) 34009, *earls@eircom.net, Fax (064) 34366* – TV P. MC VISA. DY t
15 February-7 November – **11 rm** 75.00/96.00 **st.**

Gleann Fia Country House without rest., Deerpark, North : 1 ¼ m. by Emmett's Rd ✆ (064) 35035, *gleanfia@iol.ie, Fax (064) 35000*, – TV P. MC AE VISA. AZ a
March-November – **17 rm** 35.00/56.00 **st.**

Killarney Lodge without rest., Countess Rd, ✆ (064) 36499, *klylodge@iol.ie, Fax (064) 31070*, – TV P. MC AE VISA. DX u
15 February-October – **16 rm** 70.00/84.00 **st.**

Rivermere without rest., Muckross Rd, South : ½ m. on N 71 ✆ (064) 37933, *rivermereguesthouse@eircom.net, Fax (064) 37944*, – TV. MC VISA. DY e
March-October – **8 rm** 40.00/84.00.

Kathleens Country House without rest., Tralee Rd, North : 2 m. on N 22 ✆ (064) 32810, *info@kathleens.net, Fax (064) 32340*, – TV P. MC AE VISA.
closed 8 March-7 November – **16 rm** 80.00/90.00 **st.**

Old Weir Lodge without rest., Muckross Rd, ✆ (064) 35593, *oldweirlodge@eircom.net, Fax (064) 35583* – TV P. MC AE VISA. DY r
closed 24-26 December – **31 rm** 45.00/70.00 **st.**

Lime Court without rest., Muckross Rd, ✆ (064) 34547, *limecrt@iol.ie, Fax (064) 34121* – TV P. MC AE VISA. DY s
11 February-11 November – **17 rm** 30.00/80.00 **st.**

Redwood without rest., Rockfield, Tralee Rd, North : 3 m. on N 22 ✆ (064) 34754, *rewd@indigo.ie, Fax (064) 34178*, – TV P. MC AE VISA.
6 rm 35.00/45.00 **st.**

Lohans Lodge without rest.,, North : 4 m. on N 22 ✆ (064) 33871, *Fax (064) 33871*, – TV P. MC AE VISA.
March-5 November – **5 rm** 25.00/40.00 **st.**

Naughton's Villa without rest., Muckross Rd, ✆ (064) 36025 – TV P. MC VISA.
March-13 November – **5 rm** 30.00/48.00 **st.** DY m

Hussey's Townhouse without rest., 43 High St., ✆ (064) 37454, *husseys@iol.ie, Fax (064) 33144* – TV P. MC AE VISA. DX r
April-October – **5 rm** 35.00/60.00.

Sika Lodge without rest., Ballydowney, Northwest : 1 m. on N 72 ✆ (064) 36304, *Fax (064) 36746* – TV P. MC VISA. AZ z
closed 24 to 26 December – **6 rm** 30.00/45.00 **st.**

XX **Gaby's**, 27 High St., ✆ (064) 32519, *Fax (064) 32747* – MC AE VISA DX b
closed 14 February-14 March, 21 December-4 January and Sunday – **Meals** - Seafood - (dinner only) a la carte 26.00/53.00 **t.** 9.00.

X **The Cooperage**, Old Market Lane, ✆ (064) 37716, *chezmart@iol.ie, Fax (064) 37716* – MC VISA DX s
closed Sunday lunch – **Meals** (light lunch) 25.00/35.00 **t.** and a la carte 6.95.

Beaufort *West : 6 m. by R 562 off N 72 – ✉ Killarney.*

Dunloe Castle ,, Southeast : 1 m. ✆ (064) 44111, *khl@iol.ie, Fax (064) 44583*, ← Gap of Dunloe and Macgillycuddy's Reeks, , , , , , indoor – TV P – 250. MC AE VISA
late April-October – **Meals** (dinner only) 29.00 **st.** and a la carte 9.00 – **102 rm** 108.00/170.00 **st.**, 1 suite.

Beaufort House , ✆ (064) 44764, *info@beaufortireland.com, Fax (064) 44764*, ←, « 18C former shooting lodge », , , – P. MC VISA.
April-September – **Meals** (by arrangement) (communal dining) 30.00 **st.** 8.00 – **4 rm** 80.00/150.00 **st.**

KILLEAGH (Cill Ia) *Cork* 923 H 12 – *pop. 362.*
Dublin 151 – Cork 23 – Waterford 53.

Ballymakeigh House ⑤,, North : 1 m. ℘ (024) 95184, *ballymakeigh@tinet..*, *Fax (024) 95370,* « Working farm », ⛱, ♘, ✂ – Ⓟ. MC VISA. ✻
April-October – **Meals** (by arrangement) 25.00 **st.** 8.00 – **6 rm** ☕ 45.00/90.00 **st.** – SB.

KILLINEY (Cill Iníon Léinín) *Dublin* 923 N 8.
Killiney, Ballinclea Rd ℘ (01) 285 1983.
Dublin 8 – Bray 4.

Fitzpatrick Castle, ℘ (01) 230 5400, *info@fitzpatrick.com, Fax (01) 230 5430,* ⛨, ≘, ☐, ⛱ – ⇅, ⇆ rm, ▤ rest, TV Ⓟ – 🏛 500. MC AE ⓓ VISA. ✻
Meals *(closed 25-26 December and Saturday lunch)* 14.95/16.95 **st.** (lunch) and a la car 26.15/40.20 **st.** 8.95 – ☕ 11.00 – **107 rm** 120.00/147.00 **t.**, 6 suites – SB.

Court, Killiney Bay, ℘ (01) 285 1622, *book@killineycourt.ie, Fax (01) 285 2085,* ≤, ⛱ – ⇆ rm, TV ✆ ♿ Ⓟ – 🏛 200. MC AE ⓓ VISA. ✻
Meals 16.00/30.00 **t.** and a la carte – ☕ 12.00 – **86 rm** 105.00/135.00 **st.** – SB.

KILLINICK (Cill Fhionnóg) *Wexford* 923 M 11 – *see Rosslare Harbour.*

KILLORGLIN (Cill Orglan) *Kerry* 923 C 11 – *pop. 1 278.*
Killorglin, Steelroe ℘ (066) 9761979.
Dublin 207 – Killarney 12 – Tralee 16.

Bianconi, Annadale Rd, ℘ (066) 9761146, *rsheeny@aol.ie, Fax (066) 9761950,* ⇆ rm, TV. MC AE ⓓ VISA. ✻
closed 23-28 December – **Meals** *(closed Sunday)* (bar lunch)/dinner a la carte 18.00/25.00 6.75 – **16 rm** ☕ 50.00/75.00 **t.**

Grove Lodge without rest., Killarney Rd, East : ½ m. on N 72 ℘ (066) 9761157, *grovel. @iol.ie, Fax (066) 9762330,* « Riverside setting », ⛱ – ⚓ ⇆ TV Ⓟ. MC AE ⓓ VISA. ✻
closed 22 to 30 December – **10 rm** ☕ 40.00/74.00 **st.**

The River's Edge without rest., The Bridge, ℘ (066) 9761750, *coffeya@tinet. Fax (066) 9761750,* « Riverside setting » – ⇆ TV Ⓟ. MC ⓓ VISA. ✻
closed 1 week Christmas – **10 rm** ☕ 35.00/60.00 **st.**

KILLYBEGS (Na Cealla Beaga) *Donegal* 923 G 4 *Ireland G.* – *pop. 1 408.*
Exc. : *Glengesh Pass★★, SW : 15 m. by N 56 and R 263 – Glencolmcille Folk Village★★, W : R 263 – Gweebarra Estuary★, NE : 19 m. by R 262 and R 252 – Trabane Strand★.*
Dublin 181 – Donegal 17 – Londonderry 64 – Sligo 57.

Bay View, Main St., ℘ (073) 31950, *bvhotel@iol.ie, Fax (073) 31856,* ≤, ⛨, ≘s, ☐ – ▤ rest, TV ♿ – 🏛 200. MC AE VISA. ✻
closed 24-25 December – **Meals** (bar lunch Monday to Saturday)/dinner a la carte 14.2 22.70 **t.** 8.00 – **40 rm** ☕ 60.00/116.00 **st.** – SB.

KILMEADAN (Cill Mháodáin) *Waterford* 923 K 11 – *see Waterford.*

KILTIMAGH (Coillte Mach) *Mayo* 923 EF 6 – *pop. 917.*
Dublin 138 – Galway 52 – Westport 26.

Cill Aodain, ℘ (094) 81761, *cillaodain@eircom.net, Fax (094) 81838* – TV. MC AE ⓓ VISA
closed 23 to 26 December – **Meals** (carving lunch)/dinner 8.00/22.50 **st.** and a la car 5.50 – **17 rm** ☕ 55.00/120.00 **st.** – SB.

KINNITTY (Cionn Eitigh) *Offaly* 923 I 8 – *see Birr.*

KINSALE (Cionn tSáile) *Cork* 923 G 12 *Ireland G.* – *pop. 2 007.*
See : *Town★★ – St. Multose Church★* Y – *Kinsale Regional Museum★* AC Y **M1.**
Env. : *Kinsale Harbour★ (≤★ from St. Catherine's Anglican Church, Charles Fort★).*
Exc. : *Carbery Coast★, W : 38 m. by R 600.*
Pier Rd ℘ (021) 4772234 (March-November).
Dublin 178 – Cork 17.

KINSALE

ırch Street . . . . Y 2	Guardwell . . . . Y 6	Ramparts Lane . . . . Z 13
ıis Quay . . . . Z 3	Higher O'Connel St. . . . . . YZ 8	Rose Abbey . . . . Y 15
met Street . . . . Y 5	Main Street . . . . Y 9	St John's Hill . . . . Z 16
	Market Place . . . . Y 10	Seilly Walk . . . . Z 18
	Market Quay . . . . Y 12	World's End . . . . Z 19

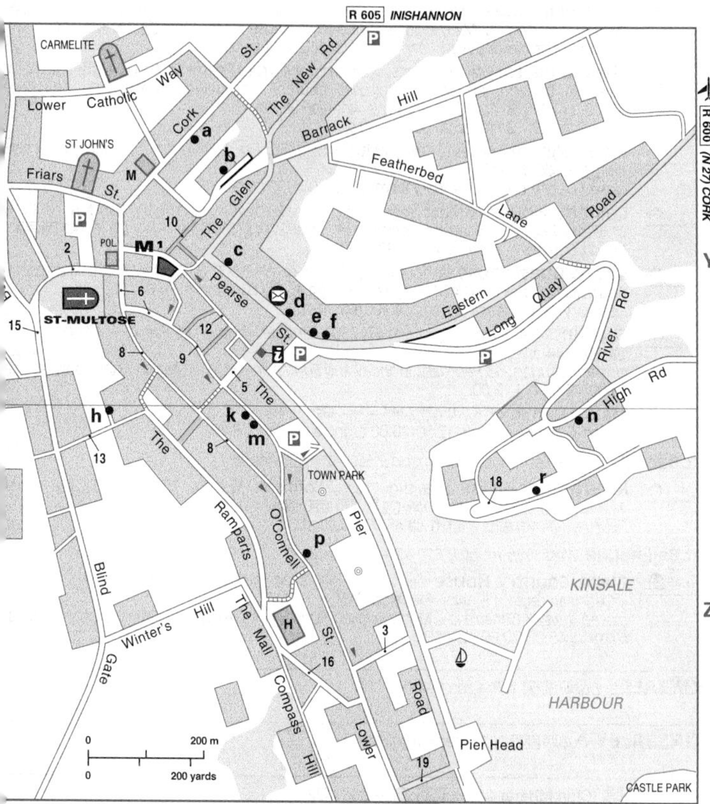

Actons, Pier Rd, ✆ (021) 4772135, *info@actonshotelkinsale.com, Fax (021) 772231,* ≼, Fō, ≘s, ⊠, 🌳 – |♦| TV ☏ P – 🏛 300. MC AE Ⓓ VISA. ✂ Z p
closed 7 January-7 February **Meals** (bar lunch Monday to Saturday)/dinner 25.00/35.00 **t.** and a la carte 🍷 7.50 – **75 rm** ⊒ 90.00/170.00 **st.** – SB.

Perryville House without rest., Long Quay, ✆ (021) 4772731, *sales@perryville.iol.ie, Fax (021) 4772298,* « Late Georgian house overlooking Kinsale harbour » – ✂ TV P. MC VISA. ✂ Y f
April-October – ⊒ 8.00 – **22 rm** 140.00/180.00 **t.**

Blue Haven, 3 Pearse St., ✆ (021) 4772209, *bluhaven@iol.ie, Fax (021) 4774268,* 🏛 – ▤ rest, TV. MC AE Ⓓ VISA. ✂ Y c
closed 24-26 December **Meals** - Seafood - (bar lunch)/dinner 31.50 **st.** and a la carte 🍷 9.90 – **17 rm** ⊒ 120.00/170.00 **st.** – SB.

Old Bank House without rest., 11 Pearse St., ✆ (021) 4774075, *oldbank@indigo.ie, Fax (021) 4774296* – |♦| TV. MC AE VISA. ✂ Y d
closed 22 to 27 December – **17 rm** ⊒ 120.00/180.00 **st.**

The Old Presbytery without rest., 43 Cork St., ✆ (021) 4772027, *info@oldpres.com, Fax (021) 4772166* – ✂ TV P. MC AE VISA. ✂ Y a
closed December and January – **16 rm** ⊒ 50.00/140.00 **t.**

Long Quay House without rest., Long Quay, ✆ (021) 4773201, *Fax (021) 4773201* – MC VISA. ✻ Y
closed 1 to 27 December – **7 rm** ☕ 50.00/70.00.

Sovereign House without rest., Newmans Mall, ✆ (021) 772850, *sovereignhouse@e om.net, Fax (021) 774723,* « Queen Anne town house », – TV. MC VISA. ✻
closed Christmas and New Year – **3 rm** ☕ 140.00, 1 suite. Y

The Old Rectory without rest., Rampart Lane, from Pearse St. follow signs for the W Museum bearing left at St. Multoses church and taking second lane on the l ✆ (021) 4772678, *Fax (021) 4772678,* – P. ✻ Y
April-October – **3 rm** ☕ 80.00/120.00 **s.**

Moorings without rest., Scilly, ✆ (021) 4772376, *Fax (021) 4772675,* ← Kinsale harbou TV P. MC AE VISA JCB. ✻ Z
closed December and January **8 rm** ☕ 120.00/130.00 **st.**

Colneth House without rest., Cappagh, Northwest : 1 m. by Bandon rd (R 6 ✆ (021) 4772824, *colnethhouse@tinet.ie, Fax (021) 4773357,* – TV P. MC AE VISA.
March-October – **8 rm** ☕ 45.00/90.00 **st.**

Kilcaw Guesthouse without rest.,, East : 1 m. on R 600 ✆ (021) 4774155, *kilcawhous hotmail.com, Fax (021) 4774755,* – TV P. MC AE VISA. ✻
February-November – **7 rm** ☕ 45.00/60.00 **st.**

The Vintage, Main St., ✆ (021) 4772502, *vintage1@indigo.ie, Fax (021) 4774828* – MC ⓓ VISA JCB. ✻ Z
closed 2 January-13 February, Monday and Sunday in winter – **Meals** (dinner only) a la ca 28.00/42.50 **t.** 🍷 12.00.

Max's, Main St., ✆ (021) 4772443 – . MC AE VISA Z
March-October – **Meals** 12.50/20.00 **t.** and a la carte 🍷 8.50.

at Barrells Cross *Southwest : 3½ m. on R 600 – Z – ✉ Kinsale.*

Rivermount House 🍃 without rest.,, Northeast : ½ m. ✆ (021) 4778033, *rivermnt@ .ie, Fax (021) 4778225,* – TV P. MC VISA. ✻
February-November – **6 rm** ☕ 35.00/50.00 **st.**

at Ballinadee *West : 7½ m. by R 600 – Z – ✉ Kinsale.*

Glebe Country House 🍃, ✆ (021) 4778294, *glebehse@indigo.ie, Fax (021) 4778[4* « Georgian rectory », – P. MC VISA
closed 1 week Christmas – **Meals** *(closed Sunday)* (residents only) (dinner only) 20.00 s
4 rm ☕ 45.00/70.00 **st.** – SB.

KINSALEY *Dublin* 923 N 7 – *see Malahide.*

KINSEALEY *Dublin* 923 N 7 – *see Malahide.*

KINVARRA (Cinn Mhara) *Galway* 923 F 8 – *pop. 432.*
Dublin 142 – Galway 17 – Limerick 37.

Merriman Inn without rest., Main St., ✆ (091) 638222, *merrimanhotel@eircom.n Fax (091) 637686* – TV ♿ P. MC AE ⓓ VISA. ✻
closed 22 December-1 February – **32 rm** ☕ 55.00/85.00 **t.**

KNIGHTS TOWN *Kerry* 923 B 12 – *see Valencia Island.*

KNOCK (An Cnoc) *Mayo* 923 F 6 *Ireland G. – pop. 575.*
See : *Basilica of our Lady, Queen of Ireland★.*
✈ *Knock (Connaught) Airport : ✆ (094) 67222, NE : 9 m. by N 17.*
ℹ *Knock Airport ✆ (094) 67247 (June-September) – Knock ✆ (094) 88193 (May-Septemb*
Dublin 132 – Galway 46 – Westport 32.
Hotels see : **Cong** *SW : 36 m. by N 17, R 331, R 334 and R 345.*

KNOCKTOPHER *Kilkenny.*
Dublin 87 – Kilkenny 12 – Waterford 18 – Wexford 45.

Carroll's, ✆ (056) 68082, *info@carrollshotel.com, Fax (056) 68290* – ▤ rest, TV P. MC VISA. ✻
closed 24 and 25 December – **Meals** (bar lunch) 10.70/20.85 **t.** and dinner a la carte – **10** ☕ 35.00/60.00 **t.** – SB.

HINCH (An Leacht) *Clare* 923 D 9 *Ireland G. – pop. 580.*

Env. : *Cliffs of Moher*★★★.

18, 18 *Lahinch* ☎ *(065) 708 1003* – 9 *Spanish Point, Miltown Malbay* ☎ *(065) 708 4198.*
Dublin 162 – Galway 49 – Limerick 41.

Aberdeen Arms, ☎ (065) 7081100, *aberdeenarms@eircom.net, Fax (065) 7081228,* – rest, TV P – 200. MC AE VISA.
closed 1 week Christmas – **Meals** (bar lunch)/dinner 15.00/25.00 **st.** and a la carte 5.50 – **55 rm** 65.00/110.00 **st.** – SB.

Moy House ,, Southwest : 2 ½ m. on N 67 (Milltown Malbay rd) ☎ (065) 7082800, *moy house@eircom.net, Fax (065) 7082500,* ← Lahinch Bay, « Early 19C country house », heated, , – TV P. MC AE VISA.
closed 23 December-14 January – **Meals** (residents only) (dinner only) 30.00 **t.** – **8 rm** 100.00/170.00 **t.**

Atlantic, Main St., ☎ (065) 7081049, *atlantichotel@eircom.net, Fax (065) 7081029* – rm, TV P. MC VISA.
closed 24 to 26 December – **Meals** (bar lunch Monday to Saturday)/dinner 20.00/25.00 **st.** and a la carte 7.00 – **14 rm** 50.00/80.00 **st.** – SB.

Shamrock Inn, Main St., ☎ (065) 7081700, *atlantic@eircom.net, Fax (065) 7081029* – TV P. MC VISA.
closed 25-26 December – **Meals** (bar lunch Monday to Saturday) a la carte 10.50/18.00 **st.** 6.00 – **10 rm** 50.00/80.00 **st.**

Greenbrier Inn without rest., Ennistymon Rd, ☎ (065) 7081242, *Fax (065) 7081247* – TV P. MC VISA.
closed January-22 February – **14 rm** 42.50/75.00 **st.**

Le Grand Londres (GREATER LONDON) est composé de la City et de 32 arrondissements administratifs (Borough) eux-mêmes divisés en quartiers ou en villages ayant conservé leur caractère propre (Area).

ENANE (An Líonán) *Galway* 923 C 7 *Ireland G.* – ✉ *Clifden.*

See : *Killary Harbour*★.

Env. : *Joyce Country*★★ – *Lough Nafooey*★, *SE : 6½ m. by R 336* – *Aasleagh Falls*★, *NE : 2½ m.*

Exc. : *Connemara*★★★ – *Lough Corrib*★★, *SE : 10 m. by R 336 and R 345* – *Doo Lough Pass*★, *NW : 9 m. by N 59 and R 335.*

Dublin 173 – Ballina 56 – Galway 41.

Delphi Lodge ,, Northwest : 8 ¼ m. by N 59 on Louisburgh rd ☎ (095) 42222, *delfish @iol.ie, Fax (095) 42296,* ←, « Georgian sporting lodge, loughside setting », , – P – 25. MC VISA.
closed mid December-mid January – **Meals** (residents only) (communal dining) (dinner only) 27.00 **t.** 8.00 – **12 rm** 90.00/160.00 **t.**

XLIP (Léim an Bhradáin) *Kildare* 923 M 7 – *pop. 13 451.*

Dublin 14 – Drogheda 39 – Galway 125 – Kilkenny 73.

Leixlip House, Captain's Hill, ☎ (01) 624 2268, *manager@leixliphouse.com, Fax (01) 624 4177,* « Georgian house » – TV P – 100. MC AE VISA.
closed 25 December – **Meals** – (see ***The Bradaun*** below) – **15 rm** 95.00/150.00 **st.** – SB.

XX **The Bradaun** (at Leixlip House H.), Captain's Hill, ☎ (01) 624 2268, *Fax (01) 624 4177* – P. MC AE VISA
closed 25 December and Monday lunch – **Meals** 15.00/18.00 **st.** and dinner a la carte 8.50.

TTERFRACK (Leitir Fraic) *Galway* 923 C 7 *Ireland G.*

Env. : *Connemara*★★★ – *Sky Road*★★ (←★★) – *Connemara National Park*★ – *Kylemore Abbey*★, *E : 3 m. by N 59.*

Dublin 189 – Ballina 69 – Galway 57.

Rosleague Manor ,, West : 1 ½ m. on N 59 ☎ (095) 41101, *rosleaguemanor@ireland. com, Fax (095) 41168,* ← Ballynakill harbour and mountains, , , , – rest, TV P. MC AE VISA JCB
April-October – **Meals** 15.00/35.00 **st.** and a la carte 7.00 – **20 rm** 100.00/170.00 **st.** – SB.

LETTERKENNY (Leitir Ceanainn) *Donegal* 923 I 3 *Ireland G. – pop. 7 606.*

Exc. : *Glenveagh National Park★★ (Gardens★★), NW : 12 m. by R 250, R 251 and R 25*
Grianan of Aileach★★ (≤★★) NE : 17½ m. by N 13 – Church Hill (Glebe House and Galler
AC) NW : 10 m. by R 250.

Dunfanaghy ℘ (074) 36335.

Derry Rd ℘ (074) 21160 (June-December).

Dublin 150 – Londonderry 21 – Sligo 72.

Holiday Inn Letterkenny, Derry Rd, Southeast : 1 ¾ m. on N 14 at junction with N ℘ (074) 24369, *Fax (074) 25389*, – rm, – 700. VISA JCB
closed 25-26 December – **Meals** (carvery lunch) 17.50 **st.** and dinner a la carte 4.95 – 7.95 – **121 rm** 75.00/105.00 **st.** – SB.

Castlegrove House, Ramelton Rd, Northeast : 4 ½ m. by N 13 off R 2 ℘ (074) 51118, *castlegrovehouse@hotmail.com, Fax (074) 51384*, ≤, « Late 17C cour house », – rm, VISA JCB.
closed 22-29 December – **Meals** *(closed Sunday November-April)* (dinner only) 18.5 30.00 **t.** and a la carte 7.50 – **13 rm** 55.00/75.00 **t.**, 1 suite – SB.

Quality Court, Main St., ℘ (074) 22977, *sales@qualitydonegal.com, Fax (074) 22928* – rm, rest, VISA JCB
Meals (bar lunch) 16.50 **t.** and a la carte – **58 rm** 55.00/88.00 **t.**, 26 suites – SB.

Gleneany House, Port Rd, ℘ (074) 26088, *Fax (074) 26090* – rest, rest, VISA.
closed 23-29 December – **Meals** a la carte 15.00/20.50 **t.** 7.00 – **23 rm** 40.00/70.00

LIMERICK (Luimneach) *Limerick* 923 G 9 *Ireland G. – pop. 52 039.*

See : *City★★ - St Mary's Cathedral★★* **Y** – *Limerick Museum★* **Z M2** – *King John's Castle★* **Y** – *John Square★* **Z 20** – *St. John's Cathedral★* **Z**.

Env. : *Hunt Museum★★ AC, E : 2 m. by N 7* **Y** – *Cratloe Wood (≤★) NW : 5 m. by N 18* **Z**.

Exc. : *Castleconnell★, E : 7 m. by N 7 – Lough Gur Interpretive Centre★ AC, S : 11 m. b 512 and R 514* **Z** – *Clare Glens★, E : 13 m. by N 7 and R 503* **Y** – *Monasteranenagh Abbe S : 13 m. by N 20* **Z**.

Shannon Airport : ℘ (061) 471444, W : 16 m. by N 18 **Z** – **Terminal** : *Limerick Railw Station.*

Arthur's Quay ℘ (061) 317522 **Y**.

Dublin 120 – Cork 58.

Plan opposite

Castletroy Park, Dublin Rd, East : 2 ¼ m. by N 7 ℘ (061) 335566, *sales@castletroy-pa e, Fax (061) 331117*, – rm, – 450. VISA.
***McLaughlin's* :** **Meals** *(closed Sunday dinner and Monday)* (dinner only and Sunday lunc dinner 20.00/26.00 **st.** and a la carte 9.00 – **105 rm** 145.00/165.00 **st.**, 2 suites – SB

South Court, Raheen Roundabout, Southwest : 2 ¾ m. on N 20 ℘ (065) 6823000, *cro nchhotels.com, Fax (065) 6823759*, – rm, rest, – 200. VISA.
***Seasons* :** **Meals** (dinner only and Sunday lunch)/dinner 19.50/21.00 **st.** and a la ca 5.00 – ***Boru's* :** **Meals** (dinner only) 16.00 **st.** and a la carte 7.50 – 8.50 – **65** 110.00/130.00 **st.** – SB.

Limerick Ryan, Ennis Rd, Northwest : 1 ¼ m. on R 587 ℘ (061) 453922, *ryan@indigo Fax (061) 326333*, – rm, rest, – 120. VISA.
Meals 8.00/20.00 **st.** and dinner a la carte 7.45 – 10.00 – **179 rm** 95.00/125.00 2 suites – SB.

Jurys Limerick, Ennis Rd, ℘ (061) 327777, *limerick-hotel@jurysdoyle.co Fax (061) 326400*, – rm, rest, – 200. **Y**
***Sorrels* :** **Meals** 12.50/18.00 **t.** and a la carte 7.00 – 9.50 – **94 rm** 109.00/170.00 1 suite.

Limerick Inn, Ennis Rd, Northwest : 4 m. on N 18 ℘ (061) 326666, *limerick-inn@limer inn.ie, Fax (061) 326281*, – rest, – 600. VISA.
closed 24 and 25 December – **Meals** 13.00/23.50 **t.** and dinner a la carte 8.00 – 8.5 **150 rm** 110.00/140.00 **st.**, 3 suites – SB.

Jurys Inn Limerick, Lower Mallow St., ℘ (061) 207000, *limerick-inn@jurysdoyle.co Fax (061) 400966* – rm, rest, – 30. VISA. **Z**
closed 25-26 December – **Meals** (dinner only) a la carte approx. 15.90 **st.** 5.50 – 7.(**151 rm** 49.00/55.00 **st.**

Greenhills, Ennis Rd, Northwest : 2 ¼ m. on R 587 ℘ (061) 453033, *info@greenhillsgr .com, Fax (061) 453307*, – rm, – 600. VISA
closed 25 December – **Meals** (carvery lunch)/dinner a la carte 17.00/25.00 **st.** 6.9 **58 rm** 75.00/120.00 **st.** – SB.

LIMERICK

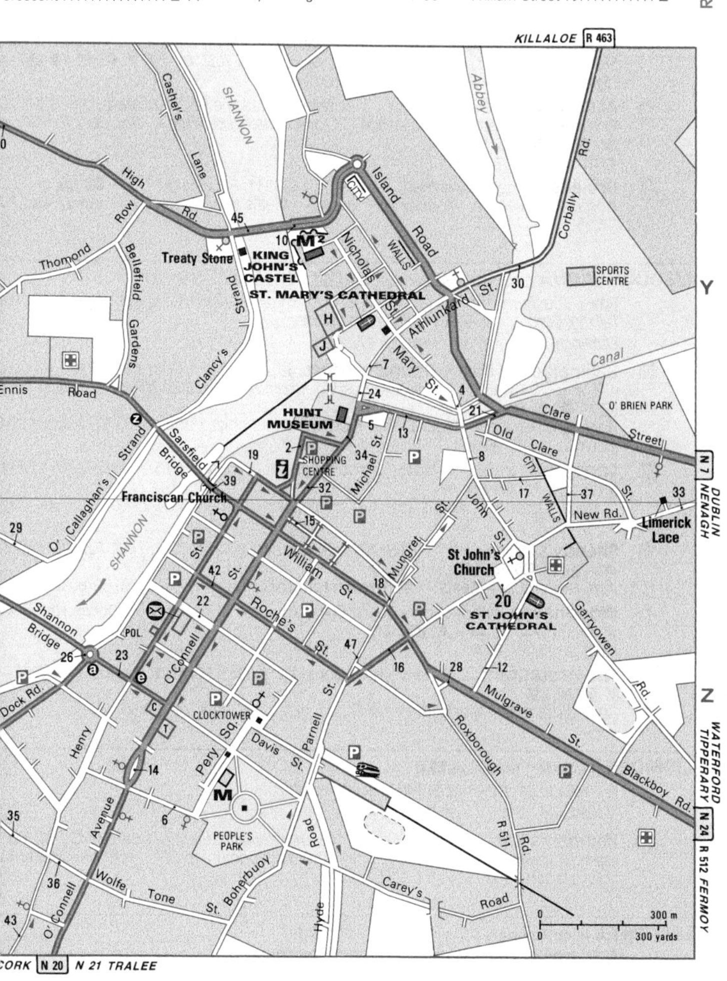

Les hôtels ou restaurants agréables sont indiqués dans le guide par un **signe rouge**.

Aidez-nous en nous signalant les maisons où, par expérience, vous savez qu'il fait bon vivre.

Votre **guide Michelin** sera encore meilleur.

Kilmurry Lodge, Castletroy, East : 3 ¼ m. by N 7 ℘ (061) 331133, *Fax (061) 330011* – ♿ P – 🎤 300. MC AE ⓓ VISA. ✗
closed 25 December – **Meals** 9.50/19.95 **t.** and dinner a la carte 🍷 5.50 – ☕ 6.50 – **43**
49.00/64.00 **st.** – SB.

Clifton House without rest., Ennis Rd, Northwest : 1 ¼ m. on R 587 ℘ (061) 451166, *c onhouse@eircom.net, Fax (061) 451224*, – TV P. MC ⓓ VISA. ✗
closed 20 December-5 January – **16 rm** ☕ 35.00/50.00 **t.**

Travelodge, Coonagh roundabout, Ennis Rd, Northwest : 2 ½ m. by R 587 at junct with N 18 ℘ (061) 457000, *Fax (061) 457000* – rm, rest, TV ♿ P. MC AE ⓓ VISA ✗
Meals (grill rest.) – **40 rm** 49.95 **t.**

Clonmacken House without rest., Clonmacken Rd, off Ennis Rd, Northwest : 2 m. b 587 ℘ (061) 327007, *clonmac@indigo.ie, Fax (061) 327785*, – TV P. MC AE ⓓ VISA. ✗
closed 25 December – **10 rm** ☕ 35.00/50.00.

Acacia Cottage without rest., 2 Foxfield, Dooradoyle Rd, Southwest : 2 m. by N 20 Ballykeefe roundabout ℘ (061) 304757, *acaciacottage@iolfree.ie, Fax (061) 304757*, TV P. MC VISA. ✗
4 rm ☕ 25.00/44.00 **st.**

Brûlées, Corner Mallow/Henry St., ℘ (061) 319931, *Fax (061) 319931* – MC VISA
closed 25 December, Monday and Tuesday – **Meals** (dinner only) a la carte 22.45/27.7
🍷 6.95. Z

LISDOONVARNA (Lios Dúin Bhearna) *Clare* 923 E 8 *Ireland G.* – *pop. 890.*

Env. : *The Burren★★ (Cliffs of Moher★★★, Scenic Routes★★, Aillwee Cave★ AC (Wa fall★★), Corcomroe Abbey★, Kilfenora Crosses★).*
Dublin 167 – Galway 39 – Limerick 47.

Ballinalacken Castle Country House ,, Northwest : 3 m. by N 67 (Doolin rd) c 477 ℘ (065) 7074025, *ballinalackencastle@eircom.net, Fax (065) 7074025*, ←, – r TV P. MC AE VISA
April-early October – **Meals** *(closed Tuesday)* (dinner only) a la carte 19.65/27.00 **t.** 🍷 10.(
12 rm ☕ 60.00/90.00 **t.** – SB.

Carrigann, ℘ (065) 7074036, *carrigannhotel@tinet.ie, Fax (065) 7074567*, – r TV P – 🎤 70. MC VISA. ✗
2 March-October – **Meals** (bar lunch)/dinner a la carte 16.50/22.00 **t.** 🍷 7.50 – **22** ☕ 47.00/70.00 **t.** – SB.

Sheedy's, Sulphir Hill, ℘ (065) 7074026, *sheedys@gofree.indigo.ie3, Fax (065) 7074* – TV P. MC VISA. ✗
April-September – **Meals** – (see ***The Restaurant*** below) – **11 rm** ☕ 50.00/80.00 **st.**

Woodhaven without rest., Doolin Coast Rd, West : 1 m. by N 67 (Doolin rd) off R ℘ (065) 7074017, – P. VISA. ✗
4 rm ☕ 25.00/38.00.

The Restaurant (at Sheedy's H.), Sulphir Hill, ℘ (065) 7074026, *Fax (065) 7074555* – P. MC AE VISA
April-September – **Meals** (dinner only) a la carte 22.40/29.85 **st.** 🍷 8.50.

LISMORE (Lios Mór) *Waterford* 923 I 11.

ℹ *Heritage Centre* ℘ *(058) 54975 (summer only).*
Dublin 143 – Cork 35 – Waterford 42.

Madden's Bar, Main St., ℘ (058) 54148, *madden@tinet.ie, Fax (058) 53343* – MC VISA
closed 2 weeks Christmas, Good Friday, Saturday, Sunday and Bank Holidays – **Meals** (lu only) a la carte 10.50/13.25 **t.** 🍷 6.00.

LISTOWEL (Lios Tuathail) *Kerry* 923 D 10 – *pop. 3 393.*

ℹ *St. John's Church* ℘ *(068) 22590 (June-September).*
Dublin 168 – Killarney 34 – Limerick 47 – Tralee 17.

Allo's with rm, 41-43 Church St., ℘ (068) 22880 – TV. MC AE VISA
closed Good Friday, 25 December, Sunday and Bank Holiday Mondays – **Meals** *(cl Sunday and Monday)* (dinner only) a la carte approx. 27.50 **t.** 🍷 8.00 – (see also below) – **3** ☕ 45.00/110.00 **t.**

Allo's Bar, 41-43 Church St., ℘ (068) 22880 – MC AE VISA
closed Good Friday, 25 December, Sunday and Bank Holiday Mondays – **Meals** (boo essential) a la carte approx. 9.45 **t.** 🍷 8.00.

NGFORD (An Longfort) *Longford* 923 I 6.

Market Sq. ✆ (043) 46566 (May-September).

Dublin 77 – Drogheda 75 – Galway 70 – Limerick 109.

Cumiskey's Farmhouse, East : 5 ½ m. by R 194 off Aghnacliffe Rd ✆ (043) 23320, *kc@iol.ie, Fax (043) 23516*, – P. MC VISA.
restricted opening November-February – **Meals** (by arrangement) 20.00 **t.** – **5 rm** 31.00/85.00 **st.**, 1 suite.

AAM CROSS *Galway* 923 D 7.

Dublin 163 – Galway 27 – Westport 33.

Peacockes, ✆ (091) 552306, *peacockes@eircom.net, Fax (091) 552215*, – rest, TV P – 100. MC AE VISA.
closed 24-26 December – **Meals** 11.50/25.00 **st.** and dinner a la carte – **25 rm** 65.00/110.00 **t.** – SB.

ACROOM (Maigh Chromtha) *Cork* 923 F 12 – *pop. 2 457.*

Lackaduve ✆ (026) 41072.

Dublin 186 – Cork 25 – Killarney 30.

Castle, Main St., ✆ (026) 41074, *castlehotel@eircom.net, Fax (026) 41505*, – rest, rest, TV P – 60. MC AE VISA.
closed 24 to 28 December – **Meals** 13.00/23.00 **st.** and a la carte 7.50 – **42 rm** 65.00/93.00 **st.** – SB.

ALAHIDE (Mullach Íde) *Dublin* 923 N 7 *Ireland G.* – *pop. 13 539.*

See : *Castle★★.*

Env. : *Fingal★.*

Beechwood, The Grange ✆ (01) 846 1611.

Dublin 9 – Drogheda 24.

Grand, ✆ (01) 845 0000, *booking@thegrand.ie, Fax (01) 845 0987*, – rm, TV P – 500. MC AE VISA.
closed 25 and 26 December – **Meals** 15.00/37.00 **t.** and a la carte 6.20 – **146 rm** 140.00/230.00 **t.**, 4 suites – SB.

Siam Thai, Gas Yard Lane, off Strand St. ✆ (01) 845 4698, *siames@eircom.net, Fax (01) 8457178* – . MC AE VISA
closed 25-26 December and Good Friday – **Meals** - Thai - (dinner only) 21.00/24.00 **t.** and a la carte.

Kinsaley *Southwest : 2½ m. by R 106 on R 107 – Malahide.*

Belcamp Hutchinson without rest., Carrs Lane, Balgriffin, D17, South : 1 m. by R 107 ✆ (01) 846 0843, *belcamphutchinson@eircom.net, Fax (01) 848 5703*, « Georgian house », – TV P. MC VISA
closed 1 week Christmas and 2 weeks November – **8 rm** 44.00/88.00 **st.**

Liscara without rest., Malahide Rd, D17, South : ½ m. on R 107 ✆ (01) 848 3751, *Fax (01) 848 3751*, – P.
March-October – **6 rm** 32.00/45.00.

ALLOW (Mala) *Cork* 923 F 11 *Ireland G.* – *pop. 6 434.*

See : *Town★ – St. James' Church★.*

Exc. : *Doneraile Wildlife Park★* AC, *NE : 6 m. by N 20 and R 581 – Buttevant Friary★, N : 7 m. by N 20 – Annes Grove Gardens★, E : 11 m. by N 72 and minor rd.*

Ballyellis ✆ (022) 21145.

Dublin 149 – Cork 21 – Killarney 40 – Limerick 41.

Longueville House, West : 3 ½ m. by N 72 ✆ (022) 47156, *info@longuevillehouse.ie, Fax (022) 47459*, « Part Georgian mansion in extensive grounds, working farm », – TV P – 30. MC AE VISA.
closed January and February – ***Presidents :*** **Meals** (booking essential) (bar lunch)/dinner 36.00/48.00 **t.** 9.00 – **20 rm** 95.00/190.00 **t.** – SB.

Springfort Hall, North : 4 ¾ m. by N 20 on R 581 ✆ (022) 21278, *stay@springfort-hall.com, Fax (022) 21557*, « Part 18C », – TV P – 300. MC AE VISA.
closed 1-6 January – **Meals** *close Sunday lunch* 16.00/35.00 **st.** and dinner a la carte 7.50 – **49 rm** 65.00/110.00 **st.** – SB.

MAYNOOTH (Maigh Nuad) *Kildare* 923 M 7 *Ireland G. – pop. 8 528.*
Env. : *Castletown House★★ AC, SE : 4 m. by R 405.*
Dublin 15.

Moyglare Manor ⑤, Moyglare, North : 2 m. ☎ (01) 628 6351, *info@moyglaremanor Fax (01) 628 5405,* ≤, « Georgian country house, extensively furnished with antiques », – P. MC AE VISA. ✻
closed 24 to 26 December – **Meals** *(closed Saturday lunch)* 22.50 **t.** and a la carte 8.5
16 rm ⊐ 110.00/180.00 **t.**

Glenroyal, Straffan Rd, ☎ (01) 629 0909, *glenroyal@hotel.ie, Fax (01) 629 0919,* – ⛶, ▤ rest, TV ☎ & P – 450. MC AE ⓓ VISA. ✻
closed 25 December – **Meals** *(closed Sunday dinner)* (carving lunch Monday to Saturd dinner a la carte 20.95/27.45 **st.** 6.95 – **57 rm** ⊐ 65.00/105.00 **st.** – SB.

Straffan Lodge, Straffan Rd, South : 1 ¾ m. on R 406 ☎ (01) 628 5002, *bookings@st anlodgehotel.com, Fax (01) 628 9781,* – ▤ rest, TV ☎ P – 170. MC AE ⓓ VISA. ✻
closed 25 December – **Meals** *(closed Sunday and Monday)* (bar lunch)/dinner a la ca 17.20/23.40 **t.** 7.95 – **17 rm** ⊐ 59.00/95.00 **st.**

MERRION (Muirfin) *Dublin – see Dublin.*

MIDLETON (Mainistir na Corann) *Cork* 923 H 12 – *pop. 3 266.*
18 *East Cork, Gortacrue ☎ (021) 631687.*
Jameson Heritage Centre ☎ (021) 613702 (March-October).
Dublin 161 – Cork 12 – Waterford 61.

Midleton Park, Old Cork Rd, ☎ (021) 4631767, *reservations@midletonparkhote Fax (021) 4631605,* – TV & P – 300. MC AE ⓓ VISA. ✻
closed 24-26 December – **Meals** 14.95 **t.** (lunch) and dinner a la carte 15.15/25.70 **t.** 8 – **39 rm** ⊐ 65.00/130.00 **t.**, 1 suite – SB.

When looking for a quiet hotel
use the maps found in the introduction
or look for establishments with the sign ⑤ *or* ⑤.

MONAGHAN (Muineachán) *Monaghan* 923 L 5 – *pop. 5 628.*
Market House ☎ (047) 81122 (April-October).
Dublin 83 – Belfast 43 – Drogheda 54 – Dundalk 22 – Londonderry 75.

Hillgrove, Old Armagh Rd, Southeast : ¾ m. by N 2 ☎ (047) 81288, *Fax (047) 84951* – ▤ rest, TV & P – 800. MC AE ⓓ VISA. ✻
Cavendish : **Meals** 12.50/21.50 **st.** and a la carte 5.50 – ***Bracken :*** **Meals** (carving lu a la carte approx. 21.50 **st.** 6.00 – **44 rm** ⊐ 50.00/110.00 **st.** – SB.

Four Seasons, Coolshannagh, North : 1 m. on N 2 ☎ (047) 81888, *Fax (047) 83131,* – TV P. MC AE ⓓ VISA. ✻
closed 25 December – **Meals** 14.00/26.00 **t.** and dinner a la carte – **38 rm** ⊐ 55 100.00 **t.**, 6 suites – SB.

Andy's, Market St., ☎ (047) 82277, *Fax (047) 84195* – MC VISA
closed 1-16 July, Good Friday, 25 December and Monday dinner – **Meals** 19.00 **st.** (ner) and a la carte 10.15/16.50 **st.**

at Glaslough *Northeast : 6½ m. by N 2 and R 168 – ✉ Monaghan.*

Castle Leslie ⑤, ☎ (047) 88109, *ultan@castle-leslie.ie, Fax (047) 88256,* ≤, « 18C ca in extensive parkland », – ✻ rest, P. MC VISA. ✻
closed 2-26 January – **Meals** (dinner only) 31.50 **s.** 7.50 – **14 rm** ⊐ 115.00/190.00 **st.** –

MONKSTOWN (Baile na Mhanaigh) *Cork* 923 G/H 12.
18 *Parkgarriffe ☎ (021) 841376.*
Dublin 162 – Cork 9 – Waterford 75.

The Bosun, The Pier, ☎ (021) 842172, *Fax (021) 842008,* ≤, – ⛶, ▤ rest, TV. MC AE VISA JCB. ✻
closed 24 to 26 December and Good Friday – **Meals** (bar lunch Monday to Saturday)/dir 25.00 **t.** and a la carte 7.75 – **15 rm** ⊐ 40.00/70.00 **t.**

MONKSTOWN (Baile na Mhanaigh) *Dublin* 923 ⑩ – *see Dublin.*

OYCULLEN (Maigh Cuilinn) *Galway* 923 E 7 – *pop. 601.*

Dublin 139 – Galway 7.

Knockferry Lodge, Knockferry (on Lough Corrib), Northeast : 6 ½ m. by Knockferry rd ☎ (091) 550122, *knockferrylodge@ireland.com, Fax (091) 550328,* – rest, P. MC AE VISA.
closed Christmas and New Year – **Meals** *(restricted opening in winter)* (dinner only) 16.00/17.50 **t.** 6.00 – **10 rm** 35.00/50.00 **t.** – SB.

Moycullen House with rm,, Southwest : 1 m. by Spiddle rd ☎ (091) 555621, *info@moycullen.com, Fax (091) 555566,* – P. MC AE VISA.
closed mid January-10 March and 23-27 December – **Meals** *(closed Wednesday)* (dinner only and Sunday lunch)/dinner 24.00 **t.** and a la carte – **3 rm** 50.00/80.00 **st.** – SB.

REPUBLIC OF IRELAND

ULLINAVAT (Muileann an Bhata) *Kilkenny* 923 K 10 – *pop. 275.*

Dublin 88 – Kilkenny 21 – Waterford 8.

Rising Sun, Main St., ☎ (051) 898173, *Fax (051) 898435* – TV P. MC AE VISA
closed 25-26 December – **Meals** (carving lunch)/dinner a la carte approx. 17.00 **t.** 6.50 – **10 rm** 38.00/60.00 **t.** – SB.

ULLINGAR (An Muileann gCearr) *Westmeath* 923 JK 7 *Ireland G.* – *pop. 8 040.*

Env. : *Belvedere House and Gardens★ AC, S : 3½ m. by N 52.*

Exc. : *Multyfarnhan Franciscan Friary★, N : 8 m. by N 4 – Tullynally Castle★ AC, N : 13 m. by N 4 and R 394 – Fore Abbey★, NE : 17 m. by R 394.*

Market House ☎ (044) 48650 (June-December).

Dublin 49 – Drogheda 36.

Austin Friar, Austin Friar St., ☎ (044) 45777, *reception@austin-friar.com, Fax (044) 45880* – TV – 50. MC AE VISA.
closed 24-26 December – **Meals** a la carte 10.50/19.00 **st.** 7.00 – **19 rm** 55.00/90.00 **st.** – SB.

Hilltop Country House without rest., Delvin Rd, Rathconnell, Northeast : 2 ½ m. by N 52 ☎ (044) 48958, *hilltopcountryhouse@eircom.net, Fax (044) 48013,* – TV P. MC VISA.
closed December and January – **5 rm** 26.00/42.00 **st.**

Crookedwood *North : 6½ m. on R 394 – Mullingar.*

Crookedwood House,, East : 1 ½ m. on Delvin rd ☎ (044) 72165, *cwood@iol.ie, Fax (044) 72166,* – TV P. MC AE VISA.
closed 4 days Christmas – **Meals** – (see ***The Restaurant*** below) – **8 rm** 60.00/110.00 **st.**

The Restaurant (at Crookedwood House H.),, East : 1 ½ m. on Delvin rd ☎ (044) 72165, *Fax (044) 72166,* « Cellars of 18C rectory », – P. MC AE VISA
closed 4 days Christmas, Sunday dinner and Monday – **Meals** (dinner only and Sunday lunch)/dinner a la carte 22.00/31.75 **st.** 9.00.

Rathconrath *West : 7 ¾ m. on R 392 – Mullingar.*

Mearescourt House,, Northwest : 3 ¾ m. by R 392, Ballnacarrigy rd on Moyvore rd ☎ (044) 55112, *Fax (044) 55112,* « Georgian mansion in parkland », – P. MC VISA.
closed 1 week Christmas – **Meals** (by arrangement) 25.00 **st.** 7.00 – **4 rm** 40.00/60.00 **st.**

AAS (An Nás) *Kildare* 923 L/M 8 – *pop. 14 074.*

Kerdiffstown, Naas ☎ (045) 874644.

Dublin 19 – Kilkenny 52 – Tullamore 53.

Jo Olive's, 10 South Main St., (above Joseph Kavanagh pub), ☎ (045) 894788, *joolive@indigo.ie* – MC VISA
closed Good Friday, 25-26 December, Sunday and Monday – **Meals** (booking essential) (dinner only) a la carte 25.20/27.75 **st.** 8.50.

AVAN (An Uaimh) *Meath* 923 L 7 *Ireland G.* – *pop. 3 447.*

Env. : *Bective Abbey★, S : 4 m. by R 161.*

Exc. : *Trim★ (castle★★), SW : 8 m. by R 161 – Kells★ (Round Tower and High Crosses★★, St. Columba's House★), NW : by N 3 – Tara★, S : 6 m. by N 3.*

Moor Park, Mooretown ☎ (046) 27661 – 18, 9 Royal Tara, Bellinter ☎ (046) 25244.

Dublin 30 – Drogheda 16 – Dundalk 32.

Newgrange, Bridge St., ℘ (046) 74100, *info@newgrangehotel.ie, Fax (046) 73977* – ⇔ rm, ▤ rest, TV ✆ & P – 🏔 550. MC AE ⊙ VISA. ✻
Bridge Brasserie : **Meals** (carvery lunch Monday to Saturday)/dinner 21.50 **t.** and a la ca
🍷 7.00 – **36 rm** ⊐ 62.50/95.50 **st.** – SB.

Ardboyne, Dublin Rd, South : 1 m. on N 3 ℘ (046) 23119, *ardboyne@quinn-hotels.cc Fax (046) 22355,* – ▤ rest, TV P – 🏔 350. MC AE ⊙ VISA. ✻
closed 25 and 26 December – **Meals** (carvery lunch Monday to Saturday) 12.00/23.00 and a la carte 🍷 10.50 – **29 rm** ⊐ 58.00/84.00 **st.** – SB.

Ma Dwyers without rest., Dublin Rd, South : ¾ m. on N 3 ℘ (046) 77992, *Fax (046) 77* – ⇔ TV P. MC VISA
closed 24-26 December – **9 rm** ⊐ 28.00/60.00 **st.**

Killyon without rest., Dublin Rd, South : 1 m. on N 3 ℘ (046) 71224, *Fax (046) 72766* – P. MC VISA. ✻
closed 24 and 25 December – **6 rm** ⊐ 30.00/50.00.

Southbank Bistro, 1 Ludlow St., ℘ (046) 72406, *dine@southbankbistro.ce Fax (046) 76824* – MC AE ⊙ VISA
*closed 25-26 December and lunch Monday and Tuesday***Meals** 9.95/12.95 (lunch) and a la carte 22.50/27.50 **t.** 🍷 7.95.

NENAGH (An tAonach) *Tipperary* 923 H 9 *Ireland G. – pop. 5 645.*

See : *Town★ – Heritage Centre★ – Castle★.*
Nenagh, Birchwood ℘ (067) 31476.
Connolly St. ℘ (067) 31610 (May-mid September).
Dublin 96 – Galway 63 – Limerick 26.

Nenagh Abbey Court, Dublin Rd, East : ¼ m. on N 7 ℘ (067) 41111, *abycourt@indi e, Fax (067) 41022* – |♦|, ⇔ rm, ▤ rest, TV ✆ & P – 🏔 450. MC AE ⊙ VISA. ✻
closed 25 December – **Meals** *(closed dinner Sunday and Monday)* (carvery lunch Monda Saturday)/dinner 22.50/30.00 **st.** and a la carte 🍷 8.95 – **46 rm** ⊐ 49.00/130.00 **st.** – SB.

Ashley Park House ⊛, Ardcrony, Northeast : 4 m. on N 52 ℘ (067) 38223, *margar ashleypark.com, Fax (067) 38013,* ≤, « 18C country house on the shores of Lough Orn – ⇔ P
Meals (by arrangement) 23.00/25.00 – **5 rm** ⊐ 33.00/60.00 **st.**

NEWBRIDGE (An Droichead Nua) *Kildare* 923 L 8 *Ireland G. – pop. 12 970.*

Env. : *Irish National Stud★★ AC (Japanese Gardens★★ AC) SW : 6 m. by N 7 – Kilda (Cathedral★★) SW : 5½ m. by N 7.*
Curragh ℘ (045) 441238.
Dublin 28 – Kilkenny 57 – Tullamore 36.

Keadeen, Ballymany, Southwest : 1 m. ℘ (045) 431666, *keadeen@iol.ie, Fax (045) 434* – ▤ rest, TV ✆ & P – 🏔 800. MC AE ⊙ VISA. ✻
closed 24-27 December – ***The Derby Room :*** **Meals** (bar lunch Monday to Saturday)/dir a la carte 18.00/30.00 – **54 rm** ⊐ 120.00/180.00 **st.**, 1 suite – SB.

NEWMARKET-ON-FERGUS (Cora Chaitlán) *Clare* 923 F 7 – *pop. 1 542.*

Dromoland Castle ℘ (061) 368444.
Dublin 136 – Ennis 8 – Limerick 15.

Dromoland Castle ⊛,, Northwest : 1½ m. on N 18 ℘ (061) 368144, *sales@dromola ie, Fax (061) 363355,* ≤, « Converted castle », – ⇔ rest, ✆ P – 🏔 450. MC AE ⊙ VISA. ✻
Earl of Thormond : **Meals** (booking essential to non-residents) 21.50/44.0 and a la carte 🍷 16.00 – ***Fig Tree*** *(at Dromoland Golf & Country Club)* (℘ (061) 3684 **Meals** a la carte 15.50/23.00 **t.** 🍷 9.50 – ⊐ 14.50 – **93 rm** 264.00/386.00 **st.**, 6 suites.

Clare Inn,, Northwest : 2 m. on N 18 ℘ (065) 6823000, *cro@lynchotels.c Fax (065) 6823759,* – ▤ rest, TV P – 🏔 400. MC AE VISA. ✻
Meals 11.00/18.00 **st.** and a la carte 🍷 8.60 – ⊐ 6.50 – **181 rm** 56.00/205.00 **st.** – SB.

NEWPORT (Baile Uí Fhiacháin) *Mayo* 923 D 6 *Ireland G. – pop. 567.*

Env. : *Burrishoole Abbey★, NW : 2 m. by N 59 – Furnace Lough★, NW : 3 m. by N 59.*
℘ (098) 41895 (June-August).
Dublin 164 – Ballina 37 – Galway 60.

Newport House ⊛, ℘ (098) 41222, *kjt1@anu.ie, Fax (098) 41613,* « Antique furnis country house », – ⇔ rest, ✆ P. MC AE ⊙ VISA. ✻
19 March-7 October – **Meals** (dinner only) 34.00 **st.** 🍷 9.00 – **18 rm** ⊐ 90.00/180.00 **st.**

EW ROSS (Ros Mhic Thriúin) *Wexford* 923 L 10 *Ireland G. – pop. 5 012 –* ✉ *Newbawn.*

See : *St. Mary's Church★.*

Exc. : *Kennedy Arboretum, Campile★* AC, *S : 7½ m. by R 733 – Dunbrody Abbey★, S : 8 m. by R 733 – Inistioge★, NW : 10 m. by N 25 and R 700 – Graiguenamanagh★ (Duiske Abbey★★ AC), N : 11 m. by N 25 and R705.*

The Quay ☎ (051) 421857 (mid June-August).

Dublin 88 – Kilkenny 27 – Waterford 15 – Wexford 23.

Clarion Brandon House, South : ¾ m. on N 25 ☎ (051) 421703, *brandonhouse@tinet.ie, Fax (051) 421567,* – rest, – 250. MC AE VISA. Meals (carving lunch Monday-Saturday)/dinner 22.00/25.00 **t.** and a la carte 8.75 – **60 rm** 75.00/140.00 **st.** – SB.

Riversdale House without rest., Lower William St., ☎ (051) 422515, *riversdalehse@eircom.net, Fax (051) 422800,* – TV P. MC VISA. *April-October* – **4 rm** 29.00/40.00 **st.**

Ballynabola *Southeast : 6 m. on N 25 –* ✉ *New Ross.*

Cedar Lodge, Carrigbyrne, East : 3 m. on N 25 ☎ (051) 428386, *cedarlodge@tinet.ie, Fax (051) 428222,* – TV P. MC AE VISA
closed December and January – **Meals** (bar lunch)/dinner 25.00/28.00 **st.** 10.95 – **28 rm** 75.00/120.00 **st.** – SB.

ONNELLOE (Tuath Ó gConaále) *Clare* 923 G 9 – *see Killaloe.*

ANMORE (Órán Mór) *Galway* 923 F 8 *Ireland G. – pop. 1 410.*

Env. : *Galway★★ (St. Nicholas Church★, Lynch's Castle★, Roman Catholic Church★, Eyre Square, Bank of Ireland Building, sword and mace★), NW : 5 m. by N 6.*

Exc. : *Athenry★, NE : 7 m. by N 6 and R 348 – Dunguaire Castle★, SW : 12 m. by N 18 and N 67 – Thoor Ballylee★, S : 15 m. by N 18 and minor rd – Coole Park★, S : 15 m. by N 18 and N 66 – Loughrea (St. Brendan's Cathedral★), SE : 17 m. by N 6 – Knockmoy Abbey★, NE : 17 m. by N 18, N 17 and N 63 – Tuam (St. Mary's Cathedral★), N : 18 m. by N 18 and N 17 – Turoe Stone★, SE : 20 m. by N 6 and north by R 348.*

Dublin 131 – Galway 7.

Galway Bay Golf & Country Club, Southwest : 3 ½ m. by Tawin rd ☎ (065) 6823000, *reservations@lynchhotels.com, Fax (065) 6823759,* ≤ Galway Bay and City, – TV P – 120. MC AE VISA.
Meals (bar lunch Monday-Saturday)/dinner a la carte 12.50/23.60 **st.** 6.75 – 7.80 – **39 rm** 109.00/190.00 **st.**, **53 suites** 265.00/304.00 **st.** – SB.

Quality,, North : ¾ m. on N 6 ☎ (091) 792244, *qualityhotelgalway@eircom.net, Fax (091) 792246,* – rm, rest, TV P – 60. MC AE VISA.
closed 25-26 December – **Meals** (carvery lunch)/dinner 17.95 **st.** and a la carte 8.00 – 5.50 – **93 rm** 105.00 **st.** – SB.

Oranmore Lodge, ☎ (091) 794400, *orlodge@eircom.net, Fax (091) 790227* – TV P – 300. MC AE VISA.
closed 22 to 27 December – **Meals** 9.20/30.00 **t.** and a la carte 9.50 – **56 rm** 120.00/180.00 **st.**

Mooring's, Main St., ☎ (091) 790462, *Fax (091) 790462* – TV P – 30. MC AE VISA.
Meals *(closed Sunday)* (dinner only) 23.00/25.00 **t.** and a la carte 6.50 – **6 rm** 35.00/60.00 **st.**

GHTERARD (Uachtar Ard) *Galway* 923 E 7 *Ireland G. – pop. 751.*

See : *Town★.*

Env. : *Lough Corrib★★ (Shore road – NW – ≤★★) – Aughnanure Castle★* AC, *SE : 2 m. by N 59.*

Gortreevagh ☎ (091) 552131.

Community Office ☎ (091) 552808.

Dublin 149 – Galway 17.

Connemara Gateway,, Southeast : ¾ m. on N 59 ☎ (091) 552328, *gateway@iol.ie, Fax (091) 552332,* – rest, TV P. MC AE VISA.
closed December and January – **Meals** (bar lunch)/dinner 22.00 **st.** and a la carte 6.95 – **61 rm** 55.00/120.00 **st.**, 1 suite – SB.

Ross Lake House, Rosscahill, Southeast : 4 ½ m. by N 59 ☎ (091) 550109, *rosslake@iol.ie, Fax (091) 550184,* – TV P. MC AE VISA
15 March-October – **Meals** (dinner only) 29.00 **st.** 11.00 – **12 rm** 75.00/170.00 **st.**, 1 suite – SB.

Currarevagh House ⑤,, Northwest : 4 m. on Glann rd ☎ (091) 552312, *currarevag reland.com, Fax (091) 552731*, ≤, « Victorian manor on Lough Corrib », ↖, ⚘, ⚘, ⚘, rest, P. MC VISA. ⚘
April-21 October – **Meals** (booking essential) (dinner only) 24.00 **t.** 5.70 – **15 rm** 55. 120.00 **t.** – SB.

River Run Lodge, Glann Rd, Northwest : ½ m. ☎ (091) 552697, *rivrun@indigo Fax (091) 552669*, ⚘ – TV P. MC AE VISA
closed 23-27 December – **Meals** (dinner only) a la carte 16.50/27.50 **st.** 8.50 – 8 35.00/75.00 **st.**

Boat Inn, The Square, ☎ (091) 552196, *info@theboatinn.com, Fax (091) 552694* – TV. AE ⊕ VISA. ⚘
closed 25 December – **Meals** a la carte 10.45/19.50 **t.** 7.25 – **10 rm** 30.00/50.00 **t.** –

PARKNASILLA (Páirc na Saileach) *Kerry* 923 C 12 *Ireland G.*

Env. : Sneem★, NW : 2½ m. by N 70.
Exc. : Iveragh Peninsula★★ (Ring of Kerry★★) – Derrynane National Historic Park★★, W m. by N 70 – Staigue Fort★, W : 13 m. by N 70.
Dublin 224 – Cork 72 – Killarney 34.

Parknasilla Great Southern ⑤, ☎ (064) 45122, *res@parknasilla.gsh Fax (064) 45323*, ≤ Kenmare River and Caha mountains, ⚘, « Collection of Irish art », ⚘, 9, ⚘, ⚘, ⚘, ⚘ – ⚘ ⚘, rest, TV ☎ P – 80. MC AE ⊕ VISA. ⚘
Pygmalion : **Meals** (dinner only) 30.00/35.00 **st.** 11.00 – 10.00 – **84 rm** 132 204.00 **st.**, 1 suite – SB.

PORTMAGEE (An Caladh) *Kerry* 923 A 12 *Ireland G.*

Exc. : Iveragh Peninsula★★ (Ring of Kerry★★).
Dublin 227 – Killarney 45 – Tralee 51.

Moorings, ☎ (066) 9477108, *moorings@iol.ie, Fax (066) 9477220*, ≤, ⚘ – rest, TV MC VISA. ⚘
March-October – **Meals** *(closed Monday dinner except Bank Holidays)* (bar lunch)/dir a la carte 21.75/32.00 **t.** 6.95 – **14 rm** 38.00/60.00 **t.** – SB.

PORTMARNOCK (Port Mearnóg) *Dublin* 923 N 7 *Ireland G. – pop. 9 145.*

Env. : Fingal★.
Dublin 5 – Drogheda 28.

Portmarnock H. and Golf Links, ☎ (01) 846 0611, *reservations@portmarnock.c Fax (01) 846 2442*, ≤, 18, ⚘ – ⚘, ⚘ rm, rest, TV ☎ ♿ P – 250. MC AE ⊕ VISA. ⚘
The Links : **Meals** a la carte 12.15/23.75 **t.** 9.00 – ***The Osborne :*** **Meals** *(closed Sur and Monday)* (dinner only) 33.50 **st.** and a la carte 12.50 – **101 rm** 145.00/210.00 2 suites – SB.

PORTUMNA (Port Omna) *Galway* 923 H 8 *Ireland G. – pop. 984.*

See : Town★ – Castle★.
Exc. : Clonfert Cathedral★ (west doorway★★), N : 15 m. by R 355 and minor roads.
Dublin 114 – Galway 42 – Limerick 45.

Shannon Oaks H. and Country Club, ☎ (0509) 41777, *sales@shannonoak Fax (0509) 41357*, ⚘, ⚘, ⚘, ⚘ – ⚘, ⚘ rm, TV ☎ ♿ P – 600. MC AE ⊕ VISA. ⚘
Castlegates : **Meals** (bar lunch Monday-Saturday)/dinner 19.95/22.50 **t.** and a la c 8.50 – **61 rm** 97.00/121.00 **st.**, 2 suites – SB.

RANELAGH *Dublin – see Dublin.*

RATHCONRATH (Ráth Conarta) *Westmeath* 923 J 7 – *see Mullingar.*

RATHGAR (Ráth Garbh) *Dublin – see Dublin.*

RATHMELTON (Ráth Mealtain) *Donegal* 923 J 2 *Ireland G.*

See : Town★.
Dublin 154 – Donegal 37 – Londonerry 27 – Sligo 76.

Ardeen ⑤ without rest., ☎ (074) 51243, *ardeenbandb@eircom.net, Fax (074) 51243*, ⚘ – P. MC VISA. ⚘
Easter-October – **4 rm** 25.00/50.00 **s.**

ATHMINES (Ráth Maonais) *Dublin* 923 ⑩ – *see Dublin.*

ATHMULLAN (Ráth Maoláin) *Donegal* 923 J 2 *Ireland G.* – *pop. 491* – ✉ *Letterkenny.*
Exc. : *Knockalla Viewpoint★, N : 8 m. by R 247 – Rathmelton★, SW : 7 m. by R 247.*
Otway, Saltpans ☎ (074) 58319.
Dublin 165 – Londonderry 36 – Sligo 87.

Rathmullan House, North : ½ m. on R 247 ☎ (074) 58188, *rathhse@iol.ie, Fax (074) 58200,* ≤, « Part 19C country house, gardens », – rest, TV P. MO AE ① VISA.
closed January-mid February and 24 to 28 December – **Meals** 30.00 **t.** (dinner) and a la carte 25.00/30.00 **t.** 7.00 – **24 rm** 65.00/150.00 **t.** – SB.

Fort Royal, North : 1 m. by R 247 ☎ (074) 58100, *fortroyal@eircom.net, Fax (074) 58103,* ≤, squash – rest, TV P. MO AE ① VISA
April-October – **Meals** (bar lunch)/dinner 27.00 **st.** 7.50 – **15 rm** 62.50/125.00 **st.** – SB.

ATHNEW (Ráth Naoi) *Wicklow* 923 N 8 – *see Wicklow.*

ECESS (Sraith Salach) *Galway* 923 C 7 *Ireland G.*
Exc. : *Connemara★★★ – Cashel★, SW : by N 59 and R 340.*
Dublin 173 – Ballina 72 – Galway 36.

Lough Inagh Lodge, Northwest : 4 ¾ m. by N 59 on R 344 ☎ (095) 34706, *inagh@iol.ie, Fax (095) 34708,* ≤ Lough Inagh and The Twelve Bens, « Part 17C former fishing lodge », – TV P. MO AE ① VISA
closed mid December-mid March – **Meals** (booking essential to non-residents) (bar lunch)/dinner a la carte 23.10/30.25 **st.** 15.45 – **12 rm** 88.00/165.00 **st.** – SB.

ENVYLE (Rinn Mhaoile) *Galway* 923 C 7 – *see Rinvyle.*

ERRIN (Raerainn) *Cork* 923 C 13 – *see Bere Island.*

NVYLE/RENVYLE (Rinn Mhaoile) *Galway* 923 C 7 *Ireland G.*
Exc. : *Connemara★★★.*
Dublin 193 – Ballina 73 – Galway 61.

Renvyle House, ☎ (095) 43511, *renvyle@iol.ie, Fax (095) 43515,* ≤ Atlantic Ocean, heated, – TV P – 120. MO AE ① VISA
closed 2 January-1 March and 25 November-23 December – **Meals** (bar lunch)/dinner 30.95 **st.** and a la carte 8.50 – **63 rm** (dinner included) 100.00/200.00 **st.**, 2 suites – SB.

VERSTOWN (Baile idir Dhá Abhainn) *Sligo* 923 G 5 – *pop. 266.*
Dublin 123 – Sligo 13.

Coopershill, ☎ (071) 65108, *ohara@coopershill.com, Fax (071) 65466,* ≤, « Georgian country house », – P. MO AE ① VISA JCB.
April-October – **Meals** (booking essential to non-residents) 29.00/32.00 **st.** 5.50 – **8 rm** 73.00/126.00 **st.** – SB.

OSKY (Rúscaigh) *Roscommon* 923 I 6.
Dublin 83 – Drogheda 81 – Galway 76 – Limerick 115.

Shannon Key West, The River Edge, ☎ (078) 38800, *shnkywst@iol.ie, Fax (078) 38811,* – rest, TV P – 300. MO AE VISA.
closed 24 and 25 December – **Meals** (carvery lunch)/dinner 18.00/25.00 **st.** and a la carte 7.00 – **40 rm** 52.00/90.00 **st.** – SB.

OSAPENNA (Rosapenna) *Donegal* 923 I 2 *Ireland G.*
Env. : *Rosguill Peninsula Atlantic Drive★ – Doe Castle★, S : by R 248 and R 245.*
Downings ☎ (074) 55301.
Dublin 216 – Donegal 52 – Londonderry 47.

Rosapenna, Downings, ☎ (074) 55301, *rosapenna@eircom.net, Fax (074) 55128,* ≤, – TV P. MO AE ① VISA
mid March-October – **Meals** (dinner only) 26.00 **t.** 8.00 – **53 rm** 72.50/115.00 **t.**, 1 suite – SB.

ROSCOMMON **(Ros Comáin)** *Roscommon* 923 H 7 *Ireland G. – pop. 1 432.*

See : *Castle★.*

Exc. : *Castlestrange Stone★, SW : 7 m. by N 63 and R 362 – Strokestown★ (Famine M seum★ AC, Strokestown Park House★ AC), N : 12 m. by N 61 and R 368 – Castlerea : Clon House★ AC, NW : 19 m. by N 60.*

Moate Park ℘ (0903) 20068.

Harrison Hall ℘ (0903) 26342 (May-August).

Dublin 94 – Galway 57 – Limerick 94.

Abbey, on N 63 (Galway rd) ℘ (0903) 26240, *cmv@indigo.ie, Fax (0903) 26021*, – 200. VISA.
closed 25 December – **Meals** 12.50/25.00 **t.** and dinner a la carte – **25 rm** 75.0 120.00 **t.** – SB.

ROSCREA **(Ros Cré)** *Tipperary* 923 I 9 *Ireland G. – pop. 4 170.*

See : *Town★ – Damer House★.*

Roscrea, Derryvale ℘ (0505) 21130.

Dublin 76 – Kilkenny 37 – Limerick 95.

Grant's, Castle St., ℘ (0505) 23300, *grantshotel@eircom.net, Fax (0505) 23209* – 500. VISA
closed 24-25 December – **Meals** *(closed Sunday dinner in winter)* 12.00/20.00 and a la carte – **25 rm** 45.00/80.00 **st.** – SB.

The Tower, Church St., ℘ (0505) 21774, *thetower@tinet.ie, Fax (0505) 22425* – VISA.
closed 25-26 December – **Meals** a la carte 14.25/20.50 **t.** – **10 rm** 30.00/53.00 **t.** – SB

Monaincha House without rest., Monaincha, East : 1 ½ m. on N 7 ℘ (0505) 231
« Georgian house, working farm »,
April-October – **3 rm** 30.00/50.00 **s.**

Great Britain and Ireland is now covered by an Atlas at a scale of 1 inch to 4.75 miles.

Three easy to use versions: Paperback, Spiralbound and Hardback.

ROSSCARBERY **(Ros Ó gCairbre)** *Cork* 923 E 13 *Ireland G. – pop. 406.*

Env. : *Drombeg Stone Circle★, SW : 2m. by R 597 – Glandore★, SW : 4 m. by R 597.*

Exc. : *Carbery Coast★.*

Dublin 194 – Cork 39 – Killarney 75.

Celtic Ross, ℘ (023) 48722, *info@celticrosshotel.com, Fax (023) 48723*, – 250. VISA.
Meals (bar lunch Monday to Saturday)/dinner 22.00 **t.** and a la carte 8.50 – **66** 90.00/150.00 **t.**, 1 suite – SB.

ROSSES POINT **(An Ros)** *Sligo* 923 G 5 *– pop. 799.*

County Sligo ℘ (071) 77134.

Dublin 139 – Belfast 132 – Sligo 6.

Yeats Country H., ℘ (071) 77211, *yeatscountry@eircom.net, Fax (071) 77203*, rm, VISA.
closed January – **Meals** (bar lunch)/dinner 18.00/22.00 **st.** and a la carte 10.00 – **98** 65.00/150.00 **st.** – SB.

ROSSLARE **(Ros Láir)** *Wexford* 923 M 11 *– pop. 929.*

Rosslare Strand ℘ (053) 32203.

Rosslare Tourist Office, Kilrane, Rosslare Harbour ℘ (053) 33622 (May-September).

Dublin 104 – Waterford 50 – Wexford 12.

Kelly's Resort, ℘ (053) 32114, *kellyhot@iol.ie, Fax (053) 32222*, door/outdoor, squash – rest, VISA.
closed 9 December-22 February – ***Kelly's :*** Meals 14.00/26.00 **t.** 7.00 – ***La Marine :*** Me a la carte 16.75/21.00 **t.** 7.00 – **99 rm** 75.00/154.00 **st.** – SB.

Crosbie Cedars, ℘ (053) 32124, *info@crosbiecedars.iol.ie, Fax (053) 32243*, – rest, – 250. VISA.
Meals (bar lunch Monday to Saturday)/dinner 22.50/25.00 **t.** and a la carte 10.00 – **34** 65.00/100.00 **t.** – SB.

OSSLARE HARBOUR (Calafort Ros Láir) *Wexford* 923 N 11 – *pop. 1 023.*

to France (Cherbourg and Roscoff) (Irish Ferries) (18 h/15 h) – to Fishguard (Stena Line) 2-4 daily (1 h 40 mn/3 h 30 mn) – to Pembroke (Irish Ferries) 2 daily (3 h 45 mn).

Kilrane (053) 33232 (April-October).

Dublin 105 – Waterford 51 – Wexford 13.

Great Southern, St. Martins Rd, (053) 33233, *res@rosslare.gsh.ie, Fax (053) 33543,* , – , rest, – 230. *closed 2 January-12 February* – **Meals** (bar lunch)/dinner 18.00/25.00 **st.** and a la carte 10.00 – 9.00 – **100 rm** 78.00/112.00 **st.** – SB.

Euro Lodge without rest.,, on N 25 (053) 33118, *eurolodge@eircom.net, Fax (053) 33910* – . *March-October* – 6.95 – **38 rm** 49.00 **st.**

Ferryport House without rest.,, on N 25 (053) 33933 – . **17 rm** 35.00/65.00.

Tagoat *West : 2½ m. on N 25 – Rosslare.*

Churchtown House ,, North : ½ m. on Rosslare rd (053) 32555, *churchtown.rosslare@indigo.ie, Fax (053) 32577,* « Part 19C », – . *March-15 November* – **Meals** *(closed Sunday and Monday)* (booking essential) (residents only) (dinner only) 25.00/27.50 8.00 – **12 rm** 65.00/138.00 **st.** – SB.

Killinick *West : 5 ¾ m. off N 25 – Rosslare.*

Danby Lodge, Rosslare Rd, on N 25 (053) 58191, *Fax (053) 58191,* – . *closed 22 to 30 December* – **Meals** a la carte approx. 20.00 6.95 – 7.95 – **24 rm** 49.00/69.00 **t.**

Assaly Lodge without rest., (053) 58300, *sales@wexford.irl.com, Fax (053) 58300,* – . *closed 15 December-15 January* – **6 rm** 35.00/50.00 **st.**

OSSNOWLAGH (Ros Neamhlach) *Donegal* 923 H 4 *Scotland G.*

See : *Rossnowlagh Strand*★★.

Dublin 153 – Donegal 14 – Sligo 31.

Sand House , (072) 51777, *info@sandhouse_hotel.ie, Fax (072) 52100,* ≤ bay, beach and mountains, , – rm, *Easter-October* – **Meals** (bar lunch Monday to Friday)/dinner 25.00/27.50 **t.** 8.50 – **45 rm** 60.00/220.00 **t.** – SB.

OUNDSTONE (Cloch na Rón) *Galway* 923 C 7 *Ireland G.* – *pop. 241.*

See : *Town*★.

Exc. : *Connemara*★★★.

Dublin 193 – Galway 47.

Eldon's, (095) 35933, *eldonshotel@tinet.ie, Fax (095) 35722,* ≤, – . *17 March-November* – ***Beola :*** **Meals** - Seafood specialities - (bar lunch)/dinner 22.00/28.00 **t.** and a la carte 6.00 – **18 rm** 40.00/100.00 **t.** – SB.

AGGART (Teach Sagard) *Dublin* 923 M 8 – *see Dublin.*

ALTHILL (Bóthar na Trá) *Galway* 923 E 8 – *see Galway.*

HULL (An Scoil) *Cork* 923 D 13 – *see Skull.*

HANAGARRY (An Seangharraí) *Cork* 923 H 12 *Ireland G.* – *pop. 230* – *Midleton.*

Env. : *Cloyne Cathedral*★, *NW : 4 m. by R 629.*

Dublin 163 – Cork 25 – Waterford 64.

Ballymaloe House ,, Northwest : 1 ¾ m. on L 35 (021) 4652531, *res@ballymaloe.ie, Fax (021) 4652021,* ≤, « Part 16C, part Georgian country house », heated, , , – rest, . *closed 24 to 26 December* – **Meals** (booking essential) (buffet dinner Sunday) 19.50/37.50 **t.** 7.50 – **34 rm** 90.00/190.00 **t.** – SB.

SHANNON (Sionainn) *Clare* 923 F 9 – *pop. 7 811.*

Shannon Airport ☎ (061) 471020.

Shannon Airport : ☎ (061) 471444.

Shannon Airport, Arrivals Hall ☎ (061) 471664.

Dublin 136 – Ennis 16 – Limerick 15.

Oak Wood Arms,, on N 19 ☎ (061) 361500, *reservations@oakwood.cc* *Fax (061) 361414,* – rm, – 400. MC AE VISA. *closed 25 December* – **Meals** (carving lunch Monday to Saturday)/dinner a la carte 26.1 30.95 **t.** 6.00 – **99 rm** 75.00/98.00 **t.**, 2 suites.

Quality, Ballycasey Rd, on N 19 ☎ (061) 364588, *sales@qualityshannon.cc* *Fax (061) 364045* – , rm, rest, . MC AE VISA. *closed 24-25 December* – **Meals** (carvery lunch Monday to Saturday)/dinner a la ca 13.40/21.50 **t.** 6.50 – **54 rm** 60.00/95.00 **st.** – SB.

at Shannon Airport *Southwest : 2½ m. on N 19 – Shannon.*

Great Southern, ☎ (061) 471122, *res@shannon.gsh.ie, Fax (061) 471982* – , rest, – 200. MC AE VISA. *closed 24 to 26 December* – **Meals** *(closed lunch Saturday, Sunday and Bank Holida* (carvery lunch)/dinner a la carte 15.00/25.00 **st.** 11.00 – 8.50 – **115 rm** 100.00 **st.** –

SHANNON AIRPORT *Clare* 923 F 9 – *see Shannon.*

SKERRIES (Na Sceirí) *Dublin* 923 N 7 *Ireland G.* – *pop. 7 339.*

Env. : *Fingal*★.

Skerries ☎ (01) 849 1204.

Skerries Mills ☎ (01) 849 5208.

Dublin 19 – Drogheda 15.

Redbank Lodge, 12 Convent Lane, ☎ (01) 849 0439, *redbank@eircom.r* *Fax (01) 849 1598,* – . MC AE VISA. *closed 24 to 27 December* – **Meals** – (see ***Redbank*** below) – **5 rm** 35.00/54.00 **t.** – S

Redbank with rm, 7 Church St., ☎ (01) 849 1005, *redbank@eircom.net, Fax (01) 849 1.* – rm, . MC AE VISA *closed 24-27 December* – **Meals** - Seafood - *(closed Sunday dinner)* (dinner only and Sun lunch)/dinner 28.00 **t.** and a la carte – **7 rm** 45.00/70.00 **t.** – SB.

SKIBBEREEN *Cork* 923 E 13 – *pop. 1 926.*

North St. ☎ (028) 21766.

Dublin 210 – Cork 53 – Killarney 65.

West Cork, Ilen St., on N 71 ☎ (028) 21277, *Fax (028) 22333* – . MC AE VISA *closed 22-28 December* – **Meals** 12.50/23.50 **st.** and dinner a la carte 8.50 – **29** 55.00/100.00 **st.**, 1 suite – SB.

Eldon, ☎ (028) 22000, *welcome@eldon_hotel.ie, Fax (028) 22191,* – . MC VISA *closed 25 December and booking essential in January* – **Meals** – (see ***Blues Bistro*** belov **19 rm** 45.00/90.00 **t.** – SB.

Blues Bistro, (at Eldon H.), ☎ (028) 23511, – . MC VISA *closed February, Christmas, Monday lunch and Bank Holidays* – **Meals** a la carte 14. 24.75 **t.** 7.00.

SKULL/SCHULL (An Scoil) *Cork* 923 D 13 *Ireland G.* – *pop. 595.*

See : *Town*★.

Exc. : *Sherkin Island*★ *(by ferry)* – *Mizen Peninsula (<★★ from pass).*

Coosheen, Coosheen, Schull ☎ (077) 28182.

Dublin 226 – Cork 65 – Killarney 64.

Corthna Lodge Country House without rest.,, West : ¾ m. by R 5 ☎ (028) 28517, *Fax (028) 28032,* <, – . MC **9 rm** 45.00/100.00 **st.**

SLIEVEROE (Sliabh Rua) *Waterford* – *see Waterford.*

.IGO (Sligeach) *Sligo* 923 G 5 *Ireland G. – pop. 17 786.*
See : *Town*★★ – *Abbey*★.
Env. : *SE : Lough Gill*★★ – *Carrowmore Megalithic Cemetery*★ *AC, SW : 3 m. – Knocknarea*★ *(≤★★) SW : 6 m. by R 292.*
Exc. : *Drumcliff*★, *N : by N 15 – Parke's Castle*★ *AC, E : 9 m. by R 286 – Glencar Waterfall*★, *NE : 9 m. by N 16 – Creevykeel Court Cairn*★, *N : 16 m. by N 15.*
Rosses Point ☎ *(071) 77134.*
Sligo Airport, Strandhill : ☎ (071) 68280.
Avar Reddan, Temple St. ☎ (071) 61201 (May-December).
Dublin 133 – Belfast 126 – Dundalk 106 – Londonderry 86.

Tree Tops without rest., Cleveragh Rd, South : ¼ m. by Dublin rd ☎ (071) 60160, *treetops @iol.ie, Fax (071) 62301,* – TV P. MC AE VISA.
closed 15 December-7 January – **5 rm** 25.50/44.00 **st.**

Benwiskin Lodge without rest., Shannon Eighter, North : 2 m. by N 15 ☎ (071) 41088, *pquigley@iol.ie, Fax (071) 41088,* – TV P. MC VISA.
closed 23 December-2 January – **5 rm** 22.00/42.00 **t.**

Ard Cuilinn Lodge without rest., Drumiskabole, Southeast : 3 m. by N 4 off R 284 ☎ (071) 62925, *ardcuiln@esatclear.ie,* – P. VISA.
March-October – **4 rm** 26.00/42.00 **st.**

Lisadorn without rest., Donegal Rd, North : 2 m. by N 15 ☎ (071) 43417, *Fax (071) 46418,* – TV P. MC VISA
7 rm 28.00/39.00 **st.**

PANISH POINT (Rinn na Spáinneach) *Clare* 923 D 9 – ✉ *Milltown Malbay.*
Dublin 171 – Galway 65 – Limerick 52.

Armada, ☎ (065) 708 4110, *armada@iol.ie, Fax (065) 708 4632,* ≤ – TV P – 300. MC VISA.
Meals 15.50 **st.** (dinner) and a la carte 16.50/18.00 **st.** 7.00 – **24 rm** 50.00/80.00 **st.** – SB.

PIDDAL/SPIDDLE (An Spidéal) *Galway* 923 E 8.
Dublin 143 – Galway 11.

Ardmor Country House without rest.,, West : ½ m. on R 336 ☎ (091) 553145, *ardmor @ireland.com, Fax (091) 553596,* ≤, – TV P. MC VISA.
April-December – **7 rm** 26.00/44.00 **t.**

PIDDLE (An Spidéal) *Galway* 923 E 8 – *see Spiddal.*

TRAFFAN (Teach Srafáin) *Kildare* 923 M 8 – *pop. 341.*
Naas, Kerdiffstown ☎ (045) 874644.
Dublin 15 – Mullingar 47.

Kildare H. & Country Club , ☎ (01) 601 7200, *hotel@kclub.ie, Fax (01) 601 7299,* , « Part early 19C country house overlooking River Liffey, riverside gardens and arboretum », , , , 18, , , indoor/outdoor, squash – TV P – 130. MC AE VISA.
Byerley Turk : **Meals** (booking essential to non-residents) 30.00/95.00 **t.** and a la carte 57.00/83.00 **t.** 9.00 – ***Legends*** (in K Club) *(☎ (01) 601 7300)* : **Meals** a la carte 28.00/43.50 **st.** 9.00 – 17.00 – **36 rm** 280.00/370.00 **t.**, 7 suites – SB.

Barberstown Castle,, North : ½ m. ☎ (01) 628 8157, *castleir@iol.ie, Fax (01) 627 7027,* ≤, « Part Elizabethan, part Victorian house with 13C castle keep », – rest, TV P – 30. MC AE VISA.
closed January-February and 24 to 26 December – **Meals** (booking essential) (dinner only) a la carte 22.00/38.50 **t.** 13.00 – **21 rm** 93.50/171.60 **st.**, 1 suite – SB.

SWORDS (Sord) *Dublin* 923 N 7 *Ireland G. – pop. 22 314.*
Env. : *Fingal★ – Newbridge House★, N : by N 1 and east by R 126.*
Exc. : *Malahide Castle★★, SE : by N 1 and R 106.*
Balheary Av. ☎ *(01) 840 9819.*
Dublin 8 – Drogheda 22.

Travelodge, Miltons Field, South : ½ m. on N 1 ☎ (01) 840 9233, *Fax (01) 840 923*
rm, TV, P. MC AE VISA JCB.
Meals (grill rest.) – **40 rm** 59.95 **t.**

Old Schoolhouse, Well Rd, on Brackenstown rd ☎ (01) 840 4160, *Fax (01) 840 5060* –
P. MC AE VISA.
closed 23 December-3 January, Easter, Saturday lunch, Sunday and Bank Holiday Monday
Meals 14.95/27.95 **t.** and a la carte 9.50.

TAGOAT (Teach Gót) *Wexford* 923 M 11 – *see Rosslare Harbour.*

TAHILLA (Tathuile) *Kerry* 923 C 12 *Ireland G.*
Exc. : *Iveragh Peninsula★★ (Ring of Kerry★★) – Sneem★, NW : 4 m. by N 70.*
Dublin 222 – Cork 70 – Killarney 32.

Tahilla Cove, ☎ (064) 45204, *tahillacove@tinet.ie, Fax (064) 45104,* ≤ Coongar C
and Caha Mountains, « Waterside setting », – , rest, TV P. MC AE VIS
April-mid October – **Meals** (bar meals lunch and Tuesday dinner)/dinner 18.00 **st.** – 9
53.00/86.00 **st.**

TALLAGHT (Tamhlacht) *Dublin* 923 N 8 – *see Dublin.*

TALLOW (Tulach an Iarainn) *Waterford* 923 H 11 – *pop. 802.*
Dublin 145 – Cork 29 – Killarney 70 – Limerick 40.

Buggys Glencairn Inn with rm,, North : 3 ¾ m. by N 72 on Glencairn
☎ (058) 56232, *buggysglencairninn@tinet.ie, Fax (058) 56232,* ≤, – rm, TV P.
VISA
closed 23 and 31 December – **Meals** (booking essential) (dinner only) a la carte 17.
24.70 **t.** – **5 rm** 48.00/76.00 **st.** – SB.

TERMONBARRY *Longford* 923 I 6 *Ireland G.*
Exc. : *Strokestown★ (Famine Museum★ AC, Strokestown Park House★ AC), NW : by N 5*
Dublin 81 – Galway 85 – Roscommon 22 – Sligo 62.

Shannonside House, ☎ (043) 26052, *keenanrestaurant@eircom.net, Fax (043) 2633*
TV P. MC VISA.
*closed 25 December*Meals (by arrangement) 14.00 **t.** – **9 rm** 29.00/46.00 **t.** – SB.

THOMASTOWN (Baile Mhic Andáin) *Kilkenny* 923 K 10 *Ireland G. – pop. 1 581 – Kilkenny.*
Env. : *Jerpoint Abbey★★, SW : 1½ m. by N9.*
Dublin 77 – Kilkenny 11 – Waterford 30 – Wexford 38.

Mount Juliet,, West : 1 ½ m. ☎ (056) 73000, *info@mountjuliet.ie, Fax (056) 730*
« 18C manor and sporting estate, ≤ River Nore and park », , , , , , , –
TV P. MC AE VISA.
Lady Helen McCalmont : Meals (dinner only) 40.00 **t.** and a la carte 10.00 – (see a
Hunters Yard at Mount Juliet below) – 12.50 – **30 rm** 200.00/300.00 **t.**, 18 sui
380.00 – SB.

Hunters Yard at Mount Juliet,, West : 1 ½ m. ☎ (056) 73000, *info@mountjuliet*
Fax (056) 73019, « Converted 18C stables », , , , , , , , – rest, TV
90. MC AE VISA.
Kendals : Meals a la carte 30.00/35.00 **t.** 9.00 – 12.50 – **16 rm** 180.00 **t.**

Abbey House without rest., Jerpoint Abbey, Southwest : 1 ¼ m. on N 9 ☎ (056) 241
Fax (056) 24192, – P. MC VISA
closed 23 to 30 December – **7 rm** 25.00/60.00 **t.**

Silks, Marshes St., ☎ (056) 54400 – MC VISA
closed 2 weeks January 24-26 December and Monday – **Meals** (dinner only and lur
Thursday to Sunday) 13.95/14.95 **t.** and a la carte.

URLES (Durlas) *Tipperary* 923 I9 – *pop. 6 603.*

Turtulla (0504) 21983.

Dublin 92 – Cork 71 – Kilkenny 30 – Limerick 47 – Waterford 58.

Anner, Dublin Rd, (0504) 21799, *info@annerhotel.com, Fax (0504) 22111,* – , rest, – 250. *closed 25-26 December* – **Meals** 11.95/28.50 **st.** and dinner a la carte – **64 rm** 45.00/80.00 **st.** – SB.

The Munster, Cathedral St., (0504) 22305, *info@munsterhotel.com, Fax (0504) 26281,* – , rest, – 600. **Meals** 12.50/25.00 **st.** and dinner a la carte 6.65 – **18 rm** 45.00/100.00 **st.** – SB.

PPERARY (Tiobraid Arann) *Tipperary* 923 H 10.

Rathanny (062) 51119.

James St. (062) 51457 (summer only).

Dublin 113 – Cork 60 – Limerick 35 – Waterford 52.

Ballyglass Country House, Glen of Aherlow Rd, South : 2 m. turning off Main St. following signs for Glen of Aherlow (062) 52104, *Fax (062) 52229,* – . **Meals** (bar lunch Monday to Saturday)/dinner a la carte 10.00/18.70 **st.** – **10 rm** 25.00/56.00 **st.** – SB.

MOLEAGUE (Tigh Molaige) *Cork* 923 F 13.

Dublin 186 – Cork 29.

Lettercollum House,, West : ¾ m. by R 600 (023) 46251, *conmc@iol.ie, Fax (023) 46270,* – . *April-November* – **Meals** *(closed Sunday dinner and Monday)* (dinner only and Sunday lunch)/dinner 24.00 **t.** 10.00.

ORMORE (An Tuar Mór) *Cork* 923 D 13 – *Goleen.*

Dublin 221 – Cork 68 – Killarney 65.

Fortview House without rest., Gurtyowen, Northeast : 1 ½ m. on Durrus rd (R 591) (028) 35324, *Fax (028) 35324,* – . *March-October* – **5 rm** 25.00/50.00 **st.**

WER *Cork* 923 G 12 – *see Blarney.*

ALEE (Trá Lí) *Kerry* 923 C 11 *Ireland G.* – *pop. 19 056.*

Env. : *Blennerville Windmill★ AC, SW : 2 m. by N 86 – Ardfert Cathedral★, NW : 5½ m. by R 551.*

Exc. : *Banna Strand★, NW : 8 m. by R 551 – Crag Cave★ AC, W : 13 m. by N 21 – Rattoo Round Tower★, N : 12 m. by R 556.*

Ashe Memorial Hall, Denny St. (066) 712188.

Dublin 185 – Killarney 20 – Limerick 64.

Ballyseede Castle,, Southeast : 3 ¼ m. by N 21 (066) 7125799, *Fax (066) 7125287,* <, « Late 18C crenellated country house in parkland », – . **Meals** *(closed Sunday and Monday to non-residents)* (booking essential to non-residents) (dinner only) 25.00 **t.** and a la carte 8.50 – 8.50 – **12 rm** 80.00/165.00.

Abbey Gate, Maine St., off Rock St., (066) 7129888, *abbeygat@aol.ie, Fax (066) 7129821* – , rm, rest, – 350. *closed 24-25 December* – **Meals** (carvery lunch Monday to Saturday)/dinner 16.95/24.00 **st.** and a la carte 6.50 – **100 rm** 80.00/100.00 **st.** – SB.

The Meadowlands, Oakpark, Northeast : ¾ m. on N 69 (066) 718 0444, *medlands@iol.ie, Fax (066) 718 0964,* – – 30. *closed 24 to 26 December* – **Meals** *(closed Sunday dinner)* (bar lunch Monday to Saturday)/dinner and a la carte 15.85/31.90 **st.** 8.00 – **27 rm** 75.00/160.00 **st.** – SB.

The Grand, Denny St., (066) 7121499, *info@grandhoteltralee.com, Fax (066) 7122877* – rest, – 250. **Meals** 9.00/19.00 **t.** and a la carte 6.00 – **44 rm** 40.00/95.00 **st.** – SB.

Ballygarry House, Killarney Rd, Southeast : 2 m. on N 21 (066) 712 3322, *ballygarry@eircom.net, Fax (066) 712 7630,* – – 500. *closed 20-26 December* – **Meals** *(closed Sunday and Monday October-May)* (bar lunch)/dinner 22.50/27.00 **t.** and a la carte 12.00 – **30 rm** 55.00/120.00 **t.** – SB.

REPUBLIC OF IRELAND

REPUBLIC OF IRELAND

Brook Manor Lodge without rest., Fenit Rd, Spa, Northwest : 2 ¼ m. by R 551 on R
(066) 7120509, *brookmanor@eircom.net, Fax (066) 7127552,* – TV P. VISA AE
7 rm 40.00/90.00 **st.**

The Forge without rest., Upper Oakpark, Northeast : 1 ½ m. on N 69 (066) 7125
Fax (066) 7125245, – TV P. VISA.
closed Christmas – **6 rm** 25.00/50.00 **st.**

Barnakyle without rest., Clogherbrien, Northwest : 1 ½ m. on R 551 (066) 7125048
rnakyl@iol.ie, Fax (066) 7181259, – TV P. VISA.
April-October – **4 rm** 25.00/38.00 **st.**

Aisling Gheal, Ivy House, Ivy Terr., (066) 7129292, *Fax (066) 7123870* – AE VIS
closed 1 week November, Sunday and Monday October-May – **Meals** (dinner only
Sunday lunch)/dinner 16.25/23.00 **t.** and a la carte 8.50.

TRAMORE (Trá Mhór) *Waterford* 923 K 11 – *pop. 6 536.*
Railway Sq. (051) 381572 (mid June-August). – Dublin 106 – Waterford 6.

Glenorney without rest., Newtown, Southwest : 1 m. by R 675 (051) 381056, *glenc*
y@iol.ie, Fax (051) 381103, – TV P. AE VISA.
6 rm 25.00/46.00 **st.**

TRIM (Baile Átha Troim) *Meath* 923 L 7 *Ireland G. – pop. 1 740.*
See : *Trim Castle★★ – Town★.* – **Env.** : *Bective Abbey★, NE : 4 m. by R 161.*
18 *County Meath, Newtownmoynagh (046) 31463.*
(046) 37111 (May-September).
Dublin 27 – Drogheda 26 – Tullamore 43.

Highfield House without rest., Maudins Rd, on Kilcock rd (046) 363
Fax (046) 38182, « 19C former maternity home », – TV P. AE VISA
closed 23 December-4 January – **7 rm** 25.00/40.00.

Crannmór without rest., Dunderry Rd, North : 1 ¼ m. (046) 31635, *crannmor@*
om.net, Fax (046) 31635, – P. VISA.
closed 22 December-7 January – **4 rm** 25.50/44.00 **st.**

TULLAMORE (Tulach Mhór) *Offaly* 923 J 8 – *pop. 9 221.*
18 *Tullamore, Brookfield (0506) 21439.*
Tullamore Dew, Heritage Centre (0506) 52617. – Dublin 65 – *Kilkenny 52 – Limerick*

Tullamore Court,, on N 80 (Portlaoise rd) (0506) 46666, *info@tullamorecourthote*
Fax (0506) 46677, – rm, rest, TV P – 750. AE VISA
closed 24-25 December – **Meals** 14.00/15.00 **st.** (lunch) and dinner a la carte 21.
30.50 **st.** 8.50 – **72 rm** 95.00/160.00 **st.** – SB.

Bridge House,, off Main St. (0506) 22000, *info@bhouse.iol.ie, Fax (0506) 41338,*
– rest, rest, TV P – 550. AE VISA.
closed 24-26 December – **Meals** (bar lunch)/dinner 15.00/22.00 **st.** and a la carte 6.9
70 rm 60.00/160.00.

VALENCIA ISLAND (Dairbhre) *Kerry* 923 A/B 12.
Dublin 237 – Killarney 55 – Tralee 57.

Knights Town.

Glanleam House, Glanleam, West : 1 ¼ m. taking right fork at top of Market
(066) 9476176, *Fax (066) 9476108,* « Part 17C and 18C country house in exten
sub-tropical gardens », – P. AE VISA.
mid March-October – **Meals** (booking essential to non-residents) (communal dining) (
ner only) 25.00/28.00 **st.** 8.50 – **6 rm** 65.00/150.00 **st.** – SB.

VIRGINIA (Achadh an Iúir) *Cavan* 923 K 6 *Ireland G. – pop. 811.*
Exc. : *Kells★ (Round Tower and High Crosses★★, St. Columba's House★), SE : 10 m. by N*
Loughcrew Passage Graves★, S : 10 m. by R 195, turning right into L 3.
9 *Virginia, Park Hotel (049) 854 8066.*
Dublin 51 – Drogheda 39 – Enniskillen 60.

Sharkey's, Main St., (049) 8547561, *sharkeys@destination_ireland.c*
Fax (049) 8547761, – TV P – 250. VISA.
Meals (carving lunch) 12.00/25.00 **st.** and dinner a la carte 5.95 – **13 rm** 35.
80.00 **st.** – SB.

ATERFORD (Port Láirge) *Waterford* 923 K 11 *Ireland G.* – *pop. 42 540.*

See : *Town*★ – *City Walls*★.

Env. : *Waterford Crystal*★, *SW : 1½ m. by N 25* **Y**.

Exc. : *Duncannon*★, *E : 12 m. by R 683, ferry from Passage East and R 374 (south)* **Z** – *Dunmore East*★, *SE : 12 m. by R 684* **Z** – *Tintern Abbey*★, *E : 13 m. by R 683, ferry from Passage East, R 733 and R 734 (south)* **Z**.

Newrath ℘ *(051) 874182.*

Waterford Airport, Killowen : ℘ *(051) 875589.*

41 The Quay ℘ *(051) 875788* **Y** – *Waterford Crystal Visitor Centre* ℘ *(051) 358397 – The Granary, Merchants Quay* ℘ *(051) 875823.*

Dublin 96 – Cork 73 – Limerick 77.

WATERFORD

Street	Grid	No.
...xander Street	Y	2
...ndel Square	Y	3
...helors Walk	Y	4
...ey's New Street	Z	5
...ybricken Green	Y	6
...onstrand Street	Y	7
...kfriars Street	Y	8
...ad Street	Y	9
...wn's Lane	Y	10
...igeen Park	Y	13
...nedral Square	Z	14
... Square Shopping Centre	YZ	
Coal Quay	Y	15
Colbeck Street	Z	16
Five Alley Lane	Y	17
George Street	Y	20
Gladstone Street	Y	19
Greyfriar's Street	Z	21
Hanover Street	Y	23
Henrietta Street	Z	24
High Street	YZ	25
Jenkin's Lane	Y	27
Keiser Street	Z	28
King's Terrace	Y	29
Lady Lane	YZ	30
Lombard Street	Z	31
Mayors Walk	Y	32
Meagher's Quay	Y	33
Newgate Street	Y	35
New Street	Y	36
Palace Lane	Z	37
Penrose Lane	Y	38
Railway Square	Y	39
St. Patrick Terrace	Y	40
Sally Park	Y	41
Scotch Quay	Z	42
Shortcourse	Y	43
Trinity Square	Y	44
Vulcan Street	Y	45
Water Side	Z	46

Y WATERFORD CRYSTAL / N 25 CORK, R 675 : TRAMORE — Z DUNMORE EAST R 683 — WEXFORD, NEW ROSS N 25

Waterford Castle H. Golf and Country Club, The Island, Ballinakill, East : 2 m. by R 683, Ballinakill Rd and private ferry (051) 878203, *info@waterfordcastle.c* *Fax (051) 879316*, « Part 15C and 19C castle, river island setting », – rest, TV. MC VISA
closed 2 January-9 February – **Meals** (bar lunch Monday-Saturday)/dinner 40.00/45.0 and a la carte 14.00 – 15.50 – **14 rm** 175.00/315.00 **t.**, 5 suites – SB.

Granville, Meagher Quay, (051) 305555, *stay@granville-hotel.ie, Fax (051) 305566* – rm, rest, TV – 250. MC AE VISA. Y
closed 25 and 26 December – **Meals** *(closed Saturday lunch)* 13.50/24.95 **st.** and a la c 7.50 – **98 rm** 75.00/180.00 **st.** – SB.

Faithlegg, Faithlegg, East : 5 m. by R 683 on Cheekpoint rd (051) 382000, *fait* *@iol.ie, Fax (051) 380010*, – rest, TV – 160. MC AE VISA.
Meals (bar lunch Monday to Saturday)/dinner 30.00 **t.** 7.00 – **80 rm** 135.00/240.00 2 suites.

Woodlands, Dunmore Rd, Southeast : 3 m. on R 683 (Dunmore East rd) (051) 3045 *woodhl@iol.ie, Fax (051) 304575*, – rest, TV – 400. MC AE
Meals (carving lunch Monday-Saturday) 14.50/22.50 **st.** and a la carte – **46 rm** 82. 130.00 **st.** – SB.

Dooley's, The Quay, (051) 873531, *hotel@iol.ie, Fax (051) 870262* – rm, TV 300. MC AE VISA. Y
closed 25-26 December – **Meals** (carvery lunch Monday to Saturday)/dinner a la c 16.00/23.00 **t.** 6.00 – **112 rm** 80.00/110.00 **t.** – SB.

Waterford Marina Quality, Canada St., The Quays, (051) 856600, *stay@irishcour* *tels.com, Fax (051) 856605*, « Riverside setting », – TV – 45. MC AE VISA. Z
closed 25 and 26 December – **Meals** (bar lunch Monday to Saturday)/dinner 14.95/17.95 and a la carte 7.95 – **81 rm** 95.00/140.00 **st.** – SB.

Bridge, The Quay, (051) 877222, *bridgehotel@treacyhotelsgroup.c* *Fax (051) 877229* – rest, TV – 400. MC AE VISA. Y
closed 25 December – **Meals** (carvery lunch Monday to Saturday)/dinner 17.00/25.00 and a la carte 8.00 – **127 rm** 45.00/100.00 **st.** – SB.

Jurys, Ferrybank, (051) 832111, *waterford-hotel@jurysdoyle.com, Fax (051) 83286* City, – rm, TV – 800. MC AE VISA. Y
closed 24 to 28 December – **Meals** 13.20/16.50 **t.** and a la carte 6.00 – 8.75 – **97** 90.00/120.00 **t.**, 1 suite.

The Belfry, Conduit Lane, (051) 844800, *info@belfryhotel.ie, Fax (051) 843719* – rest, TV. MC AE VISA. Y
closed 24 and 25 December – **Meals** (bar lunch)/dinner a la carte 11.00/19.25 **t.** – **49** 58.00/102.00 **t.** – SB.

Ivory's, Tramore Rd, South : 1 ¼ m. by N 25 on R 675 (051) 358888, *info@ivorys-ho* *e, Fax (051) 358899*, – rm, TV. MC AE VISA.
Meals *(closed Saturday lunch and Sunday dinner)* 15.95/35.00 **st.** and a la carte 6.2 **40 rm** 69.50/99.00 **st.** – SB.

Travelodge, Cork Rd, Southwest : 1 ¼ m. on N 25 (051) 358885, *Fax (051) 3588* rm, rest, TV. MC AE VISA JCB.
Meals (grill rest.) – **32 rm** 44.95 **t.**

The Anchorage without rest., 9 The Quay, (051) 854302, *anchors@indig* *Fax (051) 856979* – TV. MC VISA Y
12 rm 35.00/55.00 **st.**

Avondale without rest., 2 Parnell St., (051) 852267, *info@staywithus.net* – TV. MC Z
closed 22 to 28 December – **6 rm** 35.00/50.00.

Foxmount Country House, Passage East Rd, Southeast : 4 ½ m. by R 683, Cheekpoint rd (051) 874308, *foxmount@iol.ie, Fax (051) 854906*, « Working farm – rest.
10 March-October – **Meals** (by arrangement) 22.50 **st.** – **5 rm** 45.00/70.00 – SB.

O'Grady's with rm, Cork Rd, South : 1 m. on N 25 (051) 378851, *info@gradysh* *.com, Fax (051) 374062* – TV. MC AE VISA JCB.
closed Christmas and New Year and 2 weeks November **Meals** 16.00 **t.** and a la carte 6. **9 rm** 30.00/70.00 **st.**

X **Wine Vault,** High St., ℘ (051) 853444, *info@waterfordwinevault.com, Fax (051) 853444,* « Converted bonded warehouse of 15C origins » – ▤. MC AE VISA Z n
closed 25-26 December, Sunday and Good Friday – **Meals** 12.50/15.00 **t.** (lunch) and a la carte 16.95/27.45 **t.** 9.00.

X **McCluskeys,** 18 High St., ℘ (051) 857766, *Fax (051) 857766* – MC AE VISA Z n
closed 10 days Christmas, Sunday and Monday – **Meals** a la carte 18.25/25.50 **t.** 6.95.

Slieveroe *Northeast : 2 ¼ m. by N 25* – **Z** – ✉ *Waterford.*

Diamond Hill without rest., ℘ (051) 832855, *Fax (051) 832254*, – TV P. MC VISA.
closed 24-26 December – **17 rm** 32.00/55.00 **st.**

Cheekpoint *East : 7 m. by R 683* – **Z** – ✉ *Waterford.*

Three Rivers without rest., ℘ (051) 382520, *mail@threerivers.ie, Fax (051) 382542*, ≤ – P. MC AE VISA.
closed 20 December-10 January – **14 rm** 23.00/60.00 **st.**

Butlerstown *Southwest : 5 ¼ m. by N 25* – **Y** – ✉ *Waterford.*

Coach House without rest., Butlerstown Castle, Cork Rd, ℘ (051) 384656, *coachhse@iol.ie, Fax (051) 384751*, ≤, « Victorian house in grounds of Butlerstown Castle », ≘s, – TV P. MC AE VISA.
closed 20 December-1 February – **7 rm** 45.00/70.00 **st.**

Kilmeadan *Southwest : 6 ¾ m. on N 25* – **Y** – ✉ *Waterford.*

Kilmeaden House without rest.,, Northwest : 1 m. by N 25 on R 680 ℘ (051) 384254, *kilmeadenhouse@eircom.net, Fax (051) 384884*, ≤, « Victorian former rectory », – P. MC VISA.
May-October – **5 rm** 80.00/120.00 **st.**

ATERVILLE (An Coireán) *Kerry* 923 B 12 *Ireland G.* – *pop. 466.*

Exc. : *Iveragh Peninsula★★ (Ring of Kerry★★) – Skellig Islands★★, W : 8 m. by N 70, R 567 and ferry from Ballinskelligs – Derrynane National Historic Park★★ AC, S : 9 m. by N70 – Leacanabuaile Fort (≤★★), N : 13 m. by N 70.*

18 *Ring of Kerry ℘ (066) 9474102.*

℘ (066) 9474646 (June-September).

Dublin 238 – Killarney 48.

Butler Arms, ℘ (066) 9474144, *butarms@iol.ie, Fax (066) 9474520*, ≤, – TV P. MC AE VISA.
6 April-October – **Meals** (bar lunch)/dinner 27.50 **t.** and a la carte 6.95 – **30 rm** 95.00/180.00 **t.** – SB.

Waterville House and Golf Links without rest.,, South : ¾ m. on N 70 ℘ (066) 9474244, *Fax (066) 9474567*, ≤, ≘s, heated, 18, – TV P. MC AE VISA.
15 April-October – **6 rm** 65.00/150.00, 4 suites.

Brookhaven House without rest., New Line Rd, North : ¾ m. on N 70 ℘ (066) 9474431, *brookhaven@esatclear.ie, Fax (066) 9474724*, – TV P.
closed December and January – **5 rm** 45.00/80.00 **st.**

ESTPORT (Cathair na Mart) *Mayo* 923 D 6 *Ireland G.* – *pop. 4 253.*

See : *Town★★ (Centre★) – Westport House★★ AC.*

Exc. : *SW : Murrisk Peninsula★★ – Ballintubber Abbey★, SE : 13 m. by R 330 – Croagh Patrick★, W : 6 m. by R 335 – Bunlahinch Clapper Bridge★, W : 16 m. by R 335 – Doo Lough Pass★, W : 24 m. by R 335 – Aasleagh Falls★, S : 22 m. by N 59.*

The Mall ℘ (098) 25711.

Dublin 163 – Galway 50 – Sligo 65.

Knockranny House, Knockranny, East : ½ m. by N 5 ℘ (098) 28600, *info@khh.ie, Fax (098) 28611*, ≤ – , ▤ rest, TV P – 700. MC AE VISA.
closed 23 to 28 December – ***La Fougère :*** **Meals** (bar lunch Monday to Saturday)/dinner 32.00 **t.** – **54 rm** 130.00/220.00 **t.** – SB.

Atlantic Coast, The Quay, West : 1 m. on R 335 ℘ (098) 29000, *achotel@iol.ie, Fax (098) 29111*, ≘s, – , rm, TV P – 150. MC AE VISA.
closed 24 to 26 December – ***Blue Wave :*** **Meals** (bar lunch Monday to Saturday)/dinner 24.00 **t.** and a la carte 12.00 – **82 rm** 80.00/120.00 **st.**, 1 suite – SB.

Westport, The Demesne, Newport Rd, (098) 25122, *reservations@hotelwestpor* *Fax (098) 26739*, – 400. AE VISA.
Meals (bar lunch Monday to Saturday)/dinner 24.95 **t.** 7.00 – **129 rm** 85.00/220.00 SB.

Ardmore Country House, The Quay, West : 1 ½ m. by R 335 (098) 25994, *ardmo* *anv.ie, Fax (098) 27795*, – rm, AE VISA.
closed 3 weeks February, 1 week November and 1 week Christmas – **Meals** (dinner c 25.00/30.00 **t.** and a la carte 9.50 – **13 rm** 100.00/160.00 **t.** – SB.

Westport Woods, Quay Rd, West : ½ m. (098) 25811, *woodshotel@an* *Fax (098) 26212*, – – 300. AE VISA.
Meals (bar lunch Monday to Saturday)/dinner 18.00/22.00 **t.** and a la carte 6.00 – **95** 75.00/150.00 **t.** – SB.

Knockranny Lodge without rest., Knockranny, East : ½ m. by N 5 (098) 2859 *nockranny@anu.ie, Fax (098) 28805*, – VISA.
closed November-January – **12 rm** 60.00/80.00 **st.**

Augusta Lodge without rest., Golf Links Rd, North : ½ m. off N 59 (098) 28900, *in* *augustalodge.ie, Fax (098) 28995* – VISA.
10 rm 40.00/50.00 **st.**

Kirwan's on the Mall, South Mall, (098) 29077, *(098) 29079*, « Conver church » – AE VISA
Meals (dinner only and Sunday lunch)/dinner a la carte 21.50/28.50 **t.** 5.90.

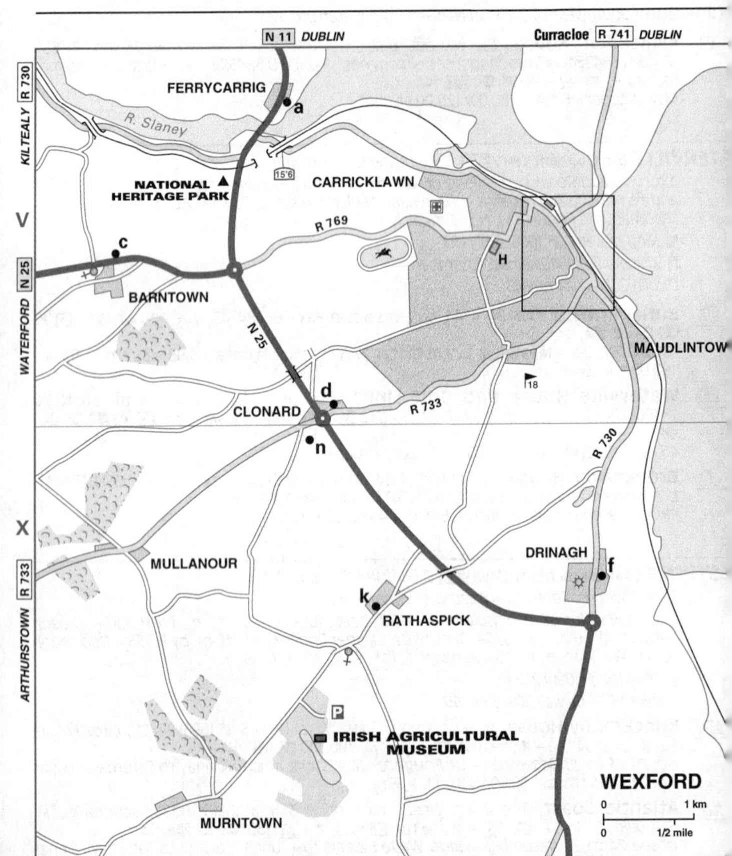

EXFORD **(Loch Garman)** *Wexford* 923 M 10 *Ireland G. – pop. 9 533.*

See : *Town★ – Main Street★* **YZ** – *Franciscan Friary★* **Z** – *St. Iberius' Church★* **Y D** – *Twin Churches★* **Z**.

Env. : *Irish Agricultural Museum, Johnstown Castle★★* **AC**, *SW : 4 1/2 m.* **X** – *Irish National Heritage Park, Ferrycarrig★* **AC**, *NW : 2 1/2 m. by N 11* **V** – *Curracloe★, NE : 5 m. by R 741 and R 743* **V**.

Exc. : *Kilmoer Quay★, SW : 15 m. by N 25 and R 739 (Saltee Islands★ - access by boat)* **X** – *Enniscorthy Castle★ (County Museum★* **AC**) *N : 15 m. by N 11* **V**.

18 Mulgannon ☎ (053) 42238.

Crescent Quay ☎ (053) 23111.

Dublin 88 – Kilkenny 49 – Waterford 38.

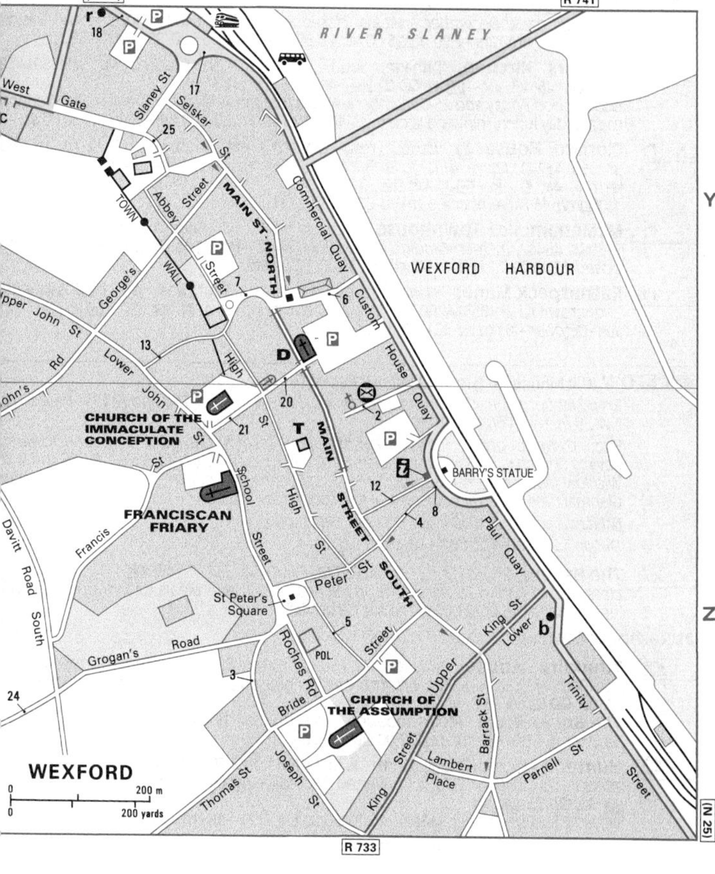

ie Street . . . . **Z** 2
rigeen Street . . . . **Z** 3
ema Lane . . . . **Z** 4
ford Street . . . . **Z** 5
nmon
uay Street . . . . **Y** 6
nmarket . . . . **Y** 7
Crescent Quay . . . . **Z** 8
Henrietta Street . . . . **Z** 12
John's Gate
Street . . . . **Y** 13
Main St. North . . . . **Y**
Main St. South . . . . **Z**
Redmond Place . . . . **Y** 17
Redmond Road . . . . **Y** 18
Rowe Street
Lower . . . . **YZ** 20
Rowe Street
Upper . . . . **Z** 21
Summerthil Road . . . . **Z** 24
Temperance Row . . . . **Y** 25

Ferrycarrig, Ferrycarrig Bridge, Northwest : 2 ¾ m. on N 11 ☎ (053) 20999, *ferrycarr griffingroup.ie, Fax (053) 20982,* ≤ River Slaney and estuary, rest, – 400. VISA. V
Tides : **Meals** *(closed Sunday and Monday) (restricted opening in winter)* (dinner o a la carte 25.50/30.50 **st.** 7.00 – ***Boathouse Bistro :*** **Meals** 13.95 **st.** (lunch) and a la ca 17.00/27.50 **st.** 7.00 – **94 rm** 90.00/190.00 **st.**, 4 suites – SB.

Talbot, Trinity St., ☎ (053) 22566, *talbotwx@tinet.ie, Fax (053) 23377,* – rm, rest, – 400. VISA. Z
closed 24-25 December – **Meals** (carving lunch)/dinner 23.00 **st.** and a la carte 9.0 **99 rm** 70.00/110.00 **st.**

Whitford House, New Line Rd, West : 2 ¼ m. on R 733 ☎ (053) 43444, *whitford@indi ie, Fax (053) 46399,* – VISA. V
closed 23 December-13 January – **Meals** (carvery lunch Monday to Saturday)/din 21.95 **st.** and a la carte 5.50 – **36 rm** 51.00/94.00 **st.** – SB.

Slaney Manor, Ferrycarrig, West : 3 m. on N 25 ☎ (053) 20051, *Fax (053) 20510,* – VISA. V
closed 23 to 30 December – **Meals** *(closed Sunday lunch)* (booking essential) (reside only) (bar lunch)/dinner 20.00/25.00 **st.** 5.50 – **10 rm** 35.00/95.00 **st.** – SB.

Farmers Kitchen, Drinagh, South : 2 ½ m. on Rosslare Rd ☎ (053) 432 *Fax (053) 45827,* – VISA. X
closed Good Friday and 25 December – **Meals** (bar meals Monday, Tuesday and Wednes to Saturday lunch)/dinner a la carte 11.10/22.75 **st.** 5.50 – **21 rm** 45.00/70.00 **st.** –

Clonard House without rest., Clonard Great, Southwest : 2 ½ m. by R ☎ (053) 43141, *khayes@indigo.ie, Fax (053) 43141,* ≤, « Georgian country house, work farm », – VISA. X
15 March-15 November – **9 rm** 27.50/45.00 **st.**

McMenamin's Townhouse without rest., 3 Auburn Terr., Redmond ☎ (053) 46442, *mcmem@indigo.ie, Fax (053) 46442* – VISA. Y
closed 10 to 30 December – **5 rm** 35.00/55.00 **st.**

Rathaspeck Manor without rest., Rathaspeck, Southwest : 4 m. by Rosslare Rd Bridgetown rd ☎ (053) 42661, « Georgian country house », – X
July-October – **6 rm** 30.00/50.00 **st.**

WICKLOW (Cill Mhantáin) *Wicklow* 923 N 9 *Ireland G. – pop. 6 416.*

Env. : *Mount Usher Gardens, Ashford★ AC, NW : 4 m. by R 750 and N 11 – Devil's Gle NW : 8 m. by R 750 and N 11.*

Exc. : *Glendalough★★★ (Lower Lake★★★, Upper Lake★★, Cathedral★★, Round Tower★, Kevin's Church★, St. Saviour's Priory★), – W : 14 m. by R 750, N 11, R 763, R 755 and R 75 Wicklow Mountains★★ (Wicklow Gap★★, Sally Gap★★, Avondale★, Meeting of the Water Glenmacnass Waterfall★, Glenmalur★, – Loughs Tay and Dan★).*

Fitzwilliam St. ☎ (0404) 69117 (June-December).

Dublin 33 – Waterford 84 – Wexford 67.

The Bakery, Church St., ☎ (0404) 66770, *Fax (0404) 66717* – VISA
closed Good Friday, 25 December and Sunday in winter – **Meals** (dinner only and Sun lunch)/dinner 16.00/21.00 **t.** and a la carte 6.50.

at Rathnew *Northwest : 2 m. on R 750 – ✉ Wicklow.*

Tinakilly House, on R 750 ☎ (0404) 69274, *reservations@tinakilly Fax (0404) 67806,* ≤, « Part Victorian country house », – rest, 80. VISA.
The Brunel Room : **Meals** (booking essential) (bar lunch Monday to Saturday)/din 39.00 **st.** 9.00 – **52 rm** 122.00/280.00 **st.** – SB.

Hunter's, Newrath Bridge, North : ¾ m. by N 11 on R 761 ☎ (0404) 40106, *reception@ nters.ie, Fax (0404) 40338,* « Converted 18C coaching inn, gardens » – rest, 30. VISA.
closed 23-25 December – **Meals** 15.00/30.00 **t.** 7.00 – **16 rm** 65.00/130.00 **t.**

This Guide is not a comprehensive list of all hotels and restaurants, nor even of all good hotels and restaurants in Great Britain and Ireland.

Since our aim is to be of service to all motorists, we must show establishments in all categories and so we have made a selection of some in each.

OODENBRIDGE *Wicklow* 923 N 9.

Woodenbridge, Arklow ☎ (0402) 35202.

Dublin 46 – Waterford 68 – Wexford 41.

Woodenbridge, Vale of Avoca, ☎ (0402) 35146, *wbhotel@iol.ie, Fax (0402) 35573,* ≤, – rest, TV ♿ P – 250. MC AE VISA.
closed 25 December – **Meals** (bar lunch Monday to Saturday)/dinner 21.00 **st.** and a la carte – **23 rm** 60.00/100.00 **st.** – SB.

OUGHAL (Eochaill) *Cork* 923 I 12 *Ireland G. – pop. 5 630.*

See : *Town★ – St. Mary's Collegiate Church★★ – Town Walls★ – Clock Gate★.*

Exc. : *Helvick Head★ (≤★), NE : 22 m. by N 25 and R 674 – Ringville (≤★), NE : 20 m. by N 25 and R 674 – Ardmore★ – Round Tower★ – Church★ (arcade★), N : 10 m. by N 25 and R 673 – Whiting Bay★, SE : 12 m. by N 25, R 673 and the coast road.*

Knockaverry ☎ (024) 92787.

Heritage Centre ☎ (024) 20170 (May-September).

Dublin 146 – Cork 30 – Waterford 47.

Aherne's, 163 North Main St., ☎ (024) 92424, *ahernes@eircom.net, Fax (024) 93633* – TV ♿ P. MC AE ⊙ VISA.
closed 24 to 30 December – **Meals** – (see ***Aherne's Seafood Restaurant and Bar*** below) – **12 rm** 85.00/160.00 **t.** – SB.

Aherne's Seafood Restaurant and Bar (at Aherne's H.), 163 North Main St., ☎ (024) 92424, *Fax (024) 93633* – P. MC AE ⊙ VISA
closed 23 to 28 December – **Meals** 16.95/30.00 **t.** and a la carte 13.50.

Distances

All distances in this edition are quoted in miles. The distance is given from each town to other nearby towns and to the capital of each region as grouped in the guide.
To avoid excessive repetition some distances have only been quoted once – you may therefore have to look under both town headings.
The distances in miles quoted are not necessarily the shortest but have been based on the roads which afford the best driving conditions and are therefore the most practical.

Distances en miles

Pour chaque région traitée, vous trouverez au texte de chacune des localités sa distance par rapport à la capitale et aux villes environnantes.
La distance d'une localité à une autre n'est pas toujours répétée aux deux villes intéressées : voyez au texte de l'une ou de l'autre.
Ces distances ne sont pas nécessairement comptées par la route la plus courte mais par la plus pratique, c'est-à-dire celle offrant les meilleures conditions de roulage.

	Belfast	Cork	Dublin	Dundalk	Galway	Killarney	Limerick	Londonderry	Omagh	Sligo	Tullamore
Cork	263										
Dublin	104	159									
Dundalk	53	210	51								
Galway	195	121	136	154							
Killarney	291	54	187	238	134						
Limerick	228	57	124	175	65	70					
Londonderry	72	297	142	102	171	296	227				
Omagh	68	264	109	69	155	256	187	34			
Sligo	124	203	136	106	90	215	146	82	66		
Tullamore	141	127	65	83	82	141	72	161	127	99	
Waterford	205	74	102	152	142	118	78	240	207	183	84

136 Miles
Dublin - Sligo

Distanze in miglia

Per ciascuna delle regioni trattate, troverete nel testo di ogni località la sua distanza dalla capitale e dalle dittà circostanti.
Le distanza da una località all'altra non è sempre ripetuta nelle due città interessate : vedere nel testo dell'una o dell'altra.
Le distanza non sono necessariamente calcolate seguendo il percorso più breve, ma vengono stabilite secondo l'itinerario più pratico, che offre cioè le migliori condizioni di viaggio.

Entfernungsangaben in meilen

Die Entfernungen der einzelnen Orte zur Landeshauptstadt und zu den nächstgrößeren Städten in der Umgebung sind im allgemeinen Orstext angegeben.
Die Entfernung zweier Städte voneinander können Sie aus den Angaben im Ortstext der einen oder der anderen Stadt ersehen.
Die Entfernungsangaben gelten nicht immer für der kürzesten, sondern für den günstigsten Weg.

Distances between major towns

Distances entre principales villes

Distanze tra le principali città

Entfernungen zwischen den größeren Städten

Edinburgh - Southampton: 438 Miles

	Aberdeen	Ayr	Birmingham	Blackpool	Brighton	Bristol	Cambridge	Cardiff	Carlisle	Coventry	Dover	Dumfries	Dundee	Edinburgh	Glasgow	Inverness	Ipswich	Kingston-upon-Hull	Leeds	Leicester	Liverpool	London	Manchester	Middlesbrough	Newcastle	Norwich	Nottingham	Oban	Oxford	Plymouth	Portsmouth	Sheffield	Southampton	Stoke-on-Trent	Swansea
Ayr	184																																		
Birmingham	431	293																																	
Blackpool	323	185	134																																
Brighton	600	463	167	303																															
Bristol	514	377	89	217	161																														
Cambridge	467	354	99	227	121	153																													
Cardiff	534	396	109	237	193	45	184																												
Carlisle	229	91	204	96	372	287	265	307																											
Coventry	447	310	22	151	156	97	79	123	220																										
Dover	588	492	204	333	106	200	123	231	402	183																									
Dumfries	208	57	237	129	406	320	298	340	35	254	436																								
Dundee	67	113	364	256	532	447	400	467	162	380	521	141																							
Edinburgh	123	81	303	195	472	386	343	406	101	320	464	80	56																						
Glasgow	148	35	300	192	469	383	361	403	98	317	499	77	77	46																					
Inverness	110	210	461	353	630	545	505	564	259	478	626	238	131	160	175																				
Ipswich	521	409	153	281	128	208	55	240	319	133	130	352	454	397	415	559																			
Kingston-upon-Hull	361	248	145	145	265	237	146	256	159	126	267	192	294	237	255	399	172																		
Leeds	325	213	122	90	266	214	154	234	123	122	275	156	258	201	220	363	208	61																	
Leicester	415	315	43	155	168	120	72	152	225	24	189	258	348	290	322	483	126	102	103																
Liverpool	357	219	103	60	271	186	196	170	130	119	301	163	290	229	226	387	250	132	77	124															
London	546	409	121	249	55	124	57	156	319	100	77	353	479	397	416	577	79	201	204	106	218														
Manchester	352	214	90	55	259	173	167	193	125	107	289	158	285	224	221	382	221	98	44	112	36	206													
Middlesbrough	274	185	180	127	324	272	205	292	96	180	326	129	207	150	192	312	259	89	64	153	147	260	114												
Newcastle	229	147	214	142	357	306	239	326	60	213	360	90	162	105	153	267	293	133	97	187	181	293	147	46											
Norwich	490	378	165	245	171	219	67	251	288	145	173	322	423	366	385	528	45	154	177	121	226	115	190	229	262										
Nottingham	395	282	53	128	197	145	90	165	193	53	218	226	328	271	289	433	144	98	75	29	110	135	73	133	167	122									
Oban	178	126	391	283	559	474	452	493	189	407	589	167	118	124	93	116	506	346	310	412	316	506	311	272	227	475	379								
Oxford	501	363	68	204	108	74	83	106	274	57	146	307	434	373	370	531	137	178	174	76	173	59	160	232	266	149	105	460							
Plymouth	632	494	207	335	215	118	272	155	405	215	291	438	565	504	501	662	309	354	332	238	304	225	291	390	423	336	263	591	198						
Portsmouth	584	446	151	287	49	96	132	152	357	140	142	390	517	456	453	614	164	261	257	159	256	80	243	315	349	197	188	543	85	175					
Sheffield	361	249	86	97	230	178	126	198	159	86	251	192	294	237	255	399	180	70	35	67	78	168	42	99	133	149	39	346	138	296	221				
Southampton	566	428	133	269	62	76	133	135	339	122	144	372	499	438	435	596	170	244	239	141	238	86	225	297	331	198	170	526	68	153	22	203			
Stoke-on-Trent	387	249	48	90	216	131	141	150	160	64	246	193	320	259	256	417	195	135	92	66	59	163	46	162	195	176	51	347	117	248	200	51	182		
Swansea	517	379	146	220	229	82	221	41	290	159	268	323	450	389	386	547	277	293	271	189	174	193	180	329	362	288	202	476	143	192	189	235	171	187	
Wick	[illegible]	[illegible]	[illegible]	[illegible]	[illegible]	[illegible]	[illegible]	[illegible]	[illegible]	[illegible]	[illegible]	[illegible]	[illegible]	[illegible]	[illegible]	[illegible]	[illegible]	[illegible]	[illegible]	[illegible]	[illegible]	[illegible]	[illegible]	[illegible]	[illegible]	[illegible]	[illegible]	[illegible]	[illegible]	[illegible]	[illegible]	[illegible]	[illegible]	[illegible]	[illegible]

Birmingham	Cardiff	Dublin	Glasgow	London	
425	453	601	720	299	**Amsterdam**
026	1054	1202	1321	899	**Barcelona**
617	644	792	911	490	**Basel**
780	807	955	1075	653	**Berlin**
674	701	849	969	547	**Bern**
569	520	719	852	614	**Bordeaux**
065	1092	1240	1359	938	**Bratislava**
453	1480	1628	1748	1326	**Brindisi**
323	351	499	618	197	**Bruxelles-Brussel**
168	120	318	470	81	**Cherbourg**
643	670	818	937	516	**Clermont-Ferrand**
449	476	624	744	322	**Düsseldorf**
566	593	741	861	439	**Frankfurt am Main**
664	691	839	958	537	**Genève**
776	703	851	972	549	**Hamburg**
70	897	1045	1165	743	**København**
766	293	442	561	139	**Lille**
316	1267	1466	1599	1361	**Lisboa**
457	485	633	752	331	**Luxembourg**

Birmingham	Cardiff	Dublin	Glasgow	London	
666	693	841	960	539	**Lyon**
1000	951	1149	1283	1045	**Madrid**
1328	1280	1478	1611	1373	**Málaga**
860	887	1035	1154	733	**Marseille**
830	857	1006	1125	703	**Milano**
777	804	952	1071	650	**München**
364	315	514	647	419	**Nantes**
1317	1344	1493	1612	1190	**Palermo**
377	404	552	671	250	**Paris**
1185	1137	1335	1468	1230	**Porto**
880	907	1055	1175	753	**Praha**
1190	1217	1366	1485	1063	**Roma**
719	670	869	1002	764	**San Sebastián**
583	610	758	877	456	**Strasbourg**
813	672	988	1108	686	**Toulouse**
1242	1014	1417	1536	1115	**Valencia**
1127	1154	1302	1422	1000	**Warszawa**
1015	1042	1190	1309	888	**Wien**
1131	1158	1306	1425	1004	**Zagreb**

· distances refer to the colour key in the table
: distances sont indiquées dans la couleur du point de passage
distanze sono indicate con il colore del punto di passaggio
· Entfernungen sind angegeben in der Farbe des betroffenen ssagepunktes

- ● FOLKESTONE (CHANNEL TUNNEL)
- ● SOUTHAMPTON
- ● TYNEMOUTH

Glasgow - Barcelona 1321 Miles

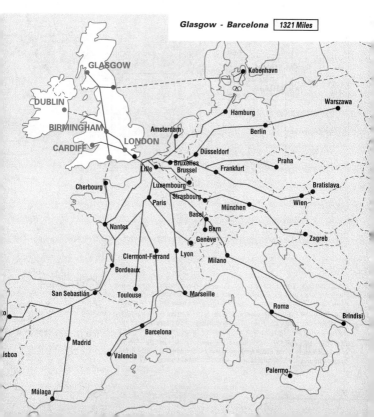

Major roads and principal shipping routes

Motorway

Road number ...... A 4. T 35. N 2

Mileage 20

Principales routes et liaisons maritimes

Autoroute

N° de route .... A 4. T 35. N 2

Distance en miles 20

Principali strade e itinerari marittimi

Autostrada

Numero di strada... A 4. T 35. N 2

Distanza in miglia 20

Hauptverkehrsstrassen und Schiffsverbindungen

Autbahn

Straßennummer .... A 4. T 35. N 2

Entfernung in Meilen .. 20

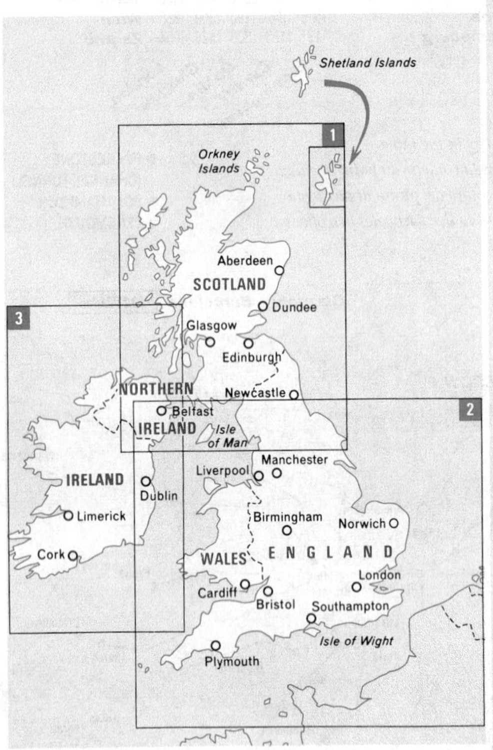

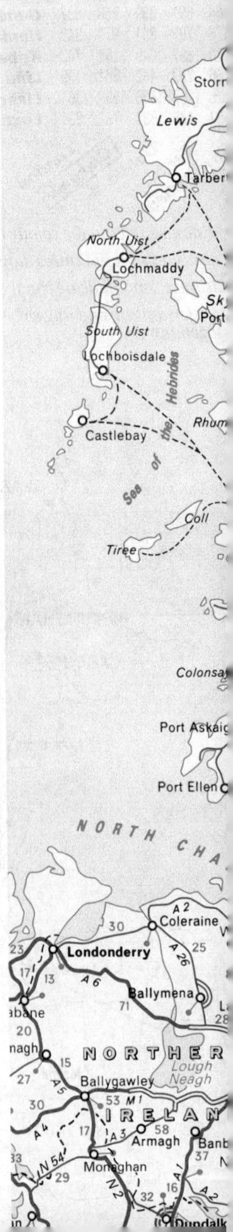

GREAT BRITAIN: the maps and town plans in the Great Britain Section of this Guide are based upon the Ordnance Survey of Great Britain with the permission of the Controller of Her Majesty's Stationery Office, © Crown Copyright 39923X.

NORTHERN IRELAND: the maps and town plans in the Northern Ireland Section of this Guide are based upon the Ordnance Survey of Northern Ireland with the sanction of the Controller of H. M. Stationery Office, Permit number 1590.

REPUBLIC OF IRELAND: the maps and town plans in the Republic of Ireland Section of this Guide are based upon the Ordnance Survey of Ireland by permission of the Government of the Republic, Permit number 7169.

1

SHETLAND ISLANDS
Unst
Yell
Whalsay
Mainland
Lerwick
Scalloway
Bergen
Aberdeen
Stromness
ORKNEY ISLANDS
Lerwick
Westray
Sanday
Rousay
Stronsay
Mainland
Stromness
Kirkwall
Hoy
Durness
Thurso
Tongue
Wick
Loch Shin
Brora
Ullapool
Garve
Elgin
Banff
Fraserburgh
Nairn
Keith
Inverness
Loch Ness
Spey
Lerwick
Torshavn
ABERDEEN
Invergarry
Kingussie
Dee
Braemar
Stonehaven
Fort William
SCOTLAND
Loch Tay
NORTH SEA
DUNDEE
Arbroath
Oban
Crianlarich
Perth
Lochearnhead
St.Andrews
Tarbet
Stirling
Firth of Forth
Kirkcaldy
Lochgilphead
Greenock
Falkirk
Dunfermline
GLASGOW
EDINBURGH
Rothesay
Largs
Motherwell
Berwick upon Tweed
Ardrossan
Peebles
Brodick
Arran
Kilmarnock
Galashiels
Ayr
Abington
Hawick
Alnwick
New Galloway
Dumfries
Tynemouth
Bergen
Stavanger
Hamburg
Cairnryan
NEWCASTLE UPON TYNE
Stranraer
Carlisle
Sunderland
Durham
Hartlepool
Workington
Penrith
Whitehaven
Keswick
Darlington
Middlesbrough
Isle of Man
Kendal
Scarborough
ENGLAND
Douglas
Barrow-in-Furness

NORTHERN IRELAND
Ballymena
Larne
Belfast
Bangor
Lough Neagh
Strangford Lough
Ballygawley
Armagh
Banbridge
Newcastle
Monaghan
Dundalk / Dun Dealgan
Drogheda/ Droichead Átha
Kells
Boyne
DUBLIN/ BAILE ÁTHA CLIATH
Dún Laoghaire
Naas
Bray
Wicklow
Carlow
Arklow
Enniscorthy
Wexford
Rosslare
Isle of Man
Douglas
IRISH SEA
ST GEORGE'S CHANNEL
Stranraer
Carlisle
Penrith
Workington
Whitehaven
Keswick
Kendal
Barrow-in-Furness
Heysham
Lancaster
ENG
Wharfe
BLACKPOOL
Preston
Blackburn
Burnley
Bolton
Southport
Wigan
LIVERPOOL
Birkenhead
Warrington
Chester
Colwyn Bay/ Bae Colwyn
Holyhead/ Caergybi
Bangor
Caernarfon
Mold/ Yr Wyddgrug
Wrexham/ Wrecsam
Dolgellau
Shrewsbury
Welshpool/ Y Trallwng
Wolverhampton
Dudley
BIRMINGHAM
Aberystwyth
Llangurig
Ludlow
Severn
Llandrindod Wells
Worcester
Wye
WALES
Fishguard/ Abergwaun
Carmarthen/ Caerfyrddin
Hereford
Brecon/ Aberhonddu
Ross
Gloucester
Merthyr Tydfil
Milford Haven/ Aberdaugleddau
Pembroke Dock/ Doc Penfro
Newport/ Casnewydd
Swansea/ Abertawe
CARDIFF/ CAERDYDD
BRISTOL
Bath
Bristol Channel
Ilfracombe
Minehead
Wells
Barnstaple
Bridgwater
Taunton
Bude
Yeovil
EXETER
Honiton
Dorchester
Exmouth
Weymouth
Newquay
Bodmin
PLYMOUTH
Torquay Torbay
Truro
Penzance
Falmouth
Isles of Scilly
Santander
Roscoff
St-Malo
Rosslare
Alderney
Guernsey
Sark
St.Peter-Port
Jersey

2

NORTH SEA

CHANNEL

Hartlepool
Middlesbrough
Scarborough
York
KINGSTON UPON HULL
Immingham
Rotterdam
Zeebrugge
Scunthorpe
Great Grimsby
Doncaster
Lincoln
Skegness
Boston
NOTTINGHAM
Cromer
King's Lynn
NORWICH
Great Yarmouth
Lowestoft
LEICESTER
Wisbech
Stamford
Peterborough
Ely
Rugby
Bury St.Edmunds
CAMBRIDGE
Ipswich
Bedford
Felixstowe
Harwich
Esbjerg
Göteborg
Hoek van Holland
Hamburg
Kingston upon Hull
Colchester
Stevenage
Luton
Aylesbury
Harlow
Chelmsford
OXFORD
Tilbury
Southend-on-Sea
Reading
Windsor
LONDON
Thames
Sheerness
Margate
Ramsgate
Canterbury
Deal
Newbury
Basingstoke
Guildford
Maidstone
Crawley
Royal Tunbridge Wells
Winchester
Dover
Folkestone
Channel Tunnel
Zeebrugge
OOSTENDE
BRUGGE
Dunkerque
Calais
BELGIË
BELGIQUE
SOUTHAMPTON
Chichester
BRIGHTON
Hastings
Worthing
Eastbourne
Newhaven
PORTSMOUTH
Newport
Isle of Wight
Boulogne
St-Omer
LILLE
Arras
Cambrai
Abbeville
St-Malo
Somme
Dieppe
AMIENS
St-Quentin
Rosslare
FRANCE
Beauvais
Compiègne
LE HAVRE
ROUEN
Senlis
CAEN
Seine

3

ATLANTIC OCEAN
NORTH CHANNEL
CELTIC SEA
ST GEORGE'S C
Tiree
Mull
Colonsay
Jura
Port Askaig
Islay
Port Ellen
NORTHERN IRELAND
IRELAND
Coleraine
Londonderry
Letterkenny
Donegal
Strabane
Omagh
Ballymena
Larne
Lough Neagh
Ballygawley
BELFAST
Enniskillen
Sligo/ Sligeach
Armagh
Banbridge
Newcastle
Monaghan
Ballina
L. Allen
Boyle
Cavan
Dundalk / Dun Dealgan
Westport
Castlebar
L. Mask
Longford
Kells
Drogheda/ Droichead Átha
Clifden
Roscommon
L. Corrib
L. Ree
Mullingar
Boyne
DUBLIN/ BAILE ÁTHA CLIATH
Galway/ Gaillimh
Athlone
Ballinasloe
Tullamore
Naas
Dún Laoghaire
Bray
Lisdoonvarna
River Shannon
Roscrea
Wicklow
Ennis/ Inis
Kilkee
Carlow
Thurles
Suir
Arklow
LIMERICK/ LUIMNEACH
Kilkenny / Cill Chainnigh
Cashel/ Caiseal
Barrow
Enniscorthy
Tralee
Dingle
Killarney/ Cill Airne
Caher
Carrick on Suir
Wexford
Fermoy
Waterford/ Port Lairge
Rosslare
R. Blackwater
Lismore
Youghal
CORK/ CORCAIGH
Cobh
Glengarriff
Bantry

Major hotel groups

Central reservation telephone numbers

Principales chaînes hôtelières

Centraux téléphoniques de réservation

Principali catene alberghiere

Centrali telefoniche di prenotazione

Die wichtigsten Hotelketten

Zentrale für telefonische Reservierung

ACCOR HOTELS (IBIS, MERCURE & NOVOTEL)	*020 8283 4550*
CHOICE HOTELS	*0800 444444 (Freephone)*
CORUS & REGAL HOTELS	*0345 334400*
DE VERE HOTELS PLC	*01925 639499*
FORTE HOTELS	*0800 404040 (Freephone)*
HILTON/STAKIS HOTELS	*0990 515151*
HOLIDAY INN WORLDWIDE	*0800 897121 (Freephone)*
HYATT HOTELS WORLDWIDE	*0345 581666*
INTERCONTINENTAL HOTELS LTD	*0800 0289387 (Freephone)*
JARVIS HOTELS PLC	*0845 7303040*
JURYS/DOYLE HOTELS	*00353 1 6070000*
MACDONALD HOTELS PLC	*0345 585593*
MARRIOTT HOTELS	*0800 221222 (Freephone)*
MILLENNIUM & COPTHORNE HOTELS PLC	*0845 3020001*
PREMIER LODGES	*08702 010203*
QUEENS MOAT HOUSES PLC	*0500 213214 (Freephone)*
RADISSON EDWARDIAN HOTELS	*0800 374411 (Freephone)*
SHERATON HOTELS	*0800 353535 (Freephone)*
THISTLE HOTELS	*0800 181716 (Freephone)*
TRAVEL INNS	*0870 2428000*
TRAVELODGES	*08700 850950*

International Dialling Codes

Note: when making an international call, do not dial the first «0» of the city coc (except for calls to Italy).

Indicatifs Téléphoniques Internationaux

Important : pour les communications internationales, le zéro (0) initial de l'indica interurbain n'est pas à composer (excepté pour les appels vers l'Italie).

from \ to	A	B	CH	CZ	D	DK	E	FIN	F	GB	GF
A Austria		0032	0041	00420	0049	0045	0034	00358	0033	0044	003
B Belgium	0043		0041	00420	0049	0045	0034	00358	0033	0044	003
CH Switzerland	0043	0032		00420	0049	0045	0034	00358	0033	0044	003
CZ Czech Republic	0043	0032	0041		0049	0045	0034	00358	0033	0044	003
D Germany	0043	0032	0041	00420		0045	0034	00358	0033	0044	003
DK Denmark	0043	0032	0041	00420	0049		0034	00358	0033	0044	003
E Spain	0043	0032	0041	00420	0049	0045		00358	0033	0044	003
FIN Finland	0043	0032	0041	00420	0049	0045	0034		0033	0044	003
F France	0043	0032	0041	00420	0049	0045	0034	00358		0044	003
GB United Kingdom	0043	0032	0041	00420	0049	0045	0034	00358	0033		003
GR Greece	0043	0032	0041	00420	0049	0045	0034	00358	0033	0044	
H Hungary	0043	0032	0041	00420	0049	0045	0034	00358	0033	0044	003
I Italy	0043	0032	0041	00420	0049	0045	0034	00358	0033	0044	003
IRL Ireland	0043	0032	0041	00420	0049	0045	0034	00358	0033	0044	003
J Japan	00143	00132	00141	001420	00149	00145	00134	001358	00133	00144	001
L Luxembourg	0043	0032	0041	00420	0049	0045	0034	00358	0033	0044	003
N Norway	0043	0032	0041	00420	0049	0045	0034	00358	0033	0044	003
NL Netherlands	0043	0032	0041	00420	0049	0045	0034	00358	0033	0044	003
PL Poland	0043	0032	0041	00420	0049	0045	0034	00358	0033	0044	003
P Portugal	0043	0032	0041	00420	0049	0045	0034	00358	0033	0044	003
RUS Russia	81043	81032	810420	6420	81049	81045	*	810358	81033	81044	*
S Sweden	0043	0032	0041	00420	0049	0045	0034	00358	0033	0044	003
USA	01143	01132	01141	001420	01149	01145	01134	01358	01133	01144	011

**Direct dialling not possible*

**Pas de sélection automatiq*

ndicativi Telefonici nternationali

ıportante: per le comunicazioni internazionali, non bisogna comporre lo zero (0) :iziale dell'indicativo interurbano (escluse le chiamate per l'Italia)

'elefon-Vorwahlnummern nternational

'ichtig: bei Auslandgesprächen darf die Null (0) der Ortsnetzkennzahl nicht ·wählt werden (ausser bei Gesprächen nach Italien).

H	I	IRL	J	L	N	NL	PL	P	RUS	S	USA	
036	0039	00353	0081	00352	0047	0031	0048	00351	007	0046	001	**A Austria**
036	0039	00353	0081	00352	0047	0031	0048	00351	007	0046	001	**B Belgium**
036	0039	00353	0081	00352	0047	0031	0048	00351	007	0046	001	**CH Switzerland**
036	0039	00353	0081	00352	0047	0031	0048	00351	007	0046	001	**CZ Czech Republic**
036	0039	00353	0081	00352	0047	0031	0048	00351	007	0046	001	**D Germany**
036	0039	00353	0081	00352	0047	0031	0048	00351	007	0046	001	**DK Denmark**
036	0039	00353	0081	00352	0047	0031	0048	00351	007	0046	001	**E Spain**
036	0039	00353	0081	00352	0047	0031	0048	00351	007	0046	001	**FIN Finland**
036	0039	00353	0081	00352	0047	0031	0048	00351	007	0046	001	**F France**
036	0039	00353	0081	00352	0047	0031	0048	00351	007	0046	001	**GB United Kingdom**
036	0039	00353	0081	00352	0047	0031	0048	00351	007	0046	001	**GR Greece**
	0039	00353	0081	00352	0047	0031	0048	00351	007	0046	001	**H Hungary**
036		00353	0081	00352	0047	0031	0048	00351	*	0046	001	**I Italy**
036	0039		0081	00352	0047	0031	0048	00351	007	0046	001	**IRL Ireland**
136	00139	001353		001352	00147	00131	00148	001351	*	00146	0011	**J Japan**
036	0039	00353	0081		0047	0031	0048	00351	007	0046	001	**L Luxembourg**
036	0039	00353	0081	00352		0031	0048	00351	007	0046	001	**N Norway**
036	0039	00353	0081	00352	0047		0048	00351	007	0046	001	**NL Netherlands**
036	0039	00353	0081	00352	0047	0031		00351	007	0046	001	**PL Poland**
036	0039	00353	0081	00352	0047	0031	0048		007	0046	001	**P Portugal**
1036	*	*	*	*	*	81031	81048	*		*	*	**RUS Russia**
036	0039	00353	0081	00352	0047	0031	0048	00351	007		001	**S Sweden**
136	01139	011353	01181	011352	01147	01131	01148	011351	*	011146		**USA**

Selezione automatica impossibile **Automatische Vorwahl nicht möglich*

The Euro

*1999 saw the launch of the European single currency: the EURO.
11 countries in the European Union are already using the EURO: Austria, Belgium, Finland, France, Germany, Ireland, Italy, Luxembourg, Netherlands, Portugal and Spain.
In each of these countries, prices will today be displayed in the local currency and in Euros.
However, as Euro notes and coins will not be available until 2002, payment in Euros is currently only possible by bank or credit cards.
We have therefore retained the local currency prices only for entries in this year's guide.
The following tables show the fixed rates between the Euro and other European currencies, together with fluctuating rates for non-Euro countries as in November 2000.*

L'Euro

*1999 a vu l'avènement de la monnaie européenne commune : l'EURO.
Onze pays de l'Union Européenne ont d'ores et déjà adopté l'EURO : l'Allemagne, l'Autriche, la Belgique, l'Espagne, la Finlande, la France, l'Irlande, l'Italie, le Luxembourg, les Pays-Bas et le Portugal.
Dans ces pays, les prix sont désormais affichés en monnaies nationales et en euros.
Toutefois, les billets de banque et pièces en euros n'étant disponibles qu'en 2002, seuls les règlements par chèques bancaires ou cartes de crédit pourront être libellés en euros.
Dans cette édition, nous avons choisi de mentionner les prix dans la monnaie nationale.
Les tableaux ci-après indiquent la parité fixe entre l'euro et les devises européennes et celle fluctuante de monnaies hors zone euro, en Novembre 2000.*

L'Euro

*Il 1999 ha segnato l'avvento della moneta unica europea: l'EURO
Undici paesi dell'Unione Europea hanno già adottato l'EURO: Austria, Belgio, Finlandia, Francia, Germania, Irlanda, Italia, Lussemburgo, Paesi Bassi, Portogallo e Spagna.
In questi paesi i prezzi sono indicati nella moneta nazionale ed in euro
Non essendo tuttavia disponibili le banconote e le monete in euro che dal 2002, saranno possibili i pagamenti in euro solo tramite assegni o carte di credito.
In questa edizione abbiamo scelto di indicare i prezzi nella moneta nazionale.
Le tabelle che seguono indicano la parità fissa tra l'euro e le valute europee e quella fluttuante delle valute al di fuori dell'euro, in Novembre 2000*

Der Euro

1999 war das Jahr der Einführung der einheitlichen europäischen Währung: der Euro.
Elf Länder der europäischen Vereinigung haben den Euro eingeführt: Deutschland, Österreich, Belgien, Spanien, Finnland, Frankreich, Irland, Italien, Luxemburg, die Niederlande und Portugal.
Die Preise werden in diesen Ländern in der nationalen Währung und in Euro ausgezeichnet.
Banknoten und Münzen in Euro sind jedoch erst ab 2002 erhältlich. Die Bezahlung in Euro kann bis zu diesem Zeitpunkt nur per Scheck oder per Kreditkarte erfolgen.
Aus diesem Grund haben wir uns entschieden in dieser Ausgabe, die Preise in der nationalen Währung anzugeben.
Die folgenden Tabellen zeigen die festgelegte Parität zwischen dem Euro und den europäischen Währungen, sowie die schwankenden Paritäten der Währungen außerhalb der Eurozone mit dem Wechselkurs von November 2000.

1 € = 13,7603 ATS	**A**	1 ATS = 0,0726728 €
1 € = 40,3399 BEF	**B**	1 BEF = 0,0247893 €
1 € = 1,9583 DEM	**D**	1 DEM = 0,5112918 €
1 € = 166,386 ESP	**E**	1 ESP = 0,0060101 €
1 € = 6,55957 FRF	**F**	1 FRF = 0,152449 €
1 € = 5,94573 FIM	**FIN**	1 FIM = 0,1681879 €
1 € = 1936,27 ITL	**I**	1 ITL = 0,0005164 €
1 € = 0,787564 IEP	**IRL**	1 IEP = 1,269738 €
1 € = 40,3399 LUF	**L**	1 LUF = 0,0247893 €
1 € = 2,20371 NLG	**NL**	1 NLG = 0,4537802 €
1 € = 200,482 PTE	**P**	1 PTE = 0,0049879 €

1 € = 0,595 £	**GB**	1 £ = 1,681 €
1 € = 92,66 Y	**J**	1 Y = 0,01079 €
1 € = 1,523 CHF	**CH**	1 CHF = 0,657 €
1 € = 0,862 $	**USA**	1 $ = 1,161 €

Index of towns
Index des localités
Indice delle località
Orlsverzeichnis

B

D

E

F

G

L

N

S

GREAT BRITAIN : "Based on Ordnance Survey of Great Britain with the permission of the controller of Her Majesty's Stationery Office, © Crown Copyright 39923X"

REPUBLIC OF IRELAND : "Based on Ordnance Survey of Ireland by permission of the Government Permit No 7169 © Government of Ireland"

NORTHERN IRELAND : "Based on Ordnance Survey of Northern Ireland with the sanction of the Controller of H.M. Stationery Office, Permit No 1590"

Manufacture française des pneumatiques Michelin
Société en commandite par actions au capital de 2 000 000 000 de F.
Place des Carmes-Déchaux – 63 Clermont-Ferrand (France)
R.C.S. Clermont-Fd B 855 200 507

Michelin et Cie, Propriétaires-Éditeurs 2001
Dépôt légal Janvier 2001 – ISBN 206 000302 4

Made in France 12-00

Photocompositeur : A.P.S. - Tours
Imposeur : CASTERMAN - Tournai (Belgique)
Imprimeur : CASTERMAN - Tournai (Belgique)
Relieur : DIGUET-DENY à Breteuil-sur-Iton

Illustrations Cécile Imbert/MICHELIN : pages 1 à 54
Narratif Systèmes/Geneclo : pages 56 à 64
Autres illustrations : Rodolphe Corbel.